S0-BAM-892

S. Pub.113-12

2013-2014

OFFICIAL CONGRESSIONAL DIRECTORY

113TH CONGRESS

CONVENED JANUARY 3, 2013

JOINT COMMITTEE ON PRINTING
UNITED STATES CONGRESS

UNITED STATES GOVERNMENT PRINTING OFFICE
WASHINGTON, DC

U.S. GOVERNMENT OFFICIAL EDITION NOTICE

Use of ISBN Prefix

This is the Official U.S. Government edition of this publication and is herein identified to certify its authenticity. Use of the 0-16 ISBN prefix is for U.S. Government Printing Office Official Editions only. The Superintendent of Documents of the U.S. Government Printing Office requests that any reprinted edition clearly be labeled as a copy of the authentic work with a new ISBN.

BERNAN
4501 Forbes Boulevard
Lanham, MD 20706
1-800-865-3457

Paperback ISBN: 978-1-60175-905-4
Cloth ISBN: 978-1-60175-904-7

NOTES

Closing date for compilation of the Congressional Directory was February 18, 2014.

SENATE

[Democrats in roman, Republicans in *italic*.]

REPRESENTATIVES

[Republicans in roman, Democrats in *italic*.]

The following changes have occurred in the membership of the 113th Congress since the election of November 6, 2012:

Name	Resigned, [Died] or 【Term Ended】	Successor	Elected or [Appointed]	Sworn in
SENATOR				
John F. Kerry, MA [1]	Feb. 1, 2013	William M. Cowan	[Feb. 1, 2013] ..	Feb. 7, 2013
Frank R. Lautenberg, NJ	[June 3, 2013]	*Jeff Chiesa*	[June 6, 2013] ..	June 10, 2013
William M. Cowan, MA	【July 16, 2013】	Edward J. Markey	June 25, 2013 ..	July 16, 2013
Jeff Chiesa, NJ	【Oct. 31, 2013】	Cory A. Booker	Oct. 16, 2013 ...	Oct. 31, 2013
Max Baucus, MT [2]	Feb. 6, 2014	John E. Walsh	[Feb. 9, 2014] ..	Feb. 11, 2014
REPRESENTATIVES				
Jo Ann Emerson, 8th MO	Jan. 22, 2013	Jason T. Smith	June 4, 2013	June 5, 2013
Robin L. Kelly, 2d IL [3]	....	....	Apr. 9, 2013	Apr. 11, 2013
Mark Sanford, 1st SC [4]	....	....	May 7, 2013	May 15, 2013
Jo Bonner, 1st AL	Aug. 2, 2013	Bradley Byrne	Dec. 17, 2013 ..	Jan. 8, 2014
Rodney Alexander, 5th LA	Sept. 27, 2013	Vance M. McAllister ...	Nov. 16, 2013 ..	Nov. 21, 2013
C. W. Bill Young, 10th FL	[Oct. 18, 2013]	....	....	
Edward J. Markey, 5th MA	July 15, 2013 [5]	*Katherine M. Clark*	Dec. 10, 2013 ..	Dec. 12, 2013
Melvin L. Watt, 12th NC	Jan. 6, 2014	....	....	
Trey Radel, 19th FL	Jan. 27, 2014	....	....	
Robert E. Andrews, 1st NJ	Feb. 18, 2014	....	....	

[1] Senator Kerry resigned to become Secretary of State.

[2] Senator Baucus resigned to become U.S. Ambassador to China.

[3] Representative Kelly elected to the 113th Congress, by special election, to fill the vacancy caused by the resignation of Representative Jesse L. Jackson, Jr., and took the oath of office on April 11, 2013.

[4] Representative Sanford elected to the 113th Congress, by special election, to fill the vacancy caused by the resignation of Representative Tim Scott, and took the oath of office on May 15, 2013.

[5] Representative Markey resigned following his election to the United States Senate.

SENATE

[Democrats in roman, Republicans in *italic*.]

REPRESENTATIVES

[Republicans in roman, Democrats in *italic*.]

The following changes have occurred in the membership of the 112th Congress since the election of November 2, 2010:

Name	Resigned, [Died] or (Interim Vacant Status)	Successor	Elected or [Appointed]	Sworn in
SENATOR				
John Ensign, NV	May 3, 2011	*Dean Heller*	[May 3, 2011] ..	May 9, 2011
Daniel K. Inouye, HI ..	[Dec. 17, 2012]	Brian Schatz	[Dec. 26, 2012]	Dec. 27, 2012
James W. DeMint, SC	Jan. 1, 2013	*Tim Scott*	[Jan. 2, 2013] ...	Jan. 3, 2013
REPRESENTATIVES				
Christopher John Lee, 26th NY	Feb. 9, 2011	*Kathleen C. Hochul*	May 24, 2011 ..	June 1, 2011
Jane Harman, 36th CA	Feb. 28, 2011	*Janice Hahn*	July 12, 2011 ...	July 19, 2011
Dean Heller, 2d NV	May 9, 2011	Mark E. Amodei	Sept. 13, 2011 ..	Sept. 15, 2011
Anthony D. Weiner, 9th NY	June 21, 2011	Robert L. Turner	Sept. 13, 2011 ..	Sept. 15, 2011
David Wu, 1st OR	Aug. 3, 2011	*Suzanne Bonamici*	Jan. 31, 2012 ...	Feb. 7, 2012
Gabrielle Giffords, 8th AZ	Jan. 25, 2012	*Ron Barber*	June 12, 2012 ..	June 19, 2012
Donald M. Payne, 10th NJ	[March 6, 2012]	*Donald M. Payne, Jr.* [1]	Nov. 6, 2012	Nov. 15, 2012
Jay Inslee, 1st WA	March 20, 2012	*Suzan K. DelBene* [2]	Nov. 6, 2012	Nov. 13, 2012
Thaddeus G. McCotter, 11th MI	July 6, 2012	David Alan Curson	Nov. 6, 2012	Nov. 13, 2012
Geoff Davis, 4th KY ...	July 31, 2012	Thomas Massie [3]	Nov. 6, 2012	Nov. 13, 2012
Dennis A. Cardoza, 18th CA	(Aug. 15, 2012) [4] ...	....	....	
Jesse L. Jackson, Jr., 2d IL	(Nov. 21, 2012) [5] ...	....	....	
Bob Filner, 51st CA	(Dec. 3, 2012) [6]	....	....	
Tim Scott, 1st SC	Jan. 2, 2012 [7]	....	....	

[1] Representative Payne, Jr. elected simultaneously to the 112th Congress and 113th Congress, by special election to fill the vacancy caused by the death of Representative Donald Milford Payne.

[2] Representative DelBene elected simultaneously to the 112th Congress and 113th Congress, by special election to fill the vacancy caused by the resignation of Representative Jay Inslee.

[3] Representative Massie elected simultaneously to the 112th Congress and 113th Congress, by special election to fill the vacancy caused by the resignation of Representative Geoff Davis.

[4] This seat was in interim vacant status until a new Representative was elected to fill the unexpired term. The seat was filled in the general elections on November 6, 2012, with term beginning in the 113th Congress.

[5] Representative Jesse L. Jackson, Jr. was elected to the 113th Congress on November 6, 2012, but declined his seat. This seat was in interim vacant status until a new Representative was elected to fill the unexpired term.

[6] This seat was in interim vacant status until a new Representative was elected to fill the unexpired term. The seat was filled in the general elections on November 6, 2012, with term beginning in the 113th Congress.

[7] Representative Scott resigned to accept appointment to the United States Senate. The seat was filled in a special election on May 7, 2013.

FOREWORD

The *Congressional Directory* is one of the oldest working handbooks within the United States Government. While there were unofficial directories for Congress in one form or another beginning with the 1st Congress in 1789, the *Congressional Directory* published in 1847 for the 30th Congress is considered by scholars and historians to be the first official edition because it was the first to be ordered and paid for by Congress. With the addition of biographical sketches of legislators in 1867, the *Congressional Directory* attained its modern format.

The *Congressional Directory* is published by the United States Congress in partnership with the Government Printing Office, at the direction of the Joint Committee on Printing under the authority of Title 44, Section 721 of the U.S. Code.

JOINT COMMITTEE ON PRINTING

Charles E. Schumer, Senator from New York, *Chair*

Gregg Harper, Representative from Mississippi, *Vice Chair*

Senate

Tom Udall, of New Mexico.
Mark R. Warner, of Virginia.
Pat Roberts, of Kansas.
Saxby Chambliss, of Georgia.

House

Candice S. Miller, of Michigan.
Richard B. Nugent, of Florida.
Robert A. Brady, of Pennsylvania.
Juan Vargas, of California.

The 2013–2014 *Congressional Directory* was compiled by the Government Printing Office, under the direction of the Joint Committee on Printing by:

Project Manager.—Evangeline R. Brown.

Editors: Farnsworth Alston; Michael Bush; Mary Ann Carter; Natoshka Faxio-Douglas; Regina G. Mitchell; Frances M. Wilson.

Typographers: Michael E. Colbert; Necandra T. Williams.

Proofreader/Editor.—Margaret Ross-Smith.

State District Maps.—Election Data Services, Inc.

Representatives' Zip Codes.—House Office of Mailing Services/U.S. Postal Service.

For sale by the Superintendent of Documents, U.S. Government Printing Office

Internet: bookstore.gpo.gov; Phone: toll free (866) 512–1800; DC area (202) 512–1800

Fax: (202) 512–2250; Mail: Stop SSOP, Washington, DC 20402–0001

Paper Cover ISBN–978–0–16–091922–0

Casebound ISBN–978–0–16–091921–3

CONTENTS

Name Index on page 1145

113th Congress*

THE VICE PRESIDENT

JOSEPH R. BIDEN, Jr., Democrat, of Wilmington, DE; born in Scranton, PA, November 20, 1942; education: St. Helena's School, Wilmington, DE; Archmere Academy, Claymont, DE; A.B., history and political science, University of Delaware; J.D., Syracuse University College of Law; married: Jill Tracy Biden; children: Joseph R. Biden III, Robert Hunter Biden, and Ashley Blazer Biden; admitted to the bar, December 1968, Wilmington, DE; engaged in private practice until 1972; served on New Castle County Council, 1970–72; elected to the U.S. Senate on November 7, 1972; reelected to each succeeding Senate term; served on committees: chair, Foreign Relations; Judiciary; elected as 47th Vice President of the United States on November 4, 2008; took the oath of office on January 20, 2009 and took the oath of office for a second time on January 20, 2013.

The Ceremonial Office of the Vice President is S–212 in the Capitol. The Vice President has offices in the Dirksen Senate Office Building, the Eisenhower Executive Office Building (EEOB) and the White House (West Wing).

Assistant to the President and Chief of Staff to the Vice President.—Bruce Reed, EEOB, room 276, 456–9000.

Deputy Assistant to the President and Chief of Staff to Dr. Jill Biden.—Sheila Nix, EEOB, room 200, 456–7458.

Deputy Assistant to the President and Director of Economic and Domestic Policy to the Vice President.—Sarah Bianchi, EEOB, room 280, 456–3460.

Deputy Assistant to the President and National Security Advisor to the Vice President.—Jacob Sullivan, EEOB, room 206, 456–2744.

Deputy Assistant to the President and Assistant to the Vice President for Communications.—Shailagh Murray, EEOB, room 288, 456–0373.

Deputy Assistant to the President and Senior Advisor to the Vice President.—Jose Cerda, EEOB, room 204, 456–9000.

Special Assistant to the President and Assistant to the Vice President for Intergovernmental Affairs, Public Engagement, and Correspondence.—Lise Clavel, EEOB, room 202A, 456–8240.

Counselor to the Vice President.—Steve Ricchetti, EEOB, room 272, 456–9000.

Counsel to the Vice President.—Demetra Lambros, EEOB, room 266, 456–3241.

Director of:

Administration to the Vice President.—Faisal Amin, EEOB, room 263, 456–2599.

Advance to the Vice President.—Chad Bolduc, EEOB, room 269, 456–3878.

Legislative Affairs to the Vice President.—Tonya Williams, EEOB, room 279A, 456–1540.

Scheduling to the Vice President.—Alex Hornbrook, EEOB, room 265, 456–6773.

Executive Assistants to the Vice President: Kathy Chung, Kellen Suber, West Wing.

---

*Biographies are based on information furnished or authorized by the respective Senators and Representatives.

ALABAMA

(Population 2010, 4,779,736)

SENATORS

RICHARD C. SHELBY, Republican, of Tuscaloosa, AL; born in Birmingham, AL, May 6, 1934; education: attended the public schools; B.A., University of Alabama, 1957; LL.B., University of Alabama School of Law, 1963; professional: attorney; admitted to the Alabama bar in 1961 and commenced practice in Tuscaloosa; member, Alabama State Senate, 1970–78; law clerk, Supreme Court of Alabama, 1961–62; city prosecutor, Tuscaloosa, 1963–71; U.S. Magistrate, Northern District of Alabama, 1966–70; special assistant Attorney General, State of Alabama, 1969–71; chairman, legislative council of the Alabama Legislature, 1977–78; former president, Tuscaloosa County Mental Health Association; member of Alabama Code Revision Committee, 1971–75; member: Phi Alpha Delta legal fraternity, Tuscaloosa County; Alabama and American bar associations; First Presbyterian Church of Tuscaloosa; Exchange Club; American Judicature Society; Alabama Law Institute; married: the former Annette Nevin in 1960; children: Richard C., Jr., and Claude Nevin; committees: ranking member, Appropriations; Banking, Housing, and Urban Affairs; Rules and Administration; elected to the 96th Congress on November 7, 1978; reelected to the three succeeding Congresses; elected to the U.S. Senate on November 4, 1986; reelected to each succeeding Senate term.

Office Listings

http://shelby.senate.gov twitter: @senshelbypress

304 Russell Senate Office Building, Washington, DC 20510 .... (202) 224–5744
Chief of Staff.—Alan Hanson. FAX: 224–3416
Personal Secretary / Appointments.—Anne Caldwell.
Press Secretary.—Jonathan Graffeo.
2005 University Boulevard, Suite 2100, Tuscaloosa, AL 35401 .... (205) 759–5047
FAX: 759–5067
Vance Federal Building, Room 321, 1800 5th Avenue North, Birmingham, AL 35203 .... (205) 731–1384
John A. Campbell Federal Courthouse, Suite 445, 113 St. Joseph Street, Mobile, AL 36602 .... (251) 694–4164
Frank M. Johnson Federal Courthouse, Suite 208, 15 Lee Street, Montgomery, AL 36104 .... (334) 223–7303
Huntsville International Airport, 1000 Glenn Hearn Boulevard, Box 20127, Huntsville, AL 35824 .... (256) 772–0460

* * *

JEFF SESSIONS, Republican, of Mobile, AL; born in Selma, AL, December 24, 1946; education: graduated Wilcox County High School, Camden, AL; B.A., Huntingdon College, Montgomery, AL, 1969; J.D., University of Alabama, Tuscaloosa, 1973; professional: U.S. Army Reserves, captain, 1973–86; attorney; Assistant U.S. Attorney, South District of Alabama, 1975–77; U.S. Attorney, South District of Alabama, 1981–93; Attorney General, State of Alabama, 1994–96; married: the former Mary Blackshear, 1969; children: Mary Abigail, Ruth and Samuel; committees: ranking member, Budget; Armed Services; Environment and Public Works; Judiciary; elected to the U.S. Senate on November 5, 1996; reelected to each succeeding Senate term.

Office Listings

http://sessions.senate.gov twitter: @senatorsessions

326 Russell Senate Office Building, Washington, DC 20510 .... (202) 224–4124
Chief of Staff.—Rick Dearborn. FAX: 224–3149
Scheduler.—Kate Hollis.
Executive Assistant.—Peggi Hanrahan.
Communications Director.—Stephen Miller.
Press Secretary.—Jack Bonnikson.
341 Vance Federal Building, 1800 Fifth Avenue North, Birmingham, AL 35203 .... (205) 731–1500
Field Representative.—Virginia Amason.
Colonial Bank Centre, Suite 2300–A, 41 West I–65 Service Road North, Mobile, AL 36608 .... (251) 414–3083
Field Representative.—Valerie Day.
200 Clinton Avenue, NW., Suite 802, Huntsville, AL 35801 .... (256) 533–0979
Field Representative.—Lisa Montgomery.
United States Courthouse, 100 West Troy Street, Room 302, Dothan, AL 36303 .... (334) 792–4924

Field Representative.—Cecelia Meeks.
7550 Halcyon Summit Drive, Suite 150, Montgomery, AL 36117 .... (334) 244–7017
State Director.—Chuck Spurlock.

REPRESENTATIVES

FIRST DISTRICT

BRADLEY BYRNE, Republican, of Fairhope, AL; born in Mobile, AL, February 16, 1955; education: B.A. in public policy and history, Duke University, 1977, J.D., the University of Alabama, 1980; professional: Alabama State Board of Education; Chancellor of two-year college system, Alabama State Senate / Organizations: Leadership Alabama, Alabama PTA, U.S. Supreme Court Bar, Alabama State Workforce Planning Council; (chair) / awards: Council for Leaders in Alabama Schools Legislative Leadership Award (2007); Alabama Wildlife Foundation Legislator of the Year Award (2005); South Alabama Literacy Champion Award (2006); religion: Episcopalian; wife: Rebecca; children: Patrick, Laura, Kathleen, and Colin; committees: Armed Services; Natural Resources; elected by special election to the 113th Congress on December 17, 2014, to fill the vacancy caused by the resignation of United States Representative Jo Bonner.

Office Listings

http://byrne.house.gov

2236 Rayburn House Office Building, Washington, DC 20515 .... (202) 225–4931
Chief of Staff.—Alex Schriver. FAX: 225–0562
Legislative Director.—Matt Weinstein.
Scheduler.—Errical Bryant.
11 North Water Street, Suite 15290, Mobile, AL 36602 .... (251) 690–2811
201 East Section Avenue, Foley, AL 36535 .... (251) 972–8545

Counties: BALDWIN, CLARKE (part), ESCAMBIA, MOBILE, MONROE, AND WASHINGTON. Population (2010), 687,841.

ZIP Codes: 36420, 36425–27, 36432, 36439, 36441, 36444–46, 36451, 36460–62, 36470–71, 36475, 36480–83, 36502–05, 36507, 36509, 36511–13, 36518, 36521–30, 36532–33, 36535–36, 36538–39, 36541–45, 36547–51, 36553, 36555–56, 6558–62, 36564, 36567–69, 36571–72, 36575–85, 36587, 36590, 36601–13, 36615–19, 36628, 36633, 36640, 36652, 36660, 36663, 36670–71, 36685, 36688–89, 36691, 36693, 36695, 36768–69

* * *

SECOND DISTRICT

MARTHA ROBY, Republican, of Montgomery, AL; born in Montgomery, July 26, 1976; education: B.M., New York University, New York, NY, 1998; J.D., Cumberland School of Law at Samford University, Birmingham, AL, 2001; professional: attorney, Copeland, Franco, Screws, and Gill, P.A.; Councilor, District Seven, City of Montgomery; religion: Christian (Presbyterian); family: husband, Riley; children: Margaret and George; committees: Appropriations; elected to the 112th Congress on November 2, 2010; reelected to the 113th Congress on November 6, 2012.

Office Listings

http://roby.house.gov http://twitter.com/repmartharoby

428 Cannon House Office Building, Washington, DC 20515 .... (202) 225–2901
Chief of Staff.—Stephen Boyd. FAX: 225–8913
Legislative Director.—Vacant.
Communications Director.—Todd Stacy.
Director of Scheduling.—Jessica Fuller.
401 Adams Avenue, Suite 160, Montgomery, AL 36104 .... (334) 277–9113
217 Graceland Drive, Suite 5, Dothan, AL 36303 .... (334) 794–9680
505 East Three Notch Street, Andalusia City Hall, Room 322, Andalusia, AL 36420 .... (334) 428–1129

Counties: AUTAUGA, BARBOUR, BULLOCK, BUTLER, COFFEE, CONECUH, COVINGTON, CRENSHAW, DALE, ELMORE, GENEVA, HENRY, HOUSTON, MONTGOMERY (part), PIKE. Population (2010), 673,887.

ZIP Codes: 35010, 36003, 36005–06, 36009–10, 36016–17, 36020, 36022, 36024–30, 36032–38, 36041–43, 36046–49, 36051–54, 36064, 36066–67, 36069, 36071, 36078–82, 36089, 36091–93, 36104–13, 36115–17, 36301, 36303, 36305,

36310–14, 36316–23, 36330, 36340, 36343–46, 36350–53, 36360, 36362, 36370–71, 36373–76, 36401, 36420–21, 36426, 36432, 36442, 36453–56, 36460, 36467, 36471, 36473–77, 36483, 36502, 36703, 36749, 36758, 36860

* * *

THIRD DISTRICT

MIKE ROGERS, Republican, of Saks, AL; born in Hammond, IN, July 16, 1958; education: B.A., Jacksonville State University, 1981; M.P.A., Jacksonville State University, 1984; J.D., Birmingham School of Law, 1991; professional: attorney; awards: Anniston Star Citizen of the Year, 1998; public service: Calhoun County Commissioner, 1987–91; Alabama House of Representatives, 1994–2002; family: married to Beth; children: Emily, Evan, and Elliot; committees: Agriculture; Armed Services; Homeland Security; elected to the 108th Congress on November 5, 2002; reelected to each succeeding Congress.

Office Listings

http://www/house.gov/mike-rogers twitter: @repmikerogersal

324 Cannon House Office Building, Washington, DC 20515 .... (202) 225–3261
Chief of Staff.—Marshall Macomber. FAX: 226–8485
Deputy Chief of Staff.—Chris Brinson.
Legislative Director.—Whitney Verett.
Press Secretary.—Shea Snider.
Scheduler.—Jessica Jennings.
1129 Noble Street, 104 Federal Building, Anniston, AL 36201 .... (256) 236–5655
District Director.—Sheri Rollins.
1819 Pepperell Parkway, Suite 203, Opelika, AL 36801 .... (334) 745–6221
Field Representative.—Cheryl Cunningham.

Counties: CALHOUN, CHAMBERS, CHEROKEE, CLAY, CLEBURNE, COOSA (part), LEE, MACON, MONTGOMERY (part), RANDOLPH, RUSSELL, ST. CLAIR, TALLADEGA, AND TALLAPOOSA. Population (2010), 682,819.

ZIP Codes: 30165, 31905, 35004, 35010, 35014, 35032, 35044, 35052, 35054, 35072, 35082, 35089, 35094, 35096, 35112, 35120–21, 35125, 35128, 35131, 35133, 35135, 35146, 35149–51, 35160, 35173, 35178, 35901, 35903, 35905, 35953, 35959–61, 35967, 35972–73, 35983, 35987, 36013, 36027, 36029, 36031, 36039, 36052, 36064, 36075, 36078, 36083, 36088–89, 36116–17, 36201, 36203, 36205–07, 36250–51, 36255–56, 36258, 36260, 36262–69, 36271–74, 36276–80, 36801, 36804, 36830, 36832, 36849–50, 36852–56, 36858–63, 36865–67, 36869–71, 36874–75, 36877, 36879

* * *

FOURTH DISTRICT

ROBERT B. ADERHOLT, Republican, of Haleyville, AL; born in Haleyville, July 22, 1965; education: graduate, Birmingham Southern University; J.D., Cumberland School of Law, Samford University; professional: attorney; assistant legal advisor to Governor Fob James, 1995–96; Haleyville municipal judge, 1992–96; George Bush delegate, Republican National Convention, 1992; Republican nominee for the 17th District, Alabama House of Representatives, 1990; married: Caroline McDonald; children: Mary Elliott and Robert Hayes; committees: Appropriations; elected to the 105th Congress; reelected to each succeeding Congress.

Office Listings

http://www.aderholt.house.gov twitter: @robert__aderholt

2369 Rayburn House Office Building, Washington, DC 20515 .... (202) 225–4876
Chief of Staff.—Brian Rell. FAX: 225–5587
Legislative Director.—Mark Dawson.
Communications Director / Press Secretary.—Anne Marie Malecha.
Administrative Director.—Stephanie Brown.
Carl Elliott Building, 1710 Alabama Avenue, Room 247, Jasper, AL 35501 .... (205) 221–2310
District Field Director.—Paul Housel.
205 Fourth Avenue, NE., Suite 104, Cullman, AL 35055 .... (256) 734–6043
Director of Constituent Services.—Jennifer Taylor.
107 Federal Building, 600 Broad Street, Gadsden, AL 35901 .... (256) 546–0201
Field Representative.—Joe Morgan.
1011 George Wallace Boulevard, Suite 146, Tuscumbia, AL 35674 .... (256) 381–3450
Field Representative.—Kreg Kennedy.

Counties: BLOUNT (part), CHEROKEE (part), COLBERT, CULLMAN, DEKALB, ETOWAH, FAYETTE, FRANKLIN, JACKSON (part), LAMAR, LAWRENCE, MARION, MARSHALL,TUSCALOOSA (part), WALKER, WINSTON. Population (2010), 682,029.

ZIP Codes: 35006, 35013, 35016, 35019, 35031, 35033, 35049, 35053, 35055, 35057–58, 35062–63, 35070, 35077, 35079, 35083, 35087, 35097–98, 35121, 35126, 35130, 35133, 35146, 35172, 35175, 35179–80, 35447, 35461, 35481, 35501,

35503–04, 35540–46, 35548–50, 35552–55, 35563–65, 35570–72, 35574–82, 35584–87, 35592–94, 35601, 35603, 35619, 35621–22, 35640, 35653–54, 35670, 35673, 35747, 35754–55, 35760, 35765, 35769, 35771, 35775–76, 35901, 35903–07, 35950–54, 35956–57, 35961–64, 35966–68, 35971–72, 35974–76, 35978–81, 35984, 35986–90, 36272

* * *

FIFTH DISTRICT

MO BROOKS, Republican, of Huntsville, AL; born in Charleston, SC, April 29, 1954; education: B.A., Duke University, Durham, NC, 1975; J.D., University of Alabama School of Law, Tuscaloosa, AL, 1978; professional: lawyer, private practice, partner in Leo and Brooks law firm; prosecutor, Office of the District Attorney, Tuscaloosa County, AL, 1978–80; clerk, Circuit Court Judge John Snodgrass, 1980–82; member of the Alabama State House of Representatives, 1983–91; district attorney, Office of the District Attorney, Madison County, AL, 1991–93; special assistant attorney general, state of Alabama, 1995–2002; commissioner, Madison County, AL, board of commissions, 1996–2010; religion: Christian; married: Martha; four children; committees: Armed Services; Science, Space, and Technology; Foreign Affairs; elected to the 112th Congress on November 2, 2010; reelected to the 113th Congress on November 6, 2012.

Office Listings

http://brooks.house.gov https://twitter.com/repmobrooks

1230 Longworth House Office Building, Washington, DC 20515 .... (202) 225–4801
Chief of Staff / Legislative Director.—Mark Pettitt. FAX: 225–4392
Scheduler / Office Manager.—Kelly Zams.
2101 West Clinton Avenue, Suite 302, Huntsville, AL 35805 .... (256) 551–0190
District Director.—Tiffany Noel.
Field Representative.—Kathy Murray.
Special Projects Coordinator and Caseworker.—Sandy Garvey.
Caseworkers: Debi Echols, Timothy Jackson.
302 Lee Street, Room 86, Decatur, AL 35601 .... (256) 355–9400
District Field Representative and Caseworker.—Johnny Turner.
102 South Court Street, Suite 310, Florence, AL 35630 .... (256) 718–5155
District Field Representative and Caseworker.—Laura Smith.

Counties: JACKSON, LAUDERDALE, LIMESTONE, MADISON, MORGAN. Population (2010), 718,724.

ZIP Codes: 35652, 35648, 35645, 35630–34, 35677, 35617, 35610–15, 35620, 35647–49, 35671, 35741, 35748–52, 35756–63, 35767, 35773–76, 35801–16, 35824, 35893–94, 35601–03, 35609–15, 35619–21, 35622, 35640, 35670, 35673, 35699, 35754, 35775, 35740, 35744–46, 35751–52, 35755–69, 35771, 35772, 35774, 35776, 35958, 35966, 35979, 35016, 35739–42, 35896, 35898–99, 35958, 35966, 35978–79

* * *

SIXTH DISTRICT

SPENCER BACHUS, Republican, of Vestavia Hills, AL; born in Birmingham, AL, December 28, 1947; education: B.A., Auburn University, 1969; J.D., University of Alabama, 1972; professional: law firm, Bachus, Dempsey, Carson, and Steed, senior partner; member: Hunter Street Baptist Church; Alabama State Representative and Senator; school board; Republican Party Chair; children: Warren, Stuart, Elliott, Candace, and Lisa; committees: chair emeritus, Financial Services; Judiciary; elected to the 103rd Congress, November 3, 1992; reelected to each succeeding Congress.

Office Listings

http://www.house.gov/bachus twitter: @bachusal06

2246 Rayburn House Office Building, Washington, DC 20515 .... (202) 225–4921
Chief of Staff.—Michael Staley. FAX: 225–2082
Press Secretary.—Tim Johnson.
Legislative Director.—Philip Swartzfager.
1900 International Park Drive, Suite 107, Birmingham, AL 35243 .... (205) 969–2296
703 Second Avenue North, P.O. Box 502, Clanton, AL 35046 .... (205) 280–0704
Scheduler.—Brett Williams.

Counties: BIBB, BLOUNT (part), CHILTON, COOSA (part), JEFFERSON (part), SHELBY. CITIES AND TOWNSHIPS: Adamsville, Allgood, Altoona, Argo, Bessemer, Birmingham, Blountsville, Brantleyville, Brent, Brook Highland, Brookside, Calera, Cardiff, Center Point, Centreville, Chelsea, Clanton, Clay, Cleveland, Columbiana, Concord, County Line, Dunnavant, Forestdale, Fultondale, Gardendale, Garden City, Goodwatter, Graysville, Harpersville, Hayden, Helena, Highland Lake, Hissop, Homewood, Hoover, Hueytown, Indian Springs Village, Irondale, Jemison, Kellyton, Kimberly, Leeds, Locust

Fork, Maplesville, Maytown, McDonald Chapel, Meadowbrook, Montevallo, Morris, Mount Olive, Mountain Brook, Mulga, Nectar, North Johns, Oneonta, Pelham, Pinson, Pleasant Grove, Rock Creek, Rockford, Rosa, Shelby, Shoal Creek, Smoke Rise, Snead, Sterrett, Susan Moore, Sylvan Springs, Tarrant, Thorsby, Trafford, Trussville, Vance, Vandiver, Vestavia Hills, Vincent, Warrior, West Blocton, West Jefferson, Westover, Wilsonville, Wilton, and Woodstock. Population (2010), 682,819.

ZIP Codes: 35004–07, 35015, 35022–23, 35035, 35040, 35043, 35046, 35048, 35051–52, 35054, 35060, 35062–63, 35068, 35071, 35073–74, 35078–80, 35085, 35091, 35094, 35096, 35111–12, 35114–20, 35123–28, 35130–31, 35133, 35135, 35137, 35139, 35142–44, 35146–48, 35151, 35171–73, 35175–76, 35178, 35180–88, 35201–03, 35205–07, 35209–10, 35212–17, 35219, 35222–26, 35230, 35233, 35235–37, 35240, 35242–46, 35249, 35253–55, 35259–61, 35266, 35277–83, 35285, 35287–99, 35402–03, 35406–07, 35444, 35446, 35452, 35456–58, 35466, 35468, 35473, 35475–76, 35480, 35482, 35490, 35546, 35579, 35953, 35987, 36006, 36051, 36064, 36091, 36750, 36758, 36790, 36792–93

* * *

SEVENTH DISTRICT

TERRI A. SEWELL, Democrat, of Birmingham, AL; born in Selma, AL, January 1, 1965; education: graduated from Selma High School, Selma, AL; B.A., *cum laude,* Princeton University, Princeton, NJ, 1986; masters degree with first class honors from Oxford University, Oxford, UK, 1988; J.D., Harvard Law School, Cambridge, MA, 1992; professional: attorney; judicial law clerk to the Honorable Chief Judge U.W. Clemon, U.S. District Court, Northern District of Alabama, in Birmingham; memberships and boards: Treasurer of the Board and Chair of the Finance Committee, St. Vincent's Foundation, Girl Scouts of Cahaba Council, Community Advisory Board for the DAB Minority Health and Research Center, Governing Board of the Alabama Council on Economic Education, Corporate Partners Council for the Birmingham Art Museum, Alpha Kappa Alpha Sorority, Inc., The Links, Inc.; professional affiliations: American Bar Association, National Bar Association, Alabama Bar Association; religion: Methodist; Chief Deputy Whip; committees: Financial Services; Permanent Select Committee on Intelligence; elected to the 112th Congress on November 2, 2010; reelected to the 113th Congress on November 6, 2012.

Office Listings

http://sewell.house.gov twitter: @repterrisewell

1133 Longworth House Office Building, Washington, DC 20515 .... (202) 225–2665
Chief of Staff.—Nichole Francis Reynolds. FAX: 226–9567
Legislative Director / Deputy Chief of Staff.—Matt Reel.
Legislative Counsel.—Cynthia Pullom.
Press Secretary / Legislative Assistant.—Hillary Beard.
Legislative Correspondent.—Will Dodd.
Scheduler.—Allison O'Connell.

Two 20th Street North, Suite 1130, Birmingham, AL 35203 .... (205) 254–1960
District Director.—Chasseny Lewis. FAX: 254–1974

186 Field of Dreams Drive, Demopolis, AL 36732 .... (334) 287–0860
FAX: 877–4489

205 North Washington Street, UWA Station 40 Webb Hall 236–237, Livingston, AL 35470 .... (205) 652–5834
FAX: 652–5935

300 Washington Street, Marion, AL 36756 .... (334) 683–2157
FAX: 683–2201

Federal Building, 908 Alabama Avenue, Suite 112, Selma, AL 36701 .... (334) 877–4414
FAX: 877–4489

2501 7th Street, Suite 300, Tuscaloosa, AL 35401 .... (205) 752–5380
FAX: 752–5899

Counties: CHOCTAW, CLARKE (part), DALLAS, GREENE, HALE, JEFFERSON (part), MARENGO, PERRY, PICKENS (part), SUMTER, TUSCALOOSA (part), AND WILCOX. Population (2010), 682,742.

ZIP Codes: 35005–06, 35020–23, 35034, 35036, 35041–42, 35061, 35064, 35068, 35071, 35073–74, 35079, 35111, 35117, 35126–27, 35173, 35175, 35184, 35188, 35203–15, 35217–18, 35221–22, 35224, 35228–29, 35233–35, 35238, 35243, 35401, 35404–06, 35440–44, 35446–49, 35452–53, 35456, 35459–60, 35462–64, 35466, 35469–71, 35473–78, 35480–81, 35485–87, 35490–91, 35546, 35601, 35603, 35640, 35754, 36030, 36032, 36040, 36064, 36105, 36435–36, 36451, 36482, 36524, 36540, 36545, 36558, 36701–03, 36720, 36722–23, 36726–28, 36732, 36736, 36738, 36740–42, 36744–45, 36748–54, 36756, 36758–59, 36761–69, 36773, 36775–76, 36782–86, 36790, 36792–93, 36901, 36904, 36906–08, 36910, 36912–13, 36915–16, 36919, 36921–22, 36925

ALASKA

(Population 2010, 710,231)

SENATORS

LISA MURKOWSKI, Republican, of Girdwood, AK; born in Ketchikan, AK, May 22, 1957; education: Willamette University, 1975–77; Georgetown University, 1978–80, B.A., economics; Willamette College of Law, 1982–85, J.D.; professional: attorney; private law practice; Alaska and Anchorage Bar Associations: public service: Anchorage Equal Rights Commission; Anchorage District Court Attorney, 1987–89; Task Force on the Homeless, 1990–91; Alaska State Representative, 1998–2002; family: married to Verne Martell; children: Nicholas and Matthew; committees: Appropriations; Energy and Natural Resources; Health, Education, Labor, and Pensions; Indian Affairs; appointed to the U.S. Senate on December 20, 2002; elected to the 109th Congress for a full Senate term on November 2, 2004; reelected as a write-in candidate to the 112th Congress on November 2, 2010.

Office Listings

http://murkowski.senate.gov

709 Hart Senate Office Building, Washington, DC 20510 .... (202) 224–6665
Chief of Staff.—Edward Hild. FAX: 224–5301
Legislative Director.—Tara Shaw.
Scheduler.—Kristen Daimler-Nothdurft.
510 L Street, Suite 600, Anchorage, AK 99501 .... (907) 271–3735
101 12th Avenue, Room 329, Fairbanks, AK 99701 .... (907) 456–0233
1900 First Avenue, Suite 225, Ketchikan, AK 99901 .... (907) 225–6880
851 East Westpoint Drive, Wasilla, AK 99654 .... (907) 376–7665
805 Frontage Road, Suite 105, Kenai, AK 99611 .... (907) 283–5808

* * *

MARK BEGICH, Democrat, of Anchorage, AK; born in Anchorage, March 30, 1962; education: Stellar High School, 1980; professional: Small Business Owner; Real Estate and Property Management; Alaska Student Loan Corporation 1995–02, chair 1996–02; Alaska Commission of Post-Secondary Education 1995–02, chair 1996–98; University of Alaska Board of Regents 2001–02; public service: Anchorage Assembly Member, 1988–98; Mayor of Anchorage, 2003–09; member: Boys & Girls Club; Association of the United States Army; Air Force Association; family: married to Deborah Bonito; children: Jacob Begich; committees: Appropriations; Commerce, Science, and Transportation; Indian Affairs; Homeland Security and Governmental Affairs; Veterans' Affairs; elected to U.S. Senate on November 4, 2008.

Office Listings

http://begich.senate.gov

111 Russell Senate Office Building, Washington, DC 20510 .... (202) 224–3004
Chief of Staff.—David Ramseur. FAX: 224–2354
Legislative Director.—Bruce Scnadling.
Scheduling Director.—Maya Ashwal.
Communications Director.—Rachel Barinbaum.
510 L Street, Suite 750, Anchorage, AK 99501 .... (907) 271–5915
101 12th Avenue, Room 328, Fairbanks, AK 99701 .... (907) 456–0261
851 East Westpoint Drive, Suite 309, Wasilla, AK 99654 .... (907) 357–9956
One Sealaska Plaza, Suite 308, Juneau, AK 99802 .... (907) 586–7700
805 Frontage Road, Suite 101, Kenai, AK 99611 .... (907) 283–4000
Whitecliff Building, Suite 230, 1900 First Avenue, Ketchikan, AK 99901 .... (907) 225–3000

REPRESENTATIVE

AT LARGE

DON YOUNG, Republican, of Fort Yukon, AK; born in Meridian, CA, June 9, 1933; education: A.A., Yuba Junior College; B.A., Chico State College, Chico, CA; Honorary Doctorate of Laws, University of Alaska, Fairbanks; State House of Representatives, 1966–70; U.S. Army, 41st Tank Battalion, 1955–57; elected member of the State Senate, 1970–73; served on the Fort Yukon City Council for six years, serving four years as mayor; educator for nine years; river boat captain; member: National Education Association, Elks, Lions, Jaycees; married: Lula Fredson of Fort Yukon; children: Joni and Dawn; committees: Natural Resources; Transportation and Infrastructure; elected to the 93rd Congress in a special election, March 6, 1973, to fill the vacancy created by the death of Congressman Nick Begich; reelected to each succeeding Congress.

Office Listings

http://www.house.gov/donyoung

2314 Rayburn House Office Building, Washington, DC 20515 .... (202) 225–5765
Administrative Assistant.—Pamela Day. FAX: 225–0425
Executive Assistant / Office Manager.—Alana Wilson.
Legislative Director.—Erik Elam.
4241 B Street, Suite 203, Anchorage, AK 99503 .... (907) 271–5978
FAX: 271–5950
100 Cushman Street, Suite 307, Fairbanks, AK 99707 .... (907) 456–0210
FAX: 456–0279
612 West Willoughby Avenue, Suite B, P.O. Box 21247, Juneau, AK 99802 .... (907) 586–7400
FAX: 586–8922

Population (2010), 710,231.

ZIP Codes: 99501–24, 99540, 99546–59, 99561, 99563–69, 99571–81, 99583–91, 99599, 99602–15, 99619–22, 99624–41, 99643–45, 99647–72, 99674–95, 99697, 99701–12, 99714, 99716, 99720–27, 99729–30, 99732–34, 99736–86, 99788–89, 99791, 99801–03, 99811, 99820–21, 99824–27, 99829–30, 99832–33, 99835–36, 99840–41, 99850

ARIZONA

(Population 2010, 6,392,017)

SENATORS

JOHN McCAIN, Republican, of Phoenix, AZ; born in the Panama Canal Zone, August 29, 1936; education: graduated Episcopal High School, Alexandria, VA, 1954; graduated, U.S. Naval Academy, Annapolis, MD, 1958; National War College, Washington, DC, 1973; retired captain (pilot), U.S. Navy, 1958–81; military awards: Silver Star, Bronze Star, Legion of Merit, Purple Heart, and Distinguished Flying Cross; chair, International Republican Institute; married to the former Cindy Hensley; seven children: Doug, Andy, Sidney, Meghan, Jack, Jim, and Bridget; committees: Armed Services; Foreign Relations; Homeland Security and Governmental Affairs; Indian Affairs; elected to the 98th Congress in November, 1982; reelected to the 99th Congress in November, 1984; elected to the U.S. Senate in November, 1986; reelected to each succeeding Senate term.

Office Listings

http://mccain.senate.gov twitter: @senjohnmccain

241 Russell Senate Office Building, Washington, DC 20510 .... (202) 224–2235
Chief of Staff.—Pablo Carrillo. TDD: 224–7132
Legislative Director.—Joseph Donoghue.
Communications Director.—Brian Rogers.
Scheduler.—Ellen Cahill.
2201 East Camelback Road, Suite 115, Phoenix, AZ 85016 .... (602) 952–2410
TDD: 952–0170
122 North Cortez Street, Suite 108, Prescott, AZ 86301 .... (928) 445–0833
407 West Congress Street, Suite 103, Tucson, AZ 85701 .... (602) 670–6334

* * *

JEFFRY ''JEFF'' FLAKE, Republican, of Mesa, born in Snowflake, AZ, December 31, 1962; education: B.A. degree in international relations, Brigham Young University, Provo, UT, 1986; M.A. degree, political science, Brigham Young University, Provo, UT, 1987; professional: executive director, Foundation for Democracy, Namibia 1989–90; director, Interface Public Affairs, Washington, DC, 1990–92; executive director, Goldwater Institute, Phoenix, AZ, 1992–99; member, United States House of Representatives, 2001–13; religion: Church of Jesus Christ of Latter-Day Saints; family: wife, Cheryl; children: Ryan, Alexis, Austin, Tanner, Dallin; grandchild: Aiden Jeffry; committees: Foreign Relations; Energy and Natural Resources; Judiciary; Special Committee on Aging; elected to the U.S. Senate on November 6, 2012.

Office Listings

www.flake.senate.gov

S–368 Russell Senate Office Building, Washington, DC 20510 .... (202) 224–4521
Chief of Staff.—Steve Voeller. FAX: 228–0515
Legislative Director.—Chandler Morse.
Administrative Director.—Celeste Gold.
Scheduler.—Megan Runyan.
2200 East Camelback Road, Suite 120, Phoenix, AZ 85016 .... (602) 840–1891
FAX: 840–4848
6840 North Oracle Road, Suite 150, Tucson, AZ 85704 .... (520) 575–8633
FAX: 797–3232

REPRESENTATIVES

FIRST DISTRICT

ANN KIRKPATRICK, Democrat, of Flagstaff, AZ; born in McNary, AZ, March 24, 1950; education: B.A., University of Arizona, Tucson, 1972; J.D., University of Arizona College of Law, Tucson, 1979; professional: Coconino Deputy County Attorney, 1980–81; Pima Deputy County Attorney, 1981–85; Sedona City Attorney, 1990–91; Partner, Kirkpatrick & Harris, Law Firm P.C., 1991–2008; Instructor, Business Law & Ethics, Coconino Community College, 2004; Representative, Arizona State House, District 2, 2005–07; Representative, 111th United States Congress, District 1, 2009–10; caucuses: Veterans' Jobs; Native American; General Aviation;

Small Brewers; United Solutions; Youth Drug Prevention; Anti-Bullying; Healthcare Innovation Task Force; Congressional Gaming; Congressional Diabetes; Mental Health; Small Business; Healthy Forests Caucus; P3 Caucus; Congressional Academic Medicine Caucus; High Performance Building Caucus; Congressional Tennis Caucus; religion: Catholic; married: husband Roger Curley, two children; committees: Transportation and Infrastructure, Veterans' Affairs; elected to the 113th Congress on November 6, 2012.

Office Listings

http://kirkpatrick.house.gov   twitter.com/repkirkpatrick   facebook.com/repkirkpatrick

330 Cannon House Office Building, Washington, DC 20515 .... (202) 225–3361
Chief of Staff.—Carmen Gallus. FAX: 225–3462
Legislative Director.—Ken Montoya.
Communications Director.—Jennifer Johnson.
Scheduler.—Samantha Frisby.
405 North Beaver Street, Suite 6, Flagstaff, AZ 86001 .... (928) 213–9977
District Director.—Ron Lee.
211 North Florence Street, Suite 1, Casa Grande, AZ 85122 .... (520) 316–0839
Deputy Director/Community Outreach.—Blanca Varela.
11555 West Civic Center Drive, Suite 104A, Marana, AZ 85653 .... (520) 382–2663
Caseworker.—Zak Royse.
550 North 9th Place, Show Low, AZ 85901 .... (928) 537–5657
Community Outreach.—Jerry Brownlow.
1400 East Ash, Globe, AZ 85501 .... (928) 425–3231
Community Outreach.—Cathy Melvin.

Counties: APACHE, COCONINO (part), GILA (part), GRAHAM, GREENLEE, MARICOPA (part), NAVAJO, PIMA (part), PINAL (part), and YAVAPAI (part). Population: (2010), 724,868.

ZIP Codes: 85122–23, 85128, 85130–32, 85135, 85137–39, 85141–42, 85145, 85172–73, 85191–94, 85226, 85248, 85339, 85501–02, 85530–36, 85539–40, 85542–43, 85545–46, 85548, 85550–52, 85618, 85623, 85631, 85643, 85652–54, 85658, 85704, 85718, 85737, 85739, 85741–43, 85755, 85901–02, 85911–12, 85920, 85922–42, 86001–04, 86011, 86015, 86017–18, 86020, 86022–25, 86028, 86030–33, 86035–36, 86038–40, 86042, 86044–47, 86052–54, 86322, 86325–26, 86335–36, 86339–42, 86351, 86434–35, 86502–08, 86510–12, 86514–15, 86520, 86535, 86538, 86540, 86544–45, 86547, 86556

* * *

SECOND DISTRICT

RON BARBER, Democrat, of Tucson, AZ; born in Wakefield, England, August 25, 1945; education: B.A., University of Arizona, Tucson, AZ, 1967; married: Nancy Barber; children: two daughters; committees: Armed Services; Homeland Security, Small Business; elected to the 112th Congress on June 12, 2012, by special election, to fill the vacancy caused by the resignation of United States Representative Gabrielle Giffords; elected to a full term in the 113th Congress on November 6, 2012.

Office Listings

http://www.barber.house.gov   twitter: @repronbarber

1029 Longworth House Office Building, Washington, DC 20515 .... (202) 225–2542
Chief of Staff.—Jennifer Cox. FAX: 225–0378
Scheduler.—Mikaela Ober Schuster.
3945 East Fort Lowell, Suite 211, Tucson, AZ 85712 .... (520) 881–3588
District Director.—Jessica Floyd.
77 Calle Portal, Suite B–160, Sierra Vista, AZ 85635 .... (520) 459–3115

Counties: COCHISE, PIMA (part), SANTA CRUZ (part). Population (2010), 722,918.

ZIP Codes: 85602–3, 85605–10, 85613–17, 85619–20, 85622, 85625–27, 85629–30, 85632, 85635–36, 85638, 85641, 85643–45, 85650, 85655, 85670, 85704–08, 85710–19, 85722, 85728, 85730–33, 85738, 85740–45, 85747–52

* * *

THIRD DISTRICT

RAÚL M. GRIJALVA, Democrat, of Tucson, AZ; born in Tucson, February 19, 1948; education: Sunnyside High School, Tucson, AZ; B.A., University of Arizona; professional: former Assistant Dean for Hispanic Student Affairs, University of Arizona; former Director of the El Pueblo Neighborhood Center; public service: Tucson Unified School District Governing Board,

1974–86; Pima County Board of Supervisors, 1989–2002; family: married to Ramona; three daughters; committees: Education and the Workforce; Natural Resources; elected to the 108th Congress on November 5, 2002; reelected to each succeeding Congress.

Office Listings

http://www.house.gov/grijalva

1511 Longworth House Office Building, Washington, DC 20515 .... (202) 225–2435
Chief of Staff.—Amy Emerick. FAX: 225–1541
Legislative Director.—Kelsey Mishking.
Communications Director.—Adam Sarvana.
Scheduler.—Cristina Villa.
738 North 5th Avenue, Suite 110, Tucson, AZ 85705 .... (520) 622–6788
146 North State Avenue, Somerton, AZ 85350 .... (928) 343–7933
13065 West McDowell Road, Suite C–123, Avondale, AZ 85392 .... (623) 536–3388

Counties: LA PAZ (part), MARICOPA (part), PIMA (part), PINAL (part), SANTA CRUZ (part), and YUMA. Population (2010), 710,224.

ZIP Codes: 85033 (part), 85035 (part), 85037 (part), 85043 (part), 85139 (part), 85193 (part), 85305 (part), 85307 (part), 85321–22, 85323 (part), 85326 (part), 85329, 85336–37, 85338 (part), 85340 (part), 85341, 85343, 85349–50, 85353 (part), 85354 (part), 85364 (part), 85365 (part), 85366, 85369, 85392 (part), 85395 (part), 85396 (part), 85601, 85611, 85621, 85622 (part), 85624, 85628, 85629 (part), 85633–34, 85637, 85639–40, 85645 (part), 85646, 85648, 85653 (part), 85662, 85701–03, 85705 (part), 85706 (part), 85709, 85713 (part), 85714 (part), 85719 (part), 85721, 85723–26, 85734–36, 85743 (part), 85745 (part), 85746, 85754, 85756 (part), 85757, 85775

* * *

FOURTH DISTRICT

PAUL GOSAR, Republican, of Flagstaff, AZ; born in Rock Springs, WY, November 27, 1958; education: graduated, Pinedale High School, Pinedale, WY; B.S., Creighton University, Omaha, NE, 1981; D.D.S., Creighton University, Omaha, NE, 1985; professional: served as the President of the Northern Arizona Dental Society; Vice-Chair of the American Dental Association's Council on Governmental Affairs; awards: Arizona Dental Association's ''Dentist of the Year''; inducted into the Arizona Dental Association Hall of Fame; religion: Catholic; family: wife, Maude; children: Elle, Gaston, and Isabelle; caucuses: GOP Doctor's caucus, Immigration Reform caucus, and Coal caucus; committees: Natural Resources; Oversight and Government Reform; elected to the 112th Congress on November 2, 2010; reelected to the 113th Congress on November 6, 2012.

Office Listings

http://www.gosar.house.gov twitter: @repgosar https://www.facebook.com/repgosar
http://www.youtube.com/repgosar http://www.flickr.com/photos/repgosar

504 Cannon House Office Building, Washington, DC 20515 .... (202) 225–2315
Chief of Staff.—Tom Van Flein. FAX: 226–9739
Legislative Director.—Jeremy Harrell.
Communications Director.—Apryl Marie Fogel.
Press Secretary.—Orlando Watson.
Scheduler / Office Manager.—Leslie Rath.
District Director.—Penny Pew.
122 North Cortez Street, Suite 104, Prescott, AZ 86301 .... (928) 445–1683
FAX: 445–3414
207 East Hunt Highway, Suite 12, San Tan Valley, AZ 85143 .... (480) 882–2697
FAX: 882–2698
220 North 4th Street, Kingman, AZ 86401.

Counties: GILA, LA PAZ, MARICOPA, MOHAVE, PINAL, YAVAPAI, YUMA. CITIES AND TOWNSHIPS: Ak-Chin Village, Apache Junction, Arcosanti, Arizona City, Arizona Village, Ash Fork, Bagdad, Beaver Dam, Big Park, Black Canyon City, Blackwater, Bouse, Buckeye, Bullhead City, Central Heights-Midland City, Chino Valley, Chloride, Chuichu, Cibola, Clarkdale, Claypool, Colorado City, Cordes Lakes, Cornville, Cottonwood-Verde Village, Desert Hills, Dewey-Humboldt, Dolan Springs, Dudleyville, Ehrenberg, Eloy, Florence, Fort Mohave, Fortuna Foothills, Gadsden, Gisela, Globe, Gold Canyon, Golden Valley, Hackberry, Hayden, Hope, Jerome, Kaibab, Kearny, Kingman, Kohls Ranch, Lake Havasu City, Lake Montezuma, Litchfield Park, Littlefield, Mammoth, Marana, Maricopa, Mayer, Meadview, Mesquite Creek, Mohave Valley, Mojave Ranch Estates, New Kingman-Butler, Nothing, Oatman, Oracle, Parker, Parker Strip, Paulden, Payson, Peach Springs, Peeples Valley, Peoria, Pine, Poston, Prescott Valley, Quartzsite, Queen Creek, Queen Valley, Sacaton, Salome, San Luis, San Manuel, San Tan Valley, Santan, Scenic, Seligman, Somerton, Spring Valley, Stanfield, Star Valley, Superior, Surprise, Tacna, Topock, Top-of-the-World, Valentine, Wellton, Wendon, Wickenburg, Wikieup, Wilhoit, Williamson, Willow Valley, Winkelman, Yarnell, Young, Yucca, and Yuma. Population (2010), 707,750.

ZIP Codes: 85118, 85140, 85142–43, 85173, 85324–26, 85328, 85334, 85340, 85344, 85346, 85348, 85352, 85356–60, 85362, 85364–65, 85367, 85371, 85383, 85387, 85390, 85541, 85544, 85547, 85554, 86021–22, 86305, 86312, 86314–

15, 86320–21, 86323–27, 86331–34, 86337, 86401–06, 86409, 86411–13, 86426, 86431–33, 86436–38, 86440–42, 86444–46

* * *

FIFTH DISTRICT

MATT SALMON, Republican, of Mesa, AZ; born in Salt Lake City, UT, January 21, 1958; education: B.A. in english, Arizona State University, Phoenix, AZ, 1981; M.P.A., Brigham Young University, Provo, UT 1986; professional: telecommunications executive; community affairs manager; member of the Arizona State Senate, 1991–95; assistant majority leader, 1993–95; religion: Church of Jesus Christ of Latter-Day Saints; family: Matt has spent the last 34 years married to Nancy; four children; six grandchildren; served in Congress from 1995–2000; committees: Education and the Work Force; Foreign Relations; elected to the 113th Congress on November 6, 2012.

Office Listings

http://www.house.gov/salmon

2349 Rayburn House Office Building, Washington, DC 20515 .... (202) 226–2635
Chief of Staff.—Adam Deguire. FAX: 226–4386
Scheduler.—Olivia Vickers.
Communications Director.—Kristine Michalson.
207 North Gilbert Road, Suite 209, Gilbert, AZ 85234 .... (480) 699–8239

Counties: MARICOPA (part), PINAL (part). CITIES AND TOWNSHIPS: Apache Junction, Chandler, Gilbert, Mesa, and Queen Creek. Population (2010), 710,224.

ZIP Codes: 85120–21, 85127, 85142, 85147, 85201, 85203–10, 85212–13, 85215–16, 85224–25, 85233–34, 85236, 85249, 85275, 85277, 85286, 85295–97

* * *

SIXTH DISTRICT

DAVID SCHWEIKERT, Republican, of Fountain Hills, AZ; born March 3, 1962; education: B.A., Arizona State University, Tempe, AZ, 1988; M.B.A., Arizona State University, Tempe, AZ, 2005; professional: business owner of a real estate company; realtor; financial consultant; member of the Arizona state house of representatives, 1989–94; member of the Arizona state board of equalization, 1995–2003; former treasurer, Maricopa County, AZ, 2004–06; religion: Catholic; married: Joyce Schweikert; committees: Science, Space, and Technology; Small Business; elected to 112th Congress on November 2, 2010; reelected to the 113th Congress on November 6, 2012.

Office Listings

http://schweikert.house.gov twitter: @repdavid

1205 Longworth House Office Building, Washington, DC 20515 .... (202) 225–2190
Chief of Staff.—Matthew Tully. FAX: 225–0096
Senior Advisor.—Oliver Schwab.
Scheduler.—Kelly Roberson.
Legislative Director.—Beau Brunson.
Communications Director.—Rachel Semmel.
10603 North Hayden Road, Suite 108, Scottsdale, AZ 85260 .... (480) 946–2411
FAX: 946–2446

Counties: MARICOPA (part). CITIES AND TOWNSHIPS: Fountain Hills, Paradise Valley, Cave Creek, Carefree, Rio Verde, Scottsdale, Phoenix (part), Yavapai Nation, and Salt River Pima Maricopa Indian Community. Population (2010), 754,482.

ZIP Codes: 85020, 85022–24, 85027–29, 85032, 85050, 85054, 85201, 85250–51, 85253–56, 85258–60, 85264, 85268

* * *

SEVENTH DISTRICT

ED PASTOR, Democrat, of Phoenix, AZ; born in Claypool, AZ, June 28, 1943; education: attended public schools in Miami, AZ; graduate of Arizona State University; B.A., chemistry, 1966; J.D., Arizona University, 1974; professional: member, Governor Raul Castro's staff; taught chemistry, North High School; former deputy director of Guadalupe Organization, Inc.;

elected supervisor, board of supervisors, Maricopa County; served board of directors for the National Association of Counties; vice chairman, Employment Steering Committee; president, Arizona County Supervisors Association; member, executive committee of the Arizona Association of Counties; resigned, May, 1991; board of directors, Neighborhood Housing Services of America; National Association of Latino Elected Officials; served as director at large, ASU Alumni Association; founding board member, ASU Los Diablos Alumni Association; served on board of directors of the National Council of La Raza; Arizona Joint Partnership Training Council; National Conference of Christians and Jews; Friendly House; Chicanos Por La Causa; Phoenix Economic Growth Corporation; Sun Angel Foundation; vice president, Valley of the Sun United Way; advisory member, Boys Club of Metropolitan Phoenix; married: Verma; two daughters: Yvonne and Laura; appointed a Chief Deputy Minority Whip; committees: Appropriations; Permanent Select Committee on Intelligence; elected by special election on September 24, 1991, to fill the vacancy caused by the resignation of Morris K. Udall; elected in November, 1992, to the 103rd Congress; reelected to each succeeding Congress.

Office Listings

http://www.pastor.house.gov

2465 Rayburn House Office Building, Washington, DC 20515 .... (202) 225–4065
Executive Assistant.—Laura Campos. FAX: 225–1655
411 North Central Avenue, Suite 150, Phoenix, AZ 85004 .... (602) 256–0551
District Director.—Elisa de la Vara.

Counties: MARICOPA (part). Population (2010), 725,197.

ZIP Codes: 85001–10, 85012–19, 85021, 85025–26, 85030–31, 85033–38, 85040–44, 85048, 85051, 85061–64, 85066–67, 85072, 85074–75, 85079, 85082, 85098, 85282–83, 85301, 85303, 85305, 85311, 85318, 85323, 85339, 85353

* * *

EIGHTH DISTRICT

TRENT FRANKS, Republican, of Phoenix, AZ; born in Uravan, CO, June 19, 1957; education: attended Ottawa University; graduate of the Center for Constitutional Studies; professional: small business owner; oil field and drilling engineer; Executive Director, Arizona Family Research Institute; conservative writer, and former radio commentator, with Family Life Radio and NBC affiliate KTKP 1280 AM; public service: Arizona House of Representatives, 1985–87; appointed in 1987 to head the Arizona Governor's Office for Children; awards: True Blue award, Family Research Council; Spirit of Enterprise award, U.S. Chamber of Commerce; Taxpayer Hero, Council for Citizens Against Government Waste; Friend of Education award, Education Freedom Coalition; religion: Baptist; member, North Phoenix Baptist Church; married: Josephine; committees: Armed Services; Judiciary; elected to the 108th Congress on November 5, 2002; reelected to each succeeding Congress.

Office Listings

http://www.house.gov/franks

2435 Rayburn House Office Building, Washington, DC 20515 .... (202) 225–4576
Chief of Staff.—Randy Kutz. FAX: 225–6328
Executive Assistant.—Lisa Teschler.
Scheduler.—Anna Hurley.
Communications Director.—Ben Carnes.
Press Assistant.—Kate Middleton.
Speech Writer.—Bethany Haley.
Legislative Director.—Bobby Cornett.
MLA.—Drew Nishiyama.
Legislative Assistant.—Stephanie Hammond.
Legislative Correspondent.—Catherine Kutz.
DoD Fellow.—Sanjit Singh.
7121 West Bell Road, Suite 200, Glendale, AZ 85308 .... (623) 776–7911
District Director.—Dan Hay.
District Representatives: Lloyd Bostrom, Steve Montenegro, Brian Van Hovel, Doyle Scott.
Field Representative.—Shari Farrington.
Business / Commerce Liaison.—Michael Jameson.
Legal Counsel.—David Sheasby.
Staff Assistant.—Terry Murray.

Counties: MARICOPA, NEW RIVER, SUN CITY, SUN CITY WEST, SURPRISE (part), NORTH GATEWAY, GLENDALE, NEW VILLAGE, PEORIA. Population (2010), 305,198.

ZIP Codes: 85083, 85085–87, 85301–10, 85312, 85318, 85331, 85335, 85338, 85340, 85345, 85351, 85361, 85363, 85372–76, 85378–83, 85385, 85387–88, 85395

* * *

NINTH DISTRICT

KYRSTEN SINEMA, Democrat, of Phoenix, AZ; born in Tucson, AZ, July 12, 1976; education: B.A. social work, Brigham Young University, Provo, UT, 1995; M.A. social work, Arizona State University, Tempe, AZ, 1999; J.D. Arizona State University, Tempe, AZ, 2004; Ph.D., social justice, social inquiry, Arizona State University, Tempe, AZ, 2012; professional: member of the Arizona House of Representatives, 2005–11; Aspen-Rodel Public Leadership Fellow, 2008; assistant minority leader, Arizona House of Representatives, 2009–11; *Time* Magazine's Top 40 Under 40, 2010; member of the Arizona State Senate, 2011–12; TED Fellow, 2012; committees: Financial Services; elected to the 113th Congress on November 6, 2012.

Office Listings

http://sinema.house.gov twitter: @repsinema

1237 Longworth House Office Building, Washington, DC 20515 .... (202) 225–9888
Chief of Staff.—JoDee Winterhof. FAX: 225–9731
Legislative Director.—Kris Pratt.
Communications Director.—Justin Unga.
Scheduler.—Melissa Rasowsky.
2944 North 44th Street, Suite 150, Maricopa County, AZ 85018 .... (602) 956–2285
District Director.—Michelle Davidson.

Counties: MARICOPA COUNTY (part). CITIES: Ahwatukee, Chandler, Guadalupe, Mesa, Phoenix, Tempe. Population (2010), 722,896.

ZIP Codes: 85008 (part), 85011, 85012 (part), 85014 (part), 85016 (part), 85018 (part), 85020 (part), 85021 (part), 85044 (part), 85045, 85060, 85068, 85069, 85076, 85201 (part), 85202, 85210, 85211, 85224 (part), 85244, 85246, 85257 (part), 85271, 85274, 85280–81, 85282 (part), 85283 (part), 85284–85, 85287

ARKANSAS

(Population 2010, 2,915,918)

SENATORS

MARK L. PRYOR, Democrat, of Little Rock, AR; born in Fayetteville, AR, January 10, 1963; education: B.A., University of Arkansas, 1985; J.D., University of Arkansas, 1988; professional: attorney; Wright, Lindsey & Jennings (law firm); public service: elected, Arkansas House of Representatives, 1990; elected, Arkansas Attorney General, 1998; children: Adams and Porter; his father, David Pryor, was a former Governor and U.S. Senator from Arkansas; committees: Appropriations; Commerce, Science, and Transportation; Homeland Security and Governmental Affairs; Rules and Administration; Small Business and Entrepreneurship; Joint Economic Committee; Select Committee on Ethics; elected to the U.S. Senate on November 5, 2002; reelected to each succeeding Senate term.

Office Listings

http://pryor.senate.gov

255 Dirksen Senate Office Building, Washington, DC 20510 .... (202) 224–2353
Chief of Staff.—Andy York. FAX: 228–0908
Legislative Director.—Kristen Sharp.
Communications Director.—Michael Teague.
Office Manager.—Patrice Bolling.
500 Clinton Avenue, Suite 401, Little Rock, AR 72201 .... (501) 324–6336

* * *

JOHN NICHOLS BOOZMAN, Republican, of Rogers, AR; born in Shreveport, LA, December 10, 1950; education: Southern College of Optometry, Memphis, TN, 1977; also attended University of Arkansas, Fayetteville, AR; professional: doctor of optometry; business owner; rancher; religion: Southern Baptist; married: Mrs. Cathy Boozman; children: three daughters; committees: Agriculture, Nutrition, and Forestry; Appropriations; Environment and Public Works; Veterans' Affairs; elected to the U.S. House of Representatives 2001–11; elected to the U.S. Senate on November 2, 2010.

Office Listings

http://boozman.senate.gov twitter: @johnboozman

320 Hart Senate Office Building, Washington, DC 20510 .... (202) 224–4843
Chief of Staff.—C. Matthew Sagely. FAX: 228–1371
Deputy Chief of Staff / Counsel.—Susan Olson.
Legislative Director.—Kathee Facchiano.
Communications Director.—Sara Lasure.
Scheduler.—Lesley Parker.
1401 West Capitol Avenue, Plaza Suite F, Little Rock, AR 72201 .... (501) 372–7153
213 West Monroe, Suite N, Lowell, AR 72745 .... (479) 725–0400
1120 Garrison Avenue, Fort Smith, AR 72901 .... (479) 573–0189
1001 Highway 62 East, Suite 11, Mountain Home, AR 72653 .... (870) 424–0129
300 South Church Street, Suite 400, Jonesboro, AR 72401 .... (870) 268–6925
620 East 22nd Street, Suite 204, Stuttgart, AR 72160 .... (870) 672–6941
106 West Main Street, Suite 104, El Dorado, AR 71730 .... (870) 863–4641

REPRESENTATIVES

FIRST DISTRICT

RICK CRAWFORD, Republican, of Jonesboro, AR; born in Homestead AFB, FL, January 22, 1966; education: graduated, Alvirne High School; B.A., agricultural business and economics, Arkansas State University, 1996; professional: U.S. Army—Bomb Disposal Technician, 1985–89, Professional Rodeo Announcer; KAIT–TV Jonesboro—News Anchor; KFIN–FM—Farm Director; Delta Farm Roundup TV Show—Producer and Anchor; Agwatch—Owner and Operator; member: National Association of Farm Broadcasting; 4-H Foundation Board of Arkansas; recipient of the NAFB Newscast Award, 2006 and 2008; married: Stacy; children: Will and Delaney; Republican Study Committee; committees: Agriculture; Transportation and Infrastructure; elected to the 112th Congress on November 2, 2010; reelected to the 113th Congress on November 6, 2012.

Office Listings

http://crawford.house.gov twitter: @reprickcrawford
https://www.facebook.com/reprickcrawford?ref=br__tf

1408 Longworth House Office Building, Washington, DC 20515 .... (202) 225–4076
Chief of Staff.—Jonah Shumate. FAX: 225–5602
Press Secretary.—Jack Pandol.
Legislative Director.—Ted Verrill.
112 South First Street, Cabot, AR 72023 .... (501) 843–3043
2400 East Highland Drive, Suite 300, Jonesboro, AR 72401 .... (870) 203–0540
1001 Highway 62 East, Suite 9, Mountain Home, AR 72653 .... (870) 424–2075

Counties: ARKANSAS, BAXTER, CHICOT, CLAY, CLEBURNE, CRAIGHEAD, CRITTENDEN, CROSS, DESHA, FULTON, GREENE, INDEPENDENCE, IZARD, JACKSON, JEFFERSON (part), LAWRENCE, LEE, LINCOLN, LONOKE, MISSISSIPPI, MONROE, PHILLIPS, POINSETT, PRAIRIE, RANDOLPH, SAINT FRANCIS, SEARCY, SHARP, STONE, AND WOODRUFF. Population (2013), 729,510.

ZIP Codes: 72003, 72005–07, 72014, 72017, 72020–21, 72023–24, 72026, 72029, 72031, 72036–38, 72040–44, 72046, 72048, 72051, 72055, 72059–60, 72064, 72067, 72069, 72072–76, 72083, 72086, 72101–02, 72108, 72112, 72121, 72123, 72130–31, 72134, 72137, 72139–40, 72142–43, 72153, 72160, 72165–66, 72169–70, 72175–76, 72179, 72189, 72301, 72303, 72310–13, 72315–16, 72319–22, 72324–33, 72335–36, 72338–42, 72346–48, 72350–55, 72358–60, 72364–70, 72372–74, 72376–77, 72383–84, 72386–87, 72389–92, 72394–96, 72401–04, 72410–17, 72419, 72421–22, 72424–45, 72447, 72449–51, 72453–62, 72464–67, 72469–76, 72478–79, 72482, 72501, 72503, 72512–13, 72515, 72517, 72519–34, 72536–40, 72542–46, 72550, 72553–56, 72560–62, 72564–69, 72571–73, 72575–79, 72581, 72583–85, 72587, 72610, 72613, 72617, 72623, 72626, 72629, 72631, 72633, 72635–36, 72639, 72642, 72645, 72650–51, 72653–54, 72658, 72663, 72669, 72675, 72679–80, 72685–86

* * *

SECOND DISTRICT

TIM GRIFFIN, Republican, of Little Rock, AR; born in Charlotte, NC, August 21, 1968; education: B.A., Hendrix College, Conway, AR, 1990; attended Pembroke College, Oxford University, 1991; J.D., Tulane Law School, New Orleans, LA, 1994; professional: United States Army Reserve; Judge Advocate General's (JAG) Corps, 1996–present; business owner; lawyer, private practice; U.S. Attorney for the Eastern District of Arkansas, 2006–07; deputy director and special assistant to the President, White House Office of Political Affairs, 2005; religion: Baptist; married, two children; caucuses: National Guard and Reserve Components Caucus (NGRCC); General Aviation Caucus; Congressional Natural Gas Caucus; Congressional Sportsmen's Caucus; Congressional Military Family Caucus; Congressional Health Care Caucus; Air Force Caucus; Army Caucus; Congressional Motorcycle Caucus; Congressional Caucus for Competitiveness in Entertainment Technology (E-TECH); International Anti-Piracy Caucus; Wounded to Work Caucus; Multiple Sclerosis Caucus; Congressional Mississippi River Delta Caucus; Congressional Arthritis Caucus; Congressional Modeling and Simulation Caucus; Congressional Prayer Caucus; Congressional Cancer Caucus; Republican Israel Caucus; Congressional Nuclear Issues Working Group; Congressional Waterways Caucus; Congressional Diabetes Caucus; Congressional Caucus on U.S.-Turkish Relations and Turkish Americans; Congressional EOD Caucus; Congressional Community Health Center (CHC) Caucus; Congressional Caucus on Intellectual Property Promotion and Piracy Prevention; House Small Brewers Caucus; Congressional Rice Caucus; Congressional Down Syndrome Caucus; House Hunger Caucus; Congressional Scouting Caucus; Congressional Community Pharmacy Caucus; Congressional Manufactured Housing Caucus; Congressional USO Caucus; Congressional Mobility Air Forces Caucus; Congressional Arts Caucus; Congressional Chicken Caucus; Congressional Nursing Caucus; Congressional Wellness Caucus; Congressional TRIO Caucus; Congressional Zoo and Aquarium Caucus; Congressional Bicycle Caucus; Congressional Addiction, Treatment and Recovery Caucus; Rare Disease Congressional Caucus; Congressional Lupus Caucus; Congressional Youth Challenge Caucus; International Religious Freedom Caucus; Congressional Afterschool Caucus; Bi-Partisan, Bi-Cameral Congressional Task Force on Alzheimer's Disease; Congressional Malaria Caucus; Congressional Biomedical Caucus; Congressional Dyslexia Caucus; Congressional Missile Defense Caucus; Congressional Animal Protection Caucus; Congressional Real Estate Caucus; Congressional Childhood Cancer Caucus; Congressional Fitness Caucus; Congressional Motorsports Caucus; Congressional French Caucus; Congressional Horse Caucus; Congressional Congenital Heart Caucus; Congressional Crohn's and Colitis Caucus; Defense Communities Caucus; Congressional Caucus on Parkinson's Disease; Majority Assistant Whip; committees: Ways and Means; elected to the 112th Congress on November 2, 2010, reelected to the 113th Congress on November 6, 2012.

Office Listings

http://www.griffin.house.gov www.facebook.com/reptimgriffin
www.twitter.com/reptimgriffin

1232 Longworth House Office Building, Washington, DC 20515 .... (202) 225–2506

Chief of Staff.—Clayton Hall. FAX: 225–5903
Communications Director.—Matt Wolking.
Legislative Director.—A. Brooke Bennett.
1501 North University, Suite 150, Little Rock, AR 72207 .... (501) 324–5941
District Director.—Carl Vogelphol.
1105 Deer Street, Suite 12, Conway, AR 72032 .... (501) 358–3481

Counties: CONWAY, FAULKNER, PERRY, PULASKI, SALINE, VAN BUREN, AND WHITE. Population (2010), 751,377.

ZIP Codes: 71772, 71909, 72001–02, 72010–13, 72015–18, 72020, 72022–23, 72025, 72027–28, 72030–35, 72039, 72045–47, 72052–53, 72057–61, 72063, 72065–68, 72070, 72076, 72078–82, 72085, 72087–89, 72099, 72102–04, 72106–08, 72110–11, 72113–22, 72124–27, 72131, 72135–37, 72139, 72141–43, 72145, 72149, 72153, 72156–57, 72164, 72167, 72173, 72178, 72180–81, 72183, 72190, 72199, 72201–07, 72209–12, 72214–17, 72219, 72221–23, 72225, 72227, 72231, 72260, 72295, 72419, 72568, 72629, 72645, 72679, 72823

* * *

THIRD DISTRICT

STEVE WOMACK, Republican, of Rogers, AR; born in Russellville, AR, February 18, 1957; education: Russellville High School, Russellville, AR; B.A., Arkansas Tech University, 1979; professional: radio station manager; financial consultant, mayor of Rogers, AR; military: retired colonel, National Guard; awards: Legion of Merit; Meritorious Service Medal; Army Commendation Medal; Army Achievement Medal; Global War on Terror Expeditionary and Service Medals; religion: Southern Baptist; family: married the former Terri Williams of DeWitt, AR; three sons; caucuses: Republican Study Committee, National Guard; committees: Appropriations; elected to the 112th Congress on November 2, 2010; reelected to the 113th Congress on November 6, 2012.

Office Listings

http://womack.house.gov

1119 Longworth House Office Building, Washington, DC 20515 .... (202) 225–4301
Chief of Staff.—Beau Walker. FAX: 225–5713
Communications Director.—Claire Burghoff.
Scheduler.—Rebekah Baer.
Legislative Director.—Chris Huffaker.
Legislative Counsel.—Adrielle Churchill.
Legislative Assistants: Corey Inglee, Ivy Williams.
Legislative Correspondent.—Amanda Ladden-Stirling.
Staff Assistant.—Jordan Bearden.
3333 Pinnacle Hills, Suite 120, Rogers, AR 72758 .... (479) 464–0446
District Director.—Bootsie Ackerman. FAX: 464–0063
Constituent Service Manager.—Janet Foster.
Caseworker.—Pam Forester.
Field Representative.—Jeff Thacker.
Projects Director.—Kyle Weaver.
423 North 6th Street, Fort Smith, AR 72902 .... (479) 424–1146
Field Representative / Military and Veterans Advisor.—Bob Moody. FAX: 424–2737
Caseworker.—Chris Bader.
303 North Main Street, Suite 102, Harrison, AR 72601 .... (870) 741–6900
Field Representative.—Teri Garrett. FAX: 741–7741

Counties: BENTON, BOONE, CARROLL, CRAWFORD, FRANKLIN, JOHNSON, MADISON, MARION, NEWTON, POPE, SEBASTIAN, WASHINGTON. Population (2010), 754,704.

ZIP Codes: 65729, 65733, 65761, 72063, 72080, 72601, 72611, 72616, 72619, 72624, 72630–34, 72638, 72640–41, 72644, 72648, 72653, 72655, 72660–62, 72668–69, 72672, 72675, 72677, 72679, 72682–83, 72685, 72687, 72701, 72703–04, 72712, 72714–15, 72717–19, 72722, 72727, 72729–30, 72732, 72734, 72736, 72738–40, 72744–45, 72747, 72749, 72751, 72753, 72756, 72758, 72761–62, 72764, 72768–69, 72773–74, 72801–02, 72823, 72837, 72839, 72843, 72846–47, 72856, 72858, 72901, 72903–04, 72908, 72916, 72921, 72923, 72927, 72932–34, 72936–37, 72940–41, 72945–46, 72948, 72952, 72955–56, 72959

* * *

FOURTH DISTRICT

TOM COTTON, Republican, of Dardanelle, AR; born in Dardanelle, AR, May 13, 1977; education: graduated Dardanelle High School; B.A., Harvard University, 1999; J.D., Harvard University, 2002; professional: attorney, management consultant; military service: United States Army Infantry Officer, 2005–09; awards: graduated Magna Cum Laude, Harvard University; Ranger Tab Recipient; Army Commendation Medal; Combat Infantryman Badge; Iraq Campaign Medal; Bronze Star Medal; committees: Financial Services; Foreign Affairs; elected to the 113th Congress on November 6, 2012.

Office Listings

http://cotton.house.gov

415 Cannon House Office Building, Washington, DC 20515 .... (202) 225–3772
Chief of Staff.—Doug Coutts. FAX: 225–1314
Legislative Director.—Jonathan Hiler.
Communications Director.—Caroline Rabbitt.
Hot Springs Federal Building, 100 Reserve Street, Suite 307, Hot Springs, AR 71901 .... (501) 520–5892
District Director.—Lesley Nelms.
George Howard Jr. Federal Building, 100 East 8th Avenue, Room 2521, Pine Bluff, AR 71601 .... (870) 536–3376
Johnson County Courthouse, 215 West Main Street, Room 300, Clarksville, AR 72830 .... (479) 754–2120
Union County Courthouse, Suite 406, 101 North Washington Street, El Dorado, AR 71730 .... (870) 881–0681

Counties: Ashley, Bradley, Calhoun, Clark, Cleveland, Columbia, Crawford, Dallas, Drew, Franklin, Garland, Grant, Hempstead, Hot Spring, Howard, Jefferson, Johnson, LaFayette, Little River, Logan, Madison, Miller, Montgomery, Nevada, Newton, Ouachita, Pike, Polk, Scott, Sebastian, Sevier, Union, and Yell. Population (2010), 717,926.

ZIP Codes: 71601–03, 71631, 71635, 71638, 71642, 71644, 71646–47, 71651–52, 71655, 71658–61, 71663, 71665, 71667, 71670–71, 71675–77, 71701, 71711, 71720, 71722, 71724–26, 71730, 71740, 71742–45, 71747, 71751–53, 71758–59, 71762–66, 71770, 71772, 71801, 71820, 71822–23, 71825–27, 71832–39, 71841–42, 71845–47, 71851–55, 71857–62, 71865–66, 71901, 71909, 71913, 71921–23, 71929, 71933, 71935, 71937, 71940–41, 71943–45, 71949–50, 71952–53, 71956–62, 71964–65, 71968–73, 71998–99, 72004, 72015, 72025, 72046, 72057, 72065, 72079, 72084, 72087, 72104, 72128–29, 72132, 72150, 72152, 72167–68, 72175, 72601, 72624, 72628, 72632, 72638, 72641, 72648, 72655, 72666, 72670, 72703, 72721, 72727, 72738, 72740, 72742, 72752, 72756, 72760, 72773, 72776, 72821, 72824, 72826–28, 72830, 72832–35, 72838–42, 72845–47, 72851–57, 72860, 72863, 72865, 72921, 72926–28, 72930, 72933–38, 72940–41, 72943–47, 72949–51, 72956, 72958–59

CALIFORNIA

(Population 2010, 37,253,956)

SENATORS

DIANNE FEINSTEIN, Democrat, of San Francisco, CA; born in San Francisco, June 22, 1933; education: B.A., Stanford University, 1955; elected to San Francisco Board of Supervisors, 1970–78; president of Board of Supervisors: 1970–71, 1974–75, 1978; mayor of San Francisco, 1978–88; candidate for governor of California, 1990; recipient: Distinguished Woman Award, *San Francisco Examiner;* Achievement Award, Business and Professional Women's Club, 1970; Golden Gate University, California, LL.D. (hon.), 1979; SCOPUS Award for Outstanding Public Service, American Friends of the Hebrew University of Jerusalem; University of Santa Clara, D.P.S. (hon.); University of Manila, D.P.A. (hon.), 1981; Antioch University, LL.D. (hon.), 1983; Los Angeles Anti-Defamation League of B'nai B'rith's Distinguished Service Award, 1984; French Legion d'Honneur from President Mitterand, 1984; Mills College, LL.D. (hon.), 1985; U.S. Army Commander's Award for Public Service, 1986; Brotherhood/Sisterhood Award, National Conference of Christians and Jews, 1986; Paulist Fathers Award, 1987; Episcopal Church Award for Service, 1987; U.S. Navy Distinguished Civilian Award, 1987; Silver Spur Award for Outstanding Public Service, San Francisco Planning and Urban Renewal Association, 1987; All Pro Management Team Award for No. 1 Mayor, *City and State* Magazine, 1987; Community Service Award Honoree for Public Service, 1987; American Jewish Congress, 1987; President's Award, St. Ignatius High School, San Francisco, 1988; Coro Investment in Leadership Award, 1988; President's Medal, University of California at San Francisco, 1988; University of San Francisco, D.H.L. (hon.), 1988; member: Coro Foundation, Fellowship, 1955–56; California Women's Board of Terms and Parole, 1960–66, executive committee; U.S. Conference of Mayors, 1983–88; Mayor's Commission on Crime, San Francisco; Bank of California, director, 1988–89; San Francisco Education Fund's Permanent Fund, 1988–89; Japan Society of Northern California, 1988–89; Inter-American Dialogue, 1988–present; Publius Award from the Center for the Study of the Presidency and Congress, 2009; chair, U.S. Senate Caucus on International Narcotics Control; married: Dr. Bertram Feinstein (dec.); married on January 20, 1980, to Richard C. Blum; children: one child; three stepchildren; religion: Jewish; committees: chair, Select Committee on Intelligence; Appropriations; Judiciary; Rules and Administration; elected to the U.S. Senate, by special election, on November 3, 1992, to fill the vacancy caused by the resignation of Senator Pete Wilson; reelected to each succeeding Senate term.

Office Listings

http://feinstein.senate.gov twitter: @senfeinstein

331 Hart Senate Office Building, Washington, DC 20510	(202) 224–3841
Chief of Staff.—Chris Thompson.	FAX: 228–3954
Legislative Director.—John Watts.	
Director of Communications.—Brian Weiss.	
750 B Street, Suite 1030, San Diego, CA 92101	(619) 231–9712
2500 Tulare Street, Suite 4290, Fresno, CA 93721	(559) 485–7430
One Post Street, Suite 2450, San Francisco, CA 94104	(415) 393–0707
11111 Santa Monica Boulevard, Suite 915, Los Angeles, CA 90025	(310) 914–7300

* * *

BARBARA BOXER, Democrat, of Rancho Mirage, CA; born in Brooklyn, NY, November 11, 1940; education: B.A. in economics, Brooklyn College, 1962; professional: stockbroker and economic researcher with securities firms on Wall Street, 1962–65; journalist and associate editor, Pacific Sun newspaper, 1972–74; congressional aide, Fifth Congressional District, California, 1974–76; elected Marin County Board of Supervisors, 1976–82; first woman president, Marin County Board of Supervisors; awards: Human Rights for Vietnam Award, Vietnamese Community of Southern California, 1994; Legislator of the Year Award, Southern California Public Health Association, 1996; Lifetime Consumer Hero, Consumer Federation of America, 1997; Edgar Wayburn Award, Sierra Club, 1997; President's Award, California State Conference of the NAACP, 2001; Phillip Burton Wilderness Award, California Wilderness Coalition (CWC), 2003; Children's Champion Award, California Head Start Association, 2003; Circle of Courage Award, Afghan Women's Association International and the Women's 2003 Intercultural Network, 2003; National End Family Violence Achievement Award, Family Violence Law Center, 2003; Leadership Award, National Foundation for Women Legislators, 2005; Champion of Affordability Award, Housing Trust of Santa Clara County, 2005; Friend of the National Parks, National Parks Conservation Association, 2005; Impossible Dream Award, Planned

Parenthood Action Council, 2005; Champion for Children Award, California Children's Hospital, 2006; Woman of the Year, Women's Image Network, 2006; Visionary Leadership Award, San Francisco Democratic Party, 2006; Award, Native American Heritage Association, 2007; Champion Award for Public Service, Endangered Species Coalition, 2007; Lifetime Achievement Award, City Year San Jose / Silicon Valley, 2008; Breakfast of Champions, Afterschool Alliance, 2008; Transportation Leader's Award, National Stone, Sand, and Gravel Association, 2008; John H. Chafee Congressional Environmental Award, Association of American Railroads, 2008; Legislative Leadership Award, National Association of Clean Water Agencies, 2008; Legislator of the Year Award, American Planning Association, 2008; Humane Champion, Humane Society of the United States, 2008; Legislator of the Year Award, Information and Technology Industry Council, 2008; Vera Shultz Visionary Leadership Award, Marin Women's Commission, 2009; 25th Annual Leadership Conference Award, Cyprus and Hellenic Leadership, 2009; Aviation Safety Award, National Air Traffic Controllers Association, 2009; Legislator of the Year Award, California Primary Care Association, 2009; Children's Champion Award, Global Action for Children, 2009; Award, Oxfam America, 2009; Legislator of the Year Award, Air Quality Management District, 2009; National Transportation Leadership Award for the 21st Century, American Association of State Highway and Transportation Officials, 2009; Defender of Children Award, First Focus Campaign for Children, 2010; Golden Triangle Award, National Farmers Union, 2010; Safety Leadership Award, Advocates for Highway and Auto Safety, 2010; Award National Association of Community Health Centers, 2010; Safety Net Award, National Association of Public Hospitals and Health Systems, 2010; President's Leadership Award, American Burn Association, 2010; Phil Burton Badge of Courage Award, The Sierra Club-San Francisco Bay Chapter, 2010; Service Award, Entertainment Leadership Initiative / Grammy Foundation, 2010; Public Service Award, American College of Nurse-Midwives, 2010; All Rise Leadership Award, National Association of Drug Court Professionals, 2011; Friends of the National Parks Award, National Parks Conservation Association, 2011; Outstanding Leadership Recognition, American Water Works Association, California-Nevada Section, 2011; Recognition, East Bay Municipal Utility District, 2011; Champion for the National Parent Helpline Award, Parents Anonymous, 2011; Nightingale Award, Nurse Alliance, 2011; Legislative Leader Award, The Humane Society, 2011; Congressional Champion Award, The Corps Network, 2012; YMCA Congressional Champion, YMCA, 2012; Distinguished Community Health Defender Award, National Association of Community Health Centers, Inc., 2012; Fearless Trailblazer Award, Feminist Majority, 2012; Certificate of Recognition, Orange County Fire Authority, 2012; Certificate of Recognition, Treasure Island Jobs Corps, 2012; Congressional Champion, American Great Outdoors, 2012; Award, Associated Professional and Contractors of CA, Inc., 2012; Award, The City of West Hollywood, 2013; Congressional Champion Award, The Corps Network, 2013; Distinguished Community Health Advocate, National Association of Community Health Centers, 2013 married: Stewart Boxer, 1962; children: Doug and Nicole; committees: chair, Environment and Public Works; chair, Select Committee on Ethics; Commerce, Science, and Transportation; Foreign Relations; elected November 2, 1982, to the 98th Congress; reelected to the 99th–102nd Congresses; elected to the U.S. Senate on November 3, 1992; reelected to each succeeding Senate term.

Office Listings

http://boxer.senate.gov twitter: @senatorboxer

112 Hart Senate Office Building, Washington, DC 20510 .... (202) 224–3553
Chief of Staff.—Laura Schiller. FAX: 228–2382
Legislative Director.—Sean Moore.
Director of Scheduling.—Kelly Boyer.
Communications Director.—Zachary Coile.
70 Washington Street, Suite 203, Oakland, CA 94607 .... (510) 286–8537
312 North Spring Street, Suite 1748, Los Angeles, CA 90012 .... (213) 894–5000
501 I Street, Suite 7–600, Sacramento, CA 95814 .... (916) 448–2787
600 B Street, Suite 2240, San Diego, CA 92101 .... (619) 239–3884
2500 Tulare Street, Suite 5290, Fresno, CA 93721 .... (559) 497–5109
3403 10th Street, Suite 704, Riverside, CA 92501 .... (951) 684–4849

REPRESENTATIVES

FIRST DISTRICT

DOUG LAMALFA, Republican, of Richvale, CA; born in Oroville, CA, July 2, 1960; education: graduated from Oroville High School; B.S., California Polytechnic State University, San Luis Obispo, CA, 1982; rice farmer; California State Assemblyman, 2002–08; California State Senator, 2010–12; married: Jill; children: four; caucuses: Congressional Western Caucus, Republican Study Committee; Congressional Sportsmen's Caucus; Small Business Caucus; Rice

Caucus; PORTS Caucus; Natural Gas Caucus; Sikh Caucus; Congressional Wine Caucus; Prayer Caucus; Values Action Team; National Guard and Reserve Components Caucus; Cement Caucus; committees: Agriculture; Natural Resources; elected to the 113th Congress on November 6, 2012.

Office Listings

http://lamalfa.house.gov twitter: @replamalfa

506 Cannon House Office Building, Washington, DC 20515 .... (202) 225–3076
Chief of Staff.—Mark Spannagel. FAX: 226–0852
Scheduler.—Caitlin Dorman.
Legislative Director.—Kevin Eastman.
Communications Director.—Kevin Eastman.
1453 Downer Street, Suite A, Oroville, CA 95965 .... (530) 534–7100
FAX: 534–7800
2885 Churn Creek Road, Suite C, Redding, CA 96002 .... (530) 223–5898
FAX: 605–4342

Counties: SISKIYOU, MODOC, SHASTA, LASSEN, TEHAMA, PLUMAS, GLENN, BUTTE, SIERRA, NEVADA, AND PLACER. Population (2010), 702,905.

ZIP Codes: 95568, 95602–03, 95712–13, 95728, 95910, 95914–17, 95923–24, 95926–30, 95934, 95936, 95938, 95940–42, 95944–49, 95954, 95956–60, 95965–66, 95968–69, 95971, 95973–78, 95980, 95983–84, 95986, 96001, 96006–09, 96011, 96013–17, 96019–23, 96025, 96027–29, 96031, 96032–35, 96037–40, 96044, 96047, 96050–51, 96054–59, 96061–62, 96064–65, 96067–71, 96073–75, 96078–80, 96084–90, 96092, 96094–97, 96101, 96104–06, 96108–19, 96121–30, 96132, 96134–37, 96161, 97635

* * *

SECOND DISTRICT

JARED W. HUFFMAN, Democrat, of San Rafael, California; born in Independence, MO, February 18, 1964; education: B.A., University of California, Santa Barbara, 1986, J.D., Boston College, 1990; professional: California Assembly, 2006–12; senior lawyer, Natural Resources Defense Council, 2001–06; board member, Marin Municipal Water District, 1994–2006; public interest attorney, 1990–2001; family: married, Susan Huffman; two children; caucuses: Congressional Progressive Caucus, Wild Salmon Caucus (Co-Chair), Sustainable Energy & Environment Coalition, Problem Solvers Caucus, National Marine Sanctuary Caucus, Congressional Wine Caucus, Congressional Labor and Working Families Caucus, Congressional Shellfish Caucus, Sensible Drug Policy Working Group, Bicameral Task Force on Climate Change, Congressional Rare Disease Caucus; committees: Budget; Natural Resources; elected to the 113th Congress on November 6, 2012.

Office Listings

http://huffman.house.gov twitter: @rephuffman https://www.facebook.com/rephuffman

1630 Longworth House Office Building, Washington, DC 20515 .... (202) 225–5161
Chief of Staff.—Benjamin Miller. FAX: 225–5163
Execuitve Assistant / Scheduler.—Melissa Burnell.
999 Fifth Avenue, Suite 290, San Rafael, CA 94901 .... (415) 258–9657
District Director.—Jeannine Callaway.
430 North Franklin Street, P.O. Box 2208, Fort Bragg, CA 95437 .... (707) 962–0933
District Representative.—Heidi Cusick Dickerson.
317 Third Street, Suite 1, Eureka, CA 95501 .... (707) 407–3585
District Representative.—John Driscoll.

Counties: HUMBOLDT, DEL NORTE, MARIN, MENDOCINO, SONOMA (part), TRINITY. CITIES AND TOWNSHIPS: ARCATA, CLOVERDALE, CRESCENT CITY, EUREKA, FORT BRAGG, GARBERVILLE, HEALDSBURG, MENDOCINO, NOVATO, PETALUMA, SAN RAFAEL, SEBASTOPOL, UKIAH, WINDSOR, AND WILLITS. Population (2010), 708,596.

ZIP Codes: 94946–50, 94952–54, 94956–57, 94960, 94963–66, 94970–79, 94998–99, 95401, 95403–4, 95410, 95412, 95415, 95417–18, 95420–21, 95425, 95427–30, 95432, 95436–37, 95441, 95444–46, 95448–51, 95454, 95456, 95459–60, 95462–63, 95465–66, 95468–73, 95480–82, 95486, 95488, 95490, 95492, 95494, 95497, 95501–03, 95511, 95514, 95518–19, 95521, 95524–28, 95531–32, 95534, 95536–38, 95540, 95542–43, 95545–52

* * *

THIRD DISTRICT

JOHN GARAMENDI, Democrat, of Walnut Grove, CA; born in Mokelumne Hill, CA, January 24, 1945; education: B.A., business, University of California-Berkeley, Berkeley, CA,

1966; M.B.A., Harvard University, Cambridge, MA, 1974; professional: small business owner; Peace Corps volunteer, 1966–68; California State Assembly member, 1974–76; member of the California State Senate, 1976–90; California Insurance Commissioner, 1991–94, and 2002–06; Deputy Secretary of the U.S. Interior Department, 1995–98; previously California Lieutenant Governor, 2007–09; regent, University of California; trustee, California State University; member of Make It In America Working Group; religion: Christian; family: married to Patricia Garamendi; six children; ten grandchildren; Deputy Whip; committees: Agriculture; Armed Services; Transportation and Infrastructure; elected by special election on November 3, 2009, to fill the vacancy caused by the resignation of U.S. Representative Ellen Tauscher; elected to each succeeding Congress.

Office Listings

http://garamendi.house.gov

2438 Rayburn House Office Building, Washington, DC 20515 .... (202) 225–1880
Chief of Staff.—Chris Austin. FAX: 225–5914
Scheduler.—Sofia Leon.
Communications Director.—Donald Lathbury.
Legislative Director.—Elizabeth Crow.
990 Klamath Lane, Suite 4, Yuba City, CA 95993 .... (530) 329–8865
FAX: 763–4248
412 G Street, Davis, CA 95616 .... (530) 753–5301
FAX: 753–5614

Counties: Colusa, Glenn (part), Lake (part), Sacramento (part), Solano (part), Sutter, Yolo (part), and Yuba. Population (2010), 712,075.

ZIP Codes: 94503, 94510, 94512, 94533–35, 94558, 94571, 94585, 94591, 95422–24, 95443, 95451, 95453, 95457–58, 95464, 95485, 95493, 95606–07, 95612, 95615–18, 95620, 95625–27, 95632, 95637, 95639, 95641, 95645, 95653–54, 95659–60, 95668, 95673–74, 95676, 95679–80, 95687–88, 95690–92, 95694–98, 95757–59, 95776, 95823, 95834–37, 95843, 95901, 95903, 95912–14, 95918–19, 95922, 95925, 95932, 95935, 95937, 95939, 95941, 95950–51, 95953, 95955, 95957, 95960–63, 95966, 95970, 95972, 95977, 95979, 95982, 95987–88, 95991–93

* * *

FOURTH DISTRICT

TOM McCLINTOCK, Republican, of Granite Bay, CA; born in Bronxville, NY, July 10, 1956; education: B.A., *cum laude* political science, UCLA, Los Angeles, CA; 1978; professional: member, California State Assembly 1982–92 and 1996–2000; member, California State Senate 2000–04; director, Center for the California Tax Payer, National Tax Limitation Foundation 1992–94; director, Economic and Regulatory Affairs, Claremount Institute 1994–96; married: Lori; two children; committees: Budget; Natural Resources; elected to the 111th Congress on November 4, 2008; reelected to each succeeding Congress.

Office Listings

http://www.mcclintock.house.gov twitter: @repmcclintock

434 Cannon House Office Building, Washington, DC 20515 .... (202) 225–2511
Chief of Staff.—Igor Birman. FAX: 225–5444
Scheduler.—Rachel Long.
Legislative Director.—Kristen Glenn.
Legislative Assistant.—Chris Tudor.
Legislative Correspondent.—Cynthia Judson.
8700 Auburn Folsom Road, Suite 100, Granite Bay, CA 95746 .... (916) 786–5560
District Director.—Rocky Deal.

Counties: Alpine, Amador, Calaveras, El Dorado, Mariposa, Tuolumne, Fresno (part), Madera (part), Nevada (part), Placer (part). Population (2010), 760,078.

ZIP Codes: 35251, 59223, 85252, 92532, 93601–02, 93604–05, 93610–11, 93614, 93619, 93621, 93623, 93626, 93628, 93633–34, 93636, 93638, 93641, 93643–45, 93649, 93651, 93653, 93657, 93664, 93667, 93669, 93675, 93701, 94248, 95147, 95221–26, 95228–30, 95232–33, 95236, 95245–49, 95251–52, 95254–57, 95256–57, 95305–06, 95309–11, 95318, 95321, 95325, 95327, 95329, 95333, 95335, 95338, 95345–47, 95364, 95369–70, 95372–73, 95379, 95383, 95389, 95601, 95603, 95613–14, 95619, 95623, 95626, 95629, 95631, 95633–36, 95640, 95642, 95644, 95646, 95648, 95650–51, 95656, 95658, 95661, 95663–69, 95672, 95675, 95678, 95681–82, 95684–85, 95689, 95699, 95709, 95713, 95715, 95720–21, 95724, 95726, 95728, 95735, 95746–47, 95762, 95765, 95945–46, 95949, 95959, 96120, 96140, 96141–43, 96145–46, 96148, 96150, 96161–62

* * *

FIFTH DISTRICT

MIKE THOMPSON, Democrat, of Napa Valley, CA; born in St. Helena, CA, January 24, 1951; education: graduated, St. Helena High School, St. Helena, CA; U.S. Army, 1969–72; Purple Heart; B.A., Chico State University, 1982; M.A., Chico State University, 1996; teacher at San Francisco State University, and Chico State University; elected to the California State Senate, 2nd District, 1990–98; former chairman of the California State Senate Budget Committee; married to Janet; two children: Christopher and Jon; committees: Ways and Means; Permanent Select Committee on Intelligence; elected to the 106th Congress; reelected to each succeeding Congress.

Office Listings

http://mikethompson.house.gov http://www.house.gov/writerep twitter: @repthompson

231 Cannon House Office Building, Washington, DC 20515 .... (202) 225–3311
Chief of Staff.—Anne Steckel. FAX: 225–4335
Legislative Directors: Melanie Rhinehart, Van Tassell.
Communications Director.—Austin Vevurka.
1040 Main Street, Suite 101, Napa, CA 94559 .... (707) 645–1888
1985 Walnut Avenue, Vallejo, CA 94592 .... (707) 269–9595
2300 County Center Drive, Suite A100, Santa Rosa, CA 95403 .... (707) 542–7182

Counties: CONTRA COSTA. CITIES AND TOWNSHIPS: Christie, Crockett, Glen Frazer, Hercules, Martinez, Pinole, Port Costa, Rodeo, Selby, Tara Hills, Tormey, Vine Hill. LAKE COUNTY. CITIES AND TOWNSHIPS: Cobb, Kelseyville, Lakeport, Middletown. SONOMA COUNTY. CITIES AND TOWNSHIPS: Boyes Hot Springs, Cotati, El Verano, Eldridge, Fetters Hot Springs, Fulton, Glen Ellen, Kenwood, Mark West, Rohnert Park, Santa Rosa, Sonoma, Vineburg. NAPA COUNTY. CITIES AND TOWNSHIPS: American Canyon, Angwin, Aetna Springs, Calistoga, Deer Park, Oakville, Pope Valley, Rutherford, St. Helena. SOLANO COUNTY. CITIES AND TOWNSHIPS: Benicia, Tiara, Vallejo. Population (2011), 547,495.

ZIP Codes: 94508, 94510, 94515, 94525, 94547, 94553, 94558–59, 94562, 94564, 94567, 94569, 94572–74, 94576, 94581, 94587, 94589–92, 94599, 94806, 94926–28, 94931, 95401, 95409, 95416, 95426, 95431, 95433, 95435, 95439, 95442, 95451–53, 95461, 95476, 95492, 95621.

* * *

SIXTH DISTRICT

DORIS OKADA MATSUI, Democrat, of Sacramento, CA; born in Posten, AZ, September 25, 1944; education: B.A., University of California, Berkeley, CA, 1966; professional: staff, White House, 1992–98; private advocate; organizations: Meridian International Center Board of Trustees; Woodrow Wilson Center Board of Trustees; California Institute Board of Directors; married: Robert Matsui, 1966; children: Brian Robert; committees: Energy and Commerce; elected by special election on March 8, 2005 to the 109th Congress, to fill the vacancy caused by the death of her husband, Representative Robert Matsui; reelected to each succeeding Congress.

Office Listings

http://www.house.gov/matsui https://twitter.com/dorismatsui

2434 Cannon House Office Building, Washington, DC 20515 .... (202) 225–7163
Chief of Staff.—Julie Eddy. FAX: 225–0566
Executive Assistant.—Clare Chmiel.
Legislative Director.—Kyle Victor.
Press Secretary.—Jonelle Trimmer.
501 I Street, 12–600, Sacramento, CA 95814 .... (916) 498–5600
District Director.—Nathan Dietrich.

County: SACRAMENTO COUNTY (part), YOLO COUNTY (part). CITY: Sacramento and West Sacramento. Population (2010), 702,905.

ZIP Codes: 95605, 95618, 95620–21, 95652, 95660, 95673, 95691, 95758, 95811, 95814–26, 95828–29, 95831–35, 95837, 95838, 95841–43, 95864

* * *

SEVENTH DISTRICT

AMI BERA, Democrat of Elk Grove, CA; born in La Palma, CA, March 2, 1965; education: B.S., University of California, Irvine, CA; M.D., University of California, Irvine, CA, 1991;

professional: military; awards: medical director for care management, Mercy Hospital, Sacramento, CA; chief medical officer, Sacramento, CA; associate dean of admissions for University of California, Davis Medical School, 2004–07; religion: Unitarian; married: Janine Bera (also a physician); children: Sydra; committees: Foreign Affairs; Science, Space, and Technology; elected to the 113th Congress on November 6, 2012.

Office Listings

http://bera.house.gov https://twitter.com/repbera

1408 Longworth House Office Building, Washington, DC 20515 .... (202) 225–5716
Chief of Staff.—Mini Timmaraju. FAX: 226–1298
Director of Operations.—Erin Fyffe.
Legislative Director.—Matt Horowitz.
Press Secretary.—Allison Teixeira.
11070 White Rock Road, Suite 195, Rancho Cordova, CA 95670 .... (916) 635–0505
District Director.—Faith Whitmore.

Counties: EASTERN HALF OF SACRAMENTO COUNTY. CITIES: Citrus Heights, Folsom, Rancho Cordova, and Elk Grove as well as the unincorporated communities of, Carmichael, Fair Oaks, Orangevale, Rosemont, La Riviera, Sloughhouse, Rancho Murieta, Vineyard, Florin, Vintage Park, Wilton, Herald and half of Arden Arcade. Population: (2010), 710,607.

ZIP Codes: 95608–11, 95621, 95624, 95628, 95630, 95632, 95638, 95655, 95662, 95670, 95678, 95683, 95693, 95741–42, 95757–58, 95763, 95821, 95823, 95825–30, 95841–42, 95864–66 (Some of these zips are only partially in the District)

* * *

EIGHTH DISTRICT

PAUL COOK, Republican, of Yucca Valley, CA, born in Meridien, CT, March 3, 1943; B.S., Southern Connecticut University, New Haven, CT, 1966; M.P.A., California State University San Bernardino, San Bernardino, CA, 1996; M.A., University of California Riverside, Riverside, CA, 2000; professional: United States Marine Corps, 1966–92; professor; member, Yucca Valley California Town Council, 1998–2006; California State Assemblyman 2006–12; married: Jeanne; committees: Armed Services; Foreign Affairs; Veterans' Affairs; elected to the 113th Congress on November 6, 2012.

Office Listings

http://cook.house.gov

1222 Longworth House Office Building, Washington, DC 20515 .... (202) 225–5861
Chief of Staff.—John Sobel. FAX: 225–6498
14955 Dale Evans Parkway, Apple Valley, CA 92307 .... (760) 247–1815
District Director.—Matthew Knox.

Counties: SAN BERNARDINO (part), MONO, INYO. CITIES AND TOWNSHIPS: Adelanto, Angelus Oaks, Apple Valley, Arrowbear, Arrowhead Farms, Baldy Mesa, Baker, Barstow, Bear Valley, Benton, Big Bear City, Big Bear Lake, Big Pine, Big River, Bishop, Bridgeport, Bums Canyon, Cartago, Cedar Glen, Cedar Pines Park, Coleville, Crestline, Daggett, Darwin, El Mirage, Erwin Lake, Fawnskin, Flamingo Heights, Forest Falls, Furnace Creek, Green Valley Lake, Helendale, Hesperia, Highland, Hinkley, Independence, Joshua Tree, June Lake, Lake Arrowhead, Keeler, Landers, Lenwood, Lee Vining, Lytle Creek, Mono City, Mount Baldy, Morongo Valley, Needles, Newberry Springs, Oak Glen, Oak Hills, Oro Grande, Paradise, Pioneertown, Pinon Hills, Phelan, Red Mountain, Rimrock, Running Springs, Skyforest, Sugarloaf, Topaz, Trona, Twentynine Palms, Twin Peaks, Victorville, Walker, Wrightwood, Yucca Valley, and Yucaipa. Population (2010) 708,578.

ZIP Codes: 91759, 92242, 92252, 92256, 92268, 92277–78, 92284–86, 92301, 92305, 92309–64, 92310–12, 92314–15, 92321–22, 92325, 92327–28, 92333, 92339–42, 92344–47, 92352, 92358, 92363, 92368, 92372, 92382, 92385–86, 92388–65, 92391–95, 92397–99, 92407, 93512–15, 93522, 93526, 93529–30, 93541, 93549, 93558, 93562–92, 95223, 95967, 95969, 96107, 96133

* * *

NINTH DISTRICT

JERRY McNERNEY, Democrat, of Stockton, CA; born in Albuquerque, NM, June 18, 1951; attended the U.S. Military Academy, West Point, NY, 1969–71; A.S., University of New Mexico, Albuquerque, NM, 1973; M.S., University of New Mexico, NM, 1975; Ph.D. in Mathematics, University of New Mexico, 1981; professional: wind engineer; entrepreneur; business owner; married: Mary; children: Michael, Windy and Greg; committees: Energy and Commerce; elected to the 110th Congress on November 7, 2006; reelected to each succeeding Congress.

Office Listings

http://mcnerney.house.gov twitter: @repmcnerney

1210 Longworth House Office Building, Washington, DC 20515 .... (202) 225–1947
Chief of Staff.—Nick Holder. FAX: 225–4060
Executive Assistant.—Teresa Frison.
Communications Director.—Lauren Smith.
Legislative Director.—Patrick Arness.
District Director.—Nicole Damasco Alioto.
4703 Lone Tree Way, Antioch, CA 94531 .... (925) 754–0716
2222 Grand Canal Boulevard, #7, Stockton, CA 95207 .... (209) 476–8552

Counties: SAN JOAQUIN (part), CONTRA COSTA (part), SACRAMENTO (part). CITIES AND TOWNSHIPS: Stockton, Antioch, Lodi, Brentwood, Oakley, Galt, Lathrop, and Discovery Bay. Population (2010), 648,766.

ZIP Codes: 94505, 94509, 94511, 94513–14, 94531, 94548, 94561, 95201–15, 95219–20, 95227, 95230–31, 95234, 95236–37, 95240–42, 95253, 95258, 95267, 95269, 95296, 95304, 95320, 95330, 95336–37, 95361, 95366, 95391, 95632, 95686, 95690, 95757

* * *

TENTH DISTRICT

JEFF DENHAM, Republican, of Turlock, CA; born in Hawthorne, CA, July 29, 1967; education: A.A., Victor Valley Junior College, Victorville, CA, 1989; B.A., California Polytechnic State University, San Luis Obispo, CA, 1992; military: United States Air Force, 1984–88; United States Air Force Reserve, 1988–2000; professional: business owner; served in the California State Senate, 2002–10; religion: Christian; family: wife-Sonia, two children; committees: Agriculture; Transportation and Infrastructure; Veterans' Affairs; elected to the 112th Congress on November 2, 2010; reelected to the 113th Congress on November 6, 2012.

Office Listings

http://www.denham.house.gov twitter: @repjeffdenham https://facebook.com/repjeffdenham
https://www.youtube.com/repjeffdenham http://www.flickr.com/photos/59309318@No4/

1730 Longworth House Office Building, Washington, DC 20515 .... (202) 225–4540
Chief of Staff.—Jason Larrabee. FAX: 225–3402
Scheduler.—Carol Kresse.
1040 East Herndon, Suite 201, Fresno, CA 93720 .... (559) 449–2490
District Director.—Bob Rucker.
4701 Sisk Road, Suite 202, Madesto, CA 95356 .... (209) 579–5458

Counties: STANISLAUS COUNTY (part), SAN JOAQUIN COUNTY (part). CITIES AND TOWNSHIPS: Airport, Bret Harte, Bystrom, Ceres, Cowan, Cowan Landing, Del Rio, Denair, Diablo Grande, East Oakdale, Empire, Escalon, Grayson, Hickman, Hughson, Keyes, Manteca, Modesto, Monterey Park Tract, Newman, Oakdale, Parklawn, Patterson, Ripon, Riverbank, Riverdale Park, Rouse, Salida, Shackelford, Tracy, Turlock, Valley Home, Waterford, West Modesto, Woodbridge, Westley, and Westport. Population (2010), 714,750.

ZIP Codes: 94550, 95230, 95304, 95307, 95313, 95316, 95319–20, 95322–23, 95326, 95328–30, 95336–37, 95350–51, 95354–58, 95360–61, 95363, 95366–68, 95376–77, 95380, 95382, 95385–87

* * *

ELEVENTH DISTRICT

GEORGE MILLER, Democrat, of Martinez, CA; born in Richmond, CA, May 17, 1945; education: attended Martinez public schools; Diablo Valley College; graduated, San Francisco State College, 1968; J.D., University of California at Davis School of Law, 1972; member: California State bar; Davis Law School Alumni Association; served five years as legislative aide to Senate majority leader, California State Legislature; past chairman and member of Contra Costa County Democratic Central Committee; past president of Martinez Democratic Club; married: the former Cynthia Caccavo; children: George and Stephen; six grandchildren; committees: Education and the Workforce; elected to the 94th Congress, November 5, 1974; reelected to each succeeding Congress.

Office Listings

http://www.georgemiller.house.gov George.Miller@mail.house.gov twitter: @askgeorge

2205 Rayburn House Office Building, Washington, DC 20515 .... (202) 225–2095

Chief of Staff.—Daniel Weiss. FAX: 225–5609
Executive Assistant / Scheduler.—Courtney Rochelle.
1333 Willow Pass Road, Suite 203, Concord, CA 94520 .... (925) 602–1880
District Director.—Barbara Johnson.
3220 Blume Drive, Suite 160, Richmond, CA 94806 .... (510) 262–6500
Field Representative.—Latressa Alford.
375 G Street, Suite 1, Vallejo, CA 94592 .... (707) 645–1888
Field Representative.—Kathy Hoffman.

Counties: CONTRA COSTA (part), SOLANO (part). CITIES AND TOWNSHIPS: Alomo, Antioch, Bay Point, Blackhawk, Clayton, Concord, El Cerrito, El Sobrante, Kensington, Lafayette, Martinez, Moraga, Orinda, Pittsburg, Pleasant Hil, Richmond, San Pablo, and Walnut Creek. (2013), 722,847.

ZIP Codes: 92526, 94506–07, 94509, 94517–24, 94527–30, 94549, 94553, 94556–57, 94563, 94565, 94595–98, 94708, 94801–08, 94820, 94850

* * *

TWELFTH DISTRICT

NANCY PELOSI, Democrat, of San Francisco, CA; born in Baltimore, MD, March 26, 1940; daughter of the late Representative Thomas D'Alesandro, Jr., of MD; education: graduated, Institute of Notre Dame High School, 1958; B.A., Trinity College, Washington, DC (major, political science; minor, history), 1962; northern chair, California Democratic Party, 1977–81; state chair, California Democratic Party, 1981–83; chair, 1984 Democratic National Convention Host Committee; finance chair, Democratic Senatorial Campaign Committee, 1985–86; member: Democratic National Committee; California Democratic Party Executive Committee; San Francisco Library Commission; Board of Trustees, LSB Leakey Foundation; married: Paul F. Pelosi, 1963; children: Nancy Corinne, Christine, Jacqueline, Paul, Jr., and Alexandra; 8 grandchildren; elected by special election, June 2, 1987, to the 100th Congress to fill the vacancy caused by the death of Representative Sala Burton; reelected to each succeeding Congress; elected Democratic Whip in the 107th Congress; Democratic Leader in the 108th and 109th Congresses; elected Speaker of the House in the 110th and 111th Congresses; elected Democratic Leader in the 112th Congress and 113th Congress.

Office Listings

http://www.house.gov/pelosi twitter: @nancypelosi

235 Cannon House Office Building, Washington, DC 20515 .... (202) 225–4965
Chief of Staff.—Catlin O'Neill. FAX: 225–8259
90 7th Street, Suite 2–800, San Francisco, CA 94103 .... (415) 556–4862
District Director.—Dan Bernal.

County: SAN FRANCISCO COUNTY (part). CITY: San Francisco. Population (2010), 702,905.

ZIP Codes: 94014, 94102–05, 94107–12, 94114–18, 94121–24, 94127, 94129–34, 94158, 94164

* * *

THIRTEENTH DISTRICT

BARBARA LEE, Democrat, of Oakland, CA; born in El Paso, TX, July 16, 1946; education: graduated, San Fernando High School; B.A., Mills College, 1973; MSW, University of California, Berkeley, 1975; congressional aide and public servant; senior advisor and chief of staff to Congressman Ronald V. Dellums in Washington, DC, and Oakland, CA, 1975–87; California State Assembly, 1990–96; California State Senate, 1996–98; Assembly committees: Housing and Land Use; Appropriations; Business and Professions; Industrial Relations; Judiciary; Revenue and Taxation; board member, California State Coastal Conservancy, District Export Council, and California Defense Conversion Council; committees: Appropriations; Budget; elected to the 105th Congress on April 7, 1998, by special election, to fill the remaining term of retiring Representative Ronald V. Dellums; reelected to each succeeding Congress.

Office Listings

http://lee.house.gov twitter: @repbarbaralee

2267 Rayburn House Office Building, Washington, DC 20515 .... (202) 225–2661

Chief of Staff.—Julie Nickson. FAX: 225–9817
Scheduler.—Tatyana Kalinga.
Communications Director.—Carrie E. Adams.
Legislative Director.—Jirair Ratevosian.
1301 Clay Street, Suite 1000–N, Oakland, CA 94612 .... (510) 763–0370

Counties: ALAMEDA COUNTY. CITIES: Alameda, Albany, Berkeley, Emeryville, Kensington, Piedmont. OAKLAND COUNTY (part). Population (2010), 691,592.

ZIP Codes: 94501–02, 94577–79, 94601–15, 94617–94621, 94623–27, 94643, 94649, 94660–62, 94666, 94701–10, 94712, 94720

* * *

FOURTEENTH DISTRICT

JACKIE SPEIER, Democrat, of Hillsborough, CA; born in San Francisco, CA, May 14, 1950; education: B.A., University of California at Davis; J.D., University of California, Hastings College of the Law, 1976; legislative council, Congressman Leo J. Ryan; member, San Mateo County Board of Supervisors; member, California State Assembly; senator, California State Senate; married: Barry Dennis; two children: Jackson Sierra and Stephanie Sierra; committees: Armed Services; Oversight and Government Reform; elected in a special election, April 8, 2008, to fill the vacancy caused by the death of Representative Thomas P. Lantos; elected to the 111th Congress on November 4, 2008; reelected to each succeeding Congress.

Office Listings

http://speier.house.gov https://www.facebook.com/jackiespeier twitter: @repspeier
http://www.youtube.com/user/jackiespeierCA12

211 Cannon House Office Building, Washington, DC 20515 .... (202) 225–3531
Chief of Staff.—Cookab Hashemi. FAX: 226–4183
Legislative Director.—Erin Ryan.
155 Bovet Road, Suite 780, San Mateo, CA 94402 .... (650) 342–0300
District Representative.—Brian Perkins. FAX: 375–8270

Counties: SAN MATEO COUNTY (part). CITIES: Belmont, Brisbane, Burlingame, Colma, Daly City, East Palo Alto, Foster City, Half Moon Bay, Hillsborough, Menlo Park, Millbrae, Montara, Moss Beach, Pacifica, Redwood City, San Bruno, San Carlos, San Gregorio, San Mateo, South San Francisco, and Woodside. SAN FRANCISCO COUNTY (part). CITIES: San Francisco. Population (2012), 726,958.

ZIP Codes: 94002, 94005, 94010–11, 94013–15, 94019, 94025, 94030, 94038, 94044, 94061–66, 94070, 94074, 94080, 94083, 94099, 94112, 94116–17, 94127–28, 94131–32, 94134, 94143, 94303, 94401–04, 94497

* * *

FIFTEENTH DISTRICT

ERIC SWALWELL, Democratic, of Dublin, CA; born in Sac City, IA, November 16, 1980; education: graduated, Dublin High School, Dublin, CA, 1999; B.A., University of Maryland, College Park, College Park, MD, 2003; J.D., University of Maryland School of Law, Baltimore, MD, 2006; professional: former city councilman at City of Dublin City Council; former Deputy District Attorney at Alameda County District Attorney's Office; Planning Commissioner at City of Dublin; Heritage & Cultural Arts Commissioner at City of Dublin; law clerk at Alameda County District Attorney's Office; commission: Tom Lantos Human Rights; caucuses: Pro-Choice; Ad Hoc Committee for Irish Affairs; Anti-Bullying; Congressional Asian Pacific America; Congressional Dyslexia; Cyber Security; Democratic Whip's Task Force on Poverty and Opportunity; Diabetes; Friends of Ireland; High Tech; India; International Religious Freedom; Internet; LGBT Equality; Ports; Science and Labs; Sikh; Soccer; Victims' Rights; Wine; committees: Homeland Security; Science, Space, and Technology; elected to the 113th Congress on November 6, 2012.

Office Listings

http://www.swalwell.house.gov twitter: @repswalwell

501 Cannon House Office Building, Washington, DC 20515 .... (202) 225–5065
Chief of Staff.—Ricky Le. FAX: 226–3805
5075 Hopyard Road, Pleasanton, CA 94588 .... (925) 460–5100
1260 B Street, Suite 150, Hayward, CA 94541 .... (510) 370–3322

Counties: ALAMEDA COUNTY (part) AND CONTRA COSTA (part). CITIES AND TOWNSHIPS: San Leandro (part), San Lorenzo, Castro Valley, Union City, Fremont (part), Hayward, Pleasanton, San Ramon, Dublin, Sunol, Ashland, Danville (part), and Fairview. Population (2010), 732,515.

ZIP Codes: 94505–06, 94514, 94526, 94536, 94538–39, 94541–42, 94544–46, 94550–52, 94555, 94566, 94568, 94577–78

* * *

SIXTEENTH DISTRICT

JIM COSTA, Democrat, of Fresno, CA; born in Fresno, April 13, 1952; education: B.A., California State University, Fresno, CA, 1974; professional: employee, Costa Brothers Dairy, 1959–74; special assistant, Congressman John Krebs, 1975–76; administrative assistant, California Assemblyman Richard Lehman, 1976–78; California State Assembly, 1978–94; California State Senate, 1994–2002; chief executive officer, Costa Group, 2002–03; religion: Catholic; committees: Agriculture; Natural Resources; elected to the 109th Congress on November 2, 2004; reelected to each succeeding Congress.

Office Listings

http://www.costa.house.govt twitter: @repjimcosta

1314 Longworth House Office Building, Washington, DC 20515 .... (202) 225–3341
Chief of Staff.—Scott Nishioki. FAX: 225–9308
Deputy Chief of Staff / Scheduler.—Juan Lopez.
855 M Street, Suite 940, Fresno, CA 93721 .... (559) 495–1620
2222 M Street, Suite 305, Merced, CA 95340 .... (209) 384–1620
District Director.—Ian LeMay.

Counties: FRESNO (part), MADERA (part), MERCED. Population (2011), 714,214.

ZIP Codes: 93606, 93610 (part), 93620 (part), 93622 (part), 93626 (part), 93630 (part), 93635, 93636 (part), 93637, 93638 (part), 93639, 93661, 93665, 93701–03, 93704–06 (part), 93707–09, 93711 (part), 93712, 93714–18, 93721, 93722–23 (part), 93724, 93725–27 (part), 93728, 92741, 93744–45, 93747, 93750, 93755, 93760–61, 93764, 93771–79, 93786, 93790–94, 93844, 93888, 95301, 95303, 95312, 95315, 95316 (part), 95317, 95322 (part), 95324, 95333–34, 95340–41, 95343–44, 95348, 95356, 95360 (part), 95369 (part), 95374, 95380 (part), 95388

* * *

SEVENTEENTH DISTRICT

MICHAEL M. HONDA, Democrat, of San Jose, CA; born in Walnut Creek, CA, June 27, 1941; education: San Jose State University, received degrees in biological sciences and spanish, and a Masters Degree in education; awards: California Federation of Teachers Legislator of the Year; Outreach Paratransit Services Humanitarian Award; AEA Legislator of the Year; Service Employees International Union Home Care Champion Award; Asian Law Alliance Community Impact Award; AFL–CIO Distinguished Friend of Labor Award; chair emeritus, Congressional Asian Pacific American Caucus; chair, Ethiopia and Ethiopian American Caucus; chair, Congressional Anti-Bullying Caucus; public service: Peace Corps; San Jose Planning Commission; San Jose Unified School Board; Santa Clara County Board of Supervisors; California State Assemblyman; family: widower; children: Mark and Michelle; committees: Appropriations; Democratic Senior Whip; elected to the 107th Congress on November 7, 2000; reelected to each succeeding Congress.

Office Listings

http://www.house.gov/honda https://www.facebook.com/repmikehonda
https://twitter.com/repmikehonda http://www.flickr.com/photos/congressman_honda/

1713 Longworth House Office Building, Washington, DC 20515 .... (202) 225–2631
Chief of Staff.—Jennifer Van der Heide. FAX: 225–2699
Legislative Director.—Eric Werwa.
Communications Director.—Ken Scudder.
2001 Gateway Place, Suite 670W, San Jose, CA 95110 .... (408) 436–2720
District Director.—Meri Maben.

Counties: ALAMEDA COUNTY (part), Santa Clara County (part). CITIES AND TOWNSHIPS: Cupertino, Fremont, Milpitas, Newark, North San Jose, Santa Clara, and Sunnyvale. Population (2010), 719,276.

ZIP Codes: 94024, 94040, 94043, 94085–89, 94536, 94538–39, 94555, 94560, 95002, 95014–15, 95035–36, 95050–56, 95070, 95101, 95110, 95112, 95116–17, 95126–29, 95131–34, 95140

* * *

EIGHTEENTH DISTRICT

ANNA G. ESHOO, Democrat, of Menlo Park, CA; born in New Britain, CT, December 13, 1942; education: attended Canada College; San Mateo County Board of Supervisors, 1982–92; committees: Energy and Commerce; elected on November 3, 1992, to the 103rd Congress; reelected to each succeeding Congress.

Office Listings

http://www.eshoo.house.gov

241 Cannon House Office Building, Washington, DC 20515 .... (202) 225–8104
Executive Assistant.—Jena Gross. FAX: 225–8890
698 Emerson Street, Palo Alto, CA 94301 .... (650) 323–2984
Chief of Staff.—Karen Chapman.

Counties: SAN MATEO, SANTA CLARA, SANTA CRUZ. CITIES AND TOWNSHIPS: Atherton, Ben Lomond, Boony Doon, Boulder Creek, Brookdale, Campbell, Cambrian Park, Davenport, Felton, Fruitdale, La Honda, Ladera, Lexington Hills, Loma Mar, Lompico, Los Altos, Los Altos Hills, Los Gatos, Menlo Park, Monte Sereno, Mountain View, Palo Alto, Pescadero, Portola Valley, Redwood City, San Jose, Saratoga, Scott's Valley, Stanford, Woodside, and Zayante. Population (2010), 702,906.

ZIP Codes: 94020–28, 94035, 94039–43, 94060–63, 94074, 94301–06, 94309, 95005–09, 95011, 95014, 95017–18, 95026, 95030–33, 95041–42, 95044, 95050, 95060, 95065–67, 95070–71, 95073, 95076, 95117–18, 95120, 95123–26, 95128–30, 95141, 95154, 95157–58, 95160, 95170

* * *

NINETEENTH DISTRICT

ZOE LOFGREN, Democrat, of San Jose, CA; born in San Mateo, CA, December 21, 1947; education: graduated Gunn High School, 1966; B.A., Stanford University, Stanford, CA, 1970; J.D., Santa Clara Law School, Santa Clara, CA, 1975; admitted to the California Bar, 1975; District of Columbia Bar, 1981; Supreme Court, 1986; member: board of trustees, San Jose Evergreen Community College District, 1979–81; board of supervisors, Santa Clara County, CA, 1981–94; married: John Marshall Collins, 1978; children: Sheila and John; committees: House Administration; Judiciary; Science, Space, and Technology; Joint Committee on the Library; elected to the 104th Congress; reelected to each succeeding Congress.

Office Listings

http://www.lofgren.house.gov twitter: @repzoelofgren

1401 Longworth House Office Building, Washington, DC 20515 .... (202) 225–3072
Chief of Staff.—Stacey Leavandosky. FAX: 225–3336
Communications Director.—Duncan Neasham.
Executive Assistant / Scheduler.—Sabrina Kirkwood.
635 North First Street, Suite B, San Jose, CA 95112 .... (408) 271–8700
Chief of Staff.—Sandra Soto.

Counties: SANTA CLARA (part). CITIES AND TOWNSHIPS: San Jose, San Martin, Gilroy and unincorporated portions of southern Santa Clara County. Population (2010), 702,904.

ZIP Codes: 94550, 95013, 95020, 95023, 95033, 95035, 95037–38, 95046, 95050, 95076, 95103, 95106, 95108–13, 95109–13, 95115–16, 95118–28, 95132–33, 95135–36, 95138–41, 95148, 95150–53, 95155–56, 95159, 95172–73, 95191–92, 95196

* * *

TWENTIETH DISTRICT

SAM FARR, Democrat, of Carmel, CA; born in San Francisco, CA, July 4, 1941; education: attended Carmel, CA, public schools; B.S., biology, Willamette University, Salem, OR; studied at the Monterey Institute of International Studies; served in the Peace Corps for two years in Colombia, South America; worked as a consultant and employee of the California Assembly; elected to the California Assembly, 1980–93; former member of California Assembly's Committees on Education, Insurance, and Natural Resources; married to Shary Baldwin; one daughter: Jessica; committees: Appropriations; elected on June 8, 1993, by special election, to fill the vacancy caused by the resignation of Representative Leon Panetta; reelected to each succeeding Congress.

Office Listings

http://www.farr.house.gov twitter: @repsamfarr http://www.facebook.com/repsamfarr

1126 Longworth House Office Building, Washington, DC 20515 .... (202) 225–2861
Chief of Staff.—Rochelle Dornatt.
Legislative Director.—Debbie Merrill.
Press Secretary.—Adam Russell.
701 Ocean Avenue, Santa Cruz, CA 95060 .... (831) 429–1976
100 West Alisal Street, Salinas, CA 93901 .... (831) 424–2229

Counties: MONTEREY, SAN BENITO, SANTA CRUZ (southern half), SANTA CLARA (souother portion). Population (2010), 744,350.

ZIP Codes: 93426, 93450–51, 93901–02, 93905–08, 93912, 93915, 93920–28, 93930, 93932–33, 93940, 93942–44, 93950, 93953–55, 93960, 93962, 95001, 95003–04, 95010, 95012, 95019, 95020–21, 95023–24, 95039, 95043, 95045, 95060–65, 95073, 95075–77

* * *

TWENTY-FIRST DISTRICT

DAVID VALADAO, Republican, of Hanford, CA; born in Hanford, CA, April 14, 1977; education: graduated from Hanford High School; attended College of the Sequoias in Visalia, CA. professional: dairy farmer; leadership: the California Milk Advisory Board, Western States Dairy Trade Association; elected as Regional Leadership Council Chairman for Land O' Lakes Inc., a Fortune 200 company; member of the California State house of representatives, 2010–12; religion: Catholic; married: Terra Valadao; three children, Connor, Madeline, and Lucas; committees: Appropriations; elected to the 113th Congress on November 6, 2012.

Office Listings

http://www.valadao.house.gov https://www.facebook.com/congressmandavidvaladao
https://twitter.com/repdavidvaladao

1004 Longworth House Office Building, Washington, DC 20515 .... (202) 225–4695
FAX: 225–3196
Chief of Staff.—Tal Eslick.
Scheduler.—Cole Rojewski.
Legislative Director.—Chris Marklund.
101 Irwin Street, Suite 110B, Hanford, CA 93230 .... (559) 582–5526
District Director.—George Andrews.
2700 M Street, Suite 250B, Bakersfield, CA 93301 .... (661) 864–7736

Counties: KINGS, TULARE (part), KERN (part), FRESNO (part). Population (2010), 714,164.

ZIP Codes: 93201–04, 93206, 93210, 93212, 93215, 93218–19, 93227, 93230, 93234, 93237, 93239, 93241–43, 93245, 93249–51, 93256–57, 93261, 93263, 93266, 93270, 93272, 93274–75, 93278–80, 93290–91, 93304–07, 93311–12, 93314, 93607–09, 93616, 93620, 93622, 93624–25, 93627, 93631, 93640, 93648, 93652, 93654, 93656–57, 93660, 93662, 93668, 93706, 93723, 93725

* * *

TWENTY-SECOND DISTRICT

DEVIN NUNES, Republican, of Tulare, CA; born in Tulare County, CA, October 1, 1973; education: A.A., College of the Sequoias; B.S., Agricultural Business, and a Masters Degree in Agriculture, from California Polytechnic State University, San Luis Obispo; graduate, California Agriculture Leadership Fellowship Program; professional: farmer and businessman; elected, College of the Sequoias Board of Trustees, 1996; reelected, 2000; appointed by President George W. Bush to serve as California State Director of the U.S. Department of Agriculture Rural Development Office, 2001; religion: Catholic; married: the former Elizabeth Tamariz, 2003; two children; committees: Ways and Means; Permanent Select Committee on Intelligence; elected to the 108th Congress on November 5, 2002; reelected to each succeeding Congress.

Office Listings

http://www.nunes.house.gov

1013 Longworth House Office Building, Washington, DC 20515 .... (202) 225–2523

Chief of Staff.—Johnny Amaral. FAX: 225–3404
Legislative Director.—Damon Nelson.
Communications Director.—Andrew House.
Scheduler.—Jennifer Morrow.
113 North Church Street, Suite 208, Visalia, CA 93291 .... (559) 733–3861
264 Clovis Avenue, Suite 206, Clovis, CA 93612 .... (559) 323–5235

Counties: TULARE, FRESNO (part). Population (2010), 702,904.

ZIP Codes: 93201, 93207–08, 93212, 93215, 93218–19, 93221, 93223, 93227, 93235, 93237, 93242, 93244, 93247, 93256–58, 93260–62, 93265, 93267, 93270–72, 93274–75, 93277–79, 93286, 93290–92, 93602–03, 93605, 93609, 93611–13, 93615–16, 93618, 93621, 93625–26, 93628, 93631, 93633–34, 93641–42, 93646–49, 93651, 93654, 93656–57, 93662, 93664, 93666–67, 93670, 93673, 93675, 93703, 93710, 93720, 93726–27, 93740, 93747

* * *

TWENTY-THIRD DISTRICT

KEVIN McCARTHY, Republican, of Bakersfield, CA; born in Bakersfield, January 26, 1965; education: graduated, Bakersfield High School, 1983; B.S., business administration, CSU–Bakersfield, 1989; M.B.A., CSU–Bakersfield, 1994; professional: intern, worked up to District Director for U.S. Congressman Bill Thomas, 1987–2002; served as Trustee, Kern Community College District, 2000–02; served in the California State Assembly, 2002–06; elected, California Assembly Republican Leader, 2003–06; married to the former Judy Wages, 1992; two children: Connor and Meghan; committees: Financial Services; elected to the 110th Congress on November 7, 2006; reelected to each succeeding Congress.

Office Listings

http://www.kevinmccarthy.house.gov twitter: @GOPWhip twitter: @kevinomccarthy

2421 Rayburn House Office Building, Washington, DC 20515 .... (202) 225–2915
Chief of Staff.—James Min. FAX: 225–2908
Scheduler.—Kristin Thomson.
Legislative Director.—Kyle Lombardi.
Press Secretary.—Mariana Diez.
4100 Empire Drive, Suite 150, Bakersfield, CA 93309 .... (661) 327–3611
District Administrator.—Robin Lake Foster.

Counties: KERN COUNTY (part). CITIES AND TOWNSHIPS: Arvin, Bakersfield, Bodfish, Boron, Caliente, California City, Cantil, China Lake, Edison, Edwards, Fellows, Frazier Park, Glennville, Havilah, Inyokern, Keene, Kernville, Lake Isabella, Lebec, Maricopa, McKittrick, Mojave, Monolith, North Edwards, Onyx, Randsberg, Ridgecrest, Rosamond, Taft, Tehachapi, Tupman, Weldon, Willow Springs, Wofford Heights, Woody. TULARE COUNTY (part). CITIES AND TOWNSHIPS: Badger, California Hot Springs, Exeter, Lemon Cove, Lindsay, Orosi, Porterville, Posey, Springville, Strathmore, Terra Bella, Three Rivers, Visalia, Woodlake. LOS ANGELES COUNTY (part). CITIES AND TOWNSHIPS: Lancaster. Population (2012) 707,345.

ZIP Codes: 93203, 93205, 93207–08, 93221–22, 93224–26, 93238, 93240, 93243–44, 93247, 93251–52, 93255, 93257, 93260, 93262, 93265, 93267–68, 93270–71, 93276, 93283, 93285–87, 93292, 93301, 93304–07, 93309, 93311–14, 93501, 93505, 93516, 93518–19, 93523, 93527–28, 93531, 93534, 93536, 93554–55, 93560–61, 93603, 93633, 93647

* * *

TWENTY-FOURTH DISTRICT

LOIS CAPPS, Democrat, of Santa Barbara, CA; born in Ladysmith, WI, January 10, 1938; education: graduated Flathead County High School, Kalispell, MT, 1955; B.S. in Nursing, Pacific Lutheran University, 1959; M.A. in Religion, Yale University, 1964; M.A. in Education, University of California at Santa Barbara, 1990; professional: head nurse, Yale New Haven Hospital; staff nurse, Visiting Nurses Association, Hamden, CT; elementary district nurse, Santa Barbara School District; director, Teenage Pregnancy and Parenting Project, Santa Barbara County; director, Santa Barbara School District Parent and Child Education Center; instructor of early childhood education, Santa Barbara City College; board member: American Red Cross, American Heart Association, Family Service Agency, Santa Barbara Women's Political Committee; married: Walter Capps, 1960; children: Lisa, Todd, and Laura; committees: Energy and Commerce; elected by special election on March 10, 1998, to the 105th Congress, to fill the vacancy caused by the death of her husband Representative Walter Capps; reelected to each succeeding Congress.

Office Listings

http://www.capps.house.gov twitter: @reploiscapps

2231 Rayburn House Office Building, Washington, DC 20515 .... (202) 225–3601

Chief of Staff.—Randolph Harrison. FAX: 225–5632
Deputy Chief of Staff / Executive Assistant.—Sarah Rubinfield.
Legislative Director.—Adriane Casalotti.
Press Secretary.—Ashley Schapitl.
1411 Marsh Street, Suite 205, San Luis Obispo, CA 93401 .... (805) 546–8348
District Representatives: Greg Haas, Betsy Umhofer.
301 East Carrillo Street, Suite A, Santa Barbara, CA 93101 .... (805) 730–1710
District Director.—Sharon Siegel.
District Representatives: Rachel Kondor, Raymond Morua.
1101 South Broadway, Suite A, Santa Maria, CA 93454 .... (805) 349–3832
District Representatives.—Blanca Figueroa.

Counties: SAN LUIS OBISPO COUNTY (All). CITIES AND TOWNSHIPS: Atascadero, Arroyo Grande, Baywood-Los Osos, Cambria, Cayucos, Grover Beach, Morro Bay, Nipomo, Oceano, Paso Robles, Pismo Beach, San Luis Obispo. SANTA BARBARA COUNTY (All). CITIES AND TOWNSHIPS: Carpinteria, Goleta, Guadalupe, Isla Vista, Mission Canyon, Montecito, Santa Barbara, Santa Maria, Summerland, Toro Canyon. VENTURA COUNTY (part). CITIES AND TOWNSHIPS: Ventura. Population (2010), 708,744.

ZIP Codes: 93001, 93013–14, 93067, 93101–21, 93130, 93140, 93150, 93160, 93190, 93199, 93254, 93401–12, 93420–24, 93427–30, 93432–37, 93440–49, 93451–58, 93460–61, 93463–65, 93475, 93483, 94338

* * *

TWENTY-FIFTH DISTRICT

HOWARD P. ''BUCK'' MCKEON, Republican, of Santa Clarita, CA; born in Los Angeles, CA, September 9, 1938; education: graduated, Verdugo Hills High School, Tujunga, CA; B.S., Brigham Young University; mayor and city councilman, Santa Clarita, 1987–92; former member: board of directors, Canyon Country Chamber of Commerce; California Republican State Central Committee; advisory council, Boy Scouts of America; president and trustee, William S. Hart School District, 1979–87; former chairman and director, Henry Mayo Newhall Memorial Hospital, 1983–87; former chairman and founding director, Valencia National Bank, 1987–92; honorary chairman, Red Cross Community Support Campaign, 1992; honorary chairman, Leukemia Society Celebrity Program, 1990 and 1994; president, Republican Freshman Class of the 103rd Congress; married: to the former Patricia Kunz, 1962; children: Tamara, Howard D., John Matthew, Kimberly, David Owen, and Tricia; committees: chair, Armed Services; Education and the Workforce; elected on November 3, 1992, to the 103rd Congress; reelected to each succeeding Congress.

Office Listings

http://www.house.gov/mckeon www.twitter.com/buckmckeon
www.facebook.com/buckmckeon

2310 Rayburn House Office Building, Washington, DC 20515 .... (202) 225–1956
Chief of Staff.—Alan Tennille. FAX: 226–0683
Executive Assistant / Appointments.—Candace Wagner.
District Director.—Morris Thomas.
26650 The Old Road, Suite 203, Santa Clarita, CA 91355 .... (661) 254–2111
1008 West Avenue, M–14, Suite E1, Palmdale, CA 93551 .... (661) 274–9688

Counties: NORTHERN LOS ANGELES (part), VENTURA (part). CITIES: Santa Clarita, Simi Valley, Palmdale, Lancaster, and Northern San Fernando Valley (part). Population (2010), 702,904.

ZIP Codes: 91042, 91214, 91310, 91321–22, 91350–51, 91354–55, 91380–81, 91383–87, 91390, 92301, 92309–12, 92328, 92342, 92345, 92347, 92364–65, 92368, 92371–72, 92384, 92389, 92392–94, 92398, 92832, 93510, 93512–17, 93524, 93526–27, 93529–30, 93534–35, 93541–46, 93549–53, 93560, 93562, 93586, 93590–92, 93599, 96107, 96133

* * *

TWENTY-SIXTH DISTRICT

JULIA BROWNLEY, Democrat, of Westlake Village, CA; born in Aiken, SC, August 28, 1952; education: B.A., The George Washington University, 1975; M.B.A., American University, 1979; professional: product manager, Steelcase, 1984–92; sales manager, Pitney Bowes, 1981–84; sales manager, Burroughs Corporation, 1976–81; Santa Monica-Malibu School Board, 1994–2006; California State Assembly, 2007–12; chair of California State Assembly Committee on Education; children: Fred and Hannah; committees: Science, Space, and Technology; Veterans Affairs; elected to the 113th Congress on November 6, 2012.

Office Listings

http://juliabrownley.house.gov

1019 Longworth House Office Building, Washington, DC 20515 .... (202) 225–5811
Chief of Staff.—Lenny Young. FAX: 225–5811
Legislative Director.—Sharon Wagener.
Communications Director.—Eric Parker.
Scheduler.—Jonathan Cousimano.
300 East Esplanade Drive, Suite 470, Oxnard, CA 93036 .... (805) 379–1779
District Director.—Carina Armenta. FAX: 379–1799
223 East Thousand Oaks Boulevard, Suite 411, Thousand Oaks, CA 91360 .... (805) 379–1779
FAX: 379–1799

Counties: LOS ANGELES (part) AND VENTURA (part). Population (2010), 702,905.

ZIP Codes: 91320, 91360–62, 91377, 93003–04, 93010, 93012, 93015, 93021–23, 93030, 93033, 93035–36, 93040–41, 93060, 93065–66

* * *

TWENTY-SEVENTH DISTRICT

JUDY M. CHU, Democrat, of El Monte, CA; born in Los Angeles, CA, July 7, 1953; education: B.A. in math from UCLA, Los Angeles, CA, 1974; Ph.D. in psychology from the California School of Professional Psychology, 1979; professional: Garvey School District Board member, 1985–88; Monterey Park City Council and Mayor, 1988–2001; California State Assembly, 2001–2006; California State Board of Equalization, 2006–2009; first Chinese American woman elected to Congress; family: married to Assemblymember Mike Eng in 1978; committees: Judiciary; Small Business; elected to the 111th Congress on July 14, 2009, by special election to fill the vacancy caused by the resignation of United States Representative Hilda Solis; reelected to each succeeding Congress.

Office Listings

http://www.chu.house.gov https://twitter.com/repjudychud

1520 Longworth House Office Building, Washington, DC 20515 .... (202) 225–5464
Chief of Staff.—Amelia Wang. FAX: 225–5467
Legislative Director.—Allison Rose.
Congressional Asian Pacific American Caucus (CAPAC) Executive Director.—Gene Kim.
Legislative Assistants: Mariana Maguire, Priscila Hammett, Moh Sharma, ESQ.
Legislative Correspondent / System Administrator.—Vacant.
Legislative Counsel.—Linda Shim.
Press Secretary.—Dan Lindner.
Scheduler.—Courtney Hruska.
Staff Assistant.—Ellen Hamilton.
527 South Lake Avenue, Suite 106, Pasadena, CA 91101 .... (626) 304–0110
District Director.—Becky Cheng. FAX: 304–0132
Deputy District Director.—Bryan Urias.
Field Representative / Case Workers: Anthony Duarte, Carina Lieu, Enrique Robles.
Caseworker / VITA Site Coordinator.—Lena Ng.
District Scheduler.—Lindsay Plake.
Staff Assistant.—Vacant.

Counties: LOS ANGELES COUNTY (part). CITIES: Alhambra, Altadena (unincorporated), Arcadia, Bradbury, Claremont, Glendora, Monterey Park, Monrovia, Pasadena, Rosemead, South Pasadena, San Gabriel, San Marino, Sierra Madre, Temple City, Upland, San Antonio Heights (unincorporated), East Pasadena (unincorporated), South San Gabriel (unincorporated). Population (2010), 684,496.

ZIP Codes: 91001, 91003, 91006–07, 91010, 91711, 91016–17, 91024–25, 91030–31, 91066–77, 91101–10, 91108, 91114–18, 91118, 91121, 91123–26, 91129, 91131, 91175, 91182, 91184–89, 91191, 91740–41, 91754–56, 91770, 91770–72, 91775–76, 91778, 91780, 91784–86, 91801–04, 91841, 91896, 91899

* * *

TWENTY-EIGHTH DISTRICT

ADAM B. SCHIFF, Democrat, of Burbank, CA; born in Framingham, MA, June 20, 1960; education: B.A., Stanford University, 1982; J.D., Harvard University, 1985; professional: attorney; U.S. Attorney's Office, served as a criminal prosecutor; chosen by the Dept. of Justice to assist the Czechoslovakian Government in reforming their criminal justice system; public service: elected to the California State Senate, 1996; involved in numerous community service activities; awards: Dept. of Justice Special Achievement Award; Council of State Governments Toll Fellowship; California League of High Schools Legislator of the Year; family: married: Eve; children: Alexa and Elijah; committees: Appropriations; Permanent Select Committee on Intelligence; elected to the 107th Congress on November 7, 2000; reelected to each succeeding Congress.

Office Listings

http://www.house.gov/schiff twitter: @repadamschiff

2411 Rayburn House Office Building, Washington, DC 20515 .... (202) 225–4176
Chief of Staff.—Timothy Bergreen. FAX: 225–5828
Communications Director.—Patrick Boland.
Executive Assistant.—Christopher Hoven.
245 East Olive Avenue, Burbank, CA 91502 .... (626) 304–2727
District Director.—Ann Peifer.

Counties: LOS ANGELES (part). CITIES: Burbank, Glendale, Hollywood, La Canada-Flintridge, La Crescenta, Los Feliz, Pasadena, Sunland, and Tujunga. Population (2010), 702,904.

ZIP Codes: 9004, 90026–29, 90031, 90036, 90038–39, 90046, 90048, 90068–69, 91011, 91020, 91040, 91042–43, 91103, 91105, 91201–08, 91214, 91352, 91501–02, 91504–06

* * *

TWENTY-NINTH DISTRICT

ANTONIO CÁRDENAS, Democrat, of San Fernando Valley, CA; born in Pacoima, CA, March 31, 1963; education: B.A., University of California at Santa Barbara, 1986; professional: businessman; public service: California State Assembly, 1996–2002; Los Angeles City Council, 2002–13; religion: Christian; family: married to Norma Sanchez; children: 4, Andres, Alina, Vanessa, Cristian; committees: Budget; Natural Resources; Oversight and Government Reform, elected to the 113th Congress on November 6, 2012.

Office Listings

http://www.house.gov/cárdenas twitter: @repcárdenas

1508 Longworth House Office Building, Washington, DC 20515 .... (202) 225–6131
Chief of Staff.—Sam Jammal. FAX: 225–0819
Legislative Director.—Miguel Franco.
9300 Laurel Canyon Boulevard, 2d Floor, Arleta, CA 91331 .... (818) 504–0090

Counties: LOS ANGELES. Population (2010), 680,661.

ZIP Codes: 91040, 91321, 91331, 91340, 91342–45, 91352, 91387, 91401–02, 91405–06, 91411, 91504–05, 91601–02, 91605–07

* * *

THIRTIETH DISTRICT

BRAD SHERMAN, Democrat, of Sherman Oaks, CA; born in Los Angeles, CA, October 24, 1954; education: B.A., *summa cum laude,* UCLA, 1974; J.D., *magna cum laude,* Harvard Law School, 1979; professional: admitted to the California Bar in 1979 and began practice in Los Angeles; attorney, CPA, certified tax law specialist; elected to the California State Board of Equalization, 1990, serving as chairman, 1991–95; committees: Financial Services; Foreign Affairs; elected to the 105th Congress; reelected to each succeeding Congress.

Office Listings

twitter: @bradsherman

2242 Rayburn House Office Building, Washington, DC 20515 .... (202) 225–5911
Chief of Staff.—Don MacDonald. FAX: 225–5879
5000 Van Nuys Boulevard, Suite 420, Sherman Oaks, CA 91403 .... (818) 501–9200
District Director.—Matthew Dababneh.

Counties: LOS ANGELES (part). Population (2010), 702,904.

ZIP Codes: 90046, 90049, 90068, 90077, 90210, 91302–04, 91306–07, 91311, 91316, 91324–26, 91330, 91335, 91342–44, 91356, 91364, 91367, 91371, 91401, 91403, 91406, 91411, 91423, 91436, 91505–06, 91601–02, 91604, 91607–08, 93064

* * *

THIRTY-FIRST DISTRICT

GARY G. MILLER, Republican, of Rancho Cucamonga, CA; born in Huntsville, AR, October 16, 1948; education: Loma Vista Elementary School, Whittier, CA; California High School, Whittier, CA; Lowell High School, LaHabra, CA; Mount San Antonio College, Walnut, CA; military service: private, U.S. Army, 1967; professional: developer; owner, G. Miller Development Company; public service: Diamond Bar, CA, City Council, 1989–95; Mayor, 1992; California State Assembly, 1995–98; married: Cathy Miller; children: Brian, Elizabeth, Loren, and Matthew; committees: Financial Services; Transportation and Infrastructure; elected to the 106th Congress; reelected to each succeeding Congress.

Office Listings

http://www.house.gov/garymiller twitter: @repgarymiller

2467 Rayburn House Office Building, Washington, DC 20515 .... (202) 225–3201
Chief of Staff.—John Rothrock. FAX: 226–6962
Legislative Director / Senior Policy Advisor.—Randy Ross.
Executive Director.—Kevin McKee.
8300 Utica Avenue, Suite 105, Rancho Cucamonga, CA 91730 .... (909) 980–1492
District Director.—Chris Marsh.

Counties: SAN BERNARDINO (part). CITIES AND TOWNSHIPS: Upland, Rancho Cucamonga, Fontana, Rialto, Colton, Grand Terrace, Loma Linda, San Bernardino, and Redlands. Population (2010), 611,336.

ZIP Codes: 91701, 91730, 91737, 91739, 91786, 92313, 92316, 92324, 92335–36, 92346, 92350, 92354, 92357, 92359, 92373–74, 92376–77, 92399, 92401, 92404–05, 92407–08, 92410–11, 92509

* * *

THIRTY-SECOND DISTRICT

GRACE F. NAPOLITANO, Democrat, of Los Angeles, CA; born in Brownsville, TX, December 4, 1936; education: Brownsville High School, Brownsville, TX; Cerritos College, Norwalk, CA; Texas Southmost College, Brownsville, TX; professional: Transportation Coordinator, Ford Motor Company; elected to Norwalk, CA, City Council, 1986; became mayor of Norwalk, CA, 1989; elected to the California Assembly, 58th District, 1992–98; organizations: Norwalk Lions Club; Veterans of Foreign Wars (auxiliary); American Legion (auxiliary); Soroptimist International; past director, Cerritos College Foundation; director, Community Family Guidance Center; League of United Latin American Citizens; director, Los Angeles County Sanitation District; director, Los Angeles County Vector Control (Southeast District); director, Southeast Los Angeles Private Industry Council; director, Los Angeles County Sheriff's Authority; National Women's Political Caucus; past national board secretary, United States-Mexico Sister Cities Association; member, Congressional Hispanic Caucus; co-chair, Congressional Mental Health Caucus; maiden name: Flores; married: Frank Napolitano; children: Yolanda Dyer, Fred Musquiz, Edward Musquiz, Michael Musquiz, and Cynthia Dowling; committees: Natural Resources; Transportation and Infrastructure; elected to the 106th Congress; reelected to each succeeding Congress.

Office Listings

http://www.house.gov/napolitano http://www.twitter.com/gracenapolitano
http://www.youtube.com/repgracenapolitano

1610 Longworth House Office Building, Washington, DC 20515 .... (202) 225–5256
Chief of Staff.—Daniel Chao. FAX: 225–0027
Legislative Director.—Joe Sheehy.
Press Secretary.—Jerry O'Donnell.
Scheduler.—Joseph Ciccone.
4401 Santa Anita Avenue, Suite 201, El Monte, CA 91731 .... (626) 350–0150
District Director.—Ben Cardenas.

Counties: LOS ANGELES (part). Population (2010), 702,905.

ZIP Codes: 91009–10, 91016–17, 91702, 91706, 91714–16, 91722–24, 91731–32, 91734–35, 91744, 91746–47, 91749–50, 91773, 91790–93, 91797

* * *

THIRTY-THIRD DISTRICT

HENRY A. WAXMAN, Democrat, of Los Angeles, CA; born in Los Angeles, September 12, 1939; education: B.A., political science, UCLA, 1961; J.D., School of Law; admitted to the California State bar, 1965; served three terms as California State Assemblyman; former chairman, California Assembly Health Committee; Select Committee on Medical Malpractice; and Committee on Elections and Reapportionment; president, California Federation of Young Democrats, 1965–67; member: Guardians of the Jewish Home for the Aged; American Jewish Congress; Sierra Club; married: the former Janet Kessler, 1971; children: Carol Lynn and Michael David; committees: Energy and Commerce; elected to the 94th Congress on November 5, 1974; reelected to each succeeding Congress.

Office Listings

http://www.house.gov/waxman https://www.facebook.com/rep.henrywaxman
twitter: @waxmanclimate

2204 Rayburn House Office Building, Washington, DC 20515 .... (202) 225–3976
Chief of Staff.—Pat Delgado. FAX: 225–4099
5055 Wilshire Boulevard, Suite 310, Los Angeles, CA 90036 .... (310) 321–7664
District Director.—Lisa Pinto.
1600 Rosecrans Avenue, 4th Floor, Manhattan Beach, CA 90266 .... (310) 321–7664
District Director.—Lisa Pinto.

Counties: LOS ANGELES COUNTY (part). CITIES AND TOWNSHIPS: Agoura Hills, Bel-Air, Beverly Hills, Brentwood, Calabasas, El Segundo, Hermosa Beach, Malibu, Manhattan Beach, Marina Del Rey, Pacific Palisades, Palos Verdes Estates, The City of Rancho Palos Verdes, Redondo Beach, Rolling Hills, Rolling Hills Estates, Santa Monica, Topanga, Venice, and Vista Del Mar. The 33rd Congressional District also includes a portion of the communities of Hancock Park, Harbor City, San Pedro, Torrance, West Los Angeles, and Westwood. Population (2010), 707,854.

ZIP Codes: 90004 (part), 90020 (part), 90024 (part), 90036, 90048–49, 90073, 90077, 90095, 90209, 90211–13, 90245, 90254, 90263–67, 90272, 90274–75, 90277–78, 90290–95, 90401–08 (part), 90409–11, 90503 (part), 90505 (part), 90710 (part), 90731 (part), 90732 (part), 90744 (part), 91301–02, 91376

* * *

THIRTY-FOURTH DISTRICT

XAVIER BECERRA, Democrat, of Los Angeles, CA; born in Sacramento, CA, January 26, 1958; education: graduated, McClatchy High School, Sacramento, 1976; B.A., Stanford University, 1980; J.D., Stanford Law School, 1984; admitted to California bar, 1985; attended Universidad de Salamanca, 1978–79; staff attorney, ''Reggie Fellow,'' Legal Assistance Corporation of Central Massachusetts, 1984–85; administrative assistant for State Senator Art Torres, California State Legislature, 1986; Deputy Attorney General, Office of the Attorney General, State of California, 1987–90; Assemblyman, California State Legislature, 1990–92; member: Mexican American State Legislators Policy Institute; Mexican American Bar Association; chairperson: Hispanic Employee Advisory Committee to the State Attorney General, 1989; honorary member: Association of California State Attorneys and Administrative Law Judges; former member: steering committee, Greater Eastside Voter Registration Project; Construction and General Laborers Union, Local 185 (Sacramento); Pitzer College Board of Trustees; National Association of Latino's Electoral and appointed to the Official Board of Directors; vice chair, Democratic Caucus of the 111th Congress; reelected vice chair, Democratic Caucus of the 112th Congress; married to Dr. Carolina Reyes; children: Clarisa, Olivia, Natalia; committees: Ways and Means; elected on November 3, 1992, to the 103rd Congress; reelected to each succeeding Congress.

Office Listings

http://www.house.gov/becerra twitter: @repbecerra

1226 Longworth House Office Building, Washington, DC 20515 .... (202) 225–6235
Chief of Staff.—Debra Dixon. FAX: 225–2202
Policy Director.—Sean McCluskie.
Scheduler.—Cynthia Palafox.
350 Souoth Bixel Street, Suite 120, Los Angeles, CA 90017 .... (213) 481–1425
District Director.—Liz Saldivar.

Counties: LOS ANGELES COUNTY (part). CITIES: Los Angeles. Population (2010), 698,741.

ZIP Codes: 90004–07, 90010, 90012–15, 90017–23, 90026, 90030–33, 90030–33, 90038, 90041–42, 90053, 90057, 90063, 90065, 90071, 90079, 90086, 90090

* * *

THIRTY-FIFTH DISTRICT

GLORIA NEGRETE MCLEOD, Democrat, of Chino, CA; born in Los Angeles, CA, September 6, 1941; education: A.A. degree, Chaffey Community College, Rancho Cucamonga, CA, 1975; professional: instructional aide; member of the Chaffey Community College board, 1995–2000; president of the Chaffey Community College board, 2000; member of the California state assembly, 2000–06; member of the California state senate, 2006–12; married: Gilbert; 10 children, 27 grandchildren and 25 great grandchildren; caucuses: Congressional Hispanic Caucus, Women's Caucus; Native American Caucus; Military Sexual Assault Prevention Caucus; USO Congressional Caucus; National Guard and Reserve Components Caucus; Congressional Steel Caucus; Gun Violence Prevention Task Force; committees: Agriculture; Veterans' Affairs; elected to the 113th Congress on November 6, 2012.

Office Listings

http://www.negretemcleod.house.gov twitter: @repmcleod facebook.com/negretemcleod

1641 Longworth House Office Building, Washington, DC 20515 .... (202) 225–6161
Chief of Staff.—Alfonso Sanchez. FAX: 225–8671
Legislative Director.—Teresa Acuna.
Communication Director.—Daniel Sanchez.
4959 Palo Verde Street, Suite 110B, Montclair, CA 91763 .... (909) 626–2054
District Director.—Marti Rodriguez.

Counties: SAN BERNARDINO COUNTY (part). CITIES: Bloomington, Chino, Fontana, Montclair, Ontario, Rialto. LOS ANGELES COUNTY (part). CITIES: Pomona. Population (2010), 710,704.

ZIP Codes: 91708–11, 91730, 91739, 91743, 91750, 91752, 91758, 91761–69, 91786, 91789, 92316, 92324, 92331, 92334–37, 92509, 92880

* * *

THIRTY-SIXTH DISTRICT

RAUL RUIZ, M.D., Democrat, of Palm Springs, CA; born in Coachella, CA, August 25, 1972; education: B.S., University of California, Los Angeles, 1994; M.D., Harvard University, 2001; M.P.P., Harvard University, 2001; M.P.H., Harvard University, 2007; professional: emergency physician, Eisenhower Medical Center; founder, Coachella Valley Healthcare Initiative, 2010; senior associate dean, School of Medicine at University of California Riverside, 2011; caucuses: Seniors Task Force; Native American Caucus; No Labels-Problem Solvers; Veterans Job Caucus; Law Enforcement Caucus; LGBT Caucus; Renewable Energy Caucus; Government Efficiency Caucus; Small Business Caucus; Specialty Crop Caucus; and Friends of Canada Caucus; committees: Natural Resources; Veterans' Affairs; elected to the 113th Congress on November 6, 2012.

Office Listings

http://ruiz.house.gov

1319 Longworth House Office Building, Washington, DC 20515 .... (202) 225–5330
Chief of Staff.—Kyle Layman. FAX: 225–1238
Legislative Director.—Orfa Torres-Jaen.
Communications Director.—Michael Ford.
Scheduler.—Joseph Abushawish.
777 East Tahquitz Canyon Way, Suite 338, Palm Springs, CA 92262 .... (760) 424–8888
District Director.—Greg Rodriguez.

Counties: RIVERSIDE COUNTY. CITIES: Palm Springs, Palm Desert, Indio, Coachella, Rancho Mirage, Desert Hot Springs, Indian Wells, and Cathedral City. Population (2010), 714,975.

ZIP Codes: 92201–03, 92210–11, 92220, 92230, 92234, 92236, 92240–41, 92253–54, 92258, 92260, 92262, 92264, 92270, 92276, 92282, 92539, 92549, 92561, 92583

* * *

THIRTY-SEVENTH DISTRICT

KAREN R. BASS, Democrat, of Los Angeles, CA; born in Los Angeles, October 3, 1953; education: B.S., health sciences, California State University, Dominguez Hills, CA, 1990; P.A.,

University of Southern California School of Medicine, Los Angeles; professional: elected first Democratic woman Speaker of the California Assembly; founded and served as Executive Director of the non-profit organization Community Coalition, Los Angeles; physician assistant, Los Angeles County General Hospital; religion: Baptist; family: daughter Emilia Bass-Lechuga, son-in-law Michael Wright; step children: Scythia, Omar, Yvette, and Jesse Lechuga; awards: JFK profiles in Courage Award; Congressional Black Caucus Phoenix Award; committees: Foreign Affairs; Judiciary; elected to the 112th Congress on November 2, 2010.

Office Listings

http://www.bass.house.gov twitter: @repkarenbass

408 Cannon Office Building, Washington, DC 20515 .... (202) 225–7084
Chief of Staff.—Carrie Kohns. FAX: 225–2422
Senior Legislative Assistant.—Susie Saavedra.
Scheduler / Executive Assistant.—Allison Fialkov.
Communications Director.—Kevin Smith.
4322 Wilshire Boulevard, Suite 302, Los Angeles, CA 90010 .... (323) 965–1422
District Director.—Solomon Rivera.

Counties: LOS ANGELES (part). CITIES: Culver and Los Angeles. COMMUNITIES OF: Ladera Heights and View Park-Windsor Hills. Population (2010), 702,904.

ZIP Codes: 90004–08, 90010–11, 90016, 90018–20, 90022, 90026–29, 90033–39, 90043–45, 90047–48, 90053, 90056–58, 90062–64, 90066, 90068, 90070, 90078, 90083, 90093, 90099, 90103, 90230–33

* * *

THIRTY-EIGHTH DISTRICT

LINDA T. SÁNCHEZ, Democrat, of Lakewood, CA; born in Orange, CA, January 28, 1969; education: B.A., University of California, Berkeley; J.D., U.C.L.A. Law School; passed bar exam in 1995; professional: attorney; has practiced in the areas of appellate, civil rights, and employment law; International Brotherhood of Electrical Workers Local 441; National Electrical Contractors Association; and Orange County Central Labor Council Executive Secretary, AFL–CIO; organizations: National Women's Political Caucus; Women in Leadership; religion: Catholic; committees: ranking member, Ethics; Ways and Means; elected to the 108th Congress on November 5, 2002; reelected to each succeeding Congress.

Office Listings

http://www.house.gov/lindasanchez twitter: @replindasanchez

2423 Rayburn House Office Building, Washington, DC 20515 .... (202) 225–6676
Chief of Staff.—Adam Brand. FAX: 226–1012
Legislative Director.—Tim Del Monico.
Communications Director.—Mattie Munoz.
17906 Crusader Avenue, Suite 100, Cerritos, CA 90703 .... (562) 860–5050
District Director.—José Delgado.

Counties: LOS ANGELES (part). Population (2010), 715,745.

ZIP Codes: 90601–06, 90623, 90638, 90701, 90703, 90706, 90716, 90712–13, 90715, 90640, 90650, 90660, 90670, 91733

* * *

THIRTY-NINTH DISTRICT

EDWARD R. ROYCE, Republican, of Fullerton, CA; born in Los Angeles, CA, October 12, 1951; education: B.A., California State University, Fullerton, 1977; professional: small business owner; controller; corporate tax manager; California State Senate, 1982–92; member: Fullerton Chamber of Commerce; board member, Literacy Volunteers of America; California Interscholastic Athletic Foundation board of advisers; married: Marie Therese Porter, 1985; committees: chair, Foreign Affairs; Financial Services; elected on November 3, 1992 to the 103rd Congress; reelected to each succeeding Congress.

Office Listings

http://www.royce.house.gov twitter: @repedroyce

2185 Rayburn House Office Building, Washington, DC 20515 .... (202) 225–4111

Chief of Staff.—Amy Porter. FAX: 226–0335
Legislative Director.—Peter Freeman.
Communications Director.—Chelsea Wilson.
210 West Birch Street, Suite 201, Brea, CA 92821 .... (714) 255–0109
District Director.—Sara Catalan. FAX: 744–4056

Counties: California's 39th district encompasses cities in northern ORANGE COUNTY, eastern LOS ANGELES COUNTY, and southwestern SAN BERNARDINO COUNTY. The cities include Brea, Buena Park, Chino Hills, Diamond Bar, Fullerton, Hacienda Heights, La Habra, Placentia, Rosemead, Rowland Heights, Walnut, and Yorba Linda. Population (2010), 643,115.

ZIP Codes: 90603, 90620–22, 90624, 90631–33, 90638, 91709–10, 91745–46, 91748–49, 91765–66, 91768, 91788–89, 92801, 92806–07, 92811, 92817, 92821–23, 92831–38, 92865, 92867, 92870–71, 92885–87, 92899

* * *

FORTIETH DISTRICT

LUCILLE ROYBAL-ALLARD, Democrat, of Los Angeles, CA; born in Los Angeles, June 12, 1941; education: B.A., California State University, Los Angeles, 1965; served in the California State Assembly, 1987–92; the first woman to serve as the chair of the California Democratic Congressional Delegation in the 105th Congress; in the 106th Congress, she became the first woman to chair the Congressional Hispanic Caucus, and the first Latina in history to be appointed to the House Appropriations Committee; married: Edward T. Allard III; two children: Lisa Marie and Ricardo; two stepchildren: Angela and Guy Mark; committees: Appropriations; the first Mexican-American woman elected to Congress on November 3, 1992 to the 103rd Congress; reelected to each succeeding Congress.

Office Listings

http://www.house.gov/roybal-allard https://www.facebook.com/reproybalallard
https://twitter.com/reproybalallard

2330 Rayburn House Office Building, Washington, DC 20515–0534 .... (202) 225–1766
Chief of Staff.—Victor G. Castillo. FAX: 226–0350
Legislative Director.—Debbie Jessup.
Executive Assistant.—Christine C. Ochoa.
500 Citadel Drive, Suite 320, Commerce, CA 90040–1572 .... (323) 721–8790
District Director.—Ana Figueroa. FAX: 721–8789

Counties: LOS ANGELES COUNTY (part). CITIES: Bill, Bell Gardens, Bellflower, Commerce, Cudahy, Downey, East Los Angeles, Florence-Graham, Huntington Park, Maywood, Paramount, South Los Angeles, Vernon, and Walnut Park. Population (2010), 694,514.

ZIP Codes: 90001, 90003, 90007, 90011, 90015, 90021–23, 90037, 90040, 90052, 90058–59, 90063, 90082, 90091, 90201–02, 90239–42, 90255, 90270, 90280, 90640, 90650, 90660, 90706, 90723, 91754

* * *

FORTY-FIRST DISTRICT

MARK TAKANO, Democrat, of Riverside, CA; born in Riverside, December 10, 1960; education: B.A. in government, Harvard College, 1983; M.A. in fine arts, University of California Riverside, 2010; professional: Public School Teacher; Riverside Community College District Board Trustee; awards: Chairman of the Asian Pacific Islander Caucus of the California Democratic Party; charter member of the Association of Latino Community College Trustees; member of the Association of California Asian American Trustees; member of Asian Pacific Americans in Higher Education; recipient of Martin Luther King Visionaries Award; religion: Methodist; committees: Science, Space, and Technology; Veterans' Affairs; elected to the 113th Congress on November 6, 2012.

Office Listings

http://takano.house.gov http://twitter.com/repmarktakano

1507 Longworth House Office Building, Washington, DC 20515 .... (202) 225–2305
Chief of Staff.—Richard McPike. FAX: 225–7018
Deputy Chief of Staff/Legislative Director.—Yuri Beckelman.
3403 10th Street, Suite 610, Riverside, CA 92501 .... (951) 222–0203
District Director.—Rafael Elizalde.

Counties: RIVERSIDE (part). CITIES: Jurupa Valley, Moreno Valley, Perris, and Riverside. Population (2010), 797,133.

ZIP Codes: 91572, 92324, 92373, 92501, 92503–09, 92518, 92551, 92553, 92555, 92557, 92570–71, 92880

* * *

FORTY-SECOND DISTRICT

KEN CALVERT, Republican, of Corona, CA; born in Corona, June 8, 1953; education: A.A., Chaffey College, CA, 1973; B.A. in economics, San Diego State University, 1975; professional: congressional aide to Representative Victor V. Veysey, CA; general manager, Jolly Fox Restaurant, Corona, 1975–79; Marcus W. Meairs Co., Corona, 1979–81; president and general manager, Ken Calvert Real Properties, 1981–92; County Youth Chairman, Representative Veysey's District, 1970–72; Corona / Norco Youth Chairman for Nixon, 1968 and 1972; Reagan-Bush campaign worker, 1980; co-chair, Wilson for Senate Campaign, 1982; chairman, Riverside Republican Party, 1984–88; co-chairman, George Deukmejian election, 1978, 1982 and 1986; co-chairman, George Bush election, 1988; co-chairman, Pete Wilson Senate elections, 1982 and 1988; co-chairman, Pete Wilson for Governor election, 1990; chairman and charter member, Lincoln Club of Riverside County, 1986–90; past president, Corona Rotary Club; Corona Elks; Navy League of Corona / Norco; Corona Chamber of Commerce; past chairman, Norco Chamber of Commerce; County of Riverside Asset Leasing; past chairman, Corona / Norco Board of Realtors; Monday Morning Group; Corona Group; executive board, Economic Development Partnership; charter member, Corona Community Hospital Corporate 200 Club; Silver Eagles (March AFB Support Group); Corona Airport Advisory Commission; committees: Appropriations; Budget; elected on November 3, 1992 to the 103rd Congress; reelected to each succeeding Congress.

Office Listings

http://www.house.gov/calvert twitter: @kencalvert

2269 Rayburn House Office Building, Washington, DC 20515 .... (202) 225–1986
Chief of Staff.—Dave Ramey. FAX: 225–2004
Legislative Director.—Rebecca Rudman.
4160 Temescal Canyon Road, Suite 214, Corona, CA 92883 .... (951) 784–4300
District Director.—Jolyn Murphy.
Press Secretary.—Jason Gagnon.

Counties: RIVERSIDE COUNTY. CITIES AND TOWNSHIPS: Canyon Lake, Corona, Eastvale, Lake Elsinore, Menifee, Murrieta, Norco, a portion of Temecula, and Wildomar. Population (2010), 710,617.

ZIP Codes: 91752, 92028, 92223, 92503–04, 92506–08, 92530–32, 92536, 92544–45, 92548, 92555, 92562–63, 92567, 92570–71, 92582, 92584–87, 92590–92, 92595–96, 92860, 92877–83

* * *

FORTY-THIRD DISTRICT

MAXINE WATERS, Democrat, of Los Angeles, CA; born in St. Louis, MO, August 15, 1938; education: B.A., California State University; honorary degrees: Harris-Stowe State College, St. Louis, MO, and Central State University, Wilberforce, OH, Spelman College, Atlanta, GA, North Carolina A&T State University, Howard University, Central State University, Bishop College, Morgan State University; elected to California State Assembly, 1976; reelected every two years thereafter; member: Assembly Democratic Caucus, Board of TransAfrica Foundation, National Women's Political Caucus; chair, Democratic Caucus Special Committee on Election Reform; chair, Ways and Means Subcommittee on State Administration; chair, Joint Committee on Public Pension Fund Investments; founding member, National Commission for Economic Conversion and Disarmament; member of the board, Center for National Policy; Clara Elizabeth Jackson Carter Foundation (Spelman College); Minority AIDS Project; married to Sidney Williams, former U.S. Ambassador to the Commonwealth of the Bahamas; two children: Karen and Edward; committees: ranking member, Financial Services; elected to the 102nd Congress on November 6, 1990; reelected to each succeeding Congress.

Office Listings

http://www.waters.house.gov twitter: @maxinewaters

2221 Rayburn House Office Building, Washington, DC 20515 .... (202) 225–2201
Chief of Staff.—Mikael Moore. FAX: 225–7854
Deputy Chief of Staff.—Janice Bashford.
10124 South Broadway, Suite 1, Los Angeles, CA 90003 .... (323) 757–8900
District Director.—Blanca Jimenez.

Counties: LOS ANGELES COUNTY (part). CITIES: Gardena, Hawthorne, Inglewood, Lawndale, Los Angeles, Playa Del Ray, Lomita, and Torrance. Population (2010), 702,983.

ZIP Codes: 90007, 90009, 90044–45, 90047, 90052, 90056, 90059, 90061, 90066, 90082, 90094, 90189, 90247–51, 90260–61, 90293, 90301–13, 90397–98, 90504, 90506, 90717

* * *

FORTY-FOURTH DISTRICT

JANICE HAHN, Democrat, of San Pedro, CA; born in Los Angeles, CA, March 30, 1952; education: B.S. in education, Abilene Christian University, Abilene, TX, 1974; professional: teacher, Good News Academy, 1974–78; stay-at-home mother, 1978–88; Director of Marketing, Alexander Haagan Company, 1988–90; Director of Community Outreach, Western Waste Industries, 1990–92; Vice President of Public Finance, Prudential Securities, 1993–95; Public Affairs Regional Manager, Southern California Edison Co., 1995–2000; elected to the Charter Reform Commission, 1997–99; Los Angeles City Council, 15th District, 2001–11; family: children, Danny, Mark, and Katy; grandchildren, McKenna, Brooklyn, Isabela, Josiah, and Luke; committees: Small Business; Transportation and Infrastructure; elected to the 112th Congress by special election, July 12, 2011, to fill the vacancy caused by the resignation of United States Representative Jane Harman, and took the oath of office July 19, 2011; elected to a full term in the 113th Congress on November 6, 2012.

Office Listings

http://www.house.gov/hahn twitter: @rep_janicehahn

404 Cannon House Office Building, Washington, DC 20515 .... (202) 225–8220
Chief of Staff.—Laurie Saroff. FAX: 226–7290
Legislative Director.—Vacant.
Scheduler.—Jeff Howell.
140 West 6th Street, San Pedro, CA 90731 .... (310) 831–1799
544 North Avalon Boulevard, Suite 307, Wilmington, CA 90744 .... (310) 549–8282
205 South Willowbrook Avenue, Compton, CA 90220 .... (310) 605–5520

Counties: LOS ANGELES (part). CITIES: Carson, Compton, Los Angeles, Lynwood, Port of Los Angeles, San Pedro, Southgate, Watts, and Wilmington. Population (2010), 702,904.

ZIP Codes: 90001 (part), 90002 (part), 90003 (part), 90004 (part), 90005 (part), 90007 (part), 90011 (part), 90015 (part), 90018 (part), 90020 (part), 90021 (part), 90022 (part), 90023 (part), 90025 (part), 90026 (part), 90031 (part), 90037 (part), 90038 (part), 90058 (part), 90059 (part), 90061 (part), 90063 (part), 90064 (part), 90089 (part), 90220, 90221 (part), 90222, 90223 (part), 90230 (part), 90248 (part), 90255 (part), 90262 (part), 90280, 90291 (part), 90292 (part), 90302 (part), 90405 (part), 90503 (part), 90504 (part), 90505 (part), 90631 (part), 90640 (part), 90706 (part), 90710 (part), 90712 (part), 90717 (part), 90731 (part), 90732 (part), 90733–34, 90744 (part), 90745–49, 90802 (part), 90805 (part), 90810 (part), 90811 (part), 90895, 91016 (part), 91030 (part), 91103 (part), 91105 (part), 91124 (part), 91321 (part), 91344 (part), 91505 (part), 91702 (part), 91711 (part), 91724 (part), 91731 (part), 91732 (part), 91740 (part), 91745 (part), 91754 (part), 91768 (part), 91770 (part), 91773 (part), 91789 (part), 93550 (part), 93551 (part)

* * *

FORTY-FIFTH DISTRICT

JOHN CAMPBELL, Republican, of Irvine, CA; born in Los Angeles, CA, July 19, 1955; education: B.A., University of California, Los Angeles, CA; M.A., University of Southern California, Los Angeles, CA; professional: certified public accountant; member of the California State Senate; married: Catherine; children: two sons; committees: Budget; Financial Services; Joint Economic Committee; elected to the 109th Congress by special election to fill the vacancy caused by the resignation of United States Representative Christopher Cox; elected to the 110th Congress; reelected to each succeeding Congress.

Office Listings

http://www.house.gov/campbell

1507 Longworth House Office Building, Washington, DC 20515 .... (202) 225–5611
Chief of Staff.—Muffy Lewis. FAX: 225–9177
Executive Assistant.—Carolyn Noble.
Legislative Director.—David Malech.
Communications Director.—Chris Bognanno.
610 Newport Center Drive, Suite 330, Newport Beach, CA 92660 .... (949) 756–2244

Counties: ORANGE COUNTY (part). CITIES: Aliso Viejo, Corona del Mar, Dana Point, Foothill Ranch, Irvine, Laguna Beach, Laguna Hills, Laguna Niguel, Laguna Woods, Lake Forest, Newport Beach, Orange, San Juan Capistrano, Santa Ana, and Tustin. Population (2010), 727,833.

ZIP Codes: 92602–04, 92606–07, 92610, 92612, 92614, 92618, 92620, 92624–25, 92629–30, 92651, 92653, 92656–57, 92660–63, 92674–75, 92677–79, 92690, 92693, 92705, 92780, 92782

* * *

FORTY-SIXTH DISTRICT

LORETTA SANCHEZ, Democrat, of Anaheim, CA; born in Lynwood, CA, January 7, 1960; education: graduate of Chapman University; M.B.A., American University; specializes in assisting public agencies with finance matters; member, Blue Dog Coalition; California Democratic Congressional Delegation; Congressional Caucus on Competitiveness in Entertainment Technology; Congressional Caucus on Entertainment Industries; Congressional Caucus on Innovation and Entrepreneurship; Congressional Caucus on Korea; Congressional Caucus on Vietnam; Congressional Caucus on Women in the Military; Congressional Cyber-Security Caucus; Congressional Human Rights Caucus; Congressional Labor and Working Families Caucus; Congressional LGBT Equality Caucus; Congressional Mental Health Caucus; Congressional Military Families Caucus; New Democrat Coalition; committees: Armed Services; Homeland Security; Joint Economic Committee; elected to the 105th Congress; reelected to each succeeding Congress.

Office Listings

http://www.house.gov/sanchez twitter: @lorettasanchez

1114 Longworth House Office Building, Washington, DC 20515 .... (202) 225–2965
Chief of Staff.—Adrienne Elrod. FAX: 225–5859
Deputy Chief of Staff / Scheduler.—Shane Moore.
Legislative Director.—Eduardo Lerma.
Legislative Assistants: Melanie Abe, Jessica Fernandez, Annie Yea.
Communications Director.—Adrienne Watson.
12397 Lewis Street, Suite 101, Garden Grove, CA 92840 .... (714) 621–0102
District Director.—Gaston Castellanos.

Counties: ORANGE COUNTY (part). CITIES: Anaheim (west and north-south of the Anaheim Stadium-Disneyland corridor), Fullerton, Garden Grove, Orange, and Santa Ana. Population (2010), 648,663.

ZIP Codes: 90620, 92606, 92626, 92701–07, 92711–12, 92735, 92780, 92799, 92801–07

* * *

FORTY-SEVENTH DISTRICT

ALAN LOWENTHAL, Democrat, of Long Beach, CA; born in Manhattan, New York County, NY, March 8, 1941; education: B.A. Hobart College, Geneva, NY, 1962; M.A. The Ohio State University, Columbus, OH, 1965; Ph.D. The Ohio State University, Columbus, OH, 1967; professional: professor; psychologist; member of the Long Beach, CA City Council, 1992–98; member of the California State Assembly, 1998–2004; member of the California State Senate, 2004–12; religion: Jewish; family: wife, Dr. Deborah Malumed; 2 children, 3 grandchildren; caucuses: Congressional Ports Caucus; Congressional Asian Pacific American Caucus; Progressive Caucus; House LGBT Equality Caucus; committees: Foreign Affairs; Natural Resources; elected to the 113th Congress on November 6, 2012.

Office Listings

http://www.lowenthal.house.gov twitter: @replowenthal

515 Cannon House Office Building, Washington, DC 20515 .... (202) 225–7924
Chief of Staff.—Tim Hysom. FAX: 225–7926
Legislative Director.—Frances Marquez.
Communications Director.—Keith Higginbotham.
Scheduler.—Amanda Slade.
100 West Broadway Street, West Tower, Suite 600, Long Beach, CA 90802 .... (562) 436–3828
District Director.—Mark Pulido.

Counties: LOS ANGELES COUNTY (part). CITIES: Avalon, Lakewood, Long Beach, Signal Hill. ORANGE COUNTY (part). CITIES: Buena Park, Cypress, Garden Grove, Los Alamitos, Midway City, Rossmoor, Stanton, and Westminster. Population (2013), 719,805.

ZIP Codes: 90620, 90623, 90630, 90680, 90704, 90712, 90713, 90716, 90720–21, 90731, 90740, 90744, 90755, 90801–10, 90813–15, 90831–35, 90840, 90842, 90844, 90846–48, 90853, 92647, 92655, 92683–85, 92703, 92801, 92802, 92804, 92840–46

* * *

FORTY-EIGHTH DISTRICT

DANA T. ROHRABACHER, Republican, of Costa Mesa, CA; born in Coronado, CA, June 21, 1947; education: graduated Palos Verdes High School, CA, 1965; attended Los Angeles Harbor College, Wilmington, CA, 1965–67; B.A., Long Beach State College, CA, 1969; M.A., University of Southern California, Los Angeles, 1975; professional: writer / journalist; speechwriter and special assistant to the President, The White House, Washington, DC, 1981–88; assistant press secretary, Reagan/Bush Committee, 1980; reporter, City News Service/Radio News West, and editorial writer, *Orange County Register*, 1972–80; family: wife and triplets; committees: Foreign Affairs; Science, Space, and Technology; elected on November 8, 1988, to the 101st Congress; reelected to each succeeding Congress.

Office Listings

http://www.house.gov/rohrabacher

2300 Rayburn House Office Building, Washington, DC 20515 .... (202) 225–2415
Chief of Staff.—Rick Dykema. FAX: 225–0145
Legislative Director.—Jeff Vanderslice.
Communications Director.—Tara Setmayer.
Senior Policy Advisor.—Tony DeTora.
Legislative Assistant.—Kevin Holsclaw.
Legislative Correspondent.—Brian Alesi.
Executive Assistant / Scheduler.—Fess Cassels.
Staff Assistant.—Justin Ahn.
101 Main Street, Suite 380, Huntington Beach, CA 92648 .... (714) 960–6483
District Director.—Kathleen Staunton.
District Executive Assistant / Scheduler.—Joyce Bassil.

Counties: ORANGE COUNTY (part). Communities of Aliso Viejo, Corona del Mar, Costa Mesa, Fountain Valley, Garden Grove, Huntington Beach, Laguna Beach, Laguna Niguel, Midway City, Newport Beach, Santa Ana, Seal Beach, Sunset Beach, Surfside, and Westminster. Population (2010), 702,905.

ZIP Codes: 90740, 90742–043, 92625–27, 92646–49, 92651, 92655–57, 92660–63, 92677, 92683, 92703–04, 92708, 92843–44

* * *

FORTY-NINTH DISTRICT

DARRELL E. ISSA, Republican, of Vista, CA; born in Cleveland, OH, November 1, 1953; education: Siena Heights College; military service: Captain U.S. Army; attended college on an ROTC scholarship; professional: Businessman; founder and CEO of Directed Electronics, Inc.; past Chairman, Consumer Electronics Association; previously on Board of Directors, Electronics Industry Association; public service: Co-Chairman of the campaign to pass the California Civil Rights Initiative (Proposition 209); Chairman of the Volunteer Committee for the 1996 Republican National Convention; Chairman of the San Diego County Lincoln Club; candidate for the U.S. Senate in 1998; architect of 2003 California recall campaign of former Governor Gray Davis; married: Kathy; children: William; committees: chair, Oversight and Government Reform; Judiciary; elected to the 107th Congress on November 7, 2000; reelected to each succeeding Congress.

Office Listings

http://issa.house.gov twitter: @darrellissa

2347 Rayburn House Office Building, Washington, DC 20515 .... (202) 225–3906
Chief of Staff.—Dale Neugebauer. FAX: 225–3303
Deputy Chief of Staff.—Veronica Wong.
Deputy Staff Director for Communication and Strategy.—Frederick Hill.
Scheduler.—Katie Weiss.
1800 Thibodo Road, Suite 310, Vista, CA 92081 .... (760) 599–5000

Counties: ORANGE (part), SAN DIEGO (part). Population (2010), 702,906.

ZIP Codes: 92003, 92007–14, 92018, 92023–24, 92028–29, 92037, 92049, 92051–52, 92054–58, 92067–69, 92075, 92078, 92081, 92083–85, 92091–93, 92121, 92127, 92130, 92624, 92629, 92672–75, 92677, 92688, 92690–94

* * *

FIFTIETH DISTRICT

DUNCAN HUNTER, Republican, of Lakeside, CA; born in San Diego, CA, December 7, 1976; education: graduated from Granite Hills High School; B.S., Business Administration, San Diego State University, San Diego, CA, 2001; professional: business analyst; military: captain, United States Marine Corps, 2002–05; United States Marine Corps Reserves, 2005–08; religion: Protestant; married: Margaret; children: Duncan, Elizabeth, and Sarah; committees: Armed Services; Education and the Workforce; Transportation and Infrastructure; elected to the 111th Congress on November 4, 2008, reelected to each succeeding Congress.

Office Listings

http://www.hunter.house.gov

223 Cannon House Office Building, Washington, DC 20515 .... (202) 225–5672
Chief of Staff.—Victoria Middleton. FAX: 225–0235
Deputy Chief of Staff / Communications Director.—Joe Kasper.
Legislative Director.—Jimmy Thomas.
Scheduler / Office Manager.—Carly DeBeikes.
Senior Legislative Assistant.—Reed Linsk.
Legislative Assistant.—Ellen Malin.
Legislative Correspondent.—Alexandra Collison.
Staff Assistant.—Nina Gandhi.
Military Fellow.—Louis Delair.
1611 North Magnolia Avenue, Suite 310, El Cajon, CA 92020 .... (619) 448–5201
333 South Juniper Street, Suite 110, Escondido, CA 92025 .... (760) 592–0271
41000 Main Street, Temecula, CA 92590 .... (951) 216–2111

Counties: SAN DIEGO COUNTY (part). CITIES AND TOWNSHIPS: Alpine, Barona I.R., Borrego Springs, Bonsall, Boulevard, Descanso, El Cajon, Escondido, Fallbrook, Guatay, Jamul, Julian, Lakeside, La Mesa, Mount Laguna, Pala, Palamar Mountain, Pauma Valley, Pine Valley, Potrero, Poway, Ramona, Ranchita, San Marcos, Santa Ysabel, Santee, Spring Valley, Temecula, Valley Center, Vista, and Warner Springs. Population (2010), 724,472.

ZIP Codes: 91901, 91903, 91916, 91931, 91935, 91941, 91948, 91962, 91978, 92003–04, 92019–21, 92025–30, 92033, 92036, 92040, 92046, 92059–61, 92064–66, 92069–72, 92078–79, 92082, 92084, 92086, 92088, 92589–93

* * *

FIFTY-FIRST DISTRICT

JUAN VARGAS, Democrat, of San Diego, CA; born in National City, CA, March 7, 1961; education: B.A., University of San Diego, San Diego, CA, 1983; M.A., Fordham University, New York, NY, 1987; J.D., Harvard University, Cambridge, MA, 1991; professional: lawyer; business executive; member of the San Diego, CA, city council, 1993–2000; member of the California State Assembly, 2000–06; member of the California State Senate, 2010–12; religion: Roman Catholic; spouse: Adrienne Vargas; children: Rosa Celina Vargas and Helena Jeanne Vargas; committees: Agriculture; Foreign Affairs; House Administration; elected to the 113th Congress on November 6, 2012.

Office Listings

http://vargas.house.gov https://twitter.com/repjuanvargas

1605 Longworth House Office Building, Washington, DC 20515 .... (202) 225–8045
Chief of Staff.—Tim Walsh. FAX: 225–9073
Special Assistant.—Rita Fernandez.
Press Secretary.—Dianna Zamora-Marroquin.
333 F Street, Suite A, Chula Vista, CA 91910 .... (619) 422–5963
FAX: 422–7290
380 North 8th Street, El Centro, CA 92243 .... (760) 355–8800
FAX: 312–9664

Counties: SAN DIEGO (part), AND IMPERIAL COUNTY. Cities: Alpine, Bard, Blythe, Bonita, Boulevard, Brawley, Calexico, Calipatria, Campo, Chula Vista, Dulzura, El Cajon, El Centro, Heber, Holtville, Imperial, Imperial Beach, Jacubma, Jamul, Lemon Grove, National City, Niland, Ocotillo, Palo Verde, Pine Valley, Potrero, San Diego, Seeley, Tecate, Thermal, Westmorland, and Winterhaven. Population (2010), 702,906.

ZIP Codes: 91901–02, 91905–06, 91909–12, 91915, 91917, 91932–35, 91945, 91947, 91950–51, 91962–63, 91980, 91987, 92019, 92101–02, 92104–05, 92113–15, 92136, 92139, 92143, 92153–54, 92158, 92165, 92170, 92173–74, 92179, 92222, 92225, 92227, 92231–33, 92243–44, 92249–51, 92257, 92259, 92266, 92273–74, 92281, 92283

* * *

FIFTY-SECOND DISTRICT

SCOTT PETERS, Democrat, of La Jolla, CA; born in Springfield, OH, June 17, 1958; education: Magna Cum Laude, Phi Beta Kappa, Duke University; New York University School of Law, professional: Environmental lawyer; City Council President; San Diego Port Commissioner; religion: Lutheran; Wife, Lynn; 2 children; committees: Armed Services; Science, Space and Technology; elected to the 113th Congress on November 6, 2012.

Office Listings

http://scottpeters.house.gov twitter: @repscottpeters

2140 Rayburn House Office Building, Washington, DC 20515 .... (202) 225–0508
Chief of Staff.—Michelle Dorothy. FAX: 225–2558
Scheduler.—Anne Moriarity.
Legislative Director.—Morgan Jones.
Communications Director.—Taylor Lavender.
4350 Executive Drive, Suite 105, San Diego, CA 92121 .... (858) 455–5550
District Director.—MaryAnne Pintar.

Counties: SAN DIEGO COUNTY (part). CITIES AND TOWNSHIPS: Carmel Valley, La Jolla, Point Loma, Downtown San Diego, Coronado and Poway. Population (2010), 704,565.

ZIP Codes: 91901, 91905–06, 91916–17, 91931, 91935, 91941–42, 91945, 91948, 91962, 91977–78, 92004, 92019, 92021, 92025, 92029, 92036, 92040, 92064–66, 92071, 92108, 92111, 92115, 92117, 92119–20, 92123–24, 92126, 92128–29, 92131, 92145

* * *

FIFTY-THIRD DISTRICT

SUSAN A. DAVIS, Democrat, of San Diego, CA; born in Cambridge, MA, April 13, 1944; education: B.S., University of California at Berkeley; M.A., University of North Carolina; public service: served three terms in the California State Assembly; served nine years on the San Diego City School Board; former President of the League of Women Voters of San Diego; awards: California School Boards Association Legislator of the Year; League of Middle Schools Legislator of the Year; family: married to Steve; children: Jeffrey and Benjamin; grandsons: Henry and Theo; granddaughter: Jane; committees: Armed Services; Education and the Workforce; elected to the 107th Congress on November 7, 2000; reelected to each succeeding Congress.

Office Listings

http://www.house.gov/susandavis

1526 Longworth House Office Building, Washington, DC 20515 .... (202) 225–2040
Chief of Staff.—Lisa Sherman. FAX: 225–2948
Press Secretary.—Aaron Hunter.
Scheduler.—Cynthia Patton.
2700 Adams Avenue, Suite 102, San Diego, CA 92116 .... (619) 280–5353
District Director.—Jessica Poole. FAX: 280–5311

Counties: SAN DIEGO COUNTY (part). Population (2010), 639,008.

ZIP Codes: 91902, 91908, 91910–11, 91913–15, 91921, 91941–46, 91976–79, 92019–22, 92101–05, 92108, 92110–11, 92114–16, 92119–20, 92123–24, 92134, 92139, 92149, 92154, 92160, 92163–64, 92168, 92171, 92175–76, 92182, 92190, 92193, 92195

COLORADO

(Population 2010, 5,029,196)

SENATORS

MARK UDALL, Democrat, of Eldorado Springs, CO; born in Tucson, AZ, July 18, 1950; B.A., Williams College, Williamstown, MA, 1972; field coordinator, Morris K. Udall for President, 1974; executive director, Colorado Outward Bound School, 1985–95; member of the Colorado State House of Representatives, 1996–98; member of the U.S. House of Representatives, 1999–2008; married: Maggie Fox; two children; committees: Armed Services; Energy and Natural Resources; Select Committee on Intelligence; elected to the U.S. Senate on November 4, 2008.

Office Listings

http://markudall.senate.gov https://www.facebook.com/markudall
https://twitter.com/markudall

SH–730 Hart Senate Office Building, Washington, DC 20510 .... (202) 224–5941
Chief of Staff.—Michael Sozan. FAX: 224–6471
Administrative Director.—John Fossum.
Legislative Director.—Jacob T. Swanton.
Deputy Chief of Staff.—Joseph Britton.
Director of Scheduling.—Jacqueline Miller.
999 18th Street, Suite 1525, North Tower, Denver, CO 80202 .... (303) 650–7820
State Director.—Jennifer Rokala.
Communications Director.—Michael Saccone.
107 West B Street, Pueblo, CO 81003 .... (719) 542–1701
954 East 2nd Avenue, Suite 106, Durango, CO 81301 .... (970) 247–1047
2880 International Circle, Suite 107, Colorado Springs, CO 80910 .... (719) 471–3993
609 Main Street, Suite 205, Alamosa, CO 81101 .... (719) 589–2101
801 8th Street, Suite 140A, Greeley, CO 80631 .... (970) 356–5586
400 Rood Avenue, Suite 220, Grand Junction, CO 81501 .... (970) 245–9553
P.O. Box 866, Clark, CO 80428 .... (303) 650–7820

* * *

MICHAEL F. BENNET, Democrat, of Denver, CO; born in New Delhi, India, November 28, 1964; education: B.A., Wesleyan University, 1987; J.D., Yale Law School, 1993; editor-in-chief of the *Yale Law Journal;* counsel to U.S. Deputy Attorney General, 1995–97; special assistant, U.S. Attorney, CT, 1997; managing director, Anschutz Investment Co., 1997–2003; chief of staff to mayor of Denver, CO, 2003–05; superintendent, Denver Public Schools, 2005–09; married: Susan D. Dagget; children: Caroline, Halina, and Anne; committees: Agriculture, Nutrition, and Forestry; Finance; Health, Education, Labor, and Pensions; appointed January 21, 2009, to the 111th United States Senate for the term ending January 3, 2011; elected to the 112th Congress for a full Senate term on November 2, 2010.

Office Listings

http://bennet.senate.gov

458 Russell Senate Office Building, Washington, DC 20510–0606 .... (202) 224–5852
Chief of Staff.—Jonathan Davidson. FAX: 228–5036
Legislative Director.—Brian Appel (acting).
Communications Director.—Adam Bozzi.
Scheduler.—Kristin Mollet.
1127 Sherman Street, Suite 150, Denver, CO 80203 .... (303) 455–7600
FAX: 455–8851
129 West B Street, Pueblo, CO 81003 .... (719) 542–7550
FAX: 542–7555
609 Main Street, Suite 110, Alamosa, CO 81101 .... (719) 587–0096
FAX: 587–0098
409 North Tejon, Suite 107, Colorado Springs, CO 80903 .... (719) 328–1100
FAX: 328–1129
1200 South College Avenue, Suite 211, Fort Collins, CO 80524 .... (970) 224–2200
FAX: 224–2205
225 North 5th Street, Suite 511, Grand Junction, CO 81501 .... (970) 241–6631
FAX: 241–8313
835 East 2nd Avenue, Suite 203, Durango, CO 81301 .... (970) 259–1710
FAX: 259–9789

REPRESENTATIVES

FIRST DISTRICT

DIANA DEGETTE, Democrat, of Denver, CO; born in Tachikowa, Japan, July 29, 1957; education: B.A., political science, *magna cum laude*, The Colorado College, 1979; J.D., New York University School of Law, 1982 (Root Tilden Scholar); professional: attorney with McDermott, Hansen, and Reilly; Colorado Deputy State Public Defender, Appellate Division, 1982–84; Colorado House of Representatives, 1992–96; board of directors, Planned Parenthood, Rocky Mountain Chapter; member and formerly on board of governors, Colorado Bar Association; member, Colorado Women's Bar Association; past memberships: board of trustees, The Colorado College; Denver Women's Commission; board of directors, Colorado Trial Lawyers Association; former editor, *Trial Talk* magazine; listed in 1994–96 edition of *Who's Who in America*; Chief Deputy Whip; committees: Energy and Commerce; elected to the 105th Congress; reelected to each succeeding Congress.

Office Listings

http://degette.house.gov

2368 Rayburn House Office Building, Washington, DC 20515 .... (202) 225–4431
Chief of Staff.—Lisa B. Cohen. FAX: 225–5657
Scheduler.—Diana Gambrel.
Communications Director.—Matt Inzeo.
600 Grant Street, Suite 202, Denver, CO 80203 .... (303) 844–4988
District Director.—Morris Price.

Counties: ARAPAHOE (part), DENVER, AND JEFFERSON (part). Population (2010), 718,457.

ZIP Codes: 80012, 80014, 80110–11, 80113, 80120–21, 80123, 80127–28, 80202–07, 80209–12, 80214–16, 80218–24, 80226–27, 80230–32, 80235–39, 80246–47, 80249, 80264, 80290, 80293–94

* * *

SECOND DISTRICT

JARED POLIS, Democrat, of Boulder, CO; born in Boulder, CO, May 12, 1975; education: B.A., political science, Princeton University, Princeton, NJ, 1996; professional: Internet entrepreneur; founder of New America Schools; chair, Colorado State Board of Education; House Democratic Steering and Policy Committee; religion: Jewish; committees: Education and the Workforce; Rules; elected to the 111th Congress on November 4, 2008; reelected to each succeeding Congress.

Office Listings

http://www.polis.house.gov

1433 Longworth House Office Building, Washington, DC 20515 .... (202) 225–2161
Chief of Staff.—Dan Turrentine.
Deputy Chief of Staff / Legislative Director.—Eve Lieberman.
Communications Director.—Scott Overland.
4770 Baseline Road, Suite 220, Boulder, CO 80303 .... (303) 484–9596
101 West Main Street, Suite 101G, P.O. Box 1453, Frisco, CO 80443 .... (970) 668–3240
300 East Horsetooth Road, Suite 103, Fort Collins, CO 80525 .... (970) 226–1239

Counties: BOULDER (part), BROOMFIELD, CLEAR CREEK, EAGLE (part), GILPIN, GRAND, JEFFERSON, LARIMER, PARK (part), AND SUMMIT. Population (2010), 732,658.

ZIP Codes: 80007, 80020–21, 80023, 80025–28, 80135, 80228, 80234, 80301–05, 80310, 80401, 80403, 80419, 80421, 80422–25, 80427, 80433, 80435–36, 80438–39, 80442–44, 80446–48, 80451–55, 80457, 80459, 80465–66, 80468, 80470–71, 80475–76, 80478, 80481–82, 80497–98, 80503–04, 80510–13, 80515–17, 80521, 80524–26, 80528, 80532, 80534–38, 80540, 80544–45, 80547, 80549–50, 80612, 81620, 81632, 81645, 81649, 81655, 81657, 82063

* * *

THIRD DISTRICT

SCOTT TIPTON, Republican, of Cortez, CO; born in Espanola, NM, November 9, 1956; education: graduated, B.S., political science, Ft. Lewis College, Durango, CO, 1978; professional: Owner/President of Mesa Verde Pottery, Cortez, CO; public service: elected to Colorado House of Representatives, 2008–10; religion: Anglican; married: Elizabeth Tipton; children: Liesl (married to Chris Ross) and Elizabeth Tipton; caucuses: chair, Small Business Caucus; Coal; Natural Gas; Western; Sportsman; Israel; Beef; Dairy; committees: Agriculture; Natural Resources; Small Business; elected to the 112th Congress on November 2, 2010; reelected to the 113th Congress on November 6, 2012.

Office Listings

http://tipton.house.gov

218 Cannon House Office Building, Washington, DC 20515 .... (202) 225–4761
Chief of Staff.—Nicholas Zupancic. FAX: 226–9669
Legislative Director.—Lindley Kratovil.
Executive Assistant.—Megan Dornan.
225 North 5th Street, Suite 702, Grand Junction, CO 81501 .... (970) 241–2499
District Director.—Joshua Green.
609 Main Street, Suite 105, Box 11, Alamosa, CO 81101 .... (719) 587–5105
503 North Main Street, Suite 658, Pueblo, CO 81003 .... (719) 542–1073
835 East Second Avenue, Suite 230, Durango, CO 81301 .... (970) 259–1490

Counties: Alamosa, Archuleta, Conejos, Costilla, Custer, Delta, Dolores, Eagle (part), Garfield, Gunnison, Hinsdale, Huerfano, Jackson, La Plata, Lake, Mesa, Mineral, Moffat, Montezuma, Montrose, Ouray, Pitkin, Pueblo, Rio Blanco, Rio Grande, Routt, Saguache, San Juan, and San Miguel. Population (2010), 718,457.

ZIP Codes: 80423, 80426, 80428, 80434, 80461, 80463, 80467, 80469, 80473, 80477, 80479–80, 80483, 80487–88, 81001, 81003–08, 81019, 81022–23, 81025, 81039–40, 81055, 81069, 81089, 81101, 81120–26, 81128–33, 81136–38, 81140–41, 81143–44, 81146–49, 81151–52, 81154–55, 81210, 81220, 81224–25, 81230–31, 81235, 81237, 81239, 81241, 81243, 81248, 81251–53, 81301, 81303, 81320–21, 81323–28, 81330–32, 81334–35, 81401, 81403, 81410–11, 81413, 81415–16, 81418–19, 81422–35, 81501, 81503–07, 81520–27, 81601, 81610–12, 81615, 81620–21, 81623–25, 81630–33, 81635, 81637–43, 81645–50, 81652–56

* * *

FOURTH DISTRICT

CORY GARDNER, Republican, of Yuma, CO; born in Yuma, CO, August 22, 1976; education: B.S., political science, Colorado State University, Fort Collins, CO, 1997; J.D., University of Colorado, Boulder, CO, 2001; professional: agricultural advocate; staff, United States Senator Wayne Allard of Colorado, 2002–05; member of the Colorado State House of Representatives, 2005–10; committees: Energy and Commerce; elected to the 112th Congress on November 2, 2010; reelected to the 113th Congress on Novmeber 6, 2012.

Office Listings

http://www.gardner.house.gov

213 Cannon House Office Building, Washington, DC 20515 .... (202) 225–4676
Chief of Staff.—Chris Hansen.
Legislative Director.—Natalie Farr.
Communications Director.—Rachel Boxer.
Director of Scheduling.—Nancy Pack.
2425 35th Avenue, Suite 202, Greeley, CO 80634 .... (970) 351–6007
7505 Village Square Drive, Suite 207, Castle Rock, CO 80108 .... (720) 508–3937
529 North Albany, Suite 1220, Yuma, CO 80759 .... (970) 848–2845
408 North Main Street, Suite F, P.O. Box 104, Rocky Ford, CO 81068 .... (719) 316–1101

Counties: Adams, Arapahoe, Baca, Boulder (part), Bent, Cheyenne, Crowley, Douglas, Elbert, Kiowa, Kit Carson, Larimer, Las Animas, Lincoln, Logan, Morgan, Phillips, Prowers, Otero (part), Sedgewick, Washington, Weld (part), and Yuma. Population (2010), 718,456.

ZIP Codes: 80101–09, 80112, 80116–08, 80124–27, 80130–31, 80134–35, 80136–38, 80501–04, 80510–13, 80515, 80517, 80521–28, 80530, 80532–43, 80545–47, 80549–51, 80553, 80603, 80610–12, 80615, 80620–24, 80631–34, 80638–39, 80642–46, 80648–54, 80701, 80705, 80720–23, 80726–29, 80731–37, 80740–47, 80749–51, 80754–55, 80757–59, 80801–02, 80804–05, 80807, 80810, 80812, 80815, 80818, 80821–26, 80828, 80830, 80832–34, 80836, 80861–62, 81020–21, 81024, 81027, 81029–30, 81033–34, 81036, 81038, 81041, 81043–47, 81049–50, 81052, 81054, 81057, 81059, 81062–64, 81071, 81073, 81076, 81084, 81087, 81090–92

* * *

FIFTH DISTRICT

DOUG LAMBORN, Republican, of Colorado Springs, CO; born in Leavenworth, KS, May 24, 1954; education: B.S., University of Kansas, Lawrence, 1978; J.D., University of Kansas,

Lawrence, 1985; lawyer, private practice (business and real estate); Colorado State House of Representatives, 1995–98; Colorado State Senate, 1998–2006; married: Jeanie; five children; committees: Armed Services; Natural Resources; Veterans' Affairs; elected to the 110th Congress on November 7, 2006; reelected to each succeeding Congress.

Office Listings

http://www.lamborn.house.gov https://www.facebook.com/congressmandouglamborn

2402 Rayburn House Office Building, Washington, DC 20515 .... (202) 225–4422
Chief of Staff.—Adam Magary. FAX: 226–2638
Legislative Director.—Vacant.
Director of Communications.—Catherine Mortensen.
Scheduler / Executive Assistant.—Jamie Dangers.
1125 Kelly Johnson Boulevard, Suite 330, Colorado Springs, CO 80920 .... (719) 520–0055

Counties: CHAFFEE, EL PASO, FREMONT, PARK (part), AND TELLER. Population (2010), 718,457.

ZIP Codes: 80106, 80132–33, 80420–21, 80432, 80440, 80448–49, 80456, 80808–09, 80813–14, 80816–17, 80819–20, 80827, 80829, 80831–33, 80840, 80860, 80863–64, 80902–11, 80913–30, 80938–39, 80951, 81008, 81201, 81211–12, 81221–23, 81226–27, 81232–33, 81236, 81240, 81242, 81244, 81253

* * *

SIXTH DISTRICT

MIKE COFFMAN, Republican, of Aurora, CO; born in Fort Leonard Wood, MO, March 19, 1955; education: attended, Aurora Central High School; B.A., University of Colorado, Boulder, CO, 1979; military: United States Army, 1972–74; United States Army Reserve, 1975–78; United States Marine Corps, 1979–82; United States Marine Corps Reserve, 1983–94, and 2005–06; professional: business owner; elected to the Colorado State House of Representatives, 1989–94; elected to the Colorado State Senate, 1994–98; Colorado State Treasurer, 1999–2007; Colorado Secretary of State, 2007–08; religion: Methodist; married: Cynthia; committees: Armed Services; Small Business; Veterans' Affairs; elected to the 111th Congress on November 4, 2008; reelected to each succeeding Congress.

Office Listings

http://www.coffman.house.gov

2443 Rayburn House Office Building, Washington, DC 20515 .... (202) 225–7882
Chief of Staff.—Jacque Ponder. FAX: 226–4623
Scheduler.—Alexandra Williams.
3300 South Parker Road, Suite 305, Aurora, CO 80014 .... (720) 748–7514

Counties: ADAMS (part), ARAPAHOE (part), DOUGLAS (part). Population (2010), 718,456.

ZIP Codes: 80013–19, 80040–42, 80044–46, 80102, 80111–12, 80120–80126, 80128–30, 80137–38, 80160–61, 80163, 80165–66, 80231, 80247

* * *

SEVENTH DISTRICT

ED PERLMUTTER, Democrat, of Golden, CO; born in Denver, CO, May 1, 1953; education: B.A., University of Colorado, 1975; J.D., University of Colorado, 1978; professional: served as a member of the Board of Governors of the Colorado Bar Association; served on the Board of Trustees and Judicial Performance Commission for the First Judicial District; Trustee, Midwest Research Institute, the primary operator of the National Renewable Energy Laboratory; board member, National Jewish Medical and Research Center; elected to two 4-year terms to represent central Jefferson County as a Colorado State Senator, 1995–2003; served on numerous committees in the State Senate, including Water, Finance, Judiciary, Child Welfare, Telecommunication, Transportation, Legal Services, and Oil and Gas; also served as chair of the Public Policy and Planning Committee, chair of the Bi-Partisan Renewable Energy Caucus, and President Pro Tem (2001–02 session); married; three children; committees: Financial Services; elected to the 110th Congress on November 7, 2006; reelected to each succeeding Congress.

Office Listings

http://perlmutter.house.gov/

1410 Longworth House Office Building, Washington, DC 20515 .... (202) 225–2645
Chief of Staff.—Danielle Radovich Piper. FAX: 225–5278
Legislative Director.—Matt Henken.
Scheduler / Executive Assistant.—Alison Inderforth.
Staff Assistant.—Daniel J. Dingmann.
12600 West Colfax Avenue, Suite B400, Lakewood, CO 80215 .... (303) 274–7944

Counties: ADAMS (part), ARAPAHOE (part), JEFFERSON (part). CITIES AND TOWNSHIPS: Arvada, Aurora, Bennett, Brighton, Commerce City, Edgewater, Golden, Lakewood, and Wheat Ridge. Population (2010), 718,456.

ZIP Codes: 80001, 80002 (part), 80003–07, 80020 (part), 80021 (part), 80022 (part), 80023 (part), 80024, 80030–31, 80033 (part), 80034–37, 80123 (part), 80127 (part), 80212 (part), 80214 (part), 80215, 80216 (part), 80221 (part), 80225, 80226 (part), 80227 (part), 80228–29, 80232 (part), 80233, 80234 (part), 80235 (part), 80239 (part), 80241 (part), 80260, 80303 (part), 80401 (part), 80402, 80403 (part), 80419, 80465 (part), 80601 (part), 80602 (part), 80603 (part), 80614, 80640 (part)

CONNECTICUT

(Population 2010, 3,574,097)

SENATORS

RICHARD BLUMENTHAL, Democrat, of Greenwich, CT; born in Brooklyn, NY, February 13, 1946; son of Martin and Jane Rosenstock Blumenthal; education: graduated, Riverdale Country School, Riverdale, NY, 1963; B.A., government, Harvard College, Cambridge, MA, 1967; J.D., Yale Law School, New Haven, CT, 1973; admitted to Connecticut Bar, 1976; admitted to District of Columbia Bar, 1977; appointed United States Attorney for the District of Connecticut, 1977–81; Connecticut State House of Representatives, 1984–87; Connecticut State Senate, 1987–90; elected Attorney General for the State of Connecticut, 1990, reelected in 1994, 1998, 2002, and 2006; military: served in the United States Marine Corps Reserves, 1970–76, honorably discharged as Sergeant; married: Cynthia M. Blumenthal; four children: Matthew, Michael, David, and Claire; committees: Armed Services; Commerce, Science, and Transportation; Judiciary; Veterans' Affairs; Special Committee on Aging; elected to the U.S. Senate on November 2, 2010.

Office Listings

http://blumenthal.senate.gov

724 Hart Senate Office Building, Washington, DC 20510 .... (202) 224–2823
Chief of Staff.—Laurie Rubiner. FAX: 224–9673
Legislative Director.—Ethan Saxon.
Scheduling Director.—Dana Sandman.
Communications Director.—Josh Zembik.
90 State House Square, 10th Floor, Hartford, CT 06103 .... (860) 258–6940
FAX: 258–6958
915 Lafayette Boulevard, Room 330, Bridgeport, CT 06604 .... (203) 330–0598
FAX: 330–0608

* * *

CHRISTOPHER S. MURPHY, Democrat, of Cheshire, CT; born in White Plains, Westchester County, NY, August 3, 1973; education: attended Exeter College, Oxford, England, 1994–95; graduated with honors with double majors in history and political science, Williams College, Williamstown, MA, 1996; J.D., University of Connecticut, Hartford, CT, 2002; professional: lawyer, private practice; Southington, Connecticut; planning and zoning commission, 1997–99; practiced real estate and banking law from 2002–06, with the firm of Ruben, Johnson & Morgan in Hartford; member of the Connecticut State House of Representatives, 1999–2003; member of the Connecticut State Senate, 2003–06; married: Cathy Holahan, a legal aid attorney who represents children in need in New Britain and Waterbury; children: Chris, Cathy, and their sons Owen and Rider; elected as a Democrat to the 110th and to the two succeeding Congresses, January 3, 2007–January 3, 2013; committees: Foreign Relations; Health, Education, Labor, and Pensions; Joint Economic Committee; elected to the U.S. Senate on November 6, 2012.

Office Listings

http://www.chrismurphy.house.gov

303 Hart Senate Office Building, Washington, DC 20510 .... (202) 224–4041
Chief of Staff.—Francis Creighton. FAX: 224–9750
Executive Assistant.—Emily Smith.
Legislative Director.—David Bonine.
One Constitution Plaza, 7th Floor, Hartford, CT 06103 .... (860) 549–8463
State Director.—Kenny Curran.

REPRESENTATIVES

FIRST DISTRICT

JOHN B. LARSON, Democrat, of East Hartford, CT; born in Hartford, CT, July 22, 1948; education: Mayberry Elementary School, East Hartford, CT; East Hartford High School; B.A., Central Connecticut State University; Senior Fellow, Yale University, Bush Center for Child Development and Social Policy; professional: high school teacher, 1972–77; insurance broker,

1978–98; president, Larson and Lyork; public service: Connecticut State Senate, 12 years, President Pro Tempore, 8 years; married: Leslie Larson; children: Carolyn, Laura, and Raymond; committees: Ways and Means; elected to the 106th Congress; reelected to each succeeding Congress.

Office Listings

http://www.house.gov/larson

1501 Longworth House Office Building, Washington, DC 20515 .... (202) 225–2265
Chief of Staff.—Lee Slater. FAX: 225–1031
Deputy Chief of Staff.—Geraldine de Puy.
Legislative Director.—David Sitcovsky.
221 Main Street, Hartford, CT 06106–1864 .... (860) 278–8888
District Chief of Staff.—John Rossi.
Press Secretary.—Edmund Skowronek.

Counties: HARTFORD (part), LITCHFIELD (part), MIDDLESEX (part). Population (2010), 714,820.

ZIP Codes: 06002, 06010, 06013, 06016, 06021, 06023, 06026–27, 06033, 06035, 06037, 06040, 06042, 06052, 06057–63, 06065, 06067, 06073–74, 06088, 06090–91, 06095–96, 06098, 06103, 06105–12, 06114, 06117–20, 06160, 06416, 06444, 06451, 06457, 06467, 06479–80, 06489, 06759, 06790

* * *

SECOND DISTRICT

JOE COURTNEY, Democrat, of Vernon, CT; born in Hartford, CT, April 6, 1953; education: B.A., Tufts University, 1971–75; University of Connecticut Law School, 1975–78; public service: Connecticut State Representative, 1987–94; Vernon Town Attorney, 2003–06; professional: attorney, Courtney, Boyan, and Foran, LLC, 1978–2006; religion: Roman Catholic; married: Audrey Courtney; children: Robert and Elizabeth; committees: Agriculture; Armed Services; Education and Workforce; elected to the 110th Congress on November 7, 2006; reelected to each succeeding Congress.

Office Listings

http://www.house.gov/courtney https://www.facebook.com/joecourtney
https://twitter.com/repjoecourtney

2348 Rayburn House Office Building, Washington, DC 20515 .... (202) 225–2076
Chief of Staff.—Jason Gross. FAX: 225–4977
Communications Director.—Elizabeth Dononvan.
Scheduler.—Christina Kostuk.
Legislative Director.—Neil McKiernan.
55 Main Street, Suite 250, Norwich, CT 06360 .... (860) 886–0139
District Director.—Jenny Contois. FAX: 886–2974
77 Hazard Avenue, Unit J, Enfield, CT 06082 .... (860) 741–6011
FAX: 741–6036

Counties: HARTFORD (part), MIDDLESEX (part), NEW HAVEN (part), NEW LONDON, TOLLAND, AND WINDHAM. Population (2010), 714,819.

ZIP Codes: 06029, 06033, 06043, 06066, 06071, 06076, 06078, 06082, 06084, 06093, 06226, 06231–32, 06234–35, 06237–39, 06241–43, 06247–50, 06254–56, 06259–60, 06262–64, 06266, 06268–69, 06277–82, 06320, 06330–36, 06339–40, 06350–51, 06353–55, 06357, 06359–60, 06365, 06370–71, 06373–80, 06382, 06384–85, 06387, 06389, 06409, 06412–15, 06417, 06419–20, 06423–24, 06426, 06438, 06441–43, 06447, 06456, 06469, 06475

* * *

THIRD DISTRICT

ROSA L. DELAURO, Democrat, of New Haven, CT; born in New Haven, March 2, 1943; education: graduated, Lauralton Hall High School; attended London School of Economics, Queen Mary College, London, 1962–63; B.A., *cum laude*, history and political science, Marymount College, NY, 1964; M.A., international politics, Columbia University, NY, 1966; professional: executive assistant to Mayor Frank Logue, city of New Haven, 1976–77; executive assistant/development administrator, city of New Haven, 1977–78; chief of staff, Senator Christopher Dodd, 1980–87; executive director, Countdown '87, 1987–88; executive director, Emily's List, 1989–90; religion: Catholic; family: married, Stanley Greenberg; children: Anna, Kathryn, and Jonathan; co-chair, Democratic Steering and Policy Committee; committees:

Appropriations; elected to the 102nd Congress on November 6, 1990; reelected to each succeeding Congress.

Office Listings

http://www.delauro.house.gov

2413 Rayburn House Office Building, Washington, DC 20515 .... (202) 225–3661
Chief of Staff.—Beverly Pheto. FAX: 225–4890
Scheduler.—Lona Watts.
59 Elm Street, New Haven, CT 06510 .... (203) 562–3718
District Director.—Jennifer Lamb.

Counties: FAIRFIELD (part), MIDDLESEX (part), NEW HAVEN (part). CITIES AND TOWNSHIPS: Ansonia, Beacon Falls, Bethany, Branford, Derby, Durham, East Haven, Guilford, Hamden, Middlefield, Middletown (part), Milford, Naugatuck, New Haven, North Branford, North Haven, Orange, Prospect, Seymour, Shelton (part), Stratford, Wallingford, Waterbury (part), West Haven, and Woodbridge. Population (2011), 718,549.

ZIP Codes: 06401, 06403, 06405, 06410, 06418, 06422, 06437, 06450, 06455, 06457, 06460, 06471–73, 06477, 06481, 06483–84, 06492–94, 06501–21, 06524–25, 06530–38, 06540, 06607, 06614–15, 06706, 06708, 06712, 06762, 06770

* * *

FOURTH DISTRICT

JAMES A. HIMES, Democrat, of Cos Cob, CT; born in Lima, Peru to American parents, July 5, 1966; education: B.A., Harvard University, Cambridge, MA, 1988; M.Phil, Oxford University, Oxford, England, 1990; professional: vice president, Goldman Sachs & Co., 1990–2002; vice president, Enterprise Community Partners, 2002–07; Commissioner, Greenwich Housing Authority; chair, Greenwich Democratic Town Committee; religion: Presbyterian; married: Mary Himes, 1994; children: Emma and Linley; committees: Financial Services; Permanent Select Committee on Intelligence; elected to the 111th Congress on November 4, 2008; reelected to each succeeding Congress.

Office Listings

http://www.himes.house.gov

119 Cannon House Office Building, Washington, DC 20515 .... (202) 225–5541
Chief of Staff.—Mark Henson. FAX: 225–9629
Executive Aide.—Cara Pavlock.
888 Washington Boulevard, Stamford, CT 06901–2927 .... (866) 453–0028
211 State Street, 2nd Floor, Bridgeport, CT 06604–4223 .... (866) 453–0028
District Director.—Tyrone McClain.

Counties: FAIRFIELD (part), NEW HAVEN (part). CITIES AND TOWNSHIPS: Bridgeport, Darien, Easton, Fairfield, Greenwich, Monroe, New Canaan, Norwalk, Oxford, Redding, Ridgefield, Shelton, Stamford, Trumbull Weston, Westport, and Wilton. Population (2010), 714,819.

ZIP Codes: 06468, 06478, 06604–08, 06610–12, 06807, 06820, 06824–25, 06830–31, 06840, 06850–51, 06853–56, 06870, 06877–78, 06880, 06883, 06890, 06896–97, 06901–03, 06905–07

* * *

FIFTH DISTRICT

ELIZABETH H. ESTY, Democrat, of Cheshire, CT; born August 25, 1959; education: graduated, A.B., Harvard College, Cambridge, MA, 1981; graduated, J.D., Yale University, New Haven, CT, 1985; professional: law clerk for a federal judge; a Supreme Court lawyer at Sidley Austin LLP in Washington, DC; professor at American University; former member, Cheshire Town Council, CT, 2005–08; member of the Connecticut State House of Representatives, 2008–10; caucuses: serves on Gun Violence Prevention Task Force; committees: Science, Space, and Technology; Transportation and Infrastructure; elected to 113th Congress on November 6, 2012.

Office Listings

http://esty.house.gov

509 Cannon House Office Building, Washington, DC 20515 .... (202) 225–4476
Chief of Staff.—Julie Sweet. FAX: 225–5933
Communications Director.—Jeb Fain.
Scheduler.—Anna Kain.
114 West Main Street, Suite 206, New Britain, CT 06053 .... (860) 223–8412

District Director.—Russell Griffin.

Counties: FAIRFIELD (part), HARTFORD (part), LITCHFIELD, NEW HAVEN (part). CITIES: Danbury, Meriden, New Britain, Torrington, and Waterbury. Population (2010), 714,820.

ZIP Codes: 06001, 06013, 06018–20, 06022, 06024, 06030–32, 06034, 06039, 06050–53, 06058–59, 06062, 06068–70, 06079, 06081, 06085, 06087, 06089, 06092, 06107, 06404, 06408, 06410–11, 06440, 06450–51, 06454, 06470, 06482, 06487–88, 06701–06, 06708, 06710, 06716, 06720–26, 06749–59, 06762–63, 06776–79, 06781–87, 06790–91, 06793–96, 06798, 06801, 06804, 06810–14, 06816–17

DELAWARE

(Population 2010, 897,934)

SENATORS

THOMAS R. CARPER, Democrat, of Wilmington, DE; born in Beckley, WV, January 23, 1947; education: B.A., Ohio State University, 1968; M.B.A., University of Delaware, 1975; military service: U.S. Navy, served during Vietnam War; public service: Delaware State Treasurer, 1977–83; U.S. House of Representatives, 1983–93; Governor of Delaware, 1993–2001; organizations: Third Way; New Democrat Network; former National Governors' Association chair; religion: Presbyterian; family: married to the former Martha Ann Stacy; children: Ben and Christopher; committees: chair, Homeland Security and Governmental Affairs; Environment and Public Works; Finance; elected to the U.S. Senate on November 7, 2000; reelected to each succeeding Senate term.

Office Listings

http://carper.senate.gov www.facebook.com/tomcarper twitter: @senatorcarper

513 Hart Senate Office Building, Washington, DC 20510 .... (202) 224–2441
Chief of Staff.—Jim Reilly. FAX: 228–2190
Legislative Director.—Bill Ghent.
Administrative Director.—Madge Farooq.
2215 Federal Building, 300 South New Street, Dover, DE 19904 .... (302) 674–3308
301 North Walnut Street, Suite 102 L–1, Wilmington, DE 19801 .... (302) 573–6291
12 The Circle, Georgetown, DE 19947 .... (302) 856–7690

* * *

CHRISTOPHER A. COONS, Democrat, of Wilmington, DE; born in Greenwich, CT, September 9, 1963; education: B.A., Amherst College, 1985; M.A.R., Yale University, 1992; J.D., Yale University, 1992; professional: associate (legal counsel), W.L. Gore & Associates, 1996–2004; president of New Castle County Council, 2000–04; county executive, New Castle County, 2005–10; religion: Presbyterian; married: Annie; children: Michael, Jack, and Maggie; committees: Appropriations; Budget; Foreign Relations; Judiciary; elected on November 2, 2010 to the United States Senate to fill the remainder of the vacancy caused by the unfinished term of Joseph R. Biden, Jr. and took the oath of office on November 15, 2010.

Office Listings

http://coons.senate.gov http://www.facebook.com/senatorchriscoons
http://www.twitter.com/sencoonsoffice

127A Russell Senate Office Building, Washington, DC 20510 .... (202) 224–5042
Chief of Staff.—Todd Webster. FAX: 228–3075
Legislative Director.—Jonathan Stahler.
Communications Director.—Ian Koski.
Office Manager.—Trinity Hall.
1105 North Market Street, Suite 100, Wilmington, DE 19801–1233 .... (302) 573–6345
State Director.—Christy Gleason (acting).
500 West Loockerman Street, Suite 450, Dover, DE 19904 .... (302) 736–5601

REPRESENTATIVE

AT LARGE

JOHN CARNEY, JR., Democrat, of Wilmington, DE; born in Wilmington, May 20, 1956; education: B.A., english, Dartmouth College, Hanover, NH, 1978; M.P.A., University of Delaware, Newark, DE, 1987; professional: staff assistant, United States Senator Joseph Biden, Jr., Delaware, 1986–89; deputy chief administrative officer, New Castle County Executive Dennis Greenhouse, Delaware, 1989–94; deputy chief of staff, Governor Tom Carper, 1994–97; secretary of finance, Delaware, 1997–2000; lieutenant governor, Delaware, 2001–2009; awards: Order of the First State; Outstanding Alumni, University of Delaware; Recipient of the Outstanding Public Service Award, National Association of Community Health Centers, 2004; Recipient of the James Ewing Layman Award, Society of Surgical Oncology, 2008; City of Wilmington Public Service Award; religion: Roman Catholic; family: wife, Tracey, two sons; caucuses: New Democrats Caucus; National Guard Caucus; committees: Financial Services;

elected to the 112th Congress on November 2, 2010; reelected to the 113th Congress on November 6, 2012.

Office Listings

http://www.johncarney.house.gov

1406 Longworth House Office Building, Washington, DC 20515 .... (202) 225–4165
Chief of Staff.—Elizabeth Hart. FAX: 225–2291
Communications Director / Legislative Director.—Sheila Grant.
DC Scheduler.—Kristy Huxhold.

233 North King Street, Suite 200, Wilmington, DE 19801 .... (302) 428–1902
State Director.—Doug Gramiak. FAX: 428–1905
DE Scheduler.—Kristy Huxhold.

Counties: KENT, NEW CASTLE, SUSSEX. CITIES AND TOWNSHIPS: Bethany Beach, Bethel, Bellefonte, Blades, Bowers, Bridgeville, Camden, Cheswold, Dagsboro, Delmar, Delaware City, Dewey Beach, Dover, Ellendale, Elsmere, Farmington, Felton, Fenwick Island, Frankford, Frederica, Georgetown, Greenwood, Harrington, Hartly, Henlopen Acres, Houston, Kenton, Laurel, Lewes, Little Creek, Leipsic, Magnolia, Middletown, Milford, Millsboro, Millville, Milton, New Castle, Newark, Newport, Ocean View, Odessa, Rehoboth Beach, Seaford, Selbyville, Slaughter Beach, South Bethany, Smyrna, Townsend, Viola, Wilmington, Woodside, and Wyoming. Population (2010), 897,934.

ZIP Codes: 19701–03, 19706–18, 19720–21, 19725–26, 19730–36, 19801–10, 19850, 19880, 19884–87, 19890–99, 19901–06, 19930–31, 19933–34, 19936, 19938–41, 19943–47, 19950–56, 19958, 19960–64, 19966–71, 19973, 19975, 19977, 19979–80

FLORIDA

(Population 2010, 18,801,310)

SENATORS

BILL NELSON, Democrat, of Orlando, FL, born in Miami, FL, September 29, 1942; education: Melbourne High School, 1960; B.A., Yale University, 1965; J.D. University of Virginia School of Law, 1968; professional: attorney; admitted to the Florida Bar, 1968; captain, U.S. Army Reserve, 1965–71; active duty, 1968–70; public service: Florida State House of Representatives, 1973–79; U.S. House of Representatives, 1979–91; Florida Treasurer, Insurance Commissioner, and State Fire Marshal, 1995–2001; Astronaut: payload specialist on the space shuttle *Columbia*, January, 1986; married: the former Grace Cavert; children: Bill Jr. and Nan Ellen; committees: chair, Special Committee on Aging; Armed Services; Budget; Commerce, Science, and Transportation; Finance; elected to the U.S. Senate on November 7, 2000; reelected to each succeeding Senate term.

Office Listings

http://billnelson.senate.gov twitter: @senbillnelson

716 Hart Senate Office Building, Washington, DC 20510 .... (202) 224–5274
Chief of Staff.—Pete Mitchell. FAX: 228–2183
Deputy Chief of Staff, Communications.—Dan McLaughlin.
Deputy Chief of Staff, Administration.—Brenda Strickland.
Legislative Director.—Susie Perez Quinn.
U.S. Courthouse Annex, 111 North Adams Street, Tallahassee, FL 32301 .... (850) 942–8415
Chief of Staff.—Pete Mitchell.
801 North Florida Avenue, 4th Floor, Tampa, FL 33602 .... (813) 225–7040
2925 Salzedo Street, Coral Gables, FL 33134 .... (305) 536–5999
3416 University Drive, Ft. Lauderdale, FL 33328 .... (954) 693–4851
413 Clematis Street, Suite 210, West Palm Beach, FL 33401 .... (561) 514–0189
225 East Robinson Street, Suite 410, Orlando, FL 32801 .... (407) 872–7161
1301 Riverplace Boulevard, Suite 2010, Jacksonville, FL 32207 .... (904) 346–4500
2000 Main Street, Suite 801, Ft. Myers, FL 33901 .... (239) 334–7760

* * *

MARCO A. RUBIO, Republican, of West Miami, FL; born in Miami, FL, May 28, 1971; education: South Miami Senior High School, 1989; B.S., political science, University of Florida, 1993; J.D., *cum laude,* University of Miami, 1996; professional: Florida House of Representatives, 2000–08; served as majority whip, majority leader and speaker of the house; attorney, Broad and Cassel; Marco Rubio, P.A.; lecturer at Florida International University's Metropolitan Center, 2009–10; Bob Dole for President, 1996, Miami-Dade County Director; religion: Roman Catholic; married: Jeanette; children: Amanda, Daniella, Anthony, and Dominick; committees: Commerce, Science, and Transportation; Foreign Relations; Small Business and Entrepreneurship; Select Committee on Intelligence; elected to the U.S. Senate on November 2, 2010.

Office Listings

http://rubio.senate.gov twitter: @marcorubio

SR–284 Russell Building, Washington, DC 20510 .... (202) 224–3041
Chief of Staff.—Cesar Conda. FAX: 228–0285
Legislative Director.—Sally Canfield.
201 South Orange Avenue, Suite 350, Orlando, FL 32801 .... (407) 254–2573
1650 Prudential Drive, Suite 220, Jacksonville, FL 32207 .... (904) 398–8586
1 North Palafox Street, Suite 159, Pensacola, FL 32502 .... (850) 433–2603
3802 Spectrum Boulevard, Suite 106, Tampa, FL 33612 .... (813) 977–6450
8669 Northwest 36th Street, Suite 110, Miami, FL 33166 .... (305) 444–8332
3299 East Tamiami Trail, Suite 106, Naples, FL 34112 .... (239) 213–1521
402 South Monroe Street, Suite 2105E, Tallahassee, FL 32399 .... (850) 599–9100
4580 PGA Boulevard, Suite 201, Palm Beach Gardens, FL 33418 .... (561) 775–3360

REPRESENTATIVES

FIRST DISTRICT

JEFF MILLER, Republican, of Chumuckla, FL, born in Pinellas County, June 27, 1959, education: B.A., University of Florida, 1984, professional: real estate broker, public service: Executive Assistant to the Commissioner of Agriculture, 1984–88, Environmental Land Management Study Commission, 1992, Santa Rosa County Planning Board Vice Chairman, 1996–98, elected to the Florida House of Representatives in 1998, reelected in 2000, served as House Majority Whip: organizations: Kiwanis Club of Milton, Florida Historical Society, Santa Rosa County United Way, Milton Pregnancy Resource Center Advisory Board, Gulf Coast Council of Boy Scouts, Florida FFA Foundation, religion: Methodist, married: Vicki Griswold, children: Scott and Clint; committees: chair, Veterans' Affairs, Armed Services, Permanent Select Committee on Intelligence, elected to the 107th Congress, by special election, on October 16, 2001; reelected to each succeeding Congress.

Office Listings

http://jeffmiller.house.gov

336 Cannon House Office Building, Washington, DC 20515 .... (202) 225–4136
Chief of Staff.—Dan McFaul. FAX: 225–3414
Legislative Director.—Diane Cihota.
Scheduler.—Jessica Sunday.
4300 Bayou Boulevard, Suite 13, Pensacola, FL 32503 .... (850) 479–1183
District Director.—Sheilah Bowman.
348 Southwest Miracle Strip Parkway, Unit 24, Ft. Walton Beach, FL 32548 .... (850) 664–1266

Counties: ESCAMBIA, HOLMES (part), OKALOOSA, SANTA ROSA, WALTON. CITIES AND TOWNSHIPS: Pensacola, Pace, Milton, Cantonment, Jay, Gulf Breeze, Fort Walton Beach, Santa Rosa Beach, DeFuniak Springs, Laurel Hill, Crestview, Destin, Ferrypass, Navarre, Valparaiso, Miramar Beach, Chumuckla, Century, Walnut Hill, Seaside. Population (2010), 687,856.

ZIP Codes: 32422, 32427, 32433–35, 32439, 32454, 32459, 32501–09, 32511–14, 32516, 32520–24, 32526, 32530, 32531, 32533–42, 32544, 32547–49, 32559–83, 32588

* * *

SECOND DISTRICT

STEVE SOUTHERLAND II, Republican, of Panama City, FL; born in Nashville, TN, October 10, 1965; education: graduated, A. Crawford Mosley High School, Panama City, FL, 1983; B.S., Troy State University, 1987; A.A., Jefferson State Community College, 1989; professional: owner / president, Southerland Family Funeral Homes; former chairman, Florida Board of Funeral Directors; former chairman, Early Learning Coalition of Northwest Florida; former member: Bay County Economic Development Alliance; Bay Defense Alliance; Covenant Hospice Foundation Board; religion: Southern Baptist; married: Susan Southerland; children: daughters, Samantha, Stephanie, Ally, and Abby; committees: Natural Resources; Transportation and Infrastructure; elected to the 112th Congress on November 2, 2010; reelected to the 113th Congress on November 6, 2012.

Office Listings

http://southerland.house.gov twitter: @rep_southerland

1229 Longworth House Office Building, Washington, DC 20515 .... (202) 225–5235
Chief of Staff.—Jonathan Hayes. FAX: 225–5615
Deputy Chief of Staff / Communications Director.—Matt McCullough.
Legislative Director.—Karen Williams.
Legislative Assistants: Kristen Callaway, Mike DeFilippis.
Executive Assistant.—Kathryn Whitehurst.
840 West 11th Street, Suite 2250, Panama City, FL 32401 .... (850) 785–0812
District Director.—Jonathan Hayes.
Deputy District Director (West).—Melissa Thompson.
3116 Capital Circle Northeast, Suite 9, Tallahassee, FL 32308 .... (850) 561–3979
Deputy District Director (East).—Lori Hutto.

Counties: BAY, CALHOUN, FRANKLIN, GADSDEN, GULF, HOLMES (part), JACKSON, JEFFERSON, LEON, LIBERTY, MADISON (part), TAYLOR, WAKULLA, AND WASHINGTON. Population (2010), 737,519.

ZIP Codes: 32008, 32013, 32024, 32038, 32055, 32060, 32062, 32064, 32066, 32071, 32094, 32096, 32126, 32140, 32170, 32175, 32267, 32301–18, 32320–24, 32326–34, 32336, 32343–44, 32346–48, 32351–53, 32355–62, 32395, 32399, 32401–13, 32417, 32420–21, 32423–24, 32426, 32428, 32430–32, 32437–38, 32440, 32442–49, 32454, 32456–57, 32459–61, 32465–66, 32541, 32550, 32578, 32628, 32648, 32680, 32692

* * *

THIRD DISTRICT

TED S. YOHO, DVM, Republican, of Gainesville, FL; born in Minneapolis, MN, April 13, 1955; education: graduated from Deerfield Beach High School, Deerfield Beach, FL, 1973; attended Florence State University (University of North Alabama), Florence, AL; A.A., Broward Community College, Fort Lauderdale, FL, 1977; B.S.A., University of Florida, Gainesville, FL, 1979; D.V.M., University of Florida, Gainesville, FL, 1983; professional: large animal veterinarian; religion: Christian; married: the former Carolyn Sue Marlin, children: Katie, Tyler, and Lauren; caucuses: active member of 4–H and Future Farmers of America Clubs; Veterinarian Caucus, Republican Study Committee; Florida Ports Caucus, Fix Congress Now Caucus; House Liberty Caucus; Regulation Reform Working Group; committees: Agriculture; Foreign Affairs; elected to the 113th Congress on November 6, 2012.

Office Listings

http://www.yoho.house.gov twitter: @reptedyoho

511 Cannon House Office Building, Washington, DC 20515 .... (202) 225–5744
Chief of Staff.—Kat Cammack. FAX: 225–3973
Scheduler.—Rachel King.
Legislative Director.—Omar Raschid.
Press Secretary.—Kelley McNabb.
5000 Northwest 27th Court, Suite E, Gainesville, FL 32606 .... (352) 505–0838
Deputy District Director.—Clay Martin.
1213 Blanding Boulevard, Orange Park, FL 32065 .... (904) 276–9626
Deputy District Director.—Lucy Hoover.

Counties: ALACHUA, BRADFORD, CLAY, COLUMBIA, DIXIE, GILCHRIST, HAMILTON, LAFAYETTE, LEVY, MARION, SUWANEE, AND UNION. Population (2010), 696,000.

ZIP Codes: 32003, 32006, 32008, 32013, 32024–26, 32030, 32038, 32042–44, 32050, 32052–56, 32058–62, 32064–68, 32071, 32073, 32079, 32083, 32087, 32091, 32094, 32096, 32140, 32160, 32234, 32340–41, 32348, 32350, 32601, 32603–12, 32614–16, 32618–19, 32621–22, 32625–26, 32628, 32631, 32633–35, 32639–41, 32643–44, 32648, 32653, 32655–56, 32658, 32666–69, 32680, 32683, 32686, 32692–94, 32696–97, 34430–32, 34449, 34474, 34476, 34481–82, 34498

* * *

FOURTH DISTRICT

ANDER CRENSHAW, Republican, of Jacksonville, FL; born in Jacksonville, September 1, 1944; education: B.A., University of Georgia, 1966; J.D., University of Florida, 1969; professional: investment banker; religion: Episcopal; public service: former member of the Florida House of Representatives and the Florida State Senate; served as President of the Florida State Senate; married: Kitty; children: Sarah and Alex; member of House Republican Leadership Whip team serving as Deputy Majority Whip; committee: Appropriations; elected to the 107th Congress on November 7, 2000; reelected to each succeeding Congress.

Office Listings

http://www.crenshaw.house.gov https://twitter.com/andercrenshaw

440 Cannon House Office Building, Washington, DC 20515 .... (202) 225–2501
Chief of Staff.—John Ariale. FAX: 225–2504
Legislative Director.—Erica Striebel.
Communications Director.—Barbara Riley.
1061 Riverside Avenue, Suite 100, Jacksonville, FL 32204 .... (904) 598–0481
District Director.—Jacqueline Smith. FAX: 598–0486
Mobile Office .... (904) 465–7743

Counties: BAKER, DUVAL, NASSAU. CITIES AND TOWNSHIPS: Jacksonville, Jacksonville Beach, Macclenny, and Yulee. Population (2010), 696,345.

ZIP Codes: 32009, 32011, 32034–35, 32040–41, 32046, 32063, 32072, 32082, 32087, 32097, 32099, 32204–05, 32207, 32210–12, 32214, 32216–29, 32233–34, 32237, 32239–41, 32244–46, 32250, 32254–59, 32266, 32277

* * *

FIFTH DISTRICT

CORRINE BROWN, Democrat, of Jacksonville, FL; born in Jacksonville, November 11, 1946; education: B.S., Florida A&M University, 1969; master's degree, Florida A&M University, 1971; education specialist degree, University of Florida; honorary doctor of law, Edward Waters College; faculty member: Florida Community College in Jacksonville; University of Florida; and Edward Waters College; served in the Florida House of Representatives for 10 years; first woman elected chairperson of the Duval County Legislative Delegation; served as a consultant to the Governor's Committee on Aging; member: Congressional Black Caucus; Women's Caucus; and Progressive Caucus; Human Rights Caucus; Missing and Exploited Children's Caucus; Diabetes Caucus; Duma Study Group; Community College Caucus; Older Americans Caucus; one child: Shantrel; committees: Transportation and Infrastructure; Veterans' Affairs; elected on November 3, 1992, to the 103rd Congress; reelected to each succeeding Congress.

Office Listings

http://www.house.gov/corrinebrown https://twitter.com/repcorrinebrown
https://www.facebook.com/congresswomanbrown

2111 Rayburn House Office Building, Washington, DC 20515 .... (202) 225–0123
Chief of Staff.—E. Ronnie Simmons. FAX: 225–2256
Executive Assistant/Scheduler.—Cathy Gass.
Legislative Director.—Nick Martinelli.
Communications Director.—David Simon.
101 East Union Street, Suite 202, Jacksonville, FL 32202 .... (904) 354–1652
455 North Garland Avenue, Suite 414, Orlando, FL 32801 .... (407) 872–2208

Counties: ALACHUA (part), CLAY (part), DUVAL (part), LAKE (part), MARION (part), ORANGE (part), PUTNAM (part), AND SEMINOLE (part). Population (2010), 696,345.

ZIP Codes: 32003, 32043, 32073, 32102, 32113, 32134, 32140, 32148, 32177, 32202, 32204–12, 32216, 32218–22, 32224, 32244, 32254, 32277, 32601, 32609, 32631, 32640–41, 32664, 32666–67, 32681, 32686, 32702–03, 32712, 32720, 32736, 32746, 32751, 32757, 32767, 32771, 32773, 32776, 32784, 32798, 32801, 32804–06, 32808–11, 32818–19, 32835, 32839, 34734, 34761

* * *

SIXTH DISTRICT

RONALD ''RON'' DESANTIS, Republican, of Ponte Vedra Beach, FL; born in Jacksonville, FL, September 14, 1978; education: *magna cum laude* B.A. in history, Yale University, New Haven, CT, 2001; J.D., Harvard Law School, Cambridge University, MA, 2005; sworn into the Judge Advocate General Corps of the U.S. Navy, while still a student at the Harvard Law School; completing U.S. Naval Justice School in 2005; professional: served in the Trial Service Office Command South East at the Naval Station Mayport, Florida as a military prosecutor; promoted to Lieutenant (O–3) and worked for the Joint Task Force-Guantanamo Commander (JTF–GTMO), at the Guantanamo Bay Joint Detention Facility, 2006; assigned to SEAL Team One and deployed to Iraq with the troop surge as the Legal Advisor to the SEAL Commander, Special Operations Task Force-West in Fallujah, 2007; earned an appointment with the U.S. Department of Justice to serve as a federal prosecutor at the U.S. Attorney's Office in the Middle District of Florida, 2008; concurrently accepted a Reserve commission as a Lieutenant, Judge Advocate General Corps, in the U.S. Navy Reserve; and currently a Lieutenant Commander; awards: Bronze Star Medal and Iraq Campaign Medal Award; authored a book entitled *Dreams From Our Founding Fathers: First Principles in the Age of Obama*, which was published in 2011; religion: Roman Catholic; married: Casey Black DeSantis; committees: Foreign Affairs; Judiciary; Oversight and Government Reform; elected to the 113th Congress on November 6, 2012.

Office Listings

http://desantis.house.gov/ https://www.facebook.com/repdesantis
https://twitter.com/repdesantis

427 Cannon House Office Building, Washington, DC 20515 .... (202) 225–2706
Chief of Staff.—Justin Roth. FAX: 226–6299
Legislative Director.—Dustin Carmack.
Scheduler.—Shira Lahav.
Communications Director.—Elizabeth Dillon.
1000 City Center Circle, 2nd Floor, Port Orange, FL 32129 .... (386) 756–9798

3940 Lewis Speedway, Suite 2104, St. Augustine, FL 32084	(904) 827–1114

Counties: ST. JOHNS, FLAGLER, PUTNAM (part), AND VOLUSIA (part). CITIES: St. Augustine and Daytona Beach. Population (2010) 696,345.

ZIP Codes: 32033, 32080–82, 32084, 32086, 32092, 32095, 32110, 32112, 32114, 32117–19, 32124, 32127–32, 32136, 32139, 32141, 32145, 32147, 32157, 32164, 32167, 32169, 32174, 32176, 32180–81, 32187, 32189, 32190, 32193, 32259, 32759

* * *

SEVENTH DISTRICT

JOHN L. MICA, Republican, of Winter Park, FL; born in Binghamton, NY, January 27, 1943; education: graduated, Miami-Edison High School, Miami, FL; B.A., University of Florida, 1967; professional: president, MK Development; managing general partner, Cellular Communications; former government affairs consultant, Mica, Dudinsky and Associates; executive director, Local Government Study Commissions, Palm Beach County, 1970–72; executive director, Orange County Local Government Study Commission, 1972–74; Florida State House of Representatives, 1976–80; administrative assistant, U.S. Senator Paula Hawkins, 1980–85; Florida State Good Government Award, 1973; one of five Florida Jaycees Outstanding Young Men of America, 1978; member: Kiwanis, U.S. Capitol Preservation Commission, Tiger Bay Club, co-chairman, Speaker's Task Force for a Drug Free America, Florida Blue Key; U.S. Capitol Preservation Commission; brother of former Congressman Daniel A. Mica; married: the former Patricia Szymanek, 1972; children: D'Anne Leigh and John Clark; committees: Oversight and Government Reform; Transportation and Infrastructure; elected on November 3, 1992 to the 103rd Congress; reelected to each succeeding Congress.

Office Listings

http://www.house.gov/mica

2187 Rayburn House Office Building, Washington, DC 20515	(202) 225–4035
Chief of Staff.—Wiley Deck.	FAX: 226–0821
Deputy Chief of Staff.—Sean McMaster.	
Legislative Director.—Brian Waldrip.	
Scheduler.—Mary Klappa.	
100 East Sybelia Avenue, Suite 340, Maitland, FL 32751	(407) 657–8080
840 Deltona Boulevard, Suite G, Deltona, FL 32725	(386) 860–1499
95 East Mitchell Hammock Boulevard, Suite 202, Oviedo, FL 32765	(407) 366–0833

Counties: ORANGE COUNTY (part). CITIES AND TOWNSHIPS: Apopka, Maitland, Winter Park. SEMINOLE COUNTY (part). CITIES AND TOWNSHIPS: Altamonte Springs, Casselberry, Heathrow, Lake Mary, Longwood, Oviedo, Sanford, and Winter Springs. VOLUSIA COUNTY (part). CITIES AND TOWNSHIPS: Deltona, Debary, and Orange City. Population, (2010), 702,203.

ZIP Codes: 32701, 32703, 32706–08, 32712–16, 32718–19, 32724–25, 32728, 32730, 32732–33, 32738–39, 32744–46, 32750–54, 32762–66, 32771, 32773–74, 32779, 32789–91, 32793–95, 32799, 32803–04, 32807, 32810, 32814, 32816–17, 32820, 32826, 32833, 32867

* * *

EIGHTH DISTRICT

BILL POSEY, Republican, of Rockledge, FL; born in Washington, DC, December 18, 1947; education: graduated Cocoa High School, 1966; A.A., Brevard Community College, Cocoa, FL; National Legislator of the Year by the American Legislative Exchange Council; married: Katie Posey; children: Pamela and Catherine; member, House Aerospace Caucus; Military Veterans Caucus; Congressional Autism Caucus; Republican Study Committee; committees: Financial Services; Science, Space, and Technology; elected to the 111th Congress on November 4, 2008; elected to each succeeding Congress.

Office Listings

http://www.posey.house.gov https://twitter.com/congbillposey
https://www.facebook.com/bill.posey15

120 Cannon House Office Building, Washington, DC 20515	(202) 225–3671
Chief of Staff.—Stuart Burns.	FAX: 225–3516
Legislative Director.—Marcus Brubaker.	
Communications Director.—George Cecala.	
Scheduler.—Tim Convy.	
2725 Judge Fran Jamieson Way Building C, Melbourne, FL 32940	(321) 632–1776

Directors of Community Relations: Patrick Gavin, Pam Gillespie, David Jackson, Rob Medina.

Counties: BREVARD, INDIAN RIVER, AND ORANGE (part). Population (2010), 696,344.

ZIP Codes: 32903–05, 32907–09, 32920, 32922, 32925–27, 32931, 32934–35, 32937, 32940, 32948–53, 32955, 32958, 32960, 32962–63, 32966–68, 32970, 32976, 32780, 32796, 32831, 32833

* * *

NINTH DISTRICT

ALAN GRAYSON, Democrat, of Orlando, FL; born in New York, NY, March 13, 1958; education: B.A., economics, Harvard College, Cambridge, MA, 1978; J.D., Harvard Law, Cambridge, MA, 1983; M.P.P., Harvard Kennedy School, Cambridge, MA, 1978; professional: co-founder and former President of IDT Corporation; founder of Grayson & Kubli, P.C.; married: Lolita Grayson; children: Skye, Star, Storm, Stone, Sage; committees: Foreign Affairs; Science, Space, and Technology; elected to the 111th Congress on November 4, 2008; elected to the 113th Congress on November 6, 2012.

Office Listings

http://www.grayson.house.gov

430 Cannon House Office Building, Washington, DC 20515 .... (202) 225–9889
Chief of Staff.—Julie Tagen. FAX: 225–9742
Legislative Director.—David Bagby.
Senior Policy Advisor.—Matt Stoller.
Communications Director.—Lauren Doney.
Legislative Correspondent.—Shilpa Deshpande Finnerty.
Scheduler / Office Manager.—Carla Coleman.
Staff Assistant.—David Holladay.
5842 South Semoran Boulevard, Orlando, FL 32822 .... (407) 615–8889
District Director.—Susannah Randolph. FAX: 615–8890
Press Secretary.—Paola Amador.
Director of Constituent Services.—Juan R. Lopez-Sanchez.
Grants Coordinator.—Mike Nichola.
101 North Church Street, Suite 550, Kissimmee, FL 34741 .... (407) 518–4983
Constituent Field Representative.—Vivian Rodriguez. FAX: 846–2087
Constituent Advocate.—Lizy H. Price.

Counties: ORANGE (part), OSCEOLA, POLK (part). Population (2010), 753,549.

ZIP Codes: 32792, 32803, 32806–07, 32809, 32812, 32817, 32821–22, 32824–32, 32837, 32857, 32862, 32872, 32877–78, 32885, 33836–38, 33844–45, 33848, 33851, 33858, 33896–97, 34739, 34741–47, 34758–59, 34769–73, 34972

* * *

TENTH DISTRICT

DANIEL WEBSTER, Republican, of Winter Garden, FL; born in Charleston, WV, April 27, 1949; education: graduated from Evans High School, Orlando, FL; B.S., Georgia Institute of Technology, Atlanta, GA, 1971; professional: owner, Webster Air Conditioning & Heating, Inc., Orlando, FL; married: Sandy Jordan; father of six children and grandfather of eight; committees: Rules; Transportation and Infrastructure; elected to the 112th Congress on November 2, 2010; reelected to the 113th Congress on November 6, 2012.

Office Listings

http://www.webster.house.gov twitter: @repwebster

1039 Longworth House Office Building, Washington, DC 20515 .... (202) 225–2176
Chief of Staff.—Frank Walker. FAX: 225–0999
District Director.—Elizabeth Tyrrell.
300 West Plant Street, Winter Garden, FL 34787 .... (407) 654–5705
FAX: 654–5814

Counties: ORANGE (part), LAKE (part), POLK (part). CITIES AND TOWNSHIPS: Astatula, Azalea, Bay Hill, Bay Lake, Belle Isle, Belleview, Conway, Doctor Phillips, Eustis, Fairview Shores, Howey-in-the-Hills, Holden Heights, Leesburg, Meadow Wood, Mid Florida Lakes, Montverde, Oakland, Ocala Part, Ocoee, Orlando, Tavares, Umatilla, Union Park, Williamsburg, Windermere, and Winter Garden. Population (2010), 696,345.

ZIP Codes: 32159, 32702–03, 32726, 32735–36, 32757, 32776, 32778, 32784, 32801, 32803–07, 32809, 32811–12, 32818–19, 32821–22, 32830, 32835–37, 32839, 33805, 33809, 33823, 33837, 33844, 33850, 33868, 33880–81, 33884, 33896–97, 34705, 34711, 34714–15, 34731, 34734, 34736–37, 34747–48, 34753, 34756, 34760–62, 34786–88, 34797

* * *

ELEVENTH DISTRICT

RICHARD NUGENT, Republican, of Spring Hill, FL; born in Evergreen Park, IL, May 26, 1951; education: B.A. in criminology, Saint Leo College, Saint Leo, FL, 1990; FBI National Academy graduate, FBI Academy, Quantico, VA, 1991; M.P.A., public administration, Troy State University, MacDill Air Force Base, FL, 1995; executive leadership training, National Sheriff's Institute, Longmount, CO, 2002; professional: Illinois Air National Guard, 1969–75; 38+ years in law enforcement; Deputy County Sheriff, Hernando County, FL; elected Sheriff, Hernando County, FL, 2001–10; military: law enforcement; family: wife, Wendy; children: three sons; committees: Armed Services; House Administration; Rules; elected to the 112th Congress on November 2, 2010; reelected to the 113th Congress on November 6, 2012.

Office Listings

http://nugent.house.gov

1727 Longworth House Office Building, Washington, DC 20515 .... (202) 225–1002
Chief of Staff.—Justin Grabelle. FAX: 226–6559
Deputy Chief of Staff / Legislative and Communications Director.—Harrison Lewis.
Scheduler.—Lindsay Reidenbach.
11035 Spring Hill Drive, Spring Hill, FL 34608 .... (352) 684–4446
FAX: 684–4484

Counties: CITRUS, HERNANDO, LAKE (part), MARION (part), PASCO (part), SUMTER. CITIES AND TOWNSHIPS: Brooksville, Ocala, and The Villages. Population (2010), 696,345.

ZIP Codes: 32113, 32133, 32159, 32162, 32179, 32195, 32617, 32686, 32702, 32784, 33513–14, 33521, 33523, 33538, 33585, 33597, 34420, 34428–29, 34432–34, 34436, 34442, 34445–46, 34448–50, 34452–53, 34461, 34465, 34470–76, 34479–82, 34484, 34488, 34491, 34601–02, 34604, 34606–07, 34609, 34613–14, 34661, 34731, 34785

* * *

TWELFTH DISTRICT

GUS M. BILIRAKIS, Republican, of Palm Harbor, FL; born in Gainesville, FL, February 8, 1963; raised in Tarpon Springs, FL; education: B.A., University of Florida, 1986; J.D., Stetson University, 1989; son of former Representative Michael Bilirakis (1983–2006); volunteered on his father's congressional campaigns; interned for President Ronald Reagan and the National Republican Congressional Committee; worked for former Representative Don Sundquist (R–TN); ran the Bilirakis Law Group, specializing in wills, trusts, and estate planning, Holiday, FL; taught government classes, St. Petersburg College; member of the Florida House of Representatives, 1998–2006; chaired several prominent panels in the State House, including Crime Prevention, Public Safety Appropriations, and the Economic Development, Trade, and Banking Committee; married: Eva; children: Michael, Teddy, Manuel, and Nicholas; Senior Republican Freshman Whip; committees: Energy and Commerce; Veterans' Affairs; elected to the 110th Congress on November 7, 2006; reelected to each succeeding Congress.

Office Listings

http://bilirakis.house.gov https://twitter.com/repgusbilirakis
https://www.facebook.com/gusbilirakis

2313 Rayburn House Office Building, Washington, DC 20515 .... (202) 225–5755
Chief of Staff.—Elizabeth Hittos. FAX: 225–4085
Press Secretary.—Sarah Criser.
Executive Assistant.—Tim Tracy.
7132 Little Road, New Port Richey, FL 34654 .... (727) 232–2921
District Director.—Summer Robertson. FAX: 232–2923
5901 Argerian Drive, Suite 102, Wesley Chapel, FL 33545 .... (813) 501–4942
FAX: 501–4944
600 Klosterman Road, Room BB–038, Tarpon Springs, FL 34689 .... (727) 940–5860
FAX: 940–5861

Counties: PASCO, HILLSBOROUGH (part), AND PINELLAS (part). CITIES AND TOWNSHIPS: Dade City, New Port Richey, Port Richey, San Antonio, St Leo, Zephyrhills, Aripeka, Bayonet Point, Beacon Square, Connerton, Crystal Springs,

Dade City North, Elfers, Heritage Pines, Holiday, Hudson, Jasmine Esastes, Key Vista, Lacoochee, Land O'Lakes, Meadow Oaks, Moon Lake, New Port Richey East, Odessa, Pasadena Hills, Quail Ridge, River Ridge, Shady Hills, Trinity, Tilby, Wesley Chapel, Zephyrhills North, Zephyrhills South, Zephyrhills West, Tarpon Springs, Palm Harbor, East Lake, Oldsmar, Keystone, Lutz, Cheval, North Dale, Citrus Park, Westchase, Lake Magdalene, and Carrollwood. Population (2010), 696,344.

ZIP Codes: 33252–24, 33526, 33537, 33539–45, 33548–49, 33558–59, 33574, 33576, 33593, 34610, 33612–13, 33618, 33624–26, 34637–39, 34652–56, 34667–69, 34674, 33677, 34679–81, 34683–85, 34688–92

* * *

THIRTEENTH DISTRICT

VACANT

Counties: PINELLAS COUNTY (part). Population (2010), 696,345.

ZIP Codes: 33701–11, 33713–16, 33744, 33755–56, 33759–67, 33770–74, 33776–78, 33781–82, 33785–86, 34677, 34683–84, 34695, 34698

* * *

FOURTEENTH DISTRICT

KATHY CASTOR, Democrat, of Tampa, FL; born in Miami, FL, August 20, 1966; education: B.A., political science, Emory University, 1988; J.D., Florida State University, 1991; professional: Assistant General Counsel, State of Florida, Department of Community Affairs, 1991–94; attorney, Icard Merrill, 1994–95; partner, Broad and Cassel, 1995–2000; ran for Florida State Senate, 2000; Hillsborough County Commissioner, 2002–06; religion: member of Palma Ceia Presbyterian Church; married: William Lewis; children: two; committees: Budget; Energy and Commerce; elected to the 110th Congress on November 7, 2006; reelected to each succeeding Congress.

Office Listings

http://castor.house.gov

205 Cannon House Office Building, Washington, DC 20515 .... (202) 225–3376
Chief of Staff.—Clay Phillips. FAX: 225–5652
Legislative Director.—Elizabeth Brown.
Scheduler.—Lara Hopkins.
4144 North Armenia Avenue, Suite 300, Tampa, FL 33607 .... (813) 871–2817
District Director.—Chloe Coney.
Press Secretary.—Marcia Mejia.

Counties: HILLSBOROUGH (part), PINELLAS (part). CITIES: Apollo Beach, Brandon, Carrollwood, Carrollwood Village, Citrus Park, Gibsonton, Riverview, Ruskin, St. Petersburg, Tampa, Temple Terrace, and Town 'N' Country, Ybor City. Population (2010), 696,345.

ZIP Codes: 33508–11, 33534, 33549, 33570, 33572, 33575, 33578, 33586, 33601–19, 33621–26, 33629–31, 33633–35, 33637, 33646, 33650, 33655, 33660–64, 33672–75, 33677, 33679–82, 33684–86, 33689, 33694, 33701, 33704–05, 33707, 33710–13, 33730–31, 33733, 33747, 33784, 34677

* * *

FIFTEENTH DISTRICT

DENNIS A. ROSS, Republican, of Lakeland, FL; born in Lakeland, October 18, 1959; education: Lakeland Senior High School; B.S., organizational management, Auburn University, Auburn, AL, 1981; J.D., Cumberland School of Law at Samford University, Birmingham, AL, 1987; professional: attorney, Holland & Knight; attorney, Walt Disney World; founder and attorney, Ross Vecchio, PA, 1989–2010; awards: Workers Compensation Section, Appreciation Award, 2001; Florida Building Material Association, Legislator of the Year Award, 2001 and 2003; Florida Workers Advocate, Outstanding Freshman Representative Award, 2001; The Trust for Public Land, Legislative Leadership Award, 2001; Polk Community College, Outstanding Legislator, 2001; Florida Crane Owners Council, Representative of the Year, 2003; Florida Association of Roofing Professionals, Legislative Achievement Award, 2003; Florida Automotive Dealer Association, Legislator of the Year, 2003; Florida Retail Federation, Legislator of the Year, 2003; Florida Bankers Association, Outstanding Leadership Award, 2004; ARC Florida, Representative of the Year, 2004; YMCA of Florida, Outstanding Leadership Award, 2005; Florida League of Cities, Legislative Appreciation Award, 2005, 2006 and 2007; Florida Insurance Council, Harry G. Landrum Outstanding Legislative Leadership, 2005 and 2008; Florida Association of Counties, Champion Award, 2005; Florida Trucking Association, Legislator of the Year, 2005 and 2006; Associated Industries of Florida, Champion for Business Award, 2005; Florida Association of Insurance and Financial Advisors, Representative of the Year, 2005; Florida Association of Mortgage Brokers, Grateful Recognition Award, 2005; Florida Association of Insurance Agents, Legislator of the Year, 2006; Florida Chamber, Most Valuable Legislator, 2008; Governor's Hurricane Conference, Legislative Award, 2008; Associated Industries of Florida Financial Securities Council, Legislator of the Year, 2008; Florida Chamber Honor Roll 2001, 2002, 2003, 2004, 2005, 2007 and 2008; religion: member, First Presbyterian Church, Lakeland; married: Cindy; children: Shane and Travis; committees: Financial Services; elected to the 112th Congress on November 2, 2010; reelected to the 113th Congress on November 6, 2012.

Office Listings

http://www.house.gov/dennisross. twitter: @repdennisross

229 Cannon House Office Building, Washington, DC 20515 .... (202) 225–1252
Chief of Staff.—Anthony Foti. FAX: 226–0585
Legislative Director.—Amie Woeber.
Office Coordinator.—Grafton Pritchartt.
170 Fitzgerald Road, Suite 1, Lakeland, FL 33813 .... (863) 644–8215
District Director.—Blaine Gravitt. FAX: 648–0749
Director of Administration / Scheduler.—Shelee Meeker.
Community Outreach Director.—Kristin Collis.

Counties: HILLSBOROUGH (part), POLK (part). CITIES AND TOWNSHIPS: Auburndale, Bartow, Brandon, Dover, Durant, Eaton Park, Highland City, Kathleen, Lakeland, Lithia, Lutz, Mulberry, Plant City, Riverview, Ruskin, Seffner, Tampa, Temple Terrace, Thonotosassa, Valrico, Winter Haven, and Zephyrhills. Population (2010), 813,570.

ZIP Codes: 33510–11, 33527, 33530, 33540, 33547–49, 33559, 33563, 33565–67, 33569, 33578, 33584, 33592, 33594, 33596, 33610, 33612–13, 33617–18, 33620, 33637, 33647, 33801, 33803, 33805, 33809–13, 33815, 33823, 33830, 33840, 33846–47, 33849, 33860, 33863, 33880

* * *

SIXTEENTH DISTRICT

VERN BUCHANAN, Republican, of Longboat Key, FL; born in Detroit, MI, May 8, 1951; education: B.B.A., business administration, Cleary University; M.B.A., University of Detroit; honorary degree: Doctorate of Science in Business Administration, Cleary University; professional: founder and chairman, Buchanan Enterprises; founder and chairman, Buchanan Automotive Group, 1992; operations include Sarasota Ford and 18 auto franchises in the southeastern United States; experience in real estate including home building and property development and management; awards: One of America's Ten Outstanding Young Men, U.S. Jaycees; Entrepreneur of the Year, Inc. Magazine and Arthur Young; Entrepreneur of the Year, Harvard Business School, Club of Detroit; One of Michigan's Five Outstanding Young Men, Michigan Jaycees; President's Award, Ford Motor Company; Certified Retailer Award, J.D. Power and Associates; Outstanding Citizen Award, United Negro College Fund; Outstanding Philanthropic Corporation Award, National Society of Fund Raising Executives; Freedom Award for Business and Industry, NAACP; The American Jewish Committee Civic Achievement Award; Tampa Bay Business Hall of Fame Award; married: Sandy Buchanan; children: James and Matt; committee: Ways and Means; elected to the 110th Congress on November 7, 2006; reelected to each succeeding Congress.

Office Listings

http://www.buchanan.house.gov twitter: @vernbuchanan
https://www.facebook.com/congressmanbuchanan

2104 Cannon House Office Building, Washington, DC 20515 .... (202) 225–5015
Chief of Staff.—Dave Karvelas. FAX: 226–0828
Deputy Chief of Staff.—Don Green.
Legislative Director.—Shane Lieberman.
Communications Director.—Max Goodman.
Scheduler.—Christina Aiuto.
111 South Orange Avenue, Suite 200W, Sarasota, FL 34236 .... (941) 951–6643

District Director.—Sally Tibbetts.
Scheduler.—Sydney Gruters.
2424 Manatee Avenue West, Suite 104, Bradenton, FL 34205 .... (941) 747–9081

Counties: MANATEE, SARASOTA. Population (2010), 639,345.

ZIP Codes: 33834, 34211–12, 34219, 34221, 34223, 34240–41, 34251, 34287–88, 34292–93

* * *

SEVENTEENTH DISTRICT

THOMAS J. ROONEY, Republican, of Tequesta, FL; born in Philadelphia, PA, November 21, 1970; education: B.A., Washington and Jefferson, Washington, PA; M.A., University of Florida, Gainesville, FL; J.D., University of Miami, Coral Gables, FL; member, Roman Catholic Church; married: Tara; children: Tommy, Sean, and Seamus; committees: Appropriations; Permanent Select Committee on Intelligence; elected to the 111th Congress on November 4, 2008; reelected to each succeeding Congress.

Office Listings

http://www.rooney.house.gov ttps://www.facebook.com/reptomrooney?ref=mf
https://twitter.com/tomrooney http://www.youtube.com/user/congressmanrooney

221 Cannon House Office Building, Washington, DC 20515 .... (202) 225–5792
Chief of Staff.—Brian Crawford. FAX: 225–3132
Communications Director.—Michael Mahaffey.
226 Taylor Street, Suite 230, Punta Gorda, FL 33950 .... (941) 575–9101
Summerfield Shoppes, 11345 Big Bend Road, Riverview, FL 33579 .... (813) 677–8646
4507 George Boulevard, Sebring, FL 33875 .... (863) 402–9082

Counties: CHARLOTTE DESOTO, GLADES, HARDEE, HIGHLANDS, HILLSBOROUGH, LEE, MANATEE, OKEECHOBEE, AND POLK. Population (2010), 696,344.

ZIP Codes: 33471, 33547, 33598, 33801, 33803, 33811, 33813, 33823, 33825, 33830, 33834, 33841, 33843, 33850, 33852, 33857, 33860, 33865, 33870, 33873, 33875–76, 33880, 33884, 33890, 33898, 33905, 33920, 33935, 33947–48, 33950, 33952–55, 33960, 33971–72, 33980–83, 34224, 34251, 34266, 34269, 34972, 34974

* * *

EIGHTEENTH DISTRICT

PATRICK E. MURPHY, Democrat, of Jupiter, FL; born in Miami, FL, March 30, 1983; education: B.S. in business administration from the University of Miami, 2006; professional: CPA, Deloitte & Touche; Vice President, Coastal Environmental Services; religion: Roman Catholic; caucuses: Co-founder & Co-Chair of the United Solutions Caucus, Co-Chair of the No Labels' Problem Solvers Group; member, New Democrat Coalition, Congressional Arts Caucus, Congressional Boating Caucus, Congressional Caucus on Access to Capital & Credit, Congressional SPA and Accountants Caucus, Congressional Everglades Caucus, Congressional Human Trafficking Caucus, Congressional Small Business Caucus, Congressional Veterans Jobs Caucus, Florida PORTS Caucus, PORTS Caucus; co-chair of the Congressional Citrus Caucus and the Disaster Relief Caucus; committees: Financial Services; Small Business; elected to the 113th Congress on November 6, 2012.

Office Listings

http://www.patrickmurphy.house.gov twitter: @repmurphyfl

1517 Longworth House Office Building, Washington, DC 20515 .... (202) 225–3026
Chief of Staff.—Eric Johnson. FAX: 225–8398
Deputy Chief of Staff.—Tiffany Muller.
Legislative Director.—Christopher Fisher.
Press Secretary.—Erin Moffet.
Scheduler.—Nick Malatesta.
2000 PGA Boulevard, Suite A3220, Palm Beach Gardens, FL 33408 .... (561) 253–8433
District Director.—Michael Kenny. FAX: 253–8436
Executive Assistant.—Sherlean Purvis.
Constituent Services Representative.—Angie Toro.
171 Southwest Flagler Avenue, Stuart, FL 34994 .... (772) 781–3266
Constituent Services Representative.—Victoria Winslett. FAX: 781–3267
121 Southwest Port St. Lucie Boulevard, Room 187, Port St. Lucie, FL 34984 ...... (772) 336–2877

Constituent Services Representative.—Candace Walls. FAX: 336–2899

Counties: MARTIN, ST. LUCIE, AND PALM BEACH (NORTHERN PART). Cities: Fort Pierce, Port St. Lucie, Tradition, Lakewood Park, Eden, Indian River Estates, Stuart, Palm City, Hutchinson Island, Hobe Sound, Indiantown, Jensen Beach, Port Salerno, Jupiter Island, Sewall's Point, Jupiter, Palm Beach Gardens, West Palm Beach (part), Riviera Beach, Singer Island (part), Jupiter Inlet Colony, Juno Beach, Loxahatchee, Palm Beach Shores, North Palm Beach, Royal Palm Beach, Tequesta, and Juno Beach. Population (2010), 696,345.

ZIP Codes: 33403–04, 33407–12, 33417–18, 33420, 33422, 33438, 33455, 33458, 33468–70, 33475, 33477–78, 34945–54, 34956–58, 34972, 34974, 34979, 34981–88, 34990–92, 34994–97

* * *

NINETEENTH DISTRICT

VACANT

Counties: LEE AND COLLIER. Population (2010), 696,345.

ZIP Codes: 33901–16, 33919, 33921–22, 33924, 33928–29, 33931–32, 33936, 33945, 33955–57, 33965–67, 33970–71, 33973–74, 33976, 33990–91, 33993–94, 34101–10, 34112–14, 34119, 34133–34, 34136, 34140, 34142, 34145–46

* * *

TWENTIETH DISTRICT

ALCEE L. HASTINGS, Democrat, of Miramar, FL; born in Altamonte Springs, FL, September 5, 1936; education: graduated, Crooms Academy, Sanford, FL, 1954; B.A., Fisk University, Nashville, TN, 1958; Howard University, Washington, DC; J.D., Florida A&M University, Tallahassee, 1963; attorney; admitted to the Florida bar, 1963; circuit judge, U.S. District Court for the Southern District of Florida; member: African Methodist Episcopal Church, NAACP, Miami-Dade Chamber of Commerce, Family Christian Association, ACLU, Southern Poverty Law Center, National Organization for Women, Planned Parenthood, Women and Children First, Inc., Sierra Club, Cousteau Society, Broward County Democratic Executive Committee, Dade County Democratic Executive Committee, Lauderhill Democratic Club, Hollywood Hills Democratic Club, Pembroke Pines Democratic Club, Urban League, National Bar Association, Florida Chapter of the National Bar Association, T.J. Reddick Bar Association, National Conference of Black Lawyers, Simon Wiesenthal Center, The Furtivist Society; Progressive Black Police Officers Club, International Black Firefighters Association; co-chair, Florida Delegation; co-chair, Helsinki Commission; three children: Alcee Lamar II, Chelsea, and Leigh; Senior Democratic Whip; committees: Rules; elected on November 3, 1992, to the 103rd Congress; reelected to each succeeding Congress.

Office Listings

http://www.house.gov/alceehastings

2353 Rayburn House Office Building, Washington, DC 20515 .... (202) 225–1313
Chief of Staff / Press Secretary.—Lale Mamaux. FAX: 225–1171
Policy Director.—Christian Sy.
Senior Policy Advisor.—Ian Wolf.
Policy Advisor.—Larry Zaragoza.
Staff Assistants: David Opong-Waddee, Evan Polisar.
Office Manager / Scheduler.—Barbara Harper.
2701 West Oakland Park Boulevard, Suite 200, Ft. Lauderdale, FL 33311 .... (954) 733–2800
Chief of Staff.—Arthur W. Kennedy.

Counties: BROWARD (part), HENDRY (part), PALM BEACH (part). Population (2010), 696,345.

ZIP Codes: 33060, 33063–64, 33068–69, 33072, 33301, 33304–05, 33309–13, 33317, 33319–22, 33334, 33336, 33340, 33345, 33351, 33359, 33401, 33403–11, 33413–15, 33417–19, 33421, 33426, 33430, 33435, 33438, 33440–42, 33459–62, 33470, 33476

* * *

TWENTY-FIRST DISTRICT

THEODORE DEUTCH, Democrat, of Boca Raton, FL; born in Bethlehem, PA, May 7, 1966; education: graduate of Liberty High School; B.A., University of Michigan, Ann Arbor, MI, 1988; J.D., University of Michigan Law School, Ann Arbor, MI, 1990; admitted to the Florida bar, 1991; attorney: Florida State Senator, 2006–10; member: Florida Bar Association; Jewish Federation of South Palm Beach County; League of Women Voters; married to the former Jill Weinstock, three children; committees: Ethics; Foreign Affairs; Judiciary; elected to the 111th Congress on April 13, 2010, by special election to fill the vacancy caused by the resignation of United States Representative Robert Wexler; reelected to each succeeding Congress.

Office Listings

http://deutch.house.gov twitter: @repteddeutch

1024 Longworth House Office Building, Washington, DC 20515 .... (202) 225–3001
Chief of Staff.—Joshua Rogin. FAX: 225–5974
Deputy Chief of Staff.—Ellen McLaren.
Communications Director.—Ashley Mushnick.
8177 West Glades Road, Suite 211 Boca Raton, FL 33434 .... (561) 470–5440
District Director.—Wendi Lipsich. FAX: 470–5446

Counties: BROWARD (part), PALM BEACH (part). CITIES AND TOWNSHIPS: Boynton Beach, Boca Raton, Delray Beach, Greenacres, Lake Worth, Lantana (only one precinct), West Palm Beach, Coral Springs, Parkland, Coconut Creek, Margate (part), Pompano Beach, and Deerfield Beach. Population (2010), 736,419.

ZIP Codes: 33063–66, 33068–69, 33071, 33073, 33075–77, 33093, 33321, 33406, 33411, 33413–15, 33417, 33426, 33428, 33431, 33433–34, 33436–37, 33441–42, 33445–46, 33448, 33454, 33461–63, 33466–67, 33481–82, 33484, 33486–88, 33496–99

* * *

TWENTY-SECOND DISTRICT

LOIS FRANKEL, Democrat, of West Palm Beach, FL; born in New York City, NY; May 17, 1948; education: B.A., Boston University, Boston, MA, 1970; J.D., Georgetown University Law Center, Washington, DC, 1973; professional: elected State Representative in the 83rd district of the Florida House of Representatives, 1986; first female Florida House Minority Leader from 1995–2003; elected Mayor of West Palm Beach from 2003–11; religion: Jewish; caucuses: member of the Congressional Progressive Caucus; Congressional Everglades Caucus; Congressional Ports Caucus; Florida Ports Caucus; Congressional Pro-Choice Caucus; Congressional Caucus for Women's Issues; Democratic Israel Working Group; committees: Foreign Affairs; Transportation and Infrastructure; elected to the 113th Congress on November 6, 2012.

Office Listings

http://frankel.house.gov https://www.facebook.com/reploisfrankel
https://twitter.com/reploisfrankel

1037 Longworth House Office Building, Washington, DC 20515 .... (202) 225–9890
Chief of Staff.—Jonathon Bray. FAX: 225–1224
Legislative Director.—Jim Cho.
Legislative Assistants: Josh Cohen, Kelsey Moran.
Communications Director.—Sarah Rothschild.
Scheduler.—Kate Regan.
Staff Assistant.—Melissa Durity.
2500 North Military Trail, Suite 490, Boca Raton, FL 33431 .... (561) 998–9045
District Director.—Felicia Goldstein. FAX: 998–9048

Counties: BROWARD (part), PALM BEACH (part). CITIES: Pompano Beach, West Palm Beach, Oakland Park, Delray Beach, Palm Springs, Boca Raton, Fort Lauderdale, Plantation, Ocean Ridge, Lantana, Boynton Beach, Highland Beach, Wilton Manors, and Lighthouse Point. Population (2010), 696,345.

ZIP Codes: 33060, 33062, 33064, 33069, 33301, 33304–06, 33308–09, 33311–12, 33315–17, 33322–25, 33334, 33401, 33404–07, 33415, 33431–36, 33441, 33444–45, 33461–63, 33480, 33483–84, 33486–87, 33496

* * *

TWENTY-THIRD DISTRICT

DEBBIE WASSERMAN SCHULTZ, Democrat, of Weston, FL; born in Forest Hills, Queens County, NY, September 27, 1966; education: B.A., University of Florida, Gainesville, FL, 1988; M.A., University of Florida, FL, 1990; professional: Public Policy Curriculum Specialist, Nova Southeastern University; Adjunct Instructor, Political Science, Broward Community College; aide to United States Representative Peter Deutsch, 1989–92; member, Florida State House of Representatives, 1992–2000; member, Florida State Senate, 2000–04; organizations: Board of Trustees, Westside Regional Medical Center; Outstanding Freshman Legislator, Florida Women's Political Caucus; Secretary; Board of Directors, American Jewish Congress; Member, Broward National Organization for Women; Board of Directors, National Safety Council, South Florida Chapter; religion: Jewish; married: Steve; children: Rebecca, Jake, Shelby; Senior Democratic Whip; elected chair, Democratic National Committee, 2011; committees: Appropriations; elected to the 109th Congress on November 2, 2004; reelected to each succeeding Congress.

Office Listings

http://wassermanschultz.house.gov twitter: @repdwstweet

118 Cannon House Office Building, Washington, DC 20515 .... (202) 225–7931
Chief of Staff.—Tracie Pough. FAX: 226–2052
Communications Director.—Jonathon Beeton.
Legislative Director / General Counsel.—Coby Dolan.
Executive Assistant.—Hannah Lerner.
10100 Pines Boulevard, Pembroke Pines, FL 33026 .... (954) 437–3926
19200 West Country Club Drive, Third Floor, Aventura, FL 33180 .... (305) 936–5724

Counties: BROWARD COUNTY (part). CITIES: Cooper City, Dania Beach, Davie, Fort Lauderdale, Hallandale Beach, Hollywood, Hollywood Hills, Pembroke Pines, Plantation, Sunrise, Southwest Ranches, and Weston. MIAMI-DADE COUNTY (part). CITIES: Aventura, Bal Harbour, Bay Harbor Islands, Golden Beach, Miami Beach, and North Bay Village. Population (2010), 703,594.

ZIP Codes: 33004, 33009, 33019–21, 33023–24, 33026–28, 33139–41, 33154, 33160, 33180, 33312, 33314–16, 33324–28, 33330–32

* * *

TWENTY-FOURTH DISTRICT

FREDERICA S. WILSON, Democrat, of Miami, FL; born in Miami, November 5; education: B.S., Fisk University; M.S., University of Miami; Florida Memorial University, Honorary Doctorate of Humane Letters; professional: executive director, Office of Alternative Education and Dropout Prevention, Miami–Dade County Schools; member, Miami–Dade County School Board, 1992–98; Minority Whip, Florida State House of Representatives, 1998–2002; Democratic Whip, Florida State Senate, 2002–04; Minority Leader Pro Tempore, Florida State Senate, 2002–10; Minority Whip, Florida State Senate, 2008–10; members: regional director, Alpha Kappa Alpha Sorority, Inc., 1986–present; founder / member, 5000 Role Models of Excellence, Inc., 1993–present; member, National Association of Black School Educators, present; member, the Links, Inc., present; founder, Stop Day Enough is Enough, 1996–present; Miami Delegate, President's Summit for America's Future, 1997; State of Florida ''STOP DAY'', Enough is Enough, founder, 1996; President's Summit for America's Future, Philadelphia, Pennsylvania, Miami Delegate, 1997; founder, Miami–Dade County ''Keep Me Safe'' summit, march, and candlelight vigil board member, Women's Action for New Directions Educational Fund, 2004; honors and awards: Southern Living, Outstanding Southerner, May 1993; Macedonia Missionary Baptist Church, Image Maker, 1993; South Florida Association of Black Journalists, Kuumba Award, 1994; St. Petersburg Junior College, In Recognition, 1996; American Red Cross, Spectrum Award, 1998; African–American Achiever Award for Education, 1998; Peace Education Foundation, Peacemaker of the Year, 1998; Youth Crime Watch / Citizens Crime Watch, A Champion for All Poor and Minority Students, 1998; Imperial Daughters of Isis Miami Beach, Florida Hall of Fame, 1999; NAACP, Florida Chapter, Morris Milton Memorial Award, 2001; Zeta Phi Beta Sorority, Inc., Leadership Award, 2001; Florida A&M University, National Alumni Association Expresses Gratitude, 2001; The Florida HIV–AIDS Ministries, Inc., Honors State Representative Frederica S. Wilson, 2001; Florida AIDS Action, Outstanding Leadership and Support for HIV / AIDS and Health Care, 2002; Alpha Kappa Alpha Sorority, Inc., In Appreciation, 2002; Western Union, L'Union Fait la Force Award, 2003; Community Action Agency, Citizen of the Year Award, 2004; American Cancer Society, Florida Chapter, Legislative Leadership Award, 2004; Florida Education Association, Educator of the Year, 2004; Association of Black Health–System Pharmacists, Legislator Achievement Award, 2004; Easter Seals of Miami–Dade, Legislator of the Year Award, 2004; Northside Seventh Day Adventist Church (Miami), Distinguished Community Leader Award, 2004; The Black Archives, History and Research Foundation of South Florida, Inc., Chairman's Award, 2004; Sierra Club, Florida Chapter, Legislative Recognition Award, 2004; Network Miami Magazine, One of Miami's 50 Most Influential Black Business Professionals, 2004; Millennium Movers, Inc., Shaker Award, 2004; Alpha Kappa Alpha Sorority, Ft. Pierce, Florida Chapter, Soror of the Year, 2005; Alpha Kappa Alpha Sorority, Ft. Walton Beach, Florida Chapter, Soror of the Year, 2005; Alpha Kappa Alpha Sorority, Thomasville, GA Chapter, Soror of the Year, 2005; Carrie P. Meek Education Leadership Achievement Award, 2005; Miami Gardens Jaycees, Distinguished Service Award, 2005; Alpha Kappa Alpha, Inc., Emerald Service Award, 2005; The Links, Inc., Links of Gold Award, 2005; Belafonte TACOLCY Center, Inc., U.S. Department of Justice / Drug Enforcement Administration in Recognition of State Senator Frederica S. Wilson, 2005; SEIU Florida Healthcare Union, Legislative Hero Award, 2006; Barry University, SGA Acknowledgement of Florida's Residents Access Grant Award, 2006; City of Miami, Women Builders of Community Dreams Award, 2006; Florida Memorial University, SGA Leadership Character and Service Award, 2006; Holy Faith Missionary Baptist Church, Participation Award, 2006; Miami–Dade Police Department, Appreciation Award, 2006; The Historic St. Agnes Episcopal Church, 108th Anniversary Appreciation Award, 2006; FAU, Small Business Development Appreciation Award, 2006; Day of the Child, Mentoring Award, 2006; Project H.O.P.E., Katrina Humanitarian Award, 2006; South Florida Chapter of the Coalition of Black Trade Unionists, Audrey McCollum Scholarship Award, 2006; CEO Magazine, Legislative Action Recognition, 2006; Community Action Agency, Youth Leadership Award, 2006; I.B.P.O.E. of W., Antlers Temple #39, Legislative Excellence Award, 2006; Community Health of South Dade, Inc., Health Hero Award, 2006; Health Council of South Florida, Inc., Health Leadership Award, 2006; National Coalition of 100 Black Women, Inc., Greater Miami Chapter, Candace Award, 2006; Kiwanis Club of Miami Shores, North Dade Exemplary Service Award, 2006; Academy of Florida Trial Lawyers, Rosemary Barkett Award, 2006; National Pan Hellenic Council, Inc., Celebration of Excellence, 2006; NAACP Milton Morris Award, 2007; Jessie C. Trice Humanitarian Award, 2007; Liberty City's Community Action Agency, Community Service Award, 2007; Miami Dade College, Pathway to Opportunity Appreciation Award, 2007; Florida Association of School Administrators, Legislator of the Year, 2007; Florida Association of Women Lawyers, Legislative Recognition Award, 2007; Florida Health Center, Jessie C. Trice Humanitarian Award, 2007; Miami Dade Community Action Agency, Liberty City Advisor Committee in Recognition of State Senator Frederica S. Wilson June 2007; The National Medical Association, Scroll of Merit for Public Education Advocacy, 2008; American School Health Association, Legislator of the Year, 2008; Alpha Kappa Alpha Sorority International, Rosa Parks Coretta Scott King Award, 2008; Florida Association of Counties (FAC), County Partner Award, 2008; Florida Cable Telecommunications Association, Leaders in Learning Award, 2008; AKA Educational Advancement Foundation, The Green Diamond Award, 2008; Bethune–Cookman University, In Tribute, 2009; Alpha Kappa Alpha Sorority, Inc., With Appreciation, 2009; The Links, Inc., In Appreciation, 2010 Alpha Kappa Alpha Sorority, Inc., Timeless Service to Mankind, 2011; Miami Dade Chamber of Commerce, H.T. Smith Lifetime Achievement Award, 2011; ICABA, Salutes South Florida's 100 Accomplished Caribbean Americans, 2012; TheGrio.com, The Grio's 100, 2012; Louie Bing Scholarship Fund, Inc., Award of Excellence, 2012; National Voices for Equality Education and Enlightenment Voices of Leadership Award, Congresswoman Wilson, April 2012; First Focus Campaign for Children, Defender of Children, 2012; Youth Power Movement, First Annual Humanitarian Award, 2012; I Am Empowered for Jobs Award, National Urban League, 2013; Broward Black Elected Officials Inaugural Lifetime Achievement Community Service Award; The Links, Inc., Services to Youth Award, 2013; City of North Miami, In Recognition, 2013; committees: Education and the Workforce; Science, Space, and Technology; elected to the 112th Congress on November 2, 2010; reelected to the 113th Congress on November 6, 2012.

Office Listings

http://wilson.house.gov https://www.facebook.com/repwilson twitter.com/repwilson

208 Cannon House Office Building, Washington, DC 20515 .... (202) 225–4506
Chief of Staff.—Kim Bowman. FAX: 226–0777
Senior Advisor.—Keenan Austin.
Legislative Director.—Justin Talbot Zorn.
Legislative Assistant / Scheduler.—Corey Solow.
Legislative Correspondent.—Jean Roseme.
Staff Assistant.—Crystal Handfield.
Staff Assistant / Press Assistant.—Steven Page.
18425 Northwest, 2nd Avenue, Suite 355, Miami, FL 33169 .... (305) 690–5905

District Chief of Staff.—Alexis Snyder.
District Office Director.—Joyce Postell.
South Florida Communications Director.—Gwen Belton.
Director of Special Community Relations.—Aaron Scavron.
Director of Special Operations.—Edward Haynes.
Director of International Relations.—Tamara Phillippeaux.
Director of Field Operations.—Shirlee Moreau-Lafleur.
District Policy Director.—Marcus Dixon.
Congressional Aides: Jessica Lopez, Walta Tolbert.

10100 Pines Boulevard, 3rd Floor, Building B, Pembroke Pines, FL 33026 .... (954) 450–6767
Director of International Relations.—Tamara Phillippeaux.

West Park City Hall, 1965 South State Road 7, West Park, FL 33023 .... (954) 989–2688
Congressional Aide.—Walta Tolbert.

Miramar City Hall, 2300 Civic Center Place, Miramar, FL 33025 .... (954) 883–6165
Congressional Aide.—Walta Tolbert.

Counties: DADE (part), BROWARD (part). Population (2010), 693,086.

ZIP Codes: 33054–56, 33083, 33101, 33127, 33142, 33147, 33150–51, 33164, 33167–69, 33179–81, 33238, 33242, 33261

* * *

TWENTY-FIFTH DISTRICT

MARIO DIAZ-BALART, Republican, of Miami, FL; born in Ft. Lauderdale, FL, September 25, 1961; education: University of South Florida; professional: president, Gordon Diaz-Balart and Partners (public relations and marketing business); religion: Catholic; public service: administrative assistant to the Mayor of Miami, 1985–88; Florida House of Representatives, 1988–92, and 2000–02; Florida State Senate, 1992–2000; committees: Appropriations; elected to the 25th District in the 108th Congress on November 5, 2002, reelected to each succeeding Congress. In 2010 ran unopposed and was elected to the 21st District in the 112th Congress on November 2, 2010. In 2012 was elected to the 25th District in the 113th Congress on November 6, 2012.

Office Listings

http://www.house.gov/mariodiaz-balart https://www.facebook.com/mdiazbalart
https://twitter.com/mariodb https://www.youtube.com/user/mariodiazbalart
http://instagram.com/repmariodb

436 Cannon House Office Building, Washington, DC 20515 .... (202) 225–4211
Chief of Staff.—Cesar A. Gonzalez. FAX: 226–8576
Legislative Director.—Miguel Mendoza.

8669 Northwest 36th Street, Suite 100, Doral, FL 33166 .... (305) 470–8555
District Director.—Miguel Otero. FAX: 470–8575
Deputy District Director.—Gloria Amor.

4715 Golden Gate Parkway, Suite 1, Naples, FL 34116 .... (239) 348–1620
Congressional Aide.—Karen Harmon. FAX: 348–3569

Counties: BROWARD COUNTY (part), COLLIER (part), HENDRY (part), MIAMI-DADE COUNTY (part). CITIES AND TOWNSHIPS: Ave Maria, Doral, Everglades City, Fontainebleau, Golden Gate, Golden Gate Estates, Hialeah, Immokalee, LaBelle, Medley, Miami Lakes, Miami Springs, Miramar, Pembroke Pines, and Sweetwater. Population (2010), 723,113.

ZIP Codes: 33002, 33010, 33012–18, 33027, 33029, 33054–55, 33102, 33112, 33122, 33126, 33135, 33147, 33152, 33166–67, 33172, 33174, 33178, 33182, 33184–85, 33194, 33199, 33222, 33331–32, 33440, 33928, 33930, 33935–36, 33972, 33975, 34104–05, 34109, 34112–14, 34116–17, 34119–20, 34135, 34137–43

* * *

TWENTY-SIXTH DISTRICT

JOSE ANTONIO ''JOE'' GARCIA, Democrat, of Miami, FL; born in Miami, FL, October 12, 1963; education: Miami Dade College, 1983–84; B.A., political science, history, and philosophy, University of Miami, Coral Gables, FL, 1987; J.D., University of Miami, Coral Gables, FL, 1991; professional: Florida Public Service Commission, 1991–2000; Executive Vice President, New Democratic Network 2004–08; chairman, Miami-Dade Democratic Party, 2007–08; executive director, Cuban American National Foundation, 2000–09; director of Economic Impact, U.S. Department of Energy, 2009–10; religion: Catholic; committees: Judiciary; Natural Resources; elected to the 113th Congress on November 6, 2012.

Office Listings

http://www.garcia.house.gov https://www.facebook.com/repjoegarcia
twitter: @repjoegarcia http://www.youtube.com/repjoegarcia

1440 Longworth House Office Building, Washington, DC 20515 .... (202) 225–2778
Chief of Staff.—Raul Martinez, Jr. FAX: 226–0346
Legislative Director.—David Montes.
Press Secretary.—Nicole Cueto.
Senior Policy Advisor.—Anna Gonzalez.
Legislative Assistants: Lindsay Marks, Natalie Raps.
Legislative Correspondent.—Andrew Connery.
Scheduler.—Stefanie Austin.
Office Manager.—Kim Fuller.
CHCI Fellow.—Elias Gonzalez.
12851 Southwest 42 Street. Suite 131, Miami, FL 33175 .... (305) 222–0160
District Director.—Julie Nissenbaum Caputo. FAX: 228–9397
Deputy District Director.—Kyle Schulberg.
Constituent Services.—Christina Elias.
Outreach Director.—Hector Caraballo.
Staff Assistant.—Annette Collazo.
404 West Palm Drive, Florida City, FL 33034 .... (305) 247–1234
South Dade Director.—Kevin Chambliss.
1100 Simonton Street, Suite 1–213, Key West, FL 33040 .... (305) 292–4485
Monroe County Director.—Jennifer George-Nichol.

Counties: DADE (part), MONROE. Population (2010), 726,532.

ZIP Codes: 33001, 33030–37, 33040, 33042–43, 33050–51, 33070, 33141, 33157, 33165, 33170, 33173–77, 33183–87, 33189, 33193–94, 33196, 34141

* * *

TWENTY-SEVENTH DISTRICT

ILEANA ROS-LEHTINEN, Republican, of Miami, FL; born in Havana, Cuba, July 15, 1952; education: B.A., English, Florida International University; M.S., educational leadership, Florida International University; Ed.D, University of Miami, 2004; certified Florida school teacher; founder and former owner, Eastern Academy; elected to the Florida House of Representatives, 1982; elected to the Florida State Senate, 1986; former president, Bilingual Private School Association; regular contributor to leading Spanish-language newspaper; during House tenure, married then-State Representative Dexter Lehtinen; two children and two step-children; committees: Chairman emeritus, Foreign Affairs; Rules; elected on August 29, 1989 to the 101st Congress; reelected to each succeeding Congress.

Office Listings

http://twitter: @roslehtinen

2206 Rayburn House Office Building, Washington, DC .... (202) 225–3931
Chief of Staff.—Arthur Estopinan. FAX: 225–5620
Deputy Director.—Christine del Portillo.
Legislative Director.—Joshua H. Salpeter.
Press Secretary.—Alex Cruz.
4960 Southwest 72nd Avenue, Suite 208, Miani, FL 33155 .... (305) 668–2285

Counties: DADE (part). CITIES AND TOWNSHIPS: Coral Gables, Cutler Bay, Hialeah, Key Biscayne, Little Havana, Miami, Pinecrest, South Miami, and Westchester. Population (2010), 696,345.

ZIP Codes: 33010, 33012–13, 33030, 33032–33, 33035, 33039, 33109, 33122, 33125–26, 33128–31, 33133–36, 33142–47, 33149, 33155–58, 33165–66, 33170, 33173–74, 33176, 33189–90

GEORGIA

(Population 2010, 9,687,653)

SENATORS

SAXBY CHAMBLISS, Republican, of Moultrie, GA; born in Warrenton, NC, November 10, 1943; education: graduated, C.E. Byrd High School, Shreveport, LA, 1962; B.B.A., University of Georgia, 1966; J.D., University of Tennessee College of Law, 1968; professional: served on the state bar of Georgia's Disciplinary Review Panel, 1969; member: Moultrie-Colquitt County Economic Development Authority; Colquitt County Economic Development Corporation; married: the former Julianne Frohbert, 1966; children: Lia Chambliss Baker, and C. Saxby (Bo), Jr.; committees: vice-chair, Select Committee on Intelligence; Agriculture, Nutrition, and Forestry; Armed Services; Rules and Administration; Joint Committee on Printing; elected to the 104th Congress; reelected to each succeeding Congress; elected to the U.S. Senate on November 5, 2002; reelected to the U.S. Senate on November 4, 2008.

Office Listings

http://chambliss.senate.gov www.twitter.com/saxbychambliss
www.facebook.com/saxbychambliss

416 Russell Senate Office Building, Washington, DC 20510 .... (202) 224–3521
Chief of Staff.—Camila Knowles. FAX: 224–0103
Deputy Chief of Staff.—Teresa Ervin.
Office Manager.—Kate Vickers.
Legislative Director.—Hugh Gamble.
Communications Director.—Lauren Claffey.
100 Galleria Parkway, Suite 1340, Atlanta, GA 30339 .... (770) 763–9090
State Director.—Camila Knowles.
585 South Main Street, P.O. Box 3217, Moultrie, GA 31776 .... (229) 985–2112
Field Representative.—Debbie Cannon.
3633 Wheeler Road, Suite 270, Augusta, GA 30909 .... (706) 650–1555
Field Representative.—Jim Hussey.
300 Mulberry Street, Suite 502, Macon, GA 31201 .... (478) 741–1417
FAX: 471–1437

* * *

JOHNNY ISAKSON, Republican, of Marietta, GA; born in Fulton County, GA, December 28, 1944; education: University of Georgia; professional: real estate executive; president, Northside Realty; public service: Georgia State House of Representatives, 1977–90; Georgia State Senate, 1993–96; appointed chairman of the Georgia Board of Election, 1996–97; awards: Republican National Committee "Best Legislator in America," 1989; organizations: chairman of the board, Georgian Club; trustee, Kennesaw State University; board of directors, Metro Atlanta and Georgia Chambers of Commerce; past president, Cobb Chamber of Commerce; executive committee, National Association of Realtors; president, Realty Alliance; advisory board, Federal National Mortgage Association; married: Dianne; children: John, Kevin, and Julie; religion: Methodist; elected to the 106th Congress on February 23, 1999, by special election; reelected to each succeeding Congress; committees: vice chair, Select Committee on Ethics; Finance; Health, Education, Labor, and Pensions; Veterans' Affairs; elected to the U.S. Senate on November 2, 2004; reelected to the U.S. Senate on November 2, 2010.

Office Listings

http://isakson.senate.gov facebook: johnnyisakson twitter: @senatorisakson

131 Russell Senate Office Building, Washington, DC 20510 .... (202) 224–3643
Chief of Staff.—Chris Carr. FAX: 228–0724
Deputy Chief of Staff/Communications Director.—Joan Kirchner.
Scheduler.—Stefanie Mohler.
One Overton Park, 3625 Cumberland Boulevard, Suite 970, Atlanta, GA 30339 ..... (770) 661–0999

REPRESENTATIVES

FIRST DISTRICT

JACK KINGSTON, Republican, of Savannah, GA; born in Bryan, TX, April, 24, 1955; education: Michigan State University, 1973–74; University of Georgia, 1974–78; insurance salesman; vice president, Palmer and Cay/Carswell; Georgia State Legislature, 1984–92; member: Savannah Health Mission, Isle of Hope Community Association, Christ Church; married: Elizabeth Morris Kingston, 1979; children: Betsy, John, Ann, and Jim; committees: Appropriations; elected on November 3, 1992 to the 103rd Congress; reelected to each succeeding Congress.

Office Listings

http://www.house.gov/kingston

2372 Rayburn House Office Building, Washington, DC 20515 .... (202) 225–5831
Chief of Staff.—Adam Sullivan. FAX: 226–2269
Legislative Director.—Allison Myers.
Legislative Assistants: Mary Carpenter, Mike Donnal.
Military Legislative Assistant.—Edward Rothgery.
Constituent Services Director.—Monya Baldwin.
Legislative Correspondent.—Elizabeth King.
Press Assistant.—Ivy Robinson.
Outreach Coordinator.—Alexandra Kendrick.
1 Diamond Causeway, Suite 7, Savannah, GA 31406 .... (912) 352–0101
Casework Manager.—Trish DePriest.
Caseworker.—Bruce Bazemore.
Scheduler / Executive Assistant.—Brianna Foran.
Field Representative.—Brooke Childers.
1510 Newcastle Street, Suite 200, Brunswick, GA 31520 .... (912) 265–9010
Field Representative.—Charles Wilson.
District Director.—Merritt Wall.

Counties: BACON, BRANTLEY, BRYAN, CAMDEN, CHARLTON, CHATHAM (part), CLINCH, COFFEE, ECHOLS, EFFINGHAM, GLYNN, LIBERTY, LONG, LOWNDES (part), MCINTOSH, PIERCE, TELFAIR, WARE, WAYNE, AND WHEELER. Population (2010), 691,974.

ZIP Codes: 30411, 30427–28, 31037, 31055, 31060, 31077, 31083, 31300–01, 31305, 31308–09, 31313–16, 31319–21, 31323–24, 31327–28, 31331–33, 31404, 31406, 31410–11, 31419, 31500–31602, 31605–24, 31627, 31630–32, 31634–36, 31637, 31639–42, 31645–99, 31749, 31794, 31798

* * *

SECOND DISTRICT

SANFORD D. BISHOP, JR., Democrat, of Albany, GA; born in Mobile, AL, February 4, 1947; education: attended Mobile County public schools; B.A., Morehouse College, 1968; J.D., Emory University, 1971; professional: attorney; admitted to the Georgia and Alabama Bars; Georgia House of Representatives, 1977–91; Georgia Senate, 1991–93; former member: Executive Board, Boy Scouts of America; YMCA; Sigma Pi Phi Fraternity; Kappa Alpha Psi Fraternity; 32nd Degree Mason, Shriner; member: Mt. Zion Baptist Church, Albany, GA; married: Vivian Creighton Bishop; child: Aeysha Reese; committees: Appropriations; elected to the 103rd Congress; reelected to each succeeding Congress.

Office Listings

http://www.bishop.house.gov

2429 Rayburn House Office Building, Washington, DC 20515 .... (202) 225–3631
Chief of Staff.—Tracey Thornton. FAX: 225–2203
Deputy Chief of Staff.—Michael Reed.
Office Manager / Scheduler.—Julian Johnson.
Legislative Director.—Jonathan Halpern.
Legislative Correspondent / Press Assistant.—Adilene Rosales.
Communications Director.—Maxwell Gigle.
Albany Towers, 235 West Roosevelt Avenue, Suite 114, Albany, GA 31701 .... (229) 439–8067
Deputy District Director / Ag Advisor.—Kenneth Cutts.
Constituent Services Director.—Sharon Richter.
Office Manager / Constituent Services.—Toni Pickel.
Staff Assistant / District Scheduler.—Shawana Kelson.
18 Ninth Street, Suite 201, Columbus, GA 31901 .... (706) 320–9477
Office Manager / Constituent Services.—Harry Crawford.
Field Representative.—Elaine Gillispie.
Staff Assistant.—Peggy Sagul.
682 Cherry Street, Suite 302, Macon, GA 31201 .... (478) 803–2361
Constituent Services.—Vanessa Mills.
Field Representative.—Michelle Sands.

Counties: BAKER, CALHOUN, CHATTAHOOCHEE, CLAY, CRAWFORD, CRISP, DECATUR, DOOLY, DOUGHERTY, EARLY, GRADY, LEE, MACON, MARION, MILLER, MITCHELL, MUSCOGEE, PEACH, QUITMAN, RANDOLPH, SCHLEY, SEMINOLE, STEWART, SUMTER, TALBOT, TAYLOR, TERRELL, AND WEBSTER. Population (2010), 631,973.

ZIP Codes: 31010, 31015, 31039, 31068–69, 31072, 31092, 31201, 31204, 31211, 31217, 31701–12, 31714, 31716, 31719–22, 31730, 31735, 31743–44, 31763–65, 31787–96, 31803, 31805, 31814–15, 31821, 31824–25, 31832, 31901–07, 31995, 31997–99, 39813, 39815, 39817–19, 39823–29, 39832, 39834, 39836–37, 39840–42, 39845–46, 39851–52, 39854, 39859, 39861–62, 39866–67, 39870, 39877, 39885–86, 39897

* * *

THIRD DISTRICT

LYNN A. WESTMORELAND, Republican, of Grantville, GA; born in Atlanta, GA, April 2, 1950; education: graduated from Therrell High School, Atlanta, GA; attended Georgia State University, Atlanta, GA, 1969–71; professional: real estate developer; public service: Minority Leader, Georgia State House, 2000–04; Representative, Georgia State House, 1992–2004; religion: Baptist; organizations: National Rifle Association; married: Joan; children: Heather, Marcy, and Trae; committees: Financial Services; Permanent Select Committee on Intelligence; elected to the 109th Congress on November 2, 2004; reelected to each succeeding Congress.

Office Listings

http://www.westmoreland.house.gov

2433 Rayburn House Office Building, Washington, DC 20515 .... (202) 225–5901
Chief of Staff.—Brad Bohannon. FAX: 225–2515
Communications Director.—Leslie Shedd.
Legislative Director.—Kevin Doran.
Office Manager.—Claire Ouiment.
1601–B East Highway 34, Suite 3, Newnan, GA 30265 .... (770) 683–2033

Counties: CARROLL. CITIES AND TOWNSHIPS: Bowdon, Carrollton, Mount Zion, Roopville, Temple, Villa Rica, and Whitesburg. COWETA (part). CITIES AND TOWNSHIPS: Grantville, Haralson, Lone Oak, Meriwether, Luthersville, Moreland, Newnan, Palmetto, Senoia, Sharpsburg, and Turin. FAYETTE. Cities and Townships: Brooks, Fayetteville, Peachtree City, Tyrone, and Woolsey. HARRIS. CITIES AND TOWNSHIPS: Cataula, Ellerslie, Fortson, Hamilton, Midland, Pine Mountain, Pine Mountain Valley, Shiloh, Waverly Hall, and West Point. HENRY (part). CITIES AND TOWNSHIPS: Hampton, Locust Grove, McDonough, and Stockbridge. LAMAR. Cities and Townships: Aldora, Barnesville, Milner. MUSCOGEE (part). CITIES AND TOWNSHIPS: Columbus. PIKE. CITIES AND TOWNSHIPS: Concord, Meansville, Molena, Williamson, and Zebulon. SPALDING. CITIES AND TOWNSHIPS: Griffin, Orchard Hill, and Sunny Side. TROUP. CITIES AND TOWNSHIPS: Hogansville, and LaGrange. UPSON. CITIES AND TOWNSHIPS: Thomaston, and Yatesville. Population (2010), 757,344.

ZIP Codes: 30257–59, 30263, 30265, 30268–69, 30275–77, 30285–86, 30290, 30292–93, 30295, 31016, 31029, 31066, 31097, 31800, 31804, 31807–08, 31811, 31816, 31820, 31822–23, 31826, 31829–31, 31833, 31901, 31904, 31906, 31909

* * *

FOURTH DISTRICT

HENRY C. ''HANK'' JOHNSON, JR., Democrat, of Lithonia, GA; born in Washington, DC, October 2, 1954; B.A., Clark College (Clark Atlanta University), Atlanta, GA, 1976; J.D., Thurgood Marshall School of Law, Texas Southern University, Houston, TX, 1979; professional: partner, Johnson & Johnson Law Group LLC, 1980–2007; judge, Magistrate Court, 1989–2001; associate, DeKalb County Commissioner, 2001–06; married: Mereda, 1979; two children: Randi and Alex; committees: Armed Services; Judiciary; elected to the 110th Congress on November 7, 2006; reelected to each succeeding Congress.

Office Listings

http://www.hankjohnson.house.gov

1427 Longworth House Office Building, Washington, DC 20515 .... (202) 225–1605
Chief of Staff.—Arthur D. Sidney. FAX: 226–0691
Legislative Director.—Scott Goldstein.
Office Manager / Scheduler.—Glenn Miles.
5700 Hillandale Drive, Suite 12D, Lithonia, GA 30058 .... (770) 987–2291
District Director.—Kathy Register.

Counties: DEKALB (part), GWINNETT (part), ROCKDALE (part), NEWTON (part). CITIES: Atlanta (part), Avondale Estates, Clarkston, Conyers, Clarkston, Decatur, Doraville, Lilburn, Lithonia, Pine Lake, Norcross, Snellville, Stone Mountain and Tucker. Population (2010), 691,976.

ZIP Codes: 30002–03, 30012–13, 30021, 30030–39, 30047, 30052, 30058, 30071, 30079, 30083–88, 30093–94, 30096, 30316–17, 30319, 30329, 30340–41, 30345

* * *

FIFTH DISTRICT

JOHN LEWIS, Democrat, of Atlanta, GA; born in Pike County, AL, February 21, 1940; education: graduated Pike County Training School, Brundidge, AL, 1957; B.A., American Baptist Theological Seminary, Nashville, TN, 1961; B.A., Fisk University, Nashville, TN, 1963; civil rights leader; Atlanta City Council, 1982–86; member: Martin Luther King Center for Social Change, African American Institute, Robert F. Kennedy Memorial; married the former Lillian Miles in 1968; one child, John Miles Lewis; appointed Senior Chief Deputy Democratic Whip for the 109th Congress; committees: Ways and Means; elected to the 100th Congress on November 4, 1986; reelected to each succeeding Congress.

Office Listings

http://www.house.gov/johnlewis www.facebook.com/repjohnlewis twitter: @repjohnlewis

343 Cannon House Office Building, Washington, DC 20515 .... (202) 225–3801
Chief of Staff.—Michael Collins. FAX: 225–0351
Officer Manager / Scheduler.—Jacob Gillison.
Director of Communications.—Brenda Jones.
Legislative Director.—Jamila Thompson.
100 Peachtree Street, NW., Suite 1920, Atlanta, GA 30303 .... (404) 659–0116
District Director.—Aaron Ward.

Counties: CLAYTON (part), DEKALB (part), AND FULTON (part). Population (2012), 691,976.

ZIP Codes: 30030, 30032–34, 30236, 30260, 30273–74, 30281, 30288, 30294, 30296–97, 30303, 30305–19, 30322, 30324, 30326–27, 30329, 30331, 30336–37, 30342, 30344–45, 30349, 30354

* * *

SIXTH DISTRICT

TOM PRICE, Republican, of Roswell, GA; born in Lansing, MI, October 8, 1954; education: B.A., University of Michigan, 1976; M.D., University of Michigan, 1979; professional: physician; member of the Georgia State Senate, 1997–2004; member: Cobb Chamber of Commerce; Civil Air Patrol; Advisory Board, Georgia Partnership for Excellence in Education; vice chair, Committee on the Budget; religion: Presbyterian; married: Elizabeth; one child, Robert; committees: Budget; Education and the Workforce; Ways and Means; elected to the 109th Congress on November 2, 2004; reelected to each succeeding Congress.

Office Listings

http://www.tomprice.house.gov

100 Cannon House Office Building, Washington, DC 20515 .... (202) 225–4501
Chief of Staff.—Kris Skrzycki. FAX: 225–4656
District Director.—Kyle McGowan.
85–C Mill Street, Suite 300, Roswell, GA 30075 .... (770) 998–0049

Counties: COBB (part), FULTON (part), AND DEKALB (part). CITIES AND TOWNSHIPS: Roswell, Johns Creek, Tucker, Alpharetta, Sandy Springs, Brookhaven, Chamblee, Doraville, and Dunwoody. Population (2010), 699,103.

ZIP Codes: 30004–07, 30009, 30022–24, 30033, 30062, 30065–68, 30075–77, 30084–85, 30092–93, 30097–98, 30102, 30144, 30188, 30319, 30324, 30326, 30328–29, 30338–42, 30345–46, 30350, 30356, 30358, 30360, 30362, 30366, 31119, 31141, 31145–46, 31150, 31156

* * *

SEVENTH DISTRICT

W. ROBERT WOODALL, Republican, of Lawrenceville, GA; born in Athens, GA, February 11, 1970; education: undergraduate, B.A., Furman University, Greenville, SC, 1992; graduate, J.D., University of Georgia, Athens, GA, 1997; awards: co-author of the New York Times bestsellling book *Fair Tax: The Truth;* religion: Methodist; committees: Budget; Oversight and Government Reform; Rules; elected to the 112th Congress on November 2, 2010; reelected to the 113th Congress on November 6, 2012.

Office Listings

http://woodall.house.gov

1725 Longworth House Office Building, Washington, DC 20515 .... (202) 225–4272
Legislative Director.—Janet Rossi. FAX: 225–4696
75 Langley Drive, Lawrenceville, GA 30046 .... (770) 232–3005
FAX: 232–2909

Counties: FORSYTH (part), AND GWINNETT (part). Population (2010), 691,975.

ZIP Codes: 30004–05, 30017, 30019, 30040–41, 30043–49, 30052, 30078, 30091–93, 30095–97, 30099, 30340, 30360, 30518–19

* * *

EIGHTH DISTRICT

AUSTIN SCOTT, Republican, of Ashburn, GA; born in Augusta, GA, December 10, 1969; B.B.A., University of Georgia, 1993; professional: business owner; member of the Georgia State House of Representatives, 1997–2010; religion: Baptist; married: wife, Vivien; one son, Wells; member, National Association of Insurance and Financial Advisors; Coastal Plains Chapter of the American Red Cross; awards: American Cancer Society's Outstanding Legislative Leadership Award, 2003 and 2004; Georgia Association of Emergency Medical Services Star of Life Legislative Award, 2007 and 2008; Republican Freshman Class President; committees: Agriculture; Armed Services; elected to the 112th Congress on November 2, 2010; reelected to the 113th Congress on November 6, 2012.

Office Listings

http://austinscott.house.gov twitter: @austinscottga08 www.facebook.com/repaustinscott

516 Cannon House Office Building, Washington, DC 20515 .... (202) 225–6531
Chief of Staff.—Joby Young. FAX: 225–3013
Legislative Director.—Jessica Robertson.
Communications Director.—Amanda Maddox.
Scheduler.—Mary Dee Beal.
127–B North Central Avenue, Tifton, GA 31794 .... (229) 396–5175
FAX: 396–5179
230 Margie Drive, Suite 500, Warner Robins, GA 31088 .... (478) 971–1776
FAX: 971–1778

Counties: ATKINSON, BEN HILL, BERRIEN, BIBB (part), BLECKLEY, BROOKS, COLQUITT, COOK, DODGE, HOUSTON, IRWIN, JONES, LANIER, LOWNDES (part), MONROE, PULASKI, TELFAIR, THOMAS, TIFT, TURNER, TWIGGS, WILCOX, WILKINSON, AND WORTH. Population (2010), 693,640.

ZIP Codes: 30233, 31001, 31033–35, 31008, 31011–17, 31020–21, 31023, 31035, 31028–33, 31036–38, 31042, 31044, 31046–47, 31054–55, 31060–61, 31065–66, 31069, 31071–72, 31077, 31079, 31083–84, 31086, 31088, 31090–93, 31095, 31098–99, 31204, 31209, 31210–11, 31217, 31220–21, 31297, 31512, 31544, 31549, 31601–66, 31620, 31622, 31624–27, 31629, 31632, 31635–39, 31641–45, 31647, 31649, 31650, 31698, 31705, 31712, ·31714, 31720, 31722, 31727, 31733, 31738, 31744, 31747, 31749–50, 31753, 31756–58, 31760, 31765, 31768–9, 31771–79, 31781, 31783–84, 31788–96, 31798–99

* * *

NINTH DISTRICT

DOUGLAS COLLINS, Republican, of Gainesville, GA; born in Gainesville, GA, August 16, 1966; education: B.A., political science, criminal law, North Georgia College and State University, Dahlonega, GA, 1988; Master of Divinity, New Orleans Baptist Theological Seminary, New Orleans, LA, 1996; Juris Doctorate, John Marshall Law School, Atlanta, GA, 2007; professional: preacher; business owner; soldier; lawyer; Georgia State House of Representatives, 2006–12; religion: Baptist: married: Lisa Collins; children: Jordan, Copelan, and Cameron; committees: Foreign Affairs; Judiciary; Oversight and Government Reform; elected by regular election to the 113th Congress on November 6, 2012 to fill the vacancy caused by the redistricting of District 9.

Office Listings

http://www.dougcollins.house.gov

513 Cannon House Office Building, Washington, DC 20515 .... (202) 225–9893

Chief of Staff.—Brendan Belair. FAX: 226–1224
Communications Director.—Kelley McNabb.
Legislative Director.—Jennifer Lackey.
Scheduler.—Lindsey Taylor.
111 Green Street Southeast, Gainesville, GA 30501 .... (770) 297–3388

Counties: BANKS, CLARKE (part), DAWSON, ELBERT, FANNIN, FORSYTH (part), FRANKLIN, GILMER, HABERSHAM, HALL, HART, JACKSON, LUMPKIN, MADISON, PICKENS (part), RABUN, STEPHENS, TOWNS, UNION, WHITE. CITIES AND TOWNSHIPS: Homer, Gillsville, Dawsonville, Elberton, Bowman, Blue Ridge, McCaysville, Morganton, Cumming, Canon, Carnesville, Franklin Springs, Lavonia, Royston, Elijay, Alto, Baldwin, Clarkesville, Cornelia, Demorest, Mount Airy, Tallulah Falls, Clermont, Flowery Branch, Gainesville, Lula, Oakwood, Bowersville, Hartwell, Arcade, Braselton, Commerce, Hoschton, Jefferson, Nicholson, Pendergrass, Talmo, Dahlonega, Carlton, Colbert, Comer, Danielsville, Hull, Ila, Jasper, Nelson, Talking Rock, Clayton, Dillard, Mountain City, Sky Valley, Martin, Toccoa, Hiawassee, Young Harris, Blairsville, Cleveland, and Helen. Population (2010), 691,975.

ZIP Codes: 30028, 30040–41, 30143, 30151, 30175, 30501–04, 30506–07, 30510–13, 30516–17, 30520–23, 30525, 30527–31, 30533–37, 30540, 30542–49, 30553–55, 30557, 30560, 30562, 30565–67, 30573, 30575, 30577, 30582, 30597, 30599, 30624, 30627–29, 30633, 30635, 30639, 30643, 30646–47, 30662

* * *

TENTH DISTRICT

PAUL C. BROUN, Republican, of Athens, GA; born in Clarke County, GA, May 14, 1946; education: B.S. in chemistry, University of Georgia, Athens, GA, 1967; M.D., Medical College of Georgia, Augusta, GA, 1971; professional: physician; served, U.S. Marine Corps Reserves, 1964–67; member: Rotary Club; Athens-Clarke County Chamber of Commerce; Prince Avenue Baptist Church; religion: Southern Baptist; married: Nancy ''Niki'' Bronson Broun; children: Carly, Collins, Lucy; grandchildren: Lucile, Tillman; committees: Homeland Security; Natural Resources; Science, Space, and Technology; elected by special election to the 110th Congress on July 17, 2007; reelected to each succeeding Congress.

Office Listings

http://www.house.gov/broun

2437 Rayburn House Office Building, Washington, DC 20515 .... (202) 225–4101
Chief of Staff.—David Bowser. FAX: 226–0776
Office Manager / Scheduler.—Teddie Norton.

Counties: BALDWIN, BARROW, BUTTS, COLUMBIA (part), CLARKE (part), GLASCOCK, GREENE, GWINNETT (part), HANCOCK, HENRY, JASPER, JEFFERSON, JOHNSON, LINCOLN, MCDUFFIE, MORGAN, NEWTON (part), OCONEE, OGLETHORPE, PUTNAM, TALIAFERRO, WALTON, WARREN, WASHINGTON, AND WILKES. Population (2010), 691,976.

ZIP Codes: 30011–12, 30014, 30016, 30019, 30025, 30043, 30045, 30052, 30054–56, 30216, 30233–34, 30248, 30252–53, 30413, 30434, 30477, 30517, 30519, 30548, 30601–02, 30605–07, 30609, 30619–23, 30625, 30627–31, 30641–42, 30648, 30650, 30655–56, 30660, 30663–69, 30773, 30677–78, 30680, 30683, 30802–03, 30807–10, 30814, 30816–18, 30820–21, 30823–24, 30828, 30833, 31002, 31018, 31024, 31029, 31031, 31033, 31035, 31038, 31045, 31049, 31061–62, 31064, 31067, 31082, 31085, 31087, 31089, 31094, 31096

* * *

ELEVENTH DISTRICT

PHIL GINGREY, Republican, of Marietta, GA; born in Augusta, GA, July 10, 1942; education: B.S., Georgia Tech, 1965; M.D., Medical College of Georgia, 1969; professional: Physician; set up a pro-life OB-GYN practice; organizations: Cobb County Medical Society; Medical Association of Georgia; American Medical Association; Georgia OB-GYN Society; public service: Marietta School Board, 1993–97; Georgia State Senate, 1999–2002; House Policy Committee; married: Billie Ayers; children: Billy, Gannon, Phyllis, and Laura; committees: Energy and Commerce; House Administration; elected to the 108th Congress on November 5, 2002; reelected to each succeeding Congress.

Office Listings

http://www.house.gov/gingrey twitter: @rephilgingrey

442 Cannon House Office Building, Washington, DC 20515 .... (202) 225–2931
Chief of Staff.—David Sours. FAX: 225–2944
Legislative Director / Deputy Chief of Staff.—Michael Calvo.
Director of Operations.—Elizabeth Ezzell.
219 Roswell Street, Marietta, GA 30060 .... (770) 429–1776
100 North Street, Suite 150, Canton, GA 30114 .... (770) 345–2931

135 West Cherokee Avenue, Cartersville, GA 30120 .... (678) 721–2509

Counties: BARTOW, CHEROKEE, COBB (part), FULTON (part). Population (2010) 794,969.

ZIP Codes: 30004, 30008, 30028, 30040, 30060–62, 30064, 30066–67, 30075, 30080, 30082, 30101–03, 30107, 30114–15, 30120–21, 30127, 30144–45, 30152, 30156, 30160, 30171, 30178, 30183–84, 30188–89, 30305, 30319, 30326–27, 30339, 30342

* * *

TWELFTH DISTRICT

JOHN BARROW, Democrat, of Augusta, GA; born in Athens, October 31, 1955; education: graduated from Clarke Central High School, Athens-Clarke County, GA, 1973; B.A., University of Georgia, Athens, GA, 1976; J.D., Harvard University, Cambridge, MA, 1979; professional: law clerk for Judge, Savannah, GA; law clerk for Judge, 50th Circuit Court of Appeals; founding member, Wilburn, Lewis, Barrow and Stotz, PC; county commissioner; lawyer, private practice; Athens-Clarke, GA, city-county commissioner, 1990–2004; religion: Baptist; children: James and Ruth; committees: Energy and Commerce; elected to the 109th Congress on November 2, 2004; reelected to each succeeding Congress.

Office Listings

http://www.barrow.house.gov

2202 Rayburn House Office Building, Washington, DC 20515 .... (202) 225–2823
Chief of Staff.—Ashley Jones. FAX: 225–3377
Legislative Director.—Hill Thomas.
Communications Director.—Richard Carbo.
Enterprise Mill, 1450 Greene Street, Suite 550, Augusta, GA 30901 .... (706) 722–4494
Statesboro City Hall, 50 East Main Street, Statesboro, GA 30458 .... (912) 489–4494
Dublin City Hall, 100 Church Street, Dublin, GA 31021 .... (478) 272–7088
Vidalia Community Center, 107 Old Airport Road, Suite A, Vidalia, GA 30474 .... (912) 537–9301

Counties: APPLING, BULLOCH, BURKE, CANDLER, COFFEE, COLUMBIA (part), EFFINGHAM (part), EMANUEL, EVANS, JEFF DAVIS, JENKINS, LAURENS, MONTGOMERY, RICHMOND, SCREVEN, TATTNALL, TOOMBS, TREUTLEN, AND WHEELER. Population (2010), 701,142.

ZIP Codes: 30401, 30410–12, 30415, 30417, 30420–21, 30423, 30425–29, 30434, 30436, 30438–39, 30441–42, 30445–46, 30448–58, 30460–61, 30464, 30467, 30470–71, 30473–75, 30802, 30805, 30809, 30812–16, 30822, 30830, 30901, 30903–07, 30909, 30912, 31002, 31009, 31019, 31021–22, 31027, 31037, 31049, 31065, 31075, 31083, 31303, 31308, 31312, 31321, 31326, 31329, 31510, 31512–13, 31518–19, 31532–33, 31535, 31539, 31549, 31552, 31554–55, 31563, 31567, 31624, 31650, 31798

* * *

THIRTEENTH DISTRICT

DAVID SCOTT, Democrat, of Atlanta, GA; born in Aynor, SC, June 27, 1945; education: Florida A&M University, graduated with honors, 1967; M.B.A., graduated with honors, University of Pennsylvania Wharton School of Finance, 1969; professional: businessman; owner and CEO, Dayn-Mark Advertising; public service: Georgia House of Representatives, 1974–82; Georgia State Senate, 1983–2002; married: Alfredia Aaron, 1969; children: Dayna and Marcye; committees: Agriculture; Financial Services; elected to the 108th Congress on November 5, 2002; reelected to each succeeding Congress.

Office Listings

http://davidscott.house.gov facebook: repdavidscott twitter: @repdavidscott

225 Cannon House Office Building, Washington, DC 20515 .... (202) 225–2939
Chief of Staff.—Michael Andel. FAX: 225–4628
Deputy Chief of Staff for Administration.—Angie Borja.
Legislative Director.—Gary Woodward.
173 North Main Street, Jonesboro, GA 30236 .... (770) 210–5073
888 Concord Road, Suite 100, Smyra, GA 30080 .... (770) 432–5405

Counties: CLAYTON, COBB, DOUGLAS, FAYETTE, FULTON, AND HENRY. Population (2010), 707,070.

ZIP Codes: 30252–53, 30260, 30268, 30273–74, 30281, 30290–91, 30294, 30296–97, 30331, 30337, 30344, 30349

* * *

FOURTEENTH DISTRICT

TOM GRAVES, Republican, of Ranger, GA; born in St. Petersburg, FL, February 3, 1970; education: B.A.A., finance, University of Georgia, Athens, GA, 1993; professional: business owner; Georgia State House of Representatives, 2003–10; religion: Baptist: married: Julie Howard Graves; children: JoAnn, John and Janey; committees: Appropriations; elected by special election to the 111th Congress on June 8, 2010, to fill the vacancy caused by the resignation of United States Representative John Nathan Deal; elected to the 112th Congress on November 2, 2010; reelected to the GA–14th district in the 113th Congress on November 6, 2012.

Office Listings

http://www.tomgraves.house.gov

432 Cannon House Office Building, Washington, DC 20515 .... (202) 225–5211
Chief of Staff.—Tim Baker. FAX: (202) 225–8272
Deputy Chief of Staff.—Jason Lawrence.
Communications Director.—John Donnelly.
Scheduler.—Maggie Newton.
702 South Thornton Avenue, Dalton, GA 30720 .... (706) 226–5320
FAX: (706) 278–0840
600 East First Street, Suite 301, Rome, GA 30161 .... (770) 535–2592
FAX: (706) 232–7864

Counties: CATOOSA, CHATTOOGA, DADE, FLOYD, GORDON, HARALSON, MURRAY, PAULDING, PICKENS (part), POLK, WALKER, AND WHITFIELD. Population (2010), 619,974.

ZIP Codes: 30101, 30103–05, 30110, 30113, 30120, 30124–25, 30127, 30129, 30132, 30134, 30138–41, 30143

HAWAII

(Population 2010, 1,360,301)

SENATORS

BRIAN SCHATZ, Democrat, of Hawaii; born in Ann Arbor, MI, October 20, 1972; education: graduated from Punahou School, Honolulu, HI, 1990; B.A., Pomona College, Claremont, CA, 1994; professional: chairman, Democratic Party of Hawaii, 2008–10; CEO, Helping Hands Hawaii, 2002–10; Hawaii House of Representatives, 1998–2006; Lieutenant Governor of Hawaii, 2010–12; appointed to the United States Senate on December 26, 2012, and took the oath of office on December 27, 2012; married: Linda Schatz; committees: Commerce, Science, and Transportation; Energy and Natural Resources; Indian Affairs.

Office Listings

http://www.schatz.senate.gov twitter: @senbrianschatz

722 Hart Senate Office Building, Washington, DC 20510 .... (202) 224–3934
Chief of Staff.—Andrew Winer. FAX: 228–1153
Scheduler.—Diane Miyasato.
Legislative Director.—Arun Revana.
Communications Director.—Meaghan Smith.
300 Ala Moana Boulevard, Room 7–212, Honolulu, HI 96850 .... (808) 523–2061
FAX: 523–2065

* * *

MAZIE HIRONO, Democrat, of Hawaii; born in Fukushima, Japan, November 3, 1947; graduated from Kaimuki High School, Honolulu, HI; B.A., University of Hawaii, Manoa, HI, 1970; J.D., Georgetown University, Washington, DC, 1978; professional: lawyer, private practice; member of the Hawaii State House of Representatives, 1981–94; Hawaii Lieutenant Governor, 1994–2002; elected to the United States House of Representatives as a Democrat to the 110th, 111th, and 112th Congresses; was not a candidate for reelection to the United States House of Representatives for the 113th Congress; committees: Armed Services; Judiciary; Veterans' Affairs; elected to the United States Senate on November 6, 2012.

Office Listings

http://www.hirono.senate.gov twitter: @maziehirono

330 Hart Senate Office Building, Washington, DC 20510 .... (202) 224–6361
Chief of Staff.—Betsy Lin. FAX: 224–2126
Prince Kuhio Federal Building, 300 Ala Moana Boulevard, Room 3–106, Honolulu, HI 96850 .... (808) 522–8970
District Director.—Alan Yamamoto.

REPRESENTATIVES

FIRST DISTRICT

COLLEEN HANABUSA, Democrat, of Waianae, HI; born in Honolulu, HI, May 4, 1951; education: graduated from St. Andrews Priory School, Honolulu, HI, 1969; B.A., University of Hawaii, Honolulu, HI, 1973; M.A., University of Hawaii, Honolulu, HI, 1975; J.D., University of Hawaii, Honolulu, HI, 1977; professional: attorney, 1977–2010; Hawaii State Senate, 1998–2010; Hawaii State Senate President, 2006–10; religion: Buddhism; married: John Souza; caucuses: Congressional Asian Pacific American Caucus (CAPAC); Seniors Caucus; Native American Caucus; National Guard Caucus, Navy/Marine Corp Caucus; Coast Guard Caucus; Air Force Caucus; Congressional Army Caucus, USO Caucus; Sustainable Energy and Environment Coalition; committees: Armed Services; Natural Resources; elected to the 112th Congress on November 2, 2010; reelected to the 113th Congress on November 6, 2012.

Office Listings

http://www.hanabusa.house.gov

238 Cannon House Office Building, Washington, DC 20515 .... (202) 225–2726
Chief of Staff.—Rod Tanonaka. FAX: 225–0688
Legislative Director.—Josh Dover.
Communications Director.—Ashley Nagaoka.
300 Ala Moana Boulevard, Room 4–104, Honolulu, HI 96850 .... (808) 541–2570

District Director.—Rod Tanonaka.

Counties: HONOLULU (part). CITIES AND TOWNSHIPS: Aiea Pearl City, Ewa Beach, Honolulu, Mililani, and Waipahu. Population (2010), 680,496.

ZIP Codes: 96701, 96706–07, 96782, 96789, 96797, 96813–19, 96821–22, 96825–26, 96850, 96853, 96859–60

* * *

SECOND DISTRICT

TULSI GABBARD, Democrat, of Hawaii; born in Leloaloa, American Samoa, April 12, 1981; education: Hawaii Pacific University, Officer Candidate School, Army; professional: member of the Hawaii House of Representatives from the 42nd District, 2002–04; member of the Honolulu City Council from the Sixth District, 2011–12; member of the U.S. House of Representatives from Hawaii's 2nd District, 2013–present; member of the Army National Guard, 2003–present; committees: Foreign Affairs; Homeland Security, elected to the 113th Congress on November 6, 2012.

Office Listings

http://gabbard.house.gov

502 Cannon House Office Building, Washington, DC 20515 .... (202) 225–4906
Chief of Staff.—Jessica Vanden Berg. FAX: 225–4987
300 Ala Moana Boulevard, 5–104 Prince Kuhio Federal Building, Honolulu, HI 96850 .... (808) 541–1986
District Director.—Col. (Ret.) Walt Kaneakua.

Counties: HAWAI'I. CITIES: Hawi, Hilo, Honoka'a, Kailua-Kona, Na'alehu, Kealakekua, Pahoa, Ocean View, Volcano, Waimea, and Waikoloa. HONOLULU COUNTY (part). CITIES: Hale'iwa, Honolulu, Kailua, Kane'ohe, Kapolei, La'ie, Makakilo, Nanakuli, Wahiawa, Waialua, Wai'anae, Waimanalo. KALAWAO COUNTY. CITY: Kalaupapa. KAUA'I COUNTY. CITIES: Hanalei, Hanapepe, Kalaheo, Kapa'a, Kekaha, Kilauea, Koloa, Lihue, Waimea. MAUI COUNTY. CITIES: Hana, Kahului, Kaunakakai, Lahaina, Lana'i City, Makawao, Wailuku. NORTHWESTERN HAWAIIAN ISLANDS. ISLANDS OF: Becker, French Frigate Shoals, Gardener Pinnacles, Hermes and Kure Atolls, Laysan, Lisianski, Maro Reef, Nihoa, and Pearl. Population (2010), 679,805.

ZIP Codes: 96703–05, 96707–08, 96710, 96712–14, 96716–17, 96719–20, 96722, 96725–32, 96734, 96737–38, 96740–44, 96746–57, 96759–66, 96768–74, 96776–81, 96783, 96785–86, 96789–93, 96795–97, 96825, 96857, 96863

IDAHO

(Population 2010, 1,567,582)

SENATORS

MIKE CRAPO, Republican, of Idaho Falls, ID; born in Idaho Falls, May 20, 1951; education: graduated, Idaho Falls High School, 1969; B.A., Brigham Young University, Provo, UT, 1973; J.D., Harvard University Law School, Cambridge, MA, 1977; professional: attorney; admitted to the California Bar, 1977; admitted to the Idaho Bar, 1979; law clerk, Hon. James M. Carter, Judge of the U.S. Court of Appeals for the Ninth Circuit, San Diego, CA, 1977–78; associate attorney, Gibson, Dunn, and Crutcher, San Diego, 1978–79; attorney, Holden, Kidwell, Hahn and Crapo, 1979–92; partner, 1983–92; Idaho State Senate, 1984–92, assistant majority leader, 1987–89, president pro tempore, 1989–92; member: American Bar Association, Boy Scouts of America, Idaho Falls Rotary Club, 1984–88; married: the former Susan Diane Hasleton, 1974; children: Michelle, Brian, Stephanie, Lara, and Paul; co-chair, Western Water Caucus; co-chair, Sportsman Caucus; COPD Caucus; committees: ranking member, Banking, Housing, and Urban Affairs; Budget; Environment and Public Works; Finance; Indian Affairs; elected on November 3, 1992, to the 103rd Congress; reelected to each succeeding Congress; elected to the U.S. Senate on November 3, 1998; reelected to each succeeding Senate term.

Office Listings

http://www.crapo.senate.gov

239 Dirksen Senate Office Building, Washington, DC 20510 .... (202) 224–6142
Chief of Staff.—Susan Wheeler. FAX: 228–1375
Communications Director.—Lindsay Nothern.
Legislative Director.—Ken Flanz.
251 East Front Street, Suite 205, Boise, ID 83702 .... (208) 334–1776
Chief of Staff.—John Hoehne.
610 Hubbard Street, Suite 209, Coeur d'Alene, ID 83814 .... (208) 664–5490
Director.—Karen Roetter.
313 D Street, Suite 105, Lewiston, ID 83501 .... (208) 743–1492
Director.—Tony Snodderly.
275 South 5th Avenue, Suite 225, Pocatello, ID 83201 .... (208) 236–9635
Director.—Farhanna Hibbert.
410 Memorial Drive, Suite 204, Idaho Falls, ID 83402 .... (208) 522–9779
Director.—Leslie Huddleston.
202 Falls Avenue, Suite 2, Twin Falls, ID 83301 .... (208) 734–2515
Director.—A.J. Church.

* * *

JAMES E. RISCH, Republican, of Boise, ID; born in Milwaukee, WI, May 3, 1943; education: St. Johns Cathedral High School, Milwaukee, WI; B.S., forestry, University of Idaho, Moscow, ID, 1965; J.D., University of Idaho, Moscow, ID, 1968, Law Review, College of Law Advisory Committee; professional: Ada County Prosecuting Attorney, 1970–74; president, Idaho Prosecuting Attorneys Association, 1973; Idaho State Senate, 1974–88, 1995–2003; Assistant Majority Leader, 1996; Majority Leader, 1997–82, 1997–2002; President Pro Tempore, 1983–1988; Lieutenant Governor of Idaho, 2003–06, 2007–09; Governor of Idaho, 2006; small business owner; ranch / farmer; former partner Risch, Goss, Insinger, Gustavel law firm; member, National Cattle Association; Idaho Cattle Association; American, Idaho and Boise Valley Angus Association; National Rifle Association; Ducks Unlimited; Rocky Mountain Elk Foundation; married: Vicki; children: James, Jason, and Jordan, 2 daughters-in-law; 6 grandchildren; Congressional Youth Leadership Council; Impact Aid Coalition; Senate Rural Health Caucus; Rural Education Caucus; WMD / Terrorism Caucus; National Guard Caucus; Western Caucus, Sportsman Caucus, Recycling Caucus, Republican High Tech Task Force; committees: Energy and Natural Resources; Foreign Relations; Small Business and Entrepreneurship; Select Committee on Ethics; Select Committee on Intelligence; elected to the U.S. Senate on November 4, 2008.

Office Listings

http://risch.senate.gov twitter: @senatorrisch

483 Russell Senate Office Building, Washington, DC 20510 .... (202) 224–2752
Chief of Staff.—John Sandy. FAX: 224–2573
Communications Director.—Brad Hoaglun.
Executive Assistant / Scheduler.—Rachel Burkett.
Legislative Director.—Chris Socha.
350 North Ninth Street, Suite 302, Boise, ID 83702 .... (208) 342–7985

610 Hubbard, Harbor Plaza, Suite 213, Coeur d'Alene, ID 83814 .... (208) 667–6130
901 Pier View Drive, Suite 202A, Idaho Falls, ID 83402 .... (208) 523–5541
313 D Street, Suite 106, Lewiston, ID 83501 .... (208) 743–0792
275 South Fifth Avenue, Suite 290, Pocatello, ID 83201 .... (208) 236–6817
1411 Falls Avenue East, Suite 201, Twin Falls, ID 83301 .... (208) 734–6780

REPRESENTATIVES

FIRST DISTRICT

RAÚL R. LABRADOR, Republican, of Eagle, ID; born in Carolina, PR, December 8, 1967; education: B.A., Brigham Young University, Provo, UT, 1992, J.D., University of Washington, Seattle, WA, 1995; professional: attorney; religion: The Church of Jesus Christ of Latter-Day Saints; married: Becca Labrador; five children; committees: Judiciary; Natural Resources; elected to the 112th Congress on November 2, 2010; reelected to the 113th Congress on November 6, 2012.

Office Listings

http://labrador.house.gov/

1523 Longworth House Office Building, Washington, DC 20515 .... (202) 225–6611
Chief of Staff.—Mike Cunningto. FAX: 225–3029
Legislative Director.—Neil Siefring.
Scheduler.—Alexa Walker.
33 East Broadway Avenue, Suite 251, Meridian, ID 83642 .... (208) 888–3188
1250 Ironwood Drive, Suite 243, Coeur d'Alene, ID 83814 .... (208) 667–0127
313 D Street, Suite 107, Lewiston, ID 83501 .... (208) 743–1388

Counties: ADA (part), ADAMS, BENEWAH, BOISE, BONNER, BOUNDARY, CANYON, CLEARWATER, GEM, IDAHO, KOOTENAI, LATAH, LEWIS, NEZ PERCE, OWYHEE, PAYETTE, SHOSHONE, VALLEY, WASHINGTON. Population (2010), 784,132.

ZIP Codes: 59847, 83302, 83316, 83501, 83520, 83522–26, 83530, 83533, 83535–37, 83539–49, 83552–55, 83602, 83604–05, 83607, 83610–12, 83615–17, 83619, 83622, 83624, 83626–29, 83631–32, 83634, 83636–39, 83641–46, 83650–51, 83654–57, 83660–61, 83666, 83669–72, 83676–77, 83686–87, 83702, 83705, 83709, 83713–14, 83716, 83801–06, 83808–15, 83821–27, 83830, 83832–37, 83839–52, 83854–58, 83860–61, 83864, 83866–74, 83876, 89832, 97910, 97913, 99128

* * *

SECOND DISTRICT

MICHAEL K. SIMPSON, Republican, of Blackfoot, ID; born in Burley, ID, September 8, 1950; education: graduated, Blackfoot High School, 1968; Utah State University, 1972; Washington University School of Dental Medicine, 1977; professional: dentist, private practice; Blackfoot, ID, City Council, 1981–85; Idaho State Legislature, 1985–98; Idaho Speaker of the House, 1992–98; married: Kathy Simpson; committees: Appropriations; elected to the 106th Congress; reelected to each succeeding Congress.

Office Listings

http://simpson.house.gov

2312 Rayburn House Office Building, Washington, DC 20515 .... (202) 225–5531
Chief of Staff.—Lindsay Slater. FAX: 225–8216
Scheduler.—Emilee Henshaw.
Legislative Director.—Nathan Greene.
Press Secretary.—Nikki Watts.
802 West Bannock, Suite 600, Boise, ID 83702 .... (208) 334–1953
1341 Fillmore, #202, Twin Falls, ID 83301 .... (208) 734–7219
410 Memorial Drive, Suite 203, Idaho Falls, ID 83402 .... (208) 523–6701
275 South Fifth Avenue, #275, Pocatello, ID 83201 .... (208) 233–2222

Counties: ADA (Part), BANNOCK, BEAR LAKE, BINGHAM, BLAINE, BONNEVILLE, BUTTE, CAMAS, CARIBOU, CASSIA, CLARK, CUSTER, ELMORE, FRANKLIN, FREMONT, GOODING, JEFFERSON, JEROME, LEMHI, LINCOLN, MADISON, MINIDOKA, ONEIDA, POWER, TETON, AND TWIN FALLS. Population (2010), 793,109.

ZIP Codes: 83201–06, 83209–15, 83217–18, 83220–21, 83223, 83226–30, 83232–39, 83241, 83243–46, 83250–56, 83261–63, 83271–72, 83274, 83276–78, 83281, 83283, 83285–87, 83301–03, 83311–14, 83316, 83318, 83320–25, 83327–28, 83330, 83332–38, 83340–44, 83346–50, 83352–55, 83401–06, 83415, 83420–25, 83427–29, 83431, 83433–36, 83438, 83440–46, 83448–52, 83454–55, 83460, 83462–69, 83601–02, 83604, 83623–24, 83627, 83633–34, 83647–48, 83701–09, 83712, 83714–17, 83720–33, 83735, 83744, 83756

ILLINOIS

(Population, 2010 12,830,632)

SENATORS

RICHARD DURBIN, Democrat, of Springfield, IL; born in East St. Louis, IL, November 21, 1944; son of William and Ann Durbin; education: graduated, Assumption High School, East St. Louis; B.S., foreign service and economics, Georgetown University, Washington, DC, 1966; J.D., Georgetown University Law Center, 1969; professional: attorney, admitted to the Illinois Bar in 1969; began practice in Springfield; legal counsel to Lieutenant Governor Paul Simon, 1969–72; legal counsel to Illinois Senate Judiciary Committee, 1972–82; parliamentarian, Illinois Senate, 1969–82; president, New Members Democratic Caucus, 98th Congress; associate professor of medical humanities, Southern Illinois University School of Medicine; elected as Assistant Democratic Leader, 2004; elected as Assistant Majority Leader, 2006; married: the former Loretta Schaefer, 1967; children: Christine, Paul, and Jennifer; committees: Appropriations; Foreign Relations; Judiciary; Rules and Administration; Joint Committee on the Library; elected to the 98th Congress, November 2, 1982; reelected to each succeeding Congress; elected to the U.S. Senate on November 5, 1996; reelected to each succeeding Senate term.

Office Listings

http://durbin.senate.gov

711 Hart Senate Office Building, Washington, DC 20510 .... (202) 224–2152
Chief of Staff.—Patrick Souders. FAX: 228–0400
Legislative Director.—Dena Morris. TTY: 224–8180
Director of Scheduling.—Claire Reuschel.
230 South Dearborn, Kluczynski Building, 38th Floor, Chicago, IL 60604 .... (312) 353–4952
Chicago Director.—Clarisol Duque.
525 South Eighth Street, Springfield, IL 62703 .... (217) 492–4062
Downstate Director.—Bill Houlihan.
1504 Third Avenue, Suite 227, Rock Island, IL 61201 .... (309) 786–5173
250 West Cherry Street, Suite 115D, Carbondale, IL 62901 .... (618) 351–1122

* * *

MARK KIRK, Republican, of Highland Park, IL; born in Champaign, IL, September 15, 1959; education: B.A., Cornell University, Ithaca, NY, 1981; M.S., London School of Economics, London, UK, 1982; J.D., Georgetown University, Washington, DC, 1992; professional: United States Naval Reserve, 1989–present; staff member, U.S. Representative John Porter, 1984–90; served, World Bank, 1990–91; special assistant, U.S. State Department, 1991–93; attorney, Baker & McKenzie, 1993–95; counsel, House International Relations Committee, 1995–99, elected to the U.S. House of Representatives, 2001–10; awards: Navy and Marine Corps Commendation Medal; Navy Achievement Medal; National Defense Service Medal; Global War on Terror Service Medal; and other various decorations; married: no; children: none; committees: Appropriations; Banking, Housing, and Urban Affairs; Health, Education, Labor, and Pensions; Special Committee on Aging; elected in a special election on November 2, 2010 and sworn-in on November 29, 2010 to the United States Senate to serve the remainder of former Senator Barack Obama's unexpired term; concurrently elected in a general election on November 2, 2010 to the United States Senate for a full six-year term.

Office Listings

http://kirk.senate.gov

524 Hart Senate Office Building, Washington, DC 20510 .... (202) 224–2854
Chief of Staff.—Kate Dickens. FAX: 228–4611
Deputy Chief of Staff.—Richard Goldberg.
Legislative Director.—Patrick Magnuson.
Policy and Communications Director.—Lance Trover.
Executive Assistant.—Lisa Radogno.
230 South Dearborn Street, Suite 3900, Chicago, IL 60604 .... (312) 886–3506
607 East Adams Street, Suite 1520, Springfield, IL 62701 .... (217) 492–5089

REPRESENTATIVES

FIRST DISTRICT

BOBBY L. RUSH, Democrat, of Chicago, IL; born in Albany, GA; November 23, 1946; education: attended Marshall High School, Marshall, IL; B.A., Roosevelt University, Chicago,

IL, 1974; M.A., University of Illinois, Chicago, IL, 1994; M.A., McCormick Theological Seminary, Chicago, IL, 1998; professional: United States Army, 1963–68; insurance agent; alderman, Chicago, Illinois, city council, 1983–93; deputy chairman, Illinois Democratic Party, 1990; unsuccessful candidate for mayor of Chicago, IL, 1999; minister; married: Carolyn; five children; committees: Energy and Commerce; elected on November 3, 1992 to the 103rd Congress; reelected to each succeeding Congress.

Office Listings

http://www.rush.house.gov

2268 Rayburn House Office Building, Washington, DC 20515 .... (202) 225–4372
Chief of Staff.—Rev. Stanley Watkins. FAX: 226–0333
Senior Policy Counsel / Legislative Director.—Timothy Robinson.
Director of Administration and Operations.—N. Lenette Myers.
Communications Director.—Debra Johnson.
700–706 East 79th Street, Chicago, IL 60619 .... (773) 224–6500
District Director.—Robyn Wheeler Grange.
3235 West 147th Street, Midlothian, IL 60445 .... (708) 385–9550
Deputy District Director.—Younus Suleman. FAX: 385–3860

Counties: COOK COUNTY (part), WILL COUNTY (part). CITIES AND TOWNSHIPS: Bremen Township, Calumet Township, Orland Township, Palos Township, Rich Township, Thornton Township, Worth Township, Will County, Frankfort Township, Green Garden Township, Jackson Township, Manhattan Township, New Lenox Township, Alsip, Blue Island, Calumet Park, Chicago Country, Club Hills, Crestwood, Dixmoor, Elwood, Evergreen Park, Frankfort, Frankfort Square, Harvey, Manhattan, Markham, Merrionette Park, Midlothian, Mokena, New Lenox, Oak Forest, Oak Lawn, Orland Hills, Orland Park, Palos Heights, Posen, Riverdale, Robbins, Tinley Park, and Worth. Population (2012), 711,982.

ZIP Codes: 60406, 60421, 60423, 60426, 60428, 60442, 60445, 60448–49, 60451–53, 60462–64, 60467–69, 60472, 60477–78, 60482, 60487, 60609, 60615–17, 60619–21, 60628–29, 60636–37, 60643, 60649, 60652–53, 60655, 60803, 60805, 60827

* * *

SECOND DISTRICT

ROBIN L. KELLY, Democrat, of Matteson, IL; born in New York, NY, April 30, 1956; education: B.A. in psychology, Bradley University, IL, 1977; M.A., counseling, Bradley University, 1982; Ph.D., political science, Northern Illinois University, IL, 2004; professional: counselor; community affairs director, Matteson, IL, 1992–2006; member, Illinois State House of Representatives, 2003–07; chief of staff, Illinois State Treasurer, 2007–10; chief administrative officer, Cook County, IL, 2010–12; caucuses: member, Congressional Black Caucus; married: Dr. Nathaniel Horn; two children; committees: Oversight and Government Reform; Science, Space, and Technology; elected to the 113th Congress on April 9, 2013, by special election, to fill the vacancy caused by the resignation of United States Representative Jesse L. Jackson, Jr.

Office Listings

http://www.robinkelly.house.gov www.facebook.com/reprobinkelly
https://twitter.com/RepRobinKelly

2419 Rayburn House Office Building, Washington, DC 20515 .... (202) 225–0773
Chief of Staff.—Brandon Garrett. FAX: 225–4583
Legislative Director.—Brandon Webb.
Legislative Assistant.—Aimee Ramirez.
Legislative Correspondent.—Jay Cho.
Director of Operations / Scheduler.—Tony Presta.
600 Holiday Plaza Drive, Suite 505, Matteson, IL 60443 .... (708) 679–0078
District Director.—Audra Wilson.
1000 E 111th Street, 11th Floor, Chicago, IL 60628 .... (773) 568–2623

Counties: COOK (part), KANKAKEE, WILL (part). CITIES AND TOWNSHIPS: Beecher, Blue Island, Bonfield, Bourbonnais, Bradley, Buckingham, Cabery, Calumet City, Chebanse, Chicago, Chicago Heights, Country Club Hills, Crete, Custer Park, Dixmoor, Dolton, Essex, Flossmoor, Ford Heights, Frankfort, Gardner, Glenwood, Grant Park, Harvey, Hazel Crest, Herscher, Homewood, Hopkins Park, Kankakee, Lansing, Lynwood, Manhattan, Manteno, Markham, Matteson, Momence, Monee, Olympia Fields, Park Forest, Pembroke Township, Peotone, Phoenix, Reddick, Richton Park, Riverdale, Saint Anne, Sauk Village, South Chicago Heights, South Holland, Steger, Tinley Park, Thornton, Union Hill, University Park, and Wilmington. Population (2010), 718,507.

ZIP Codes: 60401, 60406, 60409, 60411–12, 60417, 60419, 60422–23, 60425–26, 60428–30, 60438, 60443, 60449, 60461, 60466, 60468, 60471, 60473, 60475–78, 60481, 60484, 60615, 60617, 60628, 60633, 60637, 60649, 60827, 60901, 60913–15, 60917, 60919, 60922, 60935, 60940–42, 60944, 60950, 60954, 60958, 60961, 60964, 60969

* * *

THIRD DISTRICT

DANIEL LIPINSKI, Democrat, of Chicago, IL; born in Chicago, July 15, 1966; son of former Congressman William Lipinski, 1983–2004; education: B.S., mechanical engineering, *magna cum laude,* Northwestern University, 1988; M.S., engineering-economic systems, Stanford University, 1989; Ph.D., political science, Duke University, 1998; professional: aide to United States Representative George Sangmeister, 1993–94; aide to United States Representative Jerry Costello, 1995–96; aide to United States Representative Rod Blagojevich, 1999–2000; professor, James Madison University Washington Program, Washington, DC, 2000; professor, University of Notre Dame, South Bend, IN, 2000–01; professor, University of Tennessee, Knoxville, TN, 2001–04; married: Judy; committees: Science, Space, and Technology; Transportation and Infrastructure; elected to the 109th Congress on November 2, 2004; reelected to each succeeding Congress.

Office Listings

http://www.lipinski.house.gov

1717 Longworth House Office Building, Washington, DC 20515 .... (202) 225–5701
Chief of Staff / Legislative Director.—Eric Lausten. FAX: 225–1012
Office Administrative.—Jennifer Sypolt.
Legislative Assistant.—Brian Oszakewski.
6245 South Archer Avenue, Chicago, IL 60638 .... (312) 886–0481
District Chief of Staff.—Jerry Hurckes.
222 East 9th Street, Suite 109, Lockport, IL 60441 .... (815) 838–1990
Communications Director.—Guy Tridgell.
5309 West 95th Street, Oak Lawn, IL 60453 .... (708) 424–0853
14700 Ravinia Avenue, 1st Floor, Orland Park, IL 60462 .... (708) 403–4379

Counties: COOK (part), WILL (PART), DUPAGE (part). CITIES AND TOWNSHIPS: Alsip, Bedford Park, Berwyn, Bridgeview, Brookfield, Burbank, Burr Ridge, Chicago, Chicago Ridge, Cicero, Countryside, Crest Hill, Forest Park, Forest View, Hickory Hills, Hillside, Hinsdale, Homer Glen, Hometown, Hodgkins, Indian Head Park, Justice Burbank, LaGrange, Lemont, Lockport, Lyons, McCook, Merrionette Park, North Riverside, Oak Lawn, Oak Park, Palos Heights, Palos Hills, Palos Park, Proviso, Riverside, Romeoville, Stickney, Summit Brookfield, Western Springs, Willow Springs, and Worth. Population (2012), 704,438.

ZIP Codes: 60402 (part), 60406, 60415, 60432 (part), 60435 (part), 60439 (part), 60441 (part), 60446 (part), 60448 (part), 60451 (part), 60463 (part), 60455, 60456 (part), 60457–58, 60459 (part), 60462 (part), 60463 (part), 60464 (part), 60465, 60467 (part), 60477 (part), 60480 (part), 60482 (part), 60501, 60513 (part), 60521 (part), 60425 (part), 60526 (part), 60534 (part), 60544 (part), 60546 (part), 60558 (part), 60561 (part), 60608 (part), 60609 (part), 60616 (part), 60620 (part), 60629 (part), 60632 (part), 60636 (part), 60638 (part), 60643 (part), 60652 (part), 60655 (part), 60803 (part), 60804 (part), 60805 (part)

* * *

FOURTH DISTRICT

LUIS V. GUTIÉRREZ, Democrat, of Chicago, IL; born in Chicago, December 10, 1953; education: B.A., Northeastern Illinois University, DeKalb, IL, 1974; professional: teacher; social worker, Illinois; state department of children and family services; administrative assistant, Chicago, IL, mayor's office subcommittee on infrastructure, 1984–85; co-founder, West Town-26th Ward Independent Political Organization, 1985; alderman, Chicago, IL, city council, 1986–93, president pro tem, 1989–92; Democratic National Committee, 1984; married: Soraida Arocho; children: Omaira and Jessica; committees: Judiciary; Permanent Select Committee on Intelligence; elected on November 3, 1992, to the 103rd Congress; reelected to each succeeding Congress.

Office Listings

http://www.house.gov/gutierrez

2408 Rayburn House Office Building, Washington, DC 20515 .... (202) 225–8203
Chief of Staff.—Susan Collins. FAX: 225–7810
Communications Director.—Douglas Rivlin.
3210 West North Avenue, Chicago, IL 60647 .... (773) 342–0774
FAX: 342–0776
5531 West Cermak Road, Cicero, IL 60804 .... (708) 652–5180
FAX: 652–5118

Counties: COOK COUNTY (part). CITIES: Berkeley, Brookfield, Chicago, Cicero, Elmwood Park, Forest Park, Hillside, Maywood, Melrose Park, Northlake, Oak Park, Stickney, Stone Park, and Westchester. Population (2010), 712,813.

ZIP Codes: 60104, 60126, 60154, 60160, 60162–64, 60304–05, 60402, 60513, 60546, 60608–09, 60616, 60618, 60622–23, 60625, 60629-30, 60632, 60634, 60639, 60641, 60647, 60651, 60707, 60804

* * *

FIFTH DISTRICT

MIKE QUIGLEY, Democrat, of Chicago, IL; born in Indianapolis, October 17, 1958; education: B.A., political science, Roosevelt University, 1981; M.P.P., University of Chicago, 1985; J.D., Loyola University, 1989; professional: Cook County aldermanic aide, 1983–89; practicing attorney, 1990–present; Cook County Commissioner, 1998–2009; adjunct professor, Roosevelt University, 2006–07; adjunct professor, Loyola University, 2002–09; married: Barbara; children: Meghan and Alyson; committees: Appropriations; elected to the 111th Congress on April 7, 2009, by special election, to fill the vacancy caused by the resignation of United States Representative Rahm Emanuel; reelected to the 112th Congress on November 2, 2010; reelected to each succeeding Congress.

Office Listings

http://www.quigley.house.gov

1124 Longworth House Office Building, Washington, DC 20515 .... (202) 225–4061
Chief of Staff.—Lindsey Matese. FAX: 225–5603
Communications Director.—Laura Sisemore.
Scheduler.—Blaine Nolan.
Legislative Director.—Robyn Russell.
3742 West Irving Park Road, Chicago, IL 60618 .... (773) 267–5926
FAX: 267–6583
1057 West Belmont, Chicago, IL 60657 .... (773) 267–5926

Counties: COOK COUNTY (part). Population (2010), 648,610.

ZIP Codes: 60018, 60106, 60126, 60131, 60154, 60160, 60162, 60164, 60171, 60176, 60181, 60191, 60521, 60523, 60525–26, 60558, 60610, 60612–14, 60618, 60622, 60625, 60630–31, 60634, 60640–42, 60645–47, 60656–57, 60659, 60706–07, 60714

* * *

SIXTH DISTRICT

PETER J. ROSKAM, Republican, of Wheaton, IL; born in Hinsdale, IL, September 13, 1961; education: B.A., University of Illinois, Urbana-Champaign, IL, 1983; J.D., Illinois Institute of Technology Chicago-Kent College of Law, Chicago, IL, 1989; professional: lawyer, private practice; staff, United States Representative Tom DeLay of Texas, 1985–86; United States Representative Henry Hyde of Illinois, 1986–87; teacher; businessman; member, Illinois House of Representatives, 1993–99; member, Illinois Senate, 2000–06; married: Elizabeth; children: four; committees: Ways and Means; elected to the 110th Congress on November 7, 2006; reelected to each succeeding Congress.

Office Listings

http://www.house.gov/roskam

227 Cannon House Office Building, Washington, DC 20515 .... (202) 225–4561
Chief of Staff.—Steven Moore. FAX: 225–1166
Scheduler.—Hannah Yee.
Legislative Director.—David Mork.
Press Secretaries.—Megan Holder.
2700 International Drive, Suite 304, West Chicago, IL 60185 .... (630) 232–0006

Counties: COOK (part), DUPAGE (part). CITIES AND TOWNSHIPS: Algonquin Barrington, Barrington Hills, Bartlett, Carol Stream, Cary, Clarendon Hills, Darien, Deer Park, Downers Grove, Forest Lake, Fox River Grove, Gilberts, Glen Ellyn, Hawthorne Woods, Hinsdale, Hoffman Estates, Inverness, Jeff, Kildeer, Lake In The Hills, Lake Zurich, Lisle, Lombard, Long Grove, Naperville, North Barrington, Oak Brook, Palatine, Sleepy Hollow, South Barrington, South Elgin, Sutton, Tower Lakes, Trout Valley, Warrenville, Wayne, West Chicago, West Dundee, Westmont, Wheaton, Willowbrook, and Winfield. Population (2010) 712,813.

ZIP Codes: 60010, 60013, 60021, 60047, 60067, 60074, 60102–03, 60118, 60136–37, 60148, 60156, 60169, 60177, 60179, 60184–85, 60187–89, 60192, 60199, 60514–16, 60521, 60523, 60527, 60532, 60540, 60555, 60559, 60561, 60563–65

* * *

SEVENTH DISTRICT

DANNY K. DAVIS, Democrat, of Chicago, IL; born in Parkdale, AR, September 6, 1941; education: B.A., Arkansas AM&N College, 1961; M.A., Chicago State University; Ph.D., Union Institute, Cincinnati, OH; educator and health planner-administrator; board of directors, National Housing Partnership; Cook County Board of Commissioners, 1990–96; former alderman of the Chicago City Council's 29th ward, receiving the Independent Voters of Illinois ''Best Alderman Award'' for 1980–81, 1981–82, and 1989–90; co-chair, Clinton-Gore-Braun '92; founder and past president, Westside Association for Community Action; past president, National Association of Community Health Centers; 1987 recipient of the Leon M. Despres Award; married to Vera G. Davis; two sons: Jonathan and Stacey; committees: Oversight and Government Reform; Ways and Means; elected to the 105th Congress; reelected to each succeeding Congress.

Office Listings

http://www.davis.house.gov

2159 Rayburn House Office Building, Washington, DC 20515 .... (202) 225–5006
Chief of Staff.—Yul Edwards. FAX: 225–5641
Legislative Director.—Jill Hunter-Williams.
Director of Issues and Communications.—Ira Cohen.
2746 West Madison Street, Chicago, IL 60612 .... (773) 533–7520

Counties: COOK. CITIES AND TOWNSHIPS: Berwyn, Chicago, Oak Park, Proviso, River Forest and Riverside. Population (2010), 712,812.

ZIP Codes: 60104, 60130, 60141, 60153–55, 60160, 60162–63, 60301–12, 60614–16, 60621–24, 60629, 60632, 60636–37, 60639, 60642, 60644, 60651, 60653–54, 60661, 60707, 60804

* * *

EIGHTH DISTRICT

TAMMY DUCKWORTH, Democrat, of Hoffman Estates, IL, born in Bangkok; education: B.A., political science, University of Hawaii, 1989; M.A., George Washington University, DC, 1992; professional: Rotary International; Illinois Department of Veterans Affairs; U.S. Department of Veterans Affairs; military: Lt. Colonel, Illinois National Guard; Combat Veteran, Operation Iraqi Freedom; married: Bryan Bowlsbey; committees: Armed Services, Oversight and Government Reform; elected to the 113th Congress on November 6, 2012.

Office Listings

http://Duckworth.house.gov twitter.com/repduckworth
https://www.facebook.com/congresswomantammyduckworth

104 Cannon House Office Building, Washington, DC 20515 .... (202) 225–3711
Chief of Staff.—Kaitlin Fahey. FAX: 225–7830
1701 East Woodfield Road, Suite 900, Schaumburg, IL 60173 .... (847) 413–1959
District Director.—Sendy Soto. FAX: 413–1965

Counties: COOK COUNTY (part). TOWNSHIPS: Arlington Heights, Barrington Hills, Buffalo Grove, Chicago (part), Des Plaines, Elk Grove, Hoffman Estates, Mount Prospect, Palatine, Rolling Meadows, Rosemont, Schaumburg, Streamwood, and Wheeling. DUPAGE COUNTY (part). TOWNSHIPS: Addison, Bartlett, Bensenville, Bloomingdale, Carol Stream, Elmhurst, Glen Ellyn, Glendale, Hanover Park, Itasca, Lombard, Oak Brook, Oakbrook Terrace, Roselle, Villa Park, and Wheaton. KANE COUNTY (part). TOWNSHIPS: Algonquin, Carpentersville, East Dundee, and Elgin. Population (2010), 726,418.

ZIP Codes: 60004–05, 60007–10, 60016, 60018, 60038, 60056, 60067, 60074, 60089–90, 60101–103, 60106–108, 60110, 60116–118, 60120–21, 60123–24, 60126, 60131–33, 60137, 60139, 60143, 60148, 60157, 60168–70, 60172–173, 60177, 60179, 60181, 60187–188, 60191–195, 60399, 60523

* * *

NINTH DISTRICT

JANICE D. SCHAKOWSKY, Democrat, of Evanston, IL; born in Chicago, IL, May 26, 1944; education: B.A., University of Illinois, 1965; consumer advocate; program director, Illinois Public Action; executive director, Illinois State Council of Senior Citizens, 1985–90; State Representative, 18th District, Illinois General Assembly, 1991–99; served on Labor and

Commerce, Human Service Appropriations, Health Care, and Electric Deregulation Committees; religion: Jewish; married: Robert Creamer; children: Ian, Mary, and Lauren; committees: Energy and Commerce; Permanent Select Committee on Intelligence; elected to the 106th Congress; reelected to each succeeding Congress.

Office Listings

http://www.house.gov/schakowsky

2367 Rayburn House Office Building, Washington, DC 20515 .... (202) 225–2111
Chief of Staff.—Cathy Hurwit. FAX: 226–6890
Communications Director.—Sabrina Sangh.
Legislative Director.—Vacant.
Appointments Secretary.—Kim Muzeroll.
5533 Broadway, Chicago, IL 60640 .... (773) 506–7100
District Director.—Leslie Combs.
1852 Johns Drive, Glenview, IL 60025 .... (847) 328–3409

Counties: COOK COUNTY (part). CITIES: Chicago, Evanston, Glenview, Golf, Lincolnwood, Morton Grove, Niles, and Skokie. Population (2010), 712,813.

ZIP Codes: 60004–05, 60016, 60018–19, 60025–26, 60029, 60043, 60053, 60056, 60062, 60068, 60070, 60076–77, 60090–91, 60093, 60176, 60201–03, 60613, 60626, 60630, 60640, 60645–46, 60656–57, 60659–60, 60706, 60712, 60714

* * *

TENTH DISTRICT

BRADLEY S. SCHNEIDER, Democrat, of Deerfield, IL; born in Denver, CO, August 20, 1961; education: Cherry Creek High School, Greenwood Village, CO, 1979; B.A., Northwestern University, Evanston, IL, 1983; M.B.A., Kellogg School of Management, Evanston, IL, 1988; professional: managing principal, Davis Dann Adler Schneider, LLC; director of family business center; Blackman Kallick LLC, small business owner, Cadence Consulting Group, LLC; committees: Foreign Affairs; Small Business; elected to the 113th Congress on November 6, 2012.

Office Listings

http://schneider.house.gov

317 Cannon House Office Building, Washington, DC 20515 .... (202) 225–4835
Chief of Staff.—Reed Adamson. FAX: 225–0837
111 Barclay Boulevard, Suite 200, Lincolnshire, IL 60069 .... (847) 793–0625
District Director.—Barbara Cornew. FAX: 793–0677

Counties: COOK (part), LAKE (part). Population (2010), 709,209.

ZIP Codes: 60004, 60015–16, 60020, 60022, 60025–26, 60030–31, 60035, 60037, 60040–41, 60044–48, 60050–51, 60053, 60056, 60060–62, 60064, 60068–70, 60073, 60081, 60083, 60085, 60087–90, 60093, 60096, 60099, 60714

* * *

ELEVENTH DISTRICT

BILL FOSTER, Democrat, of Naperville, IL; born in Madison, WI, October 7, 1955; education: B.S., University of Wisconsin-Madison, 1976; Ph.D., Harvard University, 1983; professional: small business owner, physicist; committees: Financial Services; elected to the 113th Congress on November 6, 2012.

Office Listings

http://www.foster.house.gov https://twitter.com/repbillfoster
https://www.facebook.com/congressmanbillfoster?ref=hl

1224 Longworth House Office Building, Washington, DC 20515 .... (202) 225–3515
Chief of Staff.—Elizabeth Glidden. FAX: 225–9420
2711 East New York Street, Suite 204, Aurora, IL 60502 .... (630) 585–7672
195 Springfield Avenue, Suite 102, Joliet, IL 60435 .... (815) 280–5876
District Director.—Carole Cheney.

Counties: COOK (part), DUPAGE (part), KANE (part), KENDALL (part), AND WILL (part). Population (2010), 722,173.

ZIP Codes: 60403–04, 60410, 60421, 60431–36, 60439–42, 60446–48, 60451, 60480, 60490, 60502–06, 60512, 60515–17, 60519, 60525, 60527, 60532, 60538, 60540, 60542–44, 60559–65, 60586

* * *

TWELFTH DISTRICT

WILLIAM L. ENYART, Democrat, of Belleville, IL; born in Pensacola, FL, September 22, 1949; education: B.A., Southern Illinois University Edwardsville, Edwardsville, IL, 1974; M.S., Army War College, Carlisle Barracks, PA, 2000; J.D., Southern Illinois University School of Law, Carbondale, IL, 1979; professional: lawyer; military: United States Air Force, 1969–74; Illinois Army National Guard, 1982–2012, military: retired as Major General, Adjutant General of Illinois, 2007–12; awards: U.S. Military awards include, among others: Legion of Merit, Meritorious Service Medal, Army Commendation Medal; Foreign military awards include: Polish Army Gold Cross, Republic of Vietnam Gallantry Cross with Palm (unit citation); honorary doctorate, Lindenwood University-Belleville, 2013; religion: Christian Church; married: Annette Eckert, 1983; children: James (Jay), Alex; committees: Agriculture; Armed Services; elected to the 113th Congress on November 6, 2012.

Office Listings

http://www.enyart.house.gov www.facebook.com/congressmanbillenyart
https://twitter.com/repbillenyart

1722 Longworth House Office Building, Washington, DC 20515 .... (202) 225–5661
Chief of Staff.—Kevin Kern. FAX: 225–0285
Scheduler.—Karl Britton.
Legislative Director.—Willie Lyles III.
Press Secretary.—Kevin Kern.
23 Public Square, Suite 404, Belleville, IL 62220 .... (618) 233–8026
FAX: 233–8765
250 West Cherry Street, Carbondale, IL 62901 .... (618) 529–3791
FAX: 549–3768
1330 Swanwick Street, Chester, IL 62233 .... (618) 826–3043
FAX: 826–1923
SIUE East Street, Louis Center, Building A, Room 1051, East St. Louis, IL 62201 (618) 233–8026
2060 Delmar Avenue, Suite B, Granite City, IL 62040 .... (618) 451–7065
FAX: 451–2126
1100 Main Street, Mt. Vernon, IL 62864 .... (618) 316–9035
201 East Nolen Street, West Frankfort, IL 62896 .... (618) 937–6402
FAX: 937–3307

Counties: ALEXANDER, FRANKLIN, JACKSON, JEFFERSON, MADISON (part), MONROE, PERRY, PULASKI, RANDOLPH, ST. CLAIR, UNION, AND WILLIAMSON. Population (2010), 712,813.

ZIP Codes: 62002, 62010, 62018, 62024–25, 62035, 62040, 62048, 62059–60, 62067, 62084, 62087, 62090, 62095, 62201, 62203–08, 62217, 62220–21, 62223, 62225–26, 62232–34, 62236–44, 62248, 62254–55, 62257–58, 62260–61, 62263–65, 62268–69, 62272, 62274, 62277–80, 62282, 62285–86, 62288–89, 62292–95, 62297–98, 62801, 62808, 62810, 62812, 62814, 62816, 62819, 62822, 62825, 62830–32, 62836, 62841, 62846, 62851, 62856, 62860, 62864–65, 62872, 62874, 62877, 62883–84, 62888–91, 62893–94, 62896–98, 62901–03, 62905–07, 62912, 62914–18, 62920–24, 62926–27, 62932–33, 62939–42, 62948–52, 62956–59, 62961–64, 62966, 62969–70, 62974–76, 62983, 62987–88, 62990, 62992, 62994, 62996–99

* * *

THIRTEENTH DISTRICT

RODNEY DAVIS, Republican, of Taylorville, IL; born in Des Moines, IA, January 5, 1970; education: graduated from Taylorville High School, 1988; B.A., Millikin University, IL, 1992; professional: congressional aide, 1999–2012; has served on numerous local civic and community organizations and groups; religion: Catholic; married: Shannon R. Davis; children: Toryn, Clark, and Griffin; committees: Agriculture; Transportation and Infrastructure; elected to the 113th Congress on November 6, 2012.

Office Listings

http://www.rodneydavis.house.gov https://www.facebook.com/reprodneydavis
twitter.com/rodneydavis

1740 Longworth House Office Building, Washington, DC 20515 .... (202) 225–2371
Chief of Staff.—Jen Daulby.
Legislative Director.—Bobby Frederick.
Scheduler.—Drew Collins.
2004 Fox Drive, Champaign, IL 61820 .... (217) 403–4690
Communications Director.—Andrew Flach.
243 South Water Street, Suite 100, Decatur, IL 62523 .... (217) 791–6224

District Director.—Tim Butler.
104 West North Street, Normal, IL 61761 .... (309) 252–8834
108 East Market Street, Taylorville, IL 62568 .... (217) 824–5117
9 Junction Drive, Suite 9, Glen Carbon, IL 62034 .... (618) 205–8660

Counties: BOND (part), CALHOUN, CHAMPAIGN (part), CHRISTIAN, DEWITT, GREENE, JERSEY, MACON, MACOUPIN, MADISON (part), MCLEAN (part), MONTGOMERY, PIATT, SANGAMON (part). Population (2010), 710,784.

ZIP Codes: 60481, 61252, 61701–02, 61704–05, 61709–10, 61727, 61735, 61745, 61749, 61756, 61761, 61772, 61777–78, 61790–91, 61799, 61801–03, 61813, 61815, 61818, 61820–22, 61824, 61826, 61830, 61839, 61842, 61854–56, 61864, 61872, 61874, 61880, 61882, 61884, 61913, 61929, 61936, 62002, 62006, 62009, 62013–17, 61719, 61721–23, 61725–28, 62031-37, 62044–45, 62049–54, 62056, 62058, 62060, 62062–63, 62065, 62069–70, 62074–77, 62079, 62081–83, 62086, 62088–89, 62091–94, 62097, 62234, 62262, 62355, 62501, 62510, 62513, 62517, 62521–26, 62531, 62533, 62535, 62538, 62540, 62544–47, 62549–51, 62554–58, 62560, 62563, 62567–68, 62570, 62572–73, 62626, 62629–30, 62640, 62649, 62667, 62670, 62672, 62674, 62685–86, 62690, 62701–04, 62707, 62711–12

* * *

FOURTEENTH DISTRICT

RANDY HULTGREN, Republican, of Winfield, IL; born in Park Ridge, IL, March 1, 1966; education: graduated, B.A., Bethel College, 1988; J.D., Chicago-Kent College of Law, 1993; professional: elected to the DuPage County Board and county Forest Preserve Board, 1994; elected to the Illinois House of Representatives, 1999, elected to the Illinois State Senate, 2007; married: wife, Christy; four children; committees: Financial Services; Science, Space, and Technology; elected to the 112th Congress on November 2, 2010; reelected to the 113th Congress on November 6, 2012.

Office Listings

http://hultgren.house.gov facebook.com/rephultgren twitter: @rephultgren

332 Cannon House Office Building, Washington, DC 20515 .... (202) 225–2976
Chief of Staff.—Katherine McGuire FAX: 225–0697
Office Manager.—Kate Disbrow.
Deputy Chief of Staff.—Doug Thomas.
Senior Legislative Aide.—Scott Luginbill.
Communications Director.—Jameson Cunningham.
Legislative Aide.—Andrew Mooney.
Staff Assistant.—Gina Gregolunas.
1797 State Street, Suite A, Geneva, IL 60134 .... (630) 232–7104
Deputy Chief of Staff.—Sean McCarthy.
Staff Assistants: Reed Sullivan, Valerie Wright.
Caseworkers: Carol Berger, Ruth Richardson.
Coalitions Director.—Susan Russell.
Senior Field Representative.—Nick Provenzano.

Counties: DEKALB (part), DUPAGE (part), KANE (part), KENDALL (part), LAKE (part), MCHENRY (part), AND WILL (part). CITIES AND TOWNSHIPS: Alden, Algonquin, Antioch, Aurora, Batavia, Beach Park, Big Grove, Big Rock, Blackberry, Bolingbrook, Boulder Hill, Bristol, Bull Valley, Burlington, Burton, Campton, Campton Hills, Channahon, Channel Lake, Chemung, Coral, Cortland, Crystal Lake, DeKalb, Dorr, Dunham, Elburn, Elgin, Fox, Fox Lake Hills, Fox Lake, Fremont, Geneva, Grafton, Grandwood Park, Greenwood, Gurnee, Hampshire, Hartland, Harvard, Hawthorn Woods, Hebron, Hinckley, Holiday Hills, Huntley, Island Lake, Johnsburg, Joliet, Kaneville, Kendall, Lake Barrington, Lake Catherine, Lake in the Hills, Lake Villa, Lakemoor, Lakewood, Lily Lake, Lindenhurst, Lisbon, Little Rock, Maple Park, Marengo, McCullom Lake, McHenry, Millbrook, Millington, Minooka, Montgomery, Mundelein, Na-Au-Say, Naperville, Newark, Newport, North Aurora, North Barrington, Nunda, Oakwood Hills, Old Mill Creek, Oswego, Pierce, Pingree Grove, Pistakee Highlands, Pittsfield, Plainfield, Plano, Plato, Plattville, Port Barrington, Prairie Grove, Prestbury, Richmond, Riley, Ringwood, Romeoville, Rutland, Sandwich, Seneca, Seward, Shorewood, Somonauk, Spring Grove, Squaw Grove, St. Charles, Sugar Grove, Sycamore, Troy, Union, Virgil, Volo, Wadsworth, Warren, Warrenville, Wauconda, Waukegan, West Chicago, Wheatland, Winfield, Wonder Lake, Woodstock, and Yorkville. Population (2010), 721,774.

ZIP Codes: 60001–02, 60010, 60012–14, 60020, 60030–31, 60033–34, 60042, 60046–48, 60050–51, 60060, 60071–73, 60075, 60081, 60083–84, 60087, 60097–99, 60102, 60109, 60112, 60115, 60119, 60124, 60134–36, 60140, 60142, 60144, 60147, 60151–52, 60156, 60174–75, 60178, 60180, 60183, 60185–86, 60189–90, 60404, 60410, 60431, 60447, 60450, 60490, 60502–03, 60506, 60510–12, 60520, 60536–39, 60541–45, 60548, 60552, 60554–56, 60560, 60563–65, 60585, 61012, 61038

* * *

FIFTEENTH DISTRICT

JOHN SHIMKUS, Republican, of Collinsville, IL; born in Collinsville, February 21, 1958; education: graduated from Collinsville High School; B.S., West Point Military Academy, West

Point, NY, 1980; teaching certificate, Christ College, Irvine, CA, 1990; M.B.A., Southern Illinois University, Edwardsville, 1997; U.S. Army Reserves, 1980–85; government and history teacher, Metro East Lutheran High School, Edwardsville, IL; Collinsville township trustee, 1989; Madison county treasurer, 1990–96; married: the former Karen Muth, 1987; children: David, Daniel, and Joshua; committees: Energy and Commerce; elected to the 105th Congress; reelected to each succeeding Congress.

Office Listings

http://www.shimkus.house.gov https://www.facebook.com/repshimkus
https://twitter.com/repshimkus

2452 Rayburn House Office Building, Washington, DC 20515 .... (202) 225–5271
Chief of Staff.—Craig Roberts. FAX: 225–5880
Legislative Director / Deputy Chief of Staff.—Greta Joynes.
15 Professional Park Drive, Maryville, IL 62062 .... (217) 492–5090
District Director.—Deb Detmers.
101 North 4th Street, Suite 303, Effingham, IL 62401 .... (618) 532–9676
201 North Vermillion Street, Suite 218, Danville, IL 61832 .... (217) 446–0664
110 East Locust Street, Room 12, Harrisburg, IL 62946 .... (618) 252–8271

Counties: BOND, CHAMPAIGN, CLARK, CLAY, COLES, CRAWFORD, CUMBERLAND, DOUGLAS (part), EDGAR, EDWARDS, EFFINGHAM, FAYETTE, FORD, GALLATIN, HAMILTON, HARDIN, JASPER, JOHNSON, LAWRENCE, MADISON (part), MARION, MASSAC, MOULTRIE, POPE, RICHLAND, SALINE (part), SHELBY, VERMILLION, WABASH, WASHINGTON, WAYNE, AND WHITE. Population (2010), 712,813.

ZIP Codes: 60932–33, 60936 (part), 60942 (part), 60949, 60957, 60960, 60963, 61802 (part), 61810–11, 61814, 61816–17, 61822 (part), 61832–34, 61840–41, 61843–44, 61845 (part), 61846–50, 61852, 61853 (part), 61857–59, 61863 (part), 61864 (part), 61865–66, 61870–73, 61875 (part), 61876–78, 61880 (part), 61883, 61910–12, 61913 (part), 61914 (part), 61917, 61919–20, 61924, 61925 (part), 61928, 61929 (part), 61930–33, 61937 (part), 61938, 61940–44, 61949, 61951, 61953, 61955–57, 62001 (part), 62002, 62011–12, 62025 (part), 62032 (part), 62034 (part), 62035, 62040, 62046, 62061–62, 62074 (part), 62075 (part), 62080 (part), 62086 (part), 62097 (part), 62214, 62231–32, 62234 (part), 62237 (part), 62246 (part), 62249, 62253, 62255 (part), 62257 (part), 62262 (part), 62263, 62265 (part), 62266, 62268 (part), 62271, 62273, 62275, 62281 (part), 62284 (part), 62292, 62293 (part), 62294 (part), 62401, 62410–11, 62414, 62417–22, 62424, 62426–28, 62431–33, 62435–36, 62439–43, 62445–52, 62454, 62458–68, 62471, 62473–76, 62479–81, 62510 (part), 62534, 62544 (part), 62550 (part), 62553 (part), 62557 (part), 62565, 62571, 62801 (part), 62803, 62806–07, 62808 (part), 62809, 62810 (part), 62811, 62814 (part), 62815, 62817–18, 62820–21, 62823–24, 62827–28, 62830 (part), 62831 (part), 62835, 62836 (part), 62837–39, 62842–44, 62848–50, 62851 (part), 62852–54, 62858–59, 62860 (part), 62861–63, 62867–71, 62875–76, 62877 (part), 62879–82, 62886–87, 62889 (part), 62890 (part), 62892, 62893 (part), 62895, 62899 (part), 62908, 62910 (part), 62912 (part), 62917 (part), 62919, 62922 (part), 62923 (part), 62928, 62930–31, 62934–35, 62938, 62939 (part), 62941 (part), 62946, 62953–54, 62956 (part), 62960, 62965, 62967, 62977, 62979, 62982, 62984–85, 62987 (part), 62995

* * *

SIXTEENTH DISTRICT

ADAM KINZINGER, Republican, of Channahon, IL; born in Kankakee, IL, February 27, 1978; education: graduated, Normal Community West High School, 1996; B.S., Illinois State University, 2000; professional: McLean County Board, 1998–2003; Sales Representative, STL Technologies, 2000–03; United States Air National Guard, 2003–present, current rank: Major; religion: Protestant; single; Deputy Republican Whip; committees: Energy and Commerce; Foreign Affairs; elected to the 112th Congress on November 2, 2010; reelected to the 113th on November 6, 2012.

Office Listings

http://www.kinzinger.house.gov

1221 Longworth House Office Building, Washington, DC 20515 .... (202) 225–3635
Chief of Staff.—Austin Weatherford. FAX: 225–3521
Deputy Chief of Staff.—Pamela Mattox.
628 Columbus Street, Suite 507, Ottawa, IL 61350 .... (815) 431–9271
District Director.—Bonnie Walsh.
Deputy District Director.—Reed Wilson.

Counties: BOONE, BUREAU, DEKALB (part), FORD (part), GRUNDY, IROQUOIS, LASALLE, LEE, LIVINGSTON, OGLE, PUTNAM, STARK (part), WILL (part), AND WINNEBAGO (part). Population (2010), 712,813.

ZIP Codes: 60033, 60111, 60113, 60115, 60129, 60135, 60140, 60145–46, 60150, 60152, 60178, 60407–08, 60410, 60416, 60420–21, 60424, 60437, 60444, 60447, 60450, 60460, 60470, 60474, 60479, 60481, 60518, 60530–31, 60537, 60541, 60548–53, 60556–57, 60911–12, 60917–22, 60924, 60926–31, 60934–36, 60938–39, 60941–42, 60945–46, 60948, 60950–53, 60955–56, 60958–62, 60964, 60966–68, 60970, 60973–74, 61006–08, 61010–12, 61015–16, 61019–21, 61024, 61030–31, 61038–39, 61042–43, 61047, 61049, 61051–52, 61054, 61057, 61061, 61063–65, 61068, 61071–73, 61078–81, 61084, 61088, 61091, 61101–04, 61107–09, 61111–12, 61114–15, 61126, 61130–32, 61243, 61283, 61301, 61310–38, 61340–42, 61344–46, 61348–50, 61353–54, 61356, 61358–64, 61367–68, 61370–74, 61376–79, 61421, 61443, 61560, 61726, 61731, 61739–41, 61743–44, 61764, 61769, 61773, 61775, 61845

* * *

SEVENTEENTH DISTRICT

CHERI BUSTOS, Democrat, of East Moline, IL; born in Springfield, IL, October 17, 1960; education: graduated B.A., University of Maryland, College Park, MD, 1983; M.A., University of Illinois at Springfield, 1985; religion: Roman Catholic; married: Gerry; children: Tony, Nick, and Joseph; committees: Agriculture; Transportation and Infrastructure; elected to the 113th Congress on November 6, 2012.

Office Listings

http://bustos.house.gov facebook: rep. cheri bustos
twitter: @repcheri

1009 Longworth House Office Building, Washington, DC 20515 .... (202) 225–5905
Chief of Staff.—Allison Jaslow.
Legislative Director.—Todd Wolf.
Communications Director.—Colin Milligan.
Scheduler.—Melissa Miller.
Legislative Assistants: Hannah Hill, Donald Rozman.
Legislative Correspondents: Lyron Blum-Evitts, Jonathan Tauberg.
Staff Assistant.—Bruce Goldrosen.
2401 4th Avenue, Rock Island, IL 61201 .... (309) 786–3406
District Director.—Heidi Shultz.
Constituent Advocates: Miranda French, Lucie VanHecke.
Events Coordinator.—Kerry Myers.
3100 North Knoxville Avenue, Suite 205, Peoria, IL 61603 .... (309) 966–1813
Constituent Advocates: Andrew Colgan, Laura Glessing.
119 North Church Street, Suites 207 and 208, Rockford, IL 61101 .... (815) 968–8011
Outreach Director.—Alexander Finke.
Constituent Advocate.—Catherine Gray.

Counties: CARROLL, FULTON, HENDERSON, HENRY, JO DAVIESS, KNOX, MERCER, PEORIA (part), ROCK ISLAND, STEPHENSON, TAZEWELL (part), WARREN, WHITESIDE, AND WINNEBAGO (part). Population (2010), 712,813.

ZIP Codes: 61001, 61007, 61013–14, 61018–20, 61025, 61027–28, 61032, 61036–37, 61039, 61041, 61044, 61046–48, 61050–51, 61053, 61059–60, 61062–64, 61067, 61070–71, 61074–75, 61077–78, 61081, 61084–85, 61087–89, 61101–10, 61125, 61201, 61204, 61230–44, 61250–52, 61254, 61256–66, 61270, 61272–79, 61281–85, 61299, 61344, 61361, 61401–02, 61410, 61412–15, 61417–19, 61422–23, 61425, 61427–28, 61430–37, 61439, 61441–43, 61447–50, 61453–54, 61458–60, 61462, 61465–78, 61480, 61482, 61484–86, 61488–90, 61501, 61519–20, 61524, 61529, 61531, 61533–34, 61536, 61539, 61542–47, 61553–55, 61558, 61563–64, 61569, 61572, 61601–07, 61610–11, 61613–16, 61625, 61629–30, 61633–34, 61636–37, 61641, 61650–56, 62330, 62644

* * *

EIGHTEENTH DISTRICT

AARON SCHOCK, Republican, of Peoria, IL; born in Morris, MN, May 28, 1981; B.S. in finance, Bradley University, Peoria, IL, 2002; professional: President of Peoria Board of Education; Illinois House of Representatives 2005–09; religion: Christian; Deputy Republican Whip; caucuses: co-founder, Colombia Caucus; co-chair, Congressional Future Caucus; co-chair, STEAM Caucus; co-chair, Congressional Pro-Trade Caucus; committees: Ways and Means; House Administration; elected to the 111th Congress on November 4, 2008; reelected to each succeeding Congress.

Office Listings

http://www.schock.house.gov https://www.facebook.com/repaaronschock
twitter: @aaronschock

328 Cannon House Office Building, Washington, DC 20515 .... (202) 225–6201
Deputy Chief of Staff and Policy Director.—Mark Roman. FAX: 225–9249
Executive Assistant.—Sarah Rogers.
Senior Legislative Assistant.—Margie Almanza.
Legislative Assistant.—Kelli Ripp.
Staff Assistant.—Ben Jarrett.
100 Northeast Monroe Street, Room 100, Peoria, IL 61602 .... (309) 671–7027
FAX: 671–7309
201 West Morgan Street, Jacksonville, IL 62650 .... (217) 245–1431
FAX: 243–6852
235 South 6th Street, Springfield, IL 62701 .... (217) 670–1653
FAX: 670–1806

Counties: ADAMS, BROWN, CASS, HANCOCK, LOGAN, MARSHALL, MASON, MCDONOUGH, MCLEAN (part), MENARD, MORGAN, PEORIA (part), PIKE, SANGAMON (part), SCHUYLER, SCOTT, STARK (part), TAZEWELL (part), AND WOODFORD. Population (2010), 712,813.

ZIP Codes: 61321, 61358, 61369, 61375, 61377, 61411, 61415–16, 61420–22, 61424, 61426, 61434, 61438, 61440, 61449–52, 61455, 61459, 61470, 61473, 61475, 61479, 61482–84, 61489, 61491, 61516–17, 61523, 61525–26, 61528–37, 61540–41, 61545–48, 61550, 61552, 61554, 61559, 61561–62, 61565, 61567–71, 61603–04, 61607, 61610–12, 61614–16, 61635, 61638, 61643, 61701–02, 61704–05, 61709–10, 61720–26, 61728–34, 61736–38, 61742, 61744–45, 61747–49, 61751–55, 61758–61, 61770–71, 61774, 61776, 61791, 61799, 61842–43, 62082, 62301, 62305–06, 62311–14, 62316, 62319–21, 62323–26, 62329–30, 62334, 62336, 62338–41, 62343–49, 62351–63, 62365–67, 62370, 62373–76, 62378–80, 62512, 62515, 62518–20, 62530, 62536, 62539, 62541, 62543, 62545, 62548, 62558, 62561, 62563, 62601, 62610–13, 62615, 62617–18, 62621–22, 62624–25, 62627–29, 62631, 62633–35, 62638–39, 62642–44, 62650–51, 62655–56, 62659–68, 62670–71, 62673, 62675, 62677, 62681–82, 62684, 62688–95, 62702–04, 62707, 62711–12

INDIANA

(Population 2010, 6,483,802)

SENATORS

DANIEL COATS, Republican, of Indianapolis, IN; born in Jackson, MI, May 16, 1943; education: B.A., Wheaton College, Wheaton, IL, 1965; J.D., Indiana University, Indianapolis, IN, 1971; professional: served in the United States Army, 1966–68; U.S. House of Representatives, 1981–89; U.S. Senate, 1989–98; U.S. Ambassador to the Federal Republic of Germany, 2001–05; religion: Presbyterian (P.C.A.); married: Marsha Crawford, 1965; three children; eight grandchildren; committees: Appropriations; Commerce, Science and Transportation; Joint Economic Committee; Select Committee on Intelligence; elected to the U.S. Senate on November 2, 2010.

Office Listings

http://coats.senate.gov twitter: @sendancoats

SR–493 Russell Senate Office Building, Washington, DC 20510	(202) 224–5623
Chief of Staff.—Dean Hingson.	FAX: 228–1820
Legislative Director.—Viraj Mirani.	
Communications Director.—Tara DiJulio.	
Scheduler.—Stephanie Eastman.	
11035 Broadway, Suite A, Crown Point, IN 46307	(219) 663–2595
	FAX: 663–4586
101 Martin Luther King, Jr. Boulevard, Evansville, IN 47708	(812) 465–6500
	FAX: 465–6503
1300 South Harrison Street, Suite 3161, Ft. Wayne, IN 46802	(260) 426–3151
	FAX: 420–0060
1650 Market Tower, 10 West Market Street, Indianapolis, IN 46204	(317) 554–0750
	FAX: 554–0760
2 East McClain Avenue, Suite 2–A, Scottsburg, IN 47170	(812) 754–0520
	FAX: 754–0539

* * *

JOSEPH S. DONNELLY, Democrat, of Granger, IN; born in Queens, NY, September 29, 1955; education: graduated, B.A., University of Notre Dame, Notre Dame, IN, 1977; J.D., University of Notre Dame, Notre Dame, IN, 1981; religion: Roman Catholic; married: Jill Truitt, 1979; two children; committees: Agriculture, Nutrition and Forestry, Armed Services; Special Committee on Aging; elected to the U.S. Senate on November 6, 2012.

Office Listings

http://www.donnelly.senate.gov twitter.com/sendonnelly

720 Hart Senate Office Building, Washington, DC 20510	(202) 224–4814
Chief of Staff.—Joel Elliott.	FAX: 224–5011
Scheduler.—Audrey Porter.	
Legislative Director.—Andrew Lattanner.	
Communications Director.—Elizabeth Shappell.	
10 West Market Street, Suite 1180, Indianapolis, IN 46204	(317) 226–5555
205 West Colfax Avenue, South Bend, IN 46601	(574) 288–2780
5400 Federal Plaza, Suite 3200, Hammond, IN 46320	(219) 852–0089
123 Northwest 4th Street, Suite 417, Evansville, IN 47708	(812) 425–5862
702 North Shore Drive, Suite LL–101, Jeffersonville, IN 47130	(812) 284–2027
203 East Berry Street, Suite 702B, Fort Wayne, IN 46802	(260) 420–4955

REPRESENTATIVES

FIRST DISTRICT

PETER J. VISCLOSKY, Democrat, of Merrillville, IN; born in Gary, IN, August 13, 1949; education: graduated, Andrean High School, Merrillville, 1967; B.S., accounting, Indiana University Northwest, Gary, 1970; J.D., University of Notre Dame Law School, Notre Dame, IN, 1973; LL.M., international and comparative law, Georgetown University Law Center, Washington, DC, 1982; professional: attorney; admitted to the Indiana State Bar, 1974, the District of Columbia Bar, 1978, and the U.S. Supreme Court Bar, 1980; associate staff, U.S. House of Representatives, Committee on Appropriations, 1977–80, Committee on the Budget,

1980–82; practicing attorney, Merrillville law firm, 1983–84; wife: Joanne Royce; children: John Daniel and Timothy Patrick; committees: Appropriations; elected to the 99th Congress on November 6, 1984; reelected to each succeeding Congress.

Office Listings

http://www.visclosky.house.gov twitter: @repvisclosky

2256 Rayburn House Office Building, Washington, DC 20515 .... (202) 225–2461
Chief of Staff.—Mark Lopez. FAX: 225–2493
Deputy Chief of Staff.—Joe DeVooght.
Executive Assistant.—Korry Baack.
Communications Director.—Philip LaRue.
7895 Broadway, Suite A, Merrillville, IN 46410 .... (219) 795–1844
District Directors: Gregory Gulvas, Elizabeth Johnson. FAX: 795–1850
(888) 423–7383

Counties: LAKE, LAPORT (part), PORTER. Population (2010), 720,422.

ZIP Codes: 46301–04, 46307–08, 46310–12, 46319–25, 46327, 46341–42, 46345, 46347–49, 46350, 46355–56, 46360, 46368, 46373, 46375–77, 46379–85, 46390, 46392–94, 46401–11

* * *

SECOND DISTRICT

JACKIE WALORSKI, Republican, of Elkhart, IN; born in South Bend, IN, August 17, 1963; education: B.A., major: communications, Taylor University, Upland, IN, 1985; professional: served in the Indiana General Assembly from 2005–10; religion: Christian; married: Dean; committees: Armed Services; Budget; Veterans' Affairs; elected to the 113th Congress on November 6, 2012.

Office Listings

http://walorksi.house.gov https://www.facebook.com/repjackiewalorski
https://twitter.com/repwalorski

419 Cannon House Office Building, Washington, DC 20515 .... (202) 225–3915
Chief of Staff.—Brendon DelToro. FAX: 225–6798
Legislative Director.—Annie Boyajian.
Scheduler.—Katie Toskey.
Communications Director.—Elizabeth Guyton.
202 Lincolnway East, Mishawaka, IN 46544 .... (574) 204–2645
709 Main Street, Rochester, IN 46975 .... (574) 780–1330

Counties: ELKHART, FULTON, KOSCIUSKO (part), LAPORTE (part), MARSHALL, MIAMI, PULASKI, ST. JOSEPH, STARKE, AND WABASH. CITIES: Elkhart, Goshen, Knox, La Porte, Mishawaka, Peru, Plymouth, Rochester, South Bend, Syracuse, Wabash and Winamac. Population (2010), 718,237.

ZIP Codes: 46340, 46345–46, 46348, 46350, 46352, 46365–66, 46374, 46382, 46501–02, 46504, 46506–08, 46510–11, 46513–17, 46524, 46526–28, 46530–32, 46534, 46536–39, 46540, 46542–46, 46550, 46552–56, 46561, 46563, 46565, 46567, 46570, 46572–74, 46580, 46582, 46595, 46601, 46613–17, 46619, 46624, 46626, 46628, 46634–35, 46637, 46660, 46680, 46702, 46732, 46750, 46767, 46787, 46901, 46910–12, 46914, 46919, 46921–22, 46926, 46931–32, 46939, 46940–41, 46943, 46945–46, 46950–51, 46958–59, 46960, 46962, 46968, 46970–71, 46974–75, 46978, 46980, 46982, 46984–85, 46988, 46990, 46992, 46996, 47946, 47957, 47959, 47960

* * *

THIRD DISTRICT

MARLIN A. STUTZMAN, Republican, of Howe, IN; born in Sturgis, MI, August 31, 1976; education: graduated from Lake Area Christian High School, 1994; studied business at Glen Oaks Community College, Centreville, MI and Trine State University, Angola, IN; professional: co-owner and runs family's 4,000-acre farm in northeast Indiana; owner, Stutzman Farms Trucking; religion: Southern Baptist; elected to the Indiana House as the youngest member of the Legislature, 2002–08; elected to the State Senate, 2008–10; assistant Republican Whip; caucus and member: Indiana Senate Conservative Caucus, 2009; served on the Commerce, Public Policy and Interstate Cooperation Committee; Pensions and Labor Committee; Natural Resources Committee; ranking member, Utilities and Technology Committee; Association for Retarded Children (ARC); Howe Community Association; Indiana Farm Bureau; LaGrange County Farm Bureau; National Federation for Independent Businesses (NFIB); National

Rifle Association (NRA); Young Republicans of LaGrange County; married: the former Christy Chavers, 2000; children: Payton and Preston; committees: Financial Services; elected to the 111th Congress, by special election and simultaneously elected to the 112th Congress on November 2, 2010; reelected to each succeeding Congress.

Office Listings

http://stutzman.house.gov https://twitter.com/repstutzman

1728 Longworth House Office Building, Washington, DC 20515 .... (202) 225–4436
Chief of Staff.—Matthew ''Matt'' Lloyd.
Legislative Director.—John Hammond IV.
Scheduler.—Mary Wells.
1300 South Harrison, Room 3105, Fort Wayne, IN 46802 .... (260) 424–3041
District Director.—Carlin Yoder.
Communications Director.—James Wegmann.
700 Park Avenue, Suite D, Winona Lake, IN 46590 .... (574) 269–1940

Counties: ALLEN, DEKALB, KOSCIUSKO (portions), LAGRANGE, NOBLE, STEUBEN, WHITLEY. HUNTINGTON, ADAMS, WELLS, JAY, BLACKFORD (portions). Population (2010), 723,633.

ZIP Codes: 46538, 46555, 46562, 46565, 46571, 46580, 46582, 46590, 46701–03, 46705–06, 46710–11, 46714, 46721, 46723, 46725, 46730–33, 46737–38, 46740–43, 46745–48, 46750, 46755, 46759, 46760, 46762–67, 46770, 46772–74, 46776–77, 46779, 46781, 46783–85, 46787–88, 46791–95, 46797–98, 46802–09, 46814–16, 46818–19, 46825, 46835, 46845, 47326, 47359, 47369, 47371, 47373, 47381

* * *

FOURTH DISTRICT

TODD ROKITA, Republican, of Indianapolis, IN; born in Munster, IN, February 9, 1970; education: graduated with a B.A., Wabash College, Crawfordsville, IN, 1992; J.D., Indiana University School of Law, Indianapolis, IN, 1995; professional: practicing attorney, 1995–97; general counsel at the Indiana Secretary of State's office, 1997–2000; deputy Secretary of State, 2000–2002; Secretary of State, 2002–2010; President of the Association of Secretaries of State (NASS), 2007–08; awards: Indianapolis Choice Award, by the Indianapolis Chapter of the Association of Women Business Owners, 2008; ''Award of Merit'', by the International Association of Commercial Administrators (IACA), 2008 and 2010; Friend of Foreign Service Medal, by the Taiwanese Government, 2010; religion: Roman Catholic; married: Kathy Rokita; children: Teddy and Ryan; committees: Budget; Education and the Workforce; House Administration; elected to the 112th Congress on November 2, 2010; reelected to the 113th Congress on November 6, 2012.

Office Listings

http://www.rokita.house.gov twitter: @toddrokita

236 Cannon House Office Building, Washington, DC 20515 .... (202) 225–5037
Chief of Staff.—Mike Ward. FAX: 226–0544
Legislative Director.—Tom Borck.
Communications Director.—Josh Britton.
Scheduler.—Megan Wenrich.
355 South Washington Street, Danville, IN 46122 .... (317) 718–0404
District Director.—Joe McLain.
337 Columbia Street, Lafayette, IN 47901 .... (765) 838–3930

Counties: BOONE, CLINTON, FOUNTAIN (part), HENDRICKS, JOHNSON (part), LAWRENCE, MARION (part), MONROE (part) MONTGOMERY, MORGAN, TIPPECANOE, AND WHITE (part). Population (2010), 774,798.

ZIP Codes: 46035, 46039, 46041, 46049–50, 46052, 46057–58, 46065, 46069, 46071, 46075, 46077, 46105, 46112–13, 46118, 46120–23, 46128, 46135, 46147, 46149, 46151, 46157–58, 46165–68, 46171–72, 46175, 46180, 46231, 46234, 46278, 46310, 46341, 46349, 46374, 46392, 46901–02, 46913, 46917, 46920, 46923, 46926, 46929, 46932, 46947, 46950, 46970, 46978–79, 46985, 46988, 46994, 47456, 47868, 47901, 47904–07

* * *

FIFTH DISTRICT

SUSAN W. BROOKS, Republican, of Auburn, IN; born in Fort Wayne, IN, August 25, 1960; education: graduated Homestead High School, 1978; Miami University, Oxford, OH 1982; J.D. from the Indiana University Robert H. McKinney School of Law, 1985; professional: criminal defense attorney, 1985–97; Deputy Mayor of Indianapolis, 1998–99; Ice Miller Government Affairs, 1999–2001; U.S. Attorney for the Southern District of Indiana, 2001–07; Ivy Tech Community College Senior Vice President and General Counsel, 2007–11; married: David; children: Jessica and Conner; committees: Homeland Security, Education and the Workforce, Ethics; elected to the 113th Congress on November 6, 2012.

Office Listings

http://www.susanwbrooks.house.gov

1505 Longworth House Office Building, Washington, DC 20515 .... (202) 225–2276
Chief of Staff.—Mel Raines. FAX: 225–0016
Legislative Director.—Megan Savage.
Press Secretary.—Alex Damron.
Scheduler / Executive Assistant.—Michael Corr.
District Director.—Karen Glaser.
11611 North Meridian Street, Suite 415, Carmel, IN 46032 .... (317) 848–0201
120 East 8th Street, Anderson, IN 46016 .... (765) 640–5115

Counties: BLACKFORD, BOONE, GRANT, HAMILTON, HOWARD, MADISON, MARION, AND TIPTON. Population (2010), 720,423.

ZIP Codes: 46001, 46011–13, 46016–17, 46030–34, 46036–38, 46040, 46044–45, 46047–52, 46055–56, 46060, 46062–64, 46068–70, 46072, 46074–77, 46112, 46205, 46208, 46216, 46220, 46226, 46228, 46234–36, 46240, 46250, 46254, 46256, 46260, 46268, 46278, 46280, 46290–02, 46919, 46928, 46930, 46933, 46936, 46938, 46940, 46952–53, 46957, 46986–87, 46989, 46991, 47336, 47348, 47356

* * *

SIXTH DISTRICT

LUKE MESSER, Republican, of Shelbyville, IN; born in Evansville, IN, February 27, 1969; education: B.A., Wabash College, Crawfordsville, IN, 1991; J.D., Vanderbilt University, Nashville, TN, 1994; professional: attorney; religion: Presbyterian; wife, Jennifer Messer; children, Emma, Eva and Hudson; committees: Budget; Education and the Workforce; Foreign Affairs; elected to the 113th Congress on November 6, 2012.

Office Listings

http://www.messer.house.gov twitter: @replukemesser
www.facebook.com/replukemesser www.youtube.com/user/replukemesser

508 Cannon House Office Building, Washington, DC 20515 .... (202) 225–3021
Chief of Staff.—Doug Menorca. FAX: 225–3382
Legislative Director.—Jerry White.
Communications Director.—Liz Hill.
Scheduler / Office Manager.—Amy Burke.
2 Public Square, Shelbyville, IN 46176 .... (317) 421–0704
District Director.—Mike Lynch. FAX: 421–0739
Policy Director.—John Hatter.
Staff Assistant.—Tim Hawkins.
107 West Charles Street, Muncie, IN 47305 .... (765) 747–5566
Director of Constituent Services.—Kim Bennett.
Constituent Service Representative.—Karrie Pardieck.
50 North 5th Street, Richmond, IN 47374 .... (765) 962–2883
Constituent Service Representative.—Debbie Berry.

Counties: BARTHOLOMEW, DEARBORN, DECATUR, DELAWARE, FAYETTE, FRANKLIN, HANCOCK, HENRY, JEFFERSON, JENNINGS, OHIO, RANDOLPH, RIPLEY, RUSH, SCOTT (part), SHELBY, SWITZERLAND, UNION, AND WAYNE. Population (2010), 720,422.

ZIP Codes: 45003, 45030, 45053, 45056, 45347, 45390, 46001, 46012, 46017, 46040, 46055–56, 46064, 46070, 46104, 46110, 46115, 46117, 46124, 46126–27, 46130–31, 46133, 46140, 46144, 46146, 46148, 46150, 46154–56, 46161–63, 46173, 46176, 46182, 46186, 46229, 46235–36, 46239, 46259, 46725, 46989, 46994, 47001, 47003, 47006, 47010–12, 47016–18, 47020, 47022–25, 47030–32, 47034–38, 47040–43, 47060, 47102, 47138, 47141, 47147, 47170, 47177, 47201–03, 47223–27, 47229–32, 47234, 47236, 47240, 47243–47, 47250, 47261, 47263, 47265, 47270, 47272–74, 47280, 47282–83, 47302–05, 47307–08, 47320, 47322, 47324–25, 47327, 47330–31, 47334–42, 47344–46, 47351–58, 47360–62, 47366–68, 47370, 47373–75, 47380, 47382–88, 47390, 47392–94, 47396, 47448, 47546

* * *

SEVENTH DISTRICT

ANDRÉ CARSON, Democrat, of Indianapolis, IN; born in Indianapolis, October 16, 1974; graduated Arsenal Technical High School, Indianapolis, IN; education: B.A. in Criminal Justice

Management, Concordia University Wisconsin, Mequon, WI; M.B.A, Indiana Wesleyan University, Marion, IN; professional: Investigative Officer for the Indiana State Excise Police, 1997–2006; Indiana Department of Homeland Security's Intelligence Fusion Center, 2006; City County Councilor, Marion County, 2007; religion: Muslim; married: Mariama; children: Salimah; caucuses: Whip, Congressional Black Caucus; Progressive Caucus; New Democrat Coalition; committees: Armed Services; Transportation and Infrastructure; elected to the 110th Congress on March 11, 2008, by special election, to fill the vacancy caused by the death of United States Representative Julia Carson; reelected to each succeeding Congress.

Office Listings

http://www.carson.house.gov https://twiiter.com/repandrecarson

2453 Rayburn House Office Building, Washington, DC 20515 .... (202) 225–4011
Chief of Staff.—Kim Rudolph. FAX: 225–5633
Legislative Director.—Nathan Bennett.
Legislative Assistants: Matthew Klapper, Andrea Martin, Erica Powell.
Scheduler.—Asal Sayas.
300 East Fall Creek Parkway North Drive, Suite 300, Indianapolis, IN 46205 .... (317) 283–6516
District Director.—Chris Worden. FAX: 283–6567
Press Secretary.—Blake Johnson.

Counties: MARION. City of Indianapolis, township of Center, parts of the townships of Decatur, Lawrence, Perry, Pike, Warren, Washington, and Wayne, included are the cities of Beech Grove and Lawrence. Population (2010), 676,351.

ZIP Codes: 46107, 46160, 46201–09, 46211, 46214, 46216–22, 46224–31, 46234–35, 46237, 46239–42, 46244, 46247, 46249, 46251, 46253–55, 46260, 46266, 46268, 46274–75, 46277–78, 46282–83, 46285, 46291, 46295–96, 46298

* * *

EIGHTH DISTRICT

LARRY BUCSHON, Republican, of Newburgh, IN; born in Kincaid, IL, May 31, 1962; graduated from South Fork High School, Kincaid, IL, 1980; B.S., with a concentration in chemistry, University of Illinois, Urbana-Champaign, IL, 1984; M.D., University of Illinois, Chicago, 1988; residency, Medical College of Wisconsin in Milwaukee, 1988–95; cardiothoracic surgeon, 1995–2010; commissioned lieutenant, U.S. Navy Reserves, 1989; promoted, lieutenant commander, 1994; honorable discharge, 1998; married: Kathryn; children: Luke, Alec, Blair, and Zoe; committees: Education and the Workforce; Science, Space, and Technology; Transportation and Infrastructure; elected to the 112th Congress on November 2, 2010; reelected to the 113th Congress on November 6, 2012.

Office Listings

http://www.bucshon.house.gov twitter: @replarrybucshon

1005 Longworth House Office Building, Washington, DC 20515 .... (202) 225–4636
Chief of Staff.—Jon Causey. FAX: 225–3284
Press Secretary.—Nick McGee.
Legislative Director.—Teresa Buckley.
Executive Assistant.—Beth Trenti.
101 Northwest Martin Luther King, Jr. Boulevard, Room 124, Evansville, IN 47708 .... (812) 465–6484
Deputy Chief of Staff.—Steven Reeves.
901 Wabash Avenue, Suite 140, Terre Haute, IN 47807 .... (812) 232–0523

Counties: CLAY, CRAWFORD (part), DAVIESS, DUBOIS, GIBSON, GREENE, KNOX, MARTIN, OWEN, PARKE, PERRY, PIKE, POSEY, SPENCER, SULLIVAN, VANDERBURGH, VERMILLION, VIGO, AND WARRICK. Population (2010), 694,398.

ZIP Codes: 46105, 46120–21, 46128, 46135, 46165–66, 46170–72, 46175, 47403–04, 47424, 47427, 47429, 47431–33, 47438–39, 47441, 47443, 47445–46, 47449, 47453, 47455–57, 47459–60, 47462, 47465, 47469–71, 47501, 47512, 47516, 47519, 47522–24, 47527–29, 47535, 47537, 47541–42, 47553, 47557–58, 47561–62, 47564, 47567–68, 47573, 47578, 47581, 47584–85, 47590–91, 47596–98, 47601, 47610–14, 47616, 47618–20, 47629–31, 47633, 47637–40, 47647–49, 47654, 47660, 47665–66, 47670, 47683, 47701–06, 47708, 47710–16, 47719–22, 47724–25, 47727–28, 47730–37, 47739–41, 47744, 47747, 47750, 47801–05, 47807–09, 47811–12, 47830–34, 47836–38, 47840–42, 47845–66, 47868–72, 47874–76, 47878–82, 47884–85, 47917–18, 47921, 47928, 47932, 47952, 47966, 47969–70, 47974–75, 47982, 47987, 47989, 47991–93

* * *

NINTH DISTRICT

TODD C. YOUNG, Republican, of Bloomington, IN; born in Indianapolis, IN, August 24, 1972; education: B.S., political science, United States Naval Academy, Annapolis, MD, 1995;

M.B.A., University of Chicago, Chicago, IL, 2000; M.A., american history, School of Advanced Study, University of London, UK, 2001; J.D., Indiana University, Bloomington, IN, 2005; professional: legislative assistant, United States Senate, 2002–03; management consultant, Crowe Chizek, 2003–05; attorney, Tucker and Tucker, PC in Paoli, IN, 2005–09; military: United States Navy, 1990–95; United States Marine Corps, 1995–2000; member: Sherwood Oaks Christian Church, Bloomington, IN; married: Jennifer Tucker Hill; children: Tucker, Annalise, Abigal, and Ava; committees: Ways and Means; elected to the 112th Congress on November 2, 2010; reelected to the 113th Congress on November 6, 2012.

Office Listings

http://toddyoung.house.gov twitter: @reptoddyoung

1721 Longworth House Office Building, Washington, DC 20515 .... (202) 225–5315
Chief of Staff.—John Connell. FAX: 226–6866
Legislative Director.—Emily Mueller.
Communications Director.—Trevor Foughty.
Scheduler.—Jodi Richardson.
279 Quartermaster Drive, Jeffersonville, IN 47130 .... (812) 288–3999
320 West 8th Street, Suite 114, Bloomington, IN 47404 .... (812) 335–3355
2 North Madison Avenue, Greenwood, IN 46142.

Counties: BROWN, CLARK, CRAWFORD (part), FLOYD, HARRISON, JACKSON, JOHNSON, LAWRENCE, MONROE, MORGAN (part), ORANGE, SCOTT (part), and Washington. Population (2010), 726,570.

ZIP Codes: 46106, 46110–11, 46113, 46124, 46131, 46140, 46142–43, 46151, 46158, 46160, 46162, 46164, 46166, 56181, 46184, 46229, 46259, 47019, 47021, 47033, 47039, 47102, 47104, 47106–08, 47110–12, 47114–20, 47122–26, 47129–38, 47140–47, 47150–51, 47160–67, 47170, 47172, 47175, 47177, 47190, 47199, 47201, 47220, 47228–29, 47235, 47249, 47260, 47264, 47274, 47281, 47401–08, 47420–21, 47426, 47429, 47432–37, 47446, 47448, 47451–52, 47454, 47458, 47460, 47462–64, 47467–70

IOWA

(Population 2010, 3,046,355)

SENATORS

CHUCK GRASSLEY, Republican, of New Hartford, IA; born in New Hartford, IA, September 17, 1933; education: graduated, New Hartford Community High School, 1951; B.A., University of Northern Iowa, 1955; M.A., University of Northern Iowa, 1956; doctoral studies, University of Iowa, 1957–58; professional: farmer; member: Iowa State Legislature, 1959–74; Farm Bureau; State and County Historical Society; Masons; Baptist Church; and International Association of Machinists, 1962–71; co-chair, International Narcotics Control Caucus; married: the former Barbara Ann Speicher, 1954; children: Lee, Wendy, Robin Lynn, Michele Marie; committees: ranking member, Judiciary; Agriculture, Nutrition, and Forestry; Budget; Finance; Joint Committee on Taxation; elected to the 94th Congress, November 5, 1974; reelected to the 95th and 96th Congresses; elected to the U.S. Senate, November 4, 1980; reelected to each succeeding Senate term.

Office Listings

http://grassley.senate.gov https://www.facebook.com/grassley
https://twitter.com/chuckgrassley

135 Hart Senate Office Building, Washington, DC 20510	(202) 224–3744
Chief of Staff.—Jill Kozeny.	FAX: 224–6020
Legislative Director.—Kolan Davis.	
721 Federal Building, 210 Walnut Street, Des Moines, IA 50309	(515) 288–1145
State Administrator.—Robert Renaud.	
111 7th Avenue, Southeast, Suite 6800, Cedar Rapids, IA 52404	(319) 363–6832
120 Federal Courthouse Building, 320 Sixth Street, Sioux City, IA 51101	(712) 233–1860
210 Waterloo Building, 531 Commercial Street, Waterloo, IA 50701	(319) 232–6657
201 West 2nd Street, Suite 720, Davenport, IA 52801	(563) 322–4331
307 Federal Building, 8 South Sixth Street, Council Bluffs, IA 51501	(712) 322–7103

* * *

TOM HARKIN, Democrat, of Cumming, IA; born in Cumming, November 19, 1939; education: graduated, Dowling Catholic High School, Des Moines, IA; B.S., Iowa State University, Ames, 1962; U.S. Navy, 1962–67; military service: LCDR, U.S. Naval Reserves; LL.B., Catholic University of America, Washington, DC, 1972; admitted to the bar, Des Moines, IA, 1972; married: the former Ruth Raduenz, 1968; children: Amy and Jenny; committees: chair, Health, Education, Labor, and Pensions; Agriculture, Nutrition, and Forestry; Appropriations; elected to the 94th Congress on November 5, 1974; reelected to four succeeding Congresses; elected to the U.S. Senate on November 6, 1984; reelected to each succeeding Senate term.

Office Listings

http://harkin.senate.gov

731 Hart Senate Office Building, Washington, DC 20510	(202) 224–3254
Chief of Staff.—Brian Ahlberg.	FAX: 224–9369
Communications Director.—Kate Frischmann.	
Federal Building, 210 Walnut Street, Room 733, Des Moines, IA 50309	(515) 284–4574
11 7th Avenue Southeast, Box 16, Suite 480, Cedar Rapids, IA 52401	(319) 365–4504
1606 Brady Street, Suite 323, Davenport, IA 52801	(563) 322–1338
Federal Building, 320 Sixth Street, Room 110, Sioux City, IA 51101	(712) 252–1550
Federal Building, 350 West Sixth Street, Room 315, Dubuque, IA 52001	(563) 582–2130

REPRESENTATIVES

FIRST DISTRICT

BRUCE L. BRALEY, Democrat, of Waterloo, IA; born in Grinnell, IA, October 30, 1957; education: B.A., Iowa State University, Ames, IA, 1980; J.D., University of Iowa Law School, Iowa City, IA, 1983; professional: attorney, Dulton, Braun, Staack & Hellman, 1983–2006; married: Carolyn; children: Lisa, David and Paul; chair, Populist Caucus; committees: Energy and Commerce; elected to the 110th Congress on November 7, 2006; reelected to each succeeding Congress.

Office Listings

http://www.house.gov/braley

2263 Rayburn House Office Building, Washington, DC 20515	(202) 225–2911
Chief of Staff.—John Davis.	FAX: 225–6666
219 East Fourth Street, Waterloo, IA 50703	(319) 287–3233
1050 Main Street, Dubuque, IA 52001	(563) 557–7789
Deputy Director.—John Murphy.	
310 3rd Street, Southeast, Cedar Rapids, IA 52401	(319) 364–2288

Counties: ALLAMAKEE, BENTON, BLACK HAWK, BREMER, BUCHANAN, CLAYTON, DELAWARE, DUBUQUE, FAYETTE, HOWARD, IOWA, JACKSON, JONES, LINN, MARSHALL, MITCHELL, POWESHIEK, TAMA, WINNESHIEK, AND WORTH. Population (2010), 761,548.

ZIP Codes: 50005, 50027, 50051, 50078, 50106, 50112, 50120, 50136, 50141–42, 50148, 50153, 50157–58, 50162, 50171, 50173, 50206–07, 50234, 50239, 50242, 50247, 50258, 50434, 50440, 50444, 50446, 50448, 50450, 50454–56, 50458–61, 50464, 50466, 50471–72, 50476, 50603, 50606–07, 50609, 50612–13, 50621–22, 50626, 50628–30, 50632, 50634–35, 50641, 50643–45, 50647–48, 50650–52, 50654–55, 50662, 50664, 50666–71, 50674–77, 50681–82, 50701–03, 50707, 52001–03, 52030–33, 52035, 52037–50, 52052–54, 52057, 52060, 52064–66, 52068–70, 52072–74, 52076–79, 52101, 52132–36, 52140–42, 52144, 52146–47, 52151, 52154–66, 52168–72, 52175, 52201–03, 52205–25, 52227–29, 52232–33, 52236–37, 52249, 52251, 52253, 52257, 52301–02, 52305–16, 52318, 52320–21, 52323–26, 52328–30, 52332, 52334, 52336, 52338–39, 52341–42, 52345–49, 52351–52, 52354–56, 52361–62, 52401–05, 52411, 52731

* * *

SECOND DISTRICT

DAVID LOEBSACK, Democrat, of Iowa City, IA; born in Sioux City, IA, December 23, 1952; education: graduated, East High School, 1970; B.A., Iowa State University, 1974; M.A., Iowa State University, 1976; Ph.D., political science, University of California, Davis, 1985; professional: professor, political science, Cornell College, 1982–2006; married: Teresa Loebsack; four children; committees: Armed Services; Education and the Workforce; elected to the 110th Congress on November 7, 2006; reelected to each succeeding Congress.

Office Listings

http://www.loebsack.house.gov

1527 Longworth House Office Building, Washington, DC 20515	(202) 225–6576
Chief of Staff.—Eric Witte.	
Office Manager / Scheduler.—Heidi Hotopp.	
209 West 4th Street, Suite 104, Davenport, IA 52801	(563) 323–5988
District Director.—Rob Sueppel.	FAX: 323–5231
125 South Dubuque Street, Iowa City, IA 52240–4003	(319) 351–0789
	(866) 914–4692

Counties: APPANOOSE, CLARKE, CEDAR, CLINTON, DECATUR, DES MOINES, DAVIS, HENRY, JASPER, JOHNSON, JEFFERSON, KEOKUK, LOUISA, LEE, LUCAS, MUSCATINE, MAHASKA, MONROE, MARION, SCOTT, VAN BUREN, WASHINGTON, WAYNE, AND WAPELLO. Population (2010), 761,624.

ZIP Codes: 50008, 50027–28, 50044, 50049, 50052, 50054, 50057, 50060, 50062, 50065, 50067–68, 50103–04, 50108, 50116, 50119, 50123, 50127, 50135–38, 50140, 50143–44, 50147, 50150–51, 50153, 50163, 50165, 50168, 50170, 50174, 50207–08, 50213–14, 50219, 50225, 50228, 50232, 50238, 50251–52, 50255–56, 50262, 50264, 50268, 50272, 50275, 52037, 52201, 52216, 52231, 52235, 52240, 52241, 52242–48, 52254–55, 52306, 52317, 52319, 52322, 52327, 52333, 52335, 52337–38, 52340, 52353, 52355–56, 52358–59, 52531, 52533–35, 52537–38, 52540, 52542–44, 52549–52, 52555–57, 52560–63, 52565, 52567–74, 52576–77, 52580–81, 52583–86, 52588, 52590–91, 52593–95, 52601, 52619–21, 52623–27, 52630–32, 52635, 52637–42, 52644–60, 52701, 52720–22, 52726–34, 52736–39, 52742, 52745–61, 52765–69, 52771–74, 52776–78, 52801–09

* * *

THIRD DISTRICT

TOM LATHAM, Republican, of Ames, IA; born in Hampton, IA, July 14, 1948; education: attended Alexander Community School; graduated Cal (Latimer) Community College, 1966; attended Wartburg College, 1966–67; Iowa State University, 1967–70; agriculture business major; professional: marketing representative, independent insurance agent, bank teller and bookkeeper; member and past president, Nazareth Lutheran Church; past chairman, Franklin County Extension Council; secretary, Republican Party of Iowa; 5th District representative, Republican State Central Committee; co-chairman, Franklin County Republican Central Committee; Iowa delegation whip; member: 1992 Republican National Convention, Iowa Farm Bureau Federation, Iowa Soybean Association, American Seed Trade Association, Iowa Corn Growers Association, Iowa Seed Association, Agribusiness Association of Iowa, I.S.U.

Extension Citizens Advisory Council; married: Mary Katherine (Kathy), 1975; children: Justin, Jennifer, and Jill; committees: Appropriations; elected to the 104th Congress; reelected to each succeeding Congress.

Office Listings

http://www.house.gov/latham

2217 Rayburn House Office Building, Washington, DC 20515 .... (202) 225–5476
Chief of Staff.—James Carstensen. FAX: 225–3301
Scheduler.—Andrew Moore.
2700 Grand Avenue, Suite 109, Ames, IA 50312 .... (515) 282–1909
District Director.—Clarke Scanlon.
208 West Taylor Street, Creston, IA 50801 .... (641) 782–2495
Regional Representative.—Laura Hartman.
116 West Broadway Street, Council Bluffs, IA 51503 .... (712) 325–1404
Regional Representative.—Emily Clark.

Counties: ADAIR, ADAMS, CASS, DALLAS, FREMONT, GUTHRIE, MADISON, MILLS, MONTGOMERY, PAGE, POLK, POTTAWATTAMIE, RINGGOLD, TAYLOR, UNION, AND WARREN. Population (2010), 761,612.

ZIP Codes: 50001–03, 50007, 50009, 50020–23, 50026, 50029, 50032–33, 50035, 50038–39, 50047–48, 50061, 50063, 50066, 50069–70, 50072–74, 50109, 50111, 50115, 50118, 50125, 50128, 50131, 50133, 50139, 50145–46, 50149, 50155, 50160, 50164, 50166–67, 50169, 50210–11, 50216, 50218, 50220, 50222, 50226, 50229, 50233, 50237, 50240–41, 50243, 50250, 50254, 50257, 50261, 50263, 50265–66, 50273–74, 50276–77, 50301–25, 50327–36, 50339–40, 50359–64, 50367–69, 50380–81, 50391–96, 50398, 50801, 50830–31, 50833, 50835–37, 50839–43, 50845–49, 50851, 50853–54, 50857–64, 50936, 50940, 50947, 50950, 50980–83, 51501–03, 51510, 51521, 51525–26, 51532–36, 51540–42, 51544, 51548–49, 51551–54, 51559–61, 51566, 51571, 51573, 51575–77, 51591, 51601, 51603, 51630–32, 51636–40, 51645–54, 51656

* * *

FOURTH DISTRICT

STEVE KING, Republican, of Kiron, IA; born in Storm Lake, IA, May 28, 1949; education: graduated, Denison Community High School; attended Northwest Missouri State University, Maryville, MO, 1967–70; professional: agri-businessman; owner and operator of King Construction Company; public service: Iowa State Senate, 1996–2002; religion: Catholic; family: married to Marilyn; children: David, Michael, and Jeff; committees: Agriculture; Judiciary; Small Business; elected to the 108th Congress on November 5, 2002; reelected to each succeeding Congress.

Office Listings

http://www.steveking.house.gov

1131 Longworth House Office Building, Washington, DC 20515 .... (202) 225–4426
Chief of Staff.—Tracie Gibler. FAX: 225–3193
Legislative Director.—Thomas Binion.
Scheduler.—Meredith Cooke.
Press Secretary.—Sarah Wells.
526 Nebraska Street, Sioux City, IA 51101 .... (712) 224–4692
202 1st Street, SE., Suite 126, Mason City, IA 50401 .... (641) 201–1624
723 Central Avenue, Fort Dodge, IA 50501 .... (515) 573–2738
306 North Grand Avenue, Spencer, IA 51301 .... (712) 580–7754
1421 South Bell Avenue, Suite 102, Ames, IA 50010 .... (515) 232–2885

Counties: AUDUBON, BOONE, BUENA VISTA, BUTLER, CALHOUN, CARROLL, CERRO GORDO, CHEROKEE, CHICKASAW, CLAY, CRAWFORD, DICKINSON, EMMET, FLOYD, FRANKLIN, GREENE, GRUNDY, HAMILTON, HANCOCK, HARDIN, HARRISON, HUMBOLDT, IDA, KOSSUTH, LYON, MONONA, O'BRIEN, OSCEOLA, PALO ALTO, PLYMOUTH, POCAHONTAS, SAC, SHELBY, SIOUX, STORY, WEBSTER, WINNEBAGO, WOODBURY, AND WRIGHT. Population (2010), 761,571.

ZIP Codes: 50006, 50010–12, 50014, 50020, 50022, 50025–26, 50029, 50034, 50036, 50040–42, 50046, 50050, 50055–56, 50058, 50064, 50071, 50075–76, 50101–02, 50105, 50107, 50117, 50122, 50124, 50126, 50128–30, 50132, 50134, 50154, 50156, 50161, 50201, 50206, 50212, 50217, 50220, 50223, 50227, 50230–31, 50235–36, 50243–44, 50246–49, 50258, 50269, 50271, 50276, 50278, 50401, 50420–21, 50423–24, 50428, 50430–36, 50438–39, 50441, 50444, 50446, 50449–53, 50457–58, 50460–61, 50464–65, 50467–71, 50473, 50475, 50477–80, 50482–84, 50501, 50510–11, 50514–25, 50527–33, 50535–36, 50538–46, 50548, 50551, 50554, 50556–63, 50565–71, 50573–79, 50581–83, 50585–86, 50588, 50590–95, 50597–99, 50601–05, 50609, 50611, 50613, 50616, 50619–21, 50624–25, 50627, 50630, 50633, 50636, 50638, 50642–43, 50645, 50653, 50657–60, 50665–66, 50669–70, 50672–74, 50680, 51001–12, 51014, 51016, 51018–20, 51022–31, 51033–41, 51044–56, 51058, 51060–63, 51101, 51103–06, 51108–09, 51111, 51201, 51230–32, 51234–35, 51237–50, 51301, 51331, 51333–34, 51338, 51340–43, 51345–47, 51350–51, 51354–55, 51357–58, 51360, 51363–66, 51401, 51430–31, 51433, 51436, 51439–55, 51458–59, 51460–63, 51465–67, 51520–21, 51523, 51527–31, 51537, 51543, 51545–46, 51550, 51552, 51555–59, 51562–65, 51570, 51572, 51577–79, 52154, 52171

KANSAS

(Population 2010, 2,853,118)

SENATORS

PAT ROBERTS, Republican, of Dodge City, KS; born in Topeka, KS, April 20, 1936; education: graduated, Holton High School, Holton, KS, 1954; B.S., journalism, Kansas State University, Manhattan, KS, 1958; professional: captain, U.S. Marine Corps, 1958–62; editor and reporter, Arizona newspapers, 1962–67; aide to Senator Frank Carlson, 1967–68; aide to Representative Keith Sebelius, 1969–80; U.S. House of Representatives, 1980–96; founding member: bipartisan Caucus on Unfunded Mandates, House Rural Health Care Coalition; shepherded the 1996 Freedom to Farm Act through the House and Senate; married: the former Franki Fann, 1969; children: David, Ashleigh, and Anne-Wesley; committees: ranking member, Rules and Administration; Agriculture, Nutrition, and Forestry; Finance; Health, Education, Labor, and Pensions; Joint Committee on the Library; Joint Committee on Printing; Select Committee on Ethics; elected to the U.S. Senate in November, 1996; reelected to each succeeding Senate term.

Office Listings

http://roberts.senate.gov

109 Hart Senate Office Building, Washington, DC 20510 .... (202) 224–4774
Chief of Staff.—Jackie Cottrell. FAX: 224–3514
Legislative Director.—Amber Sechrist.
Scheduler.—Jensine Moyer.
Communications Director.—Sarah Little.
100 Military Plaza, P.O. Box 550, Dodge City, KS 67801 .... (620) 227–2244
District Director.—Martha Ruiz-Martinez.
155 North Market Street, Suite 120, Wichita, KS 67202 .... (316) 263–0416
District Director.—Tamara Woods.
Frank Carlson Federal Building, 444 SE Quincy, Room 392, Topeka, KS 66683 .... (785) 295–2745
District Director.—Gilda Lintz.
11900 College Boulevard, Suite 203, Overland Park, KS 66210 .... (913) 451–9343
State Director.—Chad Tenpenny.

* * *

JERRY MORAN, Republican, of Hays, Kansas; born in Plainville, Kansas, May 29, 1954; education: B.S., University of Kansas, Lawrence, KS, 1976; J.D., University of Kansas School of Law, Lawrence, KS, 1981; M.B.A., candidate, Fort Hays State University, Hays, KS; professional: bank officer; instructor; U.S. House of Representatives, 1997–2010; Kansas State Senate, 1989–97, serving as vice president, 1993–95, majority leader, 1995–97; Kansas State Special Assistant Attorney General, 1982–85; deputy attorney, Rooks County, KS, 1987–95; University of Kansas School of Law Board of Governors, served as vice president, 1993–94, president, 1994–95; Board of Directors, Kansas Chamber of Commerce and Industry, 1996–97; religion: Christian; family: married Robba; two daughters, Kelsey and Alex; caucuses: the Senate Hunger Caucus, the Senate Western Caucus, Senate Rural Health Caucus, co-chair of Community Pharmacy Caucus; committees: Appropriations; Banking, Housing, and Urban Affairs; Veterans' Affairs; elected to the U.S. Senate on November 2, 2010.

Office Listings

http://moran.senate.gov

361A Russell Senate Office Building, Washington, DC 20510 .... (202) 224–6521
Chief of Staff.—Todd Novascone. FAX: 228–6966
Legislative Director.—Alex Richard.
Scheduler.—Emily Whitfield.
Communications Director.—Garrette Silverman.
1200 Main Street, Suite 402, Hays, KS 67601 .... (785) 628–6401
State Casework Director.—Rachel Robben.
Constituent Services Representative.—Chelsey Gillogly.
23600 College Boulevard, Suite 201, Olathe, KS 66061 .... (913) 393–0711
Kansas State Scheduler.—Lisa Dethloff.
306 North Broadway, Suite 125, P.O. Box 1372, Pittsburg, KS 66762 .... (620) 232–2286
FAX: 232–2284
923 Westport Place, Suite 210, P.O. Box 067, Manhattan, KS 66502 .... (785) 539–8973
FAX: 587–0789
3450 North Rock Road, Building 200, Suite 209, P.O. Box 781753, Wichita, KS 67226 .... (316) 631–1410

State Director.—Brennen Britton. FAX: 631–1297
Deputy State Director.—Mike Zamrzia.

REPRESENTATIVES

FIRST DISTRICT

TIM HUELSKAMP, Republican, of Fowler, KS; born in Fowler, November 11, 1968; education: attended seminary of Santa Fe, NM; B.S., social science, College of Santa Fe, Santa Fe, NM, 1991; Ph.D., political science, American University of Washington, DC, 1995; professional: farmer; rancher; budget and legislative analyst for the State of New Mexico; served in the Kansas State Senate, 1996–2010; married: Angela Huelskamp; children: Natasha, Rebecca, Athan, and Alexander; committees: Small Business; Veterans' Affairs; elected to the 112th Congress on November 2, 2010; reelected to the 113th on November 6, 2012.

Office Listings

http://huelskamp.house.gov

126 Cannon House Office Building, Washington, DC 20515 .... (202) 225–2715
Chief of Staff.—Jim Pfaff. FAX: 225–5124
Legislative Director.—Mark Kelly.
Press Secretary.—Paul Nelson.
Office Manager.—Matthew Salcedo.
100 Military Avenue, Suite 205, Dodge City, KS 67801–0249 .... (620) 225–0172
One North Main, Suite 525, P.O. Box 1128, Hutchinson, KS 67504 .... (620) 665–6138
119 West Iron Avenue, Fourth Floor, Suite A, P.O. Box 766, Salina, KS 67402 .... (785) 309–0572

Counties: BARBER, BARTON, CHASE, CHEYENNE, CLARK, CLAY, CLOUD, COMANCHE, DECATUR, DICKINSON, EDWARDS, ELLIS, ELLSWORTH, FINNEY, FORD, GEARY (part), GOVE, GRAHAM, GRANT, GRAY, GREELEY, GREENWOOD (part), Hamilton, Haskell, Hodgeman, Jewell, Kearny, Kiowa, Lane, Lincoln, Logan, Lyon, McPherson, Marion (part), MARSHALL, MEADE, MITCHELL, MORRIS, MORTON, NEMAHA (part), NESS, NORTON, OSBORNE, OTTAWA, PAWNEE, PHILLIPS, PRATT, RAWLINS, RENO, REPUBLIC, RICE, ROOKS, RUSH, RUSSELL, SALINE, SCOTT, SEWARD, SHERIDAN, SHERMAN, SMITH, STAFFORD, STANTON, STEVENS, THOMAS, TREGO, WABAUNSEE, WALLACE, WASHINGTON, AND WICHITA. Population (2010), 713,278.

ZIP Codes: 66401, 66403–04, 66406–08, 66411–13, 66423, 66427, 66431, 66438, 66441, 66501–02, 66507–08, 66514, 66518, 66523, 66526, 66534, 66536, 66538, 66541, 66544, 66547–48, 66610, 66614–15, 66801, 66830, 66833–35, 66838, 66840, 66843, 66845–46, 66849–51, 66853–54, 66858–62, 66864–66, 66868–70, 66872–73, 66901, 66930, 66932–33, 66935–46, 66948–49, 66951–53, 66955–56, 66958–64, 66966–68, 66970, 67009, 67020–21, 67028–29, 67035, 67053–54, 67057, 67059, 67061–63, 67065–66, 67068, 67070, 67073, 67104, 67107–09, 67112, 67114, 67124, 67127, 67134, 67138, 67143, 67151, 67155, 67335, 67401–02, 67410, 67416–18, 67420, 67422–23, 67425, 67427–28, 67430–32, 67436–39, 67441–52, 67454–60, 67464, 67466–68, 67470, 7473–76, 67478, 67480–85, 67487, 67490–92, 67501–02, 67504–05, 67510–16, 67518–26, 67529–30, 67543–48, 67550, 67552–54, 67556–57, 67559–61, 67563–68, 67570, 67572–76, 67578–79, 67581, 67583–85, 67601, 67621–23, 67625–29, 67631–32, 67634–35, 67637–40, 67642–51, 67653–61, 67663–65, 67667, 67669, 67671–75, 67701, 67730–41, 67743–45, 67748–49, 67751–53, 67756–58, 67761–62, 67764, 67801, 67831, 67834–42, 67844, 67846, 67849–51, 67853–55, 67857, 67859–65, 67867, 67869–71, 67876–80, 67882, 67901, 67905, 67950–54

* * *

SECOND DISTRICT

LYNN JENKINS, Republican, of Topeka, KS; born in Topeka, KS, June 10, 1963; education: A.A., Kansas State University, Manhattan, KS, 1985; B.S., accounting / economics, Weber State College, Ogden, UT, 1985; professional: certified public accountant; accountant, Braunsdorf, Carson, and Clinkinbeard; accountant, Baird, Kurtz and Dobson; certified public accountant, Public Accounting / Specialty Taxation, 1985–present; Representative, Kansas State House of Representatives, 1999–2000; Senator, Kansas State Senate, 2001–02; Treasurer, State of Kansas, 2003–08; children: Hayley and Hayden; Community Pharmacy Caucus; House Army Caucus; Military Veterans Caucus; Nuclear Issues Working Group; Cystic Fibrosis Caucus; committees: Ways and Means; elected to the 111th Congress on November 4, 2008; reelected to each succeeding Congress.

Office Listings

http://lynnjenkins.house.gov

1027 Longworth House Office Building, Washington, DC 20515 .... (202) 225–6601
Chief of Staff.—Pat Leopold. FAX: 225–7986
Legislative Director.—Eric Schmutz.
Scheduler.—Lauren Hoover.
Press Aide.—Annie Dwyer.
510 Southwest 10th Avenue, Topeka, KS 66612 .... (785) 234–5966

1001 North Broadway, Suite C, Pittsburgh, KS 66762 .... (620) 231–5966

Counties: ALLEN, ANDERSON, ATCHISON, BOURBON, BROWN, CHEROKEE, COFFEY, CRAWFORD, DONIPHAN, DOUGLAS, FRANKLIN, JACKSON, JEFFERSON, LABETTE, LEAVENWORTH, LINN, MARSHALL (part), MIAMI (part), MONTGOMERY, NEMAHA, NEOSHO, OSAGE, SHAWNEE, WILSON, AND WOODSON. Population (2010), 713,272.

ZIP Codes: 66002, 66006–08, 66010, 66012, 66014–17, 66020–21, 66023–27, 66032–33, 66035, 66039–50, 66052–54, 66056, 66058, 66060, 66064, 66066–67, 66070–73, 66075–76, 66078–80, 66083, 66086–88, 66090–95, 66097, 66109, 66402–04, 66406, 66408–09, 66411–19, 66422, 66424–25, 66427–29, 66431–32, 66434, 66436, 66438–40, 66451, 66508–10, 66512, 66515–16, 66521–24, 66527–28, 66532–34, 66536–44, 66546, 66548, 66550, 66552, 66603–12, 66614–19, 66621–22, 66701, 66710–14, 66716–17, 66720, 66724–25, 66728, 66732–36, 66738–41, 66743, 66746, 66748–49, 66751, 66753–58, 66760–63, 66767, 66769–73, 66775–83, 66839, 66852, 66854, 66856–57, 66864, 66868, 66871, 67047, 67301, 67330, 67332–33, 67335–37, 67340–42, 67344, 67347, 67351, 67354, 67356–57, 67363–64

* * *

THIRD DISTRICT

KEVIN YODER, Republican, of Overland Park; born in Hutchison, KS, January 8, 1976; education: B.A., University of Kansas, Lawrence, KS, 1999; J.D., University of Kansas College of Law, Lawrence, KS, 2002; professional: attorney; admitted to the Kansas Bar, 2002; State Representative, Kansas House of Representatives, 20th District; 2003–11; chairman, House Appropriations Committee; chairman, General Government Budget Committee; serves on the Board of Directors of the Johnson County Bar Association; married: Brooke Robinson Yoder; members: member of the Kansas Sentencing Commission; Kansas City Chamber's Congressional Forum; Overland Park Rotary Club; Johnson County Bar Association; Greater Kansas City Area University of Kansas Alumni Association Board of Directors; Overland Park Republican Precinct Committeeman; committees: Appropriations; elected to the 112th Congress on November 2, 2010; reelected to the 113th Congress on November 6, 2012.

Office Listings

http://www.yoder.house.gov

215 Cannon House Office Building, Washington, DC 20515 .... (202) 225–2865
Chief of Staff.—Vacant.
Legislative Director.—Patrick Carroll.
Scheduler.—Emily Hunter.
Communications Director.—Matthew Manda.
7325 West 79th Terrace, Overland Park, KS 66204 .... (913) 621–0832
District Director.—Molly Haase. FAX: 621–1533
Constituent Services Director.—Cheyne Worley.

Counties: JOHNSON, MIAMI (part), and Wyandotte. Population (2010), 713,272.

ZIP Codes: 66012–13, 66018–19, 66021, 66025, 66030–31, 66053, 66061–62, 66071, 66083, 66085, 66101–06, 66109, 66111–12, 66115, 66118, 66202–21, 66223–24, 66226–27

* * *

FOURTH DISTRICT

MIKE POMPEO, Republican, of Wichita, KS; born in Orange, CA, December 30, 1963; education: B.S., mechanical engineering, United States Military Academy at West Point, NY, 1986, graduated first in his class; J.D., Harvard Law School, Cambridge, MA, 1994; professional: owned/founder, Thayer Aerospace; president, Sentry International; editor of *Harvard Law Review;* religion: Presbyterian; married: Susan Pompeo of Wichita, KS; children: Nick; caucus: Republican Study Committee; committees: Energy and Commerce; Permanent Select Committee on Intelligence; elected to the 112th Congress on November 2, 2010; reelected to the 113th Congress on November 6, 2012.

Office Listings

http://www.pompeo.house.gov

107 Cannon House Office Building, Washington, DC 20515 .... (202) 225–6216
Chief of Staff.—Jim Richardson. FAX: 225–3489
Legislative Director.—Chiris Parinello.
Legislative Assistants: Blake Hollander, Preston Kerr.
Legislative Aide.—Mike Netherton.
Communications Director.—J.P. Freire.
Scheduler / Office Manager.—Sarah Keeny.
Staff Assistant.—Katherine Thomas.
7701 East Kellogg, Suite 510, Wichita, KS 67207 .... (316) 262–8992

District Director.—Toni Porter.

Counties: BARBER, BUTLER, CHAUTAUQUA, COMANCHE, COWLEY, EDWARDS, ELK, GREENWOOD, HARPER, HARVEY, KINGMAN, KIOWA, PAWNEE (part), Pratt, Sedgwick, Stafford, and Sumner. Population (2010), 715,456.

ZIP Codes: 66759, 66853, 66855, 66860, 66863, 66870, 67001–05, 67008–10, 67012–13, 67016–26, 67028–31, 67035–39, 67041–42, 67045, 67047, 67049–52, 67054–62, 67065–68, 67070–72, 67074, 67101–06, 67108–12, 67114, 67117–20, 67122–24, 67127, 67131–35, 67137–38, 67140, 67142–44, 67146–47, 67149–52, 67154–56, 67159, 67201–21, 67223, 67226–28, 67230, 67232, 67235, 67260, 67275–78, 67334–46, 67349, 67352–53, 67355, 67360–61, 67511, 67519, 67523, 67529, 67547, 67550, 67552, 67563, 67574

KENTUCKY

(Population 2010, 4,339,367)

SENATORS

MITCH McCONNELL, Republican, of Louisville, KY; born in Colbert County, AL, February 20, 1942; education: graduated Manual High School, Louisville, 1960, president of the student body; B.A. with honors, University of Louisville, 1964, president of the student council, president of the student body of the College of Arts and Sciences; J.D., University of Kentucky Law School, 1967, president of student bar association, outstanding oral advocate; professional: attorney, admitted to the Kentucky Bar, 1967; chief legislative assistant to U.S. Senator Marlow Cook, 1968–70; Deputy Assistant U.S. Attorney General, 1974–75; Judge/Executive of Jefferson County, KY, 1978–84; chairman, National Republican Senatorial Committee, 1997–2000; chairman, Joint Congressional Committee on Inaugural Ceremonies, 1999–2001; Senate Majority Whip, 2002–06; Senate Republican Leader, 2007–present; married to Elaine Chao on February 6, 1993; children: Elly, Claire and Porter; committees: Agriculture, Nutrition, and Forestry; Appropriations; Rules and Administration; elected to the U.S. Senate on November 6, 1984; reelected to each succeeding Senate term.

Office Listings

http://mcconnell.senate.gov https://twitter.com/mcconnellpress
https://www.facebook.com/mitchmcconnell

317 Russell Senate Office Building, Washington, DC 20510 .... (202) 224–2541
Chief of Staff.—Reb Brownell (acting). FAX: 224–2499
Scheduler.—Stefanie Muchow.
Legislative Director / Counsel.—Russell Coleman.
Communications Director.—Robert Steurer.
601 West Broadway, Suite 630, Louisville, KY 40202 .... (502) 582–6304
State Director.—Terry Carmack.
1885 Dixie Highway, Suite 345, Fort Wright, KY 41011 .... (606) 578–0188
300 South Main Street, Suite 310, London, KY 40741 .... (606) 864–2026
Professional Arts Building, Suite 100, 2320 Broadway, Paducah, KY 42001 .... (270) 442–4554
771 Corporate Drive, Suite 108, Lexington, KY 40503 .... (606) 224–8286
Federal Building, Room 102, 241 Main Street, Bowling Green, KY 42101 .... (270) 781–1673

* * *

RAND PAUL, Republican, of Bowling Green, KY; born in Pittsburgh, PA, January 7, 1963; education: undergraduate, Baylor University, Waco, Texas, 1981–84; M.D., Duke University School of Medicine, 1988; religion: Methodist; family: married to the former Kelley Ashby; three sons, William, Duncan, and Robert; committees: Foreign Relations; Health, Education, Labor, and Pensions; Homeland Security and Government Affairs; Small Business and Entrepreneurship; elected to the U.S. Senate on November 2, 2010.

Office Listings

http://paul.senate.gov

124 Russell Senate Office Building, Washington, DC 20510 .... (202) 224–4343
Chief of Staff.—William Henderson. FAX: 228–6917
Legislative Directors: Rachel Bovard, John Gray.
Senior Communications Director.—Brian Darling.
Scheduler.—Jessica Jelgerhuis.
600 Dr. Martin Luther King, Jr. Place, Suite 1072B, Louisville, KY 40202 .... (502) 582–5341
State Director.—Jim Milliman.
1029 State Street, Bowling Green, KY 42101 .... (270) 782–8303
1100 South Main Street, Suite 12, Hopkinsville, KY 42240 .... (270) 885–1212
423 Frederica Street, Room 305, Owensboro, KY 42301 .... (270) 689–9085
541 Buttermilk Pike, Suite 102, Crescent Springs, KY 41017 .... (859) 426–0165
771 Corporate Drive, Suite 105, Lexington, KY 40503 .... (859) 219–2269

REPRESENTATIVES

FIRST DISTRICT

ED WHITFIELD, Republican, of Hopkinsville, KY; born in Hopkinsville, May 25, 1943; education: graduated, Madisonville High School, Madisonville, KY; B.S., University of Kentucky, Lexington, 1965; J.D., University of Kentucky, 1969; attended American University's Wesley Theological Seminary, Washington, DC; military service: first lieutenant, U.S. Army Reserves, 1967–73; professional: attorney, private practice, 1970–79; vice president, CSX Corporation, 1979–90; admitted to bar: Kentucky, 1970, and Florida, 1993; began practice in 1970 in Hopkinsville, KY; member, Kentucky House, 1973, one term; married: Constance Harriman Whitfield; children: Kate; committees: Energy and Commerce; elected to the 104th Congress; reelected to each succeeding Congress.

Office Listings

http://www.whitfield.house.gov http://twitter.com/repedwhitfield

2814 Rayburn House Office Building, Washington, DC 20515 .... (202) 225–3115
Chief of Staff.—Cory Hicks. FAX: 225–3547
Scheduler/Office Manager.—Emma Heydlauff.
Legislative Director.—Taylor Booth.
1403 South Main Street, Hopkinsville, KY 42240 .... (270) 885–8079
District Director.—Michael Pape.
200 North Main, Suite F, Tompkinsville, KY 42167 .... (270) 487–9509
Field Representative.—Sandy Simpson.
222 First Street, Suite 224, Henderson, KY 42420 .... (270) 826–4180
Field Representative.—Ed West.
100 Fountain Avenue, Room 104, Paducah, KY 42001 .... (270) 442–6901
Field Representative.—Janece Everett.

Counties: ADAIR, ALLEN, BALLARD, CALDWELL, CALLOWAY, CARLISLE, CASEY, CHRISTIAN, CLINTON, CRITTENDEN, CUMBERLAND, FULTON, GRAVES, HENDERSON, HICKMAN, HOPKINS, LIVINGSTON, LOGAN, LYON, MARION, MARSHALL, MCCRACKEN, MCLEAN, METCALF, MONROE, MUHLENBERG, OHIO, RUSSELL, SIMPSON, TAYLOR, TODD, TRIGG, UNION, WASHINGTON, AND WEBSTER. Population (2010), 725,929.

ZIP Codes: 40009, 40033, 40037, 40040, 40049, 40052, 40060–63, 40069, 40078, 40119, 40328, 40330, 40437, 40442, 40448, 40464, 40468, 40484, 40489, 42001–03, 42020–25, 42027–29, 42031–33, 42035–41, 42044–45, 42047–51, 42053–56, 42058, 42060–61, 42063–64, 42066, 42069–71, 42076, 42078–79, 42081–88, 42101, 42104, 42120, 42122–24, 42129, 42133–35, 42140–41, 42150–51, 42153–54, 42164, 42166–67, 42170, 42201–04, 42206, 42209–211, 42214–17, 42219–21, 42223, 42232, 42234, 42236, 42240–41, 42251–52, 42254, 42256, 42262, 42265–67, 42274, 42276, 42280, 42283, 42286–88, 42301, 42320–28, 42330, 42332–34, 42337, 42338, 42344–45, 42347, 42349–50, 42352, 42354, 42356, 42361, 42367–69, 42370, 42371–72, 42374–76, 42378, 42402–04, 42406, 42408–11, 42413,42419–20, 42431, 42436–37, 42440–42, 42444–45, 42450–53, 42455–64, 42516, 42528, 42539, 42541, 42544, 42565–67, 42602–03, 42629, 42642, 42711, 42715–16, 42718–20, 42728, 42731, 42733, 42735, 42740–43, 42746, 42749, 42753, 42758, 42759, 42786

* * *

SECOND DISTRICT

BRETT GUTHRIE, Republican, of Bowling Green, KY; born in Florence, AL, February 18, 1964; education: B.S., United States Military Academy, West Point, NY, 1987; M.P.M., Yale University, New Haven, CT, 1997; military service: U.S. Army, Field Artillery Office, 101st Airborne Division, 1987–90; professional: Vice President, Trace Die Cast, 1991–2009; member: Kentucky Senate, 1998–2009; married: Beth; children: Caroline, Robby, and Elizabeth; committees: Education and the Workforce; Energy and Commerce; elected to the 111th Congress on November 4, 2008; reelected to each succeeding Congress.

Office Listings

http://www.guthrie.house.gov

308 Cannon House Office Building, Washington, DC 20515 .... (202) 225–3501
Chief of Staff.—Eric Bergren.
Legislative Director.—Megan Spindel.
Communications Director.—Jennifer Sherman.
Scheduler.—Jennifer Beil.
1001 Center Street, Suite 300, Bowling Green, KY 42101 .... (270) 842–9896
District Director.—Mark Lord.

Counties: BARREN, WARREN, BRECKINRIDGE, DAVIESS, HANCOCK, GRAYSON, BUTLER, HARDIN, GREEN, BULLITT, SPENCER (part), WASHINGTON (part), GARRARD, BOYLE, MERCER, JESSAMINE (part), HARDIN, LARUE, MEADE, NELSON, EDMONSON, AND HART. Population (2010), 723,137.

ZIP Codes: 40004, 40008, 40012–13, 40020, 40037 (part), 40040, 40046 (part), 40047–48, 40051, 40052 (part), 40069 (part), 40071 (part), 40078, 40104, 40107–11, 40115, 40117, 40119 (part), 40121, 40140, 40142–46, 40150, 40152, 40155, 40157, 40160–62, 40165, 40170–71, 40175–76, 40177 (part), 40178, 40229 (part), 40272 (part), 40299, 40310, 40328 (part), 40330, 40339, 40356 (part), 40372 (part), 40383 (part), 40390 (part), 40403 (part), 40419 (part), 40422 (part), 40440 (part), 40444 (part), 40461 (part), 40464 (part), 40468 (part), 40484 (part), 42101–03, 42104 (part), 42122 (part), 42123, 42127, 42130, 42133 (part), 42141, 42154 (part), 42156, 42159–60, 42163, 42166 (part), 42170 (part), 42171, 42206 (part), 42207, 42210, 42214 (part), 42256 (part), 42259, 42261, 42273, 42274 (part), 42275, 42285, 42301 (part), 42303, 42320 (part), 42327 (part), 42333 (part), 42339 (part), 42343 (part), 42348, 42349 (part), 42351, 42355–56, 42361 (part), 42366 (part), 42368 (part), 42376 (part), 42378 (part), 42701, 42712–13, 42716 (part), 42718 (part), 42721–22, 42724, 42726, 42729, 42732, 42740, 42743 (part), 42746 (part), 42748, 42749 (part), 42754, 42757, 42762, 42764–65, 42776, 42782, 42784, 42788

* * *

THIRD DISTRICT

JOHN A. YARMUTH, Democrat, of Louisville, KY; born in Louisville, November 4, 1947; education: graduated, Atherton High School, Louisville, 1965; graduated, Yale University, New Haven, CT, 1969; professional: Legislative Aide for Kentucky Senator Marlow Cook, 1971–74; publisher, *Louisville Today Magazine*, 1976–82; Associate Vice President of University Relations at the University of Louisville, 1983–86; Vice President of a local healthcare firm 1986–90; founder, editor and writer *LEO Newsweekly*, 1990–2005; Television host and commentator, 2003–05; awards: 2007 Spirit of Enterprise Award; Louisville Alzheimer's Association Person of the Year; named Outstanding New Member of Congress by the Committee for Education and Funding; 16 Metro Louisville Journalism Awards for editorial and column writing; married: Cathy Yarmuth, 1981; child: Aaron; committees: Budget; Energy and Commerce; elected to the 110th Congress on November 7, 2006; reelected to each succeeding Congress.

Office Listings

http://www.yarmuth.house.gov

403 Cannon House Office Building, Washington, DC 20515 .... (202) 225–5401
Chief of Staff.—Julie Carr. FAX: 225–5776
Legislative Director.—Ashley Bromagen.
Press Secretary.—Stephen George.
Scheduler.—Erica DiCio.
600 Martin Luther King, Jr. Place, Suite 216, Louisville, KY 40202 .... (502) 582–5129
District Director.—Carolyn Tandy.

Counties: JEFFERSON. Population (2010), 741,096.

ZIP Codes: 40025, 40027, 40041, 40047, 40059 (part), 40118, 40177 (part), 40201–22, 40223 (part), 40224–25, 40228, 40229 (part), 40231–33, 40241 (part), 40242–43, 40245 (part), 40250–53, 40255–59, 40261, 40266, 40268–70, 40272 (part), 40280–83, 40285, 40289–90, 40291 (part), 40292–93, 40295, 40297–98, 40299 (part)

* * *

FOURTH DISTRICT

THOMAS MASSIE, Republican, of Garrison, KY; born in Huntington, WV, January 13, 1971; education: graduated from Lewis County High School; B.S., electrical engineering/economics, Massachusetts Institute of Technology, 1993; M.S., mechanical engineering, Massachusetts Institute of Technology, 1996; professional: inventor/engineer; founder of SensAble Devices, Inc.; farmer; Lewis County Judge Executive; married: Rhonda; four children; committees: Oversight and Government Reform; Science, Space, and Technology; Transportation and Infrastructure; elected simultaneously to the 112th and 113th Congresses on November 6, 2012, by special election to fill the vacancy caused by the resignation of United States Representative Geoffrey C. (Geoff) Davis.

Office Listings

http://massie.house.gov

314 Cannon House Office Building, Washington, DC 20515 .... (202) 225–3465
Chief of Staff.—Hans Hoeg. FAX: 225–0003
Deputy Chief of Staff.—Gary Howard.
Legislative Director.—Seana Cranston.
Legislative Correspondent/Legislative Assistant.—Stephen Johnson.
Press Secretary.—Lorenz Isidro.
Scheduler.—Lauren Wills.
Staff Assistant.—Ryan Falk.
541 Buttermilk Pike, Suite 208, Crescent Springs, KY 41017 .... (859) 426–0080
District Director.—Chris McCane. FAX: 426–0061
1700 Greenup Avenue, R–505, Ashland, KY 41101 .... (606) 324–9898
Eastern District Field Representative.—J.R. Reed.
108 West Jefferson Street, LaGrange, KY 40031 .... (502) 265–9119
Western District Field Representative.—Stacie Rockaway. FAX: 265–9126

Counties: BOYD, BOONE, BRACKEN, CARROLL, CAMPBELL, GREENUP, GALLATIN, GRANT, HENRY, HARRISON, JEFFERSON, KENTON, LEWIS, MASON, OLDHAM, OWEN, PENDLETON, SHELBY, SPENCER, AND TRIMBLE. Population (2010), 723,450.

ZIP Codes: 40003 (part), 40006–07, 40010–11, 40014, 40019, 40022–23, 40026, 40031, 40036, 40045, 40046 (part), 40050, 40055–58, 40059 (part), 40065, 40067–68, 40070, 40071 (part), 40075, 40076 (part), 40077, 40241 (part), 40245 (part), 40291 (part), 40299 (part), 40359, 40363, 40370 (part), 40379 (part), 40601 (part), 41001–03, 41004 (part), 41005–08, 41010 (part), 41011, 41014–18, 41030, 41031 (part), 41033–35, 41040, 41042–43, 41044 (part), 41045–46, 41048, 41051–52, 41055 (part), 41056, 41059, 41062–63, 41064 (part), 41071, 41073–76, 41080, 41083, 41085–86, 41091–92, 41093 (part), 41094–95, 41097–99, 41101, 41102 (part), 41121, 41129 (part), 41135, 41139, 41141, 41143 (part), 41144, 41164 (part), 41166, 41169, 41174–75, 41179, 41183, 41189

* * *

FIFTH DISTRICT

HAROLD ROGERS, Republican, of Somerset, KY; born in Barrier, KY, December 31, 1937; education: graduated, Wayne County High School, 1955; attended Western Kentucky University, 1956–57; A.B., University of Kentucky, 1962; LL.B., University of Kentucky Law School, 1964; professional: lawyer, admitted to the Kentucky State Bar, 1964; commenced practice in Somerset; member, North Carolina and Kentucky National Guard, 1957–64; associate, Smith and Blackburn, 1964–67; private practice, 1967–69; Commonwealth Attorney, Pulaski and Rockcastle Counties, KY, 1969–80; delegate, Republican National Convention, 1972, 1976, 1980, 1984, and 1988; Republican nominee for Lieutenant Governor, KY, 1979; past president, Kentucky Commonwealth Attorneys Association; member and past president, Somerset-Pulaski County Chamber of Commerce and Pulaski County Industrial Foundation; founder, Southern Kentucky Economic Development Council, 1986; member, Chowder and Marching Society, 1981–present; member, Republican Steering Committee; married the former Shirley McDowell, 1957; three children: Anthony, Allison, and John Marshall; committees: chair, Appropriations; elected to the 97th Congress, November 4, 1980; reelected to each succeeding Congress.

Office Listings

http://halrogers.house.gov

2406 Rayburn House Office Building, Washington, DC 20515 .... (202) 225–4601
Chief of Staff.—David Thomas. FAX: 225–0940
Office Manager.—Chelsea Whalen.
Legislative Correspondent.—Ashley Nichols.
Staff Assistant.—Nick Camic.
Legislative Director.—Megan O'Donnell.
Legislative Assistant.—Aaron Jones.
48 South Kentucky Highway 15, Hazard, KY 41701 .... (606) 439–0794
District Director.—Karen Kelly. FAX: 439–4647
551 Clifty Street, Somerset, KY 42503 .... (606) 679–8346
110 Resource Court, Suite A, Prestonsburg, KY 41653–1842 .... (606) 886–0844
FAX: 889–0371

Counties: BELL, BOYD, BREATHITT, CARTER, CLAY, ELLIOTT, FLOYD, HARLAN, JACKSON, JOHNSON, KNOTT, KNOX, LAUREL, LAWRENCE, LEE, LESLIE, LETCHER, LINCOLN, MAGOFFLIN, MARTIN, MORGAN, OWSLEY, PERRY, PIKE, PULASKI, ROCKCASTLE, ROWAN, WAYNE, AND WHITLEY. Population (2010), 723,228.

ZIP Codes: 40313, 40351, 40393, 40402, 40409, 40434, 40445, 40447, 40447–48, 40456, 40460, 40481, 40486, 40701, 40729, 40734, 40737, 40740–41, 40743–44, 40759, 40763, 40769, 40771, 40801, 40806–08, 40813, 40815–16, 40818–20, 40823–24, 40826–31, 40840, 40843–45, 40847, 40849, 40854–56, 40858, 40862–63, 40865, 40868, 40870, 40873–74, 40902–03, 40906, 40913–15, 40921, 40923, 40927, 40935, 40940–41, 40943, 40946, 40949, 40953, 40958, 40962, 40964–65, 40972, 40977, 40979, 40982–83, 40988, 40995, 40997, 41124, 41132, 41142, 41146, 41149, 41159, 41168, 41171, 41180, 41201, 41203–04, 41214, 41216, 41219, 41222, 41224, 41226, 41230–32, 41234, 41238, 41240, 41250, 41254–57, 41260, 41262–65, 41267–68, 41271, 41274, 41311, 41314, 41317, 41339, 41348, 41352, 41366–67, 41385, 41390, 41397, 41408, 41421, 41425, 41464–65, 41472, 41501, 41503, 41512–14, 41517, 41519, 41522, 41526, 41527–28, 41531, 41534–35, 41537–40, 41544, 41547–48, 41553–55, 41557–60, 41562–64, 41566–68, 41571, 41601–07, 41612, 41615–16, 41619, 41621–22, 41630–32, 41635–36, 41640, 41642–43, 41645, 41647, 41649–50, 41653, 41659–60, 41663, 41666–67, 41669, 41701, 41712–14, 41719, 41721–23, 41725, 41727, 41729, 41731, 41735, 41739–40, 41745–46, 41749, 41751, 41754, 41759–60, 41762–64, 41766, 41772–77, 41804, 41810, 41815, 41817, 41819, 41822, 41824–26, 41828, 41831–37, 41840, 41843–45, 41847–49, 41855, 41858, 41861–62, 42501, 42503, 42518–19, 42533, 42567, 42631, 42634–35, 42638, 42649, 42653

* * *

SIXTH DISTRICT

ANDY BARR, Republican, of Lexington, KY; born in Lexington, July 24, 1973; education: B.A. degree in government and philosophy from the University of Virginia in Charlottesville, VA, 1996, graduating with *magna cum laude* and *Phi Beta Kappa* honors; J.D., from the University of Kentucky College of Law, in Lexington, KY, 2001; religion: Episcopal; married to the former Eleanor Carol Leavell of Georgetown, Kentucky; together, they are the proud parents of two daughters; caucus: Bi-Partisan Prescription Drug Caucus; Congressional Arthritis Caucus; Congressional Automotive Caucus; Congressional Bourbon Caucus; Congressional Coal Caucus; Congressional Diabetes Caucus; Congressional Down Syndrome Caucus; chair of Congressional Horse Caucus; Congressional Natural Gas Caucus; Congressional Prayer Caucus; Congressional Recycling Caucus; Congressional Sportsmen's Caucus; Congressional United Solutions Caucus; Congressional Veterans Job Caucus; German-American Caucus; Historic Preservation Caucus; House Manufacturing Caucus; National Guard and Reserves Components Caucus; National Guard Youth Challenge Caucus; Pro-Life Caucus; USO Congressional Caucus; Republican Study Committee; committees: Financial Services, elected to the 113th Congress on November 6, 2012.

Office Listings

http://www.barr.house.gov www.facebook.com/repandybarr
www.twitter.com/repandybarr www.youtube.com/repandybarr

1432 Longworth House Office Building, Washington, DC 20515 .... (202) 225–4706
Chief of Staff.—Betsy Hawkings. FAX: 225–2122
Legislative Director.—David Stern.
Communications Director.—Catherine Gatewood.
Scheduler.—Tatum Dale.
2709 Old Rosebud Road, Lexington, KY 40509 .... (859) 219–1366

Counties: ANDERSON, BATH, BOURBON, CLARK, ESTILL, FAYETTE, FLEMING, FRANKLIN, HARRISON (part), JESSAMINE (part), MADISON, MENIFEE, MONTGOMERY, NICHOLAS, POWELL, ROBERTSON, SCOTT, WOLFE, AND WOODFORD. Population (2010), 723,203.

ZIP Codes: 40003, 40046, 40076, 40311–13, 40316, 40322, 40324, 40334, 40336–37, 40340, 40342, 40346–48, 40350, 40353, 40356, 40358, 40360–61, 40370–72, 40374, 40376, 40379–80, 40383, 40385, 40387, 40390–91, 40403–04, 40461, 40472, 40475, 40502–11, 40513–17, 40601, 40604, 41004, 41010, 41031, 41039, 41041, 41044, 41049, 41055, 41064, 41093, 41301, 41332, 41360, 41365

LOUISIANA

(Population 2010, 4,553,762)

SENATORS

MARY L. LANDRIEU, Democrat, of New Orleans, LA; born in Alexandria, VA, November 23, 1955; education: B.A., Louisiana State University, 1977; real estate broker, specializing in townhouse development; represented New Orleans House District 90 in Louisiana Legislature, 1979–87; State Treasurer, 1987–95; vice chair, Louisiana Council on Child Abuse; member, Business and Professional Women; majority council member, Emily's List; past national president, Women's Legislative Network; past vice president, Women Executives in State Government; delegate to every Democratic National Convention since 1980; married: E. Frank Snellings; children: Connor, and Mary Shannon; committees: chair, Energy and Natural Resources; Appropriations; Homeland Security and Governmental Affairs; Small Business and Entrepreneurship; elected to the U.S. Senate on November 5, 1996; reelected to each succeeding Senate term.

Office Listings

http://landrieu.senate.gov facebook.com/senatormarylandrieu twitter: @senlandrieu

703 Hart Senate Office Building, Washington, DC 20510 .... (202) 224–5824
Chief of Staff.—Donald R. Cravins, Jr. FAX: 224–9735
Scheduler.—Katie Rose Norman.
Communications Director.—Matthew Lehner.
Press Secretary.—Erin Donar.
Legislative Director.—Elizabeth Craddock.
Office Manager.—Alicia Williams.
Hale Boggs Federal Building, 500 Poydras Street, Room 1005, New Orleans, LA 70130 .... (504) 589–2427
U.S. Courthouse, 300 Fannin Street, Room 2240, Shreveport, LA 71101–3086 .... (318) 676–3085
U.S. Federal Court House, 707 Florida Street, Room 326, Baton Rouge, LA 70801 . (225) 389–0395
Hibernia Tower, One Lakeshore Drive, Suite 1260, Lake Charles, LA 70629 .... (337) 436–6650

* * *

DAVID VITTER, Republican, of Metairie, LA; born in Metairie, May 3, 1961; education: Harvard University; Oxford University Rhodes Scholar; Tulane University School of Law; professional: attorney; adjunct law professor, Tulane and Loyola Universities; religion: Catholic; public service: Louisiana House of Representatives, 1992–99; U.S. House of Representatives, 1999–2005; awards: Alliance for Good Government ''Legislator of the Year''; Victims and Citizens Against Crime ''Outstanding Legislator'' and ''Lifetime Achievement Award''; married: Wendy Baldwin Vitter; children: Sophie, Lise, Airey, and Jack; caucuses: chairman of the Border Security and Enforcement First Immigration Caucus; committees: ranking member, Environment and Public Works; Armed Services; Banking, Housing, and Urban Affairs; Small Business and Entrepreneurship; elected to the U.S. Senate on November 2, 2004; reelected to the U.S. Senate on November 2, 2010.

Office Listings

http://vitter.senate.gov

516 Hart Senate Office Building, Washington, DC 20510 .... (202) 224–4623
Chief of Staff.—Kyle Ruckert. FAX: 228–5061
2800 Veterans Boulevard, Suite 201, Metairie, LA 70002 .... (504) 589–2753
858 Convention Street, Baton Rouge, LA 70801 .... (225) 383–0331
1217 North 19th Street, Monroe, LA 71201 .... (318) 325–8120
2230 South MacArthur Street, Suite 4, Alexandria, LA 71301 .... (318) 448–0169
920 Pierremont Road, Suite 113, Shreveport, LA 71106 .... (318) 861–0437
3221 Ryan Street, Suite E, Lake Charles, LA 70601 .... (337) 436–0453
800 Lafayette Street, Suite 1200, Lafayette, LA 70501 .... (337) 262–6898

REPRESENTATIVES

FIRST DISTRICT

STEVE SCALISE, Republican, of Jefferson, LA; born in New Orleans, LA, October 6, 1965; education: B.S., Louisiana State University, Baton Rouge, LA, 1983; professional: Computer

Programmer for technology company; Louisiana House of Representatives, 1995–2007, Louisiana Senate, 2007–08; awards: Spirit of Enterprise, U.S. Chamber of Commerce; religion: Catholic; married: former Jennifer LeTulle; children: Madison and Harrison; committees: Energy and Commerce; elected to 110th Congress on May 4, 2008 in special election; reelected to each succeeding Congress.

Office Listings

http://www.scalise.house.gov www.facebok.com/repstevescalise
https://twitter.com/stevescalise

2338 Rayburn House Office Building, Washington, DC 20515 .... (202) 225–3015
Chief of Staff.—Lynnel Ruckert. FAX: 226–0386
Legislative Director.—Eric Zulkosky.
Scheduler.—Adrienne Kean.
Communications Director.—Stephen Bell.
110 Veterans Memorial Boulevard, Suite 500, Metaire, LA 70005 .... (504) 837–1259
District Director.—Charles Henry.
21454 Koop Drive, Suite 1E, Mandeville, LA 70471 .... (985) 893–9064
112 South Cypress Street, Hammond, LA 70403 .... (985) 340–2185
8026 Main Street, Suite 700, Houma, LA 70360 .... (985) 879–2300

Parishes: all or parts of: JEFFERSON, ORLEANS, ST. TAMMANY, TANGIPAHOA, ST. BERNARD, PLAQUEMINES, TERREBONNE, LAFOURCHE. Population (2010), 758,994.

ZIP Codes: 70001–06, 70009–11, 70033, 70038, 70041, 70055–56, 70060, 70062, 70064–65, 70083, 70091, 70115, 70118–19, 70121–24, 70160, 70181, 70183–84, 70343–45, 70353–54, 70357–58, 70360–61, 70363–64, 70373–74, 70377, 70401–04, 70420, 70427, 70431, 70433–38, 70445, 70447–48, 70452, 70454–67, 70469–71, 70764–65

* * *

SECOND DISTRICT

CEDRIC L. RICHMOND, Democrat, of New Orleans; born in New Orleans, LA, September 13, 1973; education: B.A., Morehouse College, Atlanta, GA, 1995: J.D., Tulane School of Law, New Orleans, LA, 1998; Harvard University Executive Education Program at the John F. Kennedy School of Government, Cambridge, MA; professional: military; member of the Louisiana State House of Representatives, 1999–2008; awards: *Time* Magazine's 2010 40 Under 40, Innocence Project Legislative Champion Award; religion: Baptist; commissions, caucuses; New Democrat Coalition; Congressional Black Caucus; Gulf Coast Caucus; committees: Homeland Security; Judiciary; elected to the 112th Congress on November 2, 2010; reelected to the 113th Congress on November 6, 2012.

Office Listings

http://www.richmond.house.gov twitter: @reprichmond
www.facebook.com/reprichmond

240 Cannon House Office Building, Washington, DC 20515 .... (202) 225–6636
Chief of Staff.—Virgil Miller. FAX: 225–1988
Office Manager / Scheduler.—Bianca Lacey.
Legislative Director.—Fabrice Coles.
Communications Director.—Monique Waters.
2021 Lakeshore Drive, Suite 309, New Orleans, LA 70122 .... (504) 288–3777
District Director.—Enix Smith.
200 Derbigny Street, Suite 3200, Gretna, LA 70053 .... (504) 365–0390
1520 Thomas H. Delpit Drive, Suite 126, Baton Rouge, LA 70802 .... (225) 636–5600

Parishes: ASCENSION (part), ASSUMPTION (part), EAST BATON ROUGE (part), IBERVILLE (part), JEFFERSON (part), ORLEANS (part), ST. CHARLES (part), ST. JAMES, ST. JOHN THE BAPTIST (part), WEST BATON ROUGE (part). Population (2010), 755,538.

ZIP Codes: 70001, 70003, 70030, 70031, 70039, 70047, 70049, 70051–53, 70056–58, 70062, 70065, 70068, 70070–72, 70076, 70080, 70084, 70086, 70087, 70090, 70094, 70112–19, 70121–31, 70139, 70163, 70301, 70341, 70346, 70372, 70390, 70391, 70393, 70710, 70714, 70719, 70721, 70723, 70725, 70734, 70737, 70743, 70763, 70764, 70767, 70776, 70780, 70788, 70791, 70802, 70805–07, 70811, 70812, 70814, 70815

* * *

THIRD DISTRICT

CHARLES W. BOUSTANY, JR., Republican, of Lafayette, LA; born in New Orleans, LA, February 21, 1956; education: graduated Cathedral Carmel High School, Lafayette, LA; B.S.,

University of Southwestern Louisiana, Lafayette, LA, 1978; M.D., Louisiana State University School of Medicine, New Orleans, LA, 1982; professional: surgeon; public service: served on the Louisiana Organ Procurement Agency Tissue Advisory Board; board of directors for the Greater Lafayette Chamber of Commerce, 2001; Chamber of Commerce as Vice President for Government Affairs, 2002; president of the Lafayette Parish Medical Society; chaired the American Heart Association's Gala; Healthcare Division of the UL-Lafayette Centennial Fundraiser, which provided $75 million of university endowed chairs, professorships and scholarships; member of Leadership Lafayette Class IIIXX, 2002; member, Lafayette Parish Republican Executive Committee, 1996–2001; Republican Policy Committee; vice-chairman of the Bush/Cheney Victory 2000 Campaign for Lafayette Parish; board of directors for Lafayette General Medical Center; married: the former Bridget Edwards; children: Erik and Ashley; committees: Ways and Means; elected to the 109th Congress on December 4, 2004; reelected to each succeeding Congress.

Office Listings

http://www.house.gov/boustany

1431 Longworth House Office Building, Washington, DC 20515 .... (202) 225–2031
Chief of Staff.—Jeff Dobrozsi. FAX: 225–5724
Legislative Director.—Terri Fish.
Scheduler.—Paige Hensgens.
800 Lafayette Street, Suite 1400, Lafayette, LA 70501 .... (337) 235–6322
One Lakeshore Drive, Suite 1775, Lake Charles, LA 70629 .... (337) 433–1747

Parishes: ACADIA, CALCASIEU, CAMERON, EVANGELINE, IBERIA, JEFFERSON DAVIS, LAFAYETTE, ST. LANDRY, ST. MARTIN, ST. MARY VERMILION. Population (2010), 760,696.

ZIP Codes: 70380, 70342, 70392, 70501–12, 70515–18, 70520, 70524–29, 70531–35, 70537, 70538, 70541–43, 70544, 70546, 70548–51, 70552, 70554–56, 70558–59, 70560, 70563, 70570–71, 70575, 70577–78, 70580–81, 70582, 70583–84, 70586, 70589, 70591–92, 70596, 70598, 70601–02, 70605–07, 70609, 70611–12, 70615–16, 70630–33, 70640, 70643, 70645–48, 70650, 70655, 70658, 70661, 70663–65, 70668–69, 70750, 71322, 71345, 71353, 71356, 71358, 71362

* * *

FOURTH DISTRICT

JOHN FLEMING, Republican, of Minden, LA; born in Meridian, MS, July 5, 1951; education: B.S., University of Mississippi, Oxford, MS, 1973; M.D., University of Mississippi, Oxford, MS, 1976; professional: family physician and businessman; military: Lieutenant Commander, U.S. Navy; awards: Louisiana Family Doctor of the Year, 2007; religion: Southern Baptist; married: Cindy; four children; committees: Armed Services; Natural Resources; elected to the 111th Congress on November 4, 2008; reelected to each succeeding Congress.

Office Listings

http://www.fleming.house.gov

416 Cannon House Office Building, Washington, DC 20515 .... (202) 225–2777
Chief of Staff.—Dana Gartzke. FAX: 225–8039
Legislative Director.—Garth Van Meter.
Scheduler/Office Manager.—Rebecca Hobbs.
Communications Director.—Doug Sachtleben.
6425 Youree Drive, Suite 350, Shreveport, LA 71105 .... (318) 798–2254
District Director.—Stephanie McKenzie.
103 North Third Street, Leesville, LA 71446 .... (337) 238–0778
District Director.—Lee Turner.
700 Benton Road, Bossier City, LA 71111 .... (318) 549–1712

Parishes: ALLEN, BEAUREGARD, BIENVILLE, BOSSIER, CADDO, CLAIBORNE, DESOTO, EVANGELINE, NATCHITOCHES, RED RIVER, SABINE, ST. LANDRY, UNION, VERNON, AND WEBSTER. Population (2010), 667,109.

ZIP Codes: 70515, 70524, 70535, 70541, 70570, 70576, 70584–86, 70589, 70634, 70637–39, 70644, 70648, 70651–60, 70662, 71001–09, 71016, 71018–19, 71021, 71023–24, 71027–34, 71037–40, 71043–52, 71055, 71058, 71060–61, 71063–73, 71075, 71078–80, 71082, 71101–13, 71115, 71118–20, 71129–30, 71133–38, 71148, 71156, 71161, 71163–66, 71171–72, 71222, 71234, 71241, 71256, 71260, 71277, 71403, 71406, 71411, 71414, 71416, 71419, 71426, 71429, 71434, 71438–39, 71443, 71446–47, 71449–50, 71456–63, 71468–69, 71474–75, 71486, 71496–97, 71526

* * *

FIFTH DISTRICT

VANCE McALLISTER, Republican, of Swartz, LA; born in Oak Grove, LA, January 7, 1974; education: attended, University of Louisiana-Monroe; professional: businessman, with a background in the oil and gas industries; military: U.S. Army, followed by Louisiana National Guard; religion: Baptist; married: Kelly; five children; committees: Agriculture; Natural Resources; elected by special election on November 16, 2013, to fill the vacancy caused by the resignation of U.S. Representative Rodney Alexander.

Office Listings

http://www.mcallister.house.gov

316 Cannon House Office Building, Washington, DC 20515 .... (202) 225–8490
Chief of Staff.—Adam Terry. FAX: 225–5639
Press Secretary.—Jennifer Dunagin.
Scheduler.—Jennifer Dunagin.
Legislative Director.—Jack Thompson.
1900 Stubbs Avenue, Suite B, Monroe, LA 71201 .... (318) 322–3500
1412 Centre Court, Suite 402, Alexandria, LA 71301 .... (318) 445–0818

Parishes: AVOYELLES, CALDWELL, CATAHOULA, CONCORDIA, EAST CARROLL, EAST FELICIANA (part), FRANKLIN, JACKSON, LASALLE, LINCOLN, MADISON, MOREHOUSE, OUACHITA, RAPIDES, RICHLAND, ST. LANDRY (part), ST. HELENA (part), TANGIPAHOA (part), TENSAS, WASHINGTON, WEST CARROLL, WEST FELICIANA, AND WINN. Population (2010), 758,851.

ZIP Codes: 70401, 70422, 70426–27, 70431, 70435–38, 70441–44, 70446, 70450–51, 70455–56, 70465–66, 70512, 70570, 70577, 70589, 70656, 70712, 70722, 70730, 70748, 70750, 70761, 70775, 70782, 70787, 70789, 71001, 71031, 71201–03, 71209, 71219–20, 71223, 71225–27, 71229, 71232–35, 71237, 71238, 71243, 71245, 71247, 71250–51, 71253–54, 71259, 71261, 71263–64, 71266, 71268–70, 71272, 71275–76, 71279–80, 71282, 71286, 71291–92, 71295, 71301–03, 71316, 71322–23, 71325–28, 71331, 71333–34, 71336, 71339–43, 71345–46, 71350–51, 71353–58, 71360, 71362, 71366–69, 71371, 71373, 71375, 71377–78, 71401, 71404–05, 71407, 71409–10, 71417, 71418, 71422–25, 71427, 71430, 71432–33, 71435, 71438, 71441, 71447, 71454–55, 71457, 71463, 71465–67, 71472–73, 71479–80, 71483, 71485

* * *

SIXTH DISTRICT

BILL CASSIDY, Republican, of Baton Rouge, LA; born in Highland Park, IL, September 28, 1957; education: graduated, Tara High School; B.S., Louisiana State University, Baton Rouge, LA, 1979; M.D., Louisiana State University medical school, New Orleans, LA, 1983; professional: medical doctor; Associate Professor, Baton Rouge; medical doctor, Associate Professor of Medicine with LSU Health Science Center; member of the Louisiana State Senate; married: Laura Layden Cassidy, M.D.; children: Will, Meg, and Kate; committees: Energy and Commerce; elected to the 111th Congress on November 4, 2008; reelected to each succeeding Congress.

Office Listings

http//:www.cassidy.house.gov

1131 Longworth House Office Building, Washington, DC 20515 .... (202) 225–3901
Chief of Staff.—James Quinn. FAX: 225–7313
Press Secretary.—John Cummins.
Executive Assistant.—Cristin Buckels Prosser.
5555 Hilton Avenue, Suite 100, Baton Rouge, LA 70808 .... (225) 929–7711
29261 Frost Road, Livingston, LA 70753 .... (225) 686–4413
200 West First Street, Thibodaux, LA 70301 .... (985) 447–1662

Parishes: ASCENSION, ASSUMPTION, EAST BATON ROUGE, EAST FELICIANA, IBERVILLE, Lafourche, Livingston, Pointe Coupee, St. Charles, St. Helena, St. John The Baptist, Terrbonne, West Baton Rouge, and West Feliciana. Population (2010), 755,607.

ZIP Codes: 70030, 70047, 70068–69, 70079, 70087, 70301–02, 70339, 70341, 70352, 70356, 70359–61, 70364, 70371–72, 70375, 70380, 70390, 70394–95, 70403, 70422, 70436, 70441, 70443, 70449, 70453, 70456, 70462, 70466, 70704, 70706–07, 70710–11, 70714–15, 70718–19, 70722, 70725–30, 70732–34, 70736–37, 70739–40, 70744, 70747–49, 70752–57, 70759–60, 70762, 70764–65, 70767, 70769–70, 70772–74, 70777–78, 70783, 70785–86, 70788, 70791, 70801–02, 70806–11, 70814–21, 70825–27, 70831, 70835–37, 70874, 70879, 70884, 70893–96, 70898

MAINE

(Population, 2010 1,328,361)

SENATORS

SUSAN M. COLLINS, Republican, of Bangor, ME; born in Caribou, ME, December 7, 1952; education: graduated, Caribou High School, 1971; B.A., *magna cum laude,* Phi Beta Kappa, St. Lawrence University, Canton, NY; Outstanding Alumni Award, St. Lawrence University, 1992; staff director, Senate Subcommittee on the Oversight of Government Management, 1981–87; for 12 years, principal advisor on business issues to former Senator William S. Cohen; Commissioner of Professional and Financial Regulation for Maine Governor John R. McKernan, Jr., 1987; New England administrator, Small Business Administration, 1992–93; appointed Deputy Treasurer of Massachusetts, 1993; executive director, Husson College Center for Family Business, 1994–96; committees: ranking member, Special Committee on Aging; Appropriations; Select Committee on Intelligence; elected to the U.S. Senate on November 5, 1996; reelected to each succeeding Senate term.

Office Listings

http://collins.senate.gov www.facebook.com/susancollins twitter: @senatorcollins

413 Dirksen Senate Office Building, Washington, DC 20510 .... (202) 224–2523
Chief of Staff.—Mary Dietrich. FAX: 224–2693
Communications Director.—Kevin Kelley.
Legislative Director.—Elizabeth McDonnell.
P.O. Box 655, 202 Harlow Street, Room 204, Bangor, ME 04402 .... (207) 945–0417
State Representative.—Carol Woodcock.
68 Sewall Street, Room 507, Augusta, ME 04330 .... (207) 622–8414
State Representative.—Bobby Reynolds.
160 Main Street, Biddeford, ME 04005 .... (207) 283–1101
State Representative.—Cathy Goodwin.
11 Lisbon Street, Lewiston, ME 04240 .... (207) 784–6969
State Representative.—Carlene Tremblay.
25 Sweden Street, Suite A, Caribou, ME 04736 .... (207) 493–5873
State Representative.—Philip Bosse.
1 Canal Plaza, Suite 802, Portland, ME 04101 .... (207) 780–3575
State Representative.—Alec Porteous.

* * *

ANGUS S. KING, JR., Independent, of Brunswick, ME; born in Alexandria, VA, March 31, 1944; education: graduated Dartmouth College, 1966; University of Virginia Law School, 1969; chief counsel to U.S. Senate Subcommittee on Alcoholism and Narcotics for former Maine Senator William Hathaway; founded Northeast Energy Management, Inc., 1989; elected Maine's 71st Governor, 1994, reelected 1998 by one of the largest margins in Maine's history; Maine's first independent U.S. Senator; committees: Armed Services; Budget; Rules and Administration; Select Committee on Intelligence; elected to the U.S. Senate on November 6, 2012.

Office Listings

http://king.senate.gov twitter: @senangusking
https://www.facebook.com/senatorangusskingjr

359 Dirksen Senate Office Building, Washington, DC 20510 .... (202) 224–5344
Chief of Staff.—Kay Rand. FAX: 224–1946
Executive Assistant.—Ryan Boyd.
Communications Director.—Crystal Canney.
Director of Scheduling.—Kathryn Shorr.
Legislative Director.—Chad Metzler.
Senior Policy Advisor.—Marge Kilkelly.
Administrative Director.—Patrick Doak.
4 Gabriel Drive, Suite F1, Augusta, ME 04330 .... (207) 622–8292
169 Academy Street, Suite A, Presque Isle, ME 04769 .... (207) 764–5124
383 U.S. Route 1, Suite 1c, Scarborough, ME 04074 .... (207) 883–1588
State Director.—Edie Smith.
Regional Representatives: Sharon Campbell, Travis Kennedy, Gail Kezer, Elizabeth Schneider MacTaggart, Bonnie Pothier, Chris Rector, Ben Tucker.

REPRESENTATIVES

FIRST DISTRICT

CHELLIE PINGREE, Democrat, of North Haven, ME; born in Minneapolis, MN, April 2, 1955; education: B.A., College of the Atlantic, Bar Harbor, ME, 1979; professional: farmer; businesswoman; religion: Lutheran; married: three children; House Oceans Caucus; Progressive Caucus, Women's Caucus; Sustainable Energy and Environment Coalition; National Guard and Reserve Component Caucus; Humanities Caucus; Bicycle Caucus; Philanthropy Caucus; House Trade Working Group; committees: Appropriations; elected to the 111th Congress on November 4, 2008; reelected to each succeeding Congress.

Office Listings

http://pingree.house.gov

1318 Longworth House Office Building, Washington, DC 20515 .... (202) 225–6116
Chief of Staff.—Jesse Connolly. FAX: 225–5590
Legislative Director.—Claire Benjamin.
Scheduler.—Karen Sudbay.
2 Portland Fish Pier, Suite 304, Portland, ME 04101 .... (207) 774–5019

Counties: CUMBERLAND, KENNEBEC (part), KNOX, LINCOLN, SAGADAHOC, YORK. Population (2010), 668,515.

ZIP Codes: 03901–11, 04001–11, 04013–15, 04017, 04019–21, 04024, 04027–30, 04032–34, 04038–40, 04042–43, 04046–50, 04053–57, 04061–64, 04066, 04069–79, 04082–87, 04090–98, 04101–10, 04112, 04116, 04122–24, 04259–60, 04265, 04284, 04287, 04330, 04332–33, 04336, 04338, 04341–55, 04357–60, 04363–64, 04530, 04541, 04543–44, 04547–48, 04551, 04553–56, 04558, 04562–65, 04567–68, 04570–76, 04578–79, 04841, 04843, 04846–56, 04858–65, 04901, 04910, 04917–18, 04922, 04926–27, 04935, 04937, 04941, 04949, 04952, 04962–63

* * *

SECOND DISTRICT

MICHAEL H. MICHAUD, Democrat, of East Millinocket, ME; born on January 18, 1955; grew up in Medway, ME; education: graduate, Harvard University John F. Kennedy School of Government Program for Senior Executives in State and Local Government; professional: mill worker; community service: actively involved in a variety of local, regional, and statewide civic and economic development organizations; public service: Maine House of Representatives, 1980–94; Maine State Senate, 1994–2002; religion: Catholic; committees: Transportation and Infrastructure; Veterans' Affairs; elected to the 108th Congress on November 5, 2002; reelected to each succeeding Congress.

Office Listings

http://www.house.gov/michaud

1724 Longworth House Office Building, Washington, DC 20515 .... (202) 225–6306
Chief of Staff.—Peter Chandler. FAX: 225–2943
Legislative Director.—Nora Todd.
Scheduler.—Diane Smith.
Communications Director.—Ed Gilman.
6 State Street, Suite 101, Bangor, ME 04401 .... (207) 942–6935
179 Lisbon Street, Ground Floor, Lewiston, ME 04240 .... (207) 782–3704
445 Main Street, Presque Isle, ME 04769 .... (207) 764–1036
108 Main Street, Waterville, ME 04901 .... (207) 873–5713

Counties: ANDROSCOGGIN, AROOSTOOK, FRANKLIN, HANCOCK, KENNEBEC (part), OXFORD, PENOBSCOT, PISCATAQUIS, SOMERSET, WALDO, WASHINGTON. Population (2010), 664,180.

ZIP Codes: 04010, 04016, 04022, 04037, 04041, 04051, 04068, 04088, 04210–12, 04216–17, 04219–28, 04230–31, 04234, 04236–41, 04243, 04250, 04252–58, 04261–63, 04266–68, 04270–71, 04274–76, 04278, 04280–83, 04285–86, 04288–92, 04294, 04354, 04401–02, 04406, 04408, 04410–24, 04426–31, 04434–35, 04438, 04441–44, 04448–51, 04453–57, 04459–64, 04467–69, 04471–76, 04478–79, 04481, 04485, 04487–93, 04495–97, 04549, 04605–07, 04609, 04611–17, 04619, 04622–31, 04634–35, 04637, 04640, 04642–46, 04648–50, 04652–58, 04660, 04662, 04664, 04666–69, 04671–77, 04679–81, 04683–86, 04691, 04693–94, 04730, 04732–47, 04750–51, 04756–66, 04768–70, 04772–77, 04779–81, 04783, 04785–88, 04848–51, 04857, 04903, 04911–12, 04915, 04920–25, 04928–30, 04932–33, 04936–45, 04947, 04949–58, 04961, 04964–67, 04969–76, 04978–79, 04981–88, 04992

MARYLAND

(Population 2010, 5,773,552)

SENATORS

BARBARA A. MIKULSKI, Democrat, of Baltimore, MD; born in Baltimore, July 20, 1936; education: B.A., Mount St. Agnes College, 1958; M.S.W., University of Maryland School of Social Work, 1965; former social worker for Catholic Charities and city of Baltimore; former adjunct professor, Department of Sociology, Loyola College; elected to the Baltimore City Council in 1971; Democratic nominee for the U.S. Senate in 1974, winning 43 percent of vote; elected to the U.S. House of Representatives in November, 1976; first woman appointed to the Energy and Commerce Committee; also served on the Merchant Marine and Fisheries Committee; became the first Democratic woman to be elected to a Senate seat not previously held by her husband, and the first Democratic woman ever to serve in both houses of Congress; Secretary, Democratic Conference; first woman to be elected to a leadership post; Secretary of the Democratic Conference; first woman to serve as Chair of the Seante Appropriations Committee; committees: chair, Appropriations; Health, Education, Labor, and Pensions; Select Committee on Intelligence; elected to the U.S. Senate in November, 1986; reelected to each succeeding Senate term.

Office Listings

http://mikulski.senate.gov http://twitter.com/senatorbarb
https://www.facebook.com/senatormikulski

503 Hart Senate Office Building, Washington, DC 20510 .... (202) 224–4654
Chief of Staff.—Julia Frifield. FAX: 224–8858
Legislative Director.—Jean Doyle.
901 South Bond Street, Suite 310, Baltimore, MD 21231 .... (410) 962–4510
State Director.—Jan Gardner.
60 West Street, Suite 202, Annapolis, MD 21401 .... (410) 263–1805
6404 Ivy Lane, Suite 406, Greenbelt, MD 20770 .... (301) 345–5517
32 West Washington Street, Suite 203, Hagerstown, MD 21740 .... (301) 797–2826
The Gallery Plaza Building, 212 Main Street, Suite 200, Salisbury, MD 21801 ...... (410) 546–7711

* * *

BENJAMIN L. CARDIN, Democrat, of Baltimore, MD; born in Baltimore, October 5, 1943; education: graduated, City College High School, 1961; B.A., *cum laude*, University of Pittsburgh, 1964; L.L.B., 1st in class, University of Maryland School of Law, 1967; professional: attorney, Rosen and Esterson, 1967–78; elected to Maryland House of Delegates in November 1966, served from 1967–87; Speaker of the House of Delegates, youngest Speaker at the time, 1979–87; elected to U.S. House of Representatives in November 1986, Maryland 3rd Congressional District, served from 1987–2007; member: Associated Jewish Charities and Welfare Fund, 1985–89; Trustee, Goucher College, 1999–2008; St. Mary's College, 1988–99; Lifetime Member, NAACP, since 1990; Board of Visitors, University of Maryland Law School, 1991–present; President's Board of Visitors, UMBC, 1998–present; Board of Visitors, U.S. Naval Academy, 2007–present; Board of Trustees, The James Madison Memorial Fellowship, 2010–present; awards: Congressional Award, Small Business Council of America, 1993, 1999, 2005; Public Sector Distinguished Award, Tax Foundation, 2003; Congressional Voice for Children Award, National PTA, 2009; Congressional Leadership Award, American College of Emergency Physicians, 2010; Whitney M. Young Award, Baltimore Urban League, 2011; Chesapeake Conservation Hero, Chesapeake Conservancy, 2012; Commissioner, Commission for Security and Cooperation in Europe (CSCE), since 1993; co-chair, CSCE, 2007–08; chair, CSCE, 2009–10; co-chair, CSCE, 2011–13; chair, CSCE, 2013–present; Vice President, Organization for Security and Cooperation in Europe Parliamentary Assembly, 2006–present; religion: Jewish; married: Myrna Edelman of Baltimore, 1964; two children, (one deceased); two grandchildren; committees: Environment and Public Works; Finance; Foreign Relations; Small Business and Entrepreneurship; elected to the U.S. Senate on November 7, 2006; reelected to the U.S. Senate on November 6, 2012.

Office Listings

http://cardin.senate.gov

509 Hart Senate Office Building, Washington, DC 20510 .... (202) 224–4524
Chief of Staff.—Chris Lynch. FAX: 224–1651
Policy Director.—Priscilla Ross. TDD: 224–3452
Appointments Secretary.—Debbie Yamada.
100 South Charles Street, Tower I, Suite 1710, Baltimore, MD 21201 .... (410) 962–4436

State Director.—Carleton Atkinson. FAX: 962–4256
10201 Martin Luther King, Jr. Highway, Suite 210, Bowie, MD 20720 .... (301) 860–0414
451 Hungerford Drive, Suite 230, Rockville, MD 20850 .... (301) 762–2974
129 East Main Street, Suite 115, P.O. Box 11, Salisbury, MD 21803 .... (410) 546–4250
13 Canal Street, Room 305, Cumberland, MD 21502 .... (301) 777–2957

REPRESENTATIVES

FIRST DISTRICT

ANDY HARRIS, Republican, of Cockeysville, MD; born in Brooklyn, NY, January 25, 1957; education: B.S., Johns Hopkins University, Baltimore, MD, 1977; M.D., Johns Hopkins University, Baltimore, 1980; M.H.S., Johns Hopkins University, Baltimore, 1995; professional: anesthesiologist, as an Associate Professor of Anesthesiology and Critical Care Medicine; member of the Maryland State Senate, 1998–2010; minority whip, Maryland State Senate; military: Commander, Johns Hopkins Medical Naval Reserve Primus Unit P0605C; religion: Catholic; married: M. Sylvia; five children; committees: Appropriations; elected to the 112th Congress on November 2, 2010; reelected to the 113th Congress on November 6, 2012.

Office Listings

http://harris.house.gov

1533 Longworth House Office Building, Washington, DC 20515 .... (202) 225–5311
Chief of Staff.—Kevin Reigrut. FAX: 225–0254
Legislative Director.—John Dutton.
Communications Director.—Matt Sauvage.
Scheduler.—Charlotte Heyworth.
100 Olde Point Village, Suite 101, Chester, MD 21619 .... (410) 643–5425
15 Churchville Road, Suite 102B, Bel Air, MD 21014 .... (410) 588–5670
212 West Main Street, Suite 204B, Salisbury, MD 21801 .... (443) 944–8624

Counties: COUNTIES: BALTIMORE (part), CAROLINE, CARROLL (part), CECIL, DORCHESTER, KENT, HARFORD (part), QUEEN ANNE'S, SOMERSET, TALBOT, WICOMICO, AND WORCESTER. Population (2010), 721,529.

ZIP Codes: 21001, 21009, 21013–15, 21018, 21023, 21028, 21030–32, 21034, 21040, 21047–48, 21050–51, 21053, 21057, 21074, 21078, 21082, 21084–85, 21087–88, 21102, 21111, 21120, 21128, 21131–32, 21136, 21154–57, 21160–62, 21234, 21236, 21286, 21601, 21606–07, 21609–10, 21612–13, 21617, 21619–20, 21622–29, 21631–32, 21634–36, 21638–41, 21643–45, 21647–73, 21675–79, 21681–85, 21687, 21690, 21757, 21784, 21787, 21791, 21801–04, 21810–11, 21813–14, 21817, 21821–22, 21824, 21826, 21829–30, 21835–38, 21840–43, 21849–53, 21856–57, 21861–67, 21869, 21871–72, 21874–75, 21890, 21901–04, 21911–22, 21930

* * *

SECOND DISTRICT

C. A. DUTCH RUPPERSBERGER, Democrat, of Cockeysville, MD; born in Baltimore, MD, January 31, 1946; education: Baltimore City College; University of Maryland, College Park; J.D., University of Baltimore Law School, 1970; professional: attorney; partner, Ruppersberger, Clark, and Mister (law firm); public service: Baltimore County Assistant State's Attorney; Baltimore County Council; Baltimore County Executive, 1994–2002; married: the former Kay Murphy; children: Cory and Jill; committees: ranking member, Permanent Select Committee on Intelligence; elected to the 108th Congress on November 5, 2002; reelected to each succeeding Congress.

Office Listings

http://dutch.house.gov twitter.com/call_me_dutch
https://www.facebook.com/dutchruppersberger

2416 Rayburn House Office Building, Washington, DC 20515 .... (202) 225–3061
Chief of Staff.—Tara Oursler. FAX: 225–3094
Deputy Chief of Staff.—Cori Duggins.
Communications Director.—Jaime Lennon.
Senior Policy Advisor.—Walter Gonzales.
The Atrium, 375 West Padonia Road, Suite 200, Timonium, MD 21093 .... (410) 628–2701
District Director.—Jennifer Riggs. FAX: 628–2708
Scheduler.—Carol Merkel.

Counties: ANNE ARUNDEL (part), BALTIMORE CITY (part), BALTIMORE COUNTY (part), HARFORD (part), HOWARD (part). Population (2010), 721,529.

ZIP Codes: 20701, 20723–24, 20755, 20794, 21001, 21005, 21009–10, 21015, 21017, 21022, 21027, 21030–31, 21034, 21040, 21043, 21052, 21057, 21062–63, 21065, 21071, 21075–78, 21085, 21090, 21093, 21113, 21117, 21128–30, 21133, 21136, 21144, 21162–63, 21204, 21206, 21208, 21212–14, 21219–22, 21224–27, 21230–31, 21234, 21236–37, 21239, 21240, 21244, 21252, 21286

* * *

THIRD DISTRICT

JOHN P. SARBANES, Democrat, of Baltimore, MD; born in Baltimore, May 22, 1962; education: A.B., *cum laude*, Woodrow Wilson School of Public and International Affairs, Princeton University, 1984; Fulbright Scholar, Greece, 1985; J.D., Harvard University School of Law, 1988; professional: law clerk to Judge J. Frederick Motz, U.S. District Court for the District of Maryland, 1988–89; admitted to Maryland Bar, 1988; member: American Bar Association; Maryland State Bar Association; attorney, Venable, LLP, 1989–2006 (chair, health care practice); founding member, Board of Trustees, Dunbar Project, 1990–94; Board of Directors, Public Justice Center, 1991–2006 (president, 1994–97); Institute for Christian and Jewish Studies, 1991–present (past chair, membership committee); Special Assistant to State Superintendent of Schools, State Department of Education, 1998–2005; awards: Unsung Hero Award, Maryland Chapter of the Association of Fundraising Professionals, 2006; Arthur W. Machen, Jr., Award, Maryland Legal Services Corp., 2006; married to Dina Sarbanes; three children; committees: Energy and Commerce; elected to the 110th Congress on November 7, 2006; reelected to each succeeding Congress.

Office Listings

http://www.sarbanes.house.gov

2444 Rayburn House Office Building, Washington, DC 20510 .... (202) 225–4016
Chief of Staff.—Jason Gleason. FAX: 225–9219
Deputy Chief of Staff / Legislative Director.—Dvora Lovinger.
Legislative Correspondent.—Caren Howard.
Scheduler / Director of Administration.—Kristen Lail.
Legislative Assistants: Helen Mastrogianis, Raymond O'Mara.
Communications Director.—Meghan Pennington.
600 Baltimore Avenue, Suite 303, Towson, MD 21204 .... (410) 832–8890
44 Calvert Street, Suite 349, Annapolis, MD 21401 .... (410) 295–1679
3901 National Drive, Burtonsville, MD 20866 .... (301) 421–4078

Counties: ANNE ARUNDEL (part), BALTIMORE (part), BALTIMORE CITY (part), HOWARD (part), AND MONTGOMERY (part). Population (2010), 720,094.

ZIP Codes: 20705, 20707, 20723–24, 20759, 20777, 20783, 20832–33, 20853, 20855, 20860–62, 20866, 20868, 20882, 20901, 20903–06, 21012, 21022, 21029, 21037, 21043–46, 21054, 21056, 21060–61, 21075–77, 21090, 21093, 21108, 21113, 21117, 21122, 21128, 21136, 21139, 21144, 21153, 21201–15, 21218, 21223–27, 21229–31, 21234, 21236–37, 21239, 21252, 21281–82, 21285–86, 21401–03, 21409, 21412, 21797

* * *

FOURTH DISTRICT

DONNA F. EDWARDS, Democrat, of Fort Washington, MD; born in Yanceyville, NC, June 28, 1959; education: B.A., Wake Forest University, Winston-Salem, NC, 1980; J.D., Franklin Pierce Law Center, Concord, NH, 1989; professional: executive director, Arca Foundation, 2000–08; founder and executive director, National Network to End Domestic Violence, 1996–99; executive director, Center for New Democracy, 1994–96; member: board of directors, National Network to End Domestic Violence; Citizens for Responsibility and Ethics in Washington; League of Conservation Voters, Common Cause; Tom Lantos Human Rights Commission; committees: Science, Space, and Technology; Transportation and Infrastructure; elected by special election on June 17, 2008, to fill the vacancy caused by the resignation of U.S. Representative Albert Russell Wynn, and elected to a full term in the 111th Congress on November 4, 2008; reelected to each succeeding Congress.

Office Listings

http://www.donnaedwards.house.gov https://twitter.com/repdonnaedwards
https://www.facebook.com/pages/congresswoman-donna-f-edwards/107297211756

2445 Rayburn House Office Building, Washington, DC 20515 .... (202) 225–8699
Chief of Staff.—Adrienne Christian. FAX: 225–8714
Legislative Director.—Chris Schloesser.
Communications Director.—Dan Weber.
5001 Silver Hill Road, Suite 106, Suitland, MD 20746 .... (301) 516–7601

877 Baltimore Annapolis Boulevard, #101, Severna Park, MD 21146 .... (301) 562–7960

Counties: ANNE ARUNDEL (part), PRINCE GEORGE'S (part). CITIES AND TOWNSHIPS: Andrews Air Force Base, Annapolis, Arnold, Beltsville, Bladensburg, Bowie, Brentwood, Capitol Heights, Clinton, College Park, Crofton, Crownsville, Davidsonville, District Heights, Edgewater, Fort Washington, Gambrills, Glen Burnie, Glenn Dale, Hyattsville, Lanham, Laurel, Millersville, Mount Rainier, Odenton, Oxon Hill, Pasadena, Riva, Riverdale, Severn, Severna Park, Sherwood Forest, Silver Spring, Suitland, Takoma Park, Temple Hills, and Upper Marlboro. Population (2010) 720,065.

ZIP Codes: 20705–08, 20710, 20712, 20720–22, 20724, 20735, 20737, 20740, 20743–48, 20762, 20769, 20772, 20774, 20781–85, 20903–04, 20912, 21012, 21032, 21035, 21037, 21054, 21061, 21108, 21113–14, 21122, 21140, 21144, 21146, 21401, 21405, 21409

* * *

FIFTH DISTRICT

STENY H. HOYER, Democrat, of Mechanicsville, MD; born in New York, NY, June 14, 1939; education: graduated Suitland High School; B.S., University of Maryland, 1963; J.D., Georgetown University Law Center, 1966; Honorary Doctor of Public Service, University of Maryland, 1988; admitted to the Maryland Bar Association, 1966; professional: practicing attorney, 1966–90; Maryland State Senate, 1967–79; vice chairman, Prince George's County, MD, Senate delegation, 1967–69; chairman, Prince George's County, MD, Senate delegation, 1969–75; president, Maryland State Senate, 1975–79; member, State Board for Higher Education, 1978–81; married: Judith Pickett, deceased, February 6, 1997; children: Susan, Stefany, and Anne; Democratic Steering Committee; Democratic Whip, 108 and 109th Congresses; House Majority Leader, 110th and 111th Congresses; Democratic Whip, 112th and 113th Congresses; elected to the 97th Congress on May 19, 1981, by special election; reelected to each succeeding Congress.

Office Listings

http://www.hoyer.house.gov www.facebook.com/whiphoyer twitter: @whiphoyer

1705 Longworth House Office Building, Washington, DC 20515 .... (202) 225–4131
Chief of Staff.—Alexis Covey-Brandt. FAX: 226–0663
Senior Advisor / Personal Office Director.—Jim Notter.
U.S. Federal Courthouse, Suite 310, 6500 Cherrywood Lane, Greenbelt, MD 20770 .... (301) 474–0119
401 Post Office Road, Suite 202, Waldorf, MD 20602 .... (301) 843–1577

Counties: ANNE ARUNDEL (part), CALVERT, CHARLES, PRINCE GEORGE'S (part), ST. MARY'S. Population (2012), 721,529.

ZIP Codes: 20601–03, 20606–09, 20611–13, 20615–26, 20628–30, 20632, 20634, 20636–37, 20639–40, 20645–46, 20650, 20653, 20657–60, 20662, 20664, 20667, 20670, 20674–76, 20678, 20680, 20684–90, 20692–93, 20695, 20705–08, 20711, 20714–16, 20720–21, 20732–33, 20735–37, 20740, 20742, 20744, 20746, 20748, 20751, 20754, 20758, 20762, 20764–65, 20769–70, 20772, 20774, 20776, 20778–79, 20781–84, 21035, 21037, 21054, 21113–14

* * *

SIXTH DISTRICT

JOHN K. DELANEY, Democrat of Potomac, MD; born in Wood-Ridge, NJ, April 16, 1963; education: B.A., Columbia University, 1985; J.D., Georgetown University Law School, 1988; professional: former practicing attorney, Shaw, Pittman, Potts & Trowbridge; Co-founder, Chair, and Chief Executive Officer, Health Care Financial Partners, Inc., 1993–99; Co-founder and Executive Chair, Capital Source, 2000–12; awards: Ernst & Young Entrepreneur of the Year, 2005; married: April; children: Summer, Brooke, Lily, Grace; committees: Financial Services; Joint Economic Committee; elected to the 113th Congress on November 6, 2012.

Office Listings

http://www.delaney.house.gov https://www.facebook.com/congressmanjohndelaney
https://twitter.com/RepJohnDelaney

1632 Longworth House Office Building, Washington, DC 20515 .... (202) 225–2721
Chief of Staff.—John Monsif.
Legislative Director.—Benjamin Turner.
Scheduler.—Jeri Sparling.
9801 Washingtonian Boulevard, Suite 330, Gaithersburg, MD 20878 .... (301) 926–0300
6 West Washington Street, Suite 210, Hagerstown, MD 21740 .... (301) 733–2900

Counties: ALLEGANY, FREDERICK (part), GARRETT, MONTGOMERY (part), WASHINGTON. CITIES AND TOWNSHIPS: Bethesda, Boonsboro, Boyds, Clarksburg, Cumberland, Darnestown, Frederick, Frostburg, Funkstown, Gaithersburg, Germantown,

Hagerstown, Hancock, Montgomery Village, Oakland, Olney, Poolesville, Potomac, Rockville, Sharpsburg, Smithburg, Urbana, Williamsport, Woodsboro. Also includes Antietam National Battlefield and Camp David. Population (2010), 728,400.

ZIP Codes: 20817, 20827, 20837–39, 20841–42, 20850, 20852–55, 20859, 20871–72, 20874–80, 20882, 20884–86, 20898–99, 20906, 21501–05, 21520–24, 21528–30, 21531–32, 21536, 21538–43, 21545, 21550, 21555–57, 21560–62, 21701–05, 21709–11, 21713, 21715–17, 21719–22, 21733–34, 21740–42, 21746–50, 21754–56, 21758, 21766–67, 21769, 21774, 21777, 21779–83, 21790, 21795

* * *

SEVENTH DISTRICT

ELIJAH E. CUMMINGS, Democrat, of Baltimore, MD; born in Baltimore, January 18, 1951; education: graduated, Baltimore City College High School, 1969; B.S., political science, Phi Beta Kappa, Howard University, Washington, DC, 1973; J.D., University of Maryland Law School, 1976; professional: attorney; admitted to the Maryland Bar in 1976; delegate, Maryland State Legislature, 1982-96; chairman, Maryland Legislative Black Caucus, 1984; speaker pro tempore, Maryland General Assembly, 1995-96; vice chairman, Constitutional and Administrative Law Committee; vice chairman, Economic Matters Committee; active in civic affairs, and recipient of numerous community awards; member, U.S. Naval Academy Board of Visitors, Morgan State University Board of Regents, University of Maryland Law School Board of Advisors; member, New Psalmist Baptist Church, Baltimore, MD; married: Dr. Maya Rockeymoore; committees: Oversight and Government Reform; Transportation and Infrastructure; Joint Economic Committee; elected to the 104th Congress by special election in April, 1996; reelected to each succeeding Congress.

Office Listings

http://www.house.gov/cummings https://www.facebook.com/elijahcummings
https://twitter.com/elijahecummings

2235 Rayburn House Office Building, Washington, DC 20515 .... (202) 225–4741
Chief of Staff.—Vernon Simms. FAX: 225–3178
Legislative Director.—Lucinda Lessley.
Legislative Assistants: Jedd Bellman, Jimmy Fremgen, Suzanne Owen.
Press Secretary.—Safiya Simmons.
1010 Park Avenue, Suite 105, Baltimore, MD 21201 .... (410) 685–9199
754 Frederick Road, Catonsville, MD 21228 .... (410) 719–8777
8267 Main Street, Room 102, Ellicott City, MD 21043 .... (410) 465–8259

Counties: BALTIMORE (part), HOWARD (part), BALTIMORE CITY (part). Population (2010), 660,523.

ZIP Codes: 21036, 21042, 21051, 21111, 21152, 21207, 21216–17, 21228, 21235, 21245, 21250–51, 21287, 21723, 21737–38, 21794, 20777, 20833, 21013, 21029–31, 21043–45, 21047, 21057, 21074–75, 21082, 21087, 21093, 21102, 21104, 21117, 21120, 21131, 21133, 21136, 21155, 21161

* * *

EIGHTH DISTRICT

CHRIS VAN HOLLEN, Democrat, of Kensington, MD; born in Karachi, Pakistan, January 10, 1959; education: B.A., Swarthmore College, 1982; masters in public policy, Harvard University, 1985; J.D., Georgetown University, 1990; professional: attorney; legislative assistant to former Maryland U.S. Senator Charles McC. Mathias, Jr.; staff member, U.S. Senate Committee on Foreign Relations; senior legislative advisor to former Maryland Governor William Donald Schaefer; public service: elected, Maryland House of Delegates, 1990; elected, Maryland State Senate, 1994; married: Katherine; children: Anna, Nicholas, and Alexander; committees: ranking member, Budget; elected to the 108th Congress on November 5, 2002; reelected to each succeeding Congress.

Office Listings

http://www.vanhollen.house.gov

1707 Longworth House Office Building, Washington, DC 20515 .... (202) 225–5341
Chief of Staff.—Bill Parsons. FAX: 225–0375
Legislative Director.—Sarah Schenning.
Legislative Assistants: Erika Appel, Ben Cook.
Communications Director.—Bridgett Frey.
51 Monroe Street, Suite 507, Rockville, MD 20850 .... (301) 424–3501

205 Center Street, Suite 206, Mount Airy, MD 21771 .... (301) 829–2181
District Director.—Joan Kleinman.

Counties: MONTGOMERY (part), FREDERICK (part), CARROLL (part). Population (2010), 721,528.

ZIP Codes: 20811–18, 20824–25, 20847–55, 20857, 20872, 20882, 20889, 20891–92, 20894–96, 20901–08, 20910–16, 20918, 21104, 21157–58, 21701–04, 21714, 21718, 21727, 21754–55, 21757, 21759, 21762, 21765, 21769–71, 21773–76, 21778, 21780, 21783–84, 21787–21788, 21791–93, 21797–98

MASSACHUSETTS

(Population 2010, 6,547,629)

SENATORS

ELIZABETH WARREN, Democrat, of Cambridge, MA; born in Oklahoma City, OK, June 22, 1949; education: B.A., University of Houston, Houston, TX, 1970; J.D., Rutgers Law School, Newark, NJ, 1976; professional: Leo Gottlieb Professor of Law, Harvard Law School, 1995–2012; Chief Advisor, National Bankruptcy Review Commission, 1995–97; chair, Congressional Oversight Panel, 2008–10; Assistant to the President and Special Advisor to the Secretary of the Treasury for the Consumer Financial Protection Bureau, 2010–11; married: Bruce Mann; two children, three grandchildren; committees: Banking, Housing, and Urban Affairs; Health, Education, Labor, and Pensions; Special Committee on Aging; elected to the U.S. Senate on November 6, 2012.

Office Listings

http://warren.senate.gov

317 Hart Senate Office Building, Washington, DC 20510 .... (202) 224–4543
Chief of Staff.—Mindy Myers.
Deputy Chief of Staff.—Dan Geldon.
Legislative Director.—Jon Donenberg.
2400 JFK Federal Building, 15 New Sudbury Street, Boston, MA 02203 .... (617) 565–3170
State Director.—Roger Lau.
1550 Main Street, Suite 406, Springfield, MA 01103 .... (413) 788–2690

* * *

EDWARD J. MARKEY, Democrat, of Malden, MA; born in Malden, MA, July 11, 1946; education: B.A., Boston College, Boston, MA, 1968; J.D., Boston College, Boston, MA, 1972; U.S. Army Reserve (1968–73); professional: member, Massachusetts House of Representatives (1973–76); U.S. House of Representatives (1976–2013); ranking member, Natural Resources Committee (2011–13); chair, Select Committee on Energy Independence and Global Warming (2007–11); chair, Subcommittee on Energy and the Environment (2009–11); chair, subcommittee on Telecommunications and the Internet (2007–09); married: Dr. Susan Blumenthal; committees: Commerce, Science, and Transportation; Environment and Public Works; Foreign Relations; Small Business and Entrepreneurship; elected to the U.S. Senate in a special election on June 25, 2013, to fill the vacancy caused by the resignation of John F. Kerry to become Secretary of State.

Office Listings

http://www.markey.senate.gov twitter: @markeymemo
https://www.facebook.com/edjmarkey

218 Russell Senate Office Building, Washington, DC 20510 .... (202) 224–2742
Chief of Staff.—Mark Bayer.
Scheduler.—Sarah Butler.
Communications Director.—Giselle Barry.
JFK Federal Building, Suite 975, 15 New Sudbury Street, Boston, MA 02203 .... (617) 565–8519
222 Milliken Boulevard, Suite 312, Fall River, MA 02721 .... (508) 677–0523
1550 Main Street, 4th Floor, Springfield, MA 01101 .... (413) 785–4610

REPRESENTATIVES

FIRST DISTRICT

RICHARD E. NEAL, Democrat, of Springfield, MA; born in Springfield, February 14, 1949; education: graduated, Springfield Technical High School, 1968; B.A., American International College, Springfield, 1972; M.A., University of Hartford Barney School of Business and Public Administration, West Hartford, CT, 1976; instructor and lecturer; assistant to mayor of Springfield, 1973–78; Springfield City Council, 1978–84; mayor, City of Springfield, 1983–89; member: Massachusetts Mayors Association; Adult Education Council; American International College Alumni Association; Boys Club Alumni Association; Emily Bill Athletic Association; Cancer Crusade; John Boyle O'Reilly Club; United States Conference of Mayors; Valley Press Club; Solid Waste Advisory Committee for the State of Massachusetts; Committee on Leadership and Government; Mass Jobs Council; trustee: Springfield Libraries and Museums Association, Springfield Red Cross, Springfield YMCA; married: Maureen; four children: Rory Christopher, Brendan Conway, Maura Katherine, and Sean Richard; committees: Ways and Means; elected on November 8, 1988 to the 101st Congress; reelected to each succeeding Congress.

Office Listings

http://www.house.gov/neal

2208 Rayburn House Office Building, Washington, DC 20515 .... (202) 225–5601
Administrative Assistant.—Ann Jablon. FAX: 225–8112
Executive Assistant.—Tim Ranstrom.
Press Secretary.—William Tranghese.
300 State Street, Suite 200, Springfield, MA 01105 .... (413) 785–0325
District Manager.—Vacant.
78 Center Street, Pittsfield, MA 01201 .... (508) 634–8198
Office Manager.—Cynthia Clark.

Counties: BERKSHIRE, FRANKLIN (part), HAMPDEN (part), HAMPSHIRE (part), and WORCESTER (part). Population (2010), 727,515.

ZIP Codes: 01001, 01008–13, 01020–22, 01026–30, 01032–34, 01036, 01039, 01040, 01050, 01056–57, 01069–71, 01073, 01075, 01077, 01079–81, 01083–86, 01089, 01092, 01095–98, 01103–09, 01118–19, 01128–29, 01151, 01199, 01201, 01220, 01222–26, 01229, 01230, 01235–38, 01240, 01242–45, 01247, 01253–60. 01262, 01264, 01266–67, 01270, 01301, 01330, 01337–41, 01343, 01346, 01350, 01367, 01370, 01506–07, 01515, 01518, 01521, 01550, 01566, 01571, 01585

* * *

SECOND DISTRICT

JAMES P. McGOVERN, Democrat, of Worcester, MA; born in Worcester, November 20, 1959; education: B.A., M.P.A., American University; legislative director and senior aide to Congressman Joe Moakley (D–South Boston); led the 1989 investigation into the murders of six Jesuit priests and two lay women in El Salvador; managed George McGovern's (D–SD) 1984 presidential campaign in Massachusetts and delivered his nomination speech at the Democratic National Convention; board of directors, Jesuit International Volunteers; former volunteer, Mt. Carmel House, an emergency shelter for battered and abused women; married: Lisa Murray McGovern; committees: Agriculture; Rules; elected to the 105th Congress; reelected to each succeeding Congress.

Office Listings

http://www.house.gov/mcgovern

438 Cannon House Office Building, Washington, DC 20515 .... (202) 225–6101
Legislative Director.—Cindy Buhl. FAX: 225–5759
Press Secretary.—Michael Mershon.
12 East Worcester Street, Suite 1, Worcester, MA 01604 .... (508) 831–7356
District Director.—Kathleen Polanowicz.
24 Church Street, Suite 29, Leominster, MA 01543 .... (978) 466–3552
District Representative.—Eladia Romero.
94 Pleasant Street, Northampton, MA 01060 .... (413) 341–8700
District Representative.—Natalie Blais.

Counties: FRANKLIN (part), HAMPDEN (part), HAMPSHIRE (part), NORFOLK (part), AND WORCESTER (part). CITIES AND TOWNSHIPS: Amherst, Athol, Auburn, Barre, Belchertown, Bellingham, Blackstone, Boylston, Deerfield, Douglas, Erving, Gill, Grafton, Greenfield, Hadley, Hardwick, Hatfield, Holden, Hubbardston, Leicester, Leominster, Leverett, Mendon, Millbury, Millville, Montague, New Braintree, New Salem, North Brookfield, Northampton, Northborough, Northbridge, Northfield, Oakham, Orange, Oxford, Palmer, Paxton, Pelham, Petersham, Phillipston, Princeton, Royalston, Rutland, Shrewsbury, Shutesbury, Spencer, Sterling, Sunderland, Sutton, Templeton, Upton, Uxbridge, Ware, Warwick, Webster, Wendell, West Boylston, West Brookfield, Westborough, Whately, Winchendon, and Worcester. Population (2010), 727,514.

ZIP Codes: 01002–03, 01005, 01007, 01031, 01035, 01037–39, 01053–54, 01060, 01062–63, 01066, 01068–69, 01072, 01074, 01082, 01088, 01093–94, 01301, 01331, 01342, 01344, 01347, 01349, 01351, 01354–55, 01360, 01364, 01366, 01368, 01370, 01373, 01375–76, 01378–79, 01420, 01436, 01438, 01440, 01452–53, 01468, 01475, 01501, 01504–05, 01516, 01519–20, 01522, 01524–25, 01527, 01529, 01531–32, 01534–37, 01540–43, 01545, 01560, 01562, 01564, 01568–70, 01581, 01583, 01585, 01588, 01590, 01602–12, 01756–57, 02019

* * *

THIRD DISTRICT

NIKI TSONGAS, Democrat, of Lowell, MA; born in Chico, CA, April 26, 1946; graduated from Narimasu American High School, Japan, 1964; B.A., Smith College, Northampton, MA, 1968; J.D., Boston University, Boston, MA, 1988; professional: social worker; lawyer, Middlesex Community College's dean of external affairs; widowed: Paul Tsongas; children: Ashley Tsongas, Katina Tsongas, and Molly Tsongas; committees: Armed Services; Natural Resources; elected to the 110th Congress, by special election, to fill the vacancy caused by the resignation of Representative Martin Meehan; elected to the 111th Congress on November 4, 2008; reelected to each succeeding Congress.

Office Listings

http://www.tsongas.house.gov

1607 Longworth House Office Building, Washington, DC 20515 .... (202) 225–3411
Chief of Staff.—Katie Enos. FAX: 226–0771
Washington Manager/Legislative Director.—Sarah Christopherson.
Scheduler.—Kristen Hagan.
11 Kearney Square, 4th Floor, Lowell, MA 01852 .... (978) 459–0101
District Director.—Chris Mullin.

Counties: ESSEX COUNTY, MIDDLESEX COUNTY, WORCESTER COUNTY. Population (2010), 732,090.

ZIP Codes: 01432, 01450–51, 01460, 01464, 01503, 01523, 01718–20, 01740–42, 01749, 01754, 01775–76, 01778, 01810, 01821, 01824, 01826–27, 01830, 01840–44, 01850–54, 01862–63, 01876, 01879, 01886

* * *

FOURTH DISTRICT

JOSEPH P. KENNEDY III, Democrat, of Brookline, MA; born in Brighton, MA, October 4, 1980; education: graduated, Buckingham, Browne & Nichols, 1999; B.S., Stanford College, 2003; J.D., Harvard University, 2009; professional: Peace Corps, 2004–06; assistant district attorney, Cape and Islands Office, 2009–11; assistant district attorney, Middlesex Office 2011–2012; committees: Foreign Affairs; Science, Space, and Technology; elected to the 113th Congress, November 6, 2012.

Office Listings

http://kennedy.house.gov

1218 Longworth House Office Building, Washington, DC 20515 .... (202) 225–5931
Chief of Staff.—Greg Mecher. FAX: 225–0182
Deputy Chief of Staff/Legislative Director.—Sarah Curtis.
Scheduler.—Rachael Goldenberg.
8 North Main Street, Suite 200, Attleboro, MA 02703 .... (508) 431–1110
29 Crafts Street, Suite 375, Newton, MA 02458 .... (617) 332–3333
District Director.—Nick Clemons.
Communications Director.—Emily Browne.

Counties: BRISTOL (part), MIDDLESEX (part), NORFOLK (part), PLYMOUTH (part), WORCESTER (part). CITIES AND TOWNSHIPS: Attleboro, Bellingham, Berkley, Brookline, Dighton, Dover, Easton, Fall River, Foxboro, Franklin, Freetown, Hopedale, Hopkinton, Lakeville, Mansfield, Medfield, Medway, Milford, Millis, Needham, Newton, Norfolk, North Attleborough, Norton, Plainville, Raynham, Rehoboth, Seekonk, Sharon, Somerset, Swansea, Taunton, Wellesley, and Wrentham. Population (2010), 727,514.

ZIP Codes: 01747–48, 01757, 02019, 02030–31, 02035, 02038, 02048, 02052–54, 02056, 02067, 02070, 02093, 02171, 02334, 02347–48, 02356–57, 02375, 02445–47, 02456–62, 02464–68, 02481–82, 02492, 02494–95, 02702–03, 02712, 02715, 02718, 02725–26, 02760–63, 02766–69, 02771, 02777, 02779–80

* * *

FIFTH DISTRICT

KATHERINE M. CLARK, Democrat, of Melrose, MA; born in New Haven, CT, July, 17 1963; education: B.A., Saint Lawrence University, 1985; J.D., Cornell School of Law, 1989; M.P.A., Harvard University, 1997; professional: admitted to the Massachusetts Bar, 1997; served as general counsel for the Massachusetts Office of Child Care Services; Chief of the Policy Division for the Massachusetts Attorney General and prosecutor; elected in March 2008 to the Massachusetts House of Representatives, elected to the Massachusetts State Senate in November of 2010; religion: Protestant; married: Rodney Dowell; children: Addison, Jared and Nathaniel; committees: Natural Resources; elected to the 113th Congress, by special election on December 10, 2013.

Office Listings

http://www.katherineclark.house.gov

2108 Rayburn House Office Building, Washington, DC 20515 .... (202) 225–2836
Chief of Staff.—Brooke Scannell. FAX: 226–0092
Legislative Director.—David Bond.
Scheduler.—George Tobias.
5 High Street, Suite 101, Medford, MA 02155 .... (781) 396–2900
Senior Advisor.—Jennifer McAndrew.

Counties: MIDDLESEX (part), SUFFOLK (part), AND WORCESTER (part). CITIES AND TOWNSHIPS: Arlington, Ashland, Belmont, Cambridge, Framingham, Holliston, Lexington, Lincoln, Malden, Medford, Melrose, Natick, Revere, Sherborn, Southborough, Stoneham, Sudbury, Waltham, Watertown, Wayland, Weston, Winchester, Winthrop, and Woburn. Population (2010), 727,515.

ZIP Codes: 01701–05, 01721, 01746, 01760, 01770, 01772–73, 01776, 01778, 01890, 02138–42, 02148, 02151–53, 02155, 02176, 02180, 02238, 02420–21, 02451–54, 02471–72, 02474, 02476–78, 02493

* * *

SIXTH DISTRICT

JOHN F. TIERNEY, Democrat, of Salem, MA; born in Salem, September 18, 1951; education: graduated, Salem High School; B.A., political science, Salem State College, 1973; J.D., Suffolk University, 1976; professional: attorney, admitted to the Massachusetts bar in 1976; sole practitioner, 1976–80; partner, Tierney, Kalis and Lucas, 1981–96; member: Salem Chamber of Commerce, 1976–96 (president, 1995); trustee, Salem State College, 1992–97; married: Patrice M., 1997; committees: Education and the Workforce; Oversight and Government Reform; elected to the 105th Congress; reelected to each succeeding Congress.

Office Listings

http://www.house.gov/tierney

2238 Rayburn House Office Building, Washington, DC 20515 .... (202) 225–8020
Chief of Staff.—Betsy Arnold Marr. FAX: 225–5915
Legislative Director.—Kevin McDermott.
Executive Assistant.—Bambi Yingst.
17 Peabody Square, Peabody, MA 01960 .... (978) 531–1669
Outreach Director.—Drew Russo.
Lynn City Hall, Room 412, Lynn, MA 01902 .... (781) 595–7375

Counties: ESSEX, MIDDLESEX. CITIES AND TOWNSHIPS: Amesbury, Bedford, Beverly, Billerica, Boxford, Burlington, Danvers, Essex, Georgetown, Gloucester, Groveland, Hamilton, Ipswich, Lynn, Lynnfield, Manchester by the Sea, Marblehead, Merrimac, Middletown, Nahant, Newbury, Newburyport, Andover, North Andover, North Reading, Peabody, Reading, Rockport, Rowley, Salem, Salisbury, Saugus, Swampscott, Tewksbury, Topsfield, Wenham, West Newbury, Wakefield, and Wilmington. Population (2010), 731,681.

ZIP Codes: 01730–31, 01801, 01803, 01805, 01810, 01821–22, 01833–34, 01845, 01860, 01864, 01867, 01876, 01880, 01885, 01887, 01889, 01901–08, 01910, 01913, 01915, 01921–23, 01929–31, 01936–38, 01940, 01944–45, 01949–52, 01960–61, 01965–66, 01969–71, 01982–85

* * *

SEVENTH DISTRICT

MICHAEL E. CAPUANO, Democrat, of Somerville, MA; born in Somerville, January 9, 1952; education: graduated, Somerville High School, 1969; B.A., Dartmouth College, 1973; J.D., Boston College Law School, 1977; professional: admitted to the Massachusetts Bar, 1977; Alderman in Somerville, MA, 1977–79; Alderman-at-Large, 1985–89; elected Mayor for five terms, 1990 to January, 1999, when he resigned to be sworn in as a U.S. Representative; Democratic Caucus; married: Barbara Teebagy of Somerville, MA, in 1974; children: Michael and Joseph; committees: Ethics; Financial Services; Transportation and Infrastructure; elected to the 106th Congress; reelected to each succeeding Congress.

Office Listings

http://www.house.gov/capuano

1414 Longworth House Office Building, Washington, DC 20515 .... (202) 225–5111
Chief of Staff.—Robert Primus. FAX: 225–9322
Office Manager / Scheduler.—Mary Doherty.
Senior Legislative Assistant.—Noelle Melton.
110 First Street, Cambridge, MA 02141 .... (617) 621–6208
District Director.—Jon Lenicheck.

Counties: MIDDLESEX (part), NORFOLK (part), SUFFOLK (part). CITIES AND TOWNSHIPS: Boston (part), Cambridge (part), Chelsea, Everett, Milton (part), Randolph, and Somerville. Population (2010), 727,514.

ZIP Codes: 02111, 02115–26, 02128–32, 02134–36, 02138–45, 02149–50, 02163, 02186, 02199, 02368

* * *

EIGHTH DISTRICT

STEPHEN F. LYNCH, Democrat, of South Boston, MA; born in South Boston, March 31, 1955; education: South Boston High School, 1973; B.S., Wentworth Institute of Technology; J.D., Boston College Law School; master in public administration, JFK School of Government, Harvard University; professional: attorney; former President of Ironworkers Local #7; organizations: South Boston Boys and Girls Club; Colonel Daniel Marr Boys and Girls Club; Friends for Children; public service: elected to the Massachusetts House of Representatives in 1994, and the State Senate in 1996; family: married to Margaret; one child: Victoria; committees: Financial Services; Oversight and Government Reform; elected to the 107th Congress, by special election, on October 16, 2001; reelected to each succeeding Congress.

Office Listings

http://lynch.house.gov

2133 Rayburn House Office Building, Washington, DC 20515 .... (202) 225–8273
Chief of Staff.—Kevin Ryan. FAX: 225–3984
Legislative Director.—Bruce Fernandez.
Scheduler.—Meghan Aldridge.
88 Black Falcon Avenue, Suite 340, Boston, MA 02210 .... (617) 428–2000
Plymouth County Registry Building, 155 West Elm Street, Brockton, MA 02401 ... (508) 586–5555
1245 Hancock Street, Suite 16, Quincy, MA 02169 .... (617) 657–6305

Counties: BRISTOL (part), NORFOLK (part), PLYMOUTH (part), SUFFOLK (part). Population (2010), 732,884.

ZIP Codes: 02021, 02025–26, 02032, 02043, 02045, 02047, 02050, 02062, 02066, 02071–72, 02081, 02090, 02108–10, 02113–14, 02118, 02122, 02124–25, 02127, 02130–32, 02136, 02169–71, 02184, 02186, 02188–91, 02203, 02210, 02301–02, 02322, 02324, 02333, 02343, 02351, 02368, 02379, 02382, 02467, 02767

* * *

NINTH DISTRICT

WILLIAM "BILL" KEATING, Democrat, of Bourne, MA; born in Norwood, MA, September 6, 1952; education: B.A., business administration, Boston College, MA, 1974; M.B.A., business administration, Boston College, MA, 1982; J.D., Suffolk University Law School, MA, 1985; professional: admitted to the Massachusetts Bar in 1985 and began practice in Stoughton, MA; Massachusetts House of Representatives, 1977–84; Massachusetts State Senate, 1985–98; chairman, Judiciary Committee; Committee on Taxation; Committee on Public Safety, Steering and Policy Committee; vice chairman, Committee on Criminal Justice; Norfolk County District Attorney, 1999–2011; religion: Roman Catholic; family: wife, Tevis, two children, Kristen and Patrick; committees: Foreign Affairs; Homeland Security; elected to the 112th Congress on November 2, 2010; reelected to the 113th Congress on November 6, 2012.

Office Listings

http://www.keating.house.gov

315 Cannon House Office Building, Washington, DC 20515 .... (202) 225–3111
Chief of Staff.—Garrett Donovan. FAX: 225–5658
2 Court Street, Plymouth, MA 02360 .... (508) 746–9000
297 North Street, Suite 312, Hyannis, MA 02061 .... (508) 771–0666

District Director.—Michael Jackman.
558 Pleasant Street, Suite 309, New Bedford, MA 02740 .... (508) 999–6462

Counties: BARNSTABLE, BRISTOL (part), DUKES, NANTUCKET, AND PLYMOUTH. Population (2010), 727,514.

ZIP Codes: 02050, 02061, 02330, 02332, 02338–09, 02341, 02344–46, 02349, 02359–60, 02364, 02367, 02370, 02532, 02534–40, 02542–43, 02553–54, 02556–59, 02561–63, 02568, 02571, 02574–76, 02601, 02631, 02633, 02635–39, 02641–53, 02655, 02657, 02659–64, 02666–73, 02675, 02713–14, 02719–24, 02738–48, 02770, 0279002018, 02020, 02025, 02035, 02040–41, 02043–45, 02047, 02050–51, 02055, 02059–61, 02065–66, 02169–71, 02184, 02186, 02188–91, 02269, 02327, 02330–32, 02339–41, 02345, 02351, 02355, 02358–62, 02364, 02366–67, 02370, 02381, 02532, 02534–37, 02539–43, 02552–54, 02556–57, 02559, 02561–65, 02568, 02573–75, 02584, 02601, 02630–35, 02637–39, 02641–53, 02655, 02657, 02659–64, 02666–73, 02675, 02713

MICHIGAN

(Population 2010, 9,883,640)

SENATORS

CARL LEVIN, Democrat, of Detroit, MI; born in Detroit, June 28, 1934; education: graduated, Central High School, Detroit, 1952; Swarthmore College, Swarthmore, PA, 1956; Harvard Law School, Boston, MA, 1959; admitted to the Michigan bar in 1959; professional: lawyer; Grossman, Hyman and Grossman, Detroit, 1959–64; assistant attorney general and general counsel for Michigan Civil Rights Commission, 1964–67; chief appellate defender for city of Detroit, 1968–69; counsel, Schlussel, Lifton, Simon, Rands and Kaufman, 1971–73; counsel, Jaffe, Snider, Raitt, Garratt and Heuer, 1978–79; member, City Council of Detroit, 1969–77 (president, 1974–77); member: Congregation T'Chiyah; American, Michigan and Detroit bar associations; former instructor at Wayne State University and the University of Detroit; married: the former Barbara Halpern, 1961; children: Kate, Laura, and Erica; committees: chair, Armed Services; Homeland Security and Governmental Affairs; Small Business and Entrepreneurship; elected to the U.S. Senate on November 7, 1978; reelected to each succeeding Senate term.

Office Listings

http://levin.senate.gov

269 Russell Senate Office Building, Washington, DC 20510 .... (202) 224–6221
Chief of Staff.—David Lyles. FAX: 224–1388
Legislative Director.—Jack Danielson.
Scheduler.—Alison Warner.
Press Secretary.—Tara Andringa.
477 Michigan Avenue, McNamara Building, Room 1860, Detroit, MI 48226 .... (313) 226–6020
Federal Building, Room 720, 110 Michigan Street, NW., Grand Rapids, MI 49503. (616) 456–2531
1810 Michigan National Tower, 124 West Allegan Street, Suite 1810, Lansing, MI 48933 .... (517) 377–1508
524 Ludington Street, Suite LL103, Escanaba, MI 49829 .... (906) 789–0052
515 North Washington, Suite 402, Saginaw, MI 48607 .... (989) 754–2494
30500 VanDyke, Suite 206, Warren, MI 48093 .... (586) 573–9145
107 Cass Street, Suite E, Traverse City, MI 49684 .... (616) 947–9569

* * *

DEBBIE STABENOW, Democrat, of Lansing, MI; born in Gladwin, MI, April 29, 1950; education: Clare High School; B.A., Michigan State University, 1972; M.S.W., Michigan State University, 1975; public service: Ingham County, MI, Commissioner, 1975–78, chairperson for two years; Michigan State House of Representatives, 1979–90; Michigan State Senate, 1991–94; religion: Methodist; children: Todd and Michelle; committees: chair, Agriculture, Nutrition, and Forestry; Budget; Finance; Energy and Natural Resources; elected to the U.S. House of Representatives in 1996 and 1998; elected to the U.S. Senate on November 7, 2000; reelected to each succeeding Senate term.

Office Listings

http://stabenow.senate.gov

133 Hart Senate Office Building, Washington, DC 20510 .... (202) 224–4822
Chief of Staff.—Dan Farough. FAX: 228–0325
Legislative Director.—Matt VanKuiken.
Scheduler.—Anne Stanski.
221 West Lake Lansing Road, Suite 100, East Lansing, MI 48823 .... (517) 203–1760
Marquette Building, 243 West Congress, Suite 550, Detroit, MI 48226 .... (313) 961–4330
432 North Saginaw, Suite 301, Flint, MI 48502 .... (810) 720–4172
3335 South Airport Road West, Suite 6B, Traverse City, MI 49684 .... (231) 929–1031
3280 Beltline Court, Suite 400, Grand Rapids, MI 49525 .... (616) 975–0052
1901 West Ridge, Suite 7, Marquette, MI 49855 .... (906) 228–8756

REPRESENTATIVES

FIRST DISTRICT

DAN BENISHEK, Republican, of Crystal Falls, MI; born in Iron Mountain, MI, April 20, 1952; education: graduated from West Iron County High School, 1970; B.S., biology, University of Michigan, 1974; M.D., Wayne State Medical School, Detroit, MI, 1978; completed, family practice internship in Flint at St. Joseph's Hospital; completed, general surgery residency at Wayne State in Detroit; professional: served as a general surgeon in Michigan's Upper Peninsula in a private practice since 1983; worked part-time at Oscar G. Johnson VA Medical Center in Iron Mountain for twenty years; married: wife Judy; five children and two grandchildren; Dr. Benishek, avid hunter and fisherman; proud member of the National Rifle Association (NRA) and Gun Owners of America (GOA); committees: Agriculture; Natural Resources; Veterans' Affairs; elected to the 112th Congress on November 2, 2010; reelected to the 113th Congress on November 6, 2012.

Office Listings

http://www.benishek.house.gov

514 Cannon House Office Building, Washington, DC 20515 .... (202) 225–4735
Chief of Staff.—James Hayes. FAX: 225–4710
Press Secretary.—Kyle Bonini.
Legislative Director.—Michelle Lane.
Scheduler/Executive Assistant.—Kay Miller.
1349 South Otsego Avenue, Suite 7A, Gaylord, MI 49735 .... (877) 376–5613
District Director.—Brandon Darin.
3301 Veterans Drive, Suite 106, Traverse City, MI 49684 .... (877) 376–5613
500 South Stephenson Avenue, Suite 500, Iron Mountain, MI 49801 .... (877) 376–5613
307 South Front Street, Suite 120, Marquette, MI 49855 .... (877) 376–5613

Counties: ALCONA, ALGER, ALPENA, ANTRIM, BARAGA, BENZIE, CHARLEVOIX, CHEBOYGAN, CHIPPEWA, CRAWFORD, DELTA, DICKINSON, EMMET, GRAND TRAVERSE, HOUGHTON, IRON, KALKASKA, KEWEENAW, LEELANAU, LUCE, MACKINAC, MANISTEE, MARQUETTE, MASON (part), MENOMINEE, MONTMORENCY, ONTONAGON, OSCODA, OTSEGO, PRESQUE ISLE, AND SCHOOLCRAFT. Population (2010), 650,222.

ZIP Codes: 48621, 48636, 48705, 48721, 48740, 48742, 49402, 49405, 49410–11, 49431, 49610–11, 49614–15, 49617, 49619, 49621–22, 49626, 49627–29, 49634–37, 49645–46, 49648, 49650, 49653–54, 49660, 49664, 49666, 49670, 49673–75, 49680, 49682, 49685–86, 49696, 49705, 49709–11, 49715, 49717, 49719, 49722–26, 49728, 49734–37, 49739–40, 49743–45, 49748–49, 49752–53, 49757, 49759–62, 49764, 49766, 49768, 49775, 49779, 49781–86, 49788, 49791–93, 49796–97, 49799, 49802, 49805–06, 49808, 49812, 49814–16, 49819–21, 49826–27, 49829, 49833–35, 49837–41, 49845, 49847–49, 49852, 49858, 49862–66, 49868, 49870–72, 49874, 49876–77, 49881, 49886–87, 49891, 49893–94, 49896, 49901–03, 49905, 49908, 49910–12, 49915–19, 49921–22, 49925, 49927, 49929–31, 49934–35, 49938, 49942, 49946, 49948, 49950, 49952–53, 49955, 49959–64, 49968–71

* * *

SECOND DISTRICT

BILL HUIZENGA, Republican, of Zeeland, MI; born in Zeeland, January 31, 1969; education: graduated, Holland Christian High School; B.A., Calvin College, Grand Rapids, MI, 1987; professional: co-owner, Huizenga Gravel Company, Jenison, MI; formerly licensed realtor and developer; married: the former Natalie Tiesma; children: Garrett, Adrian, Alexandra, Willam, and Sieger; committees: Financial Services; elected to the 112th Congress on November 2, 2010; reelected to the 113th Congress on November 6, 2012.

Office Listings

http://huizenga.house.gov

1217 Longworth House Office Building, Washington, DC 20515 .... (202) 225–4401
Chief of Staff.—Jon DeWitte. FAX: 226–0779
Legislative Director.—Marliss McManus.
Communications Director.—Brian Patrick.
Scheduler/Executive Assistant.—Rebecca Buursma.
District Director of Policy.—Greg Van Woerkom.
4555 Wilson Avenue Southwest, Suite 3, Grandville, MI 49418 .... (616) 570–0917
1 South Harbor Avenue, Suite 6B, Grand Haven, MI 49417 .... (616) 414–5516

Counties: ALLEGAN (part), KENT (part), LAKE, MASON, MUSKEGON, NEWAYGO, OCEANA, OTTAWA. Population (2010), 705,975.

ZIP Codes: 49303–04, 49307, 49309, 49312, 49315–16, 49318, 49321, 49323, 49327, 49329–30, 49337–38, 49343, 49345, 49349, 49401–05, 49409–10, 49412–13, 49415, 49417–18, 49420–31, 49434–37, 49440–46, 49448–49, 49451–52, 49454–61, 49463–64, 49504, 49508–09, 49512, 49519, 49534, 49544, 49546, 49548, 49601, 49623, 49642, 49644, 49655–56, 49677, 49688

* * *

THIRD DISTRICT

JUSTIN A. AMASH, Republican, of Cascade, MI; born in Grand Rapids, MI, April 18, 1980; education: attended Kelloggsville Christian School and Grand Rapids Christian High School;

B.A., economics, *magna cum laude,* University of Michigan, Ann Arbor, MI, 2002; J.D., University of Michigan Law School, Ann Arbor, MI, 2005; professional: small business owner; attorney; member, State Bar of Michigan, Grand Rapids Bar Association; State Representative, Michigan's 72nd district, 2009–10; religion: member, St. Nicholas Antiochian Orthodox Christian Church; married: Kara; three children: Alexander, Anwen, and Evelyn; committees: Oversight and Government Reform; Joint Economic Committee; elected to the 112th Congress on November 2, 2010; reelected to the 113th Congress on November 6, 2012.

Office Listings

http://amash.house.gov facebook.com/repjustinamash twitter: @repjustinamash

114 Cannon House Office Building, Washington, DC 20515 .... (202) 225–3831
Chief of Staff.—Ben Vanderveen. FAX: 225–5144
Deputy Chief of Staff.—Will Adams.
Executive Assistant / Scheduler.—Hayley Alexander.
Press Secretary.—Will Adams.
110 Michigan Street, NW., Suite 460, Grand Rapids, MI 49503 .... (616) 451–8383
District Director.—Jordan Bush.
70 West Michigan Avenue, Suite 212, Battle Creek, MI 49017 .... (269) 205–3823

Counties: BARRY, CALHOUN, IONIA, KENT (part), MONTCALM (part). CITIES: Albion, Battle Creek, Belding, Cedar Springs, East Grand Rapids, Grand Rapids, Hastings, Ionia, Lowell, Marshall, Portland, Rockford, and Springfield. Population (2010), 707,973.

ZIP Codes: 48809, 48815, 48838, 48845–46, 48849, 48851, 48860, 48865, 48870, 48873, 48875, 48881, 48887, 48897, 49011, 49014–18, 49020, 49029, 49033, 49035, 49037, 49046, 49050–51, 49058, 49060, 49068–69, 49073, 49092, 49224, 49245, 49301–02, 49306, 49315–17, 49319, 49321, 49325–26, 49331, 49333, 49341, 49343, 49345, 49351, 49355–57, 49501, 49503–10, 49512, 49514–16, 49518, 49523, 49525, 49528, 49534, 49544, 49546, 49548, 49550, 49555, 49560, 49599

* * *

FOURTH DISTRICT

DAVE CAMP, Republican, of Midland, MI; born in Midland, July 9, 1953; education: graduated, H.H. Dow High School, Midland, 1971; B.A., *magna cum laude*, Albion College, Albion, MI, 1975; J.D., University of San Diego, 1978; attorney; member: State Bar of Michigan; State Bar of California; District of Columbia Bar, U.S. Supreme Court; U.S. District Court, Eastern District of Michigan and Southern District of California; Midland County Bar Association; law practice, Midland, 1979–91; Special Assistant Attorney General, 1980–84; administrative assistant to Congressman Bill Schuette, Michigan's 10th Congressional District, 1985–87; State Representative, Michigan's 102nd district, 1989–91; chairman, Corrections Day Advisory Group; Deputy Minority Whip; Executive Committee, National Republican Congressional Committee; Rural Health Care Coalition; 1998 Adoption Hall of Fame Inductee; American Farm Bureau Federation 1998 Golden Plow award recipient; married: attorney Nancy Keil of Midland, 1994; three children; committees: chair, Ways and Means; chair, Joint Committee on Taxation; elected to Congress on November 6, 1990; reelected to each succeeding Congress.

Office Listings

http://www.house.gov/camp

341 Cannon House Office Building, Washington, DC 20515 .... (202) 225–3561
Chief of Staff.—Jim Brandell. FAX: 225–9679
Press Secretary.—Allie Walker.
Legislative Director.—Adam Pradko.
Scheduler.—Katelyn Wilcox.
135 Ashman Street, Midland, MI 48640 .... (989) 631–2552
District Director.—Ryan Tarrant.
112 Spruce Street, Suite A, Cadillac, MI 49601 .... (231) 876–9205

Counties: CLARE COUNTY. CITIES: Clare, Farwell, Harrison, Lake, Lake George. CLINTON COUNTY. CITIES: Dewitt, East Lansing (part), Grand Ledge (part), St. Johns. GLADWIN COUNTY. CITIES: Beaverton, Gladwin. GRATIOT COUNTY. CITIES: Alma, Ashley, Bannister, Breckenridge, Elm Hall, Elwell, Ithaca, Middleton, North Star, Perrinton, Pompeii, Riverdale, Sumner, St. Louis, Wheeler. ISABELLA COUNTY. CITIES: Blanchard, Millbrook, Mt. Pleasant, Rosebush, Shepherd, Weidman, Winn. MECOSTA COUNTY. CITIES: Barryton, Big Rapids, Canadian Lakes, Chippewa Lakes, Mecosta, Morley, Paris, Remus, Stanwood. MIDLAND COUNTY. CITIES: Coleman, Edenville, Hope, Laporte, Midland, North Bradley, Poseyville, Sanford. MISSAUKEE COUNTY. CITIES: Falmouth, Lake City, McBain, Merritt, Moorestown. MONTCALM COUNTY. CITIES: Alger, Butternut, Carson City, Cedar Lake, Coral, Crystal, Edmore, Entrican, Fenwick, Gowen, Greenville, Howard City, Lakeview, Langston, Maple Hill, McBride, Pierson, Sand Lake, Sheridan, Sidney, Six Lakes, Stanton, Trufant, Vestaburg, Vickeryville. OGEMAW COUNTY. CITIES: Rose City, West Branch. OSCEOLA COUNTY. CITIES: Evart, Hersey, LeRoy, Marion, Reed City, Sears, Tustin. ROSCOMMON COUNTY. CITIES: Higgins Lake, Houghton Lake, Houghton Lake Heights, Prudenville, Roscommon, St. Helen. SAGINAW COUNTY (part). CITIES: Birch Run, Brant, Burt, Carrollton, Chesaning, Frankenmuth, Freeland, Fremont, Hemlock, Merrill, Oakley, St. Charles, University Center.

SHIAWASSEE COUNTY. CITIES: Bancroft, Caledonia, Chapin, Corunna, Durand, Henderson, Laingsburg, Morrice, New Haven, New Lothrup, Owosso, Perry, Shaftsburg, Venice, and Vernon. WEXFORD COUNTY. CITIES: Cadillac, Manton. Population (2010), 705,974.

ZIP Codes: 48048, 48050, 48264, 48414–15, 48417–18, 48429, 48449, 48460, 48476, 48601, 48609–10, 48612, 48614–18, 48620, 48622–23, 48625–30, 48632–33, 48637, 48642, 48648–49, 48651, 48653–57, 48661–63, 48670, 48674, 48686, 48710, 48722, 48724, 48734, 48756, 48801, 48804, 48806–07, 48811–12, 48817–18, 48820, 48822, 48829–32, 48834–35, 48838, 48841, 48847–48, 48850, 48852, 48856–59, 48862, 48866–67, 48871–72, 48874, 48877–80, 48882–86, 48888–89, 48891, 48893–94, 48896, 49083, 49305, 49307, 49310, 49316, 49320, 49322, 49326, 49329, 49332, 49334, 49336, 49338–40, 49343, 49346–47, 49412–13, 49601, 49620, 49631–32, 49638–40, 49651, 49653, 49655, 49657, 49665, 49667–68, 49677, 49679, 49688, 49886

* * *

FIFTH DISTRICT

DANIEL T. KILDEE, Democrat, of Flint Township, MI; born in Flint, MI, August 11, 1958; education: graduated, Northern High School, 1976, B.S., administration, Central Michigan University, 2011; married: Jennifer, 1988; children: Ryan, Kenneth, and Katy; one granddaughter, Caitlin; Steering and Policy Committee; committees: Financial Services; elected to the 113th Congress, November 6, 2012.

Office Listings

http://www.dankildee.house.gov

327 Cannon House Office Building, Washington, DC 20515 .... (202) 225–3611
Chief of Staff.—John Blair. FAX: 225–6393
Legislative Director.—Andy Leavitt.
Communications Director.—Mitchell Rivard.
Scheduler/Executive Assistant.—Michelle Mittler.
801 South Saginaw Street, Plaza Level, Flint, MI 48502 .... (810) 238–8627
District Chief of Staff.—Amy Hovey. FAX: 238–8658

Counties: ARENAC, BAY, GENESEE, IOSCO, SAGINAW (part), TUSCOLA (part). Population (2010), 705,975.

ZIP Codes: 48411, 48415, 48418, 48420–21, 48423, 48429–30, 48433, 48436–39, 48442, 48449, 48451, 48457–58, 48462–64, 48473, 48480, 48501–07, 48509, 48519, 48529, 48531–32, 48550–57, 48601–08, 48610–11, 48613, 48623, 48631, 48634, 48638, 48642, 48650, 48652, 48658–59, 48663, 48703, 48706–08, 48710, 48722, 48724, 48730, 48732–34, 48737–39, 48743, 48745–50

* * *

SIXTH DISTRICT

FRED UPTON, Republican, of St. Joseph, MI; born in St. Joseph, April 23, 1953; education: graduated, Shattuck School, Fairbault, MN, 1971; B.A., journalism, University of Michigan, Ann Arbor, 1975; professional: field manager, Dave Stockman Campaign, 1976; staff member, Congressman Dave Stockman, 1976–80; legislative assistant, Office of Management and Budget, 1981–83; deputy director of Legislative Affairs, 1983–84; director of Legislative Affairs, 1984–85; member: First Congregational Church, Emil Verbin Society; married: the former Amey Rulon-Miller; committees: chair, Energy and Commerce; elected to the 100th Congress on November 4, 1986; reelected to each succeeding Congress.

Office Listings

http://www.upton.house.gov

2183 Rayburn House Office Building, Washington, DC 20515 .... (202) 225–3761
Chief of Staff.—Joan Hillebrands. FAX: 225–4986
Senior Advisor/Executive Assistant.—Bits Thomas.
800 Centre, Suite 106, 800 Ship Street, St. Joseph, MI 49085 .... (269) 982–1986
157 South Kalamazoo Mall, Suite 180, Kalamazoo, MI 49007 .... (269) 385–0039

Counties: ALLEGAN (part), BERRIEN, CASS, KALAMAZOO, ST. JOSEPH, VAN BUREN. CITIES AND TOWNSHIPS: Allegan, Augusta, Bangor, Baroda, Benton Harbor, Berrien Springs, Berrien Center, Bloomingdale, Breedsville, Bridgman, Buchanan, Burr Oak, Cassopolis, Centreville, Climax, Coloma, Colon, Comstock, Constantine, Covert, Decatur, Delton, Douglas, Dowagiac, Eau Claire, Edwardsburg, Fulton, Galesburg, Galien, Gobles, Grand Junction, Hagar Shores, Harbert, Hartford, Hickory Corners, Holland, Jones, Kalamazoo, Lakeside, Lawrence, Lawton, Leonidas, Marcellus, Mattawan, Mendon, Nazareth, New Troy, New Buffalo, Niles, Nottawa, Oshtemo, Otsego, Paw Paw, Plainwell, Portage, Pullman, Richland, Riverside, Saugatuck, Sawyer, Schoolcraft, Scotts, Sodus, South Haven, St. Joseph, Stevensville, Sturgis, Three Oaks, Three Rivers, Union Pier, Union, Vandalia, Vicksburg, Watervliet, and White Pigeon. Population (2010), 705,974.

ZIP Codes: 49001–49013, 49015, 49019, 49022–24, 49026–27, 49030–32, 49034, 49038–43, 49045, 49047–48, 49052–53, 49055–57, 49060–67, 49070–72, 49074–75, 49077–81, 49083–85, 49087–88, 49090–91, 49093, 49095, 49097–99, 49101–04, 49106–07, 49111–13, 49115–17, 49119–20, 49125–30, 49311, 49314–16, 49323, 49328, 49333, 49335, 49344, 49348, 49406, 49408, 49416, 49419, 49423, 49426, 49450, 49453, 49464

* * *

SEVENTH DISTRICT

TIMOTHY L. WALBERG, Republican, of Tipton, MI; born in Chicago, IL, April 12, 1951; education: studied forestry at Western Illinois University, Macomb, IL; attended Moody Bible Institute, Chicago, IL; B.A., religious education, Fort Wayne Bible College, 1975; M.A., communications, Wheaton College Graduate School, Wheaton, IL, 1978; professional: minister, Union Grace Gospel Church, 1978–82; member of the Michigan House of Representatives, 1983–98; president, Warren Reuther Center for Education and Community Impact; division manager, Moody Bible Institute; elected to the U.S. House of Representatives for the 110th Congress, 2007–09; married: Susan; three children; committees: Education and the Workforce; Oversight and Government Reform; elected to the 112th Congress on November 2, 2010; reelected to the 113th Congress on November 6, 2012.

Office Listings

http://www.walberg.house.gov

2436 Rayburn House Office Building, Washington, DC 20515 .... (202) 225–6276
Chief of Staff.—Joe Wicks. FAX: 225–6281
Legislative Director.—R.J. Laukitis.
Press Secretary.—Sarah Kuziomko.
800 West Ganson Street, Jackson, MI 49202 .... (517) 780–9075

Counties: BRANCH, EATON, HILLSDALE, JACKSON, LENAWEE, MONROE, WASHTENAW (part). Population (2010), 705,974.

ZIP Codes: 48103, 48105, 48108, 48111, 48117–18, 48130–31, 48133–34, 48137, 48140, 48144–45, 48157–62, 48164, 48166–70, 48176–79, 48182, 48189–91, 48197, 48813, 48821, 48827, 48837, 48849, 48861, 48876, 48890, 48897, 48906, 48911, 48917, 49011, 49021, 49028, 49030, 49036, 49040, 49073, 49076, 49082, 49089, 49092, 49094, 49096, 49201–03, 49220–21, 49224, 49227–30, 49232–38, 49240–42, 49245–56, 49259, 49261–72, 49274, 49276–77, 49279, 49282–89

* * *

EIGHTH DISTRICT

MIKE ROGERS, Republican, of Howell, MI; born in Livingston County, MI, June 2, 1963; education: B.S., Adrian College; also attended the University of Michigan as an Army ROTC member; military service: U.S. Army, Captain, served in a rapid deployment unit as a Company Commander; professional: FBI Special Agent, assigned to public corruption and organized crime units; businessman; co-founder of E.B.I. Builders, Inc.; organizations: American Heart Association; Women's Resource Center; Brighton Rotary Club; Society of Former Special Agents of the FBI; religion: Methodist; married: Kristi; children: Erin and Jonathan; committees: chair, Permanent Select Committee on Intelligence; Energy and Commerce; elected to the 107th Congress on November 7, 2000; reelected to each succeeding Congress.

Office Listings

http://www.house.gov/mikerogers

2112 Rayburn House Office Building, Washington, DC 20515 .... (202) 225–4872
Chief of Staff.—Andrew Hawkins. FAX: 225–5820
Legislative Director.—Diane Rinaldo.
Scheduler.—Mary Randolph Carpenter.
Press Secretary.—Kelsey Knight.
1000 West St. Joseph, Suite 300, Lansing, MI 48915 .... (517) 702–8000

Counties: INGHAM, LIVINGSTON, OAKLAND (part). CITIES AND TOWNSHIPS: Addison Township, Brandon Township, Brighton, Cohoctah, Dansville, East Lansing, Fenton, Fowlerville, Gregory, Groveland Township, Hamburg, Hartland, Haslett, Hell, Holly Township, Holt, Howell, Independence Township, Lakeland, Lansing, Leslie, Mason, Meridian Township, Oak Grove, Oakland Township, Okemos, Onondaga, Orion Township, Oxford Township, Pinckney, Rochester, Rochester Hills (part), Rose Township, Springfield Township, Stockbridge, Unadilla, Village of Clarkston, Webberville, and Williamston. Population, (2010), 705,974.

ZIP Codes: 48114, 48116, 48139, 48143, 48306–07, 48309, 48346, 48350, 48359–60, 48362–63, 48366–67, 48370–71, 48430, 48442, 48462, 48805, 48816, 48819, 48824–26, 48842–44, 48854–55, 48864, 48895, 48901, 48909–10, 48912–13, 48915–16, 48918–19, 48921–22, 48924, 48929–30, 48933, 48937, 48951, 48956, 48980, 49251

* * *

NINTH DISTRICT

SANDER M. LEVIN, Democrat, of Royal Oak, MI; born in Detroit, MI, September 6, 1931; education: graduated, Central High School, Detroit, 1949; B.A., University of Chicago, 1952; M.A., Columbia University, New York, NY, 1954; LL.B., Harvard University, Cambridge, MA, 1957; professional: attorney, admitted to the Michigan Bar in 1958 and commenced practice in Detroit, MI; member: Oakland Board of Supervisors, 1961–64; Michigan Senate, 1965–70; Democratic floor leader in State Senate; served on the Advisory Committee on the Education of Handicapped Children in the Department of Health, Education, and Welfare, 1965–68; chairman, Michigan Democratic Party, 1968–69; Democratic candidate for Governor, 1970 and 1974; fellow, Kennedy School of Government, Institute of Politics, Harvard University, 1975; assistant administrator, Agency for International Development, 1977–81; married: Dr. Pamela Cole; children: Jennifer, Andrew, Madeleine, and Matthew; committees: Ways and Means; Joint Committee on Taxation; elected on November 2, 1982, to the 98th Congress; reelected to each succeeding Congress.

Office Listings

http://www.house.gov/levin http://www.facebook.com/repsandylevin
http://twitter.com/#!/repsandylevin

1236 Longworth Office House Building, Washington, DC 20515 .... (202) 225–4961
Chief of Staff.—Hilarie Chambers. FAX: 226–1033
Scheduler.—Monica Chrzaszcz.
27085 Gratiot Avenue, Roseville, MI 48066 .... (586) 498–7122

Counties: MACOMB (part), OAKLAND (part). CITIES: Berkley, Beverly Hills, Bingham Farms, Bloomfield Township, Clawson (part), Center Line, Clinton Township, Eastpointe, Ferndale, Franklin, Fraser, Lake Township, Hazel Park, Huntington Woods, Madison Heights, Mount Clemens, Pleasant Ridge, Roseville, Royal Oak, Southfield Township, St. Clair Shores, Sterling Heights (part), and Warren. Population (2010), 705,975.

ZIP Codes: 48009, 48015, 48017, 48021, 48025–26, 48030, 48034–36, 48038, 48043, 48046, 48066–73, 48080–82, 48088–93, 48220, 48236, 48301–02, 48304, 48310, 48312–14, 48320, 48323

* * *

TENTH DISTRICT

CANDICE S. MILLER, Republican, of Harrison Township, MI; born in St. Clair Shores, MI, May 7, 1954; education: attended Macomb Community College and Northwood University; public service: Harrison Township Board of Trustees, 1979; Harrison Township Supervisor, 1980–92; Macomb County Treasurer, 1992–94; Michigan Secretary of State, 1994–2002; professional: worked in a family-owned marina business before she became involved in public service; religion: Presbyterian; married: Macomb County Circuit Court Judge Donald Miller; children: Wendy; committees: chair, House Administration; Homeland Security; Transportation and Infrastructure; Joint Committee of the Library; Joint Committee on Printing; elected to the 108th Congress on November 5, 2002; reelected to each succeeding Congress.

Office Listings

http://candicemiller.house.gov

320 Cannon House Office Building, Washington, DC 20515 .... (202) 225–2106
Chief of Staff.—Jamie Roe. FAX: 226–1169
Deputy Chief of Staff.—Sean Moran.
Legislative Director.—Dena Kozanas.
Scheduler.—John Bremer.
Press Secretary.—Erin Sayago.
48701 Van Dyke Avenue, Shelby Township, MI 48317 .... (586) 997–5010

Counties: HURON, LAPEER, MACOMB (part), SAINT CLAIR, SANILAC, TUSCOLA (part). Population (2010), 719,712.

ZIP Codes: 48001–03, 48005–06, 48014, 48022–23, 48027–28, 48032, 48035, 48039–42, 48044–45, 48047–51, 48054, 48059–60, 48062–65, 48074, 48079, 48094–97, 48306, 48312–17, 48367, 48371, 48401, 48412–13, 48416, 48419, 48421–23, 48426–28, 48432, 48435, 48438, 48441, 48444–46, 48450, 48453–56, 48461–72, 48475, 48720, 48725–27, 48729, 48731, 48735, 48759–60, 48767

* * *

ELEVENTH DISTRICT

KERRY BENTIVOLIO, Republican, of Milford, MI; born in Detroit, MI, October 6, 1951; education: B.A., St. Mary's College, M.A., Master of Education from Marygrove College; professional: teacher, small business owner, rancher; military: United States Army, Michigan Army National Guard; awards: Excellence in Competition Badge Pistol; Meritorious Service Medal; Army Commendation Medal (2nd award); Army Achievement Medal (4th award); Air Force Achievement Medal; Army Good Conduct Medal; National Defense Service Medal (3rd award); Vietnam Service Medal with 2 Bronze Stars; Global War on Terrorism Service Medal; Iraqi Campaign Medal Campaign Star; Noncommissioned Officer Professional Development Ribbon (3rd award); Army Service Ribbon; Army Reserve Component Overseas Training Ribbon (3rd award); Armed Forces Reserve Medal with ''M'' Device and 20-Year Device; Republic of Vietnam Gallantry Cross Unit Citation with Palm; Republican of Vietnam Campaign Medal with Device 1960; Combat Infantryman Badge; religion: Catholic; married: Karen; children: Kristin, Kevin; committees: Oversight and Government Reform; Small Business; elected to the 113th Congress on November 6, 2012.

Office Listings

http://www.bentivolio.house.gov

226 Cannon House Office Building, Washington, DC 20515 .... (202) 225–8171
Chief of Staff.—Rob Wasinger.
Scheduler.—Lindsay Duvall.
Legislative Director.—Tim Witt.
Communications Director.—Matt Chisholm.
800 Welch Road, Commerce, MI 48390 .... (248) 859–2982

Counties: WAYNE COUNTY. CITIES: Caton Township, Livonia, Northville, Northville Township, Plymouth, Plymouth Township. OAKLAND COUNTY. Cities: Auburn Hills, Birmingham, Bloomfield Hills, Clawson, Commerce Township, Farmington, Highland, Lake Angelus, Lyon Township, Milford, Novi, Rochester Hills, South Lyon, Troy, Walled Lake, Waterford, West Bloomfield, White Lake, Wixom, and Wolverine Lake. Population (2010), 705,974.

ZIP Codes: 48007, 48009, 48012, 48017, 48073, 48083–85, 48098–99, 48111, 48150–65, 48167–68, 48170, 48178, 48184–85, 48187–88, 48240, 48301, 48304, 48307, 48309, 48321, 48326–32, 48335–36, 48346, 48350, 48353, 48356–57, 48359, 48374–78, 48380–83, 48386–87, 48390–91, 48393, 48442

* * *

TWELFTH DISTRICT

JOHN D. DINGELL, Democrat, of Dearborn, MI; born in Colorado Springs, CO, July 8, 1926; education: B.S., Georgetown University, 1949; J.D., Georgetown University Law School, 1952; professional: World War II veteran; assistant Wayne County prosecutor, 1953–55; member: Migratory Bird Conservation Commission; married: the former Deborah Insley; committees: Energy and Commerce; elected to the 84th Congress in a special election to fill the vacant seat of his late father, the Honorable John D. Dingell, December 13, 1955; reelected to the 85th and each succeeding Congress; On June 7, 2013, he became the longest serving member of Congress in United States History, surpassing the tenure of the former Senator from West Virginia, Robert Byrd.

Office Listings

http://www.house.gov/dingell

2328 Rayburn House Office Building, Washington, DC 20515 .... (202) 225–4071
Chief of Staff.—Katie Murtha.
Legislative Director.—Andrew Woelfling.
Scheduler.—Beth Siniawsky.
Communications Director.—Christopher Schuler.
19855 West Outer Drive, Suite 103–E, Dearborn, MI 48124 .... (313) 278–2936
District Administrator.—Derek Dobies.
301 West Michigan Avenue, Ypsilanti, MI 48197 .... (734) 481–1100
Office Manager.—Donna Hoffer.

Counties: WAYNE COUNTY (part). CITIES AND TOWNSHIPS: Allen Park, Belleville, Brownstown, Brownstone Township, Dearborn, Dearborn Heights, Flat Rock, Grosse Ile, Gibraltar, Lincoln Park, New Boston, Plymouth, Riverview, Rockwood, Romulus, Southgate, Sumpter Township, Taylor, Trenton, Van Buren Township, Wayne, Woodhaven, Wyandotte. MONROE COUNTY (part). CITIES AND TOWNSHIPS: Carleton. WASHTENAW COUNTY (part). CITIES AND TOWNSHIPS: Ann Arbor, Dexter, Pittsfield Township, Saline, Superior Township, Willis, Ypsilanti, and Ypsilanti Township. Population (2010), 654,580.

ZIP Codes: 48101, 48103–05, 48108–09, 48111, 48117, 48120, 48124–26, 48128, 48130, 48134, 48138, 48146, 48164, 48170, 48173–74, 48176, 48180, 48183–84, 48191–93, 48195, 48197–98

* * *

THIRTEENTH DISTRICT

JOHN CONYERS, JR., Democrat, of Detroit, MI; born in Detroit, May 16, 1929; son of John and Lucille Conyers; education: B.A., Wayne State University, 1957; LL.B., Wayne State Law School, June 1958; served as officer in the U.S. Army Corps of Engineers, one year in Korea; awarded combat and merit citations; engaged in many civil rights and labor activities; legislative assistant to Congressman John D. Dingell, December 1958 to May 1961; appointed Referee for the Workmen's Compensation Department, State of Michigan, by Governor John B. Swainson in October 1961; former vice chairman of Americans for Democratic Action; vice chairman of the National Advisory Council of the ACLU; member: Kappa Alpha Psi; Wolverine Bar; NAACP; Tuskegee Airmen, Inc.; organizations: Congressional Black Caucus; Progressive Caucus; married: Monica Conyers; children: John III, and Carl; committees: ranking member, Judiciary; elected to the 89th Congress on November 3, 1964; reelected to each succeeding Congress.

Office Listings

http://www.house.gov/conyers

2426 Rayburn House Office Building, Washington, DC 20515 .... (202) 225–5126
Chief of Staff.—Cynthia Martin. FAX: 225–0072
Scheduler.—Rinia Shelby.
Federal Courthouse, Suite 669, 231 West Lafayette, Detroit, MI 48226 .... (313) 961–5670
District Director.—Yolanda Lipsey.
33300 Warren Road, Suite 13, Westland, MI 48185 .... (734) 675–4084
FAX: 675–4218

Counties: WAYNE COUNTY (part). CITIES AND TOWNSHIPS: Detroit, Dearborn Heights, Ecorse, Garden City, Highland Park, Inkster, Melvindale, Redford, River Rouge, Romulus, Wayne, and Westland. Population (2010), 699,214.

ZIP Codes: 48125, 48203, 48207, 48210–16, 48221, 481226–27, 48235, 48238

* * *

FOURTEENTH DISTRICT

GARY C. PETERS, Democrat, of Bloomfield Township, MI; born in Pontiac, MI, December 1, 1958; education: B.A., Alma College, Alma, MI, 1980; M.B.A., University of Detroit, Detroit, MI, 1984; J.D., Wayne State University, Detroit, MI, 1989; M.A., Michigan State University, East Lansing, MI, 2007; professional: Assistant Vice President, Merrill Lynch, 1980–89; Vice President, UBS/Paine Webber, 1989–2003; City Council, Rochester Hills, MI, 1991–93; Lt. Commander, Navy Reserve, 1993–2005; Michigan Senate, 1995–2002; Chief Administrative Officer for the Bureau of Investments, State of Michigan, 2003; Lottery Commissioner, State of Michigan, 2003–07; Griffin Endowed Chair in American Government, Central Michigan University, 2007–08; religion: Episcopalian; married: Colleen Ochoa Peters; three children: Gary Jr., Madeline, and Alana; Armenian Caucus; Congressional Automotive Caucus; Congressional Caucus on India and Indian Americans; Congressional Fire Services Caucus; Congressional Pakistan Caucus; House Bangladesh Caucus; House Manufacturing Caucus; Law Enforcement Caucus; LGBT Equality Caucus; National Guard and Reserve Component Caucus; New Democrat Coalition; Pro-Choice Caucus; committees: Financial Services; elected to the 111th Congress on November 4, 2008; reelected to each succeeding Congress.

Office Listings

http://www.peters.house.gov

1609 Longworth House Office Building, Washington, DC 20515 .... (202) 225–5802
Chief of Staff.—Eric Feldman. FAX: 226–2356
Legislative Director.—David Weinberg.
Press Secretary.—Haley Morris.
400 Monroe Street, Suite 290, Detroit, MI 48226 .... (313) 964–9960
District Office Director.—Kala Smith.

Counties: OAKLAND (part) WAYNE (part). CITIES AND TOWNSHIPS: Detroit, Farmington Hills, Grosse Pointe, Grosse Pointe Farms, Grosse Pointe Park, Grosse Pointe Shores, Grosse Pointe Woods, Hamtramck, Harper Woods, Keego Harbor,

Lathrup Village, Oak Park, Orchard Lake, Pontiac, Royal Oak Township, Southfield, Sylvan Lake, and West Bloomfield. Population (2010), 705,974.

ZIP Codes: 48033–34, 48075–76, 48203, 48205, 48207, 48209, 48212–14, 48216, 48221, 48224–26, 48230, 48234–35, 48237, 48325, 48331, 48334–36, 48343, 48320–23, 48340–42

MINNESOTA

(Population 2010, 5,303,925)

SENATORS

AMY KLOBUCHAR, Democrat, of Minneapolis, MN; born in Plymouth, MN, May 25, 1960; education: B.A., *magna cum laude*, Yale University, 1982; J.D., *magna cum laude*, University of Chicago Law School, 1985; professional: Attorney at law firm Dorsey & Whitney, 1985–93, Partner in 1993; Partner at law firm Gray, Plant, Mooty, Mooty & Bennett, 1993–98; religion: Congregationalist; public service: City of Minneapolis prosecutor, 1988; elected Hennepin County Attorney, 1998, reelected, 2002; married: John; child: Abigail; committees: Agriculture, Nutrition, and Forestry; Commerce, Science, and Transportation, Judiciary; Rules and Administration; Joint Economic Committee; elected to the U.S. Senate on November 7, 2006; reelected to the U.S. Senate on November 6, 2012.

Office Listings

http://klobuchar.senate.gov

302 Hart Senate Office Building, Washington, DC 20510 .... (202) 224–3244
Chief of Staff.—Rose Baumann.
Legislative Director.—Travis Talvitie.
Deputy Chief of Staff.—Sara Bryant.
Communications Director.—Brigit Helgen.
Scheduler.—Caroline Selby.
1200 Washington Avenue South, Suite 250, Minneapolis, MN 55415 .... (612) 727–5220
State Director.—Sammy Clark.
1130½ 7th Street Northwest, Suite 208, Rochester, MN 55901 .... (507) 288–5321
121 4th Street South, Moorhead, MN 56560 .... (218) 287–2219
Olcott Plaza, 820 9th Street North, Suite 105, Virginia, MN 55792 .... (218) 741–9690

* * *

AL FRANKEN, Democrat, of St. Louis Park, MN; raised in St. Louis Park, MN, born May 21, 1951; education: Harvard, Cambridge, MA, 1973; professional: comedy writer, author, and radio talk show host; has taken part in seven USO tours, visiting our troops overseas in Germany, Bosnia, Kosovo and Uzbekistan—as well as visiting Iraq, Afghanistan, and Kuwait four times; married: Franni Franken for 34 years; two children; committees: Energy and Natural Resources; Health, Education, Labor, and Pension; Judiciary; Indian Affairs; elected to the 111th U.S. Senate on November 4, 2008, the election was contested; following a June 30, 2009, decision in his favor by the Minnesota State Supreme Court, he took the oath of office and began service on July 7, 2009.

Office Listings

www.franken.senate.gov

H309 Hart Senate Office Building, Washington, DC 20510 .... (202) 224–5641
Chief of Staff.—Casey Aden-Wansbury. FAX: 224–0044
State Director.—Alana Petersen.
Legislative Director.—Jeff Lomonaco.
Scheduler.—Tara Mazer.
Communications Director.—Ed Shelleby.
Press Secretary.—Ed Shelleby.
60 East Plato Boulevard, Suite 220, St. Paul, MN 55107 .... (651) 221–1016
FAX: 221–1078
208 South Minnesota Avenue, Suite 6, St. Peter, MN 56082 .... (507) 931–5813
FAX: 931–7345
916 West St. Germain Street, Suite 110, St. Cloud, MN 56301 .... (320) 251–2721
FAX: 251–4164
515 West First Street, Suite 104, Duluth, MN 55802 .... (218) 722–2390
FAX: 622–4131

REPRESENTATIVES

FIRST DISTRICT

TIMOTHY J. WALZ, Democrat, of Mankato, MN; born in West Point, NE, April 6, 1964; education: B.S., Chadron State College, Chadron, NE; M.S., St. Mary's University, Winona,

MN; professional: high school teacher; military: Command Sergeant Major, Minnesota's 1st/ 34th Division of the Army National Guard, 1981–2005; awards: 2002 Minnesota Ethics in Education award winner, 2003 Mankato Teacher of the Year, and the 2003 Minnesota Teacher of Excellence; married: Gwen Whipple Walz, 1994; children: Hope and Gus; committees: Agriculture; Transportation and Infrastructure; Veterans' Affairs; elected to the 110th Congress on November 7, 2006; reelected to each succeeding Congress.

Office Listings

http://www.walz.house.gov

1034 Longworth House Office Building, Washington, DC 20515 .... (202) 225–2472
Chief of Staff.—Josh Syrjamaki. FAX: 225–3433
Legislative Director.—Elizabeth Glidden.
Scheduler.—Denise Fleming.
227 East Main Street, Suite 220, Mankato, MN 56001 .... (507) 388–2149
1130½ Seventh Street, NW., Rochester, MN 55901 .... (507) 206–0643

Counties: BLUE EARTH COUNTY. CITIES: Amboy, Eagle Lake, Garden City, Good Thunder, Lake Crystal, Madison Lake, Mankato, Mapleton, Pemberton, St. Clair, Vernon Center. BROWN COUNTY. CITIES: Comfrey, Hanska, New Ulm, Sleepy Eye, Springfield. COTTONWOOD COUNTY. CITIES: Mountain Lake, Storedon, Westbrook. DODGE COUNTY. CITIES: Claremont, Dodge Center, Hayfield, Kasson, Mantorville, West Concord, Windom. FARIBAULT COUNTY. CITIES: Blue Earth, Bricelyn, Delavan, Easton, Elmore, Frost, Huntley, Kiester, Minnesota Lake, Walters, Wells, Winnebago. FILLMORE COUNTY. CITIES: Canton, Chatfield, Fountain, Harmony, Lanesboro, Mabel, Ostrander, Peterson, Preston, Rushford, Spring Valley, Whalan, Wykoff. FREEBORN COUNTY. CITIES: Albert Lea, Alden, Clarks Grove, Conger, Emmons, Freeborn, Geneva, Glenville, Hartland, Hayward, Hollandale, London, Manchester, Myrtle, Oakland, Twin Lakes. HOUSTON COUNTY. CITIES: Brownsville, Caledonia, Eitzen, Hokah, Houston, La Crescent, Spring Grove. JACKSON COUNTY. CITIES: Heron, Jackson, Lake Field. LE SUEUR COUNTY. CITIES: Cleveland, Elysian, Heidelberg, Kasota, Kilkenny, Le Center, Le Sueur, Montgomery, New Prague, Waterville. MARTIN COUNTY. CITY: Fairmount. MOWER COUNTY. CITIES: Adams, Austin, Brownsdale, Dexter, Elkton, Grand Meadow, Lansing, LeRoy, Lyle, Rose Creek, Sargeant, Taopi, Waltham. NICOLLET COUNTY. CITIES: North Mankato, St. Peter. NOLES COUNTY. CITIES: Adrian, Worthington. OLMSTED COUNTY. CITIES: Byron, Dover, Eyota, Oronoco, Rochester, Stewartville, Viola. RICE COUNTY. CITIES: Webster, Wheatland, Warsaw, Walcott, Morristown, Shieldsville, Faribault. ROCK COUNTY. CITIES: Lurverne. STEELE COUNTY. CITIES: Blooming Prairie, Ellendale, Hope, Medford, Meriden, Owatonna. WASECA COUNTY. CITIES: Janesville, New Richland, Otisco, Waldorf, Waseca. WATONWAN COUNTY. CITIES: Madelia, St. James. WINONA COUNTY. CITIES: Altura, Dakota, Goodview, Homer, Lewiston, Minnesota City, Rollingstone, St. Charles, Stockton, Utica, and Winona. Population (2010), 644,787.

ZIP Codes: 55019, 55021, 55046, 55049, 55052, 55057, 55060, 55087–88, 55332–35, 55901–02, 55904, 55906, 55909–10, 55912, 55917–27, 55929, 55931–36, 55939–41, 55943–44, 55947, 55949–56, 55959–65, 55967, 55969–77, 55979, 55982, 55985, 55987, 55990–01, 56001, 56003, 56007, 56009–11, 56013–14, 56016–17, 56019–29, 56031–37, 56039, 56041–48, 56050–52, 56054–58, 56060, 56062–63, 56065, 56068–69, 56071–75, 56078, 56080–83, 56085, 56087–91, 56093, 56096–98, 56101, 56110–11, 56116–22, 56127–29, 56131, 56134, 56137–38, 56141, 56143–47, 56150, 56153, 56155–56, 56158–62, 56165, 56167–68, 56171, 56173, 56176, 56181, 56185, 56187, 56266

* * *

SECOND DISTRICT

JOHN KLINE, Republican, of Lakeville, MN; born in Allentown, PA, September 6, 1947; education: B.A., Rice University, 1969; M.P.A., Shippensburg University, 1988; military service: U.S. Marine Corps, 1969–94; retired at the rank of Colonel; organizations: Boy Scouts of America; Marine Corps League; Veterans of Foreign Wars; Marine Corps Association; American Legion; Retired Officers Association; past president, Marine Corps Coordinating Council of Minnesota; religion: Methodist; family: married to Vicky; children: Kathy and Dan; committees: chair, Education and the Workforce; Armed Services; elected to the 108th Congress on November 5, 2002; reelected to each succeeding Congress.

Office Listings

http://www.house.gov/kline

2439 Rayburn House Office Building, Washington, DC 20515 .... (202) 225–2271
Chief of Staff.—Jean Hinz. FAX: 225–2595
Communications Director.—Troy Young.
Scheduler.—Janelle Belland.
350 West Burnsville Parkway, Suite 135, Burnsville, MN 55337 .... (952) 808–1213
District Director.—Brooke Dorobiala.

Counties: DAKOTA COUNTY. CITIES: Apple Valley, Burnsville, Eagan, Farmington, Hastings, Inver Grove Heights, Lakeville, Rosemount, South St. Paul, West St. Paul. GOODHUE COUNTY. CITIES: Cannon Falls, Pine Island, Red Wing, Zumbrota. RICE COUNTY (part). CITIES: Northfield. SCOTT COUNTY. CITIES: Shakopee, Savage, Prior Lake, New Prague, Jordan, Belle Plaine. WASHINGTON COUNTY (part). CITIES: Cottage Grove, St. Paul Park. Population (2010), 668,891.

ZIP Codes: 55009, 55010 (part), 55016 (part), 55018, 55019 (part), 55020 (part), 55021 (part), 55024, 55026–27, 55031, 55033, 55041, 55044, 55049 (part), 55053 (part), 55054 (part), 55057 (part), 55065–66, 55068 (part), 55071 (part), 55075 (part), 55076 (part), 55077, 55085, 55088 (part), 55089 (part), 55118 (part), 55120–24, 55150 (part), 55306, 55337, 55352, 55372, 55378, 55379 (part), 55910 (part), 55932 (part), 55945, 55946 (part), 55956 (part), 55957,

55960 (part), 55963 (part), 55964 (part), 55968, 55981, 55983 (part), 55985 (part), 55991, 55992 (part), 56071 (part), 56011 (part), 56044 (part), 56071 (part)

* * *

THIRD DISTRICT

ERIK PAULSEN, Republican, of Eden Prairie, MN; born in Bakersfield, CA, May 14, 1965; education: B.A., St. Olaf College, Northfield, MN, 1987; caucuses: co-chair, Charter Schools Caucus; co-chair, Congressional Wellness Caucus; co-chair, Friends of Norway Caucus; Civility Caucus; National Parks Caucus; Land Conservation Caucus; Zoo Caucus; Diabetes Caucus; Rare Disease Caucus; National Guard Caucus; General Aviation Caucus; Law Enforcement Caucus; Financial Literacy Caucus; Sportsman's Caucus; Nuclear Issues Working Group; U.S.-China Working Group; Renewable Energy Caucus; India Caucus; Bike Caucus; religion: Lutheran; married: Kelly; children: four daughters; committees: Ways and Means; Joint Economic Committee; elected to the 111th Congress on November 4, 2008; reelected to each succeeding Congress.

Office Listings

http://www.paulsen.house.gov facebook: congressmanerikpaulsen twitter: @reperikpaulsen

127 Cannon House Office Building, Washington, DC 20515 .... (202) 225–2871
Chief of Staff.—Laurie Esau FAX: 225–6351
Legislative Director.—Noah Jacobson.
Press Secretary.—Philip Minardi.
Scheduler.—Crysten Glawe.
250 Prairie Center Drive, Suite 230, Eden Prairie, MN 55344 .... (952) 405–8510
FAX: 405–8514

Counties: ANOKA (part), CARVER (part), HENNEPIN (part). CITIES AND TOWNSHIPS: Bloomington, Brooklyn Park, Champlin, Chanhassen, Chaska, Coon Rapids, Corcoran, Dahlgren, Dayton, Deephaven, Excelsior, Eden Prairie, Edina, Greenfield, Greenwood, Independence, Laketown, Long Lake, Loretto, Maple Grove, Maple Plain, Medina, Medicine Lake, Minnetonka, Minnetonka Beach, Minnetrista, Mound, Orono, Osseo, Plymouth, Rogers, Shorewood, Spring Park, St. Bonifacuis, Tonka Bay, Victoria, Wayzata, and Woodland. Population (2010), 650,185.

ZIP Codes: 55305, 55311, 55316–18, 55327–28, 55331, 55340, 55343–47, 55356–57, 55359, 55364, 55369, 55373–75, 55384, 55386–88, 55391, 55420, 55425, 55428–31, 55433, 55435–39, 55441–48

* * *

FOURTH DISTRICT

BETTY McCOLLUM, Democrat-Farmer-Labor, of St. Paul, MN; born in Minneapolis, MN, July 12, 1954; education: A.A., Inver Hills Community College; B.S., College of St. Catherine; professional: teacher and sales manager; public service: North St. Paul City Council, 1986–92; Minnesota House of Representatives, 1992–2000; organizations: Girl Scouts of America; VFW Ladies' Auxiliary, and American Legion Ladies' Auxiliary; awards: Friend of the National Parks Award, National Parks Conservation Association, 2005; Friend of College Access Award, National Association for College Admission Counseling, 2006; Congressional Leadership Award, InterAction, 2006; Congressional Arts Leadership Award, Americans for the Arts, 2007; founder, Congressional Global Health Caucus; Senior Democratic Whip; appointments: National Council on the Arts; single; children: Sean and Katie; committees: Appropriations; elected to the 107th Congress on November 7, 2000; reelected to each succeeding Congress.

Office Listings

http://www.house.gov/mccollum

1714 Longworth House Office Building, Washington, DC 20515 .... (202) 225–6631
Chief of Staff.—Bill Harper. FAX: 225–1968
Legislative Director.—Jenn Holcomb.
Office Director.—Meredith Raimondi.
Communications Director.—Maria Reppas.
165 Western Avenue North, Suite 17, St. Paul, MN 55102 .... (651) 224–9191
District Director.—Joshua Straka.

Counties: RAMSEY, WASHINGTON (part). Population (2010), 614,624.

ZIP Codes: 55001, 55003, 55016, 55042–43, 55055, 55082, 55090, 55101–30, 55133, 55144–46, 55155, 55164–66, 55168, 55170–72, 55175, 55187–88, 55449

* * *

FIFTH DISTRICT

KEITH ELLISON, Democrat-Farmer-Labor, of Minneapolis, MN; born in Detroit, MI, August 4, 1963; education: University of Detroit Jesuit High School and Academy, 1981; Wayne State University, 1987; University of Minnesota Law School, 1990; professional: The Law Office of Lindquist & Vennum, 1990–93; Executive Director of the nonprofit Legal Rights Center in Minneapolis, 1993–98; Hassan & Reed Ltd., 1998–2001; Ellison Law Offices, 2003–06; served in Minnesota State Legislature District 58B, 2003–06, four children; Commissions: Center for Strategic and International Studies; Commission on Global Health; House Democracy Assistance Commission; Tom Lantos Human Rights Commission; Caucuses: founder, Consumer Justice Caucus; co-chair, Progressive Caucus; vice-chair, LGBT Caucus; Out of Iraq Caucus; Children's Environmental Health Caucus; Congressional Human Rights Caucus; Congressional Labor and Working Families Caucus; Congressional Anti-Terrorism Caucus; Congressional Caucus of India and Indian Americans; Congressional Arts Caucus; Law Enforcement Caucus; Congressional Caucus to Fight and Control Methamphetamine; Financial and Economic Literacy Caucus; Bicameral Congressional Caucus on Parkinson's Disease; Congressional Diabetes Caucus; Congressional E9-1-1 (Emergency Responders) Caucus; Congressional Adoption Caucus; Congressional Wildlife Caucus; Congressional Black Caucus; Populist Caucus; Pro-Choice Caucus; Green Jobs Caucus; committees: Financial Services; elected to the 110th Congress on November 7, 2006; reelected to each succeeding Congress.

Office Listings

http://ellison.house.gov

2244 Rayburn House Office Building, Washington, DC 20515 .... (202) 225–4755
Chief of Staff.—Kari Moe.
Legislative Director.—Vic Edgerton.
Communications Director.—Jeremy Slevin.
2100 Plymouth Avenue, Minneapolis, MN 55411 .... (612) 522–1212
District Director.—Jamie Long.

Counties: ANOKA (part), HENNEPIN (part), RAMSEY (part). CITIES: Minneapolis and the surrounding suburbs of Brooklyn Center, Columbia Heights, Crystal, Edina, Fridley, Fort Snelling, Golden Valley, Hilltop, Hopkins, Richfield, Robbinsdale, Spring Lake Park, St. Anthony, and St. Louis Park. Population (2010), 677,196.

ZIP Codes: 55111–12, 55305, 55343, 55401–30, 55432–33, 55440–41, 55450, 55454–55, 55458–60, 55470, 55472, 55474, 55479–80, 55483–88

* * *

SIXTH DISTRICT

MICHELE BACHMANN, Republican, of Stillwater, MN; born in Waterloo, IA, April 6, 1956; education: B.A., Winona State University, Winona, MN, 1978; J.D., Coburn School of Law, Oral Roberts University, Tulsa, OK; LL.M. in tax law at the College of William and Mary, Williamsburg, VA; professional: federal tax litigation attorney; served six years in the Minnesota State Senate; organizations: New Heights Charter School; married: Marcus; children: Lucas, Harrison, Elisa, Caroline, and Sophia; committees: Financial Services; Select Committee on Intelligence; elected to the 110th Congress on November 7, 2006; reelected to each succeeding Congress.

Office Listings

http://www.bachmann.house.gov

2417 Rayburn House Office Building, Washington, DC 20515 .... (202) 225–2331
Chief of Staff / Legislative Director (Interim).—Robert Boland. FAX: 225–6475
Communications Director.—Dan Kotman.
2850 Cutters Grove Avenue, Suite 205, Anoka, MN 55303 .... (763) 323–8922
FAX: 323–6585

Counties: ANOKA, BENTON, CARVER, HENNEPIN (part), Sherburne, Stearns, WASHINGTON (part), WRIGHT. Population (2010), 662,990.

ZIP Codes: 55005, 55011, 55014, 55025, 55038, 55047, 55070, 55073, 55079, 55082, 55092, 55110, 55126, 55301–04, 55308–09, 55313, 55315, 55318–22, 55327–30, 55339, 55341, 55349, 55353, 55357–58, 55360, 55362–63, 55367–68, 55371, 55373–76, 55382, 55387–90, 55395, 55397–98, 55434, 55449, 56011, 56301, 56303–04, 56307, 56310, 56314, 56320–21, 56329–30, 56340, 56357, 56362, 56367–69, 56373–75, 56377, 56379, 56387

* * *

SEVENTH DISTRICT

COLLIN C. PETERSON, Democrat, of Detroit Lakes, MN; born in Fargo, ND, June 29, 1944; education: graduated from Glyndon (MN) High School, 1962; B.A. in business administration and accounting, Moorhead State University, 1966; U.S. Army National Guard, 1963–69; CPA, owner and partner; Minnesota State Senator, 1976–86; member: AOPA, Safari Club, Ducks Unlimited, American Legion, Sea Plane Pilots Association, Pheasants Forever, Benevolent Protective Order of Elks, Cormorant Lakes Sportsmen Club; three children: Sean, Jason, and Elliott; committees: ranking member, Agriculture; elected to the 102nd Congress, November 6, 1990; reelected to each succeeding Congress.

Office Listings

http://collinpeterson.house.gov

2109 Rayburn House Office Building, Washington, DC 20515 .... (202) 225–2165
Chief of Staff.—Cherie Slayton. FAX: 225–1593
Legislative Director.—Robin Goracke.
Assistants: Chris Iacaruso, Richard Lee, Zach Martin, Rebekah Solem, Natalie Winters..
Lake Avenue Plaza Building, Suite 107, 714 Lake Avenue, Detroit Lakes, MN 56501 .... (218) 847–5056
Minnesota Wheat Growers Building, 2603 Wheat Drive, Red Lake, MN 56750 ..... (218) 253–4356
324 3rd Street, SW., Suite 4, Willmar, MN 56201 .... (320) 235–1061

Counties: BECKER, BELTRAMI (part), BIG STONE, CHIPPEWA, CLAY, CLEARWATER, COTTONWOOD (part), DOUGLAS, GRANT, KANDIYOHI, KITTSON, LAC QUI PARLE, LAKE OF THE WOODS, LINCOLN, LYON, MAHNOMEN, MARSHALL, MCLEOD, MEEKER, MURRAY, NORMAN, OTTER, PIPESTONE, TAIL, PENNINGTON, POLK, POPE, RED LAKE, REDWOOD, RENVILLE, ROSEAU, SIBLEY, STEARNS (part), STEVENS, SWIFT, TODD, TRAVERSE, WILKIN, AND YELLOW MEDICINE. Population (2010), 662,991.

ZIP Codes: 55307, 55310, 55312, 55314, 55321, 55324–25, 55329, 55332–36, 55338–39, 55342, 55350, 55353–55, 55366, 55368, 55370, 55381–82, 55385, 55389, 55395–96, 55409, 55970, 56011, 56044, 56054, 56058, 56083, 56085, 56087, 56113, 56115, 56129, 56132, 56136, 56142, 56149, 56152, 56157, 56164, 56166, 56169–70, 56175, 56178, 56180, 56201, 56207–12, 56214–16, 56218–32, 56235–37, 56239–41, 56243–45, 56248–49, 56251–53, 56255–58, 56260, 56262–67, 56270–71, 56273–74, 56276–85, 56287–89, 56291–97, 56301–04, 56307–12, 56314–16, 56318–21, 56323–24, 56326–27, 56329, 56331–32, 56334, 56336, 56339–40, 56343, 56345, 56347, 56349, 56352, 56354–55, 56360–62, 56368, 56372–74, 56377–79, 56381–82, 56385, 56387, 56393, 56395–99, 56433–34, 56436–38, 56440, 56443, 56446, 56453, 56458, 56461, 56464, 56466–67, 56470, 56475, 56477–79, 56481–82, 56501–02, 56510–11, 56514–25, 56527–29, 56531, 56533–38, 56540–54, 56556–57, 56560–63, 56565–81, 56583–94, 56601, 56619, 56621, 56623, 56633–34, 56644, 56646–47, 56650–52, 56661, 56663, 56666–67, 56670–71, 56673, 56676, 56678, 56682–87, 56701, 56710–11, 56713–16, 56720–29, 56731–38, 56740–42, 56744, 56748, 56750–51, 56754–63

* * *

EIGHTH DISTRICT

RICHARD M. NOLAN, Democrat-Farmer-Labor, of Crosby, MN; born in Brainerd, MN, December 17, 1943; education: attended St. John's University, Collegeville, MN, 1962; B.A., University of Minnesota, Minneapolis, MN, 1966; post-graduate work at the University of Maryland, College Park, MD, St. Cloud State, St. Cloud, MN, and Central Lakes Community College, Brainerd, MN; professional: High School Social Studies Teacher; Head Start Program Director; Curriculum Coordinator; Fingerhut Corporation Assistant to the President; MN State Representative; U.S. Congressman; U.S. Export Corporation President; Minnesota World Trade Center President; International Business Consultant; Emily Forest Products CEO; religion: Roman Catholic; married: Mary Nolan; four children; ten grandchildren; committees: Agriculture; Transportation and Infrastructure; elected to the 94th Congress and did not seek reelection after serving three terms; elected to the 113th Congress on November 6, 2012.

Office Listings

http://www.nolan.house.gov

2447 Rayburn House Office Building, Washington, DC 20515 .... (202) 225–6211
Chief of Staff.—Mike Misterek.
Deputy Chief of Staff.—Jodie Torkelson.
Legislative Director.—Jim Swiderski.
Communications Director.—Steve Johnson.
Scheduler.—Ione Yates.
Duluth Technology Village, 11 East Superior Street, Suite 125, Duluth, MN 55802 (218) 464–5095
District Director.—Jeff Anderson. FAX: 464–5098
Brainerd City Hall, 501 Laurel Street, Brainerd, MN 56401 .... (218) 454–4078

FAX: 454–4096

Chisago County Government Center, 313 North Main Street, Room 103, Center City, MN 55012 .... (218) 491–3131

Chisholm City Hall, 316 West Lake Street, Room 7, Chisholm, MN 55719 .... (218) 491–3114

Counties: AITKIN, BELTRAMI (part), CARLTON, CASS, CHISAGO, COOK, CROW WING, HUBBARD, ISANTI, ITASCA, KANABEC, KOOCHICHING, LAKE, MILLE LACS, MORRISON, PINE, ST. LOUIS, WADENA. CITIES: Baxter, Brainerd, Cambridge, Chisago City, Chisholm, Cloquet, Duluth, Ely, Eveleth, Grand Rapids, Hermantown, Hibbing, International Falls, Isanti, Lindstrom, Little Falls, Mora, North Branch, Park Rapids, Pine City, Princeton, Proctor, Rush City, Two Harbors, Virginia, Wadena, and Wyoming. Population (2010), 660,347.

ZIP Codes: 55005–08, 55012–13, 55017, 55025, 55029–30, 55032, 55036–37, 55040, 55045, 55051, 55056, 55063, 55069–70, 55072–74, 55079–80, 55084, 55092, 55371, 55398, 55601–07, 55609, 55612–16, 55702–13, 55716–26, 55731–36, 55738, 55741–42, 55744, 55746, 55748–53, 55756–58, 55760, 55763–69, 55771–72, 55775, 55779–87, 55790, 55792–93, 55795–98, 55802–08, 55810–12, 56307, 56313–14, 56317–18, 56328–31, 56336, 56338, 56340, 56342, 56344–45, 56347, 56350, 56353, 56357–59, 56363–64, 56367, 56373, 56382, 56384, 56386, 56401, 56425, 56431, 56433–36, 56441–44, 56447–50, 56452, 56455, 56458, 56461, 56464–70, 56472–75, 56477, 56479, 56481–82, 56484, 56601, 56623, 56626–31, 56633, 56636–37, 56639–41, 56647, 56649–50, 56653–55, 56657–63, 56667–69, 56672, 56678–81, 56683, 56688

MISSISSIPPI

(Population 2010, 2,967,297)

SENATORS

THAD COCHRAN, Republican, of Oxford, MS; born in Pontotoc, MS, December 7, 1937; education: B.A., University of Mississippi, 1959; J.D., University of Mississippi Law School, 1965; received a Rotary Foundation Fellowship and studied international law and jurisprudence at Trinity College, University of Dublin, Ireland, 1963–64; military service: served in U.S. Navy, 1959–61; professional: admitted to Mississippi Bar in 1965; board of directors, Jackson Rotary Club, 1970–71; Outstanding Young Man of the Year Award, Junior Chamber of Commerce in Mississippi, 1971; president, young lawyers section of Mississippi State Bar, 1972–73; married: the former Rose Clayton of New Albany, MS, 1964; two children and three grandchildren; committees: ranking member, Agriculture, Nutrition, and Forestry; Appropriations; Rules and Administration; elected to the 93rd Congress, November 7, 1972; reelected to 94th and 95th Congresses; chairman of the Senate Republican Conference, 1990–96; elected to the U.S. Senate, November 7, 1978, for the six-year term beginning January 3, 1979; subsequently appointed by the Governor, December 27, 1978, to fill the vacancy caused by the resignation of Senator James O. Eastland; reelected to each succeeding Senate term.

Office Listings

http://cochran.senate.gov

113 Dirksen Senate Office Building, Washington, DC 20510 .... (202) 224–5054
Chief of Staff.—Bruce Evans.
Legislative Director.—Adam Telle.
Press Secretary.—Chris Gallegos.
Scheduler.—Doris Wagley.
190 East Capitol Street, Suite 550, Jackson, MS 39201 .... (601) 965–4459
911 East Jackson Avenue, Suite 249, Oxford, MS 38655 .... (662) 236–1018
2012 15th Street, Suite 451, Gulfport, MS 39501 .... (228) 867–9710

* * *

ROGER F. WICKER, Republican, of Tupelo, MS; born in Pontotoc, MS, July 5, 1951; education: graduated Pontotoc High School; University of Mississippi: B.A., 1973; J.D., 1975; president, Associated Student Body, 1972–73; *Mississippi Law Journal*, 1973–75; Air Force ROTC; U.S. Air Force, 1976–80; U.S. Air Force Reserve, 1980–2004 (retired with rank of lieutenant colonel); U.S. House of Representatives Rules Committee staff for Representative Trent Lott, 1980–82; private law practice, 1982–94; Lee County Public Defender, 1984–87; Tupelo City Judge pro tempore, 1986–87; Mississippi State Senate, 1988–94, chairman: Elections Committee (1992), Public Health and Welfare Committee (1993–94); member: Lions Club, University of Mississippi Hall of Fame, Sigma Nu Fraternity Hall of Fame, Omicron Delta Kappa, Phi Delta Phi; religion: Southern Baptist, deacon, adult choir of First Baptist Church, Tupelo, MS; married: Gayle Long Wicker; children: Margaret (Manning) McPhillips, Caroline (Kirk) Sims, and McDaniel (Kellee) Wicker; grandchildren: Caroline McPhillips; Henry McPhillips; Commission on Security and Cooperation in Europe; committees: Armed Services; Budget; Commerce, Science, and Transportation; Environment and Pulbic Works; Joint Economic; elected to the 104th Congress, November 8, 1994; president, Republican freshman class, 1995; reelected to each succeeding Congress; appointed by the governor, December 31, 2007, to fill the vacancy caused by the resignation of Senator Trent Lott; elected to the U.S. Senate on November 4, 2008; reelected to the U.S. Senate on November 6, 2012.

Office Listings

http://wicker.senate.gov http://facebook.com/senatorwicker twitter: @senatorwicker

555 Dirksen Senate Office Building, Washington, DC 20510 .... (202) 224–6253
Chief of Staff.—Michelle Barlow Richardson. FAX: 228–0378
Legislative Director.—Bob Foster.
Communications Director.—Ryan Taylor.
Scheduler.—Hall Carter.
U.S. Federal Courthouse, 501 East Court Street, Suite 3.500, Jackson, MS 39201 .. (601) 965–4644
FAX: 695–4007
452 Courthouse Road, Suite F, Gulfport, MS 39507 .... (228) 604–2383
FAX: 896–4359
3118 Pascagoula Street, Suite 179, Pascagoula, MS 39567 .... (228) 762–5400
FAX: 762–0137
2801 West Main Street, Tupelo, MS 38801 .... (662) 844–5010

FAX: 844–5030

321 Losher Street, Hernando, MS 38632 .... (662) 429–1002
FAX: 429–6002

REPRESENTATIVES

FIRST DISTRICT

ALAN NUNNELEE, Republican, of Tupelo, MS; born in Columbus, MS, October 9, 1958; education: Clinton High School, Clinton, MS, 1976; B.S., Mississippi State University, Starkville, MS, 1980; professional: Mississippi State Senate, 1994–2010; chairman, Appropriations Committee, 2008–10; religion: Southern Baptist; married: Tori Nunnelee; children: Reed, Emily, and Nathan; caucuses: Congressional Prayer Caucus; Congressional Sportsmen's Caucus; Congressional Constitution Caucus; Congressional Military Family Caucus; National Guard and Reserve Components Caucus; Immigration Reform Caucus; Congressional Coal Caucus; Congressional Nursing Caucus; Congressional Manufacturing Caucus; Congressional Cement Caucus; Congressional Chicken Caucus; Congressional Peanut Caucus; Congressional Coalition on Adoption; Community College Caucus; House General Aviation Caucus; Foster Youth Caucus; Values Action Team; Congressional Pro-Life Caucus; Caucus on Orphans and Vulnerable Children; Science & National Labs Caucus; committees: Appropriations; Budget; elected to the 112th Congress on November 2, 2010; reelected to the 113th Congress on November 6, 2012.

Office Listings

http://nunnelee.house.gov

1427 Longworth House Office Building, Washington, DC 20515 .... (202) 225–4306
Chief of Staff.—Ted Maness. FAX: 225–3549
Legislative Director.—Meyer Seligman.
Communications Director.—Jordan Russell.
Scheduler.—Mabel Murphree.
133 East Commerce Street, Hernando, MS 38632 .... (662) 449–3090
431 West Main Street, Tupelo, MS 38804 .... (662) 841–8808
FAX: 841–8845
318 Seventh Street North, Columbus, MS 39701 .... (662) 327–0748
FAX: 328–5982

Counties: ALCORN, BENTON, CALHOUN, CHICKASAW, CHOCTAW, CLAY, DESOTO, ITTAWAMBA, LAFAYETTE, LEE, LOWNDES, MARSHALL, MONROE, PONTOTOC, PRENTISS, TATE, TIPPAH, TISHIMINGO, UNION, WEBSTER (part), OKTIBBEHA (part), and WINSTON (part). Population (2010), 788,095.

ZIP Codes: 38601–03, 38606, 38610–11, 38618–21, 38625, 38627, 38629, 38632–35, 38637–38, 38641–42, 38647, 38649–52, 38654–55, 38658–59, 38661, 38663, 38665–66, 38668, 38670–74, 38677, 38679–80, 38683, 38685–86, 38801–04, 38820–21, 38824–29, 38833–35, 38838–39, 38841, 38843–44, 38846–52, 38854–60, 38862–66, 38868–71, 38873–80, 38901–02, 38913–16, 38920, 38922, 38925–27, 38929, 38940, 38948–49, 38951, 38953, 38955, 38960–61, 38965, 39108, 39339, 39701–05, 39710, 39730, 39735–37, 39740–41, 39743–46, 39750–56, 39759, 39766–67, 39769, 39771–73, 39776

* * *

SECOND DISTRICT

BENNIE G. THOMPSON, Democrat, of Bolton, MS; born in Bolton, January 28, 1948; education: graduated, Hinds County Agriculture High School; B.A., Tougaloo College, 1968; M.S., Jackson State University, 1972; professional: teacher; Bolton Board of Aldermen, 1969–73; mayor of Bolton, 1973–79; Hinds County Board of Supervisors, 1980–93; Congressional Black Caucus; Congressional Gaming Caucus; Congressional Sportsmen's Caucus; House Education Caucus; Rural Caucus; Progressive Caucus; Housing Assistance Council; NAACP 100 Black Men of Jackson, MS; Southern Regional Council; Kappa Alpha Psi Fraternity; married to the former London Johnson, Ph.D.; one daughter: BendaLonne; committees: ranking member, Homeland Security; elected to the 103rd Congress in a special election; reelected to each succeeding Congress.

Office Listings

http://www.bennie thompson.house.gov

2466 Rayburn House Office Building, Washington, DC 20515 .... (202) 225–5876

Chief of Staff/Communications Director.—Lanier Avant. FAX: 225–5898
Administrative Assistant.—Vacant.
Legislative Director.—Cory Horton.
Scheduler.—Andrea Lee.
107 West Madison Street, P.O. Box 610, Bolton, MS 39041–0610 .... (601) 866–9003
District Director.—Vacant.
3607 Medgar Evers Boulevard, Jackson, MS 39213 .... (601) 982–8582
263 East Main Street, Marks, MS 38646 .... (662) 326–9003
Mound Bayou City Hall, Room 134, 106 West Green Street, Mound Bayou, MS 38762 .... (662) 741–9003
509 Highway 82 West, Greenwood, MS 38930 .... (662) 455–9003
910 Courthouse Lane, Greenville, MS 38701 .... (662) 335–9003

Counties: ATTALA, BOLIVAR, CARROLL, CLAIBORNE, COAHOMA, COPIAH, GRENADA, HINDS (part), HOLMES, HUMPHREYS, ISSAQUENA, JEFFERSON, LEAKE, LEFLORE, MADISON (part), MONTGOMERY, PANOLA, QUITMAN, SHARKEY, SUNFLOWER, TALLAHATCHIE, TUNICA, WARREN, WASHINGTON, YALOBUSHA, AND YAZOO. Population (2010), 741,862.

ZIP Codes: 38606, 38614, 38617, 38619–23, 38626, 38630–31, 38639, 38643–46, 38658, 38664–66, 38670, 38676, 38701–04, 38720–23, 38725–26, 38730–32, 38736–38, 38740, 38744–46, 38748–49, 38751, 38753–54, 38756, 38759–62, 38764–65, 38767–69, 38771–74, 38778, 38781, 38901, 38914, 38917, 38920–25, 38927–30, 38940–41, 38943–48, 38950, 38952–54, 38957–58, 38961–67, 39038–41, 39045–46, 39051, 39054, 39056, 39059, 39061, 39063, 39066–67, 39069, 39071, 39078–79, 39083, 39086, 39088, 39090, 39094–97, 39108, 39110, 39113, 39115, 39120, 39144, 39146, 39150, 39154, 39156–57, 39159–60, 39162, 39166, 39169–70, 39174–77, 39179–80, 39183, 39189, 39191–92, 39194, 39201–04, 39206, 39209, 39211–13, 39216–17, 39272, 39365, 39653, 39668, 39745, 39747, 39767

* * *

THIRD DISTRICT

GREGG HARPER, Republican, of Pearl, MS; born in Jackson, MS, June 1, 1956; education: graduated from Pearl High School, Pearl, MS, 1974; B.S., Mississippi College, Clinton, MS, 1978; J.D., University of Mississippi, Oxford, MS, 1981; professional: prosecuting attorney; member, Pearl Chamber of Commerce, Rankin County Chamber of Commerce; Republican Steering Committee; religion: Southern Baptist; married: the former Sidney Carol Hancock; children: Livingston and Maggie; committees: chair, Joint Committee on Printing; vice-chair, Joint Committee on the Library; Energy and Commerce; House Administration; elected to the 111th Congress on November 4, 2008; reelected to each succeeding Congress.

Office Listings

http://www.harper.house.gov

307 Cannon House Office Building, Washington, DC 20515 .... (202) 225–5031
Chief of Staff.—Michael Cravens. FAX: 225–5797
Policy Director.—Scot Malvaney.
Communications Director.—Adam Buckalew.
Scheduler.—Marcy Scoggins.
2507–A Old Brandon Road, Pearl, MS 39208 .... (601) 932–2410
District Director.—Chip Reynolds.
1901 Front Street, Suite A, Meridian, MS 39301 .... (601) 693–6681
Special Assistant.—Frances White.
1 Research Boulevard, Suite 206, Starkville, MS 39759 .... (662) 324–0007
Special Assistant.—Henry Moseley.
230 South Whitworth Street, Brookhaven, MS 39601 .... (601) 823–3400
District Field Representative.—Evan Gardner.

Counties: ADAMS, AMITE, COVINGTON, FRANKLIN, HINDS (part), JASPER (part), JEFF DAVIS, JONES (part), KEMPER, LAUDERDALE, LAWRENCE, LEAKE (part), LINCOLN, MADISON (part), MARION (part), NESHOBA, NEWTON, NOXUBEE, OKTIBBEHA, PIKE, RANKIN, SCOTT, SIMPSON, SMITH, WALTHALL, WEBSTER (part), WILKINSON, WINSTON. Population (2010), 745,254.

ZIP Codes: 39041–44, 39046–47, 39051, 39057, 39062, 39069, 39071, 39073–74, 39078, 39080, 39082–83, 39087, 39090, 39092, 39094, 39098, 39108–12, 39114, 39116–17, 39119–22, 39130, 39140, 39145, 39148–49, 39151–53, 39157–58, 39161, 39165, 39167–68, 39189–91, 39193, 39202, 39206, 39208–09, 39211, 39213, 39216, 39218, 39232, 39236, 39288, 39298, 39301–05, 39307, 39309, 39320, 39323, 39325–28, 39332, 39335–39, 39341–42, 39345–46, 39350, 39352, 39354, 39358–59, 39361, 39364–65, 39402, 39421–22, 39427–29, 39439, 39443, 39460, 39474, 39478–80, 39482–83, 39601–03, 39629–33, 39635, 39638, 39641, 39643, 39645, 39647–49, 39652–54, 39656–57, 39661–69, 39701, 39735, 39739, 39743, 39750, 39755, 39759–60, 39762, 39769

* * *

FOURTH DISTRICT

STEVEN M. PALAZZO, Republican, of Biloxi, MS; born in Gulfport, MS, February 21, 1970; education: B.S., University of Southern Mississippi, Hattiesburg, MS, 1994; M.P.A.,

University of Southern Mississippi, Hattiesburg, 1996; professional: accountant; military: United States Marine Corps Reserve, 1988–96; Mississippi Army National Guard, 2007–present; member of Mississippi State House of Representatives, 2007–10; commissions and caucuses: Congressional Sportmen's Caucus; Gulf Coast Caucus; Home Protection Caucus; National Guard Caucus; Shipbuilding Caucus; family: spouse, Lisa; children: Barrett, Aubrey, and Bennett; committees: Armed Services; Homeland Security; Science, Space, and Technology; elected to the 112th Congress on November 2, 2010; reelected to the 113th Congress on November 6, 2012.

Office Listings

http://www.palazzo.house.gov www.facebook.com/stevenpalazzo twitter.com/congpalazzo

331 Cannon House Office Building, Washington, DC 20515 .... (202) 225–5772
Chief of Staff.—Casey Street. FAX: 225–7074
Legislative Director.—Patrick Large.
Scheduler.—Leslie Churchwell.
1325 25th Avenue, Gulfport, MS 39501 .... (228) 864–7670
Deputy Chief of Staff.—Hunter Lipscomb.
641 Main Street, Suite 215, Hattiesburg, MS 39401 .... (601) 582–3246
3118 Pascagoula Street, Suite 181, Pascagoula, MS 39567 .... (228) 202–8104
FAX: 202–8105
72 Technology Boulevard, Suite 216, Ellisville, MS 39437 .... (601) 428–9711

Counties: CLARKE (part), FORREST, GEORGE, GREENE, HANCOCK, HARRISON, JACKSON, JONES, LAMAR, MARION, PEARL RIVER, PERRY, STONE, AND WAYNE. CITIES AND TOWNSHIPS: Biloxi, Gulfport, Hattiesburg, Laurel, and Pascagoula. Population (2010), 741,776.

ZIP Codes: 39301, 39307, 39322, 39324, 39330, 39332, 39347–48, 39355–56, 39360, 39362–63, 39366–67, 39401–04, 39406, 39422–23, 39425–26, 39429, 39436–37, 39439–43, 39451–52, 39455–57, 39459, 39461–66, 39470, 39475–78, 39480–82, 39501–03, 39505–07, 39520–22, 39525, 39529–35, 39540, 39552–53, 39555–56, 39558, 39560–69, 39571–74, 39576–77, 39581, 39595

MISSOURI

(Population 2010, 5,988,927)

SENATORS

CLAIRE McCASKILL, Democrat, of Kirkwood, MO; born in Rolla, MO, July 24, 1953; raised in Lebanon, MO and Columbia, MO; education: B.A., University of Missouri-Columbia, 1975; J.D., University of Missouri-Columbia School of Law, 1978; professional: clerk with the Missouri Court of Appeals, Western District in Kansas City, 1978; assistant prosecutor, Jackson County prosecutor's office, 1979–83; Missouri State Representative, 1983–88; practiced law in Kansas City, MO, 1983–92; Jackson County Legislator-At-Large, 1991–93; Jackson County Prosecutor, 1993–99; Missouri State Auditor, 1999–2006; married: Joseph Shephard, 2002; together, they have seven children: Benjamin, Carl, Marilyn, Michael, Austin, Maddie, Lily; appointed deputy whip for the majority, 2007; committees: Armed Services; Commerce, Science, and Transportation; Homeland Security and Governmental Affairs; Special Committee on Aging; elected to the U.S. Senate of the 110th Congress on November 7, 2006; reelected to the U.S. Senate on November 6, 2012.

Office Listings

http://mccaskill.senate.gov

506 Hart Senate Office Building, Washington, DC 20510 .... (202) 224–6154
Chief of Staff.—Julie Dwyer. FAX: 228–6326
Deputy Chief of Staff.—Tod Martin.
Legislative Director.—Stephen Hedger.
Communications Director.—John LaBombard.
5850 Delmar Boulevard, Suite A, St. Louis, MO 63112 .... (314) 367–1364
Regional Director.—Joeana Middleton.
4141 Pennsylvania Avenue, Suite 101, Kansas City, MO 64111 .... (816) 421–1639
Regional Director.—Corey Dillon.
555 Independence Avenue, Room 1600, Cape Girardeau, MO 63703 .... (573) 651–0964
District Director.—Christy Mercer.
915 East Ash Street, Columbia, MO 65201 .... (573) 442–7130
Regional Director.—Cindy Hall.
324 Park Central West, Suite 101, Springfield, MO 65806 .... (417) 868–8745
District Director.—Gail Melgren.

* * *

ROY BLUNT, Republican, of Springfield, MO; born in Niangua, MO, January 10, 1950; education: B.A., Southwest Baptist University, 1970; M.A., Missouri State University, 1972; professional: county clerk and chief election official of Greene County, 1972–84; Secretary of State of Missouri, 1984–92; president of Southwest Baptist University, 1993–96; U.S. House of Representatives for Missouri's 7th District, 1997–2010; married: Abigail Blunt; children: Governor Matthew Blunt, Amy Blunt, Andrew Blunt, Alexander Charles Blunt; committees: Appropriations; Armed Services; Commerce, Science and Transportation; Rules and Administration; elected to the U.S. Senate on November 2, 2010.

Office Listings

http://blunt.senate.gov

260 Russell Senate Office Building, Washington, DC 20510 .... (202) 224–5721
Chief of Staff.—Glen Chambers. FAX: 224–8149
Deputy Chief of Staff.—Burson Snyder.
Legislative Director.—Tracy Henke.
Communications Director.—Amber Marchand.
Director of Scheduling.—Richard Eddings.
2740B East Sunshine, Springfield, MO 65804 .... (417) 877–7814
911 Main Street, Suite 2224, Kansas City, MO 64105 .... (816) 471–7141
7700 Bonhomme, Suite 315, Clayton, MO 63105 .... (314) 725–4484
1001 Cherry Street, Suite 104, Columbia, MO 65201 .... (573) 442–8151
State Director.—Derek Coats.
308 East High, Suite 202, Jefferson City, MO 65101 .... (573) 634–2488
2502 Tanner Drive, Suite 208, Cape Girardeau, MO 63703 .... (573) 334–7044

REPRESENTATIVES

FIRST DISTRICT

WM. LACY CLAY, Democrat, of St. Louis, MO; born in St. Louis, July 27, 1956; education: Springbrook High School, Silver Spring, MD, 1974; B.A., University of Maryland, College Park, MD, 1983; public service: Missouri House of Representatives, 1983–91; Missouri State Senate, 1991–2000; nonprofit organizations: St. Louis Gateway Classic Sports Foundation; Mary Ryder Homes; William L. Clay Scholarship and Research Fund; religion: Catholic; divorced; children: Carol and William III; committees: Financial Services; Oversight and Government Reform; elected to the 107th Congress on November 7, 2000; reelected to each succeeding Congress.

Office Listings

http://www.lacyclay.house.gov

2418 Rayburn House Office Building, Washington, DC 20515 .... (202) 225–2406
Chief of Staff.—Darryl A. Piggee. FAX: 226–3717
Scheduler.—Karyn Long.
Legislative Assistants: Anthony Clark, Richard Pecantee, Marvin Steele.
Thomas F. Eagleton U.S. Courthouse, 111 South 10th Street, Suite 24–344, St. Louis, MO 63102 .... (314) 367–1970
FAX: 367–1341
6830 Gravois, St. Louis, MO 63116 .... (314) 669–9393
FAX: 669–9398

Counties: ST. LOUIS (part). Population (2010), 748,616.

ZIP Codes: 63031, 63033–34, 63042–45, 63074, 63101–25, 63130, 63132–41, 63143–44, 63146–47, 63155

* * *

SECOND DISTRICT

ANN L. WAGNER, Republican, of Ballwin, MO; born in St. Louis, MO, September 13, 1962; education: B.A.B.S. University of Missouri, Columbia, 1984; professional: businesswoman; Hallmark Cards; Ralston Purina; public service: Committeewoman for Lafayette Township; chair of Missouri Republican Party, 1999–2005; co-chair of the Republican National Committee 2001–05; U.S. Ambassador to Luxembourg, 2005–09; family: married to Raymond Jr.; children: Raymond III, Stephen, Mary Ruth; committees: Financial Services; elected to the 113th Congress on November 6, 2012.

Office Listings

http://wagner.house.gov https://www.facebook.com/repannwagner
https://twitter.com/repannwagner

435 Cannon House Office Building, Washington, DC 20515 .... (202) 225–1621
Chief of Staff.—Christian Morgan.
Scheduler.—Courtney Ellis.
301 Sovereign Court, Suite 201, St. Louis, MO 63011 .... (636) 779–5449
District Director.—Miriam Stonebraker.

Counties: JEFFERSON (part), CHARLES (part), ST. LOUIS (part). Population (2010), 706,622.

ZIP Codes: 63005, 63010–11, 63017, 63021, 63025–26, 63038, 63040, 63043–44, 63049, 63069, 63074, 63088, 63105, 63114, 63117, 63119, 63122–32, 63141, 63144, 63146, 63301, 63303–04, 63341, 63366, 63368, 63376

* * *

THIRD DISTRICT

BLAINE LUETKEMEYER, Republican, of St. Elizabeth, MO; born in Jefferson City, MO, May 7, 1952; education: graduate of Lincoln University, Jefferson City, MO, 1974; where he earned a degree with distinction in political science and a minor in business administration, 1999–2005; professional: served as Missouri State Representative and after leaving office was appointed by the Governor to serve as the Director of the Missouri Division of Tourism; lifelong member of St. Elizabeth Catholic Church; married: Jackie, three children; committees: Financial Services; Small Business (vice chairman); elected to the 111th Congress on November 4, 2008; reelected to each succeeding Congress.

Office Listings

http://luetkemeyer.house.gov

2440 Rayburn House Office Building, Washington, DC 20515 .... (202) 225–2956
Chief of Staff.—Seth Appleton. FAX: 225–5712
Legislative Director.—Chris Brown.
Legislative Assistants: Christy Knese, Chance McNeely.
Deputy Press Secretary.—Kristina Weger.
Director of Scheduling.—Amber Daniles.

2117 Missouri Boulevard, Jefferson City, MO 65109 .... (573) 635–7232
District Office Director.—Jeremy Ketterer FAX: 635–8346
Press Secretary.—Paul Sloca.
Director of Constituent Affairs.—Keri Stuart.
Caseworker.—Lori Boykin.
Office Manager.—Laura Hardecke.

516 Jefferson Street, Washington, MO 63090 .... (636) 239–2276
District Office Director.—Dan Engemann. FAX: 239–0478
Field Representative.—Mary Tinsley.

113 East Pearce, Wentzville, MO 63385 .... (573) 327–7055
District Office Director.—Tanner Smith. FAX: 327–3254

Counties: CALLAWAY, CAMDEN (part), COLE, FRANKLIN, GASCONADE, JEFFERSON (part), LINCOLN, MARIES, MILLER, MONTGOMERY, OSAGE, ST. CHARLES (part) and WARREN. Population (2010), 748,615.

ZIP Codes: 63005 (part), 63010 (part), 63012 (part), 63013–63014, 63015 (part), 63016 (part), 63019 (part), 63023 (part), 63025 (part), 63026 (part), 63028 (part), 63037, 63039, 63041 (part), 63048, 63049 (part), 63050 (part), 63051–53, 63055, 63057, 63060–61, 63068, 63069 (part), 63070 (part), 63072 (part), 63073, 63077, 63079, 63080 (part), 63084, 63089–91, 63301 (part), 63302, 63303 (part), 63332–33, 63334 (part), 63341 (part), 63342, 63343 (part), 63344 (part), 63346–51, 63352 (part), 63357, 63359 (part), 63361–63, 63365, 63366 (part), 63367, 63368 (part), 63369–70, 63373, 63376 (part), 63377–79, 63381, 63383, 63384 (part)

* * *

FOURTH DISTRICT

VICKY HARTZLER, Republican, of Harrisonville, MO; born in Archie, MO, October 13, 1960; education: B.S., in education, *summa cum laude,* University of Missouri-Columbia, Columbia, MO, 1983; M.S., in education, Central Missouri State University (now University of Central Missouri), Warrensburg, MO, 1992; professional: served as State spokesperson for the Coalition to Protect Marriage, 2004; member of the Missouri State House of Representatives, 124th District, 1995–2001; appointed chair, Missouri Women's Council, 2005; teacher of family and consumer sciences for 11 years in Lebanon and Belton, MO; religion: Evangelical Christian; family: married Lowell Hartzler; one child: Tiffany, caucuses: Pro-Life Caucus; Israel Allies Caucus; Republican Study Committee; Tea Party Caucus; Air Force Caucus; Immigration Caucus; Missile Defense Caucus; Human Trafficking Caucus; Small Business Caucus; Prayer Caucus; Military Family Caucus; Job Creators' Caucus; Rural Caucus; committees: Agriculture; Armed Services; Budget; elected to the 112th Congress on November 2, 2010; reelected to the 113th Congress on November 6, 2012.

Office Listings

http://www.hartzler.house.gov

1023 Longworth House Office Building, Washington, DC 20515 .... (202) 225–2876
Chief of Staff.—Eric Bohl. FAX: 225–0148
Legislative Director.—Daniel Burgess.
Communications Director.—Steve Walsh.
Scheduler.—Adrienne Cornelius.

2415 Carter Lane, Suite 4, Columbia, MO 65201 .... (573) 442–9311

1909 North Commercial Street, Harrisonville, MO 64701 .... (816) 884–3411

219 North Adams Street, Lebanon, MO 65536 .... (417) 532–5582

415 South Ohio Avenue, Suite 212B, Sedalia, MO 65301 .... (573) 634–4884

Counties: AUDRAIN (part), BARTON, BATES, BENTON, BOONE, CAMDEN, CASS, CEDAR, COOPER, DADE, DALLAS, HENRY, HICKORY, HOWARD, JOHNSON, LACLEDE, MONITIEAU, MORGAN, PULASKI, RANDOLPH, ST. CLAIR, VERNON, AND WEBSTER (part). Population (2010), 748,616.

ZIP Codes: 63352, 64011–12, 64019–20, 64030, 64034, 64037, 64040, 64061, 64070–71, 64076, 64078, 64080, 64082–83, 64090, 64093, 64147, 64149, 64701, 64720, 64722–26, 64728, 64730, 64733–35, 64738–48, 64750, 64752, 64755–56, 64759, 64761–63, 64765–67, 64769–72, 64776, 64778–81, 64783–84, 64788, 64790, 64832, 64855, 65010–11,

65018, 65020, 65023, 65025–26, 65034, 65037–39, 65042, 65046, 65050, 65055, 65064, 65068, 65072, 65074, 65078–79, 65081, 65084, 65201–03, 65205, 65211–12, 65215–18, 65230–33, 65237, 65239–40, 65243–44, 65247–48, 65250, 65254–57, 65259–60, 65264–65, 65270, 65274, 65276, 65278–80, 65284–85, 65287, 65299, 65301–02, 65305, 65322–26, 65329, 65332–38, 65340, 65345, 65347–48, 65350–51, 65354–55, 65360, 65452, 65457, 65459, 65461, 65463, 65470, 65473, 65534, 65536, 65543, 65550, 65552, 65556, 65567, 65583–84, 65590–91, 65603–04, 65607, 65622, 65632, 65634–36, 65644, 65646, 65648–50, 65652, 65661–62, 65668, 65674, 65682, 65685, 65706, 65713, 65722, 65724, 65732, 65735, 65742, 65746, 65752, 65757, 65764, 65767, 65770, 65774, 65779, 65783, 65785–87

* * *

FIFTH DISTRICT

EMANUEL CLEAVER II, Democrat, of Kansas City, MO; born in Waxahachie, TX, October 26, 1944; education: M. Div., Saint Paul School of Theology, MO, 1974; B.S., Prairie View A&M University, TX, 1972; professional: Senior Pastor, St. James United Methodist Church, 1973–2009; City Councilman, Kansas City, MO, 5th District, 1979–91; founder, Harmony in a World of Difference, 1991; founder, Southern Christian Leadership Conference, Kansas City Chapter; Mayor of Kansas City, MO, 1991–99; member, President-elect Bill Clinton's Transitional Team, 1992; host, Under the Clock, KCUR radio, 1999–2004; chairman of the Congressional Black Caucus, 2010–12; member, National Co-Chair of President Barack Obama Campaign Committee, 2012; married: Dianne; four children; four grandchildren; committees: Financial Services; elected to the 109th Congress on November 2, 2004; reelected to each succeeding Congress.

Office Listings

http://www.house.gov/cleaver

2335 Rayburn House Office Building, Washington, DC 20515 .... (202) 225–4535
Legislative Director.—Jennifer Shapiro. FAX: 225–4403
Scheduler.—Justin Thaxton.
101 West 31st Street, Kansas City, MO 64108 .... (816) 842–4545
Chief of Staff.—Geoff Jolley.
Communications Director.—Michele Rooney.
211 Maple Avenue, Independence, MO 64050 .... (816) 833–4545

Counties: CLAY COUNTY (part), JACKSON COUNTY (part), LAFAYETTE, RAY, AND SALINE COUNTIES. CITIES AND TOWNSHIPS: Kansas City, Independence, Lee's Summit, Raytown, Grandview, Sugar Creek, Blue Springs, Grain Valley, Oak Grove, North Kansas City, Gladstone, Claycomo, Lawson, Richmond, Concordia, Higginsville, Lexington, Odessa, Marshall, Sweet Springs, and Slater. Population (2010), 747,573.

ZIP Codes: 64001, 64011, 64017, 64020–22, 64024, 64029, 64035–37, 64062, 64067, 64071, 64074–77, 64084–85, 64096–97, 64747–48, 65320, 65327, 65330, 65339–40, 65344, 65347, 65349, 65351

* * *

SIXTH DISTRICT

SAM GRAVES, Republican, of Tarkio, MO; born in Fairfax, MO, November 7, 1963; education: B.S., University of Missouri-Columbia, 1986; professional: farmer; organizations: Missouri Farm Bureau; Northwest Missouri State University Agriculture Advisory Committee; University Extension Council; Rotary Club; awards: Associated Industries Voice of Missouri Business Award; Tom Henderson Award; Tarkio Community Betterment Award; Missouri Physical Therapy Association Award; Outstanding Young Farmer Award, 1997; Hero of the Taxpayer Award; NFIB Guardian of Small Business Award; public service: elected to the Missouri House of Representatives, 1992; and the Missouri State Senate, 1994; religion: Baptist; committees: chair, Small Business; Transportation and Infrastructure; elected to the 107th Congress on November 7, 2000; reelected to each succeeding Congress.

Office Listings

http://www.house.gov/graves

1415 Longworth House Office Building, Washington, DC 20515 .... (202) 225–7041
Chief of Staff.—Tom Brown. FAX: 225–8221
Legislative Director.—Jordan Austin.
Communications Director.—Chris Averill.
Scheduler.—Buffy Smith.
411 Jules Street, Suite 111, St. Joseph, MO 64501 .... (816) 233–9818
11724 Northwest Plaza Circle, Suite 900, Kansas City, MO 64153 .... (816) 792–3976
906 Broadway, P.O. Box 364, Hannibal, MO 63401 .... (573) 221–3400

Counties: ADAIR, ANDREW, ATCHISON, AUDRAIN (PART), BUCHANAN, CALDWELL, CARROLL, CHARITON, CLARK, CLAY (PART), CLINTON, DAVIESS, DEKALB, GENTRY, GRUNDY, HARRISON, HOLT, JACKSON (PART), KNOX, LEWIS, LINN, LIVING-

STON, MACON, MARION, MERCER, MONROE, NODAWAY, PIKE, PLATTE, PUTNAM, RALLS, SCHUYLER, SCOTLAND, SHELBY, SULLIVAN, AND WORTH. Population (2010), 748,616.

ZIP Codes: 63119, 63330, 63334, 63336, 63339, 63343–45, 63352–53, 63359, 63382, 63384, 63401, 63430–43, 63445–48, 63450–54, 63456–69, 63471–74, 63501, 63530–41, 63543–49, 63551–52, 63555–61, 63563, 63565–67, 64013–16, 64018, 64024, 64028–30, 64048, 64051, 64055–58, 64060, 64062–64, 64066, 64068–69, 64072, 64074–75, 64077, 64079, 64085–86, 64088–89, 64092, 64098, 64106, 64112, 64116, 64118–19, 64134, 64150–58, 64163–68, 64188, 64190, 64195, 64401–02, 64420–24, 64426–34, 64436–46, 64448–49, 64451, 64453–59, 64461, 64463, 64465–71, 64473–77, 64479–87, 64489–94, 64496–99, 64501–08, 64601, 64620, 64622–25, 64628, 64630–33, 64635–61, 64664, 64667–68, 64670–74, 64676, 64679, 64681–83, 64686, 64688–89, 64701, 65065, 65202, 65205, 65230, 65232, 65236, 65240, 65243–44, 65246–47, 65254–55, 65258, 65260–61, 65263–65, 65270, 65275, 65280–83, 65286

* * *

SEVENTH DISTRICT

BILLY LONG, Republican, of Springfield, MO; born in Niangua, MO, August 11, 1955; education: attended, University of Missouri, Columbia, MO, 1973–74; Missouri Auction School, Kansas City, MO, 1979; Certified Auctioneer Institute designation, University of Indiana, Bloomington, IN; professional: owner, Billy Long Auctions, LLC; radio talk show host, KWTO AM 560; member: National Association of Realtors; National Auctioneers Association; National Board of Directors; Springfield Area Chamber of Commerce; former president, Missouri Professional Auctioneers Association; Southeast Rotary Club, Springfield; awards: Missouri Professional Auctioneers' Hall of Fame; Outstanding Young Alumni Award, Greenwood Lab School; religion: Presbyterian; family: wife, Barbara Long; daughters; caucuses: Republican Caucus; committees: Energy and Commerce; elected to the 112th Congress on November 2, 2010; reelected to the 113th Congress on November 6, 2012.

Office Listings

http://long.house.gov

1541 Longworth House Office Building, Washington, DC 20515	(202) 225–6536
Chief of Staff.—Joe Lillis.	FAX: 225–5604
Legislative Director.—Scott Shiller.	
Scheduler.—Ben Elleson.	
Communications Director.—Keith Beardslee.	
3232 East Ridgeview Street, Springfield, MO 65804	(417) 889–1899
	FAX: 889–4915
2727 East 32nd Street, Suite 2, Joplin, MO 64804	(417) 781–1041
	FAX: 781–2832

Counties: BARRY, CHRISTIAN, GREENE, JASPER, LAWRENCE, MCDONALD, NEWTON, POLK, STONE, TANEY, AND WEBSTER (part). Population (2010), 721,754.

ZIP Codes: 64748, 64755–56, 64766, 64769, 64801–04, 64830–36, 64840–44, 64847–50, 64853–59, 64861–70, 64873–74, 65603–05, 65608–20, 65622–27, 65629–31, 65633, 65635, 65637–38, 65640–41, 65645–50, 65652–58, 65661, 65663–64, 65666, 65669, 65672–76, 65679–82, 65686, 65702, 65705, 65707–08, 65710, 65712, 65714–15, 65720–21, 65723, 65725–30, 65733–34, 65737–42, 65744–45, 65747, 65752–57, 65759–62, 65765–73, 65781, 65784–85, 65801–10, 65814, 65817, 65890, 65898–99

* * *

EIGHTH DISTRICT

JASON T. SMITH, Republican, of Salem, MO; born in St. Louis, MO, June 16, 1980; education: graduate of Salem High School, received B.S. degrees, agricultural economics and business administration with an emphasis in finance, University of Missouri, Columbia; earned law degree from Oklahoma City University School of Law; also spent summer studying international law, Trinity College, Cambridge, England; professional: attorney; real estate agent; small business owner and fourth generation owner of the family farm; religion: member, Grace Community Church; NRA; Missouri Bar; numerous local chambers of commerce and Missouri Farm Bureau; former president, current member of the Salem FFA Alumni Association; holds an American FFA degree; elected to the Missouri State House of Representatives, 2005 (special election), 2006, 2008; committees: Judiciary; Natural Resources; elected by special election on June 4, 2013 to the 113th Congress, to fill the vacancy caused by the resignation of United States Representative Jo Ann Emerson.

Office Listings

http://jasonsmith.house.gov http://www.facebook.com/repjasonsmith
http://twitter.com/repjasonsmith

2230 Rayburn House Office Building, Washington, DC 20515	(202) 225–4404

Chief of Staff.—Josh Haynes. FAX: 226–0326
Deputy Chief of Staff.—Justin Gibbs.
Executive Assistant / Scheduler.—Carrie Bock.
2502 Tanner Drive, Suite 205, Cape Girardeau, MO 63703 .... (573) 335–0101
830A South Bishop, Rolla, MO 65401 .... (573) 364–2455
22 East Columbia, Farmington, MO 63640 .... (573) 756–9755
35 Court Square, Suite 300, West Plains, MO 65775 .... (417) 255–1515
2911 North Westwood Boulevard, Suite C, Poplar Bluff, MO 63907.

Counties: BOLLINGER, BUTLER, CAPE GIRARDEAU, CARTER, CRAWFORD, DENT, DOUGLAS, DUNKLIN, HOWELL, IRON, JEFFERSON (part), MADISON, MISSISSIPPI, NEW MADRID, OREGON, OZARK, PEMISCOT, PERRY, PHELPS, REYNOLDS, RIPLEY, SCOTT, SHANNON, ST. FRANCOIS, STE. GENEVIEVE, STODDARD, TEXAS, WASHINGTON, WAYNE AND WRIGHT. Population (2010), 748,616.

ZIP Codes: 63036, 63071, 63601, 63620–26, 63628–33, 63636–38, 63640, 63648, 63650–51, 63653–56, 63660, 63662–66, 63674–75, 63701–03, 63730, 63732, 63735–40, 63742–48, 63750–52, 63755, 63758, 63760, 63763–64, 63766–67, 63769–72, 63774–76, 63779–85, 63787, 63801, 63820–30, 63833–34, 63837, 63839–41, 63845–53, 63855, 63857, 63860, 63862–63, 63866–70, 63873–82, 63901–02, 63931–45, 63950–57, 63960–67, 65401–02, 65409, 65436, 65438–41, 65444, 65446, 65449, 65453, 65456, 65459, 65461–62, 65464, 65466, 65468, 65479, 65483–84, 65501, 65529, 65532, 65541–42, 65546, 65548, 65550, 65552, 65555, 65557, 65564–66, 65570–71, 65586, 65588–89, 65606, 65608–09, 65614, 65616, 65618, 65620, 65626–27, 65629, 65637–38, 65652–53, 65655, 65660, 65662, 65666–67, 65676, 65679–80, 65688–90, 65692, 65701–02, 65704, 65711, 65713, 65715, 65717, 65720, 65729, 65731, 65733, 65740–41, 65744, 65746, 65753, 65755, 65759–62, 65766, 65768, 65773, 65775, 65777–78, 65784, 65788–91, 65793

MONTANA

(Population 2010, 989,415)

SENATORS

JON TESTER, Democrat, of Big Sandy, MT; born in Havre, MT, August 21, 1956; education: graduated, Big Sandy High School, 1974; B.S. in music, University of Great Falls, 1978; professional: farmer, T-Bone Farms, Big Sandy, 1978–present; teacher, Big Sandy School District, 1978–80; member, Big Sandy Soil Conservation Service Committee, 1980–83; chairman, Big Sandy School Board of Trustees, 1983–92; Past Master, Treasure Lodge #95 of the Masons; member, Chouteau County Agricultural Stabilization and Conservation Service Committee, 1990–95; member, Organic Crop Improvement Association, 1996–97; served in Montana Senate, 1999–2007; Montana Senate Democratic Whip, 2001–03; Montana Senate Democratic Leader, 2003–05; Montana Senate President, 2005–07; vice chair, Congressional Sportsmen's Caucus; married: Sharla Tester; two children: Christine and Shon; committees: chair, Indian Affairs; Appropriations; Banking, Housing, and Urban Affairs; Homeland Security and Governmental Affairs; Veterans' Affairs; elected to the U.S. Senate on November 7, 2006; reelected to the U.S. Senate on November 6, 2012.

Office Listings

http://tester.senate.gov http://www.facebook.com/senatortester twitter: @testerpress

724 Hart Senate Office Building, Washington, DC 20510 .... (202) 224–2644
Chief of Staff.—Tom Lopach. FAX: 224–8594
Legislative Director.—James Wise.
Communications Director.—Andrea Helling.
Director of Scheduling.—Trecia McEvoy.
State Director.—Bill Lombardi.
Montana Staff Director.—Dayna Swanson.
222 North 32nd Street, Suite 101, Billings, MT 59101 .... (406) 252–0550
1 East Main Street, Suite 202, Bozeman, MT 59715 .... (406) 586–4450
125 West Granite, Suite 200, Butte, MT 59701 .... (406) 723–3277
122 West Towne, Glendive, MT 59330 .... (406) 452–9585
119 First Avenue North, Suite 102, Great Falls, MT 59401 .... (406) 452–9585
208 North Montana Avenue, Suite 202, Helena, MT 59601 .... (406) 449–5401
State Director.—Bill Lombardi.
14 Third Street East, Suite 230, Kalispell, MT 59901 .... (406) 257–3360
130 West Front Street, Missoula, MT 59801 .... (406) 728–3003

* * *

JOHN E. WALSH, Democrat, of Helena, MT; born in Butte, MT, November 3, 1960; education: graduated Butte High School, 1979; attended Carroll College, Helena, MT; B.S., University of the State of New York, 1990; M.A., U.S. Army War College, Carlisle, PA, 2007; professional: served in the Montana National Guard 1979–2012; commissioned as a Second Lieutenant, 1987; led over 700 soldiers into combat in Iraq, the largest deployment of Montana soldiers and airmen since WWII, in 2004 and 2005; Adjutant General of the Montana National Guard, 2008–12; 30th Lieutenant Governor of Montana, 2013–14; awards: recipient of the Bronze Star, Legion of Merit Award; Combat Infantry Badge; married: wife, Janet who has been in the Montana public schools system for 17 years; children: Michael and Taylor; daughter-in-law, April, and a granddaughter, Kennedy; committees: Agriculture, Nutrition, and Forestry; Commerce, Science, and Transportation; Rules and Administration; Special Committee on Aging; appointed to the U.S. Senate on February 9, 2014, to fill the vacancy caused by the resignation of Max Baucus, and took the oath of office on February 11, 2014.

Office Listings

SRC–2 Russell Senate Office Building, Washington, DC 20510 .... (202) 224–2651
Chief of Staff.—Elizabeth Kelly. FAX: 228–4619
Communications Director/Deputy Chief of Staff.—Andrea Helling.
Legislative Director.—Spencer Gray.
Scheduler.—Brenda Carney.
122 West Towne Street, Glendive, MT 59330 .... (406) 365–7002
Empire Block, Suite 206, 30 West 14th Street, Helena, MT 59601 .... (406) 449–5480
FAX: 449–5484
280 East Front Street, Suite 100, Missoula, MT 59802 .... (406) 329–3123
FAX: 728–7610
220 West Lamme, Suite 1D, Bozeman, MT 59715 .... (406) 586–6104
FAX: 587–9177
222 North 32nd Street, Suite 100, Billings, MT 59101 .... (406) 657–6790

FAX: 657–6793

8 Third Street East, Kalispell, MT 59901 .... (406) 756–1150
FAX: 756–1152

245 East Park Street, Butte, MT 59701 .... (406) 782–8700
FAX: 782–6553

113 3rd Street North, Great Falls, MT 59401 .... (406) 761–1574
FAX: 727–3726

REPRESENTATIVE

AT LARGE

STEVE DAINES, Republican, of Bozeman, MT; born in Van Nuys, CA, August 20, 1962; education: B.S., Montana State University, Bozeman, MT, 1984; professional: businessman; public service: Republican National Convention delegate, 1984; married: Cindy; children: David, Annie, Michael, and Caroline; committees: Homeland Security; Natural Resources; Transportation and Infrastructure; elected to the 113th Congress on November 6, 2012.

Office Listings

http://www.daines.house.gov

206 Cannon House Office Building, Washington, DC 20515 .... (202) 225–3211
Chief of Staff.—Jason Thielman. FAX: 225–5687
Communications Director.—Alee Lockman.

910 North Last Chance Gulch, Suite B, Helena, MT 59601 .... (406) 502–1435
District Director.—Charles Robison.

222 North 32nd Street, Suite 900, Billings, MT 59101 .... (406) 969–1736

110 West Front Street, Missoula, MT 59802 .... (406) 926–2122

104 2nd Street South, Suite 103, Great Falls, MT 59401 .... (406) 315–3860

Counties: Beaverhead, Big Horn, Blaine, Broadwater, Carbon, Carter, Cascade, Chouteau, Custer, Daniels, Dawson, Deer Lodge, Fallon, Fergus, Flathead, Gallatin, Garfield, Glacier, Golden Valley, Granite, Hill, Jefferson, Judith Basin, Lake, Lewis and Clark, Liberty, Lincoln, Madison, McCone, Meagher, Mineral, Missoula, Musselshell, Park, Petroleum, Phillips, Pondera, Powder River, Powell, Prairie, Ravalli, Richland, Roosevelt, Rosebud, Sanders, Sheridan, Silver Bow, Stillwater, Sweet Grass, Teton, Toole, Treasure, Valley, Wheatland, Wibaux, and Yellowstone. Population (2010), 989,415.

ZIP Codes: 59001–04, 59006–08, 59010–16, 59018–20, 59022, 59024–39, 59041, 59043–44, 59046–47, 59050, 59052–55, 59057–59, 59061–72, 59074–79, 59081–89, 59101–08, 59201, 59211–15, 59217–19, 59221–23, 59225–26, 59230–31, 59240–44, 59247–48, 59250, 59252–63, 59270, 59273–76, 59301, 59311–19, 59322–24, 59326–27, 59330, 59332–33, 59336–39, 59341, 59343–45, 59347, 59349, 59351, 59353–54, 59401–06, 59410–12, 59414, 59416–22, 59424–25, 59427, 59430, 59432–36, 59440–48, 59450–54, 59456–57, 59460–69, 59471–72, 59474, 59477, 59479–80, 59482–87, 59489, 59501, 59520–32, 59535, 59537–38, 59540, 59542, 59544–47, 59601–02, 59604, 59620, 59623–24, 59626, 59631–36, 59638–45, 59647–48, 59701–03, 59710–11, 59713–22, 59724–25, 59727–33, 59735–36, 59739–41, 59743, 59745–52, 59754–56, 59758–62, 59771–73, 59801–04, 59806–08, 59812, 59820–21, 59823–35, 59837, 59840–48, 59851, 59853–56, 59858–60, 59863–68, 59870–75, 59901, 59903–04, 59910–23, 59925–37

NEBRASKA

(Population 2010, 1,826,341)

SENATORS

MIKE JOHANNS, Republican, of Omaha, NE; born in Osage, IA, June 18, 1950; education: B.A., St. Mary's College, Winona, MN, 1971; J.D., Creighton University, Omaha, NE, 1974; professional: Lancaster County Board, 1983–87; Lincoln City Council, 1989–91; Mayor of Lincoln, 1991–98; Nebraska Governor, 1999–2005; Secretary of Agriculture, 2005–2007; caucus: Senate Community College Caucus, Senate Impact Aid Coalition, Rural Health Caucus, Congressional Heart and Stroke Coalition, Parkinson's Action Network, Army Caucus, Air Force Caucus, Senate Cultural Caucus; Congressional Vision Caucus; Farmer Cooperative Caucus; Senate Republican Capitol Markets Task Force; Senate Western Caucus; Congressional Sportsmen's Caucus; Multiple Sclerosis Caucus; Global Internet Freedom Caucus; Military Families Caucus; Senate Biotech Caucus; Senate Diabetes Caucus; Senate General Aviation Caucus; Senate Nursing Caucus; Senate Ports-to-Plains Caucus; religion: Catholic; married: Stephanie Johanns; two children, five grandchildren; committees: Agriculture, Nutrition, and Forestry; Appropriations; Banking, Housing, and Urban Affairs; Veterans' Affairs; elected to the U.S. Senate on November 4, 2008.

Office Listings

http://johanns.senate.gov http://www.facebook.com/mikejohanns twitter: @mike__johanns

404 Russell Senate Office Building, Washington, DC 20510 .... (202) 224–4224
Chief of Staff.—Terri Moore. FAX: 224–0436
Legislative Director.—Terry Van Doren.
Communications Director.—Nick Simpson.
Administrative Director.—Cherri Carpenter.
287 Federal Building, 100 Centennial Mall, North, Lincoln, NE 68508 .... (402) 476–1400
State Director.—Nancy Johner.
9900 Nicholas Street, Suite 325, Omaha, NE 68114 .... (402) 758–8981
4111 Fourth Avenue, Suite 26, Kearney, NE 68845 .... (308) 236–7473
115 Railway Street, Suite C102, Scottsbluff, NE 69361 .... (308) 632–6032

* * *

DEB FISCHER, Republican, of Valentine, NE; born in Lincoln, NE, March 1, 1951; education: B.S., University of Nebraska-Lincoln, Lincoln, NE, 1988; professional: rancher; Senator in the Nebraska Unicameral, 2005–13; President of the Nebraska Association of School Boards; Commissioner on the Coordinating Commission for Post-Secondary Education; Valentine Rural High School Board of Education; awards: BILLD Fellow, Midwest Council of State Governments Bowhay Institute for Legislative Leadership, 2005; NRD Farm and Ranch Conservation Award, 1999; Nebraska Association of School Boards Lifetime Achievement Award, 1999; Nebraska Rural Community Schools Association Outstanding Board Member Award, 1998–99; Nebraska Cattlemen Environmental Stewardship Award, 1995; Rangeman's Award, Nebraska Section Society for Range Management, 1994; NRD State Grasslands Conservation Award, 1993; Kellogg Fellow, National Center for Food and Policy Research, Resources for the Future, Washington, DC, 1991; LEAD VIII Fellow, Nebraska Leadership Program, 1988–90; religion: Presbyterian; family, married: Bruce Fischer; three children, one grandchild; caucuses: Senate Western Caucus; Senate Rural Health Caucus; General Aviation Caucus; Republican High-Tech Task Force; National Guard Caucus; committees: Armed Services; Commerce, Science, and Transportation; Environment and Public Works; Indian Affairs; Small Business and Entrepreneurship; elected to the U.S. Senate on November 6, 2012.

Office Listings

http://fischer.senate.gov

383 Russell Senate Office Building, Washington, DC 20510 .... (202) 224–6551
Chief of Staff.—Mike Hybl. FAX: 228–1325
Legislative Director.—Stephen Higgins.
Communications Director.—Joe Hack.
Administrative Director.—Sherri Hupart.
11819 Miracle Hills Drive, Suite 205, Omaha, NE 68154 .... (402) 391–3411
State Director.—Dusty Vaughan. FAX: 391–4725
440 North 8th Street, Suite 120, Lincoln, NE 68508 .... (402) 441–4600
FAX: 476–8753
1110 Circle Drive, Suite 400, Scottsbluff, NE 69361 .... (308) 636–6344

REPRESENTATIVES

FIRST DISTRICT

JEFF FORTENBERRY, Republican, of Lincoln, NE; born in Baton Rouge, LA, December 27, 1960; education: B.A., Louisiana State University, 1982; M.P.P., Georgetown University, Washington, DC, 1986; M. Div., Franciscan University, Steubenville, Ohio, 1996; professional: Lincoln City Council, 1997–2001; publishing executive; worked as economist; managed a public relations firm; congressional aide for the Senate Subcommittee on Intergovernmental Relations; family: married to Celeste Gregory; children: five; committees: Appropriations; elected to the 109th Congress on November 2, 2004; reelected to each succeeding Congress.

Office Listings

http://www.fortenberry.house.gov twitter: @jefffortenberry
https://www.facebook.com/jefffortenberry

1514 Longworth House Office Building, Washington, DC 20515 .... (202) 225–4806
Chief of Staff.—Margaux Matter. FAX: 225–5686
Legislative Director.—Alan Feyerherm.
Press Secretary.—Jennifer Allen.
Scheduler.—Christine Capobianco.
301 South 13th Street, Suite 100, Lincoln, NE 68508 .... (402) 438–1598
629 North Broad Street, P.O. Box 377, Fremont, NE 68025 .... (402) 727–0888
125 South 4th Street, Suite 101, Norfolk, NE 68701 .... (402) 379–2064

Counties: Burt, Butler, Cass, Colfax, Cuming, Dodge, Lancaster, Madison, Otoe, Platte, Polk, Sarpy, Saunders, Seward, Stanton, Thurston, and Washington. Population (2010), 608,780.

ZIP Codes: 68001–05, 68007–09, 68014–20, 68023, 68025–26, 68029, 68031, 68033–34, 68036–42, 68044–45, 68047–48, 68050, 68055–58, 68061–68, 68070–73, 68112–13, 68122–23, 68133, 68142, 68147, 68152, 68157, 68301, 68304, 68307, 68313–14, 68317, 68320, 68324, 68329–31, 68333, 68336, 68339, 68343–44, 68346–47, 68349, 68358–60, 68364, 68366–68, 68372, 68379, 68382, 68402–05, 68407, 68409–10, 68413, 68417–19, 68421, 68423, 68428, 68430, 68434, 68438–39, 68443, 68446, 68448, 68454–56, 68460–63, 68465, 68501–10, 68512, 68514, 68516–17, 68520–24, 68526–29, 68531–32, 68542, 68583, 68588, 68601–02, 68621, 68624, 68626, 68629, 68631–35, 68640–44, 68647–49, 68651, 68653–54, 68658–59, 68661–62, 68664, 68666–67, 68669, 68701–02, 68715–16, 68733, 68748, 68752, 68758, 68768, 68779, 68781, 68784, 68788, 68791

* * *

SECOND DISTRICT

LEE TERRY, Republican, of Omaha, NE; born in Omaha, January 29, 1962; education: B.A., University of Nebraska, 1984; J.D., Creighton Law School, 1987; attorney; elected to the Omaha, NE, City Council, 1990–98; served as vice president and president, and on the audit, legislative, and cable television committees; religion: Christian; married: Robyn; children: Nolan, Ryan, and Jack; committees: Energy and Commerce; elected to the 106th Congress; reelected to each succeeding Congress.

Office Listings

http://www.leeterry.house.gov

2266 Rayburn House Office Building, Washington, DC 20515 .... (202) 225–4155
Chief of Staff.—Mark Anderson. FAX: 226–5452
Policy Director.—AT Johnston.
Executive Assistant.—Samantha Bryant.
Communications Director.—Larry Farnsworth.
11717 Burt Street, Suite 106, Omaha, NE 68154 .... (402) 397–9944
District Director.—Charles Isom.

Counties: Douglas, Sarpy (part). Cities: Bellevue, Bennington, Boys Town, Elkhorn, Gretna, La Vista, Omaha, Offutt AFB, Papillion, Plattsmouth, Ralston, Springfield, Valley, and Waterloo. Population (2010), 608,781.

ZIP Codes: 68005, 68007, 68010, 68022, 68028, 68046, 68056, 68064, 68069, 68101–14, 68116–20, 68122–24, 68127–28, 68130–35, 68137–39, 68142, 68144–45, 68147, 68152, 68154–55, 68157, 68164, 68175–76, 68178–80, 68182–83, 68197–98

* * *

THIRD DISTRICT

ADRIAN SMITH, Republican, of Gering, NE; born in Scotts Bluff, NE, December 19, 1970; education: graduated from Gering High School, Gering, NE, 1989; attended Liberty University,

Lynchburg, VA; 1989–90; B.S., University of Nebraska, 1993; professional: business owner; teacher; Gering, NE, city council, 1994–98; member of the Nebraska state legislature, 1999–2007; committees: Ways and Means; elected to the 110th Congress on November 7, 2006; reelected to each succeeding Congress.

Office Listings

http://adriansmith.house.gov

2241 Rayburn House Office Building, Washington, DC 20515 .... (202) 225–6435
Chief of Staff.—Monica Jirik. FAX: 225–0207
Legislative Director.—Josh Jackson.
Communications Director.—Rick VanMeter.
Director of Outreach and Strategic Planning (NE Schedule).—Jena Hoehne.
Scheduler.—Megan Boland.
416 Valley View Drive, Suite 600, Scottsbluff, NE 69361 .... (308) 633–6333
1811 West Second Street, Suite 275, Grand Island, NE 68803 .... (308) 384–3900

Counties: ADAMS, ANTELOPE, ARTHUR, BANNER, BLAINE, BOONE, BOX BUTTE, BOYD, BROWN, BUFFALO, CEDAR, CHASE, CHERRY, CHEYENNE, CLAY, CUSTER, DAKOTA, DAWES, DAWSON, DEUEL, DIXON, DUNDY, FILLMORE, FRANKLIN, FRONTIER, FURNAS, GAGE, GARDEN, GARFIELD, GOSPER, GRANT, GREELEY, HALL, HAMILTON, HARLAN, HAYES, HITCHCOCK, HOLT, HOOKER, HOWARD, JEFFERSON, JOHNSON, KEARNEY, KEITH, KEYA PAHA, KIMBALL, KNOX, LINCOLN, LOGAN, LOUP, MCPHERSON, MERRICK, MORRILL, NANCE, NEMAHA, NUCKOLLS, PAWNEE, PERKINS, PHELPS, PIERCE, RED WILLOW, RICHARDSON, ROCK, SALINE, SCOTTSBLUFF, SHERIDAN, SHERMAN, SIOUX, THAYER, THOMAS, VALLEY, WAYNE, WEBSTER, WHEELER, AND YORK. Population (2010), 608,438.

ZIP Codes: 60902, 68030, 68305, 68309–10, 68315, 68318, 68320–21, 68326, 68328, 68330, 68337, 68340, 68350, 68352, 68355, 68361–62, 68375, 68377, 68380, 68401, 68406, 68414–15, 68422, 68429, 68431, 68433, 68440, 68444–45, 68450, 68457, 68467, 68620, 68622, 68710–11, 68713, 68717–18, 68720, 68722–24, 68727–28, 68731, 68736, 68738, 68741–43, 68749, 68751, 68753, 68756, 68760–61, 68763, 68765–66, 68774, 68776, 68778, 68780, 68783, 68787, 68789–90, 68802, 68810, 68812, 68814, 68816, 68818, 68820–22, 68824–27, 68837–38, 68841–44, 68846–50, 68852–54, 68861–62, 68865, 68870–71, 68873, 68879, 68881, 68901, 68920, 68923, 68925–26, 68929, 68932–33, 68939–40, 68946, 68950, 68952, 68954, 68956, 68959, 68961, 68966, 68969–71, 68973, 68975–76, 69020–21, 69023, 69032, 69034, 69036–37, 69041–42, 69046, 69103, 69121, 69123, 69125, 69131–33, 69140–44, 69150–52, 69154, 69160, 69162, 69170, 69171, 69190, 69211, 69218–21, 69331, 69339, 69345–46, 69354, 69361, 69363, 69366–67, 69855

NEVADA

(Population 2010, 2,700,551)

SENATORS

HARRY REID, Democrat, of Searchlight, NV; born in Searchlight, December 2, 1939; education: graduated, Basic High School, Henderson, NV, 1957; associate degree, College of Southern Utah (now Southern Utah State College), 1959; B.S., Utah State University, Phi Kappa Phi, 1961; J.D., George Washington School of Law, Washington, DC, 1964; admitted to the Nevada State Bar in 1963, a year before graduating from law school; while attending law school, worked as a U.S. Capitol police officer; city attorney, Henderson, 1964–66; member and chairman, South Nevada Memorial Hospital Board of Trustees, 1967–69; elected: Nevada State Assembly, 1969–70; Lieutenant Governor, State of Nevada, 1970–74; served, executive committee, National Conference of Lieutenant Governors; chairman, Nevada Gaming Commission, 1977–81; member: Nevada State, Clark County and American Bar Associations; married the former Landra Gould in 1959; five children: Lana, Rory, Leif, Josh, and Key; elected to the 98th Congress on November 2, 1982, and reelected to the 99th Congress; Assistant Democratic Leader, 1998–2004; elected Democratic leader for the 109th Congress, and Majority leader for the 110th, 111th, 112th and 113th Congress; elected to the U.S. Senate on November 4, 1986; reelected to each succeeding Senate term.

Office Listings

http://reid.senate.gov

522 Hart Senate Office Building, Washington, DC 20510 .... (202) 224–3542
Chief of Staff.—David Krone. FAX: 224–7327
Deputy Chief of Staff.—David McCallum.
Executive Assistant.—Adelle Cruz.
Legislative Director.—Jason Unger.
600 East Williams Street, Room 302, Carson City, NV 89701 .... (775) 882–7343
State Director.—Mary Conelly.
333 Las Vegas Boulevard South, Suite 8016, Las Vegas, NV 89101 .... (702) 388–5020
Southern Nevada Director.—Rob Elliott.
400 South Virginia Street, Suite 902, Reno, NV 89501 .... (775) 686–5750
State Director.—Mary Conelly.

* * *

DEAN HELLER, Republican, of Carson City, NV; born in Castro Valley, CA, May 10, 1960; education: B.B.A., specializing in finance and securities analysis, University of Southern California, 1985; professional: institutional stockbroker and broker/trader on the Pacific Stock Exchange; Chief Deputy State Treasurer, Public Funds Representative; Nevada State Assemblyman, 1990–94; Secretary of State, 1994–2002; founding member of the Boys and Girls Club of Western Nevada Community College Foundation; married: Lynne Heller; children: Hillary, Harris, Drew, and Emmy; committees: Banking, Housing, and Urban Affairs; Commerce, Science, and Transportation; Energy and Natural Resources; Veterans' Affairs; Special Committee on Aging; elected to the 110th Congress on November 7, 2006, reelected to two succeeding Congresses, when he resigned to become a U.S. Senator; appointed May 3, 2011, to the U.S. Senate for the term ending January 3, 2013, to fill the vacancy caused by the resignation of John E. Ensign; took the oath of office on May 9, 2011; elected to a full term in the U.S. Senate on November 6, 2012.

Office Listings

http://Heller.Senate.gov

324 Hart Senate Office Building, Washington, DC 20510 .... (202) 224–6244
Chief of Staff.—Mac Abrams. FAX: 228–6753
Legislative Director.—Sarah Timoney Paul.
Press Secretary.—Michawn Rich.
Scheduler.—Corinne Zakzeski.
Communications Director.—Chandler Smith.
8930 West Sunset Road, Suite 230, Las Vegas, NV 89148 .... (702) 388–6605
Fax: 388–6501
Bruce Thompson Federal Building, 400 South Virginia Street, Suite 738, Reno, NV 89501 .... (775) 686–5770
Fax: 686–5729
3290 Idaho Street, Suite 2A, Elko, NV 89801 .... (775) 738–2001
Fax: 738–2004

REPRESENTATIVES

FIRST DISTRICT

DINA TITUS, Democrat, of Las Vegas, NV; born in Thomasville, Thomas County, GA, May 23, 1950; education: B.A., College of William and Mary, Williamsburg, VA., 1970; M.A., University of Georgia, Athens, GA, 1973; Ph.D., Florida State University, Tallahassee, FL, 1976; professor, University of Nevada, Las Vegas, NV, 1977–2011; member of Nevada State Senate, 1989–2008; minority leader of Nevada State Senate, 1993–2008; married: Dr. Thomas Wright; committees: Transportation and Infrastructure; Veterans' Affairs; elected to the 111th Congress; reelected to the 113th Congress on November 6, 2012.

Office Listings

http://www.titus.house.gov

401 Cannon House Office Building, Washington, DC 20515 .... (202) 225–5965
Chief of Staff.—Jay Gertsema. FAX: 225–3119
Legislative Director.—David Rosenbaum.
Communications Director.—Caitlin Teare.
Scheduler.—Joanne Rider.
550 East Charleston Boulevard, Las Vegas, NV 89104 .... (702) 220–9823
District Director.—Mike Naft. FAX: 220–9841

Counties: CLARK COUNTY (part). CITIES: Las Vegas, and North Las Vegas. Population (2010), 659,962.

ZIP Codes: 88901, 88905, 89002, 89004–06, 89009, 89011-12, 89014–16, 89019, 89028–29, 89039, 89044, 89046, 89052–54, 89074, 89077, 89105, 89113, 89117, 89118–20, 89122–23, 89134–35, 89137–41, 89144–45, 89147–48, 89157, 89159, 89161, 89163, 89178–79, 89183, 89195, 89199

* * *

SECOND DISTRICT

MARK E. AMODEI, Republican, of Carson City, NV; born in Carson City, June 12, 1958; education: B.A., University of Nevada, Reno, NV, 1980; J.D., University of Pacific, McGeorge School of Law, Sacramento, CA, 1983; professional: lawyer, Allison, MacKenzie et al., 1987–present; lawyer, United States Army Judge Advocate General Corps, 1983–87; Nevada State Assembly, 1996–98; Senator, Nevada State Senate, 1998–2010; President Pro Tempore, Nevada State Senate, 2003–08; member of Carson City Master Plan Advisory Committee; member of Education Commission of the States; vice chair of Governor's Task Force on Access to Public Health Care; member of Nevada Supreme Court's Committee on Court Funding; member of Tahoe Regional Planning Agency Legislative Oversight Committee; committees: Appropriations; elected by special election to the 112th Congress on September 13, 2011; reelected to the 113th Congress on November 6, 2012.

Office Listings

http://www.amodei.house.gov twitter: @markamodeinv2
https://www.facebook.com/markamodeinv2

222 Cannon House Office Building, Washington, DC 20515 .... (202) 225–6155
Chief of Staff.—Rick Goddard. FAX: 225–5679
905 Railroad Street, Suite 104 D, Elko, NV 89801 .... (775) 777–7705
FAX: 753–9984

5310 Kietzke Lane, Suite 103, Reno, NV 89511.

Counties: CARSON CITY, CHURCHILL, DOUGLAS, ELKO, HUMBOLDT, LANDER, LYON (part), PERSHING, STOREY, AND WASHOE. Population (2010), 679,147.

ZIP Codes: 89310, 89316, 89402–06, 89408, 89410–14, 89418–19, 89421, 89423–26, 89428–29, 89431, 89433–34, 89436, 89438–42, 89444–51, 89460, 89501–03, 89506, 89508–12, 89519, 89521, 89523, 89701–06, 89801, 89815, 89820–23, 89825–26, 89828, 89830–35, 89883

* * *

THIRD DISTRICT

JOSEPH HECK, Republican, of Henderson, NV; born in Queens, NY, October 30, 1961; education: B.A., Penn State University, 1984; D.O., Philadelphia College of Osteopathic Medicine, 1988; M.S.S., United States Army War College, Carlisle, PA, 2006; professional: colonel, U.S. Army Reserve; emergency room physician; president of emergency management consulting firm; Nevada State Senate 2004–05; religion: Roman Catholic; married: Lisa Heck; committees: Armed Services; Education and the Workforce; Permanent Select Committee on Intelligence; elected to the 112th Congress on November 2, 2010; reelected to the 113th Congress on November 6, 2012.

Office Listings

http://www.heck.house.gov

132 Cannon House Office Building, Washington, DC 20515 .... (202) 225–3252
Chief of Staff.—Greg Facchiano. FAX: 225–2185
Executive Assistant.—Caitlin Callahan.
Legislative Director.—James Langenderfer.
Communications Director.—Greg Lemon.
8485 West Sunset Road, Suite 300, Las Vegas, NV 89113 .... (702) 387–4941
District Director.—Keith Hughes.

Counties: CLARK COUNTY (part). Population (2010), 675,138.

ZIP Codes: 88901, 88905, 89002, 89004–06, 89009, 89011–12, 89014–16, 89019, 89028–29, 89039, 89044, 89046, 89052–54, 89074, 89077, 89105, 89113, 89117–20, 89122–23, 89134–35, 89137–41, 89144–45, 89147

* * *

FOURTH DISTRICT

STEVEN HORSFORD, Democrat, of North Las Vegas, NV; born in Las Vegas, NV, April 29, 1973; education: Attended University of Nevada, Reno; professional: CEO, Culinary Training Academy; member of the Nevada State Senate, 2004–12; majority leader, Nevada State Senate, 2009–12; religion: Baptist; married: Dr. Sonya Horsford; caucuses: Congressional Black Caucus; Men's Health Caucus; I–11 Caucus; Congressional Progressive Caucus; Black Men and Boys Caucus; Diabetes Caucus; committees: Homeland Security, Natural Resources, Oversight and Government Reform; elected to the 113th Congress on November 6, 2012.

Office Listings

http://www.horsford.house.gov

1330 Longworth House Office Building, Washington, DC 20515 .... (202) 225–9894
Chief of Staff.—Rodney Emery. FAX: 225–9783
Legislative Director.—John Brodtke.
Communications Director.—Tim Hogan.
Scheduler.—Marian Williams.
2250 Las Vegas Boulevard North, Suite 500, North Las Vegas, NV 89030 .... (702) 802–4500
District Director.—Edith Fernandez.

Counties: CLARK COUNTY (most of the northern part), Esmeralda, Lincoln, Lyon (part), Mineral, Nye, White Pine. Population (2010) 680,935.

ZIP Codes: 89001, 89003, 89007–08, 89010, 89013–14, 89017–18, 89020–23, 89025, 89027, 89030–32, 89034, 89040–43, 89045, 89047–49, 89060–61, 89081, 89084–86, 89101, 89103, 89106–10, 89115, 89124, 89128–31, 89134–35, 89142–43, 89149, 89156, 89158, 89161, 89166, 89191, 89301, 89310–11, 89314–19, 89409, 89415, 89420, 89422, 89427, 89430, 89444, 89447, 89833, 89883

NEW HAMPSHIRE

(Population 2010, 1,316,470)

SENATORS

JEANNE SHAHEEN, Democrat, of Madbury, NH; born in Saint Charles, MO, January 28, 1947; education: graduated, Selinsgrove Area High School, Selinsgrove, PA, 1965; B.A., Shippensburg University, Shippensburg, PA, 1969; M.S.S., University of Mississippi, 1973; professional: high school teacher; co-owner of a small retail business; consultant; New Hampshire State Senator; Governor of New Hampshire; Director of Harvard's Institute of Politics; married: William Shaheen; three children: Stefany, Stacey, and Molly; Commission on Security and Cooperation in Europe; committees: Appropriations; Armed Services; Foreign Relations; Small Business and Entrepreneurship; elected to the 111th U.S. Senate on November 4, 2008.

Office Listings

http://shaheen.senate.gov

520 Hart Senate Office Building, Washington, DC 20510 .... (202) 224–2841
Chief of Staff.—Maura Keefe.
Deputy Chief of Staff.—Justin Burkhardt.
Legislative Director.—Brian McKeon.
Communications Director.—Shripal Shah.
Scheduler.—Jennifer MacLellan.
1589 Elm Street, Suite 3, Manchester, NH 03101 .... (603) 647–7500
60 Main Street, Nashua, NH 03060 .... (603) 883–0196
340 Central Avenue, Suite 205, Dover, NH 03820 .... (603) 750–3004
50 Opera House Square, Claremont, NH 03743 .... (603) 542–4872
961 Main Street, Berlin, NH 03570 .... (603) 752–6300
12 Gilbo Avenue, Suite C, Keene, NH 03431 .... (603) 358–6604

* * *

KELLY AYOTTE, Republican, of Nashua, NH; born in Nashua, NH, June 27, 1968; education: graduated Nashua High School, 1986; B.A., Pennsylvania State University, University Park, PA, 1990; J.D., Villanova University School of Law, Villanova, PA, 1993; professional: lawyer; married: Lt. Col. Joseph Daley; two children; committees: Armed Services; Budget; Commerce, Science, and Transportation; Homeland Security and Governmental Affairs; Special Committee on Aging; elected to the 112th U.S. Senate on November 2, 2010.

Office Listings

http://ayotte.senate.gov

144 Russell Senate Office Building, Washington, DC 20510 .... (202) 224–3324
Chief of Staff.—John Easton. FAX: 224–4952
Administrative Director.—Debra Jarrett.
Legislative Director.—Adam Hechavarria.
Communications Director.—Jeff Grappone.
Scheduler.—Lauren Spivey.
1200 Elm Street, Suite 2, Manchester, NH 03101 .... (603) 622–7979
FAX: 622–0422
144 Main Street, Nashua, NH 03060 .... (603) 880–3335
14 Manchester Square, Suite 140, Portsmouth, NH 03801 .... (603) 436–7161
19 Pleasant Street, Suite 13B, Berlin, NH 03570 .... (603) 752–7702

REPRESENTATIVES

FIRST DISTRICT

CAROL SHEA-PORTER, Democrat, of Rochester, NH; born in New York City, NY, December 2, 1952; graduated from Oyster River High School, Durham, NH, 1971; B.A., University of New Hampshire, Durham, NH, 1975; M.P.A., University of New Hampshire, Durham, NH, 1979; professional: social worker; professor; married: Gene Porter; two children; committees: Armed Services; Natural Resources; elected to the 113th Congress on November 6, 2012.

Office Listings

http://shea-porter.house.gov

1530 Longworth House Office Building, Washington, DC 20515 .... (202) 225–5456

Chief of Staff.—Naomi Andrews. FAX: 225–5822
Legislative Director.—Matthew Vallone.
Press Secretary.—Ben Wakana.
Scheduler.—Emily Meneer.
33 Lowell Street, Manchester, NH 03101 .... (603) 641–9536
20 North Main Street, Rochester, NH 03867 .... (603) 335–7700

Counties: BELKNAP (part), CARROLL, ROCKINGHAM (part), STAFFORD. CITIES: Bedford, Campton, Goffstown, Hooksett, Manchester, and Merrimack. Population (2012), 657,984.

ZIP Codes: 03031–32, 03034, 03036, 03038, 03042, 03044–45, 03053–54, 03077, 03101–06, 03109–10, 03218, 03220, 03223, 03225–27, 03237, 03246, 03249, 03253–54, 03256, 03259, 03261, 03269, 03276, 03291, 03801, 03809–20, 03823–27, 03830, 03832–33, 03835–42, 03844–62, 03864–65, 03867–75, 03878, 03882–87, 03890, 03894

* * *

SECOND DISTRICT

ANN MCLANE KUSTER, Democrat, of Hopkinton, NH; born in Concord, NH, September 5, 1956; education: B.A., Dartmouth College, Hanover, NH, 1978; J.D., Georgetown University Law Center, Washington, DC, 1984; professional: consultant and owner Newfound Strategies LLC, lawyer and partner Rath, Young and Pignatelli; married: Brad Kuster; children: Zach and Travis; committees: Agriculture; Small Business; Veterans' Affairs; elected to the 113th Congress on November 6, 2012.

Office Listings

http://kuster.house.gov

137 Cannon Building, Washington, DC 20515 .... (202) 225–5206
Chief of Staff.—Abby Curran Horrell. FAX: 225–2946
Legislative Director.—Blake Anderson.
Scheduler.—Corey Garry.
Press Secretary.—Rob Friedlander.
18 North Main Street, Concord, NH 03301 .... (603) 226–1002
District Director.—Sean Downey FAX: 226–1010
70 East Pearl Street, Nashua, NH 03060 .... (603) 595–2006
FAX: 595–2016
107 Glessner Road, Bethlehem, NH 03574 .... (603) 444–7700

Counties: BELKNAP (part), CHESHIRE, COOS, GRAFTON (part), HILLSBOROUGH (part), MERRIMACK (part), ROCKINGHAM (part), SULLIVAN. Population (2013), 658,237.

ZIP Codes: 03031, 03033–34, 03037–38, 03043, 03045–49, 03051–52, 03054–55, 03057, 03060–64, 03070–71, 03073, 03076, 03079, 03082, 03084, 03086–87, 03110, 03215–17, 03220–24, 03226, 03229–31, 03233–35, 03237–38, 03240–45, 03251, 03253, 03255–58, 03260–64, 03266, 03268, 03272–73, 03275–76, 03278–82, 03284–85, 03287, 03293, 03301–05, 03307, 03431, 03435, 03440–52, 03455–58, 03461–62, 03464–70, 03561, 03570, 03574–76, 03579–86, 03588–90, 03592–93, 03595, 03597–98, 03601–05, 03607–09, 03740–41, 03743, 03745–46, 03748–56, 03765–66, 03768–71, 03773–74, 03777, 03779–82, 03784–85, 03811, 03825, 03841

NEW JERSEY

(Population 2010 8,791,894)

SENATORS

ROBERT MENENDEZ, Democrat, of North Bergen, NJ; born in New York City, NY, January 1, 1954; education: graduated, Union Hill High School, 1972; B.A., St. Peter's College, Jersey City, NJ, 1976; J.D., Rutgers Law School, Newark, NJ, 1979; professional: attorney; elected to the Union City Board of Education, 1974–78; admitted to the New Jersey Bar, 1980; mayor of Union City, 1986–92; member: New Jersey Assembly, 1987–91; New Jersey State Senate, Alliance Civic Association; U.S. House of Representatives 1993–2006; vice chair, Democratic Caucus, 1998–99; chair, Democratic Caucus, 2003–06; chair, Democratic Senatorial Campaign Committee, 2009–10; children: Alicia and Robert; committees: chair, Foreign Relations; Finance; elected on November 3, 1992 to the 103rd Congress; reelected to each succeeding Congress; appointed to the U.S. Senate on January 17, 2006 by Governor Jon S. Corzine; elected to the 110th Congress for a full Senate term on November 7, 2006; reelected to the U.S. Senate on November 6, 2012.

Office Listings

http://menendez.senate.gov

528 Hart Senate Office Building, Washington, DC 20510 .... (202) 224–4744
Chief of Staff.—Danny O'Brien. FAX: 228–2197
Deputy Chief of Staff.—Karissa Willhite.
Administrative Director.—Robert Kelly.
One Gateway Center, 11th Floor, Newark, NJ 07102 .... (973) 645–3030
208 Whitehorse Pike, Suite 18, Barrington, NJ 08007–1322 .... (856) 757–5353

* * *

CORY A. BOOKER, Democrat, of Newark, NJ; born in Washington, DC, April 27, 1969; education: graduated, Northern Valley Regional High School at Old Tappan, 1987; B.A., political science, Stanford University, 1991; M.A., sociology, Stanford University, 1992; Oxford University Rhodes Scholar, 1994; J.D., Yale Law School, 1997; professional: staff attorney, Urban Justice Center, New York, NY, 1997; member, Newark City Council, 1998–2002; partner, Booker, Rabinowitz, Trenk, Lubetkin, Tully, DiPasquale & Webster, P.C., 2002-2006; mayor, City of Newark, 2006–13; religion: Baptist; committees: Commerce, Science, and Transportation; Environment and Public Works; Small Business and Entrepreneurship; elected to the U.S. Senate on October 16, 2013 to fill the vacancy caused by the death of Frank R. Lautenberg.

Office Listings

http://www.booker.senate.gov twitter: @senbookerofc

141 Hart Senate Office Building, Washington, DC 20510 .... (202) 224–3224
Chief of Staff.—Louisa Terrell. FAX: 224–8378
Scheduler.—Unjin Lee.
Communications Director.—Kevin Griffis.
Gateway One, 11–43 Raymond Plaza West, Suite 2300, Newark, NJ 07102 .... (973) 639–8700
One Port Center, 2 Riverside Drive, Suite 505, Camden, NJ 08101 .... (856) 338–8922

REPRESENTATIVES

FIRST DISTRICT

VACANT

Counties: BURLINGTON COUNTY. CITIES AND TOWNSHIPS: Maple Shade Township, Palmyra, Riverton. CAMDEN COUNTY. CITIES AND TOWNSHIPS: Audubon, Audubon Park, Barrington, Bellmawr, Berlin, Berlin Township, Brooklawn, Camden, Chesilhurst, Clementon, Collingswood, Gibbsboro, Gloucester City, Gloucester Township, Haddon Heights, Haddon Township, Hi-Nella, Laurel Springs, Lawnside, Lindenwold, Magnolia, Merchantville, Mt. Ephraim, Oaklyn, Pennsauken Township, Pine Hill, Pine Valley, Runnemede, Somerdale, Stratford, Tavistock, Voorhees Township, Winslow Township, Woodlynne. GLOUCESTER COUNTY. CITIES AND TOWNSHIPS: Deptford, E. Greenwich, Greenwich, Logan Township,

Mantua, Monroe, National Park, Paulsboro, Washington Township, Wenonah, West Deptford Township, Westville, Woodbury Heights, and Woodbury. Population (2010), 668,011.

ZIP Codes: 08002–04, 08007, 08009, 08012, 08014, 08020–21, 08026–33, 08037, 08043, 08045, 08049, 08051–52, 08056, 08059, 08061–63, 08065–66, 08077–78, 08080–81, 08083–86, 08089–91, 08093–94, 08096–97, 08099, 08101–105, 08107–10

* * *

SECOND DISTRICT

FRANK A. LOBIONDO, Republican, of Ventnor, NJ; born in Bridgeton, NJ, May 12, 1946; education: graduated, B.S., St. Joseph's University, Philadelphia, PA, 1968; professional: operations manager, LoBiondo Brothers Motor Express, 1968–94; Cumberland County Freeholder, 1985–87; New Jersey General Assembly, 1988–94; awards and honors: honorary Coast Guard Chief Petty Officer; Board of Directors, Young Men's Christian Association; Honorary Rotarian; Taxpayer Hero Award; Watchdog of the Treasury Award; Veterans Foreign Wars ''Outstanding Federal Legislator of the Year'' Award; Humane Society of the United States-Humane Champion Award; National Association of Community Health Centers—Distinguished Community Health Superhero; Super Friend of Seniors Award; two-time winner of the Friend of the National Parks Award; March of Dimes FDR Award for community service; 2001 President's Award, Literacy Volunteers of America, NJ, Inc.; committees: Armed Services; Transportation and Infrastructure; Permanent Select Committee on Intelligence; elected to the 104th Congress; reelected to each succeeding Congress.

Office Listings

http://www.house.gov/lobiondo

2427 Rayburn House Office Building, Washington, DC 20515 .... (202) 225–6572
Chief of Staff.—Mary Annie Harper. FAX: 225–3318
Executive Assistant.—Alycia Tomaino.
5914 Main Street, Mays Landing, NJ 08330 .... (609) 625–5008
District Director.—Linda Hinckley.

Counties: BURLINGTON (part). CITIES AND TOWNSHIPS: Bass River Washington. Camden County (part). ATLANTIC COUNTY. CITIES AND TOWNSHIPS: Absecon, Atlantic City, Brigantine, Buena, Cardiff, Collings Lake, Cologne, Corbin City, Dorothy, Egg Harbor, Estell Manor, Galloway, Hammonton, Landisville, Leeds Point, Linwood, Longport, Margate, Mays Landing, Milmay, Minotola, Mizpah, Newtonville, Northfield, Oceanville, Pleasantville, Pomona, Port Republic, Richland, Somers Point, Ventnor. CAPE MAY COUNTY. CITIES AND TOWNSHIPS: Avalon, Bargaintown, Beesley's, Belleplain, Burleigh, Cape May, Cape May C.H., Cape May Point, Cold Springs, Del Haven, Dennisville, Dias Creek, Eldora, Erma, Fishing Creek, Goshen, Green Creek, Greenfield, Marmora, Ocean City, Ocean View, Rio Grande, Sea Isle, South Dennis, South Seaville, Stone Harbor, Strathmere, Tuckahoe, Villas, Whitesboro, Wildwood, Woodbine. CUMBERLAND COUNTY. CITIES AND TOWNSHIPS: Bridgeton, Cedarville, Centerton, Deerfield, Delmont, Dividing Creek, Dorchester, Elwood, Fairton, Fortescue, Greenwich, Heislerville, Hopewell, Leesburg, Mauricetown, Millville, Newport, Port Elizabeth, Port Norris, Rosenhayn, Shiloh, Vineland. GLOUCESTER COUNTY (part). CITIES AND TOWNSHIPS: Clayton, East Greenwich Ewan, Franklinville, Glassboro, Harrisonville, Malaga, Mantua, Mickleton, Mullica Hill, Newfield, Pitman, Richwood, Sewell, Swedesboro, Williamstown, Woodbury. OCEAN COUNTY (part). CITIES AND TOWNSHIPS: Barnegat Light, Harvey Cedars, Stafford Twp, Eagleswood, Tuckerton, Little Egg Harbor, Loveladies, Surf City, Ship Bottom, Long Beach Twp, Beach Haven. SALEM COUNTY. CITIES AND TOWNSHIPS: Alloway, Carney's Point, Daretown, Deepwater, Elmer, Elsinboro, Hancocks Bridge, Monroeville, Norma, Pedricktown, Penns Grove, Pennsville, Quinton, Salem, and Woodstown. Population (2010), 736,397.

ZIP Codes: 08001, 08004, 08006–09, 08019–20, 08023, 08025, 08028, 08037–39, 08050–51, 08056, 08061–62, 08067, 08069–72, 08074, 08079–80, 08085, 08087–89, 08092, 08094, 08098, 08201–05, 08210, 08212–15, 08217–21, 08223–26, 08230–32, 08234, 08240–48, 08250–52, 08260, 08270, 08302, 08310–24, 08326–30, 08332, 08340–50, 08352–53, 08360–62, 08401–04, 08406

* * *

THIRD DISTRICT

JON RUNYAN, Republican, of Mt. Laurel, NJ; born in Flint, MI, November 27, 1973; education: graduated from Carman-Ainsworth High School, Flint, MI; attended University of Michigan, Ann Arbor, MI, 1992–95; attended University of Pennsylvania, Wharton School of Business; professional: football player, NFL Philadelphia Eagles; television commentator; married: Loretta; committees: Armed Services; Natural Resources; Veterans' Affairs; elected to the 112th Congress on November 2, 2010; reelected to the 113th Congress on November 6, 2012.

Office Listings

http://www.runyan.house.gov

1239 Longworth House Office Building, Washington, DC 20515 .... (202) 225–4765

Chief of Staff.—Stacy Barton. FAX: 225–0778
4167 Church Road, Mt. Laurel, NJ 08054 .... (856) 780–6436
District Director.—Kristin Antonello. FAX: 780–6440
600 Mule Road, Unit 6, Toms River, NJ 08757 .... (732) 279–6013
FAX: 279–6062

Counties: BURLINGTON (part), OCEAN (part). Population (2010), 732,658.

ZIP Codes: 08005–06, 08008, 08010–11, 08015–16, 08019, 08022, 08036, 08041–42, 08046, 08048, 08050, 08052–55, 08057, 08060, 08064–65, 08068, 08073, 08075, 08077, 08087–88, 08092, 08501, 08505, 08511, 08515, 08518, 08554, 08562, 08610, 08620, 08640–41, 08701, 08721–24, 08731–32, 08734–35, 08738, 08740–42, 08751–53, 08755, 08757–59

* * *

FOURTH DISTRICT

CHRISTOPHER H. SMITH, Republican, of Robbinsville, NJ; born in Rahway, NJ, March 4, 1953; attended Worcester College, England, 1974; B.A., Trenton State College, 1975; businessman; executive director, New Jersey Right to Life Committee, Inc., 1976–78; religion: Catholic; married to the former Marie Hahn, 1977; four adult children; two grandchildren; caucuses: chairman, Commission on Security and Cooperation in Europe; co-chair, Congressional Pro-Life Caucus; Congressional Human Trafficking Caucus; Bipartisan; Bicameral Congressional Task Force on Alzheimer's Disease; Coalition on Autism Research and Education (C.A.R.E.), Lyme Disease Caucus; Bi-Partisan Coalition for Combating Anti-Semitism; former chairman, House Veterans' Affairs Committee; co-chairman, Congressional-Executive Commission on China; committees: Foreign Affairs; elected to the 97th Congress, November 4, 1980; reelected to each succeeding Congress.

Office Listings

http://www.house.gov/chrissmith

2373 Rayburn House Office Building, Washington, DC 20515 .... (202) 225–3765
Chief of Staff.—Mary McDermott Noonan. FAX: 225–7768
112 Village Center Drive, 2nd Floor, Freehold, NJ 07728 .... (732) 780–3035
4573 South Broad Street, First Floor, Hamilton, NJ 08619 .... (609) 585–7878
405 Route 539, Plumsted, NJ 08514 .... (609) 286–2571

Counties: MERCER. MUNICIPALITIES: Hamilton and Robbinsville. MONMOUTH. MUNICIPALITIES: Allentown, Avon-by-the-Sea, Belmar, Bradley Beach, Brielle, Colts Neck, Eatontown, Englishtown, Fair Haven, Farmingdale, Freehold Borough, Freehold Twp, Homdel, Howell, Lake Como, Little Silver, Manalapan, Manasquan, Middletown (part), Millstone, Neptune City, Neptune Twp, Ocean Twp, Red Bank, Roosevelt, Rumson, Sea Girt, Shrewsbury Twp, Spring Lake, Spring Lake Heights, Tinton Falls, Upper Freehold, and Wall. OCEAN. MUNICIPALITIES: Bay Head, Jackson, Lakehurst, Lakewood, Manchester, Plumsted, Pt. Pleasant (part), and Pt. Pleasant Beach. Population (2010), 732,657.

ZIP Codes: 07701–04, 07717, 07719–20, 07722, 07724, 07726–28, 07731, 07733, 07739, 07748, 07753, 07755, 07760, 07762, 08501, 08510, 08514, 08527, 08533, 08555, 08690–91, 08701, 08730, 08733, 08736, 08742, 08750, 08759, 08844

* * *

FIFTH DISTRICT

SCOTT GARRETT, Republican, of Wantage Township, NJ; born in Englewood, NJ, July 7, 1959; education: High Point Regional High School, 1977; B.A., Montclair State University, 1981; J.D., Rutgers University Law School, 1984; professional: attorney; counsel attorney with law firm of Sellar Richardson; organizations: Big Brothers, Big Sisters; Sussex County Chamber of Commerce; Sussex County Board of Agriculture; New Jersey State Assemblyman, 1990–2002; family: married to Mary Ellen; children: Jennifer and Brittany; committees: Budget; Financial Services; elected to the 108th Congress on November 5, 2002; reelected to each succeeding Congress.

Office Listings

http://www.garrett.house.gov twitter: @repgarrett https://www.facebook.com/repscottgarrett

2232 Russell House Office Building, Washington, DC 20515 .... (202) 225–4465
Chief of Staff.—Amy Smith. FAX: 225–9048
Legislative Director.—Andrew Shaw.
Communications Director.—Maggie Seidel.
266 Harristown Road, Suite 104, Glen Rock, NJ 07452 .... (201) 444–5454

District Director.—Rob Pettet.
83 Spring Street, Suite 302A, Newton, NJ 07860 .... (973) 300–2000

Counties: BERGEN (part), PASSAIC (part), SUSSEX (part), WARREN (part). Population (2010), 731,055.

ZIP Codes: 07401, 07410, 07416–19, 07422–23, 07428, 07430, 07432, 07436, 07446, 07450–52, 07456, 07458, 07461–63, 07466, 07480–81, 07495, 07508, 07601–04, 07607, 07620–22, 07624, 07626–28, 07630–31, 07640–49, 07652–53, 07656, 07660–61, 07663, 07666, 07675–77, 07820–23, 07825–27, 07832–33, 07838–39, 07844, 07846, 07848, 07851, 07855, 07860, 07863, 07865, 07874–75, 07877, 07879–80, 07882, 07890

* * *

SIXTH DISTRICT

FRANK PALLONE, JR., Democrat, of Long Branch, NJ; born in Long Branch, October 30, 1951; education: B.A., Middlebury College, Middlebury, VT, 1973; M.A., Fletcher School of Law and Diplomacy, 1974; J.D., Rutgers University School of Law, 1978; member of the bar: Florida, New York, Pennsylvania, and New Jersey; attorney, Marine Advisory Service; assistant professor, Cook College, Rutgers University Sea Grant Extension Program; counsel, Monmouth County, NJ, Protective Services for the Elderly; instructor, Monmouth College; Long Branch City Council, 1982–88; New Jersey State Senate, 1983–88; married the former Sarah Hospodor, 1992; committees: Energy and Commerce; Natural Resources; elected to the 100th Congress, by special election, on November 8, 1988, to fill the vacancy caused by the death of James J. Howard; reelected to each succeeding Congress.

Office Listings

http://www.house.gov/pallone www.facebook.com/repfrankpallone twitter: @reppallone

237 Cannon House Office Building, Washington, DC 20515 .... (202) 225–4671
Chief of Staff.—Jeff Carroll. FAX: 225–9665
Legislative Director.—Tiffany Guarascio.
Communications Director.—Raymond Zaccaro.
District Director.—Janice Fuller.
504 Broadway, Long Branch, NJ 07740 .... (732) 571–1140
67/69 Church Street, Kilmer Square, New Brunswick, NJ 08901–1242 .... (732) 249–8892

Counties: MIDDLESEX COUNTY. CITIES AND TOWNSHIPS: Avenel, Carteret, Colonia, Edison, Fords, Highland Park, Hopelawn, Iselin, Keasbey, Menlo Park Terrace, Metuchen, New Brunswick, Old Bridge, Perth Amboy, Piscataway, Port Reading, Sayreville, Sewaren, South Amboy, South Plainfield, and Woodbridge. MONMOUTH COUNTY. CITIES AND TOWNSHIPS: Aberdeen, Allenhurst, Asbury Park, Atlantic Highlands, Deal, Hazlet, Highlands, Interlaken, Keansburg, Keyport, Loch Arbor, Long Branch, Marlboro, Matawan, Middletown, Monmouth Beach, Oceanport, Sea Bright, Union Beach, and West Long Branch. Population (2010), 732,657.

ZIP Codes: 07001, 07008, 07060, 07064–65, 07067, 07077, 07080, 07095, 07701, 07703, 07711–12, 07716, 07718, 07721–23, 07726, 07728, 07730, 07732–35, 07737, 07740, 07746–48, 07750–53, 07755, 07757–58, 07760, 07764–65, 08812, 08817–18, 08820, 08830, 08832, 08837, 08840, 08846, 08854–55, 08857, 08859, 08861–63, 08871–73, 08879, 08899, 08901–04, 08906, 08933, 08989

* * *

SEVENTH DISTRICT

LEONARD LANCE, Republican, of Clinton Township, NJ; born in Easton, PA, June 25, 1952; education: B.A., Lehigh University, Bethlehem, PA, 1974; J.D., Vanderbilt University Law School, Memphis, TN, 1977; M.P.A., Woodrow Wilson School of Public and International Affairs at Princeton University, Princeton, NJ, 1982; professional: judicial clerk; lawyer, private practice; member, New Jersey State Assembly, 1991–2002; member, New Jersey State Senate, 2002–09; minority leader, New Jersey State Senate, 2004–08; Congressional Diabetes Caucus; Congressional Wildlife Caucus; co-chair, House Republican Israel Caucus; House Cancer Care Working Group; Passenger Rail Caucus; religion: Roman Catholic; committees: Energy and Commerce; elected to the 111th Congress on November 4, 2008; reelected to each succeeding Congress.

Office Listings

http://www.lance.house.gov

133 Cannon House Office Building, Washington, DC 20515 .... (202) 225–5361
Chief of Staff.—Todd Mitchell. FAX: 225–9460
Legislative Director.—Jon Taets.
Scheduler.—Nick Bahnsen.
Communications Director.—John Byers.
425 North Avenue East, Westfield, NJ 07090 .... (908) 518–7733

361 Route 31, Unit 1400, Flemington, NJ 08822 .... (908) 789–6900
District Director.—Amanda Woloshen.

Counties: UNION COUNTY. MUNICIPALITIES: Berkeley Heights, Clark, Cranford, Garwood, Kenilworth, Linden, Mountainside, New Providence, Springfield, Summit, Union, Westfield, Winfield. HUNTERDON COUNTY. MUNICIPALITIES: Alexandria, Bethlehem, Bloomsbury, Califon, Clinton Township, Clinton, Delaware Township, East Amwell, Flemington, Frenchtown, Glen Gardner, Hampton, High Bridge, Holland, Kingwood, Lambertville, Lebanon, Lebanon Township, Milford, Oldwick, Raritan, Readington, Whitehouse Station, Stockton, Tewksbury, Union, West Amwell. SOMERSET COUNTY. MUNICIPALITIES: Bedminster, Bernards, Bernardsville, Branchburg, Bridgewater, Far Hills, Green Brook, Hillsborough, Montgomery Township, Millstone, North Plainfield, Peapack-Gladstone, Raritan, Rocky Hill, Somerville, Warren, and Watchung. MORRIS COUNTY. MUNICIPALITIES: Chester, Dover, Long Hill, Mine Hill, Mount Arlington, Mount Olive, Netcong, Roxbury, Washington, Wharton. WARREN COUNTY. MUNICIPALITIES: Alpha, Franklin, Greenwich, Harmony, Lopatcong, and Phillipsburg. ESSEX COUNTY. MUNICIPALITIES: Millburn. Population (2010), 733,961.

ZIP Codes: 07016, 07027, 07033, 07036, 07041, 07059–60, 07066, 07069, 07081, 07083, 07090, 07092, 07416, 07676, 07801–03, 07806, 07828, 07830, 07836, 07856–57, 07869, 07885, 07901, 07920–22, 07930–31, 07933–34, 07974, 07977–78, 08323, 08502, 08504, 08530, 08540, 08551, 08553, 08557–59, 08801–04, 08807, 08809, 08812, 08821–22, 08825–27, 08829, 08833, 08836, 08844, 08848, 08853, 08858, 08865, 08867, 08869–70, 08876, 08889

* * *

EIGHTH DISTRICT

ALBIO SIRES, Democrat, of West New York, NJ; born in Bejucal, Provincia de la Habana, Cuba, January 26, 1951; education: graduated, Memorial High School; B.A., St. Peter's College, 1974; M.A., Middlebury College, Middlebury, VT, 1985; studied Spanish in Madrid, Spain; professional: businessman, teacher; part-owner, A.M. Title Agency, Union Township; mayor, West New York, NJ, 1995–2006; member: New Jersey House, 1999–2006; speaker, New Jersey House, 2002–2005; family: wife, Adrienne; stepdaughter, Tara Kole; committees: Foreign Affairs; Transportation and Infrastructure; elected to the 109th Congress by special election to fill the vacancy caused by the resignation of Robert Menendez; elected to the 110th Congress; reelected to each succeeding Congress.

Office Listings

http://www.sires.house.gov

2342 Rayburn House Office Building, Washington, DC 20515 .... (202) 225–7919
Chief of Staff.—Gene Martorony. FAX: 226–0792
Administrative Director / Scheduler.—Judi Wolford.
Legislative Director.—Kaylan Koszela.
121 Newark Avenue, Suite 200, Jersey City, NJ 07302 .... (201) 309–0301
Communications Director.—Erica Daughtrey. FAX: 309–0384
Bayonne City Hall, 630 Avenue C, Room 9, Bayonne, NJ 07002 .... (201) 823–2900
5500 Palisades Avenue, Suite A, West New York, NJ 07093 .... (201) 558–0800
800 Anna Street, Elizabeth, NJ 07201 .... (908) 820–0692
FAX: 820–0694

Counties: ESSEX (part), BERGEN (PART), HUDSON (part), UNION (part). CITIES AND TOWNSHIPS: Bayonne, Belleville, East Newark, Elizabeth, Fairview, Guttenberg, Harrison, Hoboken, Jersey City, Kearny, Newark, North Bergen, Union City, Weehawken, West New York. Population (2010), 732,658.

ZIP Codes: 07002, 07022, 07029–30, 07032, 07036, 07047 (part), 07086–87, 07093, 07097, 07099, 07101–02, 07104–05, 07107, 07109, 07114, 07184, 07188–89, 07191–93, 07195, 07198–99, 07201–02, 07206–08, 07302–08, 07310–11, 07399

* * *

NINTH DISTRICT

BILL PASCRELL, JR., Democrat, of Paterson, NJ; born in Paterson, January 25, 1937; education: B.A., journalism, and M.A., philosophy, Fordham University; veteran, U.S. Army and Army Reserves; professional: educator; elected Minority Leader Pro Tempore, New Jersey General Assembly, 1988–96; Mayor of Paterson, 1990–96; named Mayor of the Year by bipartisan NJ Conference of Mayors, 1996; started Paterson's first Economic Development Corporation; married the former Elsie Marie Botto; three children: William III, Glenn, and David; committees: Budget; Ways and Means; elected to the 105th Congress; reelected to each succeeding Congress.

Office Listings

http://www.pascrell.house.gov https://www.facebook.com/pascrell
twitter: @billpascrell

2370 Rayburn House Office Building, Washington, DC 20515 .... (202) 225–5751

Chief of Staff.—Ben Rich. FAX: 225–5782
Deputy Chief of Staff.—Assad Akhter.
Legislative Director.—Arthur Mandel.
Legislative Assistant.—Ian McTiernan.
200 Federal Plaza, Suite 500, Paterson, NJ 07505 .... (201) 523–5152
Communications Director.—Thomas A. Pietrykoski.

Counties: BERGEN COUNTY. CITIES: Carlstadt, Cliffside Park, Cresskill, East Rutherford, Edgewater, Elmwood Park, Englewood, Englewood Cliffs, Fort Lee, Garfield, Hasbrouck Heights, Leonia, Little Ferry, Lyndhurst, Moonachie, North Arlington, Palisades Park, Ridgefield, Ridgefield Park, Rutherford, Saddle Brook, South Hackensack, Teaneck (part), Tenafly, Teterboro, Wallington, Wood-Ridge. HUDSON COUNTY, CITIES: Kearny (part), Secacus. PASSAIC COUNTY, CITIES: Clifton, Haledon, Hawthorne, Passaic, Paterson, Prospect Park. Population (2010), 742,508.

ZIP Codes: 07010–15, 07020, 07024, 07026, 07031–32, 07055, 07057, 07070–75, 07094, 07096, 07099, 07407, 07501–14, 07522, 07524, 07533, 07538, 07543–44, 07604–06, 07608, 07626, 07631–32, 07643, 07650, 07657, 07660, 07663, 07666, 07670

* * *

TENTH DISTRICT

DONALD M. PAYNE, JR., Democrat, of Newark, New Jersey; born in Newark, December 17, 1958; education: graduated from Hillside High School; attended Kean College (now Kean University), Union, NJ; professional: elected to Newark Municipal Council (President) 2006–12; elected to Essex County Board of Chosen Freeholders, 2006–12; director of Student Transportation for the Essex County Educational Services Commission; married: wife, Beatrice; three children: Jack, Yvonne, and Donald III (triplets); caucuses: Congressional Black Caucus; Congressional Caucus on Sudan and South Sudan; Congressional Small Business Caucus; Ports, Opportunity, Renewable, Trade, and Security (PORTS) Caucus; Congressional Library of Congress Caucus; Foster Care Youth Caucus; Congressional Diabetes Caucus; Congressional TRIO Caucus; Congressional Down Syndrome Caucus; Congressional Irish Caucus; Indian and American Indian Caucus; House Impact Aid Coalition; Congressional Fire Services Caucus; committees: Homeland Security, Small Business; elected simultaneously to the 112th and 113th Congresses on November 6, 2012, by special election, to fill the vacancy caused by the death of United States Representative Donald Milford Payne.

Office Listings

http://payne.house.gov twitter: @repdonaldpayne

103 Cannon House Office Building, Washington, DC 20515 .... (202) 225–3436
Chief of Staff.—LaVerne Alexander. FAX: 225–4160
Communications Director.—Tiffany Haas.
60 Nelson Place, 14th Floor, Newark, NJ 07102 .... (973) 645–3213
253 Martin Luther King Drive, Jersey City, NJ 07305 .... (201) 369–0392

Counties: ESSEX, HUDSON, UNION. CITIES AND TOWNSHIPS: Bayonne, East Orange, Hillside, Irvington, Jersey City, Linden, Maplewood, Montclair, Newark, Orange, Rahway, Roselle, Roselle Park, South Orange, Union, and West Orange. Population (2010), 732,658.

ZIP Codes: 07002–03, 07017–19, 07028, 07033, 07036, 07040, 07042–44, 07050–52, 07065–67, 07079, 07083, 07088, 07102–09, 07111–12, 07114, 07175, 07202–05, 07208, 07302–06

* * *

ELEVENTH DISTRICT

RODNEY P. FRELINGHUYSEN, Republican, of Morristown, NJ; born in New York, NY, April 29, 1946; education: graduated Hobart College, NY, 1969; attended graduate school in Connecticut; served, U.S. Army, 93rd Engineer Battalion; honorably discharged, 1971; Morris County State and Federal Aid Coordinator and Administrative Assistant, 1972; member, Morris County Board of Chosen Freeholders, 1974–83 (director, 1980); served on: Welfare and Mental Health boards; Human Services and Private Industry councils; New Jersey General Assembly, 1983–94; chairman, Assembly Appropriations Committee, 1988–89 and 1992–94; member: American Legion, and Veterans of Foreign Wars; named Legislator of the Year by the Veterans of Foreign Wars, the New Jersey Association of Mental Health Agencies, and the New Jersey Association of Retarded Citizens; honored by numerous organizations; married: Virginia Frelinghuysen; children: two daughters; committees: Appropriations; elected to the 104th Congress in November, 1994; reelected to each succeeding Congress.

Office Listings

http://www.frelinghuysen.house.gov

2306 Rayburn House Office Building, Washington, DC 20515 .... (202) 225–5034
Chief of Staff.—Nancy Fox. FAX: 225–3186
Press Secretary.—Steve Wilson.
Legislative Director.—Kathleen Hazlett.
Scheduler.—Steve Silvestri.
30 Schuyler Place, 2nd Floor, Morristown, NJ 07960 .... (973) 984–0711

Counties: ESSEX COUNTY. CITIES AND TOWNSHIPS: Bloomfield, Caldwell, Cedar Grove, Essex Fells, Fairfield Township, Livingston, Montclair, North Caldwell, Nutley, Roseland, Verona, West Caldwell, and West Orange. MORRIS COUNTY. CITIES AND TOWNSHIPS: Municipalities of Boonton Town, Boonton Township, Brookside, Budd Lake, Butler, Cedar Knolls, Chatham Borough, Chatham Township, Convent Station, Denville, East Hanover, Florham Park, Green Pond, Green Village, Hanover, Harding, Hibernia, Jefferson, Kinnelon, Lake Hiawatha, Lake Hopatcong, Lincoln Park, Madison, Mendham Borough, Mendham Township, Montville, Morris Plains, Morris Township, Morristown, Mountain Lakes, Mount Tabor, Newfoundland, New Vernon, Oak Ridge, Parsippany-Troy Hills, Pequannock, Picatinny, Pine Brook, Randolph, Riverdale, Rockaway Borough, Rockaway Township, Stanhope, Towaco, Victory Gardens, and Whippany. PASSAIC COUNTY. CITIES: Bloomingdale, Haskell, Little Falls, North Haledon, Pompton Lakes, Totowa, Wanaque, Wayne and Woodland Park. SUSSEX COUNTY. CITIES AND TOWNSHIPS: Byram, Hopatcong, Ogdensburg, Sparta, and Stanhope. Population (2010), 724,761.

ZIP Codes: 07003–07, 07009, 07021, 07028, 07034–39, 07042–46, 07052, 07054, 07058, 07068, 07082, 07110, 07403, 07405, 07420, 07424, 07435, 07438–40, 07442, 07444, 07457, 07465, 07470, 07474, 07508, 07512, 07806, 07821, 07828, 07834, 07837, 07842–43, 07845, 7848–49, 07866, 07869, 07871, 07874, 07878, 07920, 07926–28, 07932, 07935–36, 07930, 07940, 07945, 07950, 07960–63, 07976, 07980, 07999

* * *

TWELFTH DISTRICT

RUSH D. HOLT, Democrat, of Hopewell Township, NJ; born in Weston, WV, October 15, 1948; son of the youngest person ever to be elected to the U.S. Senate; education: B.A., Carleton College, 1970; M.S. and Ph.D., physics, New York University, 1981; physicist; New York City Environmental Protection Administration, 1972–74; teaching fellow, New York University, 1974–80; Congressional Science Fellow, U.S. House of Representatives, Office of Representative Bob Edgar, 1982–83; professor, Swarthmore College, 1980–88; acting chief, Nuclear & Scientific Division, Office of Strategic Forces, U.S. Department of State, 1987–89; assistant director, Princeton Plasma Physics Laboratory, Princeton, NJ, 1989–97; Protestant; married: Margaret Lancefield; children: Michael, Dejan, and Rachel; committees: Education and the Workforce; Natural Resources; elected to the 106th Congress; reelected to each succeeding Congress.

Office Listings

http://holt.house.gov

1214 Longworth House Office Building, Washington, DC 20515 .... (202) 225–5801
Chief of Staff.—Chris Gaston. FAX: 225–6025
Legislative Director.—Kris Pratt.
Communications Director.—Thomas Seay.
Executive Assistant.—Andrew Black.
50 Washington Road, West Windsor, NJ 08550 .... (609) 750–9365
District Director.—Sarah Steward.

Counties: MERCER COUNTY. CITIES AND TOWNSHIPS: East Windsor, Ewing, Hightstown, Hopewell Borough, Hopewell Township, Lawrence, Pennington, Princeton, Trenton, West Windsor. MIDDLESEX COUNTY. CITIES AND TOWNSHIPS: Cranbury, Dunellen, East Brunswick, Helmetta, Jamesburg, Middlesex, Milltown, Monroe, North Brunswick, Old Bridge, Plainsboro, South Brunswick, South River, Spotswood. SOMERSET COUNTY. CITIES AND TOWNSHIPS: Bound Brook, Franklin, Manville, South Bound Brook. UNION COUNTY. CITIES AND TOWNSHIPS: Fanwood, Plainfield, Scotch Plains. Population (2010), 732,658.

ZIP Codes: 07023, 07060–63, 07076, 07747, 08512, 08520, 08525, 08528, 08530, 08534, 08536, 08540–44, 08550, 08560, 08608–11, 08618–19, 08628–29, 08638, 08648, 08691, 08805, 08810, 08812, 08816, 08823–24, 08828, 08831, 08835, 08846, 08850, 08852, 08857, 08859, 08873, 08875, 08880, 08882, 08884, 08890, 08902

NEW MEXICO

(Population 2010, 2,059,179)

SENATORS

TOM UDALL, Democrat, of Santa Fe, NM; born in Tucson, AZ, May 18, 1948; education: graduate of McLean High School, 1966; B.A., Prescott College, Prescott, AZ, 1970; LL.B., Cambridge University, Cambridge, England, 1975; J.D., University of New Mexico, Albuquerque, NM, 1977; professional: admitted to New Mexico Bar, 1978; served as New Mexico Attorney General, 1990–98; served as U.S. Representative for New Mexico's Third Congressional District, 1998–2008; married: Jill Z. Cooper; children: Amanda; member of the Commission on Security and Cooperation in Europe; committees: Appropriations; Environment and Public Works, Foreign Relations; Indian Affairs; Rules and Administration; Joint Committee on Printing; elected to the U.S. Senate on November 4, 2008.

Office Listings

http://tomudall.senate.gov

110 Hart Senate Office Building, Washington, DC 20510 .... (202) 224–6621
Chief of Staff.—Michael Collins. FAX: 228–3261
Legislative Director.—Andrew Wallace.
Communications Director.—Jennifer Talhelm.
Executive Assistant.—Donda Morgan.
219 Central Avenue, NW., Suite 210, Albuquerque, NM 87102 .... (505) 346–6791
201 North Church Street, Suite 201B, Las Cruces, NM 88001 .... (575) 526–5475
120 South Federal Place, Suite 302, Santa Fe, NM 87501 .... (505) 988–6511
102 West Hagerman, Suite A, Carlsbad, NM 88220 .... (575) 234–0366
100 South Avenue A, Suite 113, Portales, NM 88130 .... (575) 356–6811

* * *

MARTIN HEINRICH, Democrat, of Albuquerque, NM; born in Fallon, NV, October 17, 1971; education: B.S., mechanical engineering, University of Missouri, Columbia, MO, 1995; professional: Executive Director of the Cottonwood Gulch Foundation, 1996–2001; Albuquerque City Council, 2003–07; State of New Mexico Natural Resources Trustee, 2006–07; served as U.S. Representative for New Mexico's First Congressional District, 2009–12; married: Julie Heinrich; children: Carter Heinrich and Micah Heinrich; caucuses: Senate Climate Action Task Force; Congressional Sportsmen's Caucus; Congressional Dietary Supplement Caucus; committees: Energy and Natural Resources; Joint Economic Committee; Select Committee on Intelligence; elected to the U.S. Senate on November 6, 2012.

Office Listings

http://heinrich.senate.gov

702 Hart Senate Office Building, Washington, DC 20510 .... (202) 224–5521
Chief of Staff.—Steve Haro. FAX: 228–2841
Legislative Director.—Jude McCartin.
Communications Director.—Whitney Potter.
Director of Scheduling.—Catherine Melsheimer.
625 Silver Avenue Southwest, Suite 130, Albuquerque, NM 87102 .... (505) 346–6601
7450 East Main Street, Suite A, Farmington, NM 87402 .... (505) 325–5030
505 South Main Street, Suite 148, Las Cruces, NM 88001 .... (575) 523–6561
200 East 4th Street, Suite 300, Roswell, NM 88201 .... (575) 622–7113
119 East Marcy Street, Suite 101, Santa Fe, NM 87501 .... (505) 988–6647

REPRESENTATIVES

FIRST DISTRICT

MICHELLE LUJAN GRISHAM, Democrat, of Albuquerque, NM; born in Los Alamos, NM, October 24, 1959; education: B.U.S. University of New Mexico, 1981; J.D., University of New Mexico, 1987; professional: Director, New Mexico State Agency on Aging (1991–2002); Secretary, New Mexico Department of Aging and Long-Term Services (2002–04); Secretary, New Mexico Department of Health (2004–07); Bernalillo County Commissioner (2010–12); children: Taylor Stewart and Erin Grisham; committees: Agriculture; Budget; Oversight and Government Reform; elected to the 113th Congress on November 6, 2012.

Office Listings

http://www.lujangrisham.house.gov twitter: @replujangrisham
http://www.facebook.com/replujangrisham

214 Cannon House Office Building, Washington, DC 20515 .... (202) 225–6316
Chief of Staff.—Dominic Gabello.
Legislative Director.—Courtney Weaver.
Executive Assistant.—Daniel Schlegel.
505 Marquette Avenue, NW., Suite 1605, Albuquerque, NM 87102 .... (505) 346–6781

Counties: BERNALILLO (part), SANDOVAL (part), SANTA FE (part), TORRANCE, AND VALENCIA (part). CITIES AND TOWNSHIPS: Albuquerque, Bernalillo, Edgewood, Estancia, Moriarty, Mountainair, Rio Rancho, and South Valley. Population (2010), 693,772.

ZIP Codes: 87004, 87008, 87015, 87026, 87035–36, 87047–48, 87059, 87063, 87067, 87102, 87104–14, 87116–17, 87120–24, 87131, 87144, 88321

* * *

SECOND DISTRICT

STEVAN PEARCE, Republican, of Hobbs, NM; born in Lamesa, TX, August 24, 1947; education: M.B.A., Eastern New Mexico, Las Cruces, NM, 1970; B.B.A., New Mexico State University, Portales, NM, 1991; professional: owner, oil well services company; served in Vietnam as a pilot for the Air Force; member of the New Mexico State House of Representatives, 1997–2000; elected as a Republican to the 108th, 109th, 110th, 112th, and 113th Congress; religion: Baptist; married: Cynthia; caucuses: chairman of Western Caucus; member of Sportsmen's Caucus; Dairy Caucus; Republican Study Committee; committees: Financial Services; elected to the 112th Congress on November 2, 2010; reelected to the 113th Congress on November 6, 2012.

Office Listings

http://www.pearce.house.gov

2432 Rayburn House Office Building, Washington, DC 20515 .... (202) 225–2365
Chief of Staff.—Todd Willens. FAX: 225–9599
Communications Director.—Eric Layer.
Legislative Director.—Patrick Cuff.
Scheduler.—Bridget Condon.
Staff Assistant / Legislative Correspondent.—Andrew Aragon.
Legislative Aides: Katherine Mauss, Jonathan Shuffield.
570 North Telshor Boulevard, Las Cruces, NM 88011 .... (575) 522–0771
1717 West 2nd Street, Suite 110, Roswell, NM 88201 .... (575) 622–6200
111 School of Mines Road, Socorro, NM 87801 .... (575) 855–8979

Counties: BERNALILLO (part), CATRON, CHAVES, CIBOLA, DEBACA, DONA ANA, EDDY, GRANT, GUADALUPE, HIDALGO, LEA, LINCOLN, LUNA, MCKINLEY (part), OTERO, ROOSEVELT, SIERRA, SOCORRO, AND VALENCIA (part). Population (2010), 686,393.

ZIP Codes: 79821, 79835, 79922, 79932, 79934, 85534, 87002, 87005–07, 87011, 87014, 87020–23, 87026, 87028, 87031, 87034, 87038, 87040, 87045, 87049, 87051, 87062, 87068, 87105, 87121, 88024–34, 88036, 88038–49, 88051–56, 88058, 88061–63, 88065, 88072, 88081, 88113–6, 88118–9, 88123–26, 88130, 88132, 88134, 88136, 88201–03, 88210–11, 88213 88220–21, 88230–32, 88240–42, 88250, 88252–56, 88260, 88262–65, 88267–68, 88301, 88310–12, 88314, 88316–18, 88323–25, 88330, 88336–55, 88417, 88431, 88435

* * *

THIRD DISTRICT

BEN RAY LUJÁN, Democrat, of Santa Fe, NM; born in Nambe, NM; June 7, 1972; education: New Mexico Highland University; business administration, Highlands University, Las Vegas, NM; professional: elected to the New Mexico Public Regulation Commission, 2005–08; member of the Hispanic Caucus; Native American Caucus; co-chair of the Science and National Labs Caucus; co-chair of the Technology Transfer Caucus; committees: Energy and Commerce; elected to the 111th Congress on November 4, 2008; reelected to each succeeding Congress.

Office Listings

http://www.lujan.house.gov facebook.com/repbenraylujan www.twitter.com/repbenraylujan

2446 Rayburn House Office Building, Washington, DC 20515 .... (202) 225–6190

Chief of Staff.—Angela Ramirez. FAX: 226–1528
Deputy Chief of Staff / Communications Director.—Andrew Stoddard.
Legislative Director.—Andrew Jones.
Executive Assistant / Scheduler.—Chris Garcia.

1611 Calle Lorca, Suite A, Santa Fe, NM 87505 .... (505) 984–8950
District Director.—Jennifer Catechis.

800 Municipal Drive, Farmington, NM 87401 .... (505) 324–1005
Constituent Services Representative / Veterans Liaison.—Pete Valencia.

110 West Aztec, Suite 102, Gallup, NM 87301 .... (505) 863–0582
Field Representative and Navajo Nation Liaison.—Brian Lee.

903 University Avenue, P.O. Box 1368, Las Vegas, NM 87701 .... (505) 454–3038
Constituent Liaison Manager.—Pamela Garcia.

404 West Route 66 Boulevard, Tucumcari, NM 88401 .... (575) 461–3029
Field Representative.—Ron Wilmot.

3200 Civic Center Circle, NE., Suite 330, Rio Rancho, NM 87144 .... (505) 994–0499
Scheduler and Constituent Liaison.—Jeffery Bustamante.

Counties: BERNALILLO (part), NAVAJO NATION, COLFAX, CURRY, HARDING, LOS ALAMOS, MCKINLEY (part), MORA, QUAY, RIO ARRIBA, ROOSEVELT (part), SANDOVAL (part), SAN JUAN, SAN MIGUEL, SANTA FE, TAOS, UNION. Population (2010), 686,393.

ZIP Codes: 87001, 87004, 87010, 87012–13, 87015, 87017–18, 87024–25, 87027, 87029, 87037, 87041, 87044–48, 87052–53, 87056, 87064, 87072, 87083, 87114, 87120, 87123–24, 87144, 87174, 87301–02, 87305, 87310–13, 87316–17, 87319–23, 87325–26, 87328, 87347, 87364–65, 87375, 87401–02, 87410, 87412–13, 87415–21, 87455, 87461, 87499, 87501–25, 87527–33, 87535, 87537–40, 87543–45, 87548–49, 87551–54, 87556–58, 87560, 87562, 87564–67, 87569, 87571, 87573–83, 87592, 87594, 87701, 87710, 87712–15, 87718, 87722–23, 87728–36, 87740, 87742–43, 87745–47, 87749–50, 87752–53, 88101–03, 88112–13, 88115–16, 88118, 88120–26, 88130, 88132–35, 88401, 88410–11, 88414–16, 88418–19, 88421–22, 88424, 88426–27, 88430, 88433–34, 88436–37, 88439

NEW YORK

(Population 2010, 19,378,102)

SENATORS

CHARLES E. SCHUMER, Democrat, of Brooklyn and Queens, NY; born in Brooklyn, November 23, 1950; education: graduated valedictorian, Madison High School; Harvard University, *magna cum laude*, 1971; J.D. with honors, Harvard Law School, 1974; professional: admitted to the New York State Bar in 1975; elected to the New York State Assembly, 1974; served on Judiciary, Health, Education, and Cities committees; chairman, subcommittee on City Management and Governance, 1977; chairman, Committee on Oversight and Investigation, 1979; reelected to each succeeding legislative session until December 1980; married: Iris Weinshall, 1980; children: Jessica Emily and Alison Emma; committees: chair, Rules and Administration; vice chair, Joint Committee on the Library; chair, Joint Committee on Printing; Banking, Housing, and Urban Affairs; Finance; Judiciary; elected to the 97th Congress on November 4, 1980; reelected to each succeeding Congress; elected to the U.S. Senate on November 3, 1998; reelected to each succeeding Senate term.

Office Listings

http://schumer.senate.gov

322 Hart Senate Office Building, Washington, DC 20510 .... (202) 224–6542
Chief of Staff.—Mike Lynch. FAX: 228–3027
Communications Director.—Matt House.
Executive Assistant.—Alexandra Victor.
780 Third Avenue, Suite 2301, New York, NY 10017 .... (212) 486–4430
Leo O'Brien Building, 1 Clinton Square, Room 420, Albany, NY 12207 .... (518) 431–4070
130 South Elmwood Avenue, #660, Buffalo, NY 14202 .... (716) 846–4111
100 State Street, Room 3040, Rochester, NY 14614 .... (585) 263–5866
100 South Clinton, Room 841, Syracuse, NY 13261–7318 .... (315) 423–5471
Federal Office Building, 15 Henry Street, #100A–F, Binghamton, NY 13901 .... (607) 772–8109
Two Greenway Plaza, 145 Pine Lawn Road, #300N, Melville, NY 11747 .... (631) 753–0978
One Park Place, Suite 100, Peekskill, NY 10566 .... (914) 734–1532

* * *

KIRSTEN E. GILLIBRAND, Democrat, of Brunswick, NY; born in Albany, NY, December 9, 1966; education: B.A., Dartmouth College, Hanover, NH, 1988; J.D., UCLA, Los Angeles, CA, 1991; professional: attorney; Special Counsel to the U.S. Secretary of Housing and Urban Development, Andrew Cuomo; private legal practice; religion: Catholic; married: Jonathan Gillibrand 2001; two sons: Theodore 2004, Henry 2008; committees: Agriculture, Nutrition, and Forestry; Armed Services; Environment and Public Works; Special Committee on Aging; appointed to the 111th Congress on January 23, 2009, to fill the vacancy caused by the resignation of Hillary Clinton, subsequently elected on November 2, 2010, for the remaining two years of the unexpired term; reelected on November 6, 2012 to a full six year U.S. Senate term.

Office Listings

http://gillibrand.senate.gov

478 Russell Senate Office Building, Washington, DC 20510 .... (202) 224–4451
Chief of Staff.—Jess Fassler. FAX: 228–0282
Legislative Director.—Brooke Jamison.
Communications Director.—Bethany Lesser.
Scheduler.—Rachel Wilkinson.
780 Third Avenue, Suite 2601, New York, NY 10017 .... (212) 688–6262
Federal Office Building, 1 Clinton Square, Room 821, Albany, NY 12207 .... (518) 431–0120
Larkin at Exchange, 726 Exchange Street, Suite 511, Buffalo, NY 14210 .... (716) 854–9725
155 Pinelawn Road, Suite 250 North, Melville, NY 11747 .... (631) 249–2825
P.O. Box 273, Lowville, NY 13367 .... (315) 376–6118
Federal Office Building, 100 State Street, Room 4195, Rochester, NY 14614 .... (585) 263–6250
Federal Office Building, 100 South Clinton Street, Room 1470, P.O. Box 7378, Syracuse, NY 13261 .... (315) 448–0470
Lower Hudson Valley Office, P.O. Box 893, Mahopac, NY 10541 .... (845) 875–4585
Westchester County Office .... (914) 725–9294

REPRESENTATIVES

FIRST DISTRICT

TIMOTHY H. BISHOP, Democrat, of Southampton, NY; born in Southampton, June 1, 1950; education: Southampton High School, 1968; A.B., in history, from Holy Cross College; M.P.A., Long Island University, 1981; professional: educator; Provost of Southampton College, 1986–2002; community service: Southampton Rotary Club Scholarship Committee; Southampton Town Board of Ethics; Eastern Long Island Coastal Conservation Alliance; Bridgehampton Childcare and Recreation Center; religion: Catholic; married: Kathryn; children: Molly and Meghan; grandchildren: Nathan; committees: Education and the Workforce; Transportation and Infrastructure; elected to the 108th Congress on November 5, 2002; reelected to each succeeding Congress.

Office Listings

http:/www.house.gov/timbishop https://twitter.com/timbishopny
https://www.facebook.com/reptimbishop

306 Cannon House Office Building, Washington, DC 20515 .... (202) 225–3826 FAX: 225–3143
Chief of Staff.—Pete Spiro.
Legislative Director.—Eddie Shimkus.
Scheduler / Staff Assistant.—Elizabeth Dovell.
District Director / Communications Director: Brian Beedenbender, Oliver Longwell.
31 Oak Street, Suite 20, Patchogue, NY 11772 .... (631) 289–6500
137 Hampton Road, Southampton, NY 11968 .... (631) 259–8450

Counties: SUFFOLK COUNTY (part). CITIES: Brookhaven, East Hampton, Montauk, Riverhead, Smithtown, Southampton, and Southold. Population (2010), 720,071.

ZIP Codes: 00501, 00544, 11713, 11715, 11719–20, 11727, 11733, 11738, 11741–42, 11745, 11754–55, 11763–64, 11766–68, 11772, 11776–80, 11784, 11786–90, 11792, 11794, 11901, 11930–35, 11937, 11939–42, 11944, 11946–65, 11967–73, 11975–78, 11980

* * *

SECOND DISTRICT

PETER T. KING, Republican, of Seaford, NY; born in Manhattan, NY, April 5, 1944; education: B.A., St. Francis College, NY, 1965; J.D., University of Notre Dame Law School, IN, 1968; military service: served, U.S. Army Reserve National Guard, specialist 5, 1968–73; admitted to New York Bar, 1968; professional: attorney; Deputy Nassau County Attorney, 1972–74, executive assistant to the Nassau County Executive, 1974–76; general counsel, Nassau Off-Track Betting Corporation, 1977; Hempstead Town Councilman, 1978–81; Nassau County Comptroller, 1981–92; member: Ancient Order of Hiberians, Long Island Committee for Soviet Jewry, Sons of Italy, Knights of Columbus, 69th Infantry Veterans Corps, American Legion; married: Rosemary Wiedl King, 1967; children: Sean and Erin; grandson, Jack; committees: Homeland Security; Financial Services; Permanent Select Committee on Intelligence; elected on November 3, 1992 to the 103rd Congress; reelected to each succeeding Congress.

Office Listings

http://www.peteking.house.gov

339 Cannon House Office Building, Washington, DC 20515 .... (202) 225–7896 FAX: 226–2279
Chief of Staff / Press Secretary.—Kevin Fogarty.
Legislative Director.—Erin Ingraham.
1003 Park Boulevard, Massapequa Park, NY 11762 .... (516) 541–4225
District Director.—Anne Rosenfeld.
Suffolk County .... (631) 541–4225

Counties: NASSAU (part), SUFFOLK (part). CITIES AND TOWNSHIPS: Amityville, Babylon, Bayport, Bay Shore, Bethpage, Bohemia, Brentwood, Brightwaters, Copiague, Central Islip, East Islip, Deer Park, Farmingdale, Holbrook, Great River, Islip, Islip Terrace, Levittown, Lindenhurst, Massapequa, Massapequa Park, North Babylon, North Lindenhurst, Oakdale, Patemogue, Seaford, Wantagh, West Babylon, West Islip, and Wyandanch. Population (2010), 724,053.

ZIP Codes: 11701–06, 11714, 11716–18, 11722, 11726, 11730, 11735, 11739, 11741, 11751–53, 11756–58, 11756–58, 11762, 11769, 11772, 11779, 11782, 11793, 11795, 11798

* * *

THIRD DISTRICT

STEVE ISRAEL, Democrat, of Huntington, NY; born in Brooklyn, NY, May 30, 1958; education: B.A., George Washington University, 1982; professional: public relations and marketing executive; public service: legislative assistant for Rep. Richard Ottinger (D–NY), 1980–83; Suffolk County Executive for Intergovernmental Relations, 1988–91; elected to the Huntington Town Board, 1993; reelected two times; organizations: Institute on the Holocaust; Touro Law Center; Nature Conservancy; Audubon Society; awards: Child Care Council of Suffolk Leadership Award; Anti-Defamation League and Sons of Italy Purple Aster Award; elected to the 107th Congress on November 7, 2000; reelected to each succeeding Congress.

Office Listings

http://www.house.gov/israel twitter: @repsteveisrael
facebook.com/israelforcongress

2457 Rayburn House Office Building, Washington, DC 20515 .... (202) 225–3335
Chief of Staff.—Tricia Russell. FAX: 225–4669
Communications Director.—Samantha Slater.
Legislative Director.—Jessica Schwartz.
534 Broad Hollow Road, Suite 302, Melville, NY 11747 .... (631) 777–7391
District Director.—Katie Horst. FAX: 777–7610

Counties: NASSAU COUNTY (part), SUFFOLK COUNTY (part), QUEENS (part). CITIES: Albertson, Asharoken, Bay Terrace, Bayville, Beechhurst, Bellaire, Bellerose, Bethpage, Brookville, Centerport, Cold Spring Harbor, Commack, Kings Park (part), Cove Neck, Dix Hills, Douglaston, E. Northport, East Hills, East Norwich, Eaton's Neck, Elwood, Floral Park, Flower Hill, Fort Salonga, Glen Cove, Glen Head, Glen Oaks, Glenwood Landing (part), Great Neck Plaza, Great Neck, Greenlawn, Halesite, Herricks, Hicksville, Jericho, Huntington Station, Huntington, Kensington, Kings Point, Lake Success, Lattrington, Laurel Hollow, Little Neck, Lloyd Harbor, Locust Valley, Malba, Manhasset Hills, Manhasset, Manorhaven, Matinecock, Melville, Mill Neck, Muttontown, North New Hyde Park (part), Northport, Old Bethpage, Old Brookville, Old Westbury, Oyster Bay Cove, Oyster Bay, Plainview, Plandome, Port Washington, Roslyn Harbor, Roslyn Heights, Roslyn, Sands Point, Sea Cliff, Searingtown, Smithtown (part), South Huntington, Syosset, University Gardens, Upper Brookville, West Hills, Whitestone, Williston Park (part), and Woodbury. Population (2010), 724,164.

ZIP Codes: 11001–02, 11004, 11020–24, 11030, 11040, 11042, 11050, 11201, 11357, 11359–60, 11362, 11427, 11507, 11542, 11545, 11547–48, 11560, 11568, 11576–77, 11579, 11596, 11709, 11721, 11724–25, 11731–32, 11740, 11743, 11746–47, 11753–54, 11768, 11771, 11787, 11791, 11797, 11801, 11803–04, 14426

* * *

FOURTH DISTRICT

CAROLYN MCCARTHY, Democrat, of Mineola, NY; born in Brooklyn, NY, January 5, 1944; education: graduated, Mineola High School, 1962; graduated, nursing school, 1964; professional: licensed practical nurse in ICU Section, Glen Cove Hospital; married: Dennis McCarthy, 1967; widowed on December 7, 1993, when her husband was killed and her only son, Kevin, severely wounded in the Long Island Railroad Massacre; turned personal nightmare into a crusade against violence—speaking out with other families of the Long Island tragedy, not just to the victims of the shooting but to crime victims across the country; committees: Education and the Workforce; Financial Services; elected to the 105th Congress; reelected to each succeeding Congress.

Office Listings

http://www.house.gov/carolynmccarthy

2346 Rayburn House Office Building, Washington, DC 20515 .... (202) 225–5516
Chief of Staff.—Georgette Sierra. FAX: 225–5758
Executive Assistant.—Ellen McNamara.
300 Garden City Plaza, Suite 200, Garden City, NY 11530 .... (516) 739–3008
District Director.—Christopher Chaffee. FAX: 739–2973

Counties: NASSAU (part). CITIES AND TOWNSHIPS: Atlantic Beach, Baldwin, Baldwin Harbor, Barnum Island, Bay Park, Bellerose, Bellerose Terrace, Bellmore, Carle Place, Cedarhurst, East Atlantic Beach, East Garden City, East Meadow, East Rockaway, East Williston, Floral Park, Franklin Square, Freeport, Garden City, Garden City Park, Garden City South, Harbor Isle, Hempstead, Hewlett, Hewlett Bay Park, Hewlett Harbor, Hewlett Neck, Island Park, Lakeview, Lawrence, Lido Beach, Long Beach, Lynbrook, Malverne, Malverne Park Oaks, Merrick, Mineola, New Cassel, New Hyde Park, North New Hyde Park, North Woodmere, Oceanside, Pt. Lookout, Rockville Centre, Roosevelt, Salisbury, South Hempstead, Stewart Manor, South Floral Park, Uniondale, Valley Stream, Wantagh, West Hempstead, Westbury, Williston Park, Woodmere, and Woodsburgh. Population (2010), 724,357.

ZIP Codes: 11001–02, 11010, 11040, 11501, 11509–10, 11514, 11516, 11518, 11520, 11530, 11540, 11549–57, 11558, 11559, 11561, 11563–66, 11568–72, 11575, 11577, 11793, 11580–83, 11588, 11590, 11592–99, 11710

* * *

FIFTH DISTRICT

GREGORY W. MEEKS, Democrat, of Southern Queens, NY; born in Harlem, NY, September 25, 1953; education: P.S. 183; Robert F. Wagner Junior High School; Julia Richman High School, New York, NY; B.A., Adelphi University, 1971–75; J.D., Howard University School of Law, 1975–78; professional: lawyer, admitted to bar, 1979; Queens District Attorney's Office, 1978–83, Assistant Specialist Narcotic Prosecutor, 1981–83; Assistant Counsel to State Investigation Commission, 1983–85; serving as Assistant District Attorney; Supervising Judge, New York State Workers' Compensation Board; public service: New York State Assemblyman, 1992–97; organizations: Alpha Phi Alpha Fraternity; Council of Black-Elected Democrats; National Bar Association; Task Force on Financial Services; co-chair of the Congressional Services Caucus; co-chair of the Organizations of American States; active member of the Congressional Black Caucus; married: Simone-Marie Meeks, 1997; children: Aja, Ebony, and Nia-Ayana; committees: Financial Services; Foreign Affairs; elected to the 105th Congress on February 3, 1998; reelected to each succeeding Congress.

Office Listings

http://www.house.gov/meeks

2234 Rayburn House Office Building, Washington, DC 20515 .... (202) 225–3461
Chief of Staff.—Sophia Lafargue. FAX: 226–4169
Legislative Director.—Gabriel Bitol.
Office Manager / Scheduler.—Kim Fuller.
153–01 Jamaica Avenue, Jamaica, NY 11432 .... (718) 725–6000
Chief of Staff.—Robert Simmons.
6712 Rockaway Beach Bouldevard, Arverne, NY 11692 .... (347) 230–4032
District Office Manager.—Veronica Beckford.
Community Liaison.—Joseph Edwards.

Counties: NASSAU (part), QUEENS (part). CITIES AND TOWNSHIPS: Arverne, Cambria Heights, Edgemere, Elmont, Far Rockaway, Floral Park, Glen Oaks, Hammels, Hollis, Howard Beach, Inwood, Jamaica, Jamaica Estates, Kew Gardens, Laurelton, New Hyde Park, Ozone Park, Queens Village, Richmond Hill, Rosedale, St. Albans, South Jamaica, South Ozone Park, Springfield Gardens, Valley Stream, and Woodhaven. Population (2010), 717,708.

ZIP Codes: 11001, 11003, 11010, 11096, 11366, 11411–13, 11416–20, 11422–23, 11426–30, 11432–36, 11451, 11559, 11580–81, 11691–94, 11697

* * *

SIXTH DISTRICT

GRACE MENG, Democrat, of Queens, NY; born in Corona, NY, October 1, 1975; education: Stuyvesant High School; B.A, University of Michigan, 1997; J.D., Yeshiva University's Benjamin Cardozo School of Law, 2002; professional: practicing lawyer / pro bono attorney, 2003–08; New York State Assembly, 2008–12; religion: Christian; husband, Wayne Kye; children, Brandon and Tyler; caucuses: Congressional Kids Safety Caucus; Congressional Asian Pacific American Caucus; Congressional Caucus on India and Indian Americans; Congressional Bangladesh Caucus; Congressional Caucus on Sikh Americans; United Solutions Caucus; Congressional Hellenic Caucus; Congressional Caucus on Korea; committees: Foreign Affairs; Small Business; elected to the 113th Congress on November 6, 2012.

Office Listings

http://meng.house.gov https://twitter.com/repgracemeng
https://www.facebook.com/repgracemeng

1317 Longworth House Office Building, Washington, DC 20515 .... (202) 225–2601
Chief of Staff.—Jedd Moskowitz. FAX: 225–1589
Executive Assistant / Scheduler.—Brenda Connolly.
32–26 Union Street, Suite 1B, Flushing, NY 11354 .... (718) 445–7860
FAX: 445–7868
118–15 Queens Boulevard, Suite 1610, Forest Hills, NY 11375 .... (718) 445–7861
District Director.—Greg Lavine.
Communications Director.—Jordan Goldes.

Counties: QUEENS COUNTY (part), CITIES AND TOWNSHIPS: Auburndale, Bayside, Elmhurst, Electchester-Pomonok, Flushing, Forest Hills, Fresh Meadows, Glendale, Jamaica, Kew Gardens, Maspeth, Middle Village, Rego Park, Ridgewood, and Woodside. Population (2010), 724,352.

ZIP Codes: 11352, 11354–55, 11357–58, 11360–61, 11364–67, 11373–75, 11377–81, 11385, 11415, 11418, 11421, 11423–24, 11427, 11432, 11435

* * *

SEVENTH DISTRICT

NYDIA M. VELÁZQUEZ, Democrat, of New York, NY; born in Yabucoa, Puerto Rico, March 28, 1953; education: B.A. in political science, University of Puerto Rico, 1974; M.A. in political science, New York University, 1976; professional: faculty member, University of Puerto Rico, 1976–81; adjunct professor, Hunter College of the City University of New York, 1981–83; special assistant to Congressman Ed Towns, 1983; member, City Council of New York, 1984–86; national director of Migration Division Office, Department of Labor and Human Resources of Puerto Rico, 1986–89; director, Department of Puerto Rican Community Affairs in the United States, 1989–92; committees: Financial Services; Small Business; elected on November 3, 1992, to the 103rd Congress; reelected to each succeeding Congress.

Office Listings

http://www.house.gov/velazquez

2302 Rayburn House Office Building, Washington, DC 20515 .... (202) 225–2361
Chief of Staff.—Michael Day. FAX: 226–0327
Communications Director.—Alex Haurek.
Scheduler.—Vanessa Cancino.
Legislative Director.—Clarinda Landeros.
266 Broadway, Suite 201, Brooklyn, NY 11211 .... (718) 599–3658
16 Court Street, Suite 1006, Brooklyn, NY 11241 .... (718) 222–5819

Counties: KINGS (part), NEW YORK (part), AND QUEENS (part). Population (2010), 717,708.

ZIP Codes: 10002, 10004, 10007, 10009, 10012–13, 10038, 11201, 11205–08, 11211, 11215, 11217–21, 11231–32, 11237, 11378–79, 11385, 11416–18, 11421

* * *

EIGHTH DISTRICT

HAKEEM S. JEFFRIES, Democrat of New York, NY; born in Brooklyn, NY, August 04, 1970; education: graduated from Midwood High School, 1988; B.A., State University of New York at Binghamton, 1992; M.P.P., Georgetown University, 1994; J.D., New York University Law School, 1997; professional: member, New York State Assembly, 2007–13; religion: Baptist; married; two children; committees: Budget; Judiciary; elected to the 113th Congress on November 6, 2012.

Office Listings

http://www.house.gov/jeffries

1339 Longworth House Office Building, Washington, DC 20515 .... (202) 225–5936
Chief of Staff.—Cedric Grant. FAX: 225–1018
Scheduler.—Tasia Jackson.
Legislative Director.—Kirsten Zewers.
Communications Director.—Stephanie Baez.
District Director.—Stina Skewes-Cox.
55 Hanson Place, Suite 603, Brooklyn, NY 11217 .... (718) 237–2211
445 Neptune Avenue, 1st Floor, Brooklyn, NY 11224 .... (718) 373–0033

Counties: KINGS (part), QUEENS (part). Population (2010), 713,512.

ZIP Codes: 11201, 11205–08, 11210, 11212–13, 11216–17, 11221, 11224, 11233–36, 11238–39, 11414, 11416–17

* * *

NINTH DISTRICT

YVETTE D. CLARKE, Democrat, of Brooklyn, NY; born in Brooklyn, November 21, 1964; education: attended Edward R. Murrow High School; attended Oberlin College; professional: legislative aide to New York State Senator Velmanette Montgomery; executive assistant to NY Assemblywoman Barbara Clark; staff assistant, NY Compensation Board Chair Barbara Patton; Director of Youth Programs, Hospital League/Local 1199 Training and Upgrading Fund; Director of Business Development for the Bronx Empowerment Zone (BOEDC); member of City Council of New York, 2001–06; committees: Ethics; Homeland Security; Small Business; elected to the 110th Congress on November 7, 2006; reelected to each succeeding Congress.

Office Listings

http://clarke.house.gov twitter: @yvetteclarke
https://www.facebook.com/repyvettedclarke

2351 Rayburn House Office Building, Washington, DC 20515 .... (202) 225–6231
Chief of Staff.—Shelley Davis. FAX: 226–0112
Legislative Director.—Asi Ofosu.
123 Linden Boulevard, 4th Floor, Brooklyn, NY 11226 .... (718) 287–1142

Counties: KINGS (part). Population (2010), 717,708.

ZIP Codes: 11203, 11210, 11212–13, 11216–18, 11225–26, 11229–30, 11233–36, 11238

* * *

TENTH DISTRICT

JERROLD NADLER, Democrat, of New York, NY; born in Brooklyn, NY, June 13, 1947; education: graduated from Stuyvesant High School, 1965; B.A., Columbia University, 1970; J.D., Fordham University, 1978; professional: New York State Assembly, 1977–92; member: ACLU; NARAL Pro-Choice America; AIPAC; National Organization for Women; Assistant Whip; married: 1976; one child; committees: Judiciary; Transportation and Infrastructure; elected to the 102nd Congress on November 3, 1992, to fill the vacancy caused by the death of Representative Ted Weiss; at the same time elected to the 103rd Congress; reelected to each succeeding Congress.

Office Listings

http://www.house.gov/nadler

2110 Rayburn House Office Building, Washington, DC 20515 .... (202) 225–5635
Director.—John Doty. FAX: 225–6923
201 Varick Street, Suite 669, New York, NY 10014 .... (212) 367–7350
Chief of Staff.—Amy Rutkin.
6605 Fort Hamilton Parkway, NY 11229 .... (718) 373–3198

Counties: KINGS (part), NEW YORK (part). Population (2010), 716,172.

ZIP Codes: 10001, 10003–08, 10011–14, 10018–19, 10021, 10023–25, 10027–28, 10036, 10038, 10041, 10043, 10045, 10048, 10060, 10065, 10069, 10075, 10080–81, 10087, 10090, 10101–02, 10104–09, 10115–18, 10121–23, 10125, 10129–30, 10132–33, 10138, 10166, 10175–76, 10178, 10199, 10203, 10212–13, 10242, 10249, 10256–61, 10265, 10268–75, 10277–82, 10285–86, 11102, 11202, 11204, 11214, 11218–20, 11223, 11228, 11230–32, 11245, 11247

* * *

ELEVENTH DISTRICT

MICHAEL G. GRIMM, Republican, of Staten Island, NY; born in Brooklyn, NY, February 7, 1970; education: B.B.A., Accounting Baruch College, New York, NY, 1994; J.D., New York Law School, 2002; professional: U.S. Marine Corps and Reserve, 1989–97; FBI special agent, small business owner; religion: Roman Catholic; commissions and caucuses: Assistant Deputy Whip; co-chair, House Republican Israel Caucus; co-chair, Congressional Russia Caucus; co-chair, Congressional Poland Caucus; vice-chair, Congressional Dutch Caucus; co-chair, Congressional Switzerland Caucus; co-chair, Congressional Armenia Caucus; co-chair Maritime Caucus; co-chair Public Transportation Caucus; co-chair, Zoo and Aquarium Caucus; committees: Financial Services; elected to the 112th Congress on November 2, 2010; reelected to the 113th Congress on November 6, 2012.

Office Listings

http://www.grimm.house.gov

512 Cannon House Office Building, Washington, DC 20515 .... (202) 225–3371
Chief of Staff.—Chris Berardini. FAX: 226–1272
Legislative Director.—Aaron Ringel.
Communications Director.—Carol Danko.
Executive Assistant.—Blaire Bartlett.
265 New Dorp Lane, 2nd Floor, Staten Island, NY 10306 .... (718) 351–1062
District Director.—Nick Curran.
7308 13th Avenue, Brooklyn, NY 11228 .... (718) 630–5277

Brooklyn Director.—Fran Vella-Marrone.

Counties: KINGS (part), RICHMOND. Population (2010), 717,707.

ZIP Codes: 10301–10, 10312–14, 11204, 11209, 11214, 11219–20, 11223, 11228, 11252

* * *

TWELFTH DISTRICT

CAROLYN B. MALONEY, Democrat, of New York City, NY; born in Greensboro, NC, February 19, 1946; education: B.A., Greensboro College, Greensboro, NC, 1968; professional: various positions, New York City Board of Education, 1970–77; legislative aide, New York State Assembly, senior program analyst, 1977–79; executive director of advisory council, 1979–82; director of special projects, New York State Senate Office of the Minority Leader; New York City council member, 1982–93; chairperson, New York City Council Committee on Contracts; member: Council Committee on Aging, National Organization of Women, Common Cause, Sierra Club, Americans for Democratic Action, New York City Council Committee on Housing and Buildings, Citizens Union, Grand Central Business Improvement District, Harlem Urban Development Corporation (1982–91), Commission on Early Childhood Development Programs, Council of Senior Citizen Centers of New York City (1982–87); widowed (Clifton H.W. Maloney); children: Virginia Marshall Maloney and Christina Paul Maloney; committees: Financial Services; Oversight and Government Reform; Joint Economic Committee; elected on November 3, 1992, to the 103rd Congress; reelected to each succeeding Congress.

Office Listings

http://www.maloney.house.gov

2308 Rayburn House Office Building, Washington, DC 20515 .... (202) 225–7944
Chief of Staff.—Michael Iger. FAX: 225–4709
Legislative Director.—Elizabeth Darnall.
Administrative Assistant.—Rebecca Tulloch.
1651 Third Avenue, Suite 311, New York, NY 10128 .... (212) 860–0606
31–19 Newtown Avenue, Astoria, NY 11102 .... (718) 932–1804
619 Lorimer Street, Brooklyn, NY 11211 .... (718) 349–5972

Counties: KINGS (part), New York (part), QUEENS (part). CITIES AND NEIGHBORHOODS: Astoria, Brooklyn, Greenpoint, Long Island City, Manhattan, Queens, Roosevelt Island, and Williamsburg. Population (2010), 712,053.

ZIP Codes: 10001–03, 10009, 10010–12, 10016–19, 10020–22, 10028–29, 10035–36, 10044, 10055, 10065, 10075, 10087, 10103–07, 10110–13, 10118–19, 10120–21, 10123–24, 10128, 10130–31, 10150–56, 10158–59, 10162–69, 10170–79, 10199, 10259, 10261, 10276, 11101–13, 11106, 11109, 11206, 11211, 11222, 11249, 11377–78

* * *

THIRTEENTH DISTRICT

CHARLES B. RANGEL, Democrat-Liberal, of New York, NY; born in Harlem, NY, June 11, 1930; attended DeWitt Clinton High School; served in U.S. Army, 1948–52; awarded the Purple Heart, Bronze Star for Valor, U.S. and Korean presidential citations, and three battle stars while serving in combat with the Second Infantry Division in Korea; honorably discharged with rank of staff sergeant; after military duty, completed high school, 1953; graduated from New York University School of Commerce, student under the G.I. bill; 1957 dean's list; graduated from St. John's University School of Law, dean's list student under a full 3-year scholarship, 1960; lawyer; admitted to practice in the courts of the State of New York, U.S. Federal Court, Southern District of New York, and U.S. Customs Court; appointed assistant U.S. attorney, Southern District of New York, 1961; legal counsel, New York City Housing and Redevelopment Board, Neighborhood Conservation Bureau; general counsel, National Advisory Commission on Selective Service, 1966; served two terms in the New York State Assembly, 1966–70; active in 369th Veterans Association; Community Education Program; and Martin Luther King, Jr., Democratic Club; married: Alma Carter; two children: Steven and Alicia; committees: Ways and Means; Joint Committee on Taxation; elected to the 92nd Congress, November 3, 1970; reelected to each succeeding Congress.

Office Listings

http://www.house.gov/rangel

2354 Rayburn House Office Building, Washington, DC 20515 .... (202) 225–4365

Counsel / Chief of Staff.—George Henry. FAX: 225–0816
163 West 125th Street, Room 737, New York, NY 10027 .... (212) 663–3900
District Director.—Geoffrey Eaton.

Counties: BRONX (part), NEW YORK (part). Population (2012), 738,943.

ZIP Codes: 10025 (part), 10026–27, 10029–35, 10037, 10039–40, 10453, 10458, 10463, 10467–68

* * *

FOURTEENTH DISTRICT

JOSEPH CROWLEY, Democrat, of Elmhurst, Queens, NY; born in Woodside, NY, March 16, 1962; education: graduated, Power Memorial High School, 1981; B.A., political science and communications, Queens College (City University of New York), Flushing, NY, 1985; professional: elected to the New York State Assembly, 1986–98; assembly committees: Racing and Wagering; Banking, Consumer Affairs, and Protection; Election Law; Labor and Housing; serving in the leadership of the U.S. House of Representatives as vice-chair of the Democratic Caucus; founder and current chair of the Bangladesh Caucus; founder and co-chair of the Congressional Musicians Caucus; religion: Roman Catholic; married: Kasey Nilson; children: Cullen, Kenzie and Liam; committees: Ways and Means; elected to the 106th Congress; reelected to each succeeding Congress.

Office Listings

http://house.gov/crowley

1436 Longworth House Office Building, Washington, DC 20510 .... (202) 225–3965
Chief of Staff.—Kate Winkler. FAX: 225–1909
Office Manager.—Katie Papa.
Legislative Director.—Jeremy Woodrum.
82–11 37th Avenue, Suite 402, Jackson Heights, NY 11372 .... (718) 779–1400
2800 Bruckner Boulevard, Suite 301, Bronx, NY 10465 .... (718) 931–1400

Counties: BRONX (part), QUEENS (part). Population (2010), 717,708.

ZIP Codes: 10458, 10460–62, 10464–67, 10469, 10475, 11101–05, 11354, 11356–58, 11368–73, 11375, 11377

* * *

FIFTEENTH DISTRICT

JOSÉ E. SERRANO, Democrat, of Bronx, NY; born in Mayagüez, PR, October 24, 1943; education: Dodge Vocational High School, Bronx, NY; attended Lehman College, City University of New York, NY; served with the U.S. Army Medical Corps, 1964–66; employed by the Manufacturers Hanover Bank, 1961–69; Community School District 7, 1969–74; New York State Assemblyman, 1974–90; chairman, Consumer Affairs Committee, 1979–83; chairman, Education Committee, 1983–90; five children: Lisa, José Marco, Justine, Jonathan and Benjamin; committees: Appropriations; elected to the 101st Congress, by special election, March 28, 1990, to fill the vacancy caused by the resignation of Robert Garcia; reelected to each succeeding Congress.

Office Listings

http://serrano.house.gov http://www.facebook.com/repjoseserrano
http://twitter.com/repjoseserrano http://www.youtube.com/user/comgressmanserrano

2227 Rayburn House Office Building, Washington, DC 20515 .... (202) 225–4361
Deputy Chief of Staff.—Philip Schmidt. FAX: 225–6001
Legislative Director / Deputy Chief of Staff.—Matthew Alpert.
Scheduler.—Frederick Velez.
1231 Lafayette Street, 4th Floor, Bronx, NY 10474 .... (718) 620–0084
District Director.—Javier Lopez.

Counties: BRONX COUNTY (part). CITIES AND TOWNSHIPS: Bronx. Population (2010), 717,708.

ZIP Codes: 10451–60, 10463, 10468, 10472–74

* * *

SIXTEENTH DISTRICT

ELIOT L. ENGEL, Democrat, of Bronx, NY; born in Bronx, February 18, 1947; education: B.A., Hunter-Lehman College, 1969; M.A., City University of New York, 1973; J.D., New York Law School, 1987; professional: teacher and counselor in the New York City public school system, 1969–77; elected to the New York legislature, 1977–88; chaired the Assembly Committee on Alcoholism and Substance Abuse and Subcommittee on Mitchell-Lama Housing (twelve years prior to his election to Congress); member: Congressional Human Rights Caucus; Long Island Sound Caucus; co-chairman, Albanian Issues Caucus; board member, Congressional Ad Hoc Committee on Irish Affairs; Oil and National Security Caucus; EU Caucus; Fragile X Caucus; Tuberculosis Elimination Caucus; Allergy & Asthma Caucus; New Democrat Coalition; Animal Protection Caucus; Renewable and Energy Efficiency Caucus; Pro-Choice Caucus; Long Island Sound Caucus; Task Force on Anti-Semitism; HIV/AIDS Caucus; Arts Caucus; Diabetes Caucus; married: Patricia Ennis, 1980; three children; committees: ranking member, Foreign Affairs; Energy and Commerce; elected on November 8, 1988, to the 101st Congress; reelected to each succeeding Congress.

Office Listings

http://www.engel.house.gov

2161 Rayburn House Office Building, Washington, DC 20515 .... (202) 225–2464
Administrative Assistant.—E.H. ''Ned'' Michalek. FAX: 225–5513
Office Manager.—Heather Beckman.
3655 Johnson Avenue, Bronx, NY 10463 .... (718) 796–9700
Chief of Staff.—William F. Weitz. FAX: 796–5134
6 Gramatan Avenue, Suite 205, Mt. Vernon, NY 10550 .... (914) 699–4100
FAX: 699–3646
177 Dreiser Loop, Room 3, Bronx, NY 10475 .... (718) 320–2314
FAX: 320–2047

Counties: BRONX (part), WESTCHESTER (part). CITIES AND TOWNSHIPS: Parts of Bronx, Mount Vernon, New Rochelle, Yonkers. Population (2010), 717,707.

ZIP Codes: 10463, 10466–67, 10469–71, 10475, 10502, 10528, 10530, 10538, 10543, 10550–53, 10557–58, 10580, 10583, 10701–05, 10707–10, 10801–02, 10804–05

* * *

SEVENTEENTH DISTRICT

NITA M. LOWEY, Democrat, of Harrison, NY; born in New York, NY, July 5, 1937; education: graduated, Bronx High School of Science, 1955; B.A., Mount Holyoke College, 1959; assistant to Secretary of State for Economic Development and Neighborhood Preservation, and deputy director, Division of Economic Opportunity, 1975–85; Assistant Secretary of State, 1985–87; member: boards of directors, Close-Up Foundation; Effective Parenting Information for Children; Windward School, Downstate (New York Region); Westchester Jewish Conference; Westchester Opportunity Program; National Committee of the Police Corps; Women's Network of the YWCA; Legal Awareness for Women; National Women's Political Caucus of Westchester; American Jewish Committee of Westchester; married: Stephen Lowey, 1961; children: Dana, Jacqueline, and Douglas; committees: Appropriations; elected on November 8, 1988, to the 101st Congress; reelected to each succeeding Congress.

Office Listings

http://www.house.gov/lowey twitter.com/nitalowey www.facebook.com/replowey

2365 Rayburn House Office Building, Washington, DC 20515 .... (202) 225–6506
Chief of Staff.—Elizabeth Stanley. FAX: 225–0546
Executive Assistant.—Kelly Healton.
Legislative Director.—Chris Bigelow.
Communications Director.—Mark Prentice.
222 Mamaroneck Avenue, Suite 310, White Plains, NY 10605 .... (914) 428–1707
67 North Main Street, Suite 101, New City, NY 10956 .... (845) 639–3485
District Director.—Patricia Keegan.

Counties: ROCKLAND (all), WESTCHESTER (part). CITIES AND TOWNSHIPS: Briarcliff Manor; Buchanan; Chappaqua, Cortlandt, Cortlandt Manor, Crompond, Croton-on-Hudson, Dobbs Ferry, Elmsford, East Irvington, Fairview, Harrison, Hartsdale, Haverstraw, Hawthorne, Irvington, Jefferson Valley, Millwood, Mohegan Lake, Mount Kisco, Mount Pleasant, New

City, North White Plains, Ossining, Peekskill, Pleasantville, Pocantico Hills, Port Chester, Purchase, Rye Brook, Scarborough, Sleepy Hollow, Tarrytown, Thornwood, Valhalla, Verplanck, West Harrison, West Haverstraw, White Plains, and Yorktown Heights. Population (2010), 717,708.

ZIP Codes: 10510–11, 10514, 10517, 10520, 10522–23, 10528, 10530, 10532–33, 10535, 10546–49, 10562, 10566–67, 10570, 10573, 10577, 10580, 10588, 10591, 10594–96, 10598, 10601, 10603–07, 10901, 10913, 10920, 10923, 10927, 10931, 10952, 10954, 10956, 10960, 10964–65, 10968, 10970, 10974, 10976–77, 10980, 10982–84, 10986, 10989, 10993–94

* * *

EIGHTEENTH DISTRICT

SEAN PATRICK MALONEY, Democrat, of Cold Spring, NY; born in Sherbrooke, Quebec, July 30, 1966; education: graduated, Hanover High School, Hanover, NH, 1984; B.A., University of Virginia, 1988; J.D., University of Virginia, 1992; professional: Deputy White House Staff Secretary, 1997–99; White House Staff Secretary and Assistant to the President of the United States, 1999–2000; Chief Operating Officer, Kiodex, Inc., 2000–03; first deputy secretary to the Governor of New York, 2007–08; corporate partner, Kirkland & Ellis LLP, 2009–11; partner, Orrick, Herrington & Sutcliffe LLP; partner, Randy Florke, 1992–present; children: Jesus, Daley, and Essie; committees: Agriculture; Transportation and Infrastructure; elected to the 113th Congress on November 6, 2012.

Office Listings

http://seanmaloney.house.gov

1529 Longworth House Office Building, Washington, DC 20515 .... (202) 225–5441
Chief of Staff.—Timothy Persico. FAX: 225–3289
Executive Assistant.—Lara Flynn.
Legislative Director.—Jennifer Steel.
Communications Director.—Stephanie Formas.
123 Grand Street, 2nd Floor, Newburgh, NY 12550 .... (845) 561–1259
District Director.—Ed Brancati. FAX: 561–2890

Counties: NORTHERN WESTCHESTER (part), ORANGE, PUTNAM, SOUTHERN DUTCHESS (part). CITIES AND TOWNSHIPS: Arlington, Balmville, Beacon, Beaver Dam Lake, Bedford, Bedford Hills, Brewster Hill, Brewster, Brinckerhoff, Carmel Hamlet, Chester, Cold Spring, Cornwall-on-Hudson, Crown Heights, Fairview, Firthcliffe, Fishkill, Florida, Fort Montgomery, Gardnertown, Golden's Bridge, Goshen, Greenwood Lake, Harriman, Heritage Hills, Highland Falls, Hillside Lake, Hopewell Junction, Katonah, Kiryas Joel, Lake Carmel, Lincolndale, Mahopac, Maybrook, Mechanicstown, Merritt Park, Middletown, Monroe, Montgomery, Mountain Lodge Park, Myers Corner, Nelsonville, New Windsor, Newburgh, Orange Lake, Otisville, Peach Lake, Pine Bush, Port Jervis, Poughkeepsie, Putnam Lake, Red Oaks Mill, Salisbury Mills, Scotchtown, Scotts Corners, Shenorock, South Blooming Grove, Spackenkill, Titusville, Tuxedo Park, Vails Gate, Walden, Walton Park, Wappingers Falls, Warwick, Washington Heights, Washingtonville, West Point, and Woodbury. Population (2010), 717,707.

ZIP Codes: 10501, 10504–07, 10509, 10512, 10516, 10518–19, 10524, 10526–27, 10536–37, 10540–42, 10549, 10560, 10562, 10576, 10578–79, 10587, 10589–90, 10597–98, 10910, 10912, 10914–19, 10921–22, 10924–26, 10928, 10930, 10932–33, 10940–41, 10949–50, 10953, 10958–59, 10963, 10969, 10973–75, 10979, 10981, 10985, 10987–88, 12508, 12511–12, 12518, 12520, 12524, 12527, 12531, 12533, 12537–38, 12540, 12542–43, 12549–53, 12555, 12563–64, 12566, 12569, 12575, 12577, 12582, 12584, 12586, 12589–90, 12601–04, 12721, 12729, 12746, 12771, 12780, 12785

* * *

NINETEENTH DISTRICT

CHRISTOPHER GIBSON, Republican, Kinderhook, NY; born in Rockville Centre; May 13, 1964; education: graduated, B.A., *magna cum laude,* history, ROTC Commission, Siena College, Loudonville, NY, 1986; M.P.A., government, Cornell University, Ithaca, NY, 1995; Ph.D., government, Cornell University, Ithaca, 1998; professional: military, colonel, U.S. Army; Hoover National Security Affairs Fellowship, Stanford University; Congressional Fellow; awards: 2 Legions of Merit, 4 Bronze Star Medals; Purple Heart; Combat Infantryman's Badge with Star; Master Parachutist Badge, Ranger Tab; book: *Securing the State*; religion: Roman Catholic; married: Mary Jo; children: Katie, Maggie, and Connor; committees: Agriculture; Armed Services; elected to the 112th Congress on November 2, 2010; reelected to the 113th Congress on November 6, 2012.

Office Listings

http://www.gibson.house.gov

1708 Longworth House Office Building, Washington, DC 20515 .... (202) 225–5614

Chief of Staff.—Steve Stallmer. FAX: 225–1168
Deputy Chief of Staff.—Stephanie Valle.
District Director.—Steve Bulger.
Legislative Director.—Brad Gentile.
Scheduler/Executive Assistant.—Kate Better.

25 Chestnut Street, Cooperstown, NY 13326 .... (607) 282–4002
2 Hudson Street, Kinderhook, NY 12106 .... (518) 610–8133
4328 Albany Post Road, Route 9, Hyde Park, NY 12538 .... (845) 698–0132
111 Main Street, Delhi, NY 13753 .... (607) 746–9537
721 Broadway, Kingston, NY 12401 .... (845) 514–2322
92 Sullivan Avenue, Liberty, NY 12754 .... (845) 747–9273

Counties: OTSEGO, DELAWARE, SULLIVAN, ULSTER, COLUMBIA, GREENE, SCHOHARIE, MONTGOMERY (part), RENSSELAER (part), DUTCHESS (part), and BROOME (part). Population (2010), 717,708.

ZIP Codes: 12015, 12017, 12022–24, 12029, 12031, 12033, 12035–37, 12042–43, 12050–53, 12057–58, 12060–63, 12110, 12115–16, 12118, 12121, 12153–57, 12160, 12165–68, 12172–76, 12180–82, 12184–85, 12187, 12189, 12192, 12194–98, 12401, 12404–05, 12407, 12409–21, 12435–36, 12438, 12451–61, 12463–75, 12481–82, 12485–87, 12489–96, 12498, 12501–04, 12506–07, 12561, 12563–65, 12592, 12594, 12601, 12603, 12701, 12719–27, 12732–34, 12736–38, 12740–45, 12747, 12749–52, 12754, 12758–60, 12762–64, 12766–67, 12776–79, 12781, 12783–92, 12816, 13315, 13317, 13459, 13468, 13475, 13482, 13485, 13755–57, 13774, 13786, 13788, 13796, 13804, 13806–10

* * *

TWENTIETH DISTRICT

PAUL D. TONKO, Democrat, of Amsterdam, NY; born in Amsterdam, NY, June 18, 1949; education: graduated Amsterdam High School, Amsterdam, NY, in 1967; B.S. degree, mechanical and industrial engineering, Clarkson University, Potsdam, NY, 1971; professional: engineer, NYS Department of Transportation; engineer, NYS Department of Public Service; Montgomery County Board of Supervisors, 1976–83; chairman, Montgomery County Board of Supervisors, 1981–83; NYS Assembly, 1983–2007; chairman, NYS Assembly Standing Committee on Energy, 1992–07; President & CEO, NYS Energy Research and Development Authority, 2007–08; caucuses: co-chair, Sustainable Energy and Environment Coalition, co-chair, Congressional Horse Caucus; committees: Energy and Commerce; elected to the 111th Congress on November 4, 2008; reelected to each succeeding Congress.

Office Listings

http://www.tonko.house.gov https://www.facebook.com/reppaultonko

2463 Rayburn House Office Building, Washington, DC 20515 .... (202) 225–5076
Chief of Staff.—Clinton Britt. FAX: 225–5077
Communications Director.—Sean Magers.
Legislative Director.—Jean Fruci.
Director of Operations.—David Mastrangelo.
Legislative Assistants: Brendan Larkin, Jeff Morgan.
Legislative Correspondent.—Emily Duhovny.

61 Columbia Street, 4th Floor, Albany, NY 12210 .... (518) 465–0700
105 Jay Street, (Schenectady City Hall), Room 15, Schenectady, NY 12305 .... (518) 374–4547
61 Church Street, (Amsterdam City Hall), Room 309, Amsterdam, NY 12010 .... (518) 843–3400

Counties: ALBANY, MONTGOMERY (part), RENSSELAER (part), SARATOGA (part), and SCHENECTADY. Population (2010), 720,133.

ZIP Codes: 12007–10, 12016, 12019–20, 12023, 12027, 12033, 12041, 12045–47, 12053–56, 12059, 12061, 12065–70, 12072, 12074, 12077, 12083–87, 12095, 12107, 12110, 12118, 12120, 12122–23, 12128, 12137, 12141, 12143–44, 12147–48, 12150–51, 12157–61, 12166, 12170, 12177, 12180–83, 12186, 12188–89, 12193, 12196, 12198, 12201–12, 12220, 12222–24, 12226–50, 12252, 12255–57, 12260–61, 12288, 12301–09, 12325, 12345, 12460, 12469, 12866

* * *

TWENTY-FIRST DISTRICT

WILLIAM L. OWENS, Democrat, of Plattsburgh, NY; born in Brooklyn, NY, January 20, 1949; education: graduated, Chaminade High School; B.B.A., *summa cum laude*, business administration, Manhattan College, Riverdale, NY, 1971; J.D., Fordham University School of Law, New York, NY, 1974; professional: captain, U.S. Air Force active duty, 1975–79; reserves, 1979–82; attorney; economic developer; married: Jane Owens; three children: Tara, Jenna, and Brenden; four grandchildren; committees: Appropriations; elected by special election on November 3, 2009, to the 111th Congress, to fill the vacancy caused by the resignation of United States Representative John McHugh; reelected to each succeeding Congress.

Office Listings

http://www.owens.house.gov

405 Cannon House Office Building, Washington, DC 20515 .... (202) 225–4611
Chief of Staff.—Brad Katz. FAX: 226–0621
Legislative Director.—Nell Maceda.
Communications Director.—Tim Biba.
Scheduler.—Quinlan Brennan.
120 Washington Street, Suite 200, Watertown, NY 13601 .... (315) 782–3150
14 Durkee Street, Suite 320, Plattsburgh, NY 12901 .... (518) 563–1406
136 Glen Street, Glens Falls, NY 12801 .... (518) 743–0964
3 Frontage Road, Gloversville, NY 12078 .... (518) 773–4568

Counties: Clinton, Essex, Franklin, Fulton, Hamilton, Herkimer (part), Jefferson, Lewis, Saratoga (part), St. Lawrence, Warren, and Washington. Cities, Towns and Villages: Watertown, Plattsburgh, Malone, Potsdam, Canton, Massena, Ogdensburg, Glens Falls, Ballston Spa. Population (2010), 717,707.

ZIP Codes: 12010, 12025, 12032, 12070, 12078, 12086, 12095, 12108, 12117, 12134, 12139, 12164, 12190, 12801, 12804, 12808–12, 12814–17, 2819–24, 12827–28, 12832–39, 12841–58, 12860–62, 12864–65, 12870, 12872–74, 12878–79, 12883, 12885–87, 12901, 12903, 12910–24, 12926–30, 12932–37, 12939, 12941–46, 12949–53, 12955–62, 12964–67, 12969–70, 12972–81, 12983, 12985–87, 12989, 12992–93, 12995–98, 13145, 13304–05, 13312, 13316, 13324–27, 13329, 13338–39, 13343, 13345, 13353, 13360, 13365, 13367–68, 13404, 13431, 13433, 13436–38, 13452, 13470–71, 13473, 13489, 13601–03, 13605–08, 13611–28, 13630–43, 13645–52, 13654–62, 13664–85, 13687, 13690–97, 13699

* * *

TWENTY-SECOND DISTRICT

RICHARD L. HANNA, Republican, of Barneveld, NY; born in Utica, January 25, 1951; education: graduated from Witesboro High School, 1969; B.A., economics and political science with honors, Reed College, Portland, OR; 1976; professional: owner and president of Hanna Construction; married: two children; committees: Small Business; Transportation and Infrastructure; Joint Economic Committee; elected to the 112th Congress on November 2, 2010; reelected to the 113th Congress on November 6, 2012.

Office Listings

http://www.hanna.house.gov

319 Cannon House Office Building, Washington, DC 20515 .... (202) 225–3665
Chief of Staff.—Justin Stokes. FAX: 225–1891
Executive Assistant.—Carla Virgilio.
258 Genesee Street, First Floor, Utica, NY 13502 .... (315) 724–9740
FAX: 724–9746
49 Court Street, Metro Center, Suite 230, Binghamton, NY 13901 .... (607) 723–0212
FAX: 723–0215

Counties: Broome (part), Chenango, Cortland, Herkimer, Madison, Oneida, Oswego (part), Tioga (part), Tompkins (part). Cities, Towns and Villages: Binghamton, Camden, Cortland, Cortlandville, Forestport, Little Falls, New Berlin, Mexico, Norwich, Oneida, Sandy Creek, Sherrill, Sullivan, Utica, Vestal, and Windsor. Population (2010), 717,708.

ZIP Codes: 13028, 13030, 13032, 13035–37, 13040, 13042, 13044–45, 13052–54, 13061, 13072, 13076–77, 13082–83, 13087, 13101, 13103–04, 13114, 13122–24, 13126, 13131–32, 13134, 13136, 13141–42, 13144–45, 13155, 13157–59, 13162–63, 13167, 13301–04, 13308–10, 13313–14, 13316, 13318–19, 13321–24, 13328, 13332, 13334, 13338–41, 13346, 13350, 13352, 13354–55, 13357, 13361–65, 13402–03, 13406–09, 13411, 13413, 13416–18, 13421, 13424–25, 13431, 13435, 13437–41, 13456, 13460–61, 13464, 13469, 13471, 13475–78, 13480, 13483–86, 13489–95, 13501–02, 13661, 13730, 13732–33, 13736, 13744, 13746, 13748, 13760, 13777–78, 13780, 13784, 13787, 13790, 13794–95, 13797, 13801–03, 13809, 13811–13, 13815, 13826–27, 13830, 13832–33, 13835, 13841, 13843–44, 13850, 13862–63, 13865, 13901–05

* * *

TWENTY-THIRD DISTRICT

THOMAS W. REED II, Republican, of Corning, NY; born in Joliet, IL, November 18, 1971; education: graduated, B.A., Alfred University, Alfred, NY, 1993; J.D., Ohio Northern University College of Law, Ada, OH, 1996; professional: lawyer, private practice, Law Office of Thomas W. Reed II; business owner; mayor of Corning, NY, 2008–09; religion: Catholic; married: wife, Jean, and two children; committees: Ways and Means; elected November 2, 2010, to the 111th Congress by special election to fill the vacancy caused by the resignation of United States Representative Eric J.J. Massa; subsequently elected to a full term in the 112th Congress on November 2, 2010; reelected to the 113th Congress on November 6, 2012.

Office Listings

http://www.reed.house.gov

1504 Longworth House Office Building, Washington, DC 20515 .... (202) 225–3161
Chief of Staff.—Tim Kolpien. FAX: 226–6599
Deputy Chief of Staff.—Steve Pfrang.
Legislative Director.—Steve Pfrang.
Communications Director.—Elizabeth Shaffer.
District Director.—Joe Sempolinski.
89 West Market Street, Corning, NY 14830 .... (607) 654–7566
433 Exchange Street, Geneva, NY 14456 .... (315) 759–5229
401 East State Street, Suite 304–1, Ithaca, NY 14850 .... (607) 222–2027
2 East 2nd Street, Suite 300, Jamestown, NY 14701 .... (716) 708–6369
One Bluebird Square, Olean, NY 14760 .... (716) 379–8434

Counties: ALLEGANY, CATTARAUGUS, CHAUTAUQUA, CHEMUNG, ONTARIO (part), SCHUYLER, SENECA, STEUBEN, TIOGA (part), TOMPKINS, YATES. Population (2010), 717,707.

ZIP Codes: 13053, 13062, 13068, 13073, 13102, 13734, 13736, 13743, 13811–12, 13827, 13835, 13840, 13845, 13864, 14029, 14041–42, 14048, 14060, 14062–63, 14065, 14070, 14081, 14101, 14129, 14133, 14135–36, 14168, 14171, 14173, 14415, 14418, 14424, 14432, 14441, 14453, 14456, 14461, 14463, 14478, 14504, 14507, 14512, 14518, 14527, 14529, 14532, 14537, 14544, 14547–48, 14561, 14572, 14701–02, 14706–24, 14726–45, 14747–48, 14750–58, 14760, 14766–67, 14769–70, 14772, 14774–75, 14777–79, 14781–88, 14801–10, 14812–27, 14830, 14837–43, 14845, 14850, 14854–59, 14861, 14863–65, 14867, 14869–74, 14876–87, 14889, 14891–95, 14897–98, 14901–05, 14925

* * *

TWENTY-FOURTH DISTRICT

DANIEL B. MAFFEI, Democrat, of Syracuse, NY; born in Syracuse, July 4, 1968; education: graduated from Nottingham High School, 1986; B.A., Brown University, Providence, RI, 1990; M.S., Columbia University, New York, NY 1991; M.P.P., Harvard University, Cambridge, MA, 1995; professional: reporter for Channel 9 News in Syracuse, NY; Communications and policy advisor for Senator Bill Bradley and the late Senator Daniel Patrick Moynihan; married, no children; committees: Armed Services; Science, Space, and Technology; elected to the 113th Congress on November 6, 2012.

Office Listings

http://maffei.house.gov

422 Cannon House Office Building, Washington, DC 20515 .... (202) 225–3701
Chief of Staff.—Charles Kelly. FAX: 225–4042
Legislative Director.—Becky Cornell.
17 East Genesee Street, Auburn, NY 13021 .... (315) 253–4176
13 West Oneida Street, Oswego, NY 13126 .... (315) 342–2192
100 North Salina Street, 1 Clinton Square, 6th Floor, Syracuse, NY 13202 .... (315) 423–5657
FAX: 423–5604

Counties: CAYUGA, ONONDAGA, WAYNE, AND OSWEGO (part). Population: (2010), 712,871.

ZIP Codes: 13020, 13022, 13024, 13026–27, 13029, 13030 (part), 13031, 13033–35, 13036 (part), 13037 (part), 13039, 13041, 13045, 13051, 13052 (part), 13057, 13060, 13063, 13064, 13066, 13069, 13071, 13073–74, 13076 (part), 13077 (part), 13078, 13080, 13081 (part), 13082 (part), 13084, 13088–90, 13092 (part), 13093, 13104 (part), 13108, 13110–20, 13122, 13126, 13131 (part), 13132, 13135, 13137–40, 13141 (part), 13143, 13146 (part), 13147, 13148 (part), 13152–54, 13156, 13158 (part), 13158, 13159 (part), 13160, 13164, 13165 (part), 13166, 13201–07, 13209–12, 13214–15, 13217–21, 13224–25, 13235, 13244, 13250, 13252, 13261, 13290, 14413, 14432 (part), 14433, 14449–50, 14489 (part), 14502 (part), 14505, 14513, 14516, 14519 (part), 14520, 14522 (part), 14538, 14542, 14551, 14555, 14563, 14568, 14580 (part), 14589–90, 14882 (part)

* * *

TWENTY-FIFTH DISTRICT

LOUISE MCINTOSH SLAUGHTER, Democrat, of Fairport, NY; born in Harlan County, KY, August 14, 1929; education: B.S. in microbiology (1951) and M.S. in public health (1953), University of Kentucky; elected to Monroe County Legislature, two terms, 1976–79; elected to New York State Assembly, two terms, 1982–86; Distinguished Public Health Legislation Award, American Public Health Association, 1998; married: Robert Slaughter; three daughters; seven grandchildren; committees: ranking member, Rules; elected to the 100th Congress on November 4, 1986; reelected to each succeeding Congress.

Office Listings

http://www.louise.house.gov

2469 Rayburn House Office Building, Washington, DC 20515 .... (202) 225–3615
Chief of Staff.—Liam Fitzsimmons. FAX: 225–7822
Legislative Director.—Cheri Hoffman.
Press Secretary.—Eric Walker.
Scheduler.—Yodit Tewelde
3120 Federal Building, 100 State Street, Rochester, NY 14614 .... (585) 232–4850
FAX: 232–1954

Counties: MONROE (majority). CITIES AND TOWNSHIPS: Brighton, Brockport, Chili, Churchville, Clarkson, East Rochester, Fairport, Gates, Greece, Hamlin, Henrietta, Hilton, Irondequoit, Ogden, Parma, Penfield, Perinton, Pittsford, Riga, Rochester, Rush, Scottsville, Spencerport, Sweden, and Webster. Population (2010), 717,707.

ZIP Codes: 14416, 14420, 14428, 14445, 14450, 14464, 14467–68, 14502, 14514, 14519, 14526, 14534, 14543, 14546, 14559, 14564, 14580, 14586, 14604–10, 14612–13, 14615–18, 14620–26

* * *

TWENTY-SIXTH DISTRICT

BRIAN HIGGINS, Democrat, of Buffalo, NY; born in Buffalo, October 6, 1959; education: B.A., Buffalo State College, NY, 1984; M.P.A., Harvard University, Cambridge, MA, 1996; professional: lecturer, Buffalo State College; member of the Buffalo Common Council, 1988–93; member of the New York State Assembly, 1999–2004; married: Mary Jane Hannon; two children: John and Maeve; committees: Foreign Affairs; Homeland Security; elected to the 109th Congress on November 2, 2004; reelected to each succeeding Congress.

Office Listings

http://www.higgins.house.gov twittter: @repbrianhiggins
www.facebook.com/repbrianhiggins

2459 Rayburn House Office Building, Washington, DC 20515 .... (202) 225–3306
Chief of Staff.—Chuck Eaton. FAX: 226–0347
Chief of Staff/DC and Legislative Director.—Andy Tantillo.
Communications Director.—Theresa Kennedy.
Larkin at Exchange, 726 Exchange Street, Suite 601, Buffalo, NY 14210 .... (716) 852–3501
640 Park Place, Niagara Falls, NY 14301 .... (716) 282–1274

Counties: ERIE (part), NIAGARA (part). CITIES AND TOWNSHIPS: Amherst (part), Buffalo, Cheektowaga, Grand Island, Lackawanna, Niagara Falls (part), North Tonawanda, Tonawanda (city), Tonawanda (township), and West Seneca. Population (2010), 717,707.

ZIP Codes: 14026, 14043, 14051, 14068, 14072, 14120, 14127, 14150–51, 14201–28, 14260, 14301–05

* * *

TWENTY-SEVENTH DISTRICT

CHRIS COLLINS, Republican of Clarence, NY; born in Schenectady, NY, May 20, 1950; graduated Hendersonville High School, Hendersonville, NC, 1968; B.S.M.E., mechanical engineering, NC State University, Raleigh, NC, 1972; M.B.A. University of Alabama at Birmingham, Birmingham, AL, 1975; professional: businessman, elected as Erie County Executive of Erie County, NY, 2007; married to Mary Collins, children: Caitlin and Cameron; caucuses: Small Business Caucus; Manufacturing Caucus; Dairy Farmers Caucus; National Guard and Reserve Component Caucus; Northern Border Caucus; House Republican Israel Caucus; General Aviation Caucus; Aviation Safety Caucus; Law Enforcement Caucus; Fire Safety Caucus; chairman, Scouting Caucus; Congressional Job Creators Caucus; Diabetes Caucus; STEM Caucus; committees: Agriculture; Science, Space and Technology; Small Business; elected to the 113th Congress on November 6, 2012.

Office Listings

http://www.chriscollins.house.gov

1117 Longworth House Office Building, Washington, DC 20515 .... (202) 225–5265
Chief of Staff.—Christopher Grant. FAX: 225–5910
Executive Assistant.—Ashley Noland.
Legislative Director.—Jeffrey Freeland.
2813 Wehrle Drive, Suite 13, Williamsville, NY 14221 .... (716) 634–2324

Communications Director.—Grant Loomis.
District Director.—Michael Kracker.
75 Main Street, Suite C, Geneseo, NY 14454 .... (585) 519–4002

Counties: ERIE (part), NIAGARA (part), ORLEANS (part), GENESEE, WYOMING, LIVINGSTON, ONTARIO, MONROE (part). Population (2010) 717,707.

ZIP Codes: 14001, 14004–06, 14008–13, 14020–21, 14024–28, 14030–40, 14043, 14047, 14051–52, 14054–59, 14061, 14066–67, 14069–70, 14075, 14080–83, 14085–86, 14091–92, 14094–95, 14098, 14102–05, 14107–13, 14120, 14125–27, 14130–32, 14134, 14139–41, 14143–45, 14167, 14169–70, 14172, 14174, 14218–19, 14221, 14224, 14228, 14270, 14304–05, 14411, 14414, 14416, 14420, 14422–25, 14427–29, 14435, 14437, 14443, 14452–54, 14462, 14464, 14466–72, 14475–77, 14479–82, 14485–88, 14506, 14508, 14510–12, 14517, 14522, 14525, 14530, 14533–34, 14536, 14539, 14543, 14545–46, 14548–50, 14556–58, 14560, 14564, 14569, 14571–72, 14585–86, 14591–92, 14735, 14822, 14836, 14846, 14884

NORTH CAROLINA

(Population 2010, 9,535,483)

SENATORS

RICHARD BURR, Republican, of Winston-Salem, NC; born in Charlottesville, VA, November 30, 1955; education: R.J. Reynolds High School, Winston-Salem, NC, 1974; B.A., communications, Wake Forest University, Winston-Salem, NC, 1978; professional: sales manager, Carswell Distributing; member: Reynolds Rotary Club; board member, Brenner Children's Hospital; public service: U.S. House of Representatives, 1995–2005; served as vice-chairman of the Energy and Commerce Committee; married: Brooke Fauth, 1984; children: two sons; committees: ranking member, Veterans' Affairs; Finance; Health, Education, Labor, and Pensions; Select Committee on Intelligence; elected to the U.S. Senate on November 2, 2004; re-elected to the U.S. Senate on November 2, 2010.

Office Listings

http://burr.senate.gov

217 Russell Senate Office Building, Washington, DC 20510 .... (202) 224–3154
FAX: 228–2981
Chief of Staff.—Chris Joyner.
Legislative Director.—Natasha Hickman.
2000 West First Street, Suite 508, Winston-Salem, NC 27104 .... (336) 631–5125
State Director.—Dean Myers.
100 Coast Line Street, Room 210, Rocky Mount, NC 27804 .... (252) 977–9522
201 North Front Street, Suite 809, Wilmington, NC 28401 .... (910) 251–1058

* * *

KAY R. HAGAN, Democrat, of Greensboro, NC; born in Shelby, NC, May 26, 1953; education: B.A., Florida State University, 1975; J.D., Wake Forest University School of Law, 1978; professional: attorney and vice president of the Estate and Trust Division, NCNB, 1978–88; public service: North Carolina State Senator, 1999–2009; religion: Presbyterian; married: Chip Hagan; children: two daughters, one son; committees: Armed Services; Banking, Housing, and Urban Affairs; Health, Education, Labor, and Pensions; Small Business and Entrepreneurship; elected to the U.S. Senate on November 4, 2008.

Office Listings

htttp://hagan.senate.gov

521 Dirksen Senate Office Building, Washington, DC 20510 .... (202) 224–6342
FAX: 228–2563
Chief of Staff.—Mike Harney.
Deputy Chief of Staff.—Brian Nagle.
Communications Director.—Sadie Weiner.
State Director.—Melissa Midgett.
701 Green Valley Road, Suite 201, Greensboro, NC 27408 .... (877) 852–9462
82 Patton Avenue, Suite 635, Asheville, NC 28801 .... (828) 257–6510
301 South Evans Street, Suite 102, Greenville, NC 27858 .... (252) 754–0707
310 New Bern Avenue, Suite 122, Raleigh, NC 27601 .... (919) 856–4630
1520 South Boulevard, Charlotte, NC 28203 .... (704) 334–2448

REPRESENTATIVES

FIRST DISTRICT

G. K. BUTTERFIELD, Democrat, of Wilson County, NC; born, April 27, 1947; education: North Carolina Central University, graduated in 1971, with degrees in sociology and political science; North Carolina Central University School of Law, graduated in 1974, with a Juris Doctor degree; military service: U.S. Army, 1968–1970; served as a Personnel Specialist; discharged with the rank of Specialist E–4; professional: attorney; private practice, 1974–1988; public service: elected to the North Carolina Superior Court bench in November, 1988; appointed on February 8, 2001, by Governor Michael F. Easley to the North Carolina Supreme Court; after leaving the Supreme Court, following the 2002 election, Governor Easley appointed Justice Butterfield as a Special Superior Court Judge; served until his retirement on May 7, 2004; organizations: North Carolina Bar Association; North Carolina Association of Black Lawyers; Wilson Opportunities Industrialization Center; religion: Baptist; appointed Chief Deputy Whip, 110th Congress; committees: Energy and Commerce; elected to the 108th Congress, by special election, on July 20, 2004; elected to the 109th Congress on November 2, 2004; reelected to each succeeding Congress.

Office Listings

http://www.butterfield.house.gov

2305 Rayburn House Office Building, Washington, DC 20515 .... (202) 225–3101
Chief of Staff.—Troy Clair. FAX: 225–3354
Communications Director.—Kim Atterbury.
Scheduler.—Heather Asata.
216 Northeast Nash Street, Suite B, Wilson, NC 27893 .... (252) 237–9816
309 West Third Street, Weldon, NC 27890 .... (252) 538–4123

Counties: BEAUFORT (part), BERTIE, CHOWAN (part), CRAVEN (part), DURHAM (part), EDGECOMBE (part), FRANKLIN (part), GATES (part), GRANVILLE, GREENE (part), HALIFAX, HERTFORD, LENOIR (part), MARTIN (part), NASH (part), NORTHAMPTON, PASQUOTANK (part), PERQUIMANS (part), PITT (part), VANCE (part), WARREN, WASHINGTON (part), WAYNE (part), WILSON (part). Population (2010), 733,499.

ZIP Codes: 27507, 27509, 27522, 27525, 27530–34, 27536–37, 27544, 27549, 27551, 27553, 27556, 27560, 27563, 27565, 27570, 27572, 27581, 27584, 27586, 27589, 27594, 27596, 27701–05, 27707–08, 27712–13, 27801–05, 27809, 27812, 27816, 27818–20, 27822–23, 27827–29, 27831–35, 27837, 27839–47, 27849–50, 27852–53, 27855–58, 27860–63, 27866–67, 27869–77, 27881–83, 27886–95, 27897, 27906–07, 27909–10, 27922, 27924, 27926, 27930, 27932, 27937–38, 27942, 27944, 27957, 27962, 27967, 27970, 27979–80, 27983, 27985–86, 28333, 28365, 28501–04, 28523, 28526, 28537, 28551, 28560, 28562, 28578, 28580, 28586, 28590

* * *

SECOND DISTRICT

RENEE ELLMERS, Republican, of Dunn, NC; born in Ironwood, MI, February 9, 1964; education: B.S., nursing, Oakland University, Auburn Hills, MI, 1990; professional: registered nurse; president elect/vice president, Community Development for the Chamber of Commerce; member of the Betsy Johnson Hospital Foundation, member of the Dunn Planning Board, NC, 2006–10; chair, Dunn Planning Board, NC, 2008–10; member of the Harnett County Nursing Home Committee; religion: Roman Catholic; married: Dr. Brent Ellmers; one child: Ben; committees: Energy and Commerce; elected to the 112th Congress on November 2, 2010; re-elected to the 113th Congress on November 6, 2012.

Office Listings

http://www.ellmers.house.gov

426 Cannon House Office Building, Washington, DC 20515 .... (202) 225–4531
Chief of Staff.—Al Lytton. FAX: 225–5662
Legislative Director.—Elaine Acevedo.
Press Secretary.—Tom Doheny.
Scheduler.—Josie Beecher.
406 West Broad Street, Dunn, NC 28334 .... (910) 230–1910
222 Sunset Avenue, #101, Asheboro, NC 27203 .... (336) 626–7819

Counties: ALAMANCE (part), CHATHAM (part), CUMBERLAND (part), HARNETT (part), HOKE (part), LEE, MOORE, RANDOLPH (part), WAKE (part). Population (2010), 744,671.

ZIP Codes: 27207–08, 27213, 27237, 27252, 27256, 27298, 27312, 27325, 27330–32, 27344, 27349, 27355, 27405, 27501, 27504–06, 27508, 27520–21, 27524–26, 27529, 27536–37, 27540, 27542–44, 27546, 27549, 27552, 27555, 27557, 27559, 27562, 27564, 27568–70, 27576–77, 27589, 27591–93, 27596–97, 27601–03, 27605–07, 27610, 27614, 27625, 27698, 27801–04, 27807, 27809, 27816, 27822, 27829, 27850, 27856, 27863, 27878, 27880, 27882, 27891, 27893–94, 27896, 28301, 28303, 28307–08, 28310–11, 28314, 28323, 28326, 28328, 28334–35, 28339, 28341, 28355–56, 28365–66, 28368, 28382, 28385, 28390, 28393, 28441, 28444, 28447, 28453, 28458, 28466, 28478

* * *

THIRD DISTRICT

WALTER B. JONES, Republican, of Farmville, NC; born in Farmville, February 10, 1943; education: graduated Hargrave Military Academy, Chatham, VA, 1961; B.A., Atlantic Christian College, Wilson, NC, 1966; served in North Carolina National Guard; self-employed, sales; member: North Carolina House of Representatives, 1983–92; married: Joe Anne Whitehurst Jones; one child, Ashley Elizabeth Jones; committees: Armed Services; elected to the 104th Congress; reelected to each succeeding Congress.

Office Listings

https://www.facebook.com/pages/walter-jones/15083070102 twitter: @repwalterjones

2333 Rayburn House Office Building, Washington, DC 20515 .... (202) 225–3415
Chief of Staff.—Glen Downs. FAX: 225–3286
Office Manager.—Maggie Ayrea.
Communications Director.—Sarah Howard.
1105–C Corporate Drive, Greenville, NC 27858 .... (252) 931–1003
District Constituent Outreach Director.—Catherine Fodor.

Counties: BEAUFORT (part), CAMDEN, CHAOWAN, CARTERET, CRAVEN (part), CURRITUCK, DARE, GATES, GREENE, HYDE, JONES (part), LENOIR (part), MARTIN (part), NEW HANOVER, ONSLOW (part), PAMLICO, PENDER (part), PITT (part), TYRRELL, WASHINGTON, WAYNE, PASQUOTANK, PERQUIMANS (part). CITIES: Atlantic Beach, Ayden, Beaufort, Belhaven, Burgaw, Clinton, Emerald Isle, Fremont, Greenville, Havelock, Jacksonville, Kill Devil Hills, Kinston, Kitty Hawk, Morehead City, Mount Olive, Nags Head, New Bern, Newport, River Bend, Trent Woods, Wallace, Washington, Wilmington, and Winterville. Population (2010), 749,823.

ZIP Codes: 27806, 27808, 27810–12, 27814, 27817, 27821, 27824, 27826, 27828, 27834, 27836–37, 27846, 27858, 27860, 27865, 27871, 27875, 27879, 27884–85, 27888–89, 27892, 27909, 27915–17, 27919–21, 27923, 27925–30, 27932, 27935–39, 27941, 27943–44, 27946–50, 27953–54, 27956, 27958–60, 27962, 27964–66, 27968–70, 27972–74, 27976, 27978–82, 28401–03, 28405, 28407, 28412, 28421, 28425, 28429, 28435, 28445, 28447–48, 28454, 28457, 28460, 28466, 28478, 28501, 28509–13, 28515–16, 28518–24, 28526–33, 28537–47, 28552–57, 28560, 28562, 28564, 28570–75, 28577, 28579–87, 28589–90, 28594

* * *

FOURTH DISTRICT

DAVID E. PRICE, Democrat, of Chapel Hill, NC; born in Erwin, TN, August 17, 1940; education: B.A., Morehead Scholar, University of North Carolina; Bachelor of Divinity, 1964, and Ph.D., political science, 1969, Yale University; professional: professor of political science and public policy, Duke University; past chairman and executive director, North Carolina Democratic Party; author of four books and numerous book chapters, essays, and scholarly articles on Congress and the American political system; leadership roles: ranking member, House Democracy Partnership; co-chair, Democratic Budget Group; co-chair, Democratic Faith Working Group; Assistant Democratic Whip; legislative accomplishments: Home Equity Loan Consumer Protection Act (100th Congress); Scientific and Technical Education Act (102nd Congress); Education Affordability Act (105th Congress); Stand By Your Ad Act (107th Congress); Teaching Fellows Act (110th Congress); Credit Card Minimum Payment Warning Act (111th Congress); selected awards: Hubert Humphrey Public Service Award, American Political Science Association, 1990; Champion of Science Award, The Science Coalition, 2002; Charles Dick Medal of Merit, North Carolina National Guard, 2002; William Sloane Coffin Award for Peace and Justice, Yale Divinity School, 2006; Legislator of the Year, Biotechnology Industry Association, 2011; John Tyler Caldwell Award for the Humanities, North Carolina Humanities Council, 2011; past chairman of the board and Sunday School teacher, Binkley Memorial Baptist Church; married: Lisa Price; children: Karen and Michael; committees: Appropriations; elected to the 100th–103rd Congresses; elected to the 105th Congress; reelected to each succeeding Congress.

Office Listings

http://www.price.house.gov

2162 Rayburn House Office Building, Washington, DC 20515 .... (202) 225–1784
Chief of Staff.—Jean-Louise Beard. FAX: 225–2014
Legislative Director / Deputy Chief of Staff.—Asher Hildebrand.
Executive Assistant.—Jean-Louise Beard.
Systems Manager.—Sean Maxwell.
436 North Harrington Street, Suite 100, Raleigh, NC 27603 .... (919) 859–5999
District Director.—Beau Mills.
1777 Fordham Boulevard, Suite 204, Chapel Hill, NC 27514 .... (919) 967–7924
301 Green Street, Suite 315, Fayetteville, NC 28301 .... (910) 323–0260

Counties: ALAMANCE (part), CHATHAM (part), CUMBERLAND (part), DURHAM (part), HARNETT (part), ORANGE (part), and WAKE (part). Population (2010), 733,498.

ZIP Codes: 27215 (part), 27216, 27217 (part), 27228, 27231 (part), 27243 (part), 27253 (part), 27258 (part), 27278 (part), 27302 (part), 27312 (part), 27330 (part), 27332 (part), 27505 (part), 27510, 27511 (part), 27513 (part), 27514 (part), 27515–16, 27517 (part), 27518 (part), 27519 (part), 27523 (part), 27529 (part), 27540 (part), 27546 (part), 27552, 27559 (part), 27560 (part), 27562 (part), 27599, 27601–02, 27603 (part), 27604 (part), 27605 (part), 27606 (part), 27607 (part), 27608 (part), 27609 (part), 27610 (part), 27611, 27612 (part), 27613 (part), 27615 (part), 27616 (part), 27617 (part), 27619–20, 27622, 27625–27, 27629, 27634–36, 27640, 27650, 27658, 27661, 27695, 27698, 27699, 27703 (part), 27705 (part), 27707 (part), 27709, 27711, 27713 (part), 27717, 28301 (part), 28302, 28303 (part), 28304 (part), 28305 (part), 28306 (part), 28309, 28311 (part), 28312 (part), 28314 (part), 28323 (part), 28339 (part), 28356 (part), 28377 (part), 28395 (part), 28445 (part)

* * *

FIFTH DISTRICT

VIRGINIA FOXX, Republican, of Banner Elk, NC; born in New York, NY, June 29, 1943; education: A.B., University of North Carolina, Chapel Hill, NC, 1968; M.A.C.T., University of North Carolina, Chapel Hill, NC, 1972; Ed.D., University of North Carolina, Greensboro, NC, 1985; professional: instructor, Caldwell Community College, Hudson, NC; instructor, Appalachian State University, Boone, NC; Assistant Dean, Appalachian State University, Boone, NC; president, Mayland Community College, Spruce Pine, NC, 1987–94; nursery operator; deputy secretary for management, North Carolina Department of Administration; organizations: member, Watauga County Board of Education, 1967–88; member, North Carolina State Senate, 1994–2004; Executive Committee of North Carolina Citizens for Business and Industry; Z. Smith Reynolds Foundation Advisory Panel; National Advisory Council for Women's Educational Programs; Board of Directors of the NC Center for Public Research; UNC–Chapel Hill Board of Visitors; National Conference of State Legislatures' Blue Ribbon Advisory Panel on Child Care; Foscoe-Grandfather Community Center Board; family: married to Tom Foxx; one daughter; committees: Education and the Workforce; Rules; elected to the 109th Congress on November 2, 2004; reelected to each succeeding Congress.

Office Listings

http://www.foxx.house.gov

2350 Rayburn House Office Building, Washington, DC 20515 .... (202) 225–2071
Chief of Staff.—Brandon Renz. FAX: 225–2995
Legislative Director.—Leslie Goodman.
Press Secretary.—Ericka Perryman.
240 Highway 105 Extension, Suite 200, Boone, NC 28607 .... (828) 265–0240
FAX: 265–0390
3540 Clemmons Road, Suite 125, Clemmons, NC 27012 .... (336) 778–0211
FAX: 778–2290

Counties: ALEXANDER, ALLEGHANY, ASHE, AVERY, CATAWBA, DAVIDSON, DAVIE, FORSYTH, IREDELL, ROWAN, WATAUGA, WILKES, AND YADKIN. CITIES: Advance, Banner Elk, Barber, Belews Creek, Blowing Rock, Boomer, Boone, Boonville, Clemmons, Cleveland, Creston, Crumpler, Deep Gap, Dobson, East Bend, Elk Park, Elkin, Ennice, Ferguson, Fleetwood, Germanton, Glade Valley, Glendale Springs, Granite Falls, Grassy Creek, Hamptonville, Harmony, Hays, Hickory, Hiddenite, High Point, Jefferson, Jonesville, Kernersville, King, Lansing, Laurel Springs, Lenoir, Lewisville, Lexington, Linwood, McGrady, Millers Creek, Mocksville, Mooresville, Moravian Falls, Mount Ulla, North Wilkesboro, Olin, Pfafftown, Piney Creek, Purlear, Roaring Gap, Roaring River, Ronda, Rural Hall, Salisbury, Sparta, State Road, Statesville, Stokesdale, Stony Point, Sugar Grove, Taylorsville, Thomasville, Thurmond, Tobaccoville, Todd, Traphill, Troutman, Union Grove, Vilas, Walkertown, Walnut Cove, Warrensville, West Jefferson, Wilkesboro, Winston Salem, Woodleaf, Yadkinville, and Zionville. Population (2010), 741,095.

ZIP Codes: 27006, 27009–14, 27017–21, 27023, 27028, 27040, 27045, 27050–52, 27054–55, 27094, 27098–99, 27101, 27103–09, 27113–14, 27116, 27127, 27130, 27157, 27262, 27265, 27284–85, 27292, 27294–95, 27299, 27357, 27360, 27374, 28115, 28125, 28144, 28147, 28166, 28601–08, 28615, 28617–18, 28621–27, 28629–31, 28634–36, 28640, 28642–45, 28649, 28651, 28654–56, 28659–60, 28663, 28665, 28668–70, 28672, 28675–79, 28681, 28683–85, 28687, 28689, 28691–94, 28697–98

* * *

SIXTH DISTRICT

HOWARD COBLE, Republican, of Greensboro, NC; born in Greensboro, March 18, 1931; education: Appalachian State University, Boone, NC, 1949–50; A.B., history, Guilford College, Greensboro, NC, 1958; J.D., University of North Carolina School of Law, Chapel Hill, 1962; military service: U.S. Coast Guard as a seaman recruit, 1952; active duty, 1952–56 and 1977–78; reserve duty, 1960–82; retired with rank of captain; last reserve duty assignment, commanding officer, U.S. Coast Guard Reserve Unit, Wilmington, NC; professional: attorney; admitted to North Carolina Bar, 1966; field claim representative and superintendent, auto insurance, 1961–67; elected to North Carolina House of Representatives, 1969; Assistant U.S. Attorney, Middle District of North Carolina, 1969–73; commissioner (secretary), North Carolina Department of Revenue, 1973–77; North Carolina House of Representatives, 1979–83; practiced law with law firm of Turner, Enochs and Sparrow, Greensboro, NC, 1979–84; member: Alamance Presbyterian Church, American Legion, Veterans of Foreign Wars of the United States, Lions Club, Greensboro Bar Association, North Carolina Bar Association, North Carolina State Bar; North Carolina State co-chairman, American Legislative Exchange Council, 1983–84; committees: Judiciary; Transportation and Infrastructure; elected to the 99th Congress on November 6, 1984; reelected to each succeeding Congress.

Office Listings

http://coble.house.gov

2188 Rayburn House Office Building, Washington, DC 20515 .... (202) 225–3065
Chief of Staff / Press Secretary.—Ed McDonald. FAX: 225–8611
Executive Assistant.—Emily Finch.
2102 North Elm Street, Suite B, Greensboro, NC 27408–5100 .... (336) 333–5005
Office Manager.—Kathy McClellan.
1634 North Main Street, Suite 101, High Point, NC 27262–7723 .... (336) 886–5106
District Representative.—Nancy Mazza.
124 West Elm Street, P.O. Box 812, Graham, NC 27253–0812 .... (336) 229–0159
District Representative.—Janine Osborne.
107 Midtown Commons, Madison, NC 27025–1519 .... (336) 427–0044
District Representative.—Lindsay Morris.

Counties: ALAMANCE (part), CASWELL, DURHAM (part), GRANVILLE (part), GUILFORD (part), ORANGE (part), PERSON, ROCKINGHAM, STOKES, AND SURRY. Population (2010) 749,909.

ZIP Codes: 27007, 27009, 27016–17, 27019, 27021–22, 27024–25, 27027, 27030, 27041–48, 27050, 27052–53, 27201, 27212, 27214–15, 27217, 27231, 27233, 27235, 27243–44, 27249, 27253, 27258, 27260, 27262–63, 27265, 27278, 27282–84, 27288, 27291, 27298, 27301–02, 27305–06, 27310–15, 27317, 27320, 27326, 27340, 27343, 27349, 27357–58, 27377, 27379, 27401, 27403, 27405–10, 27455, 27503, 27507, 27514, 27541, 27565, 27572–74, 27582–83, 27704–05, 27712, 28621, 28676, 28683

* * *

SEVENTH DISTRICT

MIKE MCINTYRE, Democrat, of Lumberton, NC; born in Robeson County, August 6, 1956; education: B.A., Phi Beta Kappa Morehead Scholar, 1978, and J.D., 1981, University of North Carolina; upon graduation, received the Algernon Sydney Sullivan Award for ''unselfish interest in the welfare of his fellow man''; professional: attorney; past president, Lumberton Economic Advancement for Dowtown; formerly on board of directors of Lumberton Rotary Club, Chamber of Commerce and a local group home for the mentally handicapped; active in the Boy Scouts of America, and Lumberton PTA; married: the former Dee Strickland; two children; committees: Agriculture; Armed Services; elected to the 105th Congress; reelected to each succeeding Congress.

Office Listings

http://www.house.gov/mcintyre https://www.facebook.com/mikemcintyre
https://twitter.com/repmikemcintyre

2428 Rayburn House Office Building, Washington, DC 20515 .... (202) 225–2731
Chief of Staff / Press Secretary.—Dean Mitchell. FAX: 225–5773
Chief of Constituent Services.—Vivian Lipford.
Legislative Director.—Blair Miligan.
119 Courthouse Drive, P.O. Box 2107, Elizabethtown, NC 28337 .... (910) 862–1437
497 Olde Waterford Way, Suite 206, Leland, NC 28451 .... (910) 399–1134
350 East Market Street, P.O. Box 761, Smithfield, NC 27577 .... (910) 735–0610
District Chief of Staff.—Marie Thompson.

Counties: BLADEN, BRUNSWICK, COLUMBUS, CUMBERLAND (part), DUPLIN, HOKE (part), JOHNSTON, LENOIR (part), NEW HANOVER (part), PENDER (part), ROBESON (part), AND SAMPSON. Population (2010), 733,798.

ZIP Codes: 27501, 27504, 27520, 27524, 27527, 27529, 27542, 27555, 27557, 27568–69, 27576–77, 27591–92, 27597, 27603, 28306, 28312, 28318, 28320, 28325, 28328, 28332, 28334, 28337, 28341, 28344, 28348–49, 28357, 28364–66, 28371, 28376, 28337, 28382, 28384–86, 28391–93, 28399, 28401, 28403, 28405, 28409, 28411–12, 28420, 28422–24, 28428–34, 28436, 28438–39, 28441–45, 28447–53, 28455–58, 28461–70, 28472, 28478–501, 28504, 28508, 28518, 28521, 28525, 28551, 28572, 28574, 28578, 28580

* * *

EIGHTH DISTRICT

RICHARD HUDSON, Republican, of Concord, NC; born in Franklin, VA, November 4, 1971; education: B.A. in history and political science, University of North Carolina at Charlotte, 1996; professional: small business owner; served as District Director for Eighth District Congressman Robin Hayes; served as Chief of Staff for Congresswoman Virginia Foxx, Congressman John Carter and Congressman Mike Conaway; religion: Christian; married: Renee; caucuses: House Manufacturing Caucus, Congressional Textile Caucus, House National Guard and

Reserve Components Caucus, Congressional Sportsmen's Caucus, Congressional Prayer Caucus; committees: Agriculture, Education and the Workforce, Homeland Security; elected to the 113th Congress on November 6, 2012.

Office Listings

http://www.hudson.house.gov

429 Cannon House Office Building, Washington, DC 20515 .... (202) 225–3715
Chief of Staff.—Pepper Natonski. FAX: 225–4036
Communications Director.—Anna Haberlein.
Legislative Director.—Michael Thornberry.
Scheduler.—Ellie Shingleton.
325 McGill Avenue, Suite 500, Concord, NC 28027 .... (704) 786–1612
Deputy Chief of Staff.—Chris Carter.
1015 Fayetteville Road, Rockingham, NC 28379 .... (910) 997–2070

Counties: ANSON, CABARRUS (Part), DAVIDSON (part), MECKLENBURG (part), MONTGOMERY, RANDOLPH (part), RICHMOND, ROBESON (part), ROWAN (part), SCOTLAND, STANLY, AND UNION (part). Population (2010), 701,000.

ZIP Codes: 27205, 27209, 27229, 27239, 27247, 27262, 27281, 27292, 27299, 27306, 27341, 27351, 27356, 27360, 27370–71, 28001–02, 28007, 28009, 28023, 28025–27, 28041, 28071–72, 28075, 28079, 28081–83, 28088, 28091, 28097, 28102–04, 28107, 28109–12, 28115, 28119, 28124, 28127–29, 28133, 28135, 28137–38, 28144, 28146–47, 28163, 28170, 28174, 28213, 28215, 28227, 28262, 28319, 28330, 28338, 28340, 28343, 28345, 28347, 28351–53, 28357–60, 28362–64, 28367, 28369, 28371–72, 28375, 28377, 28379–80, 28383–84, 28386, 28396

* * *

NINTH DISTRICT

ROBERT M. PITTENGER, Republican, of Charlotte, NC; born in Dallas, Texas, August 15, 1948; education: psychology and political science, University of Texas, Austin, TX, 1970; professional: former Assistant to the President of Campus Crusade for Christ; founder of Pittenger Land Investments; North Carolina State Senate, 2002–08; former board member of the Presbyterian Hospital Foundation, Jesse Helms Educational Foundation, and Central Piedmont Community College Foundation; religion: Christian; family: wife: Suzanne Pittenger, four children and seven grandchildren; commissions: Congressional-Executive Commission on China; caucuses: co-chairman of the United Solutions Caucus; committees: Financial Services; elected to the 113th Congress on November 6, 2012.

Office Listings

http://pittenger.house.gov twitter: @reppittenger
www.facebook.com/congressmanpittenger

224 Cannon House Office Building, Washington, DC 20515 .... (202) 225–1976
Chief of Staff.—Brad Jones. FAX: 225–3389
Deputy Chief of Staff and Legislative Director.—Austen Jensen.
Legislative Assistants: Stephen Billy, Michelle Jelnicky.
Legislative Correspondent.—Erin Karriker.
Executive Assistant.—Erin Wall.
Staff Assistant.—Caroline Barbee.
2701 Coltsgate Road, Suite 105, Charlotte, NC 28211 .... (704) 362–1060
District Director and Veterans Specialist.—Robert Becker. FAX: 365–6384
Communications Director.—Jamie Bowers.
Constituent Services Director.—Graham Long.
Constituent Liaisons: Linda Ferster, Chris Sullivan.
Staff Assistant and Case Worker.—Lynne Davis.
116 Morlake Drive, Suite 101A, Mooresville, NC 28117 .... (704) 861–1976
Regional District Director.—Preston Curtis. FAX: 696–8190

Counties: IREDELL (part), MECKLENBURG (part), UNION (part). Population (2010), 733,498.

ZIP Codes: 27013, 28031, 28036, 28078–79, 28104–05, 28107–08, 28110, 28112, 28115, 28117, 28125, 28134, 28166, 28173, 28202–05, 28207–12, 28214–17, 28226–27, 28262, 28269–70, 28273, 28277–78, 28625, 28636, 28660, 28677–78

* * *

TENTH DISTRICT

PATRICK T. MCHENRY, Republican, of Denver, NC; born in Gastonia, NC, October 22, 1975; education: graduated Ashbrook High School, Gastonia, NC; attended North Carolina State

University, Raleigh, NC; B.A., Belmont Abbey College, Belmont, NC, 1999; professional: realtor; media executive; appointed special assistant to the U.S. Secretary of Labor by President George W. Bush in 2001; member, North Carolina House of Representatives, 2002–04; married: Giulia, 2010; organizations: Gaston Chamber of Commerce, Gastonia Rotary Club, the National Rifle Association, Saint Michael Church; board of directors, United Way's Success by Six Youth Program; committees: Financial Services; Oversight and Government Reform; elected to the 109th Congress on November 2, 2004; reelected to each succeeding Congress.

Office Listings

http://www.house.gov/mchenry ww.facebook.com/congressmanmchenry
twitter: @patrickmchenry

2334 Rayburn House Office Building, Washington, DC 20515 .... (202) 225–2576
Chief of Staff.—Parker Poling. FAX: 225–0316
Legislative Director.—Jennifer Flitton.
Press Secretary.—Jeff Butler.
Scheduler.—Lindsey Shackelford.
87 Fourth Street, NW., Suite A, P.O. Box 1830, Hickory, NC 28603 .... (828) 327–6100

Counties: BUNCOMBE (part), CATAWBA (part), CLEVELAND, GASTON, LINCOLN, POLK, AND RUTHERFORD. CITIES AND TOWNSHIPS: Hickory, Lenoir, Morganton, Shelby, and Mooresville. Population (2010), 733,499.

ZIP Codes: 28006, 28012, 28016–21, 28032–34, 28037, 28040, 28043, 28052, 28054, 28056, 28073, 28076–77, 28080, 28086, 28089–90, 28092, 28098, 28101, 28114, 28120, 28139, 28150, 28152, 28160, 28164, 28167–69, 28601–02, 28609–10, 28612–13, 28658, 28673, 28682, 28704, 28709, 28711, 28720, 28722, 28730, 28732, 28746, 28756–57, 28773, 28778, 28782, 28787, 28792, 28801, 28803–06

* * *

ELEVENTH DISTRICT

MARK R. MEADOWS, Republican, of Cashiers, NC; born in Maginot Barracks (Army), Verdun, France, July 28, 1959; education: graduated from the University of South Florida, Tampa, FL; 1980; professional: real estate developer, restaurateur; energy company customer relations director; Macon County Republican Party chairman, 2001–02; serves as a congressional liaison to the United Nations; religion: Christian; married: Debbie Meadows; two children; caucuses: appointed to the Congressional-Executive Commission on China; committees: Foreign Affairs, Oversight and Government Reform; Transportation and Infrastructure; elected to the 113th Congress on November 6, 2012.

Office Listings

http://www.meadows.house.gov

1516 Longworth House Office Building, Washington, DC 20515 .... (202) 225–6401
Chief of Staff.—Kenny West. FAX: 226–6422
Legislative Director.—Philip Newman.
Communications Director.—Emily Miller.
Scheduler.—Eliza Thurston.
200 North Grove Street, Suite 90, Hendersonville, NC 28792 .... (828) 693–5660

Counties: AVERY, BUNCOMBE (part), BURKE, CALDWELL, CHEROKEE, CLAY, GRAHAM, HAYWOOD, HENDERSON, JACKSON, MACON, MADISON, MCDOWELL, MITCHELL, SWAIN, TRANSYLVANIA, AND YANCEY. CITIES AND TOWNSHIPS: Hayesville, Hendersonville, Lenoir, Morganton, and Waynesville. Population (2010), 619,178.

ZIP Codes: 28604, 28645, 28655, 28657, 28701–02, 28704–05, 28707–08, 28712–13, 28715, 28717–19, 28721, 28723, 28730, 28734, 28736, 28739–43, 28747, 28751–54, 28759, 28763, 28771, 28774–75, 28779, 28781, 28783, 28765, 28786–87, 28789–91, 28901–02, 28904–06, 28909

* * *

TWELFTH DISTRICT

VACANT

* * *

THIRTEENTH DISTRICT

GEORGE HOLDING, Republican, of Raleigh, NC; born in Raleigh, April 17, 1968; education: B.A., classics, Wake Forest University, Winston-Salem, NC, 1991; J.D., Wake Forest University Law School, Winston-Salem, NC, 1996; professional: law clerk for U.S. District Judge Terrence Boyle; practiced law in Raleigh with Kilpatrick Stockton; served as legislative counsel to U.S. Senator Jessie Helms, 1998–2002; joined the U.S. Attorney's office for the Eastern District of North Carolina, 2002–06; confirmed by U.S. Senate as the U.S. Attorney for Eastern North Carolina, 2006–11; religion: Baptist; committees: Foreign Affairs; Judiciary; elected to the 113th Congress on November 6, 2012.

Office Listings

http://www.house.gov/holding

507 Cannon House Office Building, Washington, DC 20515 .... (202) 225–3032
Chief of Staff.—Tucker Knott. FAX: 225–0181
Legislative Director.—Jonathan Nabavi.
Press Secretary.—Lindsay Hamilton.
Scheduler.—Katie Lawrence.
3725 National Drive, Suite 101, Raleigh, NC 27605 .... (919) 782–4400
120 Main Street, Fremont, NC 27830 .... (919) 440–5247

Counties: DURHAM (part), EDGECOMBE (part), FRANKLIN (part), GRANVILLE (part), NASH (part), WAKE (part), WAYNE (part), WILSON (part), VANCE (part). Population (2010), 732,434.

ZIP Codes: 27501–02, 27508, 27511, 27513, 27518–20, 27522–26, 27529–31, 27534, 27537, 27539–40, 27542, 27544–45, 27549, 27557, 27560, 27565, 27569, 27571, 27581, 27587, 27591–92, 27596–97, 27603–10, 27612–17, 27703–04, 27801, 27803–04, 27807–09, 27813, 27816, 27822, 27829, 27830, 27851–52, 27856, 27863–64, 27878, 27880, 27882–83, 27886, 27893, 27896, 28333, 28365, 28551, 28578

NORTH DAKOTA

(Population 2010, 675,591)

SENATORS

JOHN HOEVEN, Republican, of Bismarck, ND; born in Bismarck, March 13, 1957; education: B.A., Dartmouth College, Hanover, NH, 1979; M.B.A., Northwestern University, Chicago, IL, 1981; professional: executive vice president, First Western Bank, Minot, 1986–93; president and CEO, Bank of North Dakota, 1993–2000; Governor of North Dakota, 2000–10; religion: Catholic; family: married to Mikey; two children; caucuses: Air Force Caucus; Congressional Sportsmen's Caucus; Senate Western Caucus; Norway Caucus; Rural Education Caucus; National Guard Caucus; E–911 Caucus; Rural Health Caucus; General Aviation Caucus; Impact Aid Coalition; committees: Agriculture, Nutrition, and Forestry; Appropriations; Energy and Natural Resources; Indian Affairs; elected to the U.S. Senate on November 2, 2010.

Office Listings

http://hoeven.senate.gov

338 Russell Senate Office Building, Washington, DC 20510 .... (202) 224–2551
FAX: 224–7999
Chiefs of Staff: Don Larson, Ryan Bernstein.
Legislative Director.—Tony Eberhard.
Communications Director.—Don Canton.
U.S. Federal Building, 220 East Rosser Avenue, Room 312, Bismarck, ND 58501 (701) 250–4618
FAX: 239–5112
State Director.—Don Larson.
1802 32nd Avenue South, Suite B, Fargo, ND 58103 .... (701) 239–5389
Federal Building, 102 North Fourth Street, Room 108, Grand Forks, ND 58203 ..... (701) 746–8972
315 Main Street South, Suite 204, Minot, ND 58701 .... (701) 838–1361
Williston, ND .... (701) 580–4535

* * *

HEIDI HEITKAMP, Democrat, of Mandan, ND; born in Breckenridge, MN, October 30, 1955; education: B.A., University of North Dakota, ND, 1977; J.D., Lewis and Clark Law School, 1980; professional: attorney, United States Environmental Protection Agency, 1980–81; attorney, Office of the North Dakota State Tax Commissioner, 1981–86; Tax Commissioner, State of North Dakota, 1986–92; Attorney General, State of North Dakota, 1992–2000; Director, Dakota Gasification Company, 2001–12; religion: Catholic; family: married to Dr. Darwin Lange; two children; caucuses: Afterschool Caucus; Bicameral Congressional Arthritis Caucus; Bipartisan Task Force on Tribal Colleges and Universities; Congressional Diabetes Caucus; Congressional ICBM Coalition; Congressional Next Generation 9-1-1 Caucus; Defense Communities Caucus; General Aviation Caucus; Impact Aid Coalition; Law Enforcement Caucus; National Guard Caucus; Nursing Caucus; Ports to Plains Caucus; Rural Health Caucus; Social Work Caucus; committees: Agriculture, Nutrition and Forestry; Banking, Housing and Urban Affairs; Homeland Security and Governmental Affairs; Indian Affairs; Small Business and Entrepreneurship; elected to the U.S. Senate on November 6, 2012.

Office Listings

http://heitkamp.senate.gov https://twitter.com/senatorheitkamp
www.facebook.com/senatorheidiheitkamp

502 Hart Senate Office Building, Washington, DC 20510 .... (202) 224–2043
FAX: 224–7776
Chief of Staff.—Tessa Gould.
Legislative Director.—Tracee Sutton.
220 East Rosser Avenue, Room 228, Bismarck, ND 58501 .... (701) 258–4648
657 Second Avenue North, Room 306, Fargo, ND 58102 .... (701) 232–8030
State Director.—Ryan Nagle.
33 South 3rd Street, Suite B, Grand Forks, ND 58201 .... (701) 775–9601
100 First Street, SW., Room 105, Minot, ND 58701 .... (701) 852–0703
40 First Avenue West, Suite 202, Dickinson, ND 58601 .... (701) 225–0974

REPRESENTATIVE

AT LARGE

KEVIN CRAMER, Republican, of Bismarck, ND; born in Rolette, ND, January 21, 1961; education: B.A., social work, Concordia College, Moorhead, MN, 1983; M.A., management,

University of Mary, Bismarck, ND, 2003; professional: chairman, North Dakota Republican Party, 1991–93; North Dakota Tourism Director, 1993–97; State Economic Development & Finance Director, 1997–2000; Executive Director, Harold Schafer Leadership Foundation, 2000–03; North Dakota Public Service Commissioner, 2003–12; married: Kris Cramer; children: Ian, Isaac, Rachel, Annie, and Abel; committees: Natural Resources, Science, Space, and Technology; elected to the 113th Congress on November 6, 2012.

Office Listings

http://cramer.house.gov   facebook.com/congressmankevincramer   twitter.com/repkevincramer

1032 Longworth House Office Building, Washington, DC 20515 .... (202) 225–2611
Chief of Staff.—Mark Gruman. FAX: 226–0893
Legislative Director.—Chris Marohl.
Communications Director.—Matt Becker.
Federal Building, 220 East Rosser Avenue, Room 328, Bismarck, ND 58501 .... (701) 224–0355
3217 Fiechtner Drive South, Suite D, Fargo, ND 58103 .... (701) 356–2216
315 Main Street South, Suite 203, Minot, ND 58701 .... (701) 839–0255
4200 James Ray Drive, Office 600, Grand Forks, ND 58202 .... (701) 738–4880
State Director.—Lisa Gibbens.

Population (2010), 672,591.

ZIP Codes: 58001–02, 58004–09, 58011–13, 58015–18, 58021, 58027, 58029, 58030–33, 58035–36, 58038, 58040–43, 58045–49, 58051–54, 58056–65, 58067–69, 58071–72, 58074–79, 58081, 58102–09, 58121–22, 58124–26, 58201–06, 58208, 58210, 58212, 58214, 58216, 58218–20, 58222–25, 58227–31, 58233, 58235–41, 58243–44, 58249–51, 58254–62, 58265–67, 58269–78, 58281–82, 58301, 58310–11, 58313, 58316–19, 58321, 58323–25, 58327, 58329–32, 58335, 58338–39, 58341, 58343–46, 58348, 58351–53, 58355–57, 58359, 58361–63, 58365–70, 58372, 58374, 58377, 58379–82, 58384–86, 58401–02, 58405, 58413, 58415–16, 58418, 58420–26, 58428–31, 58433, 58436, 58438–45, 58448, 58451–52, 58454–56, 58458, 58460–61, 58463–64, 58466–67, 58472, 58474–84, 58486–88, 58490, 58492, 58494–97, 58501–07, 58520–21, 58523–24, 58528–33, 58535, 58538, 58540–42, 58544–45, 58549, 58552, 58554, 58558–66, 58568–73, 58575–77, 58579–81, 58601–02, 58620–23, 58625–27, 58630–32, 58634, 58636, 58638–47, 58649–56, 58701–05, 58707, 58710–13, 58716, 58718, 58721–23, 58725, 58727, 58730–31, 58733–37, 58740–41, 58744, 58746–48, 58750, 58752, 58755–63, 58765, 58768–73, 58775–76, 58778–79, 58781–85, 58787–90, 58792–95, 58801–02, 58830–31, 58833, 58835, 58838, 58843–45, 58847, 58849, 58852–54, 58856

OHIO

(Population 2010, 11,536,504)

SENATORS

SHERROD BROWN, Democrat, of Avon Lake, OH; born in Mansfield, OH, November 9, 1952; education: B.A., Yale University, New Haven, CT, 1974; M.A., education, Ohio State University, Columbus, OH, 1979; M.A., public administration, Ohio State University, Columbus, OH, 1981; professional: Ohio House of Representatives, 1975-83; Ohio Secretary of State, 1983–91; U.S. House of Representatives, 1992–2006; member: Eagle Scouts of America; married: Connie Schultz; children: Emily, Elizabeth, Andrew and Caitlin; committees: Agriculture, Nutrition, and Forestry; Banking, Housing, and Urban Affairs; Finance; Veterans' Affairs; Select Committee on Ethics; elected to the 103rd Congress on November 3, 1992; reelected to each succeeding Congress; elected to the U.S. Senate on November 7, 2006; reelected to the U.S. Senate on November 6, 2012.

Office Listings

http://brown.senate.gov

713 Hart Senate Office Building, Washington, DC 20510 .... (202) 224–2315
Chief of Staff.—Mark Powden. FAX: 228–6321
Legislative Director.—Jeremy Hekhuis.
Communications Director.—Meghan Dubyak.
Press Secretaries: Lauren Kulik, Allison Preiss.
1301 East Ninth Street, Suite 1710, Cleveland, OH 44114 .... (216) 522–7272
State Director.—John Ryan.
Deputy State Director.—Beth Thames.
425 Walnut Street, Suite 2310, Cincinnati, OH 45202 .... (513) 684–1021
200 North High Street, Room 614, Columbus, OH 43215 .... (614) 469–2083
205 West Erie Avenue, Suite 312, Lorain, OH 44052 .... (440) 242–4100

* * *

ROBERT J. PORTMAN, Republican, of Terrace Park, OH; born in Cincinnati, December 19, 1955; education: B.A., Dartmouth College, Hanover, NH, 1979; J.D., University of Michigan Law School, Ann Arbor, MI, 1984; professional: associate counsel to George H.W. Bush, 1989; deputy assistant and director, White House Office of Legislative Affairs, 1989–91; member of the U.S. House of Representatives, 1993–2005; U.S. Trade Representative, 2005–06; Director of the Office of Management and Budget, 2006–07; religion: Methodist; married: Jane Portman; three children: Jed, Will, and Sally; committees: Budget; Energy and Natural Resources; Finance; Homeland Security and Governmental Affairs; elected to the U.S. Senate on November 2, 2010.

Office Listings

http://portman.senate.gov

448 Russell Senate Office Building, Washington, DC 20510 .... (202) 224–3353
Chief of Staff.—Rob Lehman.
Communications Director.—Vacant.
Legislative Director.—Pam Thiessen.
Director of Operations.—Jim Durrett.
37 West Broad Street, Suite 300, Columbus, OH 43215 .... (614) 469–6774
State Director.—Teri Geiger.
District Director.—Steve White.
District Representative.—Vacant.
312 Walnut Street, Suite 3075, Cincinnati, OH 45202 .... (513) 684–3265
District Director.—Connie Laug.
District Representative.—Vacant.
1240 East 9th Street, Room 3061, Cleveland, OH 44199 .... (216) 522–7095
District Director.—Caryn Candisky.
District Representative.—George Brown.
420 Madison Avenue, Room 1210, Toledo, OH 43604 .... (419) 259–3895
District Representative.—Wes Fahrbach.

REPRESENTATIVES

FIRST DISTRICT

STEVE CHABOT, Republican, of Cincinnati, OH; born in Cincinnati, January 22, 1953; education: graduated from LaSalle High School in Cincinnati; B.A., College of William and Mary, Williamsburg, VA, 1975; J.D., Salmon P. Chase College of Law, Highland Heights, KY, 1978; professional: teacher, 1975–76; member of the city council, Cincinnati, OH, 1985–90; commissioner, Hamilton County, OH, 1990–94; elected as a Republican to the 104th–110th Congresses, January 3, 1995–January 3, 2009; served as ranking member on the Committee on Small Business, 110th Congress; family: wife, Donna; two children: Erica and Randy; committees: Foreign Affairs; Judiciary; Small Business; elected to the 112th Congress on November 2, 2010; reelected to the 113th Congress on November 6, 2012.

Office Listings

http://chabot.house.gov facebook: repstevechabot twitter: @repstevechabot

2371 Rayburn House Office Building, Washington, DC 20515 .... (202) 225–2216
Chief of Staff.—Mark Wellman. FAX: 225–3012
Legislative Director.—Steve Denis.
Director of Scheduling / Administration.—Alyssa Polewski.
Carew Tower, 441 Vine Street, Room 3003, Cincinnati, OH 45202 .... (513) 684–2723
District Director.—Mike Cantwell. FAX: 421–8722
Communications Director.—Brian Griffith.
11 South Broadway Street, Third Floor, Lebanon, OH 45036 .... (513) 421–8704

Counties: HAMILTON (part), WARREN. Population (2010), 721,032.

ZIP Codes: 45001–02, 45005, 45030, 45033–34, 45036, 45039–40, 45052, 45054, 45065–66, 45068, 45111, 45140, 45152, 45162, 45202–07, 45210–11, 45214–17, 45219–21, 45223–25, 45229, 45232–33, 45237–43, 45246–49, 45251–52

* * *

SECOND DISTRICT

BRAD WENSTRUP, Republican, of Cincinnati; born in Cincinnati, OH, June 17, 1958; education: B.A., University of Cincinnati, 1980; B.S. and D.P.M., William M. Scholl College of Podiatric Medicine, Chicago, IL, 1985; professional: private practice physician/surgeon, 1986–2012; United States Army Reserve, 1998–present; religion: Catholic; married: Monica; children: Brad R. Wenstrup, Jr.; committees: Armed Services; Veterans Affairs; elected to the 113th Congress on November 6, 2012.

Office Listings

http://wenstrup.house.gov https://www.facebook.com/repbradwenstrup
twitter: @repbradwenstrup

1223 Longworth House Office Building, Washington, DC 20515 .... (202) 225–3164
Chief of Staff.—Derek Harley. FAX: 225–1992
Legislative Director.—Lisa Collins.
Communications Director.—Greg Brooks.
Scheduler.—April Lyman.
7954 Beechmont Avenue, Suite 200, Cincinnati, OH 45255 .... (513) 474–7777
District Director.—John Stanton.
170 North Main Street, Peebles, OH 45660 .... (513) 605–1380
4350 Aicholtz Road, Cincinnati, OH 45245 .... (513) 605–1389

Counties: ADAMS, BROWN, CLERMONT, HAMILTON (part), HIGHLAND, PIKE, SCIOTO (part), AND ROSS (part). CITIES AND TOWNSHIPS: Anderson TWP, Batavia, Blue Ash, Cincinnati (part), Chillicothe, Georgetown, Hillsboro, Loveland, Manchester, Milford, Mount Orab, New Richmond, Norwood, Peebles, Piketon, Portsmouth, Ripley, Sardinia, and Union TWP. Population (2010), 721,031.

ZIP Codes: 45101–03, 45106–07, 45112, 45115, 45118, 45120–22, 45130–31, 45133, 45140, 45142, 45144, 45150, 45153–54, 45156–57, 45160, 45162, 45167–68, 45171, 45174, 45176, 45202, 45206, 45208–09, 45212–13, 45226–27, 45230, 45236, 45241–46, 45255, 45601, 45612–13, 45616, 45624, 45642, 45646, 45648, 45650, 45652, 45657, 45660–63, 45671, 45679, 45684, 45690, 45693, 45697

* * *

THIRD DISTRICT

JOYCE BEATTY, Democrat, of Blacklick, OH; born in Dayton, OH, March 12, 1950; education: B.A., Central State University, Wilberforce, OH, 1972; M.S., Wright State University, Fairborn, OH, 1974; attended University of Cincinnati, Cincinnati, OH; professional: executive director, Montgomery County, OH; human services, professor; businesswoman; member, Ohio State House of Representatives, 1999–2008; administrator, The Ohio State University, 2008–12; married: Otto; stepchildren: Laurel and Otto; committees: Financial Services; elected to the 113th Congress on November 6, 2012.

Office Listings

http://www.beatty.house.gov

417 Cannon House Office Building, Washington, DC 20515 .... (202) 225–4324
Chief of Staff.—Kimberly Ross. FAX: 225–1984
Legislative Director.—Jennifer Storipan.
Scheduler / Executive Assistant.—Ashley-Dior Thomas.
471 East Broad Street, Suite 1100, Columbus, OH 43215 .... (614) 220–0003
District / Communications Director.—Greg Beswick. FAX: 220–5640

Counties: FRANKLIN (part). Population (2010), 732,258.

ZIP Codes: 43004, 43026, 43054, 43068, 43081, 43085, 43109–10, 43119, 43123, 43125, 43137, 43201–07, 43209–15, 43217, 43219, 43221–24, 43227–32

* * *

FOURTH DISTRICT

JAMES D. ''JIM'' JORDAN, Republican, of Urbana, OH; born in Troy, OH, February 17, 1964; education: graduated, Graham High School, St. Paris, OH, 1982; B.S. in economics, University of Wisconsin, Madison, WI, 1986; M.A. in education, The Ohio State University, Columbus, OH, 1991; J.D., Capital University School of Law, Columbus, OH, 2001; professional: assistant wrestling coach, The Ohio State University, 1987–95; State Representative, Ohio House of Representatives, 85th District, 1995–2001; State Senator, Ohio State Senate, 12th District, 2001–07; awards: four-time high school wrestling champion (Ohio), 1979–82; two-time NCAA Division I National Wrestling Champion, 1985–86; three-time All American, 1984–86; Wisconsin Badgers Hall of Fame; third place, Olympic Trials in Wrestling, 1988; Friend of the Taxpayer, Americans for Tax Reform, 1997; Leadership in Government Award from the Ohio Roundtable and Freedom Forum, 2001; awards from the United Conservatives of Ohio: Outstanding Freshman Legislator Award, 1996; Watchdog of the Treasury, 1996, 2000, 2004; Pro-Life Legislator of the Year, 1998; Outstanding Legislator Award, 2004; Hero of the Taxpayer, Americans for Tax Reform, 2007; National Legislator of the Year, Coalitions for America, 2012; Freedom Fighter Award, Freedom Works, 2012; activities: Grace Bible Church, Springfield; Local and National Right to Life organizations; Champaign County Republican Executive Committee; married: Polly (Stickley) Jordan; parents: John and Shirley Jordan; children: Rachel, Benjamin, Jessie, and Issac; committees: Oversight and Government Reform; Judiciary; elected to the 110th Congress on November 7, 2006; reelected to each succeeding Congress.

Office Listings

http://www.jordan.house.gov https://www.facebook.com/repjimjordan
twitter.com/jim_jordan

1524 Longworth House Office Building, Washington, DC 20515 .... (202) 225–2676
Chief of Staff.—Ray Yonkura. FAX: 226–0577
Legislative Director.—Jared Dilley.
Executive Assistant / Scheduler.—Melissa Evans.
3121 West Elm Plaza, Lima, OH 45805–2516 .... (419) 999–6455
13B East Main Street, Norwalk, OH 44857 .... (419) 663–1426
District Director.—Ray Yonkura.

Counties: ALLEN, AUGLAIZE, CHAMPAIGN, CRAWFORD, ERIE (part), HURON (part), LOGAN (part), MARION (part), MERCER (part), SANDUSKY, SENECA, SHELBY, AND UNION. Population (2010), 721,032.

ZIP Codes: 43009, 43036, 43044–45, 43047, 43060, 43067, 43070, 43072, 43077, 43084, 43310–11, 43314–26, 43330–38, 43340–51, 43356–60, 43407, 43410, 43420, 43431, 43435, 43442, 44049, 44802, 44809, 44814–16, 44818, 44820,

44828, 44836, 44841, 44846, 44849, 44853–54, 44856, 44861, 44864–65, 44867, 44875, 44881, 44883, 44887, 45302, 45306, 45312, 45317, 45326, 45333–34, 45336, 45340, 45344, 45353, 45356, 45360, 45363, 45365, 45380, 45388–89, 45502, 45801–02, 45804–10, 45812, 45819–20, 45822, 45830, 45833, 45845, 45850, 45854, 45865–66, 45969–71, 45877, 45884–85, 45887–88, 45894–96

* * *

FIFTH DISTRICT

ROBERT E. ''BOB'' LATTA, Republican, of Bowling Green, OH; born in Bluffton, OH, April 18, 1956; graduated, Bowling Green High School, Bowling Green, OH, 1974; Bowling Green State University, Bowling Green, OH, 1978; B.A., history, University of Toledo School of Law, Toledo, OH, 1981; J.D., legislator, lawyer; awards: Ohio Farm Bureau ''Friend of Farm Bureau'' Award, 2008; the United States Chamber of Commerce ''Spirit of Enterprise'' Award, 2008; American Conservative Union ''ACU Conservative'' Award, 2008; United Conservatives of Ohio ''Watchdog of the Treasury'' in 1998, 2000, and 2005; The U.S. Sportsmen's Alliance, ''Patriot Award'', 2002 and 2012; Ohio National Guard ''Major General Charles Dick Award for Legislative Excellence'', 1999; ''President's Award'', 2006; religion: Roman Catholic; family: wife, Marcia ''Sloan'' Latta; daughters, Elizabeth and Maria Latta; member, Bowling Green Noon Kiwanis, Bowling Green Chamber of Commerce; Wood County Farm Bureau; serves as an Assistant Majority Whip; co-chairman of the Congressional Sportsmen's Caucus; co-chair of the Republican New Media Caucus; committees: Energy and Commerce; elected to the 111th Congress on November 4, 2008; reelected to each succeeding Congress.

Office Listings

http://latta.house.gov

2448 Rayburn House Office Building, Washington, DC 20515 .... (202) 225–6405
Chief of Staff.—Ryan Walker. FAX: 225–1985
Legislative Director.—Allison Witt.
Scheduler.—Erin Partee.
1045 North Main Street, Suite 6, Bowling Green, OH 43402 .... (419) 354–8700
101 Clinton Street, Suite 1200, Defiance, OH 43512 .... (419) 782–1996
318 Dorney Plaza, Room 302, Findlay, OH 45840 .... (419) 422–7791

Counties: DEFIANCE, FULTON, HANCOCK, HARDIN, HENRY, LUCAS (part), MERCER (part), OTTAWA, PAULDING, PUTNAM, VAN WERT, WILLIAMS, WOOD, AND WYANDOT. Population (2010), 726,090.

ZIP Codes: 43310, 43316, 43323, 43326, 43330–32, 43337, 43340, 43345, 43347, 43351, 43359, 43402–03, 43406, 43408, 43412–13, 43416, 43430, 43432, 43437, 43443, 43445, 43447, 43449–52, 43457–58, 43460, 43462–63, 43465–69, 43501–02, 43504–06, 43511–12, 43515–19, 43521–29, 43531–37, 43540–43, 43545, 43547–49, 43551, 43553–58, 43560, 43565–67, 43569–71, 43605–06, 43613–15, 43617, 43619, 43623, 44802, 44804, 44817, 44830, 44844, 44849, 44882, 45810, 45812–14, 45816–17, 45821–22, 45827–28, 45830, 45831–33, 45835–36, 45838, 45840–41, 45843–44, 45846, 45849–51, 45853, 45855–56, 45858–59, 45861–64, 45867–68, 45872–77, 45879–82, 45886–87, 45889–91, 45894, 45896–99

* * *

SIXTH DISTRICT

WILLIAM L. ''BILL'' JOHNSON, Republican, of Marietta, OH; born in Roseboro, NC, November 10, 1954; raised in Roseboro, NC; education: B.A., graduated *summa cum laude* at Troy University; Troy, AL, 1979; M.A., computer sciences, Georgia Tech; Atlanta, GA, 1984; professional: co-founder of Johnson-Schley Management Group, Inc.; founder of J2 Business Solutions, Inc.; chief information officer of a global manufacturer of highly electronic components for the transportation industry; military: retired as Lieutenant Colonel, distinguished graduate from the Air Force Reserve Officer Training Corps, Squadron Officers School, and Air Command and Staff College, religion: Protestant; family: married to LeeAnn Johnson; children: Nathan, Joshua, Julie, and Jessica; awards: recipient of Air Force Meritorious Service Medal; Air Force Commendation Medal; National Defense Service Medal; caucuses: Pro-Life; Coal; Marcellus Shale; Air Force; House Republican Israel; Congressional Sportsmen; Congressional Prayer; Military Veterans; Congressional Anti-Terrorism; Congressional Wounded to Work; Congressional China; Congressional Turkish; United Service Organizations Congressional; Congressional Taiwan; Ohio River Basin; committees: Energy and Commerce; elected to the 112th Congress on November 2, 2010; reelected to the 113th Congress on November 6, 2012.

Office Listings

http://billjohnson.house.gov

1710 Longworth House Office Building, Washington, DC 20515 .... (202) 225–5705

Chief of Staff.—Mike Smullen.
Legislative Director.—Patrick Orth.
Communications Director.—Dan Schneider.
Scheduler.—Kaitlin Beck.
246 Front Street, Marietta, OH 45750 .... (740) 376–0868
192 East State Street, Salem, OH 44460 .... (330) 337–6951
202 Park Avenue, Suite C, Ironton, OH 45638 .... (740) 534–9431
116 Southgate Parkway, Cambridge, OH 43725 .... (740) 432–2366

Counties: ATHENS (part), BELMONT, CARROLL, COLUMBIANA, GALLIA, GUERNSEY, HARRISON, JACKSON, JEFFERSON, LAWRENCE, MAHONING (part), MEIGS, MONROE, MUSKINGUM (part), NOBLE, SCIOTO (part), TUSCARAWAS (part), AND WASHINGTON. Population (2010), 721,032.

ZIP Codes: 43701, 43711, 43713, 43716–19, 43722–25, 43732–33, 43736, 43747, 43749–50, 43754–55, 43759, 43762, 43767–68, 43772–73, 43778–80, 43786–88, 43793, 43802, 43812, 43821–22, 43830, 43832, 43837, 43842, 43901–08, 43910, 43912–15, 43917, 43920, 43925–28, 43930–35, 43938–40, 43942–48, 43950–53, 43961–64, 43967–68, 43970–74, 43976–77, 43983, 43985–86, 43988, 44401, 44406, 44408, 44413, 44423, 44427, 44431–32, 44441–45, 44449, 44451–52, 44454–55, 44460, 44493, 44514, 44601, 44607, 44609, 44615, 44620–21, 44625, 44629, 44634, 44643–44, 44651, 44653, 44656–57, 44663, 44672, 44675, 44682–83, 44688, 44693, 44695, 44699, 44730, 45601, 45613–14, 45619–21, 45623, 45629, 45631, 45634, 45636, 45638, 45640, 45645, 45648, 45650, 45652, 45653, 45656, 45658–59, 45662–63, 45669, 45672, 45674, 45678, 45680, 45682, 45685–86, 45688, 45692, 45694, 45696, 45701, 45710–11, 45714–15, 45721, 45723–24, 45727, 45729, 45734–35, 45741–46, 45750, 45760, 45767–73, 45775–76, 45779, 45784, 45786–89

* * *

SEVENTH DISTRICT

ROBERT B. GIBBS, Republican, of Lakeville, OH; born in Peru, IN, June 14, 1954; education: graduated from Bay Village Senior High School, Bay Village, OH; A.A.S., Ohio State University Agricultural Technical Institute, Wooster, OH, 1974; professional: technician; farmer; business owner; president, Ohio Farm Bureau Federation; member of the Ohio State House of Representatives, 2003–09; member of the Ohio State Senate, 2009–10; married: Jody Gibbs; children: Adam, Amy, and Andrew; committees: Agriculture; Transportation and Infrastructure; elected to the 112th Congress on November 2, 2010; reelected to the 113th Congress on November 6, 2012.

Office Listings

http://www.gibbs.house.gov

329 Cannon House Office Building, Washington, DC 20515 .... (202) 225–6265
Chief of Staff.—Ryan Stenger. FAX: 225–3394
Scheduler.—Meghan Keivel.
Legislative Director.—Corry Marshall.
Senior Policy Advisor.—Emily Tully.
Legislative Aides: Joe Price, Pat Tully.
Communications Director.—Lauren O'Toole.
110 Cottage Street, Ashland, OH 44805 .... (419) 207–0650
District Director.—Dallas Gerber. FAX: 207–0655

Counties: HURON (part), MEDINA (part), RICHLAND (part), KNOX, HOLMES, ASHLAND, COSHOCTON (part), TUSCARAWAS (part), STARK (part), LORAIN (part). Population (2010), 726,076.

ZIP Codes: 43005–06, 43011, 43014, 43019, 43022, 43028, 43037, 43050, 43080, 43749, 43804, 43811–12, 43821–22, 43824, 43832, 43836, 43843–44, 43845, 44011, 44028, 44035, 44039, 44044, 44050, 44090, 44149, 44212, 44214–15, 44235, 44253–54, 44256, 44273, 44275, 44280, 44287, 44601, 44608, 44610–13, 44618, 44624, 44626–28, 44632–34, 44637–38, 44641, 44643, 44646–47, 44652, 44654, 44657, 44661–62, 44666, 44669–70, 44676, 44681, 44685, 44687–90, 44702–10, 44714, 44718, 44720–21, 44805, 44807, 44811, 44813, 44822, 44826–27, 44833, 44837–38, 44840, 44842–43, 44847–48, 44850–51, 44855, 44857, 44859, 44864–66, 44874–75, 44878, 44880–90, 44903, 44905–07

* * *

EIGHTH DISTRICT

JOHN A. BOEHNER, Republican, of West Chester, OH; born in Reading, OH, November 17, 1949; education: graduated, Moeller High School, Cincinnati, OH, 1968; B.S., Xavier University, 1977; president, Nucite Sales, Inc.; Ohio House of Representatives, 1984–90; ranking Republican member, Commerce and Labor Committee; Energy and Environment Committee; Judiciary and Criminal Justice; elected, Union Township Trustees, 1981; elected, president, Union Township Board of Trustees, 1984; member: St. John Catholic Church; Ohio Farm Bureau; Lakota Hills Homeowners Association; Knights of Columbus, Pope John XXIII; Union Chamber of Commerce; American Heart Association Board; Butler County Mental Health Association; YMCA Capital Campaign; Union Elementary School PTA; Middletown Chamber of Commerce; American Legion Post 218 of Middletown Butler County Trustees and Clerks Association; married the former Deborah Gunlack, 1973; two children: Lindsay, Tricia; elected to the 102nd Congress; reelected to each succeeding Congress; elected Republican Leader in the 109th, 110th and 111th Congresses; elected Speaker of the House in the 112th and 113th Congresses.

Office Listings

http://johnboehner.house.gov https://twitter.com/speakerboehner
https://www.facebook.com/officeofspeakerboehner

1011 Longworth House Office Building, Washington, DC 20515 .... (202) 225–6205
Chief of Staff.—Mick Krieger. FAX: 225–5117
Press Secretary.—Brittany Bramell.
7969 Cincinnati-Dayton Road, Suite B, West Chester, OH 45069 .... (513) 779–5400
12 South Plum Street, Troy, Ohio 45373 .... (937) 339–1524
76 East High Street, 3rd Floor, Springfield, OH 45502 .... (937) 322–1120

Counties: BUTLER, CLARK, DARKE, MIAMI, PREBLE, MERCER (part). Population (2010), 721,032.

ZIP Codes: 43010, 43044, 43153, 45003–04, 45011–15, 45018, 45042, 45044, 45050, 45053, 45055–56, 45061–64, 45067, 45069–71, 45241, 45246, 45303–04, 45308, 45310–12, 45317–26, 45328, 45330–32, 45337–39, 45341, 45344, 45346–49, 45361–62, 45368–69, 45371–74, 45378, 45380–83, 45387–88, 45390, 45501–06, 45822, 45826, 45828, 45846, 45860, 45862, 45866, 45869, 45882–83, 45894, 45898

* * *

NINTH DISTRICT

MARCY KAPTUR, Democrat, of Toledo, OH; born in Toledo, June 17, 1946; education: graduated, St. Ursula Academy, Toledo, 1964; B.A., University of Wisconsin, Madison, 1968; Master of Urban Planning, University of Michigan, Ann Arbor, 1974; attended University of Manchester, England, 1974; professional: urban planner; assistant director for urban affairs, domestic policy staff, White House, 1977–79; American Planning Association and American Institute of Certified Planners Fellow; member: National Center for Urban Ethnic Affairs Advisory Committee; University of Michigan Urban Planning Alumni Association; NAACP Urban League; Polish Museum; Polish American Historical Association; Lucas County Democratic Party Executive Committee; Democratic Women's Campaign Association; Little Flower Parish Church; House Auto Parts Task Force; co-chair, Ukrainian and 4–H Caucuses; religion: Roman Catholic; committees: Appropriations; elected on November 2, 1982, to the 98th Congress; reelected to each succeeding Congress.

Office Listings

http://www.kaptur.house.gov

2186 Rayburn House Office Building, Washington, DC 20515 .... (202) 225–4146
Chief of Staff.—Steve Katich.
Deputy Chief of Staff.—Nathan Facey. FAX: (202) 225–7711
Office Manager / Scheduler.—Jennifer Holland.
One Maritime Plaza, Suite 600, Toledo, OH 43604 .... (419) 259–7500
16024 Madison Street, Suite 3, Lakewood, OH 44107 .... (216) 767–5933
FAX: (419) 255–9623
5592 Broadview Road, Room 101, Parma, OH 44134 .... (440) 799–8499
FAX: (419) 225–9623

Counties: ERIE COUNTY. CITIES AND TOWNSHIPS: Bellevue, Berlin Heights, Berlinville, Birmingham, Bloomingville, Bronson, Castalia, Chatham, Clarksfield, Collins, East Townsend, Fitchville, Hartland, Huron, Kimball, Litchfield, Milan, Mitiwanga, Monroeville, New London, Norwalk, Nova, Olena, Ridgefield, River Corners, Ruggles, Ruggles Beach, Sandusky, Shinrock, Spencer, Steuben, Sullivan, Wakeman, West Clarksfield. LORAIN COUNTY. CITIES AND TOWNSHIPS: Amherst, Beaver Park, Belden, Beulah Beach, Brownhelm, Columbia Station, Elyria, Grafton, Henrietta, Kipton, Lagrange, Linwood Park, Lorain, North Eaton, Oberlin, Ridgeville, Rochester, South Amherst, Vermilion, Wellington. LUCAS COUNTY (part). CITIES AND TOWNSHIPS: Berkey, Curtice, Gypsum, Harbor View, Holland, Maumee, Monclova, Northwood, Oregon, Swanton, Sylvania, Toledo, Waterville, Whitehouse, Woodville. OTTAWA COUNTY. CITIES AND TOWNSHIPS: Bay Shore, Bono, Catawba Island, Clay Center, Danbury, Eagle Beach, Elliston, Elmore, Gem Beach, Genoa, Graytown, Hessville, Isle St. George, Kelleys Island, Lacarne, Lakeside, Lindsey, Marblehead, Martin, Oak Harbor, Port Clinton, Portage, Put-in-Bay, Rocky Ridge, Springbrook, Vickery, Washington, Wayne, Whites Landing, and Williston. Population (2010), 721,032.

ZIP Codes: 43408, 43412, 43416, 43430, 43432–34, 43436, 43438–40, 43442, 43445–47, 43449, 43452, 43456, 43458, 43464, 43468–69, 43504, 43528, 43537, 43542, 43558, 43560, 43566, 43571, 43601–18, 43620, 43623–24, 43635, 43652, 43656–57, 43659–61, 43666–67, 43681–82, 43697, 43699, 44001, 44028, 44035, 44044, 44049–50, 44053, 44074, 44089–90, 44253, 44256, 44275, 44280, 44811, 44814, 44816, 44824, 44826, 44839, 44846–47, 44851, 44857, 44859, 44870–71, 44880, 44889

* * *

TENTH DISTRICT

MICHAEL R. TURNER, Republican, of Dayton, OH; born in Dayton, January 11, 1960; education: B.A., Ohio Northern University, 1982; J.D., Case Western Reserve University Law School, 1985; M.B.A., University of Dayton, 1992; professional: attorney; Ohio Bar Association; California Bar Association; Bar of the Supreme Court of the United States; public service: Mayor of Dayton, 1994–2002; children: Jessica and Carolyn; committees: Armed Services; Oversight and Government Reform; elected to the 108th Congress on November 5, 2002; reelected to each succeeding Congress.

Office Listings

http://www.turner.house.gov

2239 Rayburn House Office Building, Washington, DC 20515 .... (202) 225–6465
Chief of Staff.—Adam Howard. FAX: 225–6754
Legislative Director.—Vincent Erfe.
Scheduler.—Kate Pietkiewicz.
120 West Third Street, Suite 305, Dayton, OH 45402 .... (937) 225–2843
District Director.—Kelly Geers.

Counties: MONTGOMERY, GREENE, AND FAYETTE (northern part). Population (2010), 721,032.

ZIP Codes: 43106, 43128, 43142–43, 43145, 43153, 43160, 45005, 45066, 45068–69, 45301, 45305, 45307, 45309, 45314–16, 45322, 45324, 45327, 45335, 45342, 45344–45, 45354, 45368, 45370–71, 45381, 45384–85, 45387, 45402–06, 45409–10, 45414–20, 45424, 45426, 45428–34, 45439–40, 45449, 45458–59

* * *

ELEVENTH DISTRICT

MARCIA L. FUDGE, Democrat, of Cleveland, OH; born in Shaker Heights, OH, October 29, 1952; B.S., Ohio State University, 1975; J.D., Cleveland Marshall College of Law, 1983; professional: Director of Budget and Finance, Cuyahoga County Prosecutor's Office; Chief Administrator for Cuyahoga County Prosecutor Stephanie Tubbs Jones; Mayor of Warrensville Heights, OH; committees: Agriculture; Education and the Workforce; elected to the 110th Congress, by special election, to fill the vacancy caused by the death of United States Representative Stephanie Tubbs Jones; elected to the 111th Congress on November 4, 2008; reelected to each succeeding Congress.

Office Listings

http://www.fudge.house.gov

2344 Rayburn House Office Building, Washington, DC 20515 .... (202) 225–7032
Chief of Staff.—Veleter Mazyck.
Legislative Director.—Kellie Adesina.
Legislative Assistants: Jesse Barba, Clifton Williams.
Scheduler / Office Manager.—Bridgett Simmons.
4834 Richmond Road, Suite 150, Warrensville Heights, OH 44128 .... (216) 522–4900
District Director.—John Hairston.
Communications Director.—Belinda Prinz.
Scheduler / Office Manager.—Linda R. Matthews.
Congressional Staff.—Ariella Brown, Stephen Caviness, Beverly R. Charles, Anita Gray.
Staff Assistant.—Margaret McLaughlin.
1225 Lawton Street, Akron, OH 44320 .... (330) 835–4758
Outreach Coordinator.—Ginger Baylor.

Counties: CUYAHOGA COUNTY, SUMMIT COUNTY (part). CITIES: Akron, Beachwood, Bath Township, Bedford, Bedford Heights, Brahtenahl Village, Broadview Heights, Brooklyn Heights, Cleveland, Cleveland Heights, Cuyahoga Heights, East Cleveland, Euclid, Fairlawn, Garfield Heights, Glenwillow, Highland Hills Village, Newburg Heights, Maple Heights, North Randall Village, Oakwood Village, Orange Village, Pepper Pike, Richmond Heights, Shaker Heights, Seven Hills, South Euclid, University Heights, Warrensville Heights, and Woodmere. Population (2010), 705,659.

ZIP Codes: 44101–15, 44118–44130, 44132, 44135, 44137, 44143–44, 44146, 44178, 44181, 44185, 44188–95, 44197–99

* * *

TWELFTH DISTRICT

PATRICK J. TIBERI, Republican, of Columbus, OH; born in Columbus, October 21, 1962; education: B.A., Ohio State University, 1985; professional: real estate agent; assistant to U.S. Representative John Kasich (R–OH); public service: served as Majority Leader, Ohio House of Representatives, 1992–2000; organizations: Westerville Chamber of Commerce; Columbus Board of Realtors; Military Veterans and Community Service Commission; Sons of Italy; awards: Fraternal Order of Police Outstanding Legislator; Watchdog of the Treasury Award; American Red Cross Volunteer Service Award; married: Denice; committees: Ways and Means; elected to the 107th Congress on November 7, 2000; reelected to each succeeding Congress.

Office Listings

http://www.house.gov/tiberi https://twitter.com/tiberipress
https://www.facebook.com/reppattiberi

106 Cannon House Office Building, Washington, DC 20515 .... (202) 225–5355
Chief of Staff.—Mark Bell. FAX: 226–4523
Deputy Chief of Staff.—Kelli Briggs.
Legislative Director.—Whitney Daffner.
Communications Director.—Breann Gonzalez.
3000 Corporate Drive, Suite 310, Columbus, OH 43231 .... (614) 523–2555
District Director.—Walter Taylor.

Counties: DELAWARE, FRANKLIN (part), LICKING, MARION (part), MORROW, MUSKINGUM (part), and RICHLAND (part). Population (2010), 728,420.

ZIP Codes: 43001–04, 43011, 43013, 43015–17, 43023, 43025–26, 43031–33, 43035, 43040, 43046, 43054–55, 43061–62, 43065–66, 43068, 43071, 43074, 43082, 43085, 43147, 43201, 43229–30, 43235, 43240, 43334, 43342, 43344, 43356

* * *

THIRTEENTH DISTRICT

TIM RYAN, Democrat, of Niles, OH; born in Niles, July 16, 1973; education: B.S., Bowling Green University, 1995; J.D., University of New Hampshire School of Law (formerly Franklin Pierce Law Center), 2000; professional: legislative aide, Washington, DC; committees: Appropriations; Budget; elected to the 108th Congress on November 5, 2002; reelected to each succeeding Congress.

Office Listings

http://timryan.house.gov twitter: @reptimryan facebook: congressmantimryan

1421 Longworth House Office Building, Washington, DC 20515 .... (202) 225–5261
Chief of Staff.—Ron Grimes. FAX: 225–3719
Scheduler.—Erin Isenberg.
Legislative Director.—Ryan Keating.
197 West Market Street, Warren, OH 44481 .... (330) 373–0074
241 Federal Plaza West, Youngstown, OH 44503 .... (330) 740–0193

Counties: MAHONING (part), PORTAGE (part), STARK, SUMMIT (part), TRUMBULL (part). Population (2010), 723,713.

ZIP Codes: 44141, 44201, 44203, 44221, 44223–24, 44231, 44236, 44240, 44241, 44243, 44255, 44260, 44262, 44264, 44266, 44272, 44278, 44285, 44288, 44301–08, 44310–14, 44319–20, 44333, 44401–06, 44410–12, 44418, 44420, 44425, 44429–30, 44436–38, 44440, 44444, 44446, 44449, 44451, 44470–71, 44473, 44481, 44483–85, 44491, 44502–07, 44509–12, 44514–15, 44601, 44640

* * *

FOURTEENTH DISTRICT

DAVID JOYCE, Republican, of Geauga, OH; born in Cleveland, OH, March 17, 1957; education: B.S., The University of Dayton, Dayton, OH, 1979; J.D., The University of Dayton, 1982; professional: prosecuting attorney, Geauga County, 1988–2012; married: Kelly Joyce; children: Trenton, KK, and Bridey; committees: Appropriations; elected to the 113th Congress on November 6, 2012.

Office Listings

http://joyce.house.gov

1535 Longworth House Office Building, Washington, DC 20515 .... (202) 225–5731
FAX: 225–3307
Chief of Staff.—Dino DiSanto.
Scheduler.—Carla DiBlasio.
Legislative Director.—John Miceli.
Communications Director.—Christyn Keyes.
1 Victoria Place, Suite 320, Painesville, OH 44077 .... (440) 352–3939
FAX: 352–3622
10075 Ravenna Road, Twinsburg, OH 44087 .... (330) 425–9291
FAX: 425–7071

Counties: SUMMIT (part), CUYAHOGA (part), PORTAGE (part), TRUMBULL (part), LAKE, GEAUGA, AND ASHTABULA. Population (2010), 721,032.

ZIP Codes: 44003–04, 44010, 44021–24, 44026, 44030, 44032, 44040–41, 44045–48, 44056–57, 44060, 44062, 44064–65, 44067, 44072, 44076–77, 44080–82, 44084–87, 44092–95, 44099, 44122, 44124–25, 44131, 44139, 44141, 44143, 44146–47, 44202, 44221, 44223–24, 44231, 44234, 44236, 44240–41, 44255, 44262, 44264, 44266, 44278, 44313, 44402, 44404, 44410, 44417–18, 44428, 44439, 44450, 44473, 44481, 44491

* * *

FIFTEENTH DISTRICT

STEVE STIVERS, Republican, of Columbus, OH; born in Cincinnati, OH, March 24, 1965; education: B.A., Ohio State University, Columbus, OH, 1989; M.B.A., Ohio State University, 1996; M.A., U.S. Army War College; professional: military; colonel, Ohio Army National Guard, 1988–present; Ohio Company and Bank One; member of the Ohio State Senate, 2003–08; married: Karen Stivers; children: Sarah and Samuel; committees: Financial Services; elected to the 112th Congress on November 2, 2010; reelected to the 113th Congress on November 6, 2012.

Office Listings

http://www.stivers.house.gov

1022 Longworth House Office Building, Washington, DC 20515 .... (202) 225–2015
FAX: 225–3529
Chief of Staff.—Adam Kuhn.
Scheduler.—Monica Hueckel.
Legislative Director.—Jesse Walls.
Communications Director.—Courtney Whetstone.
3790 Municipal Way, Hilliard, OH 43026 .... (614) 771–4968
FAX: 771–3990
Fairfield County District Office, 123 South Broad Street, Suite 235, Lancaster, OH 43130 .... (740) 654–2654
FAX: 654–2482
Clinton County District Office, 69 North South Street, Wilimington, OH 45177 ..... (937) 283–7049
FAX: 283–7052

Counties: ATHENS (part), CLINTON, FAIRFIELD, FAYETTE (part), FRANKLIN (part), Hocking, Madison, Morgan, Perry, Pickaway, Ross (part), and Vinton. Population (2010) 721,031.

ZIP Codes: 43002, 43016–17, 43026, 43029, 43044, 43046, 43062, 43064, 43068, 43076, 43101–03, 43105, 43107, 43110–13, 43115–17, 43119, 43123, 43125–27, 43130, 43135–38, 43140, 43143–58, 43160, 43162, 43164, 43201, 43204, 43206–07, 43210, 43212, 43215, 43217, 43220–23, 43228, 43235, 43724, 43728, 43730–31, 43739, 43748, 43756, 43758, 43760–61, 43764, 43766, 43777, 43782–83, 43787, 45068, 45107, 45113, 45123, 45135, 45142, 45146, 45148, 45159, 45164, 45166, 45169, 45177, 45335, 45369, 45601, 45622, 45628, 45634, 45644, 45647, 45651, 45654, 45672, 45681, 45686, 45695, 45698, 45701, 45710–11, 45715–16, 45719, 45723, 45732, 45735, 45740, 45761, 45764, 45766, 45776, 45778, 45780, 45782

* * *

SIXTEENTH DISTRICT

JIM RENACCI, Republican, of Wadsworth, OH; born in Monongahela, PA, December 3, 1958; education: B.S., Indiana University of Pennsylvania, 1980; professional: certified public accountant (CPA); owner, nursing home facility; executive, professional arena football team; Wadsworth Board of Zoning Appeals, 1994–95; president, Wadsworth City Council, 1999–2003; mayor of Wadsworth, 2004–2008; business management consultant; religion: Roman Catholic; married: Tina Renacci; 3 children; caucuses: Congressional Coal; Congressional Steel; Northeast-Midwest Coalition; Congressional CPA; General Aviation; Hydrogen and Fuel Cell;

committees: Ways and Means; elected to the 112th Congress on November 2, 2010; reelected to the 113th Congress on November 6, 2012.

Office Listings

http://www.renacci.house.gov

130 Cannon House Office Building, Washington, DC 20515 .... (202) 225–3876
Chief of Staff.—James Slepian. FAX: 225–3059
Communications Director.—Shawn Ryan.
Scheduler.—Michelle Runk.
Legislative Director.—Jake Menefee.
1 Park Center Drive, Suite 302, Wadsworth, OH 44281 .... (330) 334–0040
Constituent Service Director.—Heidi Matthews. FAX: 493–9265

Counties: WAYNE, STARK (part), MEDINA (part), PORTAGE (part), SUMMIT (part), CUYAHOGA (part). Population (2010), 724,108.

ZIP Codes: 44017, 44070, 44107, 44116, 44126, 44129–30, 44133–34, 44136, 44138, 44142, 44145, 44147, 44149, 44201, 44203, 44212, 44214–17, 44230, 44233, 44240, 44250–51, 44254, 44256, 44260, 44265–66, 44270, 44272–74, 44276, 44278, 44281, 44287, 44306, 44312, 44319–21, 44333, 44606, 44611, 44614, 44618, 44624, 44627, 44632, 44638, 44645–47, 44659, 44662, 44666–67, 44676–77, 44685, 44691, 44706, 44708–10, 44718, 44720–21, 44840

OKLAHOMA

(Population 2010, 3,751,351)

SENATORS

JAMES M. INHOFE, Republican, of Tulsa, OK; born in Des Moines, IA, November 17, 1934; education: graduated Central High School, Tulsa, OK, 1953; B.A., University of Tulsa, OK, 1959; military service: served in the U.S. Army, private first class, 1957–58; professional: businessman; active pilot; president, Quaker Life Insurance Company; Oklahoma House of Representatives, 1967–69; Oklahoma State Senate, 1969–77; Mayor of Tulsa, OK, 1978–84; religion: member, First Presbyterian Church of Tulsa; married: Kay Kirkpatrick; children: Jim, Perry, Molly, and Katy; twelve grandchildren; committees: ranking member, Armed Services; Environment and Public Works; elected to the 100th Congress on November 4, 1986; reelected to each succeeding Congress; elected to the U.S. Senate on November 8, 1994, finishing the unexpired term of Senator David Boren; reelected to each succeeding Senate term.

Office Listings

http://inhofe.senate.gov

205 Russell Senate Office Building, Washington, DC 20510 .... (202) 224–4721
Chief of Staff.—Ryan Jackson. FAX: 228–0380
Legislative Director.—Clark Peterson.
Press Secretary.—Jared Young.
Scheduler.—Wendi Price.
1924 South Utica, Suite 530, Tulsa, OK 74104–6511 .... (918) 748–5111
1900 Northwest Expressway, Suite 1210, Oklahoma City, OK 73118 .... (405) 608–4381
302 North Independence, Suite 104, Enid, OK 73701 .... (580) 234–5105
215 East Choctaw, Suite 106, McAlester, OK 74501 .... (918) 426–0933

* * *

TOM COBURN, Republican, of Muskogee, OK; born in Casper, WY, March 14, 1948; education: Central High School, Muskogee, OK, 1966; B.S., Oklahoma State University, 1970; Oklahoma University Medical School, 1983; professional: manufacturing manager, Coburn Ophthalmic Division, Coburn Optical Industries, 1970–78; family physician, 1983–present; member, American Medical Association, Oklahoma State Medical Association, East Central County Medical Society, American Academy of Family Practice; religion: First Baptist Church, ordained deacon; member, Promise Keepers; public service: U.S. House of Representatives, 1995–2001; married: Carolyn Denton Coburn, 1968; children: Callie, Katie, and Sarah; committees: Banking, Housing, and Urban Affairs; Homeland Security and Governmental Affairs; Select Committee on Intelligence; elected to the U.S. Senate on November 2, 2004; reelected to the U.S. Senate on November 2, 2010.

Office Listings

http://coburn.senate.gov

172 Russell Hart Senate Office Building, Washington, DC 20510 .... (202) 224–5754
Chief of Staff.—Brian Treat. FAX: 224–6008
Legislative Director.—Roland Foster.
Communications Director.—John Hart.
Scheduler.—Courtney Shadegg.
1800 South Baltimore, Suite 800, Tulsa, OK 74119 .... (918) 581–7651
100 North Broadway, Suite 1820, Oklahoma City, OK 73102 .... (405) 231–4941

REPRESENTATIVES

FIRST DISTRICT

JIM BRIDENSTINE, Republican, of Tulsa, OK; born in Ann Arbor, MI, June 15, 1975; education: B.A., Rice University, Texas, 1997; M.B.A., Cornell University, New York, 2009; professional: military awards: Eagle Scout, Air Medal; Navy Commendation Medal with Combat ''V''; Navy and Marine Corps Achievement Medal x 2; National Defense Service Medal; Armed Forces Expeditionary Medal; Iraq Campaign Medal; Global War on Terrorism Expeditionary Medal; Navy Sea Service Deployment Ribbon; Expert Pistol Medal; Battle Efficiency Ribbon; religion: Baptist; family: Michelle (wife); Walker (son); Sarah (daughter); Grant (son);

Caucuses: F–35 Joint Strike Fighter Caucus; Pilot's Caucus; committees: Armed Services; Science, Space, and Technology; elected to the 113th Congress on November 6, 2012.

Office Listings

http://bridenstine.house.gov

216 Cannon House Office Building, Washington, DC 20510 .... (202) 225–2211
Chief of Staff.—Joseph Kaufman. FAX: 225–9187
Legislative Director.—James Mazol.
Communications Director.—Sheryl Kaufman.
Legislative Correspondent.—Mark Piland.
Scheduler.—Harvey Sparks.
Office Manager / Administrative Assistant.—Karen Schmitt.
2448 East 81st Street, Suite 5150, Tulsa, OK 74137 .... (918) 935–3222
District Director.—Gabe Sherman.
Deputy District Director.—G. Erik Zoellner, Ed.D.
Deputy Director of Communications.—Matt Rydin.
Constituent Services Case Worker.—Sandy Minardi.
Senior Field Representative.—Brian O'Hara.
Field Representatives: Kathy LaFortune, Joe Newhouse.
Office Manager.—Samantha Jones.

Counties: CREEK (part), ROGERS (part), TULSA, WAGONER, AND WASHINGTON. Population (2010), 750,270.

ZIP Codes: 74003, 74006, 74008, 74011–12, 74014–15, 74021–22, 74029, 74033, 74036–37, 74041, 74047, 74050–51, 74055, 74061, 74063, 74066, 74070, 74073, 74080, 74082–83, 74103–08, 74110, 74112, 74114–17, 74119–20, 74126–37, 74145–46, 74337, 74352, 74403, 74429, 74434, 74436, 74446, 74454, 74458, 74467, 74477

* * *

SECOND DISTRICT

MARKWAYNE MULLIN, Republican, of Westville, OK; born in Tulsa, OK, July 26, 1977; married on June 14, 1997; education: attended Missouri Valley College, Marshall, MO, 1996; A.A.S., Oklahoma State University Institute of Technology, Okmulgee, OK, 2010; professional: business owner; plumber; rancher; children: father of five; committees: Natural Resources; Transportation and Infrastructure; elected to the 113th Congress on November 6, 2012.

Office Listings

http://mullin.house.gov

1113 Longworth House Office Building, Washington, DC 20515 .... (202) 225–2701
Chief of Staff.—Karl Ahlgren.
Legislative Director.—Brittnee Preston.
Communications Director.—Ashley Kehl.
Executive Assistant / Scheduler.—Kayla Priehs.
431 West Broadway, Muskogee, OK 74401 .... (918) 687–2533
Claremore, OK 74017 .... (918) 341–9336
1 East Choctaw, Suite 175, McAlester, OK 74501 .... (918) 423–5951
Durant, OK 74701 .... (580) 931–0333

Counties: ADAIR, ATOKA, BRYAN, CHEROKEE, CHOCTAW, COAL, CRAIG, DELAWARE, HASKELL, HUGHES, JOHNSTON, LATIMER, LEFLORE, MARSHALL, MAYES, MCCURTAIN, MCINTOSH, MUSKOGEE, NOWATA, OKFUSKEE, OKMULGEE, OTTAWA, PITTSBURGH, PUSHMATAHA, ROGERS, SEQUOYAH. Population (2010), 750,270.

ZIP Codes: 73432, 73439–40, 73446–47, 73449–50, 73455, 73460–61, 74016–19, 74027, 74042, 74048, 74053, 74072, 74301, 74330–33, 74338–40, 74342–44, 74346–47, 74349–50, 74354, 74358–63, 74364–67, 74368–70, 74401, 74421–23, 74425–28, 74430–32, 74435, 74437–38, 74441–42, 74445, 74447, 74450–52, 74455–57, 74459–60, 74462–64, 74468–70, 74471–72, 74501, 74521–23, 74525, 74528, 74530–31, 74533–36, 74538, 74540, 74543, 74546–47, 74549, 74552–53, 74556, 74560–63, 74565, 74569–72, 74576, 74578, 74701, 74720, 74723, 74726–30, 74733, 74735–36, 74740–41, 74743, 74745, 74747–48, 74750, 74756, 74759, 74764, 74766, 74829, 74833, 74839, 74845, 74848, 74850, 74856, 74859–60, 74880, 74883, 74885, 74901–02, 74930, 74932, 74935–37, 74940–42, 74944–46, 74948, 74951, 74953–56, 74959–60, 74962, 74964–66

* * *

THIRD DISTRICT

FRANK D. LUCAS, Republican, of Cheyenne, OK; born in Cheyenne, January 6, 1960; education: B.S., agricultural economics, Oklahoma State University, 1982; professional: rancher and farmer; served in Oklahoma State House of Representatives, 1989–94; secretary, Oklahoma

House Republican Caucus, 1991–94; member: Oklahoma Farm Bureau, Oklahoma Cattlemen's Association, and Oklahoma Shorthorn Association; married: Lynda Bradshaw Lucas; children: Jessica, Ashlea, and Grant; committees: chair, Agriculture; Financial Services; Science, Space, and Technology; elected to the 103rd Congress, by special election, in May 1994; reelected to each succeeding Congress.

Office Listings

http://www.house.gov/lucas

2311 Rayburn House Office Building, Washington, DC 20515 .... (202) 225–5565
Legislative Director.—Courtney Lincoln. FAX: 225–8698
Communications Director.—Laramie Adams.
Scheduler / Office Manager.—Molly Johnson.
Legislative Assistants: Scott Ferguson, Jason Grassie, Brad Morris.
10952 Northwest Expressway, Suite B, Yukon, OK 73099 .... (405) 373–1958
Chief of Staff.—Stacey Glasscock.

Counties: ALFALFA, BEAVER, BECKHAM, BLAINE, CADDO, CANADIAN (part), CIMARRON, CREEK (part), CUSTER, DEWEY, ELLIS, GARFIELD, GRANT, GREER, HARMON, HARPER, JACKSON, KINGFISHER, KAY, KIOWA, LINCOLN, LOGAN, MAJOR, NOBLE, OSAGE, PAWNEE, PAYNE, ROGER MILLS, TEXAS, WASHITA, WOODS, AND WOODWARD. CITIES: Altus, Clinton, El Reno, Elk City, Enid, Guthrie, Guymon, Oklahoma City, Perry, Ponce City, Sapulpa, Stillwater, Tulsa, Weatherford, Woodward and Yukon. Population (2010), 745,941.

ZIP Codes: 73001, 73005–07, 73009, 73014–17, 73021–22, 73024, 73027–29, 73033–34, 73036, 73038, 73040–45, 73047–48, 73050, 73053–54, 73056, 73058–59, 73061–64, 73073, 73077–79, 73085, 73090, 73096–97, 73099, 73127, 73521–23, 73526, 73532, 73537, 73539, 73544, 73547, 73549–50, 73554, 73556, 73559–60, 73564, 73566, 73571, 73601, 73620, 73622, 73624–28, 73632, 73638–39, 73641–42, 73644–48, 73650–51, 73654–55, 73658–64, 73666–69, 73673, 73701–03, 73705–06, 73716–20, 73722, 73724, 73726–31, 73733–39, 73741–44, 73746–47, 73749–50, 73753–64, 73766, 73768, 73770–73, 73801–02, 73832, 73834–35, 73838, 73840–44, 73848, 73851–53, 73855, 73857–60, 73901, 73931–33, 73937–39, 73942, 73944–47, 73949–51, 74001–03, 74010, 74020, 74023, 74026, 74028, 74030, 74032, 74034–35, 74038–39, 74044–47, 74051–52, 74054, 74056, 74058–60, 74062–63, 74066–68, 74070–71, 74073–79, 74081, 74084–85, 74106, 74126–27, 74131–32, 74601–02, 74604, 74630–33, 74636–37, 74640–41, 74643–44, 74646–47, 74650–53, 74824, 74832, 74834, 74851, 74855, 74864, 74869, 74875, 74881

* * *

FOURTH DISTRICT

TOM COLE, Republican, of Moore, OK; born in Shreveport, LA, April 28, 1949; education: B.A., Grinnell College, 1971; M.A. Yale University, 1974; Ph.D., University of Oklahoma, 1984; Watson Fellow, 1971–72; and a Fulbright Fellow, 1977–78; professional: former college professor of history and politics; President, Cole Hargrave Snodgrass & Associates (political consulting firm); public service: Oklahoma State Senate, 1988–91; Oklahoma Secretary of State, 1995–99; has served as Chairman, and Executive Director, of the Oklahoma Republican Party; former Chairman of the National Republican Congressional Committee; and Chief of Staff of the Republican National Committee; family: married to Ellen; one child: Mason; religion: United Methodist; committees: Appropriations; Budget; Rules; Joint Committee on the Library; elected to the 108th Congress on November 5, 2002; reelected to each succeeding Congress.

Office Listings

http://www.house.gov/cole

2458 Rayburn House Office Building, Washington, DC 20515 .... (202) 225–6165
Chief of Staff.—Sean Murphy. FAX: 225–3512
Deputy Chief of Staff / Legislative Director.—Maria Bowie.
Press Secretary.—Sarah Corley.
Scheduler.—Sabrina Parker.
2424 Springer Drive, Suite 201, Norman, OK 73069 .... (405) 329–6500
711 Southwest, D Avenue, Suite 201, Lawton, OK 73501 .... (580) 357–2131
Sugg Clinic Office Building, 100 East 13th Street, Suite 213, Ada, OK 74820 .... (580) 436–5375

Counties: CANADIAN (part), CARTER, CLEVELAND, COMANCHE, COTTON, GARVIN, GRADY, JEFFERSON, LOVE, MCCLAIN, MURRAY, OKLAHOMA (part), PONTOTOC, STEPHENS, AND TILLMAN. Population (2010), 750,270.

ZIP Codes: 73002, 73004, 73006, 73010–11, 73017–20, 73026, 73030, 73032, 73051–52, 73055, 73057, 73059, 73064–69, 73071–72, 73074–75, 73079–80, 73082, 73086, 73089, 73092–93, 73095, 73098, 73110, 73130, 73135, 73139, 73141, 73145, 73149–50, 73159–60, 73165, 73169–70, 73173, 73401, 73425, 73430, 73433–34, 73437–38, 73441–44, 73448, 73453, 73456, 73458–59, 73463, 73481, 73487, 73491, 73501, 73503, 73505, 73507, 73520, 73527–31, 73533, 73538, 73540–43, 73546, 73548, 73551–53, 73555, 73557, 73559, 73562, 73564–70, 73572–73, 74572, 74820, 74825, 74831, 74842–44, 74852, 74856–57, 74865, 74871–72, 74878

* * *

FIFTH DISTRICT

JAMES LANKFORD, Republican, of Edmond, OK; professional: director of the Falls Creek Youth Camp, 1996–2009; wife: Cindy; children: Hannah, Jordan; chair, House Republican Policy Committee; committees: Budget; Oversight and Government Reform; elected to the 112th Congress on November 2, 2010; reelected to the 113th Congress on November 6, 2012.

Office Listings

http://www.lankford.house.gov

228 Cannon House Office Building, Washington, DC 20515 .... (202) 225–2132
Chief of Staff.—Randy Swanson. FAX: 226–1463
Deputy Chief of Staff/Legislative Director.—Michelle Altman.
Scheduler.—Rachel King.
Communications Director.—Kelly Ferguson.
District Director.—Mona Taylor.
1015 North Broadway Avenue, Suite 310, Oklahoma City, OK 73102 .... (405) 234–9900

Counties: OKLAHOMA (part), POTTAWATOMIE, AND SEMINOLE. CITIES: Arcadia, Asher, Aydelotte, Bethany, Bethel Acres, Bowlegs, Brooksville, Choctaw, Cromwell, Del City, Earlsboro, Edmond, Forest Park, Harrah, Johnson, Jones, Konawa, Lake Aluma, Lima, Luther, Macomb, Maud, McLoud, Midwest City, Newalla, Nichols Hills, Nicoma Park, Oklahoma City, Pink, Prague, Sasakwa, Seminole, Shawnee, Smith Village, Spencer, St. Louis, Tecumesh, The Village, Tribbey, Valley Brook, Wanette, Warr Acres, Wewoka, and Woodlawn Park. Population (2010), 750,271.

ZIP Codes: 73003, 73007–08, 73013, 73020, 73034, 73045, 73049, 73054, 73066, 73083–84, 73101–32, 73134–37, 73139, 73141–49, 73151–52, 73154–57, 73159–60, 73162, 73164, 73169, 73172–73, 73178–79, 73184–85, 73190, 73194–96, 73198, 74587, 74801–02, 74804, 74818, 74826, 74830, 74837, 74840, 74849, 74851–52, 74854, 74857, 74866–68, 74873, 74878, 74884

OREGON

(Population 2010, 3,831,074)

SENATORS

RON WYDEN, Democrat, of Portland, OR; born in Wichita, KS, May 3, 1949; education: graduated from Palo Alto High School, 1967; B.A. in political science, with distinction, Stanford University, 1971; J.D., University of Oregon Law School, 1974; professional: attorney; member, American Bar Association; former director, Oregon Legal Services for the Elderly; former public member, Oregon State Board of Examiners of Nursing Home Administrators; co-founder and codirector, Oregon Gray Panthers, 1974–80; married: Nancy Bass Wyden; children: Adam David, Lilly Anne, Ava Rose, and William Peter; committees: chair, Finance; Budget; Energy and Natural Resources; Joint Committee on Taxation; Select Committee on Intelligence; elected to the 97th Congress, November 4, 1980; reelected to each succeeding Congress; elected to the U.S. Senate on February 6, 1996, to fill the unexpired term of Senator Bob Packwood; reelected to each succeeding Senate term.

Office Listings

http://wyden.senate.gov

221 Dirksen Senate Office Building, Washington, DC 20510 .... (202) 224–5244
Chief of Staff.—Jeff Michels. FAX: 228–2717
Legislative Director.—Jayme White.
Deputy Chief of Staff.—Jocelyn Moore.
Director of Scheduling.—Wayne Binkley.
911 Northeast 11th Avenue, Suite 630, Portland, OR 97232 .... (503) 326–7525
405 East Eighth Avenue, Suite 2020, Eugene, OR 97401 .... (541) 431–0229
The Federal Courthouse, 310 West Sixth Street, Room 118, Medford, OR 97501 ... (541) 858–5122
The Jamison Building, 131 Northwest Hawthorne Avenue, Suite 107, Bend, OR 97701 .... (541) 330–9142
SAC Annex Building, 105 Fir Street, Suite 201, LaGrande, OR 97850 .... (541) 962–7691
707 Thirteenth Street, SE., Suite 285, Salem, OR 97310 .... (503) 589–4555

* * *

JEFF MERKLEY, Democrat, of Portland, OR; born in Myrtle Creek, OR; October 24, 1956; education: graduated from David Douglas High School, B.A., international relations, Stanford University, 1979; M.P.P., Woodrow Wilson School, Princeton University, 1982; professional: Presidential Fellow at the Office of the Secretary of Defense, 1982–85; Policy Analyst at the Congressional Budget Office, 1985–89; Executive Director of Portland Habitat for Humanity, 1991–94; Director of Housing Development at Human Solutions, 1995–96; President of World Affairs Council of Oregon, 1996–2003; elected to Oregon House of Representatives, 1999; Democratic Leader of the Oregon House of Representatives, 2003; elected Speaker of the Oregon House of Representatives, 2007; married: Mary Sorteberg; children: Brynne and Jonathan; committees: Appropriations; Banking, Housing, and Urban Affairs; Budget; Environment and Public Works; elected to U.S. Senate on November 4, 2008.

Office Listings

http://merkley.senate.gov

313 Hart Senate Office Building, Washington, DC 20510 .... (202) 224–3753
Chief of Staff.—Michael Zamore. FAX: 228–3997
Legislative Director.—Jeremiah Baumann.
Deputy Chief of Staff of Operations.—Jennifer Piorkowski.
Communications Director.—Matt McNally.
1400 One World Trade Center, 121 Southwest Salmon, Portland, OR 97204 .... (503) 326–3386
Jamison Building, 131 Northwest Hawthorne, Suite 208, Bend, OR 97701 .... (541) 318–1298
Wayne Morse Federal Courthouse, 405 East 8th, Suite 2010, Eugene, OR 97401 ... (541) 465–6750
10 South Bartlett Street, Suite 201, Medford, OR 97501 .... (541) 608–9102
495 State Street, Suite 330, Salem, OR 97301 .... (503) 362–8102
310 Southeast Second Street, Suite 105, Pendleton, OR 97801 .... (541) 278–1129

REPRESENTATIVES

FIRST DISTRICT

SUZANNE MARIE BONAMICI, Democrat, of Beaverton, OR; born in Michigan, October 14, 1954; education: J.D., University of Oregon, Eugene, OR, 1983; B.A., journalism, Eugene,

OR, 1980; professional: served in the Oregon State House from 2007–08, served in the Oregon State Senate from 2008–11; married: husband, Michael Simon; children: son, Andrew Simon, daughter, Sara Simon; caucuses: co-founder and co-chair of the STEAM Caucus; committees: Education and the Workforce; Science, Space, and Technology; elected to the 112th Congress on January 31st, 2012 in a special election; reelected to the 113th Congress.

Office Listings

http://www.bonamici.house.gov

439 Cannon House Office Building, Washington DC, 20515 .... (202) 225–0855
Chief of Staff.—Rachael Bornstein. FAX: 225–9497
Legislative Director.—Russ Kelley.
Scheduler.—Kimberly Koops-Wrabek.
Press Secretary.—Alex Gilliland.
12725 SW Millikan Way, Suite 220, Beaverton, OR 97005 .... (503) 469–6010
District Director.—Abigail Tibbs. FAX: 469–6018
District Scheduler.—Barbara Allen.

Counties: CLATSOP, COLUMBIA, MULTNOMAH (part), WASHINGTON, AND YAMHILL. Population (2010) 766,216.

ZIP Codes: 97005–08, 97016, 97018, 97048, 97051, 97053–54, 97056, 97064, 97103, 97106, 97109–11, 97113–17, 97119, 97121, 97123–25, 97127–28, 97133, 97138, 97144–46, 97148, 97208, 97223–24, 97229, 97231

* * *

SECOND DISTRICT

GREG WALDEN, Republican, of Hood River, OR; born in The Dalles, OR, January 10, 1957; education: B.S., journalism, University of Oregon, 1981; member: Associated Oregon Industries; Oregon Health Sciences Foundation; Hood River Rotary Club; Hood River Elk's Club; National Federation of Independent Business; Hood River Chamber of Commerce; Hood River Memorial Hospital; Columbia Bancorp; Oregon State House of Representatives, 1989–95, and majority leader, 1991–93; assistant majority leader, Oregon State Senate, 1995–97; awards: Oregon Jaycees Outstanding Young Oregonian, 1991; National Republican Legislators Association Legislator of the Year, 1993; married: Mylene Walden; one child: Anthony David Walden; committees: Energy and Commerce; elected to the 106th Congress on November 3, 1998; reelected to each succeeding Congress.

Office Listings

http://www.walden.house.gov

2182 Rayburn House Office Building, Washington, DC 20515 .... (202) 225–6730
Chief of Staff.—Brian MacDonald. FAX: 225–5774
Senior Policy Advisor.—Ray Baum.
Scheduler.—Mary Beth Spencer.
Communications Director.—Andrew Malcolm.
14 North Central Avenue, Suite 112, Medford, OR 97504 .... (541) 776–4646
1211 Washington Avenue, LaGrande, OR 97850 .... (541) 624–2400
FAX: 624–2402
1051 Northwest Bond Street, Suite 400, Bend, OR 97701 .... (541) 389–4408
FAX: 389–4452

Counties: BAKER, CROOK, DESCHUTES, GILLIAM, GRANT, HARNEY, HOOD RIVER, JACKSON, JEFFERSON, JOSEPHINE (part), KLAMATH, LAKE, MALHEUR, MORROW, SHERMAN, UMATILLA, UNION, WALLOWA, WASCO, AND WHEELER. Population (2010), 766,215.

ZIP Codes: 89421, 97001, 97014, 97021, 97029, 97031, 97033, 97037, 97039–41, 97050, 97057–58, 97063, 97065, 97497, 97501–04, 97520, 97522, 97524–27, 97530, 97535–37, 97539–41, 97601, 97603–04, 97620–27, 97630, 97632–41, 97701–02, 97707, 97710–12, 97720–22, 97730–39, 97741, 97750–56, 97758–61, 97801, 97810, 97812–14, 97817–20, 97823–28, 97830, 97833–46, 97848, 97850, 97856–57, 97859, 97862, 97864–65, 97867–70, 97873–77, 97880, 97882–86, 97901, 97903–11, 97913–14, 97918, 97920, 99362

* * *

THIRD DISTRICT

EARL BLUMENAUER, Democrat, of Portland, OR; born in Portland, August 16, 1948; education: graduated from Centennial High School; B.A., Lewis and Clark College; J.D., Northwestern School of Law; professional: assistant to the president, Portland State University;

served in Oregon State Legislature 1973–78; chaired Revenue and School Finance Committee; Multnomah County Commissioner, 1978–85; Portland City Commissioner 1986–96; served on Governor's Commission on Higher Education; National League of Cities Transportation Committee; National Civic League Board of Directors; Oregon Environmental Council; Oregon Public Broadcasting; married: Margaret Kirkpatrick; children: Jon and Anne; committees: Budget; Ways and Means; elected to the U.S. House of Representatives on May 21, 1996, to fill the vacancy created by Representative Ron Wyden's election to the U.S. Senate; reelected to each succeeding Congress.

Office Listings

http://blumenauer.house.gov

1111 Longworth House Office Building, Washington, DC 20515 .... (202) 225–4811
Chief of Staff.—Julia Pomeroy. FAX: 225–8941
Deputy Chief of Staff.—Janine Benner.
Scheduler.—Corine Weiler.
Communications Director.—Patrick Malone.
Legislative Director.—David Skillman.
729 Northeast Oregon Street, Suite 115, Portland, OR 97232 .... (503) 231–2300
District Director.—Willie Smite.

Counties: MULTNOMAH (part), CLAKAMUS (part). Population (2010), 766,215.

ZIP Codes: 97004, 97009, 97011, 97014–15, 97017, 97019, 97022–24, 97028, 97030, 97035, 97045, 97049, 97055, 97060, 97067, 97080, 97124, 97133, 97202–03, 97206, 97210–18, 97220, 97222, 97227, 97229–33, 97236, 97238, 97242, 97256, 97266–67, 97269, 97282–83, 97286, 97290, 97292–94, 97299

* * *

FOURTH DISTRICT

PETER A. DEFAZIO, Democrat, of Springfield, OR; born in Needham, MA, May 27, 1947; B.A., Tufts University, 1969; M.S., University of Oregon, 1977; professional: aide to Representative Jim Weaver, 1977–82; commissioner, Lane County, 1983–86; married: Myrnie Daut; committees: Natural Resources; Transportation and Infrastructure; elected to the 100th Congress, November 4, 1986; reelected to each succeeding Congress.

Office Listings

http://www.house.gov/defazio

2134 Rayburn House Office Building, Washington, DC 20515 .... (202) 226–3493
Chief of Staff.—Kathy Dedrick. FAX: 225–0032
Legislative Director.—Auke Mahar-Piersma.
Scheduler.—Katie Gillen.
405 East Eighth Avenue, Suite 2030, Eugene, OR 97401 .... (541) 465–6732
District Director.—Nick Batz.
125 Central Avenue, Room 350, Coos Bay, OR 97420 .... (541) 269–2609
612 Southeast Jackson Street, Room 9, Roseburg, OR 97470 .... (541) 440–3523

Counties: BENTON (part), COOS, CURRY, DOUGLAS, JOSEPHINE (part), LANE, AND LINN. CITIES: Eugene, Roseburg, and Coos Bay. Population (2010), 766,214.

ZIP Codes: 97321–22, 97324, 97326–27, 97329–31, 97333, 97345–46, 97348, 97350, 97352, 97355, 97358, 97360–61, 97370, 97374, 97377, 97383, 97386, 97389–90, 97401–06, 97408, 97410–17, 97419–20, 97423–24, 97426, 97429–31, 97434–39, 97446–59, 97461–63, 97465–67, 97469–71, 97476–81, 97484, 97486–90, 97492–99, 97523, 97526–27, 97531–32, 97534, 97538, 97543–44, 97731, 97759

* * *

FIFTH DISTRICT

KURT SCHRADER, Democrat, of Canby, OR; born in Bridgeport, CT, October 19, 1951; education; B.A., Cornell University, 1973, D.V.M., University, IL, 1977; professional: small business owner, veterinarian, farmer; past member; Oregon State Senate, Oregon House of Representatives, Canby Planning Commission; religion: Episcopalian; children: Clare, Maren, Steven, Travis, and R.J.; committees; Agriculture; Budget; Small Business; elected to the 111th Congress on November 4, 2008, reelected to each succeeding Congress.

Office Listings

http://schrader.house.gov www.facebook.com/repschrader twitter: @repschrader

108 Cannon House Office Building, Washington, DC 20515 .... (202) 225–5711
Chief of Staff.—Paul Gage. FAX: 225–5699
Deputy Chief of Staff.—Chris Huckleberry.
Executive Assistant / Scheduler.—Anne Marie Feeney.
544 Ferry Street, Suite 2, Salem, OR 97301 .... (503) 588–9100
621 High Street, Oregon City, OR 97045 .... (503) 557–1324
District Director.—Suzanne Kunse

Counties: BENTON (part), CLACKAMAS (part), LINCOLN, MARION, MULTNOMAH (part), POLK, AND TILLAMOOK. CITIES: Lincoln City, Lake Oswego, Oregon City, Salem, and Tillamook. Population (2010), 766,214.

ZIP Codes: 97002, 97013, 97015, 97017, 97020, 97023, 97026–27, 97032, 97034–36, 97038, 97042, 97045, 97062, 97068, 97070–71, 97086, 97101, 97107–08, 97112, 97118, 97122, 97130–32, 97135–37, 97140–41, 97143, 97147, 97149, 97201–02, 97206, 97219, 97222, 97236, 97239, 97266–69, 97301–12, 97314, 97317, 97321, 97324–26, 97338, 97341–44, 97346–47, 97350–52, 97357–58, 97360–62, 97364–71, 97373, 97375–76, 97378, 97380–81, 97383–85, 97388, 97390–92, 97394, 97396, 97498

PENNSYLVANIA

(Population 2010, 12,702,379)

SENATORS

ROBERT P. CASEY, JR., Democrat, of Scranton, PA; born in Scranton, April 13, 1960; education: A.B., english, College of the Holy Cross, 1982; J.D., Catholic University of America, 1988; professional: lawyer; Pennsylvania State Auditor General, 1997–2005; Pennsylvania State Treasurer, 2005–07; married: Terese; four daughters: Elyse, Caroline, Julia, and Marena; committees: chair, Joint Economic Committee; Agriculture, Nutrition, and Forestry; Finance; Health, Education, Labor, and Pension; Special Committee on Aging; elected to the U.S. Senate on November 7, 2006; reelected to the U.S. on November 6, 2012.

Office Listings

http://casey.senate.gov http://www.facebook.com/senatorbobcasey
http://twitter.com/senbobcasey http://youtube.com/senatorbobcasey

393 Russell Senate Office Building, Washington, DC 20510 .... (202) 224–6324
(866) 802–2833
Chief of Staff.—James W. Brown. FAX: 228–0604
Deputy Chief of Staff.—Kristen Gentile.
Legislative Director.—Richard D. Spiegelman.
Communications Director.—April Mellody.
22 South Third Street, Suite 6A, Harrisburg, PA 17101 .... (717) 231–7540
(866) 461–9159
FAX: 231–7542
2000 Market Street, Suite 1870, Philadelphia, PA 19103 .... (215) 405–9660
FAX: 405–9669
Grant Building, 310 Grant Street, Suite 2415, Pittsburgh, PA 15219 .... (412) 803–7370
FAX: 803–7379
409 Lackawanna Avenue, Suite 301, Scranton, PA 18503 .... (570) 941–0930
FAX: 941–0937
817 East Bishop Street, Suite C, Bellefonte, PA 16823 .... (814) 357–0314
FAX: 375–0318
17 South Park Row, Suite B–150, Erie, PA 16501 .... (814) 874–5080
FAX: 874–5084
840 Hamilton Street, Suite 301, Allentown, PA 18101 .... (610) 782–9470
FAX: 782–9474

* * *

PAT TOOMEY, Republican, of Zionsville, PA; born in East Providence, RI, November 17, 1961; education: graduated from La Salle Academy as valedictorian in 1980; B.A., political science, *cum laude,* Harvard University, Cambridge, MA, 1984; professional: worked for Chemical Bank and Morgan Grenfell in New York City before spending one year as a financial consultant in Hong Kong, 1990; founded several restaurants in Allentown, PA, with his two brothers, Steve and Michael Toomey, 1990–97; married: Kris Duncan, 1997; children: Bridget, Patrick, and Duncan; member of the Allentown Government Study Commission, 1994; elected to U.S. House of Representatives in 1998, winning two reelections, 2000–02; president, Club for Growth, 2005; co-chairman of the Board of Directors of Team Capital Bank, 2005–09; committees: Banking, Housing, and Urban Affairs; Budget; Finance; Joint Economic Committee; elected to the U.S. Senate on November 2, 2010.

Office Listings

http://toomey.senate.gov

248 Rayburn Senate Office Building, Washington, DC 20510 .... (202) 224–4254
Chief of Staff.—Christopher Gahan. FAX: 228–0284
Legislative Director.—Dan Brandt.
Director of Operations.—Laurel Edmondson.
1628 John F. Kennedy Boulevard, 8 Penn Center, Suite 1702, Philadelphia, PA 19103 .... (215) 241–1090
The Landmarks Building, 100 West Station Square Drive, Suite 225, Pittsburgh, PA 15219 .... (412) 803–3501
Federal Building, 17 South Park Row, Suite B–120, Erie, PA 16501 .... (814) 453–3010
Federal Building, 228 Walnut Street, Room 1104, Harrisburg, PA 17101 .... (717) 782–3951
1150 South Cedar Crest Boulevard, Suite 101, Allentown, PA 18103 .... (610) 434–1444
538 Spruce Street, Suite 302, Scranton, PA 18503 .... (570) 941–3540
Richland Square III, Suite 302, 1397 Eisenhower Boulevard, Johnstown, PA 15904 (814) 266–5970

REPRESENTATIVES

FIRST DISTRICT

ROBERT A. BRADY, Democrat, of Philadelphia, PA; born in Philadelphia, April 7, 1945; education: graduated from St. Thomas More High School; professional: carpenter; union official; assistant Sergeant-At-Arms, Philadelphia City Council, 1975–83; Deputy Mayor for Labor, W. Wilson Goode Administration; consultant to Pennsylvania State Senate; Pennsylvania Turnpike Commissioner; board of directors, Philadelphia Redevelopment Authority; Democratic Party Executive; ward leader; chairman, Philadelphia Democratic Party; member of Pennsylvania Democratic State Committee, and Democratic National Committee; religion: Catholic; married: Debra Brady; children: Robert and Kimberly; committees: ranking member, House Administration; Armed Services; Joint Committee on the Library; Joint Committee on Printing; elected to the 105th Congress on May 21, 1998, to fill the unexpired term of Representative Tom Foglietta; reelected to each succeeding Congress.

Office Listings

http://brady.house.gov

102 Cannon House Office Building, Washington, DC 20515 .... (202) 225–4731
Chief of Staff.—Stan White. FAX: 225–0088
Appointments Secretary.—Liz Leibowitz.
Press Secretary.—Karen Warrington.
1907–09 South Broad Street, Philadelphia, PA 19148 .... (215) 389–4627
1350 Edgemont Avenue, Suite 2575, Chester, PA 19103 .... (610) 874–7094
2637 East Clearfield Street, Philadelphia, PA 19134 .... (267) 519–2252
2630 Memphis Street, Philadelphia, PA 19121 .... (215) 426–4616

Counties: PHILADELPHIA (part), DELAWARE (part). CITIES AND TOWNSHIPS: Chester City, Chester Township, Collingdale Borough, Colwyn Borough, Darby Township, East Lansdowne Borough, Eddystone Borough, Folcroft Borough, Glenolden Borough, Lansdowne Borough, Millbourne Borough, Nether Providence Township, Philadelphia City, Ridley Township, Rose Valley Borough, Sharon Hill Borough, Swarthmore Borough, Tinicum Township, Upland Borough, Upper Darby Township and Yeadon Borough. Population (2010), 705,688.

ZIP Codes: 19013–16, 19018, 19020, 19022–23, 19026, 19029, 19032, 19036, 19050, 19063–64, 19066, 19074, 19078–79, 19081–82, 19086, 19094, 19096, 19102, 19105–09, 19112–14, 19121–25, 19130–31, 19133–37, 19139–40, 19142–43, 19145–49, 19151–53, 19171–72, 19175–77, 19181–82, 19185, 19188

* * *

SECOND DISTRICT

CHAKA FATTAH, Democrat, of Philadelphia, PA; born in Philadelphia, November 21, 1956; education: attended Overbrook High School, Community College of Philadelphia, University of Pennsylvania's Wharton School; M.A., University of Pennsylvania's Fels School of State and Local Government, 1986; completed Senior Executive Program for State Officials at Harvard University's John F. Kennedy School of Government; Pennsylvania State House of Representatives, 1988; Pennsylvania State Senate, 1988–94; author, *Gaining Early Awareness and Readiness for Undergraduate Programs* (GEAR-UP), enacted in 1998 offering college readiness preparation and scholarships for low-income students; founded Graduate Opportunity Initiative Conference, 1987; founded Philadelphia College Opportunity Resources for Education (CORE Philly) scholarship program; founded the American Cities Foundation; Chief sponser of the American Opportunity Tax Credit Act; leading advocate for the Energy Efficiency and Conservation Block Grants; Emergency Homeowners' Relief Fund; authored the White House Conference on Children and Youth Act of 2010; former trustee, Temple University, Pennsylvania State University, Lincoln University and Community College of Philadelphia; past chair, Executive Board, Pennsylvania Higher Education Assistance Agency; named one of the 50 most promising leaders in *Time* magazine, and in *Ebony* magazine as one of 50 Future Leaders; member, Mt. Carmel Baptist Church; chair, Congressional Urban Caucus; married: the former Renee' Chenault; four children; committees: Appropriations; elected to the 104th Congress on November 8, 1994; reelected to each succeeding Congress.

Office Listings

http://www.fattah.house.gov

2301 Rayburn House Office Building, Washington, DC 20515 .... (202) 225–4001
Chief of Staff.—Maisha Leek. FAX: 225–5392
Legislative Director.—Vacant.
Deputy Chief of Staff.—Debra Anderson.
Communications Director.—Allyson Freeman.
2401 North 54th Street, Philadelphia, PA 19131 .... (215) 871–4455

Counties: MONTGOMERY (part), PHILADELPHIA. Population (2010), 705,688.

ZIP Codes: 19003–04, 19010, 19035, 19038, 19041, 19066, 19072, 19083, 19085, 19087, 19092–93, 19095–96, 19101–04, 19110, 19118–22, 19126–33, 19138–41, 19143–46, 19150–51, 19161–62, 19170–72, 19175, 19178, 19182, 19187–88, 19190–92, 19195–97, 19428, 19444

* * *

THIRD DISTRICT

MIKE KELLY, Republican, of Butler, PA; born in Pittsburgh, PA, May 10, 1948; education: B.A., sociology with a minor in philosophy and theology, University of Notre Dame, South Bend, IN, 1970; professional: owner and operator of Kelly Automotive Cadillac, Chevrolet, Hyundai, and Kia car dealership; married 39 years: Vicki Kelly; four children; committees: Ways and Means; elected to the 112th Congress on November 2, 2010; reelected to the 113th Congress on November 6, 2012.

Office Listings

http://www.kelly.house.gov

1519 Longworth House Office Building, Washington, DC 20515 .... (202) 225–5406
Chief of Staff.—Matthew Stroia. FAX: 225–3103
Legislative Director.—Vacant.
Legislative Assistants: Tricia Cascio, Isaac Fong.
Press Secretary.—Tom Qualtere.
Director of Administration.—Tim Butler.
Legislative Correspondents: Suanne Edmiston, Jeff Rein.
Staff Assistant.—Carly Turk.
208 East Bayfront Parkway, Suite 102, Erie, PA 16507 .... (814) 456–8190
District Director.—Brad Moore.
101 East Diamond Street, Suite 218, Butler, PA 16001 .... (724) 282–2557
FAX: 282–3682
33 Chestnut Avenue, Sharon, PA 16146 .... (724) 885–1113
FAX: 885–1114
908 Diamond Park, Meadville, PA 16335 .... (814) 454–8190
Office Hours: Wednesday from 9 a.m. to 4 p.m. FAX: 454–8197
300 South McKean Street, Kittanning, PA 16201.
Office Hours: Thursday from 9 a.m. to 4 p.m.
430 Court Street, New Castle, PA 16101.
Office Hours: Friday from 9 a.m. to 4 p.m.

Counties: ARMSTRONG, BUTLER (part), CLARION (part), CRAWFORD (part), ERIE (part), LAWRENCE, AND MERCER. Population: (2010), 705,688.

ZIP Codes: 16001–03, 16016–18, 16020, 16022–23, 16025, 16027–30, 16033–35, 16037–41, 16045–46, 16048–53, 16055–57, 16059, 16061, 16110–11, 16113–14, 16124–25, 16127, 16130–31, 16133–34, 16137, 16142–43, 16145–46, 16148, 16150–51, 16153–54, 16156, 16159, 16201, 16210, 16218, 16222–24, 16226, 16229, 16232, 16242, 16244–45, 16249–50, 16253, 16259, 16261–63, 16311–12, 16314, 16316–17, 16327, 16335, 16342, 16354, 16360, 16362, 16388, 16401–07, 16410–12, 16415, 16417, 16420–23, 16430, 16433–35, 16438, 16440–43, 16475, 16501–12, 16514–15, 16522, 16530–34, 16538, 16541, 16544, 16546, 16550, 16553–54

* * *

FOURTH DISTRICT

SCOTT G. PERRY, Republican, of York County, PA; born in San Diego, May 27, 1962; education: Northern York High School, 1980; B.S in business administration management, Pennsylvania State University, 1991; M.S. in strategic studies, U.S. Army War College, 2012; professional: Small Business Owner at Hydrotech Mechanical Services; military: Active Colonel in Pennsylvania Army National Guard; organizations: former President of Pennsylvania Young Republicans; former Regional Director for Pennsylvania Chapter of Jaycees; Dillsburg Legion Post #2; Dillsburg VFW Post #6771; public service: Pennsylvania House of Representatives, 2006–12; married: Christy; children: Ryenn and Mattea; committees: Foreign Affairs; Homeland Security; Transportation and Infrastructure; elected to the 113th Congress on November 6, 2012.

Office Listings

http://perry.house.gov twitter: @repscottperry

126 Cannon House Office Building, Washington, DC 20515 .... (202) 225–5836

Chief of Staff.—Lauren Muglia. FAX: 226–1000
Legislative Director.—Marianne Myers.
Communications Director.—Ryan Nawrocki.
Legislative Correspondent.—Braeden Eastman.
Legislative Assistants: John Drzewicki, George O'Conner.
Staff Assistants: Justin Durbin, Hunter Presti.

22 Chambersburg Street, Gettysburg, PA 17325 .... (717) 338–1919
Field Representative.—Holly Sutphin.

2209 East Market Street, York, PA 17402 .... (717) 600–1919
Deputy Chief of Staff.—Bob Reilly.
Legislative Assistants: Donna Austin, Nicole McCleary, Ben Turner.
Staff Assistant.—Andrew Blasco.
Scheduler.—Carol Wiest.

730 North Front Street, Wormleysburg, PA 17043 .... (717) 635–9504
Director of Constituent Services.—Tyra Wallace.

Counties: ADAMS, CUMBERLAND, DAUPHIN, AND YORK. CITIES AND TOWNSHIPS: Abbottstown, Arendtsville, Bendersville, Berwick, Biglerville, Bonneauville, Butler, Camp Hill, Carroll Valley, Carroll, Chanceford, Codorus, Conewago, Cross Roads, Cumberland, Dallastown, Delta, Dillsburg, Dover, Dover, East Berlin, East Hopewell, East Manchester, East Pennsboro, East Prospect, Fairfield, Fairview, Fawn Grove, Fawn, Felton, Franklin, Franklintown, Freedom, Germany, Gettysburg, Glen Rock, Goldsboro, Hallam, Hamilton, Hamiltonban, Hampden, Hanover, Harrisburg, Heidelberg, Hellam, Highland, Hopewell, Huntington, Jackson, Jacobus, Jefferson, Latimore, Lemoyne, Lewisberry, Liberty, Littlestown, Loganville, Lower Allen, Lower Chanceford, Lower Windsor, Manchester, Manchester, Manheim, McSherrystown, Mechanicsburg, Menallen, Monaghan, Mount Joy, Mount Pleasant, Mount Wolf, New Cumberland, New Freedom, New Oxford, New Salem, Newberry, North Codorus, North Hopewell, North York, Oxford, Paradise, Peach Bottom, Penn, Railroad, Reading, Red Lion, Seven Valleys, Shiremanstown, Shrewsbury, Shrewsbury, Silver Spring, Spring Garden, Spring Grove, Springettsbury, Springfield, Stewartstown, Straban, Susquehanna, Tyrone, Union, Upper Allen, Warrington, Washington, Wellsville, West Manchester, West Manheim, West York, Windsor, Windsor, Winterstown, Wormleysburg, Wrightsville, Yoe, York Haven, York Springs, York, York, and Yorkana. Population (2010), 705,687.

ZIP Codes: 17070, 17072, 17093, 17101–04, 17109–11, 17120, 17301–02, 17304, 17306–07, 17309, 17311, 17313–22, 17324–25, 17327, 17329, 17331, 17339–40, 17343–45, 17347, 17349–50, 17352–53, 17355–56, 17360–66, 17368, 17370–72, 17401–04, 17406–08

* * *

FIFTH DISTRICT

GLENN THOMPSON, Republican, of Howard Township, PA; born in Bellefonte, PA, July 27, 1959; education: B.S., therapeutic recreation, Pennsylvania State University, 1981; M.Ed., health science / therapeutic recreation, Temple University, 1998; NHA / L, Nursing Home Administrator, Marywood University, 2006; professional: Rehabilitation Services Manager for Susquehanna Health Services, Adjunct Faculty for Cambria County Community College; Chief, Recreational Therapist for the Williamsport Hospital; Residential Services Aid for Hope Enterprises, Orderly for Centre Crest Nursing Home; Organization / Awards: Past President / Fire Fighter / EMT / Rescue Technician for Howard VFD; former, Howard Boy Scout Master; former, President and Senior VP for Juniata Valley Boy Scout Council; International Advisory Council Member for the Accreditation of Rehabilitation Facilities Commission; board member / vice chair of Private Industry Council of Central Corridors; political career: Centre County Republican chair, Pennsylvania Republican State Committee, alternate delegate for the Republican National Convention; candidate for the Pennsylvania House of Representatives, 1998 and 2000; member, Bald Eagle Area School District Board of Education; religion: Protestant; married to Penny Ammerman-Thompson; three sons, Parker, Logan and Kale; committees: Agriculture; Education and the Workforce; Natural Resources; elected to the 111th Congress on November 4, 2008; reelected to each succeeding Congress.

Office Listings

http://thompson.house.gov

124 Cannon House Office Building, Washington, DC 20515 .... (202) 225–5121
Chief of Staff.—Jordan Clark. FAX: 225–5796
Legislative Director.—Matthew Brennan.
Scheduler.—Hope Morris.
Communications Director.—Parish Braden.

127 West Spring Street, Suite C, Titusville, PA 16354 .... (814) 827–3985
District Director.—Peter Winkler.

3555 Benner Pike, Suite 101, Bellefonte, PA 16823 .... (814) 353–0215

Counties: CAMERON, CENTRE, CLARION (part), CLEARFIELD, CLINTON, CRAWFORD (part), ELK, ERIE (part), FOREST, HUNTINGDON (part), JEFFERSON, MCKEAN, POTTER, TIOGA (part), VENANGO AND WARREN. Population (2010), 705,688.

ZIP Codes: 15711, 15715, 15721, 15724, 15730, 15733, 15742, 15744, 15753, 15757, 15764, 15767, 15770, 15776, 15778, 15780–81, 15784, 15801, 15821, 15823–25, 15827–29, 15832, 15834, 15840–41, 15845–49, 15851, 15853, 15856–57, 15860–61, 15863–66, 15868, 15870, 16036, 16038, 16054, 16127, 16153, 16214, 16217, 16222, 16224,

16232–33, 16235, 16239–40, 16242, 16254–55, 16258, 16260, 16301, 16311–14, 16317, 16319, 16321–23, 16326, 16329, 16331–34, 16340–47, 16350–54, 16361–62, 16364–65, 16370–74, 16402–03, 16405, 16407, 16410, 16412, 16415–17, 16420–21, 16426–28, 16434, 16436, 16438, 16441–42, 16444, 16504, 16506, 16509–11, 16563, 16611, 16616, 16620, 16622, 16627, 16639, 16645–47, 16651–52, 16656–57, 16661, 16666, 16669, 16671, 16677, 16680, 16683, 16686, 16692, 16701, 16720, 16724–35, 16738, 16740, 16743–46, 16748–50, 16801–03, 16820–23, 16825–30, 16832–41, 16843–45, 16847–49, 16851–55, 16858–61, 16863, 16865–66, 16868, 16870–72, 16874–79, 16881–82, 16901, 16915, 16921–23, 16927–28, 16935, 16937–38, 16941, 16943, 16948, 16950, 17002, 17052, 17060, 17066, 17243, 17260, 17721, 17729, 17740, 17745, 17747–48, 17750–51, 17760, 17764, 17767, 17778–79

* * *

SIXTH DISTRICT

JIM GERLACH, Republican, of Chester Springs, PA; born in Ellwood City, PA, February 25, 1955; education: B.A., Dickinson College, 1977; J.D., Dickinson School of Law, 1980; professional: attorney; former special counsel to the regional law firm of Fox, Rothschild, O'Brien & Frankel; community service: board of directors, MECA (Mission for Educating Children with Autism); Dickinson College Board of Trustees; Chester County Agricultural Development Council; public service: Pennsylvania House of Representatives, 1991–94; Pennsylvania State Senate, 1995–2002; children: Katie, Jimmy, and Robby; committees: Ways and Means; elected to the 108th Congress on November 5, 2002; reelected to each succeeding Congress.

Office Listings

http://www.gerlach.house.gov

2442 Rayburn House Office Building, Washington, DC 20515 .... (202) 225–4315
Chief of Staff.—Annie Fultz. FAX: 225–8440
Legislative Director.—Lauryn Schothorst.
Communications Director.—Kori Walter.
111 East Uwchlan Avenue, Exton, PA 19341 .... (610) 594–1415
840 North Park Road, Wyomissing, PA 19610 .... (610) 376–7630
580 Main Street, Suite 4, Trappe, PA 19426 .... (610) 409–2780

Counties: BERKS (part), CHESTER (part), LEHIGH (part), MONTGOMERY (part). Population (2010), 720,487.

ZIP Codes: 17527, 17555, 17569, 18011, 18031, 18041, 18056, 18062, 18070, 18092, 19003–04, 19010, 19025, 19031, 19034–35, 19041, 19066, 19072, 19085, 19087, 19096, 19131, 19151, 19301, 19310, 19312, 19316, 19320, 19333, 19335, 19341, 19343–45, 19353–55, 19358, 19365–67, 19369, 19371–72, 19376, 19380, 19382, 19401, 19403–04, 19409, 19421, 19423, 19425–26, 19428, 19430, 19432, 19438, 19442, 19444, 19446, 19457, 19460, 19462, 19464–65, 19468, 19470, 19473–75, 19480–85, 19490, 19493–96, 19503–05, 19508, 19511–12, 19518–20, 19522–23, 19525, 19530, 19535, 19538–40, 19542–43, 19545, 19547–48, 19562, 19565, 19601–02, 19604–12

* * *

SEVENTH DISTRICT

PATRICK MEEHAN, Republican, of Drexel Hill, PA; born in Cheltenham, PA, October 20, 1955; education: B.S., Bowdoin College, Brunswick, ME, 1978; J.D., Temple University, Philadelphia, PA, 1985; professional: district attorney for Delaware County, 1996–2001; United States Attorney for the Eastern District of Pennsylvania, 2001–08; religion: Roman Catholic; married: Carolyn Meehan; children: Jack, Patrick, and Colin; caucuses: Autism; Congressional Fire Services; Congressional Hockey; committees: Ethics; Homeland Security; Oversight and Government Reform, Transportation and Infrastructure; elected to the 112th Congress on November 2, 2010; reelected to the 113th Congress on November 6, 2012.

Office Listings

http://meehan.house.gov

204 Cannon House Office Building, Washington, DC 20515 .... (202) 225–2011
Chief of Staff.—Brian Schubert. FAX: 226–0280
940 Sproul Road, Springfield, PA 19064 .... (610) 690–7323
District Director.—Caitlin Ganley. FAX: 690–7329

Counties: BERKS (part), CHESTER (part), DELAWARE (part), LANCASTER (part), AND MONTGOMERY (part). Population (2010), 692,866.

ZIP Codes: 17503, 17505, 17509, 17527, 17529, 17534–36, 17555, 17557, 17562, 17566, 17569, 17572, 17579, 18964, 19002–04, 19008, 19010, 19013–15, 19017–18, 19022, 19025–26, 19028–29, 19031, 19033–34, 19036–39, 19041, 19043–44, 19050, 19052, 19060–61, 19063–64, 19070, 19073–76, 19078, 19081–83, 19085, 19087, 19094, 19096, 19310–11, 19316–17, 19319–20, 19330–31, 19333, 19335, 19342–44, 19346–48, 19350–54, 19357, 19363, 19365–67, 19369, 19371–76, 19380–83, 19390, 19395, 19401, 19403–04, 19406, 19409, 19422–23, 19426, 19428, 19430, 19436–19438,

19440, 19444, 19446, 19454, 19462, 19465, 19470, 19473–74, 19477, 19484, 19486, 19490, 19501, 19508, 19512, 19518–20, 19523, 19535, 19540, 19542–43, 19547–48, 19606–09

* * *

EIGHTH DISTRICT

MICHAEL FITZPATRICK, Republican, of Levittown, PA; born in Philadelphia, PA, June 28, 1963; education: B.S., St. Thomas University, Miami Gardens, FL, 1985; J.D., Dickinson School of Law, Carlisle, PA, 1988; professional: Bucks County Board of Commissioners; practiced law at Begley Carlin and Mandio; religion: Roman Catholic; married: Kathleen; three daughters, Katie, Maggie, and Molly; three sons, Jimmy, Mick, and Tommy; committees: Financial Services; elected to the 109th Congress on November 2, 2004; elected to the 112th Congress on November 2, 2010; reelected to the 113th Congress on November 6, 2012.

Office Listings

http://www.fitzpatrick.house.gov

2400 Rayburn House Office Building, Washington, DC 20515 .... (202) 225–4276
Chief of Staff.—Athan Koutsiouroumbas. FAX: 225–9511
Legislative Director.—Kyle Whatley.
1717 Langhorne Newtown Road, Suite 400, Langhorne, PA 19047 .... (215) 579–8102
District Director.—Stacey Mulholland. FAX: 579–8109

Counties: BUCKS, AND MONTGOMERY (part). Population (2010), 705,688.

ZIP Codes: 18036, 18042, 18054–55, 18073–74, 18076–77, 18081, 18902, 18907, 18912–15, 18917, 18920, 18923, 18925, 18929–30, 18932, 18935, 18938, 18940, 18942, 18944, 18947, 18950–51, 18954–55, 18960, 18962, 18964, 18966, 18969–70, 18972, 18974, 18976–77, 18980, 19006–07, 19021, 19030, 19040, 19047, 19053–57, 19067, 19438, 19440, 19446, 19473, 19492, 19504

* * *

NINTH DISTRICT

BILL SHUSTER, Republican, of Hollidaysburg, PA; born in McKeesport, PA, January 10, 1961; education: Everett High School, Bedford County, PA; B.A., Dickinson College; M.B.A., American University; professional: businessman; Goodyear Tire & Rubber Corp.; Bandag, Inc.; President and General Manager, Shuster Chrysler; organizations: member, Zion Lutheran Church; National Federation of Independent Business; National Rifle Association; Y.M.C.A.; Precious Life, Inc.; Rotary Club; Board of Directors, Pennsylvania Automotive Association; Board of Trustees, Homewood Home Retirement Community; Sigma Chi Fraternity; family: married to Rebecca; two children: Ali and Garrett; committees: chair, Transportation and Infrastructure; Armed Services; elected to the 107th Congress, by special election, on May 15, 2001; reelected to each succeeding Congress.

Office Listings

http://www.house.gov/shuster

2209 Rayburn House Office Building, Washington, DC 20515 .... (202) 225–2431
Chief of Staff.—Eric Burgeson. FAX: 225–2486
Deputy Chief of Staff.—Kelley Halliwell.
Legislative Director.—Jamie Boone.
Scheduler.—Brittany Smith.
310 Penn Street, Suite 200, Hollidaysburg, PA 16648 .... (814) 696–6318
100 Lincoln Way East, Suite B, Chambersburg, PA 17201 .... (717) 264–8308
827 Water Street, Suite 3, Indiana, PA 15701 .... (724) 463–0516

Counties: BEDFORD, BLAIR, CAMBRIA (part), FAYETTE, FRANKLIN, FULTON, GREENE (part), HUNTINGDON (part), INDIANA, SOMERSET (part), WASHINGTON (part), and WESTMORELAND (part). Population (2010), 664,701.

ZIP Codes: 15012, 15022, 15033, 15062, 15067, 15314–15, 15320, 15322, 15325, 15327, 15332–34, 15338, 15344, 15346, 15348–49, 15351, 15357–58, 15366, 15368, 15370, 15401, 15410–13, 15415–17, 15419–25, 15427–40, 15442–47, 15449–51, 15454–56, 15458–70, 15472–78, 15480, 15482–86, 15488–92, 15501, 15510, 15521–22, 15530, 15532–42, 15545, 15550, 15552–54, 15557–60, 15562–65, 15610, 15618, 15622, 15631, 15666, 15681, 15683, 15701, 15705, 15710, 15712–14, 15716–17, 15720, 15722–25, 15727–29, 15731–31, 15734, 15737–39, 15741–43, 15745–48, 15750, 15752, 15754, 15756–59, 15761–63, 15765, 15767, 15771–75, 15777, 15783, 15920, 15924, 15926, 15929, 15931, 15938, 15940, 15944, 15946, 15949, 15954, 15957, 15961, 16211, 16222, 16246, 16256, 16601–03, 16611, 16613, 16617, 16619, 16621–25, 16627, 16629–31, 16633–41, 16644, 16646–48, 16650, 16655, 16657, 16659, 16662, 16664–65, 16667–68, 16670, 16672–75, 16678–79, 16682, 16684–86, 16689, 16691, 16693–95, 17002, 17013, 18015, 17024,

17040, 17052–53, 17060, 17066, 17068, 17201–02, 17210–15, 17217, 17219–25, 17228–29, 17231–33, 17235–41, 17243–44, 17246–47, 17249–57, 17261–65, 17267–72, 17324

* * *

TENTH DISTRICT

THOMAS A. MARINO, Republican, of Cogan Station, PA; born in Williamsport, PA, August 13, 1952; education: American Institute of Baking, 1982; A.A., general studies, Williamsport Area Community College, 1983; B.A., political science / education, Lycoming College, 1985; J.D., Dickinson School of Law, 1987; United States Army War College, 2005; professional: manufacturing manager; lawyer, private practice; served as a Lycoming County District Attorney, PA, 1992–2002; U.S. Attorney for the Middle District of Pennsylvania, 1992–2002; married: Edith, 1974; two children: Chloe, Victor; committees: Foreign Affairs; Homeland Security; Judiciary; elected to the 112th Congress on November 2, 2010; reelected to the 113th Congress on November 6, 2012.

Office Listings

http://www.marino.house.gov https://twitter.com/reptommarino
https://www.facebook.com/congressmanmarino

410 Cannon House Office Building, Washington, DC 20515 .... (202) 225–3731
Chief of Staff.—Bill Tighe. FAX: 225–9594
Legislative Director / Counsel.—Jaclyn Louis.
Director of Operations / Scheduler.—Sara Rogers.
Communications Director.—Sarah Wolf.
Senior Legislative Assistant.—Ansley Rhyne.
Legislative Assistant / Legislative Correspondent.—Peter Mihalick.
Special Assistant.—Philip Pulizzi.
Staff Assistant.—Matt Powell.
1020 Commerce Park Drive, Suite 1A, Williamsport, PA 17701 .... (570) 322–3961
Constituent Services Manager.—Jacqueline Bell.
District Representatives: Matt Hutchinson, Mike Knouse.
543 Easton Turnpike, Suite 101, Lake Ariel, PA 18436 .... (570) 689–6024
District Director.—Dave Weber.
District Representatives: Tom Cahill, Tony Herzog, Cathy Romaniello.
30 South Market Street, Suite 1A, Selinsgrove, PA 17870 .... (570) 374–9469
District Representative.—Amiee Snyder.

Counties: BRADFORD, JUNIATA, LACKAWANNA (part), LYCOMING, MIFFLIN, MONROE (part), NORTHUMBERLAND (part), PERRY, PIKE, SNYDER, SULLIVAN, SUSQUEHANNA, TIOGA, UNION, AND WAYNE. Population (2010), 669,257.

ZIP Codes: 16911–12, 16914, 16917, 16920, 16925–26, 16929–30, 16932–33, 16936, 16939–40, 16942, 16946–47, 17004, 17006, 17009, 17029, 17035, 17037, 17044–45, 17047, 17049, 17051, 17056, 17058–59, 17062–63, 17069, 17071, 17075–76, 17082, 17084, 17086, 17094, 17099, 17701–02, 17723–24, 17727–28, 17730–31, 17737, 17739, 17742, 17744, 17749, 17752, 17754, 17758, 17762–63, 17765, 17768, 17771, 17776, 17810, 17812–13, 17827, 17829, 17835, 17837, 17841–42, 17844–45, 17850, 17853, 17855–57, 17861–62, 17864–65, 17870, 17876, 17880, 17885–87, 17889, 18323, 18325, 18328, 18332, 18336–37, 18340, 18342, 18349, 18352, 18357, 18370–72, 18405, 18413, 18415, 18417, 18420–21, 18425–28, 18430–31, 18435–39, 18441, 18443, 18445, 18451, 18453–65, 18469–73, 18616, 18619, 18626, 18628, 18632, 18653, 18801, 18810, 18812, 18814, 18816–18, 18821–26, 18828–34, 18837, 18840, 18842–43, 18848, 18850–51, 18853–54

* * *

ELEVENTH DISTRICT

LOU BARLETTA, Republican, of Hazleton, PA; born in Hazleton, January 28, 1956; education: attended Bloomsburg University, Bloomsburg, PA; professional: business owner; member of city council in Hazleton, PA, 1998–2000; mayor of Hazleton, PA, 2000–10; married: Mary Grace; four daughters; committees: Education and the Workforce; Homeland Security; Transportation and Infrastructure; elected to the 112th Congress on November 2, 2010; reelected to the 113th Congress on November 6, 2012.

Office Listings

http://www.house.gov/barletta

115 Cannon House Office Building, Washington, DC 20515 .... (202) 225–6511
Chief of Staff.—Andrea Waldock. FAX: 226–6250
Legislative Director.—Kelly Hastings.
Executive Assistant.—Cherie Homa.
Press Secretary.—Time Murtaugh.
1 South Church Street, Hazleton, PA 18201–5283 .... (570) 751–0050

59 West Louther Street, Carlisle, PA 17013 .... (717) 249–0190
4813 Jonestown Road, Suite 101, Harrisburg, PA 17109 .... (717) 525–7002
106 Arch Street, Sunbury, PA 17801 .... (570) 988–7801

Counties: CARBON (part), COLUMBIA, CUMBERLAND (part), DAUPHIN (part), LUZERNE (part), MONTOUR, NORTHUMBERLAND (part), PERRY (part), and Wyoming. Population (2010), 702,158.

ZIP Codes: 17005, 17007, 17013, 17015, 17017–20, 17023–24, 17030, 17032, 17034, 17036, 17040, 17048, 17050, 17053, 17055, 17057, 17061, 17065, 17068, 17074, 17080–81, 17090, 17094, 17097, 17103–04, 17109–13, 17240–41, 17257, 17266, 17307, 17324, 17756, 17772, 17774, 17777, 17801, 17814–15, 17822–24, 17829–30, 17832, 17834, 17836, 17840, 17846–47, 17851, 17859–60, 17866–68, 17872, 17878, 17881, 17884, 17888, 17920–21, 17941, 17945, 17964, 17980, 17985, 18201–02, 18210, 18221–25, 18229–30, 18234–35, 18237, 18239, 18241, 18244, 18246, 18249, 18251, 18254–56, 18414, 18417, 18424, 18446, 18602–03, 18610, 18612, 18614–15, 18617–18, 18621–25, 18629–31, 18634–36, 18643–44, 18651, 18655–57, 18660–61, 18702, 18704, 18706–09, 18844

* * *

TWELFTH DISTRICT

KEITH J. ROTHFUS, Republican, of Sewickley, PA; born in Endicott, NY, April 25, 1962; education: B.S., information systems, State University of New York College at Buffalo, Buffalo, NY, 1984; J.D., University of Notre Dame Law School, Notre Dame, IN, 1990; profession: lawyer; religion: Roman Catholic; family: Elsie, wife; six children; caucuses: Congressional Diabetes Caucus; Congressional Cybersecurity Caucus; Congressional Down Syndrome Caucus; National Guard and Reserve Components Caucus; Congressional Steel Caucus; Congressional Multiple Sclerosis Caucus; Congressional Coal Caucus; Congressional Pro-Life Caucus; Congressional Wire and Wire Producers Caucus; Ohio River Basin Congressional Caucus; Republican Policy Committee; committees: Financial Services; elected to the 113th Congress on November 6, 2012.

Office Listings

http://www.rothfus.house.gov https://www.facebook.com/keithrothfus
https://twitter.com/keithrothfus

503 Cannon House Office Building, Washington, DC 20515 .... (202) 225–2065
Chief of Staff.—Armstrong Robinson. FAX: 225–5709
Office Manager / Schedule Coordinator.—Ana Ellis.
Legislative Director.—Danielle Janowski.
Communications Director.—Edward Yap.
Armed Services Staff.—Brian Ryckman.
Small Business Staff.—Danielle Janowski.
6000 Babcock Boulevard, Suite 104, Pittsburgh, PA 15237 .... (412) 837–1361
District Fax Number .... (412) 593–2022
District Director.—Jonathan Raso.
Deputy District Director.—Allison Beresnyak.
Constituent Advocate.—Meghan Repasky.
Military and Veterans' Affairs Representative.—Chuck Schrankel.
250 Insurance Street, Suite 203, Beaver, PA 15901 .... (724) 359–1626
District Fax Number .... (412) 593–2022
Field Representative.—Jeremy Honhold.
110 Franklin Street, Suite 150, Johnstown, PA 15901 .... (814) 619–3659
District Fax Number .... (412) 593–2022
Field Representative.—Seth McKinley.
Constituent Advocate.—Ashley Klingensmith

Counties: ALLEGHENY COUNTY (part). CITIES AND TOWNSHIPS: Allison Park, Aspinwall, Bairdford, Bakerstown, Bell Acres, Bradford Woods, Curtisville, Fawn Harrison, Fox Chapel, Franklin Park, Frazer, Hampton, Haysville, Gibsonia, Glen Osborne, Glenshaw, Indiana, Kilbuck, Marshall, McCandless, O'Hara, Ohio, Pine, Richland, Ross, Russellton, Sewickley, Sewickley Heights, Sewickley Hills, Shaler, West Deer, West View. BEAVER. CITIES AND TOWNSHIPS: Aliquippa, Ambridge, Baden, Beaver, Big Beaver, Beaver Falls, Bridgewater, Brighton Township, Center, Chippewa, Conway, Darlington, Daugherty, East Rochester, Eastvale, Economy, Fallston, Frankfort Springs, Franklin, Freedom, Georgetown, Glasgow, Greene Township, Hanover, Harmony, Homewood, Hookstown, Hopewell, Independence, Industry, Koppel, Marion, Midland, Monaca, New Brighton, New Galilee, New Sewickley, North Sewickley, Ohioville, Patterson, Patterson Heights, Potter, Pulaski, Raccoon, Rochester, Shippingport, South Beaver, South Heights, Vanport, West Mayfield, White Township. CAMBRIA (part). CITIES AND TOWNSHIPS: Barr, Beaverdale, Belmont, Blacklick, Brownstown, Cambria, Carrolltown, Cassandra, Colver, Conemaugh, Croyle, Daisytown, Dale, Dunlo, East Carroll, East Conemaugh, East Taylor, Ehrenfeld, Geistown, Ebensburg, Elim, Ferndale, Johnstown, Jackson, Lilly, Lorain, Lower Yoder, Middle Taylor, Mundy's Corner, Nanty-Glo, Portagem, Revloc, Riverside, Salix, Scalp Level, Sidman, South Fork, Spring Hill, St. Michael, Stonycreek, Summerhill, Upper Yoder, Vinco, Vintonsale, Washington, West Taylor, Westmont, Wilmore. LAWRENCE (part). CITIES AND TOWNSHIPS: Ellport, Ellwood City, Enon Valley, Little Beaver, Perry, Wampum, Wayne. SOMERSET (part). CITIES AND TOWNSHIPS: Benson, Black, Boswell, Cairnbrook, Casselman, Central City, Conemaugh, Davidsville, Edie, Friedens, Hooversville, Jefferson, Jenner, Jennersown, Jerome, Lincoln, Middle Creek, New Centerville, Ogle, Paint, Quemahoning, Rockwood, Somerset, Shade, Stoystown, Upper Turkeyfoot, Windber. WESTMORELAND (part). CITIES AND TOWNSHIPS: Allegheny, Avonmore, Bell, Bolivar, Bradenville, Delmont, Derry, East Vandergrift, Fairfield, Hyde Park, Lower Burrell, Loyalhanna, Millwood, Monroeville, Murrysville, New Alexandria, New Florence, Oklahoma, Plum, Salem, Seward, Slickville, St. Clair, Upper Burrell, Vandergrift, Washington, and West Leechburg. Population (2010), 700,573.

ZIP Codes: 15001, 15003, 15005–07, 15009–10, 15015, 15024, 15026–27, 15030, 15042–44, 15050–52, 15059, 15061, 15065–66, 15068, 15074–77, 15081, 15084, 15086, 15090, 15101, 15116, 15139, 15143, 15146–47, 15202, 15209, 15212, 15214–15, 15223, 15229, 15235, 15237–39, 15424–25, 15501–02, 15510, 15520, 15530–31, 15540–42, 15544, 15546–47, 15551, 15555, 15557, 15561, 15563, 15601, 15613, 15618, 15620, 15622, 15624, 15626–27, 15629, 15632–33, 15641, 15644, 15650, 15656, 15658, 15661, 15668, 15670–71, 15680–81, 15684, 15690, 15714, 15717, 15722, 15760, 15762, 15775, 15779, 15901–02, 15904–06, 15909, 15921–28, 15930–31, 15934–38, 15940, 15942–46, 15948, 15951–58, 15960–63, 16037, 16046, 16051, 16055, 16059, 16063, 16101, 16115, 16117, 16120, 16123, 16136, 16141, 16157, 16229

* * *

THIRTEENTH DISTRICT

ALLYSON Y. SCHWARTZ, Democrat, of Rydal, PA; born in Queens County, NY, October 3, 1948; education: graduated from the Calhoun School, New York, NY, 1966; B.A., Simmons College, Boston, MA, 1970; M.S.W., Bryn Mawr College, Bryn Mawr, PA, 1972; professional: executive director of the Elizabeth Blackwell Center, 1977–88; Deputy Commissioner of the Philadelphia Department of Human Services, 1988–90; elected to the Pennsylvania State Senate, 1991–2004; member: Pennsylvania State Board of Education; Pennsylvania Council on Higher Education; Education Commission of the States; married: Dr. David Schwartz; children: Daniel and Jordan; committees: Budget; Ways and Means; elected to the 109th Congress on November 2, 2004; reelected to each succeeding Congress.

Office Listings

http://www.house.gov/schwartz

1227 Longworth House Office Building, Washington, DC 20515 .... (202) 225–6111
Chief of Staff.—Craig Kwiecinski. FAX: 226–0611
Legislative Director.—Charlene MacDonald.
Communications Director.—Greg Vadala.
801 Old York Road, Suite 212, Jenkintown, PA 19046 .... (215) 517–6572
District Director.—Michelle Espinal.
7712 Castor Avenue, Philadelphia, PA 19152 .... (215) 335–3355

County: MONTGOMERY COUNTY. CITIES AND TOWNSHIPS: Abington Wards, Hatfield, Horsham, Lower Gwynedd, Lower Moreland, Montgomery, Plymouth, Springfield, Towamencin, Upper Dublin, Upper Frederick, Upper Gwynedd, Upper Moreland, Whitemarsh, Whitpain. BOROUGHS OF: Ambler, Hatboro, Hatfield, Jenkintown, Lansdale, North Wales, and Rockledge. PHILADELPHIA COUNTY. CITY OF: Philadelphia. Population (2010), 705,687.

ZIP Codes: 19001–02, 19006, 19009, 19019, 19025, 19027, 19038, 19040, 19044, 19046, 19075, 19090, 19095–96, 19111, 19114–16, 19118, 19120, 19124, 19126, 19128, 19136–37, 19140, 19149–50, 19152, 19154–55, 19160

* * *

FOURTEENTH DISTRICT

MICHAEL F. DOYLE, Democrat, of Forest Hills, PA; born in Swissvale, PA, August 5, 1953; graduated, Swissvale Area High School, 1971; B.S., Pennsylvania State University, 1975; co-owner, Eastgate Insurance Agency, Inc., 1983; elected and served as finance and recreation chairman, Swissvale Borough Council, 1977–81; member: Leadership Pittsburgh Alumni Association, Lions Club, Ancient Order of the Hibernians, Italian Sons and Daughters of America, and Penn State Alumni Association; member: Democratic Caucus, Democratic Study Group, Pennsylvania Democratic Delegation, Congressional Steel Caucus, Travel and Tourism CMO, Ad Hoc Committee on Irish Affairs, and National Italian-American Foundation; married Susan Beth Doyle, 1975; four children: Michael, David, Kevin, and Alexandra; committees: Energy and Commerce; elected to the 104th Congress, November 8, 1994; reelected to each succeeding Congress.

Office Listings

http://doyle.house.gov

239 Cannon House Office Building, Washington, DC 20515 .... (202) 225–2135
Administrative Assistant.—David Lucas. FAX: 225–3084
Legislative Director.—Jean Roehrenbeck.
Office Manager / Scheduler.—Ellen Young.
2637 East Carson Street, Pittsburgh, PA 15203 .... (412) 390–1499
District Director.—Paul D'Alesandro.
11 Duff Road, Penn Hills, PA 15235 .... (412) 241–6055
627 Lysle Boulevard, McKeesport, PA 15132 .... (412) 664–4049

County: ARNOLD (Westmoreland County). CITIES AND TOWNSHIPS OF: Avalon, Baldwin Borough, Baldwin Township, Bellevue, Ben Avon, Ben Avon Heights, Blawnox, Brackenridge, Braddock, Braddock Hills, Brentwood, Chalfant, Cheswick,

Churchill, Clairton, Coraopolis, Crafton, Dormont, Duquesne, Dravosburg, East Deer, East McKeesport, East Pittsburgh, Edgewood, Emsworth, Etna, Forest Hills, Glassport, Glenfield, Greentree, Harmar, Harrison (Ward 1, District 1; Ward 2; Ward 5-District 1), Homestead, Ingram, Kennedy, Liberty, Lincoln, McKees Rocks, McKeesport, Millvale, Monroeville (Ward 1; Ward 2, District 2; Ward 3, District 3; Ward 5, District 1, 2, 4; Ward 6; Ward 7), Mt. Oliver, Munhall, Neville, New Kensington (Westmoreland), North Braddock, North Versailles, Oakmont, Penn Hills, Pitcairn, Pittsburgh, Port Vue, Rankin, Robinson (Districts 3 and 5), Sharpsburg, Springdale Borough, Springdale Township, Stowe, Swissvale, Tarentum, Trafford (Allegheny), Turtle Creek, Verona, Versailles, Wall, West Homestead, West Mifflin, Whitaker, White Oak, Whitehall (Part District 1; Districts 2–16), Wilkins, Wilkinsburg, and Wilmerding. Population (2010), 705,688.

ZIP Codes: 15014, 15024–25, 15030, 15034–35, 15037, 15045, 15049, 15065, 15068, 15084–85, 15104, 15106, 15108, 15110, 15112, 15120, 15122, 15131–33, 15135–37, 15139–40, 15143–48, 15201–28, 15232–36, 15238, 15260, 15290, 15642

* * *

FIFTEENTH DISTRICT

CHARLES W. DENT, Republican, of Allentown, PA, born in Allentown, May 24, 1960; education: B.A., foreign service and international politics, Pennsylvania State University, 1982; M.A., public administration, Lehigh University, 1993; professional: Legislator Development Officer, Lehigh University, 1986–90; sales representative, P.A. Peters, Inc.; Pennsylvania State House, District 132, 1991–98; Representative, Pennsylvania State Senate, 1998–2004; religion: First Presbyterian Church; married: Pamela Jane Serfass; children: Kathryn Elizabeth, William Reed, and Charles John (Jack); committees: Appropriations; Ethics; elected to the 109th Congress on November 2, 2004; reelected to each succeeding Congress.

Office Listings

http://www.dent.house.gov https://www.facebook.com/congressmandent
https://twitter.com/dentpressshop

2455 Rayburn House Office Building, Washington, DC 20515 .... (202) 225–6411
Chief of Staff.—George McElwee. FAX: 226–0778
Legislative Director.—Kristin Dini.
3900 Hamilton Boulevard, Suite 207, Allentown, PA 18103 .... (610) 770–3490
61 North 3rd Street, Hamburg, PA 19526 .... (610) 562–4281
342 F West Main Street, Annville, PA 17003 .... (717) 867–1026
250 West Chocolate Avenue, Hershey, PA 17033 .... (717) 533–3959

Counties: BERKS (part), DAUPHIN (part), LEBANON (part), LEHIGH, AND NORTHAMPTON (part). Population (2010), 705,687.

ZIP Codes: 17003, 17010, 17022, 17026, 17028, 17033, 17036, 17038, 17041–42, 17046, 17057, 17064, 17067, 17077–78, 17087, 1711–12, 17545, 17963, 18011, 18014–18, 18020, 18031–32, 18034–38, 18040–42, 18045–46, 18049, 18051–53, 18055, 18059, 18062, 18064, 18066–69, 18072, 18077–80, 18086–88, 18091–92, 18101–06, 18109, 18195, 18951, 19504–07, 19511, 19526, 19529–30, 19533–34, 19536, 19538–39, 19541, 19544, 19550, 19554–55, 19559, 19562, 19567

* * *

SIXTEENTH DISTRICT

JOSEPH R. PITTS, Republican, of Kennett Square, PA; born in Lexington, KY, October 10, 1939; education: B.A., philosophy and religion, Asbury College, KY; military service: served in U.S. Air Force, 1963–69, rising from second lieutenant to captain; professional: nursery business owner and operator; math and science teacher, Great Valley High School, Malvern, PA, 1969–72; teacher, Mortonsville Elementary School, Versailles, KY; member: Pennsylvania House of Representatives, 1972–96, serving as chairman of Appropriations Committee, 1989–96, and of Labor Relations Committee, 1981–88; married: the former Virginia M. Pratt in 1961; children: Karen, Carol, and Daniel; committees: Energy and Commerce; elected to the 105th Congress; reelected to each succeeding Congress.

Office Listings

http://www.house.gov/pitts twitter.com/repjoepitts
https://www.facebook.com/pages/congressman-joe-pitts/94156528752?ref=ts

420 Cannon House Office Building, Washington, DC 20515 .... (202) 225–2411
Chief of Staff.—Gabe Neville. FAX: 225–2013
Legislative Director.—Monica Volante.
Press Secretary.—Andrew Wimer.
P.O. Box 837, Unionville, PA 19375 .... (610) 444–4581
150 North Queen Street, Suite 716, Lancaster, PA 17603 .... (717) 393–0667

Counties: LANCASTER COUNTY. CITY: Lancaster. TOWNSHIPS: Brecknock, Caernarvon, Clay, Conestoga, Conoy, Drumore, Earl, East Cocalico, East Donegal, East Drumore, East Earl, East Hempfield, East Lampeter, Eden, Elizabeth, Ephrata, Fulton, Lancaster, Little Britain, Manheim, Manor, Martic, Mount Joy, Penn, Pequea, Providence, Rapho, Strasburg, Upper Leacock, Warwick, West Cocalico, West Donegal, West Earl, West Hempfield, and West Lampeter. BOROUGHS OF: Adamstown, Akron, Columbia, Denver, East Petersburg, Elizabethtown, Ephrata, Lititz, Manheim, Marietta, Millersville, Mount Joy, Mountville, New Holland, Quarryville, Strasburg, and Terre Hill. BERKS COUNTY. CITY: Reading. TOWNSHIPS: Cumru (District 1 only), Lower Alsace (District 1 only), Muhlenberg (Districts 1 and 4), Spring (Districts 2, 3, 4, 9, 10, 12). BOROUGHS OF: Laureldale (Districts 1 and 2), Mount Penn, Sinking Spring, West Reading, Wyomissing (District 3). CHESTER COUNTY. CITY: Coatesville. TOWNSHIPS: Caln (District 2), East Fallowfield, East Marlborough, East Nottingham, Elk, Franklin, Kennett (District 2 and 3), London Grove, Lower Oxford, New London, Pennsbury (North District), Sadsbury (South District), Valley, West Marlborough, West Nottingham. BOROUGHS OF: Avondale, Kennett, Square, Modena, Oxford, Parkesburg, South Coatesville, and West Grove. Population (2010), 705,688.

ZIP Codes: 17022, 17073, 17501–02, 17505, 17507–08, 17512, 17516–20, 17522, 17529, 17532, 17536, 17538, 17540, 17543, 17545, 17547, 17550–52, 17554–55, 17557, 17560, 17562–63, 17565–66, 17569–70, 17572, 17576, 17578–79, 17581–82, 17584, 17601–03, 17606, 19311, 19317, 19320, 19330, 19344, 19348, 19350, 19352, 19358, 19362–63, 19365, 19367, 19375, 19382, 19390, 19501, 19540, 19543, 19551, 19560–02, 19604–11

* * *

SEVENTEENTH DISTRICT

MATT CARTWRIGHT, Democrat, of Moosic, PA; born in Erie, PA, May 1, 1961; education: B.A., history, Hamilton College, Clinton, NY, 1983; J.D., University of Pennsylvania, Philadelphia, PA, 1986; professional: attorney, Munley, Munley and Cartwright, 1987–2012; religion: Roman Catholic; family: wife, Marion; two sons, Jack and Matt; caucuses: USO Caucus, Military Sexual Assault Prevention Caucus; Military Depot Caucus; Military Mental Health Caucus; Veterans Job Caucus; Military Families Caucus; Defense Communities Caucus; Congressional Battlefield Caucus; Congressional Soils Caucus; Small Business Caucus; House Manufacturing Caucus; STEAM Caucus; School Health & Safety Caucus; Financial and Economic Literacy Caucus; Congressional Scouting Caucus; House Renewable Energy and Energy Efficiency Caucus; Safe Climate Caucus; Seniors Task Force; International Conservation Caucus; Congressional Recycling Caucus; Congressional Savings and Ownership Caucus; Structured Settlements Caucus; Congressional Ukrainan Caucus; Ad-Hoc Committee for Irish Affairs; Friends of Thailand Caucus; Congressional Academic Medicine Caucus; Congressional Nursing Caucus; Kidney Caucus; Congressional Childhood Cancer Caucus; Congressional Caucus on Parkinson's Disease; Congressional Diabetes Caucus; Congressional Fire Services Caucus; Bipartisan Disaster Relief Caucus; Public Service Caucus; LGBT Equality Caucus; International Conservation Caucus; Bi-Partisan Congressional Watchdog Caucus; Public Broadcasting Caucus; Congressional Bike Caucus; General Aviation Caucus; Congressional Public Transportation Caucus; Congressional Foster Youth Caucus; Congressional Caucus on Travel and Tourism; Military Sexual Assault Prevention Caucus; Energy and Environment Coalition (SEEC); Progressive Caucus; Democratic Caucus; committees: Natural Resources; Oversight and Government Reform; elected to the 113th Congress on November 6, 2012.

Office Listings

http://cartwright.house.gov www.facebook.com/repmattcartwright
www.twitter.com/repcartwright

1419 Longworth House Office Building, Washington, DC 20515 .... (202) 225–5546
FAX: 226–0996
Chief of Staff.—Hunter Ridgway.
Deputy Chief of Staff / Legislative Director.—Jeremy Marcus.
Deputy Chief of Staff / Communications Director.—Shane Seaver.
Scheduler.—Ambar Canales.
226 Wyoming Avenue, Scranton, PA 18503 .... (570) 341–1050
20 North Pennsylvania Avenue, Suite 201, Wilkes-Barre, PA 18711 .... (570) 371–0317
1 South Third Street, 9th Floor, Easton, PA 18042 .... (484) 546–0776
121 Progress Avenue, Suite 310, Pottsville, PA 17901 .... (570) 624–0140

Counties: CARBON (part), LACKAWANNA (part), LUZERNE (part), MONROE (part), NORTHAMPTON (part), AND SCHUYLKILL. Population: (2010), 705,687.

ZIP Codes: 17830, 17901, 17921–23, 17925, 17929–36, 17938, 17941, 17943–46, 17948–49, 17952–54, 17957, 17959–61, 17963–68, 17970, 17972, 17974, 17976, 17978–83, 17985, 18012–13, 18015, 18017, 18020, 18030, 18040, 18042–45, 18053, 18058, 18063–64, 18071–72, 18083, 18085, 18091, 18202, 18210–12, 18214, 18218, 18220, 18229, 18231–32, 18235, 18237, 18240–42, 18244–45, 18248–50, 18252, 18301–02, 18320–22, 18327, 18330–31, 18333–34, 18343–44, 18346–48, 18350–51, 18353–56, 18360, 18403, 18407, 18421, 18424, 18433–34, 18444, 18447–48, 18452, 18466, 18501–05, 18507–10, 18512, 18515, 18517–19, 18610, 18640–44, 18701–06, 18710–11, 18762, 18764, 18766–67, 18769, 18773, 19549

* * *

EIGHTEENTH DISTRICT

TIM MURPHY, Republican, of Upper St. Clair, PA; born in Cleveland, OH, September 11, 1952; education: B.S., Wheeling Jesuit University, 1974; M.A., Cleveland State University, 1976; Ph.D., University of Pittsburgh, 1979; professional: psychologist; holds two adjunct faculty positions at the University of Pittsburgh; Associate Professor in the Department of Public Health, and in the Department of Pediatrics; public service: Pennsylvania State Senate, 1996–2002; military: Lieutenant Commander, Medical Service Corps, United States Navy Reserve; religion: Catholic; family: married to Nan Missig; children: Bevin; Ad Hoc Congressional Committee for Irish Affairs / Friends of Ireland Caucus; Bipartisan Congressional Pro-Life Caucus; Congressional Caucus on Hellenic Issues; Congressional Caucus on India and Indian Americans; Congressional Cystic Fibrosis Caucus; Congressional Fire Services Caucus; Congressional Manufacturing Caucus; co-chair, Congressional Mental Health Caucus; Congressional Natural Gas Caucus; Congressional Coal Caucus; Congressional Sportsmen's Caucus; chair, Congressional Steel Caucus; National Guard and Reserve Component Caucus; GOP Doctors Caucus; Military Veteran Caucus; USO Congressional Caucus; committees: Energy and Commerce, elected to the 108th Congress on November 5, 2002; reelected to each succeeding Congress.

Office Listings

http://murphy.house.gov https://www.facebook.com/reptimmurphy
https://twitter.com/reptimmurphy

2332 Rayburn House Office Building, Washington, DC 20515 .... (202) 225–2301
Chief of Staff.—Susan Mosychuk.
Legislative Director.—Brad Grantz.
Scheduler.—Sarah Valerio.
Press Secretary.—Dain Pascocello.
504 Washington Road, Pittsburgh, PA 15228 .... (412) 344–5583

Counties: ALLEGHENY (part), GREENE (part), WASHINGTON (part), WESTMORELAND (part). CITIES AND TOWNSHIPS: Greensburg, Upper St. Clair, and Washington. Population (2010), 705,688.

ZIP Codes: 15003–04, 15012, 15017–21, 15025–26, 15028, 15031, 15037–38, 15046–47, 15053–57, 15060, 15062–64, 15067, 15071–72, 15078, 15082–83, 15085, 15087–89, 15102, 15108, 15122, 15126, 15129, 15131, 15135–37, 15143, 15146, 15205, 15216, 15220, 15226–28, 15234, 15236, 15241, 15243, 15301, 15310–14, 15316–17, 15321–24, 15329–33, 15337, 15340–42, 15344–45, 15347, 15349–50, 15352–53, 15359–64, 15367, 15370, 15376–80, 15417, 15423, 15427, 15448, 15479, 15501, 15601, 15531, 15610–12, 15615–17, 15621–25, 15628, 15632–40, 15642, 15644, 15646–47, 15650, 15655, 15658, 15660, 15662–63, 15665–66, 15670, 15672, 15675–80, 15683, 15687–89, 15691–93, 15695–98

RHODE ISLAND

(Population 2010, 1,052,567)

SENATORS

JACK REED, Democrat, of Jamestown, RI; born in Providence, RI, November 12, 1949; graduated, La Salle Academy, Providence, RI, 1967; B.S., U.S. Military Academy, West Point, NY, 1971; M.P.P., Kennedy School of Government, Harvard University, 1973; J.D., Harvard Law School, 1982; professional: served in the U.S. Army, 1967–79; platoon leader, company commander, battalion staff officer, 1973–77; associate professor, Department of Social Sciences, U.S. Military Academy, West Point, NY, 1978–79; 2nd BN (Abn) 504th Infantry, 82nd Airborne Division, Fort Bragg, NC; lawyer, admitted to the Washington, DC Bar, 1983; military awards: Army commendation medal with Oak Leaf Cluster, ranger, senior parachutist, jumpmaster, expert infantryman's badge; elected to the Rhode Island State Senate, 1985–90; committees: Appropriations; Armed Services; Banking, Housing, and Urban Affairs; elected to the 102nd Congress on November 6, 1990; served three terms in the U.S. House of Representatives; elected to the U.S. Senate, November 5, 1996; reelected to each succeeding Senate term.

Office Listings

http://reed.senate.gov

728 Hart Senate Office Building, Washington, DC 20510 .... (202) 224–4642
Chief of Staff.—Neil Campbell. FAX: 224–4680
Deputy Chief of Staff.—Cathy Nagle.
Press Secretary.—Chip Unruh.
1000 Chapel View Boulevard, Suite 290, Cranston, RI 02920 .... (401) 943–3100
Chief of Staff.—Raymond Simone.
U.S. District Courthouse, One Exchange Terrace, Suite 408, Providence, RI 02903 (401) 528–5200

* * *

SHELDON WHITEHOUSE, Democrat, of Newport, RI; born in New York City, NY, October 20, 1955; education: B.A., Yale University, New Haven, CT, 1978; J.D., University of Virginia, Charlottesville, VA, 1982; director, Rhode Island Department of Business Regulation, 1992–94; United States Attorney, 1994–98; Attorney General, Rhode Island State, 1999–2003; committees: Budget; Environment and Public Works; Health, Education, Labor, and Pensions; Judiciary; Special Committee on Aging; elected to the U.S. Senate on November 7, 2006; reelected to the U.S. Senate on November 6, 2012.

Office Listings

http://whitehouse.senate.gov

530 Hart Senate Office Building, Washington, DC 20510 .... (202) 224–2921
Chief of Staff.—Sam Goodstein. FAX: 228–6362
Legislative Director.—Joe Gaeta.
Communications Director.—Seth Larson.
170 Westminster Street, Suite 1100, Providence, RI 02903 .... (401) 453–5294
State Director.—George Carvalho.

REPRESENTATIVES

FIRST DISTRICT

DAVID N. CICILLINE, Democrat, of Providence, RI; born in Providence, RI, July 15, 1961; education: graduated, Narragansett High School, Narragansett, RI; B.A., Brown University, Providence, RI, 1983; J.D., Georgetown University Law Center, Washington, DC, 1986; professional: public defender, Washington, DC, 1986–87; lawyer, private practice; lawyer, American Civil Liberties Union; faculty, Roger Williams Law School, Bristol, RI; member of the Rhode Island State House of Representatives, 1995–2003; mayor of Providence, RI, 2002–10; committees: Foreign Affairs; Judiciary; elected to the 112th Congress on November 2, 2010; reelected to the 113th Congress on November 6, 2012.

Office Listings

http://www.cicilline.house.gov https://twitter.com/davidcicilline
https://www.facebook.com/congressmandavidcicilline

128 Cannon House Office Building, Washington, DC 20515 .... (202) 225–4911

Chief of Staff.—Peter Karafotas. FAX: 225–3290
Legislative Director.—William Walsh.
Executive Assistant / Scheduler.—Katie Spoerer.
Communications Director.—Andrew Gernt.
1070 Main Street, Suite 300, Pawtucket, RI 02860 .... (401) 729–5600

Counties: BRISTOL, NEWPORT, PROVIDENCE (part). CITIES AND TOWNSHIPS: Barrington, Bristol, Burrillville, Central Falls, Cumberland, East Providence, Jamestown, Lincoln, Little Compton, Middleton, Newport, North Providence, North Smithfield, Providence, Pawtucket, Portsmouth, Smithfield, Tiverton, Warren, and Woonsocket. Population (2010), 526,283.

ZIP Codes: 02802, 02806, 02809, 02828, 02835, 02837, 02838, 02840–42, 02860–61, 02863–65, 02871–72, 02876, 02878, 02885, 02895–96, 02903–12, 02914–17, 02919

* * *

SECOND DISTRICT

JAMES R. LANGEVIN, Democrat, of Warwick, RI; born in Providence, RI, April 22, 1964; education: B.A., political science / public administration, Rhode Island College, 1990; M.P.A., Harvard University, 1994; community service: American Red Cross; March of Dimes; Lions Club of Warwick; PARI Independent Living Center; Knights of Columbus; public service: secretary, Rhode Island Constitutional Convention, 1986; Rhode Island State Representative, 1989–95; Rhode Island Secretary of State, 1995–2000; committees: Armed Services; Permanent Select Committee on Intelligence; elected to the 107th Congress; reelected to each succeeding Congress.

Office Listings

http://www.langevin.house.gov twitter: @jimlangevin
https://www.facebook.com/congressmanjimlangevin

109 Cannon House Office Building, Washington, DC 20515 .... (202) 225–2735
Chief of Staff.—Kristin Nicholson. FAX: 225–5976
Legislative Director.—Todd Adams.
Office Manager.—Stu Rose.
The Summit South, 300 Centerville Road, Suite 200, Warwick, RI 02886 .... (401) 732–9400
District Director.—Seth Klaiman.

Counties: KENT, PROVIDENCE (part), WASHINGTON. CITIES AND TOWNSHIPS: Charleston, Coventry, Cranston, Exeter, Foster, Glocester, Greenwich (East and West), Hopkinton, Johnston, Kingstown (North and South), Narragansett, New Shoreham, Providence, Richmond, Scituate, Warwick, West Warwick, and Westerly. Population (2010), 516,587.

ZIP Codes: 02804, 02807–08, 02812–18, 02822–23, 02825, 02827–29, 02831–33, 02836, 02852, 02857, 02873–75, 02877, 02879–83, 02886–89, 02891–94, 02898, 02901–05, 02907–11, 02917, 02919–21

SOUTH CAROLINA

(Population 2010, 4,625,364)

SENATORS

LINDSEY GRAHAM, Republican, of Seneca, SC; born in Seneca, July 9, 1955; education: graduated, Daniel High School, Central, SC; B.A., University of South Carolina, 1977; awarded J.D., 1981; military service: joined the U.S. Air Force, 1982; Base Legal Office and Area Defense Counsel, Rhein Main Air Force Base, Germany, 1984; circuit trial counsel, U.S. Air Forces; Base Staff Judge Advocate, McEntire Air National Guard Base, SC, 1989–94; presently a Colonel, Air Force Reserves; award: Meritorious Service Medal for Outstanding Service; Meritorious Service Medal for Active Duty Tour in Europe; professional: established private law practice, 1988; former member, South Carolina House of Representatives; Assistant County Attorney for Oconee County, 1988–92; City Attorney for Central, SC, 1990–94; member: Walhalla Rotary; American Legion Post 120; appointed to the Judicial Arbitration Commission by the Chief Justice of the Supreme Court; religion: attends Corinth Baptist Church; committees: Appropriations; Armed Services; Budget; Judiciary; elected to the 104th Congress on November 8, 1994; reelected to each succeeding Congress; elected to the U.S. Senate on November 5, 2002, reelected to each succeeding Senate term.

Office Listings

http://lgraham.senate.gov

290 Russell Senate Office Building, Washington, DC 20510 .... (202) 224–5972
Chief of Staff.—Richard Perry. FAX: 224–3808
Legislative Director.—Mathew Rimkunas.
Scheduler / Press Secretary.—Alice James.
Deputy Communications Director.—Lorcan Connick.
130 South Main Street, Suite 700, Greenville, SC 29601 .... (864) 250–1417
State Director.—Van Cato.
Upstate Regional Director.—Laura Bauld.
530 Johnnie Dodds Boulevard, Suite 202, Mt. Pleasant, SC 29464 .... (843) 849–3887
Low Country Regional Director.—Bill Tuten.
508 Hampton Street, Suite 202, Columbia, SC 29201 .... (803) 933–0112
Midlands Regional Director.—Yvette Rowland.
John L. McMillan Federal Building, 401 West Evans Street, Suite 111, Florence, SC 29501 .... (843) 669–1505
Pee Dee Regional Director.—Celia Urquhart.
235 East Main Street, Suite 100, Rock Hill, SC 29730 .... (803) 366–2828
Piedmont Regional Director.—Philip Land.
124 Exchange Street, Suite A, Pendleton, SC 29670 .... (864) 646–4090
Senior Advisor.—Denise Bauld.

* * *

TIM SCOTT, Republican, of North Charleston, SC; born in North Charleston, September 19, 1965; education: R.B. Stall High School; B.S., Charleston Southern University, Charleston, SC, 1988; professional: former owner of Tim Scott Allstate and partner of Pathway Real Estate Group; served on Charleston County Council, 1995–2008; four terms as chair of the Charleston County Council; member of the South Carolina State House of Representatives, 2009–10; member of the U.S. House of Representatives 2010–12; committees: Commerce, Science, and Transportation; Energy and Natural Resources; Health, Education, Labor, and Pensions; Small Business and Entrepreneurship; appointed by the Governor, January 2, 2013, to fill the vacancy caused by the resignation of Senator James DeMint; appointment took effect upon his resignation from the House of Representatives on January 2, 2013; took the oath of office on January 3, 2013.

Office Listings

http://scott.senate.gov

167 Russell Senate Office Building, Washington, DC 20510 .... (202) 224–6121
Chief of Staff.—Mike Bennett. FAX: (202) 228–5143
Legislative Director.—Chuck Cogar.
Communications Director.—Sean Smith.
Scheduler.—John Don.
2500 City Hall Lane, 3rd Floor Suite, North Charleston, SC 29406 .... (843) 727–4525
State Director.—Joe McKeown. FAX: (855) 802–9355
Low Country Regional Director.—Kathy Crawford.
1301 Gervais Street, Suite 825, Columbia, SC 29201 .... (803) 771–6112

Midlands Regional Director.—Kelly Long. FAX: (855) 802–9355
PeeDee Regional Director.—Delores DaCosta.
40 West Broad Street, Suite 320, Greenville, SC 29601 .... (864) 233–5366
Upstate Regional Directors: Danielle Gibbs, Susan Aiken. FAX: (855) 802–9355

REPRESENTATIVES

FIRST DISTRICT

MARK SANFORD, Republican, of Charleston, SC; born in Ft. Lauderdale, FL, May 28, 1960; education: Furman University, B.A., Greenville, SC, 1983; Darden School of Business, University of Virginia, M.B.A., Charlottesville, VA, 1989; professional: prior congressional service, 104th–106th Congresses, committees: Government Reform and Oversight, International Relations, Joint Economic; Governor of South Carolina: 2003–11; family: son of Margaret (Peg) Sanford and the late Dr. Marshall Sanford; 4 children: Marshall III, Landon, Bolton, and Blake; committees: Homeland Security; Transportation and Infrastructure; elected to the 113th Congress, by special election, on May 7, 2013, to fill the vacancy caused by the appointment of United States Representative Tim Scott to the United States Senate.

Office Listings

http://www.sanford.house.gov fb.com/repsanfordsc
twitter: @repsanfordsc

322 Cannon House Office Building, Washington, DC 20515 .... (202) 225–3176
Chief of Staff.—Jon Kohan. FAX: 225–3407
District Director.—April Paris Derr.
530 Johnnie Dodds Bouvelard, Suite 201, Mount Pleasant, SC 29464 .... (843) 352–7572
FAX: 352–7620
710 Boundary Street, Suite 1D, Beaufort, SC 29902 .... (843) 521–2530
FAX: 521–2535

Counties: BEAUFORT (part), BERKELEY (part), CHARLESTON (part), COLLETON (part), AND DORCHESTER (part). Population (2010), 660,766.

ZIP Codes: 29401–03, 29405–07, 29410, 29412, 29414, 29417–18, 29420, 29422, 29424–25, 29429, 29430–31, 29438–39, 29445, 29450, 29453, 29455–58, 29461, 29464–66, 29469–70, 29472, 29479, 29482–85, 29487, 29492, 29901–07, 29909, 29910, 29915, 29920, 29925–26, 29928, 29935–36, 29938

* * *

SECOND DISTRICT

JOE WILSON, Republican, of Springdale, SC; born in Charleston, SC, July 31, 1947; education: graduated, B.A., Washington & Lee University, Lexington, VA; J.D., University of South Carolina School of Law; professional: attorney; Kirkland, Wilson, Moore, Taylor; former Deputy General Counsel, U.S. Department of Energy; former Judge of the town of Springdale, SC; military service: U.S. Army Reserves, 1972–75; retired Colonel in the South Carolina Army National Guard as a Staff Judge Advocate for the 218th Mechanized Infantry Brigade, 1975–2003; organizations: Cayce-West Columbia Rotary Club; Sheriff's Department Law Enforcement Advisory Council; Reserve Officers Association; Lexington County Historical Society; Columbia Home Builders Association; County Community and Resource Development Committee; American Heart Association; Mid-Carolina Mental Health Association; Cayce-West Columbia Jaycees; Kidney Foundation; South Carolina Lung Association; Alston-Wilkes Society; Cayce-West Metro Chamber of Commerce; Columbia World Affairs Council; Fellowship of Christian Athletes, Sinclair Lodge 154; Jamil Temple; Woodmen of the World; Sons of Confederate Veterans; Military Order of the World Wars; Lexington, Greater Irmo, Chapin, Columbia, West Metro, and Batesburg-Leesville Chambers of Commerce; West Metro and Dutch Fork Women's Republican Clubs; and Executive Council of the Indian Waters Council, Boy Scouts of America; awards: U.S. Chamber of Commerce Spirit of Enterprise Award; Americans for Tax Reform Friend of the Taxpayer Award; National Taxpayers' Union; Taxpayers' Friend Award; Americans for Prosperity; Friend of the American Motorist Award; public service: South Carolina State Senate, 1984–2001; family: married to Roxanne Dusenbury McCrory; four sons; Assistant GOP Whip; member, Republican Policy Committee; committees: Armed Services; Education and the Workforce; Foreign Affairs; elected to the 107th Congress, by special election, on December 18, 2001; reelected to each succeeding Congress.

Office Listings

http://joewilson.house.gov https://www.facebook.com/joewilson
twitter: @repjoewilson

2229 Rayburn House Office Building, Washington, DC 20515 .... (202) 225–2452
Chief of Staff.—Jonathan Day. FAX: 225–2455
Press Secretary.—Caroline Delleney.
Deputy Chief of Staff / Legislative Director.—Melissa Murphy.
828 Richland Avenue West, Suite 300, P.O. Box 104, Aiken, SC 29801 .... (803) 642–6416
1700 Sunset Boulevard (U.S. 378), Suite 1, West Columbia, SC 29169 .... (803) 939–0041

Counties: AIKEN, BARNWELL, LEXINGTON, ORANGEBURG (part), AND RICHLAND (part). CITIES AND TOWNSHIPS: Aiken, Arcadia Lakes, Ballentine, Barnwell, Batesburg-Leesville (part), Bath, Beech Island, Belvedere, Blackville, Blythewood, Bowman, Boyden Arbor, Branchville, Burnettown, Capitol View, Cayce, Chapin, Clearwater, Columbia (part), Cope, Cordova, Dentsville, Eastover, Eau Claire, Elko, Fairwood Acres, Gadsden, Gaston, Gilbert, Gloverville, Graniteville, Harbison, Hilda, Hilton, Hopkins, Horrell Hill, Irmo (part), Jackson, Killian, Kingville, Kline, Lake Murray, Langley, Lexington (county seat), Livingston, Lykes, Monetta, Montmorenci, Mountain Brook, Neeses, New Ellenton, North, North Augusta, Norway, Oak Grove, Pelion, Perry, Pine Ridge, Pontiac, Red Bank, Ridge Spring, Rowesville, Salley, Santee, Seven Oaks, Snelling, South Congaree, Springdale, Springfield, St. Andrews, State Park, Summit, Swansea, Vance, Vaucluse, Wagener, Warrenville, Wateree, West Columbia, Williston, Windsor, Windsor Estates, White Rock, and Woodford. Population (2010), 670,436.

ZIP Codes: 29002, 29006, 29016, 29033, 29036, 29038–39, 29044–45, 29053–54, 29061, 29063, 29070–73, 29075, 29078, 29105, 29107, 29112–13, 29115, 29123, 29129–30, 29137, 29146, 29160, 29164, 29169–72, 29177, 29180, 29203–07, 29209–10, 29212, 29219, 29223, 29229, 29260, 29801–05, 29808–09, 29812–13, 29816–17, 29822, 29826, 29898, 29829, 29831–32, 29834, 29836, 29839, 29841–43, 29847, 29849–51, 29853, 29856, 29860–61

* * *

THIRD DISTRICT

JEFF DUNCAN, Republican, of Laurens, SC; born in Greenville, SC, January 7, 1966; education: B.A., political science, Clemson University, 1988; professional: small business owner; public service: South Carolina House of Representatives, 2002–10; religion: Southern Baptist, attends Clinton First Baptist Church; married: Melody; children: Graham, John Philip, and Parker; committees: Foreign Affairs; Homeland Security; Natural Resources; elected to the 112th Congress on November 2, 2010; reelected to the 113th Congress on November 6, 2012.

Office Listings

http://jeffduncan.house.gov

116 Cannon House Office Building, Washington, DC 20515 .... (202) 225–5301
Chief of Staff.—Lance Williams. FAX: 225–3216
Legislative Director.—Joshua Gross.
303 West Beltline Boulevard, Anderson, SC 29625 .... (864) 224–7401
District Director.—Rick Adkins.
200 Courthouse Public Square, P.O. Box 471, Laurens, SC 29360 .... (864) 681–1028

Counties: ABBEVILLE, ANDERSON, EDGEFIELD, GREENWOOD, LAURENS, MCCORMICK, OCONEE, PICKENS, SALUDA, NEWBERRY (part), GREENVILLE (part). Population (2010), 660,767.

ZIP Codes: 29006, 29037, 29070, 29105, 29108, 29127, 29129, 29138, 29145, 29166, 29178, 29325, 29332, 29335, 29351, 29355, 29360, 29370, 29384, 29388, 29605, 29611, 29620–21, 29624–28, 29630–35, 29638–46, 29649, 29653–59, 29661, 29664–67, 29669–73, 29675–78, 29680, 29682, 29684–86, 29689, 29691–93, 29695–97, 29801, 29803, 29805, 29808, 29819, 29821–22, 29824, 29832, 29835, 29838, 29840, 29844–45, 29847–48, 29853, 29860, 29899

* * *

FOURTH DISTRICT

TREY GOWDY, Republican, of Spartanburg, SC; born in Greenville, SC, August 22, 1964; native of Spartanburg, SC; education: Spartanburg High School, Spartanburg, SC, 1982; B.A., Baylor University, Waco, TX, 1986; J.D., University of South Carolina Law School, Columbia, SC, 1989; professional: Nelson, Mullins, Riley & Scarborough (law firm), 1992–94; United States Attorney, 1994–2000; South Carolina Solicitor, 7th Circuit, 2001–10; religion: Baptist; member, First Baptist Church of Spartanburg; married: the former Terri Dillard, 1989; two children; committees: Education and the Workforce; Ethics; Judiciary; Oversight and Government Reform; elected to the 112th Congress on November 2, 2010; reelected to the 113th Congress on November 6, 2012.

Office Listings

http://www.gowdy.house.gov

1404 Longworth House Office Building, Washington, DC 20515 .... (202) 225–6030
Chief of Staff.—Matthew Van Patton. FAX: 226–1177
Legislative Director.—Ann Bartlett.
Legislative Assistants: Christopher Ingraham, Patrick Manion.
Executive Assistant.—Mary Ann Lynch.
Communications Director.—Amanda Duvall.
104 South Main Street, Greenville, SC 29601 .... (864) 241–0175
District Director.—Cindy Crick.
Constituent Liaison.—Belle Mercado.
101 West St. John Street, Spartanburg, SC 29306 .... (864) 583–3264
Administrative Coordinator.—Missy House.
Constituent Liaison.—Emily Davis.

Counties: GREENVILLE (part), SPARTANBURG (part). Population (2010), 660,766.

ZIP Codes: 29301–07, 29316, 29329–31, 29333–36, 29346, 29356, 29372–79, 29385–86, 29388, 29601–17, 29635–36, 29650–52, 29661–62, 29673, 29680–81, 29683, 29687–88, 29690

* * *

FIFTH DISTRICT

MICK MULVANEY, Republican, of Indian Land, SC; born in Alexandria, VA, July 21, 1967; education: graduated, Charlotte Catholic High School, 1985; B.S.F.S., international economics, commerce, and finance, Georgetown University, Washington, DC, 1989; J.D., University of North Carolina, Chapel Hill, NC, 1992; professional: Owners and Presidents Management Program, Harvard University Business School, Cambridge, MA, 2006; lawyer, private practice; real estate developer; member of the South Carolina State House of Representatives, 2007–09; member of the South Carolina State Senate, 2009–10; religion: Roman Catholic; committees: Financial Services; Small Business; elected to the 112th Congress on November 2, 2010; reelected to the 113th Congress on November 6, 2012.

Office Listings

http://www.mulvaney.house.gov facebook: rep.mickmulvaney twitter: @repmickmulvaney

1207 Longworth House Office Building, Washington, DC 20515 .... (202) 225–5501
Chief of Staff.—Al Simpson. FAX: 225–0464
Communications Director.—Stephanie Faile.
1456 Ebenezer Road, Rock Hill, SC 29731 .... (803) 327–1114
District Director.—Jeffery Sligh.

Counties: CHEROKEE, CHESTER, FAIRFIELD, KERSHAW, LANCASTER, LEE, NEWBERRY, SPARTANBURG, SUMTER (part), YORK, AND UNION. Population (2013), 675,124.

ZIP Codes: 29009–10, 29014–16, 29020, 29031–32, 29036–37, 29040, 29045, 29055, 29058, 29065, 29067, 29069, 29074–75, 29078–79, 29101–02, 29104, 29106, 29108, 29122, 29126–28, 29130, 29132, 29145, 29150–54, 29161, 29163, 29175–76, 29178, 29180, 29203, 29218, 29307, 29323, 29330, 29332, 29340–42, 29355, 29372, 29501, 29506, 29512, 29516, 29520, 29525, 29532, 29536, 29540, 29543, 29547, 29550–51, 29563, 29565, 29567, 29570, 29573–74, 29581, 29584, 29592–94, 29596, 29654, 29702–04, 29706, 29708–10, 29712, 29714–18, 29720–22, 29724, 29726–32, 29734, 29741–45

* * *

SIXTH DISTRICT

JAMES E. CLYBURN, Democrat, of Columbia, SC; born in Sumter, SC, July 21, 1940; education: graduated, Mather Academy, Camden, SC, 1957; B.S., South Carolina State University, Orangeburg, 1962; attended University of South Carolina Law School, Columbia, 1972–74; professional: South Carolina State Human Affairs Commissioner; assistant to the Governor for Human Resource Development; executive director, South Carolina Commission for Farm Workers, Inc.; director, Neighborhood Youth Corps and New Careers; counselor, South Carolina Employment Security Commission; member: lifetime member, NAACP; Southern Regional Council; Omega Psi Phi Fraternity, Inc.; Arabian Temple, No. 139; Nemiah Lodge No. 51 F&AM; married: the former Emily England; children: Mignon, Jennifer and Angela; elected vice chair, Democratic Caucus, 2002; chair, Democratic Caucus, 2006; Majority Whip; Assistant Democratic Leader, 2010 and 2012; elected on November 3, 1992, to the 103rd Congress; reelected to each succeeding Congress.

Office Listings

http://www.clyburn.house.gov

242 Cannon House Office Building, Washington, DC 20515 .... (202) 225–3315
Chief of Staff.—Yelberton Watkins. FAX: 225–2313
Deputy Chief of Staff.—Barvetta Singletary.
Scheduler.—Lindy Birch Kelly.
1225 Lady Street, Suite 200, Columbia, SC 29201 .... (803) 799–1100
District Director.—Robert Nance.
District Scheduler.—Melissa Lindler.
130 West Main Street, Kingstree, SC 29556 .... (843) 355–1211
176 Brooks Boulevard, Santee, SC 29142 .... (803) 854–4700

Counties: ALLENDALE COUNTY. CITIES AND TOWNS: Allendale, Appleton, Barton, Cave, Fairfax, Martin, Millett, Ulmer, and Sycamore. BAMBERG COUNTY. CITIES AND TOWNSHIPS: Bamberg, Denmark, Erhardt, and Olar. BEAUFORT COUNTY. CITIES AND TOWNS: Corner, Dale, Gardens, Lobeco, Sheldon, and Yemasee. BERKELEY COUNTY (part). CITIES AND TOWNSHIPS: Bethera, Cross, Daniel Island, Huger, Jamestown, Pineville, Russellville, Saint Stephen, and Wando. CALHOUN COUNTY (part). CITY OF: Cameron, Creston, Fort Motte, and St. Matthews. CHARLESTON COUNTY (part). CITIES AND TOWNSHIPS: Adams Run, Charleston, Edisto Island, Hollywood, Johns Island, Ravenel, and Wadmalaw Island. CLARENDON COUNTY. CITIES AND TOWNSHIPS: Alcolu, Davis Station, Gable, Manning, New Zion, Rimini, Summerton, and Turbeville. COLLETON COUNTY. CITIES AND TOWNSHIPS: Ashton, Cottageville, Green Pond, Hendersonville, Islandton, Jacksonboro, Lodge, Ritter, Round O, Smoaks, Walterboro, and Williams. DORCHESTER COUNTY (part). CITIES AND TOWNSHIPS: Dorchester, Harleyville, Reevesville, Ridgeville, Rosinville, and Saint George. HAMPTON COUNTY. CITIES AND TOWNS: Brunson, Crockettvillle, Cummings, Early Branch, Estill, Furman, Garnett, Gifford, Hampton, Luray, Miley, Scotia, Varnville, and Yemasee. JASPER COUNTY. CITIES AND TOWNS: Coosawhatchie, Gillisonville, Grays, Hardeeville, Pineland, Pocotaligo, Ridgeland, Robertville, Switzerland, Tarboro, and Tillman. ORANGEBURG COUNTY (part). CITIES AND TOWNSHIPS: Bowman, Branchville, Elloree, Eutawville, Holly Hill, Norway, Orangeburg, Rowesville, Santee, and Vance. RICHLAND COUNTY (part). CITIES AND TOWNSHIPS: Blythewood, Columbia, Eastover, Gadsden, and Hopkins. SUMTER COUNTY (part). CITIES AND TOWNSHIPS: Mayesville, and Sumter. WILLIAMSBURG COUNTY. CITIES AND TOWNSHIPS: Cades, Greeleyville, Hemingway, Kingstree, Lane, Nesmith, Salters, and Trio. Population (2010), 660,766.

ZIP Codes: 29001, 29003, 29016, 29018, 29030, 29039, 29042, 29044, 29047–48, 29051–53, 29056, 29059, 29061, 29078, 29080–82, 29102, 29104, 29107, 29111–12, 29114–15, 29117–18, 29125, 29133, 29135, 29142, 29147–148, 29150, 29153, 29160, 9162–63, 29201–06, 29208–10, 29212, 29223, 29225, 29229, 29401, 29403–06, 29409–10, 29418, 29420, 29426, 29431–32, 29434–37, 29445–46, 29448–50, 29452–53, 29456, 29461, 29464, 29468–72, 29474–75, 29477, 29479, 29481, 29483, 29487–88, 29492–93, 29510, 29518, 29530, 29554–56, 29560, 29564, 29580, 29583, 29590–91, 29810, 29812, 29817, 29827, 29836, 29843, 29849, 29906–07, 29909, 29911–12, 29916, 29918, 29921–24, 29927, 29929, 29932, 29934, 29936, 29939, 29940–41, 29943–45

* * *

SEVENTH DISTRICT

TOM RICE, Republican, of South Carolina, born in Charleston County, SC, August 4, 1957; education: attended high school in Myrtle Beach, SC; B.S., University of South Carolina, Columbia, SC, 1979; M.A., University of South Carolina, 1982; J.D., University of South Carolina, 1982; professional: lawyer, private practice; accountant; chairman of the Horry County Council, 2010–12; committees: Budget; Small Business; Transportation and Infrastructure; elected to the 113th Congress on November 6, 2012.

Office Listings

http://rice.house.gov

325 Cannon House Office Building, Washington, DC .... (202) 225–9895
Chief of Staff.—Jennifer Watson. FAX: 225–9690
Legislative Director.—Courtney Titus.
2411 North Oak Street, Suite 405, Myrtle Beach, SC 29577 .... (843) 445–6459
1831 West Evans Street, Suite 300, Florence, SC 29501 .... (843) 679–9781

Counties: CHESTERFIELD, DARLINGTON, DILLON, FLORENCE (part), GEORGETOWN, HORRY, MARION, AND MARLBORO. Population (2010), 660,767.

ZIP Codes: 28112, 29009, 29069, 29101, 29114, 29161, 29440, 29442, 29501, 29505–06, 29510–12, 29516, 29519–20, 29525–27, 29530, 29532, 29536, 29540–41, 29543–47, 29550, 29554–55, 29560, 29563, 29565–72, 29574–77, 29579, 29581–85, 29588–89, 29591–94, 29596, 29709, 29718, 29727–28, 29741

SOUTH DAKOTA

(Population 2010, 814,180)

SENATORS

TIM JOHNSON, Democrat, of Vermillion, SD, born in Canton, SD, December 28, 1946; education: B.A., Phi Beta Kappa, University of South Dakota, 1969; M.A., political science, University of South Dakota, 1970; post-graduate study in political science, Michigan State University, 1970–71; J.D., University of South Dakota, 1975; budget advisor to the Michigan State Senate Appropriations Committee, 1971–72; admitted to the South Dakota Bar in 1975 and began private law practice in Vermillion; elected to the South Dakota House of Representatives, 1978; reelected, 1980; elected to the South Dakota State Senate, 1982; reelected, 1984; served on the Joint Appropriations Committee and the Senate Judiciary Committee; served as Clay County Deputy State's Attorney, 1985; awards: named Outstanding Citizen of Vermillion, 1983; received South Dakota Education Association's ''Friend of Education'' Award, 1983; Billy Sutton Award for Legislative Achievement, 1984; elected to the U.S. House of Representatives, 1986; reelected to each succeeding Congress; delegate, Democratic National Convention, 1988–92; member: President's Export Council, 1999; religion: Lutheran; married: Barbara Brooks, 1969; children: Brooks, Brendan and Kelsey Marie; committees: chair, Banking, Housing, and Urban Affairs; Appropriations; Energy and Natural Resources; Indian Affairs; elected to the U.S. Senate on November 5, 1996; reelected to each succeeding Senate term.

Office Listings

http://johnson.senate.gov https://www.facebook.com/senatortimjohnson
https://twitter.com/senjohnsonsd http://www.youtube.com/senatorjohnson

136 Hart Senate Office Building, Washington, DC 20510 .... (202) 224–5842
Chief of Staff.—Drey Samuelson. FAX: 228–5765
Legislative Director.—Todd Stubbendieck.
Communications Director.—Perry Plumart.
5015 South Bur Oak, Sioux Falls, SD 57108 .... (605) 332–8896
State Director.—Sharon Boysen.
320 South First Street, Suite 103, Aberdeen, SD 57401 .... (605) 226–3440
405 East Omaha Street, Suite B, Rapid City, SD 57701 .... (605) 341–3990

* * *

JOHN THUNE, Republican, of Murdo, SD; born in Pierre, SD, January 7, 1961; education: Jones County High School, 1979; B.S., business administration, Biola University, CA; M.B.A., University of South Dakota, 1984; professional: executive director, South Dakota Municipal League; board of directors, National League of Cities; executive director, South Dakota Republican Party, 1989–91; appointed, State Railroad Director, 1991; former congressional legislative assistant, and deputy staff director; elected, U.S. House of Representatives, 1997–2003; married: Kimberly Weems, 1984; children: Brittany and Larissa; committees: Agriculture, Nutrition, and Forestry; Commerce, Science, and Transportation; Finance; elected to the U.S. Senate on November 2, 2004; reelected to each succeeding Senate term.

Office Listings

http://thune.senate.gov

511 Dirksen Senate Office Building, Washington, DC 20510 .... (202) 224–2321
Chief of Staff.—Ryan Nelson. FAX: 228–5429
Deputy Chief of Staff.—Summer Mersinger.
Legislative Director.—Brendon Plack.
Communications Director.—Andi Fouberg.
320 North Main Avenue, Suite B, Sioux Falls, SD 57104 .... (605) 334–9596
1312 West Main Street, Rapid City, SD 57701 .... (605) 348–7551
320 South First Street, Suite 101, Aberdeen, SD 57401 .... (605) 225–8823

REPRESENTATIVE

AT LARGE

KRISTI NOEM, Republican, of Castlewood, SD; born in Watertown, SD, November 30, 1971; professional: farmer; rancher; member of South Dakota State House of Representatives,

2007–10; committees: Agriculture; Armed Services; elected to the 112th Congress on November 2, 2010; reelected to the 113th Congress on November 6, 2012.

Office Listings

http://www.noem.house.gov

1323 Longworth House Office Building, Washington, DC 20515 .... (202) 225–2801
Chief of Staff.—Jordan Stoick. FAX: 225–5823
Legislative Director.—Andrew Christianson.
Communications Director.—Joshua Shields.
Scheduler.—Jennifer Fierro.

2310 West 41st Street, Suite 101, Sioux Falls, SD 57105 .... (605) 275–2868
Southeast Director.—Suzanne Veenis.

343 Quincy Street, Rapid City, SD 57701 .... (605) 791–4673
Western Director.—Brad Otten.

415 South Main Street, Suite 203, Aberdeen, SD 57401 .... (605) 262–2862
Northeast Director.—Beth Hollatz.

505 12th Street Southeast, Watertown, SD 57201 .... (605) 878–2868
Northeast Director.—Beth Hollatz.

Population (2010), 814,180.

ZIP Codes: 57001–07, 57010, 57012–18, 57020–22, 57024–59, 57061–73, 57075–79, 57101, 57103–10, 57117–18, 57186, 57188–89, 57192–98, 57201, 57212–14, 57216–21, 57223–27, 57231–39, 57241–43, 57245–49, 57251–53, 57255–66, 57268–74, 57276, 57278–79, 57301, 57311–15, 57317, 57319, 57321–26, 57328–32, 57334–35, 57337, 57339–42, 57344–46, 57348–50, 57353–56, 57358–59, 57361–71, 57373–76, 57379–86, 57399, 57401–02, 57420–22, 57424, 57426–30, 57432–42, 57445–46, 57448–52, 57454–57, 57460–61, 57465–77, 57479, 57481, 57501, 57520–23, 57528–29, 57531–34, 57536–38, 57540–44, 57547–48, 57551–53, 57555, 57559–60, 57562–64, 57566–72, 57574, 57576–77, 57579–80, 57584–85, 57601, 57620–23, 57625–26, 57630–34, 57636, 57638–42, 57644–46, 57648–52, 57656–61, 57701–03, 57706, 57709, 57714, 57716–20, 57722, 57724–25, 57730, 57732, 57735, 57737–38, 57741, 57744–45, 57747–48, 57750–52, 57754–56, 57758–64, 57766–67, 57769–70, 57772–73, 57775–77, 57779–80, 57782–83, 57785, 57787–88, 57790–94, 57799

TENNESSEE

(Population 2010, 6,346,105)

SENATORS

LAMAR ALEXANDER, Republican, of Maryville, TN; born in Maryville, TN, July 3, 1940; education: graduated with honors in Latin American history, Phi Beta Kappa, Vanderbilt University; New York University Law School; served as *Law Review* editor; professional: clerk to Judge John Minor Wisdom, U.S. Court of Appeals in New Orleans; legislative assistant to Senator Howard Baker (R–TN), 1967; executive assistant to Bryce Harlow, counselor to President Nixon, 1969; President, University of Tennessee, 1988–91; co-director, Empower America, 1994–95; helped found a company that is now the nation's largest provider of worksite day care, Bright Horizons; public service: Republican nominee for Governor of Tennessee, 1974; Governor of Tennessee, 1979–87; U.S. Secretary of Education, 1991–93; community service: chairman, Salvation Army Red Shield Family Initiative; chairman, Senate Republican Conference; and the Museum of Appalachia in Norris, TN; received Tennessee Conservation League Conservationist of the Year Award; family: married to Honey Alexander; four children; committees: Appropriations; Energy and Natural Resources; Health, Education, Labor, and Pensions; Rules and Administration; elected to the U.S. Senate on November 5, 2002; reelected to the U.S. Senate on November 4, 2008.

Office Listings

http://alexander.senate.gov https://twitter.com/senalexander handle: @senalexander
www.facebook.com/senatorlamaralexander

455 Dirksen Senate Office Building, Washington, DC 20510 .... (202) 224–4944
Chief of Staff.—David Cleary. FAX: 228–3398
Legislative Director / Counsel.—Allison Martin.
Communications Director.—Jim Jeffries.
Executive Assistant / Scheduler.—Sarah Fairchild.
3322 West End Avenue, Suite 120, Nashville, TN 37203 .... (615) 736–5129
Howard H. Baker, Jr. U.S. Courthouse; 800 Market Street, Suite 112, Knoxville, TN 37902 .... (865) 545–4253
Federal Building, 167 North Main Street, Suite 1068, Memphis, TN 38103 .... (901) 544–4224
Federal Building, 109 South Highland Street, Suite B–9, Jackson, TN 38301 .... (731) 423–9344
Joel E. Solomon Federal Building, 900 Georgia Avenue, Suite 260, Chattanooga, TN 37402 .... (423) 752–5337
Tri-Cities Regional Airport, Terminal Building, P.O. Box 1113, 2525 Highway 75, Suite 101, Blountville, TN 37617 .... (423) 325–6240

* * *

BOB CORKER, Republican, of Chattanooga, TN; born in Orangeburg, SC, August 24, 1952; education: B.S., Industrial Management, University of Tennessee, Knoxville, TN, 1974; professional: founder of Bencor Corporation, a construction company specializing in retail properties which operated in 18 states, 1978–90; founder of the Corker Group, acquisition, development, and operation of commercial real estate, 1982–2006; honors: named to the University of Tennessee at Chattanooga's ''Entrepreneurial Hall of Fame,'' 2005; community service: founding chair, Chattanooga Neighborhood Enterprise, Inc., a non-profit organization that has helped over 10,000 families secure decent, fit and affordable housing, 1986–92; public service: commissioner, State of Tennessee Department of Finance and Administration, 1995–96; mayor, City of Chattanooga, 2001–05; married: Elizabeth Corker, 1987; two children: Julia and Emily; committees: ranking member, Foreign Relations; Banking, Housing, and Urban Affairs; Special Committee on Aging; elected to the U.S. Senate on November 7, 2006; reelected to the U.S. Senate on November 6, 2012.

Office Listings

http://corker.senate.gov

425 Dirksen Senate Office Building, Washington, DC 20510 .... (202) 224–3344
Chief of Staff.—Todd Womack. FAX: 228–0566
Legislative Director.—Rob Strayer.
Executive Assistant / Scheduler.—Hallie Williams.
Communications Director.—Laura Herzog.
3322 West End Avenue, Suite 610, Nashville, TN 37203 .... (615) 279–8125
100 Peabody Place, Suite 1125, Memphis, TN 38103 .... (901) 683–1910
Howard Baker Federal Building, 800 Market Street, Suite 121, Knoxville, TN 37902 .... (865) 637–4180
1105 East Jackson Boulevard, Suite 4, Jonesborough, TN 37659 .... (423) 753–2263

10 West Martin Luther King Boulevard, Sixth Floor, Chattanooga, TN 37402 .... (423) 756–2757
91 Stonebridge Boulevard, Suite 103, Jackson, TN 38305 .... (731) 664–2294

REPRESENTATIVES

FIRST DISTRICT

DAVID ''PHIL'' ROE, Republican, of Johnson City, TN; born in Clarksville, TN; July 21, 1945; education: B.S., Austin Peay State University, Clarksville, TN, 1967; M.D., University of Tennessee, Knoxville, TN, 1970; professional: United States Army Medical Corps, 1970–72; Vice Mayor of Johnson City, 2003–07; Mayor of Johnson City, 2007–09; Physicians' Caucus; Health Caucus; religion: Members of Munsey United Methodist Church; married: Pam; children: David C. Roe, John Roe, and Whitney Larkin: committees: Education and the Workforce; Veterans' Affairs; elected to the 111th Congress; reelected to each succeeding Congress.

Office Listings

http://www.roe.house.gov https://www.facebook.com/drphilroe https://twitter.com/drphilroe

407 Cannon House Office Building, Washington, DC 20515 .... (202) 225–6356
Chief of Staff.—Matt Meyer. FAX: 225–5714
Communications Director.—Tiffany McGuffee.
Scheduler.—Barbie McCarron.
Legislative Director.—John Martin.
Staff Assistant.—Catherine Bartley.
205 Revere Street, Kingsport, TN 37660 .... (423) 247–8161
FAX: 247–0119
Higher Education Building, P.O. Box 1728, Kingsport, TN 37662
District Director.—Bill Snodgrass.
Administrative Assistant.—Sheila Houser.
Caseworker.—Carolyn Ferguson.
1609 College Park Drive, Suite 4, Morristown, TN 37813 .... (423) 254–1400
District Representative.—John Abe Teague. FAX: 254–1403
Caseworkers: Cheryl Bennett, Angie Jarnagin.

Counties: CARTER, COCKE, GREENE, HAMBLEN, HANCOCK, HAWKINS, JEFFERSON, JOHNSON, SEVIER, SULLIVAN, UNICOI, AND WASHINGTON. Population (2010), 705,123.

ZIP Codes: 37601, 37604, 37614–18, 37620, 37640–43, 37645, 37650, 37656–60, 37663–65, 37681–83, 37686–88, 37690–92, 37694, 37711, 37713, 37722, 37725, 37727, 37731, 37738, 37743, 37745, 37748, 37753, 37760, 37764–65, 37809–11, 37813–14, 37818, 37821, 37843, 37857, 37860, 37862–63, 37865, 37869, 37871, 37873, 37876–77, 37879, 37881, 37890, 37891

* * *

SECOND DISTRICT

JOHN J. DUNCAN, JR., Republican, of Knoxville, TN; born in Lebanon, TN, July 21, 1947; education: B.S. in journalism, University of Tennessee, 1969; J.D., National Law Center, George Washington University, 1973; served in both the Army National Guard and the U.S. Army Reserves, retiring with the rank of captain; private law practice, Knoxville, 1973–81; appointed State Trial Judge by Governor Lamar Alexander in 1981 and elected to a full 8-year term in 1982 without opposition, receiving the highest number of votes of any candidate on the ballot that year; member: American Legion 40 and 8, Elks, Sertoma Club, Masons, Scottish Rite and Shrine; present or past board member: Red Cross, Girl's Club, YWCA, Sunshine Center for the Mentally Retarded, Beck Black Heritage Center, Knoxville Union Rescue Mission, Senior Citizens Home Aid Service; religion: active elder at Eastminster Presbyterian Church; married: the former Lynn Hawkins; children: Tara, Whitney, John J. III and Zane; committees: Oversight and Government Reform; Transportation and Infrastructure; elected to both the 100th Congress (special election) and the 101st Congress in separate elections held on November 8, 1988; reelected to each succeeding Congress.

Office Listings

http://www.house.gov/duncan

2207 Rayburn House Office Building, Washington, DC 20515 .... (202) 225–5435
Chief of Staff.—Bob Griffitts. FAX: 225–6440
Deputy Chief of Staff.—Don Walker.
Press Secretary.—Patrick Newton.
800 Market Street, Suite 100, Knoxville, TN 37902 .... (865) 523–3772

District Director.—Bob Griffitts.
331 Court Street, Blount County Courthouse, Maryville, TN 37804 .... (865) 984–5464

Counties: BLOUNT, CAMPBELL, CLAIBORNE, GRAINGER, JEFFERSON, KNOX, LOUDON. CITIES AND TOWNSHIPS: Alcoa, Farragut, Halls (Knox Co.), Harrogate, Jefferson City, Jellico, Knoxville, Lenoir City, Loudon, Maryville, Powell, and Seymour. Population (2010), 714,622.

ZIP Codes: 37303, 37309, 37311–12, 37314, 37322–23, 37325, 37329, 37331, 37353–54, 37369–71, 37385, 37701, 37709, 37721, 37725, 37737, 37742, 37754, 37764, 37771–72, 37774, 37777, 37779, 37801–04, 37806–07, 37820, 37826, 37830, 37846, 37849, 37853, 37865, 37871, 37874, 37876, 37878, 37880, 37882, 37885–86, 37901–02, 37909, 37912, 37914–24, 37927–33, 37938–40, 37950, 37990, 37995–98

* * *

THIRD DISTRICT

CHUCK FLEISCHMANN, Republican, of Ooltewah, TN; born in New York City, NY, October 11, 1962; graduated from Elk Grove High School, Elk Grove Village, IL, 1980; B.A., political science, University of Illinois, Urbana-Champaign, IL, 1983; J.D., University of Tennessee College of Law, Knoxville, TN, 1986; professional: attorney; small business owner; former president of the Chattanooga Bar Association, 1996; former chairman of the Chattanooga Lawyers Pro Bono Committee; religion: Catholic; married: Brenda Fleischmann; three children; committees: Appropriations; elected to the 112th Congress on November 2, 2010; reelected to the 113th Congress on November 6, 2012.

Office Listings

http://www.fleischmann.house.gov http://www.facebook.com/repchuck
https://twitter.com/repchuck

230 Cannon House Office Building, Washington, DC 20515 .... (202) 225–3271
Chief of Staff.—Jim Hippe. FAX: 225–3494
Legislative Director.—Alek Vey.
Scheduler.—Courtney Butcher.
900 Georgia Avenue, Suite 126, Chattanooga, TN 37402 .... (423) 756–2342
District Director.—Bob White.
Federal Building, 200 Administration Road, Suite 100, Oak Ridge, TN 37830 .... (865) 576–1976

Counties: ANDERSON, BRADLEY (part), CAMPBELL (part), HAMILTON, MCMINN, MONROE, MORGAN, POLK, ROANE, SCOTT, AND UNION. Population (2010), 711,391.

ZIP Codes: 37302–03, 37307–11, 37315, 37317, 37322–23, 37325–26, 37329, 37331, 37333, 37336, 37338, 37341, 37343, 37350–51, 37353–54, 37361–63, 37369–70, 37373, 37377, 37379, 37385, 37391, 37402–12, 37415, 37419, 37421, 37705, 37710, 37714, 37716, 37719, 37721, 37729, 37732–33, 37754–57, 37763, 37766, 37769, 37770–71, 37774, 37779, 37801, 37807, 37825–26, 37828–30, 37840–41, 37845–49, 37852, 37854, 37866, 37870, 37872, 37874, 37880, 37885, 37887–88, 37892, 37931, 38504

* * *

FOURTH DISTRICT

SCOTT DESJARLAIS, Republican, of South Pittsburg, TN; born in Sturgis, SD, February 21, 1964; education: B.S., chemistry and psychology, University of South Dakota, 1987; M.D., University of South Dakota School of Medicine, Vermillion, 1991; professional: general practitioner, Grand View Medical Center, Jasper, TN; religion: member, Epiphany Episcopalian Church, Sherwood, TN; married: Amy; children: Tyler, Ryan, and Maggie; committees: Agriculture; Education and the Workforce; Oversight and Government Reform; elected to the 112th Congress on November 2, 2010; reelected to the 113th Congress on November 6, 2012.

Office Listings

http://www.desjarlais.house.gov

413 Cannon House Office Building, Washington, DC 20515 .... (202) 225–6831
Chief of Staff.—Richard Vaughn. FAX: 226–5172
Legislative Director.—Dayne Cutrell.
Communications Director.—Robert Jameson.
301 Keith Street, Suite 212, Cleveland, TN 37311 .... (423) 472–7500
807 South Garden Street, Columbia, TN 38401 .... (931) 381–9920
212 First Avenue Southeast, Winchester, TN 37398 .... (931) 962–3180
305 West Main Street, Murfreesboro, TN 37130 .... (931) 962–3180

Counties: BEDFORD, BLEDSOE, BRADLEY (part), FRANKLIN, GRUNDY, LINCOLN, MARION, MARSHALL, MAURY (part), MOORE, RHEA, RUTHERFORD, SEQUATCHIE, VAN BUREN (part), AND WARREN. Population (2010), 705,123.

ZIP Codes: 37014, 37018–20, 37025, 37034, 37037, 37046–47, 37060, 37063–64, 37085–86, 37090–91, 37110–11, 37118, 37122, 37127–30, 37132, 37135, 37144, 37149, 37153, 37160, 37166–67, 37174, 37180, 37183, 37190, 37301, 37305–06, 37308–13, 37318, 37321–24, 37327–28, 37330, 37332, 37334–40, 37345, 37347–49, 37352–53, 37356–57, 37359–60, 37365–67, 37373–83, 37387–89, 37394, 37396–98, 37405, 37419, 37773, 37778, 37826, 37880, 38402, 38449, 38451, 38453, 38459, 38472, 38474, 38483, 38488, 38550, 38555, 38557, 38559, 38572, 38581, 38583, 38585, 39401

* * *

FIFTH DISTRICT

JIM COOPER, Democrat, of Nashville, TN; born in Nashville, June 19, 1954; education: B.A., history and economics, University of North Carolina at Chapel Hill, 1975; Rhodes Scholar, Oxford University, 1977; J.D., Harvard Law School, 1980; admitted to Tennessee Bar, 1980; professional: attorney; Waller, Lansden, Dortch, and Davis (law firm), 1980–82; Managing Director, Equitable Securities, 1995–99; Adjunct Professor, Vanderbilt University Owen School of Management, 1995–2002 and 2006–present; partner, Brentwood Capital Advisors LLC, 1999–2002; married: Martha Hays; three children; caucuses: Blue Dog Coalition; New Democrat Coalition; committees: Armed Services; Oversight and Government Reform; elected to the U.S. House of Representatives, 1982–95; elected to the 108th Congress on November 5, 2002; reelected to each succeeding Congress.

Office Listings

http://www.cooper.house.gov https://www.facebook.com/jimcooper
https://twitter.com/repjimcooper

1536 Longworth House Office Building, Washington, DC 20515 .... (202) 225–4311
Chief of Staff.—Lisa Quigley. FAX: 226–1035
Legislative Director / Deputy Chief of Staff.—Jason Lumia.
605 Church Street, Nashville, TN 37219 .... (615) 736–5295

Counties: CHEATHAM (part), DAVIDSON, AND DICKSON. Population (2010), 713,990.

ZIP Codes: 37011, 37013, 37015, 37024–25, 37027, 37029, 37032, 37035–36, 37043, 37051–52, 37055–56, 37062, 37064, 37070, 37072–73, 37076, 37080, 37082, 37086, 37101, 37115–16, 37122, 37135, 37138, 37143, 37146, 37165, 37171, 37181, 37187, 37189, 37201–22, 37224, 37227–30, 37232, 37234–36, 37238, 37240–44, 37246, 37250

* * *

SIXTH DISTRICT

DIANE BLACK, Republican, of Gallatin, TN; born in Baltimore, MD, January 16, 1951; education: A.S.N., Arundel Community College, Baltimore, MD, 1971; B.S.N., Belmont University, Nashville, TN, 1991; professional: nurse; nonprofit community organization fundraiser; member of the Tennessee State House of Representatives, 1999–2005; member of the Tennessee State Senate, 2005–10; religion: attends Christian Community Church, Hendersonville; married: Dr. David Black; three children; six grandchildren; caucuses: member of the Congressional Caucus for Women's Issues; Pro Life Caucus; Congressional Military Families Caucus; Republican Study Committee; committees: Budget; Ways and Means; elected to the 112th Congress on November 2, 2010; reelected to the 113th Congress on November 6, 2012.

Office Listings

http://www.black.house.gov

1531 Longworth House Office Building, Washington, DC 20515 .... (202) 225–4231
Chief of Staff.—Teresa Koeberlein. FAX: 225–6887
Scheduler.—Rebecca Schussler.
29 Taylor Avenue, Suite 201, Crossville, TN 38555 .... (931) 854–0069
321 East Spring Street, Suite 301, Cookeville, TN 38501 .... (931) 854–0069
355 North Belvedere Drive, Suite 308, Gallatin, TN 37066 .... (615) 206–8204
District Director.—Charles Schneider.

Counties: CANNON, CLAY, COFFEE, CUMBERLAND, DEKALB, FENTRESS, JACKSON, MACON, OVERTON, PICKETT, PUTNAM, ROBERTSON, SMITH, SUMNER, TROUSDALE, WHITE, WILSON, CHEATHAM (part), and VAN BURDEN. CITIES AND TOWNSHIPS: Byrdstown, Carthage, Celina, Cookeville, Crossville, Gainesboro, Gallatin, Grimsley, Hartsville, Hillsboro, Lafayette, Lebanon, Livingston, Mt. Juliet, Pleasant Hill, Sparta, Smithville, Springfield, Watertown, and Woodbury. Population (2010), 705,123.

ZIP Codes: 37010, 37012, 37015–16, 37018, 37022, 37030–32, 37034–36, 37048–49, 37059, 37066, 37072–75, 37077, 37080, 37082–83, 37085, 37087, 37090, 37095, 37143, 37155, 37118–19, 37122, 37141, 37146, 37150, 37152, 37166, 37172, 37183–84, 37186–88, 37190, 37337, 37342, 37355, 37357, 37360, 37388, 37723, 37726, 37854, 38501–06,

38543–44, 38547–49, 38551, 38553, 38555–56, 38558–59, 38562, 38565, 38570–74, 38577, 38579, 38581, 38583, 38585, 38587, 38589

* * *

SEVENTH DISTRICT

MARSHA BLACKBURN, Republican, of Franklin, TN; born in Laurel, MS, June 6, 1952; education: B.S., Mississippi State University, 1973; professional: retail marketing; public service: American Council of Young Political Leaders; Executive Director, Tennessee Film, Entertainment, and Music Commission; Chairman, Governor's Prayer Breakfast; Tennessee State Senate, 1998–2002; minority whip; community service: Rotary Club; Chamber of Commerce; Arthritis Foundation; Nashville Symphony Guild Board; Tennessee Biotechnology Association; March of Dimes; American Lung Association; awards: Chi Omega Alumnae Greek Woman of the Year, 1999; Middle Tennessee 100 Most Powerful People, 1999–2002; More Magazine *Women Run The World* Honoree, April 2013; married: Chuck; children: Mary Morgan Ketchel and Chad; founding member of the Republican Women's Policy Committee; committees: vice chair, Energy and Commerce; Budget; elected to the 108th Congress on November 5, 2002; reelected to each succeeding Congress.

Office Listings

http://blackburn.house.gov/ www.facebook.com/marshablackburn
twitter: @marshablackburn

217 Cannon House Office Building, Washington, DC 20515 .... (202) 225–2811
Chief of Staff.—Mike Platt. FAX: 225–3004
Legislative Director.—Keith Studdard.
Executive Assistant.—Grace Burch.
305 Public Square, Suite 212, Franklin, TN 37064 .... (615) 591–5161
128 North 2nd Street, Suite 202, Clarksville, TN 37040 .... (931) 503–0391

Counties: BENTON (part), CHESTER, DECATUR, GILES, HARDEMAN, HARDIN, HENDERSON, HICKMAN, HOUSTON, HUMPHREYS, LAWRENCE, LEWIS, MAURY (part), McNairy, Montgomery, Perry, Stewart, Wayne, and Williamson. Population (2010), 705,192.

ZIP Codes: 37010, 37014–15, 37023, 37025, 37027–28, 37032, 37037, 37040, 37042–43, 37046–47, 37050–52, 37055, 37059–62, 37067, 37078–79, 37096–98, 37101, 37134–35, 37137, 37140, 37142, 37144, 37171, 37174–79, 37181, 37185, 37191, 37214–15, 37220, 38008, 38039, 38042, 38044, 38052, 38061, 38067, 38075, 38221, 38310, 38463–64, 38468–69, 38471–78, 38481–83, 38485–87, 42223

* * *

EIGHTH DISTRICT

STEPHEN FINCHER, Republican, of Frog Jump, TN; born in Memphis, TN, February 7, 1973; education: Crockett County High School, 1990; professional: managing partner in Fincher Farms; public service: "The Fincher Family" singing ministry; president of Alamo Dixie Youth Baseball and Crockett County Dixie Youth Baseball; chairman of the board of the PPR Committee at Archer's Chapel United Methodist Church; president of United Methodist Men; religion: Archer's Chapel United Methodist Church; married: Lynn; children: John Austin, Noah, and Sarah; committees: Agriculture; Financial Services; elected to the 112th Congress on November 2, 2010; reelected to the 113th Congress on November 6, 2012.

Office Listings

http://www.fincher.house.gov www.twitter.com/repfinchertn08
www.facebook.com/repfinchertn08

1118 Longworth House Office Building, Washington, DC 20515 .... (202) 225–4714
Chief of Staff.—Jessica Carter. FAX: 225–1765
Communications Director.—Elizabeth Lauten.
Legislative Director.—Jim Hall.
Scheduler.—Janet Angus.
Press Assistant.—Victoria Treece.
Legislative Assistants: Erin Bays, Chris Davis, Jennifer Magruder.
12015 Walker Street, Arlington, TN 38002 .... (901) 581–4718
100 South Main Street, Suite 1, Dyersburg, TN 38024 .... (731) 285–0910
117 North Liberty Street, Jackson, TN 38301 .... (731) 423–4848
406 Lindell Street South, Suite C, Martin, TN 38237 .... (731) 588–5190
5384 Poplar Avenue, Memphis, TN 38119 .... (901) 682–4422

Counties: BENTON, CARROLL, CROCKETT, DYER, FAYETTE, GIBSON, HAYWOOD, HENRY, LAKE, LAUDERDALE, MADISON, OBION, SHELBY (part), TIPTON, AND WEAKLEY. Population (2010), 705,122.

ZIP Codes: 38001–02, 38004, 38006–07, 38011–12, 38015–19, 38021, 38023–24, 38028–30, 38034, 38036–37, 38039–42, 38046–47, 38049–50, 38053–54, 38057–60, 38063, 38066, 38068–70, 38075–77, 38079–80, 38111, 38117, 38119–20, 38125, 38128, 38133–35, 38138–39, 38141, 38152, 38201, 38220–22, 38224–26, 38229–33, 38235, 38237, 38240–42, 38251, 38253–61, 38301, 38305, 38313, 38316–18, 38326, 38330, 38337, 38341–44, 38348, 38351, 38355–56, 38358, 38362, 38366, 38369, 38382, 38387, 38390–92, 38401

* * *

NINTH DISTRICT

STEPHEN IRA ''STEVE'' COHEN, Democrat, of Memphis, TN; born in Memphis, May 24, 1949 of Dr. Morris D. Cohen and Genevieve Cohen; B.A., Vanderbilt University in Nashville, TN, 1971; J.D., Cecil C. Humphreys School of Law of Memphis State University (renamed University of Memphis), 1973; legal advisor for the Memphis Police Department, 1974–77; Delegate to and Vice President of Tennessee Constitutional Convention, 1977; Commissioner on the Shelby County Commission, 1978–80; Tennessee State Senator for District 30, 1982–2006; Delegate at the 1980 and 1992 Democratic National Conventions; Commission on Security and Cooperation in Europe; committees: Judiciary; Transportation and Infrastructure; elected to the 110th Congress on November 7, 2006; reelected to each succeeding Congress.

Office Listings

http://www.cohen.house.gov https://twitter.com/repcohen
https://www.facebook.com/congressmanstevecohen

2404 Rayburn House Office Building, Washington, DC 20515 .... (202) 225–3265
Chief of Staff.—Marilyn Dillihay. FAX: 225–5663
Scheduler.—Patrick Cassidy.
Legislative Director.—David Greengrass.
Communications Director.—Ben Garmisa.
167 North Main Street, Suite 369, Memphis, TN 38103 .... (901) 544–4131
FAX: 544–4329

County: SHELBY COUNTY (part). CITY OF: Memphis. Population (2010), 705,123.

ZIP Codes: 37501, 38016–18, 38101, 38103–09, 38111–20, 38122, 38124–28, 38130–37, 38139, 38141–42, 38145–48, 38151–52, 38157, 38159, 38161, 38165–68, 38173–75, 38177, 38181–82, 38186–88, 38190, 38193–95, 38197

TEXAS

(Population 2010, 25,145,561)

SENATORS

JOHN CORNYN, Republican, of Austin, TX; born in Houston, TX, February 2, 1952; education: graduated, Trinity University, and St. Mary's School of Law, San Antonio, TX; Masters of Law, University of Virginia, Charlottesville, VA; professional: attorney; Bexar County District Court Judge; Presiding Judge, Fourth Administrative Judicial Region; Texas Supreme Court, 1990–97; Texas Attorney General, 1999–2002; community service: Salvation Army Adult Rehabilitation Council; World Affairs Council of San Antonio; Lutheran General Hospital Board; chair, National Republican Senatorial Committee; committees: Finance; Judiciary; elected to the U.S. Senate on November 5, 2002, for the term beginning January 3, 2003; appointed to the Senate on December 2, 2002, to fill the vacancy caused by the resignation of Senator Phil Gramm; reelected to the U.S. Senate on November 4, 2008.

Office Listings

http://cornyn.senate.gov

517 Hart Senate Office Building, Washington, DC 20510 .... (202) 224–2934
Republican Whip Office, S–208 Capitol Building, Washington, DC 20510 .... (202) 224–2708
Chief of Staff.—Beth Jafari. FAX: 228–2856
Legislative Director.—Jerr Rosenbaum.
5300 Memorial Drive, Suite 980, Houston, TX 77007 .... (713) 572–3337
Providence Tower, 5001 Spring Valley Road, #1125E, Dallas, TX 75244 .... (972) 239–1310
100 East Ferguson Street, Suite 1004, Tyler, TX 75702 .... (903) 593–0902
221 West Sixth Street, Suite 1530, Austin, TX 78701 .... (512) 469–6034
Wells Fargo Center, 1500 Broadway, #1230, Lubbock, TX 79401 .... (806) 472–7533
222 East Van Buren, Suite 404, Harlingen, TX 78550 .... (956) 423–0162
600 Navarro Street, Suite 210, San Antonio, TX 78205 .... (210) 224–7485

* * *

TED CRUZ, Republican, of Houston, TX; born in Calgary, Alberta, Canada, December 22, 1970; raised in Houston, TX; education: graduated *cum laude* from Princeton University with a B.A. from the Woodrow Wilson School of Public and International Affairs in 1992 and *magna cum laude* from Harvard Law School with a J.D. in 1995; Domestic Policy Advisor on the 2000 Bush-Cheney campaign; director of the Office of Policy Planning at the Federal Trade Commission; Associate Deputy Attorney General at the U.S. Department of Justice; Adjunct Professor of Law at the University of Texas School of Law; Solicitor General of the State of Texas; Partner at Morgan, Lewis & Bockius LLP; religion: Southern Baptist; married: Heidi Cruz; committees: Armed Services; Commerce, Science, and Transportation; Judiciary; Rules and Administration; Special Committee on Aging; elected to the U.S. Senate on November 6, 2012.

Office Listings

http://cruz.senate.gov https://www.facebook.com/senatortedcruz
https://twitter.com/sentedcruz

185 Dirksen Senate Office Building, Washington, DC 20510 .... (202) 224–5922
Chief of Staff.—Chip Roy. FAX: 228–0755
Legislative Director.—Brooke Bacak.
300 East 8th Street, Suite 961, Austin, TX 78701 .... (512) 916–5834
808 Travis Street, Suite 1420, Houston, TX 77002 .... (713) 718–3057
Lee Park Tower II, 3626 North Hall Street, Suite 410, Dallas, TX 75219 .... (214) 599–8749
9901 IH–10 West, Suite 950, San Antonio, TX 78230 .... (210) 340–2885
305 South Broadway Avenue, Suite 501, Tyler, TX 75702 .... (903) 593–5130

REPRESENTATIVES

FIRST DISTRICT

LOUIE GOHMERT, Republican, of Tyler, TX; born in Pittsburg, TX, August 18, 1953; education: B.A., Texas A&M University, 1975; J.D., Baylor University, Waco, TX, 1977; professional: United States Army, 1978–82; district judge, Smith County, 1992–2002; appointed by Governor Rick Perry to complete an unexpired term as Chief Justice of the 12th Court of

Appeals, 2002–03; Brigade Commander of the Corps of Cadets, Texas A&M; organizations: President of the South Tyler Rotary Club; Boy Scout District Board of Directors; religion: deacon at Green Acres Baptist Church; director of Leadership Tyler; director of Centrepoint Ministries; married: Kathy; children: Katy, Caroline, Sarah; committees: Judiciary; Natural Resources; elected to the 109th Congress on November 2, 2004; reelected to each succeeding Congress.

Office Listings

http://www.gohmert.house.gov

2243 Rayburn House Office Building, Washington, DC 20515 .... (202) 225–3035
Chief of Staff.—Connie Hair. FAX: 226–1230
Legislative Director.—Austin Smithson.
Communications Director.—Kimberly Willingham.
1121 East Southeast Loop 323, Suite 206, Tyler, TX 75701 .... (903) 561–6349

Counties: ANGELINA, GREGG, HARRISON, NACOGDOCHES, PANOLA, RUSK, SABINE, SAN AUGUSTINE, SHELBY, SMITH, WOOD, AND UPSHUR (part). Population (2010), 710,704.

ZIP Codes: 75551, 75555, 75562, 75564–65, 75601–08, 75615, 75631, 75633, 75637, 75639–45, 75647, 75650–54, 75657–63, 75666–67, 75669–72, 75680, 75682–85, 75687–89, 75691–94, 75701–13, 75750, 75755, 75757, 75760, 75762, 75771, 75788–89, 75791–92, 75797–99, 75901–04, 75915, 75929–31, 75935, 75937, 75941, 75943–44, 75946–49, 75954, 75958–59, 75961–65, 75968–69, 75972–75, 75978, 75980

* * *

SECOND DISTRICT

TED POE, Republican, of Humble, TX; born in Temple, TX, September 10, 1948; education: B.A., political science, Abilene Christian University, Abilene, TX, 1970; J.D., University of Houston, TX, 1973; professional: United States Air Force, 1970–1976; Felony Court Judge, 1981–2004; Trainer, Federal Bureau of Investigations National Academy; Chief Felony Prosecutor, District Attorney, Harris County, TX; United States Air Force Reserves Instructor, University of Houston; organizations: Congressional PORTS Caucus; Congressional Victim's Rights Caucus; committees: Foreign Affairs; Judiciary; elected to the 109th Congress on November 2, 2004; reelected to each succeeding Congress.

Office Listings

http://www.poe.house.gov

2412 Rayburn House Office Building, Washington, DC 20515 .... (202) 225–6565
Chief of Staff.—Gina Santucci. FAX: 225–5547
Press Secretary.—Shaylyn Hynes.
Scheduler.—Allyson Browning.
1801 Kingwood Drive, Suite 240, Kingwood, TX 77339 .... (866) 447–0242
710 North Post Oak, Suite 510, Houston, TX 77024 .... (713) 681–8763

Counties: HARRIS. Population (2010), 698,488.

ZIP Codes: 77002, 77004–08, 77018–19, 77024–25, 77030, 77040–41, 77043–44, 77055, 77064–66, 77069–70, 77079–80, 77084, 77086, 77088, 77092, 77095, 77098, 77336, 77338–39, 77345–46, 77357, 77365, 77373, 77375, 77377, 77379, 77388, 77396, 77429, 77532

* * *

THIRD DISTRICT

SAM JOHNSON, Republican, of Dallas, TX; born in San Antonio, TX, October 11, 1930; education: B.S., business administration, Southern Methodist University, Dallas, TX, 1951; M.A., international affairs, George Washington University, Washington, DC, 1974; military service: served in Air Force, 29 years; Korea and Vietnam (POW in Vietnam, 6 years, 10 months); director, Air Force Fighter Weapons School; flew with Air Force Thunderbirds Precision Flying Demonstration Team; graduate of Armed Services Staff College and National War College; military awards: two Silver Stars, two Legions of Merit, Distinguished Flying Cross, one Bronze Star with Valor, two Purple Hearts, four Air Medals, and three Outstanding Unit awards; ended career with rank of colonel and Air Division commander; retired, 1979; professional: opened homebuilding company, 1979; served 7 years in Texas House of Representatives; Smithsonian Board of Regents; U.S./Russian Joint Commission on POW/MIA; Texas State Society; Congressional Medal of Honor Society; National Patriot Award Recipient,

2009; caucus and award: co-chair, Air Force Caucus; Living Legends of Aviation ''Freedom of Flight'' Award recipient, 2011; Rotary International, Paul Harris Fellow; founder, Republican Study Committee (formerly Conservative Action Team); chairman of the Board of Directors, Institute of Basic Life Principles; Deputy Whip; married the former Shirley L. Melton, 1950; three children: Dr. James Robert Johnson, Shirley Virginia (Gini) Mulligan and Beverly Briney; committees: Ways and Means; Joint Committee on Taxation; elected to the 102nd Congress by special election on May 18, 1991, to fill the vacancy caused by the resignation of Steve Bartlett; reelected to each succeeding Congress.

Office Listings

http://www.samjohnson.house.gov https://twitter.com/samspressshop
https://www.facebook.com/repsamjohnson

1211 Longworth House Office Building, Washington, DC 20515 .... (202) 225–4201
Chief of Staff.—Dave Heil. FAX: 225–1485
Legislative Director.—Mark Williams.
Executive Assistant.—Christina Swisher.
1255 West 15th Street, Suite 170, Plano, TX 75075 .... (469) 304–0382

Counties: The Third District of Texas encompasses the majority of COLLIN COUNTY including all or part of the CITIES of Allen, Anna, Blue Ridge, Dallas. (COLLIN COUNTY), Fairview, Frisco, Lavon, Lowry Crossing, Lucas, McKinney, Melissa, Murphy, New Hope, Parker, Plano, Princeton, Prosper, Richardson, St. Paul, Wylie, and portions of unincorporated land in COLLIN COUNTY. Population (2010), 747,284.

ZIP Codes: 75002, 75007, 75009, 75013, 75023–26, 75030, 75034–35, 75040–42, 75044–48, 75069–71, 75074–75, 75078, 75080–82, 75085–86, 75088–89, 75093–94, 75098, 75228, 75238, 75245, 75248, 75252, 75287, 75355, 75367, 75370, 75378, 75382, 75409, 75424, 75442, 75454, 78243

* * *

FOURTH DISTRICT

RALPH M. HALL, Republican, of Rockwall, TX; born in Fate, TX, May 3, 1923; education: graduated, Rockwall High School, 1941; attended, Texas Christian University and the University of Texas; LL.B., Southern Methodist University, 1951; professional: lieutenant, carrier pilot (senior grade), U.S. Navy, 1942–45; lawyer; admitted to the Texas Bar, 1951; practiced law in Rockwall; county judge, Rockwall County, 1950–62; former president and chief executive officer, Texas Aluminum Corporation; past general counsel, Texas Extrusion Company, Inc.; past organizer, chairman, board of directors, now chairman of board, Lakeside National Bank of Rockwall (now Lakeside Bancshares, Inc.); past chairman, board of directors, Lakeside News, Inc.; past vice chairman, board of directors, Bank of Crowley; president, North and East Trading Company; vice president, Crowley Holding Co.; member: Texas State Senate, 1962–72; American Legion Post 117; VFW Post 6796; Rockwall Rotary Club; Rotary Clubs International; member: First Methodist Church; widower: (was married to the former Mary Ellen Murphy, 1944 (deceased); three sons: Hampton, Brett and Blakeley; committees: chair emeritus, Science, Space, and Technology; Energy and Commerce; elected to the 97th Congress, November 4, 1980; reelected to each succeeding Congress.

Office Listings

http://www.house.gov/ralphhall https://www.facebook.com/pages/ralph-hall/6311458773
https://twitter.com/ralphhallpress https://www.youtube.com/channel/ucyuluburkuaypekuwtqcmcq

2405 Rayburn House Office Building, Washington, DC 20515 .... (202) 225–6673
Chief of Staff.—Janet Poppleton. FAX: 225–3332
Chief Policy Advisor.—Kyle Oliver.
Legislative Director.—Christopher Schell.
104 North San Jacinto Street, Rockwall, TX 75087–2508 .... (972) 771–9118
District Director / Scheduler.—Tom Hughes. FAX: 772–0907
Constituent Services.—Linda Schenck.
123 Kaufman Street, Room 102, Linden, TX 75563 .... (903) 306–0540
Constituent Services.—Eric Cain.
Grayson County Courthouse 100 West Houston Street, 2nd Floor, Sherman, TX 75090–6019 .... (903) 813–4281
Constituent Services.—Jennyne Reeves. FAX: 868–8613
4303 Texas Boulevard, Suite 2, Texarkana, TX 75503–3094 .... (903) 794–4445
Constituent Services.—Marjorie Chandler. FAX: 794–5577

Counties: BOWIE COUNTY. CITIES AND TOWNSHIPS: DeKalb, Hooks, Leary, Maud, Nash, New Boston, Red Lick, Redwater, Texarkana, Wake Village. CAMP COUNTY. CITIES AND TOWNSHIPS: Pittsburg, Rocky Mound. CASS COUNTY. CITIES AND TOWNSHIPS: Atlanta, Avinger, Bloomburg, Domino, Douglassville, Hughes Springs, Linden, Marietta, Queen City. COLLIN COUNTY. CITIES AND TOWNSHIPS: Anna, Blue Ridge, Celina, Farmersville, Josephine, Lavon, Nevada, Royse

City, Van Alstyne, Westminster, Weston, Wylie. DELTA COUNTY. CITIES AND TOWNSHIPS: Cooper, Pecan Gap. FANNIN COUNTY. CITIES AND TOWNSHIPS: Bailey, Bonham, Dodd City, Ector, Honey Grove, Ladonia, Leonard, Pecan Gap, Ravenna, Savoy, Trenton, Whitewright, Windom. FRANKLIN COUNTY. CITIES AND TOWNSHIPS: Mount Vernon, Winnsboro. GRAYSON COUNTY. CITIES AND TOWNSHIPS: Bells, Collinsville, Denison, Dorchester, Gunter, Howe, Knollwood, Pottsboro, Sadler, Sherman, Southmayd, Tioga, Tom Bean, Van Alstyne, Whitesboro, Whitewright. HOPKINS COUNTY. CITIES AND TOWNSHIPS: Como, Cumby, Sulphur Springs, Tira. HUNT COUNTY. CITIES AND TOWNSHIPS: Caddo Mills, Campbell, Celeste, Commerce, Greenville, Hawk Cove, Josephine, Lone Oak, Neylandville, Quinlan, West Tawakoni, Wolfe City. LAMAR COUNTY. CITIES AND TOWNSHIPS: Blossom, Deport, Paris, Reno, Roxton, Sun Valley, Toco. MARION COUNTY. CITIES AND TOWNSHIPS: Jefferson City, Pine Harbor. MORRIS COUNTY. CITIES AND TOWNSHIPS: Daingerfield, Hughes Springs, Lone Star, Naples, Omaha. RAINS COUNTY. CITIES AND TOWNSHIPS: Alba, East Tawakoni, Emory, Point. RED RIVER COUNTY. CITIES AND TOWNSHIPS: Annona, Avery, Bogata, Clarksville, Deport, Detroit. ROCKWALL COUNTY. CITIES AND TOWNSHIPS: Fate, Garland, Heath, Mclendon-Chisholm, Mobile City, Rockwall, Rowlett, Royse City, Wylie. TITUS COUNTY. CITIES AND TOWNSHIPS: Miller's Cove, Mount Pleasant, Talco. UPSHUR COUNTY. CITIES AND TOWNSHIPS: Clarksville City, East Mountain, Gilmer, Gladewater, Ore City, Union Grove, and Warren City. Population (2010), 705,523.

ZIP Codes: 75002, 75009, 75013, 75019, 75030, 75032, 75034–35, 75040–41, 75058, 75069, 75071, 75074, 75076, 75078, 75087–88, 75090, 75094, 75097–98, 75132, 75135, 75164, 75166, 75173, 75189, 75407, 75409, 75413–14, 75416–18, 75422–24, 75426, 75428–29, 75431–33, 75435–36, 75438–40, 75442, 75446, 75449, 75452–55, 75457, 75459, 75460, 75462, 75469, 75472–73, 75474, 75476, 75477, 75479, 75482, 75486–87, 75683, 75489, 75490–95, 75501, 75550–51, 75554, 75556, 75559–61, 75563, 75566–73, 75572, 75630, 75638, 75644–47, 75656, 75657, 75668, 75686, 75855, 76233, 76264, 76268, 76271, 76273

* * *

FIFTH DISTRICT

JEB HENSARLING, Republican, of Dallas, TX; born in Stephenville, TX, May 29, 1957; education: B.A., economics, Texas A&M University, 1979; J.D., University of Texas School of Law, 1982; professional: businessman; vice president, Maverick Capital, 1993–96; owner, San Jacinto Ventures, 1996–2002; vice president, Green Mountain Energy Co., 1999–2001; community service: American Cancer Society for the Dallas Metro Area; Children's Education Fund; Habitat for Humanity; religion: Christian; married: Melissa; children: Claire and Travis; committees: chair, Financial Services; elected to the 108th Congress on November 5, 2002; reelected to each succeeding Congress.

Office Listings

http://www.hensarling.house.gov

2228 Rayburn House Office Building, Washington, DC 20515 .... (202) 225–3484
Chief of Staff.—Andrew Duke. FAX: 226–4888
Legislative Director.—Kyle Jackson.
Press Secretary.—Sarah Rozier.
6510 Abrams Road, Suite 243, Dallas, TX 75238 .... (214) 349–9996
810 East Corsicana Street, Suite C, Athens, TX 77571 .... (903) 675–8288

Counties: ANDERSON, CHEROKEE, DALLAS (part), HENDERSON, KAUFMAN, VAN ZANDT, AND WOOD. Population (2010), 698,498.

ZIP Codes: 75041–43, 75103, 75114, 75117–18, 75124, 75126–27, 75140, 75142–43, 75147–50, 75156–61, 75163, 75169, 75180–82, 75185, 75187, 75214, 75217–18, 75227–28, 75231, 75238, 75243, 75253, 75336, 75355, 75382, 75389, 75410, 75431, 75440, 75444, 75474, 75494, 75497, 75751–52, 75754, 75756–59, 75763–64, 75766, 75770, 75772–73, 75778–80, 75782–85, 75789–90, 75801–03, 75832, 75839, 75844, 75853, 75861, 75880, 75882, 75884, 75886, 75925, 75976

* * *

SIXTH DISTRICT

JOE BARTON, Republican, of Ennis, TX; born in Waco, TX, September 15, 1949; education: graduated Waco High School, 1968; B.S., industrial engineering, Texas A&M University, College Station, 1972; M.S., industrial administration, Purdue University, West Lafayette, IN, 1973; professional: plant manager, and assistant to the vice president, Ennis Business Forms, Inc., 1973–81; awarded White House Fellowship, 1981–82; served as aide to James B. Edwards, Secretary, Department of Energy; member, Natural Gas Decontrol Task Force in the Office of Planning, Policy and Analysis; worked with the Department of Energy task force in support of the President's Private Sector Survey on Cost Control; natural gas decontrol and project cost control consultant, Atlantic Richfield Company; cofounder, Houston County Volunteer Ambulance Service, 1976; vice president, Houston County Industrial Development Authority, 1980; chairman, Crockett Parks and Recreation Board, 1979–80; vice president, Houston County Chamber of Commerce, 1977–80; member, Dallas Energy Forum; religion: Methodist; married: Terri; son, Jack; children: Brad, Alison and Kristin, from a previous marriage; stepchildren: Lindsay and Cullen; committees: chair emeritus, Energy and Commerce; elected to the 99th Congress on November 6, 1984; reelected to each succeeding Congress.

Office Listings

http://www.joebarton.house.gov

2107 Rayburn House Office Building, Washington, DC 20515 .... (202) 225–2002
Chief of Staff.—Ryan Thompson. FAX: 225–3052
Communications Director.—Sean Brown.
Legislative Director.—Michael Weems.
Senior Legislative Assistant.—Emmanual Guillory.
Legislative Assistant.—Nina Shelat.
Legislative Correspondent.—Amy Murphy.
Staff Assistant.—Abigail Gage.
6001 West Ronald Reagan Memorial Highway, Suite 200, Arlington, TX 76017 .... (817) 543–1000
Constituent Liaison.—Deborah Rollings. FAX: 548–7029
Special Projects Director.—Jodi Sacgesser.
Deputy District Director (Tarrant Co).—Michael Taylor.
Casework Director.—Christi Townsend.
2106A West Ennis Avenue, Ennis, TX 75119 (direct phone) .... (972) 875–8488
Deputy Chief of Staff.—Linda Gillespie. FAX: 875–1907
Deputy District Director.—Dub Maines.

Counties: ELLIS, NAVARRO, AND TARRANT. CITIES AND TOWNSHIPS: Alma, Angus, Arlington, Bardwell, Barry, Blooming Grove, Burleson, Cedar Hill, Corsicana, Crowley, Dawson, Emhouse, Ennis, Eureka, Ferris, Fort Worth, Frost, Garrett, Glenn Heights, Goodlow, Grand Prairie, Italy, Kennedale, Kerens, Mansfield, Maypearl, Midlothian, Milford, Mustang, Navarro, Oak Leaf, Oak Valley, Ovilla, Palmer, Pecan Hill, Powell, Red Oak, Rendon, Retreat, Rice, Richland, Venus, and Waxahachie. Population (2010), 720,861.

ZIP Codes: 75050, 75052, 75054, 75101–02, 75104–06, 75109–10, 75119–20, 75125, 75144, 75146, 75151–55, 75165, 75167–68, 75859, 76001–04, 76006, 76010–19, 76028, 76036, 76041, 76050, 76060, 76094, 76096, 76119–20, 76123, 76133–34, 76140, 76623, 76626, 76639, 76641, 76651, 76670, 76679, 76681

* * *

SEVENTH DISTRICT

JOHN ABNEY CULBERSON, Republican, of Harris County, TX; born in Houston, TX, August 24, 1956; education: B.A., Southern Methodist University; J.D., South Texas College of Law; professional: attorney; awards: Citizens for a Sound Economy Friend of the Taxpayer Award; Texas Eagle Forum Freedom and Family Award; Houston Jaycees Outstanding Young Houstonian Award; Champion of Border Security; Ancient Coin Collectors Guild; Friend of Numismatics; Club for Growth's Defender of Economic Freedom; Congressional Management Foundation's Silver Mouse Award; Family Research Canals True Blue Award; Water Advocate ''Friend of the Shareholder'' Recognition; U.S. Chamber of Commerce; Spirit of Enterprise Guardian of Small Business by NFIB; Recognition from the 60 Plus Association; NumbersUSA ''A'' for Consistently Voting for American Workers and the Environment through Immigration Reduction; public service: Texas House of Representatives, 1987–2000; married: Belinda Burney, 1989; child: Caroline; committees: Appropriations; elected to the 107th Congress on November 7, 2000; reelected to each succeeding Congress.

Office Listings

http://www.culberson.house.gov

2352 Rayburn House Office Building, Washington, DC 20515 .... (202) 225–2571
Chief of Staff.—Jamie Gahun. FAX: 225–4381
Legislative Director.—Catherine Knowles.
10000 Memorial Drive, Suite 620, Houston, TX 77024–3490 .... (713) 682–8828
District Director.—Brittany Seabury.

County: HARRIS (part). Population (2010), 717,354.

ZIP Codes: 77005, 77019, 77024–25, 77027, 77035–36, 77040–42, 77046, 77055–57, 77063–65, 77074, 77077, 77079, 77080–82, 77084, 77094–96, 77098, 77215, 77218, 77224, 77227, 77242, 77244, 77256, 77257, 77265, 77274, 77277, 77279, 77282, 77401–02, 77429, 77433, 77449, 77450

* * *

EIGHTH DISTRICT

KEVIN BRADY, Republican, of The Woodlands, TX; born in Vermillion, SD, April 11, 1955; education: B.S., business, University of South Dakota; professional: served in Texas House of Representatives, 1991–96, the second Republican to capture the 8th District seat since the district's creation; chair, Council of Chambers of Greater Houston; president, East Texas Chamber Executive Association; president, South Montgomery County Woodlands Chamber of Commerce, 1985–present; director, Texas Chamber of Commerce Executives; Rotarian; awards: Achievement Award, Texas Conservative Coalition; Outstanding Young Texan (one of five), Texas Jaycees; Ten Best Legislators for Families and Children, State Bar of Texas; Legislative Standout, Dallas Morning News; Scholars Achievement Award for Excellence in Public Service, North Harris Montgomery Community College District; Victims Rights Equalizer Award, Texans for Equal Justice Center; Support for Family Issues Award, Texas Extension Homemakers Association; religion: attends Saints Simon and Jude Catholic Church; married: Cathy Brady; committees: chair, Joint Economic Committee; Ways and Means; Joint Committee on Taxation; elected to the 105th Congress; reelected to each succeeding Congress.

Office Listings

http://www.kevinbrady.house.gov https://www.facebook.com/kevinbrady
https://twitter.com/repkevinbrady

301 Cannon House Office Building, Washington, DC 20515 .... (202) 225–4901
Deputy Chief of Staff / Legislative Director.—Lori Harju. FAX: 225–5524
Communications Director.—Tracee Evans.
Press Secretary.—Shana Teehan.
200 River Pointe Drive, Suite 304, Conroe, TX 77304 .... (936) 441–5700
District Director.—Todd Stephens.
1300 11th Street, Suite 400, Huntsville, TX 77340 .... (936) 439–9532

Counties: GRIMES, HARRIS (part), HOUSTON, LEON, MADISON, MONTGOMERY, SAN JACINTO, TRINITY, AND WALKER. CITIES AND TOWNSHIPS: Anderson, Augusta, Bedias, Centerville, Conroe, Crockett, Decker Prairie, Grapeland, Groveton, Huntsville, Madisonville, Magnolia, Maynard, Midway, Montgomery, Navasota, New Caney, Normangee, Pinehurst, Plantersville, Point Blank, Porter Springs, Roans Prairie, Shepherd, Splendora, Spring, The Woodlands, Todd Mission, Tomball, Trinity, Weches, Willis, and Woodlake. Population (2010), 743,782.

ZIP Codes: 77371–73, 77365, 77379, 77353–59, 77375, 77377, 77070, 77340–42, 75844, 75852, 75862, 77328, 75849–51, 77365, 77830–31, 77393, 77447, 77380–89, 75835, 75856, 75858, 75926, 77316, 77318, 77320, 77331, 77333–34, 77367, 77378, 75845, 75847, 77855, 77861, 77864, 77876, 77301–06, 77354, 77447, 77868, 75833, 77328

* * *

NINTH DISTRICT

AL GREEN, Democrat, of Houston, TX; born in New Orleans, LA, September 1, 1947; raised in Florida; education: Florida A&M University, Tallahassee, FL, 1966–71; attended Tuskegee University, Tuskegee, AL; J.D., Texas Southern University, Houston, TX, 1974; professional: co-founded and co-managed the law firm of Green, Wilson, Dewberry and Fitch; Justice of the Peace, Precinct 7, Position 2, 1977–2004; organizations: former president of the Houston NAACP; Houston Citizens Chamber of Commerce; awards: Distinguished Service Award, 1978; Black Heritage Society, Outstanding Leadership Award, 1981; American Federation of Teachers, Citation for Service as a ''Courageous Defender of Due Process for Educators,'' 1983; *Ebony* Magazine's 100 Most Influential Black People, 2006; and the NAACP Fort Bend Branch Mickey Leland Humanitarian Award, 2006; Texas Black Democrats' Profiles of Courage Award, 2007; the AFL-CIO MLK Drum Major Award for Service, 2007; committees: Financial Services; elected to the 109th Congress on November 2, 2004; reelected to each succeeding Congress.

Office Listings

http://www.house.gov/algreen

2201 Rayburn House Office Building, Washington, DC 20515 .... (202) 225–7508
Chief of Staff.—Jacqueline Ellis. FAX: 225–2947
Legislative Director.—Gregg Orton.
Senior Legislative Assistant.—Gregg Orton.
Press Secretary.—Michael Mouton. (713) 383–9234
3003 South Loop West, Suite 460, Houston, TX 77054 .... (713) 383–9234
District Office Policy Manager.—Kevin Dancy. FAX: 383–9202
District Office Administrative Manager.—Crystal Webster.
Press Secretary.—Alvaro Ortiz.

Counties: FORT BEND (part), HARRIS (part). Population (2010), 698,488.

ZIP Codes: 77004, 77025, 77030–31, 77033, 77035–36, 77042, 77045, 77047–48, 77051, 77053–54, 77061, 77063, 77071–72, 77074, 77077, 77082–83, 77085, 77087, 77096, 77099, 77407, 77459, 77477, 77489, 77498, 77545

* * *

TENTH DISTRICT

MICHAEL T. McCAUL, Republican, of Austin, TX; born in Dallas, TX, January 14, 1962; education: B.S., Trinity University, San Antonio, TX, 1984; J.D., St. Mary's University, San Antonio, TX, 1987; professional: lawyer, private practice; deputy attorney general, office of Texas State Attorney General; committees: Ethics; Foreign Affairs; Homeland Security; Science, Space, and Technology; elected to the 109th Congress on November 2, 2004; reelected to each succeeding Congress.

Office Listings

http://www.mccaul.house.gov

131 Cannon House Office Building, Washington, DC 20515 .... (202) 225–2401
Chief of Staff.—Greg Hill. FAX: 225–5955
Legislative Director.—Andy Taylor.
Scheduler / Office Manager.—Jessica Nalepa.
9009 Mountain Ridge Drive, Suite 230, Austin, TX 78731 .... (512) 473–2357
Communications Director.—Mike Rosen.
Rosewood Professional Building, 990 Village Square, Suite B, Tomball, TX 77375 (281) 255–8372
1773 Westborough Drive, Suite 223, Katy, TX 77084 .... (281) 398–1247
2000 South Market Street, Suite 303, Brenham, TX 77833 .... (979) 830–8497

Counties: AUSTIN, BASTROP, BURLESON, HARRIS, LEE, TRAVIS, WALLER, AND WASHINGTON. Population (2010), 698,487.

ZIP Codes: 77070, 77084, 77094–95, 77218, 77269, 77284, 77375, 77377, 77379, 77383, 77388–89, 77391, 77410, 77413, 77418, 77423, 77426, 77429, 77433, 77445–47, 77449–50, 77452, 77466, 77473–74, 77476, 77484–85, 77491–94, 77833–36, 77838, 77852–53, 77863, 77868, 77878–80, 78602, 78615, 78621, 78650–51, 78653, 78659–60, 78664, 78682–83, 78691, 78703, 78705, 78708, 78710, 78713, 78716, 78718, 78720, 78724, 78727–31, 78733, 78746, 78751–59, 78761, 78763, 78765–66, 78779–80, 78785, 78788–89, 78931–33, 78940, 78942, 78944, 78946–48, 78950

* * *

ELEVENTH DISTRICT

K. MICHAEL CONAWAY, Republican, of Midland, TX; born in Borger, TX, June 11, 1948; education: B.B.A., Texas A&M–Commerce, 1970; professional: Spec 5 United States Army, 1970–72; tax manager, Price Waterhouse & Company, 1972–80; Chief Financial Officer, Keith D. Graham & Lantern Petroleum Company, 1980–81; Chief Financial Officer, Bush Exploration Company, 1982–84; Chief Financial Officer, Spectrum 7 Energy Corporation, 1984–86; Senior Vice President / Chief Financial Officer, United Bank, 1987–90; Senior Vice President, Texas Commerce Bank, 1990–92; owner, K. Conaway CPA, 1993–present; Deputy Republican Whip; religion: Baptist; married: Suzanne; children: Brian, Erin, Kara, and Stephanie; committees: chair, Ethics; Agriculture; Armed Services; Permanent Select Committee on Intelligence; elected to the 109th Congress on November 2, 2004; reelected to each succeeding Congress.

Office Listings

http://www.house.gov/conaway

2430 Rayburn House Office Building, Washington, DC 20515 .... (202) 225–3605
Chief of Staff.—Scott C. Graves. FAX: 225–1783
Legislative Director.—Paul Balzano.
Scheduler.—Leah Christensen.
6 Desta Drive, Suite 2000, Midland, TX 79705 .... (432) 687–2390
District Scheduler.—Patsy Bain.
33 East Twohig, Room 307, San Angelo, TX 76903 .... (325) 659–4010
Regional Director.—Joanne Powell.

Counties: ANDREWS, BROWN, CALLAHAN, COKE, COLEMAN, COMANCHE, CONCHO, DAWSON, EASTLAND, ECTOR, ERATH, GLASSCOCK, HOOD, IRION, KIMBLE, LLANO, MARTIN, MASON, MCCULLOCH, MENARD, MIDLAND, MILLS, MITCHELL, PALO PINTO, RUNNELS, SAN SABA, STEPHENS, STERLING, AND TOM GREEN. Population (2010), 698,488.

ZIP Codes: 76246, 76432, 76442, 76444, 76455, 76550, 76801–04, 76821, 76823, 76825, 76834, 76837, 76844, 76853, 76856, 76859, 76861, 76864, 76866, 76872–73, 76877, 76901–04, 76932–33, 76935–36, 76941, 76945, 76950–51, 76957, 77381–82, 77393, 78611, 78624, 78643, 78654–69, 79331, 79512, 79532, 79545, 79549–50, 79556, 79565, 79567, 79605–09, 79714, 79760–69, 79701–13, 79739, 79742, 79745, 79756, 79778, 79789

* * *

TWELFTH DISTRICT

KAY GRANGER, Republican, of Fort Worth, TX; born in Greenville, TX, January 18, 1943; education: B.S., *magna cum laude*, 1965, and Honorary Doctorate of Humane Letters, 1992, Texas Wesleyan University; professional: owner, Kay Granger Insurance Agency, Inc.; former public school teacher; elected Mayor of Fort Worth, 1991, serving three terms; during her tenure, Fort Worth received All-America City Award from the National Civic League; former Fort Worth Councilwoman; past chair, Fort Worth Zoning Commission; past board member: Dallas-Fort Worth International Airport; North Texas Commission; Fort Worth Convention and Visitors Bureau; U.S. Conference of Mayors Advisory Board; Business and Professional Women's Woman of the Year, 1989; three grown children: J.D., Brandon and Chelsea; first woman Republican to represent Texas in the U.S. House; vice chair, Republican Conference; Deputy Republican Whip; committees: Appropriations; elected to the 105th Congress; reelected to each succeeding Congress.

Office Listings

http://www.house.gov/granger

1026 Longworth House Office Building, Washington, DC 20515 .... (202) 225–5071
Chief of Staff.—Matt Leffingwell. FAX: 225–5683
Deputy Chief of Staff / Legislative Director.—Shannon Meade.
Staff Assistant.—Nicholas Vance.
Scheduler.—Amanda Hamilton.
1701 River Run Road, Suite 407, Fort Worth, TX 76107 .... (817) 338–0909
District Director.—Mattie Parker. (817) 335–5852

Counties: PARKER, TARRANT (part), and WISE. Population (2010), 698,488.

ZIP Codes: 76008, 76020, 76023, 76035–36, 76049, 76052, 76066–68, 76071, 76073, 76078, 76082, 76085–88, 76098, 76101–02, 76104, 76106–11, 76113–18, 76121–23, 76126–27, 76129–37, 76147–48, 76161–64, 76177, 76179–82, 76185, 76191–93, 76195–99, 76225, 76234, 76244, 76246, 76248, 76262, 76267, 76270, 76299, 76426, 76431, 76439, 76462, 76485–87, 76490

* * *

THIRTEENTH DISTRICT

MAC THORNBERRY, Republican, of Clarendon, TX; born in Clarendon, July 15, 1958; education: graduate, Clarendon High School; B.A., Texas Tech University; law degree, University of Texas; professional: rancher; attorney; admitted to the Texas Bar, 1983; member: Joint Forces Command Transformation; Republican Study Committee; Proliferation Prevention Forum; Congressional Rural Caucus; Rural Health Care Coalition; Anti-Terrorism Caucus; Interagency Coordination, Western Caucus; married: Sally Adams, 1986; children: Will and Mary Kemp; committees: vice chair, Permanent Select Committee on Intelligence; Armed Services; elected to the 104th Congress; reelected to each succeeding Congress.

Office Listings

http://www.thornberry.house.gov https://www.facebook.com/repmacthornberry
https://twitter.com/mactxpress http://www.youtube.com/repmacthornberry

2329 Rayburn House Office Building, Washington, DC 20515 .... (202) 225–3706
Administrative Assistant.—Lauren Hensarling. FAX: 225–3486
Office Managers: Nicole Heath, Lauren Hensarling.
905 South Filmore, Suite 520, Amarillo, TX 79101 .... (806) 371–8844
Chief of Staff.—Josh Martin.
2525 Kell Boulevard, Suite 406, Wichita Falls, TX 76308 .... (940) 692–1700

Counties: ARCHER, ARMSTRONG, BAYLOR, BRISCOE, CARSON, CHILDRESS, CLAY, COLLINGSWORTH, COOKE, COTTLE, DALLAM, DEAF SMITH, DICKENS, DONLEY, FLOYD, FOARD, GRAY, HALL, HANSFORD, HARDEMAN, HARTLEY, HEMPHILL, HUTCHINSON, JACK, KING, KNOX, LIPSCOMB, MONTAGUE, MOORE, MOTLEY, OCHILTREE, OLDHAM, POTTER, RANDALL, ROBERTS, SHERMAN, SWISHER, WHEELER, WICHITA, WILBARGER, AND WISE (part). Population (2010), 703,835.

ZIP Codes: 73448, 73539, 73562, 73848–49, 76023, 76073, 76078, 76082, 76225, 76228, 76230, 76233–34, 76238–40, 76250–52, 76255, 76259, 76261, 76263, 76265–66, 76270–73, 76301–02, 76305–06, 76308–11, 76351, 76354, 76357, 76360, 76363–67, 76371, 76373–74, 76377, 76379–80, 76384, 76389, 76426–27, 76431, 76458–59, 76486–87, 79001, 79005, 79007, 79011, 79014–16, 79018–19, 79022, 79029, 79034, 79036, 79039–40, 79042, 79044–46, 79052, 79056–59, 79061–62, 79065, 79068, 79070, 79079–81, 79083–84, 79086–88, 79092, 79094–98, 79101–04, 79106–11, 79118–19, 79121, 79124, 79178, 79201, 79220, 79225–27, 79229–30, 79234–35, 79237, 79239–41, 79243–45, 79247–48, 79251–52, 79255–57, 79259, 79261, 79370, 79529

* * *

FOURTEENTH DISTRICT

RANDY WEBER, Republican, of Friendswood, TX; born in Pearland, TX, July 2, 1953; education: B.S., University of Houston, Clear Lake, 1977; professional: owner, Weber's Air and Heat, 1981–present; married: 1976; children: Kristin, Keith, and Kyle; grandchildren: six; committees: Foreign Affairs; Science, Space, and Technology; elected to the 113th Congress on November 6, 2012.

Office Listings

http://weber.house.gov https://www.facebook.com/txrandy14
https://twitter.com/txrandy14

510 Cannon House Office Building, Washington, DC 20515 .... (202) 225–2831
Chief of Staff.—Chara McMichael. FAX: 225–0271
Legislative Director.—Artur Suchorzewski.
Communications Director.—Courtney Weaver.
505 Orleans Street, Suite 103, Beaumont, TX 77701 .... (409) 835–0108
122 West Way Street, Suite 301, Lake Jackson, TX 77566 .... (979) 285–0231
174 Calder Road, Suite 150, League City, TX 77573 .... (281) 316–0231

Counties: BRAZORIA, GALVESTON, AND JEFFERSON. Population (2010), 705,051.

ZIP Codes: 77510, 77517–18, 77539, 77546, 77549–55, 77563, 77565, 77568, 77573–74, 77590–92, 77617, 77623, 77650

* * *

FIFTEENTH DISTRICT

RUBÉN E. HINOJOSA, Democrat, of Mercedes, TX; born in Edcouch, August 20, 1940; education: B.B.A., 1962, and M.B.A., 1980, University of Texas; professional: president and chief financial officer, H&H Foods, Inc.; elected member, Texas State Board of Education, 1975–84; board of directors, National Livestock and Meat Board and Texas Beef Industry Council, 1989–93; past president and chair of the board of directors, Southwestern Meat Packers Association; chair and member, board of trustees, South Texas Community College, 1993–96; past public member, Texas State Bar Board of Directors; former adjunct professor, Pan American University School of Business; past director, Rio Grande Valley Chamber of Commerce; Knapp Memorial Hospital Board of Trustees; Our Lady of Mercy Church Board of Catholic Advisors; past member, board of trustees, Mercedes Independent School District; former U.S. Jaycee Ambassador to Colombia and Ecuador; married: Martha; children: Ruben, Jr., Laura, Iliana, Kaitlin, and Karén; committees: Education and the Workforce; Financial Services; elected to the 105th Congress; reelected to each succeeding Congress.

Office Listings

http://www.hinojosa.house.gov https://www.facebook.com/congressmanrubenhinojosa
https://twitter.com/usreprhinojosa

2262 Rayburn House Office Building, Washington, DC 20515 .... (202) 225–2531
Chief of Staff.—Connie Humphrey. FAX: 225–5688
Policy Advisor.—Rosa Garcia.
Communications Director.—Patricia Guillermo.
2864 West Trenton Road, Edinburg, TX 78539 .... (956) 682–5545
District Director.—Cindy Garza.
100 South Austin Street, Seguin, TX 78155 .... (830) 401–0457
District Director.—Mark Gonzales.

Counties: BROOKS, DUVALL, GUADALUPE, HIDALGO (part), JIM HOGG, KARNES, WILSON, LIVE OAK, AND REFUGIO. CITIES AND TOWNSHIPS: Alamo, Alice, Donna, Edcouch, Edinburg, Elsa, Goliad, Harlingen, LaVilla, Las Milpas, Lopezville, Lull, Mathis, McAllen, Mercedes, Mission, Odem, Pharr, San Juan, Sinton, Taft, Three Rivers, Weslaco and Whitsett. Population (2010), 698,488.

ZIP Codes: 78022, 78060, 78071, 78075, 78108, 78111, 78113, 78116–17, 78119, 78121, 78123–24, 78130, 78140–41, 78144, 78151, 78155, 78341, 78349–50, 78353, 78355, 78357, 78360–61, 78376, 78383–84, 78501–02, 78504–05, 78516, 78537–43, 78549, 78557–58, 78560, 78562–63, 78565, 78570, 78572–74, 78576–77, 78579, 78589, 78595–96, 78599, 78638, 78648, 78655, 78666

* * *

SIXTEENTH DISTRICT

BETO O'ROURKE, Democrat, of TX; born in El Paso, El Paso County, TX, September 26, 1972; education: B.A., Columbia University, New York, NY, 1995; professional: business owner; member of the El Paso, Texas City Council, 2005–11; committees: Homeland Security; Veterans' Affairs; elected to 113th Congress on November 6, 2012.

Office Listings

http://www.orourke.house.gov

1721 Longworth House Office Building, Washington, DC 20515 .... (202) 225–4831
Chief of Staff.—David Wysong. FAX: 225–2016
Scheduler/Office Manager.—John Andrew Meza.
Legislative Director.—Jeff Hild.
303 North Oregon Street, Suite 210, El Paso, TX 79901 .... (915) 541–1400

Counties: EL PASO (part). Population (2010), 698,488.

ZIP Codes: 79901–06, 79908, 79911–12, 79915–16, 79920, 79922, 79924–25, 79930, 79932, 79934–36

* * *

SEVENTEENTH DISTRICT

WILLIAM H. "BILL" FLORES, Republican, of Bryan, TX; born at Warren Air Force Base, Cheyenne, WY, February 25, 1954; education: graduated, Stratford High School; Stratford, TX, 1972; B.B.A., *cum laude,* Texas A&M University, College Station, TX, 1976; M.B.A., Houston Baptist University, Houston, TX, 1985; Texas Certified Public Accountant (CPA), 1978–present; commissioner, Texas Real Estate Commission (appointed by Governor Perry), 2004–09; CEO and president, Phoenix Exploration Company, 2006–09; Texas A&M University Distinguished Alumnus, 2010; married: the former Gina Bass; children: Will and John; daughter-in-law, Aimee; granddaughter, Britain Grace; committees: Budget; Natural Resources; Veterans' Affairs; elected to the 112th Congress on November 2, 2010; reelected to the 113th Congress on November 6, 2012.

Office Listings

http://flores.house.gov

1030 Longworth House Office Building, Washington, DC 20515 .... (202) 225–6105
Chief of Staff.—Jeff Morehouse. FAX: 225–0350
Press Secretary.—Andre Castro.
400 Austin Avenue, Suite 302, Waco, TX 76701 .... (254) 732–0748
District Director.—Edward Getterman.
14205 Burnet Road, Suite 230, Austin, TX 78728 .... (512) 373–3378
3000 Briarcrest Drive, Suite 406, Bryan, TX 77802 .... (979) 703–4037
FAX: 691–8939

Counties: BRAZOS, BURLESON, FALLS, FREESTONE, LEE, LEON, LIMESTONE, MCLENNAN, MILAM, ROBERTSON, AND TRAVIS, (part). Population (2010), 710,793.

ZIP Codes: 75833, 75840, 75848, 75850, 75860, 76518, 76520, 76523, 76632, 76635, 76638, 76640, 76643, 76654, 76656, 76661, 76678, 76680, 76684, 76686, 76701–05, 76707–08, 76710–12, 76714–16, 76797–99, 77801–03, 77805–06, 77837–38, 77840–45, 77850, 77852–53, 77855–57, 77862–63, 77865–67, 77870, 77878–79, 77881–82, 78660, 78691, 78727–28, 78753, 78948

* * *

EIGHTEENTH DISTRICT

SHEILA JACKSON LEE, Democrat, of Houston, TX; born in Queens, NY, January 12, 1950; education: graduated, Jamaica High School; B.A., Yale University, New Haven, CT, 1972; J.D., University of Virginia Law School, 1975; professional: practicing attorney for twelve years; AKA Sorority; Houston Area Urban League; American Bar Association; staff counsel, U.S. House Select Committee on Assassinations, 1977–78; admitted to the Texas Bar, 1975; city council (at large), Houston, 1990–94; Houston Municipal Judge, 1987–90; married

Dr. Elwyn Cornelius Lee, 1973; two children: Erica Shelwyn and Jason Cornelius Bennett; committees: Homeland Security; Judiciary; elected to the 104th Congress; reelected to each succeeding Congress.

Office Listings

http://www.jacksonlee.house.gov

2160 Rayburn House Office Building, Washington, DC 20515 .... (202) 225–3816
Chief of Staff.—Glenn Rushing. FAX: 225–3317
Chief Counsel.—Gregory Berry.
Deputy Chief of Staff.—Shashrina Thomas.
Communications Director.—Mike McQuerry.
Scheduler.—Alem Tewoldeberhan.
Executive / Staff Assistant.—Sharef Al Najjar.
1919 Smith Street, Suite 1180, Houston, TX 77002 .... (713) 655–0050
District Director.—Deidra Rasheed.
Senior Field Representative / Caseworker.—Michael Halpin.
Executive Assistant.—Janice Weaver.
Caseworkers: Ivan Sanchez, Tonya Williams.
Account and Finance.—Michelle Donches.
420 West 19th Street, Houston, TX 77008 .... (713) 861–4070
6719 West Montgomery, Suite 204, Houston, Texas 77091 .... (713) 691–4882

Counties: HARRIS COUNTY (part). CITY OF: Houston. Population (2010), 698,488.

ZIP Codes: 77001–10, 77013, 77016, 77018–24, 77026, 77028–30, 77033, 77035, 77038, 77040–41, 77045, 77047–48, 77051–52, 77054–55, 77064, 77066–67, 77076, 77078, 77080, 77086–88, 77091–93, 77097–98, 77201–06, 77208, 77210, 77212, 77216, 77219, 77221, 77226, 77230, 77233, 77238, 77240–41, 77251–53, 77255, 77265–66, 77277, 77288, 77291–93, 77297–99

* * *

NINETEENTH DISTRICT

RANDY NEUGEBAUER, Republican, of Lubbock, TX; born in St. Louis, MO, December 24, 1949; education: Texas Tech University, 1972; professional: small businessman (home building industry); organizations: West Texas Home Builders Association; Land Use and Developers Council; Texas Association of Builders; National Association of Home Builders; Campus Crusade for Christ; public service: Lubbock City Council, 1992–98; served as Mayor Pro Tempore, 1994–96; leader, coalition to create the Ports-to-Plains Trade Corridor; awards: Lubbock Chamber of Commerce Distinguished Service Award; Reese Air Force Base Friend of Reese Award; religion: Baptist; married: Dana; two children; committees: Agriculture; Financial Services; Science, Space, and Technology; elected to the 108th Congress, by special election, on June 3, 2003; reelected to each succeeding Congress.

Office Listings

http://www.randy.house.gov https://www.facebook.com/re.randy.neugebauer?ref=hl
https://twitter.com/randyneugebauer

1424 Longworth House Office Building, Washington, DC 20515 .... (202) 225–4005
Chief of Staff.—Jeanette Whitener. FAX: 225–9615
Communications Director.—Heather Vaughan.
Legislative Director.—Emily Domenech.
Legislative Assistant.—Coleman Garrison.
Office Manager / Scheduler.—Melissa James.
Legislative Correspondent.—Libby Hambleton.
Staff Assistant.—Carole Richmond.
Federal Building, 611 University Avenue, Suite 220, Lubbock, TX 79401 .... (806) 763–1611
District Director.—Mitch Barnett.

Counties: BAILEY, BORDEN, CASTRO, COCHRAN, CROSBY, FISHER, FLOYD (part), GAINES, GARZA, HALE, HASKELL, HOCKLEY, HOWARD, JONES, KENT, LAMB, LUBBOCK, LYNN, NOLAN, PARMER, SCURRY, SHACKELFORD, STEPHENS (part), STONEWALL, TAYLOR, TERRY, THROCKMORTON, YOAKUM, AND YOUNG. Population (2010), 707,772.

ZIP Codes: 76372, 76374 (part), 76388, 76424 (part), 76429 (part), 76430, 76450 (part), 76460, 76464 (part), 76481, 76483, 76491, 79009, 79021, 79027, 79031–32, 79035 (part), 79041, 79042 (part), 79043, 79045 (part), 79052 (part), 79053, 79063–64, 79072 (part), 79082, 79085, 79088 (part), 79231, 79235 (part), 79241 (part), 79250, 79311–14, 79316, 79322–26, 79329, 79330, 79331 (part), 79336, 79339, 79342–47, 79350, 79351 (part), 79353, 79355–60, 79363–64, 79366–67, 79369, 79370 (part), 79371–73, 79376, 79378–82, 79401, 79403–04, 79406–07, 79410–16, 79423–24, 79501–03, 79504 (part), 79506 (part), 79508, 79511, 79512 (part), 79517–18, 79520–21, 79525–28, 79529 (part), 79530, 79532 (part), 79533–37, 79539, 79540, 79541 (part), 79543–49, 79553, 79556, 79560–63, 79566 (part), 79567 (part), 79601 (part), 79602 (part), 79603, 79605–07, 79699, 79713 (part), 79720 (part), 79733, 79738, 79748 (part)

* * *

TWENTIETH DISTRICT

JOAQUIN CASTRO, Democrat, of San Antonio, TX; born in San Antonio, September 16, 1974; education: Thomas Jefferson High School, 1992; B.A., Stanford University, CA, 1996; J.D., Harvard University, Cambridge, MA, 2000; professional: attorney; law instructor; religion: Catholic; family: wife, Anna Flores; caucuses: Congressional Hispanic Caucus; New Democrat Coalition; committees: Armed Services; Foreign Affairs; elected to the 113th Congress on November 6, 2012.

Office Listings

http://castro.house.gov https://www.facebook.com/joaquincastrotx
twitter: @joaquincastrotx

212 Cannon House Office Building, Washington, DC 20515 .... (202) 225–3236
Chief of Staff.—Carlos Sanchez. FAX: 225–1915
Scheduler.—Jocelyn Mund.
Legislative Director.—Claudia Urrabazo.
Legislative Assistant.—Ben Thomas.
Legislative Correspondents: Sandra Alcala, Hannah Katz.
National Security Advisor.—Danny Meza.
Press Secretary.—Laura Zapata.
4715 Fredericksburg Road, Suite 512, San Antonio, TX 78229 .... (210) 348–8216

Counties: BEXAR (part). CITIES: Alamo Heights, Balcones Heights, Lackland AFB, Helotes, Leon Valley, and San Antonio. Population (2010), 716,759.

ZIP Codes: 78023, 78073, 78201, 78204, 78207, 78209, 78211–14, 78216, 78221, 78224–31, 78236–38, 78240, 78242, 78245, 78249–57

* * *

TWENTY-FIRST DISTRICT

LAMAR S. SMITH, Republican, of San Antonio, TX; born in San Antonio, November 19, 1947; education: graduated, Texas Military Institute, San Antonio, 1965; B.A., Yale University, New Haven, CT, 1969; intern, Small Business Administration, Washington, DC, 1969–70; business and financial writer, *The Christian Science Monitor*, Boston, MA, 1970–72; J.D., Southern Methodist University School of Law, Dallas, TX, 1975; admitted to the State Bar of Texas, 1975, and commenced practice in San Antonio with the firm of Maebius and Duncan, Inc.; elected chairman of the Republican Party of Bexar County, TX, 1978 and 1980; elected District 57–F State Representative, 1981; elected Precinct 3 Commissioner of Bexar County, 1982 and 1984; partner, Lamar Seeligson Ranch, Jim Wells County, TX; married: Beth Schaefer; children: Nell and Tobin; committees: chair, Science, Space, and Technology; Judiciary; Homeland Security; elected to the 100th Congress on November 4, 1986; reelected to each succeeding Congress.

Office Listings

http://lamarsmith.house.gov

2409 Rayburn House Office Building, Washington, DC 20515 .... (202) 225–4236
Chief of Staff.—Jennifer Brown. FAX: 225–8628
Legislative Director / Scheduler.—Ashlee Vinyard.
The Tetco Center, 1100 North East Loop 410, Suite 640, San Antonio, TX 78207 (210) 821–5024
District Director.—Mike Asmus.
2211 IH 35 South, Suite 106, Austin, TX 78741 .... (512) 912–7508
301 Junction Highway, Suite 346C, Kerrville, TX 78028 .... (830) 896–0154

Counties: BANDERA, BEXAR (part), BLANCO, COMAL (part), KENDALL, KERR, REAL, TRAVIS (part), GILLESPIE, AND HAYS (part). Population (2010), 698,488.

ZIP Codes: 78003, 78006, 78010, 78013, 78015, 78024–25, 78027–29, 78055, 78058, 78063, 78070, 78130–33, 78135, 78148, 78163, 78209, 78212–13, 78216–18, 78230–33, 78239, 78241, 78247, 78258–59, 78261, 78265–66, 78270, 78606, 78610, 78618–20, 78623–24, 78631, 78635–36, 78641, 78645, 78652, 78663, 78666, 78669, 78675–76, 78726, 78730–39, 78741, 78746, 78748–50, 78759, 78883, 78885

* * *

TWENTY-SECOND DISTRICT

PETE OLSON, Republican, of Sugar Land, TX; born in Fort Lewis, WA, December 9, 1962; education: B.A., Rice University, Houston, TX, 1985; Law Degree, University of Texas, Austin, TX, 1988; United States Navy, 1988–98; United States Senate, 1998–2007; Naval Aviator wings, 1991; Naval Liaison United States Senate; religion: United Methodist; married: Nancy Olson; children: Kate and Grant; committees: Energy and Commerce; elected to the 111th Congress on November 4, 2008; reelected to each succeeding Congress.

Office Listings

http://olson.house.gov

312 Cannon House Office Building, Washington, DC 20515 .... (202) 225–5951
Chief of Staff.—Steve Ruhlen. FAX: 225–5241
Legislative Director.—Sarah Whiting.
Communications Director.—Melissa Kelly.
Scheduler.—Kathy Calderon.
1650 Highway 6, Suite 150, Sugarland, TX 77478 .... (281) 494–2690
District Director.—Tyler Nelson.
6302 West Broadway Street, Suite 220, Pearland, TX 77581 .... (281) 485–4855

Counties: BRAZORIA, FORT BEND, AND HARRIS (part). CITIES OF: Alvin, Arcola, Beasley, Brookside Village, Fulshear, Frendsword, Katy, Missouri City, Manvel, Needville, Orchard, Pleak, Pearland, Richmond, Rosenberg, Sugar Land, Simonton, Stafford, Villages of Fairchild, Webster and Weston Lakes. Population (2010), 698,504.

ZIP Codes: 77058, 77062, 77089, 77406–07, 77417, 77441, 77450–51, 77459, 77461, 77464, 77469, 77471, 77476–79, 77481, 77489, 77494, 77498, 77545–46, 77571, 77578, 77581, 77583–84, 77598

* * *

TWENTY-THIRD DISTRICT

PETE P. GALLEGO, Democrat, of Alpine; born in Alpine, TX, December 2, 1961; education: attended public schools in Alpine, TX; B.A., political science, Sul Ross State University, Alpine, TX, 1982; J.D., The University of Texas at Austin, Austin, TX, 1985; professional: attorney since 1986; Assistant Attorney General of Texas; Assistant and First Assistant District Attorney, 83rd Judicial District of Texas; Of Counsel, Davis & Wilkerson, PC; Of Counsel, Brown McCarroll, LLC; private practice; elected official: Texas House of Representatives, 1991–2013; religion: Roman Catholic; spouse: María Elena Ramón; children: Nicolás Miguel Ramón Gallego; committees: Agriculture; Armed Services; elected to the 113th Congress on November 6, 2012.

Office Listings

http://www.gallego.house.gov https://twitter.com/reppetegallego
https://www.facebook.com/congressmanpetegallego

431 Cannon House Office Building, Washington, DC 20515 .... (202) 225–4511
Chief of Staff.—René Muñoz. FAX: 225–2237
Legislative Director.—Steven Snodgrass.
Administration Director.—Michael Pacheco.
Communications Director.—José Borjón.
Legislative Assistant.—Xenia Ruiz.
Legislative Correspondents: Jordan Fahle, Emily German.
1714 Southwest Military Drive, Suite 110, San Antonio, TX 78221 .... (210) 927–4592
FAX: 927–4903
124 South Horizon Boulevard, Socorro, TX 79927 .... (915) 872–1066
1915 Veterans Boulevard, Del Rio, TX 78840 .... (830) 488–6600
100 South Monroe Street, Eagle Pass, TX 78852 .... (830) 488–6600

Counties: BEXAR (part), BREWSTER, CRANE, CROCKETT, CULBERSON, DIMMIT, EDWARDS, EL PASO (part), FRIO, HUDSPETH, JEFF DAVIS, KINNEY, LA SALLE (part), LOVING, MAVERICK, MEDINA, PECOS, PRESIDIO, REAGAN, REEVES, SCHLEICHER, SUTTON, TERRELL, UPTON, UVALDE, VAL VERDE, WARD, WINKLER, AND ZAVALA. Population (2010), 698,488.

ZIP Codes: 76841, 76932, 76935–36, 76943, 76950, 78001–03, 78005–06, 78009, 78014–17, 78019, 78021, 78023, 78039, 78052, 78056–57, 78059, 78061, 78066, 78069, 78073, 78112, 78211, 78214, 78220–24, 78227, 78230–32, 78236, 78245, 78248–49, 78251–58, 78260, 78264, 78801–02, 78827–30, 78832–34, 78836–40, 78843, 78850–52, 78860–61, 78870–73, 78877, 78879–81, 78884, 78886, 79718–19, 79730–31, 79734–35, 79739, 79742–45, 79752, 79754–56, 79766, 79770, 79772, 79777–78, 79780–81, 79785, 79788–89, 79830–31, 79834, 79836–39, 79842–43, 79845–49, 79851–55, 79907, 79927–28, 79938, 79942, 88220

* * *

TWENTY-FOURTH DISTRICT

KENNY MARCHANT, Republican, of Coppell, TX; born in Bonham, TX, February 23, 1951; education: B.A., Southern Nazarene University, Bethany, OK, 1974; attended Nazarene Theological Seminary, Kansas City, MO, 1975–76; professional: real estate developer; member of the Carrollton, TX, city council, 1980–84; mayor of Carrollton, TX, 1984–87; member of the Texas State House of Representatives, 1987–2004; member, Advisory Board of Children's Medical Center; married: Donna; four children; committees: Education and the Workforce; Ways and Means; elected to the 109th Congress on November 2, 2004; reelected to each succeeding Congress.

Office Listings

http://www.house.gov/marchant https://www.facebook.com/repkennymarchant
https://twitter.com/repkenmarchant

1110 Longworth House Office Building, Washington, DC 20515 .... (202) 225–6605
Chief of Staff.—Brian Thomas. FAX: 225–0074
Legislative Director / Scheduler.—Scott Cunningham.
9901 East Valley Ranch Parkway, Suite 3035, Irving, TX 75063 .... (972) 556–0162
District Director.—Susie Miller.

Counties: DALLAS (part), DENTON (part), TARRANT (part). CITIES AND TOWNSHIPS: Addison, Bedford, Carrollton, Colleyville, Coppell, Dallas, Euless, Farmer's Branch, Fort Worth, Grapevine, Hurst, Irving, Lewisville, Plano, Southlake, and The Colony. Population (2010), 698,488.

ZIP Codes: 75001, 75006–07, 75010–11, 75014, 75016, 75019, 75022, 75024, 75028, 75038–39, 75056, 75061–63, 75067, 75093, 75099, 75209, 75220, 75229–30, 75234, 75240, 75244, 75248, 75252, 75254, 75261, 75287, 75354, 75368, 75379–81, 75391, 76021–22, 76034, 76039–40, 76051, 76053–54, 76092, 76095, 76099, 76118, 76120, 76155, 76180, 76182, 76248, 76262

* * *

TWENTY-FIFTH DISTRICT

ROGER WILLIAMS, Republican, of Austin, TX; born in Evanston, IL, September 13, 1949; education: graduated, Arlington Heights High School; B.S., Texas Christian University, Fort Worth, 1972; professional: drafted by the Atlanta Braves Organization; owner Roger Williams Car Dealerships; 105th Secretary of State of Texas, 2004–07; regional finance chair for Governor Bush, 1994, 1998; North Texas chairman for the Bush / Cheney 2000 campaign; North Texas finance chairman and national grassroots fundraising chairman for Bush / Cheney 2004, Inc.; appointed chairman of the Republican National Finance Committee's Eagles program by President George W. Bush, 2001; state finance chair for John Cornyn for U.S. Senate, Inc., 2002; chief liaison for Texas Border and Mexican Affairs, 2005; chair of the Texas Base Realignment and Closure Response Strike Force; boards: Texas Christian University Board of Trustees; National Football Foundation; College Football Hall of Fame; religion: member, University Christian Church; married: Patty Williams; children: Sabrina and Jaclyn; committees: Budget; Transportation and Infrastructure; elected to the 113th Congress on November 6, 2012.

Office Listings

http://www.williams.house.gov

1122 Longworth House Office Building, Washington, DC 20515 .... (202) 225–9896
Chief of Staff.—Colby Hale. FAX: 225–9692
Deputy Chief.—Spencer Freebairn.
Legislative Director.—Sean Dillon.
Press Secretary.—Haley Graves.
Scheduler.—Vera Minter.
1005 Congress Avenue, Suite 925, Austin, TX 78701 .... (512) 473–8910
District Director.—John Etue. FAX: 473–8946
1 Walnut Street, Suite 145, Cleburne, TX 76033 .... (817) 774–2575
Case Worker.—Robert Camacho. FAX: 774–2577

Counties: BELL (part), BOSQUE, BURNET, CORYELL, ERATH (part), HAMILTON, HAYS (part), HILL, JOHNSON, LAMPASAS, SOMERVELL, TARRANT (part), AND TRAVIS (part). Population (2010), 698,478.

ZIP Codes: 76009, 76028, 76031, 76033, 76035–36, 76043–44, 76048–49, 76050, 76055, 76058–59, 76063, 76070, 76077, 76084, 76093, 76401–02, 76433, 76436, 76446, 76457, 76522, 76525, 76526–28, 76531, 76538–39, 76544, 76549–50, 76557, 76561, 76565–66, 76621–22, 76627, 76631, 76633–34, 76636–38, 76645, 76648–49, 76652, 76657, 76660,

76665–66, 76671, 76673, 76676, 76689–90, 76692, 76853, 76877, 76880, 78605, 78608, 78610–11, 78613, 78619–20, 78623, 78639, 78641–42, 78645, 78652, 78654, 78657, 78666, 78669, 78676, 78701–03, 78705, 78712, 78721–25, 78730–34, 78736–39, 78745–46, 78749–50

* * *

TWENTY-SIXTH DISTRICT

MICHAEL C. BURGESS, Republican, of Denton County, TX; born, December 23, 1950; education: Bachelor and Masters degrees in physiology, North Texas State University, M.D., University of Texas medical school in Houston; Masters degree in Medical Management, University of Texas in Dallas; completed medical residency programs, Parkland Hospital in Dallas; professional: founder, Private Practice Specialty Group for Obstetrics and Gynecology; former Chief of Staff and Chief of Obstetrics, Lewisville Medical Center; organizations: former president, Denton County Medical Society; Denton County delegate, Texas Medical Association; alternate delegate, American Medical Association; married: Laura; three children; committees: Energy and Commerce; Rules; elected to the 108th Congress on November 5, 2002; reelected to each succeeding Congress.

Office Listings

http://www.burgess.house.gov http://www.facebok.com/michaelcburgess
twitter: @michaelcburgess

2336 Rayburn House Office Building, Washington, DC 20515 .... (202) 225–7772
Chief of Staff.—Kelle Strickland. FAX: 225–2919
Legislative Director.—James Decker.
Press Secretary.—Bruce Harvie.
Scheduler.—Amanda Stevens.
1660 South Stemmons Freeway, Suite 230, Lewisville, TX 75067 .... (972) 434–9700

Counties: DALLAS (part), DENTON (part), TARRANT (part). Population (2010) 698,488.

ZIP Codes: 75009, 75019, 75022, 75027–29, 75033–34, 75056–57, 75065, 75067–68, 75077–78, 76034, 76052, 76065, 76078, 76092, 76117, 76137, 76148, 76177, 76180, 76182, 76201–10, 76226–27, 76234, 76244, 76247–49, 76258–59, 76262

* * *

TWENTY-SEVENTH DISTRICT

BLAKE FARENTHOLD, Republican, of Corpus Christi, TX; born in Corpus Christi, December 12, 1961; education: B.S., radio television, and film, University of Texas, Austin, TX, 1985; J.D., St. Mary's University of Law School, San Antonio, TX, 1989; professional: lawyer, private practice; business owner; committees: Judiciary; Oversight and Government Reform; Transportation and Infrastructure; elected to the 112th Congress on November 2, 2010; reelected to the 113th Congress on November 6, 2012.

Office Listings

http://www.farenthold.house.gov

2110 Rayburn House Office Building, Washington, DC 20515 .... (202) 225–7742
Chief of Staff.—Beau Rothschild. FAX: 226–1134
Executive Assistant/Scheduling.—Emily Wilkes.
Legislative Director.—Blake Adami.
Communications Director.—Meaghan Cronin.
101 North Shoreline Boulevard, Suite 300, Corpus Christi, TX 78401 .... (361) 884–2222
5606 North Navarro Street, Suite 203, Victoria, TX 77904 .... (361) 894–6446

Counties: ARANSAS, BASTROP, CALDWELL, CALHOUN, GONZALES, LAVACA, WHARTON, MATAGORDA, JACKSON, VICTORIA, REFUGIO, NUECES, AND SAN PATRICIO. Population (2010), 702,804.

ZIP Codes: 77404, 77414–15, 77419–20, 77428, 77432, 77435–37, 77440, 77443, 77448, 77453–58, 77465, 77467–68, 77482–83, 77488, 77901–05, 77950–51, 77957, 77961–62, 77964, 77968–71, 77973, 77975–79, 77982–84, 77986–88, 77990–91, 77995, 78330, 78335–36, 78339–40, 78343, 78347, 78351–52, 78358–59, 78362, 78368, 78370, 78373–74, 78377, 78380–82, 78387, 78390, 78393, 78401–19, 78426–27, 78460, 78463, 78465–69, 78472, 78480, 78602, 78612, 78614, 78616, 78629, 78632, 78648, 78655–56, 78658, 78661–62, 78953, 78957

* * *

TWENTY-EIGHTH DISTRICT

HENRY CUELLAR, Democrat, of Laredo, TX; born in Laredo, September 19, 1955; education: Associate's Degree from Laredo Community College, Laredo, TX, 1976 (then known as Laredo Junior College); B.S., *cum laude*, foreign service from the Edmund A. Walsh School of Foreign Service at Georgetown University, Washington, DC, 1978; J.D., University of Texas, Austin, TX, 1981; M.B.A., international trade, from Texas A&M University, Laredo, TX, 1982; Ph.D., government, University of Texas, Austin, TX, 1998; with a total of five advanced degrees, Congressman Cuellar is the most degreed member of Congress; professional: lawyer, private practice; attorney, Law Office of Henry Cuellar, 1981–present; instructor, Department of Government, Laredo Community College, Laredo, TX, 1982–86; Licensed United States Customs Broker, 1983–present; adjunct professor, International Commercial Law, Texas A&M International, 1984–86; Representative, Texas State House of Representatives, 1986–2001; Secretary of State, State of Texas, 2001; public and civic organizations: board of directors, Kiwanis Club of Laredo, TX, 1982–83; co-founder/president, Laredo Volunteers Lawyers Program, Inc., 1982–83; board of directors, United Way, 1982–83; co-founder/treasurer, Stop Child Abuse and Neglect, 1982–83, and advisory board member, 1984; president, board of directors, Laredo Legal Aid Society, Inc., 1982–84; president, board of directors, Laredo Young Lawyers Association, 1983–84; sustaining member, Texas Democratic Party, 1984; legal advisor, American GI, local chapter, 1986–87; International Trade Association, Laredo State University, 1988; Texas Delegate, National Democratic Convention, 1992; president, board of directors, International Good Neighbor Council; member, The College of the State Bar of Texas, 1994; Texas Lyceum, 1997; policy board of advisors, Texas Hispanic Journal of Law, University of Texas Law School, 2002; member: American Bar Association; Inter-American Bar Association; Texas Bar Association; Webb/Laredo Bar Association; recipient of various awards; vice chairman of the Steering and Policy Committee; Congressional Unmanned Systems Caucus, Senior Whip; member of the Blue Dog Coalition; religion: Catholic; married: wife, Imelda; two daughters, Christina Alexandra and Catherine Ann; committees: Appropriations; elected to the 109th Congress on November 2, 2004; reelected to each succeeding Congress.

Office Listings

http://www.cuellar.house.gov twitter: @repcuellar
https://www.facebook.com/pages/us-congressman-henry-cuellar-tx-28/152569121550

2431 Rayburn House Office Building, Washington, DC 20515 .... (202) 225–1640
Chief of Staff.—Cynthia Gaona. FAX: 225–1641
Legislative Director.—Megan Swearingen.
Scheduler.—Meghan Gannon.
615 East Houston Street, Suite 451, San Antonio, TX 78205 .... (210) 271–2851
602 East Calton Road, Suite 2, Laredo, TX 78041 .... (956) 725–0639
FAX: 725–2647
117 East Tom Landry, Mission, TX 78572 .... (956) 424–3942
FAX: 424–3936
100 North F.M. 3167, Rio Grande City, Texas 78582 .... (956) 487–5603
FAX: 488–0952
615 East Houston Street, Suite 563, San Antonio, TX 78205 .... (210) 271–2851
FAX: 277–6671

Counties: ATASCOSA, BEXAR (part), HIDALGO (part), LA SALLE (part), MCMULLEN, STARR, WEBB, WILSON (part), AND ZAPATA. Population (2010), 698,488.

ZIP Codes: 78005, 78007, 78011–12, 78019, 78021, 78026, 78040–41, 78043, 78045–46, 78050, 78062, 78064–65, 78067, 78072, 78076, 78108, 78112–14, 78121, 78147, 78150, 78152, 78154, 78161, 78263, 78344, 78360–61, 78369, 78371, 78545, 78548, 78557, 78560, 78565, 78572–74, 78576, 78582, 78584–85, 78591, 78595

* * *

TWENTY-NINTH DISTRICT

GENE GREEN, Democrat, of Houston, TX; born in Houston, October 17, 1947; education: B.A., University of Houston, 1971; J.D., University of Houston Bates College of Law, 1977; admitted, Texas Bar, 1977; professional: business manager; attorney; Texas State Representative, 1973–85; Texas State Senator, 1985–92; member: Houston Bar Association; Texas Bar Association; American Bar Association; Communications Workers of America; Aldine Optimist Club; Gulf Coast Conservation Association; Lindale Lions Club; Texas Historical Society; Texas State Society; co-chair, Democratic Israel Working Group; co-chair, Natural Gas Caucus; co-chair, Tuberculosis Caucus; Traumatic Brain Injury Task Force; Bi-Cameral Congressional

Caucus on Parkinson's Disease; Community College Caucus; Congressional Steel Caucus; National Marine Sanctuary Caucus; National Wildlife Refuge Caucus; Pell Grant Caucus; Recycling Caucus; Sportsmen's Caucus; Urban Caucus; Victim's Rights Caucus; co-chair, Vision Caucus; Democratic Senior Whip; married: Helen Albers, January 23, 1970; children: Angela and Christopher; committees: Energy and Commerce; elected on November 3, 1992, to the 103rd Congress; reelected to each succeeding Congress.

Office Listings

http://www.house.gov/green

2470 Rayburn House Office Building, Washington, DC 20515 .... (202) 225–1688
Legislative Director.—Nathaniel Tipton. FAX: 225–9903
Press Secretary.—Sharlett Mena.
Legislative Assistants: Justin Ackley, Sergio Espinosa, Kristen O'Neill.
Scheduler.—Sharlett Mena.
256 North Sam Houston Parkway East, Suite 29, Houston, TX 77060 .... (281) 999–5879
Chief of Staff / Administrative Assistant.—Rhonda Jackson.
11811 Interstate–10 East, Suite 430, Houston, TX 77029 .... (713) 330–0761

Counties: HARRIS (part). CITIES AND TOWNSHIPS: Channelview, Galena Park, Houston, Humble, Jacinto City, Pasadena, and South Houston. Population (2010), 698,488.

ZIP Codes: 77003, 77009, 77011–13, 77015–17, 77020, 77022–23, 77026, 77029, 77032, 77034, 77037, 77039, 77044, 77049–50, 77060–61, 77075–76, 77087, 77089, 77091, 77093, 77396, 77502–06, 77530, 77536, 77547, 77587

* * *

THIRTIETH DISTRICT

EDDIE BERNICE JOHNSON, Democrat, of Dallas, TX; born in Waco, TX, December 3, 1935; education: nursing diploma, St. Mary's at Notre Dame, 1955; B.S., nursing, Texas Christian, 1967; M.P.A., Southern Methodist, 1976; proprietor, Eddie Bernice Johnson and Associates consulting and airport concession management; Texas House of Representatives, 1972–77; Carter Administration appointee, 1977–81; Texas State Senate, 1986–92; NABTP Mickey Leland Award for Excellence in Diversity, 2000; National Association of School Nurses, Inc., Legislative Award, 2000; the State of Texas Honorary Texan issued by the Governor of Texas, 2000; Links, Inc., Co-Founders Award, 2000; 100 Black Men of America, Inc., Woman of the Year, 2001; National Black Caucus of State Legislators Image Award, 2001; National Conference of Black Mayors, Inc. President's Award, 2001; Alpha Kappa Alpha Trailblazer, 2002; Thurgood Marshall Scholarship Community Leader, 2002; Phi Beta Sigma Fraternity Woman of the Year, 2002; CBCF Outstanding Leadership, 2002; congressional caucuses: Asian-Pacific; Airpower; Army; Arts; Biomedical Research; chair (107th Congress), Congressional Black Caucus; Children's Working Group; co-chair, Task Force on International HIV / AIDS; Fire Services; Human Rights Caucus; Korean Caucus; Livable Communities Task Force; Medical Technology; Oil & Gas Educational Forum; Singapore Caucus; Study Group on Japan; Tex-21 Transportation Caucus; Urban; Womens' Caucus; Women's Issues; member: St. John Baptist Church, Dallas; children: Dawrence Kirk; grandchildren: Kirk, Jr., David and James; committees: ranking member, Science, Space, and Technology; Transportation and Infrastructure; elected on November 3, 1992, to the 103rd Congress; reelected to each succeeding Congress.

Office Listings

http://www.ebjohnson.house.gov

2468 Rayburn House Office Building, Washington, DC 20515 .... (202) 225–8885
Chief of Staff / Legislative Director.—Murat Gokcigdem. FAX: 226–1477
Communications Director.—Cameron Trimble.
Legislative Assistants: Justin Maturo, Carrie Palmer, Bradley Watson.
Staff Assistant.—Nawaid Ladak.
3102 Maple Avenue, Suite 600, Dallas, TX 75201 .... (214) 922–8885
District Director.—Rod Givens.

Counties: DALLAS (part). CITIES AND TOWNSHIPS: Downtown Dallas, Fair Park, Kessler Park, Old East Dallas, Pleasant Grove, South Dallas and South Oak Cliff; all of Cedar Hill, DeSoto, Duncanville, Hutchins, Lancaster and Wilmer and parts of Ferris, Glenn Heights, South Grand Prairie, Oak Lawn, Ovilla, Uptown / Victory Park and West Dallas. Population (2010), 698,487.

ZIP Codes: 75051–52, 75054, 75115–16, 75125, 75134, 75137, 75141, 75146, 75149–50, 75154, 75159, 75172, 75180, 75201–04, 75207–12, 75214–20, 75223–28, 75232–33, 75235–37, 75241, 75246–47, 75249, 75253, 75270

* * *

THIRTY-FIRST DISTRICT

JOHN R. CARTER, Republican, of Round Rock, TX; born in Houston, TX, November 6, 1941; education: Texas Tech University, 1964; University of Texas Law School, 1969; professional: attorney; private law practice; public service: appointed and elected a Texas District Court Judge, 1981–2001; awards: recipient and namesake of the Williamson County ''John R. Carter Lifetime Achievement Award''; family: married to Erika Carter; children: Gilianne, John, Theodore, and Erika Danielle; committees: Appropriations; elected to the 108th Congress on November 5, 2002; reelected to each succeeding Congress.

Office Listings

http://www.carter.house.gov

409 Cannon House Office Building, Washington, DC 20515 .... (202) 225–3864
Chief of Staff.—Jonas Miller. FAX: 225–5886
Deputy Chief of Staff.—William Zito.
Communications Director.—Sara Threadgill.
Scheduler.—Holly Noles.
1717 North IH 35, Suite 303, Round Rock, TX 78664 .... (512) 246–1600
6544B South General Bruce Drive, Temple, TX 76502 .... (254) 933–1392

Counties: BELL AND WILLIAMSON. Population (2010), 739,975.

ZIP Codes: 76501, 76504, 76511, 76513, 76527, 76530, 76534, 76537, 76542–43, 76548–49, 76557, 76559, 76569, 76571, 76574, 76578, 78613, 78615, 78621, 78628, 78633–34, 78641–42, 78664–65, 78681, 78717, 78728–29

* * *

THIRTY-SECOND DISTRICT

PETE SESSIONS, Republican, of Dallas, TX; born in Waco, TX, March 22, 1955; education: B.S., in social sciences, political science, Southwestern University, Georgetown, TX, 1978; professional: worked for Southwestern Bell, and Bell Communications Research (formerly Bell Labs), 1978–94; vice president for public policy, National Center for Policy Analysis, 1994–95; board member, White Rock YMCA; trustee, Southwestern University; member, National Eagle Scout Association's national committee; advisor to president, Special Olympics Texas; past chairman, East Dallas Chamber of Commerce; awards: Honorary Doctorate, Dallas Baptist University; National Distinguished Eagle Scout Award; Boy Scouts of America; Leadership Award, American College of Emergency Physicians; Spirit of Enterprise Award, U.S. Chamber of Commerce; Best and Brightest, American Conservative Union; Guardian of Small Business Award, National Federation of Independent Business; Taxpayers' Friend Award, National Taxpayers Union; National Leadership Award, National Down Syndrome Society; Champion of Healthcare Innovation Award, Healthcare Leadership Council; Wireless Industry Achievement Award, Cellular Telecommunications and Internet Association; religion: Methodist; married: Karen Sessions; two sons: Bill and Alex; three stepsons: Conor, Liam and Nicholas; chairman, House Committee on Rules; former chairman, National Republican Congressional Committee; co-chairman, Congressional Down Syndrome Caucus; co-chairman, Congressional Missile Defense Caucus; committees: Rules; elected on November 5, 1996, to the 105th Congress; reelected to each succeeding Congress.

Office Listings

http://sessions.house.gov http://www.flickr.com/photos/petesessions
https://www.facebook.com/petesessions https://twitter.com/petesessions

2233 Rayburn House Office Building, Washington, DC 20515 .... (202) 225–2231
Chief of Staff.—Lee Padilla. FAX: 225–5878
Communications Director.—Torrie Miller.
Legislative Director.—Lindsay Pitts.
Park Central VII, 12750 Merit Drive, Suite 1434, Dallas, TX 75251 .... (972) 392–0505
Chief of Staff.—Taylor Bledsoe.

County: DALLAS (part) AND COLLIN (part). CITIES AND TOWNSHIPS: DALLAS, RICHARDSON, UNIVERSITY PARK, HIGHLAND PARK, MESQUITE, GARLAND, SACHSE, ROWLETT AND WYLIE. Population (2010), 698,488.

ZIP Codes: 75002, 75040–44, 75048, 75080–82, 75088–89, 75094, 75098, 75150, 75166, 75182, 75201, 75204–06, 75209, 75214, 75218–19, 75223, 75225–26, 75229–31, 75235, 75238, 75243–46, 75248, 75251–52

* * *

THIRTY-THIRD DISTRICT

MARC VEASEY, Democrat, of Fort Worth, TX; born in Fort Worth, January 3, 1971; education: B.S., Texas Wesleyan University, Fort Worth, TX, 1995; professional: journalist; staff, U.S. Representative J. Martin Frost of Texas; real estate broker; Texas State Representative, 2004–12; religion: Christian; married: Tonya Veasey; children: Adam Veasey; commissions, caucuses: Congressional Black Caucus; LGBT Equality Caucus; committees: Armed Services; Science, Space, and Technology; elected to the 113th Congress on November 6, 2012.

Office Listings

http://www.house.gov/veasey www.facebook.com/congressmanmarcveasey
twitter: @repveasey

414 Cannon House Office Building, Washington, DC 20515 .... (202) 225–9897
Chief of Staff.—Jane Hamilton. FAX: 225–9702
Legislative Director.—Chris Kelley.
Communications Director.—Jessica Coscia.
Executive Assistant / Scheduler.—Jane Phipps.
Legislative Assistants: Jared Hawes, Ashley Baker.
Legislative Correspondent.—Nelly Decker.
Staff Assistant.—Morgan Edwards.
4200 South Freeway, Suite 412, Fort Worth, TX 76115 .... (817) 920–9086
District Director.—Anne Hagan.
1881 Sylvan Avenue, Suite 108, Dallas, TX 75208 .... (214) 741–1387

Counties: DALLAS (part) AND TARRANT (part). CITIES AND TOWNSHIPS: Everman; Cockrell Hill; parts of Dallas, Irving, Grand Prairie, Arlington, Forest Hill, Fort Worth, Haltom City, Saginaw, and Sansom Park. Population: (2010), 698,488.

ZIP Codes: 75050–52, 75060–62, 75203, 75208, 75211–12, 75216, 75220, 75224, 75229, 75233–36, 75247, 76006, 76010–12, 76014, 76103–07, 76109–12, 76114–15, 76117–20, 76133–34, 76137, 76140, 76155, 76164, 76179

* * *

THIRTY-FOURTH DISTRICT

FILEMON VELA, Democrat, of Brownsville, TX, born in Harlingen, TX, February 13, 1963; education: B.A., Georgetown University, 1985; J.D., University of Texas at Austin School of Law, 1987; professional: attorney; admitted, Texas Bar and U.S. District Court, Western and Southern Districts of Texas, 1988; married: Rose Rivera, February 3, 1990; caucus: co-chair, Border Caucus; New Democrat Network; co-chair, Congressional LNG Export Caucus; Community Health Center Caucus; Diabetes Caucus; Disaster Relief Caucus; General Aviation Caucus; Texas Caucus on Shale Oil & Gas; TX–21 Transportation Congressional Caucus; Texas Maritime Caucus; Democratic Whip Fiscal Working Group; Democratic National Security Working Group; Democratic Whip Task Force on Poverty and Opportunity; committees: Agriculture; Homeland Security; elected to the 113th Congress on November 6, 2012.

Office Listings

http://www.house.gov/vela

437 Cannon House Office Building, Washington, DC 20515 .... (202) 225–9901
Chief of Staff.—Perry Brody.
Scheduler.—Liza Lynch.
333 Ebony Avenue, Brownsville, TX 78520 .... (956) 544–8352
District Director.—Marisela Cortez.
Press Aide.—Brenda Lopez.
500 East Main Street, Alice, TX 78332 .... (956) 544–8352
District Director.—Jose Pereida.
1390 West Expressway 83, San Benito, TX 78586 .... (956) 544–8352
District Director.—Humberto Garza.

Counties: BEE, CAMERON, DEWITT, GOLIAD, GONZALES, HIDALGO, JIM WELLS, KENEDY, KLEBERG, SAN PATRICIO, WILLACY. Population (2010), 716,416.

ZIP Codes: 77954, 77960, 77963, 77993–94, 78104, 78107, 78122, 78125, 78142, 78145–46, 78159, 78162, 78164, 78338, 78342, 78363, 78375, 78379, 78385, 78389, 78391, 78520–21, 78526, 78535, 78550, 78552, 78559, 78561, 78566–67, 78575, 78578–80, 78583, 78586, 78590, 78592–94, 78597–98, 78614, 78677

* * *

THIRTY-FIFTH DISTRICT

LLOYD DOGGETT, Democrat, of Austin, TX; born in Austin, October 6, 1946; education: graduated, Austin High School; B.B.A., University of Texas, Austin, 1967; J.D., University of Texas, 1970; president, University of Texas Student Body; associate editor, *Texas Law Review;* Outstanding Young Lawyer, Austin Association of Young Lawyers; president, Texas Consumer Association; religion: member, First United Methodist Church; admitted to the Texas State Bar, 1971; Texas State Senate, 1973-85, elected at age 26; Senate author of 124 state laws and Senate sponsor of 63 House bills enacted into law; elected president pro tempore of Texas Senate; served as acting governor; named Outstanding Young Texan by Texas Jaycees; Arthur B. DeWitty Award for outstanding achievement in human rights, Austin NAACP; honored for work by Austin Rape Crisis Center, Planned Parenthood of Austin; Austin Chapter, American Institute of Architects; Austin Council on Alcoholism; Disabled American Veterans; justice on Texas Supreme Court, 1989-94; chairman, Supreme Court Task Force on Judicial Ethics, 1992–94; Outstanding Judge (Mexican-American Bar of Texas), 1993; adjunct professor, University of Texas School of Law, 1989-94; James Madison Award, Texas Freedom of Information Foundation, 1990; First Amendment Award, National Society of Professional Journalists, 1990; member; Democratic Caucus Task Force on Education; Congressional Task Force on Tobacco and Health; Democratic Caucus Task Force on Child Care; married: Libby Belk Doggett, 1969; children: Lisa and Cathy; committees: Ways and Means, elected to the 104th Congress; reelected to each succeeding Congress.

Office Listings

http://www.house.gov/doggett https://twitter.com/repllloyddoggett
https://www.facebook.com/lloyddoggett

201 Cannon House Office Building, Washington, DC 20515 .... (202) 225–4865
Chief of Staff.—Michael J. Mucchetti. FAX: 225–3073
Digital Communications Specialist.—Elisa Santana.
Press Secretary.—Kelsey Crow.
Staff Assistant / Scheduler.—Christina Puder.
217 West Travis, San Antonio, TX 78205 .... (210) 704–1080
District Director.—Andrew Solano.
300 East 8th Street, Suite 763, Austin, TX 78701 .... (512) 916–5921

Counties: BEXAR, COMAL, GUADALUPE, CALDWELL, HAYS, AND TRAVIS. Population (2010), 698,488.

ZIP Codes: 78108, 78130, 78132, 78154, 78201–05, 78207–08, 78210, 78212, 78214–15, 78217–20, 78222–23, 78228, 78233–35, 78239, 78244, 78247, 78266, 78610, 78612, 78617, 78622, 78640, 78644, 78653, 78655–56, 78666, 78702, 78704, 78719, 78721, 78725, 78741–42, 78744–45, 78747–48, 78753–54, 78758

* * *

THIRTY-SIXTH DISTRICT

STEVE STOCKMAN, Republican, of Clear Lake, TX; born in Bloomfield Hills, MI, November 14, 1956; education: B.A., University of Houston-Clear Lake; professional: faculty member for Leadership Institute; U.S. Representative 1995–97; U.S. Representative 2013–15; caucuses: member, Bipartisan Disability Caucus; Bipartisan Congressional Prayer Caucus; Manufacturing Caucus; Natural Gas Caucus; PORTS Caucus; House Aerospace Caucus; Property Rights Action Caucus; Second Amendment Task Force; House Republican Israel Caucus; Congressional Constitution Caucus; Western Caucus; Congressional Israel Allies Caucus; Congressional Caucus on Orphans and Vulnerable Children; Congressional Army Aviation Caucus; Congressional Bi-Partisan Privacy Caucus; Congressional Coal Caucus; Congressional Air Force Caucus; Congressional Air Medical Caucus; Congressional Army Caucus; Congressional Caucus on Foster Youth; Congressional Caucus on Innovation and Entrepreneurship; Congressional Energy Caucus; Congressional Farmer Cooperative Caucus; Congressional Hearing Health Caucus; Congressional History Caucus; Congressional Homelessness Caucus; Congressional House Manufacturing Caucus; Congressional Job Creators' Caucus; Congressional Liquefied Natural Gas Export Caucus; Congressional Military Mental Health Caucus; Congressional Rural Caucus; Congressional Rural Veterans Caucus; Congressional Small Business Caucus; Congressional Steel Caucus; Congressional Tea Party Caucus; House Tea Party Caucus; married: Patti Stockman, December 10, 1988; committees: Foreign Affairs; Science, Space, and Technology; elected on November 3, 1994 to the 104th Congress; elected to the 113th Congress November 6, 2012.

Office Listings

http://www.stockman.house.gov https://twitter.com/steveworks4you
https://www.facebook.com/congressmanstockman

326 Cannon House Office Building, Washington, DC 20515 .... (202) 225–1555
Chief of Staff.—Kirk Clinkenbeard. FAX: 226–0396
Legislative Director.—John Velleco.
Press Secretary.—Donny Ferguson.
Legislative Assistants: Printus LeBlanc, Noel Fritsch, Art Harman.
Scheduler.—Kristine Nichols.
907 East Houston Street, Cleveland City Hall, Cleveland, TX 77327 .... (409) 883–8028
420 Green Avenue, Orange, TX 77630 .... (409) 886–8075
8060 Spencer Highway, San Jacinto College, Building 1, Room 108, Pasadena, TX 77505 .... (281) 478–2799

Counties: CHAMBERS, HARDIN, JASPER, LIBERTY, NEWTON, ORANGE, POLK, TYLER, AND HARRIS (part). Population (2010), 714,368.

ZIP Codes: 75326–27, 75335, 75350, 75360, 75368, 75928, 75932–39, 75942, 75951, 75956, 75960, 75966, 75977, 75979, 77369, 77374, 77376, 77505, 77507, 77514, 77519, 77520–21, 77523, 77533, 77535, 77538, 77560–62, 77564, 77571, 77575, 77580, 77585–86, 77597, 77611–12, 77614–16, 77624–25, 77630, 77632, 77656–57, 77659–64

UTAH

(Population 2010, 2,763,885)

SENATORS

ORRIN G. HATCH, Republican, of Salt Lake City, UT; born in Pittsburgh, PA, March 22, 1934; education: B.S., Brigham Young University, Provo, UT, 1959; J.D., University of Pittsburgh, 1962; practiced law in Salt Lake City, UT, and Pittsburgh, PA; senior partner, Hatch and Plumb law firm, Salt Lake City; worked his way through high school, college, and law school at the metal lathing building trade; holds ''AV'' rating in Martindale-Hubbell Law Directory; member: AFL-CIO; Salt Lake County Bar Association; Utah Bar Association; American Bar Association; Pennsylvania Bar Association; Allegheny County Bar Association and numerous other professional and fraternal organizations; honorary doctorate, University of Maryland; honorary doctor of laws: Pepperdine University; Southern Utah University; Widener University, University of Pittsburgh; honorary national ski patroller and other honorary degrees; Senate Republican High Tech Task Force; Congressional International Anti-Privacy Caucus; author of numerous national publications; member, Church of Jesus Christ of Latter-Day Saints; married: Elaine Hansen of Newton, UT; children: Brent, Marcia, Scott, Kimberly, Alysa, and Jess; committees: ranking member, Finance; Health, Education, Labor, and Pensions; Judiciary; Joint Committee on Taxation; Special Committee on Aging; elected to the U.S. Senate on November 2, 1976; reelected to each succeeding Senate term.

Office Listings

http://hatch.senate.gov

SH–104 Hart Senate Office Building, Washington, DC 20510 .... (202) 224–5251
  Chief of Staff.—Michael Kennedy. FAX: 224–6331
  Legislative Director.—Jay Khosla.
  Communications Director.—Antonia Ferrier.
  Scheduler.—Ruth Montoya.
Federal Building, Suite 8402, Salt Lake City, UT 84138 .... (801) 524–4380
  State Director.—Melanie Bowen.
Federal Building, 324 25th Street, Suite 1006, Ogden, UT 84401 .... (801) 625–5672
51 South University Avenue, Suite 320, Provo, UT 84601 .... (801) 375–7881
196 East Tabernacle, Suite 14, St. George, UT 84770 .... (435) 634–1795
77 North Main Street, Suite 112, Cedar City, UT 84720 .... (435) 586–8435

* * *

MICHAEL S. LEE, Republican, of Alpine, UT; Mesa, AZ, June 4, 1971; education: B.S., Brigham Young University, Provo, UT, 1994; J.D., Brigham Young University, 1997; professional: law clerk to Judge Dee Benson of the U.S. District Court for the District of Utah; law clerk to Judge Samuel A. Alito, Jr. on the U.S. Court of Appeals for the Third Circuit Court; attorney with the law firm Sidley & Austin; Assistant U.S. Attorney in Salt Lake City; general counsel to the Governor of Utah; law clerk to Supreme Court Justice Samuel A. Alito; partner at Howrey law firm; religion: Church of Jesus Christ of Latter-Day Saints; married: Sharon Burr of Provo, UT; children: James, John, and Eliza; committees: Armed Services; Energy and Natural Resources; Judiciary; Joint Economic Committee; elected to the U.S. Senate on November 2, 2010.

Office Listings

http://lee.senate.gov http://youtube.com/senatormikelee
http://facebook.com/senatormikelee http://twitter.com/senmikelee

316 Hart Senate Office Building, Washington, DC 20510 .... (202) 224–5444
  Chief of Staff.—Boyd Matheson. FAX: 228–1168
  Legislative Director.—Wendy Baig.
  Administrative Director.—Allyson Bell.
  Communications Director.—Brian Phillips.
  Press Secretary.—Emily Bennion.
Federal Building, 125 South State, Suite 4425, Salt Lake City, UT 84138 .... (801) 524–5933
  State Director.—Dan Hauser.
285 West Tabernacle Street, Suite 200, St. George, UT 84770 .... (435) 628–5514

REPRESENTATIVES

FIRST DISTRICT

ROB BISHOP, Republican, of Brigham City, UT; born in Kaysville, UT, July 13, 1951; education: B.A., political science, *magna cum laude,* University of Utah, 1974; professional: high school teacher; public service: Utah House of Representatives, 1979–94, Speaker of the House his last two years; elected, chair, Utah Republican Party, 1997 (served two terms); religion: Church of Jesus Christ of Latter-day Saints; family: married to Jeralynn Hansen; children: Shule, Jarom, Zenock, Maren, and Jashon; committees: Armed Servcies; Natural Resources; Rules; elected to the 108th Congress on November 5, 2002; reelected to each succeeding Congress.

Office Listings

http://www.house.gov/robbishop

123 Cannon House Office Building, Washington, DC 20515 .... (202) 225–0453
Chief of Staff.—Scott Parker. FAX: 225–5857
Legislative Assistants: Fred Ferguson, Steve Petersen, Devin Wiser.
Scheduler.—Jessica Sanford.
6 North Main Street, Brigham City, UT 84302 .... (435) 734–2270
FAX: 734–2290
324 25th Street, 1017 Federal Building, Ogden, UT 94401 .... (801) 625–0107

Counties: BOX ELDER, CACHE, DAVIS (part), DAGGETT, DUCHESNE, MORGAN, RICH, SUMMIT, UINTAH, AND WEBER. Population (2010), 690,971.

ZIP Codes: 82930, 83312, 83342, 84001–02, 84007, 84015, 84017–18, 84021, 84023–28, 84031, 84033, 84035–41, 84046, 84050–53, 84055–56, 84060–61, 84063–64, 84066–67, 84072–73, 84075–76, 84078, 84083, 84085–86, 84098, 84301–02, 84304–21, 84324–41, 84401, 84403–05, 84414, 84526, 84540

* * *

SECOND DISTRICT

CHRIS STEWART, Republican, of Farmington, UT; born in Logan, UT, July 15, 1960; education: B.S., economics, Utah State University; professional: President and CEO, Shipley Group; independent author; military: Pilot, United States Air Force; religion: Church of Jesus Christ of Latter-Day Saints; married: Evie; children: Sean, Dane, Lance, Kayla, Bryce, and Megan; committees: Appropriations; elected to the 113th Congress on November 6, 2012.

Office Listings

http://stewart.house.gov facebook.com/repchrisstewart
twitter.com/repchrisstewart instagram.com/repchrisstewart youtube.com/repchrisstewart

323 Cannon House Office Building, Washington, DC 20515 .... (202) 225–9730
Chief of Staff.—Brian Steed. FAX: 225–9627
Executive Assistant.—Nathaniel Johnson.
Press Secretary.—Allison Barker.
136 East South Temple, Suite 900, Salt Lake City, UT 84111 .... (801) 364–5550
District Director.—Dell Smith. FAX: 364–5551
253 West St. George Boulevard, Suite 100, St. George, UT 84770 .... (435) 627–1500
Southern Utah Director.—Gary Webster. FAX: 627–1911

Counties: BEAVER, DAVIS (part), GARFIELD, IRON, JUAB (part), KANE, MILLARD, PIUTE, SALT LAKE (part), SANPETE (part), SEVIER, TOOELE, WASHINGTON, AND WAYNE. CITIES: Alton Town, Annabella Town, Antimony Town, Apple Valley Town, Aurora City, Beaver City, Beryl Junction, Bicknell Town, Big Water Town, Boulder Town, Bountiful City, Brian Head Town, Bryce Canyon, Cannonville Town, Cedar City, Centerfield Town, Centerville City, Central, Central Valley Town, Circleville Town, Dammeron Valley, Delta City, Deseret, Dugway, Elsinore Town, Emigration Canyon, Enoch City, Enterprise City, Ephraim City, Erda, Escalante City, Eureka City, Farmington City (part), Fayette Town, Fillmore City, Fremont, Fruit Heights City (part), Glendale Town, Glenwood Town, Grantsville City, Gunnison City, Hanksville Town, Hatch Town, Henrieville Town, Hildale City, Hinckley Town, Holden Town, Hurricane City, Ivins City, Joseph Town, Junction Town, Kanab City, Kanarraville Town, Kanosh Town, Kaysville City (part), Kearns (part), Kingston Town, Koosharem Town, La Verkin City, Leamington Town, Leeds Town, Loa Town, Lyman Town, Lynndyl Town, Magna, Manti City, Marysvale Town, Mayfield Town, Meadow Town, Milford City, Minersville Town, Monroe City, New Harmony Town, Newcastle, North Salt Lake City, Oak City Town, Oasis, Ophir Town, Orderville Town, Panguitch City, Paragonah Town, Parowan City, Pine Valley, Redmond Town, Richfield City, Rockville Town, Rush Valley Town, Salina City, Salt Lake City (part), Santa Clara City, Scipio Town, Sigurd Town, Springdale Town, St. George City, Stansbury Park, Sterling Town, Stockton Town, Summit, Sutherland, Teasdale, Tooele City, Toquerville Town, Torrey Town, Tropic Town, Vernon Town, Veyo, Virgin Town, Washington City, Wendover City, West Bountiful City, West Valley City (part), and Woods Cross City. Population (2010), 690,971.

ZIP Codes: 84010, 84014, 84022, 84025, 84029, 84034, 84037, 84044, 84054, 84069, 84071, 84074–75, 84080–81, 84083, 84087, 84101–06, 84108–09, 84111–13, 84115–16, 84118–20, 84128, 84144, 84180, 84533, 84620–24, 84627–28, 84630–

31, 84634–38, 84640, 84642–43, 84648–49, 84652, 84654, 84656–57, 84662, 84665, 84701, 84710–16, 84718–26, 84728–47, 84749–67, 84770, 84772–76, 84779–84, 84790

* * *

THIRD DISTRICT

JASON CHAFFETZ, Republican, of Alpine, UT; born in Los Gatos, CA; March 26, 1967; education: B.A., communications, Brigham Young University, Provo, UT, 1989; professional: business executive; chief of staff, Utah Governor John Huntsman, 2004; President, Maxtera Utah, 2005–present; trustee, Utah Valley board of trustees; chair, Utah National Guard Adjutant General Review; Commissioner, Highland City Planning Commission; President, BYU Utah County Cougar Club; Cougar Club (BYU) Board of Directors; awards: starting placekicker, BYU Football Team, 1988–89; Best Run Campaign, General Election, Utah 2004, Huntsman for Governor; Western Athletic Conference Champions, 1989; Cougar Club Academic Athlete Award, 1988–89; Academic All-WAC Football Team, 1989; National All-Bowl Football Team, 1988; religion: Church of Jesus Christ of Latter-Day Saints; married: Julie, in 1991; children: Max, Ellis, and Kate; committees: Homeland Security; Judiciary; Oversight and Government Reform; elected to the 111th Congress on November 4, 2008; reelected to each succeeding Congress.

Office Listings

http://chaffetz.house.gov

2464 Rayburn House Office Building, Washington, DC 20515 .... (202) 225–7751
Chief of Staff.—Justin Harding. FAX: 225–5629
Legislative Director.—Mike Jerman.
Scheduler / Office Manager.—Camille Taylor.
Media Manager / Legislative Aide.—M.J. Henshaw.
Counsel.—Troy Stock.
Senior Legislative Assistant.—Ryan Little.
51 South University Avenue, Suite 318, Provo, UT 84601 .... (801) 851–2500
District Director.—Wade Garrett. FAX: 851–2509

Counties: CARBON, EMERY, GRAND, SALT LAKE (part), SAN JUAN, UTAH (part), WASATCH. Population (2010), 708,809.

ZIP Codes: 84003–04, 84020, 84032, 84036 (part), 84042, 84043 (part), 84047 (part), 84049, 84057–59, 84060 (part), 84062, 84070 (part), 84082, 84090–94, 84097, 84109, 84117 (part), 84121 (part), 84124 (part), 84171, 84501, 84510–13, 84515–16, 84518, 84520–23, 84525–26, 84528–37, 84539–40, 84542, 84601–06, 84651 (part), 84653, 84655 (part), 84660 (part), 84663 (part), 84664

* * *

FOURTH DISTRICT

JIM MATHESON, Democrat, of Salt Lake City, UT; born in Salt Lake City, March 21, 1960; education: B.A., Harvard University; M.B.A., University of California at Los Angeles (UCLA); professional: energy businessman; Bonneville Pacific; Energy Strategies, Inc.; The Matheson Group; organizations: Environmental Policy Institute; Salt Lake Public Utilities Board; Scott M. Matheson Leadership Forum; religion: Church of Jesus Christ of Latter-Day Saints; married: Amy; children: William and Harris; committees: Energy and Commerce; elected to the 107th Congress on November 7, 2000; reelected to each succeeding Congress.

Office Listings

http://www.matheson.house.gov

2211 Rayburn House Office Building, Washington, DC 20515 .... (202) 225–3011
Chief of Staff.—Meg Joseph. FAX: 225–5638
Scheduler.—Sarah Paulos.
9067 South 1300 West, Suite 101, West Jordan, UT 84115 .... (801) 486–1236
District Director.—Mike Reberg.

Counties: SALT LAKE (part), UTAH (part), JUAB (part), SAN PETE (part). Population (2010), 690,971.

ZIP Codes: 84003 (part), 84005–06, 84013, 84020 (part), 84043 (part), 84045, 84047 (part), 84065, 84070 (part), 84081 (part), 84084, 84088, 84095–96, 84106 (part), 84107, 84109 (part), 84115 (part), 84117 (part), 84118 (part), 84119 (part), 84120 (part), 84121 (part), 84123, 84124 (part), 84129, 84141, 84157, 84165, 84170, 84184, 84623, 84626, 84629, 84632, 84633, 84639, 84645–48, 84651 (part), 84655 (part), 84660 (part), 84662, 84663 (part), 84667

VERMONT

(Population 2010, 625,741)

SENATORS

PATRICK J. LEAHY, President Pro Tempore, December 17, 2012–present, Democrat, of Middlesex, VT; born in Montpelier, VT, March 31, 1940, son of Howard and Alba Leahy; education: graduate of St. Michael's High School, Montpelier, 1957; B.A., St. Michael's College, 1961; J.D., Georgetown University, 1964; professional: attorney, admitted to the Vermont Bar, 1964; admitted to the District of Columbia Bar, 1979; admitted to practice before: the Vermont Supreme Court, 1964; the Federal District Court of Vermont, 1965; the Second Circuit Court of Appeals in New York, 1966; and the U.S. Supreme Court, 1968; State's Attorney, Chittenden County, 1966–74; vice president, National District Attorneys Association, 1971–74; married: the former Marcelle Pomerleau, 1962; children: Kevin, Alicia, and Mark; first Democrat and youngest person in Vermont to be elected to the U.S. Senate; committees: chair, Judiciary; Agriculture, Nutrition, and Forestry; Appropriations; Rules and Administration; Joint Committee on the Library; elected to the Senate on November 5, 1974; reelected to each succeeding Senate term.

Office Listings

http://leahy.senate.gov

437 Russell Senate Office Building, Washington, DC 20515 .... (202) 224–4242
Chief of Staff.—Ed Pagano. FAX: 224–3479
Administrative Director.—Ann Berry.
Legislative Director.—John P. Dowd.
Communications Director.—David Carle.
Federal Building, Room 338, Montpelier, VT 05602 .... (802) 229–0569
199 Main Street, Courthouse Plaza, Burlington, VT 05401 .... (802) 863–2525
State Director.—John Tracy.

* * *

BERNARD SANDERS, Independent, of Burlington, VT; born in Brooklyn, NY, September 8, 1941; education: graduated, Madison High School, Brooklyn; B.S., political science, University of Chicago, 1964; professional: carpenter; writer; college professor; Mayor of Burlington, VT, 1981–89; married: the former Jane O'Meara, 1988; children: Levi, Heather, Carina and David; committees: chair, Veterans' Affairs; Budget; Energy and Natural Resources; Environment and Public Works; Health, Education, Labor, and Pensions; Joint Economic Committee; elected to the 102nd Congress on November 6, 1990; reelected to each succeeding Congress; elected to the U.S. Senate on November 7, 2006; reelected to the U.S. Senate on November 6, 2012.

Office Listings

http://sanders.senate.gov facebook.com/senatorsanders twitter.com/sensanders

332 Dirksen Senate Office Building, Washington, DC 20510 .... (202) 224–5141
Chief of Staff.—Michaeleen Crowell. FAX: 228–0776
Legislative Director.—Caryn Compton.
Communications Director.—Michael Briggs.
1 Church Street, Second Floor, Burlington, VT 05401 .... (800) 339–9834

REPRESENTATIVE

AT LARGE

PETER WELCH, Democrat, of Hartland, VT; born in Springfield, MA, May 2, 1947; education: Cathedral High School, Springfield, MA, 1969; B.A., *magna cum laude*, College of the Holy Cross, 1969; J.D., University of California at Berkeley, 1973; professional: attorney, admitted to Vermont Bar, 1974; founding partner, Welch, Graham & Manby; served in Vermont State Senate, 1981–89, 2001–07; Minority Leader, 1983–85; President pro tempore, 1985–89, 2003–07; family: wife, Joan Smith (deceased), currently married to Margaret Cheney; five children: Beth, Mary, Bill, John and Michael; three stepchildren; committees: Energy and Commerce; Oversight and Government Reform; elected to the 110th Congress on November 7, 2006; reelected to each succeeding Congress.

Office Listings

http://www.welch.house.gov twitter: @peterwelch https://www.facebook.com/peterwelch

2303 Rayburn House Office Building, Washington, DC 20515 .... (202) 225–4115
Chief of Staff.—Bob Rogan.
Scheduler / Executive Assistant.—Kelly Allen.
Legislative Director.—Jake Oster.
Communications Director.—Ryan Nickel.
128 Lakeside Avenue, Suite 235, Burlington, VT 05401 .... (802) 652–2450
State Director.—Patricia Coates.

Population (2010), 625,741.

ZIP Codes: 05001, 05009, 05030–43, 05045–56, 05058–62, 05065, 05067–77, 05079, 05081, 05083–86, 05088–89, 05091, 05101, 05141–43, 05146, 05148–56, 05158–59, 05161, 05201, 05250–55, 05257, 05260–62, 05301–04, 05340–46, 05350–63, 05401–07, 05439–66, 05468–74, 05476–79, 05481–83, 05485–92, 05494–95, 05601–04, 05609, 05620, 05633, 05640–41, 05647–58, 05660–67, 05669–82, 05701–02, 05730–48, 05750–51, 05753, 05757–70, 05772–78, 05819–30, 05832–33, 05836–43, 05845–51, 05853, 05855, 05857–63, 05866–68, 05871–75, 05901–07

VIRGINIA

(Population 2010, 8,001,024)

SENATORS

MARK R. WARNER, Democrat, of Alexandria, VA; born in Indianapolis, IN, December 15, 1954; son of Robert and Marge Warner of Vernon, CT; education: B.A., political science, George Washington University, 1977, J.D., Harvard Law School, 1980; Governor, Commonwealth of Virginia, 2002–06; chairman of the National Governor's Association, 2004–05; religion: Presbyterian; wife: Lisa Collis; children: Madison, Gillian, Eliza; committees: Banking, Housing, and Urban Affairs; Budget; Finance; Rules and Administration; Joint Committee on Printing; Select Committee on Intelligence; elected to the U.S. Senate on November 4, 2008.

Office Listings

http://warner.senate.gov

SR–475A Russell Senate Office Building, Washington, DC 20510 .... (202) 224–2023
Chief of Staff.—Luke S. Albee. FAX: 224–2530
Communications Director.—Kevin Hall.
Press Secretary.—Beth Adelson.
Scheduler.—Carrig Balderston.
Deputy Chief of Staff / Legislative Director.—David Hallock.
8000 Towers Crescent Drive, Suite 200, Vienna, VA 22182 .... (703) 442–0670
FAX: 442–0408
180 West Main Street, Abingdon, VA 24210 .... (276) 628–8158
FAX: 628–1036
101 West Main Street, Suite 4900, Norfolk, VA 23510 .... (757) 441–3079
FAX: 441–6250
919 East Main Street, Richmond, VA 23219 .... (804) 775–2314
FAX: 775–2319
129B Salem Avenue, Southwest, Roanoke, VA 24011 .... (540) 857–2676
FAX: 857–2800

* * *

TIM KAINE, Democrat, of Richmond, VA; born in St. Paul, MN, February 26, 1958; education: graduated with a B.A., University of Missouri, 1979; graduated with a J.D., Harvard University, 1983; professional: work with the Jesuit order as a Catholic missionary in Honduras, 1980–81; civil rights lawyer; professor, University of Richmond, 1987–present; Richmond City Council, 1994–98; mayor of Richmond, VA, 1998–2001; lieutenant governor of Virginia, 2002–06; Governor of Virginia, 2006–10; married: Anne Holton, who currently serves as Virginia Secretary of Education; one of the Senate's few members who speak fluent Spanish; 51st chair of the Democratic National Committee, 2009–11; caucuses: chair, Senate Career and Technical Education (CTE) Caucus; chair, U.S. / Mexico Inter-Parliamentary Group; committees: Armed Services; Budget; Foreign Relations; elected to the U.S. Senate on November 6, 2012.

Office Listings

http://kaine.senate.gov https://twitter.com/@senkaineoffice
https://www.facebook.com/senatorkaine

233 Russell Senate Office Building, Washington, DC 20510 .... (202) 224–4024
Chief of Staff.—Mike Henry. FAX: 228–6363
Communications Director.—Amy Dudley.
Legislative Director.—Mary Naylor.
Scheduler.—Kate McCarroll.
State Director.—John Knapp.
222 Central Park Avenue, Suite 120, Virginia Beach, VA 23462 .... (757) 518–1674
919 East Main Street, Suite 970, Richmond, VA 23219 .... (804) 771–2221
611 South Jefferson, Suite 5B, Roanoke, VA 24011 .... (540) 682–5693
756 Park Avenue, Norton, VA 24273 .... (276) 679–4925
9408 Grant Avenue, Suite 202, Manassas, VA 20110 .... (703) 361–3192
308 Craghead Street, Suite 102A, Danville, VA 24541 .... (434) 792–0976

REPRESENTATIVES

FIRST DISTRICT

ROBERT J. WITTMAN, Republican, of Montross, VA; born in Washington, DC, February 2, 1959; B.S., biology, Virginia Polytechnic Institute and State University, 1981; M.P.H., health policy and administration, University of North Carolina at Chapel Hill, 1989; Ph.D., Virginia Commonwealth University, Richmond, VA, 2002; professional: field director for the Virginia Health Department's Division of Shellfish Sanitation; public service: Montross Town Council, 1986–96; public policy and administration, 1992; mayor of Montross, 1992–96; Westmoreland County Board of Supervisors, 1995–2003 and chairman, 2003–05; Virginia House of Delegates, 2005–07; religion: Episcopalian; married: Kathryn Wittman; children: Devon and Joshua; committees: Armed Services; Natural Resources; elected to the 110th Congress on December 11, 2007 in a special election; elected to the 111th Congress; reelected to each succeeding Congress.

Office Listings

http://www.wittman.house.gov

2454 Rayburn House Office Building, Washington, DC 20515 .... (202) 225–4261
Chief of Staff.—Mary Springer. FAX: 225–4382
Legislative Director.—Jamie Miller.
Communications Director.—Abigail Shilling.
Scheduler/Office Manager.—Christin Parras.
401 Main Street, P.O. Box 494, Yorktown, VA 23690 .... (757) 874–6687
District Director.—Joe Schumacher.
2777 Jefferson Davis Highway, Suite 105, Stafford, VA 22554 .... (540) 659–2734
508 Church Lane, Tappahannock, VA 22560 .... (804) 443–0668

Counties: ALL OF CAROLINE, ESSEX, GLOUCESTER, KING AND QUEEN, KING GEORGE, KING WILLIAM, LANCASTER, MATHEWS, MIDDLESEX, NORTHUMBERLAND, RICHMOND, STAFFORD, WESTMORELAND, AND YORK COUNTIES; ALL OF THE CITIES of Fredericksburg, Poquoson, and Williamsburg; PART OF FAUQUIER COUNTY COMPRISED OF THE BEALETON (303), CATLETT (102), LOIS (104), AND MORRISVILLE (301) PRECINCTS AND PART OF THE REMINGTON (302) PRECINCT; PART OF JAMES CITY COUNTY COMPRISED OF THE BERKELEY A PART 1 (101), BERKELEY A PART 2 (1012), BERKELEY B PART 1 (1021), BERKELEY B PART 2 (1022), BERKELEY C (103), JAMESTOWN A (201), JAMESTOWN B (202), POWHATAN A (301), POWHATAN B (302), POWHATAN C (303), POWHATAN D (304), ROBERTS A PART 1 (5011), ROBERTS A PART 2 (5012), ROBERTS C PART 1 (5031), ROBERTS C PART 2 (5032), STONEHOUSE A (401), STONEHOUSE B (402), AND STONEHOUSE C (403) PRECINCTS AND PART OF THE ROBERTS B (502) PRECINCT; PART OF PRINCE WILLIAM COUNTY COMPRISED OF THE ASHLAND (309), BENNETT (102), BENTON (203), BRENTSVILLE (101), BRISTOW RUN (111), CEDAR POINT (112), ELLIS (106), FOREST PARK (310), GLENKIRK (408), HENDERSON (307), LAKE RIDGE (501), LIMESTONE (113), LODGE (207), MARSHALL (202), MARSTELLER (107), MCCOART (204), MONTCLAIR (308), MULLEN (411), NOKESVILLE (104), PARK (109), PATTIE (305), PENN (210), POWELL (211), QUANTICO (304), SINCLAIR (404), STONEWALL (405), SUDLEY NORTH (409), VICTORY (108), WASHINGTON REID (306), WESTGATE (407), WESTRIDGE (208), AND WOODBINE (209) PRECINCTS AND PART OF THE BUCKLAND MILLS (110) PRECINCT; PART OF SPOTSYLVANIA COUNTY COMPRISED OF THE BATTLEFIELD (701), BRENT'S MILL (702), GRANGE HALL (303), HAZEL RUN (302), PLANK ROAD (301), AND SUMMIT (401) PRECINCTS AND PART OF THE LEE HILL (403) PRECINCT; AND PART OF THE CITY OF NEWPORT NEWS COMPRISED OF THE GREENWOOD (110) PRECINCT. Population (2010), 727,366.

ZIP Codes: 20109–12, 20119, 20136, 20155–56, 20181–82, 20187, 22025, 22134–35, 22172, 22192–93, 22401–08, 22412, 22427–28, 22430, 22432, 22435–38, 22442–43, 22446, 22448, 22451, 22454, 22456, 22460, 22463, 22469, 22471–73, 22476, 22480–82, 22485, 22488, 22501, 22503–04, 22507, 22509, 22511, 22513–14, 22517, 22520, 22523–24, 22526, 22528–30, 22535, 22538–39, 22544–48, 22552, 22554–56, 22558, 22560, 22570, 22572, 22576–81, 22712, 22720, 22728, 22734, 22739, 22742, 23001, 23003, 23009, 23015, 23018, 23021, 23023, 23025, 23031–32, 23035, 23043, 23045, 23047, 23050, 23056, 23061–62, 23064, 23066, 23068–72, 23076, 23079, 23081, 23085–86, 23089–92, 23106–10, 23115, 23119, 23125–28, 23130–31, 23138, 23148–49, 23154–56, 23161, 23163, 23168–69, 23175–78, 23180–81, 23183–88, 23190, 23602–03, 23608, 23662, 23665, 23690–94, 23696

* * *

SECOND DISTRICT

E. SCOTT RIGELL, Republican, of Virginia Beach, VA; born in Titusville, FL, May 28, 1960; education: A.A., Brevard Community College, Cocoa, FL, 1981; B.B.A., Mercer University, Macon, GA, 1983; M.B.A., Regent University, Virginia Beach, VA, 1990; professional: founder and chairman of Freedom Automotive; United States Marine Corps Reserve, 1978–84; married: Teri; children: Lindsey, Mallory, Justus, and Shannon; committees: Armed Services; Budget; elected to the 112th Congress on November 2, 2010; reelected to the 113th Congress on November 6, 2012.

Office Listings

http://www.rigell.house.gov

418 Cannon House Office Building, Washington, DC 20515 .... (202) 225–4215

Chief of Staff.—Chris Connelly. FAX: 225–4218
Communications Director.—Kim Mosser Knapp.
Legislative Director.—John Thomas.
4772 Euclid Road, Suite E, Virginia Beach, VA 23462 .... (757) 687–8290
District Director.—Shannon Kendrick.
23386 Front Street, Accomac, VA 23301 .... (757) 789–5172

Counties: ACCOMACK, NORTHAMPTON. CITIES: Hampton, Newport News, Norfolk, and Virginia Beach. Population (2010), 721,969.

ZIP Codes: 23301–03, 23306–08, 23310, 23313, 23316, 23336–37, 23341, 23345, 23347, 23350, 23354, 23356–59, 23389, 23395, 23398–99, 23401, 23404–05, 23407–10, 23412–23, 23426–27, 23429, 23440–43, 23450–67, 23471, 23479–80, 23482–83, 23486, 23488, 23502–03, 23505–06, 23508–09, 23511, 23513, 23518–19, 23529, 23541, 23601–02, 23605, 23608–09, 23651, 23661, 23663–66, 23669

* * *

THIRD DISTRICT

ROBERT C. "BOBBY" SCOTT, Democrat, of Newport News, VA; born in Washington, DC, April 30, 1947; education: graduated, Groton High School; B.A., Harvard University; J.D., Boston College Law School; professional: served in the Massachusetts National Guard; attorney; admitted to the Virginia Bar; Virginia House of Delegates, 1978–83; Senate of Virginia, 1983–92; member: Alpha Phi Alpha Fraternity; NAACP; Sigma Pi Phi Fraternity; committees: Education and the Workforce; Judiciary; elected on November 3, 1992 to the 103rd Congress; reelected to each succeeding Congress.

Office Listings

http://www.bobbyscott.house.gov www.facebook.com/congressmanbobbyscott
twitter.com/repbobbyscott

1201 Longworth House Office Building, Washington, DC 20515 .... (202) 225–8351
Chief of Staff.—Joni L. Ivey. FAX: 225–8354
Executive Assistant.—Randi Petty.
Senior Counsel.—Rashage Green.
Senior Legislative Assistants: David Dailey, Carrie Hughes.
2600 Washington Avenue, Suite 1010, Newport News, VA 23607 .... (757) 380–1000
District Director.—Gisele Russell.
400 North 8th Street, Suite 430, Richmond, VA 23219 .... (804) 644–4845
District Scheduler.—Nkechi George-Winkler.

Counties: CHARLES CITY, HENRICO (part), PRINCE GEORGE, SURRY. CITIES: Hampton (part), Newport News (part), Norfolk (part), Petersburg, Portsmouth, and Richmond (part). Population (2012), 751,694.

ZIP Codes: 23030, 23075, 23140, 23147, 23150, 23185, 23218–25, 23227, 23230–32, 23234, 23241, 23249–50, 23260–61, 23269, 23274, 23276, 23278, 23282, 23284–86, 23289–93, 23298, 23501–05, 23507–11, 23513–15, 23517, 23523, 23551, 23601–05, 23607–09, 23628, 23630, 23661, 23663–64, 23666–70, 23701–05, 23707–09, 23801, 23803–05, 23839, 23842, 23846, 23860, 23875, 23881, 23883, 23888, 23890, 23899

* * *

FOURTH DISTRICT

J. RANDY FORBES, Republican, of Chesapeake, VA; born in Chesapeake, February 17, 1952; education: B.A., Randolph-Macon College; J.D., University of Virginia School of Law; professional: attorney; religion: Baptist; public service: Virginia House of Delegates, 1990–97; Virginia State Senate, 1997–2001; Republican House Floor Leader, 1994–97; Republican Senate Floor Leader, 1998–2001; Chairman of the Republican Party of Virginia, 1996–2000; married: Shirley; children: Neil, Jamie, Jordan, and Justin; committees: Armed Services; Judiciary; elected to the 107th Congress, by special election, on June 19, 2001; reelected to each succeeding Congress.

Office Listings

2135 Rayburn House Office Building, Washington, DC 20515 .... (202) 225–6365
Chief of Staff.—Dee Gilmore. FAX: 226–1170
Communications Director.—Dean Petrone.
Legislative Director.—Sarah Seitz.
District Director.—Curtis Byrd.
505 Independence Parkway, Suite 104, Chesapeake, VA 23320 .... (757) 382–0080

District Director.—Ronald White.
9401 Courthouse Road, Suite 201, Chesterfield, VA 23832 .... (804) 318–1363
Senior CSR / Senior Advocate.—Joan Fallon.

Counties: AMELIA, CHESTERFIELD (part), DINWIDDIE, GREENSVILLE, ISLE OF WIGHT (part), NOTTOWAY, POWHATAN, PRINCE GEORGE (part), SOUTHAMPTON, SUSSEX, CHESAPEAKE, COLONIAL HEIGHTS, EMPORIA, FRANKLIN, HOPEWELL, AND SUFFOLK. Population (2010), 881,217.

ZIP Codes: 23002, 23083, 23101, 23105, 23112–14, 23120, 23139, 23234, 23236–37, 23304, 23314–15, 23320–28, 23397, 23424, 23430–39, 23487, 23501, 23801, 23803–06, 23821, 23824, 23827–34, 23836–38, 23840–42, 23844–45, 23847, 23850–51, 23856–57, 23860, 23866–67, 23872–76, 23878–79, 23882, 23884–85, 23887–91, 23894, 23897–98, 23920, 23922, 23930, 23938, 23950, 23955

* * *

FIFTH DISTRICT

ROBERT HURT, Republican, of Chatham, VA; born in New York, NY, June 16, 1969; raised in Chatham, VA; education: B.S., Hampden-Sydney College, Hampden-Sydney, VA, 1991; J.D., Mississippi College School of Law, Clinton, MS, 1995; professional: attorney, Chatham Town Council, 2000–01; member of Virginia State House of Representatives, 2002–08; member of Virginia State Senate, 2008–10; committees: Financial Services; elected to the 112th Congress on November 2, 2010; reelected to the 113th Congress on November 6, 2012.

Office Listings

http://www.hurt.house.gov

125 Cannon House Office Building, Washington, DC 20515 .... (202) 225–4711
Chief of Staff.—Kelly Simpson. FAX: 225–5681
Scheduler.—Kristin Richmond.
Communications Director.—Caroline Califf.
Legislative Director.—Bryan Wood.
308 Craghead Street, Suite 102–D, Danville, VA 24541 .... (434) 791–2596
District Director.—Linda Green.
686 Berkmar Circle, Charlottesville, VA 22901 .... (434) 973–9631
515 South Main Street, P.O. Box 0, Farmville, VA 23901 .... (434) 395–0120

Counties: ALBEMARLE. CITIES AND TOWNSHIPS: Barboursville, Charlotteville, Batesville, Covesville, Crozet, Earlysville, Esmont, Free Union, Greenwood, Hatton, Ivy, Keene, Keswick, North Garden, Scottsville. APPOMATTOX. CITIES AND TOWNSHIPS: Appomattox, Evergreen, Pamplin, Spout Spring. BEDFORD. CITIES AND TOWNSHIPS: Bedford, Big Island, Coleman Falls, Forest, Goode, Goodview, Hardy, Huddleston, Lowry, Moneta, Thaxton. BRUNSWICK. CITIES AND TOWNSHIPS: Alberta, Brodnax, Lawrenceville, Gasburg, White Plains. BUCKINGHAM. CITIES AND TOWNSHIPS: Andersonville, Arvonia, Buckingham, Dillwyn, Buckingham, New Canton. CAMPBELL. CITIES AND TOWNSHIPS: Altavista, Brookneal, Concord, Evington, Gladys, Long Island, Lynch Station, Naruna, Rustburg. CHARLOTTE. CITIES AND TOWNSHIPS: Barnesville, Charlotte Court House, Cullen, Drakes Branch, Keysville, Phenix, Randolph, Red House, Red Oak, Saxe, Wylliesburg. CHARLOTTESVILLE CITY: Charlottesville. CUMBERLAND. CITIES AND TOWNSHIPS: Carterville, Cumberland, Tamworth. DANVILLE CITY: Danville. FAUQUIER. CITIES AND TOWNSHIPS: Airlie, Bealeton, Belle Meade, Belvoir, Broad Run, Calverton, Casanova, Delaplane, Germantown, Halfway, Hume, Linden, Markham, Marshall, Midland, Morrisville, New Baltimore, Old Tavern, Opal, Orlean, Paris, Rectortown, Remington, The Plains, Upperville, Warrenton. FLUVANNA. CITIES AND TOWNSHIPS: Bremo Bluff, Bybee, Carysbrook, Columbia, Fork Union, Kents Store, Palmyra, Troy. FRANKLIN. CITIES AND TOWNSHIPS: Boones Mill, Callaway, Ferrum, Glade Hill, Henry, Redwood, Penhook, Rocky Mount, Union Hall, Waidsboro, Wirtz. GREENE. CITIES AND TOWNSHIPS: Amicus, Barnes, Burtonville, Dawsonville, Dyke, Geer, Haneytown, Lydia, McMullen, Midway, Newton, Pirkey, Quinque, Ruckersville, Stanardsville, St. George, Shady Grove, Simmons Gap, Twin Lakes, Upper Pocosin, Williams Fork. HALIFAX. CITIES AND TOWNSHIPS: Alton, Clover, Cluster Springs, Crystal Hall, Denniston, Halifax, Ingram, Lennig, Mayo, Nathalie, Republican Grove, Scottsburg, Turbeville, Vernon Hill, Virgilin. HENRY. CITIES AND TOWNSHIPS: Axton, Chatmoss, Ridgeway. LUNENBURG. CITIES AND TOWNSHIPS: Tamworth, Dundas, Fort Mitchell, Kenbridge, Lunenburg, Rehoboth, Victoria. MADISON. CITIES AND TOWNSHIPS: Achash, Aroda, Aylor, Banco, Beaver Park, Big Meadows, Burnt Tree, Criglersville, Decapolis, Duet, Elly, Etlan, Five Forks, Fletcher, Fordsville, Graves Mill, Haywood, Hood, Kinderhook, Leon, Locust Dale, Madison, Madison Mills, Nethers, Novum, O'Neal, Oakpark, Oldrag, Pratts, Radiant, Repton Mills, Rochelle, Ruth, Shelby, Shifflet Corner, Syria, Tanners, Tryme, Twyman's Mill, Uno, Wolftown, Zeus. MECKLENBURG. CITIES AND TOWNSHIPS: Baskerville, Blackridge, Boydton, Bracey, Chase City, Clarksville, Forksville, LaCross, Palmer Springs, Skipwith, South Hill, Union Level Buffalo Junction, Nelson. NELSON. CITIES AND TOWNSHIPS: Afton, Arrington, Faber, Lovingston, Massies Mill, Nellysford, Montebello, Gladstone, Norwood, Piney River, Roseland, Schuyler, Shipman, Tye River, Tyro, Wingina. PITTSYLVANIA. CITIES AND TOWNSHIPS: Blairs, Callands, Cascade, Chatham, Pittsville, Sandy Level, Dry Fork, Gretna, Hurt, Java, Keeling, Ringgold, Sutherlin. PRINCE EDWARD. CITIES AND TOWNSHIPS: Farmville, Darlington Heights, Green Bay, Hampden-Sydney, Meherrin, Prospect, Rice. RAPPAHANNOCK. CITIES AND TOWNSHIPS: Amissville, Castleton, Chester Gap, Flint Hill, Huntly, Laurel Mills, Massies Corner, Peola Mills, Revercombs Corner, Sperryville, Wakefield Manor, Washington, and Woodville. Population (2010), 727,365.

ZIP Codes: 20106, 20115–17, 20119, 20128, 20130, 20137–40, 20144, 20169, 20181, 20184–89, 20198, 22623, 22627, 22630, 22639, 22640, 22642, 22643, 22701, 22709, 22711–13, 22715, 22716, 22719, 22722–23, 22725, 22727–28, 22730–32, 22734–35, 22738, 22740, 22743, 22747–49, 22901–06, 22908–11, 22920, 22922–24, 22931–32, 22935–38, 22940, 22942–43, 22945–49, 22958–60, 22963–69, 22971, 22973–74, 22976, 22987, 22989, 23004, 23022, 23027, 23038, 23040, 23055, 23084, 23093, 23123, 23139, 23821, 23824, 23843, 23845, 23847, 23856, 23857, 23868, 23873, 23876, 23887, 23889, 23893, 23901, 23909, 23915, 23917, 23919–24, 23927, 23934, 23936–39, 23941–44, 23947, 23950, 23952, 23954, 23958–60, 23962–64, 23966–68, 23970, 23974, 23976, 24054–55, 24059, 24064–65, 24067, 24069, 24079, 24088, 24091–92, 24095, 24101–02, 24104, 24112, 24137, 24139, 24148, 24151, 24161, 24174, 24176,

24179, 24184, 24464, 24483, 24501–02, 24504, 24517, 24520–23, 24527–31, 24534–35, 24538–41, 24543, 24549–51, 24553–54, 24556–58, 24562–63, 24565–66, 24569–71, 24576–77, 24580–81, 24586, 24588–90, 24592–94, 24597

* * *

SIXTH DISTRICT

BOB GOODLATTE, Republican, of Roanoke, VA; born in Holyoke, MA, September 22, 1952; education: B.A., Bates College, Lewiston, ME, 1974; J.D., Washington and Lee University, 1977; Massachusetts Bar, 1977; Virginia Bar, 1978; professional: began practice in Roanoke, VA, 1979; district director for Congressman M. Caldwell Butler, 1977–79; attorney, sole practitioner, 1979–81; partner, 1981–92; chairman of the sixth district Virginia Republican Committee, 1983–88; member: Civitan Club of Roanoke (president, 1989–90); former member, Building Better Boards Advisory Council; married: Maryellen Flaherty, 1974; children: Jennifer and Robert; Deputy Republican Whip; committees: chair, Judiciary; vice-chair, Agriculture; elected on November 3, 1992, to the 103rd Congress; reelected to each succeeding Congress.

Office Listings

http://www.goodlatte.house.gov twitter: @repgoodlatte
facebook.com/bobgoodlatte

2309 Rayburn House Office Building, Washington, DC 20515 .... (202) 225–5431
Chief of Staff.—Pete Larkin. FAX: 225–9681
Deputy Chief of Staff.—Charlie Keller.
Legislative Director.—Carrie Meadows.
Communications Director.—Beth Breeding.
10 Franklin Road, SE., Suite 540, Roanoke, VA 24011 .... (540) 857–2672
916 Main Street, Suite 300, Lynchburg, VA 24504 .... (434) 845–8306
117 South Lewis Street, Suite 215, Staunton, VA 24401 .... (540) 885–3861
District Director.—Debbie Garrett.
70 North Mason Street, Harrisonburg, VA 22802 .... (540) 432–2391

Counties: AMHERST, AUGUSTA, BATH, BEDFORD (part), BOTETOURT, HIGHLAND, PAGE, ROANOKE (part), ROCKBRIDGE, ROCKINGHAM, SHENANDOAH, AND WARREN. CITIES: Buena Vista, Harrisonburg, Lexington, Lynchburg, Roanoke, Staunton, and Waynesboro. Population (2010), 737,755.

ZIP Codes: 22610, 22626, 22630, 22641, 22644–45, 22649–50, 22652, 22654, 22657, 22660, 22664, 22801–03, 22807, 22810–12, 22815, 22820–21, 22824, 22827, 22830–35, 22840–48, 22850–51, 22853, 22920, 22922, 22939, 22952, 22967, 22980, 24001–20, 24022–38, 24040, 24042–44, 24048, 24053, 24059, 24064–66, 24070, 24077, 24079, 24083, 24085, 24087, 24090, 24101, 24121–22, 24130, 24156, 24174–75, 24178–79, 24401–02, 24411–13, 24415–16, 24421–22, 24430–33, 24435, 24437–42, 24445, 24450, 24458–60, 24463, 24465, 24467–69, 24471–73, 24476–77, 24479, 24482–87, 24501–06, 24512–15, 24521, 24523, 24526, 24533, 24536, 24550–51, 24553, 24555–56, 24572, 24574, 24578–79, 24595

* * *

SEVENTH DISTRICT

ERIC CANTOR, Republican, of Richmond, VA; born in Henrico County, June 6, 1963; education: B.A., George Washington University, 1985; J.D., College of William and Mary, 1988; M.S., Columbia University, 1989; professional: attorney; organizations: Western Henrico Rotary; elected to the Virginia State House of Delegates, 1991; appointed Chief Deputy Majority Whip, December, 2002; elected Republican Whip, December, 2008; elected Majority Leader, November, 2010; married: Diana; three children; elected to the 107th Congress on November 7, 2000; reelected to each succeeding Congress.

Office Listings

http://www.cantor.house.gov

H–329 The Capitol, Washington, DC 20515 .... (202) 225–4000
Chief of Staff.—Steve Stombres.
Policy Director.—Neil Bradley.
303 Cannon House Office Building, Washington, DC 20515 .... (202) 225–2815
Chief of Staff.—Kristi Way. FAX: 225–0011
4201 Dominion Boulevard, Suite 110, Glen Allen, VA 23060 .... (804) 747–4073
763 Madison Road, Suite 207, Culpeper, VA 22701 .... (540) 825–8960

Counties: CAROLINE (part), CHESTERFIELD (part), CULPEPER, GOOCHLAND, HANOVER, HENRICO (part), LOUISA, MADISON, ORANGE, RAPPAHANNOCK, SPOTSYLVANIA (part). CITIES: Richmond. Population (2010), 727,366.

ZIP Codes: 20106, 20186, 22407–08, 22433, 22508, 22534, 22542, 22546, 22551, 22553, 22565, 22567, 22580, 22701, 22713–14, 22716, 22718, 22724, 22726, 22729, 22733–37, 22740–41, 22923, 22942, 22947, 22957, 22960, 22972,

22974, 23005, 23015, 23024, 23038–39, 23047, 23058–60, 23063, 23065, 23067, 23069, 23084, 23093, 23102–03, 23111–14, 23116–17, 23120, 23124, 23129, 23146, 23153, 23160, 23162, 23170, 23173, 23192, 23221, 23224–30, 23233–36, 23238, 23242, 23255, 23273, 23294, 23832

* * *

EIGHTH DISTRICT

JAMES P. MORAN, Democrat, of Alexandria, VA; born in Buffalo, NY, May 16, 1945; education: B.A., College of Holy Cross; Bernard Baruch Graduate School of Finance—City University of New York; M.P.A., University of Pittsburgh Graduate School of Public and International Affairs; served on City Council of Alexandria, 1979–82; Vice Mayor, 1982–84; Mayor, 1985–90; founding member of the New Democrat Coalition; co-chair of Congressional Animal Protection Caucus; Task Force on Sovereign Wealth Funds; named as one of two ''High Technology Legislators of the Year'' by the Information Technology Industry Council; in 2000 named to the ''Legislative Hall of Fame'' by the American Electronics Association for his work on technology issues; in 2010 named ''Legislator of Year'' by the Humane Society of the United States for his work on animal welfare legislation; ''Humane Hero Award'' in 2013; 111th Congress ''Silver Mouse'' winner for Web presence; children: James, Patrick, Mary, and Dorothy; committees: Appropriations; elected to the 102nd Congress on November 6, 1990; reelected to each succeeding Congress.

Office Listings

http://moran.house.gov facebook.com/repjimmoran twitter.com/jim__moran

2252 Rayburn House Office Building, Washington, DC 20515 .... (202) 225–4376
Chief of Staff.—Austin Durrer. FAX: 225–0017
Legislative Director.—Tim Aiken.
333 North Fairfax Street, Suite 201, Alexandria, VA 22314 .... (703) 971–4700
District Director.—Susie Warner.

Counties: ARLINGTON, FAIRFAX (part). CITIES: Alexandria, and Falls Church. Population (2010), 767,596.

ZIP Codes: 22003, 22037, 22040–44, 22046, 22060, 22079, 22101–02, 22107–08, 22121–22, 22150–51, 22153, 22199, 22201–07, 22209–17, 22219, 22225–27, 22230, 22240–45, 22301–15, 22320, 22331–34, 22350

* * *

NINTH DISTRICT

H. MORGAN GRIFFITH, Republican, of Salem, VA; born March 15, 1958; education: graduated, Andrew Lewis High School, 1976; B.A., Emory and Henry College, 1980; J.D., Washington and Lee University School of Law, 1983; professional: attorney, private practice, 1983–2011; partner, Albo & Oblon, L.L.P., 2008–11; Virginia House of Delegates, 1994–2011; majority leader, Virginia House of Delegates, 2001–11; married Hilary; children: Abby, Davis, and Starke; committees: Energy and Commerce; elected to the 112th Congress on November 2, 2010; reelected to the 113th Congress on November 6, 2012.

Office Listings

http://www.morgangriffith.house.gov twitter: @repmgriffith
https://www.facebook.com/repmorgangriffith

1108 Longworth House Office Building, Washington, DC 20515 .... (202) 225–3861
Chief of Staff.—Kelly Lungren McCollum. FAX: 225–0076
Legislative Director.—Will Hupman.
Communications Director.—Andie Pivarunas.
323 West Main Street, Abingdon, VA 24210 .... (276) 525–1405
District Director.—Michelle Jenkins.
17 West Main Street, Christiansburg, VA 24073 .... (540) 381–5671

Counties: ALLEGHANY, BLAND, BUCHANAN, CARROLL, CRAIG, DICKENSON, FLOYD, GILES, GRAYSON, HENRY (part), LEE, MONTGOMERY, PATRICK, PULASKI, ROANOKE (part), RUSSELL, SCOTT, SMYTH, TAZEWELL, WASHINGTON, WISE, AND WYTHE. CITIES: Bristol, Covington, Galax, Martinsville, Norton, Radford and Salem. Population (2010), 727,366.

ZIP Codes: 24017, 24019, 24053, 24055, 24058–63, 24068, 24070, 24072–73, 24076, 24078, 24079, 24082, 24084, 24086–89, 24091, 24093, 24105, 24111–15, 24120, 24124, 24216–19, 24131–34, 24136, 24138, 24141–43, 24147–50, 24153, 24162, 24165, 24167–68, 24171, 24174–75, 24177, 24185, 24201–03, 24209–12, 24216–21, 24224–26, 24228, 24230, 24236–37, 24239, 24243–46, 24248, 24250–51, 24256, 24258, 24260, 24263, 24265–66, 24269–73, 24277, 24279–83, 24290, 24292–93, 24301, 24311–19, 24322–28, 24330, 24333, 24340, 24343, 24347–48, 24350–54, 24360–61, 24363, 24366, 24368, 24370, 24374–75, 24377–78, 24380–82, 24422, 24426, 24445, 24448, 24457, 24474, 24601–09, 24612–14, 24619–22, 24624, 24627–28, 24630–31, 24634–35, 24637, 24639–41, 24646–47, 24649, 24651, 24656–58

* * *

TENTH DISTRICT

FRANK R. WOLF, Republican, of Vienna, VA; born in Philadelphia, PA, January 30, 1939; education: B.A., Pennsylvania State University, 1961; LL.B., Georgetown University Law School, 1965; served in the U.S. Army Signal Corps (Reserves); professional: lawyer, admitted to the Virginia State Bar; legislative assistant for former U.S. Congressman Edward G. Biester, Jr., 1968–71; assistant to Secretary of the Interior Rogers C.B. Morton, 1971–74; Deputy Assistant Secretary for Congressional and Legislative Affairs, Department of the Interior, 1974–75; member, Vienna Presbyterian Church; married: the former Carolyn Stover; children: Frank, Jr., Virginia, Anne, Brenda, and Rebecca; co-chair, Tom Lantos Human Rights Commission; committees: Appropriations; elected to the 97th Congress, November 4, 1980; reelected to each succeeding Congress.

Office Listings

http://www.wolf.house.gov

233 Cannon House Office Building, Washington, DC 20515 .... (202) 225–5136
Chief of Staff.—Dan Scandling. FAX: 225–0437
Legislative Director.—Tom Culligan.
13873 Park Center Road, Suite 130, Herndon, VA 20171 .... (703) 709–5800
Director of Constituent Services.—Judy McCary.
110 North Cameron Street, Winchester, VA 22601 .... (540) 667–0900

Counties: CLARKE, FAIRFAX (part), FREDERICK, LOUDOUN, AND PRINCE WILLIAM (part), CITIES: Manassas, Manassas Park, and Winchester. Population (2010), 758,321.

ZIP Codes: 20105, 20107, 20109–11, 20117, 20120–21, 20124, 20129–30, 20132, 20135, 20137, 20141, 20143, 20147–48, 20151–52, 20155, 20158, 20164–66, 20169–71, 20175–76, 20180, 20184, 20187, 20197, 22015, 22030, 22033, 22039, 22066, 22079, 22101–02, 22124, 22151, 22153, 22182, 22601–03, 22611, 22620, 22624–25, 22630, 22637, 22645–46, 22654–56, 22663

* * *

ELEVENTH DISTRICT

GERALD E. CONNOLLY, Democrat, of Fairfax, VA; born in Boston, MA, March 30, 1950; education: graduated B.A., Maryknoll College; M.A., public administration, Harvard University, 1979; professional: member, Fairfax County Board of Supervisors, 1995–2003, chairman, 2003–07; religion: Roman Catholic; married: Cathy; children: Caitlin; committees: Foreign Affairs; Oversight and Government Reform; elected to the 111th Congress on November 4, 2008; reelected to each succeeding Congress.

Office Listings

http://www.geraldconnolly.house.gov

424 Cannon House Office Building, Washington, DC 20515 .... (202) 225–1492
Chief of Staff.—James Walkinshaw. FAX: 225–3071
Legislative Director.—Dominic Bonaiuto.
Communications Director.—George Burke.
4115 Annandale Road, Annandale, VA 22003 .... (703) 256–3071
District Director.—Sharon Stark.
4308 Ridgewood Center Drive, Woodbridge, VA 22192 .... (703) 670–4989
Prince William Director.—Colin Davenport.

Counties: FAIRFAX (part), PRINCE WILLIAM (part). CITIES: ANNANDALE, BURKE, CENTREVILLE, DALE CITY, FAIRFAX, FAIRFAX STATION, HERNDON, LORTON, MANASSAS, OAKTON, OCCOQUAN, RESTON, SPRINGFIELD, VIENNA, AND WOODBRIDGE. Population (2010), 770,944.

ZIP Codes: 20112, 20120–21, 20124, 20170–71, 20190–91, 20194, 22003, 22015, 22026–27, 22030–33, 22039, 22041–42, 22044, 22079, 22102, 22124–25, 22150–53, 22172, 22180–82, 22191–93

WASHINGTON

(Population 2010, 6,724,540)

SENATORS

PATTY MURRAY, Democrat, of Seattle, WA; born in Seattle, October 11, 1950; education: B.A., Washington State University, 1972; professional: teacher; lobbyist; Shoreline Community College; citizen lobbyist for environmental and educational issues, 1983–88; parent education instructor for Crystal Springs, 1984–87; school board member, 1985–89; elected Board of Directors, Shoreline School District, 1985–89; Washington State Senate, 1988–92; Democratic Whip, 1990–92; State Senate committees: Education; Ways and Means; Commerce and Labor; Domestic Timber Processing Select Committee; Open Government Select Committee; chair, School Transportation Safety Task Force; award: Washington State Legislator of the Year, 1990; married: Rob Murray; children: Randy and Sara; committees: chair, Budget; Appropriations; Health, Education, Labor, and Pensions; Rules and Administration; Veterans' Affairs; elected to the U.S. Senate on November 3, 1992; reelected to each succeeding Senate term.

Office Listings

http://murray.senate.gov

154 Russell Senate Office Building, Washington, DC 20510 .... (202) 224–2621
Chief of Staff.—Mike Spahn. FAX: 224–0238
Deputy Chief of Staff / Legislative Director.—Shawn Bills. TDD: 224–4430
Communications Director.—Matt McAlvanah.
2988 Jackson Federal Building, 915 Second Avenue, Seattle, WA 98174 .... (206) 553–5545
State Director.—Brian Kristjansson.
The Marshall House, 1323 Officer's Row, Vancouver, WA 98661 .... (360) 696–7797
District Director.—Kate Whittier.
10 North Post Road, Suite 600, Spokane, WA 99201 .... (509) 624–9515
District Director.—John Culton.
2930 Wetmore Avenue, Suite 903, Everett, WA 98201 .... (425) 259–6515
District Director.—Max Brown.
402 East Yakima Avenue, Suite 390, Yakima, WA 98901 .... (509) 453–7462
District Director.—Rebecca Thornton.
950 Pacific Avenue, Room 650, Tacoma, WA 98402 .... (253) 572–3636
District Director.—Kristine Reeves.

* * *

MARIA CANTWELL, Democrat, of Edmonds, WA; born in Indianapolis, IN, October 13, 1958; education: B.A., Miami University, Miami, OH, 1980; professional: businesswoman; RealNetworks, Inc.; organizations: South Snohomish County Chamber of Commerce; Alderwood Rotary; Mountlake Terrace Friends of the Library; public service: Washington State House of Representatives, 1987–92; U.S. House of Representatives, 1992–94; religion: Roman Catholic; committees: chair, Small Business and Entrepreneurship; Commerce, Science, and Transportation; Energy and Natural Resources; Finance; Indian Affairs; elected to the U.S. Senate on November 7, 2000; reelected to each succeeding Senate term.

Office Listings

http://cantwell.senate.gov twitter: @cantwellpress

311 Hart Senate Office Building, Washington, DC 20510 .... (202) 224–3441
Chief of Staff.—James Fleet. FAX: 228–0514
Legislative Director.—Pete Modaff.
Administrative Director.—Nancy Hadley.
915 Second Avenue, Suite 3206, Seattle, WA 98174 .... (206) 220–6400
The Marshall House, 1313 Officers Row, Vancouver, WA 98661 .... (360) 696–7838
950 Pacific Avenue, Suite 615, Tacoma, WA 98402 .... (253) 572–2281
U.S. Federal Courthouse, West 920 Riverside, Suite 697, Spokane, WA 99201 ...... (509) 353–2507
825 Jadwin Avenue, 204/204A, Richland, WA 99352 .... (509) 946–8106
2930 Wetmore Avenue, Suite 9B, Everett, WA 98201 .... (425) 303–0114

REPRESENTATIVES

FIRST DISTRICT

SUZAN K. DELBENE, Democrat, of Medina, WA; born in Selma, Dallas County, AL, February 17, 1962; education: B.A., Reed College, Portland, OR, 1983; M.B.A., University of

Washington, Seattle, WA, 1990; business executive; unsuccessful candidate for election to the United States House of Representatives in 2010; director, Washington State Department of Revenue, 2010–12; married: Kurt; two children: Becca and Zach; committees: Agriculture; Judiciary; elected simultaneously as a Democrat to the 112th Congress and 113th Congress, by special election to fill the vacancy caused by the resignation of U.S. Representative Jay Inslee (November 6, 2012–present).

Office Listings

http://delbene.house.gov

318 Cannon House Office Building, Washington, DC 20515 .... (202) 225–6311
Chief of Staff.—Aaron Schmidt. FAX: 226–1606
Legislative Director.—Lisa Kohn.
Communications Director.—Viet Shelton.
Scheduler.—Melissa Plummer.
Canyon Park Business Center, 22121 17th Avenue Southeast, Suite 220, Bothell, WA 98021 .... (425) 485–0085
204 West Montgomery Street, Mount Vernon, WA 98273 .... (360) 417–7879
District Director.—Julien Loh.

Counties: KING (part), SKAGIT (part), SNOHOMISH (part), WHATCOM (part). CITIES AND TOWNSHIPS: Blaine, Bothell, Carnation, Concrete, Darrington, Duvall, Everson, Ferndale, Gold Bar, Granite Falls, Hamilton, Hunts Point, Index, Kenmore, Kirkland, Lake Stevens, Lyman, Lynden, Medina, Mill Creek, Monroe, Mount Vernon, Nooksack, Point Roberts, Redmond, Skykomish, Snohomish, Sultan, Sumas, Woodinville, and Yarrow Point. Population (2010) 691,738.

ZIP Codes: 98004 (part), 98007 (part), 98008 (part), 98011, 98012 (part), 98014, 98019, 98021 (part), 98024 (part), 98028, 98033, 98034, 98036 (part), 98039, 98041, 98045 (part), 98052 (part), 98053, 98065 (part), 98072–73, 98074 (part), 98077, 98082–83, 98155 (part), 98201 (part), 98208 (part), 98220, 98223 (part), 98224, 98225 (part), 98226 (part), 98230–31, 98233 (part), 98235, 98237, 98240–41, 98244, 98247–48, 98251–52, 98255–56, 98258 (part), 98262–64, 98266–67, 98270 (part), 98272, 98273 (part), 98274 (part), 98276, 98281, 98283, 98284 (part), 98288, 98290–91, 98293–96

* * *

SECOND DISTRICT

RICK LARSEN, Democrat, of Everett, WA; born in Arlington, WA, June 15, 1965; education: B.A., Pacific Lutheran University; M.P.A., University of Minnesota; professional: economic development official at the Port of Everett; Director of Public Affairs for a health provider association; public service: Snohomish County Council; religion: Methodist; married: Tiia Karlen; children: Robert and Per; committees: Armed Services; Transportation and Infrastructure; elected to the 107th Congress on November 7, 2000; reelected to each succeeding Congress.

Office Listings

http:/www.house.gov/larsen

2113 Rayburn House Office Building, Washington, DC 20515 .... (202) 225–2605
Chief of Staff.—Kimberly Johnston. FAX: 225–4420
Legislative Director.—Terra Sabag.
Communications Director.—Bryan Thomas.
2930 Wetmore Avenue, Suite 9F, Everett, WA 98201 .... (425) 252–3188
119 North Commercial Street, Suite 1350, Bellingham, WA 98225 .... (360) 733–5144

Counties: ISLAND, SAN JUAN, SKAGIT (part), SNOHOMISH (part), WHATCOM (part). CITIES AND TOWNSHIPS: Anacortes, Arlington, Bellingham, Blakely Island, Bow, Burlington, Clinton, Conway, Coupeville, Deer Harbor, East Sound, Everett, Freeland, Friday Harbor, Greenbank, Langley, Lopez Island, Lynnwood, Marysville, Mountlake Terrace, Mukilteo, Oak Harbor, Olga, Orcas, Shaw Island, Silvana, Stanwood, Tulalip, and Waldron. Population (2010), 672,454.

ZIP Codes: 98012, 98021, 98026, 98036–37, 98043, 98207, 98221–22, 98225–29, 98232–33, 98236, 98238–39, 98243, 98245, 98249–50, 98253, 98257, 98260–61, 98270–71, 98273, 98275, 98277–80, 98284, 98286–87, 98292, 98297

* * *

THIRD DISTRICT

JAIME HERRERA BEUTLER, Republican, of Camas, born in Glendale, CA, November 3, 1978; education: communications, University of Washington, Seattle, WA, 2004; religion: Christian; family: married to Daniel Beutler; caucuses: co-vice chair of the Congressional Congress for Women's Issues / co-chair of the Women and the Economy / Business Task Force;

committees: Appropriations; Small Business; elected to the 112th Congress on November 2, 2010; reelected to the 113th Congress on November 6, 2012.

Office Listings

http://www.jaimehb.house.gov

1130 Longworth House Office Building, Washington, DC 20515 .... (202) 225–3536
Chief of Staff.—Casey Bowman. FAX: 225–3478
Legislative Director.—Chad Ramey.
Legislative Assistants: Dan Sadlosky, Jessica Wixson.
Press Secretary.—Drew Griffin.
Executive Assistant / Scheduler.—Amy Pennington.
Legislative Correspondent.—Jordon Evich.
Staff Assistant.—Christina Perez.
750 Anderson Street, Suite B, Vancouver, WA 98661 .... (360) 695–6292
District Director.—Ryan Hart.
Deputy District Director.—Shari Hildreth.
Outreach Director.—Pam Peiper.
Caseworkers: Ashley Lara, Dale Lewis, Jordan Meade.
District Staff Assistant.—Terassa Wren.

Counties: CLARK, COWLITZ, KLICKITAT, LEWIS, PACIFIC, SKAMANIA, THURSTON (part), WAHKIAKUM. Population (2010), 672,448.

ZIP Codes: 98304 (part), 98330 (part), 98336, 98355–56, 98361, 98377, 98522, 98527, 98530–33, 98537 (part), 98538–39, 98542, 98544, 98547 (part), 98554, 98561, 98564–65, 98568 (part), 98570, 98572, 98576 (part), 98577, 98579 (part), 98581–82, 98585–86, 98589 (part), 98590–91, 98593, 98596, 98597 (part), 98601–07, 98609–14, 98616–17, 98619–26, 98628–29, 98631–32, 98635, 98637–45, 98647–51, 98660–66, 98668, 98670–75, 98682–87, 98935 (part), 99322 (part), 99350 (part), 99356

* * *

FOURTH DISTRICT

DOC HASTINGS, Republican, of Pasco, WA; born in Spokane, WA, February 7, 1941; education: graduated, Pasco High School, 1959; attended Columbia Basin College and Central Washington State University, Ellensburg, WA; military service: U.S. Army Reserves, 1963–69; professional: president, Columbia Basin Paper and Supply; board of directors, Yakima Federal Savings and Loan; member: Washington State House of Representatives, 1979–87; Republican Caucus chairman, assistant majority leader, and National Platform Committee, 1984; president: Pasco Chamber of Commerce; Pasco Downtown Development Association; Pasco Jaycees (chamber president); chairman, Franklin County Republican Central Committee, 1974–78; delegate, Republican National Convention, 1976–84; married: Claire Hastings, 1967; children: Kirsten, Petrina and Colin; committees: chair, Natural Resources; Oversight and Government Reform; elected to the 104th Congress; reelected to each succeeding Congress.

Office Listings

http://www.house.gov/hastings https://www.facbook.com/repdochastings
twitter: @dochastings

1203 Longworth House Office Building, Washington, DC 20515 .... (202) 225–5816
Chief of Staff.—Jenny Gorski. FAX: 225–3251
Scheduler / Office Manager.—Ilene Clauson.
Press Secretary.—Neal Kirby.
2715 Saint Andrews Loop, Suite D, Pasco, WA 99302 .... (509) 543–9396
402 East Yakima Avenue, Suite 760, WA 98901 .... (509) 452–3243

Counties: ADAMS COUNTY. CITIES: Othello, Ritzville. BENTON COUNTY. CITIES AND TOWNSHIPS: Benton City, Kennewick, Paterson, Plymouth, Prosser, Richland, West Richland. DOUGLAS COUNTY. CITIES AND TOWNSHIPS: Bridgeport, East Wenatchee, Leahy, Mansfield, Orondo, Palisades, Rock Island, Waterville. FRANKLIN COUNTY. CITIES AND TOWNSHIPS: Basin City, Connell, Eltopia, Kahlotus, Mesa, Pasco, Windust. GRANT COUNTY. CITIES AND TOWNSHIPS: Beverly, Coulee City, Desert Aire, Electric City, Ephrata, George, Grand Coulee, Hartline, Marlin, Mattawa, Moses Lake, Quincy, Royal City, Soap Lake, Stratford, Warden, Wilson Creek. OKANOGAN COUNTY. CITIES: Brewster, Nespelem, Okanogan, Omak, Oroville, Tonasket, and Twisp. WALLA WALLA COUNTY (part). CITIES: Burbank. YAKIMA COUNTY. CITIES AND TOWNSHIPS: Brownstown, Buena, Carson, Cowiche, Grandview, Granger, Harrah, Mabton, Moxee, Naches, Outlook, Parker, Selah, Sunnyside, Tieton, Toppenish, Underwood, Wapato, White Swan, Yakima, and Zillah. Population (2010), 695,040.

ZIP Codes: 98068, 98602, 98605, 98610, 98613, 98617, 98619–20, 98623, 98628, 98635, 98648, 98650–51, 98670, 98672–73, 98801–02, 98807, 98811–13, 98815–17, 98819, 98821–24, 98826, 98828–32, 98834, 98836–37, 98840–44, 98843, 98845, 98847–48, 98850–53, 98855–56, 98857–58, 98860, 98901–04, 98907–09, 98920–23, 98925–26, 98929–30, 98932–44, 98946–48, 98950–53, 99103, 99115–16, 99123–24, 99133, 99135, 99155, 99169, 99301–02, 99320–22, 99323, 99326, 99330, 99335–38, 99343–46, 99349–50, 99352–54, 99356–57

* * *

FIFTH DISTRICT

CATHY McMORRIS RODGERS, Republican, of Spokane, WA; born in Salem, OR, May 22, 1969; education: B.A., Pensacola Christian College, Pensacola, FL, 1990; M.B.A., University of Washington, Seattle, WA, 2002; professional: fruit orchard worker; member, Washington State House of Representatives, 1994–2004; minority leader, 2002–03; organizations: member, Grace Evangelical Free Church; married: Brian Rodgers; children: Cole; chair, House Republican Conference; committees: Energy and Commerce; elected to the 109th Congress on November 2, 2004; reelected to each succeeding Congress.

Office Listings

http://www.house.gov/mcmorris https://twitter.com/cathymcmorris
https://www.facebook.com/#!/mcmorrisrodgers

203 Cannon House Office Building, Washington, DC 20515 .... (202) 225–2006
Chief of Staff.—Dave Peluso. FAX: 225–3392
Executive Assistant.—Andrea DeFelice.
Staff Assistant.—Bryce Comstock.
Legislative Director.—Melanie Steele.
Legislative Counsel.—Dr. Karen Summar.
Legislative Correspondent.—Mike Lanza.
10 North Post Street, 6th floor, Spokane, WA 99210 .... (509) 353–2374
Deputy District Director.—Louise Fendrich. FAX: 225–9379
AG & Resource Policy Director.—Mike Poulson.
Constituent Relations Liaison.—Kristy Sauer.
Executive Assistant / Finance Administration.—Rashelle Conley.
Press Secretary.—Melanie Collett.
555 South Main Street, Suite C, Colville, WA 99114 .... (509) 684–3481
Deputy District Director.—Sheila Stalp. FAX: 684–3482
Regional Representative.—Karen Dodson.
29 South Palouse Street, Walla Walla, WA 99362 .... (509) 529–9358
Deputy District Director.—Cathy Schaeffer. FAX: 529–9379

Counties: ASOTIN, COLUMBIA, FERRY, GARFIELD, PEND OREILLE, LINCOLN, SPOKANE, STEVENS, WALLA WALLA, AND WHITMAN. Population (2010), 672,455.

ZIP Codes: 98812, 98814, 98819, 98827, 98829, 98832–34, 98840–41, 98844, 98846, 98849, 98855–57, 98859, 98862, 99001, 99003–06, 99008–09, 99011–14, 99016–23, 99025–27, 99029–34, 99036–37, 99039–40, 99101–05, 99107, 99109–11, 99113–14, 99116–19, 99121–22, 99125–26, 99128–31, 99133–41, 99143–44, 99146–61, 99163–67, 99169–71, 99173–74, 99176, 99179–81, 99185, 99201–20, 99223–24, 99228, 99251–52, 99256, 99258, 99260, 99302, 99323–24, 99326, 99328–29, 99333, 99335, 99341, 99344, 99347–48, 99356, 99359–63, 99371, 99401–03

* * *

SIXTH DISTRICT

DEREK KILMER, Democrat, of Gig Harbor, WA; born in Port Angeles, January 1, 1974; education: graduated, Port Angeles High School, 1992; B.A., public affairs, Princeton University, 1996; Ph.D., University of Oxford, 1999; professional: worked as a consultant with McKinsey & Company from 1999–2002; worked for the Economic Development Board for Tacoma-Pierce County; elected to be a Washington State Representative in 2004; served in the Washington State Senate from 2007–12, caucuses: member, Democrat Caucus; New Democrats; co-chair of the Puget Sound Recovery Caucus; Rotary; married: the former Jennifer Saunders, children: Sophie and Tess; committees: Armed Services; Science, Space, and Technology; elected to the 113th Congress on November 6, 2012.

Office Listings

http://kilmer.house.gov https://twitter: @repderekkilmer
https//www.facebook.com/derek.kilmer

1429 Longworth House Office Building, Washington, DC 20515 .... (202) 225–5916
Chief of Staff.—Jonathan Smith. FAX: 226–3575
Press Secretary.—Stephen Carter.
Legislative Director.—Kevin Warnke.
Scheduler.—Andrea Friedhoff.
950 Pacific Avenue, Suite 1320, Tacoma, WA 98402 .... (253) 272–3515
District Director.—Meadow Johnson.
345 Sixth Street, Suite 500, Bremerton, WA 98337 .... (360) 373–9725
Deputy District Director.—Joe Dacca.
322 East Fifth Street, Port Angeles, WA 98362 .... (360) 797–3623

District Representative.—Judith Morris.

Counties: CLALLAM. CITIES AND TOWNSHIPS: Blyn, Forks, Joyce, LaPush, Neah Bay, Port Angeles, Sequim, and Sieku. GRAYS HARBOR. CITIES AND TOWNSHIPS: Aberdeen, Amanda Park, Cosmopolis, Elma, Hoquiam, McCleary, MoClips, Montesano, Oakville, Ocean City, Ocean Shores, Quinault, Seabrook, Taholah, and Westport. JEFFERSON. CITIES AND TOWNSHIPS: Chimicum, Nordland, Port Hadlock, Port Ludlow, Port Townsend, and Quilcene. KITSAP. CITIES AND TOWNSHIPS: Bainbridge Island, Bremerton, Hansville, Indianola, Kingston, Manchester, Olalla, Port Orchard, Poulsbo, Seabeck, Silverdale, and Southworth. MASON (part). CITIES AND TOWNSHIPS: Allyn, Belfair, Grapeview, Harstine Island, Shelton, Skokomish, and Union. PIERCE (part). CITIES AND TOWNSHIPS: Fox Island, Gig Harbor, Key Center, Lakebay, Longbranch, Purdy, Tacoma, Vaughn, and Wauna. Population: (2010), 687,387.

ZIP Codes: 98061, 98110, 98305, 98310–12, 98315, 98320, 98322, 98324–98326, 98329, 98331–33, 98335, 98337, 98339–40, 98342–43, 98345–46, 98349–51, 98353, 98357–59, 98362–68, 98370, 98376, 98378, 98380–84, 98386, 98392–95, 98401–98403, 98405–09, 98411–13, 98415, 98417–919, 98421, 98444, 98465–67, 98471, 98499, 98502, 98520, 98524, 98526, 98528, 98535–98537, 98541, 98546–48, 98550, 98552, 98555, 98557, 98559–60, 98562–63, 98566, 98568–69, 98571, 98575, 98583–84, 98587–88, 98592, 98595

* * *

SEVENTH DISTRICT

JIM McDERMOTT, Democrat, of Seattle, WA; born in Chicago, IL, December 28, 1936; education: B.S., Wheaton College, Wheaton, IL, 1958; M.D., University of Illinois Medical School, Chicago, 1963; residency in adult psychiatry, University of Illinois Hospitals, 1964–66; residency in child psychiatry, University of Washington Hospitals, Seattle, 1966–68; served, U.S. Navy Medical Corps, lieutenant commander, 1968–70; psychiatrist; Washington State House of Representatives, 1971–72; Washington State Senate, 1975–87; Democratic nominee for governor, 1980; regional medical officer, Sub-Saharan Africa, U.S. Foreign Service, 1987–88; practicing psychiatrist and assistant clinical professor of psychiatry, University of Washington, Seattle, 1970–83; member: Washington State Medical Association; King County Medical Society; American Psychiatric Association; religion: St. Mark's Episcopal Church, Seattle; grown children: Katherine and James; grandchildren; committees: Budget; Ways and Means; elected on November 8, 1988, to the 101st Congress; reelected to each succeeding Congress.

Office Listings

http://www.house.gov/mcdermott facebook.com/congressmanjimmcdermott
twitter.com/repjimmcdermott

1035 Longworth House Office Building, Washington, DC 20515 .... (202) 225–3106
Chief of Staff.—Diane Shust. FAX: 225–6197
Executive Assistant.—Myat Khaing.
Communications Director.—Amber MacDonald.
1809 Seventh Avenue, Suite 1212, Seattle, WA 98101–1313 .... (206) 553–7170
District Administrator.—Olivia Robinson.

Counties: KING COUNTY (part). CITIES AND TOWNSHIPS: Edmonds, Woodway, Burien (part), Lake Forest Park, Vashon Island, Shoreline, Normandie Park, and Seattle. Population (2010), 672,455.

ZIP Codes: 98020, 98026, 98037, 98043, 98070, 98101–09, 98112, 98115–17, 98119, 98121–22, 98125–26, 98133–34, 98136, 98146, 98148, 98154–55, 98164, 98166, 98168, 98174, 98177, 98195, 98198–99

* * *

EIGHTH DISTRICT

DAVID G. REICHERT, Republican, of Auburn, WA; born in Detroit Lakes, MI, August 29, 1950; education: graduated, Kent Meridian High School, Renton, WA, 1968; A.A., Concordia Lutheran College, Portland, OR, 1970; professional: U.S. Air Force Reserve, 1971–76; U.S. Air Force, 1976; police officer, King County, WA, 1972–97; sheriff, King County, WA, 1997–2004; member: president, Washington State Sheriff's Association; executive board member, Washington Association of Sheriffs and Police Chiefs; co-chair, Washington State Partners in Crisis; awards: recipient of the 2004 National Sheriff's Association's ''Sheriff of the Year''; two-time Medal of Valor Award Recipient from the King County sheriff's office; Washington Policy Center's Champion of Freedom Award; Families Northwest Public Policy Award; married: Julie; children: Angela, Tabitha, and Daniel; committees: Ways and Means; elected to the 109th Congress on November 2, 2004; reelected to each succeeding Congress.

Office Listings

http://www.reichert.house.gov https://www.facebook.com/repdavereichert
twitter: @davereichert

1127 Longworth House Office Building, Washington, DC 20515 .... (202) 225–7761
Chief of Staff.—Jeff Harvey. FAX: 225–4282
Legislative Director.—Zachary Rudisill.
Executive Assistant / Scheduler.—Nichole Robison.
22605 Southeast 56th Street, Suite 130, Issaquah, WA 98029 .... (425) 677–7414
District Director.—Sue Foy.
200 Palouse Street, Suite 201–1, Wenatchee, WA 98801 .... (509) 885–6615

Counties: KING COUNTY (part). CITIES AND TOWNSHIPS: Sammamish, Issaquah, Snoqualmie, North Bend, Covington, Auburn, Federal Way, Bonney Lake, Enumclaw, Issaquah, Black Diamond. CHELAN COUNTY. CITIES AND TOWNSHIPS: Wenatchee, Chelan, Cashmere, Leavenworth. KITTITAS. CITIES AND TOWNSHIPS: Cle Elum, Easton, Ellensburg, Kittitas, Snoqualmie Pass, Roslyn, Thorp. DOUGLAS. CITIES AND TOWHSHIPS: East Wenatchee. PIERCE COUNTY (part). CITIES AND TOWNSHIPS: Ashfort, Bonney Lake, Buckley, Eatonville, Graham, Orting, and Sumner. Population (2010), 690,250.

ZIP Codes: 98001–03, 98010, 98022, 98024, 98027, 98029–32, 98038, 98042, 98045, 98047, 98050–51, 98058–59, 98065, 98068, 98074–75, 98092, 98304, 98321, 98323, 98328, 98330, 98338, 98354, 98360, 98372, 98374–75, 98385, 98387, 98390–91, 98396, 98424, 98558, 98580, 98801–02, 98811, 98815–17, 98821–22, 98826, 98828, 98831, 98836, 98847, 98852, 98901, 98922, 98925–26, 98934, 98937, 98940–41, 98943, 98946, 98950

* * *

NINTH DISTRICT

ADAM SMITH, Democrat, of Tacoma, WA; born in Washington, DC, June 15, 1965; education: graduated, Tyee High School, 1983; graduated, Fordham University, NY, 1987; law degree, University of Washington, 1990; admitted to the Washington Bar in 1991; professional: prosecutor for the city of Seattle; Washington State Senate, 1990–96; member: Kent Drinking Driver Task Force; board member, Judson Park Retirement Home; married: Sara Smith, 1993; committees: ranking member, Armed Services; elected to the 105th Congress; reelected to each succeeding Congress.

Office Listings

http://www.adamsmith.house.gov

2264 Rayburn House Office Building, Washington, DC 20515 .... (202) 225–8901
Chief of Staff.—Shana Chandler. FAX: 225–5893
Communications Director.—Benjamin Halle.
101 Evergreen Building, 15 South Grady Way, Renton, WA 98057 .... (253) 593–6600
District Director.—Matt Perry.
Office Manager.—Christine Choe.

Counties: KING (part), PIERCE (part), THURSTON (part). CITIES: Bellevue, Burien, Des Moines, Federal Way, Kent, Mercer Island, Newcastle, Renton, SeaTac, Seattle, Tacoma, and Tukwila. Population (2010), 672,460.

ZIP Codes: 98001, 98003–09, 98015, 98023, 98027, 98030–32, 98040, 98042, 98055–59, 98063, 98089, 98093, 98104, 98108, 98112, 98114, 98118, 98122, 98131, 98134, 98138, 98141, 98144, 98148, 98158, 98161, 98168, 98178, 98188–89, 98198, 98402, 98421, 98422, 98424

* * *

TENTH DISTRICT

DENNY HECK, Democrat, of Olympia, WA; born in Vancouver, WA, July 29, 1952; education: graduated, Columbia River High School, WA, 1970; graduated, The Evergreen State College, WA, 1973; professional: small business owner; President and co-founder of TVW, Washington's statewide public affairs cable channel, 1993–2003; chief of staff to Governor Booth Gardner, 1989–93; elected to five consecutive terms in the Washington State House of Representatives starting in 1976; religion: member, The Lutheran Church of The Good Shepherd; former trustee, Washington State Historical Society; former trustee, The Evergreen State College; married: Paula Heck, 1976; committees: Financial Services; elected to the 113th Congress on November 6, 2012.

Office Listings

http://www.dennyheck.house.gov www.facebook.com/congressmandennyheck
twitter: www.twitter.com/repdennyheck

425 Cannon House Office Building, Washington, DC 20515 .... (202) 226–4013

Chief of Staff.—Hart Edmonson. FAX: 225–0129
Legislative Director.—Jami Burgess.
Communications Director.—Phil Gardner.
420 College Street Southeast, Suite 3000, Lacey, WA 98503 .... (360) 459–8514
6000 Main Street Southwest, Suite 3B, Lakewood, WA 98499 .... (253) 208–6172
District Director.—Roel van der Lugt.

Counties: MASON (part), PIERCE (part), THURSTON (part). CITIES: Chehalis Indian Reservation (part), DuPont, Edgewood, Fife, Fircrest, Joint Base Lewis-McChord, Lacey, Lakewood, Nisqually Indian Reservation, Olympia, Puyallup, Puyallup Indian Reservation (part), Rainier, Roy, Shelton, Squaxin Island Indian Reservation (part), Steilacoom, Sumner, Tacoma (part), Tenino, Tumwater, University Place, and Yelm. Population (2010), 672,455.

ZIP Codes: 98047, 98303, 98327, 98338, 98354, 98371–75, 98387–88, 98390–91, 98404, 98408, 98418, 98421, 98424, 98430, 98433, 98438–39, 98443–47, 98466–67, 98498–99, 98501–03, 98506, 98512–13, 98516, 98558, 98576, 98579–80, 98584, 98589, 98597

WEST VIRGINIA

(Population 2010, 1,852,994)

SENATORS

JOHN D. ROCKEFELLER IV, Democrat, of Charleston, WV; born in New York City, NY, June 18, 1937; education: graduated, Phillips Exeter Academy, Exeter, NH, 1954; A.B., Harvard University, Cambridge, MA, 1961; honorary degrees: J.D., West Virginia University; Marshall University; Davis and Elkins College; Dickinson College; University of Alabama; University of Cincinnati; doctor of humanities, West Virginia Institute of Technology; doctor of public service, Salem College; professional service: Vista volunteer, Emmons, WV, 1964; West Virginia House of Delegates, 1966–68; elected Secretary of State of West Virginia, 1968; president, West Virginia Wesleyan College, 1973–76; Governor of West Virginia, 1976–84; married: the former Sharon Percy; children: John, Valerie, Charles and Justin; committees: chair, Commerce, Science, and Transportation; Finance; Veterans' Affairs; Select Committee on Intelligence; Joint Committee on Taxation; elected to the U.S. Senate on November 6, 1984; reelected to each succeeding Senate term.

Office Listings

http://rockefeller.senate.gov

531 Hart Senate Office Building, Washington, DC 20510	(202) 224–6472
Chief of Staff.—James Reid.	FAX: 224–7665
Legislative Director.—Mark Libell.	
Communications Director.—Jenny Rosenberg.	
405 Capitol Street, Suite 508, Charleston, WV 25301	(304) 347–5372
220 North Kanawha Street, Suite 1, Beckley, WV 25801	(304) 253–9704
118 Adams Street, Suite 301, Fairmont, WV 26554	(304) 367–0122
217 West King Street, Suite 307, Martinsburg, WV 25401	(304) 262–9285

* * *

JOE MANCHIN III, Democrat, of Fairmont, WV; born in Farmington, August 24, 1947; education: graduated, Farmington High School, Farmington, 1965; B.A., West Virginia University, WV, 1970; businessman; member of the West Virginia House of Delegates, 1982–86; member of the West Virginia State Senate, 1986–96; Secretary of State, West Virginia, 2000–04; elected governor of West Virginia in 2004 and reelected in 2008; chairman of the National Governors Association, 2010; religion: Catholic; married: Gayle Conelly; three children, Heather, Joseph IV, and Brooke; seven grandchildren; committees: Armed Services; Banking, Housing, and Urban Affairs; Energy and Natural Resources; Special Committee on Aging; elected to the 111th U.S. Senate in the November 2, 2010, special election to the term ending January 3, 2013, a seat previously held by Senator Carte Goodwin, and took the oath of office on November 15, 2010.

Office Listings

http://manchin.senate.gov

306 Hart Senate Office Building, Washington, DC 20510	(202) 224–3954
Chief of Staff.—Hayden Rogers.	FAX: 228–0002
Scheduler.—Emily Castleberry.	
Communications Director.—Jonathan Kott.	
900 Pennsylvania Avenue, Suite 629, Charleston, WV 25302	(304) 342–5855
State Director.—Mara Boggs.	
217 West King Street, Room 238, Martinsburg, WV 25401	(304) 264–4626
48 Donley Street, Suite 504, Morgantown, WV 26501	(304) 284–8663
	FAX: 284–8681

REPRESENTATIVES

FIRST DISTRICT

DAVID B. MCKINLEY, P.E., Republican, of Wheeling, WV; born in Wheeling, March 28, 1947; education: B.S.C.E., civil engineering, Purdue University, West Lafayette, IN, 1969; professional: engineer (started McKinley and Associates with offices in Wheeling and Charleston, WV and Washington, PA); member of West Virginia State House of Representatives, 1981–94; chairman, West Virginia Republican Party, 1990–94; religion: Episcopalian; married: Mary

McKinley; children: David, Amy, Elizabeth, and Bennett; committees: Energy and Commerce; elected to the 112th Congress on November 2, 2010; reelected to the 113th Congress on November 6, 2012.

Office Listings

412 Cannon House Office Building, Washington, DC 20515 .... (202) 225–4172
Chief of Staff.—Mike Hamilton. FAX: 225–7564
Scheduler and Office Manager.—Tim Hershner.
Legislative Director.—Devon Seibert.
Communications Director.—Jim Forbes.
709 Beechurst Avenue, Suite 14B, Morgantown, WV 26505 .... (304) 284–8506
Horne Building, 1100 Main Street, Suite 101, Wheeling, WV 26003 .... (304) 232–3801
Federal Building, 425 Juliana Street, Suite 1004, Parkersburg, WV 26101 .... (304) 422–5972

Counties: BARBOUR, BROOKE, DODDRIDGE, GILMER, GRANT, HANCOCK, HARRISON, MARION, MARSHALL, MINERAL, MONONGALIA, OHIO, PLEASANTS, PRESTON, RITCHIE, TAYLOR, TUCKER, TYLER, WETZEL, AND WOOD. CITIES AND TOWNSHIPS: Albright, Alma, Alvy, Anmoore, Arthur, Arthurdale, Auburn, Aurora, Baldwin, Barrackville, Baxter, Bayard, Beech Bottom, Belington, Belleville, Bellview, Belmont, Bens Run, Benwood, Berea, Bethany, Big Run, Blacksville, Blandville, Booth, Brandonville, Bretz, Bridgeport, Bristol, Brownton, Bruceton Mills, Burlington, Burnt House, Burton, Cabins, Cairo, Cameron, Carolina, Cassville, Cedarville, Center Point, Central Station, Century, Chester, Clarksburg, Coburn, Colfax, Colliers, Core, Corinth, Cove, Coxs Mills, Cuzzart, Dallas, Davis, Davisville, Dawmont, Dellslow, Dorcas, Eglon, Elk Garden, Ellenboro, Elm Grove, Enterprise, Eureka, Everettville, Fairmont, Fairview, Farmington, Flemington, Flower, Follansbee, Folsom, Fort Ashby, Fort Neal, Four States, Friendly, Galloway, Gilmer, Glen Dale, Glen Easton, Glenville, Goffs, Gormania, Grafton, Grant Town, Granville, Greenwood, Gypsy, Hambleton, Harrisville, Hastings, Haywood, Hazelton, Hebron, Hendricks, Hepzibah, Highland, Hundred, Idamay, Independence, Industrial, Jacksonburg, Jere, Jordan, Junior, Keyser, Kingmont, Kingwood, Knob Fork, Lahmansville, Letter Gap, Lima, Linn, Littleton, Lockney, Lost Creek, Lumberport, MacFarlan, Mahone, Maidsville, Mannington, Masontown, Maysville, McMechen, McWhorter, Meadowbrook, Medley, Metz, Middlebourne, Mineralwells, Moatsville, Monongah, Montana Mines, Morgantown, Moundsville, Mount Clare, Mount Storm, Mountain, New Creek, New Cumberland, New England, New Manchester, New Martinsville, New Milton, Newberne, Newburg, Newell, Normantown, North Parkersburg, Nutter Fort, Osage, Owings, Paden City, Parkersburg, Parsons, Pennsboro, Pentress, Perkins, Petersburg, Petroleum, Philippi, Piedmont, Pine Grove, Porters Falls, Proctor, Pullman, Pursglove, Rachel, Reader, Red Creek, Reedsville, Reynoldsville, Riegeley, Rivesville, Rocket Center, Rockport, Rosedale, Rosemont, Rowlesburg, Saint George, Saint Marys, Salem, Sand Fork, Shinnston, Shirley, Shocks, Short Creek, Simpson, Sistersville, Smithburg, Smithfield, Smithville, Spelter, Stonewood, Stouts Mill, Stumptown, Tanner, Terra Alta, Thomas, Thornton, Toll Gate, Troy, Triadelphia, Tunnelton, Valley Grove, Vienna, Volga, Wadestown, Walker, Wallace, Wana, Warwood, Washington, Watson, Waverly, Weirton, Wellsburg, Wendel, West Liberty, West Milford, West Union, Westover, Wheeling, Wick, Wilbur, Wiley Ford, Wileyville, Williamstown, Wilson, Wilsonburg, Windsor Heights, Wolf Summit, Worthington, and Wyatt. Population (2010), 615,991.

ZIP Codes: 25267, 26003, 26030–41, 26047, 26050, 26055–56, 26059–60, 26062, 26070, 26074–75, 26101, 26104–05, 26133–34, 26136–37, 26142–43, 26146, 26148–50, 26155, 26159, 26161, 26164, 26167, 26169–70, 26175, 26178, 26180–81, 26184, 26187, 26201, 26238, 26250, 26260, 26263, 26267, 26269, 26271, 26275–76, 26283, 26287, 26292, 26301, 26320, 26323, 26325, 26327, 26330, 26335, 26337, 26339, 26342, 26346–49, 26351, 26354, 26361–62, 26366, 26369, 26374, 26377–78, 26384–86, 26404–05, 26408, 26410–12, 26415–16, 26419, 26421–22, 26424–26, 26430–31, 26435–38, 26440, 26443–44, 26448, 26451, 26456, 26501, 26505, 26508, 26519–21, 26525, 26534, 26537, 26541–43, 26547, 26554, 26559–60, 26562–63, 26568, 26570–72, 26574–76, 26581–82, 26585–88, 26590–91, 26611, 26636, 26638, 26705, 26707, 26710, 26716–17, 26719–20, 26726, 26731, 26739, 26743, 26750, 26753, 26763–64, 26767, 26833, 26847, 26855

* * *

SECOND DISTRICT

SHELLEY MOORE CAPITO, Republican, of Charleston, WV; born in Glen Dale, WV, November 26, 1953; education: B.S., Duke University; M.Ed., University of Virginia; professional: career counselor; West Virginia State College; West Virginia Board of Regents; organizations: Community Council of Kanawha Valley; YWCA; West Virginia Interagency Council for Early Intervention; Habitat for Humanity; public service: elected to the West Virginia House of Delegates, 1996; reelected in 1998; awards: Coalition for a Tobacco-Free West Virginia Legislator of the Year; religion: Presbyterian; married: to Charles L., Jr.; three children; committees: Financial Services; Transportation and Infrastructure; elected to the 107th Congress on November 7, 2000; reelected to each succeeding Congress.

Office Listings

http://www.house.gov/capito

2443 Rayburn House Office Building, Washington, DC 20515 .... (202) 225–2711
Chief of Staff.—Joel Brubaker. FAX: 225–7856
Office Manager.—Alison Bibbee.
Legislative Director.—Adam Tomlinson.
4815 MacCorkle Avenue, Southeast, Charleston, WV 25304 .... (304) 925–5964
300 Foxcroft Avenue, Suite 102, Martinsburg, WV 25401 .... (304) 264–8810

Counties: BERKELEY, BRAXTON, CALHOUN, CLAY, HAMPSHIRE, HARDY, JACKSON, JEFFERSON, KANAWHA, LEWIS, MORGAN, PENDLETON, PUTNAM, RANDOLPH, ROANE, UPSHUR, WIRT. Population (2010), 654,275.

ZIP Codes: 25002–03, 25005, 25011, 25015, 25019, 25025–26, 25030, 25033, 25035, 25039, 25043, 25045–46, 25054, 25059, 25061, 25063–64, 25067, 25070–71, 25075, 25079, 25081–83, 25085–86, 25088, 25102–03, 25106–07, 25109–13, 25123–26, 25132–34, 25136, 25139, 25141, 25143, 25147, 25150, 25156, 25159–60, 25162, 25164, 25168, 25177, 25187, 25201–02, 25211, 25213–14, 25231, 25234–35, 25239, 25241, 25243–45, 25247–48, 25251–53, 25259–62, 25264–68, 25270–71, 25275–76, 25279, 25281, 25285–87, 25301–06, 25309, 25311–15, 25317, 25320–39, 25350, 25356–58, 25360–62, 25364–65, 25375, 25392, 25396, 25401–02, 25410–11, 25413–14, 25419–23, 25425, 25427–32, 25434, 25437–38, 25440–44, 25446, 25502–03, 25510, 25515, 25520, 25523, 25526, 25541, 25550, 25560, 25569, 26133, 26136–38, 26141, 26143, 26147, 26151–52, 26160–61, 26164, 26173, 26180, 26201–02, 26205, 26210, 26215, 26218, 26224, 26228–30, 26234, 26236–38, 26241, 26253–54, 26257, 26259, 26261, 26263, 26267–68, 26270, 26273, 26276, 26278, 26280, 26282–83, 26285, 26293–94, 26296, 26321, 26335, 26338, 26342–43, 26351, 26372, 26376, 26378, 26384–85, 26412, 26430, 26443, 26447, 26452, 26546, 26590, 26601, 26610–11, 26615, 26617, 26619, 26621, 26623–24, 26627, 26629, 26631, 26636, 26638–39, 26641, 26651, 26656, 26660, 26662, 26667, 26671, 26675–76, 26678–79, 26681, 26684, 26690–91, 26704–05, 26707, 26710–11, 26714, 26717, 26722, 26731, 26739, 26743, 26750, 26755, 26757, 26761, 26763–64, 26801–02, 26804, 26807–08, 26810, 26812, 26814–15, 26817–18, 26823–24, 26836, 26838, 26845, 26847, 26851–52, 26865–66, 26884, 26886

* * *

THIRD DISTRICT

NICK J. RAHALL II, Democrat, of Beckley, WV; born in Beckley, May 20, 1949; education: graduated, Woodrow Wilson High School, Beckley, 1967; A.B., Duke University, Durham, NC, 1971; graduate work, George Washington University, Washington, DC; colonel, U.S. Air Force Civil Air Patrol; president, West Virginia Society of Washington, DC; business executive; sales representative, WWNR radio station; president, Mountaineer Tour and Travel Agency, 1974; president, West Virginia Broadcasting; awards: Coal Man of the Year, *Coal Industry News,* 1979; Young Democrat of the Year, Young Democrats, 1980; delegate, Democratic National Conventions, 1972, 1976, 1980, 1984, 1988, 1992, 1996, 2000, 2004, 2008, 2012; recipient, National Guard Association of U.S. Harry S. Truman Award, 2012; member: Rotary; Elks; Moose; Eagles; NAACP; National Rifle Association (life member); Shrine Club; Benie Kedeem Temple in Charleston; Beckley Presbyterian Church; United Mine Workers of America (honorary); Mount Hope Commandery; chairman and founder, Congressional Coal Group; Democratic Leadership Council; Congressional Appalachian Regional Commission Caucus (co chair); Congressional Arts Caucus; International Workers' Rights Caucus; Intelligent Transportation Systems Caucus; Congressional Caucus on Coal; Congressional Caucus on Prescription Drug Abuse (co chair); Congressional Labor and Working Families Caucus; Congressional Law Enforcement Caucus; Congressional Pro-Life Caucus; Congressional Qatar-American Caucus (co chair); Congressional Rural Caucus; Congressional Steel Caucus; Congressional Travel and Tourism Caucus; Democratic Congressional Campaign Committee; Democratic Study Group; Military Veterans Caucus; National Guard and Reserve Components Caucus; U.S.-Lebanon Friendship Caucus (co chair); married: the former Melinda Ross; children: Rebecca Ashley, Nick Joe III, and Suzanne Nicole; grandchildren: Madison; committees: ranking member, Transportation and Infrastructure; elected to the 95th Congress, November 2, 1976; reelected to each succeeding Congress.

Office Listings

http://www.house.gov/rahall

2307 Rayburn House Office Building, Washington, DC 20515	(202) 225–3452
Chief of Staff / Legislative Director.—David McMaster.	FAX: 225–9061
Deputy Chief of Staff / Scheduler.—Kate Denmen.	
Senior Policy Advisor.—Kent Keyser.	
Communications Director.—Diane Luensmann.	
845 Fifth Avenue, Room 152, Huntington, WV 25701–2086	(304) 522–6425
109 Main Street, Beckley, WV 25801	(304) 252–5000
220 Dingess Street, Logan, WV 25601	(304) 752–4934
601 Federal Street, Room 1005, Bluefield, WV 24701	(304) 325–6222

Counties: BOONE, CABELL, FAYETTE, GREENBRIER, LINCOLN, LOGAN, MCDOWELL, MASON, MERCER, MINGO, MONROE, NICHOLAS, POCAHONTAS, RALEIGH, SUMMERS, WAYNE, WEBSTER, AND WYOMING. Population (2010), 613,376.

ZIP Codes: 24701, 24712, 24714–16, 24719, 24724, 24726, 24729, 24731–33, 24736–40, 24747, 24751, 24801, 24808, 24811, 24813, 24815–18, 24820–31, 24834, 24836, 24839, 24842–57, 24859–62, 24866–74, 24878–82, 24884, 24887–88, 24892, 24894–99, 24901–02, 24910, 24915–18, 24920, 24924–25, 24927, 24931, 24934–36, 24938, 24941, 24943–46, 24950–51, 24954, 24957, 24961–63, 24966, 24970, 24974, 24976–77, 24981, 24983–86, 24991, 24993, 25002–04, 25007–10, 25021–22, 25024, 25028, 25031, 25036, 25040, 25043–44, 25047–49, 25051, 25053, 25057, 25059–60, 25062, 25076, 25081, 25083, 25085, 25090, 25093, 25108, 25114–15, 25118–19, 25121, 25130, 25136, 25139–40, 25142, 25148–49, 25152, 25154, 25161, 25165, 25169, 25173–74, 25180–81, 25183, 25185–86, 25193, 25202–06, 25208–09, 25213, 25247, 25265, 25082, 25106, 25123, 25239, 25241, 25253, 25260, 25264, 25287, 25502–03, 25525, 25520, 25541, 25550–01, 25504–08, 25510–12, 25514, 25517, 25520–21, 25523–24, 25526, 25529–30, 25534–35, 25537, 25540–41, 25544–45, 25547, 25555, 25557, 25559, 25562, 25564–65, 25567, 25570–73, 25601, 25606–08, 25611–12, 25614, 25617, 25621, 25624–25, 25628, 25630, 25632, 25634–39, 25644, 25646–47, 25649–54, 25661, 25665–67, 25669–72, 25674, 25676, 25678, 25682, 25685–88, 25690–92, 25694, 25696, 25699, 25701–29, 25755, 25770–79, 25801–02, 25810–13, 25816–18, 25820, 25823, 25825–27, 25831–33, 25836–37, 25839–41, 25843–49, 25851, 25853–57, 25859–60, 25862, 25864–66, 25868, 25870–71, 25873, 25875–76,

25878–80, 25882, 25901–02, 25904, 25906–09, 25911, 25913–22, 25927–28, 25931–32, 25934, 25936, 25938, 25942–43, 25951, 25958, 25961–62, 25965–67, 25969, 25971–72, 25976–79, 25981, 25984–86, 25989, 26202–03, 26205–06, 26208–09, 26217, 26222, 26230, 26234, 26261, 26264, 26266, 26288, 26291, 26294, 26298, 26610, 26617, 26639, 26651, 26656, 26660, 26662, 26674, 26676, 26678–81, 26684, 26690–91

WISCONSIN

(Population 2010, 5,686,986)

SENATORS

RONALD H. JOHNSON, Republican, of Oshkosh, WI; born in Mankato, MN, April 18, 1955; education: B.A., business administration, University of Minnesota, Twin Cities, MN, 1977; professional: CEO Pacur, LLC.; married: wife, Jane; three children: daughters, Carey and Jenna; son, Ben; committees: Budget; Commerce, Science, and Transportation; Foreign Relations; Homeland Security and Governmental Affairs; Small Business and Entrepreneurship; elected to the U.S. Senate on November 2, 2010.

Office Listings

http://ronjohnson.senate.gov

328 Hart Senate Office Building, Washington, DC 20510 .... (202) 224–5323
Chief of Staff.—Tony Blando. FAX: 228–6965
Legislative Director.—Lydia Westlake.
Press Secretary.—Melinda Schnell.
517 East Wisconsin Avenue, Room 408, Milwaukee, WI 53202 .... (414) 276–7282
219 Washington Avenue, Suite 100, Oshkosh, WI 54901 .... (920) 230–7250
Deputy Chief of Staff.—Julie Leschke.

* * *

TAMMY BALDWIN, Democrat, of Madison, WI; born in Madison, February 11, 1962; education: graduated, Madison West High School, Madison, 1980; A.B., Smith College, Northampton, MA, 1984; J.D., University of Wisconsin Law School, Madison, 1989; elected to Madison Common Council, Madison, 1986; elected to Dane County Board of Supervisors, Madison, served 1986–94; elected to the Wisconsin State Assembly, Madison, served 1992–98; elected to the U.S. House of Representatives, served 1998–2012; committees: Budget; Energy and Natural Resources; Health, Education, Labor and Pensions; Homeland Security and Government Affairs; Special Committee on Aging; elected to the U.S. Senate on November 6, 2012.

Office Listings

http://baldwin.senate.gov facebook.com/senatortammybaldwin twitter: @senatorbaldwin

717 Hart Senate Office Building, Washington, DC 20510 .... (202) 224–5653
Chief of Staff.—Bill Murat.
Legislative Director.—Dan McCarthy.
Communications Director.—John Kraus.
Executive Assistant.—Carolyn Walser.
30 West Mifflin Street, Suite 700, Madison, WI 53703 .... (608) 264–5338
State Director.—Doug Hill.
633 West Wisconsin Avenue, Suite 1920, Milwaukee, WI 53203 .... (414) 297–4451
From Wisconsin Only: (800) 247–5645
205 5th Avenue South, Room 216, La Crosse, WI 54601 .... (608) 796–0045

REPRESENTATIVES

FIRST DISTRICT

PAUL RYAN, Republican, of Janesville, WI; born in Janesville, January 29, 1970; education: Joseph A. Craig High School; economic and political science degrees, Miami University, Ohio; professional: marketing consultant, Ryan Inc., Central (construction firm); aide to former U.S. Senator Bob Kasten (R–WI); advisor to former Vice Presidential candidate Jack Kemp, and U.S. Drug Czar Bill Bennett; legislative director, U.S. Senate; organizations: Janesville Bowmen, Inc.; Ducks Unlimited; married: Janna Ryan; three children: daughter, Liza; sons, Charlie and Sam; committees: chair, Budget; Ways and Means; elected to the 106th Congress; reelected to each succeeding Congress.

Office Listings

http://paulryan.house.gov

1233 Longworth House Office Building, Washington, DC 20515 .... (202) 225–3031

Administrative Assistant.—Joyce Meyer. FAX: 225–3393
Legislative Director.—Allison Steil.
Scheduler.—Sarah Peer.
20 South Main Street, Suite 10, Janesville, WI 53545 .... (608) 752–4050
5031 Seventh Avenue, Kenosha, WI 53140 .... (262) 654–1901
216 Sixth Street, Racine, WI 53403 .... (262) 637–0510

Counties: KENOSHA, MILWAUKEE (part), RACINE, ROCK (part), WALWORTH (part), AND WAUKESHA (part). Population (2010), 728,042.

ZIP Codes: 53103–05, 53108, 53114–15, 53118–21, 53125–26, 53128–30, 53132, 53139–40, 53142–44, 53146–47, 53149–51, 53153–54, 53158, 53167–68, 53170, 53177, 53179, 53181–82, 53184–85, 53189–92, 53195, 53219–21, 53227–28, 53402–06, 53505, 53511, 53525, 53534, 53538, 53545–46, 53548, 53563

* * *

SECOND DISTRICT

MARK POCAN, Democrat, of Madison, WI; born in Kenosha, August 14, 1964; education: graduated from Bradford High School, 1982; journalism, University of Wisconsin, 1986; professional: small business owner, 1986–present; elected to the Dane County Board of Supervisors, 1991–96; elected to the State Assembly from the 78th district, 1999–2013; elected to the 113th Congress from the 2nd district; committees: Budget; Education and the Workforce; elected to the 113th Congress on November 6, 2012.

Office Listings

http://pocan.house.gov

313 Cannon House Office Building, Washington, DC 20515 .... (202) 225–2906
Chief of Staff.—Glenn Wavrunek. FAX: 225–6942
Legislative Director.—Rosalyn Kumar.
Scheduler.—Brian Walsh.
Communications Director.—Samuel Lau.
10 East Doty Street, Suite 405, Madison, WI 53703 .... (608) 258–9800
District Director.—Janet Piraino.
100 State Street, 3rd Floor, Beloit, WI 53511 .... (608) 365–8001

Counties: DANE, GREEN, IOWA, LAFAYETTE, RICHLAND (part), ROCK (part), and SAUK. Population (2010), 729,417.

ZIP Codes: 53501–02, 53503–04, 53506–08, 53510–12, 53515–17, 53520–23, 53526–37, 53541–46, 53548, 53553–56, 53558–63, 53565–56, 53569–73, 53574–78, 53580–83, 53586, 53588–89, 53593–99, 53701–08, 53711, 53713–19, 53725, 53744, 53777–79, 53782–94, 53803, 53807, 53811, 53818, 53911, 53913, 53924–25, 53937, 53940–44, 53951, 53958–61, 53965, 53968

* * *

THIRD DISTRICT

RON KIND, Democrat, of La Crosse, WI; born in La Crosse, March 16, 1963; education: B.A., Harvard University, 1985; M.A., London School of Economics, 1986; J.D., University of Minnesota Law School, 1990; admitted to the Wisconsin Bar, 1990; state prosecutor, La Crosse County District Attorney's Office; board of directors, La Crosse Boys and Girls Club; Coulee Council on Alcohol and Drug Abuse; Wisconsin Harvard Club; Wisconsin Bar Association; La Crosse County Bar Association; married: Tawni Zappa in 1994; two sons: Jonathan and Matthew; committees: Ways and Means; elected to the 105th Congress; reelected to each succeeding Congress.

Office Listings

http://www.kind.house.gov

1502 Longworth House Office Building, Washington, DC 20515 .... (202) 225–5506
Chief of Staff.—Travis Robey. FAX: 225–5739
Press Secretary.—Peter Knudsen.
Legislative Director.—Rachel Stanley.
Scheduler.—Alex Eveland.
205 Fifth Avenue South, Suite 400, La Crosse, WI 54601 .... (608) 782–2558
District Director.—Loren Kannenberg.
131 South Barstow Street, Suite 301, Eau Claire, WI 54701 .... (715) 831–9214
Staff Assistant / Case Worker.—Mark Aumann.

Counties: ADAMS, BUFFALO, CHIPPEWA, CRAWFORD, DUNN, EAU CLAIRE, GRANT, JACKSON, JUNEAU, LA CROSSE, MONROE, PEPIN, PIERCE, PORTAGE, RICHLAND, TREMPEALEAU, VERNON, AND WOOD. Population (2010), 710,873.

ZIP Codes: 53518, 53543, 53554, 53556, 53569, 53573, 53581, 53801–02, 53804, 53805–11, 53813, 53816–18, 53820–21, 53825–27, 53910, 53920, 53924, 53929, 53934, 53936–37, 53941, 53944, 53948, 53950, 53952, 53964–65, 53968, 54003, 54005, 54010–11, 54013–14, 54021–22, 54406–07, 54410, 54412–13, 54423, 54443, 54454–55, 54457–58, 54466–67, 54469, 54473, 54475, 54481–82, 54489, 54494–95, 54499, 54601, 54603, 54610–16, 54618–19, 54621–32, 54634–39, 54642–45, 54648, 54650–61, 54664–67, 54669–70, 54701, 54703, 54720–27, 54729–30, 54734, 54736–42, 54747, 54749–51, 54754–63, 54765, 54767–70, 54772–73, 54909, 54921, 54930, 54943, 54945, 54966, 54977, 54981, 54984

* * *

FOURTH DISTRICT

GWEN MOORE, Democrat, of Milwaukee, WI; born in Racine, WI, April 18, 1951; education: graduated North Division High School, Milwaukee; B.A., political science, Marquette University, Milwaukee, WI, 1978; professional: Program and Planning Analyst for the State of Wisconsin Services; housing officer, Wisconsin Housing and Development Authority; member: Wisconsin State Assembly, 1989–92; Wisconsin State Senate, 1993–2004; president pro tempore, 1997–98; three children; committees: Budget; Financial Services; elected to the 109th Congress on November 2, 2004; reelected to each succeeding Congress.

Office Listings

http://www.house.gov/moore

2245 Rayburn House Office Building, Washington, DC 20515 .... (202) 225–4572
Chief of Staff.—Minh Ta. FAX: 225–8135
219 North Milwaukee Street, Suite 3A, Milwaukee, WI 53202 .... (414) 297–1140
District Administrator.—Shirley Ellis.

Counties: MILWAUKEE (part), WAUKESHA (part). CITIES AND TOWNSHIPS: Milwaukee, Cudahy, South Milwaukee, St. Francis, West Allis, and West Milwaukee. Population (2010), 710,873.

ZIP Codes: 53007, 53051, 53110, 53154, 53172, 53201–28, 53233, 53235, 53295

* * *

FIFTH DISTRICT

F. JAMES SENSENBRENNER, JR., Republican, of Menomonee Falls, WI; born in Chicago, IL, June 14, 1943; education: graduated, Milwaukee Country Day School, 1961; A.B., Stanford University, 1965; J.D., University of Wisconsin Law School, 1968; admitted to the Wisconsin Bar, 1968; commenced practice in Cedarburg, WI; admitted to practice before the U.S. Supreme Court in 1972; professional: attorney; staff member of former U.S. Congressman J. Arthur Younger of California, 1965; elected to the Wisconsin Assembly, 1968, reelected in 1970, 1972, and 1974; elected to Wisconsin Senate in a special election, 1975, reelected in 1976 (assistant minority leader); member: Waukesha County Republican Party; Wisconsin Bar Association; Friends of Museums; American Philatelic Society; married: the former Cheryl Warren, 1977; children: Frank James III and Robert Alan; committees: Judiciary; Science, Space, and Technology; elected to the 96th Congress, November 7, 1978; reelected to each succeeding Congress.

Office Listings

http://www.sensenbrenner.house.gov

2449 Rayburn House Office Building, Washington, DC 20515 .... (202) 225–5101
Chief of Staff.—Bart Forsyth.
Legislative Director.—Amy Bos.
Communications Director.—Ben Miller.
Scheduler / Office Manager.—Jordan Berghouse.
120 Bishops Way, Room 154, Brookfield, WI 53005 .... (262) 784–1111
Deputy Chief of Staff.—Loni Hagerup.

Counties: JEFFERSON, MILWAUKEE (part), DODGE (part), WASHINGTON, WAUKESHA (part). Population (2010), 716,218.

ZIP Codes: 53005, 53007, 53018, 53022, 53029, 53032, 53035, 53036–40, 53045–46, 53051–52, 53056, 53058, 53066, 53072, 53076, 53078, 53089, 53090, 53094–95, 53098, 53122, 53137, 53146, 53151, 53156, 53178, 53186, 53188–90, 53210, 53213–14, 53219, 53220–21, 53226–28, 53538, 53549, 53551, 53579, 53594

* * *

SIXTH DISTRICT

THOMAS E. PETRI, Republican, of Fond du Lac, WI; born in Marinette, WI, May 28, 1940; education: graduated, Lowell P. Goodrich High School, 1958; B.A., Harvard University, Cambridge, MA, 1962; J.D., Harvard Law School, 1965; professional: admitted to the Wisconsin State and Fond du Lac County Bar Associations, 1965; lawyer; law clerk to Federal Judge James Doyle, 1965; Peace Corps volunteer, 1966–67; White House aide, 1969; commenced law practice in Fond du Lac, 1970; elected to the Wisconsin State Senate in 1972; reelected in 1976, and served until April, 1979; married; one daughter; committees: Education and the Workforce; Transportation and Infrastructure; elected to the 96th Congress, by special election, on April 3, 1979, to fill the vacancy caused by the death of William A. Steiger; reelected to each succeeding Congress.

Office Listings

http://www.petri.house.gov https://www.facebook.com/thomaspetri

2462 Rayburn House Office Building, Washington, DC 20515 .... (202) 225–2476
Chief of Staff / Legislative Director.—Debra Gebhardt. FAX: 225–2356
Communications Director.—Lee Brooks.
Office Manager.—Linda Towse.
490 West Rolling Meadows Drive, Suite B, Fond du Lac, WI 54937 .... (920) 922–1180
District Director.—Tyler Vorpagel.
2390 State Road 44, Suite B, Oshkosh, WI 54904 .... (920) 231–6333

Counties: COLUMBIA, DODGE (part), FOND DU LAC, GREEN LAKE, MANITOWOC, MARQUETTE, MILWAUKEE (part), OZAUKEE, SHEBOYGAN, WAUSHARA, AND WINNEBAGO (part). Population (2010), 709,482.

ZIP Codes: 53001, 53004, 53006, 53010–11, 53012–15, 53019–21, 53023–24, 53031–32, 53035, 53040, 53042, 53044, 53048–50, 53057, 53061–63, 53065, 53070, 53073–75, 53079–85, 53090–93, 53095, 53097, 53217, 53532, 53555, 53561, 53578, 53583, 53901, 53911–23, 53925–28, 53930–33, 53935, 53939, 53946–47, 53949, 53952–56, 53960, 53963–65, 53969, 54110, 54126, 54207–08, 54214, 54220–28, 54230–32, 54241–47, 54619, 54638, 54901–09, 54914–15, 54923, 54930, 54932, 54934–41, 54943, 54947, 54952–60, 54963–74, 54979–86

* * *

SEVENTH DISTRICT

SEAN P. DUFFY, Republican, of Ashland, WI; born in Hayward, WI, October 3, 1971; education: B.A., marketing, St. Mary's University, Winona, MN, 1994; J.D., William Mitchell College of Law, St. Paul, MN, 1999; professional: lawyer, private practice; prosecutor, Ashland County, WI; acting assistant district attorney and district attorney, Ashland County, WI, 2002–10; religion: Roman Catholic; married: wife, Rachel Campos-Duffy; six children; committees: Budget; Financial Services; Joint Economic Committee; elected to the 112th Congress on November 2, 2010; reelected to the 113th Congress on November 6, 2012.

Office Listings

http://duffy.house.gov

1208 Longworth House Office Building, Washington, DC 20515 .... (202) 225–3365
Chief of Staff.—Pete Meachum. FAX: 225–3240
Legislative Director.—Amie Woeber. (855) 585–4251
Communications Director.—Cassie Smedile.
Scheduler.—Jackie Reilly.
208 Grand Avenue, Wausau, WI 54403 .... (715) 298–9344
District Director.—David Anderson. FAX: 298–9348
District Scheduler.—Maggie Cronin.
Director of Constituent Services.—Tom Nimsgern.
823 Belknap Street, Suite 102, Superior, WI 54880 .... (715) 392–3984
Regional Representative.—Mary Willett. FAX: 392–3999

Counties: ASHLAND, BARRON, BAYFIELD, BURNETT, CHIPPEWA (part), CLARK, DOUGLAS, FLORENCE, FOREST, IRON, JACKSON (part), JUNEAU (part), LANGLADE, LINCOLN, MARATHON, MONROE (part), ONEIDA, POLK, PRICE, RUSK, SAWYER, ST. CROIX, TAYLOR, VILAS, WASHBURN, AND WOOD (part). Population (2010), 710,873.

ZIP Codes: 53950, 54001–02, 54004–07, 54009, 54013, 54015–17, 54020, 54022–28, 54082, 54103–04, 54120–21, 54125, 54151, 54175, 54401, 54403, 54405, 54408–14, 54417–18, 54420–22, 54424–28, 54430, 54433, 54435–37, 54440–43, 54446–49, 54451–52, 54454–57, 54459–60, 54462–63, 54465–66, 54470–71, 54473–74, 54476, 54479–80, 54484–85, 54487–91, 54493, 54495, 54498–99, 54501, 54511–15, 54517, 54519–21, 54524–27, 54529–31, 54534, 54536–42, 54545–48, 54550, 54552, 54554–66, 54568, 54611, 54615–16, 54618, 54635, 54641, 54646, 54660, 54666, 54724,

54726–34, 54741, 54745–46, 54748–49, 54754, 54757, 54762–63, 54765–68, 54771, 54801, 54805–06, 54810, 54812–14, 54817, 54819–22, 54824, 54826–30, 54832, 54835–50, 54853–59, 54861–62, 54864–65, 54867–68, 54870–76, 54880, 54888–89, 54891, 54893, 54895–96

* * *

EIGHTH DISTRICT

REID RIBBLE, Republican, of Appleton, WI; born in Neenah, WI, April 05, 1956; education: Appleton East High School, WI, 1974; Grand Rapids School of Bible and Music, MI; professional: business owner; married: DeaNa; committees: Agriculture; Budget; Transportation and Infrastructure; elected to the 112th Congress on November 2, 2010; reelected to the 113th Congress on November 6, 2012.

Office Listings

http://www.ribble.house.gov

1513 Longworth House Office Building, Washington, DC 20515 .... (202) 225–5665
Chief of Staff.—McKay Daniels. FAX: 225–5729
Legislative Director.—Paul Bleiberg.
Scheduler.—Teri Dorn.
Communications Director.—McKay Daniels.
333 West College Avenue, Appleton, WI 54911 .... (920) 380–0061
District Director.—Rick Sense.
550 North Military Avenue, Suite 4B, Green Bay, WI 54303 .... (920) 471–1950

Counties: BROWN, CALUMET, DOOR, KEWAUNEE, MARINETTE, MENOMINEE, OCONTO, OUTAGAMIE (part), SHAWANO, WAUPACA, WINNEBAGO (part). Population (2010), 706,840.

ZIP Codes: 54101–04, 54106–07, 54110–15, 54119–21, 54124–28, 54130–31, 54135, 54137–41, 54143, 54149–57, 54159, 54161–62, 54165–66, 54169–71, 54173–75, 54177, 54180, 54182, 54201–02, 54204–05, 54208–13, 54216–17, 54226–27, 54229–30, 54234–35, 54241, 54246, 54301–08, 54311, 54313, 54324, 54344, 54408–09, 54414, 54416, 54418, 54424, 54427–28, 54430, 54435, 54450, 54452, 54462–65, 54485–87, 54491, 54499, 54501, 54511–12, 54519–21, 54529, 54531, 54538–43, 54545, 54548, 54554, 54557–58, 54560–62, 54564, 54566, 54568, 54911–15, 54919, 54922, 54926, 54928–29, 54931, 54933, 54940, 54942, 54944–50

WYOMING

(Population 2010, 563,626)

SENATORS

MICHAEL B. ENZI, Republican, of Gillette, WY; born in Bremerton, WA, February 1, 1944; education: B.A., accounting, George Washington University, 1966; M.B.A., Denver University, 1968; professional: served in Wyoming National Guard, 1967–73; accounting manager and computer programmer, Dunbar Well Service, 1985–97; director, Black Hills Corporation, a New York Stock Exchange company, 1992–96; member, founding board of directors, First Wyoming Bank of Gillette, 1978–88; owner, with wife, of NZ Shoes; served in Wyoming House of Representatives, 1987–91, and in Wyoming State Senate, 1991–96; Mayor of Gillette, 1975–82; commissioner, Western Interstate Commission for Higher Education, 1995–96; served on the Education Commission of the States, 1989–93; president, Wyoming Association of Municipalities, 1980–82; president, Wyoming Jaycees, 1973–74; member: Lions Club; elder, Presbyterian Church; Eagle Scout; married: Diana Buckley, 1969; children: Amy, Brad, and Emily; committees: Budget; Finance; Health, Education, Labor, and Pensions; Homeland Security and Governmental Affairs; Small Business and Entrepreneurship; elected to the U.S. Senate in November, 1996; reelected to each succeeding Senate term.

Office Listings

http://enzi.senate.gov https://www.facebook.com/mikeenzi
https://twitter.com/senatorenzi

379–A Russell Senate Office Building, Washington, DC 20510 .... (202) 224–3424
Chief of Staff.—Flip McConnaughey. FAX: 228–0359
Legislative Director.—Tara Shaw.
Press Secretary.—Daniel Head.
Office Manager.—Christen Thompson.
Federal Center, Suite 2007, 2120 Capitol Avenue, Cheyenne, WY 82001 .... (307) 772–2477
400 South Kendrick, Suite 303, Gillette, WY 82716 .... (307) 682–6268
100 East B Street, Room 3201, P.O. Box 33201, Casper, WY 82602 .... (307) 261–6572
P.O. Box 12470, Jackson, WY 83002 .... (307) 739–9507
1285 Sheridan Avenue, Suite 210, Cody, WY 82414 .... (307) 527–9444

* * *

JOHN BARRASSO, Republican, of Casper, WY; born in Reading, PA, July 21, 1952; education: B.S., Georgetown University, Washington, DC, 1974; M.D., Georgetown University, Washington, DC, 1978; professional: Casper Orthopaedic Associates, 1983–2007; Chief of Staff, Wyoming Medical Center, 2003–05; President, Wyoming Medical Society; President, National Association of Physician Broadcasters, 1988–89; member, Wyoming State Senate, 2002–06; wife: Bobbi; children: Peter, Emma and Hadley; committees: ranking member, Indian Affairs; Energy and Natural Resources; Environment and Public Works; Foreign Relations; appointed to the United States Senate on June 22, 2007, sworn in by Vice President Cheney on June 25, 2007 to the 110th Congress to fill the vacancy caused by the death of Senator Craig Thomas; elected to the U.S. Senate on November 4, 2008; reelected to the 113th Congress for a full Senate term on November 6, 2012.

Office Listings

http://barrasso.senate.gov www.facebook.com/johnbarrasso www.twitter.com/senjohnbarrasso

307 Dirksen Senate Office Building, Washington, DC 20510 .... (202) 224–6441
Chief of Staff.—Dan Kunsman. FAX: 224–1724
Legislative Director.—Bryn Stewart.
Communications Director.—Emily Lawrimore.
Office Manager.—Amber Moyerman.
100 East B Street, Suite 2201, Casper, WY 82602 .... (307) 261–6413
FAX: 265–6706
2120 Capitol Avenue, Suite 2013, Cheyenne, WY 82001 .... (307) 772–2451
FAX: 638–3512
324 East Washington Avenue, Riverton, WY 82501 .... (307) 856–6642
FAX: 856–5901
1575 Dewar Drive, Suite 218, Rock Springs, WY 82901 .... (307) 362–5012
FAX: 362–5129
2 North Main Street, Suite 206, Sheridan, WY 82801 .... (307) 672–6456
FAX: 672–8227

REPRESENTATIVE

AT LARGE

CYNTHIA M. LUMMIS, Republican, of Cheyenne, WY; born in Cheyenne, September 10, 1954; education: graduated, B.S., animal science, University of Wyoming, 1976; B.S., biology, University of Wyoming, 1978; J.D., University of Wyoming, 1985; professional: Attorney at Law, 1986–present; rancher, 1976–present; Representative, Wyoming State House of Representatives, 1979–82; clerk, Wyoming Supreme Court, 1985; Representative, Wyoming State House of Representatives, 1985–93; Senator, Wyoming State Legislature, 1993–94; Interim Director of State Lands, State of Wyoming, 1997–98; General Counsel, Office of the Governor, 1995–97; State Treasurer, State of Wyoming, 1998–2006; chair, Western State Treasurer's Association; Advisory Board, Center for the Rocky Mountain West at the University of Montana; Board of Member, American Women's Financial Education Foundation; Director, Cheyenne Frontier Days; member, Cheyenne's Vision 2020; member, Laramie Foundation and its Wyoming Women's History House; member, Leadership Wyoming Board; Advisory Board, Ruckelshaus Institute for Environment and Natural Resources at the University of Wyoming; member, Trinity Lutheran Church; member, Wyoming Business Alliance; member, Wyoming Stock Growers Agricultural Land Trust, married: Al Wiederspahn; children: Annaliese; committees: Natural Resources; Oversight and Government Reform; Science, Space, and Technology; elected to the 111th Congress on November 4, 2008; reelected to each succeeding Congress.

Office Listings

http://lummis.house.gov https://www.facebook.com/pages/cynthia-lummis/152754318103332
https://twitter.com/cynthialummis

113 Cannon House Office Building, Washington, DC 20515 .... (202) 225–2311
Chief of Staff.—Tom Wiblemo. FAX: 225–3057
Legislative Director.—Landon Stropko.
Press Secretary.—Joe Spiering.
100 East B Street, Suite 4003, Casper, WY 82602 .... (307) 261–6595
District Representatives: Jackie King, Ryan McConnaughey.
8005 Capitol Avenue, Suite 2015, Cheyenne, WY 82001 .... (307) 772–2595
Chief of Staff.—Tucker Fagan. FAX: 772–2597
Scheduler.—Christie Clark.
District Representative.—Laura Weatherford.
45 East Loucks, Suite 300F, Sheridan, WY 82801 .... (307) 673–4608
District Representative.—Matt Jones. FAX: 673–4982

Population (2010), 563,626.

ZIP Codes: 82001, 82003, 82005–10, 82050–55, 82058–61, 82063, 82070–73, 82081–84, 82190, 82201, 82210, 82212–15, 82217–19, 82221–25, 82227, 82229, 82240, 82242–44, 82301, 82310, 82321–25, 82327, 82329, 82331–32, 82334–36, 82401, 82410–12, 82414, 82420–23, 82426, 82428, 82430–35, 82440–43, 82450, 82501, 82510, 82512–16, 82520, 82523–24, 82601–02, 82604–05, 82609, 82615, 82620, 82630, 82633, 82635–40, 82642–44, 82646, 82648–49, 82701, 82710–12, 82714–18, 82720–21, 82723, 82725, 82727, 82729–32, 82801, 82831–40, 82842, 82844–45, 82901–02, 82922–23, 82925, 82929–39, 82941–45, 83001–02, 83011–14, 83025, 83101, 83110–16, 83118–24, 83126–28

AMERICAN SAMOA

(Population 2010, 67,380)

DELEGATE

ENI F. H. FALEOMAVAEGA, Democrat, of Vailoatai, AS; born in Vailoatai, August 15, 1943; education: graduate of Kahuku High School, Hawaii, 1962; B.A., Brigham Young University, 1966; J.D., University of Houston Law School, 1972; LL.M., University of California, Berkeley, 1973; admitted to U.S. Supreme Court and American Samoa Bars; military service: enlisted, U.S. Army, 1966–69; Vietnam veteran; captain, USAR, Judge Advocate General Corps, 1982–92; professional: administrative assistant to American Samoa's Delegate to Washington, 1973–75; staff counsel, Committee on Interior and Insular Affairs, 1975–81; Deputy Attorney General, American Samoa, 1981–84; elected Lieutenant Governor, American Samoa, 1984–89; member: Democratic Study Group; National American Indian Prayer Breakfast Group; National Association of Secretaries of State; National Conference of Lieutenant Governors; Navy League of the United States; Pago Pago Lions Club; Veterans of Foreign Wars; Congressional Arts Caucus; Congressional Hispanic Caucus; Congressional Human Rights Caucus; Congressional Travel and Tourism Caucus; Central Asia Caucus; married: Hinanui Bambridge Cave of Tahiti; five children; committees: Foreign Affairs; Natural Resources; elected to the 101st Congress on November 8, 1988; reelected to each succeeding Congress.

Office Listings

http://www.house.gov/faleomavaega

2422 Rayburn House Office Building, Washington, DC 20515 .... (202) 225–8577
Chief of Staff.—Lisa Williams. FAX: 225–8757
Scheduler/Office Manager.—Hana Atuatasi.
Legislative Director.—David Richmond.
P.O. Drawer X, Pago Pago, AS 96799 .... (684) 699–8577

ZIP Codes: 96799

* * *

DISTRICT OF COLUMBIA

(Population 2010, 601,723)

DELEGATE

ELEANOR HOLMES NORTON, Democrat, of Washington, DC; born in Washington, DC, June 13, 1937; education: graduated, Dunbar High School, 1955; B.A., Antioch College, 1960; M.A., Yale Graduate School, 1963; J.D., Yale Law School, 1964; honorary degrees: Cedar Crest College, 1969; Bard College, 1971; Princeton University, 1973; Marymount College, 1974; City College of New York, 1975; Georgetown University, 1977; New York University, 1978; Howard University, 1978; Brown University, 1978; Wilberforce University, 1978; Wayne State University, 1980; Gallaudet College, 1980; Denison University, 1980; Syracuse University, 1981; Yeshiva University, 1981; Lawrence University, 1981; Emanuel College, 1981; Spelman College, 1982; University of Massachusetts, 1983; Smith College, 1983; Medical College of Pennsylvania, 1983; Tufts University, 1984; Bowdoin College, 1985; Antioch College, 1985; Haverford College, 1986; Lesley College, 1986; New Haven University, 1986; University of San Diego, 1986; Sojourner-Douglas College, 1987; Salem State College, 1987; Rutgers University, 1988; St. Joseph's College, 1988; University of Lowell, 1988; Colgate University, 1989; Drury College, 1989; Florida International University, 1989; St. Lawrence University, 1989; University of Wisconsin, 1989; University of Hartford, 1990; Ohio Wesleyan University, 1990; Wake Forest University, 1990; Fisk University, 1991; Tougalvo University, 1992; University of Southern Connecticut, 1992; professional: professor of law, Georgetown University, 1982–90; past/present member: chair, New York Commission on Human Rights, 1970–76; chair, Equal Employment Opportunity Commission, 1977–81; Community Foundation of Greater Washington, board; Yale Corporation, 1982–88; trustee, Rockefeller Foundation, 1982–90; executive assistant to the mayor of New York City (concurrent appointment); law clerk, Judge A. Leon Higginbotham, Federal District Court, 3rd Circuit; attorney, admitted to practice by examination in the District of Columbia, Pennsylvania and in the U.S. Supreme Court; Council on Foreign Relations; Overseas Development Council; U.S. Committee to Monitor the Helsinki Accords; Carter Center, Atlanta, Georgia; boards of Martin Luther King, Jr. Center for Social Change and Environmental Law Institute; Workplace Health Fund; honors awards: Harper Fellow, Yale Law School, 1976, (for "a person . . . who has made a distinguished contribution to the public life of the nation . . ."); Yale Law School Association Citation of Merit Medal to the Outstanding Alumnus of the Law School, 1980; Chancellor's Distinguished Lecturer, University of California Law School (Boalt Hall), Berkeley, 1981; Visiting Fellow, Harvard University, John F. Kennedy School of Government, spring 1984; Visiting Phi Beta Kappa Scholar, 1985; Distinguished Public Service Award, Center for National Policy, 1985; Ralph E. Shikes Bicentennial Fellow, Harvard Law School, 1987; One Hundred Most Important Women (*Ladies Home Journal*, 1988); One Hundred Most Powerful Women in Washington (The *Washingtonian* magazine, September 1989); divorced; two children: John and Katherine; committees: Oversight and Government Reform; Transportation and Infrastructure; elected to the 102nd Congress on November 6, 1990; reelected to each succeeding Congress.

Office Listings

http://www.norton.house.gov https://twitter.com/eleanornorton
https://www.facebook.com/congresswomannorton

2136 Rayburn House Office Building, Washington, DC 20515 .... (202) 225–8050
Chief of Staff.—Gwen Benson-Walker. FAX: 225–3002
Legislative Director.—Bradley Truding.
Communications Director.—Daniel van Hoogstraten.

ZIP Codes: 20001–13, 20015–20, 20024, 20026–27, 20029–30, 20032–33, 20035–45, 20047, 20049–53, 20055–71, 20073–77, 20080, 20088, 20090–91, 20099, 20201–04, 20206–08, 20210–13, 20215–24, 20226–33, 20235, 20237, 20239–42, 20244–45, 20250, 20254, 20260, 20268, 20270, 20277, 20289, 20301, 20303, 20306–07, 20310, 20314–15, 20317–19, 20330, 20340, 20350, 20370, 20372–76, 20380, 20388–95, 20398, 20401–16, 20418–29, 20431, 20433–37, 20439–42, 20444, 20447, 20451, 20453, 20456, 20460, 20463, 20469, 20472, 20500, 20503–10, 20515, 20520–27, 20530–36, 20538–44, 20546–49, 20551–55, 20557, 20559–60, 20565–66, 20570–73, 20575–77, 20579–81, 20585–86, 20590–91, 20593–94, 20597, 20599

* * *

GUAM

(Population 2010, 159,358)

DELEGATE

MADELEINE Z. BORDALLO, Democrat, of Tamuning, Guam, born on May 31, 1933; education: associate degree in music, St. Catherine's College, St. Paul, MN, 1953; professional: First Lady of Guam, 1975–78, and 1983–86; Guam Senator, 1981–82, and 1987–94 (five terms); Lt. Governor of Guam, 1995–2002 (two terms); National Committee Chair for the National Democratic Party, 1964–2004; family: Ricardo J. Bordallo (deceased); daughter, Deborah; granddaughter, Nicole; committees: Armed Services; Natural Resources; elected to the 108th Congress on November 5, 2002; reelected to each succeeding Congress.

Office Listings

http://www.house.gov/bordallo https://www.facebook.com/madeleine.bordallo

2441 Rayburn House Office Building, Washington, DC 20515 .... (202) 225–1188
Chief of Staff.—John Whitt. FAX: 226–0341
Legislative Director.—Matthew Herrmann.
Press Secretary.—Kelly Toves.
Scheduler.—Rosanne Meno.
120 Father Duenas Avenue, Suite 107, Hagåtña, GU 96910 .... (671) 477–4272

ZIP Codes: 96910, 96912–13, 96915–17, 96919, 96921, 96923, 96926, 96928–29, 96931–32

NORTHERN MARIANA ISLANDS

(Population 2010, 53,883)

DELEGATE

GREGORIO KILILI CAMACHO SABLAN, Democrat, of Saipan, MP; born in Saipan, MP, January 19, 1955; education: University of Hawaii, Manoa Honolulu, HI; 1989–90; professional: member, Northern Mariana Islands Commonwealth Legislature, 1982–86 (2 terms); special assistant to Senator Daniel Inouye; special assistant to Northern Mariana Islands Governor Pedro P. Tenorio; Executive Director of the Commonwealth Election Commission; family: married Andrea C. Sablan, son Jesse, daughter Patricia; caucuses: Congressional Asian Pacific American Caucus; Congressional Hispanic Caucus; American Citizens Abroad Caucus; Bi-Partisan Disabilities Caucus; Democratic Caucus; Community College Caucus; National Marine Sanctuary Caucus; Friends of New Zealand Caucus; International Conservation Caucus; committees: Education and the Workforce; Natural Resources; elected to the 111th Congress on November 4, 2008; reelected to each succeeding Congress.

Office Listings

http://www.sablan.house.gov

423 Cannon House Office Building, Washington, DC 20515 .... (202) 225–2646
Chief of Staff.—Robert J. Schwalbach. FAX: 226–4249
Scheduler.—Chai Cruz.
JCT II Building, Susupe, P.O. Box 504879, Saipan, MP 96950 .... (670) 323–2647
District Officer Director.—Mike Tenorio. FAX: 323–2649

ZIP Codes: 96950–52

* * *

PUERTO RICO

(Population 2010, 3,725,789)

RESIDENT COMMISSIONER

PEDRO R. PIERLUISI, Democratic, of Guaynabo, PR; born in San Juan, PR, April 26, 1959; education: contemporary U.S. history, Tulane University, New Orleans, LA, 1981; Juris Doctor, George Washington University, Washington, DC, 1984; professional: Verner & Lipfert Assoc., Washington, DC, 1984–85; Cole, Corette & Abrutyn, Washington, DC, 1985–88; Pierluisi & Pierluisi, San Juan, PR, 1990–92; Attorney General of Puerto Rico, 1993–96; O'Neill & Borges, San Jaun, PR, 1997–2007; religion: Catholic; married: Maria Elena Carrión; family: four children; committees: Ethics; Judiciary; Natural Resources, elected to the 111th Congress on November 4, 2008, reelected on November 6, 2012.

Office Listings

http://www.pierluisi.house.gov

1213 Longworth House Office Building, Washington, DC 20515 .... (202) 225–2615
Chief of Staff.—Carmen M. Feliciano. FAX: 225–2154
Communications Director.—Dennise Pérez.
Scheduler.—Frances Agosto.
Legislative Director.—John Laufer.
Senior Legislative Adviser.—Jed Bullock.
Legislative Assistant.—George Laws.
Press Aide.—Carla Escoto.
Legislative Correspondent.—Luis Miguel Lopez.
Staff Assistant.—Natalia Gandía.
157 Avenida de la Constitución Antiguo Edificio de Medicina Tropical, Ala de la Enfermería 2ndo Piso, San Juan, PR 00901 .... (787) 723–6333
District Office Director.—Rosemarie ''Maí'' Vizcarrondo. FAX: 729–7738
Deputy District Office Director.—Cristina Figueroa.
Office Manager.—Aimée Irlanda.
Constituent Liaison.—Rosario Toro.
Press Aide.—Marlena Riccio.
Staff Assistant.—Michelle Manzano.
Senior Case Worker.—Luis Ortiz.
Social Security Case Worker.—Cristina Sierra.
Veteran's Case Worker.—Jorge Mas.

ZIP Codes: 00601–06, 00610–14, 00616–17, 00622–24, 00627, 00631, 00636–38, 00641, 00646–47, 00650, 00652–53, 00656, 00659–60, 00662, 00664, 00667, 00669–70, 00674, 00676–78, 00680–83, 00685, 00687–88, 00690, 00692, 00693–94, 00698, 00703–05, 00707, 00714–21, 00723, 00725–42, 00744–45, 00751, 00754, 00757, 00765–67, 00769, 00771–73, 00775, 00777–78, 00780, 00782–86, 00791–92, 00794–95, 00901–02, 00906–31, 00933–37, 00939–40, 00949–63, 00965–66, 00968–71, 00975–79, 00981–88

* * *

VIRGIN ISLANDS

(Population 2010, 106,405)

DELEGATE

DONNA M. CHRISTENSEN, Democrat, of St. Croix, VI; born in Teaneck, NJ, September 19, 1945; B.S., St. Mary's College, Notre Dame, IN, 1966; M.D., George Washington University School of Medicine, 1970; physician, family medicine; Acting Commissioner of Health, 1994–95; medical director, St. Croix Hospital, 1987–88; founding member and vice president, Virgin Islands Medical Institute; trustee, National Medical Association; past secretary and two-time past president, Virgin Islands Medical Society; founding member and trustee, Caribbean Youth Organization; member: Democratic National Committee; Virgin Islands Democratic Territorial Committee (past vice chair); Substance Abuse Coalition; St. Dunstan's Episcopal School Board of Directors; Caribbean Studies Association; Women's Coalition of St. Croix; St. Croix Environmental Association; past chair, Christian Education Committee; Friedensthal Moravian Church; past member: Virgin Islands Board of Education; Democratic Platform Committee; cohost, Straight Up TV interview program, 1993; children: two daughters: Rabiah Layla and Karida Yasmeen; grandchildren: Nia Elena Hamilton, Kobe George, Nealia Williams and Layla Marie George; member: Congressional Black Caucus; Congressional Women's Caucus; committees: Energy and Commerce; elected to the 105th Congress; reelected to each succeeding Congress.

Office Listings

http://www.donnachristensen.house.gov

1510 Longworth House Office Building, Washington, DC 20515 .... (202) 225–1790
Chief of Staff.—Monique Clendinen Watson. FAX: 225–5517
Executive Assistant / Scheduler.—Shelley Thomas.
Office Manager.—Shanna O'Reilly.
800 Nisky Center, 2nd Floor, Suite 207, St. Thomas, VI 00802 .... (340) 774–4408
Office Manager.—Joyce Jackson.
Sunshine Mall Space 204–205, Frederiksted, P.O. Box 5980, St. Croix, VI 00823 (340) 778–5900
Office Manager.—Luz Belardo-Webster.

ZIP Codes: 00801–05, 00820–24, 00830–31, 00840–41, 00850–51

STATE DELEGATIONS

Number before names designates Congressional district. Senate Democrats in roman; Senate Republicans in *italic*; Independents in SMALL CAPS; House Republicans in roman; House Democrats in *italic*; Resident Commissioner and Delegates in ***boldface italic***.

ALABAMA

SENATORS
Richard C. Shelby
Jeff Sessions

REPRESENTATIVES
[Republicans 6, Democrat 1]

1. Bradley Byrne
2. Martha Roby
3. Mike Rogers
4. Robert B. Aderholt
5. Mo Brooks
6. Spencer Bachus
7. *Terri A. Sewell*

ALASKA

SENATORS
Lisa Murkowski
Mark Begich

REPRESENTATIVE
[Republican 1]
At Large - Don Young

ARIZONA

SENATORS
John McCain
Jeff Flake

REPRESENTATIVES
[Republicans 4, Democrats 5]

1. *Ann Kirkpartick*
2. *Ron Barber*
3. *Raúl M. Grijalva*
4. Paul A. Gosar
5. Matt Salmon
6. David Schweikert
7. *Ed Pastor*
8. Trent Franks
9. *Kyrsten Sinema*

ARKANSAS

SENATORS
Mark L. Pryor
John Boozman

REPRESENTATIVES
[Republicans 4]

1. Eric A. ''Rick'' Crawford
2. Tim Griffin
3. Steve Womack
4. Tom Cotton

CALIFORNIA

SENATORS
Dianne Feinstein
Barbara Boxer

REPRESENTATIVES
[Republicans 15, Democrats 38]

1. Doug LaMalfa
2. *Jared Huffman*
3. *John Garamendi*
4. Tom McClintock
5. *Mike Thompson*

6. *Doris O. Matsui*
7. *Ami Bera*
8. Paul Cook
9. *Jerry McNerney*
10. Jeff Denham
11. *George Miller*
12. *Nancy Pelosi*
13. *Barbara Lee*
14. *Jackie Speier*
15. *Eric Swalwell*
16. *Jim Costa*
17. *Michael M. Honda*
18. *Anna G. Eshoo*
19. *Zoe Lofgren*
20. *Sam Farr*
21. David G. Valadao
22. Devin Nunes
23. Kevin McCarthy
24. *Lois Capps*
25. Howard P. ''Buck'' McKeon
26. *Julia Brownley*
27. *Judy Chu*
28. *Adam B. Schiff*
29. *Tony Cárdenas*
30. *Brad Sherman*
31. Gary G. Miller
32. *Grace F. Napolitano*
33. *Henry A. Waxman*
34. *Xavier Becerra*
35. *Gloria Negrete McLeod*
36. *Raul Ruiz*
37. *Karen Bass*
38. *Linda T. Sánchez*
39. Edward R. Royce
40. *Lucille Roybal-Allard*
41. *Mark Takano*
42. Ken Calvert
43. *Maxine Waters*
44. *Janice Hahn*
45. John Campbell
46. *Loretta Sanchez*
47. *Alan S. Lowenthal*
48. Dana Rohrabacher
49. Darrell E. Issa
50. Duncan Hunter
51. *Juan Vargas*
52. *Scott H. Peters*
53. *Susan A. Davis*

COLORADO

SENATORS
Mark Udall
Michael F. Bennet

REPRESENTATIVES
[Republicans 4, Democrats 3]

1. *Diana DeGette*
2. *Jared Polis*
3. Scott R. Tipton
4. Cory Gardner
5. Doug Lamborn
6. Mike Coffman
7. *Ed Perlmutter*

CONNECTICUT

SENATORS
Richard Blumenthal
Christopher Murphy

REPRESENTATIVES
[Democrats 5]

1. *John B. Larson*
2. *Joe Courtney*
3. *Rosa L. DeLauro*
4. *James A. Himes*
5. *Elizabeth H. Esty*

DELAWARE

SENATORS
Thomas R. Carper
Christopher A. Coons

REPRESENTATIVE
[Democrat 1]

At Large - *John C. Carney, Jr.*

FLORIDA

SENATORS
Bill Nelson
Marco Rubio

REPRESENTATIVES
[Republicans 15, Democrats 10, Vacant 2]

1. Jeff Miller
2. Steve Southerland II
3. Ted S. Yoho
4. Ander Crenshaw
5. *Corrine Brown*
6. Ron DeSantis
7. John L. Mica
8. Bill Posey
9. *Alan Grayson*
10. Daniel Webster
11. Richard B. Nugent
12. Gus M. Bilirakis

13. ——[1]
14. *Kathy Castor*
15. Dennis A. Ross
16. Vern Buchanan
17. Thomas J. Rooney
18. *Patrick Murphy*
19. ——[2]
20. *Alcee L. Hastings*
21. *Theodore E. Deutch*
22. *Lois Frankel*
23. *Debbie Wasserman Schultz*
24. *Frederica S. Wilson*
25. Mario Diaz-Balart
26. *Joe Garcia*
27. Ileana Ros-Lehtinen

GEORGIA

SENATORS
Saxby Chambliss
Johnny Isakson

REPRESENTATIVES
[Republicans 9, Democrats 5]

1. Jack Kingston
2. *Sanford D. Bishop, Jr.*
3. Lynn A. Westmoreland
4. *Henry C. "Hank" Johnson, Jr.*
5. *John Lewis*
6. Tom Price
7. Rob Woodall
8. Austin Scott
9. Doug Collins
10. Paul C. Broun
11. Phil Gingrey
12. *John Barrow*
13. *David Scott*
14. Tom Graves

HAWAII

SENATORS
Brian Schatz
Mazie K. Hirono

REPRESENTATIVES
[Democrats 2]

1. *Colleen W. Hanabusa*
2. *Tulsi Gabbard*

IDAHO

SENATORS
Mike Crapo
James E. Risch

REPRESENTATIVES
[Republicans 2]

1. Raúl R. Labrador
2. Michael K. Simpson

ILLINOIS

SENATORS
Richard J. Durbin
Mark Kirk

REPRESENTATIVES
[Republicans 6, Democrats 12]

1. *Bobby L. Rush*
2. *Robin L. Kelly*
3. *Daniel Lipinski*
4. *Luis V. Gutiérrez*
5. *Mike Quigley*
6. Peter J. Roskam
7. *Danny K. Davis*
8. *Tammy Duckworth*
9. *Janice D. Schakowsky*
10. *Bradley S. Schneider*
11. *Bill Foster*
12. *William L. Enyart*
13. Rodney Davis
14. Randy Hultgren
15. John Shimkus
16. Adam Kinzinger
17. *Cheri Bustos*
18. Aaron Schock

INDIANA

SENATORS
Daniel Coats
Joe Donnelly

REPRESENTATIVES
[Republicans 7, Democrats 2]

1. *Peter J. Visclosky*
2. Jackie Walorski
3. Marlin A. Stutzman
4. Todd Rokita
5. Susan W. Brooks
6. Luke Messer
7. *André Carson*
8. Larry Bucshon
9. Todd C. Young

IOWA

SENATORS
Chuck Grassley
Tom Harkin

REPRESENTATIVES
[Republicans 2, Democrats 2]

1. *Bruce L. Braley*
2. *David Loebsack*
3. Tom Latham
4. Steve King

KANSAS

SENATORS
Pat Roberts
Jerry Moran

REPRESENTATIVES
[Republicans 4]

1. Tim Huelskamp
2. Lynn Jenkins
3. Kevin Yoder
4. Mike Pompeo

KENTUCKY

SENATORS
Mitch McConnell
Rand Paul

REPRESENTATIVES
[Republicans 5, Democrat 1]

1. Ed Whitfield
2. Brett Guthrie
3. *John A. Yarmuth*
4. Thomas Massie
5. Harold Rogers
6. Andy Barr

LOUISIANA

SENATORS
Mary L. Landrieu
David Vitter

REPRESENTATIVES
[Republicans 5, Democrat 1]

1. Steve Scalise
2. *Cedric L. Richmond*
3. Charles W. Boustany, Jr.
4. John Fleming
5. Vance M. McAllister
6. Bill Cassidy

MAINE

SENATORS
Susan M. Collins
ANGUS S. KING, JR.*

REPRESENTATIVES
[Democrats 2]

1. *Chellie Pingree*
2. *Michael H. Michaud*

MARYLAND

SENATORS
Barbara A. Mikulski
Benjamin L. Cardin

REPRESENTATIVES
[Republican 1, Democrats 7]

1. Andy Harris
2. *C. A. Dutch Ruppersberger*
3. *John P. Sarbanes*
4. *Donna F. Edwards*
5. *Steny H. Hoyer*
6. *John K. Delaney*
7. *Elijah E. Cummings*
8. *Chris Van Hollen*

MASSACHUSETTS

SENATORS
Elizabeth Warren
Edward J. Markey

REPRESENTATIVES
[Democrats 9]

1. *Richard E. Neal*
2. *James P. McGovern*
3. *Niki Tsongas*
4. *Joseph P. Kennedy III*
5. *Katherine M. Clark*
6. *John F. Tierney*
7. *Michael E. Capuano*
8. *Stephen F. Lynch*
9. *William R. Keating*

MICHIGAN

SENATORS
Carl Levin
Debbie Stabenow

REPRESENTATIVES
[Republicans 9, Democrats 5]

1. Dan Benishek
2. Bill Huizenga
3. Justin Amash
4. Dave Camp
5. *Daniel T. Kildee*
6. Fred Upton
7. Tim Walberg
8. Mike Rogers
9. *Sander M. Levin*
10. Candice S. Miller
11. Kerry L. Bentivolio
12. *John D. Dingell*
13. *John Conyers, Jr.*
14. *Gary C. Peters*

MINNESOTA

SENATORS
Amy Klobuchar
Al Franken

REPRESENTATIVES
[Republicans 3, Democrats 5]

1. *Timothy J. Walz*
2. John Kline
3. Erik Paulsen
4. *Betty McCollum*
5. *Keith Ellison*
6. Michele Bachmann
7. *Collin C. Peterson*
8. *Richard M. Nolan*

MISSISSIPPI

SENATORS
Thad Cochran
Roger F. Wicker

REPRESENTATIVES
[Republicans 3, Democrat 1]

1. Alan Nunnelee
2. *Bennie G. Thompson*
3. Gregg Harper
4. Steven M. Palazzo

MISSOURI

SENATORS
Claire McCaskill
Roy Blunt

REPRESENTATIVES
[Republicans 6, Democrats 2]

1. *Wm. Lacy Clay*
2. Ann Wagner
3. Blaine Luetkemeyer
4. Vicky Hartzler
5. *Emanuel Cleaver*
6. Sam Graves
7. Billy Long
8. Jason T. Smith

MONTANA

SENATORS
Jon Tester
John E. Walsh

REPRESENTATIVE
[Republican 1]

At Large - Steve Daines

NEBRASKA

SENATORS
Mike Johanns
Deb Fischer

REPRESENTATIVES
[Republicans 3]
1. Jeff Fortenberry
2. Lee Terry
3. Adrian Smith

NEVADA

SENATORS
Harry Reid
Dean Heller

REPRESENTATIVES
[Republicans 2, Democrats 2]
1. *Dina Titus*
2. Mark E. Amodei
3. Joseph J. Heck
4. *Steven A. Horsford*

NEW HAMPSHIRE

SENATORS
Jeanne Shaheen
Kelly Ayotte

REPRESENTATIVES
[Democrats 2]
1. *Carol Shea-Porter*
2. *Ann M. Kuster*

NEW JERSEY

SENATORS
Robert Menendez
Cory A. Booker

REPRESENTATIVES
[Republicans 6, Democrats 5, Vacant 1]
1. ——[3]
2. Frank A. LoBiondo
3. Jon Runyan
4. Christopher H. Smith
5. Scott Garrett
6. *Frank Pallone, Jr.*
7. Leonard Lance
8. *Albio Sires*
9. *Bill Pascrell, Jr.*
10. *Donald M. Payne, Jr.*
11. Rodney P. Frelinghuysen
12. *Rush D. Holt*

NEW MEXICO

SENATORS
Tom Udall
Martin Heinrich

REPRESENTATIVES
[Republican 1, Democrats 2]
1. *Michelle Lujan Grisham*
2. Stevan Pearce
3. *Ben Ray Luján*

NEW YORK

SENATORS
Charles E. Schumer
Kirsten E. Gillibrand

REPRESENTATIVES
[Republicans 6, Democrats 21]
1. *Timothy H. Bishop*
2. Peter T. King
3. *Steve Israel*
4. *Carolyn McCarthy*
5. *Gregory W. Meeks*
6. *Grace Meng*
7. *Nydia M. Velázquez*
8. *Hakeen S. Jeffries*
9. *Yvette D. Clarke*
10. *Jerrold Nadler*

11. Michael G. Grimm
12. *Carolyn B. Maloney*
13. *Charles B. Rangel*
14. *Joseph Crowley*
15. *José E. Serrano*
16. *Eliot L. Engel*
17. *Nita M. Lowey*
18. *Sean Patrick Maloney*
19. Christopher P. Gibson
20. *Paul Tonko*
21. *William L. Owens*
22. Richard L. Hanna
23. Tom Reed
24. *Daniel B. Maffei*
25. *Louise McIntosh Slaughter*
26. *Brian Higgins*
27. Chris Collins

NORTH CAROLINA

SENATORS
Richard Burr
Kay R. Hagan

REPRESENTATIVES
[Republicans 9, Democrats 3, Vacant 1]

1. *G. K. Butterfield*
2. Renee L. Ellmers
3. Walter B. Jones
4. *David E. Price*
5. Virginia Foxx
6. Howard Coble
7. *Mike McIntyre*
8. Richard Hudson
9. Robert Pittenger
10. Patrick T. McHenry
11. Mark Meadows
12. ——[4]
13. George Holding

NORTH DAKOTA

SENATORS
John Hoeven
Heidi Heitkamp

REPRESENTATIVE
[Republican 1]

At Large - Kevin Cramer

OHIO

SENATORS
Sherrod Brown
Rob Portman

REPRESENTATIVES
[Republicans 12, Democrats 4]

1. Steve Chabot
2. Brad R. Wenstrup
3. *Joyce Beatty*
4. Jim Jordan
5. Robert E. Latta
6. Bill Johnson
7. Bob Gibbs
8. John A. Boehner
9. *Marcy Kaptur*
10. Michael R. Turner
11. *Marcia L. Fudge*
12. Patrick J. Tiberi
13. *Tim Ryan*
14. David P. Joyce
15. Steve Stivers
16. James B. Renacci

OKLAHOMA

SENATORS
James M. Inhofe
Tom Coburn

REPRESENTATIVES
[Republicans 5]

1. Jim Bridenstine
2. Markwayne Mullin
3. Frank D. Lucas
4. Tom Cole
5. James Lankford

OREGON

SENATORS
Ron Wyden
Jeff Merkley

REPRESENTATIVES
[Republican 1, Democrats 4]

1. *Suzanne Bonamici*

2. Greg Walden
3. *Earl Blumenauer*
4. *Peter A. DeFazio*
5. *Kurt Schrader*

PENNSYLVANIA

SENATORS
Robert P. Casey, Jr.
Patrick J. Toomey

REPRESENTATIVES
[Republicans 13, Democrats 5]

1. *Robert A. Brady*
2. *Chaka Fattah*
3. Mike Kelly
4. Scott Perry
5. Glenn Thompson
6. Jim Gerlach
7. Patrick Meehan
8. Michael G. Fitzpatrick
9. Bill Shuster
10. Tom Marino
11. Lou Barletta
12. Keith J. Rothfus
13. *Allyson Y. Schwartz*
14. *Michael F. Doyle*
15. Charles W. Dent
16. Joseph R. Pitts
17. *Matt Cartwright*
18. Tim Murphy

RHODE ISLAND

SENATORS
Jack Reed
Sheldon Whitehouse

REPRESENTATIVES
[Democrats 2]

1. *David N. Cicilline*
2. *James R. Langevin*

SOUTH CAROLINA

SENATORS
Lindsey Graham
Tim Scott

REPRESENTATIVES
[Republicans 6, Democrat 1]

1. Mark Sanford
2. Joe Wilson
3. Jeff Duncan
4. Trey Gowdy
5. Mick Mulvaney
6. *James E. Clyburn*
7. Tom Rice

SOUTH DAKOTA

SENATORS
Tim Johnson
John Thune

REPRESENTATIVE
[Republican 1]

At Large - Kristi L. Noem

TENNESSEE

SENATORS
Lamar Alexander
Bob Corker

REPRESENTATIVES
[Republicans 7, Democrats 2]

1. David P. Roe
2. John J. Duncan, Jr.
3. Charles J. ''Chuck'' Fleischmann
4. Scott DesJarlais
5. *Jim Cooper*
6. Diane Black
7. Marsha Blackburn
8. Stephen Lee Fincher
9. *Steve Cohen*

TEXAS

SENATORS
John Cornyn
Ted Cruz

REPRESENTATIVES
[Republicans 24, Democrats 12]

1. Louie Gohmert
2. Ted Poe
3. Sam Johnson
4. Ralph M. Hall
5. Jeb Hensarling
6. Joe Barton
7. John Abney Culberson
8. Kevin Brady
9. *Al Green*
10. Michael T. McCaul
11. K. Michael Conaway
12. Kay Granger
13. Mac Thornberry
14. Randy K. Weber, Sr.
15. *Rubén Hinojosa*
16. *Beto O'Rourke*
17. Bill Flores
18. *Sheila Jackson Lee*
19. Randy Neugebauer
20. *Joaquin Castro*
21. Lamar Smith
22. Pete Olson
23. *Pete P. Gallego*
24. Kenny Marchant
25. Roger Williams
26. Michael C. Burgess
27. Blake Farenthold
28. *Henry Cuellar*
29. *Gene Green*
30. *Eddie Bernice Johnson*
31. John R. Carter
32. Pete Sessions
33. *Marc A. Veasey*
34. *Filemon Vela*
35. *Lloyd Doggett*
36. Steve Stockman

UTAH

SENATORS
Orrin G. Hatch
Mike Lee

REPRESENTATIVES
[Republicans 3, Democrat 1]

1. Rob Bishop
2. Chris Stewart
3. Jason Chaffetz
4. *Jim Matheson*

VERMONT

SENATORS
Patrick J. Leahy
BERNARD SANDERS*

REPRESENTATIVE
[Democrat 1]

At Large - *Peter Welch*

VIRGINIA

SENATORS
Mark R. Warner
Tim Kaine

REPRESENTATIVES
[Republicans 8, Democrats 3]

1. Robert J. Wittman
2. E. Scott Rigell
3. *Robert C. "Bobby" Scott*
4. J. Randy Forbes
5. Robert Hurt
6. Bob Goodlatte
7. Eric Cantor
8. *James P. Moran*
9. H. Morgan Griffith
10. Frank R. Wolf
11. *Gerald E. Connolly*

WASHINGTON

SENATORS
Patty Murray
Maria Cantwell

REPRESENTATIVES
[Republicans 4, Democrats 6]

1. *Suzan K. DelBene*
2. *Rick Larsen*
3. Jaime Herrera Beutler
4. Doc Hastings
5. Cathy McMorris Rodgers
6. *Derek Kilmer*
7. *Jim McDermott*
8. David G. Reichert
9. *Adam Smith*
10. *Denny Heck*

WEST VIRGINIA

SENATORS
John D. Rockefeller IV
Joe Manchin III

REPRESENTATIVES
[Republicans 2, Democrat 1]

1. David B. McKinley
2. Shelley Moore Capito
3. *Nick J. Rahall II*

WISCONSIN

SENATORS
Ron Johnson
Tammy Baldwin

REPRESENTATIVES
[Republicans 5, Democrats 3]

1. Paul Ryan
2. *Mark Pocan*
3. *Ron Kind*
4. *Gwen Moore*
5. F. James Sensenbrenner, Jr.
6. Thomas E. Petri
7. Sean P. Duffy
8. Reid J. Ribble

WYOMING

SENATORS
Michael B. Enzi
John Barrasso

REPRESENTATIVE
[Republican 1]

At Large - Cynthia M. Lummis

AMERICAN SAMOA

DELEGATE
[Democrat 1]

Eni F. H. Faleomavaega

DISTRICT OF COLUMBIA

DELEGATE
[Democrat 1]

Eleanor Holmes Norton

GUAM

DELEGATE
[Democrat 1]

Madeleine Z. Bordallo

NORTHERN MARIANA ISLANDS

DELEGATE
[Democrat 1]

Gregorio Kilili Camacho Sablan

PUERTO RICO

RESIDENT COMMISSIONER
[Democrat 1]

Pedro R. Pierluisi

VIRGIN ISLANDS

DELEGATE
[Democrat 1]

Donna M. Christensen

*Independent
[1] Vacancy due to the death of C. W. Bill Young, October 18, 2013.
[2] Vacancy due to the resignation of Trey Radel, January 27, 2014.
[3] Vacancy due to the resignation of Robert E. Andrews, February 18, 2014.
[4] Vacancy due to the resignation of Melvin L. Watt, January 6, 2014.

ALPHABETICAL LIST

SENATORS

Alphabetical list of Senators, Representatives, Delegates, and Resident Commissioner. Democrats in roman (53); Republicans in *italic* (45); Independents in SMALL CAPS (2).

Alexander, Lamar, TN
Ayotte, Kelly, NH
Baldwin, Tammy, WI
Barrasso, John, WY
Begich, Mark, AK
Bennet, Michael F., CO
Blumenthal, Richard, CT
Blunt, Roy, MO
Booker, Cory A., NJ
Boozman, John, AR
Boxer, Barbara, CA
Brown, Sherrod, OH
Burr, Richard, NC
Cantwell, Maria, WA
Cardin, Benjamin L., MD
Carper, Thomas R., DE
Casey, Robert P., Jr., PA
Chambliss, Saxby, GA
Coats, Daniel, IN
Coburn, Tom, OK
Cochran, Thad, MS
Collins, Susan M., ME
Coons, Christopher A., DE
Corker, Bob, TN
Cornyn, John, TX
Crapo, Mike, ID
Cruz, Ted, TX
Donnelly, Joe, IN
Durbin, Richard J., IL
Enzi, Michael B., WY
Feinstein, Dianne, CA
Fischer, Deb, NE
Flake, Jeff, AR
Franken, Al, MN
Gillibrand, Kirsten E., NY
Graham, Lindsey, SC
Grassley, Chuck, IA
Hagan, Kay R., NC
Harkin, Tom, IA
Hatch, Orrin G., UT
Heinrich, Martin, NM
Heitkamp, Heidi, ND
Heller, Dean, NV
Hirono, Mazie K., HI
Hoeven, John, ND
Inhofe, James M., OK
Isakson, Johnny, GA
Johanns, Mike, NE
Johnson, Ron, WI
Johnson, Tim, SD
Kaine, Tim, VA
KING, ANGUS S., JR., ME
Kirk, Mark, IL
Klobuchar, Amy, MN
Landrieu, Mary L., LA
Leahy, Patrick J., VT
Lee, Mike, UT
Levin, Carl, MI
McCain, John, AZ
McCaskill, Claire, MO
McConnell, Mitch, KY
Manchin, Joe III, WV
Markey, Edward J., MA
Menendez, Robert, NJ
Merkley, Jeff, OR
Mikulski, Barbara A., MD
Moran, Jerry, KS
Murkowski, Lisa, AK
Murphy, Christopher, CT
Murray, Patty, WA
Nelson, Bill, FL
Paul, Rand, KY
Portman, Rob, OH
Pryor, Mark L., AR
Reed, Jack, RI
Reid, Harry, NV
Risch, James E., ID
Roberts, Pat, KS
Rockefeller, John D. IV, WV
Rubio, Marco, FL
SANDERS, BERNARD, VT
Schatz, Brian, HI
Schumer, Charles E., NY
Scott, Tim, SC
Sessions, Jeff, AL
Shaheen, Jeanne, NH
Shelby, Richard C., AL
Stabenow, Debbie, MI
Tester, Jon, MT
Thune, John, SD
Toomey, Patrick J., PA
Udall, Mark, CO
Udall, Tom, NM
Vitter, David, LA
Walsh, John E., MT
Warner, Mark R., VA
Warren, Elizabeth, MA
Whitehouse, Sheldon, RI
Wicker, Roger F., MS
Wyden, Ron, OR

REPRESENTATIVES, RESIDENT COMMISSIONER, AND DELEGATES

Republicans in roman (232); Democrats in *italic* (199); Vacancies (4); Resident Commissioner and Delegates in ***boldface italic*** (6); total, 441.

Aderholt, Robert B., AL (4th)
Amash, Justin, MI (3d)
Amodei, Mark E., NV (2d)
Bachmann, Michele, MN (6th)
Bachus, Spencer, AL (6th)
Barber, Ron, AZ (2d)
Barletta, Lou, PA (11th)
Barr, Andy, KY (6th)
Barrow, John, GA (12th)
Barton, Joe, TX (6th)
Bass, Karen, CA (37th)
Beatty, Joyce, OH (3d)
Becerra, Xavier, CA (34th)
Benishek, Dan, MI (1st)
Bentivolio, Kerry L., MI (11th)
Bera, Ami, CA (7th)
Bilirakis, Gus M., FL (12th)
Bishop, Rob, UT (1st)
Bishop, Sanford D., Jr., GA (2d)
Bishop, Timothy H., NY (1st)
Black, Diane, TN (6th)
Blackburn, Marsha, TN (7th)
Blumenauer, Earl, OR (3d)
Boehner, John A., OH (8th)
Bonamici, Suzanne, OR (1st)
Boustany, Charles W., Jr., LA (3d)
Brady, Kevin, TX (8th)
Brady, Robert A., PA (1st)
Braley, Bruce L., IA (1st)
Bridenstine, Jim, OK (1st)
Brooks, Mo, AL (5th)
Brooks, Susan W., IN (5th)
Broun, Paul C., GA (10th)
Brown, Corrine, FL (5th)
Brownley, Julia, CA (26th)
Buchanan, Vern, FL (16th)
Bucshon, Larry, IN (8th)
Burgess, Michael C., TX (26th)
Bustos, Cheri, IL (17th)
Butterfield, G. K., NC (1st)
Byrne, Bradley, AL (1st)
Calvert, Ken, CA (42d)
Camp, Dave, MI (4th)
Campbell, John, CA (45th)
Cantor, Eric, VA (7th)
Capito, Shelley Moore, WV (2d)
Capps, Lois, CA (24th)
Capuano, Michael E., MA (7th)
Cárdenas, Tony, CA (29th)
Carney, John C., Jr., DE (At Large)
Carson, André, IN (7th)
Carter, John R., TX (31st)
Cartwright, Matt, PA (17th)
Cassidy, Bill, LA (6th)
Castor, Kathy, FL (14th)
Castro, Joaquin, TX (20th)
Chabot, Steve, OH (1st)
Chaffetz, Jason, UT (3d)
Chu, Judy, CA (27th)
Cicilline, David N., RI (1st)
Clark, Katherine M. MA (5th)
Clarke, Yvette D., NY (9th)
Clay, Wm. Lacy, MO (1st)
Cleaver, Emanuel, MO (5th)
Clyburn, James E., SC (6th)
Coble, Howard, NC (6th)
Coffman, Mike, CO (6th)
Cohen, Steve, TN (9th)
Cole, Tom, OK (4th)
Collins, Chris, NY (27th)
Collins, Doug, GA (9th)
Conaway, K. Michael, TX (11th)
Connolly, Gerald E., VA (11th)
Conyers, John, Jr., MI (13th)
Cook, Paul, CA (8th)
Cooper, Jim, TN (5th)
Costa, Jim, CA (16th)
Cotton, Tom, AR (4th)
Courtney, Joe, CT (2d)
Cramer, Kevin, ND (At Large)
Crawford, Eric A. ''Rick'', AR (1st)
Crenshaw, Ander, FL (4th)
Crowley, Joseph, NY (14th)
Cuellar, Henry, TX (28th)
Culberson, John Abney, TX (7th)
Cummings, Elijah E., MD (7th)
Daines, Steve, MT (At Large)
Davis, Danny K., IL (7th)
Davis, Rodney, IL (13th)
Davis, Susan A., CA (53d)
DeFazio, Peter A., OR (4th)
DeGette, Diana, CO (1st)
Delaney, John K., MD (6th)
DeLauro, Rosa L., CT (3d)
DelBene, Suzan K., WA (1st)
Denham, Jeff, CA (10th)
Dent, Charles W., PA (15th)
DeSantis, Ron, FL (6th)
DesJarlais, Scott, TN (4th)
Deutch, Theodore E., FL (21st)
Diaz-Balart, Mario, FL (25th)
Dingell, John D., MI (12th)
Doggett, Lloyd, TX (35th)
Doyle, Michael F., PA (14th)
Duckworth, Tammy, IL (8th)
Duffy, Sean P., WI (7th)
Duncan, Jeff, SC (3d)
Duncan, John J., Jr., TN (2d)
Edwards, Donna F., MD (4th)
Ellison, Keith, MN (5th)
Ellmers, Renee L., NC (2d)
Engel, Eliot L., NY (16th)
Enyart, William L., IL (12th)
Eshoo, Anna G., CA (18th)
Esty, Elizabeth H., CT (5th)
Farenthold, Blake, TX (27th)
Farr, Sam, CA (20th)
Fattah, Chaka, PA (2d)

Fincher, Stephen Lee, TN (8th)
Fitzpatrick, Michael G., PA (8th)
Fleischmann, Charles J. "Chuck", TN (3d)
Fleming, John, LA (4th)
Flores, Bill, TX (17th)
Forbes, J., Randy, VA (4th)
Fortenberry, Jeff, NE (1st)
Foster, Bill, IL (11th)
Foxx, Virginia, NC (5th)
Frankel, Lois, FL (22d)
Franks, Trent, AZ (8th)
Frelinghuysen, Rodney P., NJ (11th)
Fudge, Marcia L., OH (11th)
Gabbard, Tulsi, HI (2d)
Gallego, Pete P., TX (23d)
Garamendi, John, CA (3d)
Garcia, Joe, FL (26th)
Gardner, Cory, CO (4th)
Garrett, Scott, NJ (5th)
Gerlach, Jim, PA (6th)
Gibbs, Bob, OH (7th)
Gibson, Christopher P., NY (19th)
Gingrey, Phil, GA (11th)
Gohmert, Louie, TX (1st)
Goodlatte, Bob, VA (6th)
Gosar, Paul A., AZ (4th)
Gowdy, Trey, SC (4th)
Granger, Kay, TX (12th)
Graves, Sam, MO (6th)
Graves, Tom, GA (14th)
Grayson, Alan, FL (9th)
Green, Al, TX (9th)
Green, Gene, TX (29th)
Griffin, Tim, AR (2d)
Griffith, H. Morgan, VA (9th)
Grijalva, Raúl M., AZ (3d)
Grimm, Michael G., NY (11th)
Guthrie, Brett, KY (2d)
Gutiérrez, Luis V., IL (4th)
Hahn, Janice, CA (44th)
Hall, Ralph M., TX (4th)
Hanabusa, Colleen W., HI (1st)
Hanna, Richard L., NY (22d)
Harper, Gregg, MS (3d)
Harris, Andy, MD (1st)
Hartzler, Vicky, MO (4th)
Hastings, Alcee L., FL (20th)
Hastings, Doc, WA (4th)
Heck, Denny, WA (10th)
Heck, Joseph J., NV (3d)
Hensarling, Jeb, TX (5th)
Herrera Beutler, Jaime, WA (3d)
Higgins, Brian, NY (26th)
Himes, James A., CT (4th)
Hinojosa, Rubén, TX (15th)
Holding, George, NC (13th)
Holt, Rush, NJ (12th)
Honda, Michael M., CA (17th)
Horsford, Steven A., NV (4th)
Hoyer, Steny H., MD (5th)
Hudson, Richard, NC (8th)
Huelskamp, Tim, KS (1st)
Huffman, Jared, CA (2d)
Huizenga, Bill, MI (2d)
Hultgren, Randy, IL (14th)
Hunter, Duncan, CA (50th)
Hurt, Robert, VA (5th)
Israel, Steve, NY (3d)
Issa, Darrell E., CA (49th)
Jackson Lee, Sheila, TX (18th)
Jeffries, Hakeem S., NY (8th)
Jenkins, Lynn, KS (2d)
Johnson, Bill, OH (6th)
Johnson, Eddie Bernice, TX (30th)
Johnson, Henry C. "Hank" Jr., GA (4th)
Johnson, Sam, TX (3d)
Jones, Walter B., NC (3d)
Jordan, Jim, OH (4th)
Joyce, David P., OH (14th)
Kaptur, Marcy, OH (9th)
Keating, William R., MA (9th)
Kelly, Mike, PA (3d)
Kelly, Robin L., IL (2d)
Kennedy, Joseph P. III, MA (4th)
Kildee, Daniel T., MI (5th)
Kilmer, Derek, WA (6th)
Kind, Ron, WI (3d)
King, Peter T., NY (2d)
King, Steve, IA (4th)
Kingston, Jack, GA (1st)
Kinzinger, Adam, IL (16th)
Kirkpatrick, Ann, AZ (1st)
Kline, John, MN (2d)
Kuster, Ann M., NH (2d)
Labrador, Raúl R., ID (1st)
LaMalfa, Doug, CA (1st)
Lamborn, Doug, CO (5th)
Lance, Leonard, NJ (7th)
Langevin, James R., RI (2d)
Lankford, James, OK (5th)
Larsen, Rick, WA (2d)
Larson, John B., CT (1st)
Latham, Tom, IA (3d)
Latta, Robert E., OH (5th)
Lee, Barbara, CA (13th)
Levin, Sander M., MI (9th)
Lewis, John, GA (5th)
Lipinski, Daniel, IL (3d)
LoBiondo, Frank A., NJ (2d)
Loebsack, David, IA (2d)
Lofgren, Zoe, CA (19th)
Long, Billy, MO (7th)
Lowenthal, Alan S., CA (47th)
Lowey, Nita M., NY (17th)
Lucas, Frank D., OK (3d)
Luetkemeyer, Blaine, MO (3d)
Luján, Ben Ray, NM (3d)
Lujan Grisham, Michelle, NM (1st)
Lummis, Cynthia M., WY (At Large)
Lynch, Stephen F., MA (8th)
McAllister, Vance M., LA (5th)
McCarthy, Carolyn, NY (4th)
McCarthy, Kevin, CA (23d)
McCaul, Michael T., TX (10th)
McClintock, Tom, CA (4th)
McCollum, Betty, MN (4th)
McDermott, Jim, WA (7th)
McGovern, James P., MA (2d)
McHenry, Patrick T., NC (10th)
McIntyre, Mike, NC (7th)
McKeon, Howard P. "Buck", CA (25th)
McKinley, David B., WV (1st)

McMorris Rodgers, Cathy, WA (5th)
McNerney, Jerry, CA (9th)
Maffei, Daniel B., NY (24th)
Maloney, Carolyn B., NY (12th)
Maloney, Sean Patrick, NY (18th)
Marchant, Kenny, TX (24th)
Marino, Tom, PA (10th)
Massie, Thomas, KY (4th)
Matheson, Jim, UT (4th)
Matsui, Doris O., CA (6th)
Meadows, Mark, NC (11th)
Meehan, Patrick, PA (7th)
Meeks, Gregory W., NY (5th)
Meng, Grace, NY (6th)
Messer, Luke, IN (6th)
Mica, John L., FL (7th)
Michaud, Michael H., ME (2d)
Miller, Candice S., MI (10th)
Miller, Gary G., CA (31st)
Miller, George, CA (11th)
Miller, Jeff, FL (1st)
Moore, Gwen, WI (4th)
Moran, James P., VA (8th)
Mullin, Markwayne, OK (2d)
Mulvaney, Mick, SC (5th)
Murphy, Patrick, FL (18th)
Murphy, Tim, PA (18th)
Nadler, Jerrold, NY (10th)
Napolitano, Grace F., CA (32d)
Neal, Richard E., MA (1st)
Negrete McLeod, Gloria, CA (35th)
Neugebauer, Randy, TX (19th)
Noem, Kristi L., SD (At Large)
Nolan, Richard M., MN (8th)
Nugent, Richard B., FL (11th)
Nunes, Devin, CA (22d)
Nunnelee, Alan, MS (1st)
Olson, Pete, TX (22d)
O'Rourke, Beto, TX (16th)
Owens, William L., NY (21st)
Palazzo, Steven M., MS (4th)
Pallone, Frank, Jr., NJ (6th)
Pascrell, Bill, Jr., NJ (9th)
Pastor, Ed, AZ (7th)
Paulsen, Erik, MN (3d)
Payne, Donald M., Jr., NJ (10th)
Pearce, Stevan, NM (2d)
Pelosi, Nancy, CA (12th)
Perlmutter, Ed, CO (7th)
Perry, Scott, PA (4th)
Peters, Gary C., MI (14th)
Peters, Scott H., CA (52d)
Peterson, Collin C., MN (7th)
Petri, Thomas E., WI (6th)
Pingree, Chellie, ME (1st)
Pittenger, Robert, NC (9th)
Pitts, Joseph R., PA (16th)
Pocan, Mark, WI (2d)
Poe, Ted, TX (2d)
Polis, Jared, CO (2d)
Pompeo, Mike, KS (4th)
Posey, Bill, FL (8th)
Price, David E., NC (4th)
Price, Tom, GA (6th)
Quigley, Mike, IL (5th)
Rahall, Nick J. II, WV (3d)
Rangel, Charles B., NY (13th)
Reed, Tom, NY (23d)
Reichert, David G., WA (8th)
Renacci, James B., OH (16th)
Ribble, Reid J., WI (8th)
Rice, Tom, SC (7th)
Richmond, Cedric L., LA (2d)
Rigell, E. Scott, VA (2d)
Roby, Martha, AL (2d)
Roe, David P., TN (1st)
Rogers, Harold, KY (5th)
Rogers, Mike, AL (3d)
Rogers, Mike, MI (8th)
Rohrabacher, Dana, CA (48th)
Rokita, Todd, IN (4th)
Rooney, Thomas J., FL (17th)
Roskam, Peter J., IL (6th)
Ros-Lehtinen, Ileana, FL (27th)
Ross, Dennis A., FL (15th)
Rothfus, Keith J., PA (12th)
Roybal-Allard, Lucille, CA (40th)
Royce, Edward R., CA (39th)
Ruiz, Raul, CA (36th)
Runyan, Jon, NJ (3d)
Ruppersberger, C. A. Dutch, MD (2d)
Rush, Bobby L., IL (1st)
Ryan, Paul, WI (1st)
Ryan, Tim, OH (13th)
Salmon, Matt, AZ (5th)
Sánchez, Linda T., CA (38th)
Sanchez, Loretta, CA (46th)
Sanford, Mark, SC (1st)
Sarbanes, John P., MD (3d)
Scalise, Steve, LA (1st)
Schakowsky, Janice D., IL (9th)
Schiff, Adam B., CA (28th)
Schneider, Bradley S., IL (10th)
Schock, Aaron, IL (18th)
Schrader, Kurt, OR (5th)
Schwartz, Allyson Y., PA (13th)
Schweikert, David, AZ (6th)
Scott, Austin, GA (8th)
Scott, David, GA (13th)
Scott, Robert C. "Bobby", VA (3d)
Sensenbrenner, F. James, Jr., WI (5th)
Serrano, José E., NY (15th)
Sessions, Pete, TX (32d)
Sewell, Terri A., AL (7th)
Shea-Porter, Carol, NH (1st)
Sherman, Brad, CA (30th)
Shimkus, John, IL (15th)
Shuster, Bill, PA (9th)
Simpson, Michael K., ID (2d)
Sinema, Kyrsten, AZ (9th)
Sires, Albio, NJ (8th)
Slaughter, Louise McIntosh, NY (25th)
Smith, Adam, WA (9th)
Smith, Adrian, NE (3d)
Smith, Christopher H., NJ (4th)
Smith, Jason T., MO (8th)
Smith, Lamar, TX (21st)
Southerland, Steve II, FL (2d)
Speier, Jackie, CA (14th)
Stewart, Chris, UT (2d)
Stivers, Steve, OH (15th)
Stockman, Steve, TX (36th)

Stutzman, Marlin A., IN (3d)
Swalwell, Eric, CA (15th)
Takano, Mark, CA (41st)
Terry, Lee, NE (2d)
Thompson, Bennie G., MS (2d)
Thompson, Glenn, PA (5th)
Thompson, Mike, CA (5th)
Thornberry, Mac, TX (13th)
Tiberi, Patrick J., OH (12th)
Tierney, John F., MA (6th)
Tipton, Scott R., CO (3d)
Titus, Dina, NV (1st)
Tonko, Paul, NY (20th)
Tsongas, Niki, MA (3d)
Turner, Michael R., OH (10th)
Upton, Fred, MI (6th)
Valadao, David G., CA (21st)
Van Hollen, Chris, MD (8th)
Vargas, Juan, CA (51st)
Veasey, Marc A., TX (33d)
Vela, Filemon, TX (34th)
Velázquez, Nydia M., NY (7th)
Visclosky, Peter J., IN (1st)
Wagner, Ann, MO (2d)
Walberg, Tim, MI (7th)
Walden, Greg, OR (2d)
Walorski, Jackie, IN (2d)
Walz, Timothy J., MN (1st)
Wasserman Schultz, Debbie, FL (23d)
Waters, Maxine, CA (43d)
Waxman, Henry A., CA (33d)
Weber, Randy K., Sr., TX (14th)
Webster, Daniel, FL (10th)
Welch, Peter, VT (At Large)
Wenstrup, Brad R., OH (2d)
Westmoreland, Lynn A., GA (3d)
Whitfield, Ed, KY (1st)
Williams, Roger, TX (25th)
Wilson, Frederica S., FL (24th)
Wilson, Joe, SC (2d)
Wittman, Robert J., VA (1st)
Wolf, Frank R., VA (10th)
Womack, Steve, AR (3d)
Woodall, Rob, GA (7th)
Yarmuth, John A., KY (3d)
Yoder, Kevin, KS (3d)
Yoho, Ted S., FL (3d)
Young, Don, AK (At Large)
Young, Todd C., IN (9th)

RESIDENT COMISSIONER
Pierluisi, Pedro R., PR

DELEGATES
Faleomavaega, Eni F. H., AS
Norton, Eleanor Holmes, DC
Bordallo, Madeleine Z., GU
Sablan, Gregorio Kilili Camacho, MP
Christensen, Donna M., VI

113th Congress
Nine-Digit Postal ZIP Codes

Senate Post Office (20510): The four-digit numbers in these tables were assigned by the Senate Committee on Rules and Administration. Mail to all Senate offices is delivered by the main Post Office in the Dirksen Senate Office Building.

Senate Committees

Committee on Agriculture, Nutrition, and Forestry	–6000
Committee on Appropriations	–6025
Committee on Armed Services	–6050
Committee on Banking, Housing, and Urban Affairs	–6075
Committee on the Budget	–6100
Committee on Commerce, Science, and Transportation	–6125
Committee on Energy and Natural Resources	–6150
Committee on Environment and Public Works	–6175
Committee on Finance	–6200
Committee on Foreign Relations	–6225
Committee on Health, Education, Labor and Pensions	–6300
Committee on Homeland Security and Governmental Affairs	–6250
Committee on Indian Affairs	–6450
Committee on the Judiciary	–6275
Committee on Rules and Administration	–6325
Committee on Small Business and Entrepreneurship	–6350
Committee on Veterans' Affairs	–6375
Committee on Aging (Special)	–6400
Committee on Ethics (Select)	–6425
Committee on Intelligence (Select)	–6475

Joint Committee Offices, Senate Side

Joint Economic Committee	–6602
Joint Committee on the Library	–6625
Joint Committee on Printing	–6650
Joint Committee on Taxation	–6675

Senate Leadership Offices

President Pro Tempore	–7000
Chaplain	–7002
Majority Leader	–7010
Assistant Majority Leader	–7012
Secretary for the Majority	–7014
Minority Leader	–7020
Assistant Minority Leader	–7022
Secretary for the Minority	–7024
Democratic Policy Committee	–7050
Republican Conference	–7060
Secretary to the Republican Conference	–7062
Republican Policy Committee	–7064
Republican Steering Committee	–7066
National Security Working Group	–7070

Senate Officers

Secretary of the Senate	–7100
Curator	–7102
Disbursing Office	–7104
Printing and Document Service	–7106
Historical Office	–7108
Human Resources	–7109
Interparliamentary Services	–7110
Senate Library	–7112
Office of Senate Security	–7114
Office of Public Records	–7116
Office of Official Reporters of Debates	–7117
Stationery Room	–7118
U.S. Capitol Preservation Commission	–7122
Office of Conservation and Preservation	–7124
Information Systems	–7125
Web Technology Office	–7126
Legislative Systems	–7127
Senate Gift Shop	–7128
Senate Legal Counsel	–7130
Emergency Terror Response (COOP)	–7131
Chief Counsel for Employment	–7132
Senate Sergeant at Arms	–7200
General Counsel	–7201
Finance Division	–7205
Budget	–7205
Accounting	–7205
Hair Care Services	–7206
Procurement	–7207
Capitol Guide Service	–7209
Employee Assistance Program Office	–7211
Human Resources	–7212
Safety Program	–7212
Health Promotion / Seminars	–7213
Placement Office	–7214
Workman's Compensation	–7214
Joint Office of Education and Training	–7215
Capitol Police	–7218
Congressional Special Services Office	–7228
Office Support Services	–7230
Customer Support	–7231
IT Request Processing	–7232
Chief Information Officer	–7233
State Liaison	–7285
Periodical Press Gallery	–7234
Press Gallery	–7238
Press Photo Gallery	–7242
Radio and TV Gallery	–7246
Webster Hall	–7248
Office of Protective Services and Continuity (OPSAC)	–7249
Law Enforcement Support Office	–7249
Intelligence & Protective Services	–7249
State Office Readiness Program	–7249
Police Operations Security Emergency Preparedness (POSEP)	–7249
Office of Continuity & Emergency Preparedness (CEPO)	–7249

Other Offices on the Senate Side

Senate Legal Counsel	–7250
Central Operations—Administration	–7260
Parking / ID	–7262
Printing Graphics and Direct Mail—PSQ	–7264
Printing Graphics and Direct Mail—Capitol Hill	–7266
Facilities	–7204
Furniture Shop	–7204
Framing Shop	–7204

Cabinet Shop	-7204	Inter/Intranet Services	-7296
Photo Studio	-7216	Architect of the Capitol	-8000
Post Office	-7220	Superintendent of Senate Buildings	-8002
Recording Studio	-7220	Restaurant	-8050
Senate Legislative Counsel	-7275	Amtrak Ticket Office	-9010
Program Management	-7276	Airlines Ticket Office (CATO)	-9014
IT Support Services—Administration	-7280	Child Care Center	-9022
Telecom Support	-7281	Credit Union	-9026
Equipment Services	-7282	Veterans' Liaison	-9054
Desktop/Lan Support	-7284	Social Security Liaison	-9064
IT Research/Deployment	-7292	Caucus of International Narcotics Control	-9070
Technology Development—Administration	-7290	Army Liaison	-9082
Systems Architecture	-7277	Air Force Liaison	-9083
Information Security	-7278	Coast Guard Liaison	-9084
Applications Development	-7291	Navy Liaison	-9085
Network Engineering and Management	-7293	Marine Liaison	-9087
Enterprise IT Systems	-7294		

House Post Office (20515): Mail to all House offices is delivered by the main Post Office in the Longworth House Office Building.

House Committees Leadership

U.S. House of Representatives	-0001	Committee on Foreign Affairs	-6128
Cannon House Office Building	-0002	Committee on Homeland Security	-6480
Rayburn House Office Building	-0003	Committee on House Administration	-6157
Longworth House Office Building	-0004	Committee on the Judiciary	-6216
Ford House Office Building	-0006	Committee on Natural Resources	-6201
The Capitol	-0007	Committee on Oversight and Government Reform	-6143
Committee on Agriculture	-6001	Committee on Rules	-6269
Committee on Appropriations	-6015	Committee on Science, Space, and Technology	-6301
Committee on Armed Services	-6035	Committee on Small Business	-6315
Committee on the Budget	-6065	Committee on Transportation and Infrastructure	-6256
Committee on Education and the Workforce	-6100	Committee on Veterans' Affairs	-6335
Committee on Energy and Commerce	-6115	Committee on Ways and Means	-6348
Committee on Ethics	-6328	Permanent Select Committee on Intelligence	-6415
Committee on Financial Services	-6050		

Joint Committee Offices, House Side

Joint Economic Committee	-6432	Joint Committee on Printing	-6157
Joint Committee on the Library	-6157	Joint Committee on Taxation	-6453

House Leadership Offices

Office of the Speaker	-6501	Office of the Democratic Leader	-6537
Office of the Majority Leader	-6502	Office of the Democratic Whip	-6538
Office of the Majority Whip	-6503	House Republican Conference	-6544
Democratic Caucus	-6524	Republican Congressional Committee, National	-6547
Democratic Congressional Campaign Committee	-6525	Republican Policy Committee	-6549
Democratic Steering and Policy Committee	-6527	Republican Cloakroom	-6650
Democratic Cloakroom	-6528		

House Officers

Office of the Clerk	-6601	Office of Employee Assistance	-6619
Office of Art and Archives	-6612	ADA Services	-6860
Office of Employment and Counsel	-6622	Personnel and Benefits	-9980
Legislative Computer Systems	-6618	Child Care Center	-0001
Office of Legislative Operations	-6602	Payroll and Benefits	-6604
Legislative Resource Center	-6612	Financial Counseling	-6604
Official Reporters	-6615	Members' Services	-9970
Office of Communications	-6611	Office Supply Service	-6860
Office of Interparliamentary Affairs	-6579	House Gift Shop	-6860
Office of the Chaplain	-6655	Mail List/Processing	-6860
Office of the House Historian	-6701	Mailing Services	-6860
Office of the Parliamentarian	-6731	Contractor Management	-6860
Chief Administrative Officer	-6860	Photography	-6623
First Call	-6660	House Recording Studio	-6613
Administrative Counsel	-6660	Furniture Support Services	-6610
Periodical Press Gallery	-6624	House Office Service Center	-6860
Press Gallery	-6625	Budget	-6604
Radio/TV Correspondents' Gallery	-6627	Financial Counseling	-6604
HIR Call Center	-6165	Procurement Management	-9940
HIR Information Systems Security	-6165	Office of the Sergeant at Arms	-6634
Outplacement Services	-9920		

House Commissions and Offices

Congressional Executive Commission on China	–6481
Commission on Security and Cooperation in Europe	–6460
Commission on Congressional Mailing Standards	–6461
Office of the Law Revision Counsel	–6711
Office of Emergency Management	–6462
Office of the Legislative Counsel	–6721
General Counsel	–6532
Architect of the Capitol	–6906
Attending Physician	–6907
Congressional Budget Office	–6925

Liaison Offices

Air Force	–6854
Army	–6855
Coast Guard	–6856
Navy	–6857
Office of Personnel Management	–6858
Veterans' Administration	–6859

TERMS OF SERVICE

EXPIRATION OF THE TERMS OF SENATORS

CLASS II.—SENATORS WHOSE TERMS OF SERVICE EXPIRE IN 2015

[33 Senators in this group: Democrats, 20; Republicans, 13]

Name	Party	Residence
Alexander, Lamar	R.	Maryville, TN.
Begich, Mark	D.	Anchorage, AK.
Booker, Cory A.[1]	D.	Newark, NJ.
Chambliss, Saxby	R.	Moultrie, GA.
Cochran, Thad	R.	Oxford, MS.
Collins, Susan M.	R.	Bangor, ME.
Coons, Christopher A.[2]	D.	Wilmington, DE.
Cornyn, John	R.	Austin, TX.
Durbin, Richard J.	D.	Springfield, IL.
Enzi, Michael B.	R.	Gillette, WY.
Franken, Al[3]	D.	St. Louis Park, MN.
Graham, Lindsey	R.	Seneca, SC.
Hagan, Kay R.	D.	Greensboro, NC.
Harkin, Tom	D.	Cumming, IA.
Inhofe, James M.[4]	R.	Tulsa, OK.
Johanns, Mike	R.	Omaha, NE.
Johnson, Tim	D.	Vermillion, SD.
Landrieu, Mary L.	D.	New Orleans, LA.
Levin, Carl	D.	Detroit, MI.
McConnell, Mitch	R.	Louisville, KY.
Markey, Edward J.[5]	D.	Malden, MA.
Merkley, Jeff	D.	Portland, OR.
Pryor, Mark L.	D.	Little Rock, AR.
Reed, Jack	D.	Jamestown, RI.
Risch, James E.	R.	Boise, ID.
Roberts, Pat	R.	Dodge City, KS.
Rockefeller, John D. IV	D.	Charleston, WV.
Sessions, Jeff	R.	Mobile, AL.
Shaheen, Jeanne	D.	Madbury, NH.
Udall, Mark	D.	Eldorado Springs, CO.
Udall, Tom	D.	Santa Fe, NM.
Walsh, John E.[6]	D.	Helena, MT.
Warner, Mark R.	D.	Alexandria, VA.

[1] Elected as a Democrat to the U.S. Senate in a special election on October 16, 2013, to fill the vacancy caused by the death of Senator Frank Lautenberg, a seat subsequently held by appointed Senator Jeffrey Chiesa, and took the oath of office on October 31, 2013, for the term ending January 3, 2015.

[2] Senator Coons won a special election on November 2, 2010 to fill the vacancy caused by the resignation of Senator Joseph R. Biden, Jr. He took the oath of office on November 15, 2010, replacing appointed Senator Ted Kaufman.

[3] Contested election was resolved June 30, 2009; Senator Franken was sworn into office on July 7, 2009.

[4] Senator Inhofe won the special election held on November 8, 1994, to fill the vacancy caused by the resignation of Senator David Boren, and took the oath of office on November 17, 1994. He was elected to a full term in 1996.

[5] Representative Markey resigned to become a Senator; elected to the U.S. Senate in a special election on June 25, 2013, to fill the vacancy caused by the resignation of Senator John F. Kerry, a seat subsequently held by appointed Senator William Cowan, and took the oath of office on July 16, 2013, for the term ending January 3, 2015.

[6] Senator Walsh was appointed as a Democrat to the United States Senate on February 9, 2014, to fill the vacancy caused by the resignation of Senator Max Baucus, and took the oath of office on February 11, 2014, for the term ending January 3, 2015.

CLASS III.—SENATORS WHOSE TERMS OF SERVICE EXPIRE IN 2017

[34 Senators in this group: Democrats, 10; Republicans, 24]

Name	Party	Residence
Ayotte, Kelly	R.	Nashua, NH.
Bennet, Michael F.[1]	D.	Denver, CO.
Blunt, Roy	R.	Springfield, MO.
Blumenthal, Richard	D.	Greenwich, CT.
Boozman, John	R.	Rogers, AR.
Boxer, Barbara	D.	Rancho Mirage, CA.
Burr, Richard	R.	Winston-Salem, NC.
Coats, Daniel	R.	Indianapolis, IN.
Coburn, Tom	R.	Muskogee, OK.
Crapo, Mike	R.	Idaho Falls, ID.
Grassley, Chuck	R.	New Hartford, IA.
Hoeven, John	R.	Bismarck, ND.
Isakson, Johnny	R.	Marietta, GA.
Johnson, Ron	R.	Oshkosh, WI.
Kirk, Mark[2]	R.	Highland Park, IL.
Leahy, Patrick J.	D.	Middlesex, VT.
Lee, Mike	R.	Alpine, UT.
McCain, John	R.	Phoenix, AZ.
Mikulski, Barbara A.	D.	Baltimore, MD.
Moran, Jerry	R.	Hays, KS.
Murkowski, Lisa[3]	R.	Girdwood, AK.
Murray, Patty	D.	Seattle, WA.
Paul, Rand	R.	Bowling Green, KY.
Portman, Rob	R.	Terrace Park, OH.
Reid, Harry	D.	Searchlight, NV.
Rubio, Marco	R.	West Miami, FL.
Schatz, Brian[4]	D.	Honolulu, HI.
Schumer, Charles E.	D.	Brooklyn, NY.
Scott, Tim[5]	R.	North Charleston, SC.
Shelby, Richard C.[6]	R.	Tuscaloosa, AL.
Thune, John	R.	Murdo, SD.
Toomey, Patrick J.	R.	Zionsville, PA.
Vitter, David	R.	Metairie, LA.
Wyden, Ron[7]	D.	Portland, OR.

[1] Senator Bennet was appointed on January 21, 2009, to fill the vacancy caused by the resignation of Senator Kenneth L. Salazar. He took the oath of office on January 22, 2009. Elected to a full term on November 2, 2010.

[2] Senator Kirk won a special election on November 2, 2010, to fill the vacancy caused by the resignation of Senator Barack Obama, and at the same time was elected in the general election for the 6-year term ending January 3, 2017. He took the oath of office on November 29, 2010, replacing appointed Senator Roland Burris.

[3] Senator Murkowski was appointed on December 20, 2002, to fill the vacancy caused by the resignation of her father, Senator Frank Murkowski. Elected to a full term on November 2, 2004.

[4] Senator Schatz was appointed to the U.S. Senate on December 26, 2012, to fill the vacancy caused by the death of Senator Daniel Inouye, and took the oath of office on December 27, 2012.

[5] Senator Scott was appointed on January 2, 2013, to fill the vacancy caused by the resignation of Senator James DeMint; appointment took effect upon his resignation from the House of Representatives on January 2, 2013; took the oath of office on January 3, 2013.

[6] Senator Shelby changed party affiliation from Democrat to Republican on November 5, 1994.

[7] Senator Wyden won a special election on January 30, 1996, to fill the vacancy caused by the resignation of Senator Robert Packwood, and began service on February 6, 1996. He was elected to a full term in 1998.

CLASS I.—SENATORS WHOSE TERMS OF SERVICE EXPIRE IN 2019

[33 Senators in this group: Democrats, 23; Republicans, 8; Independents, 2]

Name	Party	Residence
Baldwin, Tammy	D.	Madison, WI.
Barrasso, John [1]	R.	Casper, WY.
Brown, Sherrod	D.	Avon, OH.
Cantwell, Maria	D.	Edmonds, WA.
Cardin, Benjamin L.	D.	Baltimore, MD.
Carper, Thomas R.	D.	Wilmington, DE.
Casey, Robert P., Jr.	D.	Scranton, PA.
Corker, Bob	R.	Chattanooga, TN.
Cruz, Ted	R.	Houston, TX.
Donnelly, Joe	D.	Granger, IN.
Feinstein, Dianne [2]	D.	San Francisco, CA.
Fischer, Deb	R.	Valentine, NE.
Flake, Jeff	R.	Mesa, AZ.
Gillibrand, Kirsten E. [3]	D.	Brunswick, NY.
Hatch, Orrin G.	R.	Salt Lake City, UT.
Heinrich, Martin	D.	Albuquerque, NM.
Heitkamp, Heidi	D.	Mandan, ND.
Heller, Dean [4]	R.	Carson City, NV.
Hirono, Mazie K.	D.	Honolulu, HI.
Kaine, Tim	D.	Richmond, VA.
King, Angus S., Jr.	I.	Brunswick, ME.
Klobuchar, Amy	D.	Minneapolis, MN.
Manchin, Joe III [5]	D.	Fairmont, WV.
McCaskill, Claire	D.	Kirkwood, MO.
Menendez, Robert [6]	D.	North Bergen, NJ.
Murphy, Christopher	D.	Cheshire, CT.
Nelson, Bill	D.	Orlando, FL.
Sanders, Bernard	I.	Burlington, VT.
Stabenow, Debbie	D.	Lansing, MI.
Tester, Jon	D.	Big Sandy, MT.
Warren, Elizabeth	D.	Cambridge, MA.
Whitehouse, Sheldon	D.	Newport, RI.
Wicker, Roger F. [7]	R.	Tupelo, MS.

[1] Senator Barrasso was appointed on June 22, 2007, to fill the vacancy caused by the death of Senator Craig Thomas. He took the oath of office on June 25, 2007; subsequently elected in a special election on November 4, 2008.

[2] Senator Feinstein won the special election held on November 3, 1992, to fill the vacancy caused by the resignation of Senator Pete Wilson. She took the oath of office on November 10, 1992. She won the seat from Senator John Seymour who had been appointed on January 7, 1991. She was elected to a full term in 1994.

[3] Senator Gillibrand was appointed on January 23, 2009, to fill the vacancy caused by the resignation of Senator Hillary Rodham Clinton. She took the oath of office on January 27, 2009; subsequently elected in a special election on November 2, 2010.

[4] Senator Heller was appointed on May 3, 2011, to fill the vacancy caused by the resignation of Senator John Ensign. He took the oath of office on May 9, 2011.

[5] Senator Manchin won a special election on November 2, 2010, to fill the vacancy caused by the death of Senator Robert C. Byrd, Senator Manchin took the oath of office on November 15, 2010, replacing appointed Senator Carte P. Goodwin.

[6] Senator Menendez was appointed on January 17, 2006, to fill the vacancy caused by the resignation of Senator Jon S. Corzine. He took the oath of office on January 18, 2006; subsequently elected to a full term in November 2006.

[7] Senator Wicker was appointed on December 31, 2007, to fill the vacancy caused by the resignation of Senator Trent Lott. He took the oath of office on December 31, 2007; subsequently elected in a special election on November 4, 2008.

CONTINUOUS SERVICE OF SENATORS

[Democrats in roman (53); Republicans in *italic* (45); Independents in SMALL CAPS (2); total, 100]

Rank	Name	State	Beginning of present service
1	Leahy, Patrick J.	Vermont	Jan. 3, 1975.
2	*Hatch, Orrin G.*	Utah	Jan. 3, 1977.
3	*Cochran, Thad* † [1]	Mississippi	Dec. 27, 1978.
4	Levin, Carl	Michigan	Jan. 3, 1979.
5	*Grassley, Chuck* †	Iowa	Jan. 3, 1981.
6	Harkin, Tom †	Iowa	Jan. 3, 1985.
	McConnell, Mitch	Kentucky	
7	Rockefeller, John D. IV [2]	West Virginia	Jan. 15, 1985.
8	*McCain, John* †	Arizona	
	Mikulski, Barbara A.†	Maryland	
	Reid, Harry †	Nevada	
	Shelby, Richard C.†	Alabama	
9	Feinstein, Dianne [3]	California	Nov. 10, 1992.‡
10	Boxer, Barbara †	California	Jan. 3, 1993.
	Murray, Patty	Washington	
11	*Inhofe, James M.* † [4]	Oklahoma	Nov. 17, 1994. ‡
12	Wyden, Ron † [5]	Oregon	Feb. 6, 1996. ‡
13	*Collins, Susan M.*	Maine	Jan. 3, 1997.
	Durbin, Richard J. †	Illinois	
	Enzi, Michael B.	Wyoming	
	Johnson, Tim †	South Dakota	
	Landrieu, Mary L.	Louisiana	
	Reed, Jack †	Rhode Island	
	Roberts, Pat †	Kansas	
	Sessions, Jeff	Alabama	
14	*Crapo, Mike* †	Idaho	Jan. 3, 1999.
	Schumer, Charles E. †	New York	
15	Cantwell, Maria †	Washington	Jan. 3, 2001.
	Carper, Thomas R.†	Delaware	
	Nelson, Bill †	Florida	
	Stabenow, Debbie †	Michigan	
16	*Cornyn, John* [6]	Texas	Dec. 2, 2002.
17	*Murkowski, Lisa* [7]	Alaska	Dec. 20, 2002.
18	*Alexander, Lamar*	Tennessee	Jan. 3, 2003.
	Chambliss, Saxby †	Georgia	
	Graham, Lindsey †	South Carolina	
	Pryor, Mark L.	Arkansas	
19	*Burr, Richard* †	North Carolina	Jan. 3, 2005.
	Coburn, Tom †	Oklahoma	
	Isakson, Johnny †	Georgia	
	Thune, John †	South Dakota	
	Vitter, David †	Louisiana	
20	Menendez, Robert † [8]	New Jersey	Jan. 18, 2006.
21	Brown, Sherrod †	Ohio	Jan. 3, 2007.
	Cardin, Benjamin L. †	Maryland	
	Casey, Robert P., Jr.	Pennsylvania	
	Corker, Bob	Tennessee	
	Klobuchar, Amy	Minnesota	
	McCaskill, Claire	Missouri	
	SANDERS, BERNARD †	Vermont	
	Tester, Jon	Montana	
	Whitehouse, Sheldon	Rhode Island	
22	*Barrasso, John* [9]	Wyoming	June 22, 2007.
23	*Wicker, Roger F.* † [10]	Mississippi	Dec. 31, 2007.

CONTINUOUS SERVICE OF SENATORS—CONTINUED

[Democrats in roman (53); Republicans in *italic* (45); Independents in SMALL CAPS (2); total, 100]

Rank	Name	State	Beginning of present service
24	Begich, Mark	Alaska	Jan. 3, 2009.
	Hagan, Kay R.	North Carolina	
	Johanns, Mike	Nebraska	
	Merkley, Jeff	Oregon	
	Risch, James E.	Idaho	
	Shaheen, Jeanne	New Hampshire	
	Udall, Mark †	Colorado	
	Udall, Tom †	New Mexico	
	Warner, Mark R.	Virginia	
25	Bennet, Michael F. [11]	Colorado	Jan. 21, 2009.
26	Gillibrand, Kirsten E.† [12]	New York	Jan. 27, 2009.
27	Franken, Al [13]	Minnesota	July 7, 2009.
28	Coons, Christopher A. [14]	Delaware	Nov. 15, 2010.
	Manchin, Joe III [15]	West Virginia	
29	*Kirk, Mark* † [16]	Illinois	Nov. 29, 2010. ‡
30	*Ayotte, Kelly*	New Hampshire	Jan. 3, 2011.
	Blumenthal, Richard	Connecticut	
	Blunt, Roy	Missouri	
	Boozman, John †	Arkansas	
	Coats, Daniel † [17]	Indiana	
	Hoeven, John	North Dakota	
	Johnson, Ron	Wisconsin	
	Lee, Mike	Utah	
	Moran, Jerry	Kansas	
	Paul, Rand	Kentucky	
	Portman, Rob	Ohio	
	Rubio, Marco	Florida	
	Toomey, Patrick J.	Pennsylvania	
31	*Heller, Dean* † [18]	Nevada	May 9, 2011.
32	Schatz, Brian E. [19]	Hawaii	Dec. 26, 2012.
33	*Scott, Tim* † [20]	South Carolina	Jan. 2, 2013.
34	Baldwin, Tammy	Wisconsin	Jan. 3, 2013.
	Flake, Jeff	Arizona	
	Donnelly, Joe	Indiana	
	Murphy, Christopher	Connecticut	
	Hirono, Mazie K.	Hawaii	
	Heinrich, Martin	New Mexico	
	KING, ANGUS S., JR.	Maine	
	Kaine, Tim	Virginia	
	Cruz, Ted	Texas	
	Warren, Elizabeth	Massachusetts	
	Fischer, Deb	Nebraska	
	Heitkamp, Heidi	North Dakota	
35	Markey, Edward J.† [21]	Massachusetts	July 16, 2013. ‡
36	Booker, Cory A. [22]	New Jersey	Oct. 31, 2013.‡
37	Walsh, John E. [23]	Montana	Feb. 11, 2014.

† Served in the House of Representatives previous to service in the Senate.

‡ Senators elected to complete unexpired terms typically begin their terms on the day following the election, but individual cases may vary.

[1] Senator Cochran was elected November 6, 1978, for the 6-year term commencing January 3, 1979; subsequently appointed December 27, 1978, to fill the vacancy caused by the resignation of Senator James Eastland. He was elected to a full term in 1984.

[2] Senator Rockefeller was elected November 6, 1984, for the 6-year term commencing January 3, 1985; did not take his seat until January 15, 1985.

[3] Senator Feinstein was elected on November 3, 1992, to fill the vacancy caused by the resignation of Senator Pete Wilson. She replaced appointed Senator John Seymour when she took the oath of office on November 10, 1992. She was elected to a full term in 1994.

[4] Senator Inhofe won the special election held on November 8, 1994, to fill the vacancy caused by the resignation of Senator David Boren, and took the oath of office on November 17, 1994. He was elected to a full term in 1996.

[5] Senator Wyden won a special election on January 30, 1996, to fill the vacancy caused by the resignation of Senator Bob Packwood. He was elected to a full term in 1998.

[6] Senator Cornyn was elected on November 5, 2002, for a 6-year term commencing January 3, 2003; subsequently appointed on December 2, 2002, to fill the vacancy caused by the resignation of Senator Phil Gramm.

[7] Senator Murkowski was appointed on December 20, 2002, to fill the vacancy caused by the resignation of her father, Senator Frank Murkowski. She was elected to a full term in 2004.

[8] Senator Menendez was appointed on January 17, 2006, to fill the vacancy caused by the resignation of Senator Jon S. Corzine; subsequently elected to a full term in November 2006.

[9] Senator Barrasso was appointed on June 22, 2007, to fill the vacancy caused by the death of Senator Craig Thomas, and took the oath of office on June 25, 2007; subsequently elected in a special election on November 2008.

[10] Senator Wicker was appointed on December 31, 2007, to fill the vacancy caused by the resignation of Senator Trent Lott; subsequently elected in a special election on November 4, 2008.

[11] Senator Bennet was appointed on January 21, 2009, to fill the vacancy caused by the resignation of Ken Salazar, and took the oath of office on January 22, 2009; subsequently elected to a full term on November 2, 2010.

[12] Senator Gillibrand was appointed on January 23, 2009, to fill the vacancy caused by the resignation of Senator Hillary Clinton, and took the oath of office on January 27, 2009; subsequently elected in a special election on November 2, 2010.

[13] The contested election case between Senator Franken and former Senator Coleman was resolved by Minnesota's Supreme Court on June 30, 2009. Franken was sworn into office on July 7, 2009. The Senate seat had remained vacant from January 3 until July 6.

[14] Senator Coons won a special election on November 2, 2010, to fill the vacancy caused by the resignation of Senator Joseph Biden, Jr. Coons took the oath of office on November 15, 2010, replacing appointed Senator Edward E. Kaufman.

[15] Senator Manchin won a special election on November 2, 2010, to fill the vacancy caused by the death of Senator Robert C. Byrd. He took the oath of office on November 15, 2010, replacing appointed Senator Carte P. Goodwin.

[16] Senator Kirk won a special election to the term ending January 3, 2011 on November 2, 2010, to fill the vacancy caused by the resignation of Senator Barack Obama, and at the same time elected in the general election for the 6-year term ending January 3, 2017; took the oath of office on November 29, 2010, replacing appointed Senator Roland Burris.

[17] Senator Coats previously served in the Senate from January 3, 1989, until January 3, 1999.

[18] Senator Heller was appointed May 3, 2011, to the United States Senate for the term ending January 3, 2013, to fill the vacancy caused by the resignation of Senator John E. Ensign; took the oath of office on May 9, 2011.

[19] Senator Schatz was appointed as a Democrat to the U.S. Senate on December 26, 2012, to fill the vacancy caused by the death of Senator Daniel Inouye, and took the oath of office on December 27, 2012.

[20] Senator Scott was appointed on January 2, 2013, to fill the vacancy caused by the resignation of Senator James DeMint; appointment took effect upon his resignation from the House of Representatives on January 2, 2013; took the oath of office on January 3, 2013.

[21] Representative Markey resigned to become a Senator; elected to the U.S. Senate in a special election on June 25, 2013, to fill the vacancy caused by the resignation of Senator John F. Kerry, a seat subsequently held by appointed Senator William Cowan, and took the oath of office on July 16, 2013, for the term ending January 3, 2015.

[22] Senator Booker elected as a Democrat to the U.S. Senate in a special election on October 16, 2013, to fill the vacancy caused by the death of Senator Frank Lautenberg, a seat subsequently held by appointed Senator Jeffrey Chiesa, and took the oath of office on October 31, 2013, for the term ending January 3, 2015.

[23] Senator Walsh was appointed as a Democrat to the United States Senate on February 9, 2014, to fill the vacancy caused by the resignation of Senator Max Baucus, and took the oath of office on February 11, 2014, for the term ending January 3, 2015.

CONGRESSES IN WHICH REPRESENTATIVES, RESIDENT COMMISSIONER, AND DELEGATES HAVE SERVED WITH BEGINNING OF PRESENT SERVICE

[* Elected to fill a vacancy; Republicans in roman (232); Democrats in *italic* (199); Vacancies (4); Resident Commissioner and Delegates in ***boldface italic*** (6); total, 441]

Name	State	Congresses (inclusive)	Beginning of present service
30 terms, consecutive			
Dingell, John D.	MI	*84th to 113th	Dec. 13, 1955
25 terms, consecutive			
Conyers, John, Jr.	MI	89th to 113th	Jan. 3, 1965
22 terms, consecutive			
Rangel, Charles B.	NY	92d to 113th	Jan. 3, 1971
21 terms, consecutive			
Young, Don	AK	*93d to 113th	Mar. 6, 1973
20 terms, consecutive			
Miller, George	CA	94th to 113th	Jan. 3, 1975
Waxman, Henry A.	CA	94th to 113th	Jan. 3, 1975
19 terms, consecutive			
Rahall, Nick J. II	WV	95th to 113th	Jan. 3, 1977
18 terms, consecutive			
Petri, Thomas E.	WI	*96th to 113th	Apr. 3, 1979
Sensenbrenner, F. James, Jr.	WI	96th to 113th	Jan. 3, 1979
17 terms, consecutive			
Hall, Ralph M.	TX	97th to 113th	Jan. 3, 1981
Hoyer, Steny H.	MD	*97th to 113th	May 19, 1981
Rogers, Harold	KY	97th to 113th	Jan. 3, 1981
Smith, Christopher H.	NJ	97th to 113th	Jan. 3, 1981
Wolf, Frank R.	VA	97th to 113th	Jan. 3, 1981
16 terms, consecutive			
Kaptur, Marcy	OH	98th to 113th	Jan. 3, 1983
Levin, Sander M.	MI	98th to 113th	Jan. 3, 1983
15 terms, consecutive			
Barton, Joe	TX	99th to 113th	Jan. 3, 1985
Coble, Howard	NC	99th to 113th	Jan. 3, 1985
Visclosky, Peter J.	IN	99th to 113th	Jan. 3, 1985
14 terms, consecutive			
DeFazio, Peter A.	OR	100th to 113th	Jan. 3, 1987
Duncan, John J., Jr.	TN	*100th to 113th	Nov. 8, 1988
Lewis, John	GA	100th to 113th	Jan. 3, 1987
Pelosi, Nancy	CA	*100th to 113th	June 2, 1987
Slaughter, Louise McIntosh	NY	100th to 113th	Jan. 3, 1987
Smith, Lamar	TX	100th to 113th	Jan. 3, 1987
Upton, Fred	MI	100th to 113th	Jan. 3, 1987

CONGRESSES IN WHICH REPRESENTATIVES, RESIDENT COMMISSIONER, AND DELEGATES HAVE SERVED WITH BEGINNING OF PRESENT SERVICE—CONTINUED

[* Elected to fill a vacancy; Republicans in roman (232); Democrats in *italic* (199); Vacancies (4); Resident Commissioner and Delegates in ***boldface italic*** (6); total, 441]

Name	State	Congresses (inclusive)	Beginning of present service
13 terms, consecutive			
Engel, Eliot L.	NY	101st to 113th	Jan. 3, 1989
Lowey, Nita M.	NY	101st to 113th	Jan. 3, 1989
McDermott, Jim	WA	101st to 113th	Jan. 3, 1989
Neal, Richard E.	MA	101st to 113th	Jan. 3, 1989
Rohrabacher, Dana	CA	101st to 113th	Jan. 3, 1989
Ros-Lehtinen, Ileana	FL	*101st to 113th	Aug. 29, 1989
Serrano, José E.	NY	*101st to 113th	Mar. 20, 1990
13 terms, not consecutive			
Price, David E.	NC	100th to 103d, 105th to 113th.	Jan 3. 1997
12 terms, consecutive			
Boehner, John A.	OH	102d to 113th	Jan. 3, 1991
Camp, Dave	MI	102d to 113th	Jan. 3, 1991
DeLauro, Rosa L.	CT	102d to 113th	Jan. 3, 1991
Johnson, Sam	TX	*102d to 113th	May 8, 1991
Moran, James P.	VA	102d to 113th	Jan. 3, 1991
Nadler, Jerrold	NY	*102d to 113th	Nov. 3, 1992
Pastor, Ed	AZ	*102d to 113th	Sep. 24, 1991
Peterson, Collin C.	MN	102d to 113th	Jan. 3, 1991
Waters, Maxine	CA	102d to 113th	Jan. 3, 1991
12 terms, not consecutive			
Cooper, Jim	TN	98th to 103d and 108th to 113th.	Jan. 3, 2003
11 terms, consecutive			
Bachus, Spencer	AL	103d to 113th	Jan. 3, 1993
Becerra, Xavier	CA	103d to 113th	Jan. 3, 1993
Bishop, Sanford D., Jr.	GA	103d to 113th	Jan. 3, 1993
Brown, Corrine	FL	103d to 113th	Jan. 3, 1993
Calvert, Ken	CA	103d to 113th	Jan. 3, 1993
Clyburn, James E.	SC	103d to 113th	Jan. 3, 1993
Eshoo, Anna G.	CA	103d to 113th	Jan. 3, 1993
Farr, Sam	CA	*103d to 113th	June 8, 1993
Goodlatte, Bob	VA	103d to 113th	Jan. 3, 1993
Green, Gene	TX	103d to 113th	Jan. 3, 1993
Gutiérrez, Luis V.	IL	103d to 113th	Jan. 3, 1993
Hastings, Alcee L.	FL	103d to 113th	Jan. 3, 1993
Johnson, Eddie Bernice	TX	103d to 113th	Jan. 3, 1993
King, Peter T.	NY	103d to 113th	Jan. 3, 1993
Kingston, Jack	GA	103d to 113th	Jan. 3, 1993
Lucas, Frank D.	OK	*103d to 113th	May 10, 1994
McKeon, Howard P. "Buck"	CA	103d to 113th	Jan. 3, 1993
Maloney, Carolyn B.	NY	103d to 113th	Jan. 3, 1993
Mica, John L.	FL	103d to 113th	Jan. 3, 1993
Roybal-Allard, Lucille	CA	103d to 113th	Jan. 3, 1993
Royce, Edward R.	CA	103d to 113th	Jan. 3, 1993
Rush, Bobby L.	IL	103d to 113th	Jan. 3, 1993

CONGRESSES IN WHICH REPRESENTATIVES, RESIDENT COMMISSIONER, AND DELEGATES HAVE SERVED WITH BEGINNING OF PRESENT SERVICE—CONTINUED

[* Elected to fill a vacancy; Republicans in roman (232); Democrats in *italic* (199); Vacancies (4); Resident Commissioner and Delegates in ***boldface italic*** (6); total, 441]

Name	State	Congresses (inclusive)	Beginning of present service
Scott, Robert C. ''Bobby''	VA	103d to 113th	Jan. 3, 1993
Thompson, Bennie G.	MS	*103d to 113th	Apr. 13, 1993
Velázquez, Nydia M.	NY	103d to 113th	Jan. 3, 1993
10 terms, consecutive			
Blumenauer, Earl	OR	*104th to 113th	May 21, 1996
Cummings, Elijah E.	MD	*104th to 113th	Apr. 16, 1996
Doggett, Lloyd	TX	104th to 113th	Jan. 3, 1995
Doyle, Michael F.	PA	104th to 113th	Jan. 3, 1995
Fattah, Chaka	PA	104th to 113th	Jan. 3, 1995
Frelinghuysen, Rodney P.	NJ	104th to 113th	Jan. 3, 1995
Hastings, Doc	WA	104th to 113th	Jan. 3, 1995
Jackson Lee, Sheila	TX	104th to 113th	Jan. 3, 1995
Jones, Walter B.	NC	104th to 113th	Jan. 3, 1995
Latham, Tom	IA	104th to 113th	Jan. 3, 1995
LoBiondo, Frank A.	NJ	104th to 113th	Jan. 3, 1995
Lofgren, Zoe	CA	104th to 113th	Jan. 3, 1995
Thornberry, Mac	TX	104th to 113th	Jan. 3, 1995
Whitfield, Ed	KY	104th to 113th	Jan. 3, 1995
9 terms			
Aderholt, Robert B.	AL	105th to 113th	Jan. 3, 1997
Brady, Kevin	TX	105th to 113th	Jan. 3, 1997
Brady, Robert A.	PA	*105th to 113th	May 19, 1998
Capps, Lois	CA	*105th to 113th	Mar. 10, 1998
Davis, Danny K.	IL	105th to 113th	Jan. 3, 1997
DeGette, Diana	CO	105th to 113th	Jan. 3, 1997
Granger, Kay	TX	105th to 113th	Jan. 3, 1997
Hinojosa, Rubén	TX	105th to 113th	Jan. 3, 1997
Kind, Ron	WI	105th to 113th	Jan. 3, 1997
Lee, Barbara	CA	*105th to 113th	Apr. 7, 1998
McCarthy, Carolyn	NY	105th to 113th	Jan. 3, 1997
McGovern, James P.	MA	105th to 113th	Jan. 3, 1997
McIntyre, Mike	NC	105th to 113th	Jan. 3, 1997
Meeks, Gregory W.	NY	*105th to 113th	Feb. 3, 1998
Pascrell, Bill, Jr.	NJ	105th to 113th	Jan. 3, 1997
Pitts, Joseph R.	PA	105th to 113th	Jan. 3, 1997
Sanchez, Loretta	CA	105th to 113th	Jan. 3, 1997
Sessions, Pete	TX	105th to 113th	Jan. 3, 1997
Sherman, Brad	CA	105th to 113th	Jan. 3, 1997
Shimkus, John	IL	105th to 113th	Jan. 3, 1997
Smith, Adam	WA	105th to 113th	Jan. 3, 1997
Tierney, John F.	MA	105th to 113th	Jan. 3, 1997
9 terms, not consecutive			
Chabot, Steve	OH	104th to 110th and 113th.	Jan. 3, 2011
8 terms			
Capuano, Michael E.	MA	106th to 113th	Jan. 3, 1999

CONGRESSES IN WHICH REPRESENTATIVES, RESIDENT COMMISSIONER, AND DELEGATES HAVE SERVED WITH BEGINNING OF PRESENT SERVICE—CONTINUED

[* Elected to fill a vacancy; Republicans in roman (232); Democrats in *italic* (199); Vacancies (4); Resident Commissioner and Delegates in ***boldface italic*** (6); total, 441]

Name	State	Congresses (inclusive)	Beginning of present service
Crowley, Joseph	NY	106th to 113th	Jan. 3, 1999
Holt, Rush D.	NJ	106th to 113th	Jan. 3, 1999
Larson, John B.	CT	106th to 113th	Jan. 3, 1999
Miller, Gary G.	CA	106th to 113th	Jan. 3, 1999
Napolitano, Grace F.	CA	106th to 113th	Jan. 3, 1999
Ryan, Paul	WI	106th to 113th	Jan. 3, 1999
Schakowsky, Janice D.	IL	106th to 113th	Jan. 3, 1999
Simpson, Michael K.	ID	106th to 113th	Jan. 3, 1999
Terry, Lee	NE	106th to 113th	Jan. 3, 1999
Thompson, Mike	CA	106th to 113th	Jan. 3, 1999
Walden, Greg	OR	106th to 113th	Jan. 3, 1999
7 terms			
Cantor, Eric	VA	107th to 113th	Jan. 3, 2001
Capito, Shelley Moore	WV	107th to 113th	Jan. 3, 2001
Clay, Wm. Lacy	MO	107th to 113th	Jan. 3, 2001
Crenshaw, Ander	FL	107th to 113th	Jan. 3, 2001
Culberson, John Abney	TX	107th to 113th	Jan. 3, 2001
Davis, Susan A.	CA	107th to 113th	Jan. 3, 2001
Forbes, J. Randy	VA	*107th to 113th	June 19, 2001
Graves, Sam	MO	107th to 113th	Jan. 3, 2001
Honda, Michael M.	CA	107th to 113th	Jan. 3, 2001
Israel, Steve	NY	107th to 113th	Jan. 3, 2001
Issa, Darrell E.	CA	107th to 113th	Jan. 3, 2001
Langevin, James R.	RI	107th to 113th	Jan. 3, 2001
Larsen, Rick	WA	107th to 113th	Jan. 3, 2001
Lynch, Stephen F.	MA	*107th to 113th	Oct. 16, 2001
McCollum, Betty	MN	107th to 113th	Jan. 3, 2001
Matheson, Jim	UT	107th to 113th	Jan. 3, 2001
Miller, Jeff	FL	*107th to 113th	Oct. 16, 2001
Rogers, Mike	MI	107th to 113th	Jan. 3, 2001
Schiff, Adam B.	CA	107th to 113th	Jan. 3, 2001
Shuster, Bill	PA	*107th to 113th	May 15, 2001
Tiberi, Patrick J.	OH	107th to 113th	Jan. 3, 2001
Wilson, Joe	SC	*107th to 113th	Dec. 18, 2001
6 terms			
Bishop, Rob	UT	108th to 113th	Jan. 3, 2003
Bishop, Timothy H.	NY	108th to 113th	Jan. 3, 2003
Blackburn, Marsha	TN	108th to 113th	Jan. 3, 2003
Burgess, Michael C.	TX	108th to 113th	Jan. 3, 2003
Butterfield, G. K.	NC	* 108th to 113th	July 20, 2004
Carter, John R.	TX	108th to 113th	Jan. 3, 2003
Diaz-Balart, Mario	FL	108th to 113th	Jan. 3, 2003
Franks, Trent	AZ	108th to 113th	Jan. 3, 2003
Garrett, Scott	NJ	108th to 113th	Jan. 3, 2003
Gerlach, Jim	PA	108th to 113th	Jan. 3, 2003
Gingrey, Phil	GA	108th to 113th	Jan. 3, 2003
Grijalva, Raúl M.	AZ	108th to 113th	Jan. 3, 2003
Hensarling, Jeb	TX	108th to 113th	Jan. 3, 2003

CONGRESSES IN WHICH REPRESENTATIVES, RESIDENT COMMISSIONER, AND DELEGATES HAVE SERVED WITH BEGINNING OF PRESENT SERVICE—CONTINUED

[* Elected to fill a vacancy; Republicans in roman (232); Democrats in *italic* (199); Vacancies (4); Resident Commissioner and Delegates in ***boldface italic*** (6); total, 441]

Name	State	Congresses (inclusive)	Beginning of present service
King, Steve	IA	108th to 113th	Jan. 3, 2003
Kline, John	MN	108th to 113th	Jan. 3, 2003
Michaud, Michael H.	ME	108th to 113th	Jan. 3, 2003
Miller, Candice S.	MI	108th to 113th	Jan. 3, 2003
Murphy, Tim	PA	108th to 113th	Jan. 3, 2003
Neugebauer, Randy	TX	*108th to 113th	June 3, 2003
Nunes, Devin	CA	108th to 113th	Jan. 3, 2003
Rogers, Mike	AL	108th to 113th	Jan. 3, 2003
Ruppersberger, C. A. Dutch	MD	108th to 113th	Jan. 3, 2003
Ryan, Tim	OH	108th to 113th	Jan. 3, 2003
Sánchez, Linda T.	CA	108th to 113th	Jan. 3, 2003
Scott, David	GA	108th to 113th	Jan. 3, 2003
Turner, Michael R.	OH	108th to 113th	Jan. 3, 2003
Van Hollen, Chris	MD	108th to 113th	Jan. 3, 2003
5 terms			
Barrow, John	GA	109th to 113th	Jan. 3, 2005
Boustany, Charles W., Jr.	LA	109th to 113th	Jan. 3, 2005
Campbell, John	CA	109th to 113th	Dec. 6, 2005
Cleaver, Emanuel	MO	109th to 113th	Jan. 3, 2005
Conaway, K. Michael	TX	109th to 113th	Jan. 3, 2005
Costa, Jim	CA	109th to 113th	Jan. 3, 2005
Cuellar, Henry	TX	109th to 113th	Jan. 3, 2005
Dent, Charles W.	PA	109th to 113th	Jan. 3, 2005
Fortenberry, Jeff	NE	109th to 113th	Jan. 3, 2005
Foxx, Virginia	NC	109th to 113th	Jan. 3, 2005
Gohmert, Louie	TX	109th to 113th	Jan. 3, 2005
Green, Al	TX	109th to 113th	Jan. 3, 2005
Higgins, Brian	NY	109th to 113th	Jan. 3, 2005
Lipinski, Daniel	IL	109th to 113th	Jan. 3, 2005
McCaul, Michael T.	TX	109th to 113th	Jan. 3, 2005
McHenry, Patrick T.	NC	109th to 113th	Jan. 3, 2005
McMorris Rodgers, Cathy	WA	109th to 113th	Jan. 3, 2005
Marchant, Kenny	TX	109th to 113th	Jan. 3, 2005
Matsui, Doris O.	CA	109th to 113th	Mar. 8, 2005
Moore, Gwen	WI	109th to 113th	Jan. 3, 2005
Poe, Ted	TX	109th to 113th	Jan. 3, 2005
Price, Tom	GA	109th to 113th	Jan. 3, 2005
Reichert, David G.	WA	109th to 113th	Jan. 3, 2005
Schwartz, Allyson Y.	PA	109th to 113th	Jan. 3, 2005
Sires, Albio	NJ	109th to 113th	Nov. 13, 2006
Wasserman Schultz, Debbie	FL	109th to 113th	Jan. 3, 2005
Westmoreland, Lynn A.	GA	109th to 113th	Jan. 3, 2005
5 terms, not consecutive			
Pearce, Stevan	NM	108th to 110th and 113th.	Jan. 3. 2011
4 terms			
Bachmann, Michele	MN	110th to 113th	Jan. 3, 2007

CONGRESSES IN WHICH REPRESENTATIVES, RESIDENT COMMISSIONER, AND DELEGATES HAVE SERVED WITH BEGINNING OF PRESENT SERVICE—CONTINUED

[*Elected to fill a vacancy; Republicans in roman (232); Democrats in *italic* (199); Vacancies (4); Resident Commissioner and Delegates in ***boldface italic*** (6); total, 441]

Name	State	Congresses (inclusive)	Beginning of present service
Braley, Bruce L.	IA	110th to 113th	Jan. 3, 2007
Broun, Paul C.	GA	*110th to 113th	July 17, 2007
Buchanan, Vern	FL	110th to 113th	Jan. 3, 2007
Carson, André	IN	*110th to 113th	Mar. 11, 2008
Castor, Kathy	FL	110th to 113th	Jan. 3, 2007
Clarke, Yvette D.	NY	110th to 113th	Jan. 3, 2007
Cohen, Steve	TN	110th to 113th	Jan. 3, 2007
Courtney, Joe	CT	110th to 113th	Jan. 3, 2007
Edwards, Donna F.	MD	*110th to 113th	June 17, 2008
Ellison, Keith	MN	110th to 113th	Jan. 3, 2007
Fudge, Marcia L.	OH	*110th to 113th	Nov. 18, 2008
Johnson, Henry C. ''Hank'', Jr.	GA	110th to 113th	Jan. 3, 2007
Jordan, Jim	OH	110th to 113th	Jan. 3, 2007
Lamborn, Doug	CO	110th to 113th	Jan. 3, 2007
Latta, Robert E.	OH	*110th to 113th	Dec. 11, 2007
Loebsack, David	IA	110th to 113th	Jan. 3, 2007
McCarthy, Kevin	CA	110th to 113th	Jan. 3, 2007
McNerney, Jerry	CA	110th to 113th	Jan. 3, 2007
Perlmutter, Ed	CO	110th to 113th	Jan. 3, 2007
Roskam, Peter J.	IL	110th to 113th	Jan. 3, 2007
Sarbanes, John P.	MD	110th to 113th	Jan. 3, 2007
Scalise, Steve	LA	*110th to 113th	May 3, 2008
Smith, Adrian	NE	110th to 113th	Jan. 3, 2007
Speier, Jackie	CA	*110th to 113th	Apr. 8, 2008
Tsongas, Niki	MA	*110th to 113th	Oct. 16, 2007
Walz, Timothy J.	MN	110th to 113th	Jan. 3, 2007
Welch, Peter	VT	110th to 113th	Jan. 3, 2007
Wittman, Robert J.	VA	*110th to 113th	Dec. 11, 2007
Yarmuth, John A.	KY	110th to 113th	Jan. 3, 2007
4 terms, not consecutive			
Nolan, Richard M.	MN	94th to 96th and 113th.	Jan. 3, 2013
Salmon, Matt	AZ	104th to 106th and 113th.	Jan. 3, 2013
Sanford, Mark	SC	*104th to 106th and 113th.	May 7, 2013
3 terms			
Cassidy, Bill	LA	111th to 113th	Jan. 3, 2009
Chaffetz, Jason	UT	111th to 113th	Jan. 3, 2009
Chu, Judy	CA	*111th and 113th	July 16, 2009
Coffman, Mike	CO	111th to 113th	Jan. 3, 2009
Connolly, Gerald E.	VA	111th to 113th	Jan. 3, 2009
Garamendi, John	CA	*111th to 113th	Nov. 3, 2009
Deutch, Theodore E.	FL	*111th to 113th	Apr. 13, 2010
Fleming, John	LA	111th to 113th	Jan. 3, 2009
Graves, Tom	GA	*111th to 113th	June 8, 2010
Guthrie, Brett	KY	111th to 113th	Jan. 3, 2009
Harper, Gregg	MS	111th to 113th	Jan. 3, 2009

CONGRESSES IN WHICH REPRESENTATIVES, RESIDENT COMMISSIONER, AND DELEGATES HAVE SERVED WITH BEGINNING OF PRESENT SERVICE—CONTINUED

[* Elected to fill a vacancy; Republicans in roman (232); Democrats in *italic* (199); Vacancies (4); Resident Commissioner and Delegates in ***boldface italic*** (6); total, 441]

Name	State	Congresses (inclusive)	Beginning of present service
Himes, James A.	CT	111th to 113th	Jan. 3, 2009
Hunter, Duncan	CA	111th to 113th	Jan. 3, 2009
Jenkins, Lynn	KS	111th to 113th	Jan. 3, 2009
Lance, Leonard	NJ	111th to 113th	Jan. 3, 2009
Luján, Ben Ray	NM	111th to 113th	Jan. 3, 2009
Lummis, Cynthia M.	WY	111th to 113th	Jan. 3, 2009
McClintock, Tom	CA	111th to 113th	Jan. 3, 2009
Olson, Pete	TX	111th to 113th	Jan. 3, 2009
Owens, William L.	NY	*111th to 113th	Nov. 3, 2009
Paulsen, Erik	MN	111th to 113th	Jan. 3, 2009
Peters, Gary C.	MI	111th to 113th	Jan. 3, 2009
Pingree, Chellie	ME	111th to 113th	Jan. 3, 2009
Polis, Jared	CO	111th to 113th	Jan. 3, 2009
Posey, Bill	FL	111th to 113th	Jan. 3, 2009
Quigley, Mike	IL	*111th to 113th	Apr. 7, 2009
Reed, Tom	NY	*111th to 113th	Nov. 2, 2010
Roe, David P.	TN	111th to 113th	Jan. 3, 2009
Rooney, Thomas J.	FL	111th to 113th	Jan. 3, 2009
Schock, Aaron	IL	111th to 113th	Jan. 3, 2009
Schrader, Kurt	OR	111th to 113th	Jan. 3, 2009
Stutzman, Marlin A.	IN	*111th to 113th	Nov. 2, 2010
Thompson, Glenn	PA	111th to 113th	Jan. 3, 2009
Tonko, Paul	NY	111th to 113th	Jan. 3, 2009
3 terms, not consecutive			
Fitzpatrick, Michael G.	PA	109th and 112th to 113th.	Jan. 3, 2011
Foster, Bill	IL	110th to 111th and 113th.	Jan. 3, 2013
Shea-Porter, Carol	NH	110th to 111th and 113th.	Jan. 3, 2013
Walberg, Tim	MI	110th and 112th to 113th.	Jan. 3, 2011
2 terms			
Amash, Justin	MI	112th and 113th	Jan. 3, 2011
Amodei, Mark E.	NV	*112th and 113th	Sept. 13, 2011
Barber, Ron	AZ	*112th and 113th	June 12, 2012
Barletta, Lou	PA	112th and 113th	Jan. 3, 2011
Bass, Karen	CA	112th and 113th	Jan. 3, 2011
Benishek, Dan	MI	112th and 113th	Jan. 3, 2011
Black, Diane	TN	112th and 113th	Jan. 3, 2011
Brooks, Mo	AL	112th and 113th	Jan. 3, 2011
Bucshon, Larry	IN	112th and 113th	Jan. 3, 2011
Carney, John C., Jr.	DE	112th and 113th	Jan. 3, 2011
Cicilline, David N.	RI	112th and 113th	Jan. 3, 2011
Crawford, Eric A. ''Rick''	AR	112th and 113th	Jan. 3, 2011
DelBene, Suzan K.	WA	*112th and 113th	Nov. 6, 2012
Denham, Jeff	CA	112th and 113th	Jan. 3, 2011
DesJarlais, Scott	TN	112th and 113th	Jan. 3, 2011

CONGRESSES IN WHICH REPRESENTATIVES, RESIDENT COMMISSIONER, AND DELEGATES HAVE SERVED WITH BEGINNING OF PRESENT SERVICE—CONTINUED

[* Elected to fill a vacancy; Republicans in roman (232); Democrats in *italic* (199); Vacancies (4); Resident Commissioner and Delegates in ***boldface italic*** (6); total, 441]

Name	State	Congresses (inclusive)	Beginning of present service
Duffy, Sean P.	WI	112th and 113th	Jan. 3, 2011
Duncan, Jeff	SC	112th and 113th	Jan. 3, 2011
Ellmers, Renee L.	NC	112th and 113th	Jan. 3, 2011
Farenthold, Blake	TX	112th and 113th	Jan. 3, 2011
Fincher, Stephen Lee	TN	112th and 113th	Jan. 3, 2011
Fleischmann, Charles J. ''Chuck''	TN	112th and 113th	Jan. 3, 2011
Flores, Bill	TX	112th and 113th	Jan. 3, 2011
Gardner, Cory	CO	112th and 113th	Jan. 3, 2011
Gibbs, Bob	OH	112th and 113th	Jan. 3, 2011
Gibson, Christopher P.	NY	112th and 113th	Jan. 3, 2011
Gosar, Paul A.	AZ	112th and 113th	Jan. 3, 2011
Gowdy, Trey	SC	112th and 113th	Jan. 3, 2011
Griffin, Tim	AR	112th and 113th	Jan. 3, 2011
Griffith, H. Morgan	VA	112th and 113th	Jan. 3, 2011
Grimm, Michael G.	NY	112th and 113th	Jan. 3, 2011
Hahn, Janice	CA	*112th and 113th	July 12, 2011
Hanabusa, Colleen W.	HI	112th and 113th	Jan. 3, 2011
Hanna, Richard L.	NY	112th and 113th	Jan. 3, 2011
Harris, Andy	MD	112th and 113th	Jan. 3, 2011
Hartzler, Vicky	MO	112th and 113th	Jan. 3, 2011
Heck, Joseph J.	NV	112th and 113th	Jan. 3, 2011
Herrera Beutler, Jaime	WA	112th and 113th	Jan. 3, 2011
Huelskamp, Tim	KS	112th and 113th	Jan. 3, 2011
Huizenga, Bill	MI	112th and 113th	Jan. 3, 2011
Hultgren, Randy	IL	112th and 113th	Jan. 3, 2011
Hurt, Robert	VA	112th and 113th	Jan. 3, 2011
Johnson, Bill	OH	112th and 113th	Jan. 3, 2011
Keating, William R.	MA	112th and 113th	Jan. 3, 2011
Kelly, Mike	PA	112th and 113th	Jan. 3, 2011
Kinzinger, Adam	IL	112th and 113th	Jan. 3, 2011
Labrador, Raúl R.	ID	112th and 113th	Jan. 3, 2011
Lankford, James	OK	112th and 113th	Jan. 3, 2011
Long, Billy	MO	112th and 113th	Jan. 3, 2011
McKinley, David B.	WV	112th and 113th	Jan. 3, 2011
Marino, Tom	PA	112th and 113th	Jan. 3, 2011
Massie, Thomas	KY	*112th and 113th	Nov. 6, 2012
Meehan, Patrick	PA	112th and 113th	Jan. 3, 2011
Mulvaney, Mick	SC	112th and 113th	Jan. 3, 2011
Noem, Kristi L.	SD	112th and 113th	Jan. 3, 2011
Nugent, Richard B.	FL	112th and 113th	Jan. 3, 2011
Nunnelee, Alan	MS	112th and 113th	Jan. 3, 2011
Payne, Donald M., Jr.	NJ	*112th and 113th	Nov. 6, 2012
Palazzo, Steven M.	MS	112th and 113th	Jan. 3, 2011
Pompeo, Mike	KS	112th and 113th	Jan. 3, 2011
Renacci, James B.	OH	112th and 113th	Jan. 3, 2011
Ribble, Reid J.	WI	112th and 113th	Jan. 3, 2011
Richmond, Cedric L.	LA	112th and 113th	Jan. 3, 2011
Rigell, E. Scott	VA	112th and 113th	Jan. 3, 2011
Roby, Martha	AL	112th and 113th	Jan. 3, 2011
Rokita, Todd	IN	112th and 113th	Jan. 3, 2011
Ross, Dennis A.	FL	112th and 113th	Jan. 3, 2011

CONGRESSES IN WHICH REPRESENTATIVES, RESIDENT COMMISSIONER, AND DELEGATES HAVE SERVED WITH BEGINNING OF PRESENT SERVICE—CONTINUED

[* Elected to fill a vacancy; Republicans in roman (232); Democrats in *italic* (199); Vacancies (4); Resident Commissioner and Delegates in ***boldface italic*** (6); total, 441]

Name	State	Congresses (inclusive)	Beginning of present service
Runyan, Jon	NJ	112th and 113th	Jan. 3, 2011
Schweikert, David	AZ	112th and 113th	Jan. 3, 2011
Scott, Austin	GA	112th and 113th	Jan. 3, 2011
Sewell, Terri A.	AL	112th and 113th	Jan. 3, 2011
Southerland, Steve II	FL	112th and 113th	Jan. 3, 2011
Stivers, Steve	OH	112th and 113th	Jan. 3, 2011
Tipton, Scott R.	CO	112th and 113th	Jan. 3, 2011
Webster, Daniel	FL	112th and 113th	Jan. 3, 2011
Wilson, Frederica S.	FL	112th and 113th	Jan. 3, 2011
Womack, Steve	AR	112th and 113th	Jan. 3, 2011
Woodall, Rob	GA	112th and 113th	Jan. 3, 2011
Yoder, Kevin	KS	112th and 113th	Jan. 3, 2011
Young, Todd C.	IN	112th and 113th	Jan. 3, 2011
2 terms, not consecutive			
Grayson, Alan	FL	111th and 113th	Jan. 3, 2013
Kirkpatrick, Ann	AZ	111th and 113th	Jan. 3, 2013
Maffei, Daniel B.	NY	111th and 113th	Jan. 3, 2013
Stockman, Steve	TX	104th and 113th	Jan. 3, 2013
Titus, Dina	NV	111th and 113th	Jan. 3, 2013
1 term			
Barr, Andy	KY	113th	Jan. 3, 2013
Beatty, Joyce	OH	113th	Jan. 3, 2013
Bentivolio, Kerry L.	MI	113th	Jan. 3, 2013
Bera, Ami	CA	113th	Jan. 3, 2013
Bridenstine, Jim	OK	113th	Jan. 3, 2013
Brooks, Susan W.	IN	113th	Jan. 3, 2013
Brownley, Julia	CA	113th	Jan. 3, 2013
Bustos, Cheri	IL	113th	Jan. 3, 2013
Byrne, Bradley	AL	*113th	Dec. 17, 2013
Cárdenas, Tony	CA	113th	Jan. 3, 2013
Cartwright, Matt	PA	113th	Jan. 3, 2013
Castro, Joaquin	TX	113th	Jan. 3, 2013
Clark, Katherine M.	MA	*113th	Dec. 10, 2013
Collins, Chris	NY	113th	Jan. 3, 2013
Collins, Doug	GA	113th	Jan. 3, 2013
Cook, Paul	CA	113th	Jan. 3, 2013
Cotton, Tom	AR	113th	Jan. 3, 2013
Cramer, Kevin	ND	113th	Jan. 3, 2013
Daines, Steve	MT	113th	Jan. 3, 2013
Davis, Rodney	IL	113th	Jan. 3, 2013
Delaney, John K.	MD	113th	Jan. 3, 2013
DeSantis, Ron	FL	113th	Jan. 3, 2013
Duckworth, Tammy	IL	113th	Jan. 3, 2013
Enyart, William L.	IL	113th	Jan. 3, 2013
Esty, Elizabeth H.	CT	113th	Jan. 3, 2013
Frankel, Lois	FL	113th	Jan. 3, 2013
Gabbard, Tulsi	HI	113th	Jan. 3, 2013
Gallego, Pete P.	TX	113th	Jan. 3, 2013

CONGRESSES IN WHICH REPRESENTATIVES, RESIDENT COMMISSIONER, AND DELEGATES HAVE SERVED WITH BEGINNING OF PRESENT SERVICE—CONTINUED

[* Elected to fill a vacancy; Republicans in roman (232); Democrats in *italic* (199); Vacancies (4); Resident Commissioner and Delegates in ***boldface italic*** (6); total, 441]

Name	State	Congresses (inclusive)	Beginning of present service
Garcia, Joe	FL	113th	Jan. 3, 2013
Heck, Denny	WA	113th	Jan. 3, 2013
Holding, George	NC	113th	Jan. 3, 2013
Horsford, Steven A.	NV	113th	Jan. 3, 2013
Hudson, Richard	NC	113th	Jan. 3, 2013
Huffman, Jared	CA	113th	Jan. 3, 2013
Jeffries, Hakeem S.	NY	113th	Jan. 3, 2013
Joyce, David P.	OH	113th	Jan. 3, 2013
Kelly, Robin L.	IL	*113th	Apr. 9, 2013
Kennedy, Joseph P. III	MA	113th	Jan. 3, 2013
Kildee, Daniel T.	MI	113th	Jan. 3, 2013
Kilmer, Derek	WA	113th	Jan. 3, 2013
Kuster, Ann M.	NH	113th	Jan. 3, 2013
LaMalfa, Doug	CA	113th	Jan. 3, 2013
Lowenthal, Alan S.	CA	113th	Jan. 3, 2013
Lujan Grisham, Michelle	NM	113th	Jan. 3, 2013
McAllister, Vance M.	LA	*113th	Nov. 16, 2013
Maloney, Sean Patrick	NY	113th	Jan. 3, 2013
Meadows, Mark	NC	113th	Jan. 3, 2013
Meng, Grace	NY	113th	Jan. 3, 2013
Messer, Luke	IN	113th	Jan. 3, 2013
Mullin, Markwayne	OK	113th	Jan. 3, 2013
Murphy, Patrick	FL	113th	Jan. 3, 2013
Negrete McLeod, Gloria	CA	113th	Jan. 3, 2013
O'Rourke, Beto	TX	113th	Jan. 3, 2013
Perry, Scott	PA	113th	Jan. 3, 2013
Peters, Scott H.	CA	113th	Jan. 3, 2013
Pittenger, Robert	NC	113th	Jan. 3, 2013
Pocan, Mark	WI	113th	Jan. 3, 2013
Rice, Tom	SC	113th	Jan. 3, 2013
Rothfus, Keith J.	PA	113th	Jan. 3, 2013
Ruiz, Raul	CA	113th	Jan. 3, 2013
Schneider, Bradley S.	IL	113th	Jan. 3, 2013
Sinema, Kyrsten	AZ	113th	Jan. 3, 2013
Smith, Jason T.	MO	*113th	June 4, 2013
Stewart, Chris	UT	113th	Jan. 3, 2013
Swalwell, Eric	CA	113th	Jan. 3, 2013
Takano, Mark	CA	113th	Jan. 3, 2013
Valadao, David G.	CA	113th	Jan. 3, 2013
Vargas, Juan	CA	113th	Jan. 3, 2013
Veasey, Marc A.	TX	113th	Jan. 3, 2013
Vela, Filemon	TX	113th	Jan. 3, 2013
Wagner, Ann	MO	113th	Jan. 3, 2013
Walorski, Jackie	IN	113th	Jan. 3, 2013
Weber, Randy K., Sr.	TX	113th	Jan. 3, 2013
Wenstrup, Brad R.	OH	113th	Jan. 3, 2013
Williams, Roger	TX	113th	Jan. 3, 2013
Yoho, Ted S.	FL	113th	Jan. 3, 2013
RESIDENT COMMISSIONER			
Pierluisi, Pedro R.	PR	111th and 113th	Jan. 3, 2009

CONGRESSES IN WHICH REPRESENTATIVES, RESIDENT COMMISSIONER, AND DELEGATES HAVE SERVED WITH BEGINNING OF PRESENT SERVICE—CONTINUED

[* Elected to fill a vacancy; Republicans in roman (232); Democrats in *italic* (199); Vacancies (4); Resident Commissioner and Delegates in ***boldface italic*** (6); total, 441]

Name	State	Congresses (inclusive)	Beginning of present service
DELEGATES			
Faleomavaega, Eni F. H.	AS	101st to 113th	Jan. 3, 1989
Norton, Eleanor Holmes	DC	102d to 113th	Jan. 3, 1991
Bordallo, Madeleine Z.	GU	108th to 113th	Jan. 3, 2003
Sablan, Gregorio Kilili Camacho ...	MP	111th to 113th	Jan. 3, 2009
Christensen, Donna M.	VI	105th to 113th	Jan. 3, 1997

NOTE: Members elected by special election are considered to begin service on the date of the election, except for those elected after a sine die adjournment. If elected after the Congress has adjourned for the session, Members are considered to begin their service on the day after the election.

STANDING COMMITTEES OF THE SENATE

[Democrats in roman; Republicans in *italic*; Independent in SMALL CAPS]

[Room numbers beginning with SD are in the Dirksen Building, SH in the Hart Building, SR in the Russell Building, and S in The Capitol]

Agriculture, Nutrition, and Forestry

328A Russell Senate Office Building 20510–6000

phone 224–2035, fax 228–2125, TTY / TDD 224–2587

http://agriculture.senate.gov

meets first and third Wednesdays of each month

Debbie Stabenow, of Michigan, *Chair*

Patrick J. Leahy, of Vermont.
Tom Harkin, of Iowa.
Sherrod Brown, of Ohio.
Amy Klobuchar, of Minnesota.
Michael F. Bennet, of Colorado.
Kirsten E. Gillibrand, of New York.
Joe Donnelly, of Indiana.
Heidi Heitkamp, of North Dakota.
Robert P. Casey, Jr., of Pennsylvania.
John E. Walsh, of Montana.

Thad Cochran, of Mississippi.
Mitch McConnell, of Kentucky.
Pat Roberts, of Kansas.
Saxby Chambliss, of Georgia.
John Boozman, of Arkansas.
John Hoeven, of North Dakota.
Mike Johanns, of Nebraska.
Chuck Grassley, of Iowa.
John Thune, of South Dakota.

SUBCOMMITTEES

[The chairwoman and ranking minority member are ex officio (non-voting) members of all subcommittees on which they do not serve.]

Commodities, Markets, Trade and Risk Management

Joe Donnelly, of Indiana, *Chair*

Heidi Heitkamp, of North Dakota.
Tom Harkin, of Iowa.
Sherrod Brown, of Ohio.
Kirsten E. Gillibrand, of New York.
John E. Walsh, of Montana.

Saxby Chambliss, of Georgia.
Pat Roberts, of Kansas.
John Boozman, of Arkansas.
John Hoeven, of North Dakota.
Mike Johanns, of Nebraska.

Conservation, Forestry and Natural Resources

Michael F. Bennet, of Colorado, *Chair*

Tom Harkin, of Iowa.
Amy Klobuchar, of Minnesota.
Patrick J. Leahy, of Vermont.
Heidi Heitkamp, of North Dakota.
John E. Walsh, of Montana.

John Boozman, of Arkansas.
Mitch McConnell, of Kentucky.
Saxby Chambliss, of Georgia.
John Thune, of South Dakota.
Pat Roberts, of Kansas.

Jobs, Rural Economic Growth and Energy Innovation

Heidi Heitkamp, of North Dakota, *Chair*

Sherrod Brown, of Ohio.
Amy Klobuchar, of Minnesota.
Michael F. Bennet, of Colorado.
Joe Donnelly, of Indiana.
Robert P. Casey, Jr., of Pennsylvania.
Mike Johanns, of Nebraska.
John Hoeven, of North Dakota.
Chuck Grassley, of Iowa.
John Thune, of South Dakota.
John Boozman, of Arkansas.

Livestock, Dairy, Poultry, Marketing and Agriculture Security

Kirsten E. Gillibrand, of New York, *Chair*

Patrick J. Leahy, of Vermont.
Amy Klobuchar, of Minnesota.
Joe Donnelly, of Indiana.
Robert P. Casey, Jr., of Pennsylvania.
John E. Walsh, of Montana.
Pat Roberts, of Kansas.
Mitch McConnell, of Kentucky.
John Boozman, of Arkansas.
Mike Johanns, of Nebraska.
Chuck Grassley, of Iowa.

Nutrition, Specialty Crops, Food and Agricultural Research

Robert P. Casey, Jr., of Pennsylvania, *Chair*

Patrick J. Leahy, of Vermont.
Tom Harkin, of Iowa.
Sherrod Brown, of Ohio.
Kirsten E. Gillibrand, of New York.
Michael F. Bennet, of Colorado.
John Hoeven, of North Dakota.
Mitch McConnell, of Kentucky.
Saxby Chambliss, of Georgia.
Chuck Grassley, of Iowa.
John Thune, of South Dakota.

STAFF

Committee on Agriculture, Nutrition, and Forestry (SR–328A), 224–2035, fax 228–2125.
Majority Staff Director.—Chris Adamo.
Senior Professional Staff: Cory Claussen, Brandon McBride, Tina May, Jacqlyn Schneider.
General Counsel.—Jonathan Cordone.
Senior Counsel.—Rostin Behnam.
Press Secretary.—Ben Becker.
Chief Counsel.—Jonathan Coppess.
Professional Staff.—Karla Thieman.
Chief Economist.—Joe Shultz.
USDA Detail.—Kevin Norton.
Legislative Correspondent.—Alexis Stanczuk.
Executive Assistant.—Hanna Abou El Seoud.
Majority Staff Assistant.—Kyle Varner.
Minority Staff Director.—T.A. Hawks.
Policy Director.—James Glueck.
Senior Professional Staff: Julian Baer, Ben Mosely, Taylor Nicholas, Andrew Vlasaty.
Chief Economist.—Keith Coble.
Professional Staff.—Darrell Dixon.
Chief Counsel.—Anne Hazlett.
General Counsel.—Steven Wall.
Conservation Policy Advisor.—Nona McCoy.
CFTC Detail.—Kevin Batteh.
Non-designated:
Staff Assistants: Simon Cook, Arohi Sharma.
IT.—Jacob Chaney.
Archivist.—Katie Salay.
GPO Detailee.—Micah Wortham.
Chief Clerk.—Jessie Williams.
Deputy Chief Clerk.—Nicole Hertenstein.

Appropriations

S–128 The Capitol 20510–6025, phone 224–7363

http://appropriations.senate.gov

meets upon call of the chair

Barbara A. Mikulski, of Maryland, *Chair*

Patrick J. Leahy, of Vermont.
Tom Harkin, of Iowa.
Patty Murray, of Washington.
Dianne Feinstein, of California.
Richard J. Durbin, of Illinois.
Tim Johnson, of South Dakota.
Mary L. Landrieu, of Louisiana.
Jack Reed, of Rhode Island.
Mark L. Pryor, of Arkansas.
Jon Tester, of Montana.
Tom Udall, of New Mexico.
Jeanne Shaheen, of New Hampshire.
Jeff Merkley, of Oregon.
Mark Begich, of Alaska.
Christopher A. Coons, of Delaware.

Richard C. Shelby, of Alabama.
Thad Cochran, of Mississippi.
Mitch McConnell, of Kentucky.
Lamar Alexander, of Tennessee.
Susan M. Collins, of Maine.
Lisa Murkowski, of Alaska.
Lindsey Graham, of South Carolina.
Mark Kirk, of Illinois.
Daniel Coats, of Indiana.
Roy Blunt, of Missouri.
Jerry Moran, of Kansas.
John Hoeven, of North Dakota.
Mike Johanns, of Nebraska.
John Boozman, of Arkansas.

SUBCOMMITTEES

[The chairwoman and ranking minority member are ex officio members of all subcommittees on which they do not serve.]

Agriculture, Rural Development, Food and Drug Administration, and Related Agencies

Mark L. Pryor, of Arkansas, *Chair*

Tom Harkin, of Iowa.
Dianne Feinstein, of California.
Tim Johnson, of South Dakota.
Jon Tester, of Montana.
Tom Udall, of New Mexico.
Jeff Merkley, of Oregon.

Roy Blunt, of Missouri.
Thad Cochran, of Mississippi.
Mitch McConnell, of Kentucky.
Susan M. Collins, of Maine.
Jerry Moran, of Kansas.
John Hoeven, of North Dakota.

Commerce, Justice, Science, and Related Agencies

Barbara A. Mikulski, of Maryland, *Chair*

Patrick J. Leahy, of Vermont.
Dianne Feinstein, of California.
Jack Reed, of Rhode Island.
Mark L. Pryor, of Arkansas.
Mary L. Landrieu, of Louisiana.
Jeanne Shaheen, of New Hampshire.
Jeff Merkley, of Oregon.
Christopher A. Coons, of Delaware.

Richard C. Shelby, of Alabama.
Mitch McConnell, of Kentucky.
Lamar Alexander, of Tennessee.
Susan M. Collins, of Maine.
Lisa Murkowski, of Alaska.
Lindsey Graham, of South Carolina.
Mark Kirk, of Illinois.
John Boozman, of Arkansas.

Department of Defense

Richard J. Durbin, of Illinois, *Chair*

Patrick J. Leahy, of Vermont.
Tom Harkin, of Iowa.
Dianne Feinstein, of California.
Barbara A. Mikulski, of Maryland.
Patty Murray, of Washington.
Tim Johnson, of South Dakota.
Jack Reed, of Rhode Island.
Mary L. Landrieu, of Louisiana.
Mark L. Pryor, of Arkansas.

Thad Cochran, of Mississippi.
Mitch McConnell, of Kentucky.
Richard C. Shelby, of Alabama.
Lamar Alexander, of Tennessee.
Susan M. Collins, of Maine.
Lisa Murkowski, of Alaska.
Lindsey Graham, of South Carolina.
Daniel Coats, of Indiana.
Roy Blunt, of Missouri.

Department of Homeland Security

Mary L. Landrieu, of Louisiana, *Chair*

Patrick J. Leahy, of Vermont.
Patty Murray, of Washington.
Jon Tester, of Montana.
Mark Begich, of Alaska.
Christopher A. Coons, of Delaware.

Daniel Coats, of Indiana.
Thad Cochran, of Mississippi.
Richard C. Shelby, of Alabama.
Lisa Murkowski, of Alaska.
Jerry Moran, of Kansas.

Department of the Interior, Environment, and Related Agencies

Jack Reed, of Rhode Island, *Chair*

Dianne Feinstein, of California.
Patrick J. Leahy, of Vermont.
Tim Johnson, of South Dakota.
Jon Tester, of Montana.
Tom Udall, of New Mexico.
Jeff Merkley, of Oregon.
Mark Begich, of Alaska.

Lisa Murkowski, of Alaska.
Thad Cochran, of Mississippi.
Lamar Alexander, of Tennessee.
Roy Blunt, of Missouri.
John Hoeven, of North Dakota.
Mike Johanns, of Nebraska.

Departments of Labor, Health and Human Services, and Education, and Related Agencies

Tom Harkin, of Iowa, *Chair*

Patty Murray, of Washington.
Mary L. Landrieu, of Louisiana.
Richard J. Durbin, of Illinois.
Jack Reed, of Rhode Island.
Mark L. Pryor, of Arkansas.
Barbara A. Mikulski, of Maryland.
Jon Tester, of Montana.
Jeanne Shaheen, of New Hampshire.
Jeff Merkley, of Oregon.

Jerry Moran, of Kansas.
Thad Cochran, of Mississippi.
Richard C. Shelby, of Alabama.
Lamar Alexander, of Tennessee.
Lindsey Graham, of South Carolina.
Mark Kirk, of Illinois.
Mike Johanns, of Nebraska.
John Boozman, of Arkansas.

Energy and Water Development

Dianne Feinstein, of California, *Chair*

Patty Murray, of Washington.
Tim Johnson, of South Dakota.
Mary L. Landrieu, of Louisiana.
Tom Harkin, of Iowa.
Jon Tester, of Montana.
Richard J. Durbin, of Illinois.
Tom Udall, of New Mexico.
Jeanne Shaheen, of New Hampshire.

Lamar Alexander, of Tennessee.
Thad Cochran, of Mississippi.
Mitch McConnell, of Kentucky.
Richard C. Shelby, of Alabama.
Susan M. Collins, of Maine.
Lisa Murkowski, of Alaska.
Lindsey Graham, of South Carolina.
John Hoeven, of North Dakota.

Financial Services, and General Government

Tom Udall, of New Mexico, *Chair*

Richard J. Durbin, of Illinois.
Christopher A. Coons, of Delaware.
Mike Johanns, of Nebraska.
Jerry Moran, of Kansas.

Legislative Branch

Jeanne Shaheen, of New Hampshire, *Chair*

Mark Begich, of Alaska.
Christopher A. Coons, of Delaware.
John Hoeven, of North Dakota.
John Boozman, of Arkansas.

Military Construction and Veterans Affairs, and Related Agencies

Tim Johnson, of South Dakota, *Chair*

Patty Murray, of Washington.
Jack Reed, of Rhode Island.
Mark L. Pryor, of Arkansas.
Jon Tester, of Montana.
Tom Udall, of New Mexico.
Mark Begich, of Alaska.
Jeff Merkley, of Oregon.
Mark Kirk, of Illinois.
Mitch McConnell, of Kentucky.
Susan M. Collins, of Maine.
Lisa Murkowski, of Alaska.
Daniel Coats, of Indiana.
John Hoeven, of North Dakota.
Mike Johanns, of Nebraska.

State, Foreign Operations, and Related Programs

Patrick J. Leahy, of Vermont, *Chair*

Tom Harkin, of Iowa.
Barbara A. Mikulski, of Maryland.
Richard J. Durbin, of Illinois.
Mary L. Landrieu, of Louisiana.
Jeanne Shaheen, of New Hampshire.
Mark Begich, of Alaska.
Christopher A. Coons, of Delaware.
Lindsey Graham, of South Carolina.
Mitch McConnell, of Kentucky.
Mark Kirk, of Illinois.
Daniel Coats, of Indiana.
Roy Blunt, of Missouri.
Mike Johanns, of Nebraska.
John Boozman, of Arkansas.

Transportation, Housing and Urban Development, and Related Agencies

Patty Murray, of Washington, *Chair*

Barbara A. Mikulski, of Maryland.
Richard J. Durbin, of Illinois.
Patrick J. Leahy, of Vermont.
Tom Harkin, of Iowa.
Dianne Feinstein, of California.
Tim Johnson, of South Dakota.
Mark L. Pryor, of Arkansas.
Jack Reed, of Rhode Island.
Tom Udall, of New Mexico.
Susan M. Collins, of Maine.
Richard C. Shelby, of Alabama.
Lamar Alexander, of Tennessee.
Lindsey Graham, of South Carolina.
Mark Kirk, of Illinois.
Daniel Coats, of Indiana.
Roy Blunt, of Missouri.
Jerry Moran, of Kansas.
John Boozman, of Arkansas.

STAFF

Committee on Appropriations (S–128), 224–7363.
Majority Staff Director.—Charles E. Kieffer (S–128).
Deputy Staff Director.—Gabrielle Batkin (S–128).
Chief Clerk.—Robert W. Putnam (SD–114).
Communications Director.—Rob Blumenthal (SD–120).
Deputy Communications Director.—Eve Goldsher (SD–120).
Professional Staff: John J. Conway (SD–114); Christine Evans (SD–134); Brigid Houton (SD–120); Daniel Katz (SD–134); Fernanda Motta (SD–114); Jessica McNiece (SD–134).

Assistant to the Chairwoman.—Ericka Rojas (S–128).
Technical Systems Manager.—Hong Nguyen (SD–114).
Security Manager.—Debbie Chiarello (SD–118).
Staff Assistant Coordinator.—Teri Curtin (SD–131).
Minority Staff Director.—William D. Duhnke III (S–146A), 4–7257.
Deputy Staff Director.—Dana Wade (S–146A).
Chief Counsel.—Christopher Ford (S–146A).
Senior Policy Advisor.—Jane Lee (S–146A).
Professional Staff.—Shelby Begany (S–146A).

Subcommittee on Agriculture, Rural Development, Food and Drug Administration, and Related Agencies (SD–129), 4–8090.
Majority Clerk.—Jessica Arden Frederick (SD–129).
Professional Staff.—Dianne Nellor (SD–129).
Staff Assistant.—Molly Barackman-Eder (SD–184).
Minority Clerk.—Stacy McBride (SD–190), 4–5270.
Professional Staff.—Carlisle Clarke (SD–190).

Subcommittee on Commerce, Justice, Science, and Related Agencies (SD–142), 4–5202.
Majority Clerk.—Jean Toal Eisen (SD–142).
Professional Staff: Jessica M. Berry (SD–142); Molly O'Rourke (SD–142); Jeremy Weirich (SD–142).
Staff Assistant.—Dan Broder (SD–142).
Minority Clerk.—Shannon Hines (SH–125), 4–7277.
Professional Staff: Amber Busby (SH–125); Allen Cutler (SH–125); Kolo Rathburn (SH–125).

Subcommittee on Department of Defense (SD–122), 4–6688.
Majority Clerk.—Betsy Schmid (SD–122).
Professional Staff: Colleen Gaydos (SD–122); David C. Gillies (SD–122); Katy Hagan (SD–122); Kate Kaufer (SD–122), Erik Raven (SD–122); Jennifer S. Santos (SD–122); Teri Spoutz (SD–122); Andy Vanlandingham (SD–122).
Staff Assistants: Kali Matalon (SD–122); Maria Veklich (SD–122).
Minority Clerk.—Stewart Holmes (SD–117), 4–7255.
Professional Staff: Alycia Farrell (SD–115); Brian Potts (SD–115); Jacqui Russell (SD–115).

Subcommittee on Department of Homeland Security (SD–135), 4–8244.
Majority Clerk.—Stephanie Gupta (SD–135).
Professional Staff: Drenan A. Dudley (SD–135); Scott Nance (SD–135); Chip Walgren (SD–135).
Staff Assistant.—Colin MacDermott (SD–135).
Minority Clerk.—Kathy Kraninger (SH–125), 4–4319.
Professional Staff: Amber Busby (SH–125); Carol Cribbs (SH–125).

Subcommittee on Department of the Interior, Environment, and Related Agencies (SD–131), 8–0774.
Majority Clerk.—Rachael Taylor (SD–131).
Professional Staff: Ryan Hunt (SD–131); Ginny James (SD–131).
Staff Assistant.—Teri Curtin (SD–131).
Minority Clerk.—Leif Fonnesbeck (SH–125), 4–7233.
Professional Staff: Amber Busby (SH–125); Brent Wiles (SH–125).

Subcommittee on Departments of Labor, Health and Human Services, and Education, and Related Agencies (SD–131), 4–9145.
Majority Clerk.—Erik Fatemi (SD–131).
Professional Staff: Lisa Bernhardt (SD–131); Michael Gentile (SD–131); Adrienne Hallett (SD–131); Robin Juliano (SD–131); Mark Laisch (SD–131).
Staff Assistant.—Teri Curtin (SD–131).
Minority Clerk.—Laura A. Friedel (SD–156), 4–7230.
Professional Staff: Jennifer Castagna (SD–156); Chol Pak (SD–156).

Subcommittee on Energy and Water Development (SD–184), 4–8119.
Majority Clerk.—Doug Clapp (SD–184).
Professional Staff: Roger Cockrell (SD–184); Leland Cogliani (SD–184).
Staff Assistant.—Molly Barackman-Eder (SD–184).
Minority Clerk.—Tom Craig (SD–188), 4–7260.
Professional Staff: Tyler Owens (SD–188); LaShawnda Smith (SH–125).

Subcommittee on Financial Services and General Government (SD–133), 4–1133.
Majority Clerk.—Marianne Upton (SD–133).
Professional Staff: Diana Gourlay Hamilton (SD–133); Emily Sharp (SD–133).
Staff Assistant.—Colin MacDermott (SD–135).
Minority Clerk.—Dale Cabaniss (SH–125), 4–2104.
Professional Staff: Andrew Newton (SH–125); LaShawnda Smith (SH–125).

Subcommittee on Legislative Branch (S–128) 4–7256.
Majority Clerk.—Melissa Zimmerman (S–128).
Staff Assistant.—Maria Veklich (SD–122).
Minority Clerk.—Rachelle G. Schroeder (S–146A), 4–9747.
Professional Staff.—Sarah Wilson Boliek (S–146A).
Subcommittee on Military Construction and Veterans Affairs, and Related Agencies (SD–125), 4–8224.
Majority Clerk.—Christina Evans (SD–125).
Professional Staff: Michael Bain (SD–125); Chad C. Schulken (SD–125).
Staff Assistant.—Kali Matalon (SD–122).
Minority Clerk.—Dennis Balkham (SH–125), 4–5245.
Professional Staff: Amber Busby (SH–125); D'Ann Lettieri (SH–125).
Subcommittee on State, Foreign Operations, and Related Programs (SD–127), 4–7284.
Majority Clerk.—Tim Rieser (SD–127).
Professional Staff: Nikole Manatt (SD–127); Janet Stormes (SD–127).
Staff Assistant.—Maria Veklich (SD–122).
Minority Clerk.—Paul Grove (SH–125), 4–2104.
Professional Staff: LaShawnda Smith (SH–125); Adam Yezerski (SH–125).
Subcommittee on Transportation, Housing and Urban Development, and Related Agencies (SD–142), 4–7281.
Majority Clerk.—Alex Keenan (SD–142).
Professional Staff: Dabney Hegg (SD–142); Meaghan L. McCarthy (SD–142); Rachel Milberg (SD–142).
Staff Assistant.—Dan Broder (SD–142).
Minority Clerk.—Heideh Shahmoradi (SD–128), 4–5310.
Professional Staff: Ken Altman (SD–128); Rajat Mathur (SD–128); Jason Woolwine (SD–128).
Editorial and Printing (SD–126): Richard L. Larson, 4–7265; Celina Inman (GPO), 4–7217; Valerie A. Hutton (GPO), 4–7267; Sonya Kunkle (GPO), 4–7266; Elmer Barnes (GPO), 4–7266.
Clerical Assistant.—George Castro (SD–120), 4–5433.

Armed Services

228 Russell Senate Office Building 20510–6050

phone 224–3871, http://www.senate.gov/~armed_services

meets every Tuesday and Thursday

Carl Levin, of Michigan, *Chair*

Jack Reed, of Rhode Island.
Bill Nelson, of Florida.
Claire McCaskill, of Missouri.
Mark Udall, of Colorado.
Kay R. Hagan, of North Carolina.
Joe Manchin III, of West Virginia.
Jeanne Shaheen, of New Hampshire.
Kirsten E. Gillibrand, of New York.
Richard Blumenthal, of Connecticut.
Joe Donnelly, of Indiana.
Mazie K. Hirono, of Hawaii.
Tim Kaine, of Virginia.
ANGUS S. KING, JR., of Maine.

James M. Inhofe, of Oklahoma.
John McCain, of Arizona.
Jeff Sessions, of Alabama.
Saxby Chambliss, of Georgia.
Roger F. Wicker, of Mississippi.
Kelly Ayotte, of New Hampshire.
Deb Fischer, of Nebraska.
Lindsey Graham, of South Carolina.
David Vitter, of Louisiana.
Roy Blunt, of Missouri.
Mike Lee, of Utah.
Ted Cruz, of Texas.

SUBCOMMITTEES

[The chairman and the ranking minority member are ex officio (non-voting) members of all subcommittees on which they do not serve.]

Airland

Joe Manchin III, of West Virginia, *Chair*

Bill Nelson, of Florida.
Claire McCaskill, of Missouri.
Kirsten E. Gillibrand, of New York.
Richard Blumenthal, of Connecticut.
Joe Donnelly, of Indiana.

Roger F. Wicker, of Mississippi.
John McCain, of Arizona.
Jeff Sessions, of Alabama.
Saxby Chambliss, of Georgia.
Roy Blunt, of Missouri.

Emerging Threats and Capabilities

Kay R. Hagan, of North Carolina, *Chair*

Jack Reed, of Rhode Island.
Bill Nelson, of Florida.
Mark Udall, of Colorado.
Joe Manchin III, of West Virginia.
Jeanne Shaheen, of New Hampshire.
Kirsten E. Gillibrand, of New York.

Deb Fischer, of Nebraska.
John McCain, of Arizona.
Roger F. Wicker, of Mississippi.
Lindsey Graham, of South Carolina.
David Vitter, of Louisiana.
Ted Cruz, of Texas.

Personnel

Kirsten E. Gillibrand, of New York, *Chair*

Kay R. Hagan, of North Carolina.
Richard Blumenthal, of Connecticut.
Mazie K. Hirono, of Hawaii.
Tim Kaine, of Virginia.
ANGUS S. KING, JR., of Maine.

Lindsey Graham, of South Carolina.
Saxby Chambliss, of Georgia.
Kelly Ayotte, of New Hampshire.
Roy Blunt, of Missouri.
Mike Lee, of Utah.

Readiness and Management Support

Jeanne Shaheen, of New Hampshire, *Chair*

Claire McCaskill, of Missouri.
Mark Udall, of Colorado.
Joe Manchin III, of West Virginia.
Joe Donnelly, of Indiana.
Mazie K. Hirono, of Hawaii.
Tim Kaine, of Virginia.
Kelly Ayotte, of New Hampshire.
Saxby Chambliss, of Georgia.
Deb Fischer, of Nebraska.
Roy Blunt, of Missouri.
Mike Lee, of Utah.
Ted Cruz, of Texas.

Seapower

Jack Reed, of Rhode Island, *Chair*

Bill Nelson, of Florida.
Kay R. Hagan, of North Carolina.
Jeanne Shaheen, of New Hampshire.
Richard Blumenthal, of Connecticut.
Mazie K. Hirono, of Hawaii.
Tim Kaine, of Virginia.
ANGUS S. KING, JR., of Maine.
John McCain, of Arizona.
Jeff Sessions, of Alabama.
Roger F. Wicker, of Mississippi.
Kelly Ayotte, of New Hampshire.
Lindsey Graham, of South Carolina.
David Vitter, of Louisiana.
Ted Cruz, of Texas.

Strategic Forces

Mark Udall, of Colorado, *Chair*

Jack Reed, of Rhode Island.
Claire McCaskill, of Missouri.
Joe Donnelly, of Indiana.
ANGUS S. KING, JR., of Maine.
Jeff Sessions, of Alabama.
Deb Fischer, of Nebraska.
David Vitter, of Louisiana.
Mike Lee, of Utah.

STAFF

Committee on Armed Services (SR–228), 224–3871.
Majority Staff Director.—Peter K. Levine.
Chief Clerk.—Travis E. Smith.
General Counsel.—Gary J. Leeling.
Counsels: Jonathan D. Clark, Jonathan S. Epstein, Gabriella E. Fahrer, Ozge Guzelsu, William G.P. Monahan, Jason W. Maroney.
Professional Staff Members: Joseph M. Bryan, Richard W. Fieldhouse, Creighton Greene, Michael J. Kuiken, Thomas K. McConnell, Michael J. Noblet, Roy F. Phillips, John H. Quirk V, Robie I. Samanta Roy, William K. Sutey.
Assistant Chief Clerk and Security Manager.—Cindy Pearson.
Nominations and Hearings Clerk.—Leah C. Brewer.
Systems Administrator.—Gary J. Howard.
Printing and Documents Clerk.—June M. Borawski.
Security Officer.—Barry C. Walker.
Legislative Clerk.—Mary J. Kyle.
Special Assistant.—Mariah K. McNamara.
Staff Assistants: Lauren M. Gillis, Daniel J. Harder, Alexandra Hathaway, Kathleen A. Kulenkampff, John L. Principato, Brendan J. Sawyer.
Minority Staff Director.—John A. Bonsell.
Executive Assistant for the Minority.—Greg R. Lilly.
Minority Counsels: Steven M. Barney, William S. Castle.
Minority Professional Staff Members: Adam J. Barker, Allen M. Edwards, Tom W. Goffus, Bruce Hock, Anthony J. Lazarski, Daniel A. Lerner, Lucian L. Niemeyer, Rob Soofer.
Subcommittee on Airland:
Majority Professional Staff Members: William K. Sutey (Lead), Creighton Greene, Michael J. Kuiken.
Minority Professional Staff Members: Bruce Hock (Lead), Anthony J. Lazarski.
Staff Assistant: John L. Principato.
Subcommittee on Emerging Threats and Capabilities:

Majority Professional Staff Members: Richard W. Fieldhouse (Lead), Jonathan S. Epstein, Ozge Guzelsu, Michael J. Kuiken, William G.P. Monahan, Michael J. Noblet, Robie I. Samanta Roy,

Minority Professional Staff Members: Tom W. Goffus (Lead), Adam J. Barker, Bruce Hock, Daniel A. Lerner, Rob Soofer.

Staff Assistant.—Kathleen A. Kulenkampff.

Subcommittee on Personnel:

Majority Professional Staff Members: Gerald J. Leeling (Lead), Jonathan D. Clark, Gabriella E. Fahrer.

Minority Professional Staff Members: Steven M. Barney (Co-Lead), Allen M. Edwards (Co-Lead).

Staff Assistant.—Brendan J. Sawyer.

Subcommittee on Readiness and Management Support:

Majority Professional Staff Members: Jason W. Maroney (Lead), Michael Noblet, John H. Quirk V.

Minority Professional Staff Members: Lucian L. Niemeyer (Lead), William S. Castle, Bruce Hock.

Staff Assistant.—Daniel J. Harder.

Subcommittee on Seapower:

Majority Professional Staff Members: Creighton Greene (Lead), Jason W. Maroney, William K. Sutey.

Minority Professional Staff Members: Daniel A. Lerner (Lead), Bruce Hock, Lucian L. Niemeyer.

Staff Assistant.—John L. Principato.

Subcommittee on Strategic Forces:

Majority Professional Staff Members: Jonathan S. Epstein (Lead), Richard W. Fieldhouse, Creighton Greene, Thomas K. McConnell.

Minority Professional Staff Members: Rob Soofer (Lead), Daniel A. Lerner.

Staff Assistant.—Lauren M. Gillis.

Majority Professional Staff Members for—

Acquisition Policy.—Jason W. Maroney.

Acquisition Workforce.—Jason W. Maroney.

Ammunition.—John H. Quirk V.

Arms Control/Non-proliferation: Jonathan S. Epstein, Richard W. Fieldhouse.

Aviation Systems: Jonathan S. Epstein, Creighton Greene.

Base Realignment and Closure (BRAC).—Michael J. Noblet, Jason W. Maroney.

Budget and Reprogramming.—Roy F. Phillips.

Buy America.—Jason W. Maroney.

Chemical-Biological Defense.—Richard W. Fieldhouse.

Chemical Demilitarization.—Richard W. Fieldhouse.

Civilian Nominations.—Gerald J. Leeling.

Civilian Personnel Policy: Alan M. Edwards, Gabriella E. Fahrer.

Combatant Commands:

AFRICOM.—Anthony J. Lazarski.

CENTCOM: Tom W. Goffus, Michael J. Kuiken, William G.P. Monahan.

EUCOM: Tom W. Goffus, William G.P. Monahan.

NORTHCOM: Adam J. Barker, Richard W. Fieldhouse.

PACOM: Tom W. Goffus, Ozge Guzelsu.

SOCOM: Adam J. Barker, Michael J. Noblet.

SOUTHCOM: Adam J. Barker, Michael J. Kuiken.

STRATCOM: Jonathan S. Epstein, Rob Soofer.

TRANSCOM: Creighton Greene, Anthony J. Lazarski.

Combating Terrorism: Ozge Guzelsu, Michael J. Kuiken, Thomas K. McConnell, William G.P. Monahan, Michael J. Noblet.

Competition Policy/Mergers and Acquisitions.—Jason W. Maroney.

Competitive Sourcing/A–76.—Jason W. Maroney.

Contracting (including service contracts).—Jason W. Maroney.

Construction, Housing, Global Basing, and Land Use.—Lucian L. Niemeyer.

Cooperative Threat Reduction Programs.—Tom W. Goffus.

Counterdrug Programs.—Adam J. Barker.

Cybersecurity/Information Assurance: Creighton Greene, Daniel A. Lerner, Thomas K. McConnell.

Defense Energy Use/Alternative Energy Issues: Lucian L. Niemeyer, John H. Quirk V, Robie I. Samanta Roy.

Defense Laboratory Management: Anthony J. Lazarski, Peter K. Levine, Robie I. Samanta Roy.

Defense Security Assistance: Tom W. Goffus, Ozge Guzelsu, Michael J. Kuiken, William G.P. Monahan.
Department of Defense Schools: Allen M. Edwards, Gabriella E. Fahrer.
Department of Energy Issues: Jonathan S. Epstein, Rob Soofer.
Depot Maintenance: Lucian L. Niemeyer, John H. Quirk V.
Detainee Policy: Peter K. Levine, William G.P. Monahan.
Domestic Preparedness: Adam J. Barker, Richard W. Fieldhouse.
Environmental Issues: Jason W. Maroney, Lucian L. Niemeyer.
Export Controls: Tom W. Goffus, Ozge Guzelsu.
Financial Management: William S. Castle, Jason W. Maroney.
Force Readiness/Training.—Lucian L. Niemeyer.
Foreign Language Policy.—Tom W. Goffus.
Foreign Policy/Geographical Region:
Afghanistan/Pakistan/Central Asia.—Tom W. Goffus.
Africa: Michael J. Kuiken, Anthony J. Lazarski.
Asia/Pacific: Tom W. Goffus, Ozge Guzelsu.
Europe/Russia: Jonathan S. Epstein, Tom W. Goffus, William G.P. Monahan.
Iraq: Tom W. Goffus, William G.P. Monahan.
Middle East: Tom W. Goffus, Michael J. Kuiken.
South and Central Americas: Tom W. Goffus, Michael J. Kuiken.
Ground Systems: William K. Sutey.
Marine Corps: Thomas K. McConnell, William K. Sutey.
Homeland Defense/Security: Adam J. Barker, Richard W. Fieldhouse.
Humanitarian, Disaster, and Civic Assistance: Tom W. Goffus, Michael J. Kuiken, William G.P. Monahan.
Information Management: Creighton Greene, Daniel A. Lerner, Jason W. Maroney.
Information Operations/Strategic Communications: Adam J. Barker, Michael J. Kuiken.
Information Technology Systems:
(IT Acquisition Policy): William S. Castle, Jason W. Maroney.
(Business Systems): William S. Castle, Michael J. Kuiken.
(Tactical Systems): Creighton Greene, Daniel A. Lerner.
Intelligence Issues: Creighton Green, Thomas K. McConnell.
Interagency Reform: William S. Castle, Michael J. Kuiken, Thomas K. McConnell, William G.P. Monahan.
International Defense Cooperation: Tom W. Goffus, Michael J. Kuiken, William G.P. Monahan.
Inventory Management: William S. Castle, John H. Quirk V.
Investigations: Joseph M. Bryan, William S. Castle, Ozge Guzelsu.
Military Personnel Issues: Jonathan D. Clark, Gabriella E. Fahrer, Gerald J. Leeling.
End Strength: Steven M. Barney, Jonathan D. Clark.
Military Family Policy: Allen M. Edwards, Gabriella E. Fahrer.
Health Care: Allen M. Edwards, Gabriella E. Fahrer.
Homosexual Conduct Policy: Steven M. Barney, Gerald J. Leeling.
Military Justice: Steven M. Barney, Gerald J. Leeling.
Military Nominations.—Steven M. Barney.
POW/MIA Issues: Jonathan D. Clark, Allen M. Edwards.
Pay and Benefits: Steven M. Barney, Jonathan D. Clark.
Military Personnel Policy: Steven M. Barney, Gerald J. Leeling.
National Guard and Reserves: Steven M. Barney, Jonathan D. Clark, Gerald J. Leeling.
Sexual Harassment/Sexual Assault Policy: Gabriella E. Fahrer, Gerald J. Leeling.
Suicide Prevention and Response: Steven M. Barney, Gerald J. Leeling.
Women in Combat.—Steven M. Barney.
Wounded Warrior Issues: Gabriella E. Fahrer, Gerald J. Leeling.
Military Space: Jonathan S. Epstein, Daniel A. Lerner.
Military Strategy: Tom W. Goffus, William K. Sutey.
Missile Defense: Richard W. Fieldhouse, Rob Soofer.
Morale, Welfare and Recreation/Commissaries/Exchanges: Allen M. Edwards, Gabriella E. Fahrer.
National Defense Stockpile: John H. Quirk V, Rob Soofer.
Nuclear Weapons Stockpile: Jonathan S. Epstein, Rob Soofer.
Peacekeeping: Tom W. Goffus, Michael J. Kuiken, William G.P. Monahan.
Personnel Protective Items: Bruce Hock, John H. Quirk V.
Quadrennial Defense Review (QDR): Tom W. Goffus, William K. Sutey.
Readiness/O&M: Bruce Hock, Anthony J. Lazarski.
Reprogramming: Daniel A. Lerner, Roy F. Phillips.
Science and Technology: Anthony J. Lazarski, Robie I. Samanta Roy.
Shipbuilding Programs: Creighton Greene, Jason W. Maroney.

Small Business: William S. Castle, Jason W. Maroney.
Special Operations Forces: Adam J. Barker, Michael J. Noblet.
Stability Operations: Tom W. Goffus, Michael J. Kuiken, William G.P. Monahan.
Strategic Programs: Jonathan S. Epstein, Rob Soofer.
Test and Evaluation: Bruce Hock, Jason W. Maroney, Robie I. Samanta Roy.
Transportation and Logistics Policy.—Anthony J. Lazarski.
Unmanned Aircraft Systems: Creighton Greene, Anthony J. Lazarski, Thomas K. McConnell.
Working Capital Fund: Daniel A. Lerner, John H. Quirk V.

Minority Professional Staff Members for—
Acquisition and Contracting Policy.—William S. Castle.
Air Force Programs, Readiness, and Operations and Maintenance.—Anthony J. Lazarski.
Arms Control and Non-proliferation.—Rob Soofer.
Army Programs, Readiness, and Operations and Maintenance.—Bruce Hock.
Budget and Reprogramming.—Daniel A. Lerner.
Chemical-Biological Defense.—Adam J. Barker.
Chemical-Demilitarization.—Adam J. Barker.
Civilian Personnel.—Steven M. Barney.
Combatant Commands:
AFRICOM.—Anthony J. Lazarski.
CENTCOM.—Tom W. Goffus.
EUCOM.—Tom W. Goffus.
NORTHCOM.—Adam J. Barker (Lead).
PACOM.—Tom W. Goffus.
SOCOM.—Adam J. Barker (Lead).
SOUTHCOM.—Adam J. Barker.
STRATCOM.—Rob Soofer.
TRANSCOM.—Anthony J. Lazarski.
Counterdrug Programs.—Adam J. Barker.
Defense Security Assistance.—Tom W. Goffus.
Depot Maintenance.—Lucian L. Niemeyer.
Detainees and Military Commissions.—William S. Castle.
Department of Energy National Security Programs.—Rob Soofer.
Environmental Issues.—Lucian L. Niemeyer.
Export Controls.—Tom W. Goffus.
Health Care.—Allen M. Edwards.
Homeland Defense.—Adam J. Barker.
Information Assurance and Cyber Security.—Daniel A. Lerner.
Information Technology.—William S. Castle.
Intelligence Programs: Daniel A. Lerner.
Laboratories.—Rob Soofer.
Marine Corps Programs, Readiness, and Operations and Maintenance.—Bruce Hock.
Military Construction and BRAC.—Lucian Niemeyer.
Military Personnel and Family Benefits: Steven M. Barney.
Missile Defense.—Rob Soofer.
National Military Strategy.—Tom W. Goffus.
Navy Programs, Readiness, and Operations and Maintenance: Daniel A. Lerner, Lucian L. Niemeyer.
Nominations.—Jonathan D. Clark.
Science and Technology.—Anthony J. Lazarski.
Space Programs.—Daniel A. Lerner.
Special Operations Forces.—Adam J. Barker.
Test and Evaluation.—Bruce Hock.

Banking, Housing, and Urban Affairs

534 Dirksen Senate Office Building 20510

phone 224–7391, http://banking.senate.gov

Tim Johnson, of South Dakota, *Chair*

Jack Reed, of Rhode Island.
Charles E. Schumer, of New York.
Robert Menendez, of New Jersey.
Sherrod Brown, of Ohio.
Jon Tester, of Montana.
Mark R. Warner, of Virginia.
Jeff Merkley, of Oregon.
Kay R. Hagan, of North Carolina.
Joe Manchin III, of West Virginia.
Elizabeth Warren, of Massachusetts.
Heidi Heitkamp, of North Dakota.

Mike Crapo, of Idaho.
Richard C. Shelby, of Alabama.
Bob Corker, of Tennessee.
David Vitter, of Louisiana.
Mike Johanns, of Nebraska.
Patrick J. Toomey, of Pennsylvania.
Mark Kirk, of Illinois.
Jerry Moran, of Kansas.
Tom Coburn, of Oklahoma.
Dean Heller, of Nevada.

SUBCOMMITTEES

[The chairman and ranking minority member are ex officio members of all subcommittees.]

Economic Policy

Jeff Merkley, of Oregon, *Chair*

Jon Tester, of Montana.
Mark R. Warner, of Virginia.
Kay R. Hagan, of North Carolina.
Joe Manchin III, of West Virginia.
Heidi Heitkamp, of North Dakota.

Dean Heller, of Nevada.
Tom Coburn, of Oklahoma.
David Vitter, of Louisiana.
Mike Johanns, of Nebraska.

Financial Institutions and Consumer Protection

Sherrod Brown, of Ohio, *Chair*

Jack Reed, of Rhode Island.
Charles E. Schumer, of New York.
Robert Menendez, of New Jersey.
Jon Tester, of Montana.
Jeff Merkley, of Oregon.
Kay R. Hagan, of North Carolina.
Elizabeth Warren, of Massachusetts.

Patrick J. Toomey, of Pennsylvania.
Richard C. Shelby, of Alabama.
David Vitter, of Louisiana.
Mike Johanns, of Nebraska.
Jerry Moran, of Kansas.
Dean Heller, of Nevada.
Bob Corker, of Tennessee.

Housing, Transportation, and Community Development

Robert Menendez, of New Jersey, *Chair*

Jack Reed, of Rhode Island.
Charles E. Schumer, of New York.
Sherrod Brown, of Ohio.
Jeff Merkley, of Oregon.
Joe Manchin III, of West Virginia.
Elizabeth Warren, of Massachusetts.
Heidi Heitkamp, of North Dakota.

Jerry Moran, of Kansas.
Bob Corker, of Tennessee.
Patrick J. Toomey, of Pennsylvania.
Mark Kirk, of Illinois.
Tom Coburn, of Oklahoma.
Dean Heller, of Nevada.
Richard C. Shelby, of Alabama.

National Security and International Trade and Finance

Mark R. Warner, of Virginia, *Chair*

Sherrod Brown, of Ohio.
Joe Manchin III, of West Virginia.

Mark Kirk, of Illinois.
Jerry Moran, of Kansas.

Securities, Insurance, and Investment

Jon Tester, of Montana, *Chair*

Jack Reed, of Rhode Island.
Charles E. Schumer, of New York.
Robert Menendez, of New Jersey.
Mark R. Warner, of Virginia.
Kay R. Hagan, of North Carolina.
Elizabeth Warren, of Massachusetts.
Heidi Heitkamp, of North Dakota.

Mike Johanns, of Nebraska.
Bob Corker, of Tennessee.
Richard C. Shelby, of Alabama.
David Vitter, of Louisiana.
Patrick J. Toomey, of Pennsylvania.
Mark Kirk, of Illinois.
Tom Coburn, of Oklahoma.

STAFF

Committee on Banking, Housing, and Urban Affairs (SD–534), 224–7391, fax 224–5137.
Majority Staff Director and Chief Counsel.—Charles Yi.
Deputy Staff Directors: Haroon Khan, Laura Swanson.
Policy Director.—Colin McGinnis.
Deputy Policy Director.—Glen Sears.
Senior Counsels: Jeff Siegel, Elisha Tuku.
Professional Staff Members: Erin Barry, Homer Carlisle, Beth Cooper, Brian Filipowich, Adam Healy.
Communications Director.—Sean Oblack.
Legislative Assistants: Brett Hewitt, Kari Johnson, Phil Rudd, Jana Steenholdt, J. Riker Vermilye.
Counsels: Patrick Grant, Jeanette Quick.
Staff Assistant.—Kelly Wismer.
Detailees: Krishna Patel, FDIC; Casey Scott, OCC.
Minority Staff Director.—Gregg Richard.
Minority Chief Counsel.—Gregory Dean.
Minority Senior Counsel.—Jelena McWilliams.
Minority Senior Investigative Counsel.—John O'Hara.
Minority Professional Staff Members: Chad Davis, Rachel Johnson, Mike Lee.
Minority Communications Director.—Amanda Critchfield.
Minority Research Assistant.—Danielle Stockton.
Minority Counsels: Travis Hill, Jared Sawyer.
Minority Detailee.—Hope Jarkowski, SEC.
Non-Designated Staff:
Chief Clerk.—Dawn Ratliff.
IT Director.—Shelvin Simmons.
Editor.—Jim Crowell.
GPO Detailees: Sheryl Arrington, Jason Parker.
Staff Assistant.—Pamela Streeter.
Subcommittee on Economic Policy (SD–534), 224–7391, fax 224–5137.
Majority Staff Director.—Andrew Green (SD–534), 224–3753.
Minority Staff Director.—Scott Riplinger (SD–534), 224–6244.
Subcommittee on Financial Institutions and Consumer Protection (SD–534), 224–7391, fax 224–5137.
Majority Staff Director.—Graham Steele (SD–534), 224–2315.
Minority Staff Director.—Tonnie Wybensinger (SD–534), 228–1487.
Subcommittee on Housing, Transportation, and Community Development (SD–534), 224–7391; fax 224–5137.
Majority Staff Director.—Brian Chernoff (SD–534), 224–4744.
Minority Staff Director.—William Ruder (SD–534), 224–6521.
Subcommittee on National Security and International Trade and Finance (SD–534), 224–7391; fax 224–5137.
Majority Staff Director.—Milan Dalal (SD–534), 224–2023.
Minority Staff Director.—Lindsey Johnson (SD–534), 224–2854.
Subcommittee on Securities, Insurance, and Investment (SD–534), 224–7391; fax 224–5137.
Majority Staff Director.—Ali O'Donnell (SD–534), 224–2644.
Minority Staff Director.—Bryan Blom (SD–534), 224–4224.

Budget

624 Dirksen Senate Office Building 20510–6100
phone 224–0642, http://budget.senate.gov

meets first Thursday of each month

Patty Murray, of Washington, *Chair*

Ron Wyden, of Oregon.
Bill Nelson, of Florida.
Debbie Stabenow, of Michigan.
BERNARD SANDERS, of Vermont.
Sheldon Whitehouse, of Rhode Island.
Mark R. Warner, of Virginia.
Jeff Merkley, of Oregon.
Christopher A. Coons, of Delaware.
Tammy Baldwin, of Wisconsin.
Tim Kaine, of Virginia.
ANGUS S. KING, JR., of Maine.

Jeff Sessions, of Alabama.
Chuck Grassley, of Iowa.
Michael B. Enzi, of Wyoming.
Mike Crapo, of Idaho.
Lindsey Graham, of South Carolina.
Rob Portman, of Ohio.
Patrick J. Toomey, of Pennsylvania.
Ron Johnson, of Wisconsin.
Kelly Ayotte, of New Hampshire.
Roger F. Wicker, of Mississippi.

(No Subcommittees)

STAFF

Committee on the Budget (SD–624), 224–0642.
Majority Staff Director.—Evan Schatz.
Deputy Staff Director.—John Righter.
Chief Counsel.—Robert Etter.
Counsel.—Dave Brown.
Chief Economist.—Brian Scholl.
Communications Director.—Eli Zupnick.
Director, Outreach and New Media.—Josh Ryan.
Senior Policy and Budget Advisor.—Sarah Bolton.
Budget and Tax Analyst.—Alex Brosseau.
Director and Senior Advisor of Health and Entitlements.—Paula Burg.
Research and Policy Fellow.—Josh Caplan.
Senior Advisor, Workforce and Business Development.—Scott Cheney.
Press Assistant.—Jeff Crooks.
Staff Assistant.—Brendon Dorgan.
Performance Budget Specialist.—Amy Edwards.
Director of Mandatory Programs and Senior Advisor for Social Security and Medicare.—Jennifer Hanson-Kilbride.
Policy Communications Specialist.—Helen Hare.
Senior Budget Analyst for Education and Appropriations.—Robyn Hiestand.
Senior Analyst and Director of Appropriations.—Mike Jones.
Budget Analyst for Energy and Environment.—Tyler Kruzich.
Economic Analyst.—Zach Moller.
Budget Review Professional.—Farouk Ophaso.
Revenues Counsel.—Jason Park.
Budget Analyst for Agriculture, Nutrition, and Trade.—Miles Patrie.
Analyst for Defense and Veterans Affairs.—Ryan Pettit.
Minority Staff Director.—Eric Ueland.
Chief Economist.—Bill Beach.
Chief Counsel.—William Smith.
Oversight Counsel.—Cari Kelly.
Senior Research Assistant.—John Selden.
Deputy Press Secretary.—Andrew Logan.
Press Assistant.—Katie Moses.
Director of Communications.—Stephen Miller.
Communication Advisor.—Garrett Murch.
Director of Budget Enforcement.—Tori Gorman.
Senior Analyst for Special Projects.—Dan Kowalski.
Budget Analyst for Science and Technology.—Greg McNeill.

Junior Budget Analyst.—Brittany Baker.
Executive Assistant.—Kimberly Proctor.
Professional Staff Members: Gregory D'Angelo, Matt Giroux, Andrew Herther, Paul Winfree.
Legislative Correspondent.—Carlton Millsap.
Budget Analyst.—Chris Jackson.
Staff Non-Designated:
Archivist.—Cathey Dugan.
Publications.—Letitia Fletcher.
Chief Clerk.—Joan Evans.
Computer Systems Administrator.—George Woodall.
Staff Assistant.—Phillip Longbrake.

Commerce, Science, and Transportation

254 Russell Senate Office Building 20510–6125

phone 224–0411, TTY / TDD 224–8418 http://commerce.senate.gov

meets first and third Tuesdays of each month

John D. Rockefeller IV, of West Virginia, *Chair*

Barbara Boxer, of California.
Bill Nelson, of Florida.
Maria Cantwell, of Washington.
Mark L. Pryor, of Arkansas.
Claire McCaskill, of Missouri.
Amy Klobuchar, of Minnesota.
Mark Begich, of Alaska.
Richard Blumenthal, of Connecticut.
Brian Schatz, of Hawaii.
Edward J. Markey, of Massachusetts.
Cory A. Booker, of New Jersey.
John E. Walsh, of Montana.

John Thune, of South Dakota.
Roger F. Wicker, of Mississippi.
Roy Blunt, of Missouri.
Marco Rubio, of Florida.
Kelly Ayotte, of New Hampshire.
Dean Heller, of Nevada.
Daniel Coats, of Indiana.
Tim Scott, of South Carolina.
Ted Cruz, of Texas.
Deb Fischer, of Nebraska.
Ron Johnson, of Wisconsin.

SUBCOMMITTEES

[The chair and the vice chair are ex officio members of all subcommittees.]

Aviation Operations, Safety, and Security

Maria Cantwell, of Washington, *Chair*

Barbara Boxer, of California.
Bill Nelson, of Florida.
Mark L. Pryor, of Arkansas.
Amy Klobuchar, of Minnesota.
Mark Begich, of Alaska.
Brian Schatz, of Hawaii.
Cory A. Booker, of New Jersey.

Kelly Ayotte, of New Hampshire.
Roger F. Wicker, of Mississippi.
Roy Blunt, of Missouri.
Marco Rubio, of Florida.
Dean Heller, of Nevada.
Tim Scott, of South Carolina.
Ted Cruz, of Texas.
Deb Fischer, of Nebraska.
Ron Johnson, of Wisconsin.

Communications and Technology, and the Internet

Mark L. Pryor, of Arkansas, *Chair*

Barbara Boxer, of California.
Bill Nelson, of Florida.
Maria Cantwell, of Washington.
Claire McCaskill, of Missouri.
Amy Klobuchar, of Minnesota.
Mark Begich, of Alaska.
Richard Blumenthal, of Connecticut.
Brian Schatz, of Hawaii.
Edward J. Markey, of Massachusetts.
Cory A. Booker, of New Jersey.

Roger F. Wicker, of Mississippi.
Roy Blunt, of Missouri.
Marco Rubio, of Florida.
Kelly Ayotte, of New Hampshire.
Dean Heller, of Nevada.
Daniel Coats, of Indiana.
Tim Scott, of South Carolina.
Ted Cruz, of Texas.
Deb Fischer, of Nebraska.
Ron Johnson, of Wisconsin.

Competitiveness, Innovation, and Export Promotion

Brian Schatz, of Hawaii, *Chair*

Mark L. Pryor, of Arkansas.
Amy Klobuchar, of Minnesota.
Mark Begich, of Alaska.
Richard Blumenthal, of Connecticut.
Edward J. Markey, of Massachusetts.

Tim Scott, of South Carolina.
Roy Blunt, of Missouri.
Daniel Coats, of Indiana.
Deb Fischer, of Nebraska.
Ron Johnson, of Wisconsin.

Consumer Protection, Product Safety, and Insurance

Claire McCaskill, of Missouri, *Chair*

Barbara Boxer, of California.
Mark L. Pryor, of Arkansas.
Amy Klobuchar, of Minnesota.
Richard Blumenthal, of Connecticut.
Brian Schatz, of Hawaii.
Cory A. Booker, of New Jersey.

Dean Heller, of Nevada.
Roy Blunt, of Missouri.
Kelly Ayotte, of New Hampshire.
Daniel Coats, of Indiana.
Ted Cruz, of Texas.
Deb Fischer, of Nebraska.

Oceans, Atmosphere, Fisheries, and Coast Guard

Mark Begich, of Alaska, *Chair*

Bill Nelson, of Florida.
Maria Cantwell, of Washington.
Richard Blumenthal, of Connecticut.
Brian Schatz, of Hawaii.
Edward J. Markey, of Massachusetts.
Cory A. Booker, of New Jersey.

Marco Rubio, of Florida.
Roger F. Wicker, of Mississippi.
Kelly Ayotte, of New Hampshire.
Daniel Coats, of Indiana.
Tim Scott, of South Carolina.
Ted Cruz, of Texas.

Science and Space

Bill Nelson, of Florida, *Chair*

Barbara Boxer, of California.
Mark L. Pryor, of Arkansas.
Amy Klobuchar, of Minnesota.
Richard Blumenthal, of Connecticut.
Edward J. Markey, of Massachusetts.

Ted Cruz, of Texas.
Roger F. Wicker, of Mississippi.
Marco Rubio, of Florida.
Dean Heller, of Nevada.
Daniel Coats, of Indiana.
Ron Johnson, of Wisconsin.

Surface Transportation and Merchant Marine Infrastructure, Safety, and Security

Richard Blumenthal, of Connecticut, *Chair*

Barbara Boxer, of California.
Maria Cantwell, of Washington.
Mark L. Pryor, of Arkansas.
Claire McCaskill, of Missouri.
Amy Klobuchar, of Minnesota.
Mark Begich, of Alaska.
Brian Schatz, of Hawaii.
Edward J. Markey, of Massachusetts.
Cory A. Booker, of New Jersey.

Roy Blunt, of Missouri.
Roger F. Wicker, of Mississippi.
Marco Rubio, of Florida.
Kelly Ayotte, of New Hampshire.
Dean Heller, of Nevada.
Daniel Coats, of Indiana.
Tim Scott, of South Carolina.
Ted Cruz, of Texas.
Deb Fischer, of Nebraska.
Ron Johnson, of Wisconsin.

STAFF

Committee on Commerce, Science, and Transportation (SR–254), 224–0411.
Majority Staff Director.—Ellen Doneski.
General Counsel.—John Williams.
Communications Director.—Jenny Rosenberg.
Press Secretary.—Kevin McAlister.
Director of Operations, Special Assistant.—Vanessa Jones.
Staff Assistant.—Andrew Clough.
Oversight and Investigations Office:
Chief Investigative Counsel and Director of Oversight.—Kristin Amerling.
Counsel.—Jennifer Epperson.
Professional Staff.—Jeff Zubricki.
Investigative Counsel.—Melanie Tiano.
Staff Assistant.—Peter Curtin.
FTC Detailee.—Kathleen Benway.
Minority Staff Director.—David Schwietert.
Deputy Minority Staff Director.—Nick Rossi.

Minority General Counsel/Chief Investigator.—Rebecca Seidel.
Legislative Assistant Investigator.—Cherilyn Pascoe.
Research and Investigative Assistant.—Matthew Plaster.
Communications Director.—Andi Fouberg.
Minority Deputy General Counsel.—Jason Van Beek.
Minority Senior Advisor.—Summer Mersinger.
Minority Office Manager.—Theresa Eugene.

Aviation Operations, Safety, and Security Staff:
Majority Professional Staff Member.—Rich Swayze.
Minority Senior Professional Staff.—Dan Neumann.

Communications and Technology, and the Internet Staff:
Communications Counsel.—John Branscome.
Counsel.—Shawn Bone.
Legislative Assistant.—Sydney Paul.
Minority Policy Director for Communications and Technology.—David Quinalty.
Minority Counsel.—Jeffrey Farrah.
Professional Staff Member.—Hap Rigby.

Competitiveness, Innovation, and Export Promotion Staff:
Senior Counsel.—Christian Fjeld.
Professional Staff.—Anna Laitin.
Counsel.—Jared Bomberg.
Legislative Assistant.—Brian No.

Consumer Protection, Product Safety, and Insurance Staff:
Senior Counsel.—Christian Fjeld.
Professional Staff.—Anna Laitin.
Counsel.—Jared Bomberg.
Legislative Assistant.—Brian No.
Minority Counsel.—Peter Feldman.

Oceans, Atmosphere, Fisheries, and Coast Guard Staff:
Oceans Counsel.—Catherine Barrett.
Counsel.—Jeff Lewis.
Legislative Assistant.—Sean Houton.
Coast Guard Detailee.—Shawn Whiteside.
Sea Grant Fellow.—Rachel Silverstein.
Minority Professional Staff.—Kelly Pennington.
Research Assistants: Sara Gibson, Andrew Timm.
Coast Guard Fellow.—Kathy Felger.

Science and Space Staff:
Senior Majority Professional Staff.—Ann Zulkosky.
Professional Staff Member.—Richard-Duane Chambers.
Legislative Assistant.—Andrew Ruffin.
Minority Professional Staff Members: Missye Brickell, Suzanne Gillen.
Minority Senior Professional Staff.—Bailey Edwards.

Surface Transportation and Merchant Marine Infrastructure, Safety, and Security Staff:
Majority Professional Staff Member.—Ian Jefferies.
Professional Staff.—Devon Barnhart.
Counsel and Professional Staff Member.—Adrian Arnakis.
Legislative Assistant.—Brandon Kaufman.
Minority Professional Staff Member.—Dan Neumann.

Bipartisan Staff:
Chief Clerk.—Anne Willis Hill.
Hearing Clerk.—Stephanie Gamache.
Director, Information Technology.—Jonathan Bowen.
Staff Editor.—Debra Miller.
Archivist.—Matthew Stahl.
GPO Detailee.—Jacqueline Washington.

Bipartisan Staff, Legislative Counsel's Office:
Legislative Counsel.—Jennifer Dorrer.
Staff Assistants: Stephanie Lieu, Kara Starr.

Energy and Natural Resources

304 Dirksen Senate Office Building 20510

phone 224–4971, fax 224–6163, http://energy.senate.gov

meets upon call of the chair

Mary L. Landrieu, of Louisiana, *Chair*

Ron Wyden, of Oregon.
Tim Johnson, of South Dakota.
Maria Cantwell, of Washington.
BERNARD SANDERS, of Vermont.
Debbie Stabenow, of Michigan.
Mark Udall, of Colorado.
Al Franken, of Minnesota.
Joe Manchin III, of West Virginia.
Brian Schatz, of Hawaii.
Martin Heinrich, of New Mexico.
Tammy Baldwin, of Wisconsin.

Lisa Murkowski, of Alaska.
John Barrasso, of Wyoming.
James E. Risch, of Idaho.
Mike Lee, of Utah.
Dean Heller, of Nevada.
Jeff Flake, of Arizona.
Tim Scott, of South Carolina.
Lamar Alexander, of Tennessee.
Rob Portman, of Ohio.
John Hoeven, of North Dakota.

SUBCOMMITTEES

[The chairman and the ranking minority member are ex officio members of all subcommittees.]

Energy

Al Franken, of Minnesota, *Chair*

Tim Johnson, of South Dakota.
Maria Cantwell, of Washington.
BERNARD SANDERS, of Vermont.
Debbie Stabenow, of Michigan.
Mark Udall, of Colorado.
Joe Manchin III, of West Virginia.
Martin Heinrich, of New Mexico.
Tammy Baldwin, of Wisconsin.

James E. Risch, of Idaho.
Dean Heller, of Nevada.
Jeff Flake, of Arizona.
Lamar Alexander, of Tennessee.
Rob Portman, of Ohio.
John Hoeven, of North Dakota.

National Parks

Mark Udall, of Colorado, *Chair*

BERNARD SANDERS, of Vermont.
Debbie Stabenow, of Michigan.
Brian Schatz, of Hawaii.
Martin Heinrich, of New Mexico.
Tammy Baldwin, of Wisconsin.

Rob Portman, of Ohio.
John Barrasso, of Wyoming.
Mike Lee, of Utah.
Lamar Alexander, of Tennessee.
John Hoeven, of North Dakota.

Public Lands, Forests, and Mining

Joe Manchin III, of West Virginia, *Chair*

Tim Johnson, of South Dakota.
Maria Cantwell, of Washington.
Mark Udall, of Colorado.
Al Franken, of Minnesota.
Brian Schatz, of Hawaii.
Martin Heinrich, of New Mexico.
Tammy Baldwin, of Wisconsin.

John Barrasso, of Wyoming.
James E. Risch, of Idaho.
Mike Lee, of Utah.
Dean Heller, of Nevada.
Jeff Flake, of Arizona.
Tim Scott, of South Carolina.
Lamar Alexander, of Tennessee.
John Hoeven, of North Dakota.

Water and Power

Brian Schatz, of Hawaii, *Chair*

Tim Johnson, of South Dakota.
Maria Cantwell, of Washington.
BERNARD SANDERS, of Vermont.
Debbie Stabenow, of Michigan.
Joe Manchin III, of West Virginia.
Al Franken, of Minnesota.

Mike Lee, of Utah.
John Barrasso, of Wyoming.
James E. Risch, of Idaho.
Dean Heller, of Nevada.
Jeff Flake, of Arizona.
Tim Scott, of South Carolina.

STAFF

Committee on Energy and Natural Resources (SD–304), 224–4971, fax 224–6163.
Majority Staff Director.—Joshua Sheinkman.
Chief Counsel.—Sam Fowler.
Senior Counsels: Dan Adamson, Patty Beneke, David Brooks, Michele Miranda, Todd Wooten.
Counsels: Andrew Johnston, Cisco Minthorn.
Chief Clerk.—Sallie Derr.
Executive Assistant.—Ian Nicholson.
Press Secretary.—Keith Chu.
Press Assistant.—Samantha Offerdahl.
Digital Coordinator.—Rebecca Steele.
Senior Professional Staff: Isaiah Akin, Meghan Conklin, Kevin Rennert, Al Stayman, Sara Tucker.
Professional Staff.—Mary Gautreaux.
Chief Investigator.—David Berick.
Investigator.—Peter Gartrell.
Legislative Aides: Abby Campbell, Danielle Deraney.
Staff Assistants: John Assini, Lauren Goldschmidt.
Detailees: Gordy Kito, Bryan Petit, Melanie Stansbury.
Fellows: Larcus Pickett, Lara Pierpoint.
Minority Staff Director.—Karen Billups.
Chief Counsel.—Patrick McCormick.
Deputy Chief Counsel.—Kellie Donnelly.
Senior Counsels: Isaac Edwards, Kaleb Froehlich.
Oil and Gas Counsel.—Kate Williams.
Public Lands Counsel.—Lucy Murfitt.
Communications Director.—Robert Dillon.
Press Secretary.—Megan Moskowitz.
Professional Staff Members: Tristan Abbey, Whitney Drew, Colin Hayes, Brian Hughes, Josh Johnson, Chuck Kleeschulte.
Legislative Aides: Chester Carson, Pasha Majdi.
Science Fellow.—Ron Faibish.
Non-Designated Staff:
Administrator Director.—Darla Ripchensky.
Receptionist.—Lindsey Stanford.
Staff Assistant.—Kari Pederson.
Systems Administrator.—Dominic Taylor.
GPO Detailees: Monica Chestnut, Wanda Green.

Environment and Public Works

410 Dirksen Senate Office Building 20510–6175

phone 224–8832, www.senate.gov/~epw

meets first and third Thursdays of each month

Barbara Boxer, of California, *Chair*

Thomas R. Carper, of Delaware.
Benjamin L. Cardin, of Maryland.
BERNARD SANDERS, of Vermont.
Sheldon Whitehouse, of Rhode Island.
Tom Udall, of New Mexico.
Jeff Merkley, of Oregon.
Kirsten E. Gillibrand, of New York.
Cory A. Booker, of New Jersey.
Edward J. Markey, of Massachusetts.

David Vitter, of Louisiana.
James M. Inhofe, of Oklahoma.
John Barrasso, of Wyoming.
Jeff Sessions, of Alabama.
Mike Crapo, of Idaho.
Roger F. Wicker, of Mississippi.
John Boozman, of Arkansas.
Deb Fischer, of Nebraska.

SUBCOMMITTEES

[The chairman and the ranking minority member are ex officio (non-voting) members of all subcommittees on which they do not serve.]

Clean Air and Nuclear Safety

Sheldon Whitehouse, of Rhode Island, *Chair*

Thomas R. Carper, of Delaware.
Benjamin L. Cardin, of Maryland.
BERNARD SANDERS, of Vermont.
Tom Udall, of New Mexico.
Edward J. Markey, of Massachusetts.

Jeff Sessions, of Alabama.
John Barrasso, of Wyoming.
Mike Crapo, of Idaho.
Roger F. Wicker, of Mississippi.
John Boozman, of Arkansas.

Green Jobs and the New Economy

Jeff Merkley, of Oregon, *Chair*

Thomas R. Carper, of Delaware.
BERNARD SANDERS, of Vermont.

Roger F. Wicker, of Mississippi.
Jeff Sessions, of Alabama.

Oversight

Cory A. Booker, of New Jersey, *Chair*

Sheldon Whitehouse, of Rhode Island.
Edward J. Markey, of Massachusetts.

James M. Inhofe, of Oklahoma.
John Boozman, of Arkansas.

Superfund, Toxics and Environmental Health

Tom Udall, of New Mexico, *Chair*

Jeff Merkley, of Oregon.
Kirsten E. Gillibrand, of New York.
Cory A. Booker, of New Jersey.
Edward J. Markey, of Massachusetts.

Mike Crapo, of Idaho.
James M. Inhofe, of Oklahoma.
Roger F. Wicker, of Mississippi.
Deb Fischer, of Nebraska.

Transportation and Infrastructure

Thomas R. Carper, of Delaware, *Chair*

Benjamin L. Cardin, of Maryland.
BERNARD SANDERS, of Vermont.
Tom Udall, of New Mexico.
Kirsten E. Gillibrand, of New York.
Cory A. Booker, of New Jersey.
Edward J. Markey, of Massachusetts.

John Barrasso, of Wyoming.
James M. Inhofe, of Oklahoma.
Jeff Sessions, of Alabama.
Mike Crapo, of Idaho.
Roger F. Wicker, of Mississippi.
Deb Fischer, of Nebraska.

Water and Wildlife

Benjamin L. Cardin, of Maryland, *Chair*

Thomas R. Carper, of Delaware.
Sheldon Whitehouse, of Rhode Island.
Jeff Merkley, of Oregon.
Kirsten E. Gillibrand, of New York.
Cory A. Booker, of New Jersey.

John Boozman, of Arkansas.
James M. Inhofe, of Oklahoma.
John Barrasso, of Wyoming.
Jeff Sessions, of Alabama.
Deb Fischer, of Nebraska.

STAFF

Committee on Environment and Public Works (SD–410), phone 224–8832; Majority fax (SD–410), 224–1273; (SH–508), 228–0574.
Majority Staff Director/Chief Counsel.—Bettina Poirier.
Majority Senior Counsels: Grant Cope, Thomas Fox.
Counsels: Alyson Cooke, Ted Illston, Tyler Rushforth.
Majority Senior Policy Advisor.—Jason Albritton.
Majority Director, Infrastructure and Economic Oversight.—David Napoliello.
Majority Senior Policy Director for Transportation.—Vacant.
Majority Chief Climate Counsel.—Joseph Mendelson III.
Office Manager.—Carolyn Mack.
Chief Clerk.—Alicia Gordon.
System Administrator.—Rae Ann Phipps.
Communications Director.—Mary Kerr.
Professional Staff Member.—Andrew Dohrmann.
Editorial Director.—Stephen Chapman.
GPO Detailees: LaVern Finks, Brenda Samuels.
Majority Press Assistants: Nathan McCray, Mara Stark-Alcala.
Majority Special Assistant.—Paul Ordal.
Majority Deputy Communications Director/Press Secretary.—Kate Gilman.
Minority fax (SD–456), 224–5167; (SH–415), 228–2322.
Staff Director.—Zak Baig.
Chief Counsel.—Bryan Zumwalt.
Director of Operations.—Kathryn Eden.
Communications Director.—Luke Bolar.
Press Secretary.—Cheyenne Steel.
Senior Clean Air Act Counsel.—Margaret Caravelli.
Senior Counsel for Oversight.—Kristina Moore.
Counsels: Laura Atcheson, Dimitri Karakitsos.
Clean Water Act Counsel.—Brandon Middleton.
Professional Staff.—Charles Brittingham, Anna Burhop, Ward Cormier, Peter Henry, Chris Tomassi.
Research Staff.—Brittany Bolen.
Research Assistant.—Jill Landry.
Staff Assistants: Rebecca Louviere, Sarah Veatch.

Finance

219 Dirksen Senate Office Building 20510

phone 224–4515, fax 224–0554, http://finance.senate.gov

meets second and fourth Tuesdays of each month

Ron Wyden, of Oregon, *Chair*

John D. Rockefeller IV, of West Virginia.
Charles E. Schumer, of New York.
Debbie Stabenow, of Michigan.
Maria Cantwell, of Washington.
Bill Nelson, of Florida.
Robert Menendez, of New Jersey.
Thomas R. Carper, of Delaware.
Benjamin L. Cardin, of Maryland.
Sherrod Brown, of Ohio.
Michael F. Bennet, of Colorado.
Robert P. Casey, Jr., of Pennsylvania.
Mark R. Warner, of Virginia.

Orrin G. Hatch, of Utah.
Chuck Grassley, of Iowa.
Mike Crapo, of Idaho.
Pat Roberts, of Kansas.
Michael B. Enzi, of Wyoming.
John Cornyn, of Texas.
John Thune, of South Dakota.
Richard Burr, of North Carolina.
Johnny Isakson, of Georgia.
Rob Portman, of Ohio.
Patrick J. Toomey, of Pennsylvania.

SUBCOMMITTEES

[The chairman and the ranking minority member are ex officio (non-voting) members of all subcommittees on which they do not serve.]

Energy, Natural Resources, and Infrastructure

Debbie Stabenow, of Michigan, *Chair*

John D. Rockefeller IV, of West Virginia.
Ron Wyden, of Oregon.
Maria Cantwell, of Washington.
Bill Nelson, of Florida.
Thomas R. Carper, of Delaware.
Michael F. Bennet, of Colorado.

John Cornyn, of Texas.
Chuck Grassley, of Iowa.
Mike Crapo, of Idaho.
Michael B. Enzi, of Wyoming.
John Thune, of South Dakota.
Richard Burr, of North Carolina.
Johnny Isakson, of Georgia.

Fiscal Responsibility and Economic Growth

Robert P. Casey, Jr., of Pennsylvania, *Chair*

Sherrod Brown, of Ohio.

Rob Portman, of Ohio.
Richard Burr, of North Carolina.

Health Care

John D. Rockefeller IV, of West Virginia, *Chair*

Debbie Stabenow, of Michigan.
Maria Cantwell, of Washington.
Bill Nelson, of Florida.
Robert Menendez, of New Jersey.
Thomas R. Carper, of Delaware.
Benjamin L. Cardin, of Maryland.
Robert P. Casey, Jr., of Pennsylvania.

Pat Roberts, of Kansas.
Orrin G. Hatch, of Utah.
Chuck Grassley, of Iowa.
Michael B. Enzi, of Wyoming.
John Cornyn, of Texas.
Richard Burr, of North Carolina.
Patrick J. Toomey, of Pennsylvania.

International Trade, Customs, and Global Competitiveness

Ron Wyden, of Oregon, *Chair*

John D. Rockefeller IV, of West Virginia.
Charles E. Schumer, of New York.
Debbie Stabenow, of Michigan.
Maria Cantwell, of Washington.
Robert Menendez, of New Jersey.
Sherrod Brown, of Ohio.
Michael F. Bennet, of Colorado.

Johnny Isakson, of Georgia.
Orrin G. Hatch, of Utah.
Chuck Grassley, of Iowa.
Pat Roberts, of Kansas.
John Thune, of South Dakota.
Rob Portman, of Ohio.

Social Security, Pensions, and Family Policy

Sherrod Brown, of Ohio, *Chair*

John D. Rockefeller IV, of West Virginia.
Charles E. Schumer, of New York.
Bill Nelson, of Florida.
Benjamin L. Cardin, of Maryland.

Patrick J. Toomey, of Pennsylvania.
Mike Crapo, of Idaho.
Johnny Isakson, of Georgia.
Rob Portman, of Ohio.

Taxation and IRS Oversight

Michael F. Bennet, of Colorado, *Chair*

Ron Wyden, of Oregon.
Charles E. Schumer, of New York.
Robert Menendez, of New Jersey.
Thomas R. Carper, of Delaware.
Benjamin L. Cardin, of Maryland.
Robert P. Casey, Jr., of Pennsylvania.

Michael B. Enzi, of Wyoming.
Orrin G. Hatch, of Utah.
Mike Crapo, of Idaho.
Pat Roberts, of Kansas.
John Cornyn, of Texas.
John Thune, of South Dakota.
Patrick J. Toomey, of Pennsylvania.

STAFF

Committees on Finance (SD–219), 224–4515, fax 228–0554.
Majority Staff Director.—Amber Cottle.
Assistant to the Director.—Kristin Smith.
General Counsel.—Mac Campbell.
Senior Advisor.—John Angell.
Counsel and Senior Advisor for Indian Affairs.—Richard Litsey.
Professional Staff.—Karen Fischer.
Research Assistant.—Sara Harshman.
Research Assistant.—Scott Levy.
Chief Tax.—Lily Batchelder.
Tax Counsels: Ryan Abraham, Ann Cammack, Kara Getz, Jude Lemke, Holly Porter, Tiffany Smith.
Tax Policy Analyst.—Anderson Heiman.
Research Associate.—Christopher Arneson.
Chief Health Counsel.—David Schwartz.
Professional Staff: Tony Clapsis, Diedra Henry-Spires.
Health Advisor.—Matt Kazan.
Professional Staff: Chelsea Thomas, Kelly Whitener.
Chief International Trade Counsel.—Bruce Hirsch.
International Trade Counsel: Elissa Alben, Lisa Pearlman.
Nomination and International Trade Advisor.—Rory Murphy.
Investigator.—Christopher Law.
Professional Staff-Social Security.—Tom Klouda.
Communication Director.—Sean Neary.
Deputy Communication Director.—Meghan Smith.
Press Assistant.—Ryan Carey.
Staff Assistants: Brandon Mourich, Logan Smith.
IT Director.—Joe Carnucci.
Archivist.—Bryan Palmer.
Detailees: Ronald Dabrowski, Laurie Dempsey, Melanie Rainer, Sibyl Tilson.
Minority Staff Director and Chief Counsel.—Chris Campbell.

Deputy Staff Director/Chief Tax Counsel.—Mark Prater.
Tax Counsels: Curt Beaulieu, Tony Coughlan, James Lyons.
Senior Tax Policy Advisor.—Christopher Hanna.
Tax Counsel.—Preston Rutledge.
Tax and Nomination Professional Staff.—Nick Wyatt.
Professional Staff Member.—Aaron Taylor.
Special Counsel.—Bryan Hickman.
Chief Healthcare Investigate Counsel.—Kim Brandt.
Chief Health Counsel and Policy Director.—Jay Khosla.
Oversight and Investigative Professional Staff.—Peter Russo.
Health Policy Advisors: Becky Shipp, Dan Todd, Kristin Welsh.
Special Assistant.—Jason Stegmaier.
Chief International Trade Counsel.—Everett Eissenstat.
International Trade Counsel.—Shane Warren.
International Trade Analyst.—Rebecca Eubank.
Chief Economist and Social Security Analyst.—Jeff Wrase.
Communications Director.—Antonia Ferrier.
Press Secretary.—Julia Lawless.
Detailees: Erik Abjornson, Anna Bonelli, John Carlo, Richard Chovanec, Justin, Kevin Rosenbaum.

Foreign Relations

450 Dirksen Senate Office Building 20510–6225

phone 224–4651, http://foreign.senate.gov

meets each Tuesday

Robert Menendez, of New Jersey, *Chair*

Barbara Boxer, of California.
Benjamin L. Cardin, of Maryland.
Jeanne Shaheen, of New Hampshire.
Christopher A. Coons, of Delaware.
Richard J. Durbin, of Illinois.
Tom Udall, of New Mexico.
Christopher Murphy, of Connecticut.
Tim Kaine, of Virginia.
Edward J. Markey, of Massachusetts.

Bob Corker, of Tennessee.
James E. Risch, of Idaho.
Marco Rubio, of Florida.
Ron Johnson, of Wisconsin.
Jeff Flake, of Arizona.
John McCain, of Arizona.
John Barrasso, of Wyoming.
Rand Paul, of Kentucky.

SUBCOMMITTEES

[The chairman and ranking minority member are ex officio (non-voting) members of all subcommittees on which they do not serve.]

African Affairs

Christopher A. Coons, of Delaware, *Chair*

Richard J. Durbin, of Illinois.
Benjamin L. Cardin, of Maryland.
Jeanne Shaheen, of New Hampshire.
Tom Udall, of New Mexico.

Jeff Flake, of Arizona.
John McCain, of Arizona.
John Barrasso, of Wyoming.
Rand Paul, of Kentucky.

East Asian and Pacific Affairs

Benjamin L. Cardin, of Maryland, *Chair*

Christopher Murphy, of Connecticut.
Barbara Boxer, of California.
Tom Udall, of New Mexico.
Edward J. Markey, of Massachusetts.

Marco Rubio, of Florida.
Ron Johnson, of Wisconsin.
Jeff Flake, of Arizona.
John McCain, of Arizona.

European Affairs

Christopher Murphy, of Connecticut, *Chair*

Jeanne Shaheen, of New Hampshire.
Edward J. Markey, of Massachusetts.
Benjamin L. Cardin, of Maryland.
Richard J. Durbin, of Illinois.

Ron Johnson, of Wisconsin.
James E. Risch, of Idaho.
Jeff Flake, of Arizona.
John Barrasso, of Wyoming.

International Development and Foreign Assistance, Economic Affairs, International Environmental Protection, and Peace Corps

Edward J. Markey, of Massachusetts, *Chair*

Tom Udall, of New Mexico.
Christopher A. Coons, of Delaware.
Christopher Murphy, of Connecticut.
Tim Kaine, of Virginia.

John Barrasso, of Wyoming.
James E. Risch, of Idaho.
Jeff Flake, of Arizona.
Rand Paul, of Kentucky.

International Operations and Organizations, Human Rights, Democracy, and Global Women's Issues

Barbara Boxer, of California, *Chair*

Jeanne Shaheen, of New Hampshire.
Richard J. Durbin, of Illinois.
Christopher A. Coons, of Delaware.
Tim Kaine, of Virginia.
Rand Paul, of Kentucky.
Marco Rubio, of Florida.
James E. Risch, of Idaho.
Ron Johnson, of Wisconsin.

Near Eastern and South and Central Asian Affairs

Tim Kaine, of Virginia, *Chair*

Barbara Boxer, of California.
Benjamin L. Cardin, of Maryland.
Christopher A. Coons, of Delaware.
Richard J. Durbin, of Illinois.
James E. Risch, of Idaho.
Marco Rubio, of Florida.
Ron Johnson, of Wisconsin.
John McCain, of Arizona.

Western Hemisphere and Global Narcotics Affairs

Tom Udall, of New Mexico, *Chair*

Tim Kaine, of Virginia.
Barbara Boxer, of California.
Jeanne Shaheen, of New Hampshire.
Christopher Murphy, of Connecticut.
John McCain, of Arizona.
Marco Rubio, of Florida.
John Barrasso, of Wyoming.
Rand Paul, of Kentucky.

STAFF

Committee on Foreign Relations (SD–444), 224–4651.
Majority Staff Director: Danny O'Brien.
Deputy Staff Director/Chief Counsel.—Jodi Herman.
Deputy Chief Counsel.—Margaret Taylor.
Senior Advisor/Counselor.—Michael Schiffer.
Research and Legislative Assistants: Christopher Barr, Brittany Beaulieu, Terrell Henry, Sanaa Khan, John Ryan, Jonathan Tsentas.
Press Secretary.—Adam Sharon.
Senior Professional Staff Members: Jason Bruder, Hal Connolly, David Fite, Damian Murphy, Charlotte Oldham-Moore, Lowell Schwartz, Dana Stroul, Brandon Yoder.
Director of Operations.—David Gins.
Legislative Correspondent.—Jenipher Camino Gonzales.
Staff Assistants: Francisco Bencosme, Davina Burgess, Nury Gambarrotti.
Non-Designated Staff:
Chief Clerk.—Susan Oursler.
Office Manager.—Samantha Hamilton.
IT Specialist.—John Dutton.
Administrative Services Coordinator.—Benjamin Schorr.
Protocol/Travel Director.—Meg Murphy.
Staff Assistant.—Vanessa Jean-Simon.
Archivist.—Lexi Simpson.
Executive/Nominations Clerk.—Gail Coppage.
Printing Clerks: Elizabeth Acton, Michael Bennet.

Health, Education, Labor, and Pensions

428 Dirksen Senate Office Building 20510–6300

phone 224–5375, http://help.senate.gov

meets second and fourth Wednesdays of each month

Tom Harkin, of Iowa, *Chair*

Barbara A. Mikulski, of Maryland.
Patty Murray, of Washington.
BERNARD SANDERS, of Vermont.
Robert P. Casey, Jr., of Pennsylvania.
Kay R. Hagan, of North Carolina.
Al Franken, of Minnesota.
Michael F. Bennet, of Colorado.
Sheldon Whitehouse, of Rhode Island.
Tammy Baldwin, of Wisconsin.
Christopher Murphy, of Connecticut.
Elizabeth Warren, of Massachusetts.

Lamar Alexander, of Tennessee.
Michael B. Enzi, of Wyoming.
Richard Burr, of North Carolina.
Johnny Isakson, of Georgia.
Rand Paul, of Kentucky.
Orrin G. Hatch, of Utah.
Pat Roberts, of Kansas.
Lisa Murkowski, of Alaska.
Mark Kirk, of Illinois.
Tim Scott, of South Carolina.

SUBCOMMITTEES

[The chairman and ranking minority member are ex officio members of all subcommittees on which they do not serve.]

* Children and Families [1]

Kay R. Hagan, of North Carolina, *Chair*

Barbara A. Mikulski, of Maryland.
Patty Murray, of Washington.
BERNARD SANDERS, of Vermont.
Robert P. Casey, Jr., of Pennsylvania.
Al Franken, of Minnesota.
Michael F. Bennet, of Colorado.
Christopher Murphy, of Connecticut.
Elizabeth Warren, of Massachusetts.

Michael B. Enzi, of Wyoming.
Mark Kirk, of Illinois.
Richard Burr, of North Carolina.
Johnny Isakson, of Georgia.
Rand Paul, of Kentucky.
Orrin G. Hatch, of Utah.
Pat Roberts, of Kansas.

Employment and Workplace Safety

Robert P. Casey, Jr., of Pennsylvania, *Chair*

Patty Murray, of Washington.
Al Franken, of Minnesota.
Michael F. Bennet, of Colorado.
Sheldon Whitehouse, of Rhode Island.
Tammy Baldwin, of Wisconsin.

Johnny Isakson, of Georgia.
Rand Paul, of Kentucky.
Orrin G. Hatch, of Utah.
Tim Scott, of South Carolina.

Primary Health and Aging [1]

BERNARD SANDERS, of Vermont, *Chair*

Barbara A. Mikulski, of Maryland.
Kay R. Hagan, of North Carolina.
Sheldon Whitehouse, of Rhode Island.
Tammy Baldwin, of Wisconsin.
Christopher Murphy, of Connecticut.
Elizabeth Warren, of Massachusetts.

Richard Burr, of North Carolina.
Pat Roberts, of Kansas.
Lisa Murkowski, of Alaska.
Michael B. Enzi, of Wyoming.
Mark Kirk, of Illinois.

STAFF

Committee on Health, Education, Labor, and Pensions (SD–644), 224–0767, fax 224–6510, TDD 224–1975.

Staff Director.—Pam Smith, SD–644, 4–0767.
Deputy Staff Director.—Lauren McFerran, SD–644, 4–0767.
Special Assistant.—Molly Click, SD–644, 4–0767.
Press Secretary.—Allison Preiss, SD–644, 4–0767.
Press Assistant.—Abraham White, SD–644, 4–0767.
Health Policy Office 4–7675
Health Policy Director.—Jenelle Krishnamoorthy, SH–527, 4–7675.
Health Policy Advisors: Andi Fristedt, Sara Singleton, SH–527, 4–7675.
Legislative Correspondent.—Brian Massa, SH–527, 4–7675.
Senior Health Policy Advisors: Nick Bath, Elizabeth Jungman, SH–527, 4–7675.
Detailee.—Sharon Boyd, SH–527, 4–7675.
Staff Assistant.—Emily Schlichting, SH–527, 4–7675.
Fellows: Nathan Brown, Maggie Linak, SH–527, 4–7675.
Education Policy Office 4–5501
Legislative Assistant.—Leanne Hotek, SH–615, 4–5501.
Staff Assistant.—Aissa Canchola, SH–615, 4–5501.
Education Policy Advisor.—Libby Masiuk, SH–615, 4–5501.
Chief Education Counsel.—Mildred Otero, SH–615, 4–5501.
Senior Education Policy Advisors: Crystal Bridgeman, SH–615, 4–5501.
Education Policy Advisors: Mario Cardona, Soncia Coleman, SH–615, 4–5501.
Detailee.—Tina Sigurdson, SH–615, 4–5501.
Fellows: Brenda Calderon, Nick Perilla, SH–615, 4–5501.
Oversight and Investigation Office 4–6403
Chief Investigative Counsel.—Beth Stein, SH–404, 4–6403.
Counsel.—Keramin Hamadanchy, SH–404, 4–6403.
Staff Assistant.—Alyssa Mowitz, SH–404, 4–6403.
Counsel.—Bryan Boroughs, SH–404, 4–6403.
Disability Office 8–3453
Senior Counsel and Disability Policy Director.—Michael Gamel-McCormick, SH–404, 8–3453.
Disability Counsel.—Lee Perselay, SH–404, 8–3453.
Subcommittee on Children and Families 4–9243
Subcommittee Staff Director.—Josh Teitelbaum, SD–648, 4–9243.
Fellow.—Jilliene Johnson, SD–648, 4–9243.
Education Policy Advisor.—Ashley Eden, SD–648, 4–9243.
Subcommittee on Employment and Workplace Safety 8–1455
Subcommittee Staff Director.—Larry Smar, SH–607, 8–1455.
Senior Policy Advisor.—Michael Waske, SH–607, 8–1455.
Subcommittee on Primary Health and Aging 4–5480
Subcommittee Staff Director.—Sophie Kasimow, SD–424, 4–5480.
Senior Staff Member.—Erica Solway, SD–424, 4–5480.
Staff Assistant.—Bill Gendell, SD–424, 4–5480.
Minority Staff
Committee on Health, Education, Labor, and Pensions (SH–835), 224–6770
Staff Director.—David Cleary, SH–833, 4–6770.
General Counsel.—Michael Merrell, SH–833, 4–6770.
Operations Director.—Misty Marshall, SH–132, 4–6770.
Senior Policy Advisor.—Lindsey Seidman, SH–132, 4–6770.
Communications Office SH–132, 4–6770
Press Secretary.—Liz Wolgemuth, SH–132, 4–6770.
Press Assistant.—Sarah Chu, SH–132, 4–6770.
Detailee.—Stacy Coggin, SH–132, 4–6770
Oversight and Investigations Office SH–622B, 4–6770.
Oversight Director.—Stacy Cline, SH–622B, 4–6770.
Detailee.—Bill Keller, SH–622B, 4–6770.
Health Policy Office SH–725, 4–0623
Health Policy Director.—MarySumpter Lapinski, SH–725, 4–0623.
Deputy Health Policy Director.—Sarah Arbes, SH–725, 4–0623.
Professional Staff Members: Melissa Pfaff, Alicia Hennie, Grace Stuntz, SH–725, 4–0623.
Education Office SH–828, 4–8484
Education Policy Director and Counsel.—Peter Oppenheim, SH–828, 4–8484.
Senior Education Policy Advisor.—Marty West, SH–828, 4–8484.

Education Policy Advisors: Bill Knudsen, Andrew LaCasse, Bob Moran, SH–828, 4–8484.

Staff Assistant.—Diane Tran, SH–828, 8–6770.

Labor Policy Office SH–828, 8–6770.

Labor Policy Director.—Kyle Fortson, SH–828, 8–6770.

Labor Counsel.—Kai Hirabayashi, SH–828, 8–6770.

Detailee.—Chris Jacob, SH–828, 8–6770.

Subcommittee on Children and Families SH–440, 4–0121

Retirement Policy Director.—Steve Perrotta, SH–440, 4–0121.

Health Policy Director.—Anna Abram, SH–440, 4–0121.

Health Policy Assistant.—Margaret Coulter, SH–440, 4–0121.

Subcommittee on Employment and Workplace Safety SH–833, 4–5800.

Staff Director.—Tommy Nguyen, SH–833, 4–5800.

Subcommittee on Primary Health and Aging SH–440, 4–5406

Staff Director.—Riley Swinehart, SH–440, 4–5406.

Professional Staff Member.—Kristen Chapman, SH–440, 4–5406.

---

[1] On January 31, 2007, the Committee was polled and agreed that the name of the Subcommittee on Education and Early Childhood Development would be changed to the Subcommittee on Children and Families, the Subcommittee on Retirement Security and Aging would be changed to the Subcommittee on Retirement and Aging, and that the Committee would discontinue the Subcommittee on Bioterrorism and Public Health Preparedness. On March 15, 2011, the Committee was polled and agreed that the name of the Subcommittee on Retirement Security and Aging would be changed to the Subcommittee on Primary Health and Aging.

*Minority Subcommittee Member order corrected March 2007.

Homeland Security and Governmental Affairs

340 Dirksen Senate Office Building 20510

phone 224–2627, fax 228–3792, http://hsgac.senate.gov

Hearing Room—SD–342 Dirksen Senate Office Building

meets first Wednesday of each month

Thomas R. Carper, of Delaware, *Chair*

Carl Levin, of Michigan.
Mark L. Pryor, of Arkansas.
Mary L. Landrieu, of Louisiana.
Claire McCaskill, of Missouri.
Jon Tester, of Montana.
Mark Begich, of Alaska.
Tammy Baldwin, of Wisconsin.
Heidi Heitkamp, of North Dakota.

Tom Coburn, of Oklahoma.
John McCain, of Arizona.
Ron Johnson, of Wisconsin.
Rob Portman, of Ohio.
Rand Paul, of Kentucky.
Michael B. Enzi, of Wyoming.
Kelly Ayotte, of New Hampshire.

SUBCOMMITTEES

[The chairman and the ranking minority member are ex officio members of all subcommittees.]

Permanent Subcommittee on Investigations (PSI)

Carl Levin, of Michigan, *Chair*

Mark L. Pryor, of Arkansas.
Mary L. Landrieu, of Louisiana.
Claire McCaskill, of Missouri.
Jon Tester, of Montana.
Tammy Baldwin, of Wisconsin.
Heidi Heitkamp, of North Dakota.

John McCain, of Arizona.
Ron Johnson, of Wisconsin.
Rob Portman, of Ohio.
Rand Paul, of Kentucky.
Kelly Ayotte, of New Hampshire.

Efficiency and Effectiveness of Federal Programs and the Federal Workforce (FPFW)

Jon Tester, of Montana, *Chair*

Mark L. Pryor, of Arkansas.
Claire McCaskill, of Missouri.
Mark Begich, of Alaska.
Tammy Baldwin, of Wisconsin.
Heidi Heitkamp, of North Dakota.

Rob Portman, of Ohio.
Ron Johnson, of Wisconsin.
Rand Paul, of Kentucky.
Michael B. Enzi, of Wyoming.

Emergency Management, Intergovernmental Relations, and the District of Columbia (EMDC)

Mark Begich, of Alaska, *Chair*

Carl Levin, of Michigan.
Mark L. Pryor, of Arkansas.
Mary L. Landrieu, of Louisiana.
Jon Tester, of Montana.
Heidi Heitkamp, of North Dakota.

Rand Paul, of Kentucky.
John McCain, of Arizona.
Rob Portman, of Ohio.
Michael B. Enzi, of Wyoming.

Financial and Contracting Oversight (FCO)

Claire McCaskill, of Missouri, *Chair*

Carl Levin, of Michigan.
Mark L. Pryor, of Arkansas.
Mary L. Landrieu, of Louisiana.
Mark Begich, of Alaska.
Tammy Baldwin, of Wisconsin.
Ron Johnson, of Wisconsin.
John McCain, of Arizona.
Michael B. Enzi, of Wyoming.
Kelly Ayotte, of New Hampshire.

STAFF

Committee on Homeland Security and Governmental Affairs (SD–340), 224–2627.
Majority Staff Director.—Richard J. Kessler, Ph.D.
Deputy Staff Director.—John Kilvington.
Chief Counsel.—Beth Grossman.
Chief Clerk.—Laura W. Kilbride.
Chief Counsel for Governmental Affairs: Troy Cribb, Lawrence B. Novey.
Chief Counsel for Homeland Security.—Mary Beth Schultz.
Deputy Chief Counsel for Homeland Security.—Stephen Viña.
Senior Counsels: Holy Idelson, Jonathan Kraden, Kata C. Sybenga.
Counsel.—Velvet D. Johnson.
Special Counsels: Deanne Millison, Laurie Rubenstein.
Senior Professional Staff: Jason Barnosky, Harlan Geer, Matt Grote, Blas Nunez-Neto, Peter P. Tyler, Jason M. Yanussi.
Professional Staff: Deirdre Armstrong, John Collins, Carly Covieo, Kristine Lam.
Legislative Assistant.—Robert Bradley.
Press Secretary.—Jennie Westbrook.
Press Assistant.—Matt Wes.
Executive Assistant/Office Manager.—Janet Burrell.
AAAS Fellow.—Carla Cotwright-Williams.
DHS Detailee.—Susan Corbin.
FBI Detailee.—Michelle Taylor.
GAO Detailee.—Walter S. Ochinko.
USSS Detailee.—Nicole Mainor.
Hearing Clerk.—Lauren Corcoran.
Publications Clerk.—Joyce Ward.
Budget and Payroll Manager.—Claudette David.
Archivist.—Katie Delacenserie.
Systems Administrator.—Dan Muchow.
Deputy Systems Administrator.—Scott Langill.
Minority Staff Director.—Keith B. Ashdown (SD–344), 224–4751.
Deputy Staff Director.—Christopher J. Barkley.
Chief Counsel.—Andrew C. Dockham.
Director of Governmental Affairs.—Katie Bailey.
Director of Homeland Security Policy.—Daniel Lips.
Director of Investigations.—Justin Rood.
Senior Investigator.—Kathryn Edelman.
Counsels: Patrick Bailey, David Demirbilek, James P. Gelfand, Sara Beth Groshart.
Investigative Counsel.—William McKenna.
Investigator.—Brian Downey.
Legislative Assistant.—Jennifer White.
Office Manager.—Rebecca Nuzzi.
USCG Detailee.—Mark Harris.
USPS OIG Detailee.—Joe Moeller.
Law Clerk.—Billy Easley.
Permanent Subcommittee on Investigations (PSI) (SR–199), 224–9505.
Majority Staff Director/Chief Counsel.—Elise Bean.
Chief Clerk.—Mary D. Robertson.
Senior Counsels: David H. Katz, Laura E. Stuber.
Counsel/Chief Investigator.—Robert Roach.
Counsels: Daniel Goshorn, Alison F. Murphy.
Professional Staff Member.—Adam Henderson.
Congressional Fellow.—Christopher Reed.
GAO Detailee.—Angela Messenger.
Minority Staff Director/Chief Counsel.—Henry J. Kerner (SR–199), 224–3721.
Counsels: Stephanie Hall, Jack Thorlin.

Senior Policy Advisor.—Brad Patout.
Research Assistants: Lauren M. Davis, Elise Mullen, Scott Wittman.
Subcommittee on Financial and Contracting Oversight (FCO) (SH–432), 224–7155.
Majority Staff Director.—Margaret Daum.
Subcommittee Clerk.—Kelsey Stroud.
Counsels: Jackson Eaton, Sarah Garcia, Charlie Moskowitz, Cathy Yu.
Commerce Detailee.—Timothy Brennan.
VA Detailee.—Nicole Wilson.
Minority Staff Director.—Rachel Weaver (SH–439), 224–2254.
Senior Professional Staff Member.—Jena Baker McNeill.
Counsel.—Ritika Rodrigues.
Professional Staff Member.—Michael Howell.
GAO Detailee.—Teague Lyons.
Subcommittee on the Efficiency and Effectiveness of Federal Programs and the Federal Workforce (FPFW) (SH–601), 224–4551.
Majority Staff Director.—Anthony McClain.
Subcommittee Clerk.—Kelsey Stroud.
Counsel.—Stephanie Wilkinson.
Professional Staff: Laura Peterson, Jorge Rueda, Liz Margolis.
DOD Detailee.—Jennifer Kowalski.
Minority Staff Director.—CAPT Brent Bombach, USN (Ret.) (SH–605), 224–3682.
General Counsel.—Rob Porter.
Research Assistant.—Darien Flowers.
Subcommittee on Emergency Management, Intergovernmental Relations and the District of Columbia (EMDC) (SH–601), 224–4462.
Majority Staff Director.—Patrick D. McQuillan III.
Subcommittee Clerk.—Kelsey Stroud.
Deputy Staff Director.—Jason Bockenstedt.
Professional Staff: Amanda Fox, Lauren McClain, Alexa Noruk.
FEMA Detailee.—Louis J. Eswood III.
GAO Detailee.—John Vocino.
Minority Staff Director.—Brandon Brooker (SH–605), 224–3682.
Professional Staff Member.—Brett King.
Research Assistant.—Adam Salmon.
State Detailee.—Paul Schirduan.

Judiciary

224 Dirksen Senate Office Building 20510–6275

phone 224–7703, fax 224–9516, http://www.judiciary.senate.gov/

meets upon call of the chair

Patrick J. Leahy, of Vermont, *Chair*

Dianne Feinstein, of California.
Charles E. Schumer, of New York.
Richard J. Durbin, of Illinois.
Sheldon Whitehouse, of Rhode Island.
Amy Klobuchar, of Minnesota.
Al Franken, of Minnesota.
Christopher A. Coons, of Delaware.
Richard Blumenthal, of Connecticut.
Mazie K. Hirono, of Hawaii.

Chuck Grassley, of Iowa.
Orrin G. Hatch, of Utah.
Jeff Sessions, of Alabama.
Lindsey Graham, of South Carolina.
John Cornyn, of Texas.
Mike Lee, of Utah.
Ted Cruz, of Texas.
Jeff Flake, of Arizona.

SUBCOMMITTEES

Antitrust, Competition Policy and Consumer Rights

Amy Klobuchar, of Minnesota, *Chair*

Charles E. Schumer, of New York.
Al Franken, of Minnesota.
Christopher A. Coons, of Delaware.
Richard Blumenthal, of Connecticut.

Mike Lee, of Utah.
Lindsey Graham, of South Carolina.
Chuck Grassley, of Iowa.
Jeff Flake, of Arizona.

Bankruptcy and the Courts

Christopher A. Coons, of Delaware, *Chair*

Richard J. Durbin, of Illinois.
Sheldon Whitehouse, of Rhode Island.
Amy Klobuchar, of Minnesota.
Al Franken, of Minnesota.

Jeff Sessions, of Alabama.
Chuck Grassley, of Iowa.
Jeff Flake, of Arizona.
Ted Cruz, of Texas.

The Constitution, Civil Rights and Human Rights

Richard J. Durbin, of Illinois, *Chair*

Al Franken, of Minnesota.
Christopher A. Coons, of Delaware.
Richard Blumenthal, of Connecticut.
Mazie K. Hirono, of Hawaii.

Ted Cruz, of Texas.
Lindsey Graham, of South Carolina.
John Cornyn, of Texas.
Orrin G. Hatch, of Utah.

Crime and Terrorism

Sheldon Whitehouse, of Rhode Island, *Chair*

Dianne Feinstein, of California.
Charles E. Schumer, of New York.
Richard J. Durbin, of Illinois.
Amy Klobuchar, of Minnesota.

Lindsey Graham, of South Carolina.
Ted Cruz, of Texas.
Jeff Sessions, of Alabama.
Mike Lee, of Utah.

Immigration, Refugees and Border Security

Charles E. Schumer, of New York, *Chair*

Patrick J. Leahy, of Vermont.
Dianne Feinstein, of California.
Richard J. Durbin, of Illinois.
Amy Klobuchar, of Minnesota.
Richard Blumenthal, of Connecticut.
Mazie K. Hirono, of Hawaii.

John Cornyn, of Texas.
Chuck Grassley, of Iowa.
Orrin G. Hatch, of Utah.
Jeff Sessions, of Alabama.
Jeff Flake, of Arizona.
Ted Cruz, of Texas.

Oversight, Federal Rights and Agency Action

Richard Blumenthal, of Connecticut, *Chair*

Patrick J. Leahy, of Vermont.
Amy Klobuchar, of Minnesota.
Orrin G. Hatch, of Utah.
Jeff Flake, of Arizona.

Privacy, Technology and the Law

Al Franken, of Minnesota, *Chair*

Dianne Feinstein, of California.
Charles E. Schumer, of New York.
Sheldon Whitehouse, of Rhode Island.
Christopher A. Coons, of Delaware.
Mazie K. Hirono, of Hawaii.
Jeff Flake, of Arizona.
Orrin G. Hatch, of Utah.
Mike Lee, of Utah.
John Cornyn, of Texas.
Lindsey Graham, of South Carolina.

STAFF

Committee on the Judiciary (SD–224), 224–7703.
Chief Clerk.—Roslyne Turner.
Hearings Clerk.—Melanie Kartzmer.
Law Librarian.—Charles Papirmeister.
Legislative Calendar Clerk.—Alberta Easter.
Majority Office (SD–224), 224–7703, fax 224–9516.
Majority Staff Director and Chief Counsel.—Kristine Lucius.
Legislative Staff Assistant to the Chief Counsel.—Emma Van Susteren.
General Counsel.—Chan Park.
Deputy General Counsel.—Anya McMurray.
Chief Counsel for Privacy and Information Policy.—Lydia Griggsby.
Chief Counsel for Nominations.—Maggie Whitney.
Senior Counsel, I.P. and Antitrust.—Aaron Cooper.
Senior Counsels: Debo Adegbile, John Amaya, Alexandra Givens, Josh Hsu, Matthew Virkstis.
Counsels: April Carson, Emily Livingston, David Pendle.
Professional Staff Members: Kelsey Kobelt, Patrick Sheahan, Scott Wilson, Adrienne Wojeciechowski.
Press Secretary.—Jessica Brady.
Archivist.—Anu Kasarabada.
Systems Administrator.—Brian Hockin.
Legislative Staff Assistants: Clark Flynt, Charles Smith, Dan Taylor, Rebekah Weber.
Staff Assistants: Camille Fordy, Logan Gregoire.
Nominations Clerk.—Jared Rosenfeld.
Minority Office (SD–152), 224–5225, fax 224–9102.
Minority Staff Director and Chief Counsel.—Kolan Davis.
Deputy Staff Director and Chief Civil Counsel.—Rita Lari Jochum.
Counsels: Fred Ansell, Nathan Hallford, Tim Kelly, Ted Lehman.
Chief Counsel for Nominations.—David Best.
Counsels.—Lake Dishman, Lauren Prieb.
Professional Staff Member.—Barbara Ledeen.
Press Secretary.—Beth Levine.
Staff Assistants: Jason Covey, Nick Davis.
Archivist.—Stuart Paine.
Director of Information Systems.—Steve Kirkland.
Investigative Counsels: Chris Lucas, Tristan Leavitt.
Chief Investigative Counsel.—Jason Foster.
Senior Investigative Counsel.—Erika Smith.
Subcommittee on Antitrust, Competition Policy and Consumer Rights (SH–807), 224–3244.
Majority Chief Counsel.—Craig Kalkut.
Minority Chief Counsel.—Bryson Bachman (SH 325), 224–5225.
Subcommittee on Bankruptcy and the Courts (SR–127A), 224–5042.
Majority Chief Counsel.—Ted Schroeder.
Minority Chief Counsel.—Danielle Cutrona (SDG–66), 224–7572.
Subcommittee on the Constitution, Civil Rights and Human Rights (SH–815), 224–1158.
Majority Chief Counsel.—Joseph Zogby.
Minority Chief Counsel.—Brooke Bacak (SD–155), 224–5225.
Subcommittee on Crime and Terrorism (SH–229), 224–3740.

Majority Chief Counsel.—Stephen Lilley.
Minority Chief Counsel.—Sergio Sarkany (SD–157). 224–5972.
Subcommittee on Immigration, Refugees and Border Security (SD–305), 224–6498.
Majority Chief Counsel.—Stephanie Martz.
Minority Chief Counsel.—Noah Phillips (SD–141), 224–7840.
Subcommittee on Oversight, Federal Rights and Agency Action (SH–702), 224–2823.
Majority Chief Counsel.—Sam Simon.
Minority Chief Counsel.—Tom Jipping (SH–202), 224–5251.
Subcommittee on Privacy, Technology and the Law (SH–223), 228–3177.
Majority Chief Counsel.—Alvaro Bedoya.
Minority Chief Counsel.—Elizabeth Taylor (SH–202), 224–5225.
Senator Feinstein Judiciary Staff (SD–524), 224–4933.
Chief Counsel.—Neil Quinter.
Senator Hirono Judiciary Staff (SD–224), 224–6361.
Senior Counsel.—Alex Harman.

Rules and Administration

305 Russell Senate Office Building 20510–6325

phone 224–6352, http://rules.senate.gov

[Legislative Reorganization Act of 1946]

meets second and fourth Wednesday of each month

Charles E. Schumer, of New York, *Chair*

Dianne Feinstein, of California.
Richard J. Durbin, of Illinois.
Patty Murray, of Washington.
Mark L. Pryor, of Arkansas.
Tom Udall, of New Mexico.
Mark R. Warner, of Virginia.
Patrick J. Leahy, of Vermont.
Amy Klobuchar, of Minnesota.
ANGUS S. KING, JR., of Maine.
John E. Walsh, of Montana.

Pat Roberts, of Kansas.
Mitch McConnell, of Kentucky.
Thad Cochran, of Mississippi.
Saxby Chambliss, of Georgia.
Lamar Alexander, of Tennessee.
Richard C. Shelby, of Alabama.
Roy Blunt, of Missouri.
Ted Cruz, of Texas.

(No Subcommittees)

STAFF

Committee on Rules and Administration (SR–305), 224–6352.
Majority Staff Director.—Jean Parvin Bordewich.
Deputy Staff Director.—Kelly Fado.
Chief Counsel.—Stacy Ettinger.
Elections Counsel.—Veronica Gillespie.
Democratic Counsel.—Ellen Zeng.
Legislative Assistant.—Abbie Sorrendino.
Assistant to Democratic Staff Director.—Sharon Larimer.
Staff Assistant.—Phillip Rumsey.
Minority Staff Director.—Mary Suit Jones.
Deputy Staff Director.—Shaun Parkin.
Chief Counsel.—Paul Vinovich.
Republican Communications.—Sarah Little.
Professional Staff: Rachel Creviston, Trish Kent.
Non-Designated Staff:
Chief Clerk.—Lynden Armstrong.
Professional Staff.—Matthew McGowan.
Director of Administration and Policy.—Maria Keebler.
Chief Auditor.—Leann Alwood.
Staff Assistants: Ben Grazda, Nathan Strege.

Small Business and Entrepreneurship

428A Russell Senate Office Building 20510

phone 224–5175, fax 224–5619, http://sbc.senate.gov/

[Created pursuant to S. Res. 58, 81st Congress]

meets first Thursday of each month

Maria Cantwell, of Washington, *Chair*

Carl Levin, of Michigan.
Mary L. Landrieu, of Louisiana.
Mark L. Pryor, of Arkansas.
Benjamin L. Cardin, of Maryland.
Jeanne Shaheen, of New Hampshire.
Kay R. Hagan, of North Carolina.
Heidi Heitkamp, of North Dakota.
Edward J. Markey, of Massachusetts.
Cory A. Booker, of New Jersey.

James E. Risch, of Idaho.
David Vitter, of Louisiana.
Marco Rubio, of Florida.
Rand Paul, of Kentucky.
Tim Scott, of South Carolina.
Deb Fischer, of Nebraska.
Michael B. Enzi, of Wyoming.
Ron Johnson, of Wisconsin.

(No Subcommittees)

STAFF

Committee on Small Business and Entrepreneurship (SR–428A), 224–5175, fax 224–5619.
Majority Staff Director.—Jane Campbell.
Deputy Staff Director.—Kevin Wheeler.
Executive Assistant.—Jim Simpson.
Policy Director.—Brian van Hook.
General Counsel.—Caroline Bruckner.
Tax Procurement Counsel.—Krystal Brumfield.
Counsels: David Gillers, Ami Sanchez.
Communications Director.—Rob Sawicki.
Policy Correspondence / Legislative Aide.—Afton Zaunbrecher.
Professional Staff Members: Ross Nodurft, Claire O'Rourke, Ashley Scott.
Chief Clerk.—Lena Postanowicz.
Systems Administrator.—Ruda Pollard.
Staff Assistant.—Christina Jones.
Minority Staff Director.—Skiffington Holderness.
Deputy Staff Director.—Wallace K. Hsueh.
Counsel.—Christina Aizcorbe.
Senior Professional Staff Members: Adam Reece, Meredith West.
Professional Staff Member.—Kristen Granchelli.
Research Analyst.—Shelley New.
Staff Assistant.—Christie Herman.

Veterans' Affairs

SR–412 Russell Senate Office Building

phone 224–9126, http://veterans.senate.gov

meets first Wednesday of each month

BERNARD SANDERS, of Vermont, *Chair*

John D. Rockefeller IV, of West Virginia.
Patty Murray, of Washington.
Sherrod Brown, of Ohio.
Jon Tester, of Montana.
Mark Begich, of Alaska.
Richard Blumenthal, of Connecticut.
Mazie K. Hirono, of Hawaii.

Richard Burr, of North Carolina.
Johnny Isakson, of Georgia.
Mike Johanns, of Nebraska.
Jerry Moran, of Kansas.
John Boozman, of Arkansas.
Dean Heller, of Nevada.

(No Subcommittees)

STAFF

Committee on Veterans' Affairs (SR–412), 224–9126, fax 224–9575.
Majority Staff Director.—Steve Robertson.
Deputy Staff Director.—Dahlia Melendrez.
General Counsel.—Travis Murphy.
Counsel.—Ann Vallandingham.
Special Projects Counsel.—Mary Ellen McCarthy.
Senior Legislative Assistants: Kathryn Monet, Kathryn Van Haste.
Legislative Assistants.—Vacant.
Legislative Aides: Elizabeth Austin, Carlos Fuentes, Rebecca Thoman.
Minority Staff Director.—Lupe Wissel (825–A Hart), 224–2074, fax 224–8908.
General Counsel.—Amanda Meredith.
Professional Staff Members: John McDonald, Maureen O'Neill.
Legislative Assistant.—Victoria Lee.
Staff Assistant.—Elijah Abram.
Non-Designated (SR–412), 224–9126.
Chief Clerk.—Heather Vachon.
Deputy Clerk / Systems Administrator.—Jeff Johnson.

SELECT AND SPECIAL COMMITTEES OF THE SENATE

Committee on Indian Affairs

838 Hart Senate Office Building 20510–6450

phone 224–2251, http://indian.senate.gov

[Created pursuant to S. Res. 4, 95th Congress; amended by S. Res. 71, 103d Congress]

meets every Wednsday of each month

Jon Tester, of Montana, *Chair*

John Barrasso, of Wyoming, *Vice Chair*

Maria Cantwell, of Washington.
Tim Johnson, of South Dakota.
Tom Udall, of New Mexico.
Al Franken, of Minnesota.
Mark Begich, of Alaska.
Brian Schatz, of Hawaii.
Heidi Heitkamp, of North Dakota.

John McCain, of Arizona.
Lisa Murkowski, of Alaska.
John Hoeven, of North Dakota.
Mike Crapo, of Idaho.
Deb Fischer, of Nebraska.

(No Subcommittees)

STAFF

Majority Staff Director/Chief Counsel.—Mary J. Pavel.
Deputy Staff Director.—Denise Desiderio.
Senior Counsel.—Anthony Walters.
Counsel.—Wendy Helgemo.
Communications Director.—Reid Walker.
Professional Staff Member.—Kenneth Martin.
Staff Assistant.—Sarah Stiltner.
Minority Staff Director/Chief Counsel.—David A. Mullon, Jr.
Deputy Chief Counsel.—Rhonda Harjo.
Legislative Assistant.—Ken Degenfelder.
Counsels: Daniel Carter, Mariah Thompson.
Clerk.—Amanda Kelly.
Administrator Director.—Jim Eismeier.
Systems Administrator.—David Stuart.
Receptionist.—Sarah Overton.
GPO Detailee.—Jack Fulmer.

Select Committee on Ethics

220 Hart Senate Office Building 20510, phone 224–2981, fax 224–7416

[Created pursuant to S. Res. 338, 88th Congress; amended by S. Res. 110, 95th Congress]

Barbara Boxer, of California, *Chair*

Johnny Isakson, of Georgia, *Vice Chair*

Mark L. Pryor, of Arkansas.
Sherrod Brown, of Ohio.

Pat Roberts, of Kansas.
James E. Risch, of Idaho.

STAFF

Staff Director/Chief Counsel.—John C. Sassaman.
Deputy Staff Director.—Annette Gillis.
Counsel and Director of Education and Training.—Tonia Smith.
Counsel and Director of Financial Disclosure Compliance.—Tremayne Bunaugh.
Counsels: Rochelle Ford, Lynn Tran, Anna Stolarz.
Professional Staff.—Adam Kamp.
Director of IT.—Danny Remington.
Legal Assistant.—Emily Chucovich.
Staff Assistants: Ben Phillips, Ben Toribio.

Select Committee on Intelligence

211 Hart Senate Office Building 20510–6475, phone 224–1700

http://www.senate.gov/~intelligence

[Created pursuant to S. Res. 400, 94th Congress]

Dianne Feinstein, of California, *Chair*

Saxby Chambliss, of Georgia, *Vice Chair*

John D. Rockefeller IV, of West Virginia.
Ron Wyden, of Oregon.
Barbara A. Mikulski, of Maryland.
Mark Udall, of Colorado.
Mark R. Warner, of Virginia.
Martin Heinrich, of New Mexico.
ANGUS S. KING, JR., of Maine.

Richard Burr, of North Carolina.
James E. Risch, of Idaho.
Daniel Coats, of Indiana.
Marco Rubio, of Florida.
Susan M. Collins, of Maine.
Tom Coburn, of Oklahoma.

Ex Officio

Harry Reid, of Nevada.
Carl Levin, of Michigan.

Mitch McConnell, of Kentucky.
James M. Inhofe, of Oklahoma.

STAFF

Majority Staff Director.—David Grannis.
Minority Staff Director.—Martha Scott Poindexter.
Chief Clerk.—Kathleen P. McGhee.

Special Committee on Aging

G–31 Dirksen Senate Office Building 20510, phone 224–5364

http://aging.senate.gov

[Reauthorized pursuant to S. Res. 4, 95th Congress]

Bill Nelson, of Florida, *Chair*

Robert P. Casey, Jr., of Pennsylvania.
Claire McCaskill, of Missouri.
Sheldon Whitehouse, of Rhode Island.
Kirsten E. Gillibrand, of New York.
Joe Manchin III, of West Virginia.
Richard Blumenthal, of Connecticut.
Tammy Baldwin, of Wisconsin.
Joe Donnelly, of Indiana.
Elizabeth Warren, of Massachusetts.
John E. Walsh, of Montana.

Susan M. Collins, of Maine.
Bob Corker, of Tennessee.
Orrin G. Hatch, of Utah.
Mark Kirk, of Illinois.
Dean Heller, of Nevada.
Jeff Flake, of Arizona.
Kelly Ayotte, of New Hampshire.
Tim Scott, of South Carolina.
Ted Cruz, of Texas.

STAFF

Majority Staff Director.—Kim Lipsky.
Deputy Staff Director.—Oliver Kim.
Senior Policy Advisor.—Rachel Pryor.
Chief Counsel.—Joel Eskovitz.
Policy Advisor.—Treon Glenn.
Chief of Oversight and Investigations.—Jack Mitchell.
Associate Investigators: Mark Kopelman, Brad Torppey.
Communications Director.—Bryan Gulley.
Press Secretary.—Clare Flannery.
Legislative Assistant.—Carissa Lewis.
Staff Assistants: Jessica Gruse, Katie Rubinger.
Chief Clerk / System Administrator.—Matt Lawrence.
Minority Staff (SH–628), 224–8710, Fax 224–9926
Staff Director.—Priscilla Hanley.
Deputy Staff Director / Communications Director.—Jen Burita.
Chief Counsel.—Mark LeDuc.
Senior Counsel.—Julie Dunne.
Senior Professional Staff Member.—John Kane.
Legislative Aide.—James Redstone.
Legislative Correspondent.—Christian Dibblee.
Staff Assistant.—Luther Whiting.

Democratic Senatorial Campaign Committee

120 Maryland Avenue, NE., 20002, phone 224–2447

Michael F. Bennet, of Colorado, *Chair*
Harry Reid, of Nevada, *Democratic Leader*

STAFF

Executive Director.—Guy Cecil.
Communications Director.—Matt Canter.
Political Director.—Anne Caprara.
Finance Director.—Angelique Cannon.
Legal Counsel.—Mark Elias.

Democratic Policy and Communications Center

419 Hart Senate Office Building, phone 224–3232

Harry Reid, of Nevada, Majority Leader

Charles E. Schumer, of New York, *Chair.*
Debbie Stabenow, of Michigan, *Vice Chair.*

STAFF

Staff Director.—Mike Lynch, Capitol / S–318, mike_lynch@dpcc.senate.gov (202) 224–2939.
Communications Director.—Matt House, Capitol / S–318, matt_house@dpcc.senate.gov, 224–2939.
Director of Hispanic Media.—Jose Parra, Capitol / S–318, jose_parra@reid.senate.gov, 224–2939.
Communication Director for NV / National Press Secretary.—Kristen Orthman, Capitol / S–318, kristen_orthman@reid.senate.gov, 224–2939.
Press Scretary for Nevada.—Sam Schumach, Capitol / S–318, sam_schumach@reid.senate.gov, 224–2939.
Deputy Press Secretary for Nevada.—Joseph Broad, Capitol, S–318, joseph_broad @reid.senate.gov, 224–2939.

Deputy Regional Press Secretary.—Carolyn Seuthe, S–112, carolyn_seuthe@dpcc.senate.gov, 224–2939.
Press Secretary for Hispanic Media.—Jorge Silva, S–112, jorge_silva@dpcc.senate.gov, 224–2939.
Press Assistant for Hispanic Media.—Reynaldo Benitez, Capitol / S–112, reynaldo_benitez@dpcc.senate.gov, 224–2939.
Press Assistants: Christopher Huntley, Capitol / S–318, christopher_huntley@dpcc.senate.gov, Hannah Leveridge, SH419, hannah_leveridge@dpcc.senate.gov, 224–2939.
Policy Director.—Ryan McConaghy, SH419, ryan_mcconaghy@dpcc.senate.gov, 224–2939.
Counsel / Policy Advisor.—Pat Collier, SH419, pat_collier@dpcc.senate.gov, 224–2939.
Policy Advisors: Julie Klein, SH419, julie_klein@dpcc.senate.gov, 224–3232; Charlie Ellsworth, SH419, charlie_ellsworth@dpcc.senate.gov, 224–3232; Matt House, S318, matt_house@dpcc.senate.gov, 224–2939; Laura Erickson Hatalsky, SH419, laura_ericksonhatalsky@dpcc.senate.gov, 224–3232.
Policy Assistant.—Karlee Tebbutt, SH419, karlee_tebbutt@dpcc.senate.gov, 224–3232.
Research Associate.—Kati Card, SH419, kati_card@dpcc.senate.gov.
Senior Rapid Response Advisor.—Dan Yoken, dan_yoken@dpcc.senate.gov, 224–2939.
Publications Director and Senior Vote Analyst.—Doug Connolly, SH705, doug_connolly@dpcc.senate.gov, 224–2939.
Votes Director.—Michael Mozden, SH705, michael_mozden@dpcc.senate.gov, 224–2939.
Communication Operations Manager.—Ryan King, ryan_king@dpcc.senate.gov, 224–2939.
Senior Advisor for Digital Media.—Faiz Shakir, S318, faiz_shakir@reid.senate.gov, 224–2939.

Steering and Outreach Committee

712 Hart Senate Office Building, phone 224–9048

Mark Begich, of Alaska, *Chair*

Jeanne Shaheen, of New Hampshire, *Vice Chair*

Harry Reid, of Nevada, *Majority Leader*

Richard J. Durbin, of Illinois, *Assistant Majority Leader*

Christopher A. Coons, of Delaware, *Chairman of Business Outreach*

Robert Menendez, of New Jersey, *Chairman of the Hispanic Task Force*

Patrick J. Leahy, of Vermont.
Carl Levin, of Michigan.
John D. Rockefeller IV, of West Virginia.
Mark L. Pryor, of Arkansas.
Tom Harkin, of Iowa.
Barbara Boxer, of California,
Kirsten E. Gillibrand, of New York.

STAFF

Staff Director.—Eloy J. Martinez.
Associate Director Business Outreach.—Marcus Fleming.
Associate Directors: Estee Sepulveda, Jason Smith.
Associate Director for Communications.—Tyrone Gayle.
Staff Assistant.—Shu-Yen Wei.

Senate Democratic Conference

154 Russell Senate Office Building, phone 224–2621, fax 224–0238

Secretary.—Patty Murray, of Washington State.
Chief of Staff.—Mike Spahn.
Senior Leadership Advisor and Floor Directors: Emma Fulkerson, Stacy Rich.

Senate Democratic Media Center

619 Hart Senate Office Building, phone 224–1430

Harry Reid, of Nevada, *Chair*

STAFF

Staff Director.—Katie Beirne.
Director of Broadcast Operations.—Brian Jones.
Director of New Media.—Faiz Shakir.
Editors: Hisham Abdelhamid, Jake Cirksena, Don Jonathan Webb.
Engineer.—Luis Mattos.
Event Coordinator.—Jason Botelho.
Graphic Design Specialist.—Perisha Gates.
Senior Developer.—Judson Blewett.
Multimedia Specialist.—Ian Shifrin.
Press Assistant.—Isaiah Calvin.
Videographers: Clare Flood, Kevin Kelleher.

National Republican Senatorial Committee

425 Second Street, NE., 20002, phone 675–6000, fax 675–6058

Jerry Moran, of Kansas, *Chair*

STAFF

Executive Director.—Rob Collins.
Director of:
Communications.—Brad Dayspring.
Finance.—Heather Larrison.
Legal Counsel.—Megan Sowards.
Political Director.—Ward Baker.
Research.—Mark McLaughlin.

Senate Republican Policy Committee

347 Russell Senate Office Building, phone 224–2946
fax 224–1235, http://rpc.senate.gov

John Barrasso, of Wyoming, *Chair*

STAFF

Staff Director.—Dan Kunsman.
Policy Director.—Arjun Mody.
Communications Director.—Emily Lawrimore.
Administrative Director.—Craig Cheney.
Analysts:
Agriculture, Energy and Environment.—Matthew Leggett.
Budget, Tax Appropriations.—Spencer Wayne.
Health Care.—Erin Dempsey.
Commerce, Transportation, Trade.—Galen Roehl.
Education, Labor, Banking, Housing.—Dana Barbieri.
Defense, Foreign Affairs, Intelligence, Veterans Affairs.—Michael Stransky.
Judiciary/Immigration.—Michael Thorpe.
Professional Staff:
Editor.—John Mitchell.
System Administrator/RVA Analyst.—Thomas Pulju.
Station Manager/Special Projects.—Carolyn Laird.
Station Operator/Project Assistant.—Katelynn Thomas.
Website/Media.—Chris Adkins.

Senate Republican Conference

405 Hart Senate Office Building, phone 224–2764
http://src.senate.gov

John Thune, of South Dakota, *Chair*

Roy Blunt, of Missouri, *Vice Chair*

STAFF

Conference of the Minority (SH–405), 224–2764.
Staff Director.—Doug Schwartz.
Media Services Director.—Dave Hodgdon.
Office Manager.—Desiree Sayle.
Communications Director.—AshLee Strong.
Senior Writer.—Mary Katherine Ascik.
Press Secretary.—Ryan Wrasse.
Internal Communications Advisor.—Amanda Hendricks.
Spanish News Coordinator.—Carlos Gonzalez.
Production Manager.—Cyrus Pearson.
Videographer/Editor.—Lane Marshall.
Audio/Video Producer.—Andrea Turnbough.
Senior Graphics Designers: Chris Angrisani, Laura Gill.
Systems Engineer.—Nate Green.
Floor Monitor.—Shane Scanlon.
Staff and Communications Assistant.—Laura Spencer.

OFFICERS AND OFFICIALS OF THE SENATE

Capitol Telephone Directory, 224–3121
Senate room prefixes:
Capitol—S, Russell Senate Office Building—SR
Dirksen Senate Office Building—SD, Hart Senate Office Building—SH

PRESIDENT OF THE SENATE

Vice President of the United States and President of the Senate.—Joseph R. Biden, Jr.

The Ceremonial Office of the Vice President is S–212 in the Capitol. The Vice President has offices in the Dirksen Senate Office Building, the Eisenhower Executive Office Building (EEOB) and the White House (West Wing).

Chief of Staff to the Vice President.—Bruce Reed, EEOB, room 276, 456–9000.
Counsel to the Vice President.—Steve Ricchetti, EEOB, room 272, 456–9590.
Assistant to the Vice President for—
Communications.—Shailagh Murray, EEOB, room 288, 456–0373.
Domestic Policy.—Brian Levine, EEOB, room 281A, 456–2728.
Legislative Affairs.—Tonya Williams, EEOB, room 243, 456–1540.
National Security Affairs.—Jake Sullivan, EEOB, room 208, 456–9501.
Executive Assistant to the Vice President.—Kathy Chung, West Wing, 456–7000.
Chief of Staff to Dr. Biden.—Sheila Nix, EEOB, room 201, 456–7458.
Deputy Assistant to the Vice President and Director of Scheduling.—Alex Hornbrook, EEOB, room 263, 456–6773.

PRESIDENT PRO TEMPORE

S–126 The Capitol, phone 224–9400

President Pro Tempore of the Senate.—Patrick J. Leahy.
Administrative Assistant to the President Pro Tempore.—Halley Ross.

MAJORITY LEADER

S–221 The Capitol, phone 224–2158, fax 224–7362

Majority Leader.—Harry Reid.
Chief of Staff.—David Krone.
Deputy Chief of Staff.—David McCallum.
Executive Assistant.—Adelle Cruz.
Scheduler.—Krysta Juris.
Deputy Chief of Staff for Policy.—Bill Dauster.
Legislative Director.—Jason Unger.
Communications Director.—Adam Jentleson.
Speechwriter.—Phoebe Sweet.
Legal Counsel.—Serena Hoy.
Executive Assistant to the Chief of Staff.—Danica Rodman.
Assistant Scheduler.—Brittany Brown.
Staff Assistant.—Devron Brown.

ASSISTANT MAJORITY LEADER

S–321 The Capitol, phone 224–9447

Assistant Majority Leader.—Richard J. Durbin.

Chief of Staff.—Pat Souders.
Director of Operations.—Sally Brown-Shaklee.
Director of Scheduling.—Claire Reuschel.
Communications Director.—Max Gleischman.
Deputy Communications Director.—Christina Mulka.
Floor Director.—Reema Dodin.
Floor Counsel.—M.J. Kenny.
Staff Assistants: Tim McMahon, Julian Miller.
Speechwriter.—Molly Rowley.

REPUBLICAN LEADER

S–230 The Capitol, phone 224–3135, fax 228–1264

Republican Leader.—Mitch McConnell.
Chief of Staff.—Sharon Soderstrom.
Deputy Chief of Staff.—Don Stewart.
Scheduler.—Stefanie Hagar.
Assistant Scheduler.—Rebecca Fleeson.
Director of Administration.—Julie Adams.
Director of Arrangements.—Katie Barnes.
Policy Advisors: Neil Chatterjee, Brendan Dunn, Jon Lieber, Denzel McGuire, Scott Raab, Dan Schneider, Erica Suarez.
Legal Counsels: John Abegg, Brian Lewis.
National Security Advisor.—Tom Hawkins.
Communications Director.—Michael Brumas.
Deputy Communications Director and Director of Speechwriting.—Brian McGuire.
Assistant Speechwriter.—Brian Forest.
Press Assistant.—Laura Hendrickson.
Systems Administrator.—Elmamoun Sulfab.
Staff Assistants: Amanda Bunning, Bridget Winstead.

REPUBLICAN COMMUNICATIONS CENTER

S–230 The Capitol, phone 228–6397

Staff Director.—John Ashbrook.
Analyst.—Matt Kenney.
Communications Advisor, New Media.—David Hauptmann.
Communications Advisor.—Ali Nepola.

OFFICE OF THE REPUBLICAN WHIP

S–208 The Capitol, phone 224–2708, fax 228–1507

Republican Whip.—John Cornyn.
Chief of Staff.—Russ Thomasson.
Whip Liaisons: Emily Kirlin, Jamie McWright.
Whip Liaison/Counsel.—Andy Moskowitz.
Policy Advisor.—Jonathan Slemrod.
Staff Assistant.—Clark Davis.

OFFICE OF THE SECRETARY

S–312 The Capitol, phone 224–3622

NANCY ERICKSON, Secretary of the Senate; elected and sworn in as the 32nd Secretary of the Senate on January 4, 2007; native of South Dakota; B.A. in government and history from Augustana College, Sioux Falls, SD; M.A. in public policy from American University, Washington, DC; Democratic Representative, Senate Sergeant at Arms (SAA); Deputy Chief of Staff, Senator Tom Daschle; General Accounting Office.

Secretary of the Senate.—Nancy Erickson (S–312), 224–3622.
Chief of Staff.—Robert W. Paxton (S–333), 224–5636.
Deputy Chief of Staff.—Mark S. Tratos (S–312), 224–9461.

Capitol Offices Liaison.—Gerald Thompson (SB–36), 224–1483.
Assistant Secretary of the Senate.—Sheila M. Dwyer (S–414C), 224–2114.
General Counsel.—Adam Bramwell (S–333), 224–8789.
Executive Accounts Administrator.—Zoraida Torres (S–414B), 224–7099.
Director (LIS Project Office).—Marsha Misenhimer (SD–B44A), 224–2500.
Bill Clerk.—Mary Anne Clarkson (S–123), 224–2120.
Captioning Services.—JoEllen R. Dicken (SVC–211), 224–4321.
Conservation and Preservation.—Beverly Adams, (S–416), 224–4550.
Curator.—Melinda Smith (S–411), 224–2955.
Daily Digest, Editor.—Elizabeth Tratos (S–421 and S–421A), 224–2658.
Assistant Editor.—Joseph Johnston, 224–2658.
Disbursing Office, Financial Clerk.—Chris J. Doby (SH–127), 224–3205.
Assistant Financial Clerk.—Ileana M. Garcia, 224–3208.
Enrolling Clerk.—Margarida Curtis (S–139), 224–8427.
Assistant Enrolling Clerk.—Cassandra Byrd, 224–7108.
Executive Clerk.—Jennifer Gorham (S–138), 224–4341.
Assistant Executive Clerk.—Brian Malloy, 224–1918.
Historian.—Donald A. Ritchie (SH–201), 224–6900.
Associate Historian.—Betty K. Koed, 224–0753.
Human Resources.—John McIlveen (SH–231B), 224–3625.
Information Systems, Systems Administrator.—Dan Kulnis (S–422), 224–4883.
Webmaster.—Arin Shapiro, 224–2020.
Interparliamentary Services.—Sally Walsh (SH–808), 224–3047.
Journal Clerk.—Scott Sanborn (S–135), 224–4650.
Legislative Clerk.—Kathleen Alvarez (S–134), 224–4350.
Assistant Legislative Clerk.—John Merlino, 224–3630.
Librarian.—Leona Faust (SR–B15), 224–3313.
Official Reporters of Debates, Chief Reporter.—Jerald D. Linnell (S–410A), 224–7525.
Coordinator of the Record.—Sylvia Oliver, 224–1939.
Morning Business Editor.—Val Mihalache (S–123), 224–3079.
Parliamentarian.—Elizabeth MacDonough (S–133), 224–6128.
Senior Assistant Parliamentarian.—Leigh Hildebrand, 224–5994.
Printing and Document Services.—Karen Moore (SH–B04), 224–0205.
Assistant to the Director.—Bud Johnson, 224–2555.
Public Records, Superintendent.—Dana McCallum (SH–232), 224–0329.
Assistant Superintendent.—Erica Omorogieva, 224–0794.
Information Specialist for—
Campaign Finance and Foreign Travel.—Malaika Nji, 224–0762.
Ethics and Disclosure.—Catina Hadijski, 224–5949.
Lobbying.—Antionette Thompson, 224–0758.
Senate Chief Counsel for Employment.—Jean Manning (SH–103), 224–5424.
Senate Gift Shop, Director.—Neil Schwartz (SDG–42), 224–7308.
Senate Page School, Principal.—Kathryn S. Weeden, 224–3926.
Senate Security, Director.—Michael P. DiSilvestro (S–407), 224–5632.
Stationery, Keeper of the Stationery.—Tony Super, 224–4846.
Joint Office of Education and Training, Director.—Megan Daly (SH–121), 224–3569.

OFFICE OF THE CHAPLAIN

S–332 The Capitol, phone 224–2510, fax 224–9686

BARRY C. BLACK, Chaplain, U.S. Senate; born in Baltimore, MD, on November 1, 1948; education: Bachelor of Arts, Theology, Oakwood College, 1970; Master of Divinity, Andrews Theological Seminary, 1973; Master of Arts, Counseling, North Carolina Central University, 1978; Doctor of Ministry, Theology, Eastern Baptist Seminary, 1982; Master of Arts, Management, Salve Regina University, 1989; Doctor of Philosophy, Psychology, United States International University, 1996; military service: U.S. Navy, 1976–2003; rising to the rank of Rear Admiral; Chief of Navy Chaplains, 2000–2003; awards: Navy Distinguished Service Medal; Legion of Merit Medal; Defense Meritorious Service Medal; Meritorious Service Medals (two awards); Navy and Marine Corps Commendation Medals (two awards); 1995 NAACP Renowned Service Award; family: married to Brenda; three children: Barry II, Brendan, and Bradford.

Chaplain of the Senate.—Barry C. Black.
Chief of Staff.—Lisa Schultz, 224–3849.
Communications Director.—Jody Spraggins-Scott, 224–2048.

Staff Scheduler/Executive Assistant.—Suzanne Chapuis, 224–7456.

OFFICE OF THE SERGEANT AT ARMS

S–151 The Capitol, phone 224–2341, fax 224–7690

TERRANCE W. GAINER, Sergeant at Arms, U.S. Senate; elected and sworn in as the 38th Sergeant at Arms on January 4, 2007; education: B.A., sociology from St. Benedict's College; M.S., management and public service; J.D. from DePaul University of Chicago; Military service: Decorated veteran who served in the Vietnam War and as a Captain in the U.S. Naval Reserve until 2000; professional: Law enforcement career began in Chicago, IL, 1968; rose through the ranks serving as Deputy IG of Illinois, Deputy Director of Illinois State Police and U.S. Department of Transportation; appointed Director of Illinois State Police in March, 1991; Gainer went on to serve as second in command of the Metropolitan Police Department of the District of Columbia beginning in May 1998 and Chief of the U.S. Capitol Police from 2002–06 until his appointment as Sergeant at Arms; Gainer served the private sector focusing on emergency preparedness issues and law enforcement programs supporting Army and Marine operations in Iraq and Afghanistan; family: married, with 6 children and 14 grandchildren.

Sergeant at Arms.—Terrance W. Gainer.
Deputy Sergeant at Arms.—Drew Willison.
Assistant Sergeant at Arms Office of Protective Services and Continuity.—Michael Stenger, SVC 305, 224–1969.
Assistant Sergeant at Arms for Operations.—Bret Swanson, SDG61, 224–7052.
Assistant Sergeant at Arms and Chief Information Officer.—Vicki Sinnett, (Postal Square), 224–0459.
Assistant Sergeant at Arms for Capitol Operations.—Kevin Morison, SB–8, 224–2506.
Deputy Assistant SAA for Operations.—Laura Parker, SD–G61, 224–1082.

APPOINTMENT DESK

Appointment Desk Manager.—Christine Catucci, North Door Capitol Building, 1st Floor, 224–7620.

CAPITOL FACILITIES

Director of Capitol Facilities.—Grace Ridgeway, SC–5, 224–2343.

CENTRAL OPERATIONS

Director of Central Operations.—Mike Brown, SD–150, 224–4035.
Hair Care Manager.—Cindi Brown, SR-B70, 224–4560.
Parking and ID Branch Manager.—Sam Jacobs, SD–G61, 224–9927.
Parking Operations.—Vacant, 224–8888.
ID Operations.—Vacant, 224–2338.
Photo Studio Manager.—Bill Allen, SD–G85, 224–6000.

DOORKEEPERS

Director of Doorkeepers.—Krista Beal, S–213, Reception Room, 224–1879.

EMPLOYEE ASSISTANCE PROGRAM

Employee Assistance Program Administrator.—Christy Prietsch, 6278 Hart, 224–3902.

FINANCIAL MANAGEMENT

Chief Financial Officer.—Christopher Dey (Postal Square), 224–6292.
Accounting Manager.—Mary Ann Sifford, 224–1035.
Accounts Payable Manager.—David Salem, 224–8844.
Budget Manager.—Jeanne Burcham, 228–5584.
Procurement Manager.—David Baker, 224–2547.

HUMAN RESOURCES

Director of Human Resources.—Patrick Murphy, SH–142, 224–2889.
SAA Safety Office Officer.—Taurus Moore, 228–0823.
Senate Placement Officer Administrator.—Brian Bean, 224–9167.
Workers' Compensation Office Manager.—Catherine Brooks, 224–3796.

IT SUPPORT SERVICES

Director of IT Support Services.—Tim Dean (acting), (Postal Square), 224–3564.
Desktop/LAN Support Manager.—Boyd Kolbe (acting), 224–9802.
Equipment Services Manager.—Win Grayson, 224–8065.
Telecom Services Manager.—Kenneth Kaus, 228–3517.

MEDIA GALLERIES

Director of the Daily Press Gallery.—Laura Eckart, S–316, 224–0241.
Director of the Periodical Press Gallery.—Edward V. Pesce, S–320, 224–0265.
Director of the Press Photographers Gallery.—Jeff Kent, S–317, 224–6548.
Director of the Radio and Television Gallery.—Michael Mastrian, S–325, 224–6421.

OFFICE OF EDUCATION AND TRAINING

Director of the Office of Education and Training.—Megan Daly, SH–121, 224–7952.

OFFICE OF INTERNAL COMMUNICATIONS

Director of the Office of Internal Communications.—Kristan Trugman, (Postal Square), 228–9852.

OFFICE OF PROTECTIVE SERVICES AND CONTINUITY

Deputy Assistant Sergeant at Arms for LESO.—Dick Attridge, SVC–305, 224–3691.
Director for Security Policy and Planning.—Michael Chandler (Postal Square), 228–0635.

OFFICE SUPPORT SERVICES

Director of Office Support Services.—Welda Wagstaff, PSB 6705, 224–0821.
State Office Liaison.—Jeanne Tessieri, PSB 6445, 224–5409.

PAGE PROGRAM

Director of the Page Program.—Elizabeth Roach (Webster Hall), 228–1291.

PRINTING, GRAPHICS AND DIRECT MAIL

Printing, Graphics and Direct Mail.—Darryl McDonald, SD–G82, 224–4871.

PROCESS MANAGEMENT AND INNOVATION

Director of Process Management and Innovation.—Ed Jankus (Postal Square), 224–7780.
IT Research and Deployment Manager.—Steve Walker, 224–1768.
Program Management Manager.—Joe Eckert, 224–2982.

PROTOCOL OFFICE

Protocol Officer.—Becky Daugherty, S–151, 224–2341.

RECORDING STUDIO

Recording Studio General Manager.—Dave Bass, SVC–160, 224–4979.

SENATE POST OFFICE

Senate Postmaster.—Donnie Cook, SD–B23, 224–5675.

TECHNOLOGY DEVELOPMENT

Director of Technology Development.—Tracy Williams (Postal Square), 224–8157.
Enterprise IT Operations Manager.—Joe LaPalme, 228–4451.
Information Technology Security Manager.—Paul Grabow, 224–4966.
Network Engineering and Management Manager.—Wes Gardner, 224–9269.
Systems Development Services Manager.—Jay Moore, 224–0092.

OFFICE OF THE SECRETARY FOR THE MAJORITY

S–309 The Capitol, phone 224–3735

Secretary for the Majority.—Gary Myrick.
Assistant Secretary for the Majority.—Tim Mitchell (S–118), 224–5551.
Administrative Assistant to the Secretary.—Nancy Iacomini.
Executive Assistant to the Secretary.—Amber Huus.

S–225 Majority Cloakroom, phone 224–4691

Cloakroom Assistants: Tequia Delgado, Stephanie Paone, Dan Tinsley, Brad Watt.

OFFICE OF THE SECRETARY FOR THE MINORITY

S–337 The Capitol, phone 224–3835, fax 224–2860

Secretary for the Minority.—Laura C. Dove (S–337).
Assistant Secretary for the Minority.—Robert Duncan (S–335).
Administrative Assistant.—Noelle Busk Ringel (S–337).
Floor Assistant.—Patrick Kilcur (S–335), phone 224–6191.

S–226 Minority Cloakroom, phone 224–6191

Cloakroom Assistants: Amanda Faulkner, Megan Mercer, Mary Elizabeth Taylor, Chris Tuck.

S–335 Republican Legislative Scheduling, phone 224–5456

OFFICE OF THE LEGISLATIVE COUNSEL

668 Dirksen Senate Office Building, phone 224–6461, fax 224–0567

Legislative Counsel.—James W. Fransen.
Deputy Legislative Counsel.—William F. Jensen III.
Senior Counsels: Charles E. Armstrong, William R. Baird, Gary L. Endicott, Elizabeth Aldridge King.
Assistant Counsels: Kimberly D. Albrecht-Taylor, John W. Baggaley, Margaret A. Bomba, Heather L. Burnham, Rachelle E. Celebrezze, Kevin M. Davis, Stephanie Easley, Ruth A. Ernst, Vincent J. Gaiani, Amy E. Gaynor, John A. Goetcheus, Robert A. Grant, John A. Henderson, Michelle L. Johnson-Weider, Heather A. Lowell, Matthew D. McGhie, Mark M. McGunagle, James L. Ollen-Smith, Allison M. Otto, Kristin K. Romero, Margaret A. Roth-Warren, Robert F. Silver, Kimberly A. Tamber, Kelly M. Thornburg.
Staff Attorneys: Kathryne M. Grendon, Thomas B. Heywood, Christina N. Jacquet, Philip B. Lynch, Christine E. Miranda, Katherine A. Scherling.
Systems Integrator.—Thomas E. Cole.
Office Manager.—Donna L. Pasqualino.
Senior Staff Assistants: Kimberly Bourne-Goldring, Rebekah J. Musgrove, Diane E. Nesmeyer, Patricia H. Olsavsky.
Staff Assistant.—Daniela A. Gonzales.

OFFICE OF SENATE LEGAL COUNSEL

642 Hart Senate Office Building, phone (202) 224–4435, fax 224–3391

Senate Legal Counsel.—Morgan J. Frankel.
Deputy Senate Legal Counsel.—Patricia Mack Bryan.
Assistant Senate Legal Counsels: Thomas E. Caballero, Grant R. Vinik.
Systems Administrator/Legal Assistant.—Sara Fox Jones.
Administrative Assistant.—Kathleen M. Parker.

STANDING COMMITTEES OF THE HOUSE

[Republicans in roman; Democrats in *italic*; Resident Commissioner and Delegates in ***boldface italic***]

[Room numbers beginning with H are in the Capitol, with CHOB in the Cannon House Office Building, with LHOB in the Longworth House Office Building, with RHOB in the Rayburn House Office Building, with H1 in O'Neill House Office Building, and with H2 in the Ford House Office Building]

Agriculture

1301 Longworth House Office Building, phone 225–2171, fax 225–8510

http://agriculture.house.gov

meets first Wednesday of each month

Frank D. Lucas, of Oklahoma, *Chair*

Bob Goodlatte, of Virginia, *Vice Chair*

Steve King, of Iowa.
Randy Neugebauer, of Texas.
Mike Rogers, of Alabama.
K. Michael Conaway, of Texas.
Glenn Thompson, of Pennsylvania.
Bob Gibbs, of Ohio.
Austin Scott, of Georgia.
Scott R. Tipton, of Colorado.
Eric A. ''Rick'' Crawford, of Arkansas.
Scott DesJarlais, of Tennessee.
Christopher P. Gibson, of New York.
Vicky Hartzler, of Missouri.
Reid J. Ribble, of Wisconsin.
Kristi L. Noem, of South Dakota.
Dan Benishek, of Michigan.
Jeff Denham, of California.
Stephen Lee Fincher, of Tennessee.
Doug LaMalfa, of California.
Richard Hudson, of North Carolina.
Rodney Davis, of Illinois.
Chris Collins, of New York.
Ted S. Yoho, of Florida.
Vance M. McAllister, of Louisiana.

Collin C. Peterson, of Minnesota.
Mike McIntyre, of North Carolina.
David Scott, of Georgia.
Jim Costa, of California.
Timothy J. Walz, of Minnesota.
Kurt Schrader, of Oregon.
Marcia L. Fudge, of Ohio.
James P. McGovern, of Massachusetts.
Suzan K. DelBene, of Washington.
Gloria Negrete McLeod, of California.
Filemon Vela, of Texas.
Michelle Lujan Grisham, of New Mexico.
Ann M. Kuster, of New Hampshire.
Richard M. Nolan, of Minnesota.
Pete P. Gallego, of Texas.
William L. Enyart, of Illinois.
Juan Vargas, of California.
Cheri Bustos, of Illinois.
Sean Patrick Maloney, of New York.
Joe Courtney, of Connecticut.
John Garamendi, of California.

SUBCOMMITTEES

[The chairman and ranking minority member are ex officio (voting) members of all subcommittees on which they do not serve.]

Conservation, Energy, and Forestry

Glenn Thompson, of Pennsylvania, *Chair*

Mike Rogers, of Alabama.
Bob Gibbs, of Ohio.
Scott R. Tipton, of Colorado.
Eric A. ''Rick'' Crawford, of Arkansas.
Reid J. Ribble, of Wisconsin.
Kristi L. Noem, of South Dakota.
Dan Benishek, of Michigan.

Timothy J. Walz, of Minnesota.
Gloria Negrete McLeod, of California.
Ann M. Kuster, of New Hampshire.
Richard M. Nolan, of Minnesota.
Mike McIntyre, of North Carolina.
Kurt Schrader, of Oregon.
Suzan K. DelBene, of Washington.

Department Operations, Oversight, and Nutrition

Steve King, of Iowa, *Chair*

Bob Goodlatte, of Virginia.
Bob Gibbs, of Ohio.
Austin Scott, of Georgia.
Stephen Lee Fincher, of Tennessee.

Marcia L. Fudge, of Ohio.
James P. McGovern, of Massachusetts.
Michelle Lujan Grisham, of New Mexico.
Gloria Negrete McLeod, of California.

General Farm Commodities and Risk Management

K. Michael Conaway, of Texas, *Chair*

Randy Neugebauer, of Texas.
Mike Rogers, of Alabama.
Bob Gibbs, of Ohio.
Austin Scott, of Georgia.
Eric A. ''Rick'' Crawford, of Arkansas.
Christopher P. Gibson, of New York.
Vicky Hartzler, of Missouri.
Kristi L. Noem, of South Dakota.
Dan Benishek, of Michigan.
Doug LaMalfa, of California.
Richard Hudson, of North Carolina.
Rodney Davis, of Illinois.
Chris Collins, of New York.

David Scott, of Georgia.
Filemon Vela, of Texas.
Pete P. Gallego, of Texas.
William L. Enyart, of Illinois.
Juan Vargas, of California.
Cheri Bustos, of Illinois.
Sean Patrick Maloney, of New York.
Timothy J. Walz, of Minnesota.
Gloria Negrete McLeod, of California.
Jim Costa, of California.
John Garamendi, of California.

Horticulture, Research, Biotechnology, and Foreign Agriculture

Austin Scott, of Georgia, *Chair*

Vicky Hartzler, of Missouri.
Jeff Denham, of California.
Stephen Lee Fincher, of Tennessee.
Doug LaMalfa, of California.
Rodney Davis, of Illinois.
Chris Collins, of New York.
Ted S. Yoho, of Florida.

Kurt Schrader, of Oregon.
Suzan K. DelBene, of Washington.
Jim Costa, of California.
Marcia L. Fudge, of Ohio.
Ann M. Kuster, of New Hampshire.
Juan Vargas, of California.
Sean Patrick Maloney, of New York.

Livestock, Rural Development, and Credit

Eric A. ''Rick'' Crawford, of Arkansas, *Chair*

Bob Goodlatte, of Virginia.
Steve King, of Iowa.
Randy Neugebauer, of Texas.
Mike Rogers, of Alabama.
K. Michael Conaway, of Texas.
Glenn Thompson, of Pennsylvania.
Scott DesJarlais, of Tennessee.
Christopher P. Gibson, of New York.
Reid J. Ribble, of Wisconsin.
Jeff Denham, of California.
Richard Hudson, of North Carolina.
Ted S. Yoho, of Florida.

Jim Costa, of California.
Mike McIntyre, of North Carolina.
David Scott, of Georgia.
Filemon Vela, of Texas.
Michelle Lujan Grisham, of New Mexico.
Pete P. Gallego, of Texas.
William L. Enyart, of Illinois.
Cheri Bustos, of Illinois.
Kurt Schrader, of Oregon.
Richard M. Nolan, of Minnesota.
Joe Courtney, of Connecticut.

STAFF

Committee on Agriculture (1301 LHOB), 225–2171.
Majority Staff
Staff Director.—Nicole Scott.
Deputy Staff Director.—Josh Mathis.
Policy Director.—Pelham Straughn.
Chief Counsel.—Kevin Kramp.
Deputy Counsel.—Patricia Straughn.
Chief Economist.—Bart Fisher.
Chief Clerk.—Debbie Smith.
Administrative Director.—Margaret Wetherald.
Communications Director.—Tamara Hinton.
Information Technology Director.—Merrick Munday.
Information Technology Assistant.—John Konya.
Counsel and Senior Professional Staff.—Brandon Lipps.
Senior Professional Staff and Counsel.—Jason Goggins.
Senior Professional Staff: Mike Dunlap, Josh Maxwell, Pete Thomson, Matthew Schertz.
Professional Staff.—R. Brent Blevins.
Science Advisor.—John Goldberg.
Counsel.—DaNita Murray.
Legislative Assistants: Caleb Crosswhite, Mary Nowak.
Clerk.—Riley Pagett.
Staff Assistant.—Skylar Sowder.
Minority Staff (1305 LHOB), 225–0317.
Staff Director.—Rob Larew.
Chief Counsel.—Andy Baker.
Senior Policy Advisor.—Anne Simmons.
Professional Staff: Keith Jones, Mary Knigge, Clark Ogilvie, Lisa Shelton.
Counsel.—Nathan Fretz.
Communications Director.—Liz Friedlander.
Office Manager.—Faye Smith.

Appropriations

H–307 The Capitol, phone 225–2771

http://www.house.gov/appropriations

Harold Rogers, of Kentucky, *Chair*

Frank R. Wolf, of Virginia.
Jack Kingston, of Georgia.
Rodney P. Frelinghuysen, of New Jersey.
Tom Latham, of Iowa.
Robert B. Aderholt, of Alabama.
Kay Granger, of Texas.
Michael K. Simpson, of Idaho.
John Abney Culberson, of Texas.
Ander Crenshaw, of Florida.
John R. Carter, of Texas.
Ken Calvert, of California.
Tom Cole, of Oklahoma.
Mario Diaz-Balart, of Florida.
Charles W. Dent, of Pennsylvania.
Tom Graves, of Georgia.
Kevin Yoder, of Kansas.
Steve Womack, of Arkansas.
Alan Nunnelee, of Mississippi.
Jeff Fortenberry, of Nebraska.
Thomas J. Rooney, of Florida.
Charles J. ''Chuck'' Fleischmann, Tennessee.
Jaime Herrera Beutler, of Washington.
David P. Joyce, of Ohio.
David G. Valadao, of California.
Andy Harris, of Maryland.
Martha Roby, of Alabama.
Mark E. Amodei, of Nevada.
Chris Stewart, of Utah.

Nita M. Lowey, of New York.
Marcy Kaptur, of Ohio.
Peter J. Visclosky, of Indiana.
José E. Serrano, of New York.
Rosa L. DeLauro, of Connecticut.
James P. Moran, of Virginia.
Ed Pastor, of Arizona.
David E. Price, of North Carolina.
Lucille Roybal-Allard, of California.
Sam Farr, of California.
Chaka Fattah, of Pennsylvania.
Sanford D. Bishop, Jr., of Georgia.
Barbara Lee, of California.
Adam B. Schiff, of California.
Michael M. Honda, of California.
Betty McCollum, of Minnesota.
Tim Ryan, of Ohio.
Debbie Wasserman Schultz, of Florida.
Henry Cuellar, of Texas.
Chellie Pingree, of Maine.
Mike Quigley, of Illinois.
William L. Owens, of New York.

SUBCOMMITTEES

[The chairman and ranking minority member are ex officio (voting) members of all subcommittees on which they do not serve.]

Agriculture, Rural Development, Food and Drug Administration, and Related Agencies

Robert B. Aderholt, of Alabama, *Chair*

Kevin Yoder, of Kansas, *Vice Chair*

Tom Latham, of Iowa.
Alan Nunnelee, of Mississippi.
Jeff Fortenberry, of Nebraska.
Thomas J. Rooney, of Florida.
David G. Valadao, of California.

Sam Farr, of California.
Rosa L. DeLauro, of Connecticut.
Sanford D. Bishop, Jr., of Georgia.
Chellie Pingree, of Maine.

Commerce, Justice, Science, and Related Agencies

Frank R. Wolf, of Virginia, *Chair*

John Abney Culberson, of Texas.
Robert B. Aderholt, of Alabama.
Andy Harris, of Maryland.
John R. Carter, of Texas.
Mario Diaz-Balart, of Florida.
Mark E. Amodei, of Nevada.

Chaka Fattah, of Pennsylvania.
Adam B. Schiff, of California.
Michael M. Honda, of California.
José E. Serrano, of New York.

Defense

Rodney P. Frelinghuysen, of New Jersey, *Chair*

Jack Kingston, of Georgia.
Kay Granger, of Texas.
Ander Crenshaw, of Florida.
Ken Calvert, of California.
Tom Cole, of Oklahoma.
Steve Womack, of Arkansas.
Robert B. Aderholt, of Alabama.
John R. Carter, of Texas.

Peter J. Visclosky, of Indiana.
James P. Moran, of Virginia.
Betty McCollum, of Minnesota.
Tim Ryan, of Ohio.
William L. Owens, of New York.
Marcy Kaptur, of Ohio.

Energy and Water Development, and Related Agencies

Michael K. Simpson, of Idaho, *Chair*

Alan Nunnelee, of Mississippi, *Vice Chair*

Rodney P. Frelinghuysen, of New Jersey.
Ken Calvert, of California.
Charles J. ''Chuck'' Fleischmann, Tennessee.
Tom Graves, of Georgia.
Jeff Fortenberry, of Nebraska.

Marcy Kaptur, of Ohio.
Peter J. Visclosky, of Indiana.
Ed Pastor, of Arizona.
Chaka Fattah, of Pennsylvania.

Financial Services and General Government

Ander Crenshaw, of Florida, *Chair*

Mario Diaz-Balart, of Florida, *Vice Chair*

Tom Graves, of Georgia.
Kevin Yoder, of Kansas.
Steve Womack, of Arkansas.
Jaime Herrera Beutler, of Washington.
Mark E. Amodei, of Nevada.

José E. Serrano, of New York.
Mike Quigley, of Illinois.
Marcy Kaptur, of Ohio.
Ed Pastor, of Arizona.

Homeland Security

John R. Carter, of Texas, *Chair*

John Abney Culberson, of Texas, *Vice Chair*

Rodney P. Frelinghuysen, of New Jersey.
Tom Latham, of Iowa.
Charles W. Dent, of Pennsylvania.
Charles J. ''Chuck'' Fleischmann, Tennessee.
Jack Kingston, of Georgia.

David E. Price, of North Carolina.
Lucille Roybal-Allard, of California.
Henry Cuellar, of Texas.
William L. Owens, of New York.

Interior, Environment, and Related Agencies

Ken Calvert, of California, *Chair*

Michael K. Simpson, of Idaho, *Vice Chair*

Tom Cole, of Oklahoma.
Jaime Herrera Beutler, of Washington.
David P. Joyce, of Ohio.
David G. Valadao, of California.
Chris Stewart, of Utah.

James P. Moran, of Virginia.
Betty McCollum, of Minnesota.
Chellie Pingree, of Maine.
José E. Serrano, of New York.

Labor, Health and Human Services, Education, and Related Agencies

Jack Kingston, of Georgia, *Chair*

Steve Womack, of Arkansas, *Vice Chair*

Charles J. ''Chuck'' Fleischmann, Tennessee.
David P. Joyce, of Ohio.
Andy Harris, of Maryland.
Martha Roby, of Alabama.
Chris Stewart, of Utah.

Rosa L. DeLauro, of Connecticut.
Lucille Roybal-Allard, of California.
Barbara Lee, of California.
Michael M. Honda, of California.

Legislative Branch

Tom Cole, of Oklahoma, *Chair*

Andy Harris, of Maryland, *Vice Chair*

Martha Roby, of Alabama.
Mark E. Amodei, of Nevada.
Chris Stewart, of Utah.
Debbie Wasserman Schultz, of Florida.
James P. Moran, of Virginia.
Sanford D. Bishop, Jr., of Georgia.

Military Construction, Veterans' Affairs, and Related Agencies

John Abney Culberson, of Texas, *Chair*

Jeff Fortenberry, of Nebraska, *Vice Chair*

Alan Nunnelee, of Mississippi.
Thomas J. Rooney, of Florida.
Tom Graves, of Georgia.
David G. Valadao, of California.
Martha Roby, of Alabama.
Sanford D. Bishop, Jr., of Georgia.
Sam Farr, of California.
David E. Price, of North Carolina.
Chaka Fattah, of Pennsylvania.

State, Foreign Operations, and Related Programs

Kay Granger, of Texas, *Chair*

Charles W. Dent, of Pennsylvania, *Vice Chair*

Frank R. Wolf, of Virginia.
Mario Diaz-Balart, of Florida.
Ander Crenshaw, of Florida.
Kevin Yoder, of Kansas.
Thomas J. Rooney, of Florida.
Nita M. Lowey, of New York.
Adam B. Schiff, of California.
Barbara Lee, of California.
Debbie Wasserman Schultz, of Florida.
Henry Cuellar, of Texas.

Transportation, Housing and Urban Development, and Related Agencies

Tom Latham, of Iowa, *Chair*

Frank R. Wolf, of Virginia, *Vice Chair*

Charles W. Dent, of Pennsylvania.
Kay Granger, of Texas.
Jaime Herrera Beutler, of Washington.
David P. Joyce, of Ohio.
Michael K. Simpson, of Idaho.
Ed Pastor, of Arizona.
David E. Price, of North Carolina.
Mike Quigley, of Illinois.
Tim Ryan, of Ohio.

STAFF

Committee on Appropriations (H–305), 225–2771.
Majority Clerk and Staff Director.—Will Smith.
Deputy Clerk and Staff Director.—Jim Kulikowski.
Staff Assistants: Dale Oak, Stephen Sepp.
Coalitions Director.—Mike Robinson.
Communications Director.—Jennifer Hing.
Press Assistant.—Marta Dehmlow.
Administrative Assistant.—Tammy Hughes.
Assistant to the Chairman.—Julia Casey.
Executive Assistant.—Victoria Luck.
Administrative Aide.—Kaitlyn Eisner-Poor.
Office Assistant.—Taylor Kelly.
Editors: Larry Boarman, Cathy Edwards (B–301A RHOB), 5–2851.
Computer Operations: Eric Jackson, Lonnie Johnson, Cathy Little, Linda Muir, Jay Sivulich (B–305 RHOB), 5–2718.
Minority Staff Director.—David Pomerantz (1016 LHOB), 5–3481.
Minority Deputy Staff Director.—Lesley Turner.
Minority Press Secretary.—Matt Dennis.
Administrative Aides: Hogan Medlin, Deborah Spriggs.
Subcommittee on Agriculture, Rural Development, Food and Drug Administration, and Related Agencies (2362–A RHOB), 5–2638.

Staff Assistants: Betsy Bina, Martin Delgado, Pam Miller, Tom O'Brien.
Administrative Aide.—Andrew Cooper.
Minority Staff Assistant.—Martha Foley (1016 LHOB), 5–3481.
Subcommittee on Commerce, Justice, Science and Related Agencies (H–310), 5–3351.
Staff Assistants: Leslie Albright, Jeff Ashford, Mike Ringler, Diana Simpson.
Administrative Aide.—Colin Samples.
Minority Staff Assistants: Bob Bonner, Matt Smith (1016 LHOB), 5–3481.
Subcommittee on Defense (H–405), 5–2847.
Staff Assistants: Brooke Boyer, Walter Hearne, Maureen Holohan, Tom McLemore, Jennifer Miller, Tim Prince, Adrienne Ramsay, Ann Reese, Megan Rosenbusch, Paul Terry, B.G. Wright.
Administrative Aide.—Sherry Young.
Minority Staff Assistants: Paul Juola, Rebecca Leggieri (1016 LHOB), 5–3481.
Subcommittee on Energy and Water Development, and Related Agencies (2362–B RHOB), 5–3421.
Staff Assistants: Rob Blair, Angie Giancarlo, Ben Hammond, Loraine Heckenberg.
Administrative Aide.—Perry Yates.
Minority Staff Assistant.—Taunja Berquam (1016 LHOB), 5–3481.
Subcommittee on Financial Services (B–300 RHOB), 5–7245.
Staff Assistants: Winnie Chang, John Martens, Ariana Sarar, Kelly Shea.
Administrative Aide.—Amy Cushing.
Minority Staff Assistants: Angela Ohm (1016 LHOB), 5–3481.
Subcommittee on Homeland Security (B–307 RHOB), 5–5834.
Staff Assistants: Valerie Baldwin, Kris Mallard, Ben Nicholson, Cornell Teague.
Administrative Aide.—Hilary May.
Minority Staff Assistant.—Darek Newby (1016 LHOB), 5–3481.
Subcommittee on Interior, Environment, and Related Agencies (B–308 RHOB), 5–3081.
Staff Assistants: Darren Benjamin, Jason Gray, Dave LesStrang.
Administrative Aide.—Colin Vickery.
Minority Staff Assistants: Rick Healy, Shalanda Young (1016 LHOB), 5–3481.
Subcommittee on Labor, Health and Human Services, Education, and Related Agencies (2358 RHOB), 5–3508.
Staff Assistants: John Bartrum, Allison Deters, Jennifer Gera, Susan Ross.
Administrative Aide.—Lori Bias.
Minority Staff Assistants: Lisa Molyneux, David Reich (1016 LHOB), 5–3481.
Subcommittee on Legislative Branch (HT–2), 6–7252.
Staff Assistants: Liz Dawson, Jennifer Panone, Chuck Turner.
Minority Staff Assistant.—Shalanda Young.
Subcommittee on Military Construction, Veterans' Affairs, and Related Agencies (HVC–227), 5–3047.
Staff Assistants: Donna Shahbaz, Sue Quantius, Sarah Young.
Administrative Aide.—Tracey Russell.
Minority Staff Assistant.—Matt Washington (1016 LHOB), 5–3481.
Subcommittee on State and Foreign Operations (HT–2), 5–2401.
Staff Assistants: Susan Adams, Anne Marie Chotvacs, Jamie Guinn, Craig Higgins, Alice Hogans.
Administrative Aide.—Clelia Alvarado.
Minority Staff Assistants: Erin Kolodjeski, Steve Marchese (1016 LHOB), 5–3481.
Subcommittee on Transportation, HUD and Independent Agencies (2358A RHOB), 5–2141.
Staff Assistants: Dena Baron, Carl Barrick, Doug Disrud, Cheryle Tucker.
Administrative Aide.—Brian Barnard.
Minority Staff Assistants: Joe Carlile, Kate Hallahan (1016 LHOB), 5–3481.

Armed Services

2120 Rayburn House Office Building, phone 225–4151, fax 225–9077

http://www.armedservices.house.gov

Howard P. ''Buck'' McKeon, of California, *Chair*

Mac Thornberry, of Texas.
Walter B. Jones, of North Carolina.
J. Randy Forbes, of Virginia.
Jeff Miller, of Florida.
Joe Wilson, of South Carolina.
Frank A. LoBiondo, of New Jersey.
Rob Bishop, of Utah.
Michael R. Turner, of Ohio.
John Kline, of Minnesota.
Mike Rogers, of Alabama.
Trent Franks, of Arizona.
Bill Shuster, of Pennsylvania.
K. Michael Conaway, of Texas.
Doug Lamborn, of Colorado.
Robert J. Wittman, of Virginia.
Duncan Hunter, of California.
John Fleming, of Louisiana.
Mike Coffman, of Colorado.
E. Scott Rigell, of Virginia.
Christopher P. Gibson, of New York.
Vicky Hartzler, of Missouri.
Joseph J. Heck, of Nevada.
Jon Runyan, of New Jersey.
Austin Scott, of Georgia.
Steven M. Palazzo, of Mississippi.
Mo Brooks, of Alabama.
Richard B. Nugent, of Florida.
Kristi L. Noem, of South Dakota.
Paul Cook, of California.
Jim Bridenstine, of Oklahoma.
Brad R. Wenstrup, of Ohio.
Jackie Walorski, of Indiana.
Bradley Byrne, of Alabama.

Adam Smith, of Washington.
Loretta Sanchez, of California.
Mike McIntyre, of North Carolina.
Robert A. Brady, of Pennsylvania.
Susan A. Davis, of California.
James R. Langevin, of Rhode Island.
Rick Larsen, of Washington.
Jim Cooper, of Tennessee.
Madeleine Z. Bordallo, of Guam.
Joe Courtney, of Connecticut.
David Loebsack, of Iowa.
Niki Tsongas, of Massachusetts.
John Garamendi, of California.
Henry C. ''Hank'' Johnson, Jr., of Georgia.
Colleen W. Hanabusa, of Hawaii.
Jackie Speier, of California.
Ron Barber, of Arizona.
André Carson, of Indiana.
Carol Shea-Porter, of New Hampshire.
Daniel B. Maffei, of New York.
Derek Kilmer, of Washington.
Joaquin Castro, of Texas.
Tammy Duckworth, of Illinois.
Scott H. Peters, of California.
William L. Enyart, of Illinois.
Pete P. Gallego, of Texas.
Marc A. Veasey, of Texas.

SUBCOMMITTEES

Intelligence, Emerging Threats and Capabilities

Mac Thornberry, of Texas, *Chair*

Jeff Miller, of Florida.
John Kline, of Minnesota.
Bill Shuster, of Pennsylvania.
Richard B. Nugent, of Florida.
Trent Franks, of Arizona.
Duncan Hunter, of California.
Christopher P. Gibson, of New York.
Vicky Hartzler, of Missouri.
Joseph J. Heck, of Nevada.

James R. Langevin, of Rhode Island.
Susan A. Davis, of California.
Henry C. ''Hank'' Johnson, Jr., of Georgia.
André Carson, of Indiana.
Daniel B. Maffei, of New York.
Derek Kilmer, of Washington.
Joaquin Castro, of Texas.
Scott H. Peters, of California.

Military Personnel

Joe Wilson, of South Carolina, *Chair*

Walter B. Jones, of North Carolina.
Joseph J. Heck, of Nevada.
Austin Scott, of Georgia.
Brad R. Wenstrup, of Ohio.
Jackie Walorski, of Indiana.
Christopher P. Gibson, of New York.
Kristi L. Noem, of South Dakota.

Susan A. Davis, of California.
Robert A. Brady, of Pennsylvania.
Madeleine Z. Bordallo, of Guam.
David Loebsack, of Iowa.
Niki Tsongas, of Massachusetts.
Carol Shea-Porter, of New Hampshire.

Oversight and Investigations

Joseph J. Heck, of Nevada, *Chair*

K. Michael Conaway, of Texas.
Mo Brooks, of Alabama.
Walter B. Jones, of North Carolina.
Austin Scott, of Georgia.
Jim Bridenstine, of Oklahoma.

Niki Tsongas, of Massachusetts.
Jackie Speier, of California.
Tammy Duckworth, of Illinois.

Readiness

Robert J. Wittman, of Virginia, *Chair*

Rob Bishop, of Utah.
Vicky Hartzler, of Missouri.
Austin Scott, of Georgia.
Kristi L. Noem, of South Dakota.
J. Randy Forbes, of Virginia.
Frank A. LoBiondo, of New Jersey.
Mike Rogers, of Alabama.
Doug Lamborn, of Colorado.
E. Scott Rigell, of Virginia.
Steven M. Palazzo, of Mississippi.

Madeleine Z. Bordallo, of Guam.
Joe Courtney, of Connecticut.
David Loebsack, of Iowa.
Colleen W. Hanabusa, of Hawaii.
Jackie Speier, of California.
Ron Barber, of Arizona.
Carol Shea-Porter, of New Hampshire.
William L. Enyart, of Illinois.
Pete P. Gallego, of Texas.

Seapower and Projection Forces

J. Randy Forbes, of Virginia, *Chair*

K. Michael Conaway, of Texas.
Duncan Hunter, of California.
E. Scott Rigell, of Virginia.
Steven M. Palazzo, of Mississippi.
Robert J. Wittman, of Virginia.
Mike Coffman, of Colorado.
Jon Runyan, of New Jersey.
Kristi L. Noem, of South Dakota.
Paul Cook, of California.
Bradley Byrne, of Alabama.

Mike McIntyre, of North Carolina.
Joe Courtney, of Connecticut.
James R. Langevin, of Rhode Island.
Rick Larsen, of Washington.
Henry C. ''Hank'' Johnson, Jr., of Georgia.
Colleen W. Hanabusa, of Hawaii.
Derek Kilmer, of Washington.
Scott H. Peters, of California.

Strategic Forces

Mike Rogers, of Alabama, *Chair*

Trent Franks, of Arizona.
Doug Lamborn, of Colorado.
Mike Coffman, of Colorado.
Mo Brooks, of Alabama.
Joe Wilson, of South Carolina.
Michael R. Turner, of Ohio.
John Fleming, of Louisiana.
Richard B. Nugent, of Florida.
Jim Bridenstine, of Oklahoma.

Jim Cooper, of Tennessee.
Loretta Sanchez, of California.
James R. Langevin, of Rhode Island.
Rick Larsen, of Washington.
John Garamendi, of California.
Henry C. ''Hank'' Johnson, Jr., of Georgia.
André Carson, of Indiana.
Marc A. Veasey, of Texas.

Tactical Air and Land Forces

Michael R. Turner, of Ohio, *Chair*

Frank A. LoBiondo, of New Jersey.
John Fleming, of Louisiana.
Christopher P. Gibson, of New York.
Jon Runyan, of New Jersey.
Paul Cook, of California.
Jim Bridenstine, of Oklahoma.
Brad R. Wenstrup, of Ohio.
Jackie Walorski, of Indiana.
Mac Thornberry, of Texas.
Walter B. Jones, of North Carolina.
Rob Bishop, of Utah.
Bradley Byrne, of Alabama.

Loretta Sanchez, of California.
Mike McIntyre, of North Carolina.
Jim Cooper, of Tennessee.
John Garamendi, of California.
Ron Barber, of Arizona.
Daniel B. Maffei, of New York.
Joaquin Castro, of Texas.
Tammy Duckworth, of Illinois.
William L. Enyart, of Illinois.
Pete P. Gallego, of Texas.
Marc A. Veasey, of Texas.

STAFF

Committee on Armed Services (2120 RHOB), 225–4151, fax 225–9077.
Staff Director.—Bob Simmons.
Deputy Staff Director.—Jenness Simler.
General Counsel.—Catherine McElroy.
Counsels: William S. Johnson, Timothy Morrison, Michele Pearce, Leonor Tomero.
Director, Legislative Operations.—Zach Steacy.
Professional Staff: Michael Amato, Paul Arcangeli, Kari Bingen, Heath R. Bope, Christopher J. Bright, Douglas Bush, Michael Casey, John D. Chapla, Jaime Cheshire, Everett Coleman, Ryan Crumpler, Alexander Gallo, Brian Garrett, Kevin Gates, David Giachetti, Craig Greene, Jeanette S. James, Stephen Kitay, Mark R. Lewis, Jamie R. Lynch, Phil MacNaughton, Timothy McClees, Elizabeth Nathan, Vickie Plunkett, Rebecca A. Ross, Jack Schuler, Catherine Sendak, Kimberly Shaw, David Sienicki, John F. Sullivan, Jesse D. Tolleson, Jr., Peter Villano, Debra S. Wada, Andrew T. Walter, John Wason, Lynn M. Williams.
Senior Advisor to the Chairman.—Jaime Cheshire.
Communications Director.—Claude Chafin.
Deputy Communications Director.—John Noonan.
Deputy Spokesman.—Robert J. McAlister.
Communications Assistant.—Joe Sangiorgio.
Security Manager.—Cyndi Howard.
Executive Assistants: Betty B. Gray, Elizabeth McWhorter.
Research Assistant.—Lauren Hauhn.
Clerks: Colin Bosse, Aaron Falk, Julie Herbert, Arthur Milikh, Nicholas Rodman, Eric L. Smith, Katie Thompson.
Staff Assistant.—John N. Johnson.

Budget

207 Cannon House Office Building 20515–6065, phone 226–7270, fax 226–7174

http://www.budget.house.gov

Paul Ryan, of Wisconsin, *Chair*

Tom Price, of Georgia, *Vice Chair*

Scott Garrett, of New Jersey.
John Campbell, of California.
Ken Calvert, of California.
Tom Cole, of Oklahoma.
Tom McClintock, of California.
James Lankford, of Oklahoma.
Diane Black, of Tennessee.
Reid J. Ribble, of Wisconsin.
Bill Flores, of Texas.
Todd Rokita, of Indiana.
Rob Woodall, of Georgia.
Marsha Blackburn, of Tennessee.
Alan Nunnelee, of Mississippi.
E. Scott Rigell, of Virginia.
Vicky Hartzler, of Missouri.
Jackie Walorski, of Indiana.
Luke Messer, of Indiana.
Tom Rice, of South Carolina.
Roger Williams, of Texas.
Sean P. Duffy, of Wisconsin.

Chris Van Hollen, of Maryland.
Allyson Y. Schwartz, of Pennsylvania.
John A. Yarmuth, of Kentucky.
Bill Pascrell, Jr., of New Jersey.
Tim Ryan, of Ohio.
Gwen Moore, of Wisconsin.
Kathy Castor, of Florida.
Jim McDermott, of Washington.
Barbara Lee, of California.
Hakeem S. Jeffries, of New York.
Mark Pocan, of Wisconsin.
Michelle Lujan Grisham,, of New Mexico.
Jared Huffman, of California.
Tony Cárdenas, of California.
Earl Blumenauer, of Oregon.
Kurt Schrader, of Oregon.

(No Subcommittees)

STAFF

Committee on Budget (207 CHOB), 226–7270, fax 226–7174.
Majority Staff Director.—Austin Smythe.
Deputy Staff Director.—Andy Morton.
Executive Assistant to the Staff Director.—Eric Davis.
Chief Counsel.—Paul Restuccia.
Senior Counsel.—Nicole Foltz.
Counsel.—Mary Popadiuk.
Chief Economist.—Timothy Flynn.
Policy Director.—Jon Burks.
Budget Analysts: Justin Bogie, Gene Emmans, Jim Herz, Matt Hoffmann, Ted McCann, Kara McKee, Stephanie Parks, Shane Skelton, Jenna Spealman, Jon Romito.
Communications Director.—Conor Sweeney.
Visual/New Media Director.—Vanessa Day.
Communications Advisor.—Brian Bolduc.
Press Secretary.—Will Allison.
Senior Advisor.—Dennis Teti.
Chief Administrator.—Alex Stoddard.
Systems Administrator.—Jose Guillen.
Committee Printer.—Richard E. Magee.
Minority Staff Director.—Tom Kahn (B71 Cannon), 226–7200, fax 225–9905.
Executive Assistant to the Staff Director.—Beth Stephenson.
Chief Counsel.—Karen Robb.
Senior Policy Coordinator.—Sarah Abernathy.
Budget Review Director.—Kimberly Overbeek.
Senior Budget Review Specialist.—Ellen J. Balis.
Senior Budget Analyst.—Diana Meredith.
Budget Analysts: Ken Cummings, Erin Miller, Scott R. Russell, Ted E. Zegers.
Communications Director.—Nu Wexler.
Office Manager.—Sheila A. McDowell.
Special Assistant to the Ranking Minority Member.—Brian Brady.
Minority Staff Assistant.—Kathleen Capstick.

Education and the Workforce

2181 Rayburn House Office Building, phone 225–4527, fax 225–9571
http://edworkforce.house.gov

John Kline, of Minnesota, *Chair*

Thomas E. Petri, of Wisconsin.
Howard P. ''Buck'' McKeon, of California.
Joe Wilson, of South Carolina.
Virginia Foxx, of North Carolina.
Tom Price, of Georgia.
Kenny Marchant, of Texas.
Duncan Hunter, of California.
David P. Roe, of Tennessee.
Glenn Thompson, of Pennsylvania.
Tim Walberg, of Michigan.
Matt Salmon, of Arizona.
Brett Guthrie, of Kentucky.
Scott DesJarlais, of Tennessee.
Todd Rokita, of Indiana.
Larry Bucshon, of Indiana.
Trey Gowdy, of South Carolina.
Lou Barletta, of Pennsylvania.
Martha Roby, of Alabama.
Joseph J. Heck, of Nevada.
Susan W. Brooks, of Indiana.
Richard Hudson, of North Carolina.
Luke Messer, of Indiana.

George Miller, of California.
Robert C. ''Bobby'' Scott, of Virginia.
Rubén Hinojosa, of Texas.
Carolyn McCarthy, of New York.
John F. Tierney, of Massachusetts.
Rush Holt, of New Jersey.
Susan A. Davis, of California.
Raúl M. Grijalva, of Arizona.
Timothy H. Bishop, of New York.
David Loebsack, of Iowa.
Joe Courtney, of Connecticut.
Marcia L. Fudge, of Ohio.
Jared Polis, of Colorado.
Gregorio Kilili Camacho Sablan, of Northern Mariana Islands.
Frederica S. Wilson, of Florida.
Suzanne Bonamici, of Oregon.
Mark Pocan, of Wisconsin.

SUBCOMMITTEES

[The chairman and ranking minority member are ex officio (non-voting) members of all subcommittees on which they do not serve.]

Early Childhood, Elementary, and Secondary Education

Todd Rokita, of Indiana, *Chair*

John Kline, of Minnesota.
Thomas E. Petri, of Wisconsin.
Virginia Foxx, of North Carolina.
Kenny Marchant, of Texas.
Duncan Hunter, of California.
David P. Roe, of Tennessee.
Glenn Thompson, of Pennsylvania.
Susan W. Brooks, of Indiana.

Carolyn McCarthy, of New York.
Robert C. ''Bobby'' Scott, of Virginia.
Susan A. Davis, of California.
Raúl M. Grijalva, of Arizona.
Marcia L. Fudge, of Ohio.
Jared Polis, of Colorado.
Gregorio Kilili Camacho Sablan, of Northern Mariana Islands.
Mark Pocan, of Wisconsin.

Health, Employment, Labor, and Pensions

David P. Roe, of Tennessee, *Chair*

Joe Wilson, of South Carolina.
Tom Price, of Georgia.
Kenny Marchant, of Texas.
Matt Salmon, of Arizona.
Brett Guthrie, of Kentucky.
Scott DesJarlais, of Tennessee.
Larry Bucshon, of Indiana.
Trey Gowdy, of South Carolina.
Lou Barletta, of Pennsylvania.
Martha Roby, of Alabama.
Joseph J. Heck, of Nevada.
Susan W. Brooks, of Indiana.
Luke Messer, of Indiana.

Rush Holt, of New Jersey.
David Loebsack, of Iowa.
Robert C. ''Bobby'' Scott, of Virginia.
Rubén Hinojosa, of Texas.
John F. Tierney, of Massachusetts.
Raúl M. Grijalva, of Arizona.
Joe Courtney, of Connecticut.
Jared Polis, of Colorado.
Frederica S. Wilson, of Florida.
Suzanne Bonamici, of Oregon.

Higher Education and Workforce Training

Virginia Foxx, of North Carolina, *Chair*

Thomas E. Petri, of Wisconsin.
Howard P. ''Buck'' McKeon, of California.
Glenn Thompson, of Pennsylvania.
Tim Walberg, of Michigan.
Matt Salmon, of Arizona.
Brett Guthrie, of Kentucky.
Lou Barletta, of Pennsylvania.
Joseph J. Heck, of Nevada.
Susan W. Brooks, of Indiana.
Richard Hudson, of North Carolina.
Luke Messer, of Indiana.

Rubén Hinojosa, of Texas.
John F. Tierney, of Massachusetts.
Timothy H. Bishop, of New York.
Suzanne Bonamici, of Oregon.
Carolyn McCarthy, of New York.
Rush Holt, of New Jersey.
Susan A. Davis, of California.
David Loebsack, of Iowa.
Frederica S. Wilson, of Florida.

Workforce Protections

Tim Walberg, of Michigan, *Chair*

John Kline, of Minnesota.
Tom Price, of Georgia.
Duncan Hunter, of California.
Scott DesJarlais, of Tennessee.
Todd Rokita, of Indiana.
Larry Bucshon, of Indiana.
Richard Hudson, of North Carolina.

Joe Courtney, of Connecticut.
Timothy H. Bishop, of New York.
Marcia L. Fudge, of Ohio.
Gregorio Kilili Camacho Sablan, of Northern Mariana Islands.
Mark Pocan, of Wisconsin.

STAFF

Committee on Education and Labor (2181 RHOB), 225–4527.
Majority Staff Director.—Juliane Sullivan.
General Counsel.—Krisann Pearce.
Director of Education and Human Services Policy.—James Bergeron.
Director of Workforce Policy.—Ed Gilroy.
Communications Director.—Alexandra Sollberger.
Deputy Press Secretary.—Nicole Sizemore.
Coalitions and Member Services Representative.—Janelle Belland.
Deputy Communications Director.—Brian Newell.
Press Assistant.—Daniel Murner.
Deputy Director of Education and Human Services Policy.—Heather Couri.
Senior Education Policy Advisor.—Brad Thomas.
Education and Human Services Oversight Counsel.—Amanda Schaumburg.
Education Policy Counsel and Senior Advisor.—Amy Jones.
Professional Staff Members-Education: Cristin Datch Kumar, Lindsay Fryer, Rosemary Lahasky, Brian Melnyk.
Legislative Assistants-Education: Dan Shorts, Emily Slack.
Deputy Director of Workforce Policy.—Molly Salmi.
Senior Policy Advisor.—Loren Sweatt.
Workforce Policy Counsel.—Marvin Kaplan.
Professional Staff Members-Workforce: Andrew Banducci, Molly Conway, Joe Wheeler.
Senior Legislative Assistant-Workforce.—Ben Hoog.
Legislative Assistant-Workforce.—Alexa Turner.
Chief Clerk.—Nancy Locke.
Deputy Clerk.—Alissa Strawcutter.
Financial Administrative Officer.—Dianna Ruskowsky.
Senior Staff Assistant.—Zachary McHenry.
Staff Assistant.—Kathlyn Ehl.
Staff Assistant-Workforce.—Jennifer Prescott.
Committee Printer.—Richard ''Dick'' Magee.
Minority Staff (2101 RHOB), 5–3725.
Staff Director.—Jody Calemine.
Deputy Staff Director.—Michael Zola.
General Counsel.—Megan O'Reilly.
Senior Economic Advisor.—Mark Zuckerman.
Special Assistant to the Staff Director.—Liz Hollis.

Clerk/Intern and Fellow Coordinator.—Tylease Alli.
Staff Assistants: Eunice Ikene, Melissa Greenberg.
Communications Director.—Julia Krahe.
Deputy Press Secretary/New Media Coordinator.—Brian P. Levin.
Chief Policy Advisory/Labor Policy Director.—Michele Varnhagen.
Senior Labor Policy Advisor.—Richard D. Miller.
Senior Policy Advisor.—Leticia Mederos.
Director of Education Policy.—Jamie P. Fasteau.
Education Policy Advisors: Jeremy Ayers, Jacque Chevalier, Scott Groginsky, Rich Williams.
Education Policy Associate.—Kelly Broughan.
Special Assistant.—Daniel Weiss.
Executive Assistant.—Katie Amundson.
Systems Administrator.—Ali Falahi.

Energy and Commerce

2125 Rayburn House Office Building, phone 225–2927

http://www.house.gov/commerce

Fred Upton, of Michigan, *Chair*

Marsha Blackburn, of Tennessee, *Vice Chair*

Ralph M. Hall, of Texas.
Joe Barton, of Texas.
Ed Whitfield, of Kentucky.
John Shimkus, of Illinois.
Joseph R. Pitts, of Pennsylvania.
Greg Walden, of Oregon.
Lee Terry, of Nebraska.
Mike Rogers, of Michigan.
Tim Murphy, of Pennsylvania.
Michael C. Burgess, of Texas.
Phil Gingrey, of Georgia.
Steve Scalise, of Louisiana.
Robert E. Latta, of Ohio.
Cathy McMorris Rodgers, of Washington.
Gregg Harper, of Mississippi.
Leonard Lance, of New Jersey.
Bill Cassidy, of Louisiana.
Brett Guthrie, of Kentucky.
Pete Olson, of Texas.
David B. McKinley, of West Virginia.
Cory Gardner, of Colorado.
Mike Pompeo, of Kansas.
Adam Kinzinger, of Illinois.
H. Morgan Griffith, of Virginia.
Gus M. Bilirakis, of Florida.
Bill Johnson, of Ohio.
Billy Long, of Missouri.
Renee L. Ellmers, of North Carolina.

Henry A. Waxman, of California.
John D. Dingell, of Michigan.
Frank Pallone, Jr., of New Jersey.
Bobby L. Rush, of Illinois.
Anna G. Eshoo, of California.
Eliot L. Engel, of New York.
Gene Green, of Texas.
Diana DeGette, of Colorado.
Lois Capps, of California.
Michael F. Doyle, of Pennsylvania.
Janice D. Schakowsky, of Illinois.
Jim Matheson, of Utah.
G. K. Butterfield, of North Carolina.
John Barrow, of Georgia.
Doris O. Matsui, of California.
Donna M. Christensen, of Virgin Islands.
Kathy Castor, of Florida.
John P. Sarbanes, of Maryland.
Jerry McNerney, of California.
Bruce L. Braley, of Iowa.
Peter Welch, of Vermont.
Ben Ray Luján, of New Mexico.
Paul Tonko, of New York.
John A. Yarmuth, of Kentucky.

SUBCOMMITTEES

[The chairman and ranking minority member are ex officio (voting) members of all subcommittees on which they do not serve.]

Commerce, Manufacturing, and Trade

Lee Terry, of Nebraska, *Chair*

Leonard Lance, of New Jersey, *Vice Chair*

Marsha Blackburn, of Tennessee.
Gregg Harper, of Mississippi.
Brett Guthrie, of Kentucky.
Pete Olson, of Texas.
David B. McKinley, of West Virginia.
Mike Pompeo, of Kansas.
Adam Kinzinger, of Illinois.
Gus M. Bilirakis, of Florida.
Bill Johnson, of Ohio.
Billy Long, of Missouri.
Joe Barton, of Texas.

Janice D. Schakowsky, of Illinois.
John P. Sarbanes, of Maryland.
Jerry McNerney, of California.
Peter Welch, of Vermont.
John A. Yarmuth, of Kentucky.
John D. Dingell, of Michigan.
Bobby L. Rush, of Illinois.
Jim Matheson, of Utah.
John Barrow, of Georgia.
Donna M. Christensen, of Virgin Islands.

Communications and Technology

Greg Walden, of Oregon, *Chair*

Robert E. Latta, of Ohio, *Vice Chair*

John Shimkus, of Illinois.
Lee Terry, of Nebraska.
Mike Rogers, of Michigan.
Marsha Blackburn, of Tennessee.
Steve Scalise, of Louisiana.
Leonard Lance, of New Jersey.
Brett Guthrie, of Kentucky.
Cory Gardner, of Colorado.
Mike Pompeo, of Kansas.
Adam Kinzinger, of Illinois.
Billy Long, of Missouri.
Renee L. Ellmers, of North Carolina.
Joe Barton, of Texas.

Anna G. Eshoo, of California.
Michael F. Doyle, of Pennsylvania.
Doris O. Matsui, of California.
Bruce L. Braley, of Iowa.
Peter Welch, of Vermont.
Ben Ray Luján, of New Mexico.
John D. Dingell, of Michigan.
Frank Pallone, Jr., of New Jersey.
Bobby L. Rush, of Illinois.
Diana DeGette, of Colorado.
Jim Matheson, of Utah.
G. K. Butterfield, of North Carolina.

Energy and Power

Ed Whitfield, of Kentucky, *Chair*

Steve Scalise, of Louisiana, *Vice Chair*

Ralph M. Hall, of Texas.
John Shimkus, of Illinois.
Joseph R. Pitts, of Pennsylvania.
Lee Terry, of Nebraska.
Michael C. Burgess, of Texas.
Robert E. Latta, of Ohio.
Bill Cassidy, of Louisiana.
Pete Olson, of Texas.
David B. McKinley, of West Virginia.
Cory Gardner, of Colorado.
Mike Pompeo, of Kansas.
Adam Kinzinger, of Illinois.
H. Morgan Griffith, of Virginia.
Joe Barton, of Texas.

Bobby L. Rush, of Illinois.
Jerry McNerney, of California.
Paul Tonko, of New York.
John A. Yarmuth, of Kentucky.
Eliot L. Engel, of New York.
Gene Green, of Texas.
Lois Capps, of California.
Michael F. Doyle, of Pennsylvania.
John Barrow, of Georgia.
Doris O. Matsui, of California.
Donna M. Christensen, of Virgin Islands.
Kathy Castor, of Florida.
John D. Dingell, of Michigan.

Environment and the Economy

John Shimkus, of Illinois, *Chair*

Phil Gingrey, of Georgia, *Vice Chair*

Ralph M. Hall, of Texas.
Ed Whitfield, of Kentucky.
Joseph R. Pitts, of Pennsylvania.
Tim Murphy, of Pennsylvania.
Robert E. Latta, of Ohio.
Gregg Harper, of Mississippi.
Bill Cassidy, of Louisiana.
David B. McKinley, of West Virginia.
Gus M. Bilirakis, of Florida.
Bill Johnson, of Ohio.
Joe Barton, of Texas.

Paul Tonko, of New York.
Frank Pallone, Jr., of New Jersey.
Gene Green, of Texas.
Diana DeGette, of Colorado.
Lois Capps, of California.
Jerry McNerney, of California.
John D. Dingell, of Michigan.
Janice D. Schakowsky, of Illinois.
John Barrow, of Georgia.
Doris O. Matsui, of California.

Health

Joseph R. Pitts, of Pennsylvania, *Chair*

Michael C. Burgess, of Texas, *Vice Chair*

Ed Whitfield, of Kentucky.
John Shimkus, of Illinois.
Mike Rogers, of Michigan.
Tim Murphy, of Pennsylvania.
Marsha Blackburn, of Tennessee.
Phil Gingrey, of Georgia.
Cathy McMorris Rodgers, of Washington.
Leonard Lance, of New Jersey.
Bill Cassidy, of Louisiana.
Brett Guthrie, of Kentucky.
H. Morgan Griffith, of Virginia.
Gus M. Bilirakis, of Florida.
Renee L. Ellmers, of North Carolina.
Joe Barton, of Texas.

Frank Pallone, Jr., of New Jersey.
John D. Dingell, of Michigan.
Eliot L. Engel, of New York.
Lois Capps, of California.
Janice D. Schakowsky, of Illinois.
Jim Matheson, of Utah.
Gene Green, of Texas.
G. K. Butterfield, of North Carolina.
John Barrow, of Georgia.
Donna M. Christensen, of Virgin Islands.
Kathy Castor, of Florida.
John P. Sarbanes, of Maryland.

Oversight and Investigations

Tim Murphy, of Pennsylvania, *Chair*

Michael C. Burgess, of Texas, *Vice Chair*

Marsha Blackburn, of Tennessee.
Phil Gingrey, of Georgia.
Steve Scalise, of Louisiana.
Gregg Harper, of Mississippi.
Pete Olson, of Texas.
Cory Gardner, of Colorado.
H. Morgan Griffith, of Virginia.
Bill Johnson, of Ohio.
Billy Long, of Missouri.
Renee L. Ellmers, of North Carolina.
Joe Barton, of Texas.

Diana DeGette, of Colorado.
Bruce L. Braley, of Iowa.
Ben Ray Luján, of New Mexico.
Janice D. Schakowsky, of Illinois.
G. K. Butterfield, of North Carolina.
Kathy Castor, of Florida.
Peter Welch, of Vermont.
Paul Tonko, of New York.
John A. Yarmuth, of Kentucky.
Gene Green, of Texas.
John D. Dingell, of Michigan.

STAFF

Committee on Energy and Commerce (2125 RHOB), 225–2927, fax 225–1919.
Majority Staff Director.—Gary Andres.
Deputy Staff Director.—Alexa Marrero.
General Counsel.—Michael Bloomquist.
Deputy Chief Counsel.—Peter Kielty.
Director, Communications.—Sean Bonyun.
Chief Counsel, Energy and Power.—Thomas Hasselboehler.
Chief Counsel, Environment and the Economy.—David McCarthy.
Chief Counsel, Oversight.—Karen Christian.
Deputy Chief Counsel, Oversight.—Alan M. Slobodin.
Chief Counsel, Health.—Clay Alspach.
Chief Counsel, Communications and Technology.—David Redl.
Chief Counsel, Commerce, Manufacturing, and Trade.—John ''Gib'' Mullan.
Counsels: Carl Anderson, Patrick Currier, Kelsey Guyselman, Sean Hayes, Jason Knox, Grace Koh, Ben Lieberman, Tina Richards, Samuel Spector, John Stone, Shannon Weinberg Taylor.
Senior Energy Counsel.—Mary Neumayr.
Counsel to Chairman Emeritus.—Krista Rosenthall.
Senior Policy Advisor, Director of Coalitions.—Marty Dannenfelser.
Senior Policy Advisor, Telecommunications.—Ray Baum.
Senior Professional Staff Member.—Brian McCullough.
Professional Staff: Matt Bravo, Annie Caputo, Gerald S. Couri II, Brenda Destro, Paul Edattel, Robert Horne, Carly McWilliams, Katie Novaria, Monica Popp, Peter Spencer.
Policy Coordinator, Energy and Power.—Allison Busbee.
Policy Coordinator, Environment and the Economy.—Christopher Sarley.
Policy Coordinator, Health.—Heidi Stirrup.
Policy Coordinator, Commerce, Manufacturing and Trade.—Nick Magallanes.

Policy Coordinator, Oversight and Investigations.—Bradley Grantz.
Policy Coordinators: Brandon Mooney, Mark Ratner.
Director, Information Technology.—Jean M. Woodrow.
Deputy Director, Information Technology.—Tim Torres.
Financial and Administrative Coordinator.—Sean Corcoran.
Human Resources and Office Administrator.—Theresa Gambo.
Press Secretaries: Charlotte Baker, Noelle Clemente.
Deputy Press Secretary.—Andrew Duberstein.
Digital Media Advisor.—Thomas Wilbur.
Legislative Coordinator.—Charlotte Savercool.
Legislative Clerks: Nick Abraham, Sydne Harwick, Brittany Havens, Brian Howard.
Staff Assistants: David Bell, Megan Capiak, Jessica Wilkerson.

Minority Staff Director.—Phil Barnett.
Deputy Committee Staff Director for Health.—Karen Nelson.
Chief Counsel.—Stacia Cardille.
Communications Director, Senior Policy Advisor.—Karen Lightfoot.
Chief Counsel, Commerce, Manufacturing, and Trade.—Michelle Ash.
Staff Director for Energy and Environment.—Greg Dotson.
Chief Counsel, Communications and Technology.—Shawn Chang.
Investigations Staff Director and Senior Policy Advisor.—Brian Cohen.
Senior Counsels, Energy and Environment: Jeff Baran, Alexandra Teitz.
Senior Counsel.—Rachel Sher.
Counsels: Bruce Ho, Kiren Gopal, Matt Siegler.
Senior Professional Staff Members: Alison Cassady, Amy Hall.
Professional Staff Members: Margaret McCarthy, Anne Reid, Will Wallace.
Chief Clerk.—Jennifer Berenholz.
Deputy Clerk.—Elizabeth Ertel.
Press Secretary.—Elizabeth Letter.
Technology Director.—Eddie Walker.
Online Communications Assistant.—Jewel Massenburg.
Policy Analysts: Caitlin Haberman, Kara van Stralen.
Special Assistant.—Stephen Salsbury.
Staff Assistants: Ziky Ababiya, Hannah Green, Ryan Skukowski.
Senior Advisors: Pat Delgado, Lisa Pinto.

Ethics

1015 Longworth House Office Building, phone 225–7103, fax 225–7392

K. Michael Conaway, of Texas, *Chair*

Charles W. Dent, of Pennsylvania.
Patrick Meehan, of Pennsylvania.
Trey Gowdy, of South Carolina.
Susan W. Brooks, of Indiana.

Linda T. Sánchez, of California.
Pedro R. Pierluisi, of Puerto Rico.
Michael E. Capuano, of Massachusetts.
Yvette D. Clarke, of New York.
Theodore E. Deutch, of Florida.

(No Subcommittees)

STAFF

Chief Counsel / Staff Director.—Tom Rust (interim).
Director of Investigations.—Tom Rust (acting).
Administrative Staff Director.—Joanne White.
Counsel to the Chairman.—Jackie Barber.
Counsel to the Ranking Member.—Dan Taylor.
Director of Advice and Education.—Carol Dixon.
Director of Investigations.—Deborah Mayer.
Senior Counsels: Heather Jones, Cliff Stoddard, John Szabo, Miguel Toruño.
Counsels: Sheria Clarke, Karena Dees, Robert Eskridge, Patrick McMullen, Tamar Nedzar, Wendy Smith, Christopher Tate.
Investigator.—Frank Davies.
Senior Financial Disclosure Advisor.—Deborah Bethea.
Systems Administrator.—Craig Barber.
Investigative Clerk.—Brittany Bohren.
Advice and Education Clerk.—Matt Scott.
Staff Assistants: Brittany Dowell, Molly McCarty, Tucker Carr.

Financial Services

2129 Rayburn House Office Building, phone 225–7502

http://www.house.gov/financialservices

meets first Tuesday of each month

Jeb Hensarling, of Texas, *Chair*

Gary G. Miller, of California, *Vice Chair*

Spencer Bachus, of Alabama.
Peter T. King, of New York.
Edward R. Royce, of California.
Frank D. Lucas, of Oklahoma.
Shelley Moore Capito, of West Virginia.
Scott Garrett, of New Jersey.
Randy Neugebauer, of Texas.
Patrick T. McHenry, of North Carolina.
John Campbell, of California.
Michele Bachmann, of Minnesota.
Kevin McCarthy, of California.
Stevan Pearce, of New Mexico.
Bill Posey, of Florida.
Michael G. Fitzpatrick, of Pennsylvania.
Lynn A. Westmoreland, of Georgia.
Blaine Luetkemeyer, of Missouri.
Bill Huizenga, of Michigan.
Sean P. Duffy, of Wisconsin.
Robert Hurt, of Virginia.
Michael G. Grimm, of New York.
Steve Stivers, of Ohio.
Stephen Lee Fincher, of Tennessee.
Marlin A. Stutzman, of Indiana.
Mick Mulvaney, of South Carolina.
Randy Hultgren, of Illinois.
Dennis A. Ross, of Florida.
Robert Pittenger, of North Carolina.
Ann Wagner, of Missouri.
Andy Barr, of Kentucky.
Tom Cotton, of Arkansas.
Keith J. Rothfus, of Pennsylvania.

Maxine Waters, of California.
Carolyn B. Maloney, of New York.
Nydia M. Velázquez, of New York.
Brad Sherman, of California.
Gregory W. Meeks, of New York.
Michael E. Capuano, of Massachusetts.
Rubén Hinojosa, of Texas.
Wm. Lacy Clay, of Missouri.
Carolyn McCarthy, of New York.
Stephen F. Lynch, of Massachusetts.
David Scott, of Georgia.
Al Green, of Texas.
Emanuel Cleaver, of Missouri.
Gwen Moore, of Wisconsin.
Keith Ellison, of Minnesota.
Ed Perlmutter, of Colorado.
James A. Himes, of Connecticut.
Gary C. Peters, of Michigan.
John C. Carney, Jr., of Delaware.
Terri A. Sewell, of Alabama.
Bill Foster, of Illinois.
Daniel T. Kildee, of Michigan.
Patrick Murphy, of Florida.
John K. Delaney, of Maryland.
Kyrsten Sinema, of Arizona.
Joyce Beatty, of Ohio.
Denny Heck, of Washington.

SUBCOMMITTEES

[The chairman and ranking minority member are ex officio (voting) members of all subcommittees on which they do not serve.]

Capital Markets and Government Sponsored Enterprises

Scott Garrett, of New Jersey, *Chair*

Robert Hurt, of Virginia, *Vice Chair*

Spencer Bachus, of Alabama.
Peter T. King, of New York.
Edward R. Royce, of California.
Frank D. Lucas, of Oklahoma.
Randy Neugebauer, of Texas.
Michele Bachmann, of Minnesota.
Kevin McCarthy, of California.
Lynn A. Westmoreland, of Georgia.
Bill Huizenga, of Michigan.
Michael G. Grimm, of New York.
Steve Stivers, of Ohio.
Stephen Lee Fincher, of Tennessee.
Mick Mulvaney, of South Carolina.
Randy Hultgren, of Illinois.
Dennis A. Ross, of Florida.
Ann Wagner, of Missouri.

Carolyn B. Maloney, of New York.
Brad Sherman, of California.
Rubén Hinojosa, of Texas.
Stephen F. Lynch, of Massachusetts.
Gwen Moore, of Wisconsin.
Ed Perlmutter, of Colorado.
David Scott, of Georgia.
James A. Himes, of Connecticut.
Gary C. Peters, of Michigan.
Keith Ellison, of Minnesota.
Bill Foster, of Illinois.
John C. Carney, Jr., of Delaware.
Terri A. Sewell, of Alabama.
Daniel T. Kildee, of Michigan.

Financial Institutions and Consumer Credit

Shelley Moore Capito, of West Virginia, *Chair*

Sean P. Duffy, of Wisconsin, *Vice Chair*

Spencer Bachus, of Alabama.
Gary G. Miller, of California.
Patrick T. McHenry, of North Carolina.
John Campbell, of California.
Kevin McCarthy, of California.
Stevan Pearce, of New Mexico.
Bill Posey, of Florida.
Michael G. Fitzpatrick, of Pennsylvania.
Lynn A. Westmoreland, of Georgia.
Blaine Luetkemeyer, of Missouri.
Marlin A. Stutzman, of Indiana.
Robert Pittenger, of North Carolina.
Andy Barr, of Kentucky.
Tom Cotton, of Arkansas.
Keith J. Rothfus, of Pennsylvania.

Gregory W. Meeks, of New York.
Carolyn B. Maloney, of New York.
Rubén Hinojosa, of Texas.
Carolyn McCarthy, of New York.
David Scott, of Georgia.
Al Green, of Texas.
Keith Ellison, of Minnesota.
Nydia M. Velázquez, of New York.
Stephen F. Lynch, of Massachusetts.
Michael E. Capuano, of Massachusetts.
Patrick Murphy, of Florida.
John K. Delaney, of Maryland.
Denny Heck, of Washington.

Housing and Insurance

Randy Neugebauer, of Texas, *Chair*

Blaine Luetkemeyer, of Missouri, *Vice Chair*

Edward R. Royce, of California.
Gary G. Miller, of California.
Shelley Moore Capito, of West Virginia.
Scott Garrett, of New Jersey.
Lynn A. Westmoreland, of Georgia.
Sean P. Duffy, of Wisconsin.
Robert Hurt, of Virginia.
Steve Stivers, of Ohio.
Dennis A. Ross, of Florida.

Michael E. Capuano, of Massachusetts.
Nydia M. Velázquez, of New York.
Emanuel Cleaver, of Missouri.
Wm. Lacy Clay, of Missouri.
Brad Sherman, of California.
James A. Himes, of Connecticut.
Carolyn McCarthy, of New York.
Kyrsten Sinema, of Arizona.
Joyce Beatty, of Ohio.

Monetary Policy and Trade

John Campbell, of California, *Chair*

Bill Huizenga, of Michigan, *Vice Chair*

Frank D. Lucas, of Oklahoma.
Stevan Pearce, of New Mexico.
Bill Posey, of Florida.
Michael G. Grimm, of New York.
Stephen Lee Fincher, of Tennessee.
Marlin A. Stutzman, of Indiana.
Mick Mulvaney, of South Carolina.
Robert Pittenger, of North Carolina.
Tom Cotton, of Arkansas.

Wm. Lacy Clay, of Missouri.
Gwen Moore, of Wisconsin.
Gary C. Peters, of Michigan.
Ed Perlmutter, of Colorado.
Bill Foster, of Illinois.
John C. Carney, Jr., of Delaware.
Terri A. Sewell, of Alabama.
Daniel T. Kildee, of Michigan.
Patrick Murphy, of Florida.

Oversight and Investigations

Patrick T. McHenry, of North Carolina, *Chair*

Michael G. Fitzpatrick, of Pennsylvania, *Vice Chair*

Peter T. King, of New York.
Michele Bachmann, of Minnesota.
Sean P. Duffy, of Wisconsin.
Michael G. Grimm, of New York.
Stephen Lee Fincher, of Tennessee.
Randy Hultgren, of Illinois.
Ann Wagner, of Missouri.
Andy Barr, of Kentucky.
Keith J. Rothfus, of Pennsylvania.

Al Green, of Texas.
Emanuel Cleaver, of Missouri.
Keith Ellison, of Minnesota.
Ed Perlmutter, of Colorado.
Carolyn B. Maloney, of New York.
John K. Delaney, of Maryland.
Kyrsten Sinema, of Arizona.
Joyce Beatty, of Ohio.
Denny Heck, of Washington.

STAFF

Committee on Financial Services (2129 RHOB), 225–7502.
Majority Staff:
Staff Director.—Shannon Flaherty McGahn.
Deputy Staff Director.—Kirsten J. Mork.
Chief Counsel.—James H. Clinger.
Deputy Staff Director/Communications.—Jeffrey W. Emerson.
General Counsel and Parliamentarian.—Travis J. Norton.
Senior Professional Staff: Michael E. Ahern, Tallman Johnson, Joe Pinder, Aaron A. Ranck.
Editor.—Terisa L. Allison.
Assistant Systems Administrator.—Steve F. Arauz.
Staff Assistants: E. Chase Burgess, Ryan A. Rusbuldt.
Counsels: Joseph R. Clark, Brian Johnson.
Research Analyst.—Andrew Davidhizar.
Chief Oversight Counsel.—Uttam A. Dhillon.
Senior Counsels: Kevin R. Edgar, Peter G. Haller, Clinton Columbus Jones III, Bethany A. Zorc.
Professional Staff.—Jennifer M. Flitton, Kylin B. McCardle, Leslie McCollum-Gooch, Geoffrey W. Okamoto, Clifford Roberti, Christopher Y. Russell, Aaron T. Sporck, Alexander H. Teel, Jeri Brett Williams.
Administrative Assistant.—Angela S. Gambo.
Digital Media Director.—Jordan Michael Haverly.
Chief Clerk.—Rosemary E. Keech.
Deputy Chief Counsel.—Francisco A. Medina.
Communications Director.—David Michael Popp.
Communications Assistant.—Adam R. Rice.
Senior Analyst.—Gisele G. Roget.
Policy Director.—Edward G. Skala.
Systems Administrator.—Kim Trimble.
Chief Economist.—John W. Verret.
Operations Manager.—Anna Bartlett Wright.
Minority Staff:
Deputy Staff Director.—Charla Ouertatani.
Deputy Staff Director.—Michael T. Beresik.

Chief Counsel.—Lawranne Stewart.
Counsels: Lisa Lederberger, Twaun Samuel.
General Counsel and Legislative Director.—Kellie Larkin.
Deputy Legislative Director.—Meredith C. Connelly.
Senior Policy Advisor.—Amanda Fischer.
Systems Administrator.—Alfred J. Forman, Jr.
Managing Director of Housing Policy.—Kirk D. Freeman.
Senior Policy Director.—Erika Jeffers.
Chief Administrative Officer.—Anita L. Johnson.
Press Assistant.—Marcos F. Manosalvas.
Senior Professional Staff: Kristofor S. Erickson, Corey S. Frayer, Daniel P. McGlinchey.
Professional Staff: Kirk Schwarzbach, Francis O. Williams.
Communications Director.—Christopher M. Spina.

Foreign Affairs

2170 Rayburn House Office Building, phone 225–5021

http://www.foreignaffairs.house.gov

meets first Tuesday of each month

Edward R. Royce, of California, *Chair*

Christopher H. Smith, of New Jersey.
Ileana Ros-Lehtinen, of Florida.
Dana Rohrabacher, of California.
Steve Chabot, of Ohio.
Joe Wilson, of South Carolina.
Michael T. McCaul, of Texas.
Ted Poe, of Texas.
Matt Salmon, of Arizona.
Tom Marino, of Pennsylvania.
Jeff Duncan, of South Carolina.
Adam Kinzinger, of Illinois.
Mo Brooks, of Alabama.
Tom Cotton, of Arkansas.
Paul Cook, of California.
George Holding, of North Carolina.
Randy K. Weber, Sr., of Texas.
Scott Perry, of Pennsylvania.
Steve Stockman, of Texas.
Ron DeSantis, of Florida.
Doug Collins, of Georgia.
Mark Meadows, of North Carolina.
Ted S. Yoho, of Florida.
Luke Messer, of Indiana.

Eliot L. Engel, of New York.
Eni F. H. Faleomavaega, of American Samoa.
Brad Sherman, of California.
Gregory W. Meeks, of New York.
Albio Sires, of New Jersey.
Gerald E. Connolly, of Virginia.
Theodore E. Deutch, of Florida.
Brian Higgins, of New York.
Karen Bass, of California.
William R. Keating, of Massachusetts.
David N. Cicilline, of Rhode Island.
Alan Grayson, of Florida.
Juan Vargas, of California.
Bradley S. Schneider, of Illinois.
Joseph P. Kennedy III, of Massachusetts.
Ami Bera, of California.
Alan S. Lowenthal, of California.
Grace Meng, of New York.
Lois Frankel, of Florida.
Tulsi Gabbard, of Hawaii.
Joaquin Castro, of Texas.

SUBCOMMITTEES

[The chairman and ranking minority member are ex officio (non-voting) members of all subcommittees on which they do not serve.]

Africa, Global Health, Global Human Rights, and International Organizations

Christopher H. Smith, of New Jersey, *Chair*

Tom Marino, of Pennsylvania.
Randy K. Weber, Sr., of Texas.
Steve Stockman, of Texas.
Mark Meadows, of North Carolina.

Karen Bass, of California.
David N. Cicilline, of Rhode Island.
Ami Bera, of California.

Asia and the Pacific

Steve Chabot, of Ohio, *Chair*

Dana Rohrabacher, of California.
Matt Salmon, of Arizona.
Mo Brooks, of Alabama.
George Holding, of North Carolina.
Scott Perry, of Pennsylvania.
Doug Collins, of Georgia.
Luke Messer, of Indiana.

Eni F. H. Faleomavaega, of American Samoa.
Ami Bera, of California.
Tulsi Gabbard, of Hawaii.
Brad Sherman, of California.
Gerald E. Connolly, of Virginia.
William R. Keating, of Massachusetts.

Europe, Eurasia, and Emerging Threats

Dana Rohrabacher, of California, *Chair*

Ted Poe, of Texas.
Tom Marino, of Pennsylvania.
Jeff Duncan, of South Carolina.
Paul Cook, of California.
George Holding, of North Carolina.
Steve Stockman, of Texas.

William R. Keating, of Massachusetts.
Gregory W. Meeks, of New York.
Albio Sires, of New Jersey.
Brian Higgins, of New York.
Alan S. Lowenthal, of California.

The Middle East and North Africa

Ileana Ros-Lehtinen, of Florida, *Chair*

Steve Chabot, of Ohio.
Joe Wilson, of South Carolina.
Adam Kinzinger, of Illinois.
Tom Cotton, of Arkansas.
Randy K. Weber, Sr., of Texas.
Ron DeSantis, of Florida.
Doug Collins, of Georgia.
Mark Meadows, of North Carolina.
Ted S. Yoho, of Florida.
Luke Messer, of Indiana.

Theodore E. Deutch, of Florida.
Gerald E. Connolly, of Virginia.
Brian Higgins, of New York.
David N. Cicilline, of Rhode Island.
Alan Grayson, of Florida.
Juan Vargas, of California.
Bradley S. Schneider, of Illinois.
Joseph P. Kennedy III, of Massachusetts.
Grace Meng, of New York.
Lois Frankel, of Florida.

Terrorism, Nonproliferation, and Trade

Ted Poe, of Texas, *Chair*

Joe Wilson, of South Carolina.
Adam Kinzinger, of Illinois.
Mo Brooks, of Alabama.
Tom Cotton, of Arkansas.
Paul Cook, of California.
Scott Perry, of Pennsylvania.
Ted S. Yoho, of Florida.

Brad Sherman, of California.
Alan S. Lowenthal, of California.
Joaquin Castro, of Texas.
Juan Vargas, of California.
Bradley S. Schneider, of Illinois.
Joseph P. Kennedy III, of Massachusetts.

The Western Hemisphere

Matt Salmon, of Arizona, *Chair*

Christopher H. Smith, of New Jersey.
Ileana Ros-Lehtinen, of Florida.
Michael T. McCaul, of Texas.
Jeff Duncan, of South Carolina.
Ron DeSantis, of Florida.

Albio Sires, of New Jersey.
Gregory W. Meeks, of New York.
Eni F. H. Faleomavaega, of American Samoa.
Theodore E. Deutch, of Florida.
Alan Grayson, of Florida.

STAFF

Committee on Foreign Affairs (2170 RHOB), 225–5021, fax 226–7269.
Majority Staff
Chief of Staff.—Amy Porter.
Majority Staff Director.—Tom Sheehy.
Deputy Staff Director.—Edward Burrier.
General Counsel.—Doug Anderson.
Chief Counsel for Oversight and Investigations.—Thomas Alexander.
Counsel for Oversight and Investigations.—Ari Fridman.
Communications Director / Counsel.—Shane Wolfe.
Deputy Communications Director.—Audra McGeorge.
Digital Director.—Ted Peterson.
Senior Director of Asia Policy.—Nien Su.
Senior Professional Staff Members: Sarah Blocher, Joan Condon, Jamie McCormick, Nilmini Rubin, Doug Seay, Matthew Zweig.
Senior Advisor.—Evan McMullin.
Professional Staff Members: Worku Gachou, Thomas Hill.
Security Officer / Professional Staff Member.—George Ritchey.
Director of Outreach and Protocol.—Elizabeth Heng.
Director of Committee Operations.—Jean Marter.
Policy Analyst.—Hunter Strupp.
Counsel and Policy Coordinator.—Jessica Kahan.
Special Assistant.—Brady Howell.
Hearing Coordinator.—Anthony Walden.
Staff Associates: Kirsten Foster, Martin Singer.
Finance Administrator.—John Gleason.
Information Resource Manager.—Vlad Cerga.
Assistant Systems Administrator.—Danny Marca.
Printing Manager / Web Assistant.—Shirley Alexander.

Minority Staff (B–360 RHOB), 226–8467.
Minority Staff Director.—Jason Steinbaum.
Deputy Staff Director.—Doug Campbell.
Chief Counsel.—Janice Kaguyutan.
Communications Director/Senior Professional Staff Member.—Daniel Harsha.
Senior Professional Staff Members: Sajit Gandhi, Robert Marcus, J.J. Ong, Peter Quilter, Jackie Quinones, Edmund Rice, Brent Woolfork.
Professional Staff Members: Heidi Ross.
Policy Analyst and Deputy Communications Director.—Robert Lattin.
Subcommittee on Africa, Global Health, Global Human Rights, and International Organizations (H2–259A FHOB), 226–7812.
Staff Director.—Gregory Simpkins.
Counsel.—Piero Tozzi.
Staff Associate.—Mark Kearny.
Minority Professional Staff.—Eric Williams.
Subcommittee on Asia and the Pacific (H2–255 FHOB), 226–7825.
Staff Director.—Kevin Fitzpatrick.
Professional Staff Member.—Priscilla Koepke.
Staff Associate.—James Burchfield.
Minority Professional Staff.—Lisa Williams.
Subcommittee on Europe, Eurasia, and Emerging Threats (H2–256 FHOB), 226–6434.
Staff Director.—Paul Berkowitz.
Professional Staff Member.—Greg McCarthy.
Staff Associate.—Jessica Roxburgh.
Minority Professional Staff.—Naz Durakoglu.
Subcommittee on the Middle East and North Africa (2401A RHOB), 225–3345.
Staff Director.—Eddy Acevedo.
Professional Staff Members: Alexander Pipas, Golan Rodgers.
Staff Associate.—Javier Pena.
Minority Professional Staff.—Casey Kustin.
Subcommittee on Terrorism, Nonproliferation, and Trade (H2–340 FHOB), 226–1500.
Staff Director.—Luke Murry.
Professional Staff Member.—Jeff Dressler.
Staff Associate.—Allie Medack.
Minority Professional Staff.—Don MacDonald.
Subcommittee on the Western Hemisphere (H2–256 FHOB), 226–9980.
Staff Director.—Mark Walker.
Professional Staff Member.—Leah Campos.
Staff Associate.—Joske Bautista.
Minority Professional Staff.—Ramon Zertuche.

Homeland Security

phone 226–8417, fax 226–3399

Michael T. McCaul, of Texas, *Chair*

Candice S. Miller, of Michigan, *Vice Chair*

Lamar Smith, of Texas.
Peter T. King, of New York.
Mike Rogers, of Alabama.
Paul C. Broun, of Georgia.
Patrick Meehan, of Pennsylvania.
Jeff Duncan, of South Carolina.
Tom Marino, of Pennsylvania.
Jason Chaffetz, of Utah.
Steven M. Palazzo, of Mississippi.
Lou Barletta, of Pennsylvania.
Richard Hudson, of North Carolina.
Steve Daines, of Montana.
Susan W. Brooks, of Indiana.
Scott Perry, of Pennsylvania.
Mark Sanford, of South Carolina.

Bennie G. Thompson, of Mississippi.
Loretta Sanchez, of California.
Sheila Jackson Lee, of Texas.
Yvette D. Clarke, of New York.
Brian Higgins, of New York.
Cedric L. Richmond, of Louisiana.
William R. Keating, of Massachusetts.
Ron Barber, of Arizona.
Donald M. Payne, Jr., of New Jersey.
Beto O'Rourke, of Texas.
Tulsi Gabbard, of Hawaii.
Filemon Vela, of Texas.
Steven A. Horsford, of Nevada.
Eric Swalwell, of California.

SUBCOMMITTEES

[The chairman and ranking minority member are ex officio members of all subcommittees on which they do not serve.]

Border and Maritime Security

Candice S. Miller, of Michigan, *Chair*

Jeff Duncan, of South Carolina.
Tom Marino, of Pennsylvania.
Steven M. Palazzo, of Mississippi.
Lou Barletta, of Pennsylvania.

Sheila Jackson Lee, of Texas.
Loretta Sanchez, of California.
Beto O'Rourke, of Texas.
Tulsi Gabbard, of Hawaii.

Counterterrorism and Intelligence

Peter T. King, of New York, *Chair*

Patrick Meehan, of Pennsylvania, *Vice Chair*

Paul C. Broun, of Georgia.
Jason Chaffetz, of Utah.

Brian Higgins, of New York.
Loretta Sanchez, of California.
William R. Keating, of Massachusetts.

Cybersecurity, Infrastructure Protection, and Security Technologies

Patrick Meehan, of Pennsylvania, *Chair*

Scott Perry, of Pennsylvania, *Vice Chair*

Mike Rogers, of Alabama.
Tom Marino, of Pennsylvania.
Jason Chaffetz, of Utah.
Steve Daines, of Montana.

Yvette D. Clarke, of New York.
William R. Keating, of Massachusetts.
Filemon Vela, of Texas.
Steven A. Horsford, of Nevada.

Emergency Preparedness, Response, and Communications

Susan W. Brooks, of Indiana, *Chair*

Steven M. Palazzo, of Mississippi, *Vice Chair*

Peter T. King, of New York.
Scott Perry, of Pennsylvania.
Mark Sanford, of South Carolina.

Donald M. Payne, Jr., of New Jersey.
Yvette D. Clarke, of New York.
Brian Higgins, of New York.

Oversight and Management Efficiency

Jeff Duncan, of South Carolina, *Chair*
Steve Daines, of Montana, *Vice Chair*

Paul C. Broun, of Georgia.
Lou Barletta, of Pennsylvania.
Richard Hudson, of North Carolina.

Ron Barber, of Arizona.
Donald M. Payne, Jr., of New Jersey.
Beto O'Rourke, of Texas.

Transportation Security

Richard Hudson, of North Carolina, *Chair*
Mike Rogers, of Alabama, *Vice Chair*

Candice S. Miller, of Michigan.
Susan W. Brooks, of Indiana.
Mark Sanford, of South Carolina.

Cedric L. Richmond, of Louisiana.
Sheila Jackson Lee, of Texas.
Eric Swalwell, of California.

STAFF

Committee on Homeland Security (H2–176 Ford House Office Building) phone 226–8417, fax 226–3399.

Chief of Staff.—Greg Hill, FHOB / H2–176 (202) 226–8417.

Deputy Chief of Staff/Policy.—R. Nicholas Palarino, FHOB / H2–176 (202) 226–8417.

Deputy Chief of Staff/Chief Counsel.—Michael Geffroy, FHOB / H2–176 (202) 226–8417.

Staff Director, Subcommittee on Border and Maritime Security.—Paul Anstine, FHOB / H2–176 (202) 226–8417.

Staff Director, Subcommittee on Counterterrorism and Intelligence.—Mandy Bowers, FHOB / H2–176 (202) 226–8417.

Staff Director, Subcommittee on Cybersecurity, Infrastructure Protection, and Security Technologies.—Alex Manning, FHOB / H2–176 (202) 226–8417.

Staff Director, Subcommittee on Emergency Preparedness, Response, and Communications.—Eric Heighberger, FHOB / H2–176 (202) 226–8417.

Staff Director, Subcommittee on Oversight and Management Efficiency.—Ryan Consaul, FHOB / H2–176 (202) 226–8417.

Staff Director, Subcommittee on Transportation Security.—Amanda Parikh, FHOB / H2–176 (202) 226–8417.

Counsel / Investigator.—Jennifer Arangio, FHOB / H2–176 (202) 226–8417.

Deputy Chief Counsel.—Joan O'Hara, FHOB / H2–176 (202) 226–8417.

Senior Counsel.—Kerry Kinirons, FHOB / H2–176 (202) 226–8417.

Senior Counsel.—Dirk Maurer, FHOB / H2–176 (202) 226–8417.

Senior Advisor.—Michael Rosen, FHOB / H2–176 (202) 226–8417.

Senior Advisor for Strategy and Coalitions.—Laura Fullerton, FHOB / H2–176 (202) 226–8417.

Senior Advisor and Coordinator for Jurisdiction.—James Murphy, FHOB / H2–176 (202) 226–8417.

Senior Advisor for Cybersecurity.—Brett DeWitt, FHOB / H2–176 (202) 226–8417.

Advisor.—Joshua Katz, FHOB / H2–176 (202) 226–8417.

Advisor for Border Security.—Tom Leonard, FHOB / H2–176 (202) 226–8417.

Advisor for Transportation Security / DHS Reauthorization.—Robert Carretta, FHOB / H2–176 (202) 226–8417.

Parliamentarian / Counsel.—Steven Giaier, FHOB / H2–176 (202) 226–8417.

Deputy Parliamentarian.—Jake Vreeburg, FHOB / H2–176 (202) 226–8417.

Chief Clerk.—Michael S. Twinchek, FHOB / H2–176 (202) 226–8417.

Deputy Chief Clerk / Administrator.—Natalie Nixon, FHOB / H2–176 (202) 226–8417.

Subcommittee Clerks.—Deborah Jordan, Dennis Terry, FHOB / H2–176 (202) 226–8417.

Communications Director.—Charlotte Sellmeyer, FHOB / H2–176 (202) 226–8417.

Director of Digital Media.—April Corbett, FHOB / H2–176 (202) 226–8417.

Chief Financial Officer.—Dawn M. Criste, FHOB / H2–176 (202) 226–8417.

Senior Professional Staff / Security Director.—Meghann Peterlin, FHOB / H2–176 (202) 226–8417.

Senior Professional Staff.—Luke Burke, FHOB / H2–176 (202) 226–8417.

Assistant Security Director.—Kyle McFarland, FHOB / H2–176 (202) 226–8417.

Professional Staff: Diana Bergwin, Kate Bonvechio, Alan Carroll, Nicole Halavik, Kyle Klein, Jason Miller, Michael Spierto, Bradley Saull, FHOB / H2–176 (202) 226–8417.

Staff Assistants: Tina Garcia, Natalie Matson, Erik Peterson, FHOB / H2–176 (202) 226–8417.

Special Assistant to the Chief of Staff.—Margaret Anne Moore, FHOB / H2–176 (202) 226–8417.

GPO Detailee, Printer.—Heather Crowell, FHOB / H2–176 (202) 226–8417.

Minority (Democratic), Staff Director.—I. Lanier Avant, FHOB / H2–117 (202) 226–2616.

Minority (Democratic), Chief Counsel for Oversight.—Cherri Branson, FHOB / H2–117 (202) 226–2616.

Minority (Democratic), Chief Counsel for Legislation.—Rosaline Cohen, FHOB / H2–117 (202) 226–2616.

Minority (Democratic), Subcommittee on Border and Maritime Security Director and Counsel.—Alison B. Northrop, FHOB / H2–117 (202) 226–2616.

Minority (Democratic), Subcommittee on Counterterrorism and Intelligence Director and Counsel.—Hope Goins, FHOB / H2–117 (202) 226–2616.

Minority (Democratic), Subcommittee on Oversight, Investigations and Management Director and Counsel.—Tamla T. Scott, FHOB / H2–117 (202) 226–2616.

Minority (Democratic), Subcommittee on Transportation Security Director.—Brian B. Turbyfill, FHOB / H2–117 (202) 226–2616.

Minority (Democratic), Senior Professional Staff Member/Counsel.—Nicole Tisdale, FHOB / H2–117 (202) 226–2616.

Minority (Democratic), Senior Professional Staff Member.—K. Christopher Schepis, FHOB / H2–117 (202) 226–2616.

Minority (Democratic), Press Secretary.—Adam M. Comis, FHOB / H2–117 (202) 226–2616.

Minority (Democratic), Professional Staff Members: Moira Bergin, Deborah R. Mack, Shaun West, FHOB / H2–117 (202) 226–2616.

Minority (Democratic), Office Manager.—Nicole Wade Johnson, FHOB / H2–117 (202) 226–2616.

Minority (Democratic), Executive Assistant.—Shante Gauthier, FHOB / H2–117 (202) 226–2616.

Minority (Democratic), Legislative Assistant.—Claytrice Henderson, FHOB / H2–117 (202) 226–2616.

House Administration

1309 Longworth House Office Building, phone 225–8281, fax 225–9957

http://cha.house.gov/

Candice S. Miller, of Michigan, *Chair*

Gregg Harper, of Mississippi.
Phil Gingrey, of Georgia.
Aaron Schock, of Illinois.
Todd Rokita, of Indiana.
Richard B. Nugent, of Florida.

Robert A. Brady, of Pennsylvania.
Zoe Lofgren, of California.
Juan Vargas, of California.

(No Subcommittees)

STAFF

Committee on House Administration (1309 LHOB), 5–2061.
Staff Director.—Kelly Craven.
Deputy Staff Director and Communications Director.—Salley Wood.
Director of Administration.—Mary Sue Englund.
Director of Policy and Planning.—John Clocker.
Director of Member and Committee Services.—George Hadijski.
Director of the Commission on Congressional Mailing Standards.—Richard Cappetto.
Director of Technology Policy.—Reynold Schweickhardt.
Deputy General Counsel.—Peter Schalestock.
Legislative Clerk.—Yael Barash.
Senior Counsel.—Bob Sensenbrenner.
Finance and Personnel Administrator.—Anne Binsted.
Shared Staffer.—Jamie Roe.
Professional Staff: Maximilian Engling, Caitlin Ryan.
Senior Staff Assistants: George Gerbo, Ryan Kelly.
Project Coordinator/Staff Assistant.—Alyssa Hinman.
Member Liaison.—Bradley Walvort.
Democratic Staff Director.—Kyle Anderson.
Deputy Staff Director.—Teri Morgan.
Chief Counsel.—Michael Harrison.
Democratic Chief Clerk.—Eddie Flaherty.
Deputy Counsel.—Khalil Abboud.
Senior Policy Adviser.—Matt Pinkus.
Senior Elections Counsel.—Thomas Hicks.
Democratic Finance Director.—Kim Stevens.
Professional Staff: Gregory Abbott, Matthew DeFreitas, Robert Henline, Kristie Muchnok, Richard Subbio.

Commission on Congressional Mailing Standards (1313 LHOB), 6–0647.
Staff Director.—Richard Cappetto.
Minority Staff Director.—Kyle Anderson.

Judiciary

2138 Rayburn House Office Building, phone 225–3951

http://www.judiciary.house.gov

meets every Wednesday

Bob Goodlatte, of Virginia, *Chair*

F. James Sensenbrenner, Jr., of Wisconsin.
Howard Coble, of North Carolina.
Lamar Smith, of Texas.
Steve Chabot, of Ohio.
Spencer Bachus, of Alabama.
Darrell E. Issa, of California.
J. Randy Forbes, of Virginia.
Steve King, of Iowa.
Trent Franks, of Arizona.
Louie Gohmert, of Texas.
Jim Jordan, of Ohio.
Ted Poe, of Texas.
Jason Chaffetz, of Utah.
Tom Marino, of Pennsylvania.
Trey Gowdy, of South Carolina.
Raúl R. Labrador, of Idaho.
Blake Farenthold, of Texas.
George Holding, of North Carolina.
Doug Collins, of Georgia.
Ron DeSantis, of Florida.
Jason T. Smith, of Missouri.

John Conyers, Jr., of Michigan.
Jerrold Nadler, of New York.
Robert C. ''Bobby'' Scott, of Virginia.
Zoe Lofgren, of California.
Sheila Jackson Lee, of Texas.
Steve Cohen, of Tennessee.
Henry C. ''Hank'' Johnson, Jr., of Georgia.
Pedro R. Pierluisi, of Puerto Rico.
Judy Chu, of California.
Theodore E. Deutch, of Florida.
Luis V. Gutiérrez, of Illinois.
Karen Bass, of California.
Cedric L. Richmond, of Louisiana.
Suzan K. DelBene, of Washington.
Joe Garcia, of Florida.
Hakeem S. Jeffries, of New York.
David N. Cicilline, of Rhode Island.

SUBCOMMITTEES

[The chairman and the ranking minority member are ex officio (non-voting) members of all subcommittees on which they do not serve.]

The Constitution and Civil Justice

Trent Franks, of Arizona, *Chair*

Jim Jordan, of Ohio, *Vice Chair*
Steve Chabot, of Ohio.
J. Randy Forbes, of Virginia.
Steve King, of Iowa.
Louie Gohmert, of Texas.
Ron DeSantis, of Florida.
Jason T. Smith, of Missouri.

Steve Cohen, of Tennessee.
Jerrold Nadler, of New York.
Robert C. ''Bobby'' Scott, of Virginia.
Henry C. ''Hank'' Johnson, Jr., of Georgia.
Theodore E. Deutch, of Florida.

Courts, Intellectual Property, and the Internet

Howard Coble, of North Carolina, *Chair*

Tom Marino, of Pennsylvania, *Vice Chair*
F. James Sensenbrenner, Jr., of Wisconsin.
Lamar Smith, of Texas.
Steve Chabot, of Ohio.
Darrell E. Issa, of California.
Ted Poe, of Texas.
Jason Chaffetz, of Utah.
Blake Farenthold, of Texas.
George Holding, of North Carolina.
Doug Collins, of Georgia.
Ron DeSantis, of Florida.
Jason T. Smith, of Missouri.

Jerry Nadler, of New York.
John Conyers, Jr., of Michigan.
Judy Chu, of California.
Theodore E. Deutch, of Florida.
Karen Bass, of California.
Cedric L. Richmond, of Louisiana.
Suzan K. DelBene, of Washington.
Hakeem S. Jeffries, of New York.
David N. Cicilline, of Rhode Island.
Zoe Lofgren, of California.
Sheila Jackson Lee, of Texas.
Steve Cohen, of Tennessee.

Crime, Terrorism, Homeland Security, and Investigations

F. James Sensenbrenner, Jr., of Wisconsin, *Chair*

Louie Gohmert, of Texas, *Vice Chair.*
Howard Coble, of North Carolina.
Spencer Bachus, of Alabama.
J. Randy Forbes, of Virginia.
Trent Franks, of Arizona.
Jason Chaffetz, of Utah.
Trey Gowdy, of South Carolina.
Raúl R. Labrador, of Idaho.
Robert C. ''Bobby'' Scott, of Virginia.
Pedro R. Pierluisi, of Puerto Rico.
Judy Chu, of California.
Luis V. Gutiérrez, of Illinois.
Karen Bass, of California.
Cedric L. Richmond, of Louisiana.

Immigration and Border Security

Trey Gowdy, of South Carolina, *Chair*

Ted Poe, of Texas, *Vice Chair.*
Lamar Smith, of Texas.
Steve King, of Iowa.
Jim Jordan, of Ohio.
Raúl R. Labrador, of Idaho.
George Holding, of North Carolina.
Zoe Lofgren, of California.
Sheila Jackson Lee, of Texas.
Luis V. Gutiérrez, of Illinois.
Joe Garcia, of Florida.
Pedro R. Pierluisi, of Puerto Rico.

Regulatory Reform, Commercial and Antitrust Law

Spencer Bachus, of Alabama, *Chair*

Blake Farenthold, of Texas, *Vice Chair.*
Darrell E. Issa, of California.
Tom Marino, of Pennsylvania.
George Holding, of North Carolina.
Doug Collins, of Georgia.
Jason T. Smith, of Missouri.
Henry C. ''Hank'' Johnson, Jr., of Georgia.
Suzan K. DelBene, of Washington.
Joe Garcia, of Florida.
Hakeem S. Jeffries, of New York.
David N. Cicilline, of Rhode Island.

STAFF

Committee on the Judiciary (2138 RHOB), 225–3951, fax 5–7680.
Chief of Staff and General Counsel.—Shelley Husband.
Deputy Chief of Staff and Chief Counsel.—Branden Ritchie.
Professional Staff.—Kayla Munro.
Parliamentarian and General Counsel.—Allison Halataei.
Legislative Clerk.—David Lazar.
Reading Clerk.—Kelsey Deterding.
Senior Counsel.—Jason Cervenak.
Counsel.—Stephanie Gadbois.
Communications Director.—Kathryn Rexrode.
Press Secretary.—Jessica Collins.
Deputy Press Secretary.—Lauren Hammond.
Director of New Media.—Amanda Walker.
Public Affairs Liaison.—Bryan Alphin.
Coalitions Director.—Joe Russo.
Staff Assistants: John Manning, Lee Towns.
Financial Administrator.—Patrick Baugh.
Constitution and Civil Justice Subcommittee H2–362 Ford, phone: 5–2825, fax: 5–4299.
Chief Counsel.—Paul Taylor.
Counsels: John Coleman, Zachary Somers.
Clerk.—Tricia White.
Courts, Intellectual Property, and the Internet Subcommittee B–352 Rayburn, phone: 5–5741, fax: 5–3673.
Chief Counsel.—Joe Keeley.
Counsels: Vishal Amin, David Whitney.
Clerk.—Olivia Lee.
IT Office 2451 Rayburn, fax: 5–1842.
Director of Information Technology.—Tom Ullrich.
Deputy Director of Information Technology.—Banyon Vassar.

Committee Publications B–29 Cannon, phone: 5–0408, fax: 5–1842.
Document Clerk.—Tim Pearson.
Committee Printing 105 Cannon, fax: 6–2362.
Committee Printer.—Doug Alexander.
Crime, Terrorism, Homeland Security, and Investigations Subcommittee B–370 Rayburn, phone: 5–5727, fax: 5–3672.
Chief Counsel.—Caroline Lynch.
Counsels: Sarah Allen, Bobby Parmiter, Sam Ramer.
Detailee.—D. Brian Northcutt.
Clerk.—Alicia Church.
Immigration and Border Security Subcommittee B–353 Rayburn, phone: 5–3926, fax: 5–3737.
Chief Counsel.—George Fishman.
Counsels: Andrea Loving, Dimple Shah.
Detailee.—Joshua Braunstein.
Clerk.—Graham Owens.
Regulatory Reform, Commercial and Antitrust Law Subcommittee 517 Cannon, phone: 6–7680, fax: 5–3746.
Chief Counsel.—Daniel Flores.
Counsels: Dan Huff, Anthony Grossi.
Clerk.—Ashley Lewis.
Minority Staff Members
Minority Chief Counsel and Staff Director.—Perry Apelbaum, 2142 Rayburn, phone: 5–6504, fax: 5–7686.
Professional Staff.—Maggie Lopatin.
Minority Offices B–351 Rayburn, B–336 Rayburn, and H2–347 Ford, phone: 5–6906, fax: 5–7682.
Minority Counsels: Danielle Brown, Jason Everett, Joe Graupensperger, Aaron Hiller, Tom Jawetz, Susan Jensen, Keenan Keller, Michelle Millben, David Lachmann, Ron LeGrand, Heather Sawyer, Stephanie Moore, David Shahoulian, Ashley McDonald, James Park, Norberto Salinas.
Press Secretary.—Andrew Schreiber.
Professional Staff: Veronica Eligan, Rosalind Jackson, Dwight Sullivan.

Natural Resources

1324 Longworth House Office Building, phone 225–2761

http://naturalresources.house.gov

meets each Wednesday

Doc Hastings, of Washington, *Chair*

Don Young, of Alaska.
Louie Gohmert, of Texas.
Rob Bishop, of Utah.
Doug Lamborn, of Colorado.
Robert J. Wittman, of Virginia.
Paul C. Broun, of Georgia.
John Fleming, of Louisiana.
Tom McClintock, of California.
Glenn Thompson, of Pennsylvania.
Cynthia M. Lummis, of Wyoming.
Dan Benishek, of Michigan.
Jeff Duncan, of South Carolina.
Scott R. Tipton, of Colorado.
Paul A. Gosar, of Arizona.
Raúl R. Labrador, of Idaho.
Steve Southerland II, of Florida.
Bill Flores, of Texas.
Jon Runyan, of New Jersey.
Markwayne Mullin, of Oklahoma.
Steve Daines, of Montana.
Kevin Cramer, of North Dakota.
Doug LaMalfa, of California.
Jason T. Smith, of Missouri.
Vance M. McAllister, of Louisiana.
Bradley Byrne, of Alabama.

Peter A. DeFazio, of Oregon.
Eni F. H. Faleomavaega, of American Samoa.
Frank Pallone, Jr., of New Jersey.
Grace F. Napolitano, of California.
Rush Holt, of New Jersey.
Raúl M. Grijalva, of Arizona.
Madeleine Z. Bordallo, of Guam.
Jim Costa, of California.
Gregorio Kilili Camacho Sablan, of Northern Mariana Islands.
Niki Tsongas, of Massachusetts.
Pedro R. Pierluisi, of Puerto Rico.
Colleen W. Hanabusa, of Hawaii.
Tony Cárdenas, of California.
Steven A. Horsford, of Nevada.
Jared Huffman, of California.
Raul Ruiz, of California.
Carol Shea-Porter, of New Hampshire.
Alan S. Lowenthal, of California.
Joe Garcia, of Florida.
Matt Cartwright, of Pennsylvania.
Katherine M. Clark, of Massachusetts.

SUBCOMMITTEES

[The chairman and ranking minority member are ex officio (non-voting) members of all subcommittees on which they do not serve.]

Energy and Mineral Resources

Doug Lamborn, of Colorado, *Chair*

Louie Gohmert, of Texas.
Rob Bishop, of Utah.
Robert J. Wittman, of Virginia.
Paul C. Broun, of Georgia.
John Fleming, of Louisiana.
Glenn Thompson, of Pennsylvania.
Cynthia M. Lummis, of Wyoming.
Dan Benishek, of Michigan.
Jeff Duncan, of South Carolina.
Paul A. Gosar, of Arizona.
Bill Flores, of Texas.
Steve Daines, of Montana.
Kevin Cramer, of North Dakota.

Rush Holt, of New Jersey.
Steven A. Horsford, of Nevada.
Matt Cartwright, of Pennsylvania.
Jim Costa, of California.
Niki Tsongas, of Massachusetts.
Jared Huffman, of California.
Alan S. Lowenthal, of California.
Tony Cárdenas, of California.
Raúl M. Grijalva, of Arizona.
Colleen W. Hanabusa, of Hawaii.
Joe Garcia, of Florida.
Katherine M. Clark, of Massachusetts.

Fisheries, Wildlife, Oceans and Insular Affairs

John Fleming, of Louisiana, *Chair*

Don Young, of Alaska.
Robert J. Wittman, of Virginia.
Glenn Thompson, of Pennsylvania.
Jeff Duncan, of South Carolina.
Steve Southerland II, of Florida.
Bill Flores, of Texas.
Jon Runyan, of New Jersey.
Vance M. McAllister, of Louisiana.
Bradley Byrne, of Alabama.

Gregorio Kilili Camacho Sablan, of Northern Mariana Islands.
Eni F. H. Faleomavaega, of American Samoa.
Frank Pallone, Jr., of New Jersey.
Madeleine Z. Bordallo, of Guam.
Pedro R. Pierluisi, of Puerto Rico.
Carol Shea-Porter, of New Hampshire.
Alan S. Lowenthal, of California.
Joe Garcia, of Florida.

Indian and Alaska Native Affairs

Don Young, of Alaska, *Chair*

Dan Benishek, of Michigan.
Paul A. Gosar, of Arizona.
Markwayne Mullin, of Oklahoma.
Steve Daines, of Montana.
Kevin Cramer, of North Dakota.
Doug LaMalfa, of California.

Colleen W. Hanabusa, of Hawaii.
Tony Cárdenas, of California.
Raul Ruiz, of California.
Eni F. H. Faleomavaega, of American Samoa.
Raúl M. Grijalva, of Arizona.

Public Lands and Environmental Regulation

Rob Bishop, of Utah, *Chair*

Don Young, of Alaska.
Louie Gohmert, of Texas.
Doug Lamborn, of Colorado.
Paul C. Broun, of Georgia.
Tom McClintock, of California.
Cynthia M. Lummis, of Wyoming.
Scott R. Tipton, of Colorado.
Raúl R. Labrador, of Idaho.
Steve Daines, of Montana.
Kevin Cramer, of North Dakota.
Doug LaMalfa, of California.
Jason T. Smith, of Missouri.
Vance M. McAllister, of Louisiana.

Raúl M. Grijalva, of Arizona.
Niki Tsongas, of Massachusetts.
Rush Holt, of New Jersey.
Madeleine Z. Bordallo, of Guam.
Gregorio Kilili Camacho Sablan, of Northern Mariana Islands.
Pedro R. Pierluisi, of Puerto Rico.
Colleen W. Hanabusa, of Hawaii.
Steven A. Horsford, of Nevada.
Carol Shea-Porter, of New Hampshire.
Joe Garcia, of Florida.
Matt Cartwright, of Pennsylvania.
Jared Huffman, of California.

Water and Power

Tom McClintock, of California, *Chair*

Cynthia M. Lummis, of Wyoming.
Scott R. Tipton, of Colorado.
Paul A. Gosar, of Arizona.
Raúl R. Labrador, of Idaho.
Doug LaMalfa, of California.
Jason T. Smith, of Missouri.
Bradley Byrne, of Alabama.

Grace F. Napolitano, of California.
Jim Costa, of California.
Jared Huffman, of California.
Tony Cárdenas, of California.
Raul Ruiz, of California.
Alan S. Lowenthal, of California.

STAFF

Committee on Natural Resources (1324 LHOB), 5–2761.
Majority Chief of Staff.—Todd Young.
Director of Legislative Operations.—Kathy Loden.
Chief Legislative Counsel.—Lisa Pittman.
Director of NW Energy and Environmental Policy, Senior Counsel.—Todd Ungerecht.
Senior Policy Advisor, Director of Outreach.—Martin Doern.
Senior Oversight Counsel, Office of Oversight and Investigations.—Byron Brown.
Senior Counsel, Office of Oversight and Investigations.—Machalagh Carr.

Counsel, Office of Oversight and Investigations: Jessica Conrad, Andrew Vecera.
Staff Assistants: Marc Alberts, Matt Schafle.
Communications Director.—Jill Strait (1328 LHOB), 6–9109.
Press Secretary.—Michael Tadeo.
Online Communications Manager.—Neal Kirby.
Deputy Press Secretary.—Mallory Micetich.
Press Assistant.—Maeve McKenna.
Personnel and Financial Officer.—Meghan Foley.
Calendar Clerk.—Joycelyn Coleman.
Director, Information Technology.—Matt Vaccaro.
Senior IT Engineer.—Ed Van Scoyoc.
Democratic Staff Director.—Penny Dodge (1329 LHOB), 5–6065.
Chief Democratic Counsel.—David Watkins.
Deputy Democratic Staff Director.—Amelia Jenkins (H2–186), 5–6065.
Democratic Senior Policy Advisors: Jean Flemma, Travis Joseph (H2–186), 5–6065.
Chief Democratic Clerk.—Jamie Harrell.
Democratic Communications Director.—Jennifer Gilbreath (H2–186), 5–6065.
Democratic Press Assistant.—Ashley Guill.
Democratic Staff Assistants: Peter Gallagher, Matthew Muirragui-Villagomez.
Democratic Director of Oversight and Investigation.—Reece Rushing.
Democratic Investigator.—Ryan Holden.

Subcommittee on Energy and Mineral Resources (1333 LHOB), 5–9297.
Majority Staff Director.—Tim Charters.
Legislative Staff: Kathy Benedetto, Katharine MacGregor, Amanda Tharpe.
Clerk.—Sophia Varnasidis.
Democratic Senior Energy Policy Advisor.—Steve Feldgus (H2–186), 5–6065.
Democratic Professional Staff Member.—Anthony Sedillo.

Subcommittee on Fisheries, Wildlife, Oceans and Insular Affairs (140 CHOB), 6–0200.
Majority Staff Director.—Harry Burroughs.
Legislative Staff: Bonnie Bruce, Dave Whaley.
Clerk.—Marc Alberts.
Democratic Counsel, Insular Affairs.—Brian Modeste (H2–186), 5–6065.
Democratic Professional Staff Member.—Matt Strickler (H2–186), 5–6065.

Subcommittee on Indian and Alaska Native Affairs (1337 LHOB), 6–9725.
Majority Staff Director.—Chris Fluhr.
Professional Legislative Staff.—Brandon Ashley.
Clerk.—Sophia Varnasidis.

Subcommittee on Public Lands and Environmental Regulation (1017 LHOB), 6–7736.
Majority Staff Director.—Jim Streeter.
Legislative Staff: Casey Hammond, Tyler Hamman, Otto Mucklo.
Clerk.—Bryson Wong.
Democratic Professional Staff Members: Brandon Bragato, Anthony Sedillo.

Subcommittee on Water and Power (1522 LHOB), 5–8331.
Majority Staff Director.—Kiel Weaver.
Legislative Staff.—Adam Eckman.
Clerk.—Matt Gall.
Democratic Professional Staff Member.—Camille Calimlim Touton (H2–186), 5–6065.

Oversight and Government Reform

2157 Rayburn House Office Building, phone 225–5074, fax 225–3974, TTY 225–6852

http://oversight.house.gov

Darrell E. Issa, of California, *Chair*

John L. Mica, of Florida.
Michael R. Turner, of Ohio.
John J. Duncan, Jr., of Tennessee.
Patrick T. McHenry, of North Carolina.
Jim Jordan, of Ohio.
Jason Chaffetz, of Utah.
Tim Walberg, of Michigan.
James Lankford, of Oklahoma.
Justin Amash, of Michigan.
Paul A. Gosar, of Arizona.
Patrick Meehan, of Pennsylvania.
Scott DesJarlais, of Tennessee.
Trey Gowdy, of South Carolina.
Blake Farenthold, of Texas.
Doc Hastings, of Washington.
Cynthia M. Lummis, of Wyoming.
Rob Woodall, of Georgia.
Thomas Massie, of Kentucky.
Doug Collins, of Georgia.
Mark Meadows, of North Carolina.
Kerry L. Bentivolio, of Michigan.
Ron DeSantis, of Florida.

Elijah E. Cummings, of Maryland.
Carolyn B. Maloney, of New York.
Eleanor Holmes Norton, of District of Columbia.
John F. Tierney, of Massachusetts.
Wm. Lacy Clay, of Missouri.
Stephen F. Lynch, of Massachusetts.
Jim Cooper, of Tennessee.
Gerald E. Connolly, of Virginia.
Jackie Speier, of California.
Matt Cartwright, of Pennsylvania.
Tammy Duckworth, of Illinois.
Robin L. Kelly, of Illinois.
Danny K. Davis, of Illinois.
Peter Welch, of Vermont.
Tony Cárdenas, of California.
Steven A. Horsford, of Nevada.
Michelle Lujan Grisham, of New Mexico.

SUBCOMMITTEES

[The chairman and ranking minority member are ex officio (voting) members of all subcommittees]

Economic Growth, Job Creation and Regulatory Affairs

Jim Jordan, of Ohio, *Chair*

Ron DeSantis, of Florida, *Vice Chair*
John J. Duncan, Jr., of Tennessee.
Patrick T. McHenry, of North Carolina.
Paul A. Gosar, of Arizona.
Patrick Meehan, of Pennsylvania.
Scott DesJarlais, of Tennessee.
Doc Hastings, of Washington.
Cynthia M. Lummis, of Wyoming.
Doug Collins, of Georgia.
Mark Meadows, of North Carolina.
Kerry L. Bentivolio, of Michigan.

Matt Cartwright, of Pennsylvania.
Tammy Duckworth, of Illinois.
Gerald E. Connolly, of Virginia.
Robin L. Kelly, of Illinois.
Danny K. Davis, of Illinois.
Steven A. Horsford, of Nevada.

Energy Policy, Health Care and Entitlements

James Lankford, of Oklahoma, *Chair*

Paul A. Gosar, of Arizona, *Vice Chair*

Patrick T. McHenry, of North Carolina.
Jim Jordan, of Ohio.
Jason Chaffetz, of Utah.
Tim Walberg, of Michigan.
Patrick Meehan, of Pennsylvania.
Scott DesJarlais, of Tennessee.
Blake Farenthold, of Texas.
Doc Hastings, of Washington.
Rob Woodall, of Georgia.
Thomas Massie, of Kentucky.

Jackie Speier, of California.
Eleanor Holmes Norton, of District of Columbia.
Jim Cooper, of Tennessee.
Matt Cartwright, of Pennsylvania.
Tammy Duckworth, of Illinois.
Danny K. Davis, of Illinois.
Tony Cárdenas, of California.
Michelle Lujan Grisham, of New Mexico.
Steven A. Horsford, of Nevada.

Federal Workforce, U.S. Postal Service and the Census

Blake Farenthold, of Texas, *Chair*

Tim Walberg, of Michigan, *Vice Chair*

Trey Gowdy, of South Carolina.
Doug Collins, of Georgia.
Ron DeSantis, of Florida.

Stephen F. Lynch, of Massachusetts.
Eleanor Holmes Norton, of District of Columbia.
Wm. Lacy Clay, of Missouri.

Government Operations

John L. Mica, of Florida, *Chair*

Mark Meadows, of North Carolina, *Vice Chair*

Michael R. Turner, of Ohio.
Justin Amash, of Michigan.
Thomas Massie, of Kentucky.

Gerald E. Connolly, of Virginia.
Jim Cooper, of Tennessee.

National Security

Jason Chaffetz, of Utah, *Chair*

Cynthia M. Lummis, of Wyoming, *Vice Chair*

John L. Mica, of Florida.
John J. Duncan, Jr., of Tennessee.
Justin Amash, of Michigan.
Paul A. Gosar, of Arizona.
Trey Gowdy, of South Carolina.
Rob Woodall, of Georgia.
Kerry L. Bentivolio, of Michigan.

John F. Tierney, of Massachusetts.
Carolyn B. Maloney, of New York.
Stephen F. Lynch, of Massachusetts.
Jackie Speier, of California.
Robin L. Kelly, of Illinois.
Peter Welch, of Vermont.
Michelle Lujan Grisham, of New Mexico.

STAFF

Oversight and Government Reform (2157 RHOB), 202–225–5074.
Majority Staff Director.—Lawrence J. Brady.
Deputy Staff Director.—John Cuaderes.
General Counsel.—Steve Castor.
Deputy General Counsel.—Jonathan Skladany.
Director of Member Services and Committee Operations.—Adam Fromm.
Deputy General Counsel and Parliamentarian.—Molly Boyl.
Deputy Staff Director for Communications and Strategy.—Frederick Hill.
Communications Director.—Rebecca Watkins.
Senior Communications Advisor.—Ali Ahmad.
Press Secretary.—Caitlin Carroll.
Press Assistant.—Will Boyington.
Legislative Policy Director.—Peter Warren.
Deputy Policy Director.—Jennifer Hemingway.

Senior Counsel.—Richard Beutel.
Senior Professional Staff Member.—Jeffrey Post, James Robertson.
Professional Staff Member.—Jenna VanSant.
Chief Clerk.—Linda Good.
Deputy Chief Clerk.—Laura Rush.
Senior Assistant Clerk.—Sharon Casey.
Assistant Clerks.—Daniel Buchelli, Sarah Vance.
Legislative Assistants: Alexa Armstrong, Michael Kiko.
Staff Assistants: Melissa Beaumont, Donna Harkins.
Executive Assistant.—Kathy Brayton.
Financial Administrator.—Robin Butler.
Deputy Chief Information Officer.—Jeff Wease.
Deputy Staff Director of Oversight.—Mark Marin.
Chief Counsel for Oversight.—Christopher Hixon.
Senior Counsels: David Brewer, Howard Denis.
Counsels: Joseph Brazauskas, Brian Daner, Mitchell Kominsky, Emily Martin, Katy Rother.
Senior Policy Advisor.—Jim Lewis.
Senior Professional Staff: Brian Blasé, Tyler Grimm, Ryan Hambleton.
Professional Staff Members: Brien Beattie, Katelyn Christ, Drew Colliatie, Meinan Goto, Tegan Millspaw, Sharon Utz, Sang Yi.
Chief Counsel for Investigations.—Ashok Pinto.
Deputy Chief Counsel for Investigations.—Ashley Callen.
Senior Counsels: Carlton Davis, Jessica Donlon.
Counsels: Jen Barblan, Lamar Echols, Jean Humbrecht.
Senior Professional Staff Member.—John Ohly.
Professional Staff: Kate Dunbar, Caroline Ingram.
Investigator.—Matthew Tallmer.

2471 Rayburn House Office Building (2471 RHOB) phone 225–5051, fax 225–4784, TTY 225–6852, http://democrats.oversight.house.gov.
Minority Staff Director.—Dave Rapallo.
Minority Deputy Staff Director/Chief Counsel.—Susanne Sachsman Grooms.
Minority Chief Oversight Counsel.—Leah Perry.
Minority Director of Legislation.—Mark Stephenson.
Minority Deputy Director of Legislation/Counsel.—Krista Boyd.
Minority Policy Director.—Lucinda Lessley.
Minority Administrative Director.—Jaron Bourke.
Minority Communications Director.—Jennifer Hoffman.
Minority Press Secretary.—Aryele Bradford.
Minority New Media Press Secretary.—Julia Krieger.
Minority Senior Investigator.—Chris Knauer.
Minority Senior Counsel.—Jason Powell.
Minority Counsels: Tamara Alexander, Meghan Berroya, Lena Chang, Yvette Cravins, Beverly Britton Fraser, Peter Kenny, Una Lee, Brian Quinn, Valerie Shen, Donald Sherman, Cecelia Thomas.
Minority Professional Staff Member.—Kevin Corbin.
Director of Operations.—Elisa LaNier.
Clerk.—Juan McCullum.
Research Assistants: Devon Hill, Adam Koshkin.
Technology Director.—Eddie Walker.

Rules

H–312 The Capitol, phone 225–9191

http://www.rules.house.gov

meets every Tuesday

Pete Sessions, of Texas, *Chair*

Virginia Foxx, of North Carolina.
Rob Bishop, of Utah.
Tom Cole, of Oklahoma.
Rob Woodall, of Georgia.
Richard B. Nugent, of Florida.
Daniel Webster, of Florida.
Ileana Ros-Lehtinen, of Florida.
Michael C. Burgess, of Texas.

Louise McIntosh Slaughter, of New York.
James P. McGovern, of Massachusetts.
Alcee L. Hastings, of Florida.
Jared Polis, of Colorado.

SUBCOMMITTEES

Legislative and Budget Process

Rob Woodall, of Georgia, *Chair*

Virginia Foxx, of North Carolina.
Richard B. Nugent, of Florida.
Daniel Webster, of Florida.
Michael C. Burgess, of Texas.

Alcee L. Hastings, of Florida.
Jared Polis, of Colorado.

Rules and Organization of the House

Richard B. Nugent, of Florida, *Chair*

Rob Bishop, of Utah.
Ileana Ros-Lehtinen, of Florida.
Daniel Webster, of Florida.
Pete Sessions, of Texas.

James P. McGovern, of Massachusetts.
Louise McIntosh Slaughter, of New York.

STAFF

Committee on Rules (H–312 The Capitol), 225–9191.
Majority Staff Director.—Hugh Halpern.
Deputy Staff Director.—Towner French.
Policy Director.—Robert Cousins.
Communications Director.—Torrie Miller.
Deputy Communications Director.—Doug Andres.
Professional Staff: Nathan Blake, Stephen Cote, Karas Pattison.
Director of Information Technology.—Chris Erb.
Director of Finance and Administration.—Sarah Minkel.
Policy Counsel.—Neil Bjorkman.
Chief Clerk.—Monica Chinn.
Legislative Clerk.—Alec Davis.
Associate Staff: Tomas Lewis (1727 LHOB); Lale Mamaux (2353 RHOB); Brandon Renz (2350 RHOB); Janet Rossi (1725 LHOB); Keith Stern (438 CHOB).
Minority Staff Director.—Miles Lackey.
Deputy Staff Director of Floor Operations.—Don Sisson.
Minority Counsel.—Adam Berg.
Minority Policy Director.—Lauren Believe.
Professional Staff: Tony Abate, David Cooper-Vince.
Chief Clerk.—Deb Delaney.
Legislative Clerk.—George Agurkis.
Press Secretary.—Eric Walker.
Speechwriter and Director of Online Communications: Andrew Lewis.
Subcommittee on Legislative and Budget Process (1725 LHOB), 5–4272.
Majority Staff Director.—Janet Rossi (Woodall).

Minority Staff Director.—Lale Mamaux (Hastings).

Subcommittee on Rules and Organization of the House (1727 LHOB), 5–1002.

Majority Staff Director.—Thomas Lewis (Nugent).

Minority Staff Director.—Keith Stern (McGovern).

Science, Space, and Technology

2321 Rayburn House Office Building, phone 225–6371, fax 226–0113

http://www.house.gov/science

meets second and fourth Wednesdays of each month

Lamar Smith, of Texas, *Chair*

Dana Rohrabacher, of California, *Vice Chair*

F. James Sensenbrenner, Jr., of Wisconsin.
Ralph M. Hall, of Texas.
Frank D. Lucas, of Oklahoma.
Randy Neugebauer, of Texas.
Michael T. McCaul, of Texas.
Paul C. Broun, of Georgia.
Steven M. Palazzo, of Mississippi.
Mo Brooks, of Alabama.
Randy Hultgren, of Illinois.
Larry Bucshon, of Indiana.
Steve Stockman, of Texas.
Bill Posey, of Florida.
Cynthia M. Lummis, of Wyoming.
David Schweikert, of Arizona.
Thomas Massie, of Kentucky.
Kevin Cramer, of North Dakota.
Jim Bridenstine, of Oklahoma.
Randy K. Weber, Sr., of Texas.
Chris Collins, of New York.

Eddie Bernice Johnson, of Texas.
Zoe Lofgren, of California.
Daniel Lipinski, of Illinois.
Donna F. Edwards, of Maryland.
Frederica S. Wilson, of Florida.
Suzanne Bonamici, of Oregon.
Eric Swalwell, of California.
Daniel B. Maffei, of New York.
Alan Grayson, of Florida.
Joseph P. Kennedy III, of Massachusetts.
Scott H. Peters, of California.
Derek Kilmer, of Washington.
Ami Bera, of California.
Elizabeth H. Esty, of Connecticut.
Marc A. Veasey, of Texas.
Julia Brownley, of California.
Mark Takano, of California.
Robin L. Kelly, of Illinois.

SUBCOMMITTEES

[The chairman and ranking minority member are ex officio (voting) members of all subcommittees on which they do not serve.]

Energy

Cynthia M. Lummis, of Wyoming, *Chair*

Randy K. Weber, Sr., of Texas, *Vice Chair*

Ralph M. Hall, of Texas.
Frank D. Lucas, of Oklahoma.
Randy Neugebauer, of Texas.
Michael T. McCaul, of Texas.
Randy Hultgren, of Illinois.
Thomas Massie, of Kentucky.
Kevin Cramer, of North Dakota.

Eric Swalwell, of California.
Alan Grayson, of Florida.
Joseph P. Kennedy III, of Massachusetts.
Marc A. Veasey, of Texas.
Mark Takano, of California.
Zoe Lofgren, of California.
Daniel Lipinski, of Illinois.

Environment

David Schweikert, of Arizona, *Chair*

Jim Bridenstine, of Oklahoma, *Vice Chair*

F. James Sensenbrenner, Jr., of Wisconsin.
Dana Rohrabacher, of California.
Randy Neugebauer, of Texas.
Paul C. Broun, of Georgia.
Randy K. Weber, Sr., of Texas.

Suzanne Bonamici, of Oregon.
Julia Brownley, of California.
Donna F. Edwards, of Maryland.
Mark Takano, of California.
Alan Grayson, of Florida.

Oversight

Paul C. Broun, of Georgia, *Chair*
Kevin Cramer, of North Dakota, *Vice Chair*

F. James Sensenbrenner, Jr., of Wisconsin.
Bill Posey, of Florida.
Daniel B. Maffei, of New York.
Eric Swalwell, of California.
Scott H. Peters, of California.

Research and Technology

Larry Bucshon, of Indiana, *Chair*
Thomas Massie, of Kentucky, *Vice Chair*

Steven M. Palazzo, of Mississippi.
Mo Brooks, of Alabama.
Randy Hultgren, of Illinois.
Steve Stockman, of Texas.
Cynthia M. Lummis, of Wyoming.
Jim Bridenstine, of Oklahoma.
Chris Collins, of New York.
Daniel Lipinski, of Illinois.
Frederica S. Wilson, of Florida.
Zoe Lofgren, of California.
Scott H. Peters, of California.
Ami Bera, of California.
Derek Kilmer, of Washington.
Elizabeth H. Esty, of Connecticut.
Robin L. Kelly, of Illinois.

Space

Steven M. Palazzo, of Mississippi, *Chair*
Mo Brooks, of Alabama, *Vice Chair*

Ralph M. Hall, of Texas.
Dana Rohrabacher, of California.
Frank D. Lucas, of Oklahoma.
Michael T. McCaul, of Texas.
Larry Bucshon, of Indiana.
Steve Stockman, of Texas.
Bill Posey, of Florida.
David Schweikert, of Arizona.
Jim Bridenstine, of Oklahoma.
Chris Collins, of New York.
Donna F. Edwards, of Maryland.
Suzanne Bonamici, of Oregon.
Daniel B. Maffei, of New York.
Joseph P. Kennedy III, of Massachusetts.
Derek Kilmer, of Washington.
Ami Bera, of California.
Marc A. Veasey, of Texas.
Julia Brownley, of California.
Frederica S. Wilson, of Florida.

STAFF

Committee on Science, Space, and Technology (2321 RHOB), 225–6371, fax 226–0113.
Majority Staff:
Chief of Staff.—Jennifer Brown.
Policy Director.—Chris Shank.
Policy Assistant.—William Henderson.
Administration:
Administrative Director.—Ashley Smith.
Financial Administrator.—John Ross.
Printer.—Sangina Wright.
IT Services.—David Hartzler, House Call.
Communications:
Deputy Chief of Staff for Communications.—Kim Smith.
Press Secretary.—Zac Kurz.
Press Assistant.—Erin Havener.
Editor/Speechwriter.—James Danford.
Counsel:
Chief Counsel.—Holt Lackey.
Deputy Chief Counsel.—Katy Flynn.
Legislative Counsel.—Lana Frost.
Energy Subcommittee
Staff Director.—Stephan Sayle.
Professional Staff.—Andy Zach.
Research Assistant.—Taylor Jordan.
AAAS Fellow.—Mahantesh Hiremath.

Environment Subcommittee
Staff Director.—Todd Johnston.
Professional Staff: Rachel Jones, Client Woods.
Research Assistant.—Taylor Jordan.
Oversight Subcommittee
Staff Director.—Raj Bharwani.
Senior Advisor to the Chairman.—Chris Wydler.
Staff Assistant.—Sarah Grady.
AAAS Fellow.—Mike McQuade.
Research and Technology Subcommittee
Staff Director.—Cliff Shannon.
Professional Staff: Kirsten Duncan, Richard Yamada.
Policy Staff.—Gabriella Ra'anan.
AAAS Fellow.—Bharat Bhushan.
Space Subcommittee
Staff Director.—Tom Hammond.
Professional Staff: Allison Rose, Jared Stout.
Policy Staff.—Gabriella Ra'anan.
Minority Staff:
Chief of Staff.—Richard Obermann.
Chief Counsel.—John Piazza.
Deputy Chief Counsel.—Russell Norman.
Administrative and Communications Director.—Kristin Kopshever.
Deputy Communications Director.—Pamitha Weerasinghe.
Energy Subcommittee
Professional Staff: Chris O'Leary, Adam Rosenberg.
Environment Subcommittee
Professional Staff.—Andrea Jones.
Oversight Subcommittee
Staff Director.—Dan Pearson.
Professional Staff.—Doug Pasternak.
Research and Technology Subcommittee
Staff Director.—Dahlia Sokolov.
Staff Director.—Marey Gallo.
Staff Director.—Brystol English.
Professional Staff.—Kim Montgomery.
Space Subcommittee
Professional Staff: Allen Li, Pam Whitney.

Small Business

2361 Rayburn House Office Building, phone 225–5821, fax 226–5276

http://www.smallbusiness.house.gov/

meets second Wednesday of each month

Sam Graves, of Missouri, *Chair*

Steve Chabot, of Ohio.
Steve King, of Iowa.
Mike Coffman, of Colorado.
Blaine Luetkemeyer, of Missouri, *Vice Chair*.
Mick Mulvaney, of South Carolina.
Scott R. Tipton, of Colorado.
Jaime Herrera Beutler, of Washington.
Richard L. Hanna, of New York.
Tim Huelskamp, of Kansas.
David Schweikert, of Arizona.
Kerry L. Bentivolio, of Michigan.
Chris Collins, of New York.
Tom Rice, of South Carolina.

Nydia M. Velázquez, of New York.
Kurt Schrader, of Oregon.
Yvette D. Clarke, of New York.
Judy Chu, of California.
Janice Hahn, of California.
Donald M. Payne, Jr., of New Jersey.
Grace Meng, of New York.
Bradley S. Schneider, of Illinois.
Ron Barber, of Arizona.
Ann M. Kuster, of New Hampshire.
Patrick Murphy, of Florida.

SUBCOMMITTEES

[The chairman and ranking minority member are ex officio (non-voting) members of all subcommittees for purposes of any meeting or hearing.]

Agriculture, Energy and Trade

Scott R. Tipton, of Colorado, *Chair*
Steve King, of Iowa.
Blaine Luetkemeyer, of Missouri.
Mick Mulvaney, of South Carolina.
Richard L. Hanna, of New York.
Tim Huelskamp, of Kansas.

Patrick Murphy, of Florida.
Kurt Schrader, of Oregon.
Grace Meng, of New York.
Ron Barber, of Arizona.

Contracting and Workforce

Richard L. Hanna, of New York, *Chair*

Steve King, of Iowa.
Mick Mulvaney, of South Carolina.
Scott R. Tipton, of Colorado.
Tim Huelskamp, of Kansas.
Kerry L. Bentivolio, of Michigan.

Grace Meng, of New York.
Yvette D. Clarke, of New York.
Judy Chu, of California.

Economic Growth, Tax and Capital Access

Tom Rice, of South Carolina, *Chair*

Steve Chabot, of Ohio.
Steve King, of Iowa.
Mike Coffman, of Colorado.
Mick Mulvaney, of South Carolina.
David Schweikert, of Arizona.

Judy Chu, of California.
Donald M. Payne, Jr., of New Jersey.
Bradley S. Schneider, of Illinois.
Ron Barber, of Arizona.

Healthcare and Technology

Chris Collins, of New York, *Chair*

Steve King, of Iowa.
Mike Coffman, of Colorado.
Blaine Luetkemeyer, of Missouri.
Jaime Herrera Beutler, of Washington.
Tim Huelskamp, of Kansas.
Janice Hahn, of California.
Kurt Schrader, of Oregon.
Bradley S. Schneider, of Illinois.

Investigations, Oversight and Regulations

Vacant, *Chair*

Steve Chabot, of Ohio.
Jaime Herrera Beutler, of Washington.
Kerry L. Bentivolio, of Michigan.
Chris Collins, of New York.
Tom Rice, of South Carolina.
Yvette D. Clarke, of New York.
Judy Chu, of California.
Ann M. Kuster, of New Hampshire.

STAFF

Committee on Small Business (2361 RHOB).
Majority Staff Director.—Lori Salley Ring (2361 RHOB) 225–5821
Deputy Staff Director.—Paul Sass.
Chief Counsel.—Barry Pineles.
Deputy Chief Counsel.—Jan Oliver.
Senior Counsel.—Emily Murphy.
Counsels: Corey Cooke, Andy Guggenheim, Viktoria Ziebarth.
Communications Director.—D.J. Jordan.
Press Secretary.—Joel Hannahs.
Clerk / Professional Staff.—Susan Marshall.
Professional Staff: Joe Hartz, Andy Karellas, Mark Ratto.
Legislative Assistant.—Andrew Huff.
Staff Assistant.—Grant Hannah.
Chief of Staff to the Member.—Tom Brown.
Minority Staff Director.—Michael Day.
Deputy Staff Director.—Adam Minehardt.
Banking Counsel.—Justin Pelletier.
Office Manager.—Mory Garcia.
Communications Director.—Alex Haurek.
Procurement Counsel.—Eminence Northcutt.
Tax Counsel.—Melissa Jung.

Transportation and Infrastructure

2165 Rayburn House Office Building, phone 225–4472, fax 225–4629

http://www.house.gov/transportation

meets first Wednesday of each month

Majority (202) 225–9446, room 2165 RHOB

Minority (202) 225–4472, room 2163 RHOB

Bill Shuster, of Pennsylvania, *Chair*

John J. Duncan, Jr., of Tennessee, *Vice Chair*

Don Young, of Alaska.
Thomas E. Petri, of Wisconsin.
Howard Coble, of North Carolina.
John L. Mica, of Florida.
Frank A. LoBiondo, of New Jersey.
Gary G. Miller, of California.
Sam Graves, of Missouri.
Shelley Moore Capito, of West Virginia.
Candice S. Miller, of Michigan.
Duncan Hunter, of California.
Eric A. ''Rick'' Crawford, of Arkansas.
Lou Barletta, of Pennsylvania.
Blake Farenthold, of Texas.
Larry Bucshon, of Indiana.
Bob Gibbs, of Ohio.
Patrick Meehan, of Pennsylvania.
Richard L. Hanna, of New York.
Daniel Webster, of Florida.
Steve Southerland II, of Florida.
Jeff Denham, of California.
Reid J. Ribble, of Wisconsin.
Thomas Massie, of Kentucky.
Steve Daines, of Montana.
Tom Rice, of South Carolina.
Markwayne Mullin, of Oklahoma.
Roger Williams, of Texas.
Mark Meadows, of North Carolina.
Scott Perry, of Pennsylvania.
Rodney Davis, of Illinois.
Mark Sanford, of South Carolina.

Nick J. Rahall II, of West Virginia.
Peter A. DeFazio, of Oregon.
Eleanor Holmes Norton, of District of Columbia.
Jerrold Nadler, of New York.
Corrine Brown, of Florida.
Eddie Bernice Johnson, of Texas.
Elijah E. Cummings, of Maryland.
Rick Larsen, of Washington.
Michael E. Capuano, of Massachusetts.
Timothy H. Bishop, of New York.
Michael H. Michaud, of Maine.
Grace F. Napolitano, of California.
Daniel Lipinski, of Illinois.
Timothy J. Walz, of Minnesota.
Steve Cohen, of Tennessee.
Albio Sires, of New Jersey.
Donna F. Edwards, of Maryland.
John Garamendi, of California.
André Carson, of Indiana.
Janice Hahn, of California.
Richard M. Nolan, of Minnesota.
Ann Kirkpatrick, of Arizona.
Dina Titus, of Nevada.
Sean Patrick Maloney, of New York.
Elizabeth H. Esty, of Connecticut.
Lois Frankel, of Florida.
Cheri Bustos, of Illinois.

SUBCOMMITTEES

[The chairman and ranking minority member are ex officio (voting) members of all subcommittees on which they do not serve.]

Aviation

Frank A. LoBiondo, of New Jersey, *Chair*

Rodney Davis, of Illinois. *Vice Chair*

Thomas E. Petri, of Wisconsin.
Howard Coble, of North Carolina.
John J. Duncan, Jr., of Tennessee.
Sam Graves, of Missouri.
Blake Farenthold, of Texas.
Larry Bucshon, of Indiana.
Patrick Meehan, of Pennsylvania.
Daniel Webster, of Florida.
Jeff Denham, of California.
Reid J. Ribble, of Wisconsin.
Thomas Massie, of Kentucky.
Steve Daines, of Montana.
Roger Williams, of Texas.
Mark Meadows, of North Carolina.

Rick Larsen, of Washington.
Peter A. DeFazio, of Oregon.
Eddie Bernice Johnson, of Texas.
Michael E. Capuano, of Massachusetts.
Daniel Lipinski, of Illinois.
Steve Cohen, of Tennessee.
André Carson, of Indiana.
Richard M. Nolan, of Minnesota.
Dina Titus, of Nevada.
Sean Patrick Maloney, of New York.
Cheri Bustos, of Illinois.
Corrine Brown, of Florida.
Elizabeth H. Esty, of Connecticut.

Coast Guard and Maritime Transportation

Duncan Hunter, of California, *Chair*

Steve Southerland II, of Florida, *Vice Chair*

Don Young, of Alaska.
Howard Coble, of North Carolina.
Frank A. LoBiondo, of New Jersey.
Patrick Meehan, of Pennsylvania.
Tom Rice, of South Carolina.
Mark Sanford, of South Carolina.

John Garamendi, of California.
Elijah E. Cummings, of Maryland.
Rick Larsen, of Washington.
Timothy H. Bishop, of New York.
Lois Frankel, of Florida.
Corrine Brown, of Florida.
Janice Hahn, of California.

Economic Development, Public Buildings, and Emergency Management

Lou Barletta, of Pennsylvania, *Chair*

Blake Farenthold, of Texas, *Vice Chair*

Thomas E. Petri, of Wisconsin.
John L. Mica, of Florida.
Eric A. "Rick" Crawford, of Arkansas.
Markwayne Mullin, of Oklahoma.
Mark Meadows, of North Carolina.
Scott Perry, of Pennsylvania.
Mark Sanford, of South Carolina.

André Carson, of Indiana.
Eleanor Holmes Norton, of District of Columbia.
Michael H. Michaud, of Maine.
Timothy J. Walz, of Minnesota.
Donna F. Edwards, of Maryland.
Richard M. Nolan, of Minnesota.
Dina Titus, of Nevada.

Highways and Transit

Thomas E. Petri, of Wisconsin, *Chair*

Reid J. Ribble, of Wisconsin, *Vice Chair*

Don Young, of Alaska.
Howard Coble, of North Carolina.
John J. Duncan, Jr., of Tennessee.
John L. Mica, of Florida.
Frank A. LoBiondo, of New Jersey.
Gary G. Miller, of California.
Sam Graves, of Missouri.
Shelley Moore Capito, of West Virginia.
Duncan Hunter, of California.
Eric A. ''Rick'' Crawford, of Arkansas.
Lou Barletta, of Pennsylvania.
Blake Farenthold, of Texas.
Larry Bucshon, of Indiana.
Bob Gibbs, of Ohio.
Richard L. Hanna, of New York.
Steve Southerland II, of Florida.
Steve Daines, of Montana.
Tom Rice, of South Carolina.
Markwayne Mullin, of Oklahoma.
Roger Williams, of Texas.
Scott Perry, of Pennsylvania.
Rodney Davis, of Illinois.

Eleanor Holmes Norton, of District of Columbia.
Peter A. DeFazio, of Oregon.
Jerrold Nadler, of New York.
Eddie Bernice Johnson, of Texas.
Michael E. Capuano, of Massachusetts.
Michael H. Michaud, of Maine.
Grace F. Napolitano, of California.
Timothy J. Walz, of Minnesota.
Steve Cohen, of Tennessee.
Albio Sires, of New Jersey.
Donna F. Edwards, of Maryland.
Janice Hahn, of California.
Richard M. Nolan, of Minnesota.
Ann Kirkpatrick, of Arizona.
Dina Titus, of Nevada.
Sean Patrick Maloney, of New York.
Elizabeth H. Esty, of Connecticut.
Lois Frankel, of Florida.
Cheri Bustos, of Illinois.

Railroads, Pipelines, and Hazardous Materials

Jeff Denham, of California, *Chair*

Richard L. Hanna, of New York, *Vice Chair*

John J. Duncan, Jr., of Tennessee.
John L. Mica, of Florida.
Gary G. Miller, of California.
Sam Graves, of Missouri.
Shelley Moore Capito, of West Virginia.
Candice S. Miller, of Michigan.
Lou Barletta, of Pennsylvania.
Larry Bucshon, of Indiana.
Bob Gibbs, of Ohio.
Patrick Meehan, of Pennsylvania.
Daniel Webster, of Florida.
Thomas Massie, of Kentucky.
Roger Williams, of Texas.
Scott Perry, of Pennsylvania.

Corrine Brown, of Florida.
Daniel Lipinski, of Illinois.
Jerrold Nadler, of New York.
Elijah E. Cummings, of Maryland.
Michael H. Michaud, of Maine.
Grace F. Napolitano, of California.
Timothy J. Walz, of Minnesota.
Albio Sires, of New Jersey.
Janice Hahn, of California.
Ann Kirkpatrick, of Arizona.
Elizabeth H. Esty, of Connecticut.
Peter A. DeFazio, of Oregon.
Michael E. Capuano, of Massachusetts.

Water Resources and Environment

Bob Gibbs, of Ohio, *Chair*

Eric A. "Rick" Crawford, of Arkansas, *Vice Chair*

Don Young, of Alaska.
Gary G. Miller, of California.
Shelley Moore Capito, of West Virginia.
Candice S. Miller, of Michigan.
Richard L. Hanna, of New York.
Daniel Webster, of Florida.
Jeff Denham, of California.
Reid J. Ribble, of Wisconsin.
Thomas Massie, of Kentucky.
Steve Daines, of Montana.
Tom Rice, of South Carolina.
Markwayne Mullin, of Oklahoma.
Mark Meadows, of North Carolina.
Rodney Davis, of Illinois.
Mark Sanford, of South Carolina.

Timothy H. Bishop, of New York.
Donna F. Edwards, of Maryland.
John Garamendi, of California.
Lois Frankel, of Florida.
Eleanor Holmes Norton, of District of Columbia.
Eddie Bernice Johnson, of Texas.
Grace F. Napolitano, of California.
Steve Cohen, of Tennessee.
Janice Hahn, of California.
Richard M. Nolan, of Minnesota.
Ann Kirkpatrick, of Arizona.
Dina Titus, of Nevada.
Sean Patrick Maloney, of New York.

STAFF

Committee on Transportation and Infrastructure (2165 RHOB) 225–9446, fax 225–6782.
Majority Full Committee Staff
Staff Director.—Chris Bertram.
Deputy Staff Director.—Stephen Martinko.
General Counsel.—Jennifer Hall.
Director of Budget and Program Analysis.—Clare Doherty.
Director of Member Services.—Matt Sturges.
Director of Outreach and Coalitions.—Beth Spivey.
Director of Facilities and Operations.—Mike Legg.
Legislative Assistants: Caryn Moore, Dennis Wirtz.
Staff Assistants: Clint Hines, Jason Klink, Tracy Zea.
Minority Full Committee Staff (2163 RHOB) 225–4472, fax 226–1270.
Staff Director.—Jim Zoia.
Chief Counsel.—Ward McCarragher.
Deputy Staff Director.—Ann Adler.
Executive Assistant.—Lisa James.
Staff Assistant.—Luke Strimer.
Information Systems (2165 RHOB) 225–9446, fax 225–6782.
Information Systems Manager.—Keven Sard.
Assistant Systems Administrator.—Scott Putz.
Majority Communications (2165 RHOB) 225–9446, fax 225–6782.
Communications Director.—Jim Billimoria.
Communications Advisor.—Justin Harclerode.
Digital Media Director.—Michael Marianccio.
Minority Communications (2163 RHOB) 225–4472, fax 226–1270.
Communications Director.—John Noble.
Clerk's Office (588 Ford HOB) 225–9960, fax 226–3475.
Clerk.—Tracy G. Mosebey.
Printer.—Jean Paffenback.
Oversight and Investigations (586 Ford HOB) 225–9446, fax 226–6012.
Majority Staff
Counsel for Oversight and Investigations.—Kim Moore.
Professional Staff.—Jason Rosa.
Subcommittee on Aviation (2251 RHOB) 226–3220, fax 225–4629.
Majority Staff
Staff Director.—Holly E. Woodruff Lyons.
Professional Staff: Mike Matousek, Simone Perez.
Staff Assistant.—Andrew Rademaker.
Minority Staff (2251 RHOB) 225–9161, fax 225–4629.
Staff Director.—Giles Giovinazzi.
Professional Staff: Rachel Carr, Megan Evans.
Subcommittee on Coast Guard and Maritime Transportation (507 Ford HOB) 226–3552, fax 226–2524.

Majority Staff
Staff Director.—John Rayfield.
Professional Staff.—Geoff Gosselin.
Staff Assistant.—Jason Klink.
Minority Staff (505 Ford HOB) 226–3587, fax 226–1898.
Staff Director.—Dave Jansen.
Staff Assistant.—Katherine Waring.
Subcommittee on Economic Development, Public Buildings, and Emergency Management (585 Ford HOB) 225–3014, fax 226–0922.
Majority Staff
Staff Director.—Dan Mathews.
Counsel.—Johanna Hardy.
Staff Assistant.—Walker Barrett.
Minority Staff (592 Ford HOB) 225–9961, fax 226–1898.
Counsels: Elliot Doomes, Janet Erickson.
Staff Assistant.—Katherine Waring.
Subcommittee on Highways and Transit (B–376 RHOB) 225–6715, fax 226–4377.
Majority Staff
Staff Director.—Murphy Barrett.
Counsel.—Shant Boyajian.
Professional Staff: Andrew Brady, Dan Veoni.
Staff Assistant.—Erin Sulla.
Minority Staff (B–375 RHOB) 225–9989, fax 226–5435.
Staff Director.—Jim Kolb.
Senior Professional Staff.—Helena Zyblikewycz.
Staff Assistant.—Madeline Pike.
Subcommittee on Railroads, Pipelines, and Hazardous Materials (B–376 RHOB) 226–0727, fax 226–4377.
Majority Staff
Staff Director.—Mike Freidburg.
Professional Staff.—David Connolly.
Counsel.—Fred Miller.
Staff Assistant.—Erin Sulla.
Minority Staff (592 Ford HOB) 225–3274, fax 226–1898.
Staff Director.—Jennifer Homendy.
Counsel.—Rachel Carr.
Staff Assistant.—Katherine Waring.
Subcommittee on Water Resources and Environment (B–370A RHOB) 225–4360.
Majority Staff
Staff Director.—John Anderson.
Professional Staff.—Geoff Bowman.
Counsel.—Jonathan Pawlow.
Staff Assistant.—Tracy Zea.
Minority Staff (B–375 RHOB) 225–0060, fax 226–5435.
Counsel.—Ryan Seiger.
Professional Staff: Jean Flemma, David Wegner.
Staff Assistant.—Katherine Waring.

Veterans' Affairs

335 Cannon House Office Building, phone 225–3527, fax 225–5486

http://www.veterans.house.gov

Jeff Miller, of Florida, *Chair*

Doug Lamborn, of Colorado.
Gus M. Bilirakis, of Florida.
David P. Roe, of Tennessee.
Bill Flores, of Texas.
Jeff Denham, of California.
Jon Runyan, of New Jersey.
Dan Benishek, of Michigan.
Tim Huelskamp, of Kansas.
Mike Coffman, of Colorado.
Brad R. Wenstrup, of Ohio.
Paul Cook, of California.
Jackie Walorski, of Indiana.

Michael H. Michaud, of Maine.
Corrine Brown, of Florida.
Mark Takano, of California.
Julia Brownley, of California.
Dina Titus, of Nevada.
Ann Kirkpatrick, of Arizona.
Raul Ruiz, of California.
Gloria Negrete McLeod, of California.
Ann M. Kuster, of New Hampshire.
Beto O'Rourke, of Texas.
Timothy J. Walz, of Minnesota.

SUBCOMMITTEES

Disability Assistance and Memorial Affairs

Jon Runyan, of New Jersey, *Chair*

Doug Lamborn, of Colorado.
Gus M. Bilirakis, of Florida.
Paul Cook, of California.

Dina Titus, of Nevada.
Beto O'Rourke, of Texas.
Raul Ruiz, of California.
Gloria Negrete McLeod, of California.

Economic Opportunity

Bill Flores, of Texas, *Chair*

Jon Runyan, of New Jersey.
Mike Coffman, of Colorado.
Paul Cook, of California.
Brad R. Wenstrup, of Ohio.

Mark Takano, of California.
Julia Brownley, of California.
Dina Titus, of Nevada.
Ann Kirkpatrick, of Arizona.

Health

Dan Benishek, of Michigan, *Chair*

David P. Roe, of Tennessee.
Jeff Denham, of California.
Tim Huelskamp, of Kansas.
Jackie Walorski, of Indiana.
Brad R. Wenstrup, of Ohio.

Julia Brownley, of California.
Corrine Brown, of Florida.
Raul Ruiz, of California.
Gloria Negrete McLeod, of California.
Ann M. Kuster, of New Hampshire.

Oversight and Investigations

Mike Coffman, of Colorado, *Chair*

Doug Lamborn, of Colorado.
David P. Roe, of Tennessee.
Tim Huelskamp, of Kansas.
Dan Benishek, of Michigan.
Jackie Walorski, of Indiana.

Ann Kirkpatrick, of Arizona.
Mark Takano, of California.
Ann M. Kuster, of New Hampshire.
Beto O'Rourke, of Texas.
Timothy J. Walz, of Minnesota.

STAFF

Committee on Veterans' Affairs (335 CHOB), 225–3527, fax 225–5486.
Majority Staff Director.—Jon Towers.
Deputy Staff Director.—Mike Brinck.
Communications Director.—Curt Cashour.
Financial Administrator and Printing Clerk.—Bernadine Dotson.
Chief Clerk and Office Manager and Legislative Coordinator.—Jessica Eggimann.
Press Assistant.—Michael Siegel.
Staff Assistant.—Kelsey Baron.
Minority Staff Director.—Nancy Dolan (333 CHOB), 225–9756, fax 225–2034.
Deputy Staff Director and Chief Counsel.—David Tucker.
Legislative Coordinator and Office Manager.—Carol Murray.
Executive and Legislative Assistant.—Carolyn Blaydes.
Subcommittee on Disability Assistance and Memorial Affairs (337 CHOB), 225–9164, fax 226–4691.
Majority Subcommittee Staff Director and Counsel.—Rory Riley.
Professional Staff Member and Counsel.—Lauren Rogan.
Minority Staff Director and Counsel.—Justin Brown.
Subcommittee on Economic Opportunity (335 CHOB), 226–5491, fax 225–5486.
Majority Staff Director.—Jon Clark.
Minority Staff Director and Counsel.—Juan Lara.
Subcommittee on Health (338 CHOB), 225–9154, fax 226–4536.
Majority Staff Director.—Dolores Dunn.
Professional Staff Member.—Samantha Gonzalez.
Research Assistant.—Megan Olmstead.
Minority Staff Director.—Cathy Wiblemo.
Subcommittee on Oversight and Investigations (337A CHOB), 225–3569, fax 225–6392.
Majority Staff Director.—Eric Hannel.
Senior Investigative Counsel.—Harold Rees.
Investigative Counsel.—Jon Hodnette.
Minority Staff Director and Counsel.—Juan Lara.

Ways and Means

1102 Longworth House Office Building, phone 225–3625

http://waysandmeans.house.gov

Dave Camp, of Michigan, *Chair*

Sam Johnson, of Texas.
Kevin Brady, of Texas.
Paul Ryan, of Wisconsin.
Devin Nunes, of California.
Patrick J. Tiberi, of Ohio.
David G. Reichert, of Washington.
Charles W. Boustany, Jr., of Louisiana.
Peter J. Roskam, of Illinois.
Jim Gerlach, of Pennsylvania.
Tom Price, of Georgia.
Vern Buchanan, of Florida.
Adrian Smith, of Nebraska.
Aaron Schock, of Illinois.
Lynn Jenkins, of Kansas.
Erik Paulsen, of Minnesota.
Kenny Marchant, of Texas.
Diane Black, of Tennessee.
Tom Reed, of New York.
Todd C. Young, of Indiana.
Mike Kelly, of Pennsylvania.
Tim Griffin, of Arkansas.
James B. Renacci, of Ohio.

Sander M. Levin, of Michigan.
Charles B. Rangel, of New York.
Jim McDermott, of Washington.
John Lewis, of Georgia.
Richard E. Neal, of Massachusetts.
Xavier Becerra, of California.
Lloyd Doggett, of Texas.
Mike Thompson, of California.
John B. Larson, of Connecticut.
Earl Blumenauer, of Oregon.
Ron Kind, of Wisconsin.
Bill Pascrell, Jr., of New Jersey.
Joseph Crowley, of New York.
Allyson Y. Schwartz, of Pennsylvania.
Danny K. Davis, of Illinois.
Linda T. Sánchez, of California.

SUBCOMMITTEES

[The chairman and ranking minority member are ex officio (non-voting) members of all subcommittees.]

Health

Kevin Brady, of Texas, *Chair*

Sam Johnson, of Texas.
Paul Ryan, of Wisconsin.
Devin Nunes, of California.
Peter J. Roskam, of Illinois.
Jim Gerlach, of Pennsylvania.
Tom Price, of Georgia.
Vern Buchanan, of Florida.
Adrian Smith, of Nebraska.

Jim McDermott, of Washington.
Mike Thompson, of California.
Ron Kind, of Wisconsin.
Earl Blumenauer, of Oregon.
Bill Pascrell, Jr., of New Jersey.

Human Resources

David G. Reichert, of Washington, *Chair*

Todd C. Young, of Indiana.
Mike Kelly, of Pennsylvania.
Tim Griffin, of Arkansas.
James B. Renacci, of Ohio.
Tom Reed, of New York.
Charles W. Boustany, Jr., of Louisiana.

Lloyd Doggett, of Texas.
John Lewis, of Georgia.
Joseph Crowley, of New York.
Danny K. Davis, of Illinois.

Oversight

Charles W. Boustany, Jr., of Louisiana, *Chair*

Diane Black, of Tennessee.
Lynn Jenkins, of Kansas.
Kenny Marchant, of Texas.
Tom Reed, of New York.
Erik Paulsen, of Minnesota.
Mike Kelly, of Pennsylvania.

John Lewis, of Georgia.
Joseph Crowley, of New York.
Danny K. Davis, of Illinois.
Linda T. Sánchez, of California.

Select Revenue Measures

Patrick J. Tiberi, of Ohio, *Chair*

Erik Paulsen, of Minnesota.
Kenny Marchant, of Texas.
Jim Gerlach, of Pennsylvania.
Aaron Schock, of Illinois.
Tom Reed, of New York.
Todd C. Young, of Indiana.

Richard E. Neal, of Massachusetts.
John B. Larson, of Connecticut.
Allyson Y. Schwartz, of Pennsylvania.
Linda T. Sánchez, of California.

Social Security

Sam Johnson, of Texas, *Chair*

Patrick J. Tiberi, of Ohio.
Tim Griffin, of Arkansas.
James B. Renacci, of Ohio.
Aaron Schock, of Illinois.
Mike Kelly, of Pennsylvania.
Kevin Brady, of Texas.

Xavier Becerra, of California.
Lloyd Doggett, of Texas.
Mike Thompson, of California.
Allyson Y. Schwartz, of Pennsylvania.

Trade

Devin Nunes, of California, *Chair*

Kevin Brady, of Texas.
David G. Reichert, of Washington.
Vern Buchanan, of Florida.
Adrian Smith, of Nebraska.
Aaron Schock, of Illinois.
Lynn Jenkins, of Kansas.
Charles W. Boustany, Jr., of Louisiana.
Peter J. Roskam, of Illinois.

Charles B. Rangel, of New York.
Richard E. Neal, of Massachusetts.
John B. Larson, of Connecticut.
Earl Blumenauer, of Oregon.
Ron Kind, of Wisconsin.

STAFF

Committee on Ways and Means (1102 LHOB), 225–3625, fax 225–2610.
Staff Director/General Council.—Jennifer Safavian.
Deputy Staff Director.—Sage Eastman.
Policy Director.—Warren Payne.
Senior Economist.—David Logan.
Economic and Media Analyst.—Mike Stober.
Senior Advisor, Public Affairs and Coalitions.—Michelle Dimarob.
Communications Director.—Sarah Swinehart.
Press Secretary.—Allie Walker.
Senior Clerk.—Michael K. Baker.
Document Clerk.—Reggie Greene.
Systems Administrator.—Wuan Perkins.
Committee Administrator.—Chris Stottmann.
Executive Assistant.—Challee Stefani.
Staff Assistant.—Andrew Rocca.
Staff Director, Select Revenue Measures.—George Callas.
Chief Tax Counsel.—Dave Olander.
Tax Counsel: Aharon Friedman, Harold Hancock, Mark Warren.
Tax Counsel and Special Advisor on Tax Reform.—Ray Beeman.

Tax Advisor.—Sean Hailey.
Legislative Assistant, Select Revenue Measures.—John Sandell.
Oversight Staff Director.—Mark Epley.
Oversight Counsel: Jennifer Acuna, Chris Armstrong.
Legislative Assistant, Oversight.—Matt Hittle.
Staff Director/Chief Trade Counsel.—Angela Ellard.
Trade Counsel: Geoffrey Antell, Stephen Claeys, Welby Leaman, Neena Shenai.
Legislative Assistant, Trade.—Paul Guaglianone.
Health Staff Director.—Brian Sutter.
Professional Staff Health: Brett Baker, Lisa Grabert, Martin Reiser.
Legislative Assistant, Health.—Nick Uehlecke.
Staff Director, Social Security.—Kim Hildred.
Professional Staff, Social Security: Margret Hostetler, Amy Shuart.
Staff Assistant, Social Security.—Jessica Cameron.
Staff Director, Human Resources.—Matt Weidinger.
Professional Staff, Human Resources.—Anne DeCesaro, Ryan Martin.
Legislative Assistant, Human Resources.—Caitlin Alcala.

Minority Chief Counsel and Staff Director.—Janice Mays.
Oversight Staff Director.—Askia Suruma.
Communications Director.—Josh Drobnyk.
Office Manager.—Jennifer Gould.
Assistant to Janice Mays.—Carrie Breidenbach.
Staff/Research Assistants: Moyer McCoy, John Young.
IT Director.—Antoine Walker.
Press Secretary.—Alex Nguyen.
Chief Tax Counsel.—Karen McAfee.
Select Revenue Measures Staff Director.—Aruna Kalyanam.
Tax Counsel.—Ji Prichard.
Staff Director, Health.—Cybele Bjorklund.
Deputy Staff Director, Health.—Jennifer Friedman.
Professional Staff, Health.—Erin Richardson.
GAO Detailee.—Melanie Egorin.
Staff Director, Human Resources.—Nick Gwyn.
Staff Director, Social Security.—Kathryn Olson.
Professional Staff, Social Security.—Morna Miller.
Staff Director, Trade.—Jason Kearns.
Trade Counsel: Behnaz Kibria, Beth Baltzan.

SELECT AND SPECIAL COMMITTEES OF THE HOUSE

Permanent Select Committee on Intelligence

HVC–304 The Capitol, phone 225–4121

[Created pursuant to H. Res. 658, 95th Congress]

Mike Rogers, of Michigan, *Chair*

Mac Thornberry, of Texas.
Jeff Miller, of Florida.
K. Michael Conaway, of Texas.
Peter T. King, of New York.
Frank A. LoBiondo, of New Jersey.
Devin Nunes, of California.
Lynn A. Westmoreland, of Georgia.
Michele Bachmann, of Minnesota.
Thomas J. Rooney, of Florida.
Joseph J. Heck, of Nevada.
Mike Pompeo, of Kansas.

C. A. Dutch Ruppersberger, of Maryland.
Mike Thompson, of California.
Janice D. Schakowsky, of Illinois.
James R. Langevin, of Rhode Island.
Adam B. Schiff, of California.
Luis V. Gutiérrez, of Illinois.
Ed Pastor, of Arizona.
James A. Himes, of Connecticut.
Terri A. Sewell, of Alabama.

SUBCOMMITTEES

[The Speaker and Minority Leader are ex officio (non-voting) members of the committee.]

Oversight and Investigations

Lynn A. Westmoreland, of Georgia, *Chair*

Jeff Miller, of Florida.
Michele Bachmann, of Minnesota.
Thomas J. Rooney, of Florida.
Mike Pompeo, of Kansas.

Janice D. Schakowsky, of Illinois.
Ed Pastor, of Arizona.
James A. Himes, of Connecticut.

Technical and Tactical Intelligence

Joseph J. Heck, of Nevada, *Chair*

Mac Thornberry, of Texas.
Frank A. LoBiondo, of New Jersey.
Michele Bachmann, of Minnesota.
Mike Pompeo, of Kansas.

Adam B. Schiff, of California.
James R. Langevin, of Rhode Island.
Terri A. Sewell, of Alabama.

Terrorism, Human Intelligence, Analysis, and Counterintelligence

K. Michael Conaway, of Texas, *Chair*

Peter T. King, of New York.
Frank A. LoBiondo, of New Jersey.
Thomas J. Rooney, of Florida.
Devin Nunes, of California.

Mike Thompson, of California.
Luis V. Gutiérrez, of Illinois.
James A. Himes, of Connecticut.

STAFF

Majority Staff Director.—Darren Dick.
Deputy Staff Director.—Kathryn Wheelbarger.
Senior Policy Advisor.—Tom Corcoran.
Senior Advisor.—Andy Keiser.
Chief Counsel.—Sarah Geffroy.
Senior Counsel.—Michael Ellis.
Budget Director.—Bryan Smith.
Budget Auditor.—Brooke Eisele.
Chief Clerk.—Ashley Lowry.
Research Assistant.—Lisa Major.
Media Director.—Susan Phalen.
Security Director.—Kristin Jepson.
Deputy Security Director.—Kevin Klein.
System Administrator.—Brandon Smith.
Professional Staff: Chelsey Campbell, Frank Garcia, Nate Hauser, Geof Kahn, Jim Hildebrand, Randy Smith, Shannon Stuart.
Minority Staff Director.—Heather Molino.
Chief Counsel.—Janet Fisher.
Deputy Chief Counsel.—Michael Bahar.
Policy Advisor.—Robert Minehart.
Media Director.—Allison Getty.
Research Assistant.—Khizer Syed.
Professional Staff: Linda Cohen, Amanda Rogers Thorpe, Carly Scott.

National Republican Congressional Committee

320 First Street, SE., 20003, phone 479–7000

Greg Walden, of Oregon, *Chair*

Lynn A. Westmoreland, of Georgia, *Deputy Chair*
Chair of:
Finance.—Steve Stivers, of Ohio.
Recruitment.—Patrick T. McHenry, of North Carolina.
Communications and Strategy.—Tim Griffin, of Arizona.
Policy.—Tom Price, of Georgia.
Digital.—Jason Chaffetz, of Utah.
Regional.—Marsha Blackburn, of Tennessee
Coalitions.—Jaime Herrera Beutler, of Washington
Coalitions.—Tom Graves, of Georgia.

EXECUTIVE COMMITTEE MEMBERS

Diane Black, of Tennessee.
John A. Boehner, of Ohio.
Eric Cantor, of Virginia.
Tom Cole, of Oklahoma.
Jeff Denham, of California.
Virginia Foxx, of North Carolina.
Tom Graves, of Georgia.
Andy Harris, of Maryland.
Jaime Herrera Beutler, of Washington.
Randy Hultgren, of Illinois.
Mike Kelly, of Pennsylvania.
Cynthia M. Lummins, of Wyoming.
Patrick T. McHenry, of North Carolina.
Mick Mulvaney, of South Carolina.
Devin Nunes, California.
Tom Price, of Georgia.
Mike Rogers, of Alabama.
Peter J. Roskam, of Illinois.
Edward R. Royce, of California.
Pete Sessions, of Texas.
Adrian Smith, of Nebraska.
Steve Stivers, of Ohio.
Patrick J. Tiberi, of Ohio.
Ann Wagner, of Missouri.
Lynn A. Westmoreland, of Georgia.
Kevin Yoder, of Kansas.
Marsha Blackburn, of Tennessee.
Susan W. Brooks, of Indiana.
Jason Chaffetz, of Utah.
Steve Daines, of Montana.
Stephen Lee Fincher, of Tennessee.
Cory Gardner, of Colorado.
Tim Griffin, of Arkansas.
Jeb Hensarling, of Texas.
Richard Hudson, of North Carolina.
Lynn Jenkins, of Kansas.
James Lankford, of Oklahoma.
Kevin McCarthy, of California.
Cathy McMorris Rodgers, of Washington.
Randy Neugebauer, of Texas.
Mike Pompeo, of Kansas.
Reid J. Ribble, of Wisconsin.
Mike Rogers, of Michigan.
Keith J. Rothfus, of Pennsylvania.
Stephen Scalise, of Louisiana.
John Shimkus, of Illinois.
Steve Southerland II, of Florida.
Mac Thornberry, of Texas.
Fred Upton, of Michigan.
Greg Walden, of Oregon.
Roger Williams, of Texas.
Todd C. Young, of Indiana.

STAFF

Executive Director.—Liesl Hickey.
Political Director.—Rob Simms.
Deputy Executive Director and General Counsel.—Jessica Furst Johnson.
Communications Director.—Andrea Bozek.
Finance Director.—Jenny Drucker.
Digital Director.—Gerrit Lansing.
Research Director.—Todd Johnson.

House Republican Policy Committee

228 Cannon House Office Building, phone 225–2132

http://policy.house.gov

meets at the call of the Chair or the Speaker

James Lankford, of Oklahoma, *Chair*

Republican Leadership:
Speaker of the House.—John A. Boehner, of Ohio.
Majority Leader.—Eric Cantor, of Virginia.
Conference Chair.—Jeb Hensarling, of Texas.
Conference Vice Chair.—Cathy McMorris Rodgers, of Washington.
Conference Secretary.—John R. Carter, of Texas.
NRCC Chair.—Pete Sessions, of Texas.

Policy Committee Staff.—228 Cannon HOB, 225–2132.
Chief of Staff.—Randy Swanson.

House Republican Conference

202A Cannon House Office Building, phone 225–5107, fax 226–0154

Cathy McMorris Rodgers, of Washington, *Chair*

Lynn Jenkins, of Kansas, *Vice Chair*

Virginia Foxx, of North Carolina, *Secretary*

STAFF

Chief of Staff.—Jeremy Deutsch.
Director of Operations.—Marjorie Connell.
Staff Assistants: Joel Graves, Amy Reagan.
Director of Member Services.—Shaughnessy Murphy.
Assistant to Member Services.—Phillip Pinegar.
Policy Director.—Kimberly Betz.
Policy Advisor.—Emily Leviner.
Policy Coordinator.—David Smentek.
Communications Director.—Nate Hodson.
Deputy Communications Director.—Riva Litman.
Deputy Press Secretaries: Dylan Colligan, John Wittman.
Deputy Press Secretary, Specialized Media.—Wadi Gaitan.
Digital Director.—Abigail Alger.
Visual Media: Michael Calvo, Scott Schmidt.
Director of Coalitions.—Nick Muzin.

Democratic Congressional Campaign Committee

430 South Capitol Street, SE., 20003, phone (202) 863–1500

Executive Committee:
Nancy Pelosi, of California, *Democratic Leader.*
Steve Israel, of New York, *Chair.*
Chairs:
James E. Clyburn, *National Mobilization, Chair.*
Joseph Crowley, *DC Finance, Chair.*
James A. Himes, *National Finance, Chair.*
Jared Polis, *National Chair for Candidate Services.*

STAFF

Executive Director.—Kelly Ward, 478–9485.
Deputy Executive Director.—Jesse Ferguson, 485–3456.
Deputy Executive Director for Finance.—Missy Kurek, 485–3455.
Chief Operating Officer.—Hayley Dierker, 485–3425.
Chief Financial Officer.—Jackie Forte-Mackay, 485–3401.
Director of:
Campaign and Recruitment Director.—Ian Russell, 485–3454.
Candidate Fundraising.—Nicole Eynard, 485–3436.
Communications.—Emily Bittner, 741–1878
Member Services.—Charles Benton, 485–3516.
Research.—Adam Broder, 485–3510.
New Media.—Brandon English, 485–3534.
National Finance Director.—Stella Ross, 485–3412.
National Press Secretary.—Josh Schwerin, 485–3417.
National Field Director.—Gabe Lifton-Zoline, 741–1848.
Policy Director.—Mike Ryan, 485–3531.
Political Director.—Brian Zuzenak, 485–3434.

Democratic Steering and Policy Committee

H–204 The Capitol, phone 225–0100

Chair.—Nancy Pelosi, Democratic Leader from California.
Co-Chairs:
Steering.—Rosa L. DeLauro, Representative from Connecticut.
Policy.—Vacant.

STAFF

Democratic Steering Committee (H–130), 225–0100, fax 225–4188.
Steering Advisors: George Kundanis, Jonathan Stivers.

Democratic Policy Committee (H–130), 225–0100, fax 226–0938.
Policy Advisors: George Kundanis, Richard Meltzer.

Democratic Caucus

1420 Longworth House Office Building, phone 225–1400, fax 226–4412

www.dems.gov

Xavier Becerra, of California, *Chair*

Joseph Crowley, of New York, *Vice Chair*

STAFF

Chief of Staff.—Debra Dixon.
Executive Director.—Fabiola Rodriguez-Ciampoli.
Deputy Director of Operations.—Stephanie Venegas.
Senior Advisor for Member Outreach.—Eric Delaney.
Member Outreach Assistants: Noel Perez, Amanda Saldaña.
Staff Assistants: Leti Davalos, Andrew Estrada.
Policy Director.—Sean McCluskie.
Senior Policy Counsel.—Sirat Attapit.
Policy Advisor.—Moh Sharma.
Communications Director.—James Gleeson.
Press Secretary and Director of Online Strategy.—Kathleen Skiles.
Press Secretary.—Daniel Herrera.
Press Assistant.—Samuel Avery.
Policy Director to the Vice Chair.—Kevin Casey.
Events and Projects Assistant to the Vice Chair.—Andrew Sachse.

OFFICERS AND OFFICIALS OF THE HOUSE

OFFICE OF THE SPEAKER

H–232 The Capitol, phone 225–0600, fax 225–5117

Speaker of the House of Representatives.—John A. Boehner.
Chief of Staff.—Mike Sommers.
Deputy Chief of Staff for Communications Operations.—Dave Schnittger.
Director of Administrative Operations.—Amy Lozupone.
Director of Scheduling and Executive Assistant.—Kristen Blake.
Deputy Scheduler.—Maura Gillespie.
Special Events Assistants: Seton Easby-Smith, Anne Pietkiewicz, Ramsey Ratcliffe.
Director of House Operations.—Kelly Craven.
Press Secretaries: Brendan Buck, Michael Steel.
Director of Advance and Media.—Rebeccah Propp.
Deputy Press Secretary.—Heather Reed.
Director of Media Affairs.—Betsy Embler.
Communications Director.—Kevin Smith.
Communications Advisor.—Sofia Boza.
Digital Communications Director.—Caleb Smith.
Deputy Communications Director.—Michael Ricci.
Assistant Communications Director.—Katie Boyd.
Director of Public Liaison.—Maria Lohmeyer.
Director of Member Services.—Trevor Kolego.
Deputy Director of Member Services.—Annie Palisi.
Outreach Director.—Bill Greene.
Director, Information Technology.—Billy Benjamin.
Systems Administrator.—Mike Sager.
General Counsel / Chief of Legislative Operations.—Jo-Marie St. Martin.
Associate General Counsel.—Greg Robinson.
Floor Director.—Anne Thorsen.
Deputy Floor Director.—Lydia Strunk.
Policy Director.—David Stewart.
Assistants to the Speaker for Policy: Brad Bailey, Maryam Brown, Natasha Eckard, Katherine Haley, Cindy Herrle, Charlotte Ivancic, Jen Stewart, Becky Tallent.
Research Assistant.—Justin Lampert.
Cloakroom Manager.—Tim Harroun.
Floor Assistants: Alex Becker, Jared Eichhorn, Annie Minkler.
Staff Assistants: Jessica Franks, Raul Henriquez, Colton Malkerson, Will Miller, Zach Mingo.

OFFICE OF THE MAJORITY LEADER

H–329 The Capitol, phone 225–4000, fax 226–1115

Majority Leader.—Eric Cantor.
Chief of Staff.—Steve Stombres.
Deputy Chiefs of Staff: Neil Bradley, Doug Heye.
Senior Policy Advisors: Aaron Cutler, Nicole Gustafson, Cheryl Jaeger, Robert Karem, Rodger Mahan.
Policy Advisor.—Wyatt Stewart.
Director of Floor Operations.—Chris Vieson.
Deputy Director of Floor Operations.—Sarah Morgan.
Floor Assistant.—Tim Pataki.
Director of Digital Media.—Connor Walsh.
Deputy Director of Digital Media.—Nick Marcelli.

Communications Director.—Rory Cooper.
Press Secretary.—Megan Whittemore.
Deputy Press Secretary.—Gena Villari.
Speechwriter.—John Stapleton.
Director of Oversight.—Rob Borden.
Director of Member Services.—Katie Patru.
Deputy Director of Member Services.—Emily Keech.
Director of Scheduling and Administration.—Amy Barrera.
Deputy Scheduler.—Courtney Joseph.
Special Assistant to the Majority Leader.—Allen Jamerson.
Staff Assistants: Molly Edwards, Lawson Kluttz.

OFFICE OF THE MAJORITY WHIP

H–107 The Capitol, phone 225–0197, fax 225–0781

Majority Whip.—Kevin McCarthy.
Chief of Staff.—Tim Berry.
Deputy Chief of Staff.—James Min.
Floor Director.—John Stipicevic.
Coalitions Director.—Brian Worth.
Policy Director and Counsel.—Mike Franc.
Communications Director.—Erica Elliott.
Member Services and Coalitions Deputy Director.—Natalie Buchanan.
Deputy Floor Director.—Kelly Dixon.
Policy Advisors: Wes McClelland, Emily Murry.
Scheduler.—Kristin Thomson.
Press Secretary.—Mike Long.
Floor Assistants: Ben Howard, John Leganski.
Press Aide.—Mathew Sparks.
Coalitions Assistant and Assistant to the Chief of Staff.—Brittany Carey.
Senior Staff Assistant.—Aaron Thiele.

OFFICE OF THE CHIEF DEPUTY REPUBLICAN WHIP

H–116 The Capitol, phone 225–0197

Chief of Staff to Chief Deputy Whip.—David Mork.
Special Assistant to Chief Deputy Whip.—Jeff Billman.
Chief of Staff.—Tim Berry.
Deputy Chief of Staff.—James Min.
Policy Advisers: Wes McClellan, Emily Murry.
Policy Director and Counsel.—Steve Pinkos.
Press Secretary.—Erica Elliott.
Press Aide.—Mike Long.
Director of New Media.—Lauren Pratapas.
Director of Strategic Communications.—Kris Anderson.
Communications Director.—Sarah Pompei.
Deputy Director of Floor Operations.—Kelly Dixon.
Director of Floor Operations.—John Stipicevic.
Floor Assistants: Freddy Barnes, Ben Howard.
Scheduler.—Kristin Thomson.
Director of Coalitions.—Brian Worth.
Deputy Director of Member Services and Coalitions.—Natalie Buchanan.
Senior Staff Assistant.—Ashley Mettler.
Staff Assistants: Brittany Carey, Tim Pataki.

OFFICE OF THE DEMOCRATIC LEADER

H–204 The Capitol, phone 225–0100, fax 225–4188

www.democraticleader.gov

Office of the Democratic Leader.—Hon. Nancy Pelosi.
Chief of Staff.—Nadeam Elshami, H–204, The Capitol, 225–0100.
Assistant to the Chief of Staff.—Ethan McClelland, H–204, The Capitol, 225–0100.
Chief of Staff (CA08 Office).—Robert Edmonson, 235 CHOB, 225–4965.
Deputy Chiefs of Staff: Diane Dewhirst, George Kundanis, H–204, The Capitol, 225–0100.
Senior Advisors: Michael Bloom, Jonathan Stivers, H–204, The Capitol, 225–0100.
Counsel to the Democratic Leader.—Bernie Raimo, H–204, The Capitol, 225–0100.
Special Assistants to the Democratic Leader: Emily Berret, Kate Knudson, Bina Surgeon, H–204, The Capitol, 225–0100.
Staff Assistant.—Emma Kaplan, H–204, The Capitol, 225–0100.
Co-Directors of Correspondence: Robyn Lea, David Silverman, 421 Cannon, 225–0100.
Director of Scheduling.—Melinda Medlin, H–204, The Capitol, 225–0100.
Deputy Director of Scheduling.—Kelsey Smith, H–204, The Capitol, 225–0100.
Policy Director.—Dick Meltzer, H–204, The Capitol, 225–0100.
Policy Advisor.—Michael Tecklenburg, H–204, The Capitol, 225–0100.
Senior Policy Advisors: Kenneth DeGraff, Wyndee Parker, Wendell Primus, H–204, The Capitol, 225–0100.
Senior Advance Policy and Communications: Margaret Capron, Kit Judge, H–204, The Capitol.
Senior Advance and Director of Member Service.—Jaime Lizarraga, H–204, The Capitol, 225–0100.
Senior Advisor for Member Services.—Michael Long, H–204, The Capitol.
Director of Protocol and Special Events.—Kate Knudson, H–204, The Capitol, 225–0100.
Director of Speechwriting.—Jonathan Powell, H–204, The Capitol, 225–0100.
Deputy Speechwriter.—Henry Connely, H–204, The Capitol, 225–0100.
IT Director.—Wil Haynes, HB–13, The Capitol, 225–0100.
Deputy IT Director.—Kamilah Keita, HB–13, The Capitol, 225–0100.
Director of Advance.—Mary-Kate Barry, H–204, The Capitol, 225–0100.
Director of Outreach.—Reva Price, H–204, The Capitol, 225–0100.

DEMOCRATIC LEADER'S PRESS OFFICE

H–204 The Capitol, phone 225–0100

Communications Director and Senior Advisor.—Drew Hammill.
Deputy Communications Director.—Ashley Etienne.
Press Secretary.—Evangeline George.
Press Advisor.—Stephanie Cherry.
Research Director.—April Greener.
Director of New Media.—Tanya Somanader.
Senior Press Assistant.—Jorge Aguilar.
Press Assistant.—Ned Adriance.

DEMOCRATIC LEADER'S FLOOR OFFICE

H–204 The Capitol, phone 225–0100

Director of Floor Operations.—Jerry Hartz.

OFFICE OF THE DEMOCRATIC WHIP

H–148 The Capitol, phone 225–3130, fax 226–0663

Democratic Whip.—Steny H. Hoyer.
Chief of Staff.—Alexis Covey-Brandt.
Whip Director and Senior Advisor.—Brian Romick.
Floor Director.—Shuwanza Goff.
Senior Floor Assistant.—Daniel Shott.
Floor Assistant.—Danielle Aviles.

Director of Member Services.—Courtney Fry.
Deputy Director of Member Services and Outreach Advisor.—Javier Martinez.
Communications Director.—Katie Grant.
Press Secretary.—Stephanie Young.
Deputy Press Secretary.—Mariel Saez.
Press and Research Assistant.—Amanda Ott.
Speechwriter.—Adam Weissman.
Policy Director.—Tom Mahr.
Senior Policy Advisors: Keith Abouchar, James Leuschen, Elizabeth Murray, Mary Frances Repko, Daniel Silverberg.
Office Manager/Executive Assistant.—Lindsey Cobia.
Director of Scheduling and Special Events.—Michelle Mittler.
Special Assistant.—Elliot Gensemer.
Digital Director and Policy Advisor.—Steve Dwyer.
Staff Assistants: Federico Rodriguez, Deborah Rowe.

OFFICE OF THE ASSISTANT DEMOCRATIC LEADER

132 The Capitol, phone 226–3210

http://assistantdemocraticleader.house.gov

Assistant Democratic Leader.—James E. Clyburn.
Chief of Staff.—Yelberton R. Watkins.
Director of Policy.—Barvetta Singletary.
Communications Director.—Patrick Devlin.
Senior Advisor.—Amy Miller Pfeiffer.
Legislative Assistant.—Matthew Ellison.
Special Assistant to the Assistant Democratic Leader.—Tamika Day.

OFFICE OF THE CLERK

H–154 The Capitol, phone 225–7000

KAREN L. HAAS, Clerk of the House of Representatives; Karen Lehman Haas, a native of Catonsville, MD, was sworn in as Clerk of the House of Representatives on January 5, 2011. She is the 34th individual to serve as Clerk. This is Ms. Haas' second occupancy of this position—in 2005, Speaker J. Dennis Hastert appointed Ms. Haas as Clerk of the U.S. House of Representatives. As Clerk, Ms. Haas plays a central role in the daily operations and legislative activities of the House. Ms. Haas began her service on Capitol Hill in 1984, when she worked for then-Minority Leader Robert H. Michel. For nearly 11 years, she served as his Executive Legislative Assistant. Following a brief leave to work in the private sector, Ms. Haas returned to Capitol Hill in June 1999 to serve as Floor Assistant to Speaker Hastert. Following her first term as Clerk, she served as Staff Director of the House Republican Conference and Minority Staff Director for the House Small Business Committee. Ms. Haas attended public schools in Maryland and received a bachelor's degree from the University of Maryland, College Park, with a major in political science and a minor in economics.

Clerk.—Karen L. Haas.
Deputy Clerk.—Robert F. Reeves.
Senior Advisor.—Marjorie ''Gigi'' Kelaher.
Chief of:
Legislative Computer Systems.—Goldey Vansant, 2401 RHOB, 225–1182.
Legislative Operations.—Frances Chiappardi, HT–13, 225–7925.
Legislative Resource Center.—Ronald Dale Thomas, B–106 CHOB, 226–5200.
Office of:
Art and Archives.—Farar Elliott, B–53 CHOB, 226–1300.
Communications.—Catherine Cooke, B–28 CHOB, 225–1908.
House Employment Counsel.—Gloria Lett, 1036 LHOB, 225–7075.
Official Reporter.—Joe Strickland, 1718 LHOB, 225–2627.
Service Groups—
Congresswomen's Suite.—225–4196.
Members and Family Committee.—225–0622.
Prayer Room.—225–8070.

CHIEF ADMINISTRATIVE OFFICER

HB–28 The Capitol, phone 225–5555

ED CASSIDY, Chief Administrative Officer of the House of Representatives; native of Westport, CT; M.P.A., American University.

Chief Administrative Officer.—Ed Cassidy.
Administrative Counsel.—Christopher Brewster, H2–217, FHOB.
Chief Financial Officer.—Traci Beaubian, H2–330, FHOB.
Human Resources Director.—Jason Hite, H2–105B, FHOB.
Chief Information Officer.—Nelson Moe, H2–631, FHOB.
Director of Communications.—Dan Weiser, H2–217, FHOB.

CHAPLAIN

HB–25 The Capitol, phone 225–2509, fax 226–4928

PATRICK J. CONROY, S.J., Chaplain, House of Representatives, residence, Portland, OR; a Jesuit of the Oregon Province of the Society of Jesus, graduated from Claremont McKenna College in CA in 1972, attended Gonzaga University Law School for one year before entering the Jesuit Order in 1973. Earned an M.A. in philosophy from Gonzaga University, a J.D. from St. Louis University, an M.Div. from the Jesuit School of Theology at Berkeley (CA), and an STM from Regis College of the University of Toronto in missiology. Practiced law for the Colville Confederated Tribes in Omak, WA and the U.S. Conference of Catholic Bishops representing Salvadoran refugees in San Francisco. Ordained a priest in 1983. From 1984 to 1989, pastored four villages on the Colville and Spokane Indian Reservations. Worked for the national Jesuit Office of Social Ministries in Washington, D.C., then began a career of university chaplaincy at Georgetown University and Seattle University. In 2003 transferred to Jesuit High School in Portland, OR, to teach freshman theology and coach the mighty JV II girls' softball team. Also served as the Oregon Province's Provincial Assistant for Formation and as superior of the Jesuit community at Jesuit High School in Portland. Sworn in as 60th House Chaplain on May 25, 2011.

Chaplain of the House.—Patrick J. Conroy.
Assistant to the Chaplain.—Elisa Aglieco.
Liaison to Staff.—Karen Bronson.

OFFICE OF THE HOUSE HISTORIAN

B–56 Cannon House Office Building, phone 226–5525

http://historian.house.gov; history@mail.house.gov; @UShousehistory

House Historian.—Mathew Wasniewski.
Associate Historian.—Ken Kato.
Manager of Historical Services.—Erin M. Hromada.
Oral Historian.—Kathleen Johnson.

OFFICE OF INTERPARLIAMENTARY AFFAIRS

HC–4 Capitol, phone 226–1766

Director.—Janice Robinson.
Assistant Director.—Vacant.

HOUSE INFORMATION RESOURCES

H2–631C, phone: 226–4103, facsimile: 226–2433

CIO (Chief Information Officer) for the House of Representatives.—Nelson P. Moe.

OFFICE OF ATTENDING PHYSICIAN

H–166 The Capitol, phone 225–5421

(After office hours, call Capitol Operator 224–2145)

Attending Physician.—Dr. Brian P. Monahan.
Chief of Staff.—Christopher R. Picaut.
Deputy Chief of Staff.—Keith Pray.

OFFICE OF INSPECTOR GENERAL

H2–386 Ford House Office Building, phone 226–1250

Inspector General.—Theresa M. Grafenstine.
Deputy Inspector Generals: Debbie B. Hunter, Michael T. Ptasienski.
Director of Support Services.—Terry Upshur.
Assistant Director of:
Finance and Administration.—Susan Kozubski.
Quality Assurance and Contract Service.—Steven Johnson.
Administrative Assistant.—Deborah E. Jones.
Director, Performance and Financial Audits and Investigations.—Kimberly Benoit.
Assistant Director of:
Financial Audits.—Susan Simpson.
Investigations.—Julie Poole.
Auditors: Ronnette Bailey, Nicole Loutsenhizer, Alexander Stewart.
Director, Information Systems Audit.—Vacant.
Assistant Director, Information Systems Audits.—Michael Howard.
Director, Management and Advisory Services.—Joseph C. Picolla.
Assistant Directors: Gregory Roberts, Donna Wolfgang.
Management Analysts: Leslie Bonnikson, Kevin Cornell, Saad Patel.

OFFICE OF THE LAW REVISION COUNSEL

H2–308 Ford House Office Building, 20515–6711, phone 226–2411, fax 225–0010

Law Revision Counsel.—Ralph V. Seep.
Deputy Counsel.—Robert M. Sukol.
Senior Counsels: Kenneth I. Paretzky, Timothy D. Trushel.
Assistant Counsels: Michelle Evans, Katrina M. Hall, Raymond Kaselonis, Katherine L. Lane, Brian Lindsey, Edward T. Mulligan, Michele K. Skarvelis, Lindsey Skouras, John F. Wagner, Jr.
Staff Assistants: Sylvia Tahirkheli, Monica Thompson.
Printing Editors: Robert E. Belcher, James Cahill.
Senior Systems Engineer.—Eric Loach.
Systems Engineer.—Ken Thomas.

OFFICE OF THE LEGISLATIVE COUNSEL

136 Cannon House Office Building, phone 225–6060

Legislative Counsel.—Sandra L. Strokoff.
Deputy Legislative Counsel.—Edward G. Grossman.
Senior Counsels: Wade Ballou, Douglass Bellis, Timothy Brown, Paul Callen, Sherry Chriss, Susan Fleishman, Rosemary Gallagher, James Grossman, Curt Haensel, Jean Harmann, Gregory M. Kostka, Edward Leong, Hank Savage, Mark Synnes, Robert Weinhagen, Noah Wofsy.
Assistant Counsels: Karen Anderson, Marshall Barksdale, Philip Bayer, Hallet Brazelton, Warren Burke, Thomas Cassidy, Henry Christrup, Jesse Cross, Lisa Daly, Thomas Dillon, Mathew Eckstein, Lucy Wolfe Goss, Ryan Greenlaw, Justin Gross, Alison Hartwich, Ellen J. Irby, Megan Lewis, Kakuti Lin, Christopher Osborne, Scott Probst, Hadley Ross, Anthony Sciascia, Jessica Shapiro, Anna Shpak, Veena Srinivasa, Michelle Vanek, Sally Walker, Brady Young.
Office Administrator.—Nancy McNeillie.
Assistant Office Administrator.—Debra Birch.

Director, Information Systems.—Willie Blount.
Senior Systems Analyst.—Peter Szwec.
Systems Administrator.—David Topper.
Publications Coordinator.—Craig Sterkx.
Paralegal.—Kristen Amarosa.
Staff Assistants/Paralegals: Elonda Blount, Kelly Meryweather.
Staff Assistants: Ashley Anderson, Tomas Contreras, Miekl Joyner, Katherine Leiden, Matthew Loggie, Tom Meryweather, Angelina Patton.

OFFICE OF THE PARLIAMENTARIAN

H–209 The Capitol, phone 225–7373

Parliamentarian.—Thomas J. Wickham, Jr.
Deputy Parliamentarian.—Ethan B. Lauer.
Assistant Parliamentarians: Anne Gooch, Severin E. Randall, Jason A. Smith, Carrie E. Wolf.
Clerk to the Parliamentarian.—Brian C. Cooper.
Assistant Clerks to the Parliamentarian: Lloyd A. Jenkins, Monica Rodriguez.
Precedent Consultant.—Charles W. Johnson III.
Precedent Editors: Andrew S. Neal, Max A. Spitzer.
Information Technology Manager.—Bryan J. Feldblum.

OFFICE OF THE SERGEANT AT ARMS

H–124 The Capitol, phone 225–2456

PAUL D. IRVING, Sergeant at Arms of the U.S. House of Representatives; born August 21st, 1957 in Tampa, FL; B.S., Justice, American University; J.D., Whittier Law School; career record: clerk, Federal Bureau of Investigation, Los Angeles Field Office, 1980; special agent, U.S. Secret Service's, Los Angeles Field Office, 1983; Assistant Director for Government and Public Affairs, 2002; elected 36th Sergeant at Arms of the U.S. House of Representatives on January 17, 2012, for the 112th Congress.

Sergeant at Arms.—Paul D. Irving.
Deputy Sergeant at Arms.—Donald T. Kellaher.
Counsel to the Sergeant at Arms.—Tim Blodgett.
Assistant Sergeant at Arms, Administration.—Kathleen Joyce.
Assistant Sergeant at Arms, Protocol and Chamber Operations.—Ted Daniel.
Assistants to the Sergeant at Arms, Floor Security: Joyce Hamlett, Rick Villa.
Assistant Sergeant at Arms, Emergency Management.—Bob Dohr.
Assistant Sergeant at Arms, Interoffice Coordination.—Curt Coughlin.
Chief Information Officer.—Jim Kaelin.
Directors:
Division of Garage and Parking Security.—Dorian Coward.
Division of House Security.—William McFarland.
Identification Services.—Jack Looney.
Managers:
Appointments Desk.—Teresa Johnson.
Chamber Support Services.—Andrew Burns.
Senior Advisor for Police Services/Law Enforcement.—Larry Thompson.
Assistant to the Sergeant at Arms, Operations.—Stefan J. Bieret.
Staff Assistant.—KaSandra Greenhow.

JOINT COMMITTEES

Joint Economic Committee

G01 Dirksen Senate Office Building 20510–6432, phone 224–5171

[Created pursuant to sec. 5(a) of Public Law 304, 79th Congress]

Kevin Brady, Representative, Texas, *Chair*
Amy Klobuchar, Senator, Minnesota, *Vice Chair*

HOUSE

John Campbell, of California.
Sean P. Duffy, of Wisconsin.
Justin Amash, of Michigan.
Erik Paulsen, of Minnesota.
Richard L. Hanna, of New York.

Carolyn B. Maloney, of New York.
Loretta Sanchez, of California.
Elijah E. Cummings, of Maryland.
John K. Delaney, of Maryland.

SENATE

Robert P. Casey, Jr., of Pennsylvania.
BERNARD SANDERS, of Vermont.
Christopher Murphy, of Connecticut.
Martin Heinrich, of New Mexico.
Mark L. Pryor, of Arkansas.

Daniel Coats, of Indiana.
Mike Lee, of Utah.
Roger F. Wicker, of Mississippi.
Patrick J. Toomey, of Pennsylvania.

STAFF

Joint Economic Committee (G–01), 224–5171, fax 224–0240.
Republican Staff:
Executive Director.—Robert O'Quinn.
Senior Advisor.—Jeff Schlagenhauf.
Director of Communications.—Alvin Felzenberg.
Research and Press Assistant.—Andrew Silvia.
Senior Economist and Energy Policy Advisor.—Theodore Boll.
Economist.—Christina Forsberg.
Senior Policy Advisors: Doug Branch, Steve Robinson.
Executive Assistant.—Connie Foster.
Research Assistants: Hank Butler, John Trantin.
Financial Director.—Colleen Healy.
System Administrator.—Barry Dexter.
Senate Republican Staff Director.—Corey Astill.
Senior Policy Advisor and Tax Counsel.—Karin Hope.
Senior Policy Advisors: Brian Robertson, Sue Sweet.
Professional Staff Member.—Paige Hallen.
Research Assistant.—Jon Foltz.
Democratic Staff:
Staff Director.—Niles Godes.
Deputy Staff Director and Chief Economist.—Gail Gohen.
Chief Macroeconomist.—Matt Salomon.
Senior Economist.—Cary Elliott.
Senior Policy Advisors: Annabelle Tamerjan, Jim Whitney.
Policy Advisors: Martha Gimbel, Jason Kanter, Brian Phillips.
Communications Director.—Sarah Elkins.
Press Secretary.—Ian Jannetta.

Senior Research Assistant.—J.D. Mateus.
Research Assistants: Conor Carroll, Patrick Miller.
Policy Aide.—Maria Laverdiere.

Joint Committee on the Library of Congress

1309 Longworth House Office Building, 20515, phone 225–8281

Gregg Harper, Representative from Mississippi, *Chair*
Charles E. Schumer, Senator from New York, *Vice Chair*

HOUSE

Candice S. Miller, of Michigan.
Tom Cole, of Oklahoma.
Robert A. Brady, of Pennsylvania.
Zoe Lofgren, of California.

SENATE

Richard J. Durbin, of Illinois.
Patrick J. Leahy, of Vermont.
Pat Roberts, of Kansas.
Roy Blunt, of Missouri.

Joint Committee on Printing

SR–305 Russell Senate Office Building, 20515, phone 224–6352

[Created by act of August 3, 1846 (9 Stat. 114); U.S. Code 44, Section 101]

Charles E. Schumer, Senator from New York, *Chair*
Gregg Harper, Representative from Mississippi, *Vice Chair*

SENATE

Tom Udall, of New Mexico.
Mark R. Warner, of Virginia.
Pat Roberts, of Kansas.
Saxby Chambliss, of Georgia.

HOUSE

Candice S. Miller, of Michigan.
Richard B. Nugent, of Florida.
Robert A. Brady, of Pennsylvania.
Juan Vargas, of California.

Joint Committee on Taxation

1625 Longworth House Office Building 20515–6453, phone 225–3621
http://www.jct.gov

[Created by Public Law 20, 69th Congress]

Dave Camp, Representative from Michigan, *Chair*

HOUSE

Sam Johnson, of Texas.
Kevin Brady, of Texas.
Sander M. Levin, of Michigan.
Charles B. Rangel, of New York.

SENATE

John D. Rockefeller IV, of West Virginia.
Ron Wyden, of Oregon.
Orrin G. Hatch, of Utah.
Chuck Grassley, of Iowa.

NON-DESIGNATED STAFF

Joint Committee on Taxation (1625 LHOB), 225–3621.

Chief of Staff.—Thomas Barthold, 1625 LHOB, 225–3621.

Deputy Chief of Staff.—Bernard Schmitt, 596 FHOB, 226–7575.

Executive Assistants: Jean Best, 596 FHOB, 226–7575; Jayne Northern, SD G–18, 224–5561; Lucia Rogers, 596 FHOB, 226–7575; Patricia Smith, 1625 LHOB, 225–7377; Sharon Watts, 1111 (IRS), 317–4463.

Senior Refund Counsel.—Norman Brand, 1111 (IRS), 317–4463.

Senior Economists: Nicholas Bull, 596 FHOB, 226–7575; James Cilke, 596 FHOB, 226–7575; Tim Dowd, 596 FHOB, 226–7575; Robert Harvey, 596 FHOB, 226–7575; Thomas Holtmann, 596 FHOB, 226–7575; Deirdre James, 1625 LHOB, 225–7377; Pamela Moomau, 596 FHOB, 226–7575; John Navratil, 1625 LHOB, 225–7377; Christopher Overend, 596 FHOB, 226–7575.

Statistical Analyst.—Tanya Butler, 596 FHOB, 226–7575.

Economists: Aaron Butz, 596 FHOB, 225–7575; Paul Chen, 1625 LHOB, 225–7377; Chris Giosa, 597 FHOB, 226–7575; Sally Kwak, SD G–18, 224–5561; Paul Landefeld, 596 FHOB, 226–7575; Jeff Larrimore, 596 FHOB, 226–7575; James McGuire, 596 FHOB, 226–7575; Anne Moore, 596 FHOB, 226–7575; Rachel Moore, 596 FHOB, 226–7575; Zachary Richards, 596 FHOB, 226–7575; Karl Russo, 1625 LHOB, 225–7377; David Splinter, 596 FHOB, 226–7575; Lori Stuntz, 596 FHOB, 226–7575; Kathleen Toma, 596 FHOB, 226–7575; Brent Trigg, 596 FHOB, 226–7575.

Legislation Counsels: Gordon Clay, SD G–18, 224–5561; Adam Gropper, SD G–18, 224–5561; Andrew Grossman, 1625 LHOB, 225–7377; Viva Hammer, 1625 LHOB, 225–7377; Marjorie Hoffman, 1625 LHOB, 225–7377; David Lenter, 1625 LHOB, 225–7377; Patricia McDermott, 1625 LHOB, 225–7377; Kristine Roth, SD G–18, 224–5561; Kashi Way, 1625 LHOB, 225–7377; Kristeen Witt, 1625 LHOB, 225–7377.

Senior Legislation Counsels: Laurie Coady, Harold Hirsch, Cecily Rock, 1625 LHOB, 225–7377.

Legal Research Assistant.—Genevieve Cowan, SD G–18, 224–5561.

Refund Counsels: Chase Gibson, Robert Gotwald, 1111 (IRS), 317–4463.

Computer Specialists: Mark High, Damion Jedlicka, Jonathan Newton, 596 FHOB, 226–7575.

Chief Statistical Analyst.—Melani Houser, 596 FHOB, 226–7575.

Legislation Tax Accountants: Stephanie Jones, Natalie Tucker, SD G–18, 224–5561.

Senior Staff Assistant.—Debra McMullen, 1625 LHOB, 225–7377.

Staff Assistants: Neval McMullen, Kristine Means, 1625 LHOB, 225–7377.

Tax Resource Specialist.—Melissa O'Brien, SD G–18, 224–0494.

Administrative Specialist.—Frank Shima, 1625 LHOB, 225–3621.

Document Production Specialist.—Chris Simmons, 1625 LHOB, 225–7377.

Executive Assistant to COS.—Pamela Williams, 1625 LHOB, 225–3621.

ASSIGNMENTS OF SENATORS TO COMMITTEES

[Democrats in roman (53); Republicans in *italic* (45); Independent in SMALL CAPS (2); total, 100]

Senator	Committees (Standing, Joint, Select, and Special)
Alexander	Appropriations. Energy and Natural Resources. Health, Education, Labor, and Pensions. Rules and Administration.
Ayotte	Armed Services. Budget. Commerce, Science, and Transportation. Homeland Security and Governmental Affairs. Special Committee on Aging.
Baldwin	Budget. Energy and Natural Resources. Homeland Security and Governmental Affairs. Health, Education, Labor, and Pensions. Special Committee on Aging.
Barrasso	Indian Affairs, *vice chair.* Energy and Natural Resources. Environment and Public Works. Foreign Relations.
Begich	Appropriations. Commerce, Science, and Transportation. Homeland Security and Governmental Affairs. Indian Affairs. Veterans' Affairs.
Bennet	Agriculture, Nutrition, and Forestry. Finance. Health, Education, Labor, and Pensions.
Blumenthal	Armed Services. Commerce, Science, and Transportation. Judiciary. Veterans' Affairs. Special Committee on Aging.
Blunt	Appropriations. Armed Services. Commerce, Science, and Transportation. Rules and Administration. Joint Committee on the Library.
Booker	Commerce, Science, and Transportation. Environment and Public Works. Small Business and Entrepreneurship.
Boozman	Agriculture, Nutrition, and Forestry. Appropriations. Environment and Public Works. Veterans' Affairs.
Boxer	Environment and Public Works, *chair.* Select Committee on Ethics, *chair.* Commerce, Science, and Transportation. Foreign Relations.

Senator	Committees (Standing, Joint, Select, and Special)
Brown	Agriculture, Nutrition, and Forestry. Banking, Housing, and Urban Affairs. Finance. Veterans' Affairs. Select Committee on Ethics.
Burr	Finance. Health, Education, Labor, and Pensions. Veterans' Affairs. Select Committee on Intelligence.
Cantwell	Small Business and Entrepreneurship, *chair.* Commerce, Science, and Transportation. Energy and Natural Resources. Finance. Indian Affairs.
Cardin	Environment and Public Works. Finance. Foreign Relations. Small Business and Entrepreneurship.
Carper	Homeland Security and Governmental Affairs, *chair.* Environment and Public Works. Finance.
Casey	Agriculture, Nutrition, and Forestry. Finance. Health, Education, Labor, and Pensions. Joint Economic Committee. Special Committee on Aging.
Chambliss	Select Committee on Intelligence, *vice chair.* Agriculture, Nutrition, and Forestry. Armed Services. Rules and Administration. Joint Committee on Printing.
Coats	Appropriations. Commerce, Science, and Transportation. Joint Economic Committee. Select Committee on Intelligence.
Coburn	Banking, Housing, and Urban Affairs. Homeland Security and Governmental Affairs. Select Committee on Intelligence.
Cochran	Agriculture, Nutrition, and Forestry. Appropriations. Rules and Administration.
Collins	Appropriations. Select Committee on Intelligence. Special Committee on Aging.
Coons	Appropriations. Budget. Foreign Relations. Judiciary.
Corker	Banking, Housing, and Urban Affairs. Foreign Relations. Special Committee on Aging.
Cornyn	Finance. Judiciary.

Senator	Committees (Standing, Joint, Select, and Special)
Crapo	Banking, Housing, and Urban Affairs. Budget. Environment and Public Works. Finance. Indian Affairs.
Cruz	Armed Services. Commerce, Science, and Transportation. Judiciary. Rules and Administration. Special Committee on Aging.
Donnelly	Agriculture, Nutrition, and Forestry. Armed Services. Special Committee on Aging.
Durbin	Appropriations. Foreign Relations. Judiciary. Rules and Administration. Joint Committee on the Library.
Enzi	Budget. Finance. Homeland Security and Governmental Affairs. Health, Education, Labor, and Pensions. Small Business and Entrepreneurship.
Feinstein	Select Committee on Intelligence, *chair*. Appropriations. Judiciary. Rules and Administration.
Fischer	Armed Services. Commerce, Science, and Transportation. Environment and Public Works. Indian Affairs. Small Business and Entrepreneurship.
Flake	Energy and Natural Resources. Foreign Relations. Judiciary. Special Committee on Aging.
Franken	Energy and Natural Resources. Health, Education, Labor, and Pensions. Indian Affairs. Judiciary.
Gillibrand	Agriculture, Nutrition, and Forestry. Armed Services. Environment and Public Works. Special Committee on Aging.
Graham	Appropriations. Armed Services. Budget. Judiciary.
Grassley	Agriculture, Nutrition, and Forestry. Budget. Finance. Judiciary. Joint Committee on Taxation.
Hagan	Armed Services. Banking, Housing, and Urban Affairs. Health, Education, Labor, and Pensions. Small Business and Entrepreneurship.

Senator	Committees (Standing, Joint, Select, and Special)
Harkin	Health, Education, Labor, and Pensions, *chair.* Agriculture, Nutrition, and Forestry. Appropriations.
Hatch	Finance. Health, Education, Labor, and Pensions. Judiciary. Joint Committee on Taxation. Special Committee on Aging.
Heinrich	Energy and Natural Resources. Joint Economic Committee. Select Committee on Intelligence.
Heitkamp	Agriculture, Nutrition, and Forestry. Banking, Housing, and Urban Affairs. Homeland Security and Governmental Affairs. Indian Affairs. Small Business and Entrepreneurship.
Heller	Banking, Housing, and Urban Affairs. Commerce, Science, and Transportation. Energy and Natural Resources. Veterans' Affairs. Special Committee on Aging.
Hirono	Armed Services. Judiciary. Veterans' Affairs.
Hoeven	Agriculture, Nutrition, and Forestry. Appropriations. Energy and Natural Resources. Indian Affairs.
Inhofe	Armed Services. Environment and Public Works. Select Committee on Intelligence.
Isakson	Select Committee on Ethics, *vice chair.* Finance. Health, Education, Labor, and Pensions. Veterans' Affairs.
Johanns	Agriculture, Nutrition, and Forestry. Appropriations. Banking, Housing, and Urban Affairs. Veterans' Affairs.
Johnson, Ron, of Wisconsin	Budget. Commerce, Science, and Transportation. Foreign Relations. Homeland Security and Governmental Affairs. Small Business and Entrepreneurship.
Johnson, Tim, of South Dakota	Banking, Housing, and Urban Affairs, *chair.* Appropriations. Energy and Natural Resources. Indian Affairs.
Kaine	Armed Services. Budget. Foreign Relations.
KING	Armed Services. Budget. Rules and Administration. Select Committee on Intelligence.

Senator	Committees (Standing, Joint, Select, and Special)
Kirk	Appropriations. Banking, Housing, and Urban Affairs. Health, Education, Labor, and Pensions. Special Committee on Aging.
Klobuchar	Joint Economic Committee, *vice chair.* Agriculture, Nutrition, and Forestry. Commerce, Science, and Transportation. Judiciary. Rules and Administration.
Landrieu	Energy and Natural Resources, *chair.* Appropriations. Homeland Security and Governmental Affairs. Small Business and Entrepreneurship.
Leahy	Judiciary, *chair.* Agriculture, Nutrition, and Forestry. Appropriations. Rules and Administration. Joint Committee on the Library.
Lee	Armed Services. Energy and Natural Resources. Judiciary. Joint Economic Committee.
Levin	Armed Services, *chair.* Homeland Security and Governmental Affairs. Small Business and Entrepreneurship. Select Committee on Intelligence.
Manchin	Armed Services. Banking, Housing, and Urban Affairs. Energy and Natural Resources. Special Committee on Aging.
Markey	Commerce, Science, and Transportation. Environment and Public Works. Foreign Relations. Small Business and Entrepreneurship.
McCain	Armed Services. Foreign Relations. Homeland Security and Governmental Affairs. Indian Affairs.
McCaskill	Armed Services. Commerce, Science, and Transportation. Homeland Security and Governmental Affairs. Special Committee on Aging.
McConnell	Agriculture, Nutrition, and Forestry. Appropriations. Rules and Administration. Select Committee on Intelligence.
Menendez	Foreign Relations, *chair.* Banking, Housing, and Urban Affairs. Finance.
Merkley	Appropriations. Banking, Housing, and Urban Affairs. Budget. Environment and Public Works.
Mikulski	Appropriations, *chair.* Health, Education, Labor, and Pensions. Select Committee on Intelligence.

Senator	Committees (Standing, Joint, Select, and Special)
Moran	Appropriations. Banking, Housing, and Urban Affairs. Veterans' Affairs.
Murkowski	Appropriations. Energy and Natural Resources. Health, Education, Labor, and Pensions. Indian Affairs.
Murphy	Foreign Relations. Health, Education, Labor, and Pensions. Joint Economic Committee.
Murray	Budget, *chair.* Appropriations. Health, Education, Labor, and Pensions. Rules and Administration. Veterans' Affairs.
Nelson	Armed Services, *chair.* Special Committee on Aging, *chair.* Budget. Commerce, Science, and Transportation. Finance.
Paul	Foreign Relations. Homeland Security and Governmental Affairs. Health, Education, Labor, and Pensions. Small Business and Entrepreneurship.
Portman	Budget. Energy and Natural Resources. Finance. Homeland Security and Governmental Affairs.
Pryor	Appropriations. Commerce, Science, and Transportation. Homeland Security and Governmental Affairs. Rules and Administration. Small Business and Entrepreneurship. Joint Economic Committee. Select Committee on Ethics.
Reed	Appropriations. Armed Services. Banking, Housing, and Urban Affairs.
Reid	Select Committee on Intelligence.
Risch	Energy and Natural Resources. Foreign Relations. Small Business and Entrepreneurship. Select Committee on Ethics. Select Committee on Intelligence.
Roberts	Agriculture, Nutrition, and Forestry. Finance. Health, Education, Labor, and Pensions. Rules and Administration. Joint Committee on the Library. Joint Committee on Printing. Select Committee on Ethics.
Rockefeller	Commerce, Science, and Transportation, *chair.* Finance. Veterans' Affairs. Joint Committee on Taxation. Select Committee on Intelligence.

Senator	Committees (Standing, Joint, Select, and Special)
Rubio	Commerce, Science, and Transportation. Foreign Relations. Small Business and Entrepreneurship. Select Committee on Intelligence.
SANDERS	Veterans' Affairs, *chair.* Budget. Energy and Natural Resources. Environment and Public Works. Health, Education, Labor, and Pensions. Joint Economic Committee.
Schatz	Commerce, Science, and Transportation. Energy and Natural Resources. Indian Affairs.
Schumer	Rules and Administration, *chair.* Joint Committee on Printing, *chair.* Joint Committee on the Library, *vice chair.* Banking, Housing, and Urban Affairs. Finance. Judiciary.
Scott	Commerce, Science, and Transportation. Energy and Natural Resources. Health, Education, Labor, and Pensions. Small Business and Entrepreneurship. Special Committee on Aging.
Sessions	Armed Services. Budget. Environment and Public Works. Judiciary.
Shaheen	Appropriations. Armed Services. Foreign Relations. Small Business and Entrepreneurship.
Shelby	Appropriations, *vice chair.* Banking, Housing, and Urban Affairs. Rules and Administration.
Stabenow	Agriculture, Nutrition, and Forestry, *chair.* Budget. Energy and Natural Resources. Finance.
Tester	Indian Affairs, *chair.* Appropriations. Banking, Housing, and Urban Affairs. Homeland Security and Governmental Affairs. Veterans' Affairs.
Thune	Agriculture, Nutrition, and Forestry. Commerce, Science, and Transportation. Finance.
Toomey	Banking, Housing, and Urban Affairs. Budget. Finance. Joint Economic Committee.
Udall, Mark, of Colorado	Armed Services. Energy and Natural Resources. Select Committee on Intelligence.

Senator	Committees (Standing, Joint, Select, and Special)
Udall, Tom, of New Mexico	Appropriations. Environment and Public Works. Foreign Relations. Indian Affairs. Rules and Administration. Joint Committee on Printing.
Vitter	Armed Services. Banking, Housing, and Urban Affairs. Environment and Public Works. Small Business and Entrepreneurship.
Walsh	Agriculture, Nutrition, and Forestry. Commerce, Science, and Transportation. Rules and Administration. Special Committee on Aging.
Warner	Banking, Housing, and Urban Affairs. Budget. Finance. Rules and Administration. Joint Committee on Printing. Select Committee on Intelligence.
Warren	Banking, Housing, and Urban Affairs. Health, Education, Labor, and Pensions. Special Committee on Aging.
Whitehouse	Budget. Environment and Public Works. Health, Education, Labor, and Pensions. Judiciary. Special Committee on Aging.
Wicker	Armed Services. Budget. Commerce, Science, and Transportation. Environment and Public Works. Joint Economic Committee.
Wyden	Finance, *chair.* Budget. Energy and Natural Resources. Joint Committee on Taxation. Select Committee on Intelligence.

ASSIGNMENTS OF REPRESENTATIVES, RESIDENT COMMISSIONER, AND DELEGATES TO COMMITTEES

[Republicans in roman (232); Democrats in *italic* (199); Vacancies (4); Resident Commissioner and Delegates in ***boldface italic*** (6); total, 441]

Representative	Committees (Standing, Joint, and Select)
Aderholt	Appropriations.
Amash	Oversight and Government Reform. Joint Economic Committee.
Amodei	Appropriations.
Bachmann	Financial Services. Permanent Select Committee on Intelligence.
Bachus	Financial Services. Judiciary.
Barber	Armed Services. Homeland Security. Small Business.
Barletta	Education and the Workforce. Homeland Security. Transportation and Infrastructure.
Barr	Financial Services.
Barrow, John, of Georgia	Energy and Commerce.
Barton	Energy and Commerce.
Bass	Foreign Affairs. Judiciary.
Beatty	Financial Services.
Becerra	Ways and Means.
Benishek	Agriculture. Natural Resources. Veterans' Affairs.
Bentivolio	Oversight and Government Reform. Small Business.
Bera, Ami, of California	Foreign Affairs. Science, Space, and Technology.
Bilirakis	Energy and Commerce. Veterans' Affairs.
Bishop, Rob, of Utah	Armed Services. Natural Resources. Rules.
Bishop, Sanford D., Jr., of Georgia	Appropriations.
Bishop, Timothy H., of New York	Education and the Workforce. Transportation and Infrastructure.
Black	Budget. Ways and Means.
Blackburn	Budget. Energy and Commerce.

Representative	Committees (Standing, Joint, and Select)
Blumenauer	Budget. Ways and Means.
Boehner	The Speaker.
Bonamici	Education and the Workforce. Science, Space, and Technology.
Bordallo	Armed Services. Natural Resources.
Boustany	Ways and Means.
Brady, Kevin, of Texas	Joint Economic Committee, *chair*. Ways and Means. Joint Committee on Taxation.
Brady, Robert A., of Pennsylvania	Armed Services. House Administration. Joint Committee on the Library. Joint Committee on Printing.
Braley, Bruce L., of Iowa	Energy and Commerce.
Bridenstine	Armed Services. Science, Space, and Technology.
Brooks, Mo, of Alabama	Armed Services. Foreign Affairs. Science, Space, and Technology.
Brooks, Susan W., of Indiana	Education and the Workforce. Ethics. Homeland Security.
Broun, Paul C., of Georgia	Homeland Security. Natural Resources. Science, Space, and Technology.
Brown, Corrine, of Florida	Transportation and Infrastructure. Veterans' Affairs.
Brownley, Julia, of California	Science, Space, and Technology. Veterans' Affairs.
Buchanan	Ways and Means.
Bucshon	Education and the Workforce. Science, Space, and Technology. Transportation and Infrastructure.
Burgess	Energy and Commerce. Rules.
Bustos	Agriculture. Transportation and Infrastructure.
Butterfield	Energy and Commerce.
Byrne	Armed Services. Natural Resources.
Calvert	Appropriations. Budget.
Camp	Ways and Means, *chair*. Joint Committee on Taxation, *chair*.
Campbell	Budget. Financial Services. Joint Economic Committee.
Cantor	Majority Leader.

Representative	Committees (Standing, Joint, and Select)
Capito	Financial Services. Transportation and Infrastructure.
Capps	Energy and Commerce.
Capuano	Ethics. Financial Services. Transportation and Infrastructure.
Cárdenas	Budget. Natural Resources. Oversight and Government Reform.
Carney	Financial Services.
Carson, André, of Indiana	Armed Services. Transportation and Infrastructure.
Carter	Appropriations.
Cartwright	Natural Resources. Oversight and Government Reform.
Cassidy	Energy and Commerce.
Castor, Kathy, of Florida	Budget. Energy and Commerce.
Castro, Joaquin, of Texas	Armed Services. Foreign Affairs.
Chabot	Foreign Affairs. Judiciary. Small Business.
Chaffetz	Homeland Security. Judiciary. Oversight and Government Reform.
Christensen	Energy and Commerce.
Chu	Judiciary. Small Business.
Cicilline	Foreign Affairs. Judiciary.
Clark, Katherine M., of Massachusetts	Natural Resources.
Clarke, Yvette D., of New York	Ethics. Homeland Security. Small Business.
Clay	Financial Services. Oversight and Government Reform.
Cleaver	Financial Services.
Clyburn	Assistant Democratic Leader.
Coble	Judiciary. Transportation and Infrastructure.
Coffman	Armed Services. Small Business. Veterans' Affairs.
Cohen	Judiciary. Transportation and Infrastructure.
Cole	Appropriations. Budget. Rules. Joint Committee on the Library.

Representative	Committees (Standing, Joint, and Select)
Collins, Chris, of New York	Agriculture. Science, Space, and Technology. Small Business.
Collins, Doug, of Georgia	Foreign Affairs. Judiciary. Oversight and Government Reform.
Conaway	Ethics, *chair*. Agriculture. Armed Services. Permanent Select Committee on Intelligence.
Connolly	Foreign Affairs. Oversight and Government Reform.
Conyers	Judiciary.
Cook	Armed Services. Foreign Affairs. Veterans' Affairs.
Cooper	Armed Services. Oversight and Government Reform.
Costa	Agriculture. Natural Resources.
Cotton	Financial Services. Foreign Affairs.
Courtney	Agriculture. Armed Services. Education and the Workforce.
Cramer	Natural Resources. Science, Space, and Technology.
Crawford	Agriculture. Transportation and Infrastructure.
Crenshaw	Appropriations.
Crowley	Ways and Means.
Cuellar	Appropriations.
Culberson	Appropriations.
Cummings	Oversight and Government Reform. Transportation and Infrastructure. Joint Economic Committee.
Daines	Homeland Security. Natural Resources. Transportation and Infrastructure.
Davis, Danny K., of Illinois	Oversight and Government Reform. Ways and Means.
Davis, Rodney, of Illinois	Agriculture. Transportation and Infrastructure.
Davis, Susan A., of California	Armed Services. Education and the Workforce.
DeFazio	Natural Resources. Transportation and Infrastructure.
DeGette	Energy and Commerce.
Delaney	Financial Services. Joint Economic Committee.
DeLauro	Appropriations.

Representative	Committees (Standing, Joint, and Select)
DelBene	Agriculture. Judiciary.
Denham	Agriculture. Transportation and Infrastructure. Veterans' Affairs.
Dent	Appropriations. Ethics.
DeSantis	Foreign Affairs. Judiciary. Oversight and Government Reform.
DesJarlais	Agriculture. Education and the Workforce. Oversight and Government Reform.
Deutch	Ethics. Foreign Affairs. Judiciary.
Diaz-Balart	Appropriations.
Dingell	Energy and Commerce.
Doggett	Ways and Means.
Doyle	Energy and Commerce.
Duckworth	Armed Services. Oversight and Government Reform.
Duffy	Budget. Financial Services. Joint Economic Committee.
Duncan, Jeff, of South Carolina	Foreign Affairs. Homeland Security. Natural Resources.
Duncan, John J., Jr., of Tennessee	Oversight and Government Reform. Transportation and Infrastructure.
Edwards	Science, Space, and Technology. Transportation and Infrastructure.
Ellison	Financial Services.
Ellmers	Energy and Commerce.
Engel	Energy and Commerce. Foreign Affairs.
Enyart	Agriculture. Armed Services.
Eshoo	Energy and Commerce.
Esty	Science, Space, and Technology. Transportation and Infrastructure.
Faleomavaega	Foreign Affairs. Natural Resources.
Farenthold	Judiciary. Oversight and Government Reform. Transportation and Infrastructure.
Farr	Appropriations.
Fattah	Appropriations.
Fincher	Agriculture. Financial Services.
Fitzpatrick	Financial Services.

Representative	Committees (Standing, Joint, and Select)
Fleischmann	Appropriations.
Fleming	Armed Services. Natural Resources.
Flores	Budget. Natural Resources. Veterans' Affairs.
Forbes	Armed Services. Judiciary.
Fortenberry	Appropriations.
Foster	Financial Services.
Foxx	Education and the Workforce. Rules.
Frankel, Lois, of Florida	Foreign Affairs. Transportation and Infrastructure.
Franks, Trent, of Arizona	Armed Services. Judiciary.
Frelinghuysen	Appropriations.
Fudge	Agriculture. Education and the Workforce.
Gabbard	Foreign Affairs. Homeland Security.
Gallego	Agriculture. Armed Services.
Garamendi	Agriculture. Armed Services. Transportation and Infrastructure.
Garcia	Judiciary. Natural Resources.
Gardner	Energy and Commerce.
Garrett	Budget. Financial Services.
Gerlach	Ways and Means.
Gibbs	Agriculture. Transportation and Infrastructure.
Gibson	Agriculture. Armed Services.
Gingrey, Phil, of Georgia	Energy and Commerce. House Administration.
Gohmert	Judiciary. Natural Resources.
Goodlatte	Judiciary, *chair.* Agriculture.
Gosar	Natural Resources. Oversight and Government Reform.
Gowdy	Education and the Workforce. Ethics. Judiciary. Oversight and Government Reform.
Granger	Appropriations.
Graves, Sam, of Missouri	Small Business, *chair.* Transportation and Infrastructure.

Representative	Committees (Standing, Joint, and Select)
Graves, Tom, of Georgia	Appropriations.
Grayson	Foreign Affairs. Science, Space, and Technology.
Green, Al, of Texas	Financial Services.
Green, Gene, of Texas	Energy and Commerce.
Griffin, Tim, of Arkansas	Ways and Means.
Griffith, H. Morgan, of Virginia	Energy and Commerce.
Grijalva	Education and the Workforce. Natural Resources.
Grimm	Financial Services.
Guthrie	Education and the Workforce. Energy and Commerce.
Gutiérrez	Judiciary. Permanent Select Committee on Intelligence.
Hahn	Small Business. Transportation and Infrastructure.
Hall	Energy and Commerce. Science, Space, and Technology.
Hanabusa	Armed Services. Natural Resources.
Hanna	Small Business. Transportation and Infrastructure. Joint Economic Committee.
Harper	Joint Committee on the Library, *chair.* Joint Committee on Printing, *vice chair.* Energy and Commerce. House Administration.
Harris	Appropriations.
Hartzler	Agriculture. Armed Services. Budget.
Hastings, Alcee L., of Florida	Rules.
Hastings, Doc, of Washington	Natural Resources, *chair.* Oversight and Government Reform.
Heck, Denny, of Washington	Financial Services.
Heck, Joseph J., of Nevada	Armed Services. Education and the Workforce. Permanent Select Committee on Intelligence.
Hensarling	Financial Services, *chair.*
Herrera Beutler	Appropriations. Small Business.
Higgins	Foreign Affairs. Homeland Security.
Himes	Financial Services. Permanent Select Committee on Intelligence.
Hinojosa	Education and the Workforce. Financial Services.
Holding	Foreign Affairs. Judiciary.

Representative	Committees (Standing, Joint, and Select)
Holt	Education and the Workforce. Natural Resources.
Honda	Appropriations.
Horsford	Homeland Security. Natural Resources. Oversight and Government Reform.
Hoyer	Democratic Whip.
Hudson	Agriculture. Education and the Workforce. Homeland Security.
Huelskamp	Small Business. Veterans' Affairs.
Huffman	Budget. Natural Resources.
Huizenga, Bill, of Michigan	Financial Services.
Hultgren	Financial Services. Science, Space, and Technology.
Hunter	Armed Services. Education and the Workforce. Transportation and Infrastructure.
Hurt	Financial Services.
Israel	Democratic Congressional Campaign Committee, *chair.*
Issa	Oversight and Government Reform, *chair.* Judiciary.
Jackson Lee	Homeland Security. Judiciary.
Jeffries	Budget. Judiciary.
Jenkins	Ways and Means.
Johnson, Bill, of Ohio	Energy and Commerce.
Johnson, Eddie Bernice, of Texas	Science, Space, and Technology. Transportation and Infrastructure.
Johnson, Henry C. "Hank", Jr., of Georgia	Armed Services. Judiciary.
Johnson, Sam, of Texas	Ways and Means. Joint Committee on Taxation.
Jones	Armed Services.
Jordan	Judiciary. Oversight and Government Reform.
Joyce	Appropriations.
Kaptur	Appropriations.
Keating	Foreign Affairs. Homeland Security.
Kelly, Mike, of Pennsylvania	Ways and Means.
Kelly, Robin L., of Illinois	Oversight and Government Reform. Science, Space, and Technology.
Kennedy	Foreign Affairs. Science, Space, and Technology.
Kildee	Financial Services.

Representative	Committees (Standing, Joint, and Select)
Kilmer	Armed Services. Science, Space, and Technology.
Kind	Ways and Means.
King, Peter T., of New York	Financial Services. Homeland Security. Permanent Select Committee on Intelligence.
King, Steve, of Iowa	Agriculture. Judiciary. Small Business.
Kingston	Appropriations.
Kinzinger, Adam, of Illinois	Energy and Commerce. Foreign Affairs.
Kirkpatrick	Transportation and Infrastructure. Veterans' Affairs.
Kline	Education and the Workforce, *chair.* Armed Services.
Kuster	Agriculture. Small Business. Veterans' Affairs.
Labrador	Judiciary. Natural Resources.
LaMalfa	Agriculture. Natural Resources.
Lamborn	Armed Services. Natural Resources. Veterans' Affairs.
Lance	Energy and Commerce.
Langevin	Armed Services. Permanent Select Committee on Intelligence.
Lankford	Budget. Oversight and Government Reform.
Larsen, Rick, of Washington	Armed Services. Transportation and Infrastructure.
Larson, John B., of Connecticut	Ways and Means.
Latham	Appropriations.
Latta	Energy and Commerce.
Lee	Appropriations. Budget.
Levin	Ways and Means. Joint Committee on Taxation.
Lewis	Ways and Means.
Lipinski	Science, Space, and Technology. Transportation and Infrastructure.
LoBiondo	Armed Services. Transportation and Infrastructure. Permanent Select Committee on Intelligence.
Loebsack	Armed Services. Education and the Workforce.
Lofgren	House Administration. Judiciary. Science, Space, and Technology. Joint Committee on the Library.

Representative	Committees (Standing, Joint, and Select)
Long	Energy and Commerce.
Lowenthal	Foreign Affairs. Natural Resources.
Lowey	Appropriations.
Lucas	Agriculture, *chair.* Financial Services. Science, Space, and Technology.
Luetkemeyer	Financial Services. Small Business.
Luján, Ben Ray, of New Mexico	Energy and Commerce.
Lujan Grisham, Michelle, of New Mexico	Agriculture. Budget. Oversight and Government Reform.
Lummis	Natural Resources. Oversight and Government Reform. Science, Space, and Technology.
Lynch	Financial Services. Oversight and Government Reform.
McAllister	Agriculture. Natural Resources.
McCarthy, Carolyn, of New York	Education and the Workforce. Financial Services.
McCarthy, Kevin, of California	Majority Whip. Financial Services.
McCaul	Homeland Security, *chair.* Foreign Affairs. Science, Space, and Technology.
McClintock	Budget. Natural Resources.
McCollum	Appropriations.
McDermott	Budget. Ways and Means.
McGovern	Agriculture. Rules.
McHenry	Financial Services. Oversight and Government Reform.
McIntyre	Agriculture. Armed Services.
McKeon	Armed Services, *chair.* Education and the Workforce.
McKinley	Energy and Commerce.
McMorris Rodgers	Energy and Commerce.
McNerney	Energy and Commerce.
Maffei	Armed Services. Science, Space, and Technology.
Maloney, Carolyn B., of New York	Financial Services. Oversight and Government Reform. Joint Economic Committee.

Representative	Committees (Standing, Joint, and Select)
Maloney, Sean Patrick, of New York	Agriculture. Transportation and Infrastructure.
Marchant	Education and the Workforce. Ways and Means.
Marino	Foreign Affairs. Homeland Security. Judiciary.
Massie	Oversight and Government Reform. Science, Space, and Technology. Transportation and Infrastructure.
Matheson	Energy and Commerce.
Matsui	Energy and Commerce.
Meadows	Foreign Affairs. Oversight and Government Reform. Transportation and Infrastructure.
Meehan	Ethics. Homeland Security. Oversight and Government Reform. Transportation and Infrastructure.
Meeks	Financial Services. Foreign Affairs.
Meng	Foreign Affairs. Small Business.
Messer	Budget. Education and the Workforce. Foreign Affairs.
Mica	Oversight and Government Reform. Transportation and Infrastructure.
Michaud	Transportation and Infrastructure. Veterans' Affairs.
Miller, Candice S., of Michigan	House Administration, *chair.* Homeland Security. Transportation and Infrastructure. Joint Committee on the Library. Joint Committee on Printing.
Miller, Gary G., of California	Financial Services. Transportation and Infrastructure.
Miller, George, of California	Education and the Workforce.
Miller, Jeff, of Florida	Veterans' Affairs, *chair.* Armed Services. Permanent Select Committee on Intelligence.
Moore	Budget. Financial Services.
Moran	Appropriations.
Mullin	Natural Resources. Transportation and Infrastructure.
Mulvaney	Financial Services. Small Business.
Murphy, Patrick, of Florida	Financial Services. Small Business.
Murphy, Tim, of Pennsylvania	Energy and Commerce.

Representative	Committees (Standing, Joint, and Select)
Nadler	Judiciary. Transportation and Infrastructure.
Napolitano	Natural Resources. Transportation and Infrastructure.
Neal	Ways and Means.
Negrete McLeod	Agriculture. Veterans' Affairs.
Neugebauer	Agriculture. Financial Services. Science, Space, and Technology.
Noem	Agriculture. Armed Services.
Nolan	Agriculture. Transportation and Infrastructure.
Norton	Oversight and Government Reform. Transportation and Infrastructure.
Nugent	Armed Services. House Administration. Rules. Joint Committee on Printing.
Nunes	Ways and Means. Permanent Select Committee on Intelligence.
Nunnelee	Appropriations. Budget.
Olson	Energy and Commerce.
O'Rourke	Homeland Security. Veterans' Affairs.
Owens	Appropriations.
Palazzo	Armed Services. Homeland Security. Science, Space, and Technology.
Pallone	Energy and Commerce. Natural Resources.
Pascrell	Budget. Ways and Means.
Pastor, Ed, of Arizona	Appropriations. Permanent Select Committee on Intelligence.
Paulsen	Ways and Means. Joint Economic Committee.
Payne	Homeland Security. Small Business.
Pearce	Financial Services.
Pelosi	Democratic Leader.
Perlmutter	Financial Services.
Perry	Foreign Affairs. Homeland Security. Transportation and Infrastructure.
Peters, Gary C., of Michigan	Financial Services.

Representative	Committees (Standing, Joint, and Select)
Peters, Scott H., of California	Armed Services. Science, Space, and Technology.
Peterson	Agriculture.
Petri	Education and the Workforce. Transportation and Infrastructure.
Pierluisi	Ethics. Judiciary. Natural Resources.
Pingree, Chellie, of Maine	Appropriations.
Pittenger	Financial Services.
Pitts	Energy and Commerce.
Pocan	Budget. Education and the Workforce.
Poe, Ted, of Texas	Foreign Affairs. Judiciary.
Polis	Education and the Workforce. Rules.
Pompeo	Energy and Commerce. Permanent Select Committee on Intelligence.
Posey	Financial Services. Science, Space, and Technology.
Price, David E., of North Carolina	Appropriations.
Price, Tom, of Georgia	Budget. Education and the Workforce. Ways and Means.
Quigley	Appropriations.
Rahall	Transportation and Infrastructure.
Rangel	Ways and Means. Joint Committee on Taxation.
Reed	Ways and Means.
Reichert	Ways and Means.
Renacci	Ways and Means.
Ribble	Agriculture. Budget. Transportation and Infrastructure.
Rice, Tom, of South Carolina	Budget. Small Business. Transportation and Infrastructure.
Richmond	Homeland Security. Judiciary.
Rigell	Armed Services. Budget.
Roby	Appropriations.
Roe, David P., of Tennessee	Education and the Workforce. Veterans' Affairs.
Rogers, Harold, of Kentucky	Appropriations, *chair*.
Rogers, Mike, of Alabama	Agriculture. Armed Services. Homeland Security.

Representative	Committees (Standing, Joint, and Select)
Rogers, Mike, of Michigan	Permanent Select Committee on Intelligence, *chair*. Energy and Commerce.
Rohrabacher	Foreign Affairs. Science, Space, and Technology.
Rokita	Budget. Education and the Workforce. House Administration.
Rooney	Appropriations. Permanent Select Committee on Intelligence.
Roskam	Ways and Means.
Ros-Lehtinen	Foreign Affairs. Rules.
Ross	Financial Services.
Rothfus	Financial Services.
Roybal-Allard	Appropriations.
Royce	Foreign Affairs, *chair*. Financial Services.
Ruiz	Natural Resources. Veterans' Affairs.
Runyan	Armed Services. Natural Resources. Veterans' Affairs.
Ruppersberger	Permanent Select Committee on Intelligence.
Rush	Energy and Commerce.
Ryan, Paul, of Wisconsin	Budget, *chair*. Ways and Means.
Ryan, Tim, of Ohio	Appropriations. Budget.
Sablan	Education and the Workforce. Natural Resources.
Salmon	Education and the Workforce. Foreign Affairs.
Sánchez, Linda T., of California	Ethics. Ways and Means.
Sanchez, Loretta, of California	Armed Services. Homeland Security. Joint Economic Committee.
Sanford	Homeland Security. Transportation and Infrastructure.
Sarbanes	Energy and Commerce.
Scalise	Energy and Commerce.
Schakowsky	Energy and Commerce. Permanent Select Committee on Intelligence.
Schiff	Appropriations. Permanent Select Committee on Intelligence.
Schneider	Foreign Affairs. Small Business.
Schock	House Administration. Ways and Means.

Representative	Committees (Standing, Joint, and Select)
Schrader	Agriculture. Budget. Small Business.
Schwartz	Budget. Ways and Means.
Schweikert	Science, Space, and Technology. Small Business.
Scott, Austin, of Georgia	Agriculture. Armed Services.
Scott, David, of Georgia	Agriculture. Financial Services.
Scott, Robert C. ''Bobby'', of Virginia	Education and the Workforce. Judiciary.
Sensenbrenner	Judiciary. Science, Space, and Technology.
Serrano	Appropriations.
Sessions	Rules, *chair.*
Sewell, Terri A., of Alabama	Financial Services. Permanent Select Committee on Intelligence.
Shea-Porter	Armed Services. Natural Resources.
Sherman	Financial Services. Foreign Affairs.
Shimkus	Energy and Commerce.
Shuster	Transportation and Infrastructure, *chair.* Armed Services.
Simpson	Appropriations.
Sinema	Financial Services.
Sires	Foreign Affairs. Transportation and Infrastructure.
Slaughter	Rules.
Smith, Adam, of Washington	Armed Services.
Smith, Adrian, of Nebraska	Ways and Means.
Smith, Christopher H., of New Jersey	Foreign Affairs.
Smith, Jason T., of Missouri	Judiciary. Natural Resources.
Smith, Lamar, of Texas	Science, Space, and Technology, *chair.* Homeland Security. Judiciary.
Southerland	Natural Resources. Transportation and Infrastructure.
Speier	Armed Services. Oversight and Government Reform.
Stewart	Appropriations.
Stivers	Financial Services.
Stockman	Foreign Affairs. Science, Space, and Technology.
Stutzman	Financial Services.

Representative	Committees (Standing, Joint, and Select)
Swalwell, Eric, of California	Homeland Security. Science, Space, and Technology.
Takano	Science, Space, and Technology. Veterans' Affairs.
Terry	Energy and Commerce.
Thompson, Bennie G., of Mississippi	Homeland Security.
Thompson, Glenn, of Pennsylvania	Agriculture. Education and the Workforce. Natural Resources.
Thompson, Mike, of California	Ways and Means. Permanent Select Committee on Intelligence.
Thornberry	Armed Services. Permanent Select Committee on Intelligence.
Tiberi	Ways and Means.
Tierney	Education and the Workforce. Oversight and Government Reform.
Tipton	Agriculture. Natural Resources. Small Business.
Titus	Transportation and Infrastructure. Veterans' Affairs.
Tonko	Energy and Commerce.
Tsongas	Armed Services. Natural Resources.
Turner	Armed Services. Oversight and Government Reform.
Upton	Energy and Commerce, *chair.*
Valadao	Appropriations.
Van Hollen	Budget.
Vargas	Agriculture. Foreign Affairs. House Administration. Joint Committee on Printing.
Veasey	Armed Services. Science, Space, and Technology.
Vela	Agriculture. Homeland Security.
Velázquez	Financial Services. Small Business.
Visclosky	Appropriations.
Wagner	Financial Services.
Walberg	Education and the Workforce. Oversight and Government Reform.
Walden	Energy and Commerce.
Walorski	Armed Services. Budget. Veterans' Affairs.

Representative	Committees (Standing, Joint, and Select)
Walz	Agriculture. Transportation and Infrastructure. Veterans' Affairs.
Wasserman Schultz	Appropriations.
Waters	Financial Services.
Waxman	Energy and Commerce.
Weber, Randy K., Sr., of Texas	Foreign Affairs. Science, Space, and Technology.
Webster, Daniel, of Florida	Rules. Transportation and Infrastructure.
Welch	Energy and Commerce. Oversight and Government Reform.
Wenstrup	Armed Services. Veterans' Affairs.
Westmoreland	Financial Services. Permanent Select Committee on Intelligence.
Whitfield	Energy and Commerce.
Williams	Budget. Transportation and Infrastructure.
Wilson, Frederica S., of Florida	Education and the Workforce. Science, Space, and Technology.
Wilson, Joe, of South Carolina	Armed Services. Education and the Workforce. Foreign Affairs.
Wittman	Armed Services. Natural Resources.
Wolf	Appropriations.
Womack	Appropriations.
Woodall	Budget. Oversight and Government Reform. Rules.
Yarmuth	Budget. Energy and Commerce.
Yoder	Appropriations.
Yoho	Agriculture. Foreign Affairs.
Young, Don, of Alaska	Natural Resources. Transportation and Infrastructure.
Young, Todd C., of Indiana	Ways and Means.

CONGRESSIONAL ADVISORY BOARDS, COMMISSIONS, AND GROUPS

UNITED STATES AIR FORCE ACADEMY BOARD OF VISITORS

[Title 10, U.S.C., Section 9355(a)]

Board Member	**Year Appointed**
Appointed by the President:	
Arlen Jameson (Vice Chair)	2010
Marcelite Harris	2010
Thomas L. McKiernan	2011
Fletcher Wiley	2011
Sue Hoppin	2013
Dr. Paula Thronhill	2013
Appointed by the Vice President or the Senate President Pro Tempore:	
Senator *Lindsey Graham,* of South Carolina	2011
Senator *John Hoeven,* of North Dakota	2011
Appointed by the Speaker of the House of Representatives:	
Alfredo Sandoval (Chair)	2010
Representative Doug Lamborn, of Colorado	2007
Representative *Jared Polis,* of Colorado	2009
Appointed by the Chairman, Senate Armed Services Committee:	
Senator Michael F. Bennet, of Colorado	2011
Appointed by the Chairman, House Armed Services Committee:	
Representative *Niki Tsongas,* of Massachusetts	2008

UNITED STATES MILITARY ACADEMY BOARD OF VISITORS

[Title 10, U.S.C., Section 4355(a)]

Members of Congress

Senate

Jack Reed, of Rhode Island.
Mary L. Landrieu, of Louisiana.
Richard Burr, of North Carolina.

House

John Shimkus, Representative of Illinois, *Chair.*
K. Michael Conaway, Representative of Texas.
Steve Womack, Representative of Arkansas.
Steve Israel, Representative of New York.
Loretta Sanchez, Representative of California.

Presidential Appointees:

Hon. Bob Archuleta, of California, *Vice Chair.*
Brenda Sue Fulton, of New Jersey.
Elizabeth McNally, of New York.

John Travis Morrison, of Missouri.
Patrick Murphy, of Pennsylvania.
Major General Errol Schwartz, of Washington, DC.

UNITED STATES NAVAL ACADEMY BOARD OF VISITORS

[Title 10, U.S.C., Section 6968(a)]

Appointed by the President:

(Vice Chairman) Lt. Gen. Frank Petersen, USMC (Ret.) Chairman Emeritus, National Marrow Donor Program.
ADM John Nathman, USN (Ret.) Former Commander, U.S. Fleet Forces.
VADM Michelle Howard, USN, Deputy Chief of Naval Operations for Operations, Plans and Strategy.
Roland Garcia, Litigator, Office of Greenberg Tauring, LLP.
RADM Veronica Froman, USN (Ret.) CEO and chair of REBOOT, Chairman of Monarch School BoD.
Robert Stein, President of The Regency Group, King Distribution and St. John's Utilities, Kerrco Inc. board member.

Appointed by the Vice President:

Senator Barbara A. Mikulski, of Maryland.
Senator Benjamin L. Cardin, of Maryland.
Senator *Mark Kirk,* of Illinois.

Designees of the Chairmen, SASC/HASC:

Senator *John McCain,* of Arizona.
(Chairman) Representative Robert J. Wittman, of Virginia.

Appointed by the Speaker of the House:

Representative *C. A. Dutch Ruppersberger,* of Maryland.
Representative *Elijah E. Cummings,* of Maryland.
Representative John Kline, of Minnesota.

UNITED STATES COAST GUARD ACADEMY BOARD OF VISITORS *

[Title 14 U.S.C., Section 194(a)]

John D. Rockefeller IV, of West Virginia.
Mark Begich, of Alaska.
Roger F. Wicker, of Mississippi.
Patrick J. Toomey, of Pennsylvania.
John L. Mica, of Florida.
Howard Coble, of North Carolina.
Frank C. Guinta, of New Hampshire.
Andy Harris, of Maryland.
Joe Courtney, of Connecticut.
Rick Larsen, of Washington.

BRITISH-AMERICAN PARLIAMENTARY GROUP

Senate Hart Building, Room 808, phone 224–3047

[Created by Public Law 98–164]

Senate Delegation:
Chair.—Patrick J. Leahy, Senator from Vermont.
Vice Chair.—*Thad Cochran,* Senator from Mississippi.

*As appointed by the 112th Congress. No Board of Visitors has yet been appointed for the 113th Congress.

CANADA–UNITED STATES INTERPARLIAMENTARY GROUP

Senate Hart Building, Room 808, 224–3047

[Created by Public Law 86–42, 22 U.S.C., 1928a–1928d, 276d–276g]

Senate Delegation:
Chair.—Amy Klobuchar, Senator from Minnesota.
Vice Chair.—*Mike Crapo,* Senator from Idaho.

House Delegation:
Chair.—Bill Huizenga, Representative of Michigan.
Vice Chair.—Candice S. Miller, Representative of Michigan.

CHINA–UNITED STATES INTERPARLIAMENTARY GROUP

Senate Hart Building, Room 808, phone 224–3047

[Created by Public Law 108–199, Section 153]

Senate Delegation:
Chair.—Mark Begich, Senator from Alaska.
Vice Chair.—Vacant.

JAPAN–INTERPARLIAMENTARY GROUP

Senate Delegation:
Chair.—Vacant.
Vice Chair.—Vacant.

KOREA–UNITED STATES INTERPARLIAMENTARY GROUP

House Delegation:
Chair.—Edward R. Royce, Representative of California.

MEXICO–UNITED STATES INTERPARLIAMENTARY GROUP

Senate Hart Building, Room 808, phone 224–3047

[Created by Public Law 82–420, 22 U.S.C. 276h–276k]

Senate Delegation:
Chair.—Tom Udall, Senator from New Mexico.
Vice Chair.—*Kay Bailey Hutchison,* Senator from Texas.

House Delegation:
Chair.—Michael T. McCaul, Representative of Texas.
Vice Chair.—Sean P. Duffy, Representative of Wisconsin.

NATO PARLIAMENTARY ASSEMBLY

Headquarters: Place du Petit Sablon 3, B–1000 Brussels, Belgium

[Created by Public Law 84–689, 22 U.S.C., 1928z]

Senate Delegation:
Chair.—Vacant.
Vice Chair.—Vacant.

House Delegation:
Chair.—Michael R. Turner, Representative of Ohio.
Vice Chair.—Ted Poe, Representative of Texas.

STAFF

Secretary, Senate Delegation.—Julia Hart Reed, Interparliamentary Services, SH–808, 224–3047.
Secretary, House Delegation.—Jeff Dressler.

RUSSIA–UNITED STATES INTERPARLIAMENTARY GROUP

Senate Hart Building, Room 808, phone 224–3047

[Created by Public Law 108–199, Section 154]

Senate Delegation:
Chair.—Vacant
Vice Chair.—Vacant.

COMMISSION ON CONGRESSIONAL MAILING STANDARDS

1313 Longworth House Office Building, phone 226–0647

[Created by Public Law 93–191]

Chairman.—Candice S. Miller, of Michigan.
Tom Price, of Georgia.
Robert E. Latta, of Ohio.
Susan A. Davis, of California.
Brad Sherman, of California.
Cedric L. Richmond, of Louisiana.

STAFF

Majority Staff Director.—Richard Cappetto, 226–0647.
Professional Staff: George Hadijski, Ryan Kelly, Brad Walvort.
Counsel.—Peter Schalestock.
Minority Staff Director.—Kyle Anderson, 225–9337.
Professional Staff: Gregory Abbott, Matthew A. DeFreitas, Aislan Sims, Kimberly Stevens.
Counsel.—Michael Harrison.

COMMISSION ON SECURITY AND COOPERATION IN EUROPE

234 Ford House Office Building, phone 225–1901, fax 226–4199

http://www.csce.gov

Benjamin L. Cardin, Senator from Maryland, *Chair*

Christopher H. Smith, Representative from New Jersey, *Co-Chair*

LEGISLATIVE BRANCH COMMISSIONERS

Senate

Sheldon Whitehouse, of Rhode Island.
Tom Udall, of New Mexico.
Jeanne Shaheen, of New Hampshire.
Richard Blumenthal, of Connecticut.
Roger F. Wicker, of Mississippi.
Saxby Chambliss, of Georgia.
John Boozman, of Arkansas.

House

Joseph R. Pitts, of Pennsylvania.
Robert B. Aderholt, of Alabama.
Phil Gingrey, of Georgia.
Michael C. Burgess, of Texas.
Alcee L. Hastings, of Florida.
Louise McIntosh Slaughter, of New York.
Mike McIntyre, of North Carolina.
G. K. Butterfield, of North Carolina.
Steve Cohen, of Tennessee.

EXECUTIVE BRANCH COMMISSIONERS

Department of State.—Vacant.
Department of Commerce.—Vacant.
Department of Defense.—Vacant.

COMMISSION STAFF

Chief of Staff.—Fred L. Turner.
Deputy Chief of Staff.—Mark S. Milosch.
Policy Advisors: Orest Deychakiwsky, Shelly Han, Robert Hand, Janice Helwig, Alex T. Johnson, Winsome Packer, Kyle Parker, Mischa E. Thompson.
Counsel.—Allison B. Hollabaugh.
General Counsel.—Marlene Kaufmann.
Director of Administration.—Daniel R. Redfield.
Counsel for International Law.—Erika B. Schlager.

CONGRESSIONAL AWARD FOUNDATION

379 Ford House Office Building, phone (202) 226–0130, fax 226–0131

[Created by Public Law 96–114]

Chair.—Paxton K. Baker, BET Networks.
Vice Chairs:
Linda Mitchell, Mississippi State University Extension Service.
Hon. Rodney E. Slater, Patton Boggs, LLP.
Secretary.—Cheryl Maddox, Humana, Inc.
Treasurer.—Lee Klumpp, Financial Accounting Standards Board.
Members:
Cliff Akiyama, Philadelphia College of Osteopathic Medicine.
Ed Blansitt, Montgomery County Inspector General Office.
Laurel Call, Texas.
Nick Cannon, New York.
Dan Cohen, Enteromedics, Inc.
Edward Cohen, Lerner Enterprises.
Kathy Didawick, BlueCross BlueShield Association.
Dr. Wiley Dobbs, Idaho.
Mitch Draizin, Longview Capital Advisors, Inc.
David Falk, FAME.
George B. Gould, Washington, DC.
Dr. Lawrence Green, Maryland.
J. Steven Hart, Esq., Williams and Jensen, P.C.
Erica Wheelan Heyse, National Director.
Jesse Hill, Edward Jones.
Hon. Richard Hudson, United States Congress.
David W. Hunt, Esq., Nexant.
Hon. Johnny Isakson, United States Senate.
Hon. Sheila Jackson Lee, United States Congress.
Paul Kelly, The Federal Group, Inc.
Boris Kodjoe, California.
Lynn Lyons, Florida.
Raul Magdaleno, Magdaleno Consulting Group.
Patrick McLain, Sanofi, U.S.
Marc Monyek, McDonald's Corporation.

Major General Robert B. Newman, Jr., Virginia.
Kimberly Norman, G2 Secure Staff.
Jerry Prout, FMC Corporation.
Glenn Reynolds, USTelecom Association.
Adam Ruiz, Kentucky.
Beth Ann Ruoff, Ogilvy Public Relations.
Dan Scherder, Scherder and Associates.
Mike Schmid, SOS Well Services, LLC.
DeMaurice Smith, NFL Players Association.
Jimmie Lee Solomon, Florida.
Jason Van Pelt, Merck, Inc.
Rita Vaswani, Nevada State Bank.
Kathryn Weeden, United States Senate Page School.
Amos Winbush, CyberSynchs, LLC.
Jon Wood, Jon Wood & Associates, LLC.
Charmaine Yoest, Americans United for Life.

CONGRESSIONAL CLUB

2001 New Hampshire Avenue, NW., 20009, phone (202) 332–1155, fax 797–0698

Executive Board
President.—Julie Reichert.
Vice Presidents:
(1st) Vera G. Davis.
(2d) Billie Gingrey.
(3d) Helen Green.
(4th) Sandy Buchanan.
(5th) Betty Ann Tanner.
(6th) Debbie Boehner.
Treasurer.—Linda Bachus.
Recording Secretary.—Ginny Pitts.
Corresponding Secretary.—Jan English.
Administrative Assistant.—Lydia de La Vina de Foley.

CONGRESSIONAL EXECUTIVE COMMISSION ON CHINA

243 Ford House Office Building, phone 226–3766, fax 226–3804

[Created by Public Law 106–286]

Sherrod Brown, Senator from Ohio, *Chair.*
Christopher H. Smith, Representative from New Jersey, *Co-Chair.*

LEGISLATIVE BRANCH COMMISSIONERS

Senate

Carl Levin, of Michigan.
Dianne Feinstein, of California.
Jeff Merkley, of Oregon.

House

Frank R. Wolf, Representative of Virginia.
Mark Meadows, Representative of North Carolina.
Robert Pittenger, Representative of North Carolina.
Timothy J. Walz, Representative of Minnesota.
Marcy Kaptur, Representative of Ohio.
Michael M. Honda, Representative of California.

EXECUTIVE BRANCH COMMISSIONERS

Nisha Desai Biswal, U.S. Department of State.

COMMISSION STAFF

Staff Director.—Lawrence Liu.
Deputy Staff Director.—Paul B. Protic.
Director of Administration.—Judy Wright.
Senior Advisor.—Anna Brettell.
Senior Advisor and Prisoner Database Program Director.—Steve Marshall.
Senior Research Associate.—Jesse Heatley.
Senior Research Associate and Manager of Special Projects.—Abigail Story.
Research Associates: Amy Reger, Jen Salen.
Research Associate and Prisoner Database Program Deputy Director.—David Machinist.
Printer and Outreach Associate.—Deidre Jackson.

HOUSE DEMOCRACY PARTNERSHIP

227 Cannon House Office Building, phone 225–4561, fax 225–1166

democracy@mail.house.gov, http://democracy.house.gov

[Created by H. Res. 5, 112th Congress]

Chair.—Peter J. Roskam, of Illinois.
Ranking Member.—*David E. Price,* of North Carolina.

COMMISSIONERS

Jeff Fortenberry, of Nebraska.
Charles W. Boustany, Jr., of Louisiana.
K. Michael Conaway, of Texas.
Vern Buchanan, of Florida.
Ander Crenshaw, of Florida.
Joe Wilson, of South Carolina.
Susan W. Brooks, of Indiana.
Tom Latham, of Iowa.
Diane Black, of Tennessee.
Reid J. Ribble, of Wisconsin.
Sam Farr, of California.
Lois Capps, of California.
Keith Ellison, of Minnesota.
Lucille Roybal-Allard, of California.
Gwen Moore, of Wisconsin.
Susan A. Davis, of California.
Dina Titus, of Nevada.
Jim McDermott, of Washington.

Legislative Director for Representative (Roskam).—Mike Dankler.
Legislative Director for Representative (Price).—Justin Wein.

HOUSE OFFICE BUILDING COMMISSION

H–232 The Capitol, phone 225–0600

[Title 40, U.S.C. 175–176]

Chair.—John A. Boehner, Speaker of the House of Representatives.
Eric Cantor, House Majority Leader.
Nancy Pelosi, House Minority Leader.

JAPAN–UNITED STATES FRIENDSHIP COMMISSION

1201 15th Street, NW., Suite 330, phone (202) 653–9800, fax 653–9802

[Created by Public Law 94–118]

Chairman.—Harry A. Hill, President and CEO Oaklawn Marketing, Inc.
Vice-Chairman.—Dr. Sheila Smith, Senior Fellow for Japan Studies, Council on Foreign Relations (CFR).
Executive Director.—Paige Cottingham-Streater.
Assistant Executive Director.—Margaret P. Mihori.
Assistant Executive Director, CULCON.—Pamela L. Fields.
Executive Assistant.—Sylvia L. Dandridge.

Members:

Hon. Daniel Russel, Assistant Secretary of State for East Asian and Pacific Affairs, U.S. Department of State.

Hon. Evan Ryan, Assistant Secretary of State for Educational and Cultural Affairs, U.S. Department of State.

Dr. Deanna Marcum, Managing Director, Ithaka.

Dr. Patricia Maclachlan, Associate Professor of Government and Asian Studies, University of Texas.

Dr. Edward Lincoln, Professorial Lecturer, George Washington University.

David Sneider, Simpson Thacher & Bartlett, LLP.

Joan Shigekawa (acting) Chairman, National Endowment for the Arts.

Carole M. Watson (acting) Chairman, National Endowment for the Humanities.

Hon. Jim McDermott, U.S. House of Representatives.

Dr. Anne Nishimura Morse, Curator of Japanese Art, Museum of Fine Arts, Boston.

Hon. Lisa Murkowski, U.S. Senate.

Hon. Brenda Dann-Messier (acting) Assistant Secretary of Education for Post-Secondary Education, U.S. Department of Education.

Dr. T.J. Pempel, Professor of Political Science, University of California, Berkeley.

Hon. Thomas E. Petri, U.S. House of Representatives.

Dr. Leonard J. Schoppa, Jr., Director, Woodrow Wilson Department of Politics, The University of Virginia.

Hon. John D. Rockefeller IV, U.S. Senate.

MIGRATORY BIRD CONSERVATION COMMISSION

4401 North Fairfax Drive, Room 622, Arlington, VA 22203
phone (703) 358–1716, fax (703) 358–2223

[Created by act of February 18, 1929, 16 U.S.C. 715a]

Chair.—Sally Jewell, Secretary of the Interior.

Mark L. Pryor, Senator from Arkansas.

Thad Cochran, Senator from Mississippi.

John D. Dingell, Representative from Michigan.

Robert J. Wittman, Representative from Virginia.

Tom Vilsack, Secretary of Agriculture.

Gina McCarthy, Administrator of Environmental Protection Agency.

Secretary.—A. Eric Alvarez.

PERMANENT COMMITTEE FOR THE OLIVER WENDELL HOLMES DEVISE FUND

Library of Congress, 20540, phone 707–1082

[Created by act of Congress approved Aug. 5, 1955 (Public Law 246, 84th Congress), to administer Oliver Wendell Holmes Devise Fund, established by same act]

Chairman ex officio.—James H. Billington.

Administrative Officer for the Devise.—James H. Hutson.

UNITED STATES–CHINA ECONOMIC AND SECURITY REVIEW COMMISSION

444 North Capitol Street, NW., Suite 602, phone 624–1407, fax 624–1406

[Created by Public Law 106–398, 114 STAT]

COMMISSIONERS

Chair.—Hon. Dennis C. Shea.

Vice Chair.—Hon. William A. Reinsch.

Members:

Carolyn Bartholomew.

Peter T.R. Brookes.

Robin Cleveland.

Jeffrey L. Fiedler.

Hon. Carte P. Goodwin.

Daniel M. Slane.
Hon. James M. Talent.
Hon. Katherine C. Tobin, Ph.D.
Michael R. Wessel.
Larry M. Wortzel, Ph.D.

COMMISSION STAFF

Executive Director.—Michael R. Danis.
Staff Assistant.—Rickisha C. Berrien-Lopez.
Research Director and Foreign Affairs/Energy Analyst.—Caitline E. Campbell.
Congressional Liaison and Communications Director.—C. Reed Eckhold.
Management Analyst.—Christopher P. Fioravante.
Military and Security Analysts: Kimberly C. Hsu, Ethan S. Meick, Matthew O. Southerland.
Economic and Trade Analysts: Iacob N. Koch-Weser, Kevin J. Rosier, Nargiza S. Salidjanova, Anna R. Tucker.
Senior Economic and Trade Analyst.—Paul C. Magnusson.
Senior Military and Security Analyst.—R. Craig Murray.
Finance and Operations Director.—Kathleen Wilson.

SENATE NATIONAL SECURITY WORKING GROUP

311 Hart Senate Office Building, 20510, phone 228–6425

Administrative Co-Chair.—Dianne Feinstein, Senator from California.
Administrative Co-Chair.—Marco Rubio, Senator from Florida.
Democratic Leader.—Harry Reid, Senator from Nevada.
Republican Leader.—Mitch McConnell, Senator from Kentucky.
Co-Chair.—Carl Levin, Senator from Michigan.
Co-Chair.—Thad Cochran, Senator from Mississippi.
Co-Chair.—Robert Menendez, Senator from New Jersey.
Co-Chair.—Barbara A. Mikulski, Senator from Maryland.
Co-Chair.—Lindsey Graham, Senator from South Carolina.

Members:
Richard J. Durbin, Senator from Illinois.
Robert P. Casey, Jr., Senator from Pennsylvania.
Bill Nelson, Senator from Florida.
Heidi Heitkamp, Senator from North Dakota.
Benjamin L. Cardin, Senator from Maryland.
James M. Inhofe, Senator from Oklahoma.
Jeff Sessions, Senator from Alabama.
Bob Corker, Senator from Tennessee.
Roy Blunt, Senator from Missouri.
John McCain, Senator from Arizona.
James E. Risch, Senator from Idaho.

STAFF

Democratic Staff Director.—Chris Gaspar, 224–3841.
Republican Staff Director.—Jamie Fly, 224–3041.

U.S. ASSOCIATION OF FORMER MEMBERS OF CONGRESS

1401 K Street, NW., Suite 503, 20005

phone (202) 222–0972, fax 222–0977

The nonpartisan United States Association of Former Members of Congress was founded in 1970 as a nonprofit, educational, research and social organization. It has been chartered by the United States Congress and has approximately 600 members who represented American citizens in both the U.S. Senate and the House of Representatives. The Association promotes improved public understanding of the role of Congress as a unique institution as well as the crucial importance of representative democracy as a system of government, both domestically and internationally.

President.—Constance A. ''Connie'' Morella, of Maryland.
Vice President.—Barbara B. Kennelly, of Connecticut.
Treasurer.—Jim Walsh, of New York.

Secretary.—Bill Delahunt, of Massachusetts.
Immediate Past President.—Dennis Hertel, of Michigan.
Honorary Co-Chair.—Dennis Hastert, of Illinois.
Chief Executive Officer.—Peter M. Weichlein.
Counselors: Dan Glickman, of Kansas; Margaret M. Heckler, of Massachusetts; Matthew F. McHugh, of New York; Mike Parker, of Mississippi; Richard T. Schulze, of Pennsylvania; James W. Symington, of Missouri.

U.S. CAPITOL HISTORICAL SOCIETY

200 Maryland Avenue, NE., 20002, phone (202) 543–8919, fax 544–8244

[Congressional Charter, October 20, 1978, Public Law 95–493, 95th Congress, 92 Stat. 1643]

Chairman of the Board.—Hon. E. Thomas Coleman.
President.—Hon. Ron Sarasin.
Treasurer.—L. Neale Cosby.
Vice President of:
Finance and Administration.—Paul E. McGuire.
Membership and Development.—Rebecca A. Evans.
Merchandising.—Diana E. Wailes.
Scholarship and Education.—Donald R. Kennon, Ph.D.

BOARD OF TRUSTEES

STAFF

Director of:
Historical Programs.—Lauren Borchard
Public Programs and Chief Guide.—Steve Livengood.
Manager of:
Accounting Department.—Sheri Williams.
Corporate Giving.—Marilyn Green.
Membership Programs.—Dorothy Mejia-Smith.
Development Associate.—Samantha Wolfe.
Associate Historian.—William diGiacomantonio.
Receptionist, Merchandise Clerk.—Samantha Neveleff.
Receiving Supervisor.—Vince Scott.
Fulfillment Clerk—Mike Lawson.

U.S. CAPITOL PRESERVATION COMMISSION

[Created pursuant to Public Law 100–696]

Co-Chairs:
John A. Boehner, Speaker of the House.
Patrick J. Leahy, Senate President Pro Tempore.

Senate Members:
Harry Reid, Majority Leader.
Mitch McConnell, Republican Leader.
Charles E. Schumer.
Pat Roberts.
Richard J. Durbin.
John Hoeven.
Vacant.
Vacant.

House Members:
Eric Cantor, Majority Leader.
Nancy Pelosi, Democratic Leader.
Candice S. Miller.
Robert A. Brady.
Gregg Harper.
Marcy Kaptur.
Vacant.
Vacant.

Ex-Officio Member-Architect of the Capitol.—Stephen T. Ayers, AIA, LEED AP.

U.S. HOUSE OF REPRESENTATIVES FINE ARTS BOARD

1309 Longworth House Office Building, phone 225–8281

[Created by Public Law 101–696]

Chair.—Candice S. Miller, of Michigan.

Members:
Gregg Harper, of Mississippi.
Tom Cole, of Oklahoma.
Robert A. Brady, of Pennsylvania.
Zoe Lofgren, of California.

U.S. SENATE COMMISSION ON ART

S–411 The Capitol, phone 224–2955

[Created by Public Law 100–696]

Chair.—Harry Reid, of Nevada.
Vice Chair.—Mitch McConnell, of Kentucky.

Members:
Patrick J. Leahy, of Vermont.
Charles E. Schumer, of New York.
Pat Roberts, of Kansas.

STAFF

Executive Secretary.—Nancy Erickson.
Curator.—Melinda K. Smith.
Administrator.—Scott M. Strong.
Historic Preservation Officer.—Kelly Steele.
Collections Manager.—Deborah Wood.
Registrar.—Courtney Morfeld.
Collections Specialist.—Theresa Malanum.
Museum Specialist.—Richard L. Doerner.
Assistant Curator.—Amy Elizabeth Burton.

OTHER CONGRESSIONAL OFFICIALS AND SERVICES

ARCHITECT OF THE CAPITOL

ARCHITECT'S OFFICE

SB–15, U.S. Capitol, phone 228–1793, fax 228–1893, http://www.aoc.gov

Architect of the Capitol.—Stephen T. Ayers, FAIA, LEED AP, 228–1793.
Assistant Architect of the Capitol.—Michael G. Turnbull, 228–1221.
Chief Operating Officer.—Christine Merdon, P.E., CMM, 228–1793.
Chief Executive Officer for Visitor Services.—Beth Plemmons, 593–1837.
Inspector General.—Kevin Mulshine, 593–0260.
Director of:
Communications and Congressional Relations.—Mike Culver, 228–1701.
Safety, Fire and Environmental Programs.—Susan Adams, 226–0630.
Chief Administrative Officer.—David Ferguson, 228–1205.
Chief Financial Officer.—Tom Carroll, 225–0038.
Budget Officer.—Ramon Jimenez, 228–1793.
Communications Officer.—Laura Condeluci, 228–1793.
General Counsel.—Jason Baltimore, 228–1793.
Executive Officer, U.S. Botanic Garden.—Holly Shimizu, 225–6670.
Curator.—Barbara Wolanin, 228–1222.

U.S. CAPITOL

HT–42, Capitol Superintendent's Service Center, phone 228–8800, fax 225–1957

[The Capitol Superintendent's Service Center provides Facility Services for the Capitol and CVC.]

Superintendent.—Carlos Elias.
Deputy Superintendent.—Vacant, 228–8800
Assistant Superintendent.—John Deubler, 228–8800.

U.S. CAPITOL VISITOR CENTER

U.S. Capitol Visitor Center, Room SVC–101, 20515, phone 593–1816

Recorded Information 226–8000, Special Services 224–4048, TTY 224–4049

CEO for Visitor Services.—Beth Plemmons.
Director of:
Communications and Marketing.—Tom Fontana.
Exhibits and Education.—Carol Beebe.
Gift Shops.—Susan Sisk.
Restaurant/Special Events.—Miguel Lopez.
Visitor Services.—Tina Pearson.
Volunteer Coordinator.—Wayne Kehoe.

SENATE OFFICE BUILDINGS

G–45 Dirksen Senate Office Building, phone 224–3141, fax 224–0652

Superintendent.—Takis Tzamaras, 224–2021.

Deputy Superintendent.—Lawrence Barr, 224–7002.
Assistant Superintendents: Jean Gilles, Michael Shirven, 224–8023; Eric Swanson, 228–5002.

HOUSE OFFICE BUILDINGS

B–341 Rayburn House Office Building, phone 225–4141, fax 225–3003

Superintendent.—William M. Weidemeyer, P.E., CFM, 225–7012.
Deputy Superintendent.—Mark Reed, P.E., CFM, 225–4142.
Assistant Superintendents: Barron Dill, Jason McIntyre, Daniel Murphy, William Wood, 225–4142.

CAPITOL TELEPHONE EXCHANGE

6110 Postal Square Building, phone 224–3121

Supervisors: Joan Sartori, Debra Morgan.

CHILD CARE CENTERS

HOUSE OF REPRESENTATIVES CHILD CARE CENTER

147 Ford House Office Building
Virginia Avenue and 3rd Street, SW., 20515
phone 226–9320, fax 225–6908

Director.—Monica Barnabae.
Program Director.—Paige Beatty.

SENATE EMPLOYEES' CHILD CARE CENTER

United States Senate, 20510
phone 224–1461, fax 228–3686

Director.—Shannon Mara.

COMBINED AIRLINES TICKET OFFICES (CATO)

344 Maple West, Suite 224, Vienna, VA 22180

phone (703) 522–8664, 1 (888) 205–4482

General Manager.—Susan Willis.

SENATE AND HOUSE

B–222 Longworth House Office Building

phone (703) 522–2286, fax (202) 226–5992

Manager.—Misty Conner.

CONGRESSIONAL RECORD DAILY DIGEST

HOUSE SECTION

HT–13 The Capitol, phone 225–2868 (committees), 225–1501 (chamber)

Editors for—
Committee Meetings.—Kevie Niland.

Chamber Action.—Jenelle Pulis.

SENATE SECTION

S–421 The Capitol, phone 224–2658, fax 224–1220

Editor.—Elizabeth Tratos.
Assistant Editor.—Joseph Johnston.

CONGRESSIONAL RECORD INDEX OFFICE

U.S. Government Printing Office, Room C–738

North Capitol and H Streets, NW., 20401, phone 512–0275

Director.—Marcia Thompson, 512–2010, ext. 3–1975.
Deputy Director.—Philip C. Hart, 512–2010, ext. 3–1973.
Historian of Bills.—Barbre A. Brunson, 512–2010, ext. 3–1957.
Editors: Grafton J. Daniels, Jason Parsons.
Indexers: Ytta B. Carr, Joel K. Church, Jennifer E. Jones, Jane M. Wallace.

OFFICE OF CONGRESSIONAL ACCESSIBILITY SERVICES

S–156 Crypt of the Capitol 20510, phone 224–4048, TTY 224–4049

Director.—David Hauck.

LIAISON OFFICES

AIR FORCE

B–322 Rayburn House Office Building

phone 225–6656, 685–4530, DSN 325–4530, fax 685–2592

Chief.—Col. Patrick McKenzie.
Deputy Chief.—Lt. Col. Derek Blough.
Liaison Officers: Maj. Jeanetta Grover, Lt. Col. Stacy Wharton.
Budget and Appropriations Liaison Officer.—Lt. Col. Michelle ''Shelli'' Brunswick.
Legislative Assistant.—MSgt Purvis ''Alex'' Alexander.
Civilian.—Vacant.

182 Russell Senate Office Building, phone 224–2481, 685–2573, fax 685–2575

Chief.—Col. Billie Thompson.
Deputy Chief.—Lt. Col. Dawn Lancaster.
Liaison Officers: Maj. Lori Ambers, Lt. Col. Ian Dinesen, Lt. Col. Amanda Steffi.
Appropriations Liaison Officer.—Lt. Col. Bernadette Maldonado.
Legislative Assistant.—Charlotte ''Charli'' Kiley.

ARMY

B–325 Rayburn House Office Building, phone (202) 685–2676, fax 685–2674

Chief.—COL La'Tonya Lynn.
Deputy Chief.—LTC John Raffferty.
Liaison Officers: MAJ Eric Christopher, LTC Michael Davidson, MAJ Eric Harrison, MAJ Adrian Foster, MAJ Mike Poche, MAJ Kevin Tann, SGM Tonia Walker, MAJ Brian Whittier, CPT Krystyl Watson, MAJ Raymond Windmiller.
Congressional Caseworker.—Gail Warren.

183 Russell Senate Office Building, phone 224–2881, fax 685–2570

Chief.—COL Robert McAleer.
Deputy Chief.—LTC Michael Katona.
Liaison Officers: LTC Ann Marie Amaral, MAJ Rich Anderson, LTC Ned Ash, MAJ Chris Bala, MAJ Kevin Kahre, MAJ Kim McGhee, CPT Sean Smith.
Congressional Caseworkers: Nikki Barnes, Cynthia Gray.

COAST GUARD

B–320 Rayburn House Office Building, phone 225–4775, fax 426–6081

Director, House Liaison Officer.—CDR Bion Stewart.
Deputy, House Liaison Officer.—LCDR Jay Guyer.
Assistant House Liaison.—LT Brittany Lee.

183 Russell Senate Office Building, phone 224–2913, fax 755–1695

Liaison Officer.—CDR Daniel Walsh.
Liaison Assistant.—LCDR Robert Potter.

NAVY / MARINE CORPS

B–324 Rayburn House Office Building, phone: Navy 225–7126; Marine Corps 225–7124

Director.—CAPT Paul Gronemeyer, USN.
Deputy Director.—CDR Jason Grizzle, USN.
USN Liaison Officers: LCDR Chester Morgan, USN (contracts); LT Pia Chapman, USN; LT Victoria Marum, USN; LT Neil Szymczak, USN; LT Jonathan Wachtel, USN.
Director USMC.—COL Daniel Greenwood, USMC.
USMC Liaison Officers: MAJ Alex Cross, USMC; MAJ Janine Garner, USMC; CAPT Sam Howe, USMC; CAPT Anthony Garofano, USMC.
Office Manager/Administrative Clerk.—GYSGT Lacorie Delaney, USMC; SGT Abraham Cruz.

182 Russell Senate Office Building, phone: Navy 685–6003, Marine Corps 685–6010

Director.—CAPT Cedric Pringle, USN.
Deputy Director.—CDR Mike Vitali, USN.
USN Liaison Officers: LT Cameron Lindsay, USN; LT Mike Mullee, USN; LT Kate Rosenberg, USN; LT Cory Pleasanton, USN.
Director, USMC.—COL Robert Jones, USMC.
USMC Liaison Officers.—MAJ Myle Hammond, USMC; CAPT Brian O'Shea, USMC; CAPT Dave Kinzler, USMC.
Assistant Liaison Officers: GYSGT Kurt Woodard, USMC; SGT Christine Bloomfield, USMC.

GOVERNMENT ACCOUNTABILITY OFFICE

Room 7125, 441 G Street, 20548, phone 512–4400, fax 512–7919 or 512–4641

Managing Director, Congressional Relations.—Katherine Siggerud, 512–6570.
Executive Assistant.—Jane Lusby, 512–4378.
Legislative Advisers: Carlos Diz, 512–8256; Rosa Harris, 512–9492; Carolyn Kirby, 512–9843; Anne Laffoon, 512–4199; David Lewis, 512–7176; Tim Minelli, 512–8443; Paul Thompson, 512–9867; Mary Frances Widner, 512–3804.
Associate Legislative Adviser.—Kisha Clark, 512–3208.
Congressional Information Systems Specialist.—Ellen Wedge, 512–6817.

Engagement and Administrative Operations Assistant.—Theodora Guardado-Gallegos, 512–6224.

OFFICE OF PERSONNEL MANAGEMENT

B–332 Rayburn House Office Building, phone 225–4955

Chief.—Vacant.
Constituent Services Officers: Fatima Moghis, Kristen Soper, Carlos Tingle.

SOCIAL SECURITY ADMINISTRATION

G3, L1, Rayburn House Office Building, phone 225–3133, fax 225–3144

Director.—Robert Forrester.
Congressional Relations Liaisons: Sylvia Taylor-Mackey, Latrice Wingo.

STATE DEPARTMENT LIAISON OFFICES

B–330 Rayburn House Office Building, phone 226–4640, fax 226–4643

Director.—Scott Feeken, 226–4644.
Deputy Director.—Nicholas Psyhos, 226–4642.
Consular Officer.—Lisa Gisvold, 226–4641.

189 Russell Senate Office Building, fax 224–1400

Director.—Marlene Menard, 228–1602.
Deputy Director.—Nicholas Psyhos, 228–1603.
Consular Officer.—Scott Boswell, 228–1605.

VETERANS' AFFAIRS

B–328 Rayburn House Office Building, phone 225–2280, fax 453–5225

Director.—Dr. Ron Maurer.
Assistant Director.—Vacant.
Liaison Assistants: Frank Morgan, Elaine Waldrop.
Representatives: Tasha Adams, Richard Armstrong, Jr., Gloria Galloway.
Outreach.—Mandy Martin.

189 Russell Senate Office Building, phone 224–5351, fax 453–5218

Communications.—Tim Embree.
Assistant Director.—Vacant.
Liaison Representative.—Matt Steiner.
Representative.—Stuart A. Weiner.
Outreach.—Jennifer McCarthy.

UNITED STATES SENATE PAGE SCHOOL

United States Senate, Washington, DC 20510–7248, fax 224–1838

Principal.—Kathryn S. Weeden, 224–3926.
English.—Frances Owens, 228–1024.
Mathematics.—Raymond Cwalina, 228–1018.
Science.—John Malek, 228–1025.

Social Studies.—Michael Bowers, 228–1012.
Secretary.—Kathleen Martin, 224–3927.

U.S. CAPITOL POLICE

119 D Street, NE., 20510–7218

Office of the Chief 224–9806, Command Center 224–0908
Communications 224–5151, Emergency 224–0911

U.S. CAPITOL POLICE BOARD

Sergeant at Arms, U.S. House of Representatives.—Paul D. Irving.
Sergeant at Arms, U.S. Senate.—Terrance W. Gainer.
Architect of the Capitol.—Stephen T. Ayers, FAIA, LEED AP.

OFFICE OF THE CHIEF

Chief of Police.—Kim C. Dine.
Chief of Staff.—William M. Goldman.
Office of:
Diversity, Opportunity and Inclusiveness.—Deborah Lewis.
General Counsel.—Gretchen DeMar.
Professional Responsibility.—Capt. Kimberlie Bolinger.
Public Information.—Lt. Kimberly Schneider.

CHIEF OF OPERATIONS

Assistant Chief of Police.—Daniel B. Malloy, Jr.
Executive Officer.—Lt. Debbie T. Proctor.
Operational Readiness Projects.—Deputy Chief Yancey Garner, Jr.

MISSION ASSURANCE BUREAU

Bureau Commander.—Scott Linsky (acting).
Command Center: Insp. Wesley Mahr, Capt. Kenneth Wheeler.
Communications.—Capt. Jeff Wills.
Emergency Management Division.—Scott Linsky.
Special Events.—Lt. Stefanie Bloxson.

OPERATIONAL SERVICES BUREAU

Bureau Commander.—Deputy Chief Fredinal Rogers.
Hazardous Incident Response Division.—Insp. Alan Morris.
Patrol/Mobile Response Division.—Insp. Richard Rudd.

PROTECTIVE SERVICES BUREAU

Bureau Commander.—Deputy Chief Chad Thomas.
Dignitary Protection Division.—Insp. Jeffrey Pickett.
Investigations Division.—Capt. Andrew Bolinger.

SECURITY SERVICES BUREAU

Bureau Commander.—Robert Ford (acting).

UNIFORM SERVICES BUREAU

Bureau Commander.—Deputy Chief Donald Rouiller.
Capitol Division Commander.—Insp. Elizabeth Dodgson.
House Division Commander.—Insp. Thomas Loyd.
Library Division Commander.—Insp. Lawrence Loughery.
Senate Division Commander.—Insp. Matthew Perkins.

CHIEF ADMINISTRATIVE OFFICER

Chief Administrative Officer.—Richard L. Braddock.
Executive Officer.—Dominic A. Storelli.
Director, Office of:
Employment Counsel.—Frederick Herrera.
Facilities and Logistics.—Cathleen English.
Financial Management.—Jay Miller.
Human Resources.—Jacqueline Whitaker.
Information Systems.—Norman Farley.
Policy and Management Systems.—Jeffrey Miller (acting).
Training Services Bureau.—Vacant.
Task Force (Discipline Process Review).—Deputy Chief Matthew Verderosa.

STATISTICAL INFORMATION

VOTES CAST FOR SENATORS IN 2008, 2010, and 2012

[Compiled from official statistics obtained by the Clerk of the House. Figures in the last column, for the 2012 election, may include totals for more candidates than the ones shown.]

State	Vote						Total vote cast in 2012
	2008		2010		2012		
	Democrat	Republican	Democrat	Republican	Democrat	Republican	
Alabama	752,391	1,305,383	515,619	968,181			
Alaska	1,51,767	147,814	60,045	90,839			
Arizona			592,011	1,005,615	1,036,542	1,104,457	2,243,422
Arkansas	804,678		288,156	451,618			
California			5,218,441	4,217,366	7,864,624	4,713,887	12,578,511
Colorado	1,230,994	990,755	851,590	822,731			
Connecticut			605,204	498,341	792,983	604,569	1,511,764
Delaware	257,539	140,595	174,012	123,053	265,415	115,700	399,606
Florida			1,092,936	2,645,743	4,523,451	3,458,267	8,189,946
Georgia	909,923	1,228,033	996,516	1,489,904			
Hawaii			277,228	79,939	269,489	160,994	437,159
Idaho	219,903	371,744	112,057	319,953			
Illinois	3,615,844	1,520,621	1,719,478	1,778,698			
Indiana			697,775	952,116	1,281,181	1,133,621	2,560,102
Iowa	941,665	560,006	371,686	718,215			
Kansas	441,399	727,121	220,971	587,175			
Kentucky	847,005	953,816	600,052	755,706			
Louisiana	988,298	867,177	476,572	715,415			
Maine	279,510	444,300			92,900 (1)	215,399	724,720
Maryland			1,140,531	655,666	1,474,028	693,291	2,633,234
Massachusetts	1,971,974	926,044			1,696,346	1,458,048	3,184,196
Michigan	3,038,386	1,641,070			2,735,826	1,767,386	4,652,918
Minnesota	1,212,629	1,212,317			1,854,595	867,974	2,843,207
Mississippi	480,915	1,449,520			503,467	709,626	1,241,568
Missouri			789,736	1,054,160	1,494,125	1,066,159	2,725,793
Montana	348,289	129,369			236,123	218,051	486,066
Nebraska	317,456	455,854			332,979	455,593	788,572
Nevada			362,785	321,361	446,080	457,656	997,805
New Hampshire	358,438	314,403	167,545	273,218			
New Jersey	1,951,218	1,461,025			1,987,680	1,329,534	3,376,649
New Mexico	505,128	318,522			395,717	351,260	775,793
New York			3,047,880	1,239,605	4,420,043	1,514,647	7,116,628
North Carolina	2,249,311	1,887,510	1,145,074	1,458,046			
North Dakota			52,955	181,689	161,337	158,401	321,144
Ohio			1,503,297	2,168,742	2,762,690	2,435,712	5,449,018
Oklahoma	527,736	763,375	265,814	718,482			
Oregon	864,392	805,159	825,507	566,199			
Pennsylvania			1,948,716	2,028,945	3,021,364	2,509,132	5,627,422
Rhode Island	320,644	116,174			271,034	146,222	418,189
South Carolina	790,621	1,076,534	364,598	810,771			
South Dakota	237,889	142,784		227,947			
Tennessee	767,236	1,579,477			705,882	1,506,443	2,321,477
Texas	3,389,365	4,337,469			3,194,927	4,440,137	7,864,822
Utah			191,732	360,403	301,873	657,608	1,006,901
Vermont			151,281	72,699	(2)	72,898	292,762
Virginia	2,369,327	1,228,830			2,010,067	1,785,542	3,802,196
Washington			1,314,930	1,196,164	1,855,493	1,213,924	3,069,417
West Virginia	447,560	254,629	283,358	230,013	399,898	240,787	660,202
Wisconsin			1,020,958	1,125,999	1,547,104	1,380,126	3,009,411
Wyoming	126,833	372,109			53,019	185,250	250,700

[1] Independent Angus S. King, Jr. was elected on November 6, 2012 with 370,580 votes.
[2] Independent Bernard Sanders was elected on November 6, 2012 with 207,848 votes.

VOTES CAST FOR REPRESENTATIVES, RESIDENT COMMISSIONER, AND DELEGATES IN 2008, 2010, and 2012

[The figures, compiled from official statistics obtained by the Clerk of the House, show the votes for the Republican and Democratic nominees, except as otherwise indicated. Figures in the last column, for the 2012 election, may include totals for more candidates than the ones shown.]

State and district	Vote cast in 2008		State and district	Vote cast in 2010		State and district	Vote cast in 2012		Total vote cast in 2012
	Democrat	Republican		Republican	Democrat		Republican	Democrat	
AL:			AL:			AL:			
1st	....	210,660	1st	129,063	....	1st	196,374	....	200,676
2d	144,368	142,578	2d	111,645	106,865	2d	180,591	103,092	283,953
3d	121,080	142,708	3d	117,736	80,204	3d	175,306	98,141	273,930
4th	66,077	196,741	4th	167,714	....	4th	199,071	69,706	269,118
5th	158,324	147,314	5th	131,109	95,192	5th	189,185	101,772	291,293
6th	....	280,902	6th	205,288	....	6th	219,262	88,267	308,102
7th	228,518	....	7th	51,890	136,696	7th	73,835	232,520	306,558
AK:			AK:			AK:			
At large	142,560	158,939	At large	175,384	77,606	At large	185,296	82,927	289,804
AZ:			AZ:			AZ:			
1st	155,791	109,924	1st	112,816	99,233	1st	113,594	122,774	251,595
2d	125,611	200,914	2d	173,173	82,891	2d	144,884	147,338	292,279
3d	115,759	148,800	3d	108,689	85,610	3d	62,663	98,468	168,698
4th	89,721	26,435	4th	25,300	61,524	4th	162,907	69,154	243,760
5th	149,033	122,165	5th	110,374	91,749	5th	183,470	89,589	273,059
6th	115,457	208,582	6th	165,649	72,615	6th	179,706	97,666	293,177
7th	124,304	64,425	7th	70,385	79,935	7th	....	104,489	127,827
8th	179,629	140,553	8th	134,124	138,280	8th	172,809	95,635	272,791
						9th	111,630	121,881	250,131
AR:			AR:			AR:			
1st	(1)	....	1st	93,224	78,267	1st	138,800	96,601	246,843
2d	212,303	....	2d	122,091	80,687	2d	158,175	113,156	286,598
3d	....	215,196	3d	148,581	56,542	3d	186,467	....	245,660
4th	203,178	....	4th	71,526	102,479	4th	154,149	95,013	258,953
CA:			CA:			CA:			
1st	197,812	67,853	1st	72,803	147,307	1st	168,827	125,386	294,213
2d	118,878	163,459	2d	130,837	98,092	2d	91,310	226,216	317,526
3d	137,971	155,424	3d	131,169	113,128	3d	107,086	126,882	233,968
4th	183,990	185,790	4th	186,397	95,653	4th	197,803	125,885	323,688
5th	164,242	46,002	5th	43,577	124,220	5th	69,545	202,872	272,417
6th	229,672	77,073	6th	77,361	172,216	6th	53,406	160,667	214,073
7th	170,962	51,166	7th	56,764	122,435	7th	132,050	141,241	273,291
8th	204,996	27,614	8th	31,711	167,957	8th	179,644	....	179,644
9th	238,915	26,917	9th	23,054	180,400	9th	94,704	118,373	213,077
10th	192,226	91,877	10th	88,512	137,578	10th	110,265	98,934	209,199
11th	164,500	133,104	11th	112,703	115,361	11th	87,136	200,743	287,879
12th	200,442	49,258	12th	44,475	152,044	12th	44,478	253,709	298,187
13th	166,829	51,447	13th	45,575	118,278	13th	....	250,436	288,582
14th	190,301	60,610	14th	60,917	151,217	14th	54,455	203,828	258,283
15th	170,977	55,489	15th	60,468	126,147	15th	....	231,034	231,034
16th	146,481	49,399	16th	37,913	105,841	16th	62,801	84,649	147,450
17th	168,907	59,037	17th	53,176	118,734	17th	57,336	159,392	216,728
18th	130,192	....	18th	51,716	72,853	18th	89,103	212,831	301,934
19th	....	179,245	19th	128,394	69,912	19th	59,313	162,300	221,613
20th	93,023	32,118	20th	43,197	46,247	20th	60,566	172,996	233,562
21st	66,317	143,498	21st	135,979	....	21st	67,164	49,119	116,283
22d	....	224,549	22d	173,490	....	22d	132,386	81,555	213,941
23d	171,403	80,385	23d	72,744	111,768	23d	158,161	....	216,003
24th	125,560	174,492	24th	144,055	96,279	24th	127,746	156,749	284,495
25th	105,929	144,660	25th	118,308	73,028	25th	129,593	106,982	236,575
26th	108,039	140,615	26th	112,774	76,093	26th	124,863	139,072	263,935
27th	145,812	52,852	27th	55,056	102,927	27th	86,817	154,191	241,008
28th	137,471	....	28th	28,493	88,385	28th	58,008	188,703	246,711
29th	146,198	56,727	29th	51,534	104,374	29th	....	111,287	150,281
30th	242,792	....	30th	75,948	153,663	30th	....	247,851	247,851
31st	110,955	....	31st	14,740	76,363	31st	161,219	....	161,219
32d	130,142	....	32d	31,697	77,759	32d	65,208	124,903	190,111
33d	186,924	26,536	33d	21,342	131,990	33d	....	171,860	318,520
34th	98,503	29,266	34th	20,457	69,382	34th	20,223	120,367	140,590
35th	150,778	24,169	35th	25,561	98,131	35th	....	142,680	142,680
36th	171,948	78,543	36th	66,706	114,489	36th	97,953	110,189	208,142
37th	131,342	....	37th	29,159	85,799	37th	32,541	207,039	239,580
38th	130,211	....	38th	30,883	85,459	38th	69,807	145,280	215,087
39th	125,289	54,533	39th	42,037	81,590	39th	145,607	106,360	251,967
40th	86,772	144,923	40th	119,455	59,400	40th	....	125,553	125,553
41st	99,214	159,486	41st	127,857	74,394	41st	72,074	103,578	175,652
42d	104,909	158,404	42d	127,161	65,122	42d	130,245	84,702	214,947
43d	108,259	48,312	43d	36,890	70,026	43d	....	200,894	200,894
44th	123,890	129,937	44th	107,482	85,784	44th	....	165,898	165,898
45th	111,026	155,166	45th	106,472	87,141	45th	171,417	121,814	293,231
46th	122,891	149,818	46th	139,822	84,940	46th	54,121	95,694	149,815
47th	85,878	31,432	47th	37,679	50,832	47th	99,919	130,093	230,012
48th	125,537	171,658	48th	145,481	88,465	48th	177,144	113,358	290,502
49th	90,138	140,300	49th	119,088	59,714	49th	159,725	114,893	274,618
50th	141,635	157,502	50th	142,247	97,818	50th	174,838	83,455	258,293

VOTES CAST FOR REPRESENTATIVES, RESIDENT COMMISSIONER, AND DELEGATES IN 2008, 2010, and 2012—CONTINUED

[The figures, compiled from official statistics obtained by the Clerk of the House, show the votes for the Republican and Democratic nominees, except as otherwise indicated. Figures in the last column, for the 2012 election, may include totals for more candidates than the ones shown.]

State and district	Vote cast in 2008		State and district	Vote cast in 2010		State and district	Vote cast in 2012		Total vote cast in 2012
	Demo-crat	Repub-lican		Repub-lican	Demo-crat		Repub-lican	Demo-crat	
51st	148,281	49,345	51st	57,488	86,423	51st	45,464	113,934	159,398
52d	111,051	160,724	52d	139,460	70,870	52d	144,459	151,451	295,910
53d	161,315	64,658	53d	57,230	104,800	53d	103,482	164,825	268,307
CO:			CO:			CO:			
1st	203,755	67,345	1st	59,747	140,073	1st	93,217	237,579	348,210
2d	215,571	116,591	2d	98,171	148,720	2d	162,639	234,758	421,580
3d	203,455	126,762	3d	129,257	118,048	3d	185,291	142,619	347,247
4th	187,347	146,028	4th	138,634	109,249	4th	200,006	125,800	342,336
5th	113,025	183,178	5th	152,829	68,039	5th	199,639	....	307,231
6th	162,639	250,877	6th	217,368	104,104	6th	163,938	156,937	342,914
7th	173,931	100,055	7th	88,026	112,667	7th	139,066	182,460	340,970
CT:			CT:			CT:			
1st	194,493	76,860	1st	84,076	130,538	1st	82,321	192,840	297,061
2d	198,984	104,574	2d	95,671	140,888	2d	88,103	189,444	299,960
3d	204,761	58,583	3d	74,107	134,544	3d	73,726	197,163	291,301
4th	149,345	146,854	4th	102,030	110,746	4th	117,503	167,320	293,432
5th	161,178	117,914	5th	102,092	118,231	5th	128,927	137,631	284,757
DE:			DE:			DE:			
At large	146,434	235,437	At large	125,442	173,543	At large	129,757	249,933	388,059
FL:			FL:			FL:			
1st	98,797	232,559	1st	170,821	....	1st	238,440	92,961	342,594
2d	216,804	133,404	2d	136,371	105,211	2d	175,856	157,634	333,718
3d	(2)	....	3d	50,932	94,744	3d	204,331	102,468	315,669
4th	119,330	224,112	4th	178,238	....	4th	239,988	....	315,470
5th	168,446	265,186	5th	208,815	100,858	5th	70,700	190,472	269,153
6th	146,655	228,302	6th	179,349	....	6th	195,962	146,489	342,451
7th	146,292	238,721	7th	185,470	83,206	7th	185,518	130,479	316,010
8th	172,854	159,490	8th	123,586	84,167	8th	205,432	130,870	348,909
9th	126,346	216,591	9th	165,433	66,158	9th	98,856	164,891	263,747
10th	118,430	182,781	10th	137,943	71,313	10th	164,649	153,574	318,269
11th	184,106	72,825	11th	61,817	91,328	11th	218,360	120,303	338,663
12th	137,465	185,698	12th	102,704	87,769	12th	209,604	108,770	330,167
13th	137,967	204,382	13th	183,811	83,123	13th	189,605	139,742	329,347
14th	93,590	224,602	14th	188,341	74,525	14th	83,480	197,121	280,601
15th	151,951	192,151	15th	157,079	85,595	15th	(2)	....	....
16th	139,373	209,874	16th	162,285	80,327	16th	187,147	161,929	349,076
17th	(2)	....	17th	....	106,361	17th	165,488	116,766	282,266
18th	102,372	140,617	18th	102,360	46,235	18th	164,353	166,257	330,665
19th	202,465	83,357	19th	78,733	132,098	19th	189,833	109,746	306,216
20th	202,832	....	20th	63,845	100,787	20th	....	214,727	244,285
21st	99,776	137,226	21st	(2)	....	21st	....	221,263	284,400
22d	169,041	140,104	22d	118,890	99,804	22d	142,050	171,021	313,071
23d	172,835	37,431	23d	26,414	100,066	23d	98,096	174,205	275,430
24th	211,284	151,863	24th	146,129	98,787	24th	....	(2)	....
25th	115,820	130,891	25th	74,859	61,138	25th	151,466	....	200,229
						26th	108,820	135,694	252,957
						27th	138,488	85,020	230,171
GA:			GA:			GA:			
1st	83,444	165,890	1st	117,270	46,449	1st	157,181	92,399	249,580
2d	158,435	71,351	2d	81,673	86,520	2d	92,410	162,751	255,161
3d	117,522	225,055	3d	168,304	73,932	3d	232,380	....	232,380
4th	224,494	....	4th	44,707	131,760	4th	75,041	208,861	283,902
5th	231,368	....	5th	46,622	130,782	5th	43,335	234,330	277,665
6th	106,551	231,520	6th	198,100	....	6th	189,669	104,365	294,034
7th	128,159	209,354	7th	160,898	78,996	7th	156,689	95,377	252,066
8th	157,241	117,446	8th	102,770	92,250	8th	197,789	....	197,789
9th	70,537	217,493	9th	173,512	....	9th	192,101	60,052	252,153
10th	114,638	177,265	10th	138,062	66,905	10th	211,065	....	211,065
11th	95,220	204,082	11th	163,515	....	11th	196,968	90,353	287,321
12th	164,562	84,773	12th	70,938	92,459	12th	119,973	139,148	259,121
13th	205,919	92,320	13th	61,771	140,294	13th	79,550	201,988	281,538
						14th	159,947	59,245	219,192
HI:			HI:			HI:			
1st	154,208	38,115	1st	82,723	94,140	1st	96,824	116,505	217,876
2d	165,748	44,425	2d	46,404	132,290	2d	40,707	168,503	219,283
ID:			ID:			ID:			
1st	175,898	171,687	1st	126,231	102,135	1st	199,402	97,450	316,724
2d	83,878	205,777	2d	137,468	48,749	2d	207,412	110,847	318,494
IL:			IL:			IL:			
1st	233,036	38,361	1st	29,253	148,170	1st	83,989	236,854	320,844
2d	251,052	29,721	2d	25,883	150,666	2d	69,115	188,303	297,712
3d	172,581	50,336	3d	40,479	116,120	3d	77,653	168,738	246,398
4th	112,529	16,024	4th	11,711	63,273	4th	27,279	133,226	160,509
5th	170,728	50,881	5th	38,935	108,360	5th	77,289	177,729	270,377
6th	109,007	147,906	6th	114,456	65,379	6th	193,138	132,991	326,129

VOTES CAST FOR REPRESENTATIVES, RESIDENT COMMISSIONER, AND DELEGATES IN 2008, 2010, and 2012—CONTINUED

[The figures, compiled from official statistics obtained by the Clerk of the House, show the votes for the Republican and Democratic nominees, except as otherwise indicated. Figures in the last column, for the 2012 election, may include totals for more candidates than the ones shown.]

State and district	Vote cast in 2008		State and district	Vote cast in 2010		State and district	Vote cast in 2012		Total vote cast in 2012
	Demo- crat	Repub- lican		Repub- lican	Demo- crat		Repub- lican	Demo- crat	
7th	235,343	41,474	7th	29,575	149,846	7th	31,466	242,439	286,435
8th	179,444	116,081	8th	98,115	97,825	8th	101,860	123,206	225,066
9th	181,948	53,593	9th	55,182	117,553	9th	98,924	194,869	293,807
10th	138,176	153,082	10th	109,941	105,290	10th	130,564	133,890	264,454
11th	185,652	109,608	11th	129,108	96,019	11th	105,348	148,928	254,295
12th	212,891	74,382	12th	74,046	121,272	12th	129,902	157,000	303,949
13th	147,430	180,888	13th	152,132	86,281	13th	137,034	136,032	294,385
14th	185,404	135,653	14th	112,369	98,645	14th	177,603	124,351	301,954
15th	104,393	187,121	15th	136,915	75,948	15th	205,775	94,162	299,937
16th	112,648	190,039	16th	138,299	66,037	16th	181,789	112,301	294,090
17th	220,961	....	17th	104,583	85,454	17th	134,623	153,519	288,161
18th	117,642	182,589	18th	152,868	57,046	18th	244,467	85,164	329,631
19th	105,338	203,434	19th	166,166	67,132				
IN:			IN:			IN:			
1st	199,954	76,647	1st	65,558	99,387	1st	91,291	187,743	279,034
2d	187,416	84,455	2d	88,803	91,341	2d	134,033	130,113	273,475
3d	112,309	155,693	3d	116,140	61,267	3d	187,872	92,363	280,235
4th	129,038	192,526	4th	138,732	53,167	4th	168,688	93,015	272,268
5th	123,357	234,705	5th	146,899	60,024	5th	194,570	125,347	333,359
6th	94,265	180,608	6th	126,027	56,647	6th	162,613	96,678	275,253
7th	172,650	92,645	7th	55,213	86,011	7th	95,828	162,122	257,950
8th	188,693	102,769	8th	117,259	76,265	8th	151,533	122,325	283,992
9th	181,281	120,529	9th	118,040	95,353	9th	165,332	132,848	298,180
IA:			IA:			IA:			
1st	186,991	102,439	1st	100,219	104,428	1st	162,465	222,422	390,849
2d	175,218	118,778	2d	104,319	115,839	2d	161,977	211,863	381,275
3d	176,904	132,136	3d	111,925	122,147	3d	202,000	168,632	386,842
4th	120,746	185,458	4th	152,588	74,300	4th	200,063	169,470	377,883
5th	99,601	159,430	5th	128,363	63,160				
KS:			KS:			KS:			
1st	34,771	214,549	1st	142,281	44,068	1st	211,337	....	211,337
2d	142,013	155,532	2d	130,034	66,588	2d	167,463	113,735	293,718
3d	202,541	142,307	3d	136,246	90,193	3d	201,087	....	293,762
4th	90,706	177,617	4th	119,575	74,143	4th	161,094	81,770	258,922
KY:			KY:			KY:			
1st	98,674	178,107	1st	153,840	62,090	1st	199,956	87,199	287,155
2d	143,379	158,936	2d	155,906	73,749	2d	181,508	89,541	282,267
3d	203,843	139,527	3d	112,627	139,940	3d	111,452	206,385	322,656
4th	111,549	190,210	4th	151,813	66,694	4th	186,036	104,734	299,444
5th	....	177,024	5th	151,019	44,034	5th	195,408	55,447	250,855
6th	203,764	111,378	6th	119,164	119,812	6th	153,222	141,438	303,000
LA:			LA:			LA:			
1st	98,839	189,168	1st	157,182	38,416	1st	218,340	61,703	290,410
2d	31,318	33,132	2d	43,378	83,705	2d	50,146	230,417	287,354
3d	([3])	....	3d	108,963	61,914	3d	240,558	67,070	311,393
4th	44,151	44,501	4th	105,223	54,609	4th	187,894	....	249,531
5th	....	([3])	5th	122,033	....	5th	202,536	....	260,216
6th	125,886	150,332	6th	138,607	72,577	6th	243,553	....	306,713
7th	98,280	177,173	7th	([3])	....				
ME:			ME:			ME:			
1st	205,629	168,930	1st	128,501	169,114	1st	128,440	236,363	380,715
2d	226,274	109,268	2d	119,669	147,042	2d	137,542	191,456	343,908
MD:			MD:			MD:			
1st	177,065	174,213	1st	155,118	120,400	1st	214,204	92,812	337,760
2d	198,578	68,561	2d	69,523	134,133	2d	92,071	194,088	295,940
3d	203,711	87,971	3d	86,947	147,448	3d	94,549	213,747	319,859
4th	258,704	38,739	4th	31,467	160,228	4th	64,560	240,385	311,512
5th	253,854	82,631	5th	83,575	155,110	5th	95,271	238,618	343,820
6th	128,207	190,926	6th	148,820	80,455	6th	117,313	181,921	309,549
7th	227,379	53,147	7th	46,375	152,669	7th	67,405	247,770	323,818
8th	229,740	66,351	8th	52,421	153,613	8th	113,033	217,531	343,256
MA:			MA:			MA:			
1st	215,696	80,067	1st	74,418	128,011	1st	....	261,936	336,555
2d	234,369	....	2d	91,209	122,751	2d	....	259,257	342,736
3d	227,619	....	3d	85,124	122,708	3d	109,372	212,119	335,111
4th	203,032	75,571	4th	101,517	126,194	4th	129,936	221,303	373,114
5th	225,947	....	5th	94,646	122,858	5th	82,944	257,490	364,201
6th	226,216	94,845	6th	107,930	142,732	6th	176,612	180,942	389,852
7th	212,304	67,978	7th	73,467	145,696	7th	....	210,794	285,134
8th	185,530	....	8th	....	134,974	8th	82,242	263,999	371,694
9th	242,166	....	9th	59,965	157,071	9th	116,531	212,754	385,799
10th	272,899	....	10th	120,029	132,743				
MI:			MI:			MI:			
1st	213,216	107,340	1st	120,523	94,824	1st	167,060	165,179	347,037
2d	119,506	214,100	2d	148,864	72,118	2d	194,653	108,973	318,267

VOTES CAST FOR REPRESENTATIVES, RESIDENT COMMISSIONER, AND DELEGATES IN 2008, 2010, and 2012—CONTINUED

[The figures, compiled from official statistics obtained by the Clerk of the House, show the votes for the Republican and Democratic nominees, except as otherwise indicated. Figures in the last column, for the 2012 election, may include totals for more candidates than the ones shown.]

State and district	Vote cast in 2008		State and district	Vote cast in 2010		State and district	Vote cast in 2012		Total vote cast in 2012
	Demo-crat	Repub-lican		Repub-lican	Demo-crat		Repub-lican	Demo-crat	
3d	117,961	203,799	3d	133,714	83,953	3d	171,675	144,108	326,283
4th	117,665	204,259	4th	148,531	68,458	4th	197,386	104,996	312,949
5th	221,841	85,017	5th	89,680	107,286	5th	103,931	214,531	330,146
6th	123,257	188,157	6th	123,142	66,729	6th	174,955	136,563	320,475
7th	157,213	149,781	7th	113,185	102,402	7th	169,668	136,849	318,069
8th	145,491	204,408	8th	156,931	84,069	8th	202,217	128,657	345,054
9th	183,311	150,035	9th	119,325	125,730	9th	114,760	208,846	337,316
10th	108,354	230,471	10th	168,364	58,530	10th	226,075	97,734	328,612
11th	156,625	177,461	11th	141,224	91,710	11th	181,788	158,879	358,139
12th	225,094	74,565	12th	71,372	124,671	12th	92,472	216,884	319,223
13th	167,481	43,098	13th	23,462	100,885	13th	38,769	235,336	284,270
14th	227,841	....	14th	29,902	115,511	14th	51,395	270,450	328,792
15th	231,784	81,802	15th	83,488	118,336				
MN:			MN:			MN:			
1st	207,753	109,453	1st	109,242	122,365	1st	142,164	193,211	335,880
2d	164,093	220,924	2d	181,341	104,809	2d	193,587	164,338	358,446
3d	150,787	178,932	3d	161,177	100,240	3d	222,335	159,937	382,705
4th	216,267	98,936	4th	80,141	136,746	4th	109,659	216,685	347,991
5th	228,776	71,020	5th	55,222	154,833	5th	88,753	262,102	351,969
6th	175,786	187,817	6th	159,476	120,846	6th	179,240	174,944	355,153
7th	227,187	87,062	7th	90,652	133,096	7th	114,151	197,791	327,576
8th	241,831	114,871	8th	133,490	129,091	8th	160,520	191,976	353,663
MS:			MS:			MS:			
1st	185,959	149,818	1st	121,074	89,388	1st	186,760	114,076	309,177
2d	201,606	90,364	2d	64,499	105,327	2d	99,160	214,978	320,244
3d	127,698	213,171	3d	132,393	60,737	3d	234,717	....	293,322
4th	216,542	73,977	4th	105,613	95,243	4th	182,998	82,344	285,432
MO:			MO:			MO:			
1st	242,570	....	1st	43,649	135,907	1st	60,832	267,927	340,583
2d	132,068	232,276	2d	180,481	77,467	2d	236,971	146,272	394,448
3d	202,470	92,759	3d	94,757	99,398	3d	214,843	111,189	338,385
4th	200,009	103,446	4th	113,489	101,532	4th	192,237	113,120	318,723
5th	197,249	109,166	5th	84,578	102,076	5th	122,149	200,290	330,942
6th	121,894	196,526	6th	154,103	67,762	6th	216,906	108,503	333,688
7th	91,010	219,016	7th	141,010	67,545	7th	203,565	98,498	318,740
8th	72,790	198,798	8th	128,499	56,377	8th	216,083	73,755	300,391
9th	152,956	161,031	9th	162,724	46,817				
MT:			MT:			MT:			
At large	155,930	308,470	At large	217,696	121,954	At large	255,468	204,939	479,740
NE:			NE:			NE:			
1st	77,897	184,923	1st	116,871	47,106	1st	174,889	81,206	256,095
2d	131,901	142,473	2d	93,840	60,486	2d	133,964	129,767	263,731
3d	55,087	183,117	3d	117,275	29,932	3d	187,423	65,266	252,689
NV:			NV:			NV:			
1st	154,860	64,837	1st	58,995	103,246	1st	56,521	113,967	179,278
2d	136,548	170,771	2d	169,458	87,421	2d	162,213	102,019	281,449
3d	165,912	147,940	3d	128,916	127,168	3d	137,244	116,823	272,523
						4th	101,261	120,501	240,492
NH:			NH:			NH:			
1st	176,435	156,338	1st	121,655	95,503	1st	158,659	171,650	345,022
2d	188,332	138,222	2d	108,610	105,060	2d	152,977	169,275	337,394
NJ:			NJ:			NJ:			
1st	206,453	74,001	1st	58,562	106,334	1st	92,459	210,470	308,519
2d	110,990	167,701	2d	109,460	51,690	2d	166,677	116,462	289,069
3d	166,390	153,122	3d	110,215	104,252	3d	174,253	145,506	324,399
4th	100,036	202,972	4th	129,752	52,118	4th	195,145	107,991	306,247
5th	131,033	172,653	5th	124,030	62,634	5th	167,501	130,100	304,371
6th	164,077	77,469	6th	65,413	81,933	6th	84,360	151,782	239,638
7th	124,818	148,461	7th	105,084	71,902	7th	175,662	123,057	307,315
8th	159,279	63,107	8th	51,023	88,478	8th	31,763	130,853	167,790
9th	151,182	69,503	9th	52,082	83,564	9th	55,091	162,822	220,133
10th	169,945	....	10th	14,357	95,299	10th	24,271	201,435	230,060
11th	113,510	189,696	11th	122,149	55,472	11th	182,237	123,897	309,859
12th	193,732	108,400	12th	93,634	108,214	12th	80,906	189,926	274,378
13th	120,382	34,735	13th	19,538	62,840				
NM:			NM:			NM:			
1st	166,271	132,485	1st	104,215	112,010	1st	112,473	162,924	275,856
2d	129,572	101,980	2d	94,053	75,708	2d	133,180	92,162	225,515
3d	161,292	86,618	3d	90,617	120,048	3d	97,616	167,103	264,719
NY:			NY:			NY:			
1st	141,727	100,036	1st	78,300	98,316	1st	106,678	134,205	294,578
2d	143,759	70,145	2d	58,525	94,594	2d	....	93,375	271,832
3d	93,481	149,344	3d	131,674	51,346	3d	....	146,016	306,274
4th	151,792	84,444	4th	69,323	94,483	4th	84,982	152,590	299,484
5th	105,836	43,039	5th	36,861	72,239	5th	17,875	167,835	224,508

VOTES CAST FOR REPRESENTATIVES, RESIDENT COMMISSIONER, AND DELEGATES IN 2008, 2010, and 2012—CONTINUED

[The figures, compiled from official statistics obtained by the Clerk of the House, show the votes for the Republican and Democratic nominees, except as otherwise indicated. Figures in the last column, for the 2012 election, may include totals for more candidates than the ones shown.]

State and district	Vote cast in 2008		State and district	Vote cast in 2010		State and district	Vote cast in 2012		Total vote cast in 2012
	Democrat	Republican		Republican	Democrat		Republican	Democrat	
6th	141,180	....	6th	10,057	85,096	6th	45,992	107,505	186,932
7th	113,988	19,373	7th	13,751	71,247	7th	....	132,456	178,825
8th	152,153	36,897	8th	29,514	98,839	8th	15,841	178,687	236,292
9th	106,097	....	9th	37,750	67,011	9th	20,899	178,168	238,957
10th	155,090	8,204	10th	7,419	95,485	10th	35,440	155,908	236,323
11th	158,235	11,644	11th	9,119	104,297	11th	91,030	87,718	214,755
12th	115,633	12,486	12th	....	68,624	12th	41,969	184,864	268,287
13th	107,640	62,441	13th	55,821	60,773	13th	12,132	170,470	233,172
14th	176,426	43,385	14th	32,065	107,327	14th	19,191	116,117	170,995
15th	170,372	15,676	15th	10,678	91,225	15th	3,487	150,243	178,645
16th	123,312	3,941	16th	2,257	61,642	16th	53,935	173,885	270,320
17th	149,676	35,994	17th	29,792	95,346	17th	91,899	161,624	297,379
18th	167,365	73,237	18th	60,513	115,619	18th	113,386	132,456	295,436
19th	141,173	103,813	19th	88,734	98,766	19th	122,654	120,302	305,882
20th	178,996	99,930	20th	110,813	107,075	20th	79,102	181,092	317,678
21st	159,849	85,267	21st	70,211	124,889	21st	104,368	117,856	268,741
22d	147,238	76,569	22d	75,558	98,661	22d	145,042	102,080	280,189
23d	70,037	120,778	23d	73,646	82,232	23d	117,641	114,590	279,796
24th	121,345	103,379	24th	85,702	89,809	24th	105,584	133,908	303,567
25th	148,290	106,653	25th	81,380	103,954	25th	109,292	168,761	322,760
26th	109,615	124,845	26th	151,449	54,307	26th	57,368	195,234	304,961
27th	169,196	50,420	27th	63,015	119,085	27th	137,250	140,008	329,768
28th	155,409	42,016	28th	45,630	102,514				
29th	131,526	116,137	29th	93,167	....				
NC:			NC:			NC:			
1st	192,765	81,506	1st	70,867	103,294	1st	77,288	254,644	338,066
2d	199,730	93,323	2d	93,876	92,393	2d	174,066	128,973	311,397
3d	104,364	201,686	3d	143,225	51,317	3d	195,571	114,314	309,885
4th	265,751	153,947	4th	116,448	155,384	4th	88,951	259,534	348,485
5th	136,103	190,820	5th	140,525	72,762	5th	200,945	148,252	349,197
6th	108,873	221,018	6th	156,252	51,507	6th	222,116	142,467	364,583
7th	215,383	97,472	7th	98,328	113,957	7th	168,041	168,695	336,736
8th	157,185	126,634	8th	73,129	88,776	8th	160,695	137,139	302,280
9th	138,719	241,053	9th	158,790	71,450	9th	194,537	171,503	375,690
10th	126,699	171,774	10th	130,813	52,972	10th	190,826	144,023	334,849
11th	211,112	122,087	11th	110,246	131,225	11th	190,319	141,107	331,426
12th	215,908	85,814	12th	55,315	103,495	12th	63,317	247,591	310,908
13th	221,379	114,383	13th	93,099	116,103	13th	210,495	160,115	370,610
ND:			ND:			ND:			
At large	194,577	119,388	At large	129,802	106,542	At large	173,585	131,870	316,224
OH:			OH:			OH:			
1st	155,455	140,683	1st	103,770	92,672	1st	201,907	131,490	349,716
2d	124,213	148,671	2d	139,027	82,431	2d	194,296	137,077	331,373
3d	115,976	200,204	3d	152,629	71,455	3d	77,901	201,897	295,652
4th	99,499	186,154	4th	146,029	50,533	4th	182,643	114,214	312,998
5th	105,840	188,905	5th	140,703	54,919	5th	201,514	137,806	351,878
6th	176,330	92,968	6th	103,170	92,823	6th	164,536	144,444	308,980
7th	125,547	174,915	7th	135,721	70,400	7th	178,104	137,708	315,812
8th	95,510	202,063	8th	142,731	65,883	8th	246,378	....	248,316
9th	222,054	76,512	9th	83,423	121,819	9th	68,668	217,771	298,164
10th	157,268	107,918	10th	83,809	101,343	10th	208,201	131,097	349,671
11th	212,667	36,708	11th	28,754	139,693	11th	....	258,359	258,359
12th	152,234	197,447	12th	150,163	110,307	12th	233,869	134,605	368,474
13th	192,593	105,050	13th	94,367	118,806	13th	88,120	235,492	323,612
14th	125,214	188,488	14th	149,878	72,604	14th	183,657	131,637	339,894
15th	139,584	137,272	15th	119,471	91,077	15th	205,274	128,188	333,462
16th	169,044	136,293	16th	114,652	90,833	16th	185,165	170,600	355,765
17th	218,896	61,216	17th	57,352	102,758				
18th	164,187	110,031	18th	107,426	80,756				
OK:			OK:			OK:			
1st	98,890	193,404	1st	151,173	45,656	1st	181,084	91,421	285,312
2d	173,757	72,815	2d	83,226	108,203	2d	143,701	96,081	250,612
3d	62,297	184,306	3d	161,927	45,689	3d	201,744	53,472	268,003
4th	79,674	180,080	4th	(4)	....	4th	176,740	71,846	260,331
5th	88,996	171,925	5th	123,236	68,074	5th	153,603	97,504	261,677
OR:			OR:			OR:			
1st	237,567	....	1st	122,858	160,357	1st	109,699	197,845	331,980
2d	87,649	236,560	2d	206,245	72,173	2d	228,043	....	332,255
3d	254,235	71,063	3d	67,714	193,104	3d	70,325	264,979	355,875
4th	275,143	....	4th	129,877	162,416	4th	....	212,866	360,088
5th	181,577	128,297	5th	130,313	145,319	5th	139,223	177,229	327,970
PA:			PA:			PA:			
1st	242,799	24,714	1st	....	149,944	1st	41,708	235,394	277,102
2d	276,870	34,466	2d	21,907	182,800	2d	33,381	318,176	356,386
3d	146,846	139,707	3d	111,909	88,924	3d	165,826	123,933	302,514

VOTES CAST FOR REPRESENTATIVES, RESIDENT COMMISSIONER, AND DELEGATES IN 2008, 2010, and 2012—CONTINUED

[The figures, compiled from official statistics obtained by the Clerk of the House, show the votes for the Republican and Democratic nominees, except as otherwise indicated. Figures in the last column, for the 2012 election, may include totals for more candidates than the ones shown.]

State and district	Vote cast in 2008	
	Democrat	Republican
4th	186,536	147,411
5th	112,509	155,513
6th	164,952	179,423
7th	209,955	142,362
8th	197,869	145,103
9th	98,735	174,951
10th	160,837	124,681
11th	146,379	137,151
12th	155,268	113,120
13th	196,868	108,271
14th	242,326	....
15th	128,333	181,433
16th	120,193	170,329
17th	192,699	109,909
18th	119,661	213,349
19th	109,533	218,862
RI:		
1st	145,254	51,340
2d	158,416	67,433
SC:		
1st	163,724	177,540
2d	158,627	184,583
3d	101,724	186,799
4th	113,291	184,440
5th	188,785	113,282
6th	193,378	93,059
SD:		
At large	256,041	122,966
TN:		
1st	57,525	168,343
2d	63,639	227,120
3d	73,059	184,964
4th	146,776	94,447
5th	181,467	85,471
6th	194,264	....
7th	99,549	217,332
8th	180,465	....
9th	198,798	....
TX:		
1st	....	189,012
2d	....	175,101
3d	108,693	170,742
4th	88,067	206,906
5th	....	162,894
6th	99,919	174,008
7th	123,242	162,635
8th	70,758	207,128
9th	143,868	....
10th	143,719	179,493
11th	....	189,625
12th	82,250	181,662
13th	51,841	180,078
14th	....	191,293
15th	107,578	52,303
16th	130,375	16,348
17th	134,592	115,581
18th	148,617	39,095
19th	58,030	168,501
20th	127,298	44,585
21st	....	243,471
22d	140,160	161,996
23d	134,090	100,799
24th	111,089	151,434
25th	191,755	88,693
26th	118,167	195,181
27th	104,864	69,458
28th	123,494	52,524
29th	79,718	25,512
30th	168,249	32,361
31st	106,559	175,563
32d	82,406	116,283

State and district	Vote cast in 2010	
	Republican	Democrat
4th	116,958	120,827
5th	127,427	52,375
6th	133,770	100,493
7th	137,825	110,314
8th	130,759	113,547
9th	141,904	52,322
10th	110,599	89,846
11th	102,179	84,618
12th	91,170	94,056
13th	91,987	118,710
14th	49,997	122,073
15th	109,534	79,766
16th	134,113	70,994
17th	95,000	118,486
18th	161,888	78,558
19th	165,219	53,549
RI:		
1st	71,542	81,269
2d	55,409	104,442
SC:		
1st	152,755	67,008
2d	138,861	113,625
3d	126,235	66,497
4th	137,586	62,438
5th	125,834	102,296
6th	72,661	125,459
SD:		
At large	153,703	146,589
TN:		
1st	123,006	26,045
2d	141,796	25,400
3d	92,032	45,387
4th	103,969	70,254
5th	74,204	99,162
6th	128,517	56,145
7th	158,916	54,347
8th	98,759	64,960
9th	33,879	99,827
TX:		
1st	129,398	....
2d	130,020	....
3d	101,180	47,848
4th	136,338	40,975
5th	106,742	41,649
6th	107,140	50,717
7th	143,655	....
8th	161,417	34,694
9th	24,201	80,107
10th	144,980	74,086
11th	125,581	23,989
12th	109,882	38,434
13th	113,201	....
14th	140,623	44,431
15th	39,964	53,546
16th	31,051	49,301
17th	106,696	63,138
18th	33,067	85,108
19th	106,059	25,984
20th	31,757	58,645
21st	162,924	65,927
22d	140,537	62,082
23d	74,853	67,348
24th	100,078	....
25th	84,849	99,967
26th	120,984	55,385
27th	50,976	50,179
28th	46,740	62,773
29th	22,825	43,257
30th	24,668	86,322
31st	126,384	....
32d	79,433	44,258

State and district	Vote cast in 2012		Total vote cast in 2012
	Republican	Democrat	
4th	181,603	104,643	303,980
5th	177,740	104,725	282,465
6th	191,725	143,803	335,528
7th	209,942	143,509	353,451
8th	199,379	152,859	352,238
9th	169,177	105,128	274,305
10th	179,563	94,227	273,790
11th	166,967	118,231	285,198
12th	175,352	163,589	338,941
13th	93,918	209,901	303,819
14th	75,702	251,932	327,634
15th	168,960	128,764	297,724
16th	156,192	111,185	284,781
17th	106,208	161,393	267,601
18th	216,727	122,146	338,873
RI:			
1st	83,737	108,612	205,115
2d	78,189	124,067	222,660
SC:			
1st	179,908	98,154	290,013
2d	196,116	....	203,718
3d	169,512	84,735	254,763
4th	173,201	84,087	266,884
5th	154,324	113,904	278,003
6th	....	218,717	233,615
7th	153,068	114,594	275,738
SD:			
At large	207,640	153,789	361,429
TN:			
1st	182,252	47,663	239,672
2d	196,894	54,522	264,505
3d	157,830	91,094	256,909
4th	128,568	102,022	230,590
5th	86,240	171,621	263,095
6th	184,383	....	241,241
7th	182,730	61,679	257,306
8th	190,923	79,490	279,422
9th	59,742	188,422	250,987
TX:			
1st	178,322	67,222	249,658
2d	159,664	80,512	246,328
3d	187,180	....	187,180
4th	182,679	60,214	250,343
5th	134,091	69,178	208,230
6th	145,019	98,053	249,936
7th	142,793	85,553	234,837
8th	194,043	51,051	251,052
9th	36,139	144,075	183,566
10th	159,783	95,710	264,019
11th	177,742	41,970	226,023
12th	175,649	66,080	247,712
13th	187,775	....	206,388
14th	131,460	109,697	245,839
15th	54,056	89,296	146,661
16th	51,043	101,403	155,005
17th	143,284	....	179,262
18th	44,015	146,223	194,932
19th	163,239	....	192,063
20th	62,376	119,032	186,177
21st	187,015	109,326	308,865
22d	160,668	80,203	250,911
23d	87,547	96,676	192,169
24th	148,586	87,645	243,489
25th	154,245	98,827	263,932
26th	176,642	74,237	258,723
27th	120,684	83,395	212,651
28th	49,309	112,456	165,645
29th	....	86,053	95,611
30th	41,222	171,059	217,014
31st	145,348	82,977	237,187
32d	146,653	99,288	251,636
33d	30,252	85,114	117,375
34th	52,448	89,606	144,778
35th	52,894	105,626	165,179

VOTES CAST FOR REPRESENTATIVES, RESIDENT COMMISSIONER, AND DELEGATES IN 2008, 2010, and 2012—CONTINUED

[The figures, compiled from official statistics obtained by the Clerk of the House, show the votes for the Republican and Democratic nominees, except as otherwise indicated. Figures in the last column, for the 2012 election, may include totals for more candidates than the ones shown.]

State and district	Vote cast in 2008		State and district	Vote cast in 2010		State and district	Vote cast in 2012		Total vote cast in 2012
	Demo-crat	Repub-lican		Repub-lican	Demo-crat		Repub-lican	Demo-crat	
						36th	165,405	62,143	233,832
UT:			UT:			UT:			
1st	92,469	196,799	1st	135,247	46,765	1st	175,487	60,611	245,528
2d	220,666	120,083	2d	116,001	127,151	2d	154,523	83,176	248,545
3d	80,626	187,035	3d	139,721	44,320	3d	198,828	60,719	259,547
						4th	119,035	119,803	245,277
VT:			VT:			VT:			
At large ..	248,203	....	At large ..	76,403	154,006	At large ..	67,543	208,600	289,931
VA:			VA:			VA:			
1st	150,432	203,839	1st	135,564	73,824	1st	200,845	147,036	356,806
2d	141,857	128,486	2d	88,340	70,591	2d	166,231	142,548	309,222
3d	239,911	....	3d	44,553	114,754	3d	58,931	259,199	318,936
4th	135,041	199,075	4th	123,659	74,298	4th	199,292	150,190	350,046
5th	158,810	158,083	5th	119,560	110,562	5th	193,009	149,214	348,111
6th	114,367	192,350	6th	127,487	....	6th	211,278	111,949	323,893
7th	138,123	233,531	7th	138,209	79,616	7th	222,983	158,012	381,909
8th	222,986	97,425	8th	71,145	116,404	8th	107,370	226,847	351,187
9th	207,306	....	9th	95,726	86,743	9th	184,882	116,400	301,658
10th	147,357	223,140	10th	131,116	72,604	10th	214,038	142,024	366,444
11th	196,598	154,758	11th	110,739	111,720	11th	117,902	202,606	332,243
WA:			WA:			WA:			
1st	233,780	111,240	1st	126,737	172,642	1st	151,187	177,025	328,212
2d	217,416	131,051	2d	148,722	155,241	2d	117,465	184,826	302,291
3d	216,701	121,828	3d	152,799	135,654	3d	177,446	116,438	293,884
4th	99,430	169,940	4th	156,726	74,973	4th	154,749	78,940	233,689
5th	112,382	211,305	5th	177,235	101,146	5th	191,066	117,512	308,578
6th	205,991	102,081	6th	109,800	151,873	6th	129,725	186,661	316,386
7th	291,963	57,054	7th	....	232,649	7th	76,212	298,368	374,580
8th	171,358	191,568	8th	161,296	148,581	8th	180,204	121,886	302,090
9th	176,295	93,080	9th	101,851	123,743	9th	76,105	192,034	268,139
						10th	115,381	163,036	278,417
WV:			WV:			WV:			
1st	187,734	....	1st	90,660	89,220	1st	133,809	80,342	214,151
2d	110,819	147,334	2d	126,814	55,001	2d	158,206	68,560	226,766
3d	133,522	66,005	3d	65,611	83,636	3d	92,238	108,199	200,437
WI:			WI:			WI:			
1st	125,268	231,009	1st	179,819	79,363	1st	200,423	158,414	365,058
2d	277,914	122,513	2d	118,099	191,164	2d	124,683	265,422	390,898
3d	225,208	122,760	3d	116,838	126,380	3d	121,713	217,712	339,764
4th	222.728	....	4th	61,543	143,559	4th	80,787	235,257	325,788
5th	....	275,271	5th	229,642	90,634	5th	250,335	118,478	369,664
6th	126,090	221,875	6th	183,271	75,926	6th	223,460	135,921	359,745
7th	212,666	136,938	7th	132,551	113,018	7th	201,720	157,524	359,669
8th	193,662	164,621	8th	143,998	118,646	8th	198,874	156,287	355,464
WY:			WY:			WY:			
At large ..	106,758	131,244	At large ..	131,661	45,768	At large ..	166,452	57,573	250,700

[Table continues on next page]

VOTES CAST FOR REPRESENTATIVES, RESIDENT COMMISSIONER, AND DELEGATES IN 2008, 2010, and 2012—CONTINUED

[The figures, compiled from official statistics obtained by the Clerk of the House, show the votes for the Republican and Democratic nominees, except as otherwise indicated. Figures in the last column, for the 2012 election, may include totals for more candidates than the ones shown.]

Commonwealth of Puerto Rico	Vote						Total vote cast in 2012
	2008		2010		2012		
	Popular Democrat	New Progressive	New Progressive	Popular Democrat	Popular Democrat	Democrat	
Resident Commissioner (4-year term)	810,093	1,010,285	....	....	881,181	905,066	1,868,480

District of Columbia	Vote						Total vote cast in 2012
	2008		2010		2012		
	Democrat	Republican	Republican	Democrat	Libertarian	Democrat	
Delegate	245,800	17,367	8,109	117,990	16,524	246,664	278,563

Guam	Vote						Total vote cast in 2012
	2008		2010		2012		
	Democrat	Write-in	Write-in	Democrat	Republican	Democrat	
Delegate	28,247	1,617	1,502	35,919	12,995	19,765	33,006

Virgin Islands	Vote						Total vote cast in 2012
	2008		2010		2012		
	Democrat	Write-in	Republican	Democrat	Republican	Democrat	
Delegate	19,286	69	2,329	19,844	2,131	11,512	19,170

American Samoa	Vote						Total vote cast in 2012
	2008		2010		2012		
	Democrat	Republican	Republican	Democrat	Conservative	Democrat	
Delegate	7,499	4,350	4,422	6,182	4,420	7,221	13,076

Northern Mariana Islands	Vote						Total vote cast in 2012
	2008		2010		2012		
	Independent	Republican	Republican	Democrat	Republican	Democrat	
Delegate	2,474	2,117	2,049	4,852	2,503	9,829	12,332

[1] According to Arkansas law, it is not required to tabulate votes for unopposed candidates.
[2] According to Florida law, the names of those with no opposition are not printed on the ballot.
[3] According to Louisiana law, the names of those with no opposition are not printed on the ballot.
[4] According to Oklahoma law, the names of those with no opposition are not printed on the ballot.

SESSIONS OF CONGRESS, 1st–113th CONGRESSES, 1789–2013

[Closing date for this table was January 2, 2014.]

MEETING DATES OF CONGRESS: Pursuant to a resolution of the Confederation Congress in 1788, the Constitution went into effect on March 4, 1789. From then until the 20th amendment took effect in January 1934, the term of each Congress began on March 4th of each odd-numbered year; however, Article I, section 4, of the Constitution provided that ''The Congress shall assemble at least once in every Year, and such Meeting shall be on the first Monday in December, unless they shall by law appoint a different day.'' The Congress therefore convened regularly on the first Monday in December until the 20th amendment became effective, which changed the beginning of Congress's term as well as its convening date to January 3rd. So prior to 1934, a new Congress typically would not convene for regular business until 13 months after being elected. One effect of this was that the last session of each Congress was a ''lame duck'' session. After the 20th amendment, the time from the election to the beginning of Congress's term as well as when it convened was reduced to two months. Recognizing that the need might exist for Congress to meet at times other than the regularly scheduled convening date, Article II, section 3 of the Constitution provides that the President ''may, on extraordinary occasions, convene both Houses, or either of them''; hence these sessions occur only if convened by Presidential proclamation. Except as noted, these are separately numbered sessions of a Congress, and are marked by an E in the session column of the table. Until the 20th amendment was adopted, there were also times when special sessions of the Senate were convened, principally for confirming Cabinet and other executive nominations, and occasionally for the ratification of treaties or other executive business. These Senate sessions were also called by Presidential proclamation (typically by the outgoing President, although on occasion by incumbents as well) and are marked by an S in the session column. MEETING PLACES OF CONGRESS: Congress met for the first and second sessions of the First Congress (1789 and 1790) in New York City. From the third session of the First Congress through the first session of the Sixth Congress (1790 to 1800), Philadelphia was the meeting place. Congress has convened in Washington since the second session of the Sixth Congress (1800).

Congress	Session	Convening Date	Adjournment Date	Length in days[1]	Recesses[2]		President pro tempore of the Senate[3]	Speaker of the House of Representatives
					Senate	House of Representatives		
1st	1	Mar. 4, 1789	Sept. 29, 1789	210			John Langdon, of New Hampshire	Frederick A.C. Muhlenberg, of Pennsylvania.
	2	Jan. 4, 1790	Aug. 12, 1790	221			...do.	
	3	Dec. 6, 1790	Mar. 3, 1791	88			...do.	
2d	S	Mar. 4, 1791	Mar. 4, 1791	1			...do.	
	1	Oct. 24, 1791	May 8, 1792	197			Richard Henry Lee, of Virginia	Jonathan Trumbull, of Connecticut.
	2	Nov. 5, 1792	Mar. 2, 1793	119			John Langdon, of New Hampshire.	
3d	S	Mar. 4, 1793	Mar. 4, 1793	1			...do.	
	1	Dec. 2, 1793	June 9, 1794	190			John Langdon, of New Hampshire; Ralph Izard, of South Carolina.	Frederick A.C. Muhlenberg, of Pennsylvania.
	2	Nov. 3, 1794	Mar. 3, 1795	121			Henry Tazewell, of Virginia.	
4th	S	June 8, 1795	June 26, 1795	19			...do.	
	1	Dec. 7, 1795	June 1, 1796	177			Henry Tazewell, of Virginia; Samuel Livermore, of New Hampshire.	Jonathan Dayton, of New Jersey.
	2	Dec. 5, 1796	Mar. 3, 1797	89			William Bingham, of Pennsylvania.	
5th	S	Mar. 4, 1797	Mar. 4, 1797	1				
	1–E	May 15, 1797	July 10, 1797	57			William Bradford, of Rhode Island	Do.
	S	July 17, 1798	July 19, 1798	3				
	2	Nov. 13, 1797	July 16, 1798	246			Jacob Read, of South Carolina; Theodore Sedgwick, of Massachusetts.	
	3	Dec. 3, 1798	Mar. 3, 1799	91			John Laurance, of New York; James Ross, of Pennsylvania.	
6th	1	Dec. 2, 1799	May 14, 1800	164			Samuel Livermore, of New Hampshire; Uriah Tracy, of Connecticut.	Theodore Sedgwick, of Massachusetts.
	2	Nov. 17, 1800	Mar. 3, 1801	107	Dec. 23–Dec. 30, 1800	Dec. 24–Dec. 29, 1800	John E. Howard, of Maryland; James Hillhouse, of Connecticut.	
7th	S	Mar. 4, 1801	Mar. 5, 1801	2				
	1	Dec. 7, 1801	May 3, 1802	148			Abraham Baldwin, of Georgia	Nathaniel Macon, of North Carolina.

	2	Dec. 6, 1802	Mar. 3, 1803	88			Stephen R. Bradley, of Vermont.	
8th	1–E	Oct. 17, 1803	Mar. 27, 1804	163			John Brown, of Kentucky; Jesse Franklin, of North Carolina.	Do.
	2	Nov. 5, 1804	Mar. 3, 1805	119			Joseph Anderson, of Tennessee.	
9th	1	Dec. 2, 1805	Apr. 21, 1806	141			Samuel Smith, of Maryland	Do.
	2	Dec. 1, 1806	Mar. 3, 1807	93			...do.	
10th	1–E	Oct. 26, 1807	Apr. 25, 1808	182			...do	Joseph B. Varnum, of Massachusetts.
	2	Nov. 7, 1808	Mar. 3, 1809	117			Stephen R. Bradley, of Vermont; John Milledge, of Georgia.	
11th	S	Mar. 4, 1809	Mar. 7, 1809	4				
	1	May 22, 1809	June 28, 1809	38			Andrew Gregg, of Pennsylvania	Do.
	2	Nov. 27, 1809	May 1, 1810	156			John Gaillard, of South Carolina.	
	3	Dec. 3, 1810	Mar. 3, 1811	91			John Pope, of Kentucky.	
12th	1–E	Nov. 4, 1811	July 6, 1812	245			William H. Crawford, of Georgia	Henry Clay, of Kentucky.
	2	Nov. 2, 1812	Mar. 3, 1813	122			...do.	
13th	1	May 24, 1813	Aug. 2, 1813	71			...do	Do.[4]
	2	Dec. 6, 1813	Apr. 18, 1814	134			Joseph B. Varnum, of Massachusetts; John Gaillard, of South Carolina.	Langdon Cheves, of South Carolina.[4]
	3–E	Sept. 19, 1814	Mar. 3, 1815	166			John Gaillard, of South Carolina.	
14th	1	Dec. 4, 1815	Apr. 30, 1816	148			...do	Henry Clay, of Kentucky.
	2	Dec. 2, 1816	Mar. 3, 1817	92			...do.	
15th	S	Mar. 4, 1817	Mar. 6, 1817	3			...do.	
	1	Dec. 1, 1817	Apr. 20, 1818	141	Dec. 24–Dec. 29, 1817	Dec. 25–Dec. 28, 1817	...do	Do.
	2	Nov. 16, 1818	Mar. 3, 1819	108			James Barbour, of Virginia.	
16th	1	Dec. 6, 1819	May 15, 1820	162			James Barbour, of Virginia; John Gaillard, of South Carolina.	Do.[5]
	2	Nov. 13, 1820	Mar. 3, 1821	111			John Gaillard, of South Carolina	John W. Taylor, of New York.[5]
17th	1	Dec. 3, 1821	May 8, 1822	157			...do	Philip P. Barbour, of Virginia.
	2	Dec. 2, 1822	Mar. 3, 1823	92			...do.	
18th	1	Dec. 1, 1823	May 27, 1824	178			...do	Henry Clay, of Kentucky.
	2	Dec. 6, 1824	Mar. 3, 1825	88			...do.	
19th	S	Mar. 4, 1825	Mar, 9, 1825	6			...do.	
	1	Dec. 5, 1825	May 22, 1826	169			Nathaniel Macon, of North Carolina	John W. Taylor, of New York.
	2	Dec. 4, 1826	Mar. 3, 1827	90			...do.	
20th	1	Dec. 3, 1827	May 26, 1828	175			Samuel Smith, of Maryland	Andrew Stevenson, of Virginia.
	2	Dec. 1, 1828	Mar. 3, 1829	93	Dec. 24–Dec. 29, 1828	Dec. 25–Dec. 28, 1828	...do.	
21st	S	Mar. 4, 1829	Mar. 17, 1829	14			...do.	
	1	Dec. 7, 1829	May 31, 1830	176			...do	Do.
	2	Dec. 6, 1830	Mar. 3, 1831	88			...do.	
22d	1	Dec. 5, 1831	July 16, 1832	225			Littleton Waller Tazewell, of Virginia	Do.
	2	Dec. 3, 1832	Mar. 2, 1833	91			Hugh Lawson White, of Tennessee.	
23d	1	Dec. 2, 1833	June 30, 1834	211			Hugh Lawson White, of Tennessee; George Poindexter, of Mississippi.	Do.[6]
	2	Dec. 1, 1834	Mar. 3, 1835	93			John Tyler, of Virginia	John Bell, of Tennessee.[6]
24th	1	Dec. 7, 1835	July 4, 1836	211			William R. King, of Alabama	James K. Polk, of Tennessee.
	2	Dec. 5, 1836	Mar. 3, 1837	89			...do.	
25th	S	Mar. 4, 1837	Mar. 10, 1837	7			...do.	
	1–E	Sept. 4, 1837	Oct. 16, 1837	43			...do	Do.
	2	Dec. 4, 1837	July 9, 1838	218			...do.	
	3	Dec. 3, 1838	Mar. 3, 1839	91			...do.	
26th	1	Dec. 2, 1839	July 21, 1840	233			...do	Robert M.T. Hunter, of Virginia.
	2	Dec. 7, 1840	Mar. 3, 1841	87			...do.	
27th	S	Mar. 4, 1841	Mar. 15, 1841	12			William R. King, of Alabama; Samuel L. Southard, of New Jersey.	

SESSIONS OF CONGRESS, 1st–113th CONGRESSES, 1789–2013—CONTINUED

[Closing date for this table was January 2, 2014.]

MEETING DATES OF CONGRESS: Pursuant to a resolution of the Confederation Congress in 1788, the Constitution went into effect on March 4, 1789. From then until the 20th amendment took effect in January 1934, the term of each Congress began on March 4th of each odd-numbered year; however, Article I, section 4, of the Constitution provided that "The Congress shall assemble at least once in every Year, and such Meeting shall be on the first Monday in December, unless they shall by law appoint a different day." The Congress therefore convened regularly on the first Monday in December until the 20th amendment became effective, which changed the beginning of Congress's term as well as its convening date to January 3rd. So prior to 1934, a new Congress typically would not convene for regular business until 13 months after being elected. One effect of this was that the last session of each Congress was a "lame duck" session. After the 20th amendment, the time from the election to the beginning of Congress's term as well as when it convened was reduced to two months. Recognizing that the need might exist for Congress to meet at times other than the regularly scheduled convening date, Article II, section 3 of the Constitution provides that the President "may, on extraordinary occasions, convene both Houses, or either of them"; hence these sessions occur only if convened by Presidential proclamation. Except as noted, these are separately numbered sessions of a Congress, and are marked by an E in the session column of the table. Until the 20th amendment was adopted, there were also times when special sessions of the Senate were convened, principally for confirming Cabinet and other executive nominations, and occasionally for the ratification of treaties or other executive business. These Senate sessions were also called by Presidential proclamation (typically by the outgoing President, although on occasion by incumbents as well) and are marked by an S in the session column. MEETING PLACES OF CONGRESS: Congress met for the first and second sessions of the First Congress (1789 and 1790) in New York City. From the third session of the First Congress through the first session of the Sixth Congress (1790 to 1800), Philadelphia was the meeting place. Congress has convened in Washington since the second session of the Sixth Congress (1800).

Congress	Session	Convening Date	Adjournment Date	Length in days [1]	Recesses [2]		President pro tempore of the Senate [3]	Speaker of the House of Representatives
					Senate	House of Representatives		
	1–E	May 31, 1841	Sept. 13, 1841	106			Samuel L. Southard, of New Jersey	John White, of Kentucky.
	2	Dec. 6, 1841	Aug. 31, 1842	269			Willie P. Mangum, of North Carolina.	
	3	Dec. 5, 1842	Mar. 3, 1843	89			...do.	
28th	1	Dec. 4, 1843	June 17, 1844	196			...do	John W. Jones, of Virginia.
	2	Dec. 2, 1844	Mar. 3, 1845	92			...do.	
29th	S	Mar. 4, 1845	Mar. 20, 1845	17				
	1	Dec. 1, 1845	Aug. 10, 1846	253			Ambrose H. Sevier; David R. Atchison, of Missouri.	John W. Davis, of Indiana.
	2	Dec. 7, 1846	Mar. 3, 1847	87			David R. Atchison, of Missouri.	
30th	1	Dec. 6, 1847	Aug. 14, 1848	254			...do	Robert C. Winthrop, of Massachusetts.
	2	Dec. 4, 1848	Mar. 3, 1849	90			...do.	
31st	S	Mar. 5, 1849	Mar. 23, 1849	19			...do.	
	1	Dec. 3, 1849	Sept. 30, 1850	302			William R. King, of Alabama	Howell Cobb, of Georgia.
	2	Dec. 2, 1850	Mar. 3, 1851	92			...do.	
32d	S	Mar. 4, 1851	Mar. 13, 1851	10				
	1	Dec. 1, 1851	Aug. 31, 1852	275			...do	Linn Boyd, of Kentucky.
	2	Dec. 6, 1852	Mar. 3, 1853	88			David R. Atchison, of Missouri.	
33d	S	Mar. 4, 1853	Apr. 11, 1853	39			...do.	
	1	Dec. 5, 1853	Aug. 7, 1854	246			...do	Do.
	2	Dec. 4, 1854	Mar. 3, 1855	90			Lewis Cass, of Michigan; Jesse D. Bright, of Indiana.	
34th	1	Dec. 3, 1855	Aug. 18, 1856	260			Charles E. Stuart, of Michigan; Jesse D. Bright, of Indiana.	Nathaniel P. Banks, of Massachusetts.
	2–E	Aug. 21, 1856	Aug. 30, 1856	10			Jesse D. Bright, of Indiana.	
	3	Dec. 1, 1856	Mar. 3, 1857	93			James M. Mason, of Virginia.	
35th	S	Mar. 4, 1857	Mar. 14, 1857	11			James M. Mason, of Virginia; Thomas J. Rusk, of Texas.	
	1	Dec. 7, 1857	June 14, 1858	189	Dec. 23, 1857–Jan. 4, 1858	Dec. 24, 1857–Jan. 3, 1858	Benjamin Fitzpatrick, of Alabama	James L. Orr, of South Carolina.

	S	June 15, 1858	June 16, 1858	2				
	2	Dec. 6, 1858	Mar. 3, 1859	88	Dec. 23, 1858–Jan. 4, 1859	Dec. 24, 1858–Jan. 3, 1859	...do.	
36th	S	Mar. 4, 1859	Mar. 10, 1859	7			...do.	
	1	Dec. 5, 1859	June 25, 1860	202			Benjamin Fitzpatrick, of Alabama; Jesse D. Bright, of Indiana.	William Pennington, of New Jersey.
	S	June 26, 1860	June 28, 1860	3			Benjamin Fitzpatrick, of Alabama.	
	2	Dec. 3, 1860	Mar. 3, 1861	93			Solomon Foot, of Vermont.	
37th	S	Mar. 4, 1861	Mar. 28, 1861	25			...do.	
	1–E	July 4, 1861	Aug. 6, 1861	34			...do	Galusha A. Grow, of Pennsylvania.
	2	Dec. 2, 1861	July 17, 1862	228			...do.	
	3	Dec. 1, 1862	Mar. 3, 1863	93	Dec. 23, 1862–Jan. 5, 1863	Dec. 24, 1862–Jan. 4, 1863	...do.	
38th	S	Mar. 4, 1863	Mar. 14, 1863	11			...do.	
	1	Dec. 7, 1863	July 4, 1864	209	Dec. 23, 1863–Jan. 5, 1864	Dec. 24, 1863–Jan. 4, 1864	Solomon Foot, of Vermont; Daniel Clark, of New Hampshire.	Schuyler Colfax, of Indiana.
	2	Dec. 5, 1864	Mar. 3, 1865	89	Dec. 22, 1864–Jan. 5, 1865	Dec. 22, 1864–Jan. 4, 1865	Daniel Clark, of New Hampshire.	
39th	S	Mar. 4, 1865	Mar. 11, 1865	8			Lafayette S. Foster, of Connecticut.	
	1	Dec. 4, 1865	July 28, 1866	237	Dec. 6–Dec. 11, 1865 Dec. 21, 1865–Jan. 5, 1866	Dec. 7–Dec. 10, 1865 Dec. 23, 1865–Jan. 4, 1866	...do	Do.
	2	Dec. 3, 1866	Mar. 3, 1867	91	Dec. 20, 1866–Jan. 3, 1867	Dec. 20, 1866–Jan. 3, 1867	Benjamin F. Wade, of Ohio.	
40th	1	Mar. 4, 1867	Dec. 1, 1867	273	Mar. 30–July 3, 1867 July 20–Nov. 21, 1867	Mar. 31–July 2, 1867 July 21–Nov. 20, 1867	...do	Do.[7]
	S	Apr. 1, 1867	Apr. 20, 1867	20				
	2	Dec. 2, 1867	Nov. 10, 1868	345	Dec. 20, 1867–Jan. 6, 1868 July 27–Sept. 21, 1868 Sept. 21–Oct. 16, 1868 Oct. 16–Nov. 10, 1868	Dec. 21, 1867–Jan. 5, 1868 July 26–Sept. 20, 1868 Sept. 22–Oct. 15, 1868 Oct. 17–Nov. 9, 1868		
	3	Dec. 7, 1868	Mar. 3, 1869	87	Dec. 21, 1868–Jan. 5, 1869	Dec. 22, 1868–Jan. 4, 1869	...do	Theodore M. Pomeroy, of New York.[7]
41st	1	Mar. 4, 1869	Apr. 10, 1869	38			Henry B. Anthony, of Rhode Island	James G. Blaine, of Maine.
	S	Apr. 12, 1869	Apr. 22, 1869	11				
	2	Dec. 6, 1869	July 15, 1870	222	Dec. 22, 1869–Jan. 10, 1870	Dec. 23, 1869–Jan. 9, 1870	...do.	
	3	Dec. 5, 1870	Mar. 3, 1871	89	Dec. 23, 1870–Jan. 4, 1871	Dec. 23, 1870–Jan. 3, 1871	...do.	
42d	1	Mar. 4, 1871	Apr. 20, 1871	48			...do	Do.
	S	May 10, 1871	May 27, 1871	18			...do.	
	2	Dec. 4, 1871	June 10, 1872	190	Dec. 21, 1871–Jan. 8, 1872	Dec. 22, 1871–Jan. 7, 1872	...do.	
	3	Dec. 2, 1872	Mar. 3, 1873	92	Dec. 20, 1872–Jan. 6, 1873	Dec. 21, 1872–Jan. 5, 1873	...do.	
43d	S	Mar. 4, 1873	Mar. 26, 1873	23			Matthew H. Carpenter, of Wisconsin.	
	1	Dec. 1, 1873	June 23, 1874	204	Dec. 19, 1873–Jan. 5, 1874	Dec. 20, 1873–Jan. 4, 1874	...do	Do.
	2	Dec. 7, 1874	Mar. 3, 1875	87	Dec. 23, 1874–Jan. 5, 1875	Dec. 24, 1874–Jan. 4, 1875	Matthew H. Carpenter, of Wisconsin; Henry B. Anthony, of Rhode Island.	
44th	S	Mar. 5, 1875	Mar. 24, 1875	20			Thomas W. Ferry, of Michigan.	
	1	Dec. 6, 1875	Aug. 15, 1876	254	Dec. 20, 1875–Jan. 5, 1876	Dec. 21, 1875–Jan. 4, 1876	...do	Michael C. Kerr, of Indiana.[8]
	2	Dec. 4, 1876	Mar. 3, 1877	90			...do	Samuel J. Randall, of Pennsylvania.[8]
45th	S	Mar. 5, 1877	Mar. 17, 1877	13			...do.	
	1–E	Oct. 15, 1877	Dec. 3, 1877	50			...do	Do.
	2	Dec. 3, 1877	June 20, 1878	200	Dec. 15, 1877–Jan. 10, 1878	Dec. 16, 1877–Jan. 10, 1878	...do.	
	3	Dec. 2, 1878	Mar. 3, 1879	92	Dec. 20, 1878–Jan. 7, 1879	Dec. 21, 1878–Jan. 6, 1879	...do.	
46th	1–E	Mar. 18, 1879	July 1, 1879	106			Allen G. Thurman, of Ohio	Do.
	2	Dec. 1, 1879	June 16, 1880	199	Dec. 19, 1879–Jan. 6, 1880	Dec. 20, 1879–Jan. 5, 1880	...do.	
	3	Dec. 6, 1880	Mar. 3, 1881	88	Dec. 23, 1880–Jan. 5, 1881	Dec. 23, 1880–Jan. 4, 1881	...do.	
47th	S	Mar. 4, 1881	May. 20, 1881	78				
	S	Oct. 10, 1881	Oct. 29, 1881	20			Thomas F. Bayard, of Delaware; David Davis, of Illinois.	
	1	Dec. 5, 1881	Aug. 8, 1882	247	Dec. 22, 1881–Jan. 5, 1882	Dec. 22, 1881–Jan. 4, 1882	David Davis, of Illinois	J. Warren Keifer, of Ohio.

SESSIONS OF CONGRESS, 1st–113th CONGRESSES, 1789–2013—CONTINUED

[Closing date for this table was January 2, 2014.]

MEETING DATES OF CONGRESS: Pursuant to a resolution of the Confederation Congress in 1788, the Constitution went into effect on March 4, 1789. From then until the 20th amendment took effect in January 1934, the term of each Congress began on March 4th of each odd-numbered year; however, Article I, section 4, of the Constitution provided that ''The Congress shall assemble at least once in every Year, and such Meeting shall be on the first Monday in December, unless they shall by law appoint a different day.'' The Congress therefore convened regularly on the first Monday in December until the 20th amendment became effective, which changed the beginning of Congress's term as well as its convening date to January 3rd. So prior to 1934, a new Congress typically would not convene for regular business until 13 months after being elected. One effect of this was that the last session of each Congress was a ''lame duck'' session. After the 20th amendment, the time from the election to the beginning of Congress's term as well as when it convened was reduced to two months. Recognizing that the need might exist for Congress to meet at times other than the regularly scheduled convening date, Article II, section 3 of the Constitution provides that the President ''may, on extraordinary occasions, convene both Houses, or either of them''; hence these sessions occur only if convened by Presidential proclamation. Except as noted, these are separately numbered sessions of a Congress, and are marked by an E in the session column of the table. Until the 20th amendment was adopted, there were also times when special sessions of the Senate were convened, principally for confirming Cabinet and other executive nominations, and occasionally for the ratification of treaties or other executive business. These Senate sessions were also called by Presidential proclamation (typically by the outgoing President, although on occasion by incumbents as well) and are marked by an S in the session column. MEETING PLACES OF CONGRESS: Congress met for the first and second sessions of the First Congress (1789 and 1790) in New York City. From the third session of the First Congress through the first session of the Sixth Congress (1790 to 1800), Philadelphia was the meeting place. Congress has convened in Washington since the second session of the Sixth Congress (1800).

Congress	Session	Convening Date	Adjournment Date	Length in days [1]	Recesses [2] Senate	Recesses [2] House of Representatives	President pro tempore of the Senate [3]	Speaker of the House of Representatives
	2	Dec. 4, 1882	Mar. 3, 1883	90			George F. Edmunds, of Vermont.	J. Warren Keifer, of Ohio.
48th	1	Dec. 3, 1883	July 7, 1884	218	Dec. 24, 1883–Jan. 7, 1884	Dec. 25, 1883–Jan. 6, 1884	...do	John G. Carlisle, of Kentucky.
	2	Dec. 1, 1884	Mar. 3, 1885	93	Dec. 24, 1884–Jan. 5, 1885	Dec. 25, 1884–Jan. 4, 1885	...do.	
49th	S	Mar. 4, 1885	Apr. 2, 1885	30				
	1	Dec. 7, 1885	Aug. 5, 1886	242	Dec. 21, 1885–Jan. 5, 1886	Dec. 22, 1885–Jan. 4, 1886	John Sherman, of Ohio	Do.
	2	Dec. 6, 1886	Mar. 3, 1887	88	Dec. 22, 1886–Jan 4, 1887	Dec. 23, 1886–Jan. 3, 1887	John J. Ingalls, of Kansas.	
50th	1	Dec. 5, 1887	Oct. 20, 1888	321	Dec. 22, 1887–Jan. 4, 1888	Dec. 23, 1887–Jan. 3, 1888	...do	Do.
	2	Dec. 3, 1888	Mar. 3, 1889	91	Dec. 21, 1888–Jan. 2, 1889	Dec. 22, 1888–Jan. 1, 1889	...do.	
51st	S	Mar. 4, 1889	Apr. 2, 1889	30			...do.	
	1	Dec. 2, 1889	Oct. 1, 1890	304	Dec. 21, 1889–Jan. 6, 1890	Dec. 22, 1889–Jan. 5, 1890	...do	Thomas B. Reed, of Maine.
	2	Dec. 1, 1890	Mar. 3, 1891	93			Charles F. Manderson, of Nebraska.	
52d	1	Dec. 7, 1891	Aug. 5, 1892	251			...do	Charles F. Crisp, of Georgia.
	2	Dec. 5, 1892	Mar. 3, 1893	89	Dec. 22, 1892–Jan. 4, 1893	Dec. 23, 1892–Jan. 3, 1893	...do.	
53d	S	Mar. 4, 1893	Apr. 15, 1893	43			Charles F. Manderson, of Nebraska; Isham G. Harris, of Tennessee.	
	1–E	Aug. 7, 1893	Nov. 3, 1893	89			Isham G. Harris, of Tennessee	Do.
	2	Dec. 4, 1893	Aug. 28, 1894	268		Dec. 22, 1893–Jan. 2, 1894	...do.	
	3	Dec. 3, 1894	Mar. 3, 1895	97		Dec. 23, 1894–Jan. 2, 1895	Matt W. Ransom, of North Carolina; Isham G. Harris, of Tennessee.	
54th	1	Dec. 2, 1895	June 11, 1896	193			William P. Frye, of Maine	Thomas B. Reed, of Maine.
	2	Dec. 7, 1896	Mar. 3, 1897	87	Dec. 22, 1896–Jan. 5, 1897	Dec. 23, 1896–Jan. 4, 1897	...do.	
55th	S	Mar. 4, 1897	Mar. 10, 1897	11			...do.	
	1–E	Mar. 15, 1897	July 24, 1897	131			...do	Do.
	2	Dec. 6, 1897	July 8, 1898	215	Dec. 18, 1897–Jan. 5, 1898	Dec. 19, 1897–Jan. 4, 1898	...do.	
	3	Dec. 5, 1898	Mar. 3, 1899	89	Dec. 21, 1898–Jan. 4, 1899	Dec. 20, 1898–Jan. 3, 1899	...do.	
56th	1	Dec. 4, 1899	June 7, 1900	186	Dec. 20, 1899–Jan. 3, 1900	Dec. 21, 1899–Jan. 2, 1900	...do	David B. Henderson, of Iowa.
	2	Dec. 3, 1900	Mar. 3, 1901	91	Dec. 20, 1900–Jan. 3, 1901	Dec. 22, 1900–Jan. 2, 1901	...do.	
57th	S	Mar. 4, 1901	Mar. 9, 1901	6			...do.	

	1	Dec. 2, 1901	July 1, 1902	212	Dec. 19, 1901–Jan. 6, 1902	Dec. 20, 1901–Jan. 5, 1902	...do	Do.
	2	Dec. 1, 1902	Mar. 3, 1903	93	Dec. 20, 1902–Jan. 5, 1903	Dec. 21, 1902–Jan. 4, 1903	...do.	
58th	S	Mar. 5, 1903	Mar. 19, 1903	15			...do.	
	1–E	Nov. 9, 1903	Dec. 7, 1903	29			...do	Joseph G. Cannon, of Illinois.
	2	Dec. 7, 1903	Apr. 28, 1904	144	Dec. 19, 1903–Jan. 4, 1904	Dec. 19, 1903–Jan. 4, 1904	...do.	
	3	Dec. 5, 1904	Mar. 3, 1905	89	Dec. 21, 1904–Jan. 4, 1905	Dec. 22, 1904–Jan. 3, 1905	...do.	
59th	S	Mar. 4, 1905	Mar. 18, 1905	15			...do.	
	1	Dec. 4, 1905	June 30, 1906	209	Dec. 21, 1905–Jan. 4, 1906	Dec. 22, 1905–Jan. 3, 1906	...do	Do.
	2	Dec. 3, 1906	Mar. 3, 1907	91	Dec. 20, 1906–Jan. 3, 1907	Dec. 21, 1906–Jan. 2, 1907	...do.	
60th	1	Dec. 2, 1907	May 30, 1908	181	Dec. 21, 1907–Jan. 6, 1908	Dec. 22, 1907–Jan. 5, 1908	...do	Do.
	2	Dec. 7, 1908	Mar. 3, 1909	87	Dec. 19, 1908–Jan. 4, 1909	Dec. 20, 1908–Jan. 3, 1909	...do.	
61st	S	Mar. 4, 1909	Mar. 6, 1909	3			...do.	
	1–E	Mar. 15, 1909	Aug. 5, 1909	144			...do	Do.
	2	Dec. 6, 1909	June 25, 1910	202	Dec. 21, 1909–Jan. 4, 1910	Dec. 22, 1909–Jan. 3, 1910	...do.	
	3	Dec. 5, 1910	Mar. 3, 1911	89	Dec. 21, 1910–Jan. 5, 1911	Dec. 22, 1910–Jan. 4, 1911	...do.	
62d	1–E	Apr. 4, 1911	Aug. 22, 1911	141			...do.[9]	Champ Clark, of Missouri.
	2	Dec. 4, 1911	Aug. 26, 1912	267	Dec. 21, 1911–Jan. 3, 1912	Dec. 22, 1911–Jan. 2, 1912	Charles Curtis, of Kansas; Augustus O. Bacon, of Georgia; Jacob H. Gallinger, of New Hampshire; Henry Cabot Lodge, of Massachusetts; Frank B. Brandegee, of Connecticut.	
	3	Dec. 2, 1912	Mar. 3, 1913	92	Dec. 19, 1912–Jan. 2, 1913	Dec. 20, 1912–Jan. 1, 1913	Augustus O. Bacon, of Georgia; Jacob H. Gallinger, of New Hampshire.	
63d	S	Mar. 4, 1913	Mar. 17, 1913	14			James P. Clarke, of Arkansas.	
	1–E	Apr. 7, 1913	Dec. 1, 1913	239			...do	Do.
	2	Dec. 1, 1913	Oct. 24, 1914	328	Dec. 23, 1913–Jan. 12, 1914	Dec. 24, 1913–Jan. 11, 1914	...do.	
	3	Dec. 7, 1914	Mar. 3, 1915	87	Dec. 23–Dec. 28, 1914	Dec. 24–Dec. 28, 1914	...do.	
64th	1	Dec. 6, 1915	Sept. 8, 1916	278	Dec. 17, 1915–Jan. 4, 1916	Dec. 18, 1915–Jan. 3, 1916	...do[10]	Do.
	2	Dec. 4, 1916	Mar. 3, 1917	90	Dec. 22, 1916–Jan. 2, 1917	Dec. 23, 1916–Jan. 1, 1917	Willard Saulsbury, of Delaware[10]	
65th	S	Mar. 5, 1917	Mar. 16, 1917	12			...do.	
	1–E	Apr. 2, 1917	Oct. 6, 1917	188			...do	Do.
	2	Dec. 3, 1917	Nov. 21, 1918	354	Dec. 18, 1917–Jan. 3, 1918	Dec. 19, 1917–Jan. 2, 1918	...do.	
	3	Dec. 2, 1918	Mar. 3, 1919	92			...do.	
66th	1–E	May 19, 1919	Nov. 19, 1919	185	July 1–July 8, 1919	July 2–July 7, 1919	Albert B. Cummins, of Iowa	Frederick H. Gillett, of Massachusetts.
	2	Dec. 1, 1919	June 5, 1920	188	Dec. 20, 1919–Jan. 5, 1920	Dec. 21, 1919–Jan. 4, 1920	...do.	
	3	Dec. 6, 1920	Mar. 3, 1921	88			...do.	
67th	S	Mar. 4, 1921	Mar. 15, 1921	12			...do.	
	1–E	Apr. 11, 1921	Nov. 23, 1921	227	Aug. 24–Sept. 21, 1921	Aug. 25–Sept. 20, 1921	...do	Do.
	2	Dec. 5, 1921	Sept. 22, 1922	292	Dec. 22, 1921–Jan. 3, 1922	Dec. 23, 1921–Jan. 2, 1922 July 1–Aug. 14, 1922	...do.	
	3–E	Nov. 20, 1922	Dec. 4, 1922	15			...do.	
	4	Dec. 4, 1922	Mar. 3, 1923	90			...do.	
68th	1	Dec. 3, 1923	June 7, 1924	188	Dec. 20, 1923–Jan. 3, 1924	Dec. 21, 1923–Jan. 2, 1924	...do	Do.
	2	Dec. 1, 1924	Mar. 3, 1925	93	Dec. 20–Dec. 29, 1924	Dec. 21–Dec. 28, 1924	...do.	
69th	S	Mar. 4, 1925	Mar. 18, 1925	15			Albert B. Cummins, of Iowa; George H. Moses, of New Hampshire.	
	1	Dec. 7, 1925	July 3, 1926	209	Dec. 22, 1925–Jan. 4, 1926	Dec. 23, 1925–Jan. 3, 1926	...do	Nicholas Longworth, of Ohio.
	2	Dec. 6, 1926	Mar. 4, 1927	88	Dec. 22, 1926–Jan. 3, 1927	Dec. 23, 1926–Jan. 2, 1927	...do.	
70th	1	Dec. 5, 1927	May 29, 1928	177	Dec. 21, 1927–Jan. 4, 1928	Dec. 22, 1927–Jan. 3, 1928	...do	Do.
	2	Dec. 3, 1928	Mar. 3, 1929	91	Dec. 22, 1928–Jan. 3, 1929	Dec. 23, 1928–Jan. 2, 1929	...do.	
71st	S	Mar. 4, 1929	Mar. 5, 1929	2			...do.	
	1–E	Apr. 15, 1929	Nov. 22, 1929	222	June 19–Aug. 19, 1929	June 20–Sept. 22, 1929	...do	Do.
	2	Dec. 2, 1929	July 3, 1930	214	Dec. 21, 1929–Jan. 6, 1930	Dec. 22, 1929–Jan. 6, 1930	...do.	

SESSIONS OF CONGRESS, 1st–113th CONGRESSES, 1789–2013—CONTINUED

[Closing date for this table was January 2, 2014.]

MEETING DATES OF CONGRESS: Pursuant to a resolution of the Confederation Congress in 1788, the Constitution went into effect on March 4, 1789. From then until the 20th amendment took effect in January 1934, the term of each Congress began on March 4th of each odd-numbered year; however, Article I, section 4, of the Constitution provided that ''The Congress shall assemble at least once in every Year, and such Meeting shall be on the first Monday in December, unless they shall by law appoint a different day.'' The Congress therefore convened regularly on the first Monday in December until the 20th amendment became effective, which changed the beginning of Congress's term as well as its convening date to January 3rd. So prior to 1934, a new Congress typically would not convene for regular business until 13 months after being elected. One effect of this was that the last session of each Congress was a ''lame duck'' session. After the 20th amendment, the time from the election to the beginning of Congress's term as well as when it convened was reduced to two months. Recognizing that the need might exist for Congress to meet at times other than the regularly scheduled convening date, Article II, section 3 of the Constitution provides that the President ''may, on extraordinary occasions, convene both Houses, or either of them''; hence these sessions occur only if convened by Presidential proclamation. Except as noted, these are separately numbered sessions of a Congress, and are marked by an E in the session column of the table. Until the 20th amendment was adopted, there were also times when special sessions of the Senate were convened, principally for confirming Cabinet and other executive nominations, and occasionally for the ratification of treaties or other executive business. These Senate sessions were also called by Presidential proclamation (typically by the outgoing President, although on occasion by incumbents as well) and are marked by an S in the session column. MEETING PLACES OF CONGRESS: Congress met for the first and second sessions of the First Congress (1789 and 1790) in New York City. From the third session of the First Congress through the first session of the Sixth Congress (1790 to 1800), Philadelphia was the meeting place. Congress has convened in Washington since the second session of the Sixth Congress (1800).

Congress	Session	Convening Date	Adjournment Date	Length in days [1]	Recesses [2]		President pro tempore of the Senate [3]	Speaker of the House of Representatives
					Senate	House of Representatives		
	S	July 7, 1930	July 21, 1930	15			...do.	
	3	Dec. 1, 1930	Mar. 3, 1931	93	Dec. 20, 1930–Jan. 5, 1931	Dec. 21, 1930–Jan. 4, 1931	George H. Moses, of New Hampshire	Nicholas Longworth, of Ohio.
72d	1	Dec. 7, 1931	July 16, 1932	223	Dec. 22, 1931–Jan. 4, 1932	Dec. 23, 1931–Jan. 3, 1932	...do	John N. Garner, of Texas.
	2	Dec. 5, 1932	Mar. 3, 1933	89			...do.	
73d	S	Mar. 4, 1933	Mar. 6, 1933	3			...do.	
	1–E	Mar. 9, 1933	June 15, 1933	99			Key Pittman, of Nevada	Henry T. Rainey, of Illinois.
	2	Jan. 3, 1934	June 18, 1934	167			...do.	
74th	1	Jan. 3, 1935	Aug. 26, 1935	236			...do	Joseph W. Byrns, of Tennessee.[11]
	2	Jan. 3, 1936	June 20, 1936	170	June 8–June 15, 1936	June 9–June 14, 1936	...do	William B. Bankhead, of Alabama.[11]
75th	1	Jan. 5, 1937	Aug. 21, 1937	229			...do	Do.
	2–E	Nov. 15, 1937	Dec. 21, 1937	37			...do.	
	3	Jan. 3, 1938	June 16, 1938	165			...do.	
76th	1	Jan. 3, 1939	Aug. 5, 1939	215			...do	Do.[12]
	2–E	Sept. 21, 1939	Nov. 3, 1939	44			...do.	
	3	Jan. 3, 1940	Jan. 3, 1941	366	July 11–July 22, 1940	June 23–June 30, 1940 July 12–July 21, 1940	Key Pittman, of Nevada;[13] William H. King, of Utah.[13]	Sam Rayburn, of Texas.[12]
77th	1	Jan. 3, 1941	Jan. 2, 1942	365			Pat Harrison, of Mississippi;[14] Carter Glass, of Virginia.[14]	Do.
	2	Jan. 5, 1942	Dec. 16, 1942	346			Carter Glass, of Virginia.	
78th	1	Jan. 6, 1943	Dec. 21, 1943	350	July 8–Sept. 14, 1943	Apr. 23–May 2, 1943 July 8–Sept. 13, 1943	...do	Do.
	2	Jan. 10, 1944	Dec. 19, 1944	345	Apr. 1–Apr. 12, 1944 June 23–Aug. 1, 1944 Sept. 21–Nov. 14, 1944	Apr. 2–Apr. 11, 1944 June 24–June 31, 1944 Sept. 22–Nov. 13, 1944	...do.	
79th	1	Jan. 3, 1945	Dec. 21, 1945	353	Aug. 1–Sept. 5, 1945	July 22–Sept. 4, 1945	Kenneth McKellar, of Tennessee	Do.
	2	Jan. 14, 1946	Aug. 2, 1946	201		Apr. 19–Apr. 29, 1946	...do.	
80th	[15] 1	Jan. 3, 1947	Dec. 19, 1947	351	July 27–Nov. 17, 1947	July 28–Nov. 16, 1947	Arthur H. Vandenberg, of Michigan	Joseph W. Martin, Jr., of Massachusetts.

	[15]2	Jan. 6, 1948	Dec. 31, 1948	361	June 20–July 26, 1948 Aug. 7–Dec. 31, 1948	June 21–July 25, 1948 Aug. 8–Dec. 30, 1948	...do.	
81st	1	Jan. 3, 1949	Oct. 19, 1949	290	Apr. 15–May 2, 1949	....	Kenneth McKellar, of Tennessee	Sam Rayburn, of Texas.
	2	Jan. 3, 1950	Jan. 2, 1951	365	....	Apr. 6–Apr. 18, 1950 Sept. 23–Nov. 27, 1950	...do.	
82d	1	Jan. 3, 1951	Oct. 20, 1951	291	....	Mar. 23–Apr. 1, 1951 Aug. 24–Sept. 11, 1951	...do	Do.
	2	Jan. 8, 1952	July 7, 1952	182	....	Apr. 11–Apr. 21, 1952	...do.	
83d	1	Jan. 3, 1953	Aug. 3, 1953	213	....	Apr. 3–Apr. 12, 1953	Styles Bridges, of New Hampshire	Joseph W. Martin, Jr., of Massachusetts.
	2	Jan. 6, 1954	Dec. 2, 1954	331	Aug. 20–Nov. 8, 1954 Nov. 18–Nov. 29, 1954	Apr. 16–Apr. 25, 1954 Adjourned sine die Aug. 20, 1954	...do.	
84th	1	Jan. 5, 1955	Aug. 2, 1955	210	Apr. 4–Apr. 13, 1955	Apr. 5–Apr. 12, 1955	Walter F. George, of Georgia	Sam Rayburn, of Texas.
	2	Jan. 3, 1956	July 27, 1956	207	Mar. 29–Apr. 9, 1956	Mar. 30–Apr. 8, 1956	...do.	
85th	1	Jan. 3, 1957	Aug. 30, 1957	239	Apr. 18–Apr. 29, 1957	Apr. 19–Apr. 28, 1957	Carl Hayden, of Arizona	Do.
	2	Jan. 7, 1958	Aug. 24, 1958	230	Apr. 3–Apr. 14, 1958	Apr. 4–Apr. 13, 1958	...do.	
86th	1	Jan. 7, 1959	Sept. 15, 1959	252	Mar. 26–Apr. 7, 1959	Mar. 27–Apr. 6, 1959	...do	Do.
	2	Jan. 6, 1960	Sept. 1, 1960	240	Apr. 14–Apr. 18, 1960 May 27–May 31, 1960 July 3–Aug. 8, 1960	July 4–Aug. 14, 1960	...do.	
87th	1	Jan. 3, 1961	Sept. 27, 1961	268	....	Mar. 31–Apr. 9, 1961	...do	Do.[16]
	2	Jan. 10, 1962	Oct. 13, 1962	277	....	Apr. 20–Apr. 29, 1962	...do	John W. McCormack, of Massachusetts.[16]
88th	1	Jan. 9, 1963	Dec. 30, 1963	356	....	Apr. 11–Apr. 21, 1963	...do	Do.
	2	Jan. 7, 1964	Oct. 3, 1964	270	July 10–July 20, 1964 Aug. 21–Aug. 31, 1964	Mar. 27–Apr. 5, 1964 July 3–July 19, 1964 Aug. 22–Aug. 30, 1964	...do.	
89th	1	Jan. 4, 1965	Oct. 23, 1965	293	....	....	...do	Do.
	2	Jan. 10, 1966	Oct. 22, 1966	286	Apr. 7–Apr. 13, 1966 June 30–July 11, 1966	Apr. 8–Apr. 17, 1966 June 1–June 10, 1966	...do.	
90th	1	Jan. 10, 1967	Dec. 15, 1967	340	Mar. 23–Apr. 3, 1967 June 29–July 10, 1967 Aug. 31–Sept. 11, 1967 Nov. 22–Nov. 27, 1967	Mar. 24–Apr. 2, 1967 June 30–July 9, 1967 Sept. 1–Sept. 10, 1967 Nov. 23–Nov. 26, 1967	...do	Do.
	2	Jan. 15, 1968	Oct. 14, 1968	274	Apr. 11–Apr. 17, 1968 May 29–June 3, 1968 June 3–July 8, 1968 Aug. 2–Sept. 4, 1968	Apr. 12–Apr. 21, 1968 May 30–June 2, 1968 July 4–July 7, 1968 Aug. 3–Sept. 3, 1968	...do.	
91st	1	Jan. 3, 1969	Dec. 23, 1969	355	Feb. 7–Feb. 17, 1969 Apr. 3–Apr. 14, 1969 July 2–July 7, 1969 Aug. 13–Sept. 3, 1969 Nov. 26–Dec. 1, 1969	Feb. 8–Feb. 16, 1969 Apr. 4–Apr. 13, 1969 May 29–June 1, 1969 July 3–July 6, 1969 Aug. 14–Sept. 2, 1969 Nov. 7–Nov. 11, 1969 Nov. 27–Nov. 30, 1969	Richard B. Russell, of Georgia	Do.

SESSIONS OF CONGRESS, 1st–113th CONGRESSES, 1789–2013—CONTINUED

[Closing date for this table was January 2, 2014.]

MEETING DATES OF CONGRESS: Pursuant to a resolution of the Confederation Congress in 1788, the Constitution went into effect on March 4, 1789. From then until the 20th amendment took effect in January 1934, the term of each Congress began on March 4th of each odd-numbered year; however, Article I, section 4, of the Constitution provided that "The Congress shall assemble at least once in every Year, and such Meeting shall be on the first Monday in December, unless they shall by law appoint a different day." The Congress therefore convened regularly on the first Monday in December until the 20th amendment became effective, which changed the beginning of Congress's term as well as its convening date to January 3rd. So prior to 1934, a new Congress typically would not convene for regular business until 13 months after being elected. One effect of this was that the last session of each Congress was a "lame duck" session. After the 20th amendment, the time from the election to the beginning of Congress's term as well as when it convened was reduced to two months. Recognizing that the need might exist for Congress to meet at times other than the regularly scheduled convening date, Article II, section 3 of the Constitution provides that the President "may, on extraordinary occasions, convene both Houses, or either of them"; hence these sessions occur only if convened by Presidential proclamation. Except as noted, these are separately numbered sessions of a Congress, and are marked by an E in the session column of the table. Until the 20th amendment was adopted, there were also times when special sessions of the Senate were convened, principally for confirming Cabinet and other executive nominations, and occasionally for the ratification of treaties or other executive business. These Senate sessions were also called by Presidential proclamation (typically by the outgoing President, although on occasion by incumbents as well) and are marked by an S in the session column. MEETING PLACES OF CONGRESS: Congress met for the first and second sessions of the First Congress (1789 and 1790) in New York City. From the third session of the First Congress through the first session of the Sixth Congress (1790 to 1800), Philadelphia was the meeting place. Congress has convened in Washington since the second session of the Sixth Congress (1800).

Congress	Session	Convening Date	Adjournment Date	Length in days [1]	Recesses [2] Senate	Recesses [2] House of Representatives	President pro tempore of the Senate [3]	Speaker of the House of Representatives
	2	Jan. 19, 1970	Jan. 2, 1971	349	Feb. 10–Feb. 16, 1970 .... Mar. 26–Mar. 31, 1970 Sept. 2–Sept. 8, 1970 Oct. 14–Nov. 16, 1970 Nov. 25–Nov. 30, 1970 Dec. 22–Dec. 28, 1970	Feb. 11–Feb. 15, 1970 .... Mar. 27–Mar. 30, 1970 May 28–May 31, 1970 July 2–July 5, 1970 Aug. 15–Sept. 8, 1970 Oct. 15–Nov. 15, 1970 Nov. 26–Nov. 29, 1970 Dec. 23–Dec. 28, 1970	...do.	
92d	1	Jan. 21, 1971	Dec. 17, 1971 ...	331	Feb. 11–Feb. 17, 1971 .... Apr. 7–Apr. 14, 1971 May 26–June 1, 1971 June 30–July 6, 1971 Aug. 6–Sept. 8, 1971 Oct. 21–Oct. 26, 1971 Nov. 24–Nov. 29, 1971	Feb. 11–Feb. 16, 1971 .... Apr. 8–Apr. 18, 1971 May 28–May 31, 1971 July 2–July 5, 1971 Aug. 7–Sept. 7, 1971 Oct. 8–Oct. 11, 1971 Oct. 22–Oct. 25, 1971 Nov. 20–Nov. 28, 1971	Richard B. Russell, of Georgia; [17] Allen J. Ellender, of Louisiana.[17]	Carl B. Albert, of Oklahoma.
	2	Jan. 18, 1972	Oct. 18, 1972 ...	275	Feb. 9–Feb. 14, 1972 .... Mar. 30–Apr. 4, 1972 May 25–May 30, 1972 June 30–July 17, 1972 Aug. 18–Sept. 5, 1972	Feb. 10–Feb. 15, 1972 .... Mar. 30–Apr. 9, 1972 May 25–May 29, 1972 June 1–July 16, 1972 Aug. 19–Sept. 4, 1972	Allen J. Ellender, of Louisiana;[18] James O. Eastland, of Mississippi.[18]	

93d	1	Jan. 3, 1973	Dec. 22, 1973	354	Feb. 8–Feb. 15, 1973 Apr. 18–Apr. 30, 1973 May 23–May 29, 1973 June 30–July 9, 1973 Aug. 3–Sept. 5, 1973 Oct. 18–Oct. 23, 1973 Nov. 21–Nov. 26, 1973	Feb. 9–Feb. 18, 1973 Apr. 20–Apr. 29, 1973 May 25–May 28, 1973 July 1–July 9, 1973 Aug. 4–Sept. 4, 1973 Oct. 5–Oct. 8, 1973 Oct. 19–Oct. 22, 1973 Nov. 16–Nov. 25, 1973	James O. Eastland, of Mississippi	Do.
	2	Jan. 21, 1974	Dec. 20, 1974	334	Feb. 8–Feb. 18, 1974 Mar. 13–Mar. 19, 1974 Apr. 11–Apr. 22, 1974 May 23–May 28, 1974 Aug. 22–Sept. 4, 1974 Oct. 17–Nov. 18, 1974 Nov. 26–Dec. 2, 1974	Feb. 8–Feb. 12, 1974 Apr. 12–Apr. 21, 1974 May 24–May 27, 1974 July 4–July 8, 1974 Aug. 23–Sept. 10, 1974 Oct. 18–Nov. 17, 1974 Nov. 27–Dec. 2, 1974	...do.	
94th	1	Jan. 14, 1975	Dec. 19, 1975	340	Mar. 26–Apr. 7, 1975 May 22–June 2, 1975 June 27–July 7, 1975 Aug. 1–Sept. 3, 1975 Oct. 9–Oct. 20, 1975 Oct. 23–Oct. 28, 1975 Nov. 20–Dec. 1, 1975	Mar. 27–Apr. 6, 1975 May 23–June 1, 1975 June 27–July 7, 1975 Aug. 2–Sept. 2, 1975 Oct. 10–Oct. 19, 1975 Oct. 24–Oct. 27, 1975 Nov. 21–Nov. 30, 1975	...do	Do.
	2	Jan. 19, 1976	Oct. 1, 1976	257	Feb. 6–Feb. 16, 1976 Apr. 14–Apr. 26, 1976 May 28–June 2, 1976 July 2–July 19, 1976 Aug. 10–Aug. 23, 1976 Sept. 1–Sept. 7, 1976	Feb. 12–Feb. 15, 1976 Apr. 15–Apr. 25, 1976 May 28–May 31, 1976 July 3–July 18, 1976 Aug. 11–Aug. 22, 1976 Sept. 3–Sept. 7, 1976	...do.	
95th	1	Jan. 4, 1977	Dec. 15, 1977	346	Feb. 11–Feb. 21, 1977 Apr. 7–Apr. 18, 1977 May 27–June 6, 1977 July 1–July 11, 1977 Aug. 6–Sept. 7, 1977	Feb. 10–Feb. 15, 1977 Apr. 7–Apr. 17, 1977 May 27–May 31, 1977 July 1–July 10, 1977 Aug. 6–Sept. 6, 1977 Oct. 7–Oct. 10, 1977	...do	Thomas P. O'Neill, Jr., of Massachusetts.
	2	Jan. 19, 1978	Oct. 15, 1978	270	Feb. 10–Feb. 20, 1978 Mar. 23–Apr. 3, 1978 May 26–June 5, 1978 June 29–July 10, 1978 Aug. 25–Sept. 6, 1978	Feb. 10–Feb. 13, 1978 Mar. 23–Apr. 2, 1978 May 26–May 30, 1978 June 30–July 9, 1978 Aug. 18–Sept. 5, 1978	...do.	
96th	1	Jan. 15, 1979	Jan. 3, 1980	354	Feb. 9–Feb. 19, 1979 Apr. 10–Apr. 23, 1979 May 24–June 4, 1979 June 27–July 9, 1979 Aug. 3–Sept. 5, 1979 Nov. 20–Nov. 26, 1979 Adjourned sine die, Dec. 20, 1979	Feb. 9–Feb. 12, 1979 Apr. 11–Apr. 22, 1979 May 25–May 29, 1979 June 30–July 8, 1979 Aug. 3–Sept. 4, 1979 Nov. 21–Nov. 25, 1979	Warren G. Magnuson, of Washington	Do.

SESSIONS OF CONGRESS, 1st–113th CONGRESSES, 1789–2013—CONTINUED

[Closing date for this table was January 2, 2014.]

MEETING DATES OF CONGRESS: Pursuant to a resolution of the Confederation Congress in 1788, the Constitution went into effect on March 4, 1789. From then until the 20th amendment took effect in January 1934, the term of each Congress began on March 4th of each odd-numbered year; however, Article I, section 4, of the Constitution provided that ''The Congress shall assemble at least once in every Year, and such Meeting shall be on the first Monday in December, unless they shall by law appoint a different day.'' The Congress therefore convened regularly on the first Monday in December until the 20th amendment became effective, which changed the beginning of Congress's term as well as its convening date to January 3rd. So prior to 1934, a new Congress typically would not convene for regular business until 13 months after being elected. One effect of this was that the last session of each Congress was a ''lame duck'' session. After the 20th amendment, the time from the election to the beginning of Congress's term as well as when it convened was reduced to two months. Recognizing that the need might exist for Congress to meet at times other than the regularly scheduled convening date, Article II, section 3 of the Constitution provides that the President ''may, on extraordinary occasions, convene both Houses, or either of them''; hence these sessions occur only if convened by Presidential proclamation. Except as noted, these are separately numbered sessions of a Congress, and are marked by an E in the session column of the table. Until the 20th amendment was adopted, there were also times when special sessions of the Senate were convened, principally for confirming Cabinet and other executive nominations, and occasionally for the ratification of treaties or other executive business. These Senate sessions were also called by Presidential proclamation (typically by the outgoing President, although on occasion by incumbents as well) and are marked by an S in the session column. MEETING PLACES OF CONGRESS: Congress met for the first and second sessions of the First Congress (1789 and 1790) in New York City. From the third session of the First Congress through the first session of the Sixth Congress (1790 to 1800), Philadelphia was the meeting place. Congress has convened in Washington since the second session of the Sixth Congress (1800).

Congress	Session	Convening Date	Adjournment Date	Length in days [1]	Recesses [2]		President pro tempore of the Senate [3]	Speaker of the House of Representatives
					Senate	House of Representatives		
	2	Jan. 3, 1980	Dec. 16, 1980	349	Apr. 3–Apr. 15, 1980 May 22–May 28, 1980 July 2–July 21, 1980 Aug. 6–Aug. 18, 1980 Aug. 27–Sept. 3, 1980 Oct. 1–Nov. 12, 1980 Nov. 25–Dec. 1, 1980	Jan. 18–21, 1980 Feb. 14–Feb. 18, 1980 Apr. 3–Apr. 14, 1980 May 23–May 27, 1980 July 3–July 20, 1980 Aug. 2–Aug. 17, 1980 Aug. 29–Sept. 2, 1980 Oct. 3–Nov. 11, 1980 Nov. 22–Nov. 30, 1980	Warren G. Magnuson, of Washington; Milton Young, of North Dakota;[19] Warren G. Magnuson, of Washington.[19]	
97th	1	Jan. 5, 1981	Dec. 16, 1981	347	Feb. 6–Feb. 16, 1981 Apr. 10–Apr. 27, 1981 June 25–July 8, 1981 Aug. 3–Sept. 9, 1981 Oct. 7–Oct. 14, 1981 Nov. 24–Nov. 30, 1981	Feb. 7–Feb. 16, 1981 Apr. 11–Apr. 26, 1981 June 27–July 7, 1981 Aug. 5–Sept. 8, 1981 Oct. 8–Oct. 12, 1981 Nov. 24–Nov. 29, 1981	Strom Thurmond, of South Carolina	Do.
	2	Jan. 25, 1982	Dec. 23, 1982	333	Feb. 11–Feb. 22, 1982 Apr. 1–Apr. 13, 1982 May 27–June 8, 1982 July 1–July 12, 1982 Aug. 20–Sept. 8, 1982 Oct. 1–Nov. 29, 1982	Feb. 11–Feb. 21, 1982 Apr. 7–Apr. 19, 1982 May 29–June 1, 1982 July 2–July 11, 1982 Aug. 21–Sept. 7, 1982 Oct. 3–Nov. 28, 1982	...do	
98th	1	Jan. 3, 1983	Nov. 18, 1983	320	Jan. 3–Jan. 25, 1983 Feb. 3–Feb. 14, 1983 Mar. 24–Apr. 5, 1983 May 26–June 6, 1983 June 29–July 11, 1983 Aug. 4–Sept. 12, 1983 Oct. 7–Oct. 17, 1983	Jan. 7–Jan. 24, 1983 Feb. 18–Feb. 21, 1983 Mar. 25–Apr. 4, 1983 May 27–May 31, 1983 July 1–July 10, 1983 Aug. 5–Sept. 11, 1983 Oct. 7–Oct. 16, 1983	Strom Thurmond, of South Carolina	Thomas P. O'Neill, Jr., of Massachusetts.

	2	Jan. 23, 1984	Oct. 12, 1984	264	Feb. 9–Feb. 20, 1984 Apr. 12–Apr. 24, 1984 May 24–May 31, 1984 June 29–July 23, 1984 Aug. 10–Sept. 5, 1984	Feb. 10–Feb. 20, 1984 Apr. 13–Apr. 23, 1984 May 25–May 29, 1984 June 30–July 22, 1984 Aug. 11–Sept. 4, 1984	...do.	
99th	1	Jan. 3, 1985	Dec. 20, 1985	352	Jan. 7–Jan. 21, 1985 Feb. 7–Feb. 18, 1985 Apr. 4–Apr. 15, 1985 May 9–May 14, 1985 May 24–June 3, 1985 June 27–July 8, 1985 Aug. 1–Sept. 9, 1985 Nov. 23–Dec. 2, 1985	Jan. 8–Jan. 20, 1985 Feb. 8–Feb. 18, 1985 Mar. 8–Mar. 18, 1985 Apr. 5–Apr. 14, 1985 May 24–June 2, 1985 June 28–July 7, 1985 Aug. 2–Sept. 3, 1985 Nov. 22–Dec. 1, 1985	...do	Do.
	2	Jan. 21, 1986	Oct. 18, 1986	278	Feb. 7–Feb. 17, 1986 Mar. 27–Apr. 8, 1986 May 21–June 2, 1986 June 26–July 7, 1986 Aug. 15–Sept. 8, 1986	Feb. 7–Feb. 17, 1986 Mar. 25–Apr. 7, 1986 May 23–June 2, 1986 June 27–July 13, 1986 Aug. 17–Sept. 7, 1986	...do.	
100th	1	Jan. 6, 1987	Dec. 22, 1987	351	Jan. 6–Jan. 12, 1987 Feb. 5–Feb. 16, 1987 Apr. 10–Apr. 21, 1987 May 21–May 27, 1987 July 1–July 7, 1987 Aug. 7–Sept. 9, 1987 Nov. 20–Nov. 30, 1987	Jan. 9–Jan. 19, 1987 Feb. 12–Feb. 17, 1987 Apr. 10–Apr. 20, 1987 May 22–May 26, 1987 July 2–July 6, 1987 July 16–July 19, 1987 Aug. 8–Sept. 9, 1987 Nov. 11–Nov. 15, 1987 Nov. 21–Nov. 29, 1987	John C. Stennis, of Mississippi	James C. Wright, Jr., of Texas.
	2	Jan. 25, 1988	Oct. 22, 1988	272	Feb. 4–Feb. 15, 1988 Mar. 4– Mar. 14, 1988 Mar. 31–Apr. 11, 1988 Apr. 29–May 9, 1988 May 27–June 6, 1988 June 29–July 6, 1988 July 14–July 25, 1988 Aug. 11–Sept. 7, 1988	Feb. 10–Feb. 15, 1988 Apr. 1–Apr. 10, 1988 May 27–May 31, 1988 July 1–July 5, 1988 July 15–July 25, 1988 Aug. 12–Sept. 6, 1988	...do.	
101st	1	Jan. 3, 1989	Nov. 22, 1989	324	Jan. 4–Jan. 20, 1989 Jan. 20–Jan. 25, 1989 Feb. 9–Feb. 21, 1989 Mar. 17–Apr. 4, 1989 Apr. 19–May 1, 1989 May 18–May 31, 1989 June 23–July 11, 1989 Aug. 4–Sept. 6, 1989	Jan. 5–Jan. 18, 1989 Feb. 10–Feb. 20, 1989 Mar. 24–Apr. 2, 1989 Apr. 19–Apr. 24, 1989 May 26–May 30, 1989 June 30–July 9, 1989 Aug. 6–Sept. 5, 1989	Robert C. Byrd, of West Virginia	James C. Wright, Jr., of Texas;[20] Thomas S. Foley, of Washington.[20]
	2	Jan. 23, 1990	Oct. 28, 1990	260	Feb. 8–Feb. 20, 1990 Mar. 9–Mar. 20, 1990 Apr. 5–Apr. 18, 1990 May 24–June 5, 1990 June 28–July 10, 1990 Aug. 4–Sept. 10, 1990	Feb. 8–Feb. 19, 1990 Apr. 5–Apr. 17, 1990 May 26–June 4, 1990 June 29–July 9, 1990 Aug. 5–Sept. 4, 1990	...do.	

SESSIONS OF CONGRESS, 1st–113th CONGRESSES, 1789–2013—CONTINUED

[Closing date for this table was January 2, 2014.]

MEETING DATES OF CONGRESS: Pursuant to a resolution of the Confederation Congress in 1788, the Constitution went into effect on March 4, 1789. From then until the 20th amendment took effect in January 1934, the term of each Congress began on March 4th of each odd-numbered year; however, Article I, section 4, of the Constitution provided that ''The Congress shall assemble at least once in every Year, and such Meeting shall be on the first Monday in December, unless they shall by law appoint a different day.'' The Congress therefore convened regularly on the first Monday in December until the 20th amendment became effective, which changed the beginning of Congress's term as well as its convening date to January 3rd. So prior to 1934, a new Congress typically would not convene for regular business until 13 months after being elected. One effect of this was that the last session of each Congress was a ''lame duck'' session. After the 20th amendment, the time from the election to the beginning of Congress's term as well as when it convened was reduced to two months. Recognizing that the need might exist for Congress to meet at times other than the regularly scheduled convening date, Article II, section 3 of the Constitution provides that the President ''may, on extraordinary occasions, convene both Houses, or either of them''; hence these sessions occur only if convened by Presidential proclamation. Except as noted, these are separately numbered sessions of a Congress, and are marked by an E in the session column of the table. Until the 20th amendment was adopted, there were also times when special sessions of the Senate were convened, principally for confirming Cabinet and other executive nominations, and occasionally for the ratification of treaties or other executive business. These Senate sessions were also called by Presidential proclamation (typically by the outgoing President, although on occasion by incumbents as well) and are marked by an S in the session column. MEETING PLACES OF CONGRESS: Congress met for the first and second sessions of the First Congress (1789 and 1790) in New York City. From the third session of the First Congress through the first session of the Sixth Congress (1790 to 1800), Philadelphia was the meeting place. Congress has convened in Washington since the second session of the Sixth Congress (1800).

Congress	Session	Convening Date	Adjournment Date	Length in days [1]	Recesses [2]		President pro tempore of the Senate [3]	Speaker of the House of Representatives
					Senate	House of Representatives		
102d ...	1	Jan. 3, 1991	Jan. 3, 1992	366	Feb. 7–Feb. 19, 1991 .... Mar. 22–Apr. 9, 1991 Apr. 25–May 6, 1991 May 24–June 3, 1991 June 28–July 8, 1991 Aug. 2–Sept. 10, 1991 Nov. 27, 1991–Jan. 3, 1992	Feb. 7–Feb. 18, 1991 .... Mar. 23–Apr. 8, 1991 May 24–May 28, 1991 June 28–July 8, 1991 Aug. 3–Sept. 10, 1991 Nov. 28, 1991–Jan. 2, 1992	...do	Thomas S. Foley, of Washington.
	2	Jan. 3, 1992	Oct. 9, 1992	281	Jan. 3–Jan. 21, 1992 .... Apr. 10–Apr. 28, 1992 May 21–June 1, 1992 July 2–July 20, 1992 Aug. 12–Sept. 8, 1992	Jan. 4–Jan. 21, 1992 .... Apr. 11–Apr. 27, 1992 May 22–May 25, 1992 July 3–July 6, 1992 July 10–July 20, 1992 Aug. 13–Sept. 8, 1992	...do.	
103d ...	1	Jan. 5, 1993	Nov. 26, 1993 ..	326	Jan. 7–Jan. 20, 1993 .... Feb. 4–Feb. 16, 1993 Apr. 7–Apr. 19, 1993 May 28–June 7, 1993 July 1–July 13, 1993 Aug. 7–Sept. 7, 1993 Oct. 7–Oct. 13, 1993 Nov. 11–Nov. 16, 1993	Jan. 7–Jan. 19, 1993 .... Jan. 28–Feb. 1, 1993 Feb. 5–Feb. 15, 1993 Apr. 8–Apr. 18, 1993 May 28–June 7, 1993 July 2–July 12, 1993 Aug. 7–Sept. 7, 1993 Sept. 16–Sept. 20, 1993 Oct. 8–Oct. 11, 1993 Nov. 11–Nov. 14, 1993	Robert C. Byrd, of West Virginia	Thomas S. Foley, of Washington.

	2	Jan. 25, 1994	Dec. 1, 1994	311	Feb. 11–Feb. 22, 1994 Mar. 26–Apr. 11, 1994 May 25–June 7, 1994 July 1–July 11, 1994 Aug. 25–Sept. 12, 1994 Oct. 8–Nov. 30, 1994	Jan. 27–Jan. 31, 1994 Feb. 12–Feb. 21, 1994 Mar. 25–Apr. 11, 1994 May 27–June 7, 1994 July 1–July 11, 1994 Aug. 27–Sept. 11, 1994 Oct. 8–Nov. 28, 1994	...do.	
104th	1	Jan. 4, 1995	Jan. 3, 1996	365	Feb. 16–Feb. 22, 1995 Apr. 7–Apr. 24, 1995 May 26–June 5, 1995 June 30–July 10, 1995 Aug. 11–Sept. 5, 1995 Sept. 29–Oct. 10, 1995 Nov. 20–Nov. 27, 1995	Feb. 17–Feb. 20, 1995 Mar. 17–Mar. 20, 1995 Apr. 8–Apr. 30, 1995 May 4–May 8, 1995 May 26–June 5, 1995 July 1–July 9, 1995 Aug. 5–Sept. 5, 1995 Sept. 30–Oct. 5, 1995 Nov. 21–Nov. 27, 1995	Strom Thurmond, of South Carolina	Newt Gingrich, of Georgia.
	2	Jan. 3, 1996	Oct. 4, 1996	276	Jan. 10–Jan. 22, 1996 Mar. 29–Apr. 15, 1996 May 24–June 3, 1996 June 28–July 8, 1996 Aug. 2–Sept. 3, 1996	Jan. 10–Jan. 21, 1996 Mar. 30–Apr. 14, 1996 May 24–May 28, 1996 June 29–July 7, 1996 Aug. 3–Sept. 3, 1996	...do.	
105th	1	Jan. 7, 1997	Nov. 13, 1997	311	Jan. 9–Jan. 21, 1997 Feb. 13–Feb. 24, 1997 Mar. 21–Apr. 7, 1997 June 27–July 7, 1997 July 31–Sept. 2, 1997 Oct. 9–Oct. 20, 1997	Jan. 10–Jan. 19, 1997 Jan. 22–Feb. 3, 1997 Feb. 14–Feb. 24, 1997 Mar. 22–Apr. 7, 1997 June 27–July 7, 1997 Aug. 2–Sept. 2, 1997 Oct. 10–Oct. 20, 1997	...do	Do.
	2	Jan. 27, 1998	Dec. 19, 1998	327	Feb. 13–Feb. 23, 1998 Apr. 3–Apr. 20, 1998 May 22–June 1, 1998 June 26–July 6, 1998 July 31–Aug. 31, 1998 Adjourned sine die, Oct. 21, 1998.	Jan. 29–Feb. 2, 1998 Feb. 6–Feb. 10, 1998 Feb. 13–Feb. 23, 1998 Apr. 2–Apr. 20, 1998 May 23–June 2, 1998 June 25–July 13, 1998 Aug. 8–Sept. 8, 1998 Oct. 22–Dec. 16, 1998	...do.	
106th	1	Jan. 6, 1999	Nov. 22, 1999	321	Feb. 12–Feb. 22, 1999 Mar. 25–Apr. 12, 1999 May 27–June 7, 1999 July 1–July 12, 1999 Aug. 5–Sept. 8, 1999	Jan. 7–Jan. 18, 1999 Jan. 20–Feb. 1, 1999 Feb. 13–Feb. 22, 1999 Mar. 26–Apr. 11, 1999 May 28–June 6, 1999 July 2–July 11, 1999 Aug. 7–Sept. 7, 1999	...do	J. Dennis Hastert, of Illinois.
	2	Jan. 24, 2000	Dec. 15, 2000	326	Feb. 10–Feb. 22, 2000 Mar. 9–Mar. 20, 2000 Apr. 13–Apr. 25, 2000 May 25–June 6, 2000 June 30–July 10, 2000 July 27–Sept. 5, 2000 Nov. 2–Nov. 14, 2000 Nov. 14–Dec. 5, 2000	Feb. 17–Feb. 28, 2000 Apr. 14–May 1, 2000 May 26–June 5, 2000 July 1–July 9, 2000 July 28–Sept. 5, 2000 Nov. 4–Nov. 12, 2000 Nov. 15–Dec. 3, 2000	...do.	

SESSIONS OF CONGRESS, 1st–113th CONGRESSES, 1789–2013—CONTINUED

[Closing date for this table was January 2, 2014.]

MEETING DATES OF CONGRESS: Pursuant to a resolution of the Confederation Congress in 1788, the Constitution went into effect on March 4, 1789. From then until the 20th amendment took effect in January 1934, the term of each Congress began on March 4th of each odd-numbered year; however, Article I, section 4, of the Constitution provided that ''The Congress shall assemble at least once in every Year, and such Meeting shall be on the first Monday in December, unless they shall by law appoint a different day.'' The Congress therefore convened regularly on the first Monday in December until the 20th amendment became effective, which changed the beginning of Congress's term as well as its convening date to January 3rd. So prior to 1934, a new Congress typically would not convene for regular business until 13 months after being elected. One effect of this was that the last session of each Congress was a ''lame duck'' session. After the 20th amendment, the time from the election to the beginning of Congress's term as well as when it convened was reduced to two months. Recognizing that the need might exist for Congress to meet at times other than the regularly scheduled convening date, Article II, section 3 of the Constitution provides that the President ''may, on extraordinary occasions, convene both Houses, or either of them''; hence these sessions occur only if convened by Presidential proclamation. Except as noted, these are separately numbered sessions of a Congress, and are marked by an E in the session column of the table. Until the 20th amendment was adopted, there were also times when special sessions of the Senate were convened, principally for confirming Cabinet and other executive nominations, and occasionally for the ratification of treaties or other executive business. These Senate sessions were also called by Presidential proclamation (typically by the outgoing President, although on occasion by incumbents as well) and are marked by an S in the session column. MEETING PLACES OF CONGRESS: Congress met for the first and second sessions of the First Congress (1789 and 1790) in New York City. From the third session of the First Congress through the first session of the Sixth Congress (1790 to 1800), Philadelphia was the meeting place. Congress has convened in Washington since the second session of the Sixth Congress (1800).

Congress	Session	Convening Date	Adjournment Date	Length in days [1]	Recesses [2]		President pro tempore of the Senate [3]	Speaker of the House of Representatives
					Senate	House of Representatives		
107th	1	Jan. 3, 2001	Dec. 20, 2001	352	Jan. 8–Jan. 20, 2001 Feb. 15–Feb. 26, 2001 Apr. 6–Apr. 23, 2001 May 26–June 5, 2001 June 29–July 9, 2001 Aug. 3–Sept. 4, 2001 Oct. 18–Oct. 23, 2001 Nov. 16–Nov. 27, 2001	Jan. 7–Jan. 19, 2001 Jan. 21–Jan 29, 2001 Feb. 1–Feb. 5, 2001 Feb. 15–Feb. 25, 2001 Apr. 5–Apr. 23, 2001 May 27–June 4, 2001 June 29–July 9, 2001 Aug. 3–Sept. 4, 2001 Oct. 18–Oct. 22, 2001 Nov. 20–Nov. 26, 2001	Robert C. Byrd, of West Virginia; [21] Strom Thurmond, of South Carolina; [21] Robert C. Byrd, of West Virginia. [21]	Do.
	2	Jan. 23, 2002	Nov. 22, 2002	304	Jan. 29–Feb. 4, 2002 Feb. 15–Feb. 25, 2002 Mar. 22–Apr. 8, 2002 May 23–June 3, 2002 June 28–July 8, 2002 Aug. 1–Sept. 3, 2002	Jan. 30–Feb. 3, 2002 Feb. 15–Feb. 25, 2002 Mar. 21–Apr. 8, 2002 May 25–June 3, 2002 June 29–July 7, 2002 July 28–Sept. 3, 2002	Robert C. Byrd, of West Virginia.	
108th	1	Jan. 7, 2003	Dec. 9, 2003	337	Feb. 14–Feb. 24, 2003 Apr. 11–Apr. 28, 2003 May 23–June 2, 2003 June 27–July 7, 2003 Aug. 1–Sept 2, 2003 Oct. 3–Oct. 14, 2003 Nov. 25–Dec. 9, 2003	Jan. 9–Jan. 26, 2003 Feb. 14–Feb. 24, 2003 Apr. 13–Apr. 28, 2003 May 24–June 1, 2003 June 28–July 6, 2003 July 30–Sept. 2, 2003 Nov. 26–Dec. 7, 2003	Ted Stevens, of Alaska	J. Dennis Hastert, of Illinois.

	2	Jan. 20, 2004	Dec. 8, 2004	324	Feb. 12–Feb. 23, 2004 Mar. 12–Mar. 22, 2004 Apr. 8–Apr. 19, 2004 May 21–June 1, 2004 June 9–June 14, 2004 June 25–July 6, 2004 July 22–Sept. 7, 2004 Oct. 11–Nov. 16, 2004 Nov. 24–Dec. 7, 2004	Feb. 12–Feb. 23, 2004 Apr. 3–Apr. 19, 2004 May 21–May 31, 2004 June 10–June 13, 2004 June 26–July 5, 2004 July 23–Sept. 6, 2004 Oct. 10–Nov. 15, 2004 Nov. 25–Dec. 5, 2004	...do.	
109th	1	Jan. 4, 2005	Dec. 22, 2005	353	Jan. 6–Jan. 20, 2005 Jan. 26–Jan. 31, 2005 Feb. 18–Feb. 28, 2005 Mar. 20–Apr. 4, 2005 Apr. 29–May 9, 2005 May 26–June 6, 2005 July 1–July 11, 2005 July 29–Sept. 1, 2005 Sept. 1–Sept. 6, 2005 Oct. 7–Oct. 17, 2005 Nov. 18–Dec. 12, 2005	Jan. 7–Jan. 19, 2005 Jan. 21–Jan. 24, 2005 Jan. 27–Jan. 31, 2005 Feb. 3–Feb. 7, 2005 Feb. 18–Feb. 28, 2005 Mar. 22–Apr. 4, 2005 May 27–June 6, 2005 July 1–July 8, 2005 July 30–Sept. 1, 2005 Oct. 8–Oct. 16, 2005 Nov. 19–Dec. 5, 2005	...do	Do.
	2	Jan. 3, 2006	Dec. 9, 2006	341	Jan. 3–Jan. 18, 2006 Feb. 17–Feb. 27, 2006 Mar. 16–Mar. 27, 2006 Apr. 7–Apr. 24, 2006 May 26–June 5, 2006 June 29–July 10, 2006 Aug. 4–Sept. 5, 2006 Sept. 30–Nov. 9, 2006 Nov. 16–Dec. 4, 2006	Jan. 4–Jan. 30, 2006 Feb. 2–Feb. 6, 2006 Feb. 9–Feb. 13, 2006 Feb. 17–Feb. 27, 2006 Mar. 17–Mar. 27, 2006 Apr. 7–Apr. 24, 2006 May 26–June 5, 2006 June 30–July 9, 2006 Aug. 3–Sept. 5, 2006 Oct. 1–Nov. 8, 2006 Nov. 16–Dec. 3, 2006	...do.	
110th	1	Jan. 4, 2007	Dec. 31, 2007	362	Feb. 17–Feb. 26, 2007 Mar. 29–Apr. 10, 2007 May 25–June 4, 2007 June 29–July 9, 2007 Aug. 3–Sept. 4, 2007 Oct. 5–Oct. 15, 2007	Jan. 25–Jan. 28, 2007 Feb. 1–Feb. 4, 2007 Feb. 17–Feb. 26, 2007 Mar. 31–Apr. 15, 2007 May 25–June 4, 2007 June 29–July 9, 2007 Aug. 6–Sept. 3, 2007 Nov. 16–Dec. 3, 2007	Robert C. Byrd, of West Virginia	Nancy Pelosi, of California.
	2	Jan. 3, 2008	Jan. 3, 2009	367	June 27–July 7, 2008	Jan. 4–Jan. 14, 2008 Jan. 24–Jan. 27, 2008 Jan. 30–Feb. 5, 2008 Mar. 15–Mar. 30, 2008 May 23–June 2, 2008 June 27–July 7, 2008 Aug. 2–Sept. 7, 2008 Oct. 4–Nov. 18, 2008 Nov. 21–Dec. 8, 2008 Dec. 11, 2008–Jan. 3, 2009	...do.	

SESSIONS OF CONGRESS, 1st–113th CONGRESSES, 1789–2013—CONTINUED

[Closing date for this table was January 2, 2014.]

MEETING DATES OF CONGRESS: Pursuant to a resolution of the Confederation Congress in 1788, the Constitution went into effect on March 4, 1789. From then until the 20th amendment took effect in January 1934, the term of each Congress began on March 4th of each odd-numbered year; however, Article I, section 4, of the Constitution provided that ''The Congress shall assemble at least once in every Year, and such Meeting shall be on the first Monday in December, unless they shall by law appoint a different day.'' The Congress therefore convened regularly on the first Monday in December until the 20th amendment became effective, which changed the beginning of Congress's term as well as its convening date to January 3rd. So prior to 1934, a new Congress typically would not convene for regular business until 13 months after being elected. One effect of this was that the last session of each Congress was a ''lame duck'' session. After the 20th amendment, the time from the election to the beginning of Congress's term as well as when it convened was reduced to two months. Recognizing that the need might exist for Congress to meet at times other than the regularly scheduled convening date, Article II, section 3 of the Constitution provides that the President ''may, on extraordinary occasions, convene both Houses, or either of them''; hence these sessions occur only if convened by Presidential proclamation. Except as noted, these are separately numbered sessions of a Congress, and are marked by an E in the session column of the table. Until the 20th amendment was adopted, there were also times when special sessions of the Senate were convened, principally for confirming Cabinet and other executive nominations, and occasionally for the ratification of treaties or other executive business. These Senate sessions were also called by Presidential proclamation (typically by the outgoing President, although on occasion by incumbents as well) and are marked by an S in the session column. MEETING PLACES OF CONGRESS: Congress met for the first and second sessions of the First Congress (1789 and 1790) in New York City. From the third session of the First Congress through the first session of the Sixth Congress (1790 to 1800), Philadelphia was the meeting place. Congress has convened in Washington since the second session of the Sixth Congress (1800).

Congress	Session	Convening Date	Adjournment Date	Length in days [1]	Recesses [2]		President pro tempore of the Senate [3]	Speaker of the House of Representatives
					Senate	House of Representatives		
111th	1	Jan. 6, 2009	Dec. 24, 2009	353	Apr. 2–Apr. 20, 2009 May 21–June 1, 2009 June 25–July 6, 2009 Nov. 10–Nov. 16, 2009 Nov. 21–Nov. 30, 2009	Jan. 29–Feb. 1, 2009 Feb. 5–Feb. 8, 2009 Feb. 14–Feb. 22, 2009 Apr. 3–Apr. 20, 2009 May 22–June 1, 2009 June 27–July 6, 2009 Aug. 1–Sept. 7, 2009 Nov. 8–Nov. 15, 2009 Nov. 20–Nov. 30, 2009	...do	Do.
	2	Jan. 5, 2010	Dec. 22, 2010	352	Feb. 11–Feb. 23, 2010 Mar. 26–Apr. 12, 2010 May 28–June 7, 2010 June 30–July 12, 2010 Aug. 5–Aug. 12, 2010 Aug. 12–Sept. 13, 2010 Nov. 19–Nov. 29, 2010	Jan. 6–Jan. 11, 2010 Feb. 10–Feb. 21, 2010 Mar. 26–Apr. 12, 2010 May 29–June 7, 2010 July 2–July 12, 2010 July 31–Aug. 8, 2010 Aug. 11–Sept. 13, 2010 Oct. 1–Nov. 14, 2010 Nov. 19–Nov. 28, 2010	Robert C. Byrd, of West Virginia; [22] Daniel K. Inouye, of Hawaii. [22]	
112th	1	Jan. 5, 2011	Dec. 30, 2011	360	Jan. 5 –Jan. 25, 2011 Feb. 17–Feb. 28, 2011 Mar. 17–Mar. 28, 2011 Apr. 14–May 2, 2011	Jan. 13–Jan. 17, 2011 Jan. 27–Feb. 7, 2011 Feb. 20–Feb. 27, 2011 Mar. 18–Mar. 28, 2011 Apr. 16–May 1, 2011 May 14–May 22, 2011	Daniel K. Inouye, of Hawaii	John A. Boehner, of Ohio.

Congress	Session	Convening date	Adjournment date	Length in days	Recesses (Senate)	Recesses (House)	President pro tempore of the Senate	Speaker of the House
	2	Jan. 3, 2012	Jan. 3, 2013	367	Aug. 3–Sept. 10, 2012	Mar. 31–Apr. 15, 2012 Apr. 28–May 6, 2012 June 30–July 8, 2012 Aug. 8–Sept. 9, 2012 Nov. 17–Nov. 26, 2012	Daniel K. Inouye, of Hawaii;[23] Patrick J. Leahy, of Vermont.[23]	
113th.	1	Jan. 3, 2013	Dec. 24, 2013	356	Jan. 4–Jan. 22, 2013 Feb. 15–Feb. 25, 2013 Mar. 22–Apr. 8, 2013 May 23–June 3, 2013 June 28–July 8, 2013 Aug. 2–Aug. 12, 2013 Aug. 12–Sept. 6, 2013	Jan. 5–Jan. 13, 2013 Feb. 16–Feb. 24, 2013 Mar. 26–Apr. 8, 2013 May 25–June 2, 2013 June 29–July 7, 2013 Aug. 3–Sept. 5, 2013 Oct. 31–Nov. 11, 2013 Nov. 23–Dec. 1, 2013 Dec. 27, 2013–Jan. 2, 2014	...do	Do.

[1] For the purposes of this table, a session's "length in days" is defined as the total number of calendar days from the convening date to the adjournment date, inclusive. It does not mean the actual number of days that Congress met during that session.

[2] For the purposes of this table, a "recess" is defined as a break in House or Senate proceedings of three or more days, excluding Sundays. According to Article I, section 5 of the U.S. Constitution, neither house may adjourn for more than three days without tne consent of the other.

[3] The election and role of the President pro tempore has evolved considerably over the Senate's history. "*Pro tempore* is Latin for 'for the time being'; thus, the post was conceived as a temporary presiding officer. In the eighteenth and nineteenth centuries, the Senate frequently elected several Presidents pro tempore during a single session. Since Vice Presidents presided routinely, the Senate thought it necessary to choose a President pro tempore only for the limited periods when the Vice President might be ill or otherwise absent." Since no provision was in place (until the 25th amendment was adopted in 1967) for replacing the Vice President if he died or resigned from office, or if he assumed the Presidency, the President pro tempore would continue under such circumstances to fill the duties of the chair until the next Vice President was elected. Since Mar. 12, 1890, however, Presidents pro tempore have served until "the Senate otherwise ordered." Since 1949, while still elected, the position has gone to the most senior member of the majority party (see footnote 19 for a minority party exception). To gain a more complete understanding of this position, see Robert C. Byrd's *The Senate 1789–1989: Addresses on the History of the United States Senate*, vol. 2, ch. 6 "The President Pro Tempore," pp. 167–183, from which the quotes in this footnote are taken. Also, a complete listing of the dates of election of the Presidents pro tempore is in vol. 4 of the Byrd series (*The Senate 1789–1989: Historical Statistics, 1789–1992*), table 6–2, pp. 647–653.

[4] Henry Clay resigned as Speaker on Jan. 19, 1814. He was succeeded by Langdon Cheves who was elected on that same day.

[5] Henry Clay resigned as Speaker on Oct. 28, 1820, after the sine die adjournment of the first session of the 16th Congress. He was succeeded by John W. Taylor who was elected at the beginning of the second session.

[6] Andrew Stevenson resigned as Speaker on June 2, 1834. He was succeeded by John Bell who was elected on that same day.

[7] Speaker Schuyler Colfax resigned as Speaker on the last day of the 40th Congress, Mar. 3, 1869, in preparation for becoming Vice President of the United States on the following day. Theodore M. Pomeroy was elected Speaker on Mar. 3, and served for only that one day.

[8] Speaker Michael C. Kerr died on Aug. 19, 1876, after the sine die adjournment of the first session of the 44th Congress. Samuel J. Randall was elected Speaker at the beginning of the second session.

[9] William P. Frye resigned as President pro tempore on Apr. 27, 1911.

[10] President pro tempore James P. Clarke died on Oct. 1, 1916, after the sine die adjournment of the first session of the 64th Congress. Willard Saulsbury was elected President pro tempore during the second session.

[11] Speaker Joseph W. Byrns died on June 4, 1936. He was succeeded by William B. Bankhead who was elected Speaker on that same day.

[12] Speaker William B. Bankhead died on Sept. 15, 1940. He was succeeded by Sam Rayburn who was elected Speaker on that same day.

[13] President pro tempore Key Pittman died on Nov. 10, 1940. He was succeeded by William H. King who was elected President pro tempore on Nov. 19, 1940.

[14] President pro tempore Pat Harrison died on June 22, 1941. He was succeeded by Carter Glass who was elected President pro tempore on July 10, 1941.

[15] President Harry S. Truman called the Congress into extraordinary session twice, both times during the 80th Congress. Each time Congress had essentially wrapped up its business for the year, but for technical reasons had not adjourned sine die, so in each case the extraordinary session is considered an extension of the regularly numbered session rather than a separately numbered one. The dates of these extraordinary sessions were Nov. 17 to Dec. 19, 1947, and July 26 to Aug. 7, 1948.

[16] Speaker Sam Rayburn died on Nov. 16, 1961, after the sine die adjournment of the first session of the 87th Congress. John W. McCormack was elected Speaker at the beginning of the second session.

[17] President pro tempore Richard B. Russell died on Jan. 21, 1971. He was succeeded by Allen J. Ellender who was elected to that position on Jan. 22, 1971.

[18] President pro tempore Allen J. Ellender died on July 27, 1972. He was succeeded by James O. Eastland who was elected President pro tempore on July 28, 1972.

[19] Milton Young was elected President pro tempore for one day, Dec. 5, 1980, which was at the end of his 36-year career in the Senate. He was a Republican, which was the minority party at that time. Warren G. Magnuson resumed the position of President pro tempore on Dec. 6, 1980.

[20] James C. Wright, Jr., resigned as Speaker on June 6, 1989. He was succeeded by Thomas S. Foley who was elected on that same day.

[21] The 2000 election resulted in an even split in the Senate between Republicans and Democrats. From the date the 107th Congress convened on Jan. 3, 2001, until Inauguration Day on Jan. 20, 2001, Vice President Albert Gore's tie breaking vote resulted in a Democratic majority, hence Robert C. Byrd served as President pro tempore during this brief period. When Vice President Richard B. Cheney took office on Jan. 20, the Republicans became the majority party, and Strom Thurmond was elected President pro tempore. On June 6, 2001, Republican Senator James Jeffords became an Independent, creating a Democratic majority, and Robert C. Byrd was elected President pro tempore on that day.

[22] President pro tempore Robert C. Byrd died on June 28, 2010. He was succeeded by Daniel K. Inouye who was elected President pro tempore on that same day.

[23] President pro tempore Daniel K. Inouye died on December 17, 2012. He was succeeded by Patrick J. Leahy who was elected President pro tempore on that same day.

CEREMONIAL MEETINGS OF CONGRESS

The following ceremonial meetings of Congress occurred on the following dates, at the designated locations, and for the reasons indicated. Please note that Congress was not in session on these occasions.

-July 16, 1987, 100th Congress, Philadelphia, Pennsylvania, Independence Hall and Congress Hall—In honor of the bicentennial of the Constitution, and in commemoration of the Great Compromise of the Constitutional Convention which was agreed to on July 16, 1787.

-September 6, 2002, 107th Congress, New York City, New York, Federal Hall—In remembrance of the victims and heroes of September 11, 2001, and in recognition of the courage and spirit of the City of New York.

JOINT SESSIONS AND MEETINGS, ADDRESSES TO THE SENATE OR THE HOUSE, AND INAUGURATIONS

1st–113th CONGRESSES, 1789–2013 [1]

The parliamentary difference between a joint session and a joint meeting has evolved over time. In recent years the distinctions have become clearer: a joint session is more formal, and occurs upon the adoption of a concurrent resolution; a joint meeting occurs when each body adopts a unanimous consent agreement to recess to meet with the other legislative body. Joint sessions typically are held to hear an address from the President of the United States or to count electoral votes. Joint meetings typically are held to hear an address from a foreign dignitary or visitors other than the President.

The Speaker of the House of Representatives usually presides over joint sessions and joint meetings; however, the President of the Senate does preside over joint sessions where the electoral votes are counted, as required by the Constitution.

In the earliest years of the Republic, 1789 and 1790, when the national legislature met in New York City, joint gatherings were held in the Senate Chamber in Federal Hall. In Philadelphia, when the legislature met in Congress Hall, such meetings were held in the Senate Chamber, 1790–1793, and in the Hall of the House of Representatives, 1794–1799. Once the Congress moved to the Capitol in Washington in 1800, the Senate Chamber again was used for joint gatherings through 1805. Since 1809, with few exceptions, joint sessions and joint meetings have occurred in the Hall of the House.

Presidential messages on the state of the Union were originally known as the ''Annual Message,'' but since the 80th Congress, in 1947, have been called the ''State of the Union Address.'' After President John Adams's Annual Message on November 22, 1800, these addresses were read by clerks to the individual bodies until President Woodrow Wilson resumed the practice of delivering them to joint sessions on December 2, 1913.

In some instances more than one joint gathering has occurred on the same day. For example, on January 6, 1941, Congress met in joint session to count electoral votes for President and Vice President, and then met again in joint session to receive President Franklin Delano Roosevelt's Annual Message.

Whereas in more recent decades, foreign dignitaries invited to speak before Congress have typically done so at joint meetings, in earlier times (and with several notable exceptions), such visitors were received by the Senate and the House separately, or by one or the other singly, a tradition begun with the visit of General Lafayette of France in 1824. At that time a joint committee decided that each body would honor Lafayette separately, establishing the precedent. (See footnote 7 for more details.) Not all such occasions included formal addresses by such dignitaries (e.g., Lafayette's reception by the Senate in their chamber, at which he did not speak before they adjourned to greet him), hence the ''occasions'' listed in the third column of the table include not only addresses, but also remarks (defined as brief greetings or off-the-cuff comments often requested of the visitor at the last minute) and receptions. Relatively few foreign dignitaries were received by Congress before World War I.

Congress has hosted inaugurations since the first occasion in 1789. They always have been formal joint gatherings, and sometimes they also were joint sessions. Inaugurations were joint sessions when both houses of Congress were in session, and they processed to the ceremony as part of the business of the day. In many cases, however, one or both houses were not in session or were in recess at the time of the ceremony. In this table, inaugurations that were not joint sessions are listed in the second column. Those that were joint sessions are so identified and described in the third column.

JOINT SESSIONS AND MEETINGS, ADDRESSES TO THE SENATE OR THE HOUSE, AND INAUGURATIONS

[See notes at end of table]

Congress & Date	Type	Occasion, topic, or inaugural location	Name and position of dignitary (where applicable)
		NEW YORK CITY	
1st CONGRESS			
Apr. 6, 1789	Joint session	Counting electoral votes	N.A.
Apr. 30, 1789	...do	Inauguration and church service [2]	President George Washington; Right Reverend Samuel Provoost, Senate-appointed Chaplain.
Jan. 8, 1790	...do	Annual Message	President George Washington.
		PHILADELPHIA	
Dec. 8, 1790	...do	...do	Do.
2d CONGRESS			
Oct. 25, 1791	...do	...do	Do.
Nov. 6, 1792	...do	...do	Do.
Feb. 13, 1793	...do	Counting electoral votes	N.A.
3d CONGRESS			
Mar. 4, 1793	Inauguration	Senate Chamber	President George Washington.
Dec. 3, 1793	Joint session	Annual Message	Do.
Nov. 19, 1794	...do	...do	Do.
4th CONGRESS			
Dec. 8, 1795	...do	...do	Do.
Dec. 7, 1796	...do	...do	Do.
Feb. 8, 1797	...do	Counting electoral votes	N.A.
5th CONGRESS			
Mar. 4, 1797	Inauguration	Hall of the House	President John Adams.
May 16, 1797	Joint session	Relations with France	Do.
Nov. 23, 1797	...do	Annual Message	Do.
Dec. 8, 1798	...do	...do	Do.
6th CONGRESS			
Dec. 3, 1799	...do	...do	Do.
Dec. 26, 1799	...do	Funeral procession and oration in memory of George Washington.[3]	Representative Henry Lee.
		WASHINGTON	
Nov. 22, 1800	...do	Annual Message	President John Adams.
Feb. 11, 1801	...do	Counting electoral votes [4]	N.A.
7th CONGRESS			
Mar. 4, 1801	Inauguration	Senate Chamber	President Thomas Jefferson.
8th CONGRESS			
Feb. 13, 1805	Joint session	Counting electoral votes	N.A.
9th CONGRESS			
Mar. 4, 1805	Inauguration	Senate Chamber	President Thomas Jefferson.
10th CONGRESS			
Feb. 8, 1809	Joint session	Counting electoral votes	N.A.
11th CONGRESS			
Mar. 4, 1809	Inauguration	Hall of the House	President James Madison.
12th CONGRESS			
Feb. 10, 1813	Joint session	Counting electoral votes	N.A.
13th CONGRESS			
Mar. 4, 1813	Inauguration	Hall of the House	President James Madison.
14th CONGRESS			
Feb. 12, 1817	Joint session	Counting electoral votes [5]	N.A.
15th CONGRESS			
Mar. 4, 1817	Inauguration	In front of Brick Capitol	President James Monroe.
16th CONGRESS			
Feb. 14, 1821	Joint session	Counting electoral votes [6]	N.A.
17th CONGRESS			
Mar. 5, 1821	Inauguration	Hall of the House	President James Monroe.
18th CONGRESS			
Dec. 9, 1824	Senate	Reception	General Gilbert du Motier, Marquis de Lafayette, of France.

JOINT SESSIONS AND MEETINGS, ADDRESSES TO THE SENATE OR THE HOUSE, AND INAUGURATIONS—CONTINUED

[See notes at end of table]

Congress & Date	Type	Occasion, topic, or inaugural location	Name and position of dignitary (where applicable)
Dec. 10, 1824	House[7]	Address	Speaker Henry Clay; General Gilbert du Motier, Marquis de Lafayette, of France.
Feb. 9, 1825	Joint session	Counting electoral votes[8]	N.A.
19th CONGRESS			
Mar. 4, 1825	Inauguration	Hall of the House	President John Quincy Adams.
20th CONGRESS			
Feb. 11, 1829	Joint session	Counting electoral votes	N.A.
21st CONGRESS			
Mar. 4, 1829	Inauguration	East Portico[9]	President Andrew Jackson.
22d CONGRESS			
Feb. 13, 1833	Joint session	Counting electoral votes	N.A.
23d CONGRESS			
Mar. 4, 1833	Inauguration	Hall of the House[10]	President Andrew Jackson.
Dec. 31, 1834	Joint session	Lafayette eulogy	Representative and former President John Quincy Adams; ceremony attended by President Andrew Jackson.
24th CONGRESS			
Feb. 8, 1837	...do	Counting electoral votes	N.A.
25th CONGRESS			
Mar. 4, 1837	Inauguration	East Portico	President Martin Van Buren.
26th CONGRESS			
Feb. 10, 1841	Joint session	Counting electoral votes	N.A.
27th CONGRESS			
Mar. 4, 1841	Inauguration	East Portico	President William Henry Harrison.
28th CONGRESS			
Feb. 12, 1845	Joint session	Counting electoral votes	N.A.
29th CONGRESS			
Mar. 4, 1845	Inauguration	East Portico	President James Knox Polk.
30th CONGRESS			
Feb. 14, 1849	Joint session	Counting electoral votes	N.A.
31st CONGRESS			
Mar. 5, 1849	Inauguration	East Portico	President Zachary Taylor.
July 10, 1850	Joint session	Oath of office to President Millard Fillmore.[11]	N.A.
32d CONGRESS			
Jan. 5, 1852	Senate	Reception	Louis Kossuth, exiled Governor of Hungary.
Jan. 7, 1852	House	Remarks and Reception	Do.
Feb. 9, 1853	Joint session	Counting electoral votes	N.A.
33d CONGRESS			
Mar. 4, 1853	Inauguration	East Portico	President Franklin Pierce.
34th CONGRESS			
Feb. 11, 1857	Joint session	Counting electoral votes	N.A.
35th CONGRESS			
Mar. 4, 1857	Inauguration	East Portico	President James Buchanan.
36th CONGRESS			
Feb. 13, 1861	Joint session	Counting electoral votes	N.A.
37th CONGRESS			
Mar. 4, 1861	Inauguration	East Portico	President Abraham Lincoln.
Feb. 22, 1862	Joint session	Reading of Washington's farewell address.	John W. Forney, Secretary of the Senate.
38th CONGRESS			
Feb. 8, 1865	...do	Counting electoral votes	N.A.
39th CONGRESS			
Mar. 4, 1865	Inauguration	East Portico	President Abraham Lincoln.
Feb. 12, 1866	Joint session	Memorial to Abraham Lincoln	George Bancroft, historian; ceremony attended by President Andrew Johnson.

JOINT SESSIONS AND MEETINGS, ADDRESSES TO THE SENATE OR THE HOUSE, AND INAUGURATIONS—CONTINUED

[See notes at end of table]

Congress & Date	Type	Occasion, topic, or inaugural location	Name and position of dignitary (where applicable)
40th CONGRESS			
June 9, 1868	House	Address	Anson Burlingame, Envoy to the U.S. from China, and former Representative.
Feb. 10, 1869	Joint session	Counting electoral votes	N.A.
41st CONGRESS			
Mar. 4, 1869	Inauguration	East Portico	President Ulysses S. Grant.
42d CONGRESS			
Mar. 6, 1872	House	Address	Tomomi Iwakura, Ambassador from Japan.
Feb. 12, 1873	Joint session	Counting electoral votes [12]	N.A.
43d CONGRESS			
Mar. 4, 1873	Inauguration	East Portico	President Ulysses S. Grant.
Dec. 18, 1874	Joint meeting	Reception and Remarks	Speaker James G. Blaine; David Kalakaua, King of the Hawaiian Islands.[13]
44th CONGRESS			
Feb. 1, 1877 Feb. 10, 1877 Feb. 12, 1877 Feb. 19, 1877 Feb. 20, 1877 Feb. 21, 1877 Feb. 24, 1877 Feb. 26, 1877 Feb. 28, 1877 Mar. 1, 1877 Mar. 2, 1877	Joint session	Counting electoral votes [14]	N.A.
45th CONGRESS			
Mar. 5, 1877	Inauguration	East Portico	President Rutherford B. Hayes.
46th CONGRESS			
Feb. 2, 1880	House	Address	Charles Stewart Parnell, member of Parliament from Ireland.
Feb. 9, 1881	Joint session	Counting electoral votes	N.A.
47th CONGRESS			
Mar. 4, 1881	Inauguration	East Portico	President James A. Garfield.
Feb. 27, 1882	Joint session	Memorial to James A. Garfield	James G. Blaine, former Speaker, Senator, and Secretary of State; ceremony attended by President Chester A. Arthur.
48th CONGRESS			
Feb. 11, 1885	...do	Counting electoral votes	N.A.
Feb. 21, 1885	...do	Completion of Washington Monument	Representative John D. Long; Representative-elect John W. Daniel,[15] ceremony attended by President Chester A. Arthur.
49th CONGRESS			
Mar. 4, 1885	Inauguration	East Portico	President Grover Cleveland.
50th CONGRESS			
Feb. 13, 1889	Joint session	Counting electoral votes	N.A.
51st CONGRESS			
Mar. 4, 1889	Inauguration	East Portico	President Benjamin Harrison.
Dec. 11, 1889	Joint session	Centennial of George Washington's first inauguration.	Melville W. Fuller, Chief Justice of the United States; ceremony attended by President Benjamin Harrison.
52d CONGRESS			
Feb. 8, 1893	...do	Counting electoral votes	N.A.
53d CONGRESS			
Mar. 4, 1893	Inauguration	East Portico	President Grover Cleveland.
54th CONGRESS			
Feb. 10, 1897	Joint session	Counting electoral votes	N.A.
55th CONGRESS			
Mar. 4, 1897	Inauguration	In front of original Senate Wing of Capitol.	President William McKinley.

JOINT SESSIONS AND MEETINGS, ADDRESSES TO THE SENATE OR THE HOUSE, AND INAUGURATIONS—CONTINUED

[See notes at end of table]

Congress & Date	Type	Occasion, topic, or inaugural location	Name and position of dignitary (where applicable)
56th CONGRESS			
Dec. 12, 1900	Joint meeting	Centennial of the Capital City	Representatives James D. Richardson and Sereno E. Payne, and Senator George F. Hoar; ceremony attended by President William McKinley.
Feb. 13, 1901	Joint session	Counting electoral votes	N.A.
57th CONGRESS			
Mar. 4, 1901	Inauguration	East Portico	President William McKinley.
Feb. 27, 1902	Joint session	Memorial to William McKinley	John Hay, Secretary of State; ceremony attended by President Theodore Roosevelt and Prince Henry of Prussia.
58th CONGRESS			
Feb. 8, 1905	...do	Counting electoral votes	N.A.
59th CONGRESS			
Mar. 4, 1905	Inauguration	East Portico	President Theodore Roosevelt.
60th CONGRESS			
Feb. 10, 1909	Joint session	Counting electoral votes	N.A.
61st CONGRESS			
Mar. 4, 1909	Inauguration	Senate Chamber [16]	President William Howard Taft.
Feb. 9, 1911	House	Address	Count Albert Apponyi, Minister of Education from Hungary.
62d CONGRESS			
Feb. 12, 1913	Joint session	Counting electoral votes	N.A.
Feb. 15, 1913	...do	Memorial for Vice President James S. Sherman.[17]	Senators Elihu Root, Thomas S. Martin, Jacob H. Gallinger, John R. Thornton, Henry Cabot Lodge, John W. Kern, Robert M. LaFollette, John Sharp Williams, Charles Curtis, Albert B. Cummins, George T. Oliver, James A. O'Gorman; Speaker Champ Clark; President William Howard Taft.
63d CONGRESS			
Mar. 4, 1913	Inauguration	East Portico	President Woodrow Wilson.
Apr. 8, 1913	Joint session	Tariff message	Do.
June 23, 1913	...do	Currency and bank reform message	Do.
Aug. 27, 1913	...do	Mexican affairs message	Do.
Dec. 2, 1913	...do	Annual Message	Do.
Jan. 20, 1914	...do	Trusts message	Do.
Mar. 5, 1914	...do	Panama Canal tolls	Do.
Apr. 20, 1914	...do	Mexico message	Do.
Sept. 4, 1914	...do	War tax message	Do.
Dec. 8, 1914	...do	Annual Message	Do.
64th CONGRESS			
Dec. 7, 1915	...do	...do	Do.
Aug. 29, 1916	...do	Railroad message (labor-management dispute).	Do.
Dec. 5, 1916	...do	Annual Message	Do.
Jan. 22, 1917	Senate	Planning ahead for peace	Do.
Feb. 3, 1917	Joint session	Severing diplomatic relations with Germany.	Do.
Feb. 14, 1917	...do	Counting electoral votes	N.A.
Feb. 26, 1917	...do	Arming of merchant ships	President Woodrow Wilson.
65th CONGRESS			
Mar. 5, 1917	Inauguration	East Portico	Do.
Apr. 2, 1917	Joint session	War with Germany	Do.
May 1, 1917	Senate	Address	René Raphaël Viviani, Minister of Justice from France; Jules Jusserand, Ambassador from France; address attended by Marshal Joseph Jacques Césaire Joffre, member of French Commission to U.S.
May 3, 1917	House	...do	Do.
May 5, 1917	...do	...do	Arthur James Balfour, British Secretary of State for Foreign Affairs.
May 8, 1917	Senate	...do	Do.
May 31, 1917	...do	...do	Ferdinando di'Savoia, Prince of Udine, Head of Italian Mission to U.S.
June 2, 1917	House	...do	Ferdinando di'Savoia, Prince of Udine, Head of Italian Mission to U.S.; Guglielmo Marconi, member of Italian Mission to U.S.

JOINT SESSIONS AND MEETINGS, ADDRESSES TO THE SENATE OR THE HOUSE, AND INAUGURATIONS—CONTINUED

[See notes at end of table]

Congress & Date	Type	Occasion, topic, or inaugural location	Name and position of dignitary (where applicable)
June 22, 1917	Senate	Address	Baron Moncheur, Chief of Political Bureau of Belgian Foreign Office at Havre.
June 23, 1917	House	...do	Boris Bakhmetieff, Ambassador from Russia.[18]
June 26, 1917	Senate	...do	Do.
June 27, 1917	House	...do	Baron Moncheur, Chief of Political Bureau of Belgian Foreign Office at Havre.
Aug. 30, 1917	Senate	...do	Kikujirō Ishii, Ambassador from Japan.
Sept. 5, 1917	House	...do	Do.
Dec. 4, 1917	Joint session	Annual Message/War with Austria-Hungary.	President Woodrow Wilson.
Jan. 4, 1918	...do	Federal operation of transportation systems.	Do.
Jan. 5, 1918	Senate	Address	Milenko Vesnic, Head of Serbian War Mission.
Jan. 8, 1918	House	...do	Do.
Do	Joint session	Program for world's peace	President Woodrow Wilson.
Feb. 11, 1918	...do	Peace message	Do.
May 27, 1918	...do	War finance message	Do.
Sept. 24, 1918	Senate	Address and Reception[19]	Jules Jusserand, Ambassador from France; Vice President Thomas R. Marshall.
Sept. 30 1918	...do	Support of woman suffrage	President Woodrow Wilson.
Nov. 11, 1918	Joint session	Terms of armistice signed by Germany	Do.
Dec. 2, 1918	...do	Annual Message	Do.
Feb. 9, 1919	...do	Memorial to Theodore Roosevelt	Senator Henry Cabot Lodge, Sr.; ceremony attended by former President William Howard Taft.
66th CONGRESS			
June 23, 1919	Senate	Address	Epitácio da Silva Pessoa, President-elect of Brazil.
July 10, 1919	...do	Versailles Treaty	President Woodrow Wilson.
Aug. 8, 1919	Joint session	Cost of living message	Do.
Sept. 18, 1919	...do	Address	President pro tempore Albert B. Cummins; Speaker Frederick H. Gillett; Representative and former Speaker Champ Clark; General John J. Pershing.
Oct. 28, 1919	Senate	...do	Albert I, King of the Belgians.
Do	House	...do	Do.
Feb. 9, 1921	Joint session	Counting electoral votes	N.A.
67th CONGRESS			
Mar. 4, 1921	Inauguration	East Portico	President Warren G. Harding.
Apr. 12, 1921	Joint session	Federal problem message	Do.
July 12, 1921	Senate	Adjusted compensation for veterans of the World War[20].	Do.
Dec. 6, 1921	Joint session	Annual Message	Do.
Feb. 28, 1922	...do	Maintenance of the merchant marine	Do.
Aug. 18, 1922	...do	Coal and railroad message	Do.
Nov. 21, 1922	...do	Promotion of the American merchant marine.	Do.
Dec. 8, 1922	...do	Annual Message[21]	Do.
Feb. 7, 1923	...do	British debt due to the United States	Do.
68th CONGRESS			
Dec. 6, 1923	...do	Annual Message	President Calvin Coolidge.
Feb. 27, 1924	...do	Memorial to Warren G. Harding	Charles Evans Hughes, Secretary of State; ceremony attended by President Calvin Coolidge.
Dec. 15, 1924	...do	Memorial to Woodrow Wilson	Dr. Edwin Anderson Alderman, President of the University of Virginia; ceremony attended by President Calvin Coolidge.
Feb. 11, 1925	...do	Counting electoral votes	N.A.
69th CONGRESS			
Mar. 4, 1925	Inauguration	East Portico	President Calvin Coolidge.
Feb. 22, 1927	Joint session	George Washington birthday message	Do.
70th CONGRESS			
Jan. 25, 1928	House	Reception and Address	William Thomas Cosgrave, President of Executive Council of Ireland.
Feb. 13, 1929	Joint session	Counting electoral votes	N.A.
71st CONGRESS			
Mar. 4, 1929	Inauguration	East Portico	President Herbert Hoover.

JOINT SESSIONS AND MEETINGS, ADDRESSES TO THE SENATE OR THE HOUSE, AND INAUGURATIONS—CONTINUED

[See notes at end of table]

Congress & Date	Type	Occasion, topic, or inaugural location	Name and position of dignitary (where applicable)
Oct. 7, 1929	Senate	Address	James Ramsay MacDonald, Prime Minister of the United Kingdom.
Jan. 13, 1930	...do	Reception	Jan Christiaan Smuts, former Prime Minister of South Africa.
72d CONGRESS			
Feb. 22, 1932	Joint session	Bicentennial of George Washington's birth.	President Herbert Hoover.
May 31, 1932	Senate	Emergency character of economic situation in U.S.	Do.
Feb. 6, 1933	Joint meeting	Memorial to Calvin Coolidge	Arthur Prentice Rugg, Chief Justice of the Supreme Judicial Court of Massachusetts; ceremony attended by President Herbert Hoover.
Feb. 8, 1933	Joint session	Counting electoral votes	N.A.
73d CONGRESS			
Mar. 4, 1933	Inauguration	East Portico	President Franklin Delano Roosevelt.
Jan. 3, 1934	Joint session	Annual Message	Do.
May 20, 1934	...do	100th anniversary, death of Lafayette	André de Laboulaye, Ambassador of France; President Franklin Delano Roosevelt; ceremony attended by Count de Chambrun, great-grandson of Lafayette.
74th CONGRESS			
Jan. 4, 1935	...do	Annual Message	President Franklin Delano Roosevelt.
May 22, 1935	...do	Veto message	Do.
Jan. 3, 1936	...do	Annual Message	Do.
75th CONGRESS			
Jan. 6, 1937	...do	Counting electoral votes	N.A.
Do	...do	Annual Message	President Franklin Delano Roosevelt.
Jan. 20, 1937	Inauguration	East Portico	President Franklin Delano Roosevelt; Vice President John Nance Garner.[22]
Apr. 1, 1937	Senate	Address	John Buchan, Lord Tweedsmuir, Governor General of Canada.
Do	House	...do	Do.
Jan. 3, 1938	Joint session	Annual Message	President Franklin Delano Roosevelt.
76th CONGRESS			
Jan. 4, 1939	...do	...do	Do.
Mar. 4, 1939	...do	Sesquicentennial of the 1st Congress	Do.
May 8, 1939	Senate	Address	Anastasio Somoza Garcia, President of Nicaragua.
Do	House	...do	Do.
June 9, 1939	Joint meeting	Reception[23]	George VI and Elizabeth, King and Queen of the United Kingdom.
Sept. 21, 1939	Joint session	Neutrality address	President Franklin Delano Roosevelt.
Jan. 3, 1940	...do	Annual Message	Do.
May 16, 1940	...do	National defense message	Do.
77th CONGRESS			
Jan. 6, 1941	...do	Counting electoral votes	N.A.
Do	...do	Annual Message	President Franklin Delano Roosevelt.
Jan. 20, 1941	...do	Inauguration, East Portico	President Franklin Delano Roosevelt; Vice President Henry A. Wallace.
Dec. 8, 1941	...do	War with Japan	President Franklin Delano Roosevelt.
Dec. 26, 1941	Joint meeting[24]	Address	Winston Churchill, Prime Minister of the United Kingdom.
Jan. 6, 1942	Joint session	Annual Message	President Franklin Delano Roosevelt.
May 11, 1942	Senate	Address	Manuel Prado, President of Peru.
Do	House	...do	Do.
June 2, 1942	...do	...do	Manuel Luis Quezon, President of the Philippines.[25]
June 4, 1942	Senate	...do	Do.
June 15, 1942	...do	...do	George II, King of Greece.[26]
Do	House	...do	Do.
June 25, 1942	Senate	...do	Peter II, King of Yugoslavia.[26]
Do	House	...do	Do.
Aug. 6, 1942	Senate[27]	...do	Wilhelmina, Queen of the Netherlands.[26]
Nov. 24, 1942	House	...do	Carlos Arroyo del Río, President of Ecuador.
Nov. 25, 1942	Senate	...do	Do.
Dec. 10, 1942	House	...do	Fulgencio Batista, President of Cuba.
78th CONGRESS			
Jan. 7, 1943	Joint session	Annual Message	President Franklin Delano Roosevelt.
Feb. 18, 1943	Senate	Remarks	Madame Chiang Kai-shek, of China.
Do	House	Address	Do.

JOINT SESSIONS AND MEETINGS, ADDRESSES TO THE SENATE OR THE HOUSE, AND INAUGURATIONS—CONTINUED

[See notes at end of table]

Congress & Date	Type	Occasion, topic, or inaugural location	Name and position of dignitary (where applicable)
May 6, 1943	Senate	Address	Enrique Peñaranda, President of Bolivia.
Do	House	...do	Do.
May 13, 1943	Senate	...do	Edvard Beneš, President of Czechoslovakia.[26]
Do	House	...do	Do.
May 19, 1943	Joint meeting	...do	Winston Churchill, Prime Minister of the United Kingdom.
May 27, 1943	Senate	Remarks	Edwin Barclay, President of Liberia.
Do	House	Address	Do.
June 10, 1943	Senate	...do	President Hininio Moriñigo M., President of Paraguay.
Do	House	...do	Do.
Oct. 15, 1943	Senate	...do	Elie Lescot, President of Haiti.
Nov. 18, 1943	Joint meeting	Moscow Conference	Cordell Hull, Secretary of State.
Jan. 20, 1944	Senate	Address	Isaías Medina Angarita, President of Venezuela.
Do	House	...do	Do.
79th CONGRESS			
Jan. 6, 1945	Joint session	Counting electoral votes	N.A.
Do	...do	Annual Message	President Roosevelt was not present. His message was read before the Joint Session of Congress.
Jan. 20, 1945	Inauguration	South Portico, The White House[28]	President Franklin Delano Roosevelt; Vice President Harry S. Truman.
Mar. 1, 1945	Joint session	Yalta Conference	President Franklin Delano Roosevelt.
Apr. 16, 1945	...do	Prosecution of the War	President Harry S. Truman.
May 21, 1945	...do	Bestowal of Congressional Medal of Honor on Tech. Sgt. Jake William Lindsey.	General George C. Marshall, Chief of Staff, U.S. Army; President Harry S. Truman.
June 18, 1945	Joint meeting	Address	General Dwight D. Eisenhower, Supreme Commander, Allied Expeditionary Force.
July 2, 1945	Senate	United Nations Charter	President Harry S. Truman.
Oct. 5, 1945	Joint meeting	Address	Admiral Chester W. Nimitz, Commander-in-Chief, Pacific Fleet.
Oct. 23, 1945	Joint session	Universal military training message	President Harry S. Truman.
Nov. 13, 1945	Joint meeting	Address	Clement R. Attlee, Prime Minister of the United Kingdom.
May 25, 1946	Joint session	Railroad strike message	President Harry S. Truman.
July 1, 1946	...do	Memorial to Franklin Delano Roosevelt	John Winant, U.S. Representative on the Economic and Social Council of the United Nations; ceremony attended by President Harry S. Truman and Mrs. Franklin Delano Roosevelt.
80th CONGRESS			
Jan. 6, 1947	...do	State of the Union Address[29]	President Harry S. Truman.
Mar. 12, 1947	...do	Greek-Turkish aid policy	Do.
May 1, 1947	Joint meeting	Address	Miguel Alemán, President of Mexico.
Nov. 17, 1947	Joint session	Aid to Europe message	President Harry S. Truman.
Jan. 7, 1948	...do	State of the Union Address	Do.
Mar. 17, 1948	...do	National security and conditions in Europe.	Do.
Apr. 19, 1948	...do	50th anniversary, liberation of Cuba	President Harry S. Truman; Guillermo Belt, Ambassador of Cuba.
July 27, 1948	...do	Inflation, housing, and civil rights	President Harry S. Truman.
81st CONGRESS			
Jan. 5, 1949	...do	State of the Union Address	Do.
Jan. 6, 1949	...do	Counting electoral votes	N.A.
Jan. 20, 1949	...do	Inauguration, East Portico	President Harry S. Truman; Vice President Alben W. Barkley.
May 17, 1949	House	Reception	General Lucius D. Clay.
Do	Senate	Address	Do.
May 19, 1949	Joint meeting	...do	Eurico Gaspar Dutra, President of Brazil.
Aug. 9, 1949	House	...do	Elpidio Quirino, President of the Philippines.
Do	Senate	...do	Do.
Oct. 13, 1949	...do	...do	Jawaharlal Nehru, Prime Minister of India.
Do	House	...do	Do.
Jan. 4, 1950	Joint session	State of the Union Address	President Harry S. Truman.
Apr. 13, 1950	Senate	Address	Gabriel González-Videla, President of Chile.
May 4, 1950	...do	...do	Liaquat Ali Khan, Prime Minister of Pakistan.
Do	House	...do	Do.
May 31, 1950	Joint meeting	...do	Dean Acheson, Secretary of State.

JOINT SESSIONS AND MEETINGS, ADDRESSES TO THE SENATE OR THE HOUSE, AND INAUGURATIONS—CONTINUED

[See notes at end of table]

Congress & Date	Type	Occasion, topic, or inaugural location	Name and position of dignitary (where applicable)
July 28, 1950	Senate	Address	Chōjirō Kuriyama, member of Japanese Diet.
July 31, 1950	House	...do	Tokutarō Kitamura, member of Japanese Diet.
Aug. 1, 1950	...do	...do	Robert Gordon Menzies, Prime Minister of Australia.
Do	Senate	...do	Do.
82d CONGRESS			
Jan. 8, 1951	Joint session	State of the Union Address	President Harry S. Truman.
Feb. 1, 1951	Joint meeting [30]	North Atlantic Treaty Organization	General Dwight D. Eisenhower.
Apr. 2, 1951	...do	Address	Vincent Auriol, President of France.
Apr. 19, 1951	...do	Return from Pacific Command	General Douglas MacArthur.
June 21, 1951	...do	Address	Galo Plaza, President of Ecuador.
July 2, 1951	Senate	Addresses	Tadao Kuraishi, and Aisuke Okamoto, members of Japanese Diet.
Aug. 23, 1951	...do	Address	Zentarō Kosaka, member of Japanese Diet.
Sept. 24, 1951	Joint meeting	...do	Alcide de Gasperi, Prime Minister of Italy.
Jan. 9, 1952	Joint session	State of the Union Address	President Harry S. Truman.
Jan. 17, 1952	Joint meeting	Address	Winston Churchill, Prime Minister of the United Kingdom.
Apr. 3, 1952	...do	...do	Juliana, Queen of the Netherlands.
May 22, 1952	...do	Korea	General Matthew B. Ridgway.
June 10, 1952	Joint session	Steel industry dispute	President Harry S. Truman.
83d CONGRESS			
Jan. 6, 1953	...do	Counting electoral votes	N.A.
Jan. 20, 1953	...do	Inauguration, East Portico	President Dwight D. Eisenhower; Vice President Richard M. Nixon.
Feb. 2, 1953	...do	State of the Union Address	President Dwight D. Eisenhower.
Jan. 7, 1954	...do	...do	Do.
Jan. 29, 1954	Joint meeting	Address	Celal Bayar, President of Turkey.
May 4, 1954	...do	...do	Vincent Massey, Governor General of Canada.
May 28, 1954	...do	...do	Haile Selassie I, Emperor of Ethiopia.
July 28, 1954	...do	...do	Syngman Rhee, President of South Korea.
Nov. 12, 1954	Senate	Remarks	Shigeru Yoshida, Prime Minister of Japan.
Nov. 17, 1954	...do	Address [31]	Sarvepalli Radhakrishnan, Vice President of India.
Nov. 18, 1954	...do	Remarks	Pierre Mendès-France, Premier of France.
84th CONGRESS			
Jan. 6, 1955	Joint session	State of the Union Address	President Dwight D. Eisenhower.
Jan. 27, 1955	Joint meeting	Address	Paul E. Magliore, President of Haiti.
Mar. 16, 1955	Senate	...do	Robert Gordon Menzies, Prime Minister of Australia.
Do	House	...do	Do.
Mar. 30, 1955	Senate	...do	Mario Scelba, Prime Minister of Italy.
Do	House	...do	Do.
May 4, 1955	Senate	...do	P. Phibunsongkhram, Prime Minister of Thailand.
Do	House	...do	Do.
June 30, 1955	Senate	...do	U Nu, Prime Minister of Burma.
Do	House	...do	Do.
Jan. 5, 1956	Senate	...do	Juscelino Kubitschek de Oliverira, President-elect of Brazil.
Feb. 2, 1956	...do	...do	Anthony Eden, Prime Minister of the United Kingdom.
Do	House	...do	Do.
Feb. 29, 1956	Joint meeting	...do	Giovanni Gronchi, President of Italy.
Mar. 15, 1956	Senate	...do	John Aloysius Costello, Prime Minister of Ireland.
Do	House	...do	Do.
Apr. 30, 1956	Senate	...do	João Goulart, Vice President of Brazil.
May 17, 1956	Joint meeting	...do	Sukarno, President of Indonesia.
85th CONGRESS			
Jan. 5, 1957	Joint session	Middle East message	President Dwight D. Eisenhower.
Jan. 7, 1957	...do	Counting electoral votes	N.A.
Jan. 10, 1957	...do	State of the Union Address	President Dwight D. Eisenhower.
Jan. 21, 1957	...do	Inauguration, East Portico	President Dwight D. Eisenhower; Vice President Richard M. Nixon.
Feb. 27, 1957	House	Address	Guy Mollet, Premier of France.
Do	Senate	...do	Do.
May 9, 1957	Joint meeting	...do	Ngo Dinh Diem, President of Vietnam.

JOINT SESSIONS AND MEETINGS, ADDRESSES TO THE SENATE OR THE HOUSE, AND INAUGURATIONS—CONTINUED

[See notes at end of table]

Congress & Date	Type	Occasion, topic, or inaugural location	Name and position of dignitary (where applicable)
May 28, 1957	House	Address	Konrad Adenauer, Chancellor of West Germany.
Do	Senate	...do	Do.
June 20, 1957	...do	...do	Nobusuke Kishi, Prime Minister of Japan.
Do	House	...do	Do.
July 11, 1957	Senate	...do	Husseyn Shaheed Suhrawardy, Prime Minister of Pakistan.
Jan. 9, 1958	Joint session	State of the Union Address	President Dwight D. Eisenhower.
June 5, 1958	Joint meeting	Address	Theodor Heuss, President of West Germany.
June 10, 1958	Senate	...do	Harold Macmillan, Prime Minister of the United Kingdom.
June 18, 1958	Joint meeting	...do	Carlos F. Garcia, President of the Philippines.
June 25, 1958	House	...do	Muhammad Daoud Khan, Prime Minister of Afghanistan.
Do	Senate	...do	Do.
July 24, 1958	...do	...do	Kwame Nkrumah, Prime Minister of Ghana.
July 25, 1958	House	...do	Do.
July 29, 1958	Senate	...do	Amintore Fanfani, Prime Minister of Italy.
Do	House	...do	Do.
86th CONGRESS			
Jan. 9, 1959	Joint session	State of the Union Address	President Dwight D. Eisenhower.
Jan. 21, 1959	Joint meeting	Address	Arturo Frondizi, President of Argentina.
Feb. 12, 1959	Joint session	Sesquicentennial of Abraham Lincoln's birth.	Fredric March, actor; Carl Sandburg, poet.
Mar. 11, 1959	Joint meeting	Address	Jose Maria Lemus, President of El Salvador.
Mar. 18, 1959	...do	...do	Sean T. O'Kelly, President of Ireland.
May 12, 1959	...do	...do	Baudouin, King of the Belgians.
Jan. 7, 1960	Joint session	State of the Union Address	President Dwight D. Eisenhower.
Mar. 30, 1960	Senate	Address	Harold Macmillan, Prime Minister of the United Kingdom.
Apr. 6, 1960	Joint meeting	...do	Alberto Lleras-Camargo, President of Colombia.
Apr. 25, 1960	...do	...do	Charles de Gaulle, President of France.
Apr. 28, 1960	...do	...do	Mahendra, King of Nepal.
June 29, 1960	...do	...do	Bhumibol Adulyadej, King of Thailand.
87th CONGRESS			
Jan. 6, 1961	Joint session	Counting electoral votes	N.A.
Jan. 20, 1961	...do	Inauguration, East Portico	President John F. Kennedy; Vice President Lyndon B. Johnson.
Jan. 30, 1961	...do	State of the Union Address	President John F. Kennedy.
Apr. 13, 1961	Senate	Remarks	Konrad Adenauer, Chancellor of West Germany.
Apr. 18, 1961	House	Address	Constantine Karamanlis, Prime Minister of Greece.
May 4, 1961	Joint meeting	...do	Habib Bourguiba, President of Tunisia.
May 25, 1961	Joint session	Urgent national needs: foreign aid, defense, civil defense, and outer space.	President John F. Kennedy.
June 22, 1961	Senate	Remarks	Hayato Ikeda, Prime Minister of Japan.
Do	House	Address	Do.
July 12, 1961	Joint meeting	...do	Mohammad Ayub Khan, President of Pakistan.
July 26, 1961	House	...do	Abubakar Tafawa Balewa, Prime Minister of Nigeria.
Sept. 21, 1961	Joint meeting	...do	Manuel Prado, President of Peru.
Jan. 11, 1962	Joint session	State of the Union Address	President John F. Kennedy.
Feb. 26, 1962	Joint meeting	Friendship 7: 1st United States orbital space flight.	Lt. Col. John H. Glenn, Jr., USMC; Friendship 7 astronaut.
Apr. 4, 1962	...do	Address	João Goulart, President of Brazil.
Apr. 12, 1962	...do	...do	Mohammad Reza Shah Pahlavi, Shahanshah of Iran.
88th CONGRESS			
Jan. 14, 1963	Joint session	State of the Union Address	President John F. Kennedy.
May 21, 1963	Joint meeting	Flight of Faith 7 Spacecraft	Maj. Gordon L. Cooper, Jr., USAF, Faith 7 astronaut.
Oct. 2, 1963	Senate	Address	Haile Selassie I, Emperor of Ethiopia.
Nov. 27, 1963	Joint session	Assumption of office	President Lyndon B. Johnson.
Jan. 8, 1964	...do	State of the Union Address	Do.
Jan. 15, 1964	Joint meeting	Address	Antonio Segni, President of Italy.
May 28, 1964	...do	...do	Eamon de Valera, President of Ireland.
89th CONGRESS			
Jan. 4, 1965	Joint session	State of the Union Address	President Lyndon B. Johnson.

JOINT SESSIONS AND MEETINGS, ADDRESSES TO THE SENATE OR THE HOUSE, AND INAUGURATIONS—CONTINUED

[See notes at end of table]

Congress & Date	Type	Occasion, topic, or inaugural location	Name and position of dignitary (where applicable)
Jan. 6, 1965	Joint session	Counting electoral votes	N.A.
Jan. 20, 1965	...do [32]	Inauguration, East Portico	President Lyndon B. Johnson; Vice President Hubert H. Humphrey.
Mar. 15, 1965	...do	Voting rights	President Lyndon B. Johnson.
Sept. 14, 1965	Joint meeting	Flight of Gemini 5 Spacecraft	Lt. Col. Gordon L. Cooper, Jr., USAF; and Charles Conrad, Jr., USN; Gemini 5 astronauts.
Jan. 12, 1966	Joint session	State of the Union Address	President Lyndon B. Johnson.
Sept. 15, 1966	Joint meeting	Address	Ferdinand E. Marcos, President of the Philippines.
90th CONGRESS			
Jan. 10, 1967	Joint session	State of the Union Address	President Lyndon B. Johnson.
Apr. 28, 1967	Joint meeting	Vietnam policy	General William C. Westmoreland.
Aug. 16, 1967	Senate	Address	Kurt George Kiesinger, Chancellor of West Germany.
Oct. 27, 1967	Joint meeting	...do	Gustavo Diaz Ordaz, President of Mexico.
Jan. 17, 1968	Joint session	State of the Union Address	President Lyndon B. Johnson.
91st CONGRESS			
Jan. 6, 1969	...do	Counting electoral votes [33]	N.A.
Jan. 9, 1969	Joint meeting	Apollo 8: 1st flight around the moon	Col. Frank Borman, USAF; Capt. James A. Lowell, Jr., USN; Lt. Col. William A. Anders, USAF; Apollo 8 astronauts.
Jan. 14, 1969	Joint session	State of the Union Address	President Lyndon B. Johnson.
Jan. 20, 1969	...do [32]	Inauguration, East Portico	President Richard M. Nixon; Vice President Spiro T. Agnew.
Sept. 16, 1969	Joint meeting	Apollo 11: 1st lunar landing	Neil A. Armstrong; Col. Edwin E. Aldrin, Jr., USAF; and Lt. Col. Michael Collins, USAF; Apollo 11 astronauts.
Nov. 13, 1969	House	Executive-Legislative branch relations and Vietnam policy.	President Richard M. Nixon.
Do	Senate	...do	Do.
Jan. 22, 1970	Joint session	State of the Union Address	Do.
Feb. 25, 1970	Joint meeting	Address	Georges Pompidou, President of France.
June 3, 1970	...do	...do	Rafael Caldera, President of Venezuela.
Sept. 22, 1970	...do	Report on prisoners of war	Col. Frank Borman, Representative to the President on Prisoners of War.
92d CONGRESS			
Jan. 22, 1971	Joint session	State of the Union Address	President Richard M. Nixon.
Sept. 9, 1971	...do	Economic policy	Do.
Do	Joint meeting	Apollo 15: lunar mission	Col. David R. Scott, USAF; Col. James B. Irwin, USAF; and Lt. Col. Alfred M. Worden, USAF; Apollo 15 astronauts.
Jan. 20, 1972	Joint session	State of the Union Address	President Richard M. Nixon.
June 1, 1972	...do	European trip report	Do.
June 15, 1972	Joint meeting	Address	Luis Echeverria Alvarez, President of Mexico.
93d CONGRESS			
Jan. 6, 1973	Joint session	Counting electoral votes	N.A.
Jan. 20, 1973	Inauguration	East Portico	President Richard M. Nixon; Vice President Spiro T. Agnew.
Dec. 6, 1973	Joint meeting	Oath of office to, and Address by Vice President Gerald R. Ford.	Vice President Gerald R. Ford; ceremony attended by President Richard M. Nixon.
Do	Senate	Remarks and Reception	Vice President Gerald R. Ford.
Jan. 30, 1974	Joint session	State of the Union Address	President Richard M. Nixon.
Aug. 12, 1974	...do	Assumption of office	President Gerald R. Ford.
Oct. 8, 1974	...do	Economy	Do.
Dec. 19, 1974	Senate	Address [34]	Vice President Nelson A. Rockefeller.
94th CONGRESS			
Jan. 15, 1975	Joint session	State of the Union Address	President Gerald R. Ford.
Apr. 10, 1975	...do	State of the World message	Do.
June 17, 1975	Joint meeting	Address	Walter Scheel, President of West Germany.
Nov. 5, 1975	...do	...do	Anwar El Sadat, President of Egypt.
Jan. 19, 1976	Joint session	State of the Union Address	President Gerald R. Ford.
Jan. 28, 1976	Joint meeting	Address	Yitzhak Rabin, Prime Minister of Israel.
Mar. 17, 1976	...do	...do	Liam Cosgrave, Prime Minister of Ireland.
May 18, 1976	...do	...do	Valery Giscard d'Estaing, President of France.
June 2, 1976	...do	...do	Juan Carlos I, King of Spain.

JOINT SESSIONS AND MEETINGS, ADDRESSES TO THE SENATE OR THE HOUSE, AND INAUGURATIONS—CONTINUED

[See notes at end of table]

Congress & Date	Type	Occasion, topic, or inaugural location	Name and position of dignitary (where applicable)
Sept. 23, 1976	Joint meeting	Address	William R. Tolbert, Jr., President of Liberia.
95th CONGRESS			
Jan. 6, 1977	Joint session	Counting electoral votes	N.A.
Jan. 12, 1977	...do	State of the Union Address	President Gerald R. Ford.
Jan. 20, 1977	Inauguration	East Portico	President Jimmy Carter; Vice President Walter F. Mondale.
Feb. 17, 1977	House	Address	José López Portillo, President of Mexico.
Feb. 22, 1977	Joint meeting	...do	Pierre Elliot Trudeau, Prime Minister of Canada.
Apr. 20, 1977	Joint session	Energy	President Jimmy Carter.
Jan. 19, 1978	...do	State of the Union Address	Do.
Sept. 18, 1978	...do	Middle East Peace agreements	President Jimmy Carter; joint session attended by Anwar El Sadat, President of Egypt, and by Menachem Begin, Prime Minister of Israel.
96th CONGRESS			
Jan. 23, 1979	...do	State of the Union Address	Do.
June 18, 1979	...do	Salt II agreements	Do.
Jan. 23, 1980	...do	State of the Union Address	Do.
97th CONGRESS			
Jan. 6, 1981	...do	Counting electoral votes	N.A.
Jan. 20, 1981	...do[32]	Inauguration, West Front	President Ronald Reagan; Vice President George Bush.
Feb. 18, 1981	...do	Economic recovery	President Ronald Reagan.
Apr. 28, 1981	...do	Economic recovery—inflation	Do.
Jan. 26, 1982	...do	State of the Union Address	Do.
Jan. 28, 1982	Joint meeting	Centennial of birth of Franklin Delano Roosevelt.	Dr. Arthur Schlesinger, historian; Senator Jennings Randolph; Representative Claude Pepper; Averell Harriman, former Governor of New York[35]; former Representative James Roosevelt, son of President Roosevelt.
Apr. 21, 1982	...do	Address	Beatrix, Queen of the Netherlands.
98th CONGRESS			
Jan. 25, 1983	Joint session	State of the Union Address	President Ronald Reagan.
Apr. 27, 1983	...do	Central America	Do.
Oct. 5, 1983	Joint meeting	Address	Karl Carstens, President of West Germany.
Jan. 25, 1984	Joint session	State of the Union Address	President Ronald Reagan.
Mar. 15, 1984	Joint meeting	Address	Dr. Garett FitzGerald, Prime Minister of Ireland.
Mar. 22, 1984	...do	...do	François Mitterand, President of France.
May 8, 1984	...do	Centennial of birth of Harry S. Truman	Representatives Ike Skelton and Alan Wheat; former Senator Stuart Symington; Margaret Truman Daniel, daughter of President Truman; and Senator Mark Hatfield.
May 16, 1984	...do	Address	Miguel de la Madrid, President of Mexico.
99th CONGRESS			
Jan. 7, 1985	Joint session	Counting electoral votes	N.A.
Jan. 21, 1985	Inauguration	Rotunda[36]	President Ronald Reagan; Vice President George Bush.
Feb. 6, 1985	Joint session	State of the Union Address	President Ronald Reagan.
Feb. 20, 1985	Joint meeting	Address	Margaret Thatcher, Prime Minister of the United Kingdom.
Mar. 6, 1985	...do	...do	Bettino Craxi, President of the Council of Ministers of Italy.
Mar. 20, 1985	...do	...do	Raul Alfonsin, President of Argentina.
June 13, 1985	...do	...do	Rajiv Gandhi, Prime Minister of India.
Oct. 9, 1985	...do	...do	Lee Kuan Yew, Prime Minister of Singapore.
Nov. 21, 1985	Joint session	Geneva Summit	President Ronald Reagan.
Feb. 4, 1986	...do	State of the Union Address	Do.
Sept. 11, 1986	Joint meeting	Address	Jose Sarney, President of Brazil.
Sept. 18, 1986	...do	...do	Corazon C. Aquino, President of the Philippines.
100th CONGRESS			
Jan. 27, 1987	Joint session	State of the Union Address	President Ronald Reagan.
Nov. 10, 1987	Joint meeting	Address	Chaim Herzog, President of Israel.
Jan. 25, 1988	Joint session	State of the Union Address	President Ronald Reagan.
Apr. 27, 1988	Joint meeting	Address	Brian Mulroney, Prime Minister of Canada.

JOINT SESSIONS AND MEETINGS, ADDRESSES TO THE SENATE OR THE HOUSE, AND INAUGURATIONS—CONTINUED

[See notes at end of table]

Congress & Date	Type	Occasion, topic, or inaugural location	Name and position of dignitary (where applicable)
June 23, 1988	Joint meeting	Address	Robert Hawke, Prime Minister of Australia.
101st CONGRESS			
Jan. 4, 1989	Joint session	Counting electoral votes	N.A.
Jan. 20, 1989	Inauguration	West Front	President George Bush; Vice President Dan Quayle.
Feb. 9, 1989	Joint session	Building a Better America	President George Bush.
Mar. 2, 1989	Joint meeting	Bicentennial of the 1st Congress	President Pro Tempore Robert C. Byrd; Speaker James C. Wright, Jr.; Representatives Lindy Boggs, Thomas S. Foley, and Robert H. Michel; Senators George Mitchell and Robert Dole; Howard Nemerov, Poet Laureate of the United States; David McCullough, historian; Anthony M. Frank, Postmaster General; former Senator Nicholas Brady, Secretary of the Treasury.
Apr. 6, 1989	Senate[37]	Addresses on the 200th anniversary commemoration of Senate's first legislative session.	Former Senators Thomas F. Eagleton and Howard H. Baker, Jr.
June 7, 1989	Joint meeting	Address	Benazir Bhutto, Prime Minister of Pakistan.
Oct. 4, 1989	...do	...do	Carlos Salinas de Gortari, President of Mexico.
Oct. 18, 1989	...do	...do	Roh Tae Woo, President of South Korea.
Nov. 15, 1989	...do	...do	Lech Walesa, chairman of Solidarność labor union, Poland.
Jan. 31, 1990	Joint session	State of the Union Address	President George Bush.
Feb. 21, 1990	Joint meeting	Address	Vaclav Hável, President of Czechoslovakia.
Mar. 7, 1990	...do	...do	Giulio Andreotti, President of the Council of Ministers of Italy.
Mar. 27, 1990	...do	Centennial of birth of Dwight D. Eisenhower.	Senator Robert Dole; Walter Cronkite, television journalist; Winston S. Churchill, member of British Parliament and grandson of Prime Minister Churchill; Clark M. Clifford, former Secretary of Defense; James D. Robinson III, chairman of Eisenhower Centennial Foundation; Arnold Palmer, professional golfer; John S.D. Eisenhower, former Ambassador to Belgium and son of President Eisenhower; Representatives Beverly Byron, William F. Goodling, and Pat Roberts.
June 26, 1990	...do	Address	Nelson Mandela, Deputy President of the African National Congress, South Africa.
Sept. 11, 1990	Joint session	Invasion of Kuwait by Iraq	President George Bush.
102d CONGRESS			
Jan. 29, 1991	...do	State of the Union Address	Do.
Mar. 6, 1991	...do	Conclusion of Persian Gulf War	Do.
Apr. 16, 1991	Joint meeting	Address	Violeta B. de Chamorro, President of Nicaragua.
May 8, 1991	House[38]	...do	General H. Norman Schwarzkopf.
May 16, 1991	Joint meeting	...do	Elizabeth II, Queen of the United Kingdom; joint meeting also attended by Prince Philip.
Nov. 14, 1991	...do	...do	Carlos Saul Menem, President of Argentina.
Jan. 28, 1992	Joint session	State of the Union Address	President George Bush.
Apr. 30, 1992	Joint meeting	Address	Richard von Weizsäcker, President of Germany.
June 17, 1992	...do	...do	Boris Yeltsin, President of Russia.
103d CONGRESS			
Jan. 6, 1993	Joint session	Counting electoral votes	N.A.
Jan. 20, 1993	Inauguration	West Front	President William J. Clinton; Vice President Albert Gore.
Feb. 17, 1993	Joint session	Economic Address[39]	President William J. Clinton.
Sept. 22, 1993	...do	Health care reform	Do.
Jan. 25, 1994	...do	State of the Union Address	Do.
May 18, 1994	Joint meeting	Address	Narasimha Rao, Prime Minister of India.
July 26, 1994	...do	Addresses	Hussein I, King of Jordan; Yitzhak Rabin, Prime Minister of Israel.
Oct. 6, 1994	...do	Address	Nelson Mandela, President of South Africa.

JOINT SESSIONS AND MEETINGS, ADDRESSES TO THE SENATE OR THE HOUSE, AND INAUGURATIONS—CONTINUED

[See notes at end of table]

Congress & Date	Type	Occasion, topic, or inaugural location	Name and position of dignitary (where applicable)
104th CONGRESS			
Jan. 24, 1995	Joint session	State of the Union Address	President William J. Clinton.
July 26, 1995	Joint meeting	Address	Kim Yong-sam, President of South Korea.[40]
Oct. 11, 1995	...do	Close of the Commemoration of the 50th Anniversary of World War II.	Speaker Newt Gingrich; Vice President Albert Gore; President Pro Tempore Strom Thurmond; Representatives Henry J. Hyde and G.V. "Sonny" Montgomery; Senators Daniel K. Inouye and Robert Dole; former Representative Robert H. Michel; General Louis H. Wilson (ret.), former Commandant of the Marine Corps.
Dec. 12, 1995	...do	Address	Shimon Peres, Prime Minister of Israel.
Jan. 30, 1996	Joint session	State of the Union Address	President William J. Clinton.
Feb. 1, 1996	Joint meeting	Address	Jacques Chirac, President of France.
July 10, 1996	...do	...do	Binyamin Netanyahu, Prime Minister of Israel.
Sept. 11, 1996	...do	...do	John Bruton, Prime Minister of Ireland.
105th CONGRESS			
Jan. 9, 1997	Joint session	Counting electoral votes	N.A.
Jan. 20, 1997	Inauguration	West Front	President William J. Clinton; Vice President Albert Gore.
Feb. 4, 1997	Joint session	State of the Union Address[41]	President William J. Clinton.
Feb. 27, 1997	Joint meeting	Address	Eduardo Frei, President of Chile.
Jan. 27, 1998	Joint session	State of the Union Address	President William J. Clinton.
June 10, 1998	Joint meeting	Address	Kim Dae-jung, President of South Korea.
July 15, 1998	...do	...do	Emil Constantinescu, President of Romania.
106th CONGRESS			
Jan. 19, 1999	Joint session	State of the Union Address	President William J. Clinton.
Jan. 27, 2000	...do	...do	Do.
Sept. 14, 2000	Joint meeting	Address	Atal Bihari Vajpayee, Prime Minister of India.
107th CONGRESS			
Jan. 6, 2001	Joint session	Counting electoral votes	N.A.
Jan. 20, 2001	Inauguration	West Front	President George W. Bush; Vice President Richard B. Cheney.
Feb. 27, 2001	Joint session	Budget message[39]	President George W. Bush.
Sept. 6, 2001	Joint meeting	Address	Vicente Fox, President of Mexico.
Sept. 20, 2001	Joint session	War on terrorism	President George W. Bush; joint session attended by Tony Blair, Prime Minister of the United Kingdom, by Tom Ridge, Governor of Pennsylvania, by George Pataki, Governor of New York, and by Rudolph Giuliani, Mayor of New York City.
Jan. 29, 2002	...do	State of the Union Address	President George W. Bush; joint session attended by Hamid Karzai, Chairman of the Interim Authority of Afghanistan.
June 12, 2002	Joint meeting	Address[42]	John Howard, Prime Minister of Australia.
108th CONGRESS			
Jan. 28, 2003	Joint session	State of the Union Address	President George W. Bush.
July 17, 2003	Joint meeting	Address	Tony Blair, Prime Minister of the United Kingdom; joint meeting attended by Mrs. George W. Bush.
Jan. 20, 2004	Joint session	State of the Union Address	President George W. Bush.
Feb. 4, 2004	Joint meeting	Address	Jose Maria Aznar, President of the Government of Spain.
June 15, 2004	...do	...do	Hamid Karzai, President of Afghanistan.
Sept. 23, 2004	...do	...do	Ayad Allawi, Interim Prime Minister of Iraq.
109th CONGRESS			
Jan. 6, 2005	Joint session	Counting electoral votes[43]	N.A.
Jan. 20, 2005	Inauguration	West Front	President George W. Bush; Vice President Richard B. Cheney.
Feb. 2, 2005	Joint session	State of the Union Address	President George W. Bush.
Apr. 6, 2005	Joint meeting	Address	Viktor Yushchenko, President of Ukraine.
July 19, 2005	...do	...do	Dr. Manmohan Singh, Prime Minister of India.
Jan. 31, 2006	Joint session	State of the Union Address	President George W. Bush.
Mar. 1, 2006	Joint meeting	Address	Silvio Berlusconi, Prime Minister of Italy.

JOINT SESSIONS AND MEETINGS, ADDRESSES TO THE SENATE OR THE HOUSE, AND INAUGURATIONS—CONTINUED

[See notes at end of table]

Congress & Date	Type	Occasion, topic, or inaugural location	Name and position of dignitary (where applicable)
Mar. 15, 2006	Joint meeting	Address	Ellen Johnson Sirleaf, President of Liberia.
May 24, 2006	...do	...do	Ehud Olmert, Prime Minister of Israel.
June 7, 2006	...do	...do	Dr. Vaira Vike-Freiberga, President of Latvia.
July 26, 2006	...do	...do	Nouri Al-Maliki, Prime Minister of Iraq.
110th CONGRESS			
Jan. 23, 2007	Joint session	State of the Union Address	President George W. Bush.
Mar. 7, 2007	Joint meeting	Address	Abdullah II Ibn Al Hussein, King of Jordan.
Nov. 7, 2007	...do	...do	Nicolas Sarkozy, President of France.
Jan. 28, 2008	Joint session	State of the Union Address	President George W. Bush.
Apr. 30, 2008	Joint meeting	Address	Bertie Ahern, Prime Minister of Ireland.
111th CONGRESS			
Jan. 8, 2009	Joint session	Counting electoral votes	N.A.
Jan. 20, 2009	Inauguration	West Front	President Barack H. Obama; Vice President Joseph R. Biden, Jr.
Feb. 24, 2009	Joint session	Economic Address	President Barack H. Obama.
Mar. 4, 2009	Joint meeting	...do	Gordon Brown, Prime Minister of the United Kingdom.
Sept. 9, 2009	Joint session	Health care reform	President Barack H. Obama.
Nov. 2, 2009	Joint meeting	Address	Angela Merkel, Chancellor of Germany.
Jan. 27, 2010	Joint session	State of the Union Address	President Barack H. Obama.
May 20, 2010	Joint meeting	Address	Felipe Calderon Hinojosa, President of Mexico.
112th CONGRESS			
Jan. 25, 2011	Joint session	State of the Union Address	President Barack H. Obama.
Mar. 9, 2011	Joint meeting	Address	Julia Gillard, Prime Minister of Australia.
May 24, 2011	...do	...do	Binyamin Netanyahu, Prime Minister of Israel.
Sept. 8, 2011	Joint session	American Jobs Act	President Barack H. Obama.
Oct. 13, 2011	Joint meeting	Address	Lee Myung-bak, President of the Republic of Korea.
Jan. 24, 2012	Joint session	State of the Union Address	President Barack H. Obama.
113th CONGRESS			
Jan. 4, 2013	...do	Counting electoral votes	N.A.
Jan. 21, 2013	Inauguration	West Front	President Barack H. Obama; Vice President Joseph R. Biden, Jr.
Feb. 12, 2013	Joint session	State of the Union Address	President Barack H. Obama.
May 8, 2013	Joint meeting	Address	Park Geun-hye, President of the Republic of Korea.
Jan. 28, 2014	Joint session	State of the Union Address	President Barack H. Obama.

[1] Closing date for this table was January 28, 2014.

[2] The oath of office was administered to George Washington outside on the gallery in front of the Senate Chamber, after which the Congress and the President returned to the chamber to hear the inaugural address. They then proceeded to St. Paul's Chapel for the "divine service" performed by the Chaplain of the Congress. Adjournment of the ceremony did not occur until the Congress returned to Federal Hall.

[3] Funeral oration was delivered at the German Lutheran Church in Philadelphia.

[4] Because of a tie in the electoral vote between Thomas Jefferson and Aaron Burr, the House of Representatives had to decide the election. Thirty-six ballots were required to break the deadlock, with Jefferson's election as President and Burr's as Vice President on February 17. The Twelfth Amendment was added to the Constitution to prevent the 1800 problem from recurring.

[5] During most of the period while the Capitol was being reconstructed following the fire of 1814, the Congress met in the "Brick Capitol," constructed on the site of the present Supreme Court building. This joint session took place in the Representatives' chamber on the 2d floor of the building.

[6] The joint session to count electoral votes was dissolved because the House and Senate disagreed on Missouri's status regarding statehood. The joint session was reconvened the same day and Missouri's votes were counted.

[7] While this occasion has historically been referred to as the first joint meeting of Congress, the Journals of the House and Senate indicate that Lafayette actually addressed the House of Representatives, with some of the Senators present as guests of the House (having been invited at the last minute to attend). Similar occasions, when members of the one body were invited as guests of the other, include the Senate address by Queen Wilhelmina of the Netherlands on Aug. 6, 1942, and the House address by General H. Norman Schwarzkopf on May 8, 1991.

[8] Although Andrew Jackson won the popular vote by a substantial amount and had the highest number of electoral votes from among the several candidates, he did not receive the required majority of the electoral votes. The responsibility for choosing the new President therefore devolved upon the House of Representatives. As soon as the Senators left the chamber, the balloting proceeded, and John Quincy Adams was elected on the first ballot.

[9] The ceremony was moved outside to accommodate the extraordinarily large crowd of people who had come to Washington to see the inauguration.

[10] The ceremony was moved inside because of cold weather.

[11] Following the death of President Zachary Taylor, Vice President Millard Fillmore took the Presidential oath of office in a special joint session in the Hall of the House.

[12] The joint session to count electoral votes was dissolved three times so that the House and Senate could resolve several electoral disputes.

[13] Because of a severe cold and hoarseness, the King could not deliver his speech, which was read by former Representative Elisha Hunt Allen, then serving as Chancellor and Chief Justice of the Hawaiian Islands.

[14] The contested election between Rutherford B. Hayes and Samuel J. Tilden created a constitutional crisis. Tilden won the popular vote by a close margin, but disputes concerning the electoral vote returns from four states deadlocked the proceedings of the joint session. Anticipating this development, the Congress had created a special commission of five Senators, five Representatives, and five Supreme Court Justices to resolve such disputes. The Commission met in the Supreme Court Chamber (the present Old Senate Chamber) as each problem arose. In each case, the Commission accepted the Hayes electors, securing his election by one electoral vote. The joint session was convened on 15 occasions, with the last on March 2, just three days before the inauguration.

[15] The speech was written by former Speaker and Senator Robert C. Winthrop, who could not attend the ceremony because of ill health.

[16] Because of a blizzard, the ceremony was moved inside, where it was held as part of the Senate's special session. President William Howard Taft took the oath of office and gave his inaugural address after Vice President James S. Sherman's inaugural address and the swearing-in of the new senators.

[17] Held in the Senate Chamber.

[18] Bakhmetieff represented the provisional government of Russia set up after the overthrow of the monarchy in March 1917 and recognized by the United States. The Bolsheviks took over in November 1917.

[19] The address and reception were in conjunction with the presentation to the Senate by France of two Sèvres vases in appreciation of the United States' involvement in World War I. The vases are today in the Senate lobby, just off the Senate floor. Two additional Sèvres vases were given without ceremony to the House of Representatives, which today are in the Rayburn Room, not far from the floor of the House.

[20] Senators later objected to President Harding's speech (given with no advance notice to most of the Senators) as an unconstitutional effort to interfere with the deliberations of the Senate, and Harding did not repeat visits of this kind.

[21] This was the first Annual Message broadcast live on radio.

[22] This was the first inauguration held pursuant to the Twentieth Amendment, which changed the date from March 4 to January 20. The Vice Presidential oath, which previously had been given earlier on the same day in the Senate Chamber, was added to the inaugural ceremony as well, but the Vice Presidential inaugural address was discontinued.

[23] A joint reception for the King and Queen of the United Kingdom was held in the Rotunda, authorized by Senate Concurrent Resolution 17, 76th Congress. Although the concurrent resolution was structured to establish a joint meeting, the Senate, in fact, adjourned rather than recessed as called for by the resolution.

[24] Held in the Senate Chamber.

[25] At this time, the Philippines was still a possession of the United States, although it had been made a self-governing commonwealth in 1935, in preparation for full independence in 1946. From 1909 to 1916, Quezon had served in the U.S. House of Representatives as the resident commissioner from the Philippines.

[26] In exile.

[27] For this Senate Address by Queen Wilhelmina, the members of the House of Representatives were invited as guests. This occasion has sometimes been mistakenly referred to as a joint meeting.

[28] The oaths of office were taken in simple ceremonies at the White House because the expense and festivity of a Capitol ceremony were thought inappropriate because of the war. The Joint Committee on Arrangements of the Congress was in charge, however, and both the Senate and the House of Representatives were present.

[29] This was the first time the term "State of the Union Address" was used for the President's Annual Message. Also, it was the first time the address was shown live on television.

[30] This was an informal meeting in the Coolidge Auditorium of the Library of Congress.

[31] Presentation of new ivory gavel to the Senate.

[32] According to the Congressional Record, the Senate adjourned prior to the inaugural ceremonies, even though the previously adopted resolution had stated the adjournment would come immediately following the inauguration. The Senate Journal records the adjournment as called for in the resolution, hence this listing as a joint session.

[33] The joint session to count electoral votes was dissolved so that the House and Senate could each resolve the dispute regarding a ballot from North Carolina. The joint session was reconvened the same day and the North Carolina vote was counted.

[34] Rockefeller was sworn in as Vice President by Chief Justice Warren E. Burger, after which, by unanimous consent, he was allowed to address the Senate.

[35] Because the Governor had laryngitis, his speech was read by his wife, Pamela.

[36] The ceremony was moved inside because of extremely cold weather.

[37] These commemorative addresses were given in the Old Senate Chamber during a regular legislative session.

[38] For this House Address by General Schwarzkopf, the members of the Senate were invited as guests.

[39] This speech was mislabeled in many sources as a State of the Union Address.

[40] President Kim Yong-sam was in Washington for the dedication of the Korean Veterans' Memorial, held the day after this joint meeting.

[41] This was the first State of the Union Address carried live on the Internet.

[42] Prime Minister Howard was originally scheduled to address a joint meeting on September 12, 2001, but because of the attack on the United States on September 11, 2001, the event was postponed until this occasion.

[43] The joint session to count electoral votes was dissolved so that the House and Senate could each discuss the dispute regarding the ballots from Ohio. The joint session was reconvened the same day and the Ohio votes were counted.

REPRESENTATIVES UNDER EACH APPORTIONMENT

The original apportionment of Representatives was assigned in 1787 in the Constitution and remained in effect for the 1st and 2d Congresses. Subsequent apportionments based on the censuses over the years have been figured using several different methods approved by Congress, all with the goal of dividing representation among the states as equally as possible. After each census up to and including the thirteenth in 1910, Congress would enact a law designating the specific changes in the actual number of Representatives as well as the increase in the ratio of persons-per-Representative. After having made no apportionment after the Fourteenth census in 1920, Congress by statute in 1929 fixed the total number of Representatives at 435 (the number attained with the apportionment after the 1910 census), and since that time, only the ratio of persons-per-Representative has continued to increase, in fact, significantly so. Since the total is now fixed, the specific number of Representatives per state is adjusted after each census to reflect its percentage of the entire population. Since the Sixteenth Census in 1940, the "equal proportions" method of apportioning Representatives within the 435 total has been employed. A detailed explanation of the entire apportionment process can be found in *The Historical Atlas of United States Congressional Districts, 1989–1983.* Kenneth C. Martis, The Free Press, New York, 1982.

State	Constitutional apportionment	First Census, 1790	Second Census, 1800	Third Census, 1810	Fourth Census, 1820	Fifth Census, 1830	Sixth Census, 1840	Seventh Census, 1850	Eighth Census, 1860	Ninth Census, 1870	Tenth Census, 1880	Eleventh Census, 1890	Twelfth Census, 1900	Thirteenth Census, 1910	Fifteenth Census, 1930 [1]	Sixteenth Census, 1940	Seventeenth Census, 1950	Eighteenth Census, 1960	Nineteenth Census, 1970	Twentieth Census, 1980	Twenty-First Census, 1990	Twenty-Second Census, 2000	Twenty-Third Census, 2010
AL	......	......	......	[2]	3	5	7	7	6	8	8	9	9	10	9	9	9	8	7	7	7	7	7
AK	......	......	......	......	......	......	......	......	......	......	......	......	......	......	......	......	[2,3]	1	1	1	1	1	1
AZ	......	......	......	......	......	......	......	......	......	......	......	......	[2]	[4]1	1	2	2	3	4	5	6	8	9
AR	......	......	......	......	......	[2]	1	2	3	4	5	6	7	7	7	7	6	4	4	4	4	4	4
CA	......	......	......	......	......	......	[2]	[4]2	3	4	6	7	8	11	20	23	30	38	43	45	52	53	53
CO	......	......	......	......	......	......	......	......	......	[2]	1	2	3	4	4	4	4	4	5	6	6	7	7
CT	5	7	7	7	6	6	4	4	4	4	4	4	5	5	6	6	6	6	6	6	6	5	5
DE	1	1	1	2	1	1	1	1	1	1	1	1	1	1	1	1	1	1	1	1	1	1	1
FL	......	......	......	......	......	......	[2]	1	1	2	2	2	3	4	5	6	8	12	15	19	23	25	27
GA	3	2	4	6	7	9	8	8	7	9	10	11	11	12	10	10	10	10	10	10	11	13	14
HI	......	......	......	......	......	......	......	......	......	......	......	......	......	......	......	......	[2,3]	2	2	2	2	2	2
ID	......	......	......	......	......	......	......	......	......	......	[2]	1	1	2	2	2	2	2	2	2	2	2	2
IL	......	......	......	[2]	1	3	7	9	14	19	20	22	25	27	27	26	25	24	24	22	20	19	18
IN	......	......	......	[2]	3	7	10	11	11	13	13	13	13	13	12	11	11	11	11	10	10	9	9
IA	......	......	......	......	......	......	[2]	2	6	9	11	11	11	11	9	8	8	7	6	6	5	5	4
KS	......	......	......	......	......	......	......	[2]	[4]1	3	7	8	8	8	7	6	6	5	5	5	4	4	4
KY	[2]	[4]2	6	10	12	13	10	10	9	10	11	11	11	11	9	9	8	7	7	7	6	6	6
LA	......	......	......	[2]	3	3	4	4	5	6	6	6	7	8	8	8	8	8	8	8	7	7	6
ME	......	......	......	[5]	7	8	7	6	5	5	4	4	4	4	3	3	3	2	2	2	2	2	2
MD	6	8	9	9	9	8	6	6	5	6	6	6	6	6	6	6	7	8	8	8	8	8	8
MA	8	14	17	[5]20	13	12	10	11	10	11	12	13	14	16	15	14	14	12	12	11	10	10	9
MI	......	......	......	......	......	[2]	3	4	6	9	11	12	12	13	17	17	18	19	19	18	16	15	14
MN	......	......	......	......	......	......	......	[2]	2	3	5	7	9	10	9	9	9	8	8	8	8	8	8
MS	......	......	......	[2]	1	2	4	5	5	6	7	7	8	8	7	7	6	5	5	5	5	4	4
MO	......	......	......	[2]	[4]1	2	5	7	9	13	14	15	16	16	13	13	11	10	10	9	9	9	8
MT	......	......	......	......	......	......	......	......	......	......	[2]	1	1	2	2	2	2	2	2	2	1	1	1
NE	......	......	......	......	......	......	......	......	[2]	1	3	6	6	6	5	4	4	3	3	3	3	3	3
NV	......	......	......	......	......	......	......	......	[2]	1	1	1	1	1	1	1	1	1	1	2	2	3	4
NH	3	4	5	6	6	5	4	3	3	3	2	2	2	2	2	2	2	2	2	2	2	2	2
NJ	4	5	6	6	6	6	5	5	5	7	7	8	10	12	14	14	14	15	15	14	13	13	12
NM	......	......	......	......	......	......	......	......	......	......	......	......	[2]	[4]1	1	2	2	2	2	3	3	3	3
NY	6	10	17	27	34	40	34	33	31	33	34	34	37	43	45	45	43	41	39	34	31	29	27
NC	5	10	12	13	13	13	9	8	7	8	9	9	10	10	11	12	12	11	11	11	12	13	13
ND	......	......	......	......	......	......	......	......	......	......	[2]	1	2	3	2	2	2	2	1	1	1	1	1
OH	......	......	[2]	6	14	19	21	21	19	20	21	21	21	22	24	23	23	24	23	21	19	18	16
OK	......	......	......	......	......	......	......	......	......	......	......	......	[2]	8	9	8	6	6	6	6	6	5	5
OR	......	......	......	......	......	......	......	[2]	1	1	1	2	2	3	3	4	4	4	4	5	5	5	5
PA	8	13	18	23	26	28	24	25	24	27	28	30	32	36	34	33	30	27	25	23	21	19	18
RI	1	2	2	2	2	2	2	2	2	2	2	2	2	3	2	2	2	2	2	2	2	2	2
SC	5	6	8	9	9	9	7	6	4	5	7	7	7	7	6	6	6	6	6	6	6	6	7
SD	......	......	......	......	......	......	......	......	......	......	[2]	2	2	3	2	2	2	2	2	1	1	1	1
TN	......	[2]	3	6	9	13	11	10	8	10	10	10	10	10	9	10	9	9	8	9	9	9	9
TX	......	......	......	......	......	......	[2]	2	4	6	11	13	16	18	21	21	22	23	24	27	30	32	36
UT	......	......	......	......	......	......	......	......	......	......	......	[2]	1	2	2	2	2	2	2	3	3	3	4
VT	[2]	[4]2	4	6	5	5	4	3	3	3	2	2	2	2	1	1	1	1	1	1	1	1	1
VA	10	19	22	23	22	21	15	13	[6]11	9	10	10	10	10	9	9	10	10	10	10	11	11	11
WA	......	......	......	......	......	......	......	......	......	......	[2]	2	3	5	6	6	7	7	7	8	9	9	10
WV	......	......	......	......	......	......	......	......	[6]	3	4	4	5	6	6	6	6	5	4	4	3	3	3
WI	......	......	......	......	......	......	[2]	3	6	8	9	10	11	11	10	10	10	10	9	9	9	8	8
WY	......	......	......	......	......	......	......	......	......	......	[2]	1	1	1	1	1	1	1	1	1	1	1	1
Total	65	105	141	181	213	240	223	234	241	292	325	356	386	435	435	435	435	435	435	435	435	435	435

NOTE: Information for table obtained from the U.S. Census Bureau.

[1] No apportionment was made after the 1920 census.

[2] The following Representatives were added after the indicated apportionments when these states were admitted in the years listed. The number of these additional Representatives for each state remained in effect until the next census's apportionment (with the exceptions of California and New Mexico, as explained in footnote 4). They are not included in the total for each column. In reading this table, please remember that the apportionments made after each census took effect with the election two years after the census date. As a result, in the table footnote 2 is placed for several states under the decade preceding the one in which it entered the Union, since the previous decade's apportionment was still in effect at the time of statehood. *Constitutional:* Vermont (1791), 2; Kentucky (1792), 2; *First:* Tennessee (1796), 1; *Second:* Ohio (1803), 1; *Third:* Louisiana (1812), 1; Indiana (1816), 1; Mississippi (1817), 1; Illinois (1818), 1; Alabama (1819), 1; Missouri (1821), 1; *Fifth:* Arkansas (1836), 1; Michigan (1837), 1; *Sixth:* Florida (1845), 1; Texas (1845), 2; Iowa (1846), 2; Wisconsin (1848), 2; California (1850), 2; *Seventh:* Minnesota (1858), 2; Oregon (1859), 1; Kansas (1861), 1; *Eighth:* Nevada (1864), 1; Nebraska (1867), 1; *Ninth:* Colorado (1876), 1; *Tenth:* North Dakota (1889), 1; South Dakota (1889), 2; Montana (1889), 1; Washington (1889), 1; Idaho (1890), 1; Wyoming (1890), 1; *Eleventh:* Utah (1896), 1; *Twelth:* Oklahoma (1907), 5; New Mexico (1912), 2; Arizona (1912), 1; *Seventeenth:* Alaska (1959), 1; Hawaii (1959), 1.

[3] When Alaska and then Hawaii joined the Union in 1959, the law was changed to allow the total membership of the House of Representatives to increase to 436 and then to 437, apportioning one new Representative for each of those states. The total returned to 435 in 1963, when the 1960 census apportionment took effect.

[4] Even though the respective censuses were taken before the following states joined the Union, Representatives for them were apportioned either because of anticipation of statehood or because they had become states in the period between the census and the apportionment, hence they are included in the totals of the respective columns. *First:* Vermont (1791); Kentucky (1792); *Fourth:* Missouri (1821); *Seventh:* California (1850); *Eighth:* Kansas (1861); *Thirteenth:* New Mexico (1912); Arizona (1912). (Please note: These seven states are also included in footnote 2 because they became states while the previous decade's apportionment was still in effect for the House of Representatives.) California's situation was unusual. It was scheduled for inclusion in the figures for the 1850 census apportionment; however, when the apportionment law was passed in 1852, California's census returns were still incomplete so Congress made special provision that the state would retain "the number of Representatives [two] prescribed by the act of admission * * * into the Union until a new apportionment [i.e., after the 1860 census]" would be made. The number of Representatives from California actually increased before the next apportionment to three when Congress gave the state an extra Representative during part of the 37th Congress, from 1862 to 1863. Regarding New Mexico, the 1911 apportionment law, passed by the 62d Congress in response to the 1910 census and effective with the 63d Congress in 1913, stated that "if the Territor[y] of * * * New Mexico shall become [a State] in the Union before the apportionment of Representatives under the next decennial census [it] shall have one Representative * * *." When New Mexico became a state in 1912 during the 62d Congress, it was given two Representatives. The number was decreased to one beginning the next year in the 63d.

[5] The "Maine District" of Massachusetts became a separate state during the term of the 16th Congress, in 1820. For the remainder of that Congress, Maine was assigned one "at large" Representative while Massachusetts continued to have 20 Representatives, the number apportioned to it after the 1810 census. For the 17th Congress (the last before the 1820 census apportionment took effect), seven of Massachusetts's Representatives were reassigned to Maine, leaving Massachusetts with 13.

[6] Of the 11 Representatives apportioned to Virginia after the 1860 census, three were reassigned to West Virginia when that part of Virginia became a separate state in 1863. Since the Virginia seats in the House were vacant at that time because of the Civil War, all of the new Representatives from West Virginia were able to take their seats at once. When Representatives from Virginia reentered the House in 1870, only eight members represented it.

IMPEACHMENT PROCEEDINGS

The provisions of the United States Constitution which apply specifically to impeachments are as follows: Article I, section 2, clause 5; Article I, section 3, clauses 6 and 7; Article II, section 2, clause 1; Article II, section 4; and Article III, section 2, clause 3.

For the officials listed below, the date of impeachment by the House of Representatives is followed by the dates of the Senate trial, with the result of each listed at the end of the entry.

WILLIAM BLOUNT, a Senator of the United States from Tennessee; impeached July 7, 1797; tried Monday, December 17, 1798, to Monday, January 14, 1799; charges dismissed for want of jurisdiction.

JOHN PICKERING, judge of the United States District Court for the District of New Hampshire; impeached March 2, 1803; tried Thursday, March 3, 1803, to Monday, March 12, 1804; removed from office.

SAMUEL CHASE, Associate Justice of the Supreme Court of the United States; impeached March 12, 1804; tried Friday, November 30, 1804, to Friday, March 1, 1805; acquitted.

JAMES H. PECK, judge of the United States District Court for the District of Missouri; impeached April 24, 1830; tried Monday, April 26, 1830, to Monday, January 31, 1831; acquitted.

WEST H. HUMPHREYS, judge of the United States District Court for the Middle, Eastern, and Western Districts of Tennessee; impeached May 6, 1862; tried Wednesday, May 7, 1862, to Thursday, June 26, 1862; removed from office and disqualified from future office.

ANDREW JOHNSON, President of the United States; impeached February 24, 1868; tried Tuesday, February 25, 1868, to Tuesday, May 26, 1868; acquitted.

MARK DELAHAY, judge of the United States District Court of Kansas; impeached February 28, 1873; resigned office Friday, December 12, 1873, before the Senate trial was held, with no further action taken by the Senate.

WILLIAM W. BELKNAP, Secretary of War; impeached March 2, 1876; tried Friday, March 3, 1876, to Tuesday, August 1, 1876; acquitted.

CHARLES SWAYNE, judge of the United States District Court for the Northern District of Florida; impeached December 13, 1904; tried Wednesday, December 14, 1904, to Monday, February 27, 1905; acquitted.

ROBERT W. ARCHBALD, associate judge, United States Commerce Court; impeached July 11, 1912; tried Saturday, July 13, 1912, to Monday, January 13, 1913; removed from office and disqualified from future office.

GEORGE W. ENGLISH, judge of the United States District Court for the Eastern District of Illinois; impeached April 1, 1926; tried Friday, April 23, 1926, to Monday, December 13, 1926; resigned office Thursday, November 4, 1926; Court of Impeachment adjourned to December 13, 1926, when, on request of House managers, the proceedings were dismissed.

HAROLD LOUDERBACK, judge of the United States District Court for the Northern District of California; impeached February 24, 1933; tried Monday, May 15, 1933, to Wednesday, May 24, 1933; acquitted.

HALSTED L. RITTER, judge of the United States District Court for the Southern District of Florida; impeached March 2, 1936; tried Monday, April 6, 1936, to Friday, April 17, 1936; removed from office.

HARRY E. CLAIBORNE, judge of the United States District Court of Nevada; impeached July 22, 1986; tried Tuesday, October 7, 1986, to Thursday, October 9, 1986; removed from office.

ALCEE L. HASTINGS, judge of the United States District Court for the Southern District of Florida; impeached August 3, 1988; tried Wednesday, October 18, 1989, to Friday, October 20, 1989; removed from office.

WALTER L. NIXON, judge of the United States District Court for the Southern District of Mississippi; impeached May 10, 1989; tried Wednesday, November 1, 1989, to Friday, November 3, 1989; removed from office.

WILLIAM JEFFERSON CLINTON, President of the United States; impeached December 19, 1998; tried Thursday, January 7, 1999, to Friday, February 12, 1999; acquitted.

SAMUEL B. KENT, judge of the United States District Court for the Southern District of Texas; impeached June 19, 2009; resigned office effective Tuesday, June 30, 2009; Court of Impeachment convened on Wednesday, July 22, 2009, when, on request of House managers, proceedings were dismissed.

G. THOMAS PORTEOUS, JR., judge of the United States District Court for the Eastern District of Louisiana; impeached March 11, 2010; tried Tuesday, December 7, 2010, to Wednesday, December 8, 2010; removed from office and disqualified from future office.

REPRESENTATIVES, SENATORS, DELEGATES, AND RESIDENT COMMISSIONERS SERVING IN THE 1st–113th CONGRESSES*

Since the U.S. Congress convened on March 4, 1789, 12,106 individuals have served as Representatives, Senators, or in both capacities. There have been 10,156 Members who served only as Representatives, 1,288 Members who served only in the Senate, and 662 Members with service in both chambers. The total number of Representatives (including individuals serving in both bodies) is 10,818.

These numbers do not include statutory representatives: Resident Commissioners and Delegates. An additional 143 people have served only as Territorial Delegates in the House and 32 people have served only as Resident Commissioners from Puerto Rico or the Philippines.

State/Territory	Date Became a U.S. Territory	Date Entered the Union	Delegates (Only)	Resident Commissioners[1]	Representatives (Only)[2]	Representatives and Delegates	Senators (Only)[3]	Senators and Representatives[4]	Senators and Delegates	Senators, Representatives, and Delegates	Total House Members
Alabama	Mar. 3, 1817	Dec. 14, 1819 (22d)	0	0	168	1	27	13	0	0	182
Alaska	Aug. 24, 1912	Jan. 3, 1959 (49th)	7	0	4	0	6	0	1	0	12
American Samoa	Apr. 17, 1900	....	2	0	0	0	0	0	0	0	2
Arizona	Feb. 24, 1863	Feb. 14, 1912 (48th)	10	0	32	0	5	4	2	0	48
Arkansas	Mar. 2, 1819	June 15, 1836 (25th)	2	0	86	0	22	11	1	0	100
California	....	Sept. 9, 1850 (31st)	0	0	349	0	34	9	0	0	358
Colorado	Feb. 28, 1861	Aug. 1, 1876 (38th)	2	0	59	0	23	9	2	1	73
Connecticut	....	Jan. 9, 1788 (5th)	0	0	209	0	29	26	0	0	235
Delaware	....	Dec. 7, 1787 (1st)	0	0	62	0	37	14	0	0	76
District of Columbia	July 16, 1790	....	3	0	0	0	0	0	0	0	3
Florida	Mar. 20, 1822	Mar. 3, 1845 (27th)	4	0	127	0	27	6	1	0	138
Georgia	....	Jan. 2, 1788 (4th)	0	0	280	0	38	22	0	0	302
Guam	Apr. 11, 1899	....	4	0	0	0	0	0	0	0	4
Hawaii	June 14, 1900	Aug. 21, 1959 (50th)	10	0	9	0	3	4	0	0	23
Idaho	Mar. 3, 1863	July 3, 1890 (43d)	8	0	27	0	19	6	1	0	42
Illinois	Feb. 3, 1809	Dec. 3, 1818 (21st)	3	0	449	0	31	19	0	0	471
Indiana	May 7, 1800	Dec. 11, 1816 (19th)	2	0	301	1	27	18	0	0	322
Iowa	June 12, 1838	Dec. 28, 1846 (29th)	1	0	169	0	21	11	1	0	182
Kansas	May 30, 1854	Jan. 29, 1861 (34th)	2	0	108	0	24	9	0	0	119
Kentucky	....	June 1, 1792 (15th)	0	0	312	0	38	28	0	0	340
Louisiana[5]	Mar. 4, 1804	Apr. 30, 1812 (18th)	2	0	148	0	35	13	0	0	163
Maine	....	Mar. 15, 1820 (23d)	0	0	134	0	22	15	0	0	149
Mariana Islands	Apr. 11, 1899	....	1	0	0	0	0	0	0	0	1
Maryland	....	Apr. 28, 1788 (7th)	0	0	280	0	29	27	0	0	307
Massachusetts	....	Feb. 6, 1788 (6th)	0	0	403	0	24	29	0	0	432
Michigan	Jan. 11, 1805	Jan. 26, 1837 (26th)	5	0	256	0	23	13	1	1	276
Minnesota	Mar. 3, 1849	May 11, 1858 (32d)	2	0	121	0	28	10	1	0	134
Mississippi	Apr. 17, 1798	Dec. 10, 1817 (20th)	3	0	110	0	29	14	0	1	128
Missouri	June 4, 1812	Aug. 10, 1821 (24th)	2	0	293	1	35	10	0	0	306
Montana	May 26, 1864	Nov. 8, 1889 (41st)	5	0	26	0	15	5	0	1	37

REPRESENTATIVES, SENATORS, DELEGATES, AND RESIDENT COMMISSIONERS SERVING IN THE—CONTINUED 1st–113th CONGRESSES *

Since the U.S. Congress convened on March 4, 1789, 12,106 individuals have served as Representatives, Senators, or in both capacities. There have been 10,156 Members who served only as Representatives, 1,288 Members who served only in the Senate, and 662 Members with service in both chambers. The total number of Representatives (including individuals serving in both bodies) is 10,818.

These numbers do not include statutory representatives: Resident Commissioners and Delegates. An additional 143 people have served only as Territorial Delegates in the House and 32 people have served only as Resident Commissioners from Puerto Rico or the Philippines.

State/Territory	Date Became a U.S. Territory	Date Entered the Union	Delegates (Only)	Resident Commissioners [1]	Representatives (Only) [2]	Representatives and Delegates	Senators (Only) [3]	Senators and Representatives [4]	Senators and Delegates	Senators, Representatives, and Delegates	Total House Members
Nebraska	May 30, 1854	Mar. 1, 1867 (37th)	5	0	86	0	30	6	1	0	98
Nevada	Mar. 2, 1861	Oct. 31, 1864 (36th)	2	0	30	0	19	6	0	0	38
New Hampshire		June 21, 1788 (9th)	0	0	136	0	37	26	0	0	162
New Jersey		Dec. 18, 1787 (3d)	0	0	321	0	51	15	0	0	336
New Mexico	Sept. 9, 1850	Jan. 6, 1912 (47th)	16	0	23	1	11	5	1	0	46
New York		July 26, 1788 (11th)	0	0	1,443	0	36	23	0	0	1,466
North Carolina		Nov. 21, 1789 (12th)	0	0	330	0	36	18	0	0	348
North Dakota [6]	Mar. 2, 1861	Nov. 2, 1889 (39th)	9	0	14	0	17	6	0	0	29
Ohio		Mar. 1, 1803 (17th)	2	0	632	0	36	19	0	1	654
Oklahoma	May 2, 1890	Nov. 16, 1907 (46th)	3	0	75	1	11	6	0	0	85
Oregon	Aug. 14, 1848	Feb. 14, 1859 (33d)	1	0	57	0	32	4	1	0	63
Pennsylvania		Dec. 12, 1787 (2d)	0	0	1,051	0	33	21	0	0	1,072
Philippines [7]	Apr. 11, 1899		0	13	0	0	0	0	0	0	13
Puerto Rico [7]	Apr. 11, 1899		0	19	0	0	0	0	0	0	19
Rhode Island		May 29, 1790 (13th)	0	0	78	0	38	10	0	0	88
South Carolina		May 23, 1788 (8th)	0	0	225	0	37	17	0	0	242
South Dakota [6]	Mar. 2, 1861	Nov. 2, 1889 (40th)	9	0	14	1	15	10	1	0	35
Tennessee		June 1, 1796 (16th)	1	0	246	0	40	18	0	0	265
Texas		Dec. 29, 1845 (28th)	0	0	247	0	23	9	0	0	256
Utah	Sept. 9, 1850	Jan. 4, 1896 (45th)	5	0	34	0	11	3	2	0	44
Vermont		Mar. 4, 1791 (14th)	0	0	80	0	24	16	0	0	96
Virgin Islands	Mar. 31, 1917		4	0	0	0	0	0	0	0	4
Virginia		June 25, 1788 (10th)	0	0	413	0	27	27	0	0	439
Washington	Mar. 2, 1853	Nov. 11, 1889 (42d)	12	0	72	0	12	10	1	0	95
West Virginia		June 20, 1863 (35th)	0	0	86	0	24	8	0	0	94
Wisconsin	Apr. 20, 1836	May 29, 1848 (30th)	4	0	171	1	19	8	1	0	185
Wyoming	July 25, 1868	July 10, 1890 (44th)	6	0	15	0	17	3	1	0	25

* State Representation March 4, 1789 to February 11, 2014.

[1] Includes 3 members who served as Representatives and 2 members who served as Senators from a different state.

[2] Includes 3 members who served as Delegates and 18 members who served as Senators from a different state.

[3] Includes 18 members who served as Representatives from a different state. One Senator served from two states and one Senator served from three states.
[4] Includes only those members who served as both a Representative and a Senator from the same state. Eighteen members served as a Senator from one state and a Representative from a different state.
[5] Designated Orleans Territory before attaining statehood in 1812.
[6] Dakota Territory became North and South Dakota in 1889. The nine Delegates from this territory are included in counts for both states. The two Delegates who became Representatives from South Dakota are included only in that state's count.
[7] Resident Commissioners served the Philippines (1902–1946) and continue to serve Puerto Rico (1900 to present). Floor and committee privileges granted to statutory representatives (Territorial Delegates and Resident Commissioners) have changed over time; however, they have never been permitted to vote on the final passage of a bill. The Resident Commissioner's duties vary from that of a Delegate in that he has diplomatic privileges as well as most of those of a Member of Congress. The Puerto Rican Resident Commissioner has served a four-year term since 1917. For more information, see ''Status of Delegates and Resident Commissioner,'' Deschler's Precedents, H.Doc. 94–661, Volume 2, Chapter 7, Section 3.

SOURCE: Biographical Directory of the United States Congress.

POLITICAL DIVISIONS OF THE SENATE AND HOUSE FROM 1855 TO 2013

[All Figures Reflect Immediate Result of Elections. Figures Supplied by the Clerk of the House]

Congress	Years	SENATE					HOUSE OF REPRESENTATIVES				
		No. of Senators	Democrats	Republicans	Other parties	Vacancies	No. of Representatives	Democrats	Republicans	Other parties	Vacancies
34th	1855–1857	62	42	15	5	....	234	83	108	43	....
35th	1857–1859	64	39	20	5	....	237	131	92	14	....
36th	1859–1861	66	38	26	2	....	237	101	113	23	....
37th	1861–1863	50	11	31	7	1	178	42	106	28	2
38th	1863–1865	51	12	39	....	....	183	80	103	....	....
39th	1865–1867	52	10	42	....	....	191	46	145	....	....
40th	1867–1869	53	11	42	....	....	193	49	143	....	1
41st	1869–1871	74	11	61	....	2	243	73	170	....	....
42d	1871–1873	74	17	57	....	....	243	104	139	....	....
43d	1873–1875	74	19	54	....	1	293	88	203	....	2
44th	1875–1877	76	29	46	....	1	293	181	107	3	2
45th	1877–1879	76	36	39	1	....	293	156	137	....	....
46th	1879–1881	76	43	33	....	....	293	150	128	14	1
47th	1881–1883	76	37	37	2	....	293	130	152	11	....
48th	1883–1885	76	36	40	....	....	325	200	119	6	....
49th	1885–1887	76	34	41	....	1	325	182	140	2	1
50th	1887–1889	76	37	39	....	....	325	170	151	4	....
51st	1889–1891	84	37	47	....	....	330	156	173	1	....
52d	1891–1893	88	39	47	2	....	333	231	88	14	....
53d	1893–1895	88	44	38	3	3	356	220	126	10	....
54th	1895–1897	88	39	44	5	....	357	104	246	7	....
55th	1897–1899	90	34	46	10	....	357	134	206	16	1
56th	1899–1901	90	26	53	11	....	357	163	185	9	....
57th	1901–1903	90	29	56	3	2	357	153	198	5	1
58th	1903–1905	90	32	58	....	....	386	178	207	....	1
59th	1905–1907	90	32	58	....	....	386	136	250	....	....
60th	1907–1909	92	29	61	....	2	386	164	222	....	....
61st	1909–1911	92	32	59	....	1	391	172	219	....	....
62d	1911–1913	92	42	49	....	1	391	228	162	1	....
63d	1913–1915	96	51	44	1	....	435	290	127	18	....
64th	1915–1917	96	56	39	1	....	435	231	193	8	3
65th	1917–1919	96	42	53	1	....	435	[1] 210	216	9	....
66th	1919–1921	96	47	48	1	....	435	191	237	7	....
67th	1921–1923	96	37	59	....	....	435	132	300	1	2
68th	1923–1925	96	43	51	2	....	435	207	225	3	....
69th	1925–1927	96	40	54	1	1	435	183	247	5	....
70th	1927–1929	96	47	48	1	....	435	195	237	3	....
71st	1929–1931	96	39	56	1	....	435	163	267	1	4
72d	1931–1933	96	47	48	1	....	435	[2] 216	218	1	....
73d	1933–1935	96	59	36	1	....	435	313	117	5	....
74th	1935–1937	96	69	25	2	....	435	322	103	10	....
75th	1937–1939	96	75	17	4	....	435	333	89	13	....
76th	1939–1941	96	69	23	4	....	435	262	169	4	....
77th	1941–1943	96	66	28	2	....	435	267	162	6	....
78th	1943–1945	96	57	38	1	....	435	222	209	4	....
79th	1945–1947	96	57	38	1	....	435	243	190	2	....
80th	1947–1949	96	45	51	....	....	435	188	246	1	....
81st	1949–1951	96	54	42	....	....	435	263	171	1	....
82d	1951–1953	96	48	47	1	....	435	234	199	2	....
83d	1953–1955	96	46	48	2	....	435	213	221	1	....
84th	1955–1957	96	48	47	1	....	435	232	203	....	....
85th	1957–1959	96	49	47	....	....	435	234	201	....	....
86th	1959–1961	98	64	34	....	....	[3] 436	283	153	....	....
87th	1961–1963	100	64	36	....	....	[4] 437	262	175	....	....
88th	1963–1965	100	67	33	....	....	435	258	176	....	1
89th	1965–1967	100	68	32	....	....	435	295	140	....	....
90th	1967–1969	100	64	36	....	....	435	248	187	....	....
91st	1969–1971	100	58	42	....	....	435	243	192	....	....
92d	1971–1973	100	54	44	2	....	435	255	180	....	....
93d	1973–1975	100	56	42	2	....	435	242	192	1	....
94th	1975–1977	100	60	37	2	....	435	291	144	1	....
95th	1977–1979	100	61	38	1	....	435	292	143	....	....
96th	1979–1981	100	58	41	1	....	435	277	158	....	....
97th	1981–1983	100	46	53	1	....	435	242	192	1	....
98th	1983–1985	100	46	54	....	....	435	269	166	....	....
99th	1985–1987	100	47	53	....	....	435	253	182	....	....
100th	1987–1989	100	55	45	....	....	435	258	177	....	....
101st	1989–1991	100	55	45	....	....	435	260	175	....	....
102d	1991–1993	100	56	44	....	....	435	267	167	1	....
103d	1993–1995	100	57	43	....	....	435	258	176	1	....
104th	1995–1997	100	48	52	....	....	435	204	230	1	....
105th	1997–1999	100	45	55	....	....	435	207	226	2	....
106th	1999–2001	100	45	55	....	....	435	211	223	1	....
107th	2001–2003	100	50	50	....	....	435	212	221	2	....
108th	2003–2005	100	48	51	1	....	435	204	229	1	1
109th	2005–2007	100	44	55	1	....	435	202	232	1	....
110th	2007–2009	100	49	49	2	....	435	233	202	....	....
111th	2009–2011	100	55	41	2	2	435	256	178	....	1
112th	2011–2013	100	51	47	2	....	435	193	242	....	....
113th	2013–2015	100	53	45	2	....	435	200	234	....	1

[1] Democrats organized House with help of other parties.
[2] Democrats organized House because of Republican deaths.
[3] Proclamation declaring Alaska a State issued January 3, 1959.
[4] Proclamation declaring Hawaii a State issued August 21, 1959.

GOVERNORS OF THE STATES, COMMONWEALTH, AND TERRITORIES—2013

State, Commonwealth, or Territory	Capital	Governor	Party	Term of service	Expiration of term
STATE				*Years*	
Alabama	Montgomery	Robert Bentley	Republican	[c] 4	Jan. 2015
Alaska	Juneau	Sean Parnell	Republican	[f] 4	Dec. 2014
Arizona	Phoenix	Jan Brewer	Republican	[f] 4	Jan. 2015
Arkansas	Little Rock	Mike Beebe	Democrat	[c] 4	Jan. 2015
California	Sacramento	Jerry Brown	Democrat	[c] 4	Jan. 2015
Colorado	Denver	John Hickenlooper	Democrat	[c] 4	Jan. 2015
Connecticut	Hartford	Dan Malloy	Democrat	[b] 4	Jan. 2015
Delaware	Dover	Jack Markell	Democrat	[c] 4	Jan. 2017
Florida	Tallahassee	Rick Scott	Republican	[f] 4	Jan. 2015
Georgia	Atlanta	Nathan Deal	Republican	[f] 4	Jan. 2015
Hawaii	Honolulu	Neil Abercrombie	Democrat	[c] 4	Dec. 2014
Idaho	Boise	C.L. "Butch" Otter	Republican	[b] 4	Jan. 2015
Illinois	Springfield	Pat Quinn	Democrat	[b] 4	Jan. 2015
Indiana	Indianapolis	Mike Pence	Republican	[f] 4	Jan. 2017
Iowa	Des Moines	Terry Branstad	Republican	[b] 4	Jan. 2015
Kansas	Topeka	Sam Brownback	Republican	[c] 4	Jan. 2015
Kentucky	Frankfort	Steven L. Beshear	Democrat	[c] 4	Dec. 2015
Louisiana	Baton Rouge	Bobby Jindal	Republican	[f] 4	Jan. 2016
Maine	Augusta	Paul LePage	Republican	[f] 4	Jan. 2015
Maryland	Annapolis	Martin O'Malley	Democrat	[f] 4	Jan. 2015
Massachusetts	Boston	Deval Patrick	Democrat	[b] 4	Jan. 2015
Michigan	Lansing	Rick Snyder	Republican	[b] 4	Jan. 2015
Minnesota	St. Paul	Mark Dayton	Democrat	[b] 4	Jan. 2015
Mississippi	Jackson	Phil Bryant	Republican	[c] 4	Jan. 2016
Missouri	Jefferson City	Jay Nixon	Democrat	[c] 4	Jan. 2017
Montana	Helena	Steve Bullock	Democrat	[g] 4	Jan. 2017
Nebraska	Lincoln	Dave Heineman	Republican	[c] 4	Jan. 2015
Nevada	Carson City	Brian Sandoval	Republican	[c] 4	Jan. 2015
New Hampshire	Concord	Maggie Hassan	Democrat	[b] 2	Jan. 2015
New Jersey	Trenton	Chris Christie	Republican	[c] 4	Jan. 2018
New Mexico	Santa Fe	Susana Martinez	Republican	[c] 4	Jan. 2015
New York	Albany	Andrew Cuomo	Democrat	[b] 4	Jan. 2015
North Carolina	Raleigh	Pat McCrory	Republican	[c] 4	Jan. 2017
North Dakota	Bismarck	Jack Dalrymple	Republican	[b] 4	Dec. 2016
Ohio	Columbus	John Kasich	Republican	[c] 4	Jan. 2015
Oklahoma	Oklahoma City	Mary Fallin	Republican	[c] 4	Jan. 2015
Oregon	Salem	John Kitzhaber	Democrat	[f] 4	Jan. 2015
Pennsylvania	Harrisburg	Tom Corbett	Republican	[c] 4	Jan. 2015
Rhode Island	Providence	Lincoln Chafee	Independent	[c] 4	Jan. 2015
South Carolina	Columbia	Nikki R. Haley	Republican	[c] 4	Jan. 2015
South Dakota	Pierre	Dennis Daugaard	Republican	[c] 4	Jan. 2015
Tennessee	Nashville	Bill Haslam	Republican	[c] 4	Jan. 2015
Texas	Austin	Rick Perry	Republican	[b] 4	Jan. 2015
Utah	Salt Lake City	Gary R. Herbert	Republican	[b] 4	Jan. 2017
Vermont	Montpelier	Peter Shumlin	Democrat	[b] 2	Jan. 2015
Virginia	Richmond	Terry McAuliffe	Democrat	[a] 4	Jan. 2018
Washington	Olympia	Jay Inslee	Democrat	[d] 4	Jan. 2017
West Virginia	Charleston	Earl Ray Tomblin	Democrat	[c] 4	Jan. 2017
Wisconsin	Madison	Scott Walker	Republican	[b] 4	Jan. 2015
Wyoming	Cheyenne	Matthew Mead	Republican	[c] 4	Jan. 2015
COMMONWEALTH OF					
Puerto Rico	San Juan	Alejandro García Padilla	Popular Democrat.	[b] 4	Jan. 2017
TERRITORIES					
Guam	Agana	Eddie Calvo	Republican	[c] 4	Jan. 2015
Virgin Islands	Charlotte Amalie	John deJongh, Jr.	Democrat	[c] 4	Jan. 2015
American Samoa	Pago Pago	Lolo Matalasi Moliga	Independent	[c] 4	Jan. 2017
Northern Mariana Islands.	Saipan	Eloy S. Inos	Covenant	[h] 5	Jan. 2015

[a] Cannot succeed himself. [b] No limit. [c] Can serve 2 consecutive terms. [d] Can serve 3 consecutive terms. [e] Can serve 4 consecutive terms. [f] Can serve no more than 8 years in a 12-year period. [g] Can serve no more than 8 years in a 16-year period. [h] The dates for gubernatorial elections in the Northern Mariana Islands are being changed from odd-numbered years to even-numbered ones, beginning in November 2014 (rather than November 2013); therefore, for the current term only, the governor is serving a 5-year term rather than a 4-year term.

NOTE: Information for table obtained from the National Governors Association.

PRESIDENTS AND VICE PRESIDENTS AND THE CONGRESSES COINCIDENT WITH THEIR TERMS [1]

President	Vice President	Service	Congresses
George Washington	John Adams	Apr. 30, 1789–Mar. 3, 1797	1, 2, 3, 4.
John Adams	Thomas Jefferson	Mar. 4, 1797–Mar. 3, 1801	5, 6.
Thomas Jefferson	Aaron Burr	Mar. 4, 1801–Mar. 3, 1805	7, 8.
Do	George Clinton	Mar. 4, 1805–Mar. 3, 1809	9, 10.
James Madison	..do. [2]	Mar. 4, 1809–Mar. 3, 1813	11, 12.
Do	Elbridge Gerry [3]	Mar. 4, 1813–Mar. 3, 1817	13, 14.
James Monroe	Daniel D. Tompkins	Mar. 4, 1817–Mar. 3, 1825	15, 16, 17, 18, 19
John Quincy Adams	John C. Calhoun	Mar. 4, 1825–Mar. 3, 1829	19, 20.
Andrew Jackson	..do. [4]	Mar. 4, 1829–Mar. 3, 1833	21, 22.
Do	Martin Van Buren	Mar. 4, 1833–Mar. 3, 1837	23, 24.
Martin Van Buren	Richard M. Johnson	Mar. 4, 1837–Mar. 3, 1841	25, 26.
William Henry Harrison [5]	John Tyler	Mar. 4, 1841–Apr. 4, 1841	27.
John Tyler		Apr. 6, 1841 –Mar. 3, 1845	27, 28.
James K. Polk	George M. Dallas	Mar. 4, 1845–Mar. 3, 1849	29, 30.
Zachary Taylor [5]	Millard Fillmore	Mar. 5, 1849–July 9, 1850	31.
Millard Fillmore		July 10, 1850–Mar. 3, 1853	31, 32.
Franklin Pierce	William R. King [6]	Mar. 4, 1853–Mar. 3, 1857	33, 34.
James Buchanan	John C. Breckinridge	Mar. 4, 1857–Mar. 3, 1861	35, 36.
Abraham Lincoln	Hannibal Hamlin	Mar. 4, 1861–Mar. 3, 1865	37, 38.
Do. [5]	Andrew Johnson	Mar. 4, 1865–Apr. 15, 1865	39.
Andrew Johnson		Apr. 15, 1865–Mar. 3, 1869	39, 40.
Ulysses S. Grant	Schuyler Colfax	Mar. 4, 1869–Mar. 3, 1873	41, 42.
Do	Henry Wilson [7]	Mar. 4, 1873–Mar. 3, 1877	43, 44.
Rutherford B. Hayes	William A. Wheeler	Mar. 4, 1877–Mar. 3, 1881	45, 46.
James A. Garfield [5]	Chester A. Arthur	Mar. 4, 1881–Sept. 19, 1881	47.
Chester A. Arthur		Sept. 20, 1881–Mar. 3, 1885	47, 48.
Grover Cleveland	Thomas A. Hendricks [8]	Mar. 4, 1885–Mar. 3, 1889	49, 50.
Benjamin Harrison	Levi P. Morton	Mar. 4, 1889–Mar. 3, 1893	51, 52.
Grover Cleveland	Adlai E. Stevenson	Mar. 4, 1893–Mar. 3, 1897	53, 54.
William McKinley	Garret A. Hobart [9]	Mar. 4, 1897–Mar. 3, 1901	55, 56.
Do. [5]	Theodore Roosevelt	Mar. 4, 1901–Sept. 14, 1901	57.
Theodore Roosevelt		Sept. 14, 1901–Mar. 3, 1905	57, 58.
Do	Charles W. Fairbanks	Mar. 4, 1905–Mar. 3, 1909	59, 60.
William H. Taft	James S. Sherman [10]	Mar. 4, 1909–Mar. 3, 1913	61, 62.
Woodrow Wilson	Thomas R. Marshall	Mar. 4, 1913–Mar. 3, 1921	63, 64, 65, 66, 67.
Warren G. Harding [5]	Calvin Coolidge	Mar. 4, 1921–Aug. 2, 1923	67.
Calvin Coolidge		Aug. 3, 1923–Mar. 3, 1925	68.
Do	Charles G. Dawes	Mar. 4, 1925–Mar. 3, 1929	69, 70.
Herbert C. Hoover	Charles Curtis	Mar. 4, 1929–Mar. 3, 1933	71, 72.
Franklin D. Roosevelt	John N. Garner	Mar. 4, 1933–Jan. 20, 1941	73, 74, 75, 76, 77.
Do	Henry A. Wallace	Jan. 20, 1941–Jan. 20, 1945	77, 78, 79.
Do. [5]	Harry S. Truman	Jan. 20, 1945–Apr. 12, 1945	79.
Harry S. Truman		Apr. 12, 1945–Jan. 20, 1949	79, 80, 81.
Do	Alben W. Barkley	Jan. 20, 1949–Jan. 20, 1953	81, 82, 83.
Dwight D. Eisenhower	Richard M. Nixon	Jan. 20, 1953–Jan. 20, 1961	83, 84, 85, 86, 87.
John F. Kennedy [5]	Lyndon B. Johnson	Jan. 20, 1961–Nov. 22, 1963	87, 88, 89.
Lyndon B. Johnson		Nov. 22, 1963–Jan. 20, 1965	88, 89.
Do	Hubert H. Humphrey	Jan. 20, 1965–Jan. 20, 1969	89, 90, 91.
Richard M. Nixon	Spiro T. Agnew [11]	Jan. 20, 1969–Dec. 6, 1973	91, 92, 93.
Do. [13]	Gerald R. Ford [12]	Dec. 6, 1973–Aug. 9, 1974	93.
Gerald R. Ford		Aug. 9, 1974–Dec. 19, 1974	93.
Do	Nelson A. Rockefeller [14]	Dec. 19, 1974–Jan. 20, 1977	93, 94, 95.
James Earl "Jimmy" Carter	Walter F. Mondale	Jan. 20, 1977–Jan. 20, 1981	95, 96, 97.
Ronald Reagan	George Bush	Jan. 20, 1981–Jan. 20, 1989	97, 98, 99, 100, 101.
George Bush	Dan Quayle	Jan. 20, 1989–Jan. 20, 1993	101, 102, 103.
William J. Clinton	Albert Gore	Jan. 20, 1993–Jan. 20, 2001	103, 104, 105, 106, 107.
George W. Bush	Richard B. Cheney	Jan. 20, 2001–Jan. 20, 2009	107, 108, 109, 110, 111.
Barack H. Obama	Joseph R. Biden, Jr.	Jan. 20, 2009–	111, 112, 113.

[1] From 1789 until 1933, the terms of the President and Vice President and the term of the Congress coincided, beginning on March 4 and ending on March 3. This changed when the 20th amendment to the Constitution was adopted in 1933. Beginning in 1934 the convening date for Congress became January 3, and beginning in 1937 the starting date for the Presidential term became January 20. Because of this change, the number of Congresses overlapping with a Presidential term increased from two to three, although the third only overlaps by a few weeks.

[2] Died Apr. 20, 1812.

[3] Died Nov. 23, 1814.

[4] Resigned Dec. 28, 1832, to become a United States Senator from South Carolina.

[5] Died in office.

[6] Died Apr. 18, 1853.

[7] Died Nov. 22, 1875.

[8] Died Nov. 25, 1885.

[9] Died Nov. 21, 1899.

[10] Died Oct. 30, 1912.

[11] Resigned Oct. 10, 1973.

[12] Nominated to be Vice President by President Richard M. Nixon on Oct. 12, 1973; confirmed by the Senate on Nov. 27, 1973; confirmed by the House of Representatives on Dec. 6, 1973; took the oath of office on Dec. 6, 1973 in the Hall of the House of Representatives. This was the first time a Vice President was nominated by the President and confirmed by the Congress pursuant to the 25th amendment to the Constitution.

[13] Resigned from office.

[14] Nominated to be Vice President by President Gerald R. Ford on Aug. 20, 1974; confirmed by the Senate on Dec. 10, 1974; confirmed by the House of Representatives on Dec. 19, 1974; took the oath of office on Dec. 19, 1974, in the Senate Chamber.

CAPITOL BUILDINGS AND GROUNDS

UNITED STATES CAPITOL

Overview of the Building and its Function

The United States Capitol is among the most architecturally impressive and symbolically important buildings in the world. It has housed the chambers of the Senate and the House of Representatives for more than two centuries. Begun in 1793, the Capitol has been built, burnt, rebuilt, extended, and restored; today, it stands as a monument not only to its builders but also to the American people and their government.

As the focal point of the government's legislative branch, the Capitol is the centerpiece of the Capitol complex, which includes the six principal congressional office buildings and three Library of Congress buildings constructed on Capitol Hill in the 19th and 20th centuries.

In addition to its active use by Congress, the Capitol is a museum of American art and history. Each year, it is visited by millions of people from around the world.

A fine example of 19th-century neoclassical architecture, the Capitol combines function with aesthetics. Its design was derived from ancient Greece and Rome and evokes the ideals that guided the nation's founders as they framed their new republic. As the building was expanded from its original design, harmony with the existing portions was carefully maintained.

Today, the Capitol covers a ground area of 175,170 square feet, or about 4 acres, and has a floor area of approximately 16½ acres. Its length, from north to south, is 751 feet 4 inches; its greatest width, including approaches, is 350 feet. Its height above the base line on the east front to the top of the Statue of Freedom is 288 feet; from the basement floor to the top of the dome is an ascent of 365 steps.

The building is divided into five levels. The first, or ground, floor is occupied chiefly by committee rooms and the spaces allocated to various congressional officers. The areas accessible to visitors on this level include the Hall of Columns, the restored Old Supreme Court Chamber, and the Crypt beneath the Rotunda.

The second floor holds the chambers of the House of Representatives (in the south wing) and the Senate (in the north wing). This floor also contains three major public areas. In the center under the dome is the Rotunda, a circular ceremonial space that also serves as a gallery of paintings and sculpture depicting significant people and events in the nation's history. The Rotunda is 96 feet in diameter and rises 180 feet 3 inches to the canopy. The semicircular chamber south of the Rotunda served as the Hall of the House until 1857; now designated National Statuary Hall, it houses part of the Capitol's collection of statues donated by the states in commemoration of notable citizens. The Old Senate Chamber northeast of the Rotunda, which was used by the Senate until 1859, has been returned to its mid-19th-century appearance.

The third floor allows access to the galleries from which visitors to the Capitol may watch the proceedings of the House and the Senate when Congress is in session. The rest of this floor is occupied by offices, committee rooms, and press galleries.

The fourth floor and the basement/terrace level of the Capitol are occupied by offices, machinery rooms, workshops, and other support areas.

Located beneath the East Front plaza, the newest addition to the Capitol is the Capitol Visitor Center (CVC). Preparatory construction activities began in 2002, and the CVC was opened to the public on December 2, 2008. This date was chosen for its significance in the Capitol's history: it was on December 2, 1863, that the Statue of Freedom was placed atop the Capitol. The CVC occupies 580,000 square feet of space on three levels and includes an Exhibition Hall, a restaurant, orientation theaters, gift shops, and other visitor amenities as well as meeting space for the House and Senate.

Location of the Capitol

The Capitol is located at the eastern end of the Mall on a plateau 88 feet above the level of the Potomac River, commanding a westward view across the Capitol Reflecting

Pool to the Washington Monument 1.4 miles away and the Lincoln Memorial 2.2 miles away.

Before 1791, the Federal Government had no permanent site. The early Congresses met in eight different cities: Philadelphia, Baltimore, Lancaster, York, Princeton, Annapolis, Trenton, and New York City. The subject of a permanent capital for the Government of the United States was first raised by Congress in 1783; it was ultimately addressed in Article I, Section 8 of the Constitution (1787), which gave the Congress legislative authority over ''such District (not exceeding ten Miles square) as may, by Cession of Particular States, and the Acceptance of Congress, become the Seat of the Government of the United States. . . .''

In 1788, the State of Maryland ceded to Congress ''any district in this State, not exceeding ten miles square,'' and in 1789 the State of Virginia ceded an equivalent amount of land. In accordance with the ''Residence Act'' passed by Congress in 1790, President Washington in 1791 selected the area that is now the District of Columbia from the land ceded by Maryland (private landowners whose property fell within this area were compensated by a payment of £25 per acre); that ceded by Virginia was not used for the capital and was returned to Virginia in 1846. Also under the provisions of that Act, he selected three commissioners to survey the site and oversee the design and construction of the capital city and its government buildings. The commissioners, in turn, selected the French-American engineer Pierre Charles L'Enfant to plan the new city of Washington. L'Enfant's plan, which was influenced by the gardens at Versailles, arranged the city's streets and avenues in a grid overlaid with baroque diagonals; the result is a functional and aesthetic whole in which government buildings are balanced against public lawns, gardens, squares, and paths. The Capitol itself was located at the elevated east end of the Mall, on the brow of what was then called Jenkins' Hill. The site was, in L'Enfant's words, ''a pedestal waiting for a monument.''

Selection of a Plan

L'Enfant was expected to design the Capitol and to supervise its construction. However, he refused to produce any drawings for the building, claiming that he carried the design ''in his head''; this fact and his refusal to consider himself subject to the commissioners' authority led to his dismissal in 1792. In March of that year the commissioners announced a competition, suggested by Secretary of State Thomas Jefferson, that would award $500 and a city lot to whoever produced ''the most approved plan'' for the Capitol by mid-July. None of the 17 plans submitted, however, was wholly satisfactory. In October, a letter arrived from Dr. William Thornton, a Scottish-trained physician living in Tortola, British West Indies, requesting an opportunity to present a plan even though the competition had closed. The commissioners granted this request.

Thornton's plan depicted a building composed of three sections. The central section, which was topped by a low dome, was to be flanked on the north and south by two rectangular wings (one for the Senate and one for the House of Representatives). President Washington commended the plan for its ''grandeur, simplicity and convenience,'' and on April 5, 1793, it was accepted by the commissioners; Washington gave his formal approval on July 25.

Brief Construction History

1793–1829

The cornerstone was laid by President Washington in the building's southeast corner on September 18, 1793, with Masonic ceremonies. Work progressed under the direction of three architects in succession. Stephen H. Hallet (an entrant in the earlier competition) and George Hadfield were eventually dismissed by the commissioners because of inappropriate design changes that they tried to impose; James Hoban, the architect of the White House, saw the first phase of the project through to completion.

Construction was a laborious and time-consuming process: the sandstone used for the building had to be ferried on boats from the quarries at Aquia, Virginia; workers had to be induced to leave their homes to come to the relative wilderness of Capitol Hill; and funding was inadequate. By August 1796 the commissioners were forced to focus the entire work effort on the building's north wing so that it at least could be ready for government occupancy as scheduled. Even so, some third-floor rooms were still unfinished when the Congress, the Supreme Court, the Library of Congress, and the courts of the District of Columbia occupied the Capitol in late 1800.

In 1803, Congress allocated funds to resume construction. A year earlier, the office of the Commissioners had been abolished and replaced by a superintendent of the city of Washington. To oversee the renewed construction effort, Benjamin Henry Latrobe was appointed surveyor of public buildings. The first professional architect and engineer to work in America, Latrobe modified Thornton's plan for the south wing to include space for offices and committee rooms; he also introduced alterations to simplify the construction work. Latrobe began work by removing a squat, oval, temporary building known as "the Oven," which had been erected in 1801 as a meeting place for the House of Representatives. By 1807 construction on the south wing was sufficiently advanced that the House was able to occupy its new legislative chamber, and the wing was completed in 1811.

In 1808, as work on the south wing progressed, Latrobe began the rebuilding of the north wing, which had fallen into disrepair. Rather than simply repair the wing, he redesigned the interior of the building to increase its usefulness and durability; among his changes was the addition of a chamber for the Supreme Court. By 1811, he had completed the eastern half of this wing, but funding was being increasingly diverted to preparations for a second war with Great Britain. By 1813, Latrobe had no further work in Washington and so he departed, leaving the north and south wings of the Capitol connected only by a temporary wooden passageway.

The War of 1812 left the Capitol, in Latrobe's later words, "a most magnificent ruin": on August 24, 1814, British troops set fire to the building, and only a sudden rainstorm prevented its complete destruction. Immediately after the fire, Congress met for one session in Blodget's Hotel, which was at Seventh and E Streets, NW. From 1815 to 1819, Congress occupied a building erected for it on First Street, NE., on part of the site now occupied by the Supreme Court Building. This building later came to be known as the Old Brick Capitol.

Latrobe returned to Washington in 1815, when he was rehired to restore the Capitol. In addition to making repairs, he took advantage of this opportunity to make further changes in the building's interior design (for example, an enlargement of the Senate Chamber) and introduce new materials (for example, marble discovered along the upper Potomac). However, he came under increasing pressure because of construction delays (most of which were beyond his control) and cost overruns; finally, he resigned his post in November 1817.

On January 8, 1818, Charles Bulfinch, a prominent Boston architect, was hired to succeed Latrobe. Continuing the restoration of the north and south wings, he was able to make the chambers for the Supreme Court, the House, and the Senate ready for use by 1819. Bulfinch also redesigned and supervised the construction of the Capitol's central section. The copper-covered wooden dome that topped this section was made higher than Bulfinch considered appropriate to the building's size (at the direction of President James Monroe and Secretary of State John Quincy Adams). After completing the last part of the building in 1826, Bulfinch spent the next few years on the Capitol's decoration and landscaping. In 1829, his work was done and his position with the government was terminated. In the 38 years following Bulfinch's tenure, the Capitol was entrusted to the care of the commissioner of public buildings.

1830–1868

The Capitol was by this point already an impressive structure. At ground level, its length was 351 feet 7½ inches and its width was 282 feet 10½ inches. Up to the year 1827—records from later years being incomplete—the project cost was $2,432,851.34. Improvements to the building continued in the years to come (running water in 1832, gas lighting in the 1840s), but by 1850 its size could no longer accommodate the increasing numbers of Senators and Representatives from newly admitted states. The Senate therefore voted to hold another competition, offering a prize of $500 for the best plan to extend the Capitol. Several suitable plans were submitted, some proposing an eastward extension of the building and others proposing the addition of large north and south wings. However, Congress was unable to decide between these two approaches, and the prize money was divided among five architects. Thus, the tasks of selecting a plan and appointing an architect fell to President Millard Fillmore.

Fillmore's choice was Thomas U. Walter, a Philadelphia architect who had entered the competition. On July 4, 1851, in a ceremony whose principal oration was delivered by Secretary of State Daniel Webster, the president laid the cornerstone in the northeast corner of the House wing. Over the next 14 years, Walter supervised the construction of the extension, ensuring their compatibility with the architectural style of the existing building. However, because the Aquia Creek sandstone used earlier had deteriorated noticeably, he chose to use marble for the exterior. For the veneer, Walter selected marble quarried at Lee, Massachusetts, and for the columns he used marble from Cockeysville, Maryland.

Walter faced several significant challenges during the course of construction. Chief among these was the steady imposition by the government of additional tasks without additional pay. Aside from his work on the Capitol extension, Walter designed the wings of the Patent

Office building, extensions to the Treasury and Post Office buildings, and the Marine barracks in Pensacola and Brooklyn. When the Library of Congress in the Capitol's west central section was gutted by a fire in 1851, Walter was commissioned to restore it. He also encountered obstacles in his work on the Capitol extensions. His location of the legislative chambers was changed in 1853 at the direction of President Franklin Pierce, based on the suggestions of the newly appointed supervising engineer, Captain Montgomery C. Meigs. In general, however, the project progressed rapidly: the House of Representatives was able to meet in its new chamber on December 16, 1857, and the Senate first met in its present chamber on January 4, 1859. The old House chamber was later designated National Statuary Hall. In 1861 most construction was suspended because of the Civil War, and the Capitol was used briefly as a military barracks, hospital, and bakery. In 1862 work on the entire building was resumed.

As the new wings were constructed, more than doubling the length of the Capitol, it became apparent that the dome erected by Bulfinch no longer suited the building's proportions. In 1855 Congress voted for its replacement based on Walter's design for a new, fireproof cast-iron dome. The old dome was removed in 1856 and 5,000,000 pounds of new masonry was placed on the existing rotunda walls. Iron used in the dome construction had an aggregate weight of 8,909,200 pounds and was lifted into place by steam-powered derricks.

In 1859, Thomas Crawford's plaster model for the Statue of Freedom, designed for the top of the dome, arrived from the sculptor's studio in Rome. With a height of 19 feet 6 inches, the statue was almost 3 feet taller than specified, and Walter was compelled to make revisions to his design for the dome. When cast in bronze by Clark Mills at his foundry on the outskirts of Washington, it weighed 14,985 pounds. The statue was lifted into place atop the dome in 1863, its final section being installed on December 2 to the accompaniment of gun salutes from the forts around the city.

The work on the dome and the extension was completed under the direction of Edward Clark, who had served as Walter's assistant and was appointed Architect of the Capitol in 1865 after Walter's resignation. In 1866, the Italian-born artist Constantino Brumidi finished the canopy fresco, a monumental painting entitled *The Apotheosis of George Washington.* The Capitol extension was completed in 1868.

1869–1902

Clark continued to hold the post of Architect of the Capitol until his death in 1902. During his tenure, the Capitol underwent considerable modernization. Steam heat was gradually installed in the old Capitol. In 1874 the first elevator was installed, and in the 1880s electric lighting began to replace gas lights.

Between 1884 and 1891, the marble terraces on the north, west, and south sides of the Capitol were constructed. As part of the landscape plan devised by Frederick Law Olmsted, these terraces not only added over 100 rooms to the Capitol but also provided a broader, more substantial visual base for the building.

On November 6, 1898, a gas explosion and fire in the original north wing dramatically illustrated the need for fireproofing. The roofs over the Statuary Hall wing and the original north wing were reconstructed and fireproofed, the work being completed in 1902 by Clark's successor, Elliott Woods. In 1901, the space in the west central front vacated by the Library of Congress was converted to committee rooms.

1903–1970

During the remainder of Woods's service, which ended with his death in 1923, no major structural work was required on the Capitol. The activities performed in the building were limited chiefly to cleaning and refurbishing the interior. David Lynn, the Architect of the Capitol from 1923 until his retirement in 1954, continued these tasks. Between July 1949 and January 1951, the corroded roofs and skylights of both wings and the connecting corridors were replaced with new roofs of concrete and steel, covered with copper. The cast-iron and glass ceilings of the House and Senate chambers were replaced with ceilings of stainless steel and plaster, with a laylight of carved glass and bronze in the middle of each. The House and Senate chambers were completely redecorated, modern lighting was added, and acoustical problems were solved. During this renovation program, the House and Senate vacated their chambers on several occasions so that the work could progress.

The next significant modification made to the Capitol was the east front extension. This project was carried out under the supervision of Architect of the Capitol J. George Stewart, who served from 1954 until his death in 1970. Begun in 1958, it involved the construction of a new east front 32 feet 6 inches east of the old front, faithfully reproducing the sandstone structure in marble. The old sandstone walls were not destroyed; rather, they were left in place to become a part of the interior wall and are now buttressed by the addition. The marble columns of the connecting corridors were also moved and reused. Other elements of this project included repairing the dome, constructing a subway terminal under the Senate steps, reconstructing those steps, cleaning both wings, birdproofing the building, providing furniture and furnishings for 90 new rooms created by the extension, and improving the lighting throughout the building. The project was completed in 1962.

1971–PRESENT

During the nearly 25-year tenure (1971–1995) of Architect of the Capitol George M. White, FAIA, the building was both modernized and restored. Electronic voting equipment was installed in the House chamber in 1973; facilities were added to allow television coverage of the House and Senate debates in 1979 and 1986, respectively; and improved climate control, electronic surveillance systems, and new computer and communications facilities have been added to bring the Capitol up-to-date. The Old Senate Chamber, National Statuary Hall, and the Old Supreme Court Chamber, on the other hand, were restored to their mid-19th-century appearance in the 1970s.

In 1983, work began on the strengthening, renovation, and preservation of the west front of the Capitol. Structural problems had developed over the years because of defects in the original foundations, deterioration of the sandstone facing material, alterations to the basic building fabric (a fourth-floor addition and channeling of the walls to install interior utilities), and damage from the fires of 1814 and 1851 and the 1898 gas explosion.

To strengthen the structure, over 1,000 stainless steel tie rods were set into the building's masonry. More than 30 layers of paint were removed, and damaged stonework was repaired or replicated. Ultimately, 40 percent of the sandstone blocks were replaced with limestone. The walls were treated with a special consolidant and then painted to match the marble wings. The entire project was completed in 1987.

A related project, completed in January 1993, effected the repair of the Olmsted terraces, which had been subject to damage from settling, and converted the terrace courtyards into several thousand square feet of meeting space.

As the Capitol enters its third century, restoration and modernization work continues. Alan M. Hantman, FAIA, was appointed in February 1997 to a 10-year term as Architect of the Capitol. Projects under his direction included rehabilitation of the Capitol dome; conservation of murals; improvement of speech-reinforcement, electrical, and fire-protection systems in the Capitol and the Congressional office buildings; work on security improvements within the Capitol complex; restoration of the U.S. Botanic Garden Conservatory; the design and construction of the National Garden adjacent to the Botanic Garden Conservatory; renovation of the building systems in the Dirksen Senate Office Building; publication of the first comprehensive history of the Capitol to appear in a century; and construction of the Capitol Visitor Center. At the end of Mr. Hantman's term in February 2007, Mr. Stephen T. Ayers, FAIA, LEED AP, assumed the position of Acting Architect of the Capitol. On February 24, 2010, President Barack Obama nominated Mr. Ayers to serve as the 11th Architect of the Capitol. On May 12, 2010, the United States Senate, by unanimous consent, confirmed Mr. Ayers, and on May 13, 2010, the President officially appointed Mr. Ayers to a 10-year term as Architect of the Capitol.

HOUSE OFFICE BUILDINGS

CANNON HOUSE OFFICE BUILDING

An increased membership of the Senate and House resulted in a demand for additional rooms for the accommodations of the Senators and Representatives. On March 3, 1903, the Congress authorized the erection of a fireproofed office building for the use of the House. It was designed by the firm of Carrere & Hastings of New York City in the Beaux Arts style. The first brick was laid July 5, 1905, in square No. 690, and formal exercises were held at the laying of the cornerstone on April 14, 1906, in which President Theodore Roosevelt participated. The building was completed and occupied January 10, 1908. A subsequent change in the basis of congressional representation made necessary the building of an additional story in 1913–1914. The total cost of the building, including site, furnishings, equipment, and the subway connecting it with the U.S. Capitol, amounted to $4,860,155.

This office building contains about 500 rooms, and was considered at the time of its completion fully equipped for all the needs of a modern building for office purposes. A garage was added in the building's courtyard in the 1960s.

Pursuant to authority in the Second Supplemental Appropriations Act, 1955, and subsequent action of the House Office Building Commission, remodeling of the Cannon Building began in 1966. The estimated cost of this work was $5,200,000. Pursuant to the provisions of Public Law 87–453, approved May 21, 1962, the building was named in honor of Joseph G. Cannon of Illinois, who was Speaker at the time the building was constructed.

Longworth House Office Building

Under legislation contained in the Authorization Act of January 10, 1929, and in the urgent deficiency bill of March 4, 1929, provisions were made for an additional House office building, to be located on the west side of New Jersey Avenue (opposite the first House office building). The building was designed by the Allied Architects of Washington in the Neoclassical Revival style.

The cornerstone was laid June 24, 1932, and the building was completed on April 20, 1933. It contains 251 two-room suites and 16 committee rooms. Each suite and committee room is provided with a storeroom. Eight floors are occupied by members. The basement and subbasement contain shops and mechanical areas needed for the maintenance of the building. A cafeteria was added in the building's courtyard in the 1960s. The cost of this building, including site, furnishings, and equipment, was $7,805,705. Pursuant to the provisions of Public Law 87–453, approved May 21, 1962, the building was named in honor of Nicholas Longworth of Ohio, who was Speaker when the second House office building was constructed.

Rayburn House Office Building and Other Related Changes and Improvements

Under legislation contained in the Second Supplemental Appropriations Act, 1955, provision was made for construction of a fireproof office building for the House of Representatives.

All work was carried forward by the Architect of the Capitol under the direction of the House Office Building Commission at a cost totaling $135,279,000.

The Rayburn Building is connected to the Capitol by a subway. Designs for the building were prepared by the firm of Harbeson, Hough, Livingston & Larson of Philadelphia, Associate Architects. The building contains 169 congressional suites; full-committee hearing rooms for 9 standing committees, 16 subcommittee hearing rooms, committee staff rooms and other committee facilities; a large cafeteria and other restaurant facilities; an underground garage; and a variety of liaison offices, press and television facilities, maintenance and equipment shops or rooms, and storage areas. This building has nine stories and a penthouse for machinery.

The cornerstone was laid May 24, 1962, by John W. McCormack, Speaker of the House of Representatives. President John F. Kennedy participated in the cornerstone laying and delivered the address.

A portion of the basement floor was occupied beginning March 12, 1964, by House of Representatives personnel moved from the George Washington Inn property. Full occupancy of the Rayburn Building, under the room-filing regulations, was begun February 23, 1965, and completed April 2, 1965. Pursuant to the provisions of Public Law 87–453, approved May 21, 1962, the building was named in honor of Sam Rayburn of Texas.

House Office Building Annex No. 2, named the "Gerald R. Ford House of Representatives Office Building," was acquired in 1975 from the General Services Administration. The structure, located at Second and D Streets, SW., was built in 1939 for the Federal Bureau of Investigation as a fingerprint file archives. This building has approximately 432,000 square feet of space.

SENATE OFFICE BUILDINGS

Richard Brevard Russell Senate Office Building

In 1891 the Senate provided itself with office space by the purchase of the Maltby Building, then located on the northwest corner of B Street (now Constitution Avenue) and New Jersey

Avenue, NW. When it was condemned as an unsafe structure, Senators needed safer and more commodious office space. Under authorization of the Act of April 28, 1904, square 686 on the northeast corner of Delaware Avenue and B Street, NE. was purchased as a site for the Senate Office Building. The plans for the House Office Building were adapted for the Senate Office Building by the firm of Carrere & Hastings, with the exception that the side of the building fronting on First Street, NE. was temporarily omitted. The cornerstone was laid without special exercises on July 31, 1906, and the building was occupied March 5, 1909. In 1931, the completion of the fourth side of the building was commenced. In 1933 it was completed, together with alterations to the C Street facade, and the construction of terraces, balustrades, and approaches. The cost of the completed building, including the site, furnishings, equipment and the subway connecting it with the United States Capitol, was $8,390,892.

The building was named the ''Richard Brevard Russell Senate Office Building'' by Senate Resolution 296, 92nd Congress, agreed to October 11, 1972, as amended by Senate Resolution 295, 96th Congress, agreed to December 3, 1979.

Everett McKinley Dirksen Senate Office Building

Under legislation contained in the Second Deficiency Appropriations Act, 1948, Public Law 80–785, provision was made for an additional office building for the United States Senate with limits of cost of $1,100,000 for acquisition of the site and $20,600,000 for constructing and equipping the building.

The construction cost limit was subsequently increased to $24,196,000. All work was carried forward by the Architect of the Capitol under the direction of the Senate Office Building Commission. The New York firm of Eggers & Higgins served as the consulting architect.

The site was acquired and cleared in 1948–49 at a total cost of $1,011,492.

A contract for excavation, concrete footings, and mats for the new building was awarded in January 1955, in the amount of $747,200. Groundbreaking ceremonies were held January 26, 1955.

A contract for the superstructure of the new building was awarded September 9, 1955, in the amount of $17,200,000. The cornerstone was laid July 13, 1956.

As a part of this project, a new underground subway system was installed from the Capitol to both the Old and New Senate Office Buildings.

An appropriation of $1,000,000 for furniture and furnishings for the new building was provided in 1958. The building was accepted for beneficial occupancy on October 15, 1958.

The building was named the ''Everett McKinley Dirksen Senate Office Building'' by Senate Resolution 296, 92nd Congress, agreed to October 11, 1972, and Senate Resolution 295, 96th Congress, agreed to December 3, 1979.

Philip A. Hart Senate Office Building

Construction as an extension to the Dirksen Senate Office Building was authorized on October 31, 1972; legislation enacted in subsequent years increased the scope of the project and established a total cost ceiling of $137,700,400. The firm of John Carl Warnecke & Associates served as Associate Architect for the project.

Senate Resolution 525, passed August 30, 1976, amended by Senate Resolution 295, 96th Congress, agreed to December 3, 1979, provided that upon completion of the extension it would be named the ''Philip A. Hart Senate Office Building'' to honor the Senator from Michigan.

The contract for clearing of the site, piping for utilities, excavation, and construction of foundation was awarded in December 1975. Groundbreaking took place January 5, 1976. The contract for furnishing and delivery of the exterior stone was awarded in February 1977, and the contract for the superstructure, which included wall and roof systems and the erection of all exterior stonework, was awarded in October 1977. The contract for the first portion of the interior and related work was awarded in December 1978. A contract for interior finishing was awarded in July 1980. The first suite was occupied on November 22, 1982. Alexander Calder's mobile/stabile *Mountains and Clouds* was installed in the building's atrium in November 1986.

CAPITOL POWER PLANT

During the development of the plans for the Cannon and Russell Buildings, the question of heat, light, and power was considered. The Senate and House wings of the Capitol were heated by separate heating plants. The Library of Congress also had a heating plant for that building. It was determined that needs for heating and lighting and electrical power could be met by a central power plant.

A site was selected in Garfield Park. Since this park was a Government reservation, an appropriation was not required to secure title. The determining factors leading to the selection of this site were its proximity to the tracks of what is now the Penn Central Railroad and to the buildings to be served.

The dimensions of the Capitol Power Plant, which was authorized on April 28, 1904, and completed in 1910, were 244 feet 8 inches by 117 feet.

The buildings originally served by the Capitol Power Plant were connected to it by a reinforced-concrete steam tunnel.

In September 1951, when the demand for electrical energy was reaching the maximum capacity of the Capitol Power Plant, arrangements were made to purchase electrical service from the local public utility company and to discontinue electrical generation. The heating and cooling functions of the Capitol Power Plant were expanded in 1935, 1939, 1958, 1973, and 1980. A new refrigeration plant modernization and expansion project was completed in 2007.

U.S. CAPITOL GROUNDS

A Description of the Grounds

Originally a wooded wilderness, the U.S. Capitol Grounds today provide a park-like setting for the Nation's Capitol, offering a picturesque counterpoint to the building's formal architecture. The grounds immediately surrounding the Capitol are bordered by a stone wall and cover an area of 58.8 acres. Their boundaries are Independence Avenue on the south, Constitution Avenue on the north, First Street, NE./SE. on the east, and First Street, NW./SW. on the west. Over 100 varieties of trees and bushes are planted around the Capitol, and thousands of flowers are used in seasonal displays. In contrast to the building's straight, neoclassical lines, most of the walkways in the grounds are curved. Benches along the paths offer pleasant spots for visitors to appreciate the building, its landscape, and the surrounding areas, most notably the Mall to the west.

The grounds were designed by Frederick Law Olmsted (1822–1903), who planned the landscaping of the area that was performed from 1874 to 1892. Olmsted, who also designed New York's Central Park, is considered the greatest American landscape architect of his day. He was a pioneer in the development of public parks in America, and many of his designs were influenced by his studies of European parks, gardens, and estates. In describing his plan for the Capitol Grounds, Olmsted noted that, "The ground is in design part of the Capitol, but in all respects subsidiary to the central structure." Therefore, he was careful not to group trees or other landscape features in any way that would distract the viewer from the Capitol. The use of sculpture and other ornamentation has also been kept to a minimum.

Many of the trees on the Capitol Grounds have historic or memorial associations. Over 30 states have made symbolic gifts of their state trees to the Capitol Grounds. Many of the trees on the grounds bear plaques that identify their species and their historic significance.

At the East Capitol Street entrance to the Capitol plaza are two large rectangular stone fountains. Six massive red granite lamp piers topped with light fixtures in wrought-iron cages, and 16 smaller bronze light fixtures, line the paved plaza. Three sets of benches are enclosed with wrought-iron railings and grilles; the roofed bench was originally a shelter for streetcar passengers.

The northern part of the grounds offers a shaded walk among trees, flowers, and shrubbery. A small, hexagonal brick structure named the Summer House may be found in the northwest corner of the grounds. This structure contains shaded benches, a central ornamental fountain, and three public drinking fountains. In a small grotto on the eastern side of the Summer House, a stream of water flows and splashes over rocks to create a pleasing sound and cool the summer breezes.

A Brief History of the Grounds Before Olmsted

The land on which the Capitol stands was first occupied by the Manahoacs and the Monacans, who were subtribes of the Algonquin Indians. Early settlers reported that these tribes occasionally held councils not far from the foot of the hill. This land eventually became a part of Cerne Abbey Manor, and at the time of its acquisition by the Federal Government it was owned by Daniel Carroll of Duddington.

The "Residence Act" of 1790 provided that the Federal Government should be established in a permanent location by the year 1800. In early March 1791, the commissioners of the city of Washington, who had been appointed by President George Washington, selected the French engineer Pierre Charles L'Enfant to plan the new federal city. L'Enfant decided to locate the Capitol at the elevated east end of the Mall (on what was then called Jenkins' Hill); he described the site as "a pedestal waiting for a monument."

At this time the site of the Capitol was a relative wilderness partly overgrown with scrub oak. Oliver Wolcott, a signer of the Declaration of Independence, described the soil as an "*exceedingly stiff* clay, becoming dust in dry and mortar in rainy weather."

In 1825, a plan was devised for imposing order on the Capitol Grounds, and it was carried out for almost 15 years. The plan divided the area into flat, rectangular grassy areas bordered by trees, flower beds, and gravel walks. The growth of the trees, however, soon deprived the other plantings of nourishment, and the design became increasingly difficult to maintain in light of sporadic and small appropriations. John Foy, who had charge of the grounds during most of this period, was "superseded for political reasons," and the area was then maintained with little care or forethought. Many rapidly growing but short-lived trees were introduced and soon depleted the soil; a lack of proper pruning and thinning left the majority of the area's vegetation ill-grown, feeble, or dead. Virtually all was removed by the early 1870s, either to make way for building operations during Thomas U. Walter's enlargement of the Capitol or as required by changes in grading to accommodate the new work on the building or the alterations to surrounding streets.

The Olmsted Plan

The mid-19th-century extension of the Capitol, in which the House and Senate wings and the new dome were added, also required that the Capitol Grounds be enlarged, and in 1874 Frederick Law Olmsted was commissioned to plan and oversee the project. As noted above, Olmsted was determined that the grounds should complement the building. In addition, he addressed an architectural problem that had persisted for some years: from the west (the growth of the city had nothing to do with the terraces)—the earthen terraces at the building's base made it seem inadequately supported at the top of the hill. The solution, Olmsted believed, was to construct marble terraces on the north, west, and south sides of the building, thereby causing it to "gain greatly in the supreme qualities of stability, endurance, and repose." He submitted his design for these features in 1875, and after extensive study it was approved.

Work on the grounds began in 1874, concentrating first on the east side and then progressing to the west, north, and south sides. First, the ground was reduced in elevation. Almost 300,000 cubic yards of earth and other material were eventually removed, and over 200 trees were removed. New sewer, gas, and water lines were installed. The soil was then enriched with fertilizers to provide a suitable growth medium for new plantings. Paths and roadways were graded and laid.

By 1876, gas and water service was completed for the entire grounds, and electrical lamp-lighting apparatuses had been installed. Stables and workshops had been removed from the northwest and southwest corners. A streetcar system north and south of the west grounds had been relocated farther from the Capitol, and ornamental shelters were in place at the north and south car-track termini. The granite and bronze lamp piers and ornamental bronze lamps for the east plaza area were completed.

Work accelerated in 1877. By this time, according to Olmsted's report, "altogether 7,837 plants and trees [had] been set out." However, not all had survived: hundreds were stolen or destroyed by vandals, and, as Olmsted explained, "a large number of cattle [had] been caught trespassing." Other work met with less difficulty. Foot-walks were laid with artificial stone, a mixture of cement and sand, and approaches were paved with concrete. An ornamental iron trellis had been installed on the northern east-side walk, and another was under way on the southern walk.

The 1878 appointment of watchmen to patrol the grounds was quite effective in preventing further vandalism, allowing the lawns to be completed and much shrubbery to be added. Also in that year, the roads throughout the grounds were paved.

Most of the work required on the east side of the grounds was completed by 1879, and effort thus shifted largely to the west side. The Pennsylvania Avenue approach was virtually finished, and work on the Maryland Avenue approach had begun. The stone walls on the west side of the grounds were almost finished, and the red granite lamp piers were placed at the eastward entrance from Pennsylvania Avenue.

In the years 1880–1882, many features of the grounds were completed. These included the walls and coping around the entire perimeter, the approaches and entrances, and the Summer House. Work on the terraces began in 1882, and most work from this point until 1892 was concentrated on these structures.

In 1885, Olmsted retired from superintendency of the terrace project; he continued to direct the work on the grounds until 1889. Landscaping work was performed to adapt the surrounding areas to the new construction, grading the ground and planting shrubs at the bases of the walls, as the progress of the masonry work allowed. Some trees and other types of vegetation were removed, either because they had decayed or as part of a careful thinning-out process.

In 1888, the wrought-iron lamp frames and railings were placed at the Maryland Avenue entrance, making it the last to be completed. In 1892, the streetcar track that had extended into grounds from Independence Avenue was removed.

The Grounds After Olmsted

In the last years of the 19th century, work on the grounds consisted chiefly of maintenance and repairs as needed. Trees, lawns, and plantings were tended, pruned, and thinned to allow their best growth. This work was quite successful: by 1894, the grounds were so deeply shaded by trees and shrubs that Architect of the Capitol Edward Clark recommended an all-night patrol by watchmen to ensure public safety. A hurricane in September 1896 damaged or destroyed a number of trees, requiring extensive removals in the following year. Also in 1897, electric lighting replaced gas lighting in the grounds.

Between 1910 and 1935, 61.4 acres north of Constitution Avenue were added to the grounds. Approximately 100 acres was added in subsequent years, bringing the total area to 274 acres. Late in 2011, care for the Grant Memorial and the reflecting pool at the eastern end of the National Mall was transferred from the National Park Service to the Architect of the Capitol.

Since 1983, increased security measures have been put into effect, however, the area still functions in many ways as a public park, and visitors are welcome to use the walks to tour the grounds. Demonstrations and ceremonies are often held on the grounds. In the summer, a series of evening concerts by the bands of the Armed Forces is offered free of charge on the west front plaza. On various holidays, concerts by the National Symphony Orchestra are held on the west front lawn.

LEGISLATIVE BRANCH AGENCIES

CONGRESSIONAL BUDGET OFFICE

H2–405 Ford House Office Building, Second and D Streets, SW., 20515
phone (202) 226–2600, http://www.cbo.gov

[Created by Public Law 93–344]

Director.—Douglas W. Elmendorf, 6–2700.
Deputy Director.—Robert A. Sunshine, 6–2700.
General Counsel.—Mark P. Hadley, 6–2633.
Assistant Director for—
Budget Analysis.—Peter H. Fontaine, 6–2800.
Health, Retirement, and Long-Term Analysis.—Linda Bilheimer, 6–2666.
Macroeconomic Analysis.—Wendy Edelberg, 6–2750.
Management, Business and Information Services.—Rod Goodwin, 6–2600.
Microeconomic Studies.—Joseph Kile, 6–2940.
National Security.—David E. Mosher, 6–2900.
Tax Analysis.—Frank J. Sammartino, 6–2680.

GOVERNMENT ACCOUNTABILITY OFFICE

441 G Street, NW., 20548, phone (202) 512–3000

http://www.gao.gov

Comptroller General of the United States.—Gene L. Dodaro, 512–5500, fax 512–5507.
Chief Operating Officer.—Patricia Dalton, 512–5600.
Chief Administrative Officer.—David Fisher, 512–5800.
General Counsel.—Lynn Gibson, 512–5207.
Deputy General Counsel and Ethics Counselor.—Tom Armstrong, 512–8257.
Deputy Ethics Counselor.—James Lager, 512–8170.

TEAMS

Acquisition and Sourcing Management.—Paul Francis, 512–2811.
Applied Research and Methods.—Nancy Kingsbury, 512–2700.
Defense Capabilities and Management.—Janet St. Laurent, 512–4300.
Education Workforce and Income Security.—Barbara D. Bovbjerg, 512–7215.
Financial Management and Assurance.—Steve Sebastiam, 512–2600.
Financial Markets and Community Investments.—Orice Williams Brown, 512–8678.
Forensic Audits and Special Investigations.—Cathleen A. Berrick, 512–3404.
Health Care.—Cynthia A. Bascetta, 512–7207.
Homeland Security and Justice.—Cathleen Berrick, 512–3404.
Information Technology.—Joel Willemssen, 512–6408.
International Affairs and Trade.—Loren Yager, 512–4347.
Natural Resources and Environment.—Mark Gaffigan, 512–3841.
Physical Infrastructure.—Phil Herr, 512–8509.
Strategic Issues.—J. Christopher Mihm, 512–6806.

SUPPORT FUNCTIONS

Congressional Relations.—Katherine Siggerud, 512–6570.
Legislative Advisers: Blake Ainsworth, 512–4609; Seto Bagdoyan, 512–4749; Carlos Diz, 512–8256; Rosa Harris, 512–9492; Carolyn Kirby, 512–9843; Anne Laffoon, 512–4199; Paul Thompson, 512–9867; Mary Frances Widner, 512–3804.

Associate Legislative Adviser.—Martene Bryan, 512–5414.
Continuous Process Improvement Office.—Thomas Williams, 512–7007.
Field Operations.—Denise Hunter (617) 788–0575.
Inspector General.—Adam Trzeciak, 512–8110.
Deputy Inspector General.—Cathy L. Helm, 512–5748.
Opportunity and Inclusiveness.—Reginald E. Jones, 512–8401.
Personnel Appeals Board.—Stuart Melnick, 512–3836.
Public Affairs.—Charles ''Chuck'' Young, 512–3823.
Audit Policy and Quality Assurance.—Tim Bowling, 512–6100.
Strategic Planning and External Liaison.—Helen Hsing, 512–2639.

MISSION SUPPORT OFFICES

Chief Information Officer.—Howard Williams, Jr., 512–5589.
Controller/Deputy Chief Financial Officer.—William Anderson, 512–2908.
Human Capital Officer.—Carolyn Taylor, 512–2974.
Infrastructure Operations.—Terry Dorn, 512–6923.
Professional Development Program.—Denise Hunter, (617) 788–0575.

U.S. GOVERNMENT PRINTING OFFICE

732 North Capitol Street, NW., 20401

Phone (202) 512–0000, http://www.gpo.gov

Public Printer of the United States.—Davita Vance-Cooks, 512–0014, dvance-cooks@gpo.gov.
Deputy Public Printer.—Jim Bradley, 512–0111, jbradley@gpo.gov.
Superintendent of Documents.—Mary Alice Baish, 512–1313, mabaish@gpo.gov.
Chief of Staff.—Andrew M. Sherman, 512–1100, asherman@gpo.gov.
Chief Financial Officer.—Steven T. Shedd, 512–2073, sshedd@gpo.gov.
Chief Administrative Officer.—Herbert H. Jackson, Jr., 512–0952, hjackson@gpo.gov.
Managing Director, Equal Employment Opportunity.—Juanita M. Flores, 512–2014, jflores@gpo.gov.
General Counsel.—Drew Spalding, 512–0033, dspalding@gpo.gov.
Inspector General.—Michael A. Raponi, 512–0039, mraponi@gpo.gov.

GENERAL COUNSEL

General Counsel.—Drew Spalding, 512–0033, dspalding@gpo.gov.
Deputy General Counsel.—Kerry L. Miller, 512–0033, kmiller@gpo.gov.
Director, Labor Relations.—Melissa S. Hatfield, 512–1336, mhatfield@gpo.gov.

FINANCE AND ADMINISTRATION

Chief Financial Officer.—Steven T. Shedd, 512–2073, sshedd@gpo.gov.
Deputy Chief Financial Officer.—William L. Boesch, Jr., 512–2073, wboesch@gpo.gov.
Controller, Plant.—June Vance (acting), 512–2073, jvance@gpo.gov.
Controller, Information Dissemination.—William J. Grennon III, 512–2010, wgrennon@gpo.gov.
Director of:
Accounts Receivable and Collections.—Donald L. Bartolomei, 512–1078, dbartolomei@gpo.gov.
Financial Planning and Control.—Frank P. McCraw, 512–0832, fmccraw@gpo.gov.

CHIEF OF STAFF

Chief of Staff.—Andrew M. Sherman, 512–1100, asherman@gpo.gov.

PROGRAMS, STRATEGY, AND TECHNOLOGY

Chief Technology Officer.—Richard G. Davis, 512–1622, rdavis@gpo.gov.

COMMUNICATIONS

Director, Congressional Relations.—Andrew M. Sherman (acting), 512–1100, asherman @gpo.gov.
Manager, Media and Public Relations.—Gary G. Somerset, 512–1957, gsomerset@gpo.gov.
Specialist, Employee Communications.—Terri Ehrenfeld, 512–0129, tehrenfeld@gpo.gov.

CHIEF ADMINISTRATIVE OFFICER

Chief Administrative Officer.—Herbert H. Jackson, Jr., 512–0952, hjackson@gpo.gov.

HUMAN CAPITAL

Chief Human Capital Officer.—Ginger T. Thomas, 512–1182, gthomas@gpo.gov.
Director of:
Human Capital Operations.—LaShon A. Adams, 512–0954, ladams@gpo.gov.
Workforce Development, Education and Training.—Dan M. Mielke, 512–1144, dmielke @gpo.gov.
Chief Medical Officer.—Sheridan B. Easterling, M.D., 512–2061, seasterling@gpo.gov.

INFORMATION TECHNOLOGY AND SYSTEMS

Chief Information Officer.—Charles E. Riddle, Jr., 512–1040, criddle@gpo.gov.
Deputy Chief Information Officer.—R. Tracee Boxley, 512–1394, tboxley@gpo.gov.
Director of:
Applications Development and Management.—Jeremy A. Wood, 512–1024, jwood @gpo.gov.
Customer Support.—John E. Matthews, 512–1349, jmatthews@gpo.gov.
Enterprise Architecture.—Layton F. Clay, 512–2001, lclay@gpo.gov.
Enterprise Management.—Richard G. Leeds, Jr., 512–0029, rleeds@gpo.gov.
Information Technology Security.—John L. Hannan, 512–1021, jhannan@gpo.gov.
Systems Integration.—Byron C. Blocker, 512–2198, bcblocker@gpo.gov.

SECURITY SERVICES

Chief Security Officer.—LaMont R. Vernon, 512–1103, lvernon@gpo.gov.
Deputy Director.—Gresham W. Harkless, 512–1367, gharkless@gpo.gov.
Commander, Uniformed Police Branch.—Paul D. Epley, 512–1084, pepley@gpo.gov.
Chief of:
Product Security.—Jeffrey T. Dorn, Jr., 512–0708, jdorn@gpo.gov.
Physical Security.—Shirley Garner, 512–0988, sgarner@gpo.gov.

ACQUISITION SERVICES

Director, Acquisition Operations.—Damon McClure, 512–0351, dmcclure@gpo.gov.
Chief of:
Complex and Specialized Procurement.—Beverly J. Williams, 512–0937, bwilliams @gpo.gov.
Paper and General Procurements.—Vacant, 512–0966.

DEPUTY PUBLIC PRINTER

Deputy Public Printer, Operations.—Jim Bradley, 512–0111, jbradley@gpo.gov.

OFFICIAL JOURNALS OF GOVERNMENT

Managing Director.—Lyle L. Green, 512–0224, llgreen@gpo.gov.
Director of:
Congressional Publishing Services.—Vacant, 512–0224.
Congressional Record Index Office.—Marcia Thompson, 512–0275, mthompson2 @gpo.gov.
Office of Federal Register Publishing Services.—Jeffrey D. MacAfee, 512–2100, jmacafee @gpo.gov.

PLANT OPERATIONS

Managing Director.—John W. Crawford, 512–0707, jcrawford@gpo.gov.
Deputy Managing Director.—Gregory E. Estep, 512–0707, gestep@gpo.gov.
Director, Engineering Services.—Katherine L. Taylor, 512–1018, ktaylor@gpo.gov.
Manager, Quality Control and Technical Department.—Michael P. Mooney, 512–0766, mmooney@gpo.gov.
Technical Manager, Strategic Planning and Analysis.—Sylvia S.Y. Subt, 512–0707, ssubt@gpo.gov.
Production Manager.—Vacant.
Assistant Production Manager (shift 1).—Shelley N. Welcher, 512–0589, swelcher@gpo.gov.
Assistant Production Manager (shift 2).—Richard C. Lewis, 512–0688, rclewis@gpo.gov.
Assistant Production Manager (shift 3).—Dannie E. Young, 512–0625, dyoung@gpo.gov.
Manager, Production Engineering.—David J. Robare, 512–1370, drobare@gpo.gov.
Manager of:
Pre-Press.—David K. Camp, 512–0625, dcamp@gpo.gov.
Press.—Vacant.
Binding.—Walter H. Wingo, Jr., 512–0593, wwingo@gpo.gov.
Production Planning and Control.—Robert M. Martein, 512–1470, rmartein@gpo.gov.

SECURITY AND INTELLIGENT DOCUMENTS

Managing Director.—Stephen G. LeBlanc, 512–2285, sleblanc@gpo.gov.
Operations Manager.—David H. Ford, 512–1194, dford@gpo.gov.
Director of:
Business Development.—Gerald Egan, 512–2010, gegan@gpo.gov.
Secure Production Manager.—Robert H. Allegar, 512–1485, rallegar@gpo.gov.

CUSTOMER SERVICES

Managing Director.—Bruce A. Seger, 512–2213, bseger@gpo.gov.
Deputy Managing Director.—Sandra K. MacAfee, 512–0320, smacafee@gpo.gov.
Director of:
Agency Publishing Services, Regional Operations.—Vacant.
Agency Strategic Teams, Central Office.—Julie A. Hasenfus, 512–0655, jhasenfus@gpo.gov.
Office of Development and Program Support.—Kirk D. Knoll, 512–1147, kknoll@gpo.gov.
Print Support Operations.—Teddy J. Priebe, 512–2015, tpriebe@gpo.gov.
Manager of:
Creative and Digital Media Services.—Ronald J. Keeney, 512–2012, rkeeney@gpo.gov.
Internal Branding, Design and Web Services.—Dean A. Gardei, 512–0245, dgardei@gpo.gov.

GPO REGIONAL PRINTING PROCUREMENT OFFICES

Atlanta.—Elizabeth A. Bluestein, Manager, 3715 Northside Parkway, Suite 4–305, Atlanta, GA 30327, (404) 605–9160, fax 605–9185, ebluestein@gpo.gov.

Boston.—Debra L. Rozdzielski, Assistant Manager, John F. Kennedy Federal Building, 15 New Sudbury Street, E270, Boston, MA 02203–0002 (617) 565–1370, fax 565–1385, drozdzielski@gpo.gov.

Charleston Satellite Office.—Richard W. Gilbert, Assistant Manager, 2825 Noisette Boulevard, Charleston, SC 29405–1819 (843) 743–2036, fax 743–2068, rgilbert@gpo.gov.

Chicago.—Clint J. Mixon, Manager, 200 North La Salle Street, Suite 810, Chicago, IL 60601–1055 (312) 353–3916, fax 886–3163, cmixon@gpo.gov.

Columbus.—Michael J. Sommer, Manager, 1335 Dublin Road, Suite 112–B, Columbus, OH 43215–7034 (614) 488–4616, fax 488–4577, msommer@gpo.gov.

Dallas.—Kelle J. Chatham, Manager, Federal Office Building, 1100 Commerce Street, Room 731, Dallas, TX 75242–1027 (214) 767–0451, fax 767–4101, kchatham@gpo.gov.

Denver.—Diane L. Abeyta, Manager, 12345 West Alameda Parkway, Suite 208, Lakewood, CO 80228–2824 (303) 236–5292, fax 236–5304, dabeyta@gpo.gov.

Virginia Beach, VA.—Richard W. Gilbert, Assistant Manager, 11836 Canon Boulevard, Suite 400, Newport News, VA 23606–2591 (757) 873–2800, fax 873–2805, rgilbert@gpo.gov.

New York.—Debra L. Rozdzielski, Assistant Manager, 26 Federal Plaza, Room 2930, New York, NY 10278–0004 (212) 264–2252, fax 264–2413, drozdzielski@gpo.gov.

Oklahoma City Satellite Office.—Diane L. Abeyta, Manager, 3420 D Avenue, Suite 100, Tinker AFB, OK 73145–9188 (405) 610–4146, fax 610–4125, dabeyta@gpo.gov.

Philadelphia.—Debra L. Rozdzielski, Assistant Manager, 928 Jaymore Road, Suite A190, Southampton, PA 18966–3820 (215) 364–6465, fax 364–6479, drozdzielski@gpo.gov.

San Antonio Satellite Office.—Kelle J. Chatham, Manager, 1531 Connally Street, Suite 2, Lackland AFB, TX 78236–5515 (210) 675–1480, fax 675–2429, kchatham@gpo.gov.

San Diego Satellite Office.—Michael A. Barnes, Manager, 8880 Rio San Diego Drive, 8th Floor, San Diego, CA 92108–3609 (619) 209–6178, fax 209–6179, mbarnes@gpo.gov.

San Francisco.—Michael A. Barnes, Manager, 536 Stone Road, Suite 1, Benicia, CA 94510–1170 (707) 748–1970, fax 748–1980, mbarnes@gpo.gov.

Seattle.—David S. Goldberg, Manager, Federal Center South, 4735 East Marginal Way South, Seattle, WA 98134–2397 (206) 764–3726, fax 764–3301, dgoldberg@gpo.gov.

SUPERINTENDENT OF DOCUMENTS

Superintendent of Documents.—Mary Alice Baish, 512–1313, mabaish@gpo.gov.

LIBRARY SERVICES AND CONTENT MANAGEMENT

Managing Director.—Jane Sánchez, 512–0185, jsanchez@gpo.gov.

Director of:

Outreach and Support.—Robin L. Haun-Mohamed, 512–0052, rhaun-mohamad@gpo.gov.

Projects and Systems.—Anthony Smith, 512–1431, adsmith@gpo.gov.

Technical Services.—Laurie Beyer Hall, 512–1114, lhall@gpo.gov.

PUBLICATION AND INFORMATION SALES

Managing Director.—Jane Sanchez, 512–0185, jsanchez@gpo.gov.

Director of:

Sales Distribution and Outreach.—Lisa L. Williams, 512–1065, llwilliams@gpo.gov.

Sales Planning and Development.—Jeffrey Turner, 512–1055, jturner@gpo.gov.

Content Acquisitions and Contact Center.—Esther R. Edmonds, 512–1694, eedmonds @gpo.gov.

GPO BOOKSTORE

Supervisor.—Darlene R. Matthews, 512–1800, dmatthews@gpo.gov.

Washington, DC, Metropolitan Area: GPO Bookstore, 710 North Capitol Street, NW., Washington, DC 20401, 512–0132.

TO ORDER PUBLICATIONS

Phone toll free (866) 512–1800 [DC area: (202) 512–1800, fax (202) 512–2104]. Mail orders to Superintendent of Documents, P.O. Box 371954, Pittsburgh, PA 15250–7954, or order online from http://bookstore.gpo.gov. GPO Access technical support: contactcenter@gpo.gov.

LAUREL FACILITY

Manager, Distribution Facilities.—Robert E. Mitchell, 8660 Cherry Lane, Mail Stop: SSR, Room 236D1, Laurel, MD 20707–4982 (301) 953–9751, remitchell@gpo.gov.

CONGRESSMAN FRANK EVANS GOVERNMENT PRINTING OFFICE

DISTRIBUTION CENTER

Operations Manager.—Thomas Hunt, P.O. Box 4007, Pueblo, CO 81003 (719) 295–2678, fax 948–3315, thunt@gpo.gov.

LIBRARY OF CONGRESS

101 Independence Avenue, SE., 20540, phone (202) 707–5000, fax 707–5844

http://www.loc.gov

OFFICE OF THE LIBRARIAN, LM 608

The Librarian of Congress.—James H. Billington, LM 608, 707–5205.
Confidential Assistant to the Librarian.—Timothy L. Robbins, LM 608, 707–5205.
The Deputy Librarian of Congress.—Robert Dizard, Jr., LM 608, 707–0351.
Special Assistant to the Deputy Librarian.—Alana Calfee, LM 608, 707–5216.
Director, Office of:
Communications.—Gayle Osterberg, LM 105, 707–2905.
Editor for—
Calendar of Events.—Erin Allen Sanchez, LM 105, 707–7302.
Library of Congress Magazine.—Audrey Fischer, LM 105, 707–0022.
The Gazette.—Mark Hartsell, LM 605, 707–9194.
Congressional Relations.—Kathleen Ott, LM 611, 707–6577.
Development.—Susan Siegel, LM 605, 707–1447.
Special Events and Public Programs.—Larry Stafford, LM 612, 707–5218.
General Counsel.—Elizabeth Pugh, LM 601, 707–6316.

OFFICE OF INSPECTOR GENERAL, LM 630

Inspector General.—Kurt Hyde (acting), LM 630, 707–6314.
Director, Office of Investigations.—Thomas Williams, LA 319, 707–5543.

OFFICE OF THE CHIEF FINANCIAL OFFICER, LM 613

Chief Financial Officer.—Jeffrey Page, LM 613, 707–7350.
Budget Officer.—Mary Klutts, LM 613, 707–2418.
Director, Financial Reports Office.—Nina Latterell, LM 613, 707–9142.
Accounting Operations Officer.—Nicole Broadus, LM 613, 707–5547.
Director, Strategic Planning Office.—Karen Lloyd, LM 603, 707–6074.
Director, Financial Systems Office.—Steve Johnson, LM 613, 707–0670.

OFFICE OF STRATEGIC INITIATIVES, LM 637

Associate Librarian for Strategic Initiatives/Chief Information Officer.—Vacant.
Director, Digital Resource Management and Planning.—Molly H. Johnson, LM 630, 707–0809.
Director, Integration Management.—Elizabeth S. Dulabahn, LM 630, 707–2369.
Director for Information Technology Services.—Al Banks, LM G51, 707–9562.

LAW LIBRARY, OFFICE OF THE LAW LIBRARIAN, LM 240

Law Librarian.—David S. Mao, LM 240, 707–5065.
Assistant Law Librarians for—
Administrative Operations.—Donald Simon, LM 240, 707–4884.
Legislative and External Affairs.—Robert R. Newlen, LM 240, 707–4313.
Chief of:
Collections Services.—Kurt Carroll, LM 232, 707–9863.
Global Legal Research Directorate.—Peter Roudik, LM 235, 707–9861.
Public Services Division.—Debora Keysor, LM 201, 707–0368.

LIBRARY SERVICES, OFFICE OF THE ASSOCIATE LIBRARIAN FOR LIBRARY SERVICES, LM 642

Associate Librarian.—Roberta I. Shaffer, LM 642, 707–5325.
Deputy Associate Librarian/Planning and Project Management.—Blane Dessy, LM 642, 707–3032.
Deputy Associate Librarian/Operations.—Sandra Lawson, LM 641, 707–3332.
Director, American Folklife Center.—Elizabeth Peterson, LJ G49, 707–5510.

Director, Veterans History Project.—Robert W. Patrick, LA 143, 707–6072.
Collections Development Officer.—Joseph Puccio, LM 642, 707–1413.
External Relations and Program Development Officer.—David A. Taylor, LM 642, 707–1737.
Director of Acquisitions and Bibliographic Access.—Beacher Wiggins, LM 642, 707–5797.
Chief of:
African, Latin American and Western European Division.—Angela Kinney, LM 543, 707–5572.
Asian and Middle Eastern Division.—Angela Kinney (acting), LM 542, 707–5572.
Cooperative and Instructional Programs Division.—Judith Cannan, LA 140, 707–2031.
Germanic and Slavic Division.—Linda T. Stubbs, LM 527, 707–7108.
Overseas Operations Division.—Beacher Wiggins (acting), LM 642, 707–5797.
Policy and Standards Division.—Beacher Wiggins (acting), LM 642, 707–5797.
Director, Collections and Services Directorate.—Jeremy Adamson, LM 642, 707–7789.
Chief of:
African and Middle Eastern Division.—Mary Jane Deeb, LJ 220, 707–4112.
Asian Division.—Dongfang Shao, LJ 149, 707–5420.
Children's Literature Center.—Sybille A. Jagusch, LJ 100, 707–5535.
Collections, Access, Loan, and Management Division.—Steven J. Herman, LJ G02, 707–7400.
European Division.—Georgette Dorn (acting), LJ 250, 707–5414.
Federal Research Division.—Sandra W. Meditz, LA 5281, 707–3900.
Geography and Map Division.—Ralph Ehrenberg, LM B02, 707–8530.
Hispanic Division.—Georgette Dorn, LJ 240, 707–5400.
Humanities and Social Sciences Division.—Barbara Morland, James Sweany (acting), LJ 140, 707–5530.
Manuscript Division.—James H. Hutson, LM 102, 707–5383.
Motion Picture, Broadcasting, and Recorded Sound Division.—Gregory Lukow, PC 2013, 707–5840.
Music Division.—Susan H. Vita, LM 113, 707–7124.
Packard Campus of the National Audio-Visual Conservation Center.—Gregory Lukow, PC 2013, 707–5840.
Prints and Photographs Division.—Helena Zinkham, LM 339, 707–2922.
Rare Book and Special Collections Division.—Mark G. Dimunation, LJ 230, 707–5434.
Science, Technology, and Business Division.—Ronald S. Bluestone, LA 5203, 707–0948.
Serial and Government Publications Division.—Teresa V. Sierra, LM 139, 707–5647.
Director, Partnerships and Outreach Programs.—Kathryn Mendenhall, LM 642, 707–1312.
Director, Center for the Book.—John Y. Cole, Jr., LM 650, 707–5221.
Poetry and Literature Center.—Rob Casper, LJ A02, 707–5394.
Young Readers Center.—Karen Jaffe, LJ G29, 707–1950.
Executive Director, Federal Library and Information Center Committee.—Kathryn Mendenhall (acting), LA 217, 707–1312.
Interpretive Programs Officer.—William Jacobs, LA G25, 707–5223.
Director, National Library Service for the Blind and Physically Handicapped.—Karen Keninger, TSA, 707–5100.
Director, Office of Scholarly Programs.—Carolyn Brown, LJ 120, 707–3302.
Director, Publishing Office.—William Jacobs (acting), LM 602, 707–3892.
Visitor Services Officer.—Guilia Adelfio, LJ G59, 707–9779.
Business Enterprises Officer.—Eugene Flanagan, LA 130, 707–7332.
Director, Preservation Directorate.—Mark Sweeney, LM 642, 707–2958.
Binding and Collections Care Division.—Jeanne Drewes, LM G21, 707–5330.
Conservation Division.—Elmer Eusman, LM G38, 707–5838.
Preservation Reformatting Division.—Adrija Henley, LM G05, 707–5918.
Preservation Research and Testing Division.—Fanella France, LM G38, 707–5525.
Director, Technology Policy.—Roberta I. Shaffer (acting), LM 642, 707–8338.
Automation Planning and Liaison Office.—Judith Conklin, LM 532, 707–3165.
Integrated Library Systems Program Office.—Ann Della Porta, LM 301, 707–4077.
Network Development and MARC Standards Office.—Sally H. McCallum, LA 308, 707–6237.

CONGRESSIONAL RESEARCH SERVICE, LM 203

Director.—Mary B. Mazanec, LM 203, 707–5775.
Deputy Director.—Colleen J. Shogan, LM–203, 707–8231.

Chief Information Officer.—Lisa M. Hoppis, LM 413, 707–2559.
Counselor to the Director.—Lizanne D. Kelley, LM 209, 707–8833.
Associate Director of:
Congressional Information and Publishing.—Cliff Cohen, LM 223, 707–1858.
Finance and Administration.—Edward Jablonski, LM 209, 707–8397.
Workforce Management and Development.—Monica M. Woods, LM 208, 707–7654.
Assistant Director of:
American Law Division.—Karen L. Lewis, LM 227, 707–7460.
Domestic Social Policy Division.—Laura B. Shrestha, LM 323, 707–7046.
Foreign Affairs, Defense and Trade Division.—Michael L. Moodie, LM 315, 707–8470.
Government and Finance Division.—John R. Haskell, LM 303, 707–2198.
Knowledge Services Group.—Lillian W. Gassie, LM 215, 707–7573.
Resources, Science and Industry Division.—John L. Moore, LM 423, 707–7232.

U.S. COPYRIGHT OFFICE, LM 403

Register of Copyrights and Director of the U.S. Copyright Office.—Maria A. Pallante, LM 403, 707–8359.
General Counsel and Associate Register of Copyrights.—Jacqueline C. Charlesworth, LM 403, 707–8772.
Deputy General Counsel.—Vacant.
Chief of Operations.—David J. Christopher, LM 403, 707–8825.
Budget Officer.—Megan Rivet, LM 403, 707–8385.
Chief of:
Administrative Services Office.—Bruce J. McCubbin, LM 458, 707–8395.
Copyright Acquisition Division.—Stephen Want, LM 526, 707–6781.
Information and Records Division.—Vacant.
Licensing Division.—James B. Enzinna, LM 504, 707–6801.
Receipts Analysis and Control Division.—Victor A. Holmes, LM 422, 707–8244.
Chief Information Officer.—Douglas Ament, LM 403, 707–6353.
Deputy Director of Copyright Technology Office.—Denise D. Wofford, LM 560, 707–2638.
Associate Register and Director of Policy and International Affairs.—Karyn Temple Claggett, LM 403, 707–7845.
Associate Register and Director of Registration Policy and Practices.—Robert J. Kasunic, LM 443, 707–0229.
Registration Program Manager.—Susan Harley Todd, LM 443, 707–8299.
Chief of:
Literary Division.—Ted Hirakawa, LM 443, 707–6181.
Performing Arts Division.—Laura Lee Fischer, LM 443, 707–5751.
Visual Arts Division.—John Ashley, LM 433, 707–8223.

OFFICE OF SUPPORT OPERATIONS, LM 643

Chief, Office of Support Operations.—Lucy D. Suddreth, LM 643, 707–2758.
Deputy Chief, Office of Support Operations.—James M. Duda, LM 643, 707–2124.
Director, Integrated Support Services.—Elizabeth Scheffler, LM 327, 707–6042.
Chief of:
Facility Services.—Neal Graham, LM 225, 707–1863.
Health Services.—Sandra Charles, LM G40, 707–8035.
Logistics Services.—Michael England, LM G58, 707–9303.
Safety Services.—Robert Browne, LM B25, 707–1508.
Space Utilization Planning and Design.—Charon Johnson, LM G30, 707–3537.
Director, Office of Security and Emergency Preparedness.—Kenneth Lopez, LM G03, 707–8708.
Emergency Preparedness.—Michael Salmons, LM G03, 707–2850.
Personnel Security.—Taylor Hilliker, LM B15, 707–5618.
Director, Office of Opportunity, Inclusiveness and Compliance.—Kirk Rascoe, LM 623, 707–0348.
Alternative Dispute Resolution and EEO Complaints.—Vicki Magnus, LM 623, 707–6024.
Reasonable Accommodations (ADA).—Vacant, LM 623, 707–6024.
Interpreting Services.—Vacant, LM 623, 707–6024.
Director, Human Resources Services.—Dennis Hanratty, LM 645, 707–0029.
Director, Office of:
HRS Customer Service Center.—Vacant, LM 107, 707–5627.

Workforce Acquisitions.—Susan Frieswyk (acting), LM 645, 707–6959.
Workforce Management.—Catherine Hurst Weber, LM 653, 707–0903.
Workforce Performance and Development.—Kimberly Powell, LM 654, 707–8976.
Worklife Services.—Susan Frieswyk, LM 645, 707–6949.

UNITED STATES BOTANIC GARDEN

245 First Street, SW., Washington, DC 20024

(202) 225–8333 (information); (202) 226–8333 (receptionist)

http://www.usbg.gov

Director.—Stephen T. Ayers (acting), Architect of the Capitol, 228–1204.
Executive Director.—Holly H. Shimizu, 225–6670.
Administrative Officer.—Tonda S. Cave, 225–5002.
Public Programs Manager.—Ari Novy, 225–1269.
Horticulture Division Manager.—James T. Kaufmann, 225–6647.
Facility Manager.—John M. Gallagher, 225–6646.

THE CABINET

Vice President of the United States	JOSEPH R. BIDEN, JR.
Secretary of State	JOHN F. KERRY.
Secretary of the Treasury	JACK LEW.
Secretary of Defense	CHUCK HAGEL.
Attorney General	ERIC H. HOLDER, JR.
Secretary of the Interior	SALLY JEWELL.
Secretary of Agriculture	THOMAS J. VILSACK.
Secretary of Commerce	PENNY PRITZKER.
Secretary of Labor	THOMAS E. PEREZ.
Secretary of Health and Human Services	KATHLEEN SEBELIUS.
Secretary of Housing and Urban Development	SHAUN L.S. DONOVAN.
Secretary of Transportation	ANTHONY FOXX.
Secretary of Energy	ERNEST MONIZ.
Secretary of Education	ARNE DUNCAN.
Secretary of Veterans Affairs	ERIC K. SHINSEKI.
Secretary of Homeland Security	JEH CHARLES JOHNSON.
Chief of Staff	DENIS MCDONOUGH.
Administrator, Environmental Protection Agency	GINA MCCARTHY.
Director, Office of Management and Budget	SYLVIA BURWELL.
U.S. Trade Representative	MICHAEL FROMAN.
Ambassador, United States Ambassador to the United Nations	SAMANTHA POWER.
Chair, Council of Economic Advisers	JASON FURMAN.
Administrator, Small Business Administration	MARIA CONTRERAS-SWEET.

EXECUTIVE BRANCH

THE PRESIDENT

BARACK H. OBAMA, Senator from Illinois and 44th President of the United States; born in Honolulu, Hawaii, August 4, 1961; received a B.A. in 1983 from Columbia University, New York City; worked as a community organizer in Chicago, IL; studied law at Harvard University, where he became the first African American president of the *Harvard Law Review,* and received a J.D. in 1991; practiced law in Chicago, IL; lecturer on constitutional law, University of Chicago; member, Illinois State Senate, 1997–2004; elected as a Democrat to the U.S. Senate in 2004; and served from January 3, 2005, to November 16, 2008, when he resigned from office, having been elected President; family: married to Michelle; two children: Malia and Sasha; elected as President of the United States on November 4, 2008, and took the oath of office on January 20, 2009.

EXECUTIVE OFFICE OF THE PRESIDENT

1600 Pennsylvania Avenue, NW., 20500

Eisenhower Executive Office Building (EEOB), 17th Street and Pennsylvania Avenue, NW., 20500, phone (202) 456–1414, http://www.whitehouse.gov

The President of the United States.—Barack H. Obama.
Special Assistant to the President and Personal Aide to the President.—Anita Decker Breckenridge.
Director of Oval Office Operations.—Brian Mosteller.

OFFICE OF THE VICE PRESIDENT

phone (202) 456–1414

The Vice President.—Joseph R. Biden, Jr.
Assistant to the President and Chief of Staff to the Vice President.—Bruce Reed, EEOB, room 276, 456–9000.
Deputy Assistant to the President and Chief of Staff to Dr. Jill Biden.—Sheila Nix, EEOB, room 200, 456–7458.
Deputy Assistant to the President and Counsel to the Vice President.—Cynthia Hogan, EEOB, room 266, 456–3241.
Deputy Assistant to the President and Director of Economic and Domestic Policy to the Vice President.—Sarah Bianchi, EEOB, room 280, 456–3460.
Deputy Assistant to the President and National Security Advisor to the Vice President.—Jacob Sullivan, EEOB, room 206, 456–2744.
Deputy Assistant to the President and Senior Advisor to the Vice President.—Mike Donilon, West Wing, 456–1723.
Deputy Assistant to the President and Senior Advisor to the Vice President.—Jose Cerda, EEOB, room 204, 456–9000.
Special Assistant to the President and Assistant to the Vice President for Communications.—Shailagh Murray, EEOB, room 288, 456–0373.
Special Assistant to the President and Assistant to the Vice President for Intergovernmental Affairs, Public Engagement, and Correspondence.—Evan Ryan, EEOB, room 202A, 456–8240.
Counselor to the Vice President.—Steve Ricchetti, EEOB, room 272, 456–9000.
Director of Administration to the Vice President.—Faisal Amin, EEOB, room 263, 456–2599.
Director of Advance to the Vice President.—Chad Bolduc, EEOB, room 269, 456–3878.
Director of Legislative Affairs to the Vice President.—Tonya Williams, EEOB, room 279A, 456–1540.

Director of Scheduling to the Vice President.—Alex Hornbrook, EEOB, room 265, 456–6773.
Executive Assistants to the Vice President: Kathy Chung, Kellen Suber, West Wing.

COUNCIL OF ECONOMIC ADVISERS

725 Seventeenth Street, NW., 20006, phone (202) 395–5084
http://www.whitehouse.gov/cea

Chair.—Jason Furman.
Chief of Staff.—Jessica Schumer.
Members: Betsey Stevenson, James H. Stock.

COUNCIL ON ENVIRONMENTAL QUALITY

730 Jackson Place, NW., 20503, phone (202) 456–6224
http://www.whitehouse.gov/ceq

Chair.—Nancy Sutley.
Special Assistant to the Chair.—Shira Miller.
Scheduler to the Chair.—Rebecca Ferdman.
Chief of Staff.—Michael ''Mike'' Boots.
Deputy Chief of Staff.—Lowery Crook.
Deputy Director and General Counsel.—Gary Guzy.
Senior Counsel.—Ellen Athas.
Deputy General Counsel.—Brandi Colander.
Deputy Associate Director for—
International Affairs.—Vacant.
Regulatory Policy.—Manisha Patel.
Attorney Advisor.—Diana Csank.
Operations Manager.—Angela Stewart.
Administrative Services Specialist.—Essence Washington.
Administrative Assistant.—Brenda Butler.
Federal Environmental Executive.—Jonathan Powers.
Deputy Associate Director for OFEE.—William Garvey.
OFEE Senior Program Manager for Federal Outreach.—Vacant.
OFEE Senior Program Managers: Juan Lopez, Benjamin Steinberg.
Deputy Associate Director for GreenGov.—Vacant.
Associate Director for Energy and Climate Change.—Richard Duke.
Special Assistant to the Associate Director for Energy and Climate Change.—Candace Vahlsing.
Deputy Associate Directors for Energy and Climate Change: Kate Larsen, Jia Li, Laura Morton, Monisha Shah, Ali Zaidi.
Deputy Associate Director for Climate Change Adaptation.—Susan Ruffo.
Climate Change Adaptation Analyst.—Jamie Pool.
Deputy Associate Director for Transmission and Renewable Energy Siting.—Vacant.
Deputy Associate Director for Electricity and Consumer Policy.—Vacant.
Senior Advisor to the Chair.—Andrew ''Drew'' McConville.
Presidential Management Fellow for Energy Efficiency.—Stephen Capanna.
Deputy Associate Directors for—
Chemical Regulations.—Norman Birchfield.
Energy Efficiency.—Vacant.
Associate Director for Land and Water Ecosystems.—Jay Jensen.
Special Assistant to the Associate Director for Land and Water Ecosystems.—Ann Hunter-Pirtle.
Deputy Associate Directors for—
America's Great Outdoors.—Sarah Guy.
Ecosystems.—Vacant.
Lands.—Ann Acheson.
Land and Water Policy Analyst.—Ilana Cohen.
Ocean and Coastal Policy.—Michael Weiss.
Water.—Nancy Andrews.
Water Resources.—Catherine Shuman.
NOC Policy Analysts: Jonathan Anderchik, Chris Corvo.
Asian Carp Director.—John Goss.
Special Assistant to the Asian Carp Director.—Paul Angelone.

Deputy Asian Carp Director.—James Bredin.
Associate Director for Communications.—Taryn Tuss.
Special Assistant to the Associate Director for Commuications.—Scott Falin.
Deputy Associate Director for Communications.—Miguel Ayala.
Associate Director for NEPA Oversight.—Horst Greczmiel.
Associate Director for Legislative Affairs.—Trent Bauserman.
Special Assistant to the Associate Director for Legislative Affairs.—Joshua Friedmann.
Deputy Associate Director for Legislative Affairs.—Monica Neukomm.
Associate Director for Public Engagement.—Rohan Patel.
Special Assistant to the Associate Director for Public Engagement.—Vacant.
Deputy Associate Directors for Policy Outreach.—Vacant.
Deputy Associate Director for Let's Move Outside!.—Vacant.

PRESIDENT'S INTELLIGENCE ADVISORY BOARD

phone (202) 456–2352

Executive Director.—Stefanie Osburn.
General Counsel.—Athena Arguello.

NATIONAL SECURITY COUNCIL

Eisenhower Executive Office Building, 20504

phone, 202–456–1414. Internet, http://www.whitehouse.gov/nsc

MEMBERS

The President.—Barack H. Obama.
The Vice President.—Joseph R. Biden, Jr.
The Secretary of State.—John F. Kerry.
The Secretary of Defense.—Charles Timothy ''Chuck'' Hagel.

STATUTORY ADVISERS

Director of National Intelligence.—James R. Clapper, Jr.
Chairman, Joint Chiefs of Staff.—Gen. Martin E. Dempsey, USA

STANDING PARTICIPANTS

The Secretary of the Treasury.—Jacob J. Lew.
Chief of Staff to the President.—Denis R. McDonough.
Counsel to the President.—Kathryn H. Ruemmler.
National Security Adviser.—Thomas E. Donilon.
Assistant to the President for Economic Policy.—Eugene B. Sperling.

OFFICIALS

Assistant to the President for National Security Affairs.—Thomas E. Donilon.
Assistant to the President for National Security Affairs and Deputy National Security Adviser.—Antony J. Blinken.

OFFICE OF ADMINISTRATION

Eisenhower Executive Office Building, phone (202) 395–5555

Director of the Office of Administration.—Beth Jones.
Chief, Office of:
Equal Employment Opportunity.—Clara Patterson.
Finance.—Cathy Solomon.
General Counsel.—Angela Ohm.
Information.—Karen Britton.
Operations.—Erica De Vos.

OFFICE OF MANAGEMENT AND BUDGET

Eisenhower Executive Office Building, phone (202) 395–4840

Director.—Jeffrey D. Zients (acting).
Deputy Director.—Vacant.
Deputy Director for Management.—Jeffrey Zients.
Executive Associate Director.—Vacant.
Administrator, Office of:
Federal Procurement Policy.—Joseph Jordan.
Information and Regulatory Affairs.—Dominic Mancini (acting).
Assistant Director for—
Budget.—Courtney Timberlake.
Legislative Reference.—Matthew Vaeth.
Associate Director for—
Economic Policy.—Michael Falkenheim (acting).
Education, Income Maintenance and Labor Programs.—Martha Coven.
General Government Programs.—Dana Hyde.
Health Programs.—Vacant.
Legislative Affairs.—Kristen J. Sarri.
National Security Programs.—Steve Kosiak.
Natural Resources, Energy and Science Programs.—Sally Ericsson.
Strategic Planning and Communications.—Steven Posner.
General Counsel.—Tom Lue (acting).

OFFICE OF NATIONAL DRUG CONTROL POLICY

750 17th Street, NW., phone (202) 395–6700, fax 395–6711

Director.—R. Gil Kerlikowske, room 810, 395–6700.
Deputy Director.—Michael P. Botticelli, room 803, 395–6700.
Chief of Staff.—Regina M. LaBelle, room 809, 395–6762.
Deputy Chief of Staff.—Jon E. Rice (acting), room 805, 395–6762.
Deputy Director of:
Demand Reduction.—David K. Mineta, room 609, 395–6751.
State and Local Affairs.—Benjamin B. Tucker, room 661, 395–7252.
Supply Reduction.—Marilyn A. Quagliotti, room 713, 395–7225.
Assistant Deputy Director, Office of:
Demand Reduction.—Martha M. Gagné, room 610, 395–4622.
Supply Reduction.—Gerard Burns (acting), room 712, 395–5535.
General Counsel.—Jeffrey J. Teitz, room 518, 395–6601.
Associate Director, Office of:
Legislative Affairs.—Vacant, room 825, 395–7225.
Management and Administration.—Michele C. Marx, room 326, 395–6883.
Performance and Budget.—Jon E. Rice, room 535, 395–6791.
Public Affairs.—Rafael E. Lemaitre, room 846, 395–6649.
Research/Data Analysis.—Terry W. Zobeck, room 836, 395–5503.
Intergovernmental Public Liaison.—Kathryn A. Greene, room 845, 395–5758.

OFFICE OF SCIENCE AND TECHNOLOGY POLICY

Eisenhower Executive Office Building, phone (202) 456–4444, fax 456–6021
http://www.ostp.gov

Director.—John P. Holdren.
Deputy Director for Technology and Innovation.—Thomas Kalil.
U.S. Chief Technology Officer.—Todd Park.
Chief of Staff.—Rick Siger.
Associate Director for—
Energy and Environment.—Vacant.
National Security and International Affairs.—Patricia Falcone.
Science.—Vacant.
General Counsel.—Rachael Leonard.
Assistant Directors:
Legislative Affairs.—Donna Pignatelli.
Strategic Communications.—Rick Weiss.

Executive Director for President's Council of Advisors on Science and Technology (PCAST).—Amber Hartman Scholz.
Executive Director for National Science and Technology Council (NSTC).—Pedro Espina.

OFFICE OF THE UNITED STATES TRADE REPRESENTATIVE

600 17th Street, NW., 20508, phone (202) 395–6890
http://www.ustr.gov

United States Trade Representative.—Demetrios Marantis (acting).
Deputy United States Trade Representative.—Miriam Sapiro.
Deputy U.S. Trade Representative, Geneva.—Michael Punke.
Special Textile Negotiator.—Gail Strickler.
Chief Agricultural Negotiator.—Isi Siddiqui.
General Counsel.—Timothy Reif.
Assistant U.S. Trade Representative for—
Administration.—Fred Ames.
Africa.—Florie Liser.
Agricultural Affairs.—Vacant.
China Affairs.—Claire Reade.
Congressional Affairs.—Rene Muñoz.
Economic Affairs.—William Shpiece.
Environment and Natural Resources.—Mark Linscott.
Europe and the Mediterranean.—Dan Mullaney.
Industry.—Jim Sanford.
Intergovernmental Affairs and Public Liaison.—Tiffany Enoch.
Japan, Korea and APEC Affairs.—Wendy Cutler.
Monitoring and Enforcement.—Dan Brinza.
Office of the Americas.—Vacant.
Policy Coordination.—Carmen Suro-Bredie.
Public/Media Affairs.—Carol Guthrie.
Services, Investment and Intellectual Property.—Christine Bliss.
South Asian Affairs.—Douglas Hartwick.
Southeast Asia, Pacific and Pharmaceutical Policy.—Barbara Weisel.
Trade and Labor.—Lewis Karesh.
World Trade Organization (WTO) and Multilateral Affairs.—Mark Linscott.

THE WHITE HOUSE OFFICE

CABINET AFFAIRS

Assistant to the President and Cabinet Secretary.—Danielle Gray.
Deputy Assistant to the President and Deputy Cabinet Secretary.—Ruchana Bhowmik.

CHIEF OF STAFF

Assistant to the President and Chief of Staff.—Denis McDonough.
Counselor to the President.—Peter Rouse.
Assistant to the President and Deputy Chief of Staff for Operations.—Alyssa Mastromonaco.
Assistant to the President and Deputy Chief of Staff for Policy.—Rob Nabors.
Assistant to the President and Senior Advisor.—Dan Pfeiffer.
Assistant to the President and Deputy Chief of Staff for Planning.—Mark Childress.
Assistant to the President and Deputy Senior Advisor for Communications and Strategy.—David Simas.

COMMUNICATIONS

Assistant to the President and Director of Communications.—Jennifer Palmieri.
Assistant to the President and Director of Speechwriting.—Cody Keenan.
Assistant to the President and Press Secretary.—James Carney.

OFFICE OF DIGITAL STRATEGY

Special Assistant to the President and Director of Digital Strategy.—Macon Phillips.

DOMESTIC POLICY COUNCIL

Assistant to the President and Director of the Domestic Policy Council.—Cecilia Muñoz.

Deputy Assistant to the President and Deputy Director of the Domestic Policy Council.—James Kvaal.

Deputy Assistant to the President for Health Policy.—Jeanne Lambrew.

Deputy Assistant to the President for Energy and Climate Change.—Heather R. Zichal.

Deputy Assistant to the President for Urban Affairs and Economic Mobility.—Racquel Russell.

Special Assistant to the President and Director, Office of Social Innovation and Civic Participation.—Jonathan Greenblatt.

Special Assistant to the President for Education Policy.—Roberto Rodriguez.

Special Assistant to the President and Executive Director of the White House Office of Faith-Based and Neighborhood Partnerships.—Melissa Rogers.

Special Assistant to the President for Justice and Regulatory Policy.—Tonya Robinson.

Special Assistant to the President for Labor and Workforce Policy.—Portia Wu.

Special Assistant to the President and Chief of Staff of the Domestic Policy Council.—Carlos Monje.

Director of the Office of National AIDS Policy.—Grant Colfax.

OFFICE OF THE FIRST LADY

Assistant to the President and Chief of Staff to the First Lady.—Christina Tchen.

Deputy Assistant to the President and Senior Advisor to the First Lady.—Melissa Winter.

Special Assistant to the President and Director of Strategic Planning.—Andrea Mokros.

Special Assistant to the President and Director of Communications for the First Lady.—Kristina Schake.

Special Assistant to the President and White House Social Secretary.—Jeremy Bernard.

OFFICE OF LEGISLATIVE AFFAIRS

Assistant to the President and Director, Office of Legislative Affairs.—Miguel Rodriguez.

Deputy Assistant to the President for Legislative Affairs and Senate Liaison.—Edward Pagano.

Deputy Assistant to the President for Legislative Affairs and House Liaison.—Jonathan Samuels.

OFFICE OF MANAGEMENT AND ADMINISTRATION

Assistant to the President for Management and Administration.—Katy Kale.

Special Assistant to the President for Management and Administration.—Katherine Platt.

Special Assistant to the President and Director of Visitors Office.—Ellie Schafer.

NATIONAL ECONOMIC COUNCIL

Assistant to the President for Economic Policy and Director of the National Economic Council.—Eugene Sperling.

Assistant to the President and Principal Deputy Director of the National Economic Council.—Jason Furman.

Assistant to the President and Deputy National Security Advisor for International Economics.—Michael Froman.

OFFICE OF THE NATIONAL SECURITY ADVISOR

Assistant to the President and National Security Advisor.—Thomas Donilon.

Assistant to the President and Deputy National Security Advisor.—Tony Blinken.
Assistant to the President for Homeland Security and Counterterrorism and Deputy National Security Advisor.—Lisa Monaco.

PRESIDENTIAL PERSONNEL OFFICE

Assistant to the President and Director of Presidential Personnel.—Nancy Hogan.
Deputy Assistant to the President and Deputy Director of Presidential Personnel.—Jonathan McBride.
Special Assistant to the President and Chief of Staff for Presidential Personnel.—Margaret McLaughlin.

OFFICE OF PUBLIC ENGAGEMENT AND INTERGOVERNMENTAL AFFAIRS

Senior Advisor and Assistant to the President for Intergovernmental Affairs and Public Engagement.—Valerie Jarrett.
Deputy Assistant to the President and Director of the Office of Public Engagement.—Paulette Aniskoff.
Deputy Assistant to the President and Director of Intergovernmental Affairs.—David Agnew.

OFFICE OF SCHEDULING AND ADVANCE

Assistant to the President and Director of Scheduling and Advance.—Danielle Crutchfield.
Deputy Assistant to the President and Director of Scheduling.—Jessica Wright.
Deputy Assistant to the President and Director of Advance and Operations.—Peter Selfridge.
Special Assistant to the President, Trip Director and Personal Aide to the President.—Marvin Nicholson.

OFFICE OF THE STAFF SECRETARY

Deputy Assistant to the President and Staff Secretary.—Douglas Kramer.
Special Assistant to the President and Director of Presidential Correspondence.—Elizabeth Olson.

WHITE HOUSE COUNSEL

Assistant to the President and Counsel to the President.—Kathryn Ruemmler.
Deputy Assistants to the President and Deputy Counsel to the President: Steven Croley, Avril Haines, Leslie Kiernan, Edward Siskel.

PRESIDENT'S COMMISSION ON WHITE HOUSE FELLOWSHIPS

Director.—Cindy Moelis.

WHITE HOUSE MILITARY OFFICE

Director.—George Mulligan.

DEPARTMENT OF STATE

2201 C Street, NW., 20520, phone (202) 647–4000

JOHN F. KERRY, Secretary of State; born in Denver, CO, December 11, 1943; education: graduated, St. Paul's School, Concord, NH, 1962; B.A., Yale University, New Haven, CT, 1966; J.D., Boston College Law School, Boston, MA, 1976; served, U.S. Navy, discharged with rank of lieutenant; decorations: Silver Star, Bronze Star with Combat ''V'', three Purple Hearts, various theatre campaign decorations; attorney, admitted to Massachusetts Bar, 1976; appointed first assistant district attorney, Middlesex County, 1977; elected lieutenant governor, Massachusetts, 1982; married: Teresa Heinz; Senator from Massachusetts, 1985–2013; committees: chair, Foreign Relations; Commerce, Science, and Transportation; Finance; Small Business and Entrepreneurship; appointed to the Democratic Leadership for 104th and 105th Congresses; nominated by President Barack Obama to become the 68th Secretary of State, and was confirmed by the U.S. Senate on January 29, 2013.

OFFICE OF THE SECRETARY

Secretary of State.—John F. Kerry, room 7226, 647–9572.
Deputy Secretary.—William Burns.
Deputy Secretary for Management and Resources.—Vacant.
Executive Assistant.—David E. Wade, 647–9572.
Deputy Chief of Staff.—William L. Danvers, 647–5697.

AMBASSADOR-AT-LARGE FOR WAR CRIMES ISSUES

Ambassador-at-Large.—Stephen J. Rapp, room 7419A, 647–8218.
Deputy.—Elizabeth Van Schaack, 647–9880.

OFFICE OF THE CHIEF OF PROTOCOL

Chief of Protocol.—Capricia Penavic Marshall, room 1232, 647–4543.
Deputy Chiefs: Natalie Jones, 647–1144; Mark Walsh, 647–4120.

OFFICE OF CIVIL RIGHTS

Director.—John M. Robinson, room 7428, 647–9295.
Deputy Director.—Gregory B. Smith.

OFFICE OF COORDINATOR FOR COUNTERTERRORISM

Coordinator.—Jerry Lanier (acting), room 2509, 647–9892.
Principal Deputy Coordinator.—Jerry Lanier, 647–8949.

BUREAU FOR CONFLICT AND STABILIZATION OPERATIONS

Assistant Secretary.—Rick Barton, room 7123 SA–3 (202) 663–0805.

EXECUTIVE SECRETARIAT

Special Assistant and Executive Secretary.—John Bass, room 7224, 647–5301.
Deputy Executive Secretaries: Theodore Allegra, 647–5302; Julieta Valls Noyes, 647–5302; Francisco Palmieri, 647–8448.

OFFICE OF THE INSPECTOR GENERAL
2121 Virginia Avenue, NW., 20037

Inspector General.—Vacant, room 8100, 663–0361.
Deputy Inspector General.—Harold W. Geisel, 663–0361.

BUREAU OF INTELLIGENCE AND RESEARCH

Assistant Secretary.—Philip S. Goldberg, room 6468, 647–9177.
Principal Deputy Assistant Secretary.—Daniel H. Rubinstein, 647–7826.
Deputy Assistant Secretaries: Catherine Brown, 647–7754; James Buchanan, 647–9633.

OFFICE OF LEGAL ADVISER

The Legal Adviser.—Vacant, room 6421, 647–9598.
Principal Deputy Legal Adviser.—Mary McLeod, 647–5036.
Deputy Legal Advisers: Susan Biniaz, 647–7942; Jonathan B. Schwartz, 647–5036; Richard C. Visek, 647–7942.

BUREAU OF LEGISLATIVE AFFAIRS

Assistant Secretary.—Thomas Gibbons (acting), room 7531, 647–1050.
Deputy Assistant Secretary (Global, Regional and Functional).—Ur Jadaov, 647–2623.
Deputy Assistant Secretary (Senate).—Joshua Blumenfeld, 647–8733.
Deputy Assistant Secretary.—Joy Drucker, 647–1656.

POLICY PLANNING STAFF

Director.—David McKean, room 7311, 647–2972.
Principal Deputy Director.—Bathsheba Crocker.

OFFICE OF THE U.S. GLOBAL AIDS COORDINATOR

Coordinator.—Amb. Eric Goosby, room SA–29, 663–2462.
Principal Deputy U.S. Global AIDS Coordinator.—Deborah Von Zinkernagel, 663–2802.
Chief Operations Officer.—Julia Martin, 663–2339.
Director of Multilateral Outreach.—Jason Lawrence, 663–2577.

UNDER SECRETARY FOR POLITICAL AFFAIRS

Under Secretary.—Wendy Sherman, room 7250, 647–2471.
Executive Assistant.—Kamala Lakhdhir, 647–1598.

AFRICAN AFFAIRS

Assistant Secretary.—Johnnie Carson, room 6234A, 647–2530.
Principal Deputy Assistant Secretary.—Donald Yamamoto, 647–2447.

EAST ASIAN AND PACIFIC AFFAIRS

Assistant Secretary.—Joseph Yun (acting), 647–6904.
Principal Deputy Assistant Secretary.—James Zumwalt (acting), 736–4393.
Deputy Assistant Secretaries: Michael Fuchs, 647–4612; Edgard Kagan, 647–8929; Kin Moy, 647–7156; Susan Stevenson, 647–7234.

EUROPEAN AND EURASIAN AFFAIRS

Assistant Secretary.—Vacant, room 6226, 647–9626.
Principal Deputy Assistant Secretary.—Marie Yovanovitch, 647–5146.
Deputy Assistant Secretaries: Kathleen A. Doherty, 647–9373; Bay Fang, 647–5447; Brent Hartley, 647–6233; Philip T. Reeker, 647–6415; Eric S. Rubin, 647–5447; Daniel A. Russell, 647–5174.

NEAR EASTERN AFFAIRS

Assistant Secretary.—Beth Jones (acting), room 6242, 647–7209.
Principal Deputy Assistant Secretary.—Liz Dibble, 647–7207.
Deputy Assistant Secretaries: Nazanin Ash, 647–7170; Robert Ford, 647–9539; Barbara Leaf, 647–0554; Richard Schmierer, 647–4199; Stephen Seche, 647–7166.

SOUTH AND CENTRAL ASIAN AFFAIRS

Assistant Secretary.—Robert Blake, room 6254, 736–4325.
Principal Deputy Assistant Secretary.—Geoffrey Pyatt, 736–4331.
Deputy Assistant Secretaries: Alyssa Ayres, 736–4328; James Moore, 736–4315; Lynn Tracy, 736–4062.

WESTERN HEMISPHERE AFFAIRS

Assistant Secretary.—Roberta Jacobson, room 6262, 647–5780.
Principal Deputy Assistant Secretaries.—John Feeley, 647–8387; Alex Lee (acting), 647–1313.
Deputy Assistant Secretaries: Liliana Ayalde, 647–7337; Matthew Rooney, 647–6755; Kevin Whitaker, 647–8563.

INTERNATIONAL NARCOTICS AND LAW ENFORCEMENT AFFAIRS

Assistant Secretary.—William Brownfield, room 7826, 647–8464.
Principal Deputy Assistant Secretary.—Brian Nichols, 647–6642.
Deputy Assistant Secretaries: Carol Perez, 647–6054; Todd Robinson, 647–9822.

INTERNATIONAL ORGANIZATION AFFAIRS

Assistant Secretary.—Esther Brimmer, room 6323, 647–9600.
Principal Deputy Assistant Secretary.—H. Dean Pittman, 647–9602.
Deputy Assistant Secretaries: Nerissa J. Cook, 647–5798; Victoria K. Holt, 647–9604; Paula G. Schriefer, 647–9431.

UNDER SECRETARY FOR ECONOMIC, GROWTH ENERGY, AND THE ENVIRONMENT

Under Secretary.—Robert Hormats, room 7256, 647–7575.
Executive Assistant.—William Heidt, 647–7674.

ECONOMIC, ENERGY AND BUSINESS AFFAIRS

Assistant Secretary.—Jose W. Fernandez, room 4932/4934, 647–7971.
Principal Deputy Assistant Secretary.—William E. Craft (acting), 647–9496.
Deputy Assistant Secretaries: Whitney Baird, 647–6324; Krishna Urs, 647–4045.

UNDER SECRETARY FOR ARMS CONTROL AND INTERNATIONAL SECURITY

Under Secretary.—Rose E. Gottemoeller (acting), room 7208, 647–1049.
Executive Assistant.—Wade Boese, 647–6634.

INTERNATIONAL SECURITY AND NONPROLIFERATION

Assistant Secretary.—Thomas Countryman, room 3932, 647–9612.
Principal Deputy Assistant Secretary.—Vann H. Van Diepen, room 3932, 647–5122.
Deputy Assistant Secretary.—Eliott Kang, room 3932, 647–5999.
Deputy Assistant Secretary for Nonproliferation Programs.—Simon Limage, 647–9612.

POLITICAL–MILITARY AFFAIRS

Assistant Secretary.—Andrew J. Shapiro, room 6212, 647–9022.

Principal Deputy Assistant Secretary.—Tom Kelly, 647–9023.
Deputy Assistant Secretaries: Beth McCormick, 647–0337; Samuel Perez, 647–9023.

ARMS CONTROL, VERIFICATION AND COMPLIANCE

Assistant Secretary.—Rose E. Gottemoeller, room 5950, 647–5315.
Principal Deputy Assistant Secretary.—Anita Friedt, 647–6830.
Deputy Assistant Secretaries: Greg Delawie, 647–5553; Frank Rose, 647–7821.

UNDER SECRETARY FOR PUBLIC DIPLOMACY AND PUBLIC AFFAIRS

Under Secretary.—Tara D. Sonenshine, room 5932, 647–9199.
Chief of Staff.—Aviva Rosenthal.
Executive Assistant.—Michelle Logsdon.

EDUCATIONAL AND CULTURAL AFFAIRS

Assistant Secretary.—Ann Stock, 632–6445.
Principal Deputy Assistant Secretary.—Adam Ereli, 632–9444.
Deputy Assistant Secretaries: Meghann Curtis, 632–9327; Robin Lerner, 632–9386; Lee Satterfield, 632–3346.

INTERNATIONAL INFORMATION PROGRAMS

Coordinator.—Dawn McCall, 632–9942.

PUBLIC AFFAIRS

Assistant Secretary.—Mike Hammer, room 6634, 647–6088.
Deputy Assistant Secretaries: Cheryl Benton, Dana Smith.
Deputy Spokesman.—Mark Toner, 647–9606.

UNDER SECRETARY FOR MANAGEMENT

Under Secretary.—Patrick F. Kennedy, room 7207, 647–1500.
Executive Assistant.—Kathleen Austin-Ferguson, 647–1501.

ADMINISTRATION

Assistant Secretary.—James A. Barr, room 6330, 647–1492.
Deputy Assistant Secretaries: Catherine Ebert-Gray (703) 875–6956; Margaret Grafeld, 261–8300; Keith Miller, 647–3427.

CONSULAR AFFAIRS

Assistant Secretary.—Janice L. Jacobs, room 6811, 647–9576.
Principal Deputy Assistant Secretary.—Michelle Bond, 647–7753.
Deputy Assistant Secretaries: James Pettit, 647–6541; Edward Ramotow, 647–6541; Brenda Sprague, 647–5366.

DIPLOMATIC SECURITY AND OFFICE OF FOREIGN MISSIONS

Assistant Secretary.—Gregory Starr (acting), room 6316, 647–6290.
Principal Deputy Assistant Secretary.—Gregory Starr (571) 345–3815.
Deputy Assistant Secretaries: Bill Miller (571) 345–3492; Gentry O. Smith (571) 345–3836.

DIRECTOR GENERAL OF THE FOREIGN SERVICE AND
DIRECTOR OF HUMAN RESOURCES

Director General.—Linda Thomas-Greenfield, room 6218, 647–9898.

Principal Deputy Assistant Secretary.—Hans Klemm, 647–5942.
Deputy Assistant Secretaries: Marcia Bernicat, 647–9438; Philippe Lussier, 647–5152; Linda Taglialatela, 647–5152.

FOREIGN SERVICE INSTITUTE

Director.—Amb. Nancy McEldowney, room F2102 (703) 302–6703.
Deputy Director.—Marc Oestfield (703) 302–6707.

INFORMATION RESOURCE MANAGEMENT

Chief Information Officer.—Steven Taylor (acting), 634–3084.
Chief Technology Officer of Operations.—Glen Johnson, 634–3084.
Chief Knowledge Officer of Business Management and Planning.—Janice Fedak, 634–3083.
Chief Information Security Officer of Information Assurance.—William Lay (703) 812–2555.

MEDICAL SERVICES

Medical Director.—Dr. Gary Tenner, 663–1649.
Deputy Medical Director.—Charles Rosenfarb, 663–1649.

OVERSEAS BUILDINGS OPERATIONS

Director.—Lydia Munic (703) 875–4114.
Deputy Director.—Heather Townsend (703) 875–6366.
Executive Assistant.—Tomekah Burl (703) 875–5036.

UNDER SECRETARY OF STATE FOR CIVILIAN SECURITY, DEMOCRACY, AND HUMAN RIGHTS

Under Secretary.—Vacant, room 7261, 647–6240.
Executive Assistant.—Kathleen Fitzpatrick, 647–7818.

DEMOCRACY, HUMAN RIGHTS AND LABOR

Assistant Secretary.—Vacant, room 7827, 647–2126.
Principal Deputy Assistant Secretary.—Uzra Zeya, 647–3273.

OCEANS AND INTERNATIONAL ENVIRONMENTAL AND SCIENTIFIC AFFAIRS

Assistant Secretary.—Dr. Kerri-Ann Jones, room 3880, 647–1554.
Principal Deputy Assistant Secretary.—Amb. Judith Garber, 647–6950.
Deputy Assistant Secretaries: David A. Balton, 647–2396; Jonathan Margolis, 647–3584; Daniel Reifsnyder, 647–2232.

POPULATION, REFUGEES AND MIGRATION

Assistant Secretary.—Anne C. Richard, room 6825, 647–7360.
Principal Deputy Assistant Secretary.—David Robinson, 647–5982.
Deputy Assistant Secretaries: Kelly Clements, 647–5822; Catherine Wiesner, 647–5822.

U.S. MISSION TO THE UNITED NATIONS

U.S. Permanent Representative.—Susan E. Rice, room 633, 736–7555.
Deputy to the Ambassador.—Rexon Y. Ryu.

OFFICE OF U.S. FOREIGN ASSISTANCE RESOURCES

Director.—Robert Goldberg, room 5923, 647–2608.

Executive Assistant.—Lisa Greene, 647–3690.

UNITED STATES DIPLOMATIC OFFICES—FOREIGN SERVICE

(C= Consular Office, N= No Embassy or Consular Office)

http://usembassy.state.gov

LIST OF CHIEFS OF MISSION

AFGHANISTAN, ISLAMIC REPUBLIC OF (Kabul).
Hon. James B. Cunningham.
ALBANIA, REPUBLIC OF (Tirana).
Hon. Alexander A. Arvizu.
ALGERIA, DEMOCRATIC AND POPULAR REPUBLIC OF (Algiers).
Hon. Henry S. Ensher.
ANDORRA (Andorra La Vella) (N)
Hon. Alan D. Solomont.
ANGOLA, REPUBLIC OF (Luanda).
Hon. Christopher J. McMullen.
ANTIGUA AND BARBUDA (St. John's) (N).
Hon. Larry Leon Palmer.
ARGENTINA (Buenos Aires).
Hon. Vilma S. Martinez.
ARMENIA, REPUBLIC OF (Yerevan).
Hon. John A. Heffern.
AUSTRALIA (Canberra).
Hon. Jeffrey L. Bleich.
AUSTRIA, REPUBLIC OF (Vienna).
Hon. William Carlton Eacho III.
AZERBAIJAN, REPUBLIC OF (Baku).
Hon. Richard Morningstar.
BAHAMAS, THE COMMONWEALTH OF THE (Nassau).
Vacant.
BAHRAIN, STATE OF (Manama).
Hon. Thomas Charles Krajeski.
BANGLADESH, PEOPLE'S REPUBLIC OF (Dhaka).
Hon. Dan W. Mozena.
BARBADOS (Bridgetown).
Hon. Larry Leon Palmer.
BELARUS, REPUBLIC OF (Minsk).
Vacant.
BELGIUM (Brussels).
Howard G. Gutman.
BELIZE (Belmopan).
Hon. Vinai Thummalapally.
BENIN, REPUBLIC OF (Cotonou).
Hon. Michael Raynor.
BOLIVIA, REPUBLIC OF (La Paz).
Vacant.
BOSNIA–HERZEGOVINA (Sarajevo).
Hon. Patrick S. Moon.
BOTSWANA, REPUBLIC OF (Gaborone).
Hon. Michelle D. Gavin.
BRAZIL, FEDERATIVE REPUBLIC OF (Brasilia).
Hon. Thomas Alfred Shannon, Jr.
BRUNEI DARUSSALAM (Bandar Seri Begawan).
Hon. Daniel L. Shields III.
BULGARIA, REPUBLIC OF (Sofia).
Hon. Marcie B. Ries.
BURKINA FASO (Ouagadougou).
Hon. J. Thomas Dougherty.
BURMA, UNION OF (Rangoon).
Hon. Derek J. Mitchell.
BURUNDI, REPUBLIC OF (Bujumbura).
Hon. Dawn M. Liberi.
CAMBODIA, KINGDOM OF (Phnom Penh).
Hon. William E. Todd.
CAMEROON, REPUBLIC OF (Yaounde).
Hon. Robert Porter Jackson.
CANADA (Ottawa).
Amb. David C. Jacobson.
CAPE VERDE, REPUBLIC OF (Praia).
Hon. Adrienne S. O'Neal.
CENTRAL AFRICAN REPUBLIC (Bangui).
Hon. Laurence D. Wohlers.
CHAD, REPUBLIC OF (N'Djamena).
Hon. Mark M. Boulware.
CHILE, REPUBLIC OF (Santiago).
Hon. Alexandro Daniel Wolff.
CHINA, PEOPLE'S REPUBLIC OF (Beijing).
Hon. Max Baucus.
COLOMBIA, REPUBLIC OF (Bogota).
Hon. Peter Michael McKinley.
COMOROS, UNION OF (Moroni) (N).
Vacant.
CONGO, DEMOCRATIC REPUBLIC OF THE (Kinshasa).
Hon. James Frederick Entwistle.
CONGO, REPUBLIC OF THE (Brazzaville).
Hon. Christopher W. Murray.
COSTA RICA, REPUBLIC OF (San Jose).
Hon. Anne Slaughter Andrew.
COTE D'IVOIRE, REPUBLIC OF (Abidjan).
Hon. Phillip Carter III.
CROATIA, REPUBLIC OF (Zagreb).
Hon. Kenneth Merten.
CUBA (Havana).
Principal Officer John Caulfield.
CURACAO and ST. MAARTEN
Principal Officer Valerie L. Belon.
CYPRUS, REPUBLIC OF (Nicosia).
Hon. John M. Koenig.
CZECH REPUBLIC (Prague).
Hon. Norman L. Eisen.
DENMARK (Copenhagen).
Hon. Laurie Susan Fulton.
DJIBOUTI, REPUBLIC OF (Djibouti).
Hon. Geeta Pasi.
DOMINICAN REPUBLIC (Santo Domingo).
Hon. Raul Yzaguirre.
EAST TIMOR, DEMOCRATIC REPUBLIC OF (Dili).
Hon. Judith R. Fergin.
ECUADOR, REPUBLIC OF (Quito).

Hon. Adam E. Namm.
EGYPT, ARAB REPUBLIC OF (Cairo).
Hon. Anne Woods Patterson.
EL SALVADOR, REPUBLIC OF (San Salvador).
Hon. Mari Carmen Aponte.
EQUATORIAL GUINEA, REPUBLIC OF (Malabo) (N).
Hon. Mark L. Asquino.
ERITREA, STATE OF (Asmara).
Vacant.
ESTONIA, REPUBLIC OF (Tallinn).
Hon. Jeffrey D. Levine.
ETHIOPIA, FEDERAL DEMOCRATIC REPUBLIC OF (Addis Ababa).
Hon. Donald E. Booth.
FIJI ISLANDS, REPUBLIC OF THE (Suva).
Hon. Frankie Annette Reed.
FINLAND, REPUBLIC OF (Helsinki).
Hon. Bruce J. Oreck.
FRANCE (Paris).
Hon. Charles H. Rivkin.
GABONESE REPUBLIC (Libreville).
Hon. Eric D. Benjaminson.
GAMBIA, REPUBLIC OF THE (Banjul).
Hon. Edward M. Alford.
GEORGIA (Tbilisi).
Hon. Richard B. Norland.
GERMANY, FEDERAL REPUBLIC OF (Berlin).
Hon. Philip D. Murphy.
GHANA, REPUBLIC OF (Accra).
Hon. Gene Allan Cretz.
GREECE (Athens).
Hon. Daniel Bennett Smith.
GRENADA (St. George) (N).
Hon. Larry Leon Palmer.
GUATEMALA, REPUBLIC OF (Guatemala).
Hon. Arnold A. Chacón.
GUINEA, REPUBLIC OF (Conakry).
Hon. Alexander Mark Laskaris.
GUINEA-BISSAU, REPUBLIC OF (Bissau) (N).
Hon. Lewis Alan Lukens.
GUYANA, CO-OPERATIVE REPUBLIC OF (Georgetown).
Hon. D. Brent Hardt.
HAITI, REPUBLIC OF (Port-au-Prince).
Hon. Pamela A. White.
HOLY SEE (Vatican City).
Vacant.
HONDURAS, REPUBLIC OF (Tegucigalpa).
Hon. Lisa J. Kubiske.
HONG KONG (Hong Kong) (C).
Principal Officer Stephen M. Young.
HUNGARY, REPUBLIC OF (Budapest).
Hon. Eleni Tsakopoulos Kounalakis.
ICELAND, REPUBLIC OF (Reykjavik).
Hon. Luis E. Arreaga-Rodas.
INDIA (New Delhi).
Hon. Nancy J. Powell.
INDONESIA, REPUBLIC OF (Jakarta).
Hon. Scot Alan Marciel.
IRAQ, REPUBLIC OF (Baghdad).
Hon. Robert Stephen Beecroft.
IRELAND (Dublin).
Vacant.
ISRAEL, STATE OF (Tel Aviv).
Hon. Daniel Benjamin Shapiro.
ITALY (Rome).
Hon. David H. Thorne.
JAMAICA (Kingston).
Hon. Pamela E. Bridgewater Awkard.
JAPAN (Tokyo).
Hon. Caroline Kennedy.
JERUSALEM
Consul General Michael Ratney.
JORDAN, HASHEMITE KINGDOM OF (Amman).
Hon. Stuart E. Jones.
KAZAKHSTAN, REPUBLIC OF (Almaty).
Hon. Kenneth J. Fairfax.
KENYA, REPUBLIC OF (Nairobi).
Hon. Robert F. Godec.
KIRIBATI, REPUBLIC OF (Tarawa) (N).
Hon. Frankie Annette Reed.
KOREA, REPUBLIC OF (Seoul).
Hon. Sung Y. Kim.
KOSOVO (Pristina).
Hon. Tracey Ann Jacobson.
KUWAIT, STATE OF (Kuwait City).
Hon. Matthew H. Tueller.
KYRGYZ REPUBLIC (Bishkek).
Hon. Pamela L. Spratlen.
LAO PEOPLE'S DEMOCRATIC REPUBLIC (Vientiane).
Hon. Karen Brevard Stewart.
LATVIA, REPUBLIC OF (Riga).
Hon. Mark A. Pekala.
LEBANON, REPUBLIC OF (Beirut).
Hon. Maura Connelly.
LESOTHO, KINGDOM OF (Maseru).
Vacant.
LIBERIA, REPUBLIC OF (Monrovia).
Hon. Deborah Ruth Malac.
LIBYA (Tripoli).
Vacant.
LIECHTENSTEIN, PRINCIPALITY OF (Vaduz) (N).
Hon. Donald Sternoff Beyer, Jr.
LITHUANIA, REPUBLIC OF (Vilnius).
Hon. Deborah Ann McCarthy.
LUXEMBOURG, GRAND DUCHY OF (Luxembourg).
Hon. Robert A. Mandell.
MACEDONIA, REPUBLIC OF (Skopje).
Hon. Paul D. Wohlers.
MADAGASCAR, REPUBLIC OF (Antananarivo).
Vacant.
MALAWI, REPUBLIC OF (Lilongwe).
Hon. Jeanine E. Jackson.
MALAYSIA (Kuala Lumpur).
Hon. Paul W. Jones.
MALDIVES, REPUBLIC OF (Male) (N).
Hon. Michele Jeanne Sison.
MALI, REPUBLIC OF (Bamako).
Hon. Mary Beth Leonard.
MALTA, REPUBLIC OF (Valletta).
Hon. Gina K. Abercrombie-Winstanley.
MARSHALL ISLANDS, REPUBLIC OF THE (Majuro).

Hon. Thomas Hart Armbruster.
MAURITANIA, ISLAMIC REPUBLIC OF (Nouakchott).
Hon. Jo Ellen Powell.
MAURITIUS, REPUBLIC OF (Port Louis).
Hon. Sharon English Woods Villarosa.
MEXICO (Mexico City).
Hon. Earl Anthony Wayne.
MICRONESIA, FEDERATED STATES OF (Kolonia).
Hon. Dorothea-Maria Rosen.
MOLDOVA, REPUBLIC OF (Chisinau).
Hon. William H. Moser.
MONACO (Monaco).
Hon. Charles H. Rivkin.
MONGOLIA (Ulaanbaatar).
Hon. Piper Anne Wind Campbell.
MONTENEGRO, REPUBLIC OF (Podgorica).
Hon. Sue Katharine Brown.
MOROCCO, KINGDOM OF (Rabat).
Hon. Samuel Louis Kaplan.
MOZAMBIQUE, REPUBLIC OF (Maputo).
Hon. Douglas M. Griffiths.
NAMIBIA, REPUBLIC OF (Windhoek).
Hon. Wanda L. Nesbitt.
NAURU, REPUBLIC OF (Yaren) (N).
Hon. Frankie Annette Reed.
NEPAL, KINGDOM OF (Kathmandu).
Hon. Peter William Bodde.
NETHERLANDS, KINGDOM OF THE (The Hague).
Vacant.
NEW ZEALAND (Wellington).
David Huebner.
NICARAGUA, REPUBLIC OF (Managua).
Hon. Phyllis Marie Powers.
NIGER, REPUBLIC OF (Niamey).
Hon. Bisa Williams.
NIGERIA, FEDERAL REPUBLIC OF (Abuja).
Hon. Terence Patrick McCulley.
NORWAY (Oslo).
Hon. Barry B. White.
OMAN, SULTANATE OF (Muscat).
Hon. Greta Christine Holtz.
PAKISTAN, ISLAMIC REPUBLIC OF (Islamabad).
Hon. Richard G. Olson.
PALAU, REPUBLIC OF (Koror).
Hon. Helen Patricia Reed-Rowe.
PANAMA, REPUBLIC OF (Panama).
Hon. Jonathan D. Farrar.
PAPUA NEW GUINEA (Port Moresby).
Hon. Walter North.
PARAGUAY, REPUBLIC OF (Asuncion)
Hon. James Harold Thessin.
PERU, REPUBLIC OF (Lima).
Hon. Rose M. Likins.
PHILIPPINES, REPUBLIC OF THE (Manila).
Hon. Harry K. Thomas, Jr.
POLAND, REPUBLIC OF (Warsaw).
Hon. Stephen D. Mull.
PORTUGAL, REPUBLIC OF (Lisbon).
Allan J. Katz.
QATAR, STATE OF (Doha).
Hon. Susan Laila Ziadeh.
ROMANIA (Bucharest).
Vacant.
RUSSIAN FEDERATION (Moscow).
Hon. Michael Anthony McFaul.
RWANDA, REPUBLIC OF (Kigali).
Hon. Donald W. Koran.
SAINT KITTS AND NEVIS (Basseterre) (N).
Hon. Larry Leon Palmer.
SAINT LUCIA (Castries) (N).
Hon. Larry Leon Palmer.
SAINT VINCENT AND THE GRENADINES (Kingstown) (N).
Hon. Larry Leon Palmer.
SAMOA (Apia) (N).
Hon. David Huebner.
SAN MARINO, REPUBLIC OF (San Marino) (N).
Hon. David H. Thorne.
SAO TOME AND PRINCIPE, DEMOCRATIC REPUBLIC OF (Sao Tome) (N).
Hon. Eric D. Benjaminson.
SAUDI ARABIA, KINGDOM OF (Riyadh).
Hon. James B. Smith.
SENEGAL, REPUBLIC OF (Dakar).
Hon. Lewis Alan Lukens.
SERBIA (Belgrade)
Hon. Michael D. Kirby.
SEYCHELLES, REPUBLIC OF (Victoria) (N).
Hon. Sharon English Woods Villarosa.
SIERRA LEONE, REPUBLIC OF (Freetown).
Hon. Michael S. Owen.
SINGAPORE, REPUBLIC OF (Singapore).
Hon. David Adelman.
SLOVAK REPUBLIC (Bratislava).
Hon. Theodore Sedgwick.
SLOVENIA, REPUBLIC OF (Ljubljana).
Hon. Joseph A. Mussomeli.
SOLOMON ISLANDS (Honiara) (N).
Hon. Walter North.
SOUTH AFRICA, REPUBLIC OF (Pretoria).
Vacant.
SOUTH SUDAN, REPUBLIC OF (Juba).
Hon. Susan Denise Page.
SPAIN (Madrid).
Hon. Alan D. Solomont.
SRI LANKA, DEMOCRATIC SOCIALIST REPUBLIC OF (Colombo).
Hon. Michele Jeanne Sison.
SUDAN, REPUBLIC OF THE (Khartoum).
Charge d' Affaires Joseph Stafford.
SURINAME, REPUBLIC OF (Paramaribo).
Hon. Jay Nicholas Anania.
SWAZILAND, KINGDOM OF (Mbabane).
Hon. Makila James.
SWEDEN (Stockholm).
Hon. Mark Francis Brzezinski.
SWITZERLAND (Bern).
Hon. Donald Sternoff Beyer, Jr.
SYRIAN ARAB REPUBLIC (Damascus).
Hon. Robert Stephen Ford.
TAJIKISTAN, REPUBLIC OF (Dushanbe).
Hon. Susan Marsh Elliott.
TANZANIA, UNITED REPUBLIC OF (Dar es Salaam).

Hon. Alfonso E. Lenhardt.
THAILAND, KINGDOM OF (Bangkok).
Hon. Kristie Anne Kenney.
TOGOLESE REPUBLIC (Lome).
Hon. Robert E. Whitehead.
TONGA, KINGDOM OF (Nuku'alofe) (N).
Hon. Frankie Annette Reed.
TRINIDAD AND TOBAGO, REPUBLIC OF (Port-of-Spain).
Vacant.
TUNISIA, REPUBLIC OF (Tunis).
Hon. Jacob Walles.
TURKEY, REPUBLIC OF (Ankara).
Hon. Francis Joseph Ricciardone, Jr.
TURKMENISTAN (Ashgabat).
Hon. Robert Patterson.
TUVALU (Funafuti) (N).
Hon. Frankie Annette Reed.
UGANDA, REPUBLIC OF (Kampala).
Hon. Scott H. DeLisi.
UKRAINE (Kyiv).
Hon. John F. Tefft.
UNITED ARAB EMIRATES (Abu Dhabi).
Hon. Michael H. Corbin.
UNITED KINGDOM OF GREAT BRITAIN AND NORTHERN IRELAND (London).
Hon. Louis B. Susman.
URUGUAY, ORIENTAL REPUBLIC OF (Montevideo).
Hon. Julissa Reynoso.
UZBEKISTAN, REPUBLIC OF (Tashkent).
Hon. George Albert Krol.
VANUATU, REPUBLIC OF (Port Vila) (N).
Hon. Walter North.
VENEZUELA, BOLIVARIAN REPUBLIC OF (Caracas).
Vacant.
VIETNAM, SOCIALIST REPUBLIC OF (Hanoi).
Hon. David Bruce Shear.
YEMEN, REPUBLIC OF (Sanaa).
Hon. Gerald M. Feierstein.
ZAMBIA, REPUBLIC OF (Lusaka).
Hon. Mark Charles Storella.
ZIMBABWE, REPUBLIC OF (Harare).
Hon. David Bruce Wharton.

UNITED STATES PERMANENT DIPLOMATIC MISSIONS TO INTERNATIONAL ORGANIZATIONS

ASSOCIATION OF SOUTHEAST ASIAN NATIONS (Jakarta).
Hon. David Lee Carden.
AFRICAN UNION (Addis Ababa).
Hon. Michael Anthony Battle, Sr.
EUROPEAN UNION (Brussels).
Amb. William E. Kennard.
NORTH ATLANTIC TREATY ORGANIZATION (Brussels).
Hon. Ivo Daalder.
ORGANIZATION FOR ECONOMIC COOPERATION AND DEVELOPMENT (Paris).
Vacant.
ORGANIZATION FOR SECURITY AND COOPERATION IN EUROPE (Vienna).
Hon. Ian C. Kelly.
ORGANIZATION OF AMERICAN STATES (Washington, DC).
Hon. Carmen Lomellin.
UNITED NATIONS (Geneva).
Hon. Betty E. King.
UNITED NATIONS (New York).
Hon. Susan E. Rice.
UNITED NATIONS (Vienna).
Hon. Joseph E. Macmanus.

DEPARTMENT OF THE TREASURY

1500 Pennsylvania Avenue, NW., 20220, phone (202) 622–2000, http://www.ustreas.gov

JACOB J. LEW, Secretary of the Treasury; born in New York, NY, August 29, 1955; education: A.B., Harvard College, 1978; J.D., Georgetown University Law Center, 1983; professional: Deputy Director of Program Analysis, Office of Management and Budget, City of Boston, 1978–79; Deputy Director, U.S. House Democratic Steering and Policy Committee, 1979–85; Executive Director, U.S. House Democratic Steering and Policy Committee, 1985–87; Of Counsel, Van Ness, Feldman and Curtiss, 1987; Partner, Van Ness, Feldman and Curtiss, 1988–91; Campaign '88 Issues Director, Democratic National Committee, 1988; Executive Director, Center for Middle East Research, 1992–93; Special Assistant to the President, White House, 1993–94; Associate Director, Office of Management and Budget, 1994; Executive Associate Director, Office of Management and Budget, 1995; Deputy Director, Office of Management and Budget, 1995–98; Director, Office of Management and Budget, 1998–2001; Research Professor, Georgetown University Public Policy Institute, 2001; Executive Vice President and Clinical Professor of Public Policy, New York University, 2001–06; Managing Director and Chief Operating Officer of Global Wealth Management Division, Citigroup, 2006–07; Managing Director and Chief Operating Officer of Citi Alternative Investments Division, Citigroup, 2008–09; Deputy Secretary of State for Management and Resources, 2009–10; Director, Office of Management and Budget, 2010–12; White House Chief of Staff, 2012–13; married: Ruth; children: Shoshana and Isaac; nominated by President Barack Obama to become the 76th Secretary of the Treasury and confirmed by the U.S. Senate on February 27, 2013.

OFFICE OF THE SECRETARY

Secretary of the Treasury.—Jacob J. Lew, room 3330 (202) 622–1100.
Executive Assistant.—Shirley E. Gathers, 622–5377.
Confidential Assistant.—Cheryl L. Matera, 622–0190.

OFFICE OF THE DEPUTY SECRETARY

Deputy Secretary.—Mary J. Miller (acting), room 3312 (202) 622–1703.
Executive Assistants: Shirley Chisolm, room 3312-B, 622–1257; Sally Wrennall-Montes, room 3312-A, 622–0204.

OFFICE OF THE CHIEF OF STAFF

Chief of Staff.—Christian A. Weideman, room 3408 (202) 622–1906.
Deputy Chief of Staff.—Adewale Adeyemo, room 3414, 622–1906.
Executive Secretary.—David G. Clunie, room 3410, 622–1906.
White House Liaison.—Margaret Buford, room 3420, 622–1906.
Review Analyst.—Anita Maria Hunt, room 3408, 622–0502.

OFFICE OF THE GENERAL COUNSEL

General Counsel.—Christopher Meade, room 3000 (202) 622–0283.
Principal Deputy General Counsel.—Christopher Meade (202) 622–0283.
Deputy General Counsel.—Christian Weideman, 622–1135.
Staff Assistants: Aloma A. Shaw, Kim Wilson, 622–0283.
Senior Advisor to the General Counsel.—Alexander Krulic, room 3006, 622–1223.
Assistant General Counsel for—
Banking and Finance.—Peter Bieger, room 2304, 622–1975.
Enforcement and Intelligence.—Brian Egan, room 3014, 622–1143.
General Law, Ethics and Regulation.—Rochelle Granat, room 2312, 622–6052.

International Affairs.—Himamauli ''Him'' Das, room 2308, 622–1147.

Deputy Assistant General Counsel for—

Banking and Finance.—Steve Laughton (acting), room 2001, 622–8413.

Banking and Finance (FSOC).—Eric Froman, room 3023, 622–1942.

Enforcement and Intelligence.—Vacant, room 2301, 622–3654.

General Law, Ethics and Regulation.—Brian Sonfield, room 2020, 622–9804.

General Law, Ethics and Regulation (Ethics).—Elizabeth ''Beth'' Horton, room 2221, 622–9794.

International Affairs.—Jeffrey Klein, room 2306, 622–2122.

Chief Counsel, Foreign Assets Control.—Vacant, Annex 3123, 622–9880.

Deputy Chief Counsel.—Matthew Tuchband, Annex 3121, 622–1654.

OFFICE OF THE INSPECTOR GENERAL

Inspector General.—Eric Thorson, room 4436 (202) 622–1090.

Deputy Inspector General.—Vacant.

Counsel to the Inspector General.—Richard Delmar, suite 510, 927–0650.

Assistant Inspector General for—

Audit.—Marla Freedman, suite 600, 927–5400.

Investigations.—P. Brian Crane, 1425 New York Avenue, NW., suite 500, 927–5260.

Management Services.—Patricia Hollis, suite 510, 927–5200.

Deputy Assistant Inspector General for—

Audit.—Robert Taylor, suite 600, 927–5400.

Investigations.—Vacant.

Management.—Debra McGruder, suite 510, 927–5229.

OFFICE OF THE UNDER SECRETARY FOR DOMESTIC FINANCE

Under Secretary.—Mary J. Miller, room 3312 (202) 622–1703.

Senior Advisors to the Under Secretary: Bret Hester, room 3419, 622–1677; Sam Valverde, room 3024, 622–6388.

OFFICE OF THE ASSISTANT SECRETARY FOR FINANCIAL INSTITUTIONS

Assistant Secretary.—Cyrus Amir-Mokri, room 2326 (202) 622–2610.

Senior Advisor.—Vacant.

Deputy Assistant Secretary, Office of:

Consumer Policy.—Melissa Koide, 622–9892.

Financial Institutions Policy.—Katheryn Rosen, 622–1443.

Small Business, Community Development, and Housing Policy.—Don Graves, 622–9939.

Director, Office of:

Critical Infrastructure Protection.—Brian Peretti, 622–0821.

Federal Insurance Office.—Michael McRaith, 622–6081.

Financial Education.—Louisa Quittman, 622–8103.

Financial Institutions Policy.—Tim Karpoff, 622–7811.

Deputy Director.—Patty Kao, 622–3610.

Small Business, Community Development, and Housing Policy.—Benson Roberts, 622–9802.

Executive Director, Office of:

Community Development Financial Institutions Fund.—Donna Gambrell, 601 13th Street, 2nd floor, 622–4203.

Small Business Lending Fund.—Jason Tepperman, 655 15th Street, 4th floor, 622–1869.

State Small Business Credit Initiative.—Clifton Kellogg, 655 15th Street, 4th floor, 622–8917.

Terrorism Risk Insurance Program.—Jeffrey S. Bragg, 1425 New York Avenue, NW., room 2114, 622–6770.

OFFICE OF THE ASSISTANT SECRETARY FOR FINANCIAL MARKETS

Assistant Secretary.—Matthew S. Rutherford, room 2334 (202) 622–5571.

Senior Advisor.—Jamie Franco, 622–1269.

Deputy Assistant Secretary, Office of:

Capital Markets.—Timothy Bowler, 622–8811.

Federal Finance.—James Clark, 622–0509.

Government Financial Policy.—Gary Grippo, 622–2344.

Director, Office of:
Capital Markets.—Monique Rollins, 622–1745.
Debt Management.—Fred Pietrangeli, 622–1876.
Federal Lending.—Gary Burner, National Press Building, suite 228, 622–2470.
Financial Markets Regulation and Policy.—Heidilynne Schultheiss, 622–2692.
Policy and Legislative Review.—Paula Farrell, National Press Building, suite 1148, 622–2450.
State Housing Finance Agency Initiative.—Preston Atkins, 622–0699.

OFFICE OF THE FISCAL ASSISTANT SECRETARY

Assistant Secretary.—Richard Gregg, room 2118 (202) 622–0560.
Senior Advisor.—Renata Maziarz, 622–3196.
Deputy Assistant Secretary for—
Accounting Policy.—Mark Reger, room 2104, 622–6943.
Fiscal Operations and Policy.—Sheryl Morrow, room 2108, 622–2205.
Director, Office of:
Financial Agents.—Theodore Kowalsky, 622–9445.
Fiscal Projections.—David Monroe, room 2040, 622–0580.
Recovery Act Programs.—Ellen Neubauer, 622–5338.
Director, Office of Financial Innovation and Transformation.—Elizabeth Angerman, 622–9870.

OFFICE OF THE ASSISTANT SECRETARY FOR FINANCIAL STABILITY

Assistant Secretary.—Timothy Massad, room 2428 (202) 622–0178.
Senior Advisor.—J.D. Grom, 622–1258.
Chief Office of:
Compliance Officer.—Joyce Philip (acting), 927–8079.
Finance and Operations.—Lorenzo Rasetti, 927–9458.
Homeownership Officer.—Mark McArdle (acting), 622–5739.
Investment Officer.—Chairmian Uy, 622–6991.
Reporting Officer.—Carole Florman, 927–9474.

FINANCIAL MANAGEMENT SERVICE

401 14th Street, SW., 20227, phone (202) 874–6740, fax 874–7016

Commissioner.—David A. Lebryk.
Deputy Commissioner.—Wanda Rogers.
Assistant Commissioner for—
Enterprise Business Information Security and Services (EBISS).—Kim McCoy.
Debt Management Services.—Jeffrey Schramek.
Federal Finance.—Kristine Conrath.
Government-wide Accounting.—Christina Ho.
Management (Chief Financial Officer).—Marty Greiner.
Payments Management.—John Hill.
Chief Counsel.—Margaret Marquette.
Director for Legislative and Public Affairs.—Joyce Harris.

BUREAU OF THE FISCAL SERVICE

401 14th Street, SW., 20227, phone (202) 874–7000, fax (202) 874–6743

[Codified under U.S.C. 31, section 306]

Commissioner.—David Lebryk (202) 874–7000.
Chief Counsel.—Margaret Marquette (202) 874–6680.
Deputy Commissioner/Finance and Administration.—Anita Shandor (202) 504–3500.
Deputy Commissioner/Financial Services and Operations.—Wanda Rogers (202) 874–7000.
Deputy Commissioner/Accounting and Shared Services.—Cynthia Springer (304) 480–7888.
Executive Director for Government Securities Regulations Staff.—Lori Santamorena (202) 504–3632.
Assistant Commissioner, Office of:
CIO/Information and Security Services.—Kimberly McCoy (304) 480–6204.
CFO/Management.—Marty Greiner (202) 874–7100.

Debt Management.—Jeff Schramek (205) 912–6112.
Financing.—Dara Seaman (202) 504–3550.
Government-wide Accounting.—Christina Ho (202) 874–8518.
Office of Administrative Services.—Doug Anderson (304) 480–8760.
Payment Management.—John Hill (202) 874–6790.
Public Debt Accounting.—Matthew Miller (304) 480–5101.
Retail Securities.—Paul Crowe (304) 480–6516.
Revenue Collections Management.—Kristine Conrath (202) 874–6720.
Director, Office of Legislative and Public Affairs.—Joyce Harris (202) 504–6760.

OFFICE OF THE UNDER SECRETARY FOR INTERNATIONAL AFFAIRS

Under Secretary.—Lael Brainard, room 3436 MT (202) 622–1270.
Deputy Assistant Secretary for—
International Policy Analysis.—Bradley Setser, room 4464 MT, 662–1191.
Director, Strategic Initiatives.—Monica Mills, room 3034 MT, 622–6427.
Senior Advisors: Sameera Fazili, room 3217, 622–6508; Lyndsay Huot, room 3432A MT, 622–1193; Michael Love, room 4456A MT, 662–1025.
Senior Advisor and Director, IA Business Operations.—Gordon McDonald, room 3224 MT; 662–6427.
Staff Assistant.—Karen DeLaBarre Chase, room 3432B, 622–0060.
Executive Secretary and Senior Coordinator for China and the Strategic and Economic Dialogue.—Sharon Yuan, DAS, Trade and Investment Policy, room 3205 MT, 622–6883.

OFFICE OF THE ASSISTANT SECRETARY FOR INTERNATIONAL AFFAIRS

Assistant Secretary for International Finance.—Charles Collyns, room 3428 MT, 622–0656.
Deputy Assistant Secretary for—
Africa and the Middle East.—Andy Baukol, room 3218A MT, 622–2159.
Asian Nations.—Robert Dohner, room 3218B MT, 622–7222.
Europe and Eurasia.—Christopher Smart, room 3213 MT, 622–0117.
Western Hemisphere.—Leonardo Martinez, room 3037 MT, 622–2916.
Senior Advisor.—Michael Strauss, room 3041A MT, 622–7110.
Staff Assistant.—Pat Griffin, room 3430 MT, 622–7588.
Assistant Secretary for International Markets and Developments.—Marisa Lago, room 4138A MT, 622–0200.
Deputy Assistant Secretary for—
Environment and Energy.—Matthew J. Kotchen, room 3221 MT, 622–0173.
International Development, Finance and Debt.—Karen Mathiasen (acting), room 3204A MT, 622–8125.
International Monetary and Financial Policy.—Mark Sobel, room 3034 MT, 622–0168.
Investment Security.—Mark Jaskowiak, room 3203 MT, 622–0478.
Technical Assistance Policy.—W. Larry McDonald, room 3037 MT, 622–5504.
Trade and Investment Policy.—Sharon Yuan, room 3205A MT, 622–6883.
Senior Advisor.—Laura Black, 4138C MT, 622–9066.
Staff Assistant.—Kimberly Richards, 4138B MT, 622–4826.
Directors for International Affairs:
Afghanistan (IEA).—Michael Kaplan, room 4440M MT, 622–4262.
Africa (INN).—Clay Berry, room 1064C MT, 622–5280.
East Asia (ISA).—Robert Kaproth, room 4462 MT, 622–0132.
Environment and Energy Policy.—Abigail Demopulos (acting), room 1024C MT, 622–5671.
Europe and Eurasia (ICN).—Jeff Baker, room 4122C MT, 622–4845.
Global Economics Group (IMG).—John Weeks, room 5428 MT, 622–9885.
International Banking and Securities Markets (IMB).—William Murden, room 5310 MT, 622–2775.
International Debt Policy (IDD).—John Hurley, room 5417B MT, 622–9124.
International Monetary Policy (IMF).—Mathew Haarsager, room 5326 MT, 622–1041.
International Trade (ITT).—Bill Schall (acting), room 5204K MT, 622–0208.
Investment Security (IFI).—Aimen Mir, room 5211A MT, 622–0184.
Middle East and North Africa (INM).—Luyen Tran, room 5008 MT, 622–0763.
Multilateral Development Banks (IDB).—Karen Mathiasen, room 5313M MT, 622–0070.
South and Southeast Asia (ISS).—Michael Kaplan, room 4440 MT, 622–4262.
Technical Assistance.—Mike Ruffner, 740 15th Street, NW., 622–2886.

Trade Finance and Investment Negotiations (ITF).—David Drysdale, room 5419J MT, 622–1749.
Western Hemisphere (IWH).—Carrie McKellogg, room 1458A MT, 622–4072.

U.S. BANKS

U.S. Executive Director of:
Inter-American Development Bank.—Gustavo Arnavat (202) 623–1075.
International Monetary Fund.—Meg Lundsager, 623–7764.
World Bank.—Ian H. Solomon, 458–0115.

OVERSEAS

U.S. Executive Director of:
African Development Bank and Fund (Tunis, Tunisia).—Walter Jones, 011–216–71–102–010.
Asian Development Bank (Manila, Philippines).—Robert M. "Skipp" Orr, 011–632–632–6050.
European Bank for Reconstruction and Development (London, England).—James L. Hudson, 011–44–207–338–6459.

UNDER SECRETARY FOR TERRORISM AND FINANCIAL INTELLIGENCE

Under Secretary.—David S. Cohen, MT room 4326 (202) 622–8260.

ASSISTANT SECRETARY FOR TERRORIST FINANCING

Assistant Secretary.—Daniel L. Glaser, room 4316, MT 622–1943.
Deputy Assistant Secretary for Terrorist Financing and Financial Crimes.—Jennifer Fowler (acting), MT room 4000, 622–1634.
Director, Office of:
Global Affairs.—Colleen Stack, MT room 4001, 622–3447.
Strategic Policy.—Chip Poncy, MT room 4308, 622–9761.

ASSISTANT SECRETARY FOR INTELLIGENCE AND ANALYSIS

Assistant Secretary.—S. Leslie Ireland, room 4332 (202) 622–1835.
Deputy Assistant Secr: .ary.—A. Daniel McGlynn, room 2441, 622–1841.
Deputy Assistant Secretary for Security.—Charles Cavella, room 2523, 622–2585.
Director, Emergency Programs.—Michael Thomas, room 1020, 622–2195.

OFFICE OF FOREIGN ASSETS CONTROL

Director.—Adam J. Szubin, room 2240 (202) 622–2510.

EXECUTIVE OFFICE FOR ASSET FORFEITURE

1341 G Street, NW., Suite 900, 20005, phone (202) 622–9600

Director.—Eric E. Hampl.

FINANCIAL CRIMES ENFORCEMENT NETWORK (FINCEN)

P.O. Box 39, Vienna, VA 22183, phone (703) 905–3591

Director.—Jennifer Shasky Calvery (202) 354–6393.
Deputy Director.—Frederick Reynolds (202) 354–6392.

OFFICE OF THE ASSISTANT SECRETARY FOR ECONOMIC POLICY

Assistant Secretary.—Janice C. Eberly, room 3454, (202) 622–2200.
Senior Advisor to the Assistant Secretary.—Lisa Abraham, room 3445–D, 622–3552.
Deputy Assistant Secretary for Policy Coordination.—Vacant, room 3449, 622–2220.

Deputy Assistant Secretary for Macroeconomic Analysis.—David Arseneau, room 3450, 622–2734.
Director, Office of Macroeconomic Analysis.—Rachel Cononi, room 2449, 622–0156.
Deputy Assistant Secretary for Microeconomic Analysis.—Alexander Gelber, room 3439, 622–1513.
Director, Office of Microeconomic Analysis.—Jason Brown, room 4426, 622–1757.

OFFICE OF THE ASSISTANT SECRETARY FOR LEGISLATIVE AFFAIRS

Assistant Secretary for Legislative Affairs.—Alastair M. Fitzpayne, room 3134, 622–1900.
Senior Advisor.—Patrick Maloney, room 3464, 622–1900.
Special Assistant.—Kathryn Alvarez, room 3134, 622–1900.
Administrative Specialist.—Linda L. Powell, room 3453–D, 622–0535.
Legislative Research Analyst.—Gail Harris-Berry, room 3453–C, 622–4401.
Deputy Assistant Secretary (Banking and Finance and TFI).—Kathleen Mellody, 3124–B, 622–1900.
Special Assistant.—Cara Camacho, room 3128–B, 622–1900.
Deputy Assistant Secretary (Appropriations and Management).—Lisa L. Pena, room 3462, 622–1900.
Deputy Assistant Secretary (Tax and Budget).—Sandra Salstrom, room 3132, 622–1900.
Special Assistant.—Namrata Mujumdar, room 3128–D, 622–1900.
Deputy Assistant Secretary (International).—Stephane J. Le Bouder, room 3127, 622–1900.
Special Assistant.—Andrea Ambriz, room 3128–A, 622–1900.
Deputy Assistant Secretary (Housing, Small Business and TARP).—Megan O. Moore, room 3124–C, 622–1900.
Special Assistant.—J. Drew Colbert, room 3128–C, 622–1900.

OFFICE OF THE ASSISTANT SECRETARY FOR MANAGEMENT / CHIEF FINANCIAL OFFICER

Assistant Secretary for Management and Chief Performance Officer.—Nani Coloretti, room 2438, Main Treasury, 202–622–0410.
Special Assistant.—John Costello, 622–0410.
Senior Advisors: Mike Lewis, 622–3068; Benjamin Mann, 622–0527.
Deputy Assistant Secretary for Management and Budget.—Sharon Kershbaum (acting), 622–0323.
Departmental Budget Director.—Robert Mahaffie, 622–1471.
Conference Events and Meeting Services.—Lucinda Gooch, room 1128, 622–2071.
Strategic Planning and Performance Management.—James Bae, 927–9640.
Director of the Office of Financial Management.—Giancarlo Brizzi (acting), 622–0101.
Director of Departmental Offices Operations.—Karen Melanson (acting), 622–7478.
Environmental Safety and Health.—Clayt Lauter, 622–1712.
Facilities Management.—Polly Dietz, room 1155, 622–7067.
Printing and Graphics.—Craig Larsen, room 6100, Annex, 622–1409.
Deputy Assistant Secretary for Information Systems and Chief Information Officer.—Robyn East, 622–5093.
Deputy Assistant Secretary for Human Resources and Chief Human Capital Officer.—Anita Blair, 1801 L Street, NW., 927–0341.
Equal Opportunity and Diversity.—Mariam Harvey, 1801 L Street, NW., 622–1160.
Human Resource Strategy and Solutions.—Nicole Johnson, 1801 L Street, NW., room 6120, 622–4822.
Human Resources Operations.—Kristy Kaptur, 1801 L Street, NW., room 6626, 927–4919.
Deputy Assistant Secretary for Privacy, Transparency and Records.—Veronica Marco (acting), 622–2477.
Deputy Chief Financial Officer.—Dorrice Roth, 622–1693.
Director of Accounting and Internal Control.—Carole Banks, room 6263, 927–5281.
Senior Procurement Executive.—Cathy Higginbotham (acting), 622–6585.
Accounting Officer.—David Legge, room 6070, Met Square, 622–1167.
Director of the Office of:
Emergency Programs.—Mike Thomas, 622–2195.
Minority and Women Inclusion.—Lorraine Cole, 927–8181.

OFFICE OF THE ASSISTANT SECRETARY FOR PUBLIC AFFAIRS

Assistant Secretary.—Vacant, room 3438 MT (202) 622–2910.
Deputy Assistant Secretary, Public Affairs Operations.—Natalie Earnest, room 3122 MT, 622–2910.
Deputy Assistant Secretary, Public Affairs.—Anthony Coley, room 3446 MT, 622–2920.
Senior Advisor, Public Affairs.—Marissa Secreto, room 2126 MT, 622–2307.
Deputy Assistant Secretary/Public Liaison.—Victoria Suarez-Palomo, room 3108 MT, 622–9760.
Review Analyst and Scheduling Coordinator.—Carmen Alvarado, room 3442 MT, 622–7483.
Spokesperson for—
Domestic Finance.—Suzanne Elio, room 2124 MT, 622–2960.
Enforcement Specialist.—John Sullivan, room 2124 MT, 622–2960.
International Affairs.—Holly Shulman, room 2124 MT, 622–2960.
MHA & HHF.—Andrea Risotto, 1801 L Street, room 817 MT, 927–8726.
OFS.—Matthew Anderson, room 2124 MT, 622–2960.
Tax, Budget, Economic Policy.—Sabrina Siddiqui, room 2124 MT, 622–2960.
Speechwriter to the Secretary.—Mark Cohen, room 3111 MT, 622–5176.
Media Coordinator.—Anthony Reyes, room 2124 MT, 622–0470.
Media Affairs Specialist.—Matt Anderson, room 2124 MT, 622–0631.
Senior Advisor (Public Liaison).—Lance "Edward" Williams, room 3111 MT, 622–9760.
Press Assistant.—Stephanie Ma, room 2124 MT, 622–2960.

OFFICE OF THE ASSISTANT SECRETARY FOR TAX POLICY

Assistant Secretary.—Mark J. Mazur, room 3120 MT (202) 622–0050.
Deputy Assistant Secretary for—
International Tax Affairs.—Vacant, room 3045 MT, 622–1317.
Tax Analysis.—Vacant, room 3064 MT, 622–0120.
Tax Policy.—Emily McMahon, room 3112 MT, 622–0140.
Tax, Trade and Tariff Policy.—Timothy Skud, room 3104 MT, 622–0220.
Retirement and Health Policy and Senior Advisor to the Secretary—J. Mark Iwry, room 3063 MT, 622–7827.
Tax Legislative Counsel.—Lisa Zarlenga, room 3040 MT, 622–0835.
Deputy Tax Legislative Counsel.—Jessica Hauser, room 4202 MT, 622–1335.
International Tax Counsel.—Vacant, room 3054 MT, 622–1317.
Deputy International Tax Counsel: Ginny Chung, room 5104C MT, 622–9461; Henry Louis, room 5064 MT, 622–1791.
Benefits Tax Counsel.—George Bostick, room 3050 MT, 622–1341.
Deputy Benefits Tax Counsel.—Robert Neis, room 4224 MT, 622–5293.
Director, Office of Tax Analysis.—James Mackie, room 4116 MT, 622–1326.
Director, Division of:
Business and International Taxation.—William Randolph, room 4221 MT, 622–1782.
Economic Modeling and Computer Applications.—Robert Gillette, room 4039 MT, 622–0852.
Individual Taxation.—Janet McCubbin, room 4043 MT, 622–0589.
Revenue and Receipts Forecasting/Individual Revenue Division.—Scott Jaquette, room 4064 MT, 622–1319.
Revenue and Receipts Forecasting/Business Revenue Division.—Curtis Carlson, room 4112 MT, 622–0130.

BUREAU OF ENGRAVING AND PRINTING

14th and C Streets, NW., 20228, phone (202) 874–2000

[Created by act of July 11, 1862; codified under U.S.C. 31, section 303]

Director.—Larry R. Felix.
Deputy Director.—Leonard R. Olijar, 874–2016.
Chief Counsel.—Vacant, 874–2306.
Associate Directors:
Chief Financial Officer (CFO).—Vacant, 874–2020.
Chief Information Officer (CIO).—Peter O. Johnson, 874–3000.
Associate Director for—
Eastern Currency Facility.—Jon J. Cameron, 874–2032.

Western Currency Facility.—Charlene Williams (817) 847–3802.
Management.—Will Levy III, 874–2040.
Product and Technology Development.—Judith Diaz-Myers, 874–2008.
Corporate Planning and Strategic Analysis.—Andrew Brunhart, 874–4340.

OFFICE OF THE COMPTROLLER OF THE CURRENCY

400 7th Street, SW., 20219, phone (202) 649–6800

Comptroller.—Thomas Curry (acting), 649–6400.
Chief of Staff and Public Affairs.—Paul Nash (acting), 649–6480.
Chief Counsel.—Amy Friend, 649–5400.
Senior Deputy Comptroller for—
Bank Supervision Policy and Chief National Bank Examiner.—John Lyons, 649–6770.
Chief Financial Officer.—Thomas R. Bloom, 649–5480.
Economics.—Mark Levonian, 649–5410.
Large Bank Supervision.—Michael L. Brosnan, 649–5590.
Midsize and Community Bank Supervision.—Jennifer C. Kelly, 649–5420.
Director for Congressional Liaison.—Carrie Moore, 649–6737.
Ombudsman.—Larry Hattix, 649–6857.
Chief Information Officer.—Edward J. Dorris, 649–6001.

INTERNAL REVENUE SERVICE

1111 Constitution Avenue, NW., 20224, phone (202) 622–5000

[Created by act of July 1, 1862; codified under U.S.C. 26, section 7802]

Commissioner.—John Koskinen, 622–9511.
Chief of Staff.—W. Todd Grams, 622–9511.
Deputy Commissioner, Services and Enforcement.—John Dalrymple, 622–6860
Commissioner of:
Large Business and International Division.—Heather Maloy, 283–8710.
Small Business/Self-Employed.—Faris Fink, 622–0600.
Tax Exempt and Government Entities.—Joseph H. Grant, 283–2500.
Wage and Investment.—Peggy Bogadi (404) 338–7060.
Chief, Criminal Investigation.—Richard Weber, 622–3200.
Directors:
Office of Professional Responsibility.—Karen Hawkins, 927–3812.
Whistleblower Office.—Steve Whitlock, 622–0351.
Deputy Commissioner, Operations Support.—Beth Tucker, 622–4255.
Chief:
Agency-Wide Shared Services.—Dave Grant, 622–7500.
Appeals.—Sheldon Kay, 435–5600.
Communications and Liaison.—Terry Lemons, 622–5440.
Equity, Diversity and Inclusion.—Monica Davy, 622–5400.
Financial Officer.—Pamela LaRue, 622–6400.
IRS Human Capital Officer.—David Krieg, 622–7676.
Office of Privacy, Information Protection and Data Security.—Rebecca A. Chiaramida, 622–2988.
Technology Officer.—Terence Milholland, 622–6800.
Chief Counsel.—William J. Wilkins, 622–3300.
National Taxpayer Advocate.—Nina E. Olson, 622–6100.
Director, Office of Research, Analysis and Statistics.—Rosemary Marcuss, 874–0100.
Office of Legislative Affairs.—Cathy Barre, 622–3720.

INSPECTOR GENERAL FOR TAX ADMINISTRATION (TIGTA)

1401 H Street, NW., Suite 469, 20005

phone (202) 622–6500, fax 927–0001

Inspector General.—J. Russell George.
Principal Deputy Inspector General.—Joseph Hungate.
Congressional Liaison.—Matthew S. Sutphen, 927–7266.

Chief Counsel.—Michael T. McCarthy, 622–3139.
Deputy Inspector General for Audit.—Michael R. Phillips, 927–7085.
Assistant Inspector General for—
Compliance and Enforcement Operations.—Randee Cook (acting), (770) 617–6434.
Management Planning and Workforce Development.—Nancy A. Nakamura, 622–3837.
Management Services and Organizations.—Greg D. Kutz, 622–5089.
Returns Processing and Accounts Services.—Russ Martin (acting), (978) 809–0296.
Security and Information Technology.—Alan R. Duncan, 622–5894.
Deputy Inspector General for Investigations.—Timothy P. Camus, 927–7160.
Assistant Inspectors General for Investigations (HQ Ops).—Michael A. Delgado, 927–7183.
Assistant Inspectors General for Investigations (Field Ops).—Randy M. Silvis, 927–0150.
Deputy Assistant Inspector General for Investigations.—Marsha L. Griffith, 927–7182.
Deputy Inspector General for Inspections and Evaluations.—David Holmgren, 927–7048.
Associate Inspector General for Mission Support.—Margaret E. Begg, 622–5959.

OFFICE OF THE TREASURER OF THE UNITED STATES

Treasurer.—Rosie Rios (202) 622–0100.
Senior Advisor.—Kristin Ward.
Executive Assistant.—Susan McDonald.
Director, Advanced Counterfeit Deterrence.—Reese Fuller.

UNITED STATES MINT

801 9th Street, NW., 20002, phone (202) 354–7200, fax 756–6160

Director.—Richard Peterson (acting).
Executive Assistant to the Director.—Arnetta Cain.
Deputy Director.—Richard Peterson.
Executive Assistant to the Deputy Director.—Judy Dixon.
Chief Counsel.—Dan Shaver (202) 354–7280.
Director, Legislative and Intergovernmental Affairs.—William Norton (202) 354–6700.
Director, Public Affairs.—Tom Jurkowsky (202) 354–7720.
Associate Director for Protection.—Dennis O'Connor (202) 354–7300.
Deputy Associate Director.—Bill R. Bailey (202) 354–7300.
Associate Director/Chief Information Officer.—Cathy Jantzen.
Deputy Associate Director.—Sid Sinha (202) 354–7700.
Associate Director/Chief Financial Officer.—Dave Motl (202) 354–7800.
Deputy Associate Director.—Peggy Yauss (202) 354–7800.
Associate Director, Sales and Marketing.—Mark Landry (202) 354–7500.
Deputy Associate Director.—Mary Lhotsky (202) 354–7800.
Associate Director, Manufacturing.—David Croft.
Deputy Associate Director.—Tom Walkinshaw.

DEPARTMENT OF DEFENSE

The Pentagon 20301–1155, phone (703) 545–6700

fax 695–3362/693–2161, http://www.defenselink.mil

CHUCK HAGEL, Secretary of Defense; born in North Platte, NE, October 4, 1946, the eldest of four brothers; he joined the United States Army and volunteered to go to Vietnam, rising to the rank of Sergeant and serving as an infantry squad leader alongside his brother, Tom, with the Army's 9th Infantry Division in 1968; he earned numerous military decorations and honors, including two Purple Hearts. Following his tour in Vietnam, Secretary Hagel graduated from the University of Nebraska at Omaha using the G.I. Bill. Continuing his commitment to public service, Secretary Hagel became Chief of Staff to Nebraska Congressman John Y. McCollister. In 1981, Secretary Hagel was nominated by President Ronald Reagan to serve as Deputy Administrator of the Veterans Administration. In that post he helped pioneer early electronic health recordkeeping and pushed for increased benefits for Vietnam veterans suffering from Agent Orange. This fight became one of the causes of his life, later helping federal courts distribute hundreds of millions of dollars for Agent Orange victims through the Court settlement that set up the Agent Orange Payment Program which he chaired. In the mid-1980's, Secretary Hagel co-founded Vanguard Cellular Systems, Inc., which became one of the largest independent cellular networks in the country. Secretary Hagel also served as President and CEO of the USO; the Chief Operating Officer of the 1990 Economic Summit of Industrialized Nations (G–7 Summit) in Houston, Texas; Deputy Commissioner General of the United States for the 1982 World's Fair, President of the Private Sector Council and President of McCarthy & Company, an Omaha based investment bank. In 1996, Secretary Hagel was elected to the United States Senate and represented Nebraska until 2009; while in the Senate, he was a senior member of the Foreign Relations; Banking, Housing and Urban Affairs; and Intelligence Committees; he chaired the Foreign Relations International Economic Policy, Export and Trade Promotion Subcommittee; and the Banking Committee's International Trade and Finance, and Securities Subcommittees. Secretary Hagel also served as the Chairman of the Congressional-Executive Commission on China and the Senate Climate Change Observer Group. Following his Senate career, Secretary Hagel served as Co-Chairman of President Obama's Intelligence Advisory Board and a member of the Secretary of Defense Policy Board. He was a Distinguished Professor in the Practice of National Governance at the Georgetown University School of Foreign Service and Chairman of the Atlantic Council, a non-partisan institution devoted to promoting transatlantic cooperation and international security; he also served on the board of PBS and a number of corporations and financial institutions. Secretary Hagel is author of the 2008 book *America: Our Next Chapter*; he and his wife Lilibet have a daughter, Allyn, and a son, Ziller; nominated by President Barack Obama to become the 24th Secretary of Defense, becoming the first enlisted combat veteran to lead the Department of Defense, and was confirmed by the U.S. Senate on February 26, 2013.

OFFICE OF THE SECRETARY

1000 Defense Pentagon, Room 3E880, 20301–1000

phone (703) 692–7100, fax (703) 571–8951

Secretary of Defense.—Chuck Hagel.

OFFICE OF THE DEPUTY SECRETARY

1010 Defense Pentagon, Room 3E944, 20301–1010, phone (703) 692–7150

Deputy Secretary of Defense.—Ashton B. Carter.

EXECUTIVE SECRETARIAT

Pentagon, Room 3E880, 20301–1000, phone (703) 692–7120, fax 571–8951

Executive Secretary.—Michael Bruhn.

GENERAL COUNSEL

Pentagon, Room 3E788, 20301–1600, phone (703) 695–3341, fax 693–7278

General Counsel.—Robert S. Taylor (acting).
Principal Deputy.—Paul S. Koffsky (acting), (703) 697–9341.

OPERATIONAL TEST AND EVALUATION

Pentagon, Room 3E1088, 20301–1700, phone (703) 697–3655, fax 614–9103

Director.—Dr. J. Michael Gilmore.

INSPECTOR GENERAL

4800 Mark Center Drive, Suite 15G27, Alexandria, VA 22350–1500
phone (703) 604–8300, fax 604–8310
hotline 1–800–424–9098, hotline fax (703) 604–8567

Inspector General.—Vacant.
Principal Deputy Inspector General.—Lynne M. Halbrooks.

UNDER SECRETARY OF DEFENSE FOR ACQUISITION, TECHNOLOGY AND LOGISTICS

Pentagon, Room 3E1010, phone (703) 697–7021

Under Secretary.—Frank Kendall.
Principal Deputy Under Secretary.—Vacant.
Deputy Under Secretary for—
Industrial Policy.—Brett Lambert.
Installations and Environment.—John Conger (acting).
Logistics and Materiel Readiness.—Alan Estevez.
Director, Office of Small Business Program.—Andre Gudger.
Director, Defense Research and Engineering.—Alan Shaffer (acting).
Assistant to the Secretary of Defense for Nuclear and Chemical and Biological Defense Programs.—Andrew Weber.

JOINT STRIKE FIGHTER PROGRAM OFFICE

200 12th Street South, Suite 600, Arlington, VA 22202–5402,
phone (703) 602–7640, fax 602–7649

Program Executive Officer.—Lt. Gen. Christopher Bogdan.

UNDER SECRETARY OF DEFENSE (COMPTROLLER) AND CHIEF FINANCIAL OFFICER

Pentagon, Room 3E770, 20301–1100, phone (703) 695–3237

Under Secretary/Chief Financial Officer.—Robert F. Hale.
Principal Deputy Under Secretary.—Michael J. McCord.

UNDER SECRETARY OF DEFENSE FOR PERSONNEL AND READINESS

Pentagon, Room 3E986, 20301–4000, phone (703) 695–5254

Under Secretary.—Jessica L. Wright (acting).

Principal Deputy Under Secretary.—Vacant.
Military Deputy.—Lt. Gen. John Hesterman.
Assistant Secretary for—
Health Affairs.—Dr. Jonathan Woodson, 697–2111.
Reserve Affairs (Principal Deputy).—Richard Wightman, 697–6631.
Readiness and Force Management.—Fred Vollrath (703) 614–3240.

UNDER SECRETARY OF DEFENSE FOR POLICY

Pentagon, Room 3E806, 20301–2000, phone (703) 697–7200

Under Secretary.—Hon. James N. Miller.
Principal Deputy.—Hon. Kathleen H. Hicks.
Assistant Secretary of Defense for—
Asian and Pacific Security Affairs.—Dr. Peter Lavoy (acting).
Global Strategic Affairs.—Hon. Madelyn Creedon.
Homeland Defense and America's Security Affairs.—Todd Rosenblum (acting).
International Security Affairs.—Hon. Derek Chollet.
Special Operations/Low-Intensity Conflict and Interdependent Capabilities.—Hon. Michael Sheehan.

DEPARTMENT OF DEFENSE CHIEF INFORMATION OFFICER (DoD CIO)

Pentagon, Room 3E1030, 20301–6000, phone (703) 695–0348

DoD CIO.—Teresa M. Takai.
Principal Deputy DoD CIO.—Robert J. Carey.

ASSISTANT SECRETARY FOR LEGISLATIVE AFFAIRS

Pentagon, Room 3E970, 20301–1300, phone (703) 697–6210, fax 695–5860

Assistant Secretary.—Elizabeth King.
Principal Deputy.—Eric Pierce.

ASSISTANT TO THE SECRETARY OF DEFENSE FOR INTELLIGENCE OVERSIGHT

Pentagon, Room 2E1052, 20301–7200

phone (703) 697–1346, public inquiries (571) 372–6363

Assistant to the Secretary.—Michael H. Decker.
Deputy Assistant to the Secretary.—Michael E. Goodroe.

ASSISTANT SECRETARY FOR PUBLIC AFFAIRS

Pentagon, Room 2E694, 20301–1400, phone (703) 697–9312, fax 695–4299
public inquiries 571–3343

Assistant Secretary.—George E. Little.
Principal Deputy.—Bryan G. Whitman.

ADMINISTRATION AND MANAGEMENT

Pentagon, Room 3E971, 20301–1950, phone (703) 692–7138

Director.—Michael L. Rhodes, room 3E971, 692–7138.
Deputy Director.—William E. Brazis, room 3E971, 693–7906.

DEPARTMENT OF DEFENSE FIELD ACTIVITIES

DEFENSE MEDIA ACTIVITY

6700 Taylor Avenue, Fort George G. Meade, MD 20755

phone (301) 222–6700, http://www.dma.mil/

Director.—Ray B. Shepherd.
Executive Officer.—Roger L. King.

DEPARTMENT OF DEFENSE EDUCATION ACTIVITY

4800 Mark Center Drive, Arlington, VA 22350–1400

School Information (571) 372–0610

Director.—Marilee Fitzgerald (571) 372–0590.
Principal Deputy Director and Associate Director for Education.—Adrian Talley (571) 372–5832.
Associate Director for Finance and Business Operations.—Vacant.
General Counsel.—Edwin Daniel (571) 372–0976.

DEPARTMENT OF DEFENSE HUMAN RESOURCES ACTIVITY

4800 Mark Center Drive, Suite 0625–01, Alexandria, VA 22350–4000

Director.—Sharon H. Cooper.
Chief of Staff.—Jeff Register.
Executive Assistant.—Michelle Watson.

TRICARE MANAGEMENT ACTIVITY

7700 Arlington Boulevard, Falls Church, VA 22042–5101, phone (703) 681–8707

Director.—Dr. Jonathan Woodson.
Deputy Director.—Allen W. Middleton (acting).

DEFENSE PRISONER OF WAR/MISSING PERSONNEL OFFICE

241 18th Street South, Suite 800, Arlington, VA 22202, phone (703) 699–1102, fax 602–1890

Director.—Robert Newberry.

OFFICE OF ECONOMIC ADJUSTMENT

2231 Crystal Drive, Suite 520, Arlington, VA 22202, phone (703) 697–2130

Director.—Patrick J. O'Brien.
Deputy Director of:
Operations.—Ronald Adkins, 697–2206.
Programs.—Dave Larson, 697–2148.
Sacramento Regional Manager.—Gary Kuwabara (916) 557–7365.

WASHINGTON HEADQUARTERS SERVICES

Pentagon, phone (703) 693–7906

Director.—William ''Bill'' Brazis.
Deputy Director.—Vacant.
Directors for—
Acquisition Directorate.—Linda Allen (703) 545–0444.
Enterprise Information Technology Services Directorate.—Lytwaive Hutchinson (703) 695–2865.
Enterprise Management.—Sajeel Ahmed (703) 693–7995.
Executive Services.—Craig Glassner, 693–7965.

Financial Management.—Roberta Lowe, 699–3350.
Human Resources Directorate.—Susan Yarwood (571) 256–4504.
OSD Chief Information Office.—Ron Bechtold (703) 692–7453.
Raven Rock Mountain Complex.—COL Ramona Plemmons (717) 878–3343.
WHS General Counsel.—John Albanese (acting), 693–7374.

JOINT CHIEFS OF STAFF

OFFICE OF THE CHAIRMAN

Pentagon, Room 2E872, 20318–0001, phone (703) 697–9121

Chairman.—GEN Martin E. Dempsey, USA.
Vice Chairman.—ADM James A. Winnefeld, USN, room 2E724, 614–8949.
Assistant to the Chairman, Joint Chiefs of Staff.—VADM Hary B. Harris, USN, room 2E868, 695–4605.

JOINT STAFF

Director.—LTG Curtis M. Scaparrotti, USA, room 2E936, 614–5221.
Vice Director.—RADM Nora W. Tyson, USN, room 2E936, 614–5223.
Director for—
Manpower and Personnel, J–1.—RDML Dwight D. Shepherd, USN, room 1E948, 697–6098.
Joint Staff Intelligence, J–2.—RADM Elizabeth Train, USN, room 1E880, 697–9773.
Operations, J–3.—VADM Kurt W. Tidd, USN, room 2D874, 697–3702.
Logistics, J–4.—Lt. Gen. Brooks L. Bash, USAF, room 2E828, 697–7000.
Strategic Plans and Policy, J–5.—LTG Terry A. Wolff, USA, room 2E996, 695–5618.
Command, Control, Communications and Computer Systems, J–6.—LTG Mark S. Bowman, USA, room 2D860, 695–6478.
Operational Plans and Joint Force Development, J–7.—Lt. Gen. George Flynn, USMC, room 2B865, 697–9031.
Force Structure, Resources, and Assessment, J–8.—Lt. Gen. Mark F. Ramsay, USAF, room 1E962, 697–8853.

DEFENSE AGENCIES

MISSILE DEFENSE AGENCY

5700 18th Street, Fort Belvoir, VA 22060–5573

Director.—VADM James D. Syring, USN (571) 231–8006.
Deputy Director.—MG Samuel A. Greaves, USAF (256) 450–5456.
Director, Public Affairs.—Richard Lehner (571) 231–8212.
Director, Legislative Affairs.—Kimo Hollingsworth (571) 231–8105.

DEFENSE ADVANCED RESEARCH PROJECTS AGENCY

675 North Randolph Street, Arlington, VA 22203

Director.—Dr. Arati Prabhakar, 696–2400.
Deputy Director.—Dr. Steve Walker, 696–2402.

DEFENSE COMMISSARY AGENCY

1300 E Avenue, Fort Lee, VA 23801–1800, phone (804) 734–8720/8330

Director.—Joseph H. Jeu, 734–8720.
Chief Operating Officer.—Michael J. Dowling, 734–8330.

WASHINGTON OFFICE

4100 Defense Pentagon, Room 5D636, 20301–4100, phone (703) 571–7186/7185

Chief.—Thomas Owens.

DEFENSE CONTRACT AUDIT AGENCY

8725 John J. Kingman Road, Suite 2135, Fort Belvoir, VA 22060
phone (703) 767–3200

Director.—Patrick J. Fitzgerald, 767–3200.
Deputy Director.—Anita F. Bales.

DEFENSE FINANCE AND ACCOUNTING SERVICE

4800 Mark Center Drive, Suite 08J25–01, Alexandria, VA 22350–3000
phone (571) 372–7883

Director.—Teresa A. McKay.
Principal Deputy Director.—Audrey Y. Davis.

DEFENSE INFORMATION SYSTEMS AGENCY

P.O. Box 549, Command Building, Fort Meade, Maryland 20755

Director.—Lt. Gen. Ronnie D. Hawkins, USAF (301) 225–6001.
Vice Director.—RADM David G. Simpson, USN, 225–6010.
Chief of Staff.—BG Frederick A. Henry, USA, 225–6020.

DEFENSE INTELLIGENCE AGENCY

200 MacDill Boulevard, Washington, DC 20340, phone (202) 231–0800

Director.—LTG Michael T. Flynn, USA.
Deputy Director.—David R. Shedd.

DEFENSE LEGAL SERVICES AGENCY

Pentagon, Room 3E788, 20301–1600, phone (703) 695–3341, fax 693–7278

Director/General Counsel.—Robert S. Taylor (acting).
Principal Deputy Director.—Robert S. Taylor, 697–7248.

DEFENSE LOGISTICS AGENCY

8725 John J. Kingman Road, Suite 2533, Ft. Belvoir, VA 22060
phone (703) 767–5264

Director.—VADM Mark D. Harnitchek, SC, USN.
Vice Director.—Edward J. Case.

DEFENSE SECURITY COOPERATION AGENCY

201 12th Street South, Suite 203, Arlington, VA 22202–5408, phone (703) 604–6605

Director.—VADM William E. Landay III, USN.
Deputy Director.—Richard Genaille, 604–6606.

DEFENSE SECURITY SERVICE

27130 Telegraph Road, Quantico, VA 22134, phone (703) 617–2352

Director.—Stanley L. Sims.

DEFENSE THREAT REDUCTION AGENCY

8725 John J. Kingman Road, Stop 6201, Ft. Belvoir, VA 22060–6201
phone (703) 767–7594

Director.—Kenneth A. Myers III.

Deputy Director.—Maj. Gen. Jay G. Santee, USAF.
Chief, Governmental and Legislative Affairs.—Don Minner.

NATIONAL GEOSPATIAL—INTELLIGENCE AGENCY

7500 GEOINT Drive, Springfield, VA 22150, phone (571) 557–7300

Director.—Letitia A. Long.
Deputy Director.—Michael A. Rodrigue.

NATIONAL SECURITY AGENCY / CENTRAL SECURITY SERVICE

Ft. George G. Meade, MD 20755, phone (301) 688–6524

Director, NSA / Chief, CSS.—GEN Keith B. Alexander, USA.
Deputy Director, NSA.—John C. Inglis.
Deputy Chief, CSS.—Brig. Gen. D. Scott George, USAF.

JOINT SERVICE SCHOOLS

9820 Belvoir Road, Ft. Belvoir, VA 22060, phone (800) 845–7606

DEFENSE ACQUISITION UNIVERSITY

President.—James McMichael (acting), (703) 805–4592.
Vice President.—James McMichael (703) 805–4592.
Chief of Staff.—Joseph Johnson (703) 805–2828.

NATIONAL INTELLIGENCE UNIVERSITY

President.—David R. Ellison (202) 231–3344.

NATIONAL DEFENSE UNIVERSITY

Fort McNair, Building 62, 300 Fifth Avenue, 20319
phone (202) 685–3912

President.—MG Gregg F. Martin, USA, Building 62, room 307, 685–3936.
Senior Vice President.—Vacant, Building 62, room 307A, 685–3923.
Provost and Vice President for Academic Affairs.—Dr. John Yaeger, Building 62, room 309C, 685–0080.

COLLEGE OF INTERNATIONAL SECURITY AFFAIRS

Chancellor.—Dr. Michael Bell, Building 64, room 2102 (202) 685–7209.

INFORMATION RESOURCES MANAGEMENT COLLEGE

Chancellor.— Dr. Robert D. Childs, Building 62, room 201G (202) 685–3886.

JOINT FORCES STAFF COLLEGE

7800 Hampton Boulevard, Norfolk, VA 23511–1702, phone (757) 443–6200

Commandant.—RDML John ''Boomer'' Smith, USN, room A202.

INDUSTRIAL COLLEGE OF THE ARMED FORCES

Commandant.—Brig. Gen. Thomas S. Gorry, USMC, Building 59, room 200 (202) 685–4337.

NATIONAL WAR COLLEGE

Commandant.—BG Tom Cosentino, USA, Building 61, room 124 (202) 685–4341.

DWIGHT D. EISENHOWER SCHOOL FOR NATIONAL SECURITY AND RESOURCE STRATEGY

Commandant.—Brig. Gen. Thomas A. Gorry, USMC, room 200 (202) 685–4337.

UNIFORMED SERVICES UNIVERSITY OF THE HEALTH SCIENCES

4301 Jones Bridge Road, Bethesda, MD 20814

President.—Charles L. Rice, M.D., room 1018 (301) 295–3013.

DEPARTMENT OF THE AIR FORCE

Pentagon, 1670 Air Force, Washington, DC 20330–1670

phone (703) 697–7376, fax 695–8809

SECRETARY OF THE AIR FORCE

Secretary of the Air Force.—Hon. Deborah Lee James, room 4E878.
Confidential Assistant.—Vacant.
Senior Military Assistant.—Col. Stephen Oliver.
Deputy Military Assistant.—Lt. Col. Randall Ackerman.
Military Aid.—Maj. Michael Lake.

SECAF / CSAF EXECUTIVE ACTION GROUP

Director.—Col. Anthony Krawietz (703) 697–5540.
Deputy Chief.—Karen Pound.

UNDER SECRETARY OF THE AIR FORCE

Pentagon, 1670 Air Force, Room 4E858, 20330–1670, phone (703) 697–1361

Under Secretary.—Hon. Eric K. Fanning.
Confidential Assistant.—Ms. Lisa Speeder.
Senior Military Assistant.—Col. Wayne R. Monteith.
Military Assistant.—Maj. Damen A. Forte.
Executive Assistants: MSgt Wallace Macon, TSgt Monieka Stewart.

CHIEF OF STAFF

Pentagon, 1670 Air Force, Room 4E924, 20330

phone (703) 697–9225

Chief of Staff.—Gen. Mark A. Welsh III.
Confidential Assistant.—Fern Jones-Byrd.
Special Assistant.—Jason Yaley, 5E980, 697–1930.
Executive Officer.—Col. Scott L. Pleus.
Vice Chief of Staff.—Gen. Larry Spencer, room 4E938, 695–7911.
Assistant Vice Chief of Staff.—Lt. Gen. Frank Gorenc, room 4E944, 695–7913.
Chief Master Sergeant of the Air Force.—CMSAF James A. Cody, room 4E941, 695–0498.

DEPUTY UNDER SECRETARY FOR INTERNATIONAL AFFAIRS

Pentagon, 1080 Air Force Pentagon, Room 4E192, 20330–1080

Deputy Under Secretary.—Heidi H. Grant (703) 695–7262.
Assistant Deputy.—Maj. Gen. Richard C. Johnston, 695–7261.
Senior Executive Officer.—Lt. Col. Scott McKeever, 695–7261.
Executive Officer.—Maj. Scott Giller, 693–1941.
Executive Assistant.—Georgia Smothers, 695–7263.

Pentagon, 1080 Air Force Pentagon, Room 4C253, 20330–1080

Director of Policy.—Gerald R. Hust (571) 256–7491.
Executive Officer.—Lt. Col. Nicholas Gregor, 256–7494.

Executive Assistant.—Saybah Sammy, 256–7495.

Pentagon, 1080 Air Force Pentagon, Room 4C947, 20330–1080

Director of Regional Affairs.—Brig. Gen. Lawrence Martin (703) 695–2022.
Executive Officer.—Matthew Merighi, 695–2096.
Executive Assistant.—Sanura Wade, 695–2080.

Pentagon, 1080 Air Force Pentagon, Room 4C253, 20330–1080

Director of Strategy, Operations, and Resources.—Kelli Seybolt (571) 256–9492.
Executive Assistant.—Jared Kylan, 256–9491.

ASSISTANT SECRETARY FOR ACQUISITION

Pentagon, 1060 Air Force, 20330

1745 Jefferson Davis Highway, Suite 307, Arlington, VA 22202

110 Luke Avenue, Suite 200, Bolling AFB, DC 20032–6400

Assistant Secretary.—Vacant (703) 697–6361.
Senior Military Assistant.—Col. C.J. Johnson, 697–6990.
Military Assistant.—Vacant, 697–6362.

Principal Deputy.—Dr. William LaPlante, 697–9373.
Military Assistant.—Lt. Col. Kevin Massey, 693–9350.

Military Deputy.—Lt. Gen. Charles Davis, 697–6363.
Executive Officer.—Maj. Chad Searle, 695–7311.

DEPUTY ASSISTANT SECRETARY FOR ACQUISITION INTEGRATION

Deputy Assistant Secretary.—Rich Lombardi (571) 256–0355.
Associate Deputy Assistant Secretary.—Bobby Smart, 256–0351.
Executive Officer.—Maj. Justin Cezano, 256–0356.

DEPUTY ASSISTANT SECRETARY FOR CONTRACTING

Deputy Assistant Secretary.—Maj. Gen. Wendy Masiello (571) 256–2397.
Associate Deputy Assistant Secretary.—Thomas Robinson, 256–2397.
Executive Officer.—Lt. Col. Richard Marsh, 256–2397.

DEPUTY ASSISTANT SECRETARY FOR SCIENCE, TECHNOLOGY AND ENGINEERING

Deputy Assistant Secretary.—Dr. David Walker (571) 256–0303.
Associate Deputy Assistant Secretary.—Col. Ralph Sandfry, 256–0303.
Executive Officer.—Maj. David Leach, 256–0294.

CAPABILITY DIRECTORATE FOR GLOBAL POWER PROGRAMS

Director.—Maj. Gen. John Posner (571) 256–0191.
Deputy Director.—Col. Aaron Clark, 256–0192.
Executive Officer.—Maj. Jeff Zdenek, 256–0196.

CAPABILITY DIRECTORATE FOR GLOBAL REACH PROGRAMS

Director.—Maj. Gen. Kenneth Merchant (571) 256–0489.
Deputy Director.—Col. Darren Cochran, 256–0497.
Executive Officer.—Maj. Jay Rueschoff, 256–0522.

CAPABILITY DIRECTORATE FOR INFORMATION DOMINANCE

Director.—Randall Walden (571) 256–0081.
Deputy Director.—Col. Bob Yahn, 256–0082.

Executive Officer.—Maj. Brian Clifford, 256–0083.

CAPABILITY DIRECTORATE FOR SPACE PROGRAMS

Director.—Brig. Gen. Robert McMurry (571) 695–3423.
Deputy Director.—Col. Christopher Warack, 695–3499.
Executive Officer.—Maj. Jung Ha, 695–3435.

DIRECTORATE FOR SPECIAL PROGRAMS

Director.—Col. Ken Plaks (571) 767–3890.
Deputy Director.—Col. Chris DiNenna, 256–0005.
Associate Director.—Ryan Dow (202) 767–3939.
Executive Assistant.—Alesia Clark (202) 767–3890.

DIRECTORATE FOR AIR FORCE RAPID CAPABILITIES

Director.—David E. Hamilton (202) 767–1800.
Deputy and Technical Director.—Vacant.
Executive Officer.—Maj. John Fontejon, 767–3203.

ASSISTANT SECRETARY FOR FINANCIAL MANAGEMENT AND COMPTROLLER OF THE AIR FORCE (SAF/FM)

Pentagon, 1130 Air Force Pentagon, 20330–1130

Air Force Cost Analysis Agency, Jones Building

1500 West Perimeter Road, Joint Base Andrews-Naval Air Facility

Washington, MD 20762

Assistant Secretary.—Dr. Jamie M. Morin, room 4E978 (703) 695–0829.
Senior Military Assistant.—Lt. Col. Jason E. Corrothers, 695–0829.
Chief, Enlisted Matters.—CMSgt John A. Writer, 614–5429.

PRINCIPAL DEPUTY ASSISTANT SECRETARY FOR FINANCIAL MANAGEMENT

Principal Deputy Assistant Secretary.—Marilyn M. Thomas (703) 697–1974.
Military Assistant.—Capt. Charles J. Dunar III, 695–1974.

DEPUTY ASSISTANT SECRETARY FOR BUDGET (SAF/FMB)

Deputy Assistant Secretary.—Brig. Gen. James F. Martin, room 5D912 (703) 695–1876.
Executive Officer.—Lt. Col. Doug Pierce, 695–1876.
Deputy.—Caral Spangler, 697–1876.
Director of:
Budget and Appropriations Liaison.—Col. Sam Grable, room 5C949, 614–8114.
Budget Investment.—Pamela Schwenke, room 5D912, 697–1220.
Budget Management and Execution.—Judith Oliva, room 5D912, 695–9737.
Budget Operations and Personnel.—Col. John Pletcher, room 5D912, 697–0627.
Budget Programs.—Col. Michael Monson, room 5C950, 614–7883.

DEPUTY ASSISTANT SECRETARY FOR COST AND ECONOMICS (SAF/FMC)

Deputy Assistant Secretary.—Kathy L. Watern, room 5E975 (703) 697–5311.
Associate Deputy Assistant Secretary.—Grant McVicker, room 5E975 (703) 697–5313.
Executive Officer.—Lt. Col. Brian Kehl, room 5E975 (703) 697–5312.
Technical Director for Cost and Economics.—Ranae Woods, suite 3500 (240) 612–5615.
Director, Economics and Business Management.—Stephen M. Connair, room 4C843 (703) 693–9347.
Director, Cost Analysis Division.—Col. Chuck Shea, room 4C943 (703) 697–0288.

DEPUTY ASSISTANT SECRETARY FOR FINANCIAL OPERATIONS (SAF/FMP)

Deputy Assistant Secretary.—Douglas M. Bennett, room 5D739 (703) 614–4180.
Associate Deputy Assistant Secretary.—Stephen Herrera, 5D739 (703) 614–4180.
Military Assistant.—Lt. Col. Mark Snow (703) 614–4180.
Director for—
Accounting Policy and Reporting.—Fred Carr, Andrews AFB, MD (240) 612–5212.
AFAFO.—Lee Franklin, Denver, CO (720) 847–2200.
AF Financial Systems Organization.—Glena Gibson, Wright-Patterson AFB, OH (937) 257–2262.
AF–IPPS.—Lt. Col. Mark Snow, Andrews AFB, MD (240) 612–5322.
DEAMS.—Shirley Reed, Wright-Patterson AFB, OH (937) 257–5675.
FIAR.—Lori Stacey, Andrews AFB, MD (240) 612–5281.
Financial Services.—Gary Gualano, Ellsworth AFB, SD (605) 385–8532.
Information Systems and Technology.—John Koski, Andrews AFB, MD (240) 612–5283.
Management Services Compliance.—Randy Newcome, Wright-Patterson AFB, OH (937) 522–4400.

ASSISTANT SECRETARY FOR INSTALLATIONS, ENVIRONMENT AND LOGISTICS

Assistant Secretary.—Kathleen Ferguson (acting), room 4E996 (703) 697–4936.
Principal Deputy Assistant Secretary.—Kathleen Ferguson, 697–4936.
Executive Officer.—Lt. Col. Harry Seibert, 697–4219.
Military Assistant.—Lt. Col. Matt Greene, 697–5023.
Special Assistant.—Dr. Camron Gourguinpour, 697–6300.
Confidential Assistant.—Cathy Hudock, 697–4936.
Resource Manager.—Everette Dewaine Longus, 697–4391.

DEPUTY ASSISTANT SECRETARY FOR INSTALLATIONS (SAF/IEI)

Deputy Assistant Secretary.—Timothy K. Bridges, room 4B941 (703) 695–3592.
Deputy for Installation Policy.—James P. Holland, 614–6232.
Administrative Support Specialist/Secretary.—Sheenia T. Williams, 695–3592.
Executive Officer.—Vacant, 695–6456.
Director, Planning and Programs.—Col. Frank Freeman III, 697–7003.
Director, Encroachment Management.—Steve Zander, 571–5771.
Strategic Basing Analyst.—Geoff Oliver, 571–3325.
Legislative/Public Affairs Manager.—Frank Smolinsky, 697–1980.
Air Force Real Property Agency Liaison.—Robert McCann, 697–7244.
Director, Air National Guard and Reserve Affairs.—Lt. Col. Michael McDonald, 697–0997.
Director, Asset Management.—Edward Pokora, 693–9328.
Workflow Manager.—Lynette Brown, 697–6492.

BRAC PROGRAM MANAGEMENT OFFICE (SAF/IEI–PMO)

Director.—Col. Frank Freeman III (703) 697–7003.
Resources: Wellington Selden Jr., 614–0014; Paul G. Freund, 614–0861; Helen Griffith, 614–0012.
Information Management.—JJ Cook, 693–9339.
Program Management: Tim Brennan, 695–5730; Rick Rankin, 697–6492; Paul G. Freund, 614–0861; Robert Niswonger, 614–6230.

AIR FORCE REAL PROPERTY AGENCY

2261 Hughes Avenue, Suite 121, San Antonio, TX 78236–9821

Director.—Vacant (210) 395–9501.
Secretary to the Director.—Linda Cosper, 395–9503.
Executive Officer.—Tonda Sallee (210) 395–9505.

DEPUTY ASSISTANT SECRETARY FOR ENVIRONMENT, SAFETY AND OCCUPATIONAL HEALTH (SAF/IEE)

Deputy Assistant Secretary.—Gerald F. Pease, room 4B941, (703) 697–9297.

Deputy.—Michael McGhee, 697–1019.
Executive Secretary.—Maryann Fontana, 697–9297.
Executive Officer.—Maj. Mark Paine, 693–3254.
Safety Policy.—Vance Lineberger, 693–7706.
Environment Policy.—Michele Indermark, 614–8458.
Occupational Health Policy.—Lt. Col. Victor Caravello, 571–256–4397.
Director for Plans and Policy.—Lt. Col. Kirk Phillips, 692–9515

DEPUTY ASSISTANT SECRETARY FOR LOGISTICS (SAF/IEL)

Deputy Assistant Secretary.—S. Mark Reynolds, room 4B941, 697–7070.
Director, Logistics and Transformation.—Mark Van Gilst, 692–9090.
NCOIC, Knowledge Ops/Admin Support.—Vacant, 614–6240.
Chief, Depot Operations and Strategic Planning/Executive Officer.—Lt. Col. Jonathan Dowing, 693–2185.
Director, Life Cycle Management.—Al Bello, 697–1641.
Chief, Life Cycle Integration.—Kim Powell, 697–1016.
Chief, Depot Maintenance Integration.—Gene Pierre, 697–0893.

DEPUTY ASSISTANT SECRETARY FOR ENERGY (SAF/IEN)

Deputy Assistant Secretary.—Dr. Kevin T. Geiss, room 5E1000, 256–4711.
Deputy for Energy Policy.—Dr. Pasquale Gambatese, 697–1207.
Executive Officer.—Lt. Col. Jason Nulton, 697–6032.
Logistics Energy Management Specialist.—Jennifer Riley, 697–1098.
Senior Energy Facilities Engineer.—Douglas Tucker, 697–1113.
Energy Facilities Engineer.—Christa Gunn, 256–3944.
Renewable Energy Program Manager.—Megan McCluer, 697–1113.
Aviation Energy Program Analyst.—Raul Bennett, 571–5773.

ASSISTANT SECRETARY FOR MANPOWER AND RESERVE AFFAIRS
1660 Air Force Pentagon, Room 4E1010, 20330–1660

Assistant Secretary.—Daniel B. Ginsberg (703) 697–2302.
Principal Deputy Assistant Secretary.—Sheila M. Earle (703) 697–1258.
Mobilization Assistant.—Brig. Gen. Muriel McCarthy, 604–8136.
Confidential Assistant.—Ruth N. Thornton, 695–6677.
Military Assistant.—Col. Amy Johnson, 697–2303.
Executive Officer.—Lt. Col. Lawrence Colby, 697–1258.
Superintendent.—William Coates, 614–5654.

DEPUTY ASSISTANT SECRETARY FOR FORCE MANAGEMENT INTEGRATION

Deputy Assistant Secretary.—Francine C. Blackmon (703) 614–4751.
Executive Secretary.—Alicia K. Bobbitt, 614–4751.
Assistant Deputy for—
Family Programs.—Clifford Tompkins, 693–9574.
Force Management and Development.—Chief David Henry, 695–2459.
Force Management Integration.—Vacant, 614–4753.
Force Support Services.—Capt. Richard Laca, 693–9765.
Health Policy.—Norma Inabinet, 693–9764.
Military Force Management.—Thomas E. Booth, 697–7783.
Officer Accessions and Programs.—Dr. Thomas Langdon, 693–9333.
Plans and Legislative Integration.—Col. Gina Oliver, 697–7058.

DEPUTY ASSISTANT SECRETARY FOR RESERVE AFFAIRS

Deputy Assistant Secretary.—William H. Booth Sr., room 5D742 (703) 697–6376.
Executive Secretary.—Stephanie Parry (703) 697–6375.
Assistant for—
Air Force Reserve Matters.—Col. Michelle Barrett (703) 697–6431.
ANG Matters.—Col. Mark Doll (703) 697–6429.
Chief RC Business Integration.—Vacant (703) 693–9511.

Director, AF Auxiliary Programs.—Thomas Shubert (571) 256–4044.
Enlisted Matters.—CMSgt. Malinda Price (703) 693–9505.
Executive Director for Air Reserve Forces Policy Committee.—Col. Pamela Powers (703) 697–6430.
Assistant Deputy Total Force Manpower Management.—Todd Remington (703) 693–9512.
IMA to SAF/MRR: Lt. Col. Elizabeth Chamberlain (571) 256–4043; Maj. Jeremie Huot (703) 693–9504.

DEPUTY ASSISTANT SECRETARY FOR STRATEGIC DIVERSITY INTEGRATION

Deputy Assistant Secretary.—Dr. Jarris L. Taylor, Jr., room 5E783 (703) 697–6586.
Assistant Deputy.—Kathleen Ryan (703) 697–6583.
Executive Secretary.—Karen Sauls (703) 697–6586.

AIR FORCE REVIEW BOARDS AGENCY (SAF/MRB)

1500 West Perimeter Road, Suite 3700, Joint Base Andrews NAF–Washington, MD 20762

Director.—R. Philip Deavel (240) 612–5400.
Deputy Director.—Michael F. LoGrande, 612–5403.
Chief Information Officer.—Michael K. Gallogly, 612–5396.
Director of Operations.—Thomas Kearney, 612–5342.
Legal Advisor.—Ralph Arnold, 612–5404.
Medical Advisor.—Dr. Horace Carson, 612–5405.
Senior Enlisted Advisor.—CMSgt Michelle Thomas, 612–4528.
Human Resources.—Donna Atchison, 612–5401.
Confidential Assistant.—Marilyn Redmond, 612–5400.

AIR FORCE BOARD FOR CORRECTION OF MILITARY RECORDS (AFBCMR) SAF/MRBC

Executive Director.—Michael LoGrande (240) 612–5403.
Deputy.—Phillip Horton, 612–5371.
Chief Examiners: Janet Hutson, 612–5373; Daryl Lawrence, 612–5381; John Vallario, 612–5392.
Chief, AFBCMR Operations.—Charles Hollings, 612–5387.

AIR FORCE CIVILIAN APPELLATE REVIEW OFFICE (AFCARO), SAF/MRBA

Director.—Rita S. Looney (240) 612–5330.
Assistant Director.—Vacant, 612–5331.

SECRETARY OF THE AIR FORCE PERSONNEL COUNCIL (SAFPC), SAF/MRBP

Director.—Col. Cheryl J. Beineke (240) 612–5353.
Deputy Director.—Col. Andrew Weaver, 612–5369.
Senior Legal Advisor.—Col. William Gampel, 612–4529.
Senior Medical Advisor.—Col. Richard Stahlman, 612–5360.
Chief, Air Force Discharge Review Board.—Col. Elizabeth Hill, 612–5365.
Chief, Awards/Decorations/Air Force Reserve Advisor.—Col. Martha Mann, 612–5355.
Executive Secretary/Attorney Advisor on Clemency/Parole Board.—Bruce Brown, 612–5364.
Executive Secretary, DoD Civilian/Military Service Review Board.—Bruce Brown, 612–5364.
President Remissions Board.—Bruce Brown, 612–5364.

AIR FORCE PERSONNEL SECURITY APPEAL BOARD (PSAB), SAF/MRBS

President.—Al Walker (240) 612–5380.
Deputy.—Joseph Schott, 612–5350.

DoD PHYSICAL DISABILITY BOARD OF REVIEW (PDBR), SAF/MRBD

President.—James Davis (703) 325–0803.
Deputy.—Christopher Honeycutt, 325–0841.

CHIEF OF WARFIGHTING INTEGRATION AND CHIEF INFORMATION OFFICER

1800 Air Force Pentagon, Room 4E1050, 20330

Chief of Warfighting Integration and Chief Information Officer.—Lt. Gen. Michael J. Basla (703) 695–6829.
Deputy Chief of Warfighting Integration and Deputy Chief Information Officer.—Teresa M. Salazar, 695–6829.
Director of:
Warfighter Systems Integration.—Brig. Gen. Jeffrey Kendall, room 1D857, 695–1835.
Cyberspace Operations.—Maj. Gen. Earl Matthews, room 1D857, 614–2997.
Policy and Resources.—Dr. Fred Lewis, room 1D857, 695–1839.

DEPUTY CHIEF OF STAFF FOR INTELLIGENCE, SURVEILLANCE AND RECONNAISSANCE (ISR)

Deputy Chief of Staff.—Lt. Gen. Robert Otto (703) 695–5613.
Assistant Deputy Chief of Staff.—Maj. Gen. Jim Keffer.
Executive Officer.—Lt. Col. Andres Nazario.
Director of:
ISR Capabilities.—Maj. Gen. Eugene Haase, 695–5818.
ISR Interoperability.—James Clark, 693–3377.
ISR Resources.—Kenneth Dumm, 614–2144.
ISR Strategy, Plans, Doctrine and Force Development.—Brig. Gen. Donald Bacon, 614–3478.
Special Program Integration.—Dean Yount, 693–5201.

DEPUTY CHIEF OF STAFF FOR LOGISTICS, INSTALLATIONS AND MISSION SUPPORT

Pentagon, 1030 Air Force, 20330

Deputy Chief of Staff.—Lt. Gen. Judith A. Fedder, room 4E154 (703) 695–5590.
Assistant Deputy.—Patricia M. Young, Pentagon, room 4E260, 695–6236.
Director of:
Transformation.—Brig. Gen. Kathryn Johnson, Pentagon, room 4B1060, 697–0772.
Logistics.—Maj. Gen. John Cooper, Pentagon, room 4E278, 695–4900.
Resources Integration.—Shelton, Pentagon, room 4C1088, 697–2822.
Security Forces.—Brig. Gen. Allen Jamerson, Pentagon, room 5E1040, 693–5401.
The Civil Engineer.—Maj. Gen. Theresa Carter, Pentagon, room 4C1057, 693–4308.

DEPUTY CHIEF OF STAFF FOR MANPOWER, PERSONNEL AND SERVICES

Pentagon, 1040 Air Force, Room 4E168, 20330

Deputy Chief of Staff.—Lt. Gen. Darrell D. Jones (703) 697–6088.
Assistant Deputy Chief of Staff.—Robert E. Corsi, Jr.
Chief, Personnel Issues Team.—Lt. Col. Anthony Haught, room 4E169, 695–4212.
Director of:
Air Force General Officer Management.—Brig. Gen. Schneider, room 4D1066, 697–1181.
Services.—Brig. Gen. Eden Murrie, room 4D1054, 256–8598.
Force Development.—Russell Frasz, room 4D950, 695–2144.
Force Management Policy.—Brig. Gen. Gina Grosso, room 4D950A, 695–6770.
Manpower, Organization, and Resources.—Brig. Gen. Richard Murphy, room 5A328, 692–1601.
Plans and Integration.—Michelle LoweSolis, room 4D1054A, 697–5222.

DEPUTY CHIEF OF STAFF FOR OPERATIONS, PLANS AND REQUIREMENTS

Pentagon, 1630 Air Force, Room 4E1024, 20330

Deputy Chief of Staff.—Lt. Gen. Burton Field (703) 697–9991.
Assistant Deputy.—Maj. Gen. Mike Holmes, 697–9881.
Mobility Assistant.—Maj. Gen. John Winters, 697–3087.
Director of:
Cyber Operations.—Maj. Gen. Earl Matthews, room 1D857, 614–2997.
Operational Capability Requirements.—Maj. Gen. Thomas Bergeson, room 5C889A, 695–3018.
Operational Planning, Policy and Strategy.—Maj. Gen. Timothy Ray, room 5E857, 614–2711.
Operations.—Maj. Gen. James J. Jones, room 5D756, 695–7602.
Resource Integration.—Mark Budgeon, room 5E873, 697–7833.
Space Operations.—Brig. Gen. Burke Wilson, room 5D756, 697–9500.

DEPUTY CHIEF OF STAFF FOR STRATEGIC PLANS AND PROGRAMS

Pentagon, 1070 Air Force, Room 4E1082, 20330–1070

Deputy Chief of Staff.—Lt. Gen. Michael R. Moeller (703) 697–4469.
Assistant Deputy Chief of Staff.—Richard Hartley (703) 692–9944.
Military Assistant Deputy Chief of Staff.—Maj. Gen. Joseph Balskus (703) 614–7698.
Directorate of Programs.—Maj. Gen. Michael Bora, room 5D1088 (703) 614–2863.
Director for Strategic Planning.—Maj. Gen. Richard Klumpp, room 5D1050 (703) 697–3117.

DIRECTORATE OF STUDIES AND ANALYSIS ASSESSMENTS AND LESSONS LEARNED

Pentagon, 1570 Air Force, Room 4E214

Washington, DC 20330–1570

Director.—Dr. Jacqueline R. Henningsen, Ph.D., SES (571) 256–2015.
Principal Deputy Director.—Kevin E. Williams, SES.
Military Deputy Director.—Col. Michael E. Newman.
Senior Advisor.—Vacant.
Technical Director.—Dr. Mark A. Gallagher, Ph.D., SL.
Chief Analyst.—Col. Scott Long.

STRATEGIC DETERRENCE AND NUCLEAR INTEGRATION (A10)

Pentagon, 1488 Air Force, Suite 4E240, 20330

Assistant Chief of Staff.—Maj. Gen. Garrett Harencak (703) 693–9747.
Deputy Assistant Chief of Staff.—Michael Shoults, SES, 693–9747.
Associate Assistant Chief of Staff.—Dr. Billy Mullins, Ph.D., SES, 693–9747.
HQE.—Dr. Jim Blackwell, Ph.D., 695–1365.
MA.—Vacant, 697–0808.
Director of Staff.—Bob Tilson, 693–9747.
Senior Executive.—Lt. Col. Justin McMillian, 693–9747.
Junior Executive.—Maj. Matt Hlivko, 693–9747.
Administrative Assistant.—Rhonda Gill, 693–9747.
Division Chiefs:
Assessments.—David O'Donnell (202) 767–7420.
Capabilities.—Col. (sel) David Smith (202) 404–7938.
Executive Services.—Wilbert Smith, 695–7810.
Functional Authority.—Col. Zannis Pappas, 697–6056.
Operations.—Col. Eric Beene (202) 767–4259.
Planning, Policy and Strategy.—Col. Norm Worthen (703) 697–4098.

ADMINISTRATIVE ASSISTANT TO THE SECRETARY

Pentagon, 1720 Air Force, 20330

Administrative Assistant.—Tim Beyland, Pentagon, room 4E824 (703) 695–9492.

Deputy Administrative Assistant.—Patricia Zarodkiewicz, 695–9492.
Director of Staff.—Lt. Col. Heather Meyer, 695–9492.
Executive Assistants: Maj. Carey Miller, 695–9492; Maj. Meghan Szwarc, 695–9492.
Confidential Assistant.—Ruby Hill, 695–9492.
Executive Administrators: SSgt. Jenny Collins, 695–9492; TSgt. Eric Perez, 695–9492.
Director of:
Executive Dining Facility.—Shad Glover, room 4D869, 697–1112.
Information Management.—Essye Miller, 5E915, 697–6529.
Operations.—Susan Bench-Snow, room 5D855, 697–8222.
Resources-Personnel.—Anne Graham, room 5E940, 692–9516.
Resources-Finance.—Lydia Newson, room 4D845, 695–3148.
Security, Counterintelligence and Special Programs Oversight Division.—Daniel McMillin, room MD779, 693–2013.
Sensitive Activities Office.—Russell Wyler (571) 432–1581.

AUDITOR GENERAL

Pentagon, 1120 Air Force, 20330

4170 Hebble Creek Road, Building 280, Door 1

Wright-Patterson AFB, OH 45433–5643 (WPAFB)

1500 West Perimeter Road, Suite 4700

Joint Base Andrews, MD 20762

470 I Street East, Randolph AFB, TX 78150–4332

Auditor General.—Theodore J. Williams, room 4E204 (703) 614–5626.

AIR FORCE AUDIT AGENCY

Director of Operations.—Michael V. Barbino, JBA Andrews (240) 612–5110.
Assistant Auditor General for—
Acquisition, Logistics, and Financial Audits.—Valerie L. Muck, WPAFB (937) 257–7473.
Field Activities Audits.—Sharon Puschmann, Pentagon (703) 614–5738.
Operations and Support Audits.—Michael D. Petersen, Randolph AFB (210) 652–0550.

CHIEF OF CHAPLAINS

1380 AF Pentagon, Room 4E260, Washington, DC 20330

Chief.—Chaplain (Maj. Gen.) Howard D. Stendahl (571) 256–7729.
Deputy Chief.—Chaplain (Brig. Gen.) Bobby V. Page, 256–7729.

AIR FORCE CHIEF OF SAFETY

Pentagon, 1400 Air Force Pentagon, Room 4E252, 20330–1400

Chief of Air Force Safety/Commander, Air Force Safety Center.—Vacant (703) 693–7281.
Deputy Chief of Air Force Safety/Executive Director, Air Force Safety Center.—James Rubeor (505) 846–2372.
Executive Officer.—Maj. Eric Westby (703) 614–3389.
Director, Safety Issues Division.—Col. Paul Beineke, 693–3333.

AIR FORCE GENERAL COUNSEL

Pentagon, 1740 Air Force Pentagon, Suite 4E836, 20330

General Counsel.—Hon. Charles A. Blanchard (703) 697–0941.
Principal Deputy.—Gordon O. Tanner (703) 697–4406.
Military Assistant.—Col. Margarete P. Ashmore (703) 693–7304.
Executive Assistant.—Rudy A. Sheffer (703) 697–8418.
Deputy General Counsel for—
Acquisition.—Lynda O'Sullivan, room 5B914 (703) 693–7284.
Contractor Responsibility.—Rodney Grandon, Crystal City (703) 604–0423.

Fiscal, Ethics and Administrative Law.—Cheri Cannon, room 4C934 (703) 693–9291.
Intelligence, International and Military Affairs.—Craig A. Smith, room 4C756 (703) 695–5663.
Installations, Energy and Environment.—Jennifer Miller, room 5E773 (571) 256–4809.

AIR FORCE HISTORIAN

1190 Air Force Pentagon, Room 4E284, Washington, DC 20330–1190

Director.—Walter Grudzinskas (acting), (703) 697–5600.
Executive Officer.—William Stevens (202) 404–2180.
Director, Air Force Historical Research Agency, Maxwell AFB, AL.—Dr. Charles O'Connell (334) 953–5342.

INSPECTOR GENERAL

Pentagon, 1140 Air Force, Room 4E1040, 20330–1140

Inspector General.—Lt. Gen. Stephen P. Mueller (703) 697–6733.
Deputy Inspector General.—Maj. Gen. Frank J. Padilla (703) 697–4351.
Executive Officer.—Lt. Col. John M. Destazio (703) 697–4787.
Advisor for—
Air National Guard Matters.—Col. Suzanne B. Lipcaman, room 4E1037 (703) 697–0339.
Reserve Matters.—Col. Kathleen R. Mikkelson, room 4E1037 (703) 614–3863.
Director of:
Complaints Resolution Directorate.—Col. Lawrence A. Brundidge, JBAB-Building 5863, room 150 (202) 404–5262.
Inspections.—Col. Robert D. Hyde, JBAB-Building 5863, room 350 (202) 404–3263.
Senior Officials Inquiries.—Col. John R. Taylor, room 5B937 (703) 693–3579.
Special Investigations.—Col. Keith M. Givens, room 5B919 (703) 697–0411.

JUDGE ADVOCATE GENERAL

Pentagon, 1420 Air Force, 20330

1501 West Perimeter Road, Joint Base Andrews Naval Air

Facility Washington, MD 20762

The Judge Advocate General.—Lt. Gen. Richard C. Harding, room 4E180 (703) 614–5732.
Deputy Judge Advocate General.—Maj. Gen. Steven J. Lepper, room 4E180, 614–5732.
Senior Paralegal Manager.—CMSgt Steven Wallace, room 5D116, 614–9004.
Director for—
Acquisition Law and Litigation.—Col. Barbara Shestko, JBANAFW, suite 1780 (240) 612–6620.
Administrative Law.—Conrad Von Wald, room 5D116 (703) 614–4075.
Civil Law and Litigation.—Col. Mark Garney, JBANAFW, suite 1530 (240) 612–4610.
Operations and International Law.—Col. Craig Miller, room 5D116 (703) 695–9633.
Plans and Programs.—David Sprowls, room 5D116, 692–2828.
Professional Development.—Col. John Hartsel, room 5D116, 614–3021.
USAF Court of Criminal Appeals.—Col. Holly Stone, JBANAFW, suite 1900 (240) 612–5070.
USAF Judiciary.—Col. Tonya Hagmaier, JBANAFW, suite 1310, 612–4760.
USAF Trial Judiciary.—Col. Mark Allred, JBANAFW, suite 1150, 612–4570.

LEGAL OPERATIONS

Commander, Air Force Legal Operations Agency.—Col. Jeffrey Rockwell, JB Andrews, suite 1320 (240) 612–4590.
Command Paralegal Manager, Air Force Legal Operations Agency.—CMSgt Rebecca Simmons, suite 1320 (240) 612–4594.

DIRECTORATE OF LEGISLATIVE LIAISON

Pentagon, 1160 Air Force, 20330

Rayburn House Office Building, Room B–322, 20515 (RHOB)

Russell Senate Office Building, Room SR–182, 20510 (RSOB)

Director.—Maj. Gen. Tod D. Wolters, room 4E812 (703) 697–8153.
Deputy Director.—Anthony Reardon (703) 697–2650.
Director of Staff.—Col. Daniel A. Blake, 4B852, 693–0315.
Mobilization Assistant to the Director.—Col. Mark Loeben, 695–2650.
Executive Officer to the Director.—Capt. Jeanetta Grover, 697–4142.
Congressional Actions.—Stephen Frye, room 4B852, 695–0182.
Congressional Inquiry and Travel.—Col. John Larson, room 4B852, 697–3783.
House Liaison Office.—Col. Patrick McKenzie, RHOB (202) 685–4531.
Programs and Legislation.—Col. Douglas McCobb, room 4B852 (703) 697–7950.
Senate Liaison Office.—Col. Billy D. Thompson, RSOB (202) 685–2573.
Weapons Systems.—Col. James Bowen, room 4B852 (703) 697–3376.

NATIONAL GUARD BUREAU

1411 Jefferson Davis Highway, Arlington, VA 22202

Chief.—GEN Frank G. Grass, Pentagon, room 1E169 (703) 614–3087.
Legislative Liaison.—Brig. Gen. James K. Vogel, Pentagon, room 1D157 (571) 256–7339.
Director for—
Air National Guard.—Lt. Gen. Stanley Clarke, Pentagon, room 4E126 (703) 614–8033.
Army National Guard.—LTG William R. Ingram, Readiness Center, Arlington, VA, 693–8464.

OFFICE OF PUBLIC AFFAIRS

Director.—Brig. Gen. Les Kodlick (703) 697–6061.
Executive Officer.—Maj. Toni Whaley.
Chief of:
Current Operations.—Lt. Col. Brett Ashworth, 695–0640.
Engagement.—Wendy Varhegyi, 695–9664.
Requirements and Development.—Sherry Medders, 697–6701.
Strategy and Assessment.—Col. William Murphey, 697–6715.

AIR FORCE RESERVE

Pentagon, 1150 Air Force, Room 4E138, 20330

Chief, Air Force Reserve/Commander, Air Force Reserve Command.—Lt. Gen. James F. Jackson (703) 695–9225.
Deputy to Chief of Air Force Reserve.—Maj. Gen. Maryanne Miller, 695–5528.
Executive Officer.—Col. D. Scott Durham, 695–5528.
Assistant Executive Officer.—Lt. Col. Angela Gundersen, 695–5528.
Executive NCO.—SMSgt Eric D. McCross, 614–7307.

SCIENTIFIC ADVISORY BOARD

1500 West Perimeter Road, Suite 3300, Joint Base Andrews, MD 20762

Chair.—Eliahu Niewood (240) 612–5500.
Vice Chair.—David Miller (240) 612–5500.
Military Director.—Lt. Gen. Charles Davis (Pentagon 4E962), (703) 697–6363.
Executive Director.—Lt. Col. Derek Lincoln (240) 612–5502.
Administration.—MSgt Monique Thompson (240) 612–5500.

AIR FORCE SCIENTIST

Pentagon, 1075 Air Force, Room 4E130, 20330

Chief Scientist.—Dr. Mica R. Endsley (703) 697–7842.

Military Assistant.—Col. James L. Greer.

AIR FORCE OFFICE OF SMALL BUSINESS PROGRAMS

1060 Air Force Pentagon, Room 4E268, Washington, DC 20330–1060

Director.—Joseph M. McDade (571) 256–8052.

SURGEON GENERAL

Pentagon, 1780 Air Force, Room 4E114, 20330–1780

7700 Arlington Boulevard, Suite 5152, Falls Church, VA 22042–5152

Surgeon General.—Lt. Gen. Thomas Travis (703) 692–6800.
Executive Officer.—Lt. Col. Al Flowers, 692–6990.
Deputy Surgeon General.—Maj. Gen. Mark Ediger, 681–6994.
Executive Officer.—Maj. Thomas Lesnick, 681–6994.
Director for—
Congressional and Public Affairs.—Donna Tinsley, 681–7921.
Financial Management.—Col. Billy Cecil, 681–6933.
Force Development.—Maj. Gen. Kimberly Siniscalchi, 681–8157.
Medical Operations.—Brig. Gen. Charles Potter, 681–7113.
Modernization.—Brig. Gen. James Carroll, 681–8137.
Strategic Plans and Programs.—Farah Sharshar, 681–5639.
Corps Directors for—
Biomedical Sciences.—Col. Richard Mooney, 681–7616.
Dental Corps.—Col. David Stanczyk, 681–6993.
Medical.—Col. Dominic Hootsman, 681–6993.
Medical Services.—Col. Patrick Dawson, 681–6993.
Nursing.—Col. Rose Layman, 681–8157.

DIRECTORATE OF TEST AND EVALUATION

Pentagon, 1650 Air Force, Room 4E276, 20330

Director.—Randall Walden (703) 697–4774.
Deputy Director.—Devin Cate.
Executive Assistant.—Ruby Chason.

ARMY AND AIR FORCE EXCHANGE SERVICE

3911 S. Walton Walker Boulevard, Dallas, TX 75236, phone 1–800–527–6790

Director/Chief Executive Officer.—Thomas C. Shull.
Deputy Director.—Brig. Gen. Casey D. Blake.
Chief Operating Officer.—Michael P. Howard.

WASHINGTON OFFICE/OFFICE OF THE BOARD OF DIRECTORS

2530 Crystal Drive, Suite 4158, 4th Floor
Arlington, VA 22202, phone (703) 602–3439

Director/Executive Secretary.—Gregg Cox.
Deputy Director.—Denise Hunter.

DEPARTMENT OF THE ARMY

The Pentagon Washington, DC 20310

phone (703) 695–2442

OFFICE OF THE SECRETARY

101 Army Pentagon, Room 3E700, Washington, DC 20310–0101

phone (703) 695–1717, fax (703) 697–8036

Secretary of the Army.—Hon. John M. McHugh.
Executive Officer.—COL Douglas C. Crissman.

OFFICE OF THE UNDER SECRETARY

102 Army Pentagon, Room 3E700, Washington, DC 20310–0102

phone (703) 695–4311, fax (703) 697–8036

Under Secretary of the Army.—Hon. Joseph W. Westphal.
Executive Officer.—COL Reginald E. Allen.

CHIEF OF STAFF (CSA)

200 Army Pentagon, Room 3E672, Washington, DC 20310–0200

phone (703) 697–0900, fax (703) 614–5268

Chief of Staff, Army.—GEN Raymond T. Odierno.
Executive Officer.—COL Michael J. Tarsa.
Vice Chief of Staff, Army.—GEN John F. Campbell (703) 695–4371.
Executive Officer.—COL Patrick D. Frank (703) 695–4371.
Director, CSA Staff Group.—COL Andrew Rohling, room 3D654 (703) 693–8371.
Director of the Army Staff.—LTG William T. Grisoli, room 3E663 (703) 693–7707.
Sergeant Major of the Army.—SMA Raymond F. Chandler III, room 3E677 (703) 695–2150.
Directors:
Army Protocol.—Heidi Hulst, room 3A532 (703) 692–6701.
Executive Communications and Control.—Thea Harvell III, room 3D664 (703) 695–7552.
Joint and Defense Affairs.—COL Kevin Dunlop, room 3D644 (703) 614–8217.

Direct Reporting Unit
U.S. Army Test and Evaluation Command, Commanding General.—MG Genaro J. Dellarocco (703) 681–9360 / (410) 306–3327.
U.S. Military Academy, Superintendent.—LTG Robert L. Caslen, Jr. (845) 938–2610.
U.S. Army Military District of Washington, Commanding General.—MG Jeffrey S. Buchanan (202) 685–2807.

DEPUTY UNDER SECRETARY OF THE ARMY (DUSA)

101 Army Pentagon, Room 3E650, Washington, DC 20310–0001

phone (703) 697–5075, fax (703) 697–3145

Deputy Under Secretary.—Thomas E. Hawley.
Deputy.—Vacant.
Executive Officer.—Mark Von Heeringen, room 3A514 (703) 695–8375.
Executive Assistant.—Vacant, room 3E650 (703) 697–5075.

ASSISTANT SECRETARY OF THE ARMY
(ACQUISITION, LOGISTICS AND TECHNOLOGY) (ASA(ALT))
103 Army Pentagon, Room 2E532, Washington, DC 20310–0103
phone (703) 693–6154

Assistant Secretary.—Hon. Heidi Shyu.
Principal Deputy.—Gabriel O. Camarillo, room 2E520 (703) 614–4372.
Principal Military Deputy.—LTG William N. Phillips, room 2E532 (703) 697–0356.
Chief of Staff.—COL William E. Cole (703) 695–5749.
Executive Officer.—LTC Wayne ''Ed'' Barker (703) 695–6742.
Confidential Assistant.—Anita J. Odom (703) 695–6154.
Executive Assistant to the Military Deputy.—Patty Laws (703) 693–3927.
Deputy Assistant Secretaries of the Army (DASA):
Acquisition and Systems Management.—MG Harold J. Greene (703) 695–3115.
Acquisition, Policy and Logistics.—Wimpy Pybus (703) 697–5050.
Defense Exports and Cooperation.—Ann Castiglione-Cataldo (703) 614–3434.
Plans, Programs and Resources.—Thomas E. Mullins (703) 697–0387.
Procurement.—Harry P. Hallock (703) 695–2488.
Research and Technology.—Mary J. Miller (703) 692–1830.

Direct Reporting Units
Director, U.S. Army Acquisition Support Center.—Craig Spisak (703) 805–1018.

ASSISTANT SECRETARY OF THE ARMY (CIVIL WORKS) (ASA(CW))
108 Army Pentagon, Room 3E446, Washington, DC 20310–0108
phone (703) 697–4672, fax (703) 697–7401

Assistant Secretary.—Hon. Jo-Ellen Darcy.
Principal Deputy.—Marie Therese Dominguez (703) 695–1370.
Executive Officer.—COL Reinhard W. Koenig (703) 697–9809.
Military Assistant.—LTC Michael C. Derosier (703) 695–0482.
Executive Assistant.—Regena Townsend-Treleaven (703) 697–4672.
Deputy Assistant Secretaries of the Army (DASA):
Management and Budget.—Eric V. Hansen, room 3E441 (703) 695–1376.
Policy, Planning and Review.—Douglas W. Lamont, GAO–6S91 (202) 761–0016.

ASSISTANT SECRETARY OF THE ARMY
(FINANCIAL MANAGEMENT AND COMPTROLLER) (ASA(FM&C))
109 Army Pentagon, Room 3E320, Washington, DC 20310–0109
phone (703) 614–4356

Assistant Secretary.—Hon. Mary Sally Matiella.
Principal Deputy.—Robert M. Speer (703) 614–4337.
Military Deputy for Budget.—LTG Joseph E. Martz (703) 614–4034.
Executive Officer.—COL Bradley Dreyer (703) 614–4292.
Military Assistant.—MAJ Lance Sneed (703) 614–5548.
Executive Assistant.—Deborah Glembocki (703) 614–1506.
Deputy Assistant Secretaries of the Army:
Cost and Economics.—Stephen G. Barth, room 3E352 (703) 614–7550.
Financial Information Management.—Kristy E. Jones, room 3A320 (703) 692–8529.
Financial Operations.—James Watkins, room 3A320A (703) 693–2758.
Director, Army Budget.—MG Karen E. Dyson, room 3E336, 614–1573.
Director, U.S. Army Financial Management Command.—COL Stanley M. Brown (803) 751–3997.

ASSISTANT SECRETARY OF THE ARMY
(INSTALLATIONS, ENERGY AND ENVIRONMENT) (ASA(IE&E))
110 Army Pentagon, Room 3E464, Washington, DC 20310–0110
phone (703) 692–9800, fax (703) 692–9808

Assistant Secretary.—Hon. Katherine G. Hammack.

Principal Deputy.—J. Randall Robinson (703) 692–9802.
Executive Officer.—COL Andrew W. Backus (703) 692–9804.
Military Assistant.—LTC Jason Taliaferro (703) 692–9805.
Executive Assistant.—Jo Ann Ginsberg (703) 692–9800.
Deputy Assistant Secretaries of the Army:
Energy and Sustainability.—Richard G. Kidd IV, room 3D453 (703) 692–9890.
Environment, Safety and Occupational Health.—Hershel ''Hew'' E. Wolfe, room 3D453 (703) 697–1913.
Installations, Housing and Partnerships.—Paul D. Cramer, room 3E475 (703) 697–0867.
Strategic Integration.—Mark D. Rocke, room 3D453 (703) 692–9817.

ASSISTANT SECRETARY OF THE ARMY (MANPOWER AND RESERVE AFFAIRS) (ASA(M&RA))

111 Army Pentagon, Room 2E460, Washington, DC 20310–0111
phone (703) 697–9253, fax (703) 692–9000

Assistant Secretary.—Karl F. Schneider (acting).
Principal Deputy.—Karl F. Schneider (703) 692–1292.
Executive Officer.—COL Lawrence J. Wark (703) 614–2850.
Executive Assistant.—Wanda L. Artis (703) 697–9253.
Deputy Assistant Secretaries of the Army:
Army Review Boards/Director, Army Review Boards Agency.—Wilson ''Bud'' Shatzer (acting), Crystal City (703) 545–5637.
Civilian Personnel and Quality of Life.—Anthony J. Stamilio, room 2D484 (703) 614–1648.
Force Management, Manpower and Resources/Director, Civilian Senior Leader Management Office.—Gwendolyn R. DeFilippi, room 2E485 (703) 614–8143.
Diversity and Leadership.—Larry Stubblefield (703) 614–5284.
Marketing/Director, Army Marketing Research Group.—Mark S. Davis (703) 545–3439.
Military Personnel.—Samuel B. Retherford, room 2E469 (703) 697–2044.
Training, Readiness and Mobilization.—MG Steven W. Smith (acting), room 2E482 (703) 697–2631.

Direct Reporting Unit
U.S. Army Accessions Support Brigade.—COL Brian M. Cavanaugh (502) 626–1751.

ARMY GENERAL COUNSEL (GC)

104 Army Pentagon, Room 2E724, Washington, DC 20310–0104
phone (703) 697–9235, fax (703) 693–9254

General Counsel.—Hon. Brad R. Carson.
Principal Deputy General Counsel.—Levator Norsworthy, Jr. (acting).
Executive Officer/Special Counsel.—COL Lisa Anderson-Lloyd.
Executive Assistant.—Christopher J. McCombs (703) 693–7721.
Deputy General Counsel:
Acquisition.—Levator Norsworthy, Jr., room 3C546 (703) 697–5120.
Ethics and Fiscal Law.—Susan D. Tigner, room 3C546 (703) 695–4296.
Installations, Environment and Civil Works.—Craig R. Schmauder, room 3C546 (703) 695–3024.
Operations and Personnel.—Stephanie A. Barna, room 3C546 (703) 695–0562.

ADMINISTRATIVE ASSISTANT TO THE SECRETARY OF THE ARMY (AASA)

105 Army Pentagon, room 3E733, Washington, DC 20310–0105
phone (703) 695–2442, fax (703) 697–6194

Administrative Assistant to the Secretary of the Army.—Gerald B. O'Keefe.
Deputy Administrative Assistant.—Vacant (703) 697–7741.
Executive Officer.—Karan L. Reidenbach (703) 695–7444.
Executive Assistant.—Paula J. Galloway (703) 695–2442.
Director, Civilian Aides to the Secretary of the Army (CASA).—Laura L. DeFrancisco, room 3D742 (703) 697–2639.

Director, Resource Operations Center.—Sandra F. Stillerman, Fort Belvoir, Building 1458 (703) 545–2663.

Executive Directors:

U.S. Army Center of Military History.—Robert J. Dalessandro, Fort McNair Building, room 35 (202) 685–2705.

U.S. Army Headquarters Services.—Vacant, Fort Belvoir, Building 1458 (703) 545–4870.

U.S. Army Information Technology Agency.—Gregory L. Garcia, room ME882 (571) 256–1660.

U.S. Army Resources and Programs Agency.—Vacant, Fort Belvoir, Building 1458 (703) 545–0527.

ARMY AUDITOR GENERAL

6000 6th Street, Bldg 1464, Fort Belvoir, VA 22060–5609

phone (703) 545–5907, fax (703) 806–1199

Auditor General.—Randall L. Exley.

Principal Deputy Auditor General.—Joseph P. Bentz (703) 545–5910.

Executive Officer.—COL Sheila C. Denham (703) 545–5909.

Executive Assistant.—Carolyn Selquist (703) 545–5907.

General Counsel.—Michael Hoadley (703) 545–5879.

Director, Policy and Operations Management.—Felix Strelsky (703) 545–5874.

Deputy Auditors General:

Acquisition, Logistics and Technology Audits.—Kathleen Nelson (703) 545–5903.

Financial Management and Comptroller Audits.—Kevin Kelly (703) 545–5851.

Installations, Energy and Environment Audits.—Vacant.

Manpower, Reserve Affairs and Training Audits.—Monique Ferrell (703) 545–5877.

ARMY NATIONAL MILITARY CEMETERIES (ANMC)

phone (703) 614–0615, fax (571) 256–3366

Executive Director.—Patrick K. Hallinan.

Chief of Staff.—COL Michelle J. Stewart (571) 256–4324.

Executive Officer.—Christa Petry (703) 614–0615.

Executive Assistant.—Vacant.

Direct Reporting Unit

Executive Director, Arlington National Cemetery.—Patrick K. Hallinan.

Superintendent, Arlington National Cemetery.—Vacant.

ASSISTANT CHIEF OF STAFF FOR INSTALLATION MANAGEMENT (ACSIM)

600 Army Pentagon, Room 3E484, Washington, DC 20310–0600

phone (703) 693–3233, fax (703) 693–3507

Assistant Chief of Staff.—LTG Michael Ferriter.

Deputy Assistant.—Diane M. Randon.

Executive Officer.—COL John J. Strycula.

Executive Assistant.—Patricia L. Weaver.

Director, Army Installation Management Support Activity.—Diane M. Randon.

Direct Reporting Unit

U.S. Army Installation Management Command, Commanding General.—LTG Michael Ferriter.

CHIEF ARMY RESERVE (CAR)

2400 Army Pentagon, Room 3E562, Washington, DC 20310–2400

phone (703) 695–0031

Chief.—LTG Jeffrey W. Talley.

Assistant Chief.—James L. Snyder (703) 695–0047.

Executive Officer.—COL Tyra A. Harding (703) 695–0042.
Executive Assistant.—Janet L. Pendergraph (703) 695–0031.
Congressional Affairs Contact Officer.—Dorothy G. Singletary (703) 806–7546.

CHIEF INFORMATION OFFICER, G–6 (CIO, G–6)

107 Army Pentagon, Room 3E608, Washington, DC 20310–0107

phone (703) 695–4366, fax (703) 695–3091

Chief Information Officer.—Michael E. Krieger (acting).
Deputy Chief.—Michael E. Krieger (703) 695–6604.
Executive Officer.—COL Dana S. Tankins (703) 697–5503.
Civilian Executive Officer.—Marilyn Al-Mansoor (703) 695–4366.

Direct Reporting Unit
U.S. Army Network Enterprise Technology Command (NETCOM)/9th Signal Command (Army), Commander.—BG Peter A. Gallagher (502) 538–6161.

CHIEF LEGISLATIVE LIAISON (CLL)

1600 Army Pentagon, Room 1E416, Washington, DC 20310–1600

phone (703) 697–6767, fax (703) 614–7599

Chief.—MG William E. Rapp.
Principal Deputy.—Bernard P. Ingold (703) 697–0278.
Deputy.—COL David P. Anders (703) 695–1235.
Executive Officer.—COL Richard D. Root (703) 695–3524.
Enlisted Aide.—SGT Kendra N. Bilger (703) 696–4779.
Executive Assistant.—Dellar M. Burch (703) 697–6767.
Chief Congressional Inquiry.—Harry B. Williams, room 1E423 (703) 697–8381.
Chief House Liaison Division.—COL Latonya Lynn, room B325, Rayburn House Office Building, Washington, DC (202) 685–2675.
Chief Investigations and Legislative Division.—COL Susan K. Arnold, room 1E433 (703) 697–8218.
Chief Program Division.—COL Brian E. Winski, room 1E385 (703) 693–8766.
Chief Senate Liaison Division.—COL Robert McAleer, room SR183, Senate Russell Office Building, Washington, DC (202) 224–2881.
ACoS Operations.—COL Fletcher V. Washington, room 1D437 (703) 697–3206.
ACoS Plans.—LTC (P) James Vizzard, room 1D437 (703) 693–1324.
ACoS Support.—LTC Mary Williams-Lynch, room 1E423 (703) 692–4159.

CHIEF NATIONAL GUARD BUREAU (CNGB)

Pentagon, room 1E169, Washington, DC 20301–1636

phone (703) 614–3087, fax (703) 614–0274

Chief.—GEN Frank J. Grass.
Vice Chief.—Lt. Gen. Joseph L. Lengyel (703) 614–3038.
Executive Officer.—COL Jeffrey B. Cashman (703) 614–3087.
Executive Assistant.—Carol Lagasse (703) 614–3117.
Directors:
Air National Guard.—Lt. Gen. Stanley E. Clarke III (703) 614–8033.
Army National Guard.—LTG William E. Ingram, Jr., room 2A514B (703) 693–8464.

CHIEF OF CHAPLAINS (CCH)

2700 Army Pentagon, Room 3E524, Washington, DC 20310–2700

phone (703) 695–1133, fax (703) 695–9834

Chief of Chaplains.—(MG) Donald L. Rutherford.
Deputy Chief of Chaplains.—(BG) Charles Ray Bailey (703) 695–1135.
Executive Officer.—Chaplain (LTC) Brad Baumann (703) 695–1133.
Executive Assistant.—Caridad Gelineau (703) 695–1135.

CHIEF OF ENGINEERS (CoE)

GAO Building, 441 G Street NW., 20314–0001

phone (202) 761–0000, fax (202) 761–4463

Chief of Engineers.—LTG Thomas P. Bostick.
Deputy.—MG Todd T. Semonite (202) 761–0002.
Director.—COL David C. Hill (703) 693–4407.

Direct Reporting Unit
U.S. Army Corps of Engineers, Commanding General.—LTG Thomas P. Bostick.
Deputy.—MG Todd T. Semonite (202) 761–0002.
Chief of Staff.—COL R. Mark Toy (202) 761–0761.
Executive Officer.—LTC Marc F. Hoffmeister (202) 761–0468.
Executive Assistant.—Karen Huff (202) 761–0001.

CHIEF, PUBLIC AFFAIRS (CPA)

1500 Army Pentagon, Room 1E484, Washington, DC 20310–1500

phone (703) 695–5135, fax (703) 693–8362

Chief.—BG Gary J. Volesky.
Principal Deputy.—Stephanie L. Hoehne (703) 693–0616.
Deputy.—COL Thomas W. Collins (703) 697–4482.
Chief of Staff.—COL Ken Boehme.
Executive Officer.—LTC Chad G. Carroll (703) 697–4200.
Executive Assistant.—Barbara I. Callahan (703) 695–5135.
Director, Media Relations Division.—COL Dave Patterson (703) 693–4723.
Director, U.S. Army Public Affairs Center.—COL Rich Patterson (301) 677–7270.
Director, The United States Army Field Band.—COL Tim Holtan (301) 677–5763.

DEPUTY CHIEF OF STAFF, G–1 (DCS, G–1) (PERSONNEL)

300 Army Pentagon, Room 2E446, Washington, DC 20310–0300

phone (703) 697–8060

Deputy Chief of Staff.—LTG Howard B. Bromberg.
Assistant Deputy Chief of Staff.—Roy A. Wallace (703) 692–1585.
Executive Officer.—COL Steve R. Shappell (703) 697–2893.
Military Assistant.—MAJ Regina Pistone (703) 614–1862.
Executive Assistant.—Debora Van Heest (703) 697–8060.
U.S. Army Human Resources Command, Commanding General.—MG Richard P. Mustion (502) 613–8844.
Director, U.S. Army Civilian Human Resources Agency.—Barbara P. Panther (410) 306–1701.
Director, Assistant G–1 for Civilian Personnel.—Jay Aronowitz (703) 695–5701.
Director, Military Personnel Management.—MG Thomas Seamands (703) 695–5871.
Director, Human Resources Policy.—BG Henry Huntley (703) 571–7215.
Plans and Resources.—Dr. Robert Steinrauf (703) 697–5263.

DEPUTY CHIEF OF STAFF, G–2 (DCS, G–2) (INTELLIGENCE)

1000 Army Pentagon, Room 2E408, Washington, DC 20310–1000

phone (703) 695–3033, fax (703) 697–7605

Deputy Chief of Staff.—LTG Mary A. Legere.
Assistant Deputy Chief.—James "Tom" Faust.
Executive Officer.—COL Karen H. Gibson.
Executive Assistant.—Anne H. Fesmire.

Direct Reporting Unit
U.S. Army Intelligence and Security Command, Commanding General.—MG Stephen G. Fogarty.

DEPUTY CHIEF OF STAFF, G–3/5/7 (DCS, G–3/5/7) (OPERATIONS)

400 Army Pentagon, Room 2E670, Washington, DC 20310–0400

phone (703) 695–2904

Deputy Chief of Staff.—LTG James L. Huggins, Jr.
Deputy Chief.—Dr. David Markowitz (703) 692–7883.
Military Deputy Chief.—MG Gary H. Cheek (703) 697–5180.
Executive Officer.—COL Timothy J. Daughterty (703) 697–4521.
Executive Assistant.—MAJ Spring A. Kivett (703) 695–3447.
Director, U.S. Army Capabilities and Integration Directorate.—Peter Bechtel (703) 692–7906.
Director, U.S. Army Force Management Support Agency.—BG Roger Cloutier (703) 693–3227.
Director, U.S. Army Nuclear and Combating WMD Agency.—COL Juan ''Ariel'' Cuadrado (703) 614–2670.
Director, U.S. Army Operations, Readiness, and Mobilization Directorate.—BG Ryan F. Gonsalves (703) 695–0526.
Director, U.S. Army Strategy, Plans, and Policy Directorate.—MG Jeffrey J. Snow (703) 692–8805.
Director, U.S. Army Training Directorate.—BG Wayne Grigsby.

DEPUTY CHIEF OF STAFF, G–4 (DCS, G–4) (LOGISTICS)

500 Army Pentagon, Room 1E394, Washington, DC 20310–0500

phone (703) 695–4104, fax (703) 692–0759

Deputy Chief of Staff.—LTG Raymond V. Mason.
Assistant Deputy Chief.—Kathleen S. Miller (703) 697–9138.
Assistant Deputy Chief/Operations.—MG Edward F. Dorman III (703) 697–5032.
Executive Officer.—COL Jeffrey W. Drushal (703) 697–9039.
Executive Assistant.—Torwanna D. Herbert (703) 695–4102.
Director, Corporate Information Office.—Carlos D. Morrison, room 1E391 (703) 695–6160.
Director, Force Projection and Distribution.—COL Eric D. Martin, room 1E380 (703) 697–2281.
Director, Logistics Innovation Agency.—Michael K. Williams (703) 805–5440.
Director, Logistics Readiness.—Mark R. Illg (acting), room 1E367 (703) 697–8007.
Director, Maintenance Policy, Program and Processes.—Christopher J. Lowman, room 1E360 (703) 693–1624.
Director, Resource Management.—Mark F. Averill, room 1E380 (703) 693–1900.
Director, Strategy and Integration.—COL Richard B. Dix (acting), room 1E369 (703) 692–5127.
Director, Supply.—Michael B. Cervone, room 1E360 (703) 693–1584.

DEPUTY CHIEF OF STAFF, G–8 (DCS, G–8) (PROGRAMS)

700 Army Pentagon, Room 3E406, Washington, DC 20310–0700

phone (703) 697–8232, fax (703) 697–8242

Deputy Chief of Staff.—LTG James O. Barclay III.
Assistant Deputy Chief.—Donald C. Tison (703) 692–9099.
Executive Officer.—COL Eric O. Schacht.
Executive Assistant.—Jessica M. Collins (703) 697–8236.
Director, Center for Army Analysis.—Dr. William F. Crain (703) 806–5510.
Director, Force Development.—MG Robert M. Dyess, Jr. (703) 692–7707.
Director, Program Analysis and Evaluation.—MG Michael T. Harrison, Sr. (703) 697–1475.
Director, Quadrennial Defense Review.—MG John G. Rossi (703) 695–8997.

DIRECTOR OF THE ARMY STAFF (DAS)

202 Army Pentagon, room 3E663, Washington, DC 20310–0202

phone (703) 693–5300, fax (703) 695–6117

Director of the Army Staff.—LTG William T. Grisoli.

Vice Director.—Steven J. Redmann, room 3D644 (703) 697–2899.
Executive Officer.—COL Jefferson M. Ryscavage (703) 693–7710.
Executive Assistant.—Hallie Johnson (703) 695–3542.
U.S. Army Combat Readiness/Safety Center, Commanding General.—BG Timothy J. Edens (334) 255–9360.

PROVOST MARSHAL GENERAL (PMG)

2800 Army Pentagon, room 3E588, Washington, DC 203103–2800

phone (703) 692–6966, fax (703) 614–5628

Provost Marshal General.—MG David E. Quantock.
Deputy.—COL David P. Glaser (703) 692–7290.
Executive Officer.—COL Rosendo ''Ross'' T. Guieb (703) 692–6970.
Chief of Staff.—Trina M. Powell (703) 692–6829.
Executive Assistant.—Meribeth M. Puckett (703) 695–4036.
U.S. Army Corrections Command, Commanding General.—MG David E. Quantock.
Director, Defense Forensics and Biometrics Agency.—Donald G. Salo, Jr. (703) 571–0507.

Direct Reporting Unit
U.S. Army Criminal Investigation Command, Commanding General.—MG David E. Quantock.

OFFICE SMALL BUSINESS PROGRAMS (OSBP)

106 Army Pentagon, Room 3B514, Washington, DC 20310–0106

phone (703) 697–2868, fax (703) 693–3898

Director.—Tracey L. Pinson.
Deputy/Executive Officer.—Peggy W. Butler-Mason (703) 693–6113.
Executive Assistant.—Veronica D. Atkinson (703) 697–2868.

THE INSPECTOR GENERAL (TIG)

1700 Army Pentagon, Room 3E588, Washington, DC 20310–1700

phone (703) 695–1500, fax (703) 614–5628

Inspector General.—LTG Peter M. Vangjel.
Deputy Inspector General.—MG Ross E. Ridge (703) 695–1501.
Executive Officer.—Jay F. Klaus (703) 695–1502.
Executive Assistant.—SFC Robin L. Foe (703) 695–1500.
U.S. Army Inspector General Agency, Commanding General.—LTG Peter M. Vangjel.

THE JUDGE ADVOCATE GENERAL (TJAG)

2200 Army Pentagon, Room 3E542, Washington, DC 20310–2200

phone (703) 697–5151, fax (703) 693–0600

The Judge Advocate General.—LTG Flora D. Darpino.
Deputy Judge Advocate General.—MG Thomas E. Ayres (703) 693–5112.
Executive Officer.—COL George R. Smawley (703) 695–3786.
Executive Assistant.—Cindy G. Mitchell (703) 697–5151.
U.S. Army Legal Services Agency, Commander.—BG Charles N. Pede (703) 693–1100.
U.S. Army Judge Advocate General's Legal Center and School Commander/Commandant.—COL Sharon E. Riley (acting), (434) 971–3301.

THE SURGEON GENERAL (TSG)

57700 Arlington Boulevard, Defense Health Headquarters (DHHQ)

Falls Church, VA 22042, phone (703) 681–3001, fax (703) 681–3167

The Surgeon General.—LTG Patricia D. Horoho.

Deputy.—MG Brian C. Lein (703) 681–3002.
Chief of Staff.—Uldric L. Fiore, Jr. (703) 681–9514.
Executive Officer.—COL Robert D. Tenhet (703) 681–3004.
Command Sergeant Major.—CSM Donna A. Brock (703) 681–8046.
Operations Center.—Duty Officer-in-Charge (703) 681–8052.

Direct Reporting Unit
U.S. Army Medical Command (MEDCOM), Commanding General.—LTG Patricia D. Horoho.

ARMY COMMANDS

U.S. ARMY FORCES COMMAND (FORSCOM)

4700 Knox Street, Fort Bragg, NC 28310–5000
phone (910) 570–5052, fax (910) 570–1971

Commanding General.—GEN Daniel B. Allyn.
Deputy.—LTG William B. Garrett III (910) 570–5001.
Chief of Staff.—MG Leslie Carroll (910) 570–5002.
Executive Officer.—COL John Kolasheski (910) 570–5053.
Command Sergeant Major.—CSM Christopher Greca (910) 570–5003.
Secretary of the General Staff.—COL Ronald P. Elron (910) 570–5004.
Operations Center.—COL Larry A. Jackson (910) 570–6765.
Staff Action Control Officers.—Robert L. Bakeley (910) 570–5040 and Annette Taiwo (910) 570–5041.
Liaison Office (Washington, DC): Jennifer Bhartiya (703) 697–2252; COL Russell H. Bittle, Jr. (703) 614–2844.
Congressional Relations Officers: John Hughes (910) 570–5077; John Raines (910) 570–5078.

U.S. ARMY MATERIEL COMMAND (AMC)

4400 Martin Road, Redstone Arsenal, AL 35898–5000
phone (256) 450–6000, fax (256) 450–8833

Commanding General.—GEN Dennis L. Via.
Deputy Commanding General.—LTG Patricia E. McQuistion (256) 450–6100.
Executive Deputy Commanding General.—John B. Nerger (256) 450–6200.
Chief of Staff.—MG Darrell K. Williams (256) 450–7867.
Executive Officer.—COL Rodney D. Fogg (256) 450–6005.
Command Sergeant Major.—CSM Ronald T. Rilling II (256) 450–6300.
Secretary of the General Staff.—LTC Frank A. Ras (256) 450–6440.
Operations Center.—Duty Officer-in-Charge (256) 450–9496.

U.S. ARMY TRAINING AND DOCTRINE COMMAND (TRADOC)

950 Jefferson Avenue, Fort Eustis, VA 23604–5700
phone (757) 501–6474

Commanding General.—GEN Robert W. Cone.
Executive Officer.—COL Scott L. Efflandt (757) 501–6472.
Deputy Commanding General/Chief of Staff.—LTG David D. Halverson (757) 501–6478.
Executive Officer.—COL Robert H. Risberg (757) 501–6466.
Deputy Chief of Staff.—MG Mark J. MacCarley (757) 501–6495.
Executive Officer.—LTC Douglas J. Hayes (757) 501–6485.
Command Sergeant Major.—CSM Daniel A. Dailey (757) 501–6464.
Director, Command Group Actions Office.—Radames Cornier, Jr. (757) 501–5204.
Director, G–33/Operations Center.—James G. Lynch (757) 501–5094.

ARMY SERVICE COMPONENT COMMANDS

LIAISON OFFICES

Pentagon, Washington, DC 203100

U.S. Army Africa/Southern European Task Force (USARAF/SETAF).—COL Melvin Hull, room 3D513 (571) 256–1803.

U.S. Army Central (USARCENT): Hank Foresman, room 2A474 (703) 693–4033; Mark R. Seeger, room 2B485 (703) 693–4035.
U.S. Army Europe (USAREUR).—Timothy C. Touzinsky, room 1E1074 (703) 692–6886.
U.S. Army North (USARNORTH).—John D. Nelson, room 2A474 / 2B485 (703) 693–4034.
U.S. Army Pacific (USARPAC).—Robert Ralston, room 2A474 / 2B485 (703) 693–4032.
U.S. Army South (USARSO).—LTC Phil Johnson, room 2D337 (703) 692–8221.
U.S. Army Space and Missile Defense Command/Army Strategic Command (SMCD/ ARSTRAT): LTC Scott W. Anderson (703) 614–9594; Christine Kral (703) 614–9592, room 2D831; COL Clark H. Risner (703) 614–9593.
Military Surface Deployment and Distribution Command (SDDC): COL Riley Cheramie (703) 571–9708; Melissa Higginbotham (703) 571–9710, room 2B858.

JOINT FORCE HEADQUARTERS–NATIONAL CAPITAL REGION AND MILITARY DISTRICT OF WASHINGTON (JFHQ–NCR / MDW)

102 3rd Avenue, Building 39, Fort Lesley J. McNair, 20319

phone (202) 685–2807, fax (202) 685–3481

Commanding General.—MG Jeffrey S. Buchanan.
Executive Officer.—MAJ Irvin Nelms III (202) 685–2817.
Aide de Camp.—CPT Jason Halligan (202) 685–2807.
Secretary.—Kai Brown (202) 685–2808.
Deputy Commander.—Egon F. Hawrylak (202) 685–0641.
Executive Officer to the Deputy.—Bill Hegedusich (202) 685–1949.
JTF Deputy.—Rear Adm. Markham K. Rich (202) 433–2777.
Command Sergeant Major.—CSM David O. Turnbull (202) 685–2923.
Admin NCO.—CPL Matthew T. Morgan (202) 685–2923.
Chief of Staff.—COL Mark Bertolini (202) 685–2812.
Executive Assistant.—Sherri Williams, 685–4926.
Secretary of the General Staff.—Corey R. Langenwalter (202) 685–0640.

U.S. ARMY SPECIAL OPERATIONS COMMAND

Fort Bragg, NC 28310–5200

phone (910) 432–3000, fax (910) 432–4243

Commanding General.—LTG Charles T. Cleveland.
Deputy Commanding General.—BG Darsie D. Rogers (910) 432–6622.
Chief of Staff.—COL Kurt L. Sonntag (910) 432–7898.
Executive Officer.—LTC Philip J. Ryan (910) 432–2577.
Command Sergeant Major.—George A. Bequer (910) 432–0946.
Secretary of the General Staff.—Charles E. Pimble (910) 432–7209.

DEPARTMENT OF THE NAVY

Pentagon 20350–1000, phone (703) 695–3131

OFFICE OF THE SECRETARY OF THE NAVY

Pentagon, Room 4E686, phone (703) 695–3131

Secretary of the Navy.—Ray Mabus.
Confidential Assistant.—J. Scarbrough.
Executive Assistant.—CAPT L. Franchetti, USN.
Special Assistant.—T. Oppel.
Administrative Aide.—CDR V. Burks, USN, 695–5410.
Marine Personal Aide.—MAJ J. Livingston, USMC, 614–3100.
Navy Personal Aide.—LCDR K. Jones, USN, 614–6473.
Special Assistant for Public Affairs.—CAPT P. Kunze, 697–7491.
Senior Military Assistant.—COL K. Heckl, USMC.

OFFICE OF THE UNDER SECRETARY OF THE NAVY

Pentagon, Room 4E720, phone (703) 695–3141

Under Secretary of the Navy.—Vacant.
Executive Assistant and Naval Aide.—Vacant.
Executive Assistant and Marine Aide.—COL Ronald Jones.
Special Assistant.—Vacant.
Administrative Assistants: YN1 Granville Johns, SSgt Mauricio Tellez.

GENERAL COUNSEL

Pentagon, Room 4E782, phone (703) 614–1994

General Counsel.—Hon. Paul L. Oostburg Sanz.
Principal Deputy General Counsel.—Anne Brennan, 614–8733.
Executive Assistant and Special Counsel.—CAPT Gordon Modari, JAGC, USN.
Associate General Counsel for—
Litigation.—R. Borro, Washington Navy Yard, Building 36, (202) 685–6989.
Deputy General Counsel.—Thomas Ledvina, room 4E791, 614–6870.
Assistant General Counsel for—
Ethics.—Joel Weger (acting), room 4D641, 614–7425.
Manpower and Reserve Affairs.—R. Woods, room 4D548, 614–1377.
Research, Development and Acquisition.—Tom Frankfurt, room 4C682, 614–6985.
Military Assistant.—Lt. Col. Stephen Stewartl, USMC, room 4E782, 692–6164.
Administrative Assistant.—LT John Erickson, USN, room 4E782, 693–7813.

NAVAL INSPECTOR GENERAL

Washington Navy Yard, 1254 9th Street, SE., Building 172, 20374, phone (202) 433–2000

Inspector General.—VADM James P. Wisecup.
Deputy Naval Inspector General.—Andrea Brotherton.

U.S. NAVY OFFICE OF INFORMATION

1200 Navy Pentagon, Room 4B463, Phone (703) 697–7391

Duty (703) 850–1047

Chief of Information (CI).—RDML John F. Kirby.
Vice Chief of Information (VCI).—RDML Vic M. Beck.
Deputy, Chief of Information (DCI).—CAPT Dawn E. Cutler.
Executive Assistant to Chief of Information (EA).—CDR Tamara D. Lawrence.
Flag Aide to Chief of Information.—LT Rebecca Rebarich.

Senior Enlisted Advisor (SEA).—MCPO Jon McMillan.
Staff Senior Enlisted Leader (SEL).—CPO Cody Harmon.
Flag Writer-PO1.—Juan P. Cisneros.
Assistant Chief for—
Administration and Resource Management (OI–1).—William Mason, 692–4747.
Afloat Media Systems (OI–7).—Janet Quigley (202) 781–3313.
Communication Integration and Strategy (OI–9).—CDR Elissa Smith, 692–4728.
Community Outreach (OI–6).—Rob Newell, 614–1879.
Defense Media Activity (DMA) Liaison (OI–4).—LCDR David Luckett (301) 222–6401.
Media Operations (OI–3).—CDR Ryan Perry, 697–5342.
Navy Media Content Services (OI–2).—Chris Madden, 614–9154.
Requirements and Policy (OI–8).—Bruce Cole, 695–0911.

JUDGE ADVOCATE GENERAL

Pentagon, Room 4C 642

Washington Navy Yard, 1322 Patterson Avenue, Suite 3000, 20374–5066

phone (703) 614–7420, fax (703) 697–4610

Judge Advocate General.—VADM Nanette M. DeRenzi.
Executive Assistant.—CAPT David Grogan.
Deputy Judge Advocate General.—RADM James W. Crawford III.
Executive Assistant to the Deputy Judge Advocate General.—CDR Laurin Eskridge.
Assistant Judge Advocate General for Civil Law.—CAPT Kirk R. Foster, Pentagon, room 4D640, 614–7415, fax 614–9400.
Deputy Assistant Judge Advocate General for—
Administrative Law.—CAPT Scott Thompson, 614–7415.
Admiralty.—CAPT Anne B. Fischer (202) 685–5075.
Claims, Investigations and Tort Litigation.—Patricia A. Leonard (202) 685–4600, fax 685–5484.
General Litigation.—Grant Lattin (202) 685–5450, fax 685–5472.
International and Operational Law.—CAPT Stuart W. Belt, 697–5406.
Legal Assistance.—CDR Andrew R. House (202) 685–4642, fax 685–5486.
National Security Litigation and Intelligence Law.—CDR Andrew Levitz (202) 685–5464, fax 685–5467.
Assistant Judge Advocate General for Military Justice.—COL John Ewers, USMC, Building 58, 3rd Floor, Washington Navy Yard, 20374–1111 (202) 685–7053, fax 685–7084.
Deputy Assistant Judge Advocate General for Criminal Law.—CAPT Robert J. Crow, USN (202) 685–7056, fax 685–7687.
Assistant Judge Advocate General for Operations and Management.—CAPT John Hannink (202) 685–5190, fax 685–8510.
Deputy Assistant Judge Advocate General for—
Military Personnel.—CAPT Mark F. Klein (202) 685–7254, fax 685–5489.
Reserve and Retired Personnel Programs.—LCDR Kathleen A. Elkins (202) 685–5397, fax 685–8510.
Technology, Operations and Plans.—CDR Melissa Powers (202) 685–5230, fax 685–5479.
Special Assistants to the Judge Advocate General—
Command Master Chief.—LNCM Paul C. St. Sauver (202) 685–5194, fax 685–8510.
Comptroller.—Dawn C. Rooney (202) 685–5274, fax 685–5455.
Inspector General.—Vacant (202) 685–5192, fax 685–5461.

LEGISLATIVE AFFAIRS

Room 4C549, phone (703) 697–7146, fax 697–1009

Chief.—RADM Michael T. Franken.
Deputy Chief.—CAPT Mark Davis.
Executive Assistant.—LCDR Micah Murphy.
Congressional Information and Public Affairs.—CDR Gary Ross, 695–0395.
Congressional Operations.—Dee Wingfield, 693–5764.
Director for—
House Liaison.—CAPT Paul Gronemeyer (202) 225–7808.
Assistant House Liaison.—LCDR Jason Grizzle (202) 225–3075.
Legislation.—CDR Dom Flatt, 697–2851.

Naval Programs.—Tom Crowley, 693–2919.
Senate Liaison.—CAPT James Loeblein (202) 685–6006.
Assistant Senate Liaison.—CDR Mike Vitali (202) 685–6007.

ASSISTANT SECRETARY FOR FINANCIAL MANAGEMENT AND COMPTROLLER

Pentagon, Room 4E618, phone (703) 697–2325

Executive Assistant and Naval Aide.—CAPT Daniel H. Fillion, USN.
Military Assistant and Marine Aide.—MAJ Edna Rodriguez, USMC.
Director, Office of:
Budget.—RADM Joseph R. Mulloy, USN, room 4E348, 697–7105.
Financial Operations.—D. Taitano, WNY (202) 685–6701.

ASSISTANT SECRETARY FOR ENERGY, INSTALLATIONS AND ENVIRONMENT

Pentagon, Room 4E739, phone (703) 693–4530

Assistant Secretary.—Vacant.
Executive Assistant and Naval Aide.—CAPT Yancy Lindsey.
Confidential Assistant.—Sgt Karl Strong.
Military Aide.—LCDR Ben Wainwright.
Principal Deputy for Energy, Installations and Environment.—Roger Natsuhara, room 4E739, 693–4530.
Assistant General Counsel.—Craig Jensen, 614–1098.
Deputy of:
Energy.—Tom Hicks (571) 256–7879.
Environment.—D. Schregardus, 614–5493.
Safety.—Paul Hanley, 614–5516.

ASSISTANT SECRETARY FOR MANPOWER AND RESERVE AFFAIRS

Pentagon, Room 4E598, phone (703) 695–4333

Assistant Secretary.—Hon. Juan M. Garcia, room 4E598, 695–4333.
Principal Deputy.—Robert Cali, room 4E598, 692–6162.
Executive Assistant and Naval Aide.—CAPT Michael Selby, room 4E598, 695–4537.
Military Assistant and Marine Aide.—COL Samuel Mowery, room 4E598, 697–0975.
Secretary.—Antonio Sturgis, room 4E598, 695–4333.
Administrative Officer.—Michael Stokes, room 4E590, 697–2179.
Administrative Chief.—YNC Tyrone Pierce, room 4E590, 695–6472.
Administrative Assistant.—Sgt Peter Barko, room 4E590, 614–4439.
Deputy Assistant Secretary of:
Civilian Human Resources.—Patricia C. Adams, room 4D548, 695–2633.
Manpower Personnel Policy.—Dr. Russell W. Beland, room 4D548, 693–1213.
Reserve Affairs.—Dennis Biddick, room 4D548, 614–1327.

SECRETARY OF THE NAVY COUNCIL OF REVIEW BOARDS

Washington Navy Yard, 720 Kennon Street, SE., Room 309, 20374–5023

phone (202) 685–6408, fax 685–6610

Director.—Jeffrey Riehl.
Counsel.—Roger R. Claussen.
Office Administrator.—Reginald B. Clark.
Physical Evaluation Board.—Robert Powers.
Naval Clemency and Parole Board.—Randall Lamoureux.
Naval Discharge Review Board.—John D. Reeser.
Combat-Related Special Compensation Board.—Leif Larsen.
Board of Decorations and Medals.—James Nierle.

ASSISTANT SECRETARY FOR RESEARCH, DEVELOPMENT AND ACQUISITION

Pentagon, Room 4E665, phone (703) 695–6315

Assistant Secretary.—Hon. Sean J. Stackley.

Special Assistant.—Candy R. Hearn.
Executive Assistant and Naval Aide.—CAPT Brian Eckerle, USN.
Military Assistant and Marine Aide.—LT COL Eldon Metzger, USMC.
Principal Military Deputy.—VADM Paul Grosklags, USN.
Executive Assistant and Naval Aide.—CAPT Todd Siddall, USN.
Principal Civilian Deputy.—James Thomsen, 614–6430.
Executive Assistant and Naval Aide.—CDR Dave Norley, USN.
Deputy Assistant Secretary of the Navy for—
Acquisition and Logistics Management.—Elliott Branch, BF992, 614–9445.
Air Programs.—Richard Gilpin, room 4C712, 614–7794.
C4I and Space Programs.—Dr. John Zangardi, room BF963, 914–6589.
Expeditionary Warfare Programs.—Tom Dee, room 4C712, 614–4794.
International Programs.—RDML Jim Shannon, WNY (202) 433–5900.
Management and Budget.—BJ White-Olson, room 4C656, 695–6370.
Ship Programs.—Allison Stiller, room 4C712, 697–1710.

DEPARTMENT OF THE NAVY CHIEF INFORMATION OFFICER

Chief Information Officer.—Terry A. Halvorsen, Pentagon, room 4A268 (703) 695–1840.

CHIEF OF NAVAL OPERATIONS

Pentagon, Room 4E662, phone (703) 695–5664, fax 693–9408

Chief of Naval Operations.—ADM Jonathan Greenert.
Vice Chief of Naval Operations.—ADM Mark Ferguson.
Judge Advocate General of the Navy.—VADM Nanette DeRenzi.
Director:
Naval Criminal Investigative Service.—Mark Ridley (acting).
Naval Intelligence.—VADM Kendall Card.
Naval Nuclear Propulsion Program.—ADM John Richardson.
Navy Staff.—VADM Richard Hunt.
Chief of:
Chaplains.—RADM Mark Tidd.
Information.—RDML John Kirby.
Legislative Affairs.—RADM Michael Franken.
Navy Reserve.—VADM Robin Braun.
Surgeon General of the Navy.—VADM Matthew Nathan.
Oceanographer of the Navy.—RADM Jonathan White.
Master Chief Petty Officer of the Navy.—MCPON Michael Stevens.
President, Board of Inspection and Survey.—RADM Robert Wray.
Commander, Naval Education and Training.—RADM Donald Quinn.
Commander, Naval Safety Center.—RDML Kenneth Norton.
Deputy Chief of Naval Operations for—
Fleet Readiness and Logistics.—VADM Philip Cullom.
Integration of Capabilities and Resources.—VADM Allen Myers IV.
Manpower, Personnel, Training, and Education.—VADM Scott Van Buskirk.
Operations, Plans, and Strategy.—VADM Mark Fox.
Warfare Systems.—VADM Joseph Aucoin.

BUREAU OF MEDICINE AND SURGERY

7700 Arlington Boulevard, Suite 5113, Arlington, VA 22042–5113

phone (703) 681–5200, fax 681–9527

Chief.—VADM Matthew L. Nathan, MC, USN.

MILITARY SEALIFT COMMAND

914 Charles Morris Court, SE., Washington Navy Yard, 20398–5540

phone (202) 685–5001, fax 685–5020

Commander.-RADM Thomas K. Shannon.

WALTER REED NATIONAL MILITARY MEDICAL CENTER

8901 Wisconsin Avenue, Bethesda, MD 20889–5600, phone (301) 295–5800/5802, fax 295–5336.

Commander.—RADM Alton L. Stocks, MC, USN.

NAVAL AIR SYSTEMS COMMAND

47123 Buse Road, Building 2272, Patuxent River, MD 20670
phone (301) 757–7825

Commander.—VADM David A. Dunaway.

NAVAL CRIMINAL INVESTIGATIVE SERVICE HEADQUARTERS

27130 Telegraph Road, Quantico, VA 22134, phone (571) 305–9000

Director.—Mark D. Ridley (acting).

NAVAL DISTRICT OF WASHINGTON

1343 Dahlgren Avenue, SE., 20374–5001, phone (202) 433–2777, fax 433–2207

Commandant.—RDML Markham K. Rich.
Chief of Staff.—CAPT Richard W. Kitchens.

NAVAL FACILITIES ENGINEERING COMMAND

1322 Patterson Avenue, SE., Washington Navy Yard, 20374–5065
phone (202) 685–9499, fax 685–1463

Commander.—RADM Katherine L. Gregory, CEC, USN.

OFFICE OF NAVAL INTELLIGENCE

4251 Suitland Road, 20395, phone (301) 669–3001, fax 669–3509

Commander.—RADM Samuel Cox.

NAVAL SEA SYSTEMS COMMAND

Washington Navy Yard, 1333 Isaac Hull Avenue, SE., Stop 1010, 20376–1010
phone (202) 781–0100

Commander.—VADM William H. Hilarides.

NAVAL SUPPLY SYSTEMS COMMAND

Mechanicsburg, PA, phone (717) 605–3433

Commander.—RADM Jon Yuen.

SPACE AND NAVAL WARFARE SYSTEMS COMMAND SPACE FIELD ACTIVITY

14675 Lee Road, Chantilly, VA 20151
phone (703) 808–6104, fax (703) 808–8504

Commander.—CAPT Mark Rudesill.

U.S. NAVAL ACADEMY

Annapolis, MD 21402, phone (410) 293–1000

Superintendent.—VADM Michael H. Miller, USN, 293–1500.

U.S. MARINE CORPS HEADQUARTERS

Pentagon, Room 4E734, phone (703) 614–2500

Commandant.—Gen. J.F. Amos.
Assistant Commandant.—Gen. J.M. Paxton, 614–1201.
Aide-de-Camp.—Lt. Col. D.W. Hudspeth.
Chaplain.—RADM M.G. Kibben, 614–4627.
Dental Officer.—CAPT J.L. Haun.
Fiscal Director of the Marine Corps.—SES A.C. McDermott.
Inspector General of the Marine Corps.—Vacant, 614–1533.
Judge Advocate.—Maj. Gen. V.A. Ary, 614–8661.
Legislative Assistant.—Brig. Gen. D.J. Furness, 614–1686.
Medical Officer.—RADM M. Anderson.
Military Secretary.—Col. R.B. Turner.
Sergeant Major of the Marine Corps.—Sgt. Maj. M.P. Barrett, 614–8762.
Deputy Commandant of Marine Corps for—
Aviation.—Lt. Gen. R.E. Schmidle, 614–1010.
Installations and Logistics.—Lt. Gen. W.M. Faulkner, 695–8572.
Manpower and Reserve Affairs.—Lt. Gen. R.E. Milstead, 695–1929.
Plans, Policies, and Operations.—Lt. Gen. R.L. Bailey, 614–8521.
Programs and Resources.—Lt. Gen. G.M. Walters, 614–3435.
Public Affairs.—Col. T.V. Williams, 614–8010.
Director of:
Intelligence.—Col. M.S. Groen.
Marine Corps History and Museums.—Dr. C.P. Neimeyer.

MARINE BARRACKS

Eighth and I Streets, SE., 20390, phone (202) 433–4094

Commanding Officer.—Col. C.G. Cabaniss.

TRAINING AND EDUCATION COMMAND

3300 Russell Road, Quantico, VA 22134, phone (703) 784–3730, fax 784–3724

Commanding General.—Maj. Gen. T.M. Murray.

DEPARTMENT OF JUSTICE

Robert F. Kennedy Department of Justice Building

950 Pennsylvania Avenue, NW., 20530, phone (202) 514–2000

http://www.usdoj.gov

ERIC H. HOLDER, JR., Attorney General; born in New York City, NY, education: Columbia College, 1973; Columbia Law School, 1976; professional: Department of Justice Criminal Division, 1976–88; Associate Judge of the Superior Court of the District of Columbia, 1988–93; United States Attorney for the District of Columbia, 1993–97; Deputy Attorney General, 1997–2001; partner with law firm of Covington & Burling L.L.P., 2001–09; nominated by President Barack Obama to become the Attorney General of the United States on December 1, 2008 and was confirmed by the U.S. Senate on February 2, 2009.

OFFICE OF THE ATTORNEY GENERAL

RFK Main Justice Building, Room 5111, phone (202) 514–2001

Attorney General.—Eric H. Holder, Jr.

Chief of Staff and Counselor to the Attorney General.—Margaret Richardson, room 5115, 514–3892.

Counselors to the Attorney General: Denise Cheung, room 5116, 305–7378; Molly Moran, room 5119, 305–8674; Channing Phillips, room 5224, 514–4969; Karl Thompson, room 5110, 514–9798.

Counsel to the Attorney General.—Jenny Mosier, room 5112, 514–9797.

White House Liaison.—Sharon Werner, room 5214, 616–2372.

Director of Advance.—Vacant, room 5131, 514–6333.

Director of Scheduling.—Theresa Watson (acting), room 5127, 514–4195.

Confidential Assistant.—Annie Bradley, room 5111, 514–2001.

OFFICE OF THE DEPUTY ATTORNEY GENERAL

RFK Main Justice Building, Room 4111, phone (202) 514–2101

Deputy Attorney General.—James M. Cole, room 4111.

Principal Associate Deputy Attorney General.—Stuart M. Goldberg, room 4208, 514–2105.

Chief of Staff and Associate Deputy Attorney General.—David A. O'Neil, room 4210, 514–3712.

Associate Deputy Attorneys General: Matthew S. Axelrod, room 4217, 305–0273; Charlotte A. Burrows, room 4129, 514–6753; Matthew P. Cohen, room 4216, 305–4127; Robin E. Jacobsohn, room 4214, 307–1045; Iris Lan, room 4311, 514–6907; David Margolis, room 4113, 514–4945.

Associate Deputy Attorney General and Director, OCDETF.—James H. Dinan, room 4115, 514–0049.

Senior Counsels to the Deputy Attorney General: Armando O. Bonilla, room 4313, 616–1621; Trisha Anderson, room 4220, 353–3030; Chrystal L. Brown, room 4216, 514–7473; Eric R. Columbus, room 4131, 307–2510; Miriam Vogel, room 4215, 514–7473.

Counsels to the Deputy Attorney General: Heather G. Childs, room 4114, 514–8699; Kiran Raj, room 4315, 305–9886.

Emergency Preparedness and Crisis Response Coordinator.—Mark E. Michalic, room 4112, 514–0438.

Confidential Assistant to the Deputy Attorney General.—Melanie L. Dix, room 4111, 514–1904.

Chief Privacy and Civil Liberties Officer.—Vacant, room 4222, 307–0697.

Executive Director, Financial Fraud Enforcement Task Forces.—Michael J. Bresnick, room 4114, 514–4680.

National Coordinator for Child Exploitation Prevention and Interdiction.—Anne C. Gannon, room 4317, 514–9340.

Counsel for Rule of Law-Afghanistan.—Brian Tomney, room 4413, 305–8657.

OFFICE OF THE ASSOCIATE ATTORNEY GENERAL

RFK Main Justice Building, Room 5706, phone (202) 514–9500

Associate Attorney General.—Derek "Tony" West (acting).

Principal Deputy Associate Attorney General.—Elizabeth G. Taylor.

Deputy Associate Attorneys General: A. Marisa Chun, room 5724, 305–1777; Helaine Greenfeld, room 5722, 616–0038; Samuel Hirsch, room 5732, 616–2728; Julie McEvoy, room 5726, 514–0624.

Chief of Staff to the Acting Associate Attorney General.—Brian Martinez, room 5722, 616–0038.

Counsels to the Associate Attorney General: Mala Adiga, 307–5803; Varu Chilakammari, room 5730, 353–2811.

Special Assistant to the Acting Associate Attorney General.—Cindy Chang, room 5738, 532–6866.

Confidential Assistant.—Currie Gunn, room 5708, 305–2636.

Staff Assistant.—Nathaniel Gamble, room 5706, 514–5732.

OFFICE OF THE SOLICITOR GENERAL

RFK Main Justice Building, Room 5143, phone (202) 514–2201

http://www.usdoj.gov/osg

Solicitor General.—Donald B. Virrelli, Jr., room 5143, 514–2201.

Principal Deputy Solicitor General.—Sri Srinivasan, room 5143, 514–4038.

Executive Officer.—Valerie H. Yancey, room 5142, 514–3957.

Supervisory Case Management Specialist.—Vacant, room 5608, 514–2218.

Chief, Research and Publications Section.—Mary Cornaby, room 6634, 514–4459.

ANTITRUST DIVISION

RFK Main Justice Building, 950 Pennsylvania Avenue, NW., 20530

Liberty Square Building, 450 5th Street, NW., 20530 (LSB)

Assistant Attorney General.—William J. Baer, room 3109 (202) 514–2401.

Deputy Assistant Attorneys General: Scott M. Hammond, room 3214, 514–3543; Renata B. Hesse, room 3214, 353–1535; Aviv Nevo, room 3121, 353–0163; Leslie C. Overton, room 3210, 353–4651.

Director of:

Civil Enforcement.—Patricia A. Brink, room 3213, 514–2562.

Criminal Enforcement.—Marvin N. Price, Jr., room 3214, 307–0719.

Economics Enforcement.—W. Robert Majure, room 3416.

Freedom of Information Act Officer.—SueAnn Slates (LSB), room 1040, 307–1398.

Executive Officer.—Thomas D. King (LSB), room 10150, 514–4005.

Section Chiefs:

Appellate.—Catherine G. O'Sullivan, room 3222, 514–2413.

Competition Policy.—W. Robert Majure, room 3416, 9400, 307–6341.

Economic Litigation.—Norman Familant (LSB), room 9912, 307–6323.

Economic Regulatory.—Beth Armington (LSB), room 3700, 307–6332.

Foreign Commerce.—Edward T. Hand (LSB), room 11000, 514–2464.

Legal Policy.—Robert A. Potter (LSB), room 11700, 514–2512.

Litigation I.—Peter J. Mucchetti (LSB), room 4700, 307–0001.

Litigation II.—Maribeth Petrizzi (LSB), room 8700, 307–0924.

Litigation III.—John R. Read (LPB), room 300, 616–5935.

National Criminal Enforcement.—Lisa M. Phelan (LSB), room 11400, 307–6694.

Networks and Technology.—James Tierney (LSB), room 7700, 307–6640.

Telecommunications and Media.—Scott A. Scheele (LSB), room 7000, 307–6132.

Transportation, Energy, and Agriculture.—William H. Stallings (LSB), room 8000, 514–0323.

FIELD OFFICES

California: Phillip H. Warren, 450 Golden Gate Avenue, Room 10–0101, Box 36046, San Francisco, CA 94102 (415) 436–6660.

Illinois: Frank J. Vondrak (acting), Rookery Building, 209 South LaSalle Street, Suite 600, Chicago, IL 60604 (312) 353–7530.

New York: Deirdre A. McEvoy, 26 Federal Plaza, Room 3630, New York, NY 10278–1040 (212) 264–0391.

CIVIL DIVISION

RFK Main Justice Building, 950 Pennsylvania Avenue, NW., 20530

20 Massachusetts Avenue, NW., 20530 (20MASS)

1100 L Street, NW., 20530 (L ST)

National Place Building, 1331 Pennsylvania Avenue, NW., 20530 (NPB)

1425 New York Avenue, NW., 20530 (NYA)

Patrick Henry Building, 601 D Street, NW., 20530 (PHB)

Liberty Square Building, 450 5th Street, NW., 20530

Assistant Attorney General.—Stuart F. Delery (acting), room 3601, (202) 514–3301.
Associate Attorney General.—Tony West (acting), room 5714, 514–9500.
Chief of Staff.—Brian Martinez, room 5722, 616–0038.

APPELLATE STAFF

Deputy Assistant Attorney General.—Beth Brinkmann, room 3135, 353–8679.
Director.—Douglas Letter, room 7519, 514–3602.
Deputy Director.—Barbara Biddle, room 7517, 514–2541.

COMMERCIAL LITIGATION BRANCH

Deputy Assistant Attorney General.—Joyce Branda, room 3607, 307–0231.
Directors: David M. Cohen (L ST), room 12124, 514–7300; John N. Fargo (L ST), room 11116, 514–7223; J. Christopher Kohn (L ST), room 10036, 514–7450.
Office of Foreign Litigation.—Robert Hollis (L ST), room 11006, 514–7455.
Deputy Directors: Jeanne Davidson (L ST), room 12132, 307–0290; Michael Granston (PHB), room 9902, 305–0632.
Legal Officer.—Donna C. Maizel, Esq., U.S. Department of Justice, Civil Division European Office, The American Embassy, London, England, PSC 801, Box 42, FPO AE, 09498–4042, 9+011–44–20–7894–0840.
Attorney-in-Charge.—Barbara Williams, Suite 359, 26 Federal Plaza, New York, NY 10278 (212) 264–9240.

CONSUMER LITIGATION

Deputy Assistant Attorney General.—Maame Ewusi-Mensah Frimpong, room 3129, 307–6482.
Director.—Michael S. Blume (LSB), room 6254, 307–3009.

FEDERAL PROGRAMS BRANCH

Deputy Assistant Attorney General.—Ian Gershengorn, room 3137, 514–2331.
Directors: Felix Baxter (20MASS), room 7100, 514–4651; Joseph H. Hunt, room 7348, 514–1259; Jennifer D. Richetts (20MASS), room 6100, 514–3671.
Deputy Directors: Tony Coppolino (20MASS), room 6102, 514–4782; Sheila M. Lieber (20MASS), room 7102, 514–3786.

IMMIGRATION LITIGATION

Deputy Assistant Attorney General.—August Flentje (acting), room 3613, 514–3309.
Director.—Thomas W. Hussey (NPB), room 7026S, 616–4852.
Deputy Directors: Donald E. Keener (NPB), room 7022S, 616–4878; David J. Kline (NPB), room 7006N, 616–4856; David M. McConnell (NPB), room 7260N, 616–4881.

MANAGEMENT PROGRAMS

Director.—Kenneth L. Zwick, room 3140, 514–4552.
Directors, Office of:
Administration.—Donna Cornett (L ST), room 9018, 307–0261.
Planning, Budget, and Evaluation.—Linda S. Liner (L ST), room 9042, 307–0034.
Management Information.—Dorothy Bahr (L ST), room 8044, 616–8026.
Litigation Support.—Vacant (L ST), room 9126, 616–5014.

Policy and Management Operations.—Vacant (L ST), room 8128, 616–8073.

TORTS BRANCH

Deputy Assistant Attorney General.—Brian Hauck, room 3611, 616–4171.
Directors: Rupa Bhattacharyya (NYA), room 8122, 305–0008; J. Patrick Glynn (NPB), room 8028S, 616–4200; James Touhey (NPB), room 8064N, 616–4292.
Deputy Directors: JoAnn J. Bordeaux (NPB), room 8024S, 616–4204; Paul F. Figley (NPB), room 8096N, 616–4248.
Attorneys-in-Charge: Robert Underhill, 450 Golden Gate Avenue, 10/6610, Box 36028, San Francisco, CA 94102–3463, FTS: (415) 436–6630; Vacant, Suite 320, 26 Federal Plaza, New York, NY 10278–0140, FTS: (212) 264–0480.

CIVIL RIGHTS DIVISION

RFK Main Justice Building, 950 Pennsylvania Avenue, NW., 20530

1425 New York Avenue, NW., 20035 (NYAV)

601 D Street, NW., 20004 (PHB)

100 Indiana Avenue, NW., 20004 (NALC)

1800 G Street, NW., 20004 (NWB)

http://www.usdoj.gov/crt

Assistant Attorney General.—Thomas Perez, room 5643 (202) 514–2151.
Principal Deputy Assistant Attorney General.—Jocelyn Samuels, room 5748, 307–6639.
Deputy Assistant Attorneys General: Roy Austin, room 5531, 514–3845; Matthew Colangelo, room 5637, 514–5441; Greg Friel, room 5744, 353–9418.
Counsels to the Assistant Attorney General: Eric Halperin, room 5529, 307–3033; Emily Loeb, room 5646, 307–2502; Eve Hill, room 5646, 353–9390; Becky Monroe, room 5535, 305–0864.
Chief of Staff.—Vacant.
Section Chiefs:
Appellate.—David K. Flynn, room 3704, 514–2195.
Criminal.—Robert Moossy (PHB), room 5102, 514–3204.
Disability Rights.—Rebecca Bond (NYAV), room 4055, 307–2227.
Educational Opportunities.—Anurima Bhargava (PHB), room 4002, 514–4092.
Employment Litigation.—Delora Kenebrew (PHB), room 4040, 514–3831.
Housing and Civil Enforcement.—Steven Rosenbaum (NWB), room 7036, 514–4713.
Policy and Strategy Section.—Aaron Schuham (PHB), room 5006, 305–4151.
Special Litigation.—Jonathan Smith (PHB), room 5034, 514–5393.
Voting.—Chris Herren (NWB), room 7254, 307–2767.
Office Special Counsel.—Seema Nanda (acting), room 9030, 616–5594.

OFFICE OF COMMUNITY ORIENTED POLICING SERVICES

145 N Street, NE., 20530

DIRECTOR'S OFFICE

Director.—Joshua Ederheimer (acting), 11th floor (202) 514–9079.
Chief of Staff.—Rebekah Whiteaker.
Deputy Director for Management.—Wayne Henry (acting).

EXTERNAL AFFAIRS DIVISION

Assistant Director.—Dean Kueter, 11th floor, 514–9079.

COMMUNITY RELATIONS SERVICE

600 E Street, NW., Suite 6000, 20530, phone (202) 305–2935
fax 305–3009 (BICN)

Director.—Grande Lum.

Deputy Director.—Gilbert Moore.
Attorney Advisor.—George Henderson.
Media Affairs Officer.—Vacant.

REGIONAL DIRECTORS

New England.—Francis Amoroso, 408 Atlantic Avenue, Suite 222, Boston, MA 02110–1032 (617) 424–5715.

Northeast Region.—Reinaldo Rivera, 26 Federal Plaza, Suite 36–118, New York, NY 10278 (212) 264–0700.

Mid-Atlantic Region.—Harpreet Singh Mokha, Customs House, Second and Chestnut Streets, Suite 208, Philadelphia, PA 19106 (215) 597–2344.

Southeast Region.—Thomas Battles, 61 Forsyth Street, SW., Suite 7B65, Atlanta, GA 30303 (404) 331–6883.

Midwest Region.—Mary Gorecki, 230 South Dearborn Street, Suite 2130, Chicago, IL 60604 (312) 353–4391.

Southwest Region.—Vacant, Hardwood Center, 1999 Bryan Street, Suite 2050, Dallas, TX 75201 (214) 655–8175.

Central Region.—Pascual Marquez, 601 East 12th Street, Suite 0802, Kansas City, MO 64106 (816) 426–7434.

Rocky Mountain Region.—Vacant, 1244 Speer Boulevard, Suite 650, Denver, CO 80204–3584 (303) 844–2973.

Western Region.—Ronald Wakabayashi, 888 South Figueroa Street, Suite 2010, Los Angeles, CA 90017 (213) 894–2941.

Northwest Region.—Rosa Melendez, Federal Office Building, 915 Second Avenue, Suite 1808, Seattle, WA 98174 (206) 220–6700.

CRIMINAL DIVISION

RFK Main Justice Building, 950 Pennsylvania Avenue, NW., 20530

phone (202) 514–2601

Bond Building, 1400 New York Avenue, NW., 20005 (Bond)

1331 F Street, NW., 20004 (F Street)

John C. Keeney Building, 1301 New York Avenue, NW., 20530 (1301 NY)

Patrick Henry Building, 601 D Street, NW., 20530 (PHB)

2CON Building, 2 Constitution Square, 145 N Street NE., 20530 (2Con)

Assistant Attorney General.—Mythili Raman (acting), room 2107, 514–7200.

Chief of Staff and Principal Deputy Assistant Attorney General.—John D. Buretta, room 2206, 514–2601.

Deputy Assistant Attorneys General: David Bitkower, room 2113, 353–0182; Kenneth A. Blanco, room 2121, 514–3027; Paul O'Brien, room 2115, 514–0169; Denis McInerney, room 2212, 514–0762; Bruce C. Swartz, room 2119, 514–2333.

Deputy Chief of Staff.—Daniel Suleiman, room 2208, 514–9724.

Counselor to the Assistant Attorney General.—Jonathan Wroblewski, room 2218, 514–4730.

Senior Counsels to the Assistant Attorney General: Daniel Lenerz, room 2220, 532–6045; Vijay Shanker, room 2222, 353–0268.

Counselor for Transnational Organized Crime and International Affairs.—Bruce Ohr, room 2214, 514–3595.

Executive Officer.—Karl Maschino (Bond), room 5100, 514–2641.

Section Chiefs / Office Directors:

Appellate.—Patty M. Stemler, room 1264, 514–2611.

Asset Forfeiture and Money Laundering.—Jaikumar Ramaswamy (Bond), suite 10100, 514–1263.

Capital Case Unit.—Kevin Carwile (1301 NY), room 6140, 353–7172.

Child Exploitation and Obscenity.—Andrew G. Oosterbaan (Bond), suite 6000, 514–5780.

Computer Crime and Intellectual Property.—John Lynch (1301 NY), suite 600, 305–8732.

Enforcement Operations.—Monique Roth (1301 NY), suite 1200, 353–6200.

Fraud.—Jeffrey Knox (Bond), room 4100, 616–2634.

Human Rights and Special Prosecution.—Teresa McHenry (1301 NY), room 112, 616–5731.

International Affairs.—Mary Ellen Warlow (1301 NY), suite 900, 514–0000.

International Criminal Investigative Training Assistant Program.—Carr Trevillian IV (F Street), suite 500, 305–8190.
Narcotics and Dangerous Drugs.—Arthur Wyatt (Bond), room 11100, 514–0917.
Organized Crime and Gangs.—James Trusty (1301 NY), suite 700, 307–0207.
Overseas Prosecutorial Development, Assistance and Training.—Faye Ehrenstamm (F Street), room 400, 514–1323.
Policy and Legislation.—Jonathan Wroblewski, room 7730, 514–4194.
Public Integrity.—Jack Smith (Bond), suite 12100, 514–1412.

OFFICE OF DISPUTE RESOLUTION

RFK Main Justice Building, Room 4531, phone (202) 616–9471 / 616–9472

http://www.usdoj.gov/odr

Director and Senior Counsel.—Joanna M. Jacobs, room 4529, 305–4439.

DRUG ENFORCEMENT ADMINISTRATION

Lincoln Place-1 (East), 600 Army-Navy Drive, Arlington, VA 22202 (LP–1)

Lincoln Place-2 (West), 700 Army-Navy Drive, Arlington, VA 22202 (LP–2)

Administrator.—Michele M. Leonhart, room W–12060 (202) 307–8000.
Chief of Staff.—Vacant, room 12060, 307–8003.
Deputy Administrator.—Thomas M. Harrigan, room W–12058–F, 307–7345.
Equal Employment Opportunity Officer.—Oliver C. Allen, room E–11275, 307–8888.
Executive Assistants: Alan Bassham, room W–12058–C, 307–8246; Susan Nave, room W–12060–E, 353–1250.
Chief, Congressional and Public Affairs.—Vacant, room W–12228, 307–7363.
Chief, Executive Policy and Strategic Planning.—Vacant, room W–11100, 307–7420.
Section Chiefs:
Communications Section.—Vacant, room W–12232, 307–7967.
Congressional Affairs.—Eric Akers (acting), room W–12104, 307–7988.
Demand Reduction.—Eric Akers, room W–9049–E, 307–7988.
Public Affairs.—Dawn Dearden, 307–2402.
Chief Counsel.—Wendy H. Goggin, room W–12142–C, 307–7322.
Deputy Chief Counsel.—Robert C. Gleason, room E–12375, 307–8020.
Chief, Office of Administrative Law Judges.—John Mulrooney, 307–8188.

FINANCIAL MANAGEMENT DIVISION

Chief Financial Officer.—Frank M. Kalder, room W–12138, 307–7330.
Deputy Assistant Administrators for—
Acquisition Management.—Christinia K. Sisk, room W–5100, 307–7888.
Finance.—Daniel Gillette, room E–7397, 307–7002.
Resource Management.—Brian Horn, room E–5102, 307–4800.
Section Chiefs:
Acquisition Management.—Nancy Costello, room E–8281, 307–5364.
Controls and Coordination.—Brian Parks, room E–5384, 307–5276.
Financial Integrity.—Bradley J. Honkus, room E–7331, 307–7082.
Financial Operations.—Tammy Balas, room E–7165, 307–9933.
Financial Reports.—Sherri Woodle, room E–7297, 307–7040.
Financial Systems.—Renaldo Prillman, room E–8001, 307–7043.
Organization and Staffing Management.—Susan Mosser, room E–5284, 307–5052.
Policy and Transportation.—Vacant, room W–5018, 307–7808.
Program Liaison and Analysis.—James Evans, room E–5104, 353–9545.
Statistical Services.—Gamaliel Rose, room E–5332, 307–8276.

HUMAN RESOURCES DIVISION

Assistant Administrator.—Raymond Pagliarini, room W–12020, 307–4195.
Section Chiefs:
Administrative Management.—Glenda A. Rollins, room W–6108, 307–4701.
Recruitment and Placement.—Joyce Thomas, room W–3262, 307–4097.

Career Board Executive Secretary.—Bruce Travers, room W–2270, 307–7349.
Chairman, Board of Professional Conduct.—David Aldridge, room E–9333, 307–7875.
Special Agent-in-Charge, Office of Training.—James R. Gregorius, 2500 Investigation Parkway, DEA Academy, Quantico, VA 22135 (703) 632–5010.
Assistant Special Agents-in-Charge:
Domestic Training Section 1.—David Zon (703) 632–5110.
Domestic Training Section 2.—Michael Blackwood (703) 632–5310.
International Training Section.—James T. Farnsworth (703) 632–5330.

INSPECTIONS DIVISION

Chief Inspector.—James Kasson, room W–12042A, 307–7358.
Deputy Chief Inspector, Office of:
Inspections.—Kevin M. Foley, room W–4348, 307–4866.
Professional Responsibility.—K. Scott McRory (acting), room W–4176, 307–8235.
Security Programs.—Mark Mazzei (acting), room W–2340, 307–3465.

INTELLIGENCE DIVISION

Assistant Administrator.—Rodney Benson, room W–12036, 307–3607.
Director/Special Agent in Charge, El Paso Intelligence Center.—Tim Jennings, Building 11339, SSG Sims Street, El Paso, TX 79908–8098 (915) 760–2011.
Deputy Assistant Administrator, Office of Intelligence.—Douglas Poole, room W–12020C, 307–3607.
Executive Assistants: Marilyn Wankel, Greg Cherundolo, 307–3607.
Deputy Assistant Administrator, Office of:
Fusion Center.—Stephen E. Murphy (703) 561–7117.
National Security Intelligence.—W. Bond Wells, 307–7923.
Special Intelligence.—Arthur Doty, Merrifield, VA, 561–7111.
Section Chiefs:
Data Management.—Cheryl Hooper (703) 561–7671.
Indications/Warnings.—Benjamin C. Sanborn, 307–4358.
Intelligence Section.—Lourdes Border, 307–9284.
Investigative Support.—Thomas E. Neal (703) 488–4246.
Management and Production Section.—James A. Curtin, room W–7174, 307–7534.
Operation Support.—Craig Estancona, room E–5015 (703) 561–7604.
Intelligence Plans and Program.—Pat Lowery, 307–8541.
Requirements/Production.—Vacant (202) 307–7923.
Strategic Intelligence.—Sallie Castro, 353–9581.
Technical Support.—Gisele Gatjanis (703) 561–7107.

OPERATIONS DIVISION

Chief of Operations.—James Capra, room W–12050, 307–7340.
Chiefs of:
Enforcement/Administrative Support.—Vacant.
Financial Operations.—Vacant, room W–10190, 307–4379.
Global Enforcement Operations.—Vacant, room W–11070, 307–7927.
International Programs.—Vacant, room W–11024, 307–4233.
Operations Management.—Robert Brisolari, room W–11148, 307–4200.
Special Projects.—Curt Clements, 307–4233.
Deputy Assistant Administrator, Office of Diversion Control.—Joseph T. Rannazzisi, room E–6295, 307–7165.
Special Agent in Charge, Aviation Division.—Jeffrey B. Stamm, Fort Worth, TX (817) 837–2186.
Special Agent in Charge, Special Operations Division.—Derek S. Maltz, Chantilly, VA (703) 488–4205.

OPERATIONAL SUPPORT DIVISION

Assistant Administrator.—Preston Grubbs, room W–12142, 307–4730.
Deputy Assistant Administrator, Office of:
Administration.—Mary E. Colarusso, room W–9088, 307–7708.

Forensic Sciences.—Nelson Santos, room W–7342, 307–8866.
Information Systems.—Dennis R. McCrary, room E–3105, 307–3653.
Investigative Technology.—Gary Tennant, Lorton, VA (703) 495–6500.

Section Chiefs:

Administrative Operations.—Janet Gates, room W–5104–A, 307–7866.
Business Program Management.—Millie Tyler, room E–3007, 307–9895.
Facilities and Finance.—Vacant, room W–5244, 307–7792.
Hazardous Waste Disposal.—Stephen Wasem, room W–7310, 307–7206.
Integration and Management.—Venita Phillips, room E–4063, 307–9892.
Laboratory Operations.—Lance Kvetko, room W–7312, 307–8880.
Software Operations.—Michelle Bower, room E–3285, 307–9896.
Surveillance Support.—Richard Rosa, Lorton, VA (703) 495–6574.
Technology Officer.—Mark Shafernich (703) 285–4456.
Telecommunications/Intercept Support.—John Sinkovits, Lorton, VA (703) 495–6734.

Associate Deputy Assistant Administrator, Office of:

Information Systems.—Vacant, room E–3005, 307–5269.
Forensic Sciences: Scott Oulton, room W–7344, 307–8866; Steven M. Sottolano, room W–7346, 307–8868.

FIELD OFFICES

Special Agent-in-Charge:

Atlanta Division.—Harry Sommers, Room 800, 75 Spring Street, SW., Atlanta, GA 30303 (404) 893–7100.

Boston Division.—John Arvanitis, JFK Federal Building, Room E–400, 15 New Sudbury Street, Boston, MA 02203–0402 (617) 557–2100.

Caribbean Division.—Javier Pena, Metro Office Park, Millennium Park Plaza #15, 2nd Street, Suite 710, Guaynabo, PR 00968 (787) 277–4700.

Chicago Division.—John J. Riley, Suite 1200, John C. Kluczynski Federal Building, 230 South Dearborn Street, Chicago, IL 60604 (312) 353–7875.

Dallas Division.—James L. Capra, 10160 Technology Boulevard East, Dallas, TX 75220 (214) 366–6900.

Denver Division.—Kevin R. Merrill (acting), 115 Inverness Drive East, Englewood, CO 80112–5116 (303) 705–7300.

Detroit Division.—Robert L. Corso, 431 Howard Street, Detroit, MI 48226 (313) 234–4000.

El Paso Division.—Joseph Arabit, 660 Mesa Hills Drive, Suite 2000, El Paso, TX 79912 (915) 832–6000.

Houston Division.—Thomas Hinojosa (acting), 1433 West Loop South, Suite 600, Houston, TX 77027–9506 (713) 693–3000.

Los Angeles Division.—Timothy J. Landrum, 255 East Temple Street, 20th Floor, Los Angeles, CA 90012 (213) 621–6700.

Miami Division.—Mark Trouville, Phoenix Building, 8400 NW., 53rd Street, Miami, FL 33166 (305) 994–4870.

Newark Division.—John McCabe (acting), 80 Mulberry Street, 2nd Floor, Newark, NJ 07102–4206 (973) 776–1100.

New Orleans Division.—Jimmy S. Fox III, 3838 North Causeway Boulevard, Suite 1800, 3 Lakeway Center, Metaire, LA 70002 (504) 840–1100.

New York Division.—John P. Gilbride, 99 10th Avenue, New York, NY 10011 (212) 337–3900.

Philadelphia Division.—Joseph Bryfonski, William J. Green Federal Building, 600 Arch Street, Room 10224, Philadelphia, PA 19106 (215) 861–3474.

Phoenix Division.—Douglas W. Coleman (acting), 3010 North Second Street, Suite 301, Phoenix, AZ 85012 (602) 664–5600.

San Diego Division.—William R. Sherman (acting), 4560 Viewridge Avenue, San Diego, CA 92123–1672 (858) 616–4100.

San Francisco Division.—Anthony D. Williams, 450 Golden Gate Avenue, 14th Floor, San Francisco, CA 94102 (415) 436–7900.

Seattle Division.—Mark C. Thomas (acting), 400 Second Avenue West, Seattle, WA 98119 (206) 553–5443.

St. Louis Division.—Harry Sommers, 317 South 16th Street, St. Louis, MO 63103 (314) 538–4600.

Washington, DC Division.—Ava Cooper-Davis, 800 K Street, NW., Suite 500, Washington, DC 20001 (202) 305–8500.

OTHER DEA OFFICES

Special Agents-in-Charge:

Arthur A. Doty, El Paso Intelligence Center, Building 11339, SSG Sims Street, El Paso, TX 79908 (915) 760–2000.

Gary G. Olenkiewicz, Aviation Operations Division, 2300 Horizon Drive, Fort Worth, TX 76177 (817) 837–2000.

Derek S. Maltz, Special Operations Division, 14560 Avion Parkway, Chantilly, VA 20151 (703) 488–4200.

William Faiella (acting), Office of Training, P.O. Box 1475, Quantico, VA 22134 (703) 632–5000.

FOREIGN OFFICES

Ankara, Turkey: American Embassy Ankara, DEA / Justice, PSC 93, Box 5000, APO AE 09823–5000, 9–011–90–312–468–6136.

Asuncion, Paraguay: DEA / Justice, American Embassy Asuncion, Unit 4740, APO AA 34036, 9–011–595–21–210–738.

Athens, Greece: American Embassy Athens, DEA / Justice, PSC 108, Box 14, APO AE 09842, 9–011–30–210–643–4328.

Bangkok, Thailand: American Embassy, DEA / Justice, Box 49, APO AP 96546–0001, 9–011–662–205–4984.

Beijing, China: American Embassy Beijing, DEA / Justice, PSC 461, Box 50, FPO AP 96521–0002, 9–011–8610–8529–6880.

Belmopan, Belize: American Embassy Belmopan, DEA / Justice, PSC 120, Unit 7405, APO AA 34025, 301–985–9387.

Bern, Switzerland: Department of State, DEA / Justice, 5110 Bern Place, Washington, DC 20521–5110, 9–011–41–31–357–7367.

Bogota, Colombia: American Embassy Bogota, DEA / Justice, Unit 5116, APO AA 34038, 9–011–571–315–2121.

Brasilia, Brazil: DEA / Justice, American Embassy Brasilia, Unit 3500, APO AA 34030, 9–011–55–61–3312–7122.

Bridgetown, Barbados: American Embassy Bridgetown, CMR 1014, DEA / Justice, FPO AA 34055, 9–1–246–227–4171.

Brussels, Belgium: American Embassy Brussels, DEA / Justice, PSC 82, Box 137, APO AE 09710, 9–011–32–2–508–2420.

Buenos Aires, Argentina: DEA / Justice, American Embassy Buenos Aires, Unit 4309, APO AA 34034, 9–011–5411–5777–4696.

Cairo, Egypt: American Embassy Cairo, DEA / Justice, Unit 64900, Box 25, APO AE 09839–4900, 9–011–20–2–2797–2461.

Canberra, Australia: American Embassy Canberra, DEA / Justice, APO AP 96549, 9–011–61–2–6214–5903.

Caracas, Venezuela: American Embassy Caracas, DEA / Justice, Unit 4962, APO AA 34037, 9–011–582–212–975–8380 / 8443 / 8407.

Cartagena, Resident Office: American Embassy, DEA Cartagena, Unit 5141, APO AA 34038, 9–011–575–664–9369.

Chiang-Mai, Resident Office: American Embassy Chiang-Mai, Box C, APO AP 96546, 9–011–66–53–217–285.

Ciudad, Resident Office: U.S. Consulate / Ciudad Juarez Resident Office, P.O. Box 10545, El Paso, TX 79925, 9–011–52–656–611–1179.

Cochabamba, Resident Office: Unit 3220, Box 211, APO AA 34032, 9–011–591–4–429–3320.

Copenhagen, Denmark: American Embassy Copenhagen, DEA / Justice, PSC 73, APO AE 09716, 9–011–45–35–42–2680.

Curacao, Netherlands Antilles: American Consulate Curacao, DEA / Justice, Washington, DC 20521, 9–011–5999–461–6985.

Dubai, United Arab Emirates: U.S. Consulate General, DEA / Justice, 6020 Dubai Place, Dulles, VA 20189–6020, 9–011–971–4–311–6220.

Dushanbe, Tajikistan: American Embassy Dushanbe, DEA / Justice, Drug Enforcement Administration, 7090 Dushanbe Place, Dulles, VA 20189–7090, 9–011–992–37–229–2807.

Frankfurt, Resident Office: American Consulate General Frankfurt, DEA / Justice, PSC 115, Box 1017, APO AE 09213–0115, 9–011–49–69–7535–3770.

Freeport, Bahamas Resident Office: GPS, c/o U.S. Embassy, DEA, 5115 Northwest 17th Terrace, Hanger #39A, Ft. Lauderdale, FL 33309, 9–1–242–352–5353 / 5354.

Guadalajara, Resident Office: DEA, Guadalajara Resident Office, P.O. Box 9001, Brownsville, TX 78520, 9–011–52–33–3268–2191.

Guatemala City, Guatemala: American Embassy Guatemala City, DEA / Justice, Unit 3311, APO AA 34024, 9–011–502–331–4389.

Guayaquil, Resident Office: DEA / Justice, American Embassy Guayaquil, Unit 5350, APO AA, 34039, 9–011–593–42–32–3715.

The Hague, Netherlands: American Embassy The Hague, DEA / Justice, Unit 6707, Box 8, APO AE 09715, 9–011–31–70–310–2327.

Hanoi, Vietnam: American Embassy Hanoi, DEA / Justice, PSC 461, Box 400, FPO AP 96521–0002, 9–011–844–850–5011.

Hermosillo, Resident Office: U.S. Consulate-Hermosillo, P.O. Box 1689, Nogales, AZ 85628–1689, 9–011–52–662–289–3550.

Hong Kong, Resident Office: U.S. Consulate General Hong Kong, DEA / Justice, PSC 461, Box 16, FPO AP 96521–0006, 9–011–852–2521–4536.

Islamabad, Pakistan Country Office: DEA / Justice, American Embassy Islamabad, DEA / Justice, Unit 62215, APO AE 09812–2215, 9–011–92–51–208–2918.

Istanbul, Turkey Resident Office: American Consulate General, DEA / Justice, PSC 97, Box 0002, APO AE 09827, 9–011–90–212–335–9179.

Kabul, Afghanistan Country Office: DEA / Justice, American Embassy Kabul, 8160 Kabul Place, Washington, DC 20521–6180, 301–490–1042.

Kingston, Jamaica Country Office: U.S. Embassy Kingston, 142 Old Hope Road, Kingston 6, Jamaica 9–1–876–702–6004.

Kuala Lumpur, Malaysia Country Office: American Embassy Kuala Lumpur, DEA / Justice, APO AP 96535–8152, 9–011–603–2142–1779.

Lagos, Nigeria: Department of State, DEA / Justice, 8300 Lagos Place, Washington, DC 20521–8300, 9–011–234–1–261–9837.

La Paz, Bolivia: American Embassy La Paz, DEA / Justice, Unit 3220, DPO AA 34032, 9–011–591–2–216–8313.

Lima, Peru: American Embassy Lima, DEA / Justice, Unit 3810, APO AA 34031, 9–011–511–618–2475.

London, England: American Embassy London, DEA / Justice, Unit 8400, Box 0008, FPO AE 09498–4008, 9–011–44–207–894–0826.

Madrid, Spain: American Embassy Madrid, DEA / Justice, PSC 61, Box 0014, APO AE 09642, 9–011–34–91–587–2280.

Managua, Nicaragua: DEA, American Embassy Nicaragua, Unit 2700, Box 21, APO AA 34021, 9–011–505–252–7738.

Manila, Philippines: American Embassy Manila, DEA / Justice, PSC 500, Box 11, FPO AP 96515, 9–011–632–301–2084.

Matamoros, Mexico Resident Office: Matamoros DEA, P.O. Box 9004, Brownsville, TX 78501, 9–011–52–868–149–1285.

Mazatlan, Resident Office: DEA, Mazatlan Resident Office, P.O. Box 9006, Brownsville, TX 78520–0906, 9–011–669–982–1775.

Merida, Mexico: U.S. Consulate-Merida, P.O. Box 9003, Brownsville, TX 78520–0903, 9–011–52–999–942–5738.

Mexico City, Mexico: DEA / Justice, U.S. Embassy Mexico City, P.O. Box 9000, Brownsville, TX 78520, 9–011–52–55–5080–2600.

Milan, Resident Office: American Consulate Milan, DEA / Justice, PSC 833, Box 60–M, FPO AE 09624, 9–011–39–02–2903–5422.

Monterrey, Resident Office: U.S. Consulate General, Monterrey Resident Office, P.O. Box 9002, Brownsville, TX 78520–0902, 9–011–5281–8340–1299.

Moscow, Russia: American Embassy Moscow, DEA / Justice, PSC 77, APO AE 09721, 9–011–7–495–728–5218.

Nassau: Nassau Country Office, DEA / Justice, American Embassy Nassau, 3370 Nassau Place, Washington, DC 20520, 9–1–242–322–1700.

New Delhi, India: American Embassy New Delhi, Department of State, 9000 New Delhi Place, Washington, DC 20521, 9–011–91–11–2419–8495.

Nicosia, Cyprus: American Embassy Nicosia, DEA / Justice, PSC 815, Box 1, FPO AE 09836–0001, 9–011–357–22–393–302.

Nuevo Laredo, Mexico: DEA, Nuevo Laredo Resident Office, P.O. Box 3089, Laredo, TX 78044–3089, 9–011–52–867–714–0512.

Ottawa, Canada: American Embassy Ottawa, DEA / Justice, P.O. Box 35, Ogdensburg, New York 13669, 9–1–613–238–5633.

Panama City, Panama: American Embassy Panama, DEA / Justice, Unit 0945, APO AA 34002, 9–011–507–317–5541.

Paramaribo, Suriname: American Embassy Paramaribo, DEA / Justice, 3390 Paramaribo Place, Dulles, VA 20189–3390, 301–985–8693.

Paris, France: American Embassy Paris, DEA / Justice, PSC 116, Box A–224, APO AE 09777, 9–011–33–1–4312–2732.

Peshawar, Pakistan: American Consulate Peshawar, DEA / Justice, Unit 62217, APO AE 09812–2217, 9–011–92–91–584–0424 / 0425.

Port-au-Prince, Haiti: U.S. Department of State, 3400 Port-au-Prince, DEA, Washington, DC 20521, 9–011–509–2–229–8413.

Port of Spain, Trinidad and Tobago: Department of State, DEA / Justice, Port of Spain Country Office, 3410 Port of Spain Place, Washington, DC 20537, 9–1–868–628–8136.

Pretoria, South Africa: American Embassy Pretoria, Department of State, DEA / Justice, Washington, DC 20521–9300, 9–011–2712–362–5008.

Quito, Ecuador: DEA / Justice, American Embassy Quito, Unit 5338, APO AA 34039, 9–011–593–22–231–547.

Rangoon, Burma: American Embassy Rangoon, DEA / Justice, Box B, APO AP 96546, 9–011–95–1–536–509.

Rome, Italy: American Embassy Rome, DEA / Justice, PSC 833, Box 22, FPO AE 09624, 9–011–39–06–4674–2319.

San Jose, Costa Rica: American Embassy San Jose, DEA / Justice, Unit 3440, Box 376, APO AA 34020–0376, 9–011–506–22–20–2433.

San Salvador, El Salvador: American Embassy San Salvador, DEA / Justice, Unit 3130, APO AA 34023, 9–011–503–2278–6005.

Santa Cruz, Resident Office: DEA / Justice, American Embassy, Unit 3913 (Santa Cruz), APO AA 34032, 9–011–591–332–7153.

Santiago, Chile: DEA / Justice, American Embassy Santiago, Unit 3460, Box 136, APO AA 34033–0136, 9–011–56–2–330–3401.

Santo Domingo, Dominican Republic: American Embassy Santo Domingo, DEA / Justice, Unit 3470, APO AA 34041, 9–1–809–687–3754.

Sao Paulo, Resident Office: DEA / Justice, American Embassy Sao Paulo, Unit 3502, APO AA 34030, 301–985–9364.

Seoul, Korea: American Embassy Seoul, DEA / Justice, Unit 15550, APO AP 96205–0001, 9–011–82–2–397–4260.

Singapore: American Embassy Singapore, Unit 4280 Box #30, FPO AP 96507–90030, 9–011–65–6476–9021.

Tashkent: Uzbekistan Country Office, DEA / Justice, 7110 Tashkent Place, Washington, DC 20521, 9–011–998–371–120–8924.

Tegucigalpa, Honduras: American Embassy Tegucigalpa, Tegucigalpa Country Office, Unit 3480, Box 212, APO AA 34022, 301–985–9321.

Tijuana, Resident Office: DEA, Tijuana Resident Office, P.O. 439039, San Diego, CA 92143–9039, 9–011–526–646–22–7452.

Tokyo, Japan: American Embassy Tokyo, DEA / Justice, Unit 45004, Box 224, APO AP 96337–5004, 9–011–81–3–3224–5452.

Trinidad, Bolivia Resident Office: American Embassy La Paz, DEA / Justice, Unit 3220 TRO, DPO AA 34032, 301–985–9398.

Udorn, Thailand Resident Office: American Embassy (Udorn), Box UD, APO AP 96546, 9–011–66–42–247–636.

Vancouver Resident Office: DEA Vancouver, 1574 Gulf Road #1509, Point Roberts, WA 98281, 9–1–604–694–7710.

Vienna, Austria: Vienna Country Office, DEA / Justice, American Embassy, 9900 Vienna Place, Dulles, VA 20189–9900, 9–011–43–1–31339–7551.

Vientiane, Laos: American Embassy Vientiane, DEA / Justice, Unit 8165, Box V, APO AP 96546, 9–011–856–21–219–565.

Warsaw, Poland Country Office: DEA / Justice, American Embassy Warsaw, Unit 5010, Box 27, DPO AE 09730–5010, 9–011–48–22–504–2000.

ENVIRONMENT AND NATURAL RESOURCES DIVISION

RFK Main Justice Building, 950 Pennsylvania Avenue, NW., 20530

601 D Street, NW., 20004 (PHB)

Assistant Attorney General.—Ignacia S. Moreno, room 2143 (202) 514–2701.

Principal Deputy Assistant Attorney General.—Robert G. Dreher, room 2141, 514–3370.

Deputy Assistant Attorneys General: Bruce Gelber, room 2131, 514–4624; Ethan Shenkman, room 2135, 616–7349; Steve Silverman, room 2611, 514–0943; Jean Williams, room 2129, 305–0228.

Executive Officer.—Andrew Collier (PHB), room 2038, 616–3147.
Section Chiefs:
Appellate.—James C. Kilbourne (PHB), room 2339, 514–2748.
Environmental Crimes.—Stacey H. Mitchell (PHB), room 2102, 305–0363.
Environmental Defense.—Letitia J. Grishaw (PHB), room 8002, 514–2219.
Environmental Enforcement.—Ben Fisherow (PHB), room 6108, 514–2750.
General Litigation.—Tom Clark (acting), (PHB), room 3102, 305–0438.
Indian Resources.—Craig Alexander (PHB), room 3016, 514–9080.
Land Acquisition.—Andrew Goldfrank (PHB), room 3638, 305–0316.
Policy, Legislation, and Special Litigation.—Karen Wardzinski (RFK), room 2617, 514–0474.
Wildlife and Marine Resources.—Seth Barsky (PHB), room 3902, 305–0210.

FIELD OFFICES

801 B Street, Suite 504, Anchorage, AK 99501–3657

Trial Attorneys: Regina Belt (907) 271–3456; Dean Dunsmore (907) 271–5452.

501 I Street, Suite 9–700, Sacramento, CA 95814–2322

Trial Attorneys: Stephen Macfarlane (916) 930–2204; Charles Shockey (916) 930–2203.

301 Howard Street, Suite 1050, San Francisco, CA 94105–2001

Trial Attorneys: David Glazer (415) 744–6477; Robert Mullaney (415) 744–6483; Bradley O'Brien (415) 744–6484; Judith Rabinowitz (415) 744–6486; Mark Rigau (415) 744–6487.

999 18th Street, Suite 945, North Tower, Denver, CO 80202

Trial Attorneys: David Askman (303) 844–1381; Bruce Bernard (303) 844–1361; Bradley Bridgewater (303) 844–1359; Dave Carson (303) 844–1349; Jerry Ellington (303) 844–1363; Robert Foster (303) 844–1362; Jim Freeman (303) 844–1489; Dave Gehlert (303) 844–1386; Alan Greenberg (303) 844–1366; David Harder (303) 844–1372; Robert Homiak (303) 844–1391; Lee Leininger (303) 844–1364; John Moscato (303) 844–1380; Mark Nitcynski (303) 844–1498; Terry Petrie (303) 844–1369; Daniel Pinkston (303) 844–1804; Susan Schneider (303) 844–1348.
Administrative Officer.—David Jones (303) 844–1807.

161 East Mallard Drive, Suite A, Boise, ID 83706

Trial Attorneys: David Negri (208) 334–1936; Ronald Sutcliffe (208) 334–9124.

One Gateway Center, Suite 6116, Newton Corner, MA 02158

Trial Attorneys: Catherine Fiske (617) 450–0444; Donald Frankel (617) 450–0442.

c/o U.S. Attorney's Office, 105 East Pine Street, 2nd Floor, Missoula, MT 59802

Trial Attorney.—Robert Anderson (406) 829–3322.

c/o U.S. Attorney's Office, 555 Pleasant Street, Suite 352, Concord, NH 03301

Trial Attorney.— Kristine Tardiff (603) 225–1562, ext. 283.

c/o U.S. Attorney's Office, 201 Third Street, NW., Suite 900, Albuquerque, NM 87102

Trial Attorney.—Andrew Smith (505) 224–1468.

c/o NOAA / DARCNW, 7600 San Point Way, NE., Seattle, WA 98115–0070

Trial Attorneys: Brian McLachlan (206) 526–6681; Mike Zevenbergen (206) 526–6607.

EXECUTIVE OFFICE FOR IMMIGRATION REVIEW (EOIR)

5107 Leesburg Pike, Suite 2600, Falls Church, VA 22041

Director.—Juan P. Osuna, 2600 SKYT (703) 305–0169.
Deputy Director.—Ana Kocur.
Associate Director / Chief of Staff.—Vacant.
Executive Secretariat.—Rhonda Caldwell.
Assistant Director / General Counsel.—Jeff Rosenblum, 2600 SKYT, 305–0470.
Deputy General Counsel.—Jean King.
Assistant Director of:
Administration.—Thom Ingles (acting), 2300 SKYT, 305–1171.
Management Programs.—Frances A. Mooney, 2600 SKYT, 305–0289.
Planning, Analysis and Technology.—Amy Dale, 2600 SKYT, 605–0445.
Chairman, Board of Immigration Appeals.—David L. Neal, 2400 SKYT, 305–1194.
Chief, Office of the Chief Administrative Hearing Officer.—Robin Stutman, 2500 SKYT, 305–0864.
Chief Judge, Office of the Chief Immigration Judge.—Brian M. O'Leary, 2500 SKYT, 305–1247.
Deputy Chief Immigration Judge.—Michael C. McGoings.
Telephone Directory Coordinator.—Annette Thomas, 2300 SKYT, 605–1336.

EXECUTIVE OFFICE FOR UNITED STATES ATTORNEYS (EOUSA)

RFK Main Justice Building, Room 2245, phone (202) 252–1300

Director.—H. Marshall Jarrett, room 2243.
Principal Deputy Director / Chief of Staff.—Monty Wilkinson, room 2244.
Deputy Director and Counsel to the Director.—Norman Wong, room 2246.
Deputy Director for Administration and Management.—Katherine C. Gugulis, room 2247.
Deputy Director for Legal Management.—Suzanne L. Bell, room 2242.
Special Counsel to Principal Deputy Director.—Judith Wish, room 2515, 252–1324.
Administrative Officer.—Patricia Mallette, room 6804, BICN, 252–5555.
Executive Assistant / Attorney Generals Advisory Committee Liaison.—Judith Beeman, room 2235, RFK, 252–1374.
Director, Office of Legal Education.—Chammy Chandler, National Advocacy Center, 1620 Pendleton Street, Columbia, SC 29201 (803) 705–5100.
Palmetto Project Manager Staff.—Paul Suddes (803) 705–5678.
General Counsel.—Jay Macklin, room 5000 BICN, (202) 252–1600.
Chief, Planning, Evaluation and Performance (PEP) Staff.—Wayne Gibson, room 8108, BICN, 252–5802.
Assistant Directors:
Communication and Law Enforcement Coordinator Staff.—David Ausiello, room 7600, BICN, 252–5490.
Data Analysis Staff.—Michelle Slusher, room 2000, BICN, 252–5571.
Detailee Management Staff.—Louisa McCarter Dadzie, room 2200, BICN, 252–5624.
District Management and Assistance Program.—Mary Lapitino (919) 264–3618
Equal Employment Opportunity Staff.—Jason Osborne, room 5100, BICN, 252–1460.
Evaluation and Review Staff.—Dayle Elieson, room 8501, BICN, 252–5909.
FOIA and Privacy Act Staff.—Susan Gerson, room 7300, BICN, 252–6020.
Planning and Performance Staff.—Robert Carr, room 8110, BICN, 252–5909.
Counsels for—
Crisis Management and Resource.—Vacant.
Legal and Victim Programs.—Dan Villegas, room 7600, BICN, 252–5888.
Legal Initiatives.—David Smith, room 2256, RFK, 252–1326.
Legislative Counsel.—Scott Laragy, room 2509, 252–1435.
Asset Recovery Staff.—Mark Redmiles, room 7600, 252–5877.
Indian Violent and Cyber Crimes Staff.—Gretchen C. Shappert, room 7622, BICN, 252–5841.
Victim Witness Staff.—Kristina Neal, room 7600, BICN, 252–5833.
White Collar and Civil Litigation Staff.—Tammy Reno, room 7600, 252–5493.

Chief Financial Officer.—Lisa Bevels, room 2200, BICN, 252–5605.
Assistant Director of:
Audit and Review.—Louisa McCarter Dadzie, room 2200, BICN, 252–5624.
Budget Execution.—Mary Ellen Kline, room 2200, BICN, 252–5607.
Budget Formulation.—Vacant.
Financial Systems Staff.—Christopher Kraft, room 2213, BICN, 252–5610.
Chief Information Officer.—Mark Fleshman, room 9078, BICN, 252–6246.
Assistant Director of:
Case Management Staff.—Siobhan Sperin, room 9125, BICN, 252–6120.
EVOIP Program Staff.—Burke Daidy, room 9012, BICN, 272–4462.
Information Security Staff.—Ted Shelkey, room 9074, BICN, 252–6090.
Office Automation Staff.—Ram Murthy, room 9208A, BICN, 252–6270.
Records and Information Management Staff (RIM).—Bonnie Curtin, room 9080, BICN, 252–6488.
Telecommunications and Technology Development Staff.—Denny Ko, room 9136, BICN, 252–6430.
Assistant Director of:
Acquisitions Staff.—Andrew Payne, room 5200, BICN, 252–5405.
Employee Assistance Staff.—Ed Neunlist, room 2400, BICN, 252–5455.
Facilities/Support Services Staff.—Ana Indovina, room 5200, BICN, 252–5964.
Chief Human Resources Officer, Human Resources Staff.—Shawn Flinn, room 8430, BICN, 252–5310.
HR Operations Staff.—Ellen Cook, room 8426, BICN, 252–5354.
HR Policy Staff.—Jane Reimus, room 8401, BICN, 252–5315.
Litigation Technology Service Center.—Sarah Montgomery, room 5738, 514–9500.
Pre-Employment Security.—Robin McMillian, room 2000, BICN, 252–5333.
Security Programs Staff.—Tim George, room 2600, BICN, 252–5694.
Victims Rights Ombudsman.—Marie O'Rourke, room 2245, RFK Main Justice Building, 252–1317.

EXECUTIVE OFFICE FOR UNITED STATES TRUSTEES

441 G Street, NW., 20530, phone (202) 307–1391

http://www.usdoj.gov/ust

Director.—Clifford J. White III, suite 6150.
Deputy Director Field Operations.—William T. Neary (acting).
Deputy Director General Counsel.—Ramona D. Elliott, suite 6150, 307–1399.
Deputy Director Management.—Phillip E. Crewson.
Chief Information Officer.—Barbara A. Brown, 353–8754.
Assistant Director, Office of:
Administration.—Monique K. Bourque, suite 6150, 353–3548.
Oversight.—Doreen Solomon, suite 6150, 305–0222.
Planning and Evaluation.—Thomas Kearns, suite 6150, 305–7827.

U.S. TRUSTEES

Region I:

Suite 1000, 5 Post Office Square, Boston, MA 02109 (617) 788–0400.
Suite 303, 537 Congress Street, Portland, ME 04101 (207) 780–3564.
14th Floor, Sovereign Tower Bldg., 446 Main, Worcester, MA 01608 (508) 793–0555.
Suite 605, 1000 Elm Street, Manchester, NH 03101 (603) 666–7908.
Suite 910, 10 Dorrance Street, Providence, RI 02903 (401) 528–5551.

Region II:

21st floor, 33 Whitehall Street, New York, NY 10004 (212) 510–0500.
Suite 200, 74 Chapel Street, Albany, NY 12207 (518) 434–4553.
Suite 401, 300 Pearl Street, Buffalo, NY 14202 (716) 551–5541.
Long Island Federal Courthouse, 560 Federal Plaza, Central Islip, NY 11722–4456 (631) 715–7800.
Suite 302, 150 Court Street, New Haven, CT 06510 (203) 773–2210.
Room 609, 100 State Street, Rochester, NY 14614 (585) 263–5812.
Room 105, 10 Broad Street, Utica, NY 13501 (315) 793–8191.
Suite 4529, 271 Cadman Plaza East, Brooklyn, NY 11201 (718) 422–4960.

Region III:

Suite 500, 833 Chestnut Street, Philadelphia, PA 19107 (215) 597–4411.
Suite 2100, One Newark Center, Newark, NJ 07102 (973) 645–3014.
Suite 970, 1001 Liberty Avenue, Pittsburgh, PA 15222 (412) 644–4756.
Suite 1190, 228 Walnut Street, Harrisburg, PA 17101 or P.O. Box 969, Harrisburg, PA 17108 (717) 221–4515.
Suite 2207, 844 King Street, Wilmington, DE 19801 (302) 573–6491.

Region IV:

Suite 953, 1835 Assembly Street, Columbia, SC 29201 (803) 765–5250.
Room 210, 115 S. Union Street, Alexandria, VA 22314 (703) 557–7176.
Room 625, 200 Granby Street, Norfolk, VA 23510 (757) 441–6012.
Room 2025, 300 Virginia Street East, Charleston, WV 25301 (304) 347–3400.
First Campbell Square Building, 210 First Street, SW., Suite 505, Roanoke, VA 24011 (540) 857–2806.
Suite 4304, U.S. Courthouse, 701 East Broad Street, Richmond, VA 23219 (804) 771–2310.
Suite 600, 6305 Ivy Lane, Greenbelt, MD 20770 (301) 344–6216.
Suite 2625, 101 West Lombard Street, Baltimore, MD 21201 (410) 962–4300.

Region V:

Suite 2110, 400 Poydras Street, New Orleans, LA 70130 (504) 589–4018.
Suite 3196, 300 Fannin Street, Shreveport, LA 71101–3099 (318) 676–3456.
Suite 6–430, 501 East Court Street, Jackson, MS 39201 (601) 965–5241.

Region VI:

Room 976, 1100 Commerce Street, Dallas, TX 75242 (214) 767–8967.
Room 300, 110 North College Avenue, Tyler, TX 75702 (903) 590–1450.

Region VII:

Suite 3516, 515 Rusk Avenue, Houston, TX 77002 (713) 718–4650.
Room 230, 903 San Jacinto, Austin, TX 78701 (512) 916–5328.
Suite 533, 615 East Houston Street, San Antonio, TX 78205 (210) 472–4640.
Suite 1107, 606 North Carancahua Street, Corpus Christi, TX 78476 (361) 888–3261.

Region VIII:

Suite 400, 200 Jefferson Avenue, Memphis, TN 38103 (901) 544–3251.
Suite 512, 601 West Broadway, Louisville, KY 40202 (502) 582–6000.
Fourth floor, 31 East 11th Street, Chattanooga, TN 37402 (423) 752–5153.
Room 318, 701 Broadway, Nashville, TN 37203 (615) 736–2254.
Suite 500, 100 East Vine Street, Lexington, KY 40507 (859) 233–2822.

Region IX:

Suite 441, BP Building, 201 Superior Avenue East, Cleveland, OH 44114 (216) 522–7800.
Suite 200, Schaff Building, 170 North High Street, Columbus, OH 43215–2403 (614) 469–7411.
Suite 2030, 36 East Seventh Street, Cincinnati, OH 45202 (513) 684–6988.
Suite 700, 211 West Fort Street, Detroit, MI 48226 (313) 226–7999.
Suite 200R, 125 Ottawa Street, Grand Rapids, MI 49503 (616) 456–2002.

Region X:

Room 1000, 101 West Ohio Street, Indianapolis, IN 46204 (317) 226–6101.
Suite 1100, 401 Main Street, Peoria, IL 61602 (309) 671–7854.
Suite 555, 100 East Wayne Street, South Bend, IN 46601 (574) 236–8105.

Region XI:

Suite 873, 219 S. Dearborn Street, Chicago, IL 60606 (312) 886–5794.
Room 430, 517 East Wisconsin Avenue, Milwaukee, WI 53202 (414) 297–4499.
Suite 304, 780 Regent Street, Madison, WI 53715 (608) 264–5522.

Region XII:

Suite 2800, 111 Seventh Avenue, SE., Cedar Rapids, IA 52401 (319) 364–2211.
Suite 1015, U.S. Courthouse, 300 S. Fourth Street, Minneapolis, MN 55415 (612) 334–1353.
Room 793, 210 Walnut Street, Des Moines, IA 50309–2108 (515) 284–4982.
Suite 303, 314 South Main Avenue, Sioux Falls, SD 57104 (605) 330–4450.

Region XIII:

Suite 3440, 400 East 9th Street, Kansas City, MO 64106–1910 (816) 512–1940.
Suite 6353, 111 South 10th Street, St. Louis, MO 63102 (314) 539–2976.
Suite 1200, 200 West Capital Avenue, Little Rock, AR 72201–3344 (501) 324–7357.
Suite 1148, 111 South 18th Plaza, Omaha, NE 68102 (402) 221–4300.

Region XIV:

Suite 204, 230 North First Avenue, Phoenix, AZ 85003 (602) 682–2600.

Region XV:

Suite 600, 402 West Broadway Street, San Diego, CA 92101–8511 (619) 557–5013.
Suite 602, 1132 Bishop Street, Honolulu, HI 96813–2836 (808) 522–8150.

Region XVI:

Suite 2600, 725 South Figueroa, Los Angeles, CA 90017 (213) 894–6811.
Suite 9041, 411 West Fourth Street, Santa Ana, CA 92701–8000 (714) 338–3400.
Suite 720, 3801 University Avenue, Riverside, CA 92501 (951) 276–6990.
Suite 115, 21051 Warner Center Lane, Woodland Hills, CA 91367 (818) 716–8800.

Region XVII:

Suite 700, 235 Pine Street, San Francisco, CA 94104–3401 (415) 705–3300.
Suite 7–500, U.S. Courthouse, 501 I Street, Sacramento, CA 95814–2322 (916) 930–2100.
Suite 1401, 2500 Tulare Street, Fresno, CA 93721 (559) 487–5002.
Suite 690N, 1301 Clay Street, Oakland, CA 94612–5217 (510) 637–3200.
Room 4300, 300 Las Vegas Boulevard South, Las Vegas, NV 89101 (702) 388–6600.
Suite 3009, 300 Booth Street, Reno, NV 89509 (775) 784–5335.
Room 268, 280 South First Street, San Jose, CA 95113 (408) 535–5525.

Region XVIII:

Suite 5103, 700 Stewart Street, Seattle, WA 98101 (206) 553–2000.
Suite 213, 620 Southwest Main Street, Portland, OR 97205 (503) 326–4000.
Suite 220, 720 Park Boulevard, Boise, ID 83712 (208) 334–1300.
Room 593, 920 West Riverside, Spokane, WA 99201 (509) 353–2999.
Suite 204, 301 Central Avenue, Great Falls, MT 59401 (406) 761–8777.
Suite 258, 605 West Fourth Avenue, Anchorage, AK 99501 (907) 271–2600.
Suite 1100, 405 East Eighth Avenue, Eugene, OR 97401 (541) 465–6330.

Region XIX:

Suite 1551, 999 Eighteenth Street, Denver, CO 80202 (303) 312–7230.
Suite 203, 308 West 21st Street, Cheyenne, WY 82001 (307) 772–2790.
Suite 300, 405 South Main Street, Salt Lake City, UT 84111 (801) 524–5734.

Region XX:

Room 1150, Epic Center, 301 North Main Street, Wichita, KS 67202 (316) 269–6637.
Suite 112, 421 Gold Street, SW., Albuquerque, NM 87102 (505) 248–6544.
Suite 408, 215 Northwest Dean A. McGee Avenue, Oklahoma City, OK 73102 (405) 231–5950.
Suite 225, 224 South Boulder Avenue, Tulsa, OK 74103 (918) 581–6670.

Region XXI:

Room 362, 75 Spring Street, SW., Atlanta, GA 30303 (404) 331–4437.
Suite 301, EDIFICIO OCHOA, 500 Tanca Street, San Juan, PR 00901 (787) 729–7444.
Room 1204, 51 Southwest First Avenue, Miami, FL 33130 (305) 536–7285.
Suite 725, 2 East Bryan Street, Savannah, GA 31401 (912) 652–4112.
Suite 1200, 501 East Polk Street, Tampa, FL 33602 (813) 228–2000.
Suite 302, 440 Martin Luther King Boulevard, Macon, GA 31201 (478) 752–3544.
Suite 128, 110 East Park Avenue, Tallahassee, FL 32301 (850) 942–1660.
Suite 1101, 400 West Washington Street, Orlando, FL 32801 (407) 648–6301.

BUREAU OF ALCOHOL, TOBACCO, FIREARMS, AND EXPLOSIVES (ATF)

99 New York Avenue, NE., 20226

OFFICE OF THE DIRECTOR

Director.—B. Todd Jones (acting), (202) 648–8700.
Deputy Director.—Thomas E. Brandon, 648–8710.
Chief of Staff.—Joseph J. Allen, 648–7113.
Special Assistant to the Chief of Staff.—Cherie Knoblock, 648–9211.

OFFICE OF DIVERSITY AND INCLUSION (ODI)

145 North Street, NE., Suite 8S.1415, 20530

Chief Diversity Officer.—Stacie Brockman, 648–8770
Deputy Chief Officer.—Dora Silas, 648–8770

OFFICE OF CHIEF COUNSEL

Chief Counsel.—Charles R. Gross, 648–7000.
Deputy Chief Counsel.—Vacant.

OFFICE OF ENFORCEMENT PROGRAMS AND SERVICES

99 New York Avenue, NE., Washington, DC 20226

Assistant Director.—Arthur Herbert, 648–7080.
Deputy Assistant Director.—Marvin G. Richardson, 648–7080.

OFFICE OF EQUAL OPPORTUNITY

Chief.—Rachel A. Bouman, 648–8760.

OFFICE OF FIELD OPERATIONS

Assistant Director.—Ronald B. Turk, 648–8410.
Deputy Assistant Director for—
Central.—B.J. Zapor.
East.—Glenn Anderson.
West.—Stephen K. Martin.
Industry Operations.—Curtis W. Gilbert.

OFFICE OF MANAGEMENT/CFO

Assistant Director.—Mark W. Potter, 648–7800.
Deputy Assistant Director/CFO.—Vivian B. Michalic, 648–7800.

OFFICE OF OMBUDSMAN

Ombudsman.—Henry J. Lescault, 648–7375.

OFFICE OF PROFESSIONAL RESPONSIBILITY AND SECURITY OPERATIONS

Assistant Director.—Michael P. Gleysteen, 648–7500.
Deputy Assistant Director.—Vacant.

OFFICE OF PUBLIC AND GOVERNMENTAL AFFAIRS

Assistant Director.—Richard W. Marianos, 648–8520.
Deputy Assistant Director.—George D. Lennon, 648–8520
Chief of:
Legislative Affairs Division.—John T. Hageman, 648–7191.
Public Affairs Division.—Ginger L. Colbrun, 648–7938.

OFFICE OF SCIENCE AND TECHNOLOGY/CIO

Assistant Director/Chief Information Officer.—H. Richard Holgate, 648–8390.
Deputy Assistant Director.—Victoria Gold, 648–7915
Deputy Assistant Director for Forensic Services.—Greg Czarnopys, 648–6104.

OFFICE OF STRATEGIC INTELLIGENCE AND INFORMATION

Assistant Director.—James E. McDermond, 648–7600.
Deputy Assistant Director.—John A. Torres.

OFFICE OF HUMAN RESOURCES AND PROFESSIONAL DEVELOPMENT

Assistant Director.—Theresa R. Stoop, 648–8416.
Deputy Assistant Director.—Vacant.

FEDERAL BUREAU OF INVESTIGATION

J. Edgar Hoover Building, 935 Pennsylvania Avenue, NW., 20535–0001

phone (202) 324–3000, http://www.fbi.gov

Director.—James B. Comey, 324–3444.
Deputy Director.—Mark Giuliano, 324–3315.
Associate Deputy Director.—Kevin L. Perkins, 324–4180.
Chief of Staff.—Chuck Rosenberg, 324–3444.

OFFICE OF THE DIRECTOR / DEPUTY DIRECTOR / ASSOCIATE DEPUTY DIRECTOR

Office of the General Counsel.—James A. Baker, 324–6829.
Office of Public Affairs.—Michael Kortan, 324–5352.
Office of Congressional Affairs.—Stephen Kelly, 324–5051.
Office of Professional Responsibility.—Candice M. Will, 324–8284.
Office of Equal Employment Opportunity Affairs.—Kevin M. Walker, 324–4128.
Office of the Ombudsman.—Monique Bookstein, 324–2156.
Inspection Division.—Keith L. Bennett, 324–2901.
Facilities and Logistics Services Division.—Patrick G. Findlay, 324–2875.
Finance Division.—Richard Haley II, 324–4104.
Records Management Division.—Michelle Ann Jupina, 324–7141.
Security Division.—Alex J. Turner, 324–7112.

OFFICE OF THE CHIEF INFORMATION OFFICER

Executive Assistant Director / Chief Information Officer.—Jerome M. Pender, 324–6165.
Associate EAD and Deputy Chief Information Officer.—Dean E. Hall.
Assistant Director of:
Information Technology Services Division.—Jenifer Sanchez (703) 872–5050.
Information Management Technology Division.—John Martin Hope.
Information Technology Engineering Division.—Jeffery Johnson, 324–2559.
Office of the Chief Technology Officer.—Clayton Grigg (703) 872–5270.

CRIMINAL INVESTIGATIONS BRANCH

Executive Assistant Director.—Richard McFeely, 324–4880.
Assistant Director of:
Criminal Investigative Division.—Ronald T. Hosko, 324–4260.
Critical Incident Response Group.—Robert Blecksmith (703) 632–4100.
Cyber Division.—Joseph Dermarest, Jr., 651–3044.
International Operations Division.—Michael S. Welch, 324–5904.
Law Enforcement Coordination Office.—Ronald Ruecker, 324–7126.

HUMAN RESOURCES BRANCH

Executive Assistant Director.—Janet Kamerman, 324–3000.
Assistant Director of:
Human Resources Division.—David G. Bennett, 324–3514.
Training and Development Division.—Owen D. Harris (703) 632–1100.

NATIONAL SECURITY BRANCH

Executive Assistant Director.—Stephanie Douglas, 324–7045.
Assistant Director of:
Counterintelligence Division.—Robert Anderson Jr., 324–4614.
Counterterrorism Division.—Vacant.
Directorate of Intelligence.—Eric Velez-Villar, 324–7605.
Weapons of Mass Destruction Directorate.—John G. Perren, 324–4965.

SCIENCE AND TECHNOLOGY BRANCH

Executive Assistant Director.—Vacant.

Assistant Director of:
Criminal Justice Information Services Division.—Vacant.
Laboratory Division.—D. Christian Hassell (703) 632–7001.
Operational Technology Division.—Amy S. Hess (703) 632–6100.

FIELD DIVISIONS

Albany: 200 McCarty Avenue, Albany, NY 12209 (518) 465–7551.
Albuquerque: 4200 Luecking Park Avenue, NE., Albuquerque, NM., 87107 (505) 224–2000.
Anchorage: 101 East Sixth Avenue, Anchorage, AK 99501 (907) 258–5322.
Atlanta: 2635 Century Center Parkway, NE., Suite 400, Atlanta, GA 30345 (404) 679–9000.
Baltimore: 2600 Lord Baltimore Avenue, Baltimore, MD 21244 (410) 265–8080.
Birmingham: 1000 18th Street North, Birmingham, AL 35203 (205) 326–6166.
Boston: One Center Plaza, Suite 600, Boston, MA 02108 (617) 742–5533.
Buffalo: One FBI Plaza, Buffalo, NY 14202 (716) 856–7800.
Charlotte: Wachovia Building, 400 South Tryon Street, Suite 900, Charlotte, NC 28285 (704) 377–9200.
Chicago: 2111 West Roosevelt Road, Chicago, IL 60608–1128 (312) 431–1333.
Cincinnati: Federal Office Building, 550 Main Street, Room 9000, Cincinnati, OH 45202 (513) 421–4310.
Cleveland: 1501 Lakeside Avenue, Cleveland, OH 44114 (216) 522–1400.
Columbia: 151 Westpark Boulevard, Columbia, SC 29210 (803) 551–4200.
Dallas: J. Gordon Shanklin Building, One Justice Way, Dallas, TX 75220 (972) 559–5000.
Denver: Federal Office Building, 1961 Stout Street, Room 1823, Denver, CO 80294 (303) 629–7171.
Detroit: P.V. McNamara Federal Office Building, 477 Michigan Avenue, 26th Floor, Detroit, MI 48226 (313) 965–2323.
El Paso: 660 South Mesa Hills Drive, Suite 3000, El Paso, TX 79912 (915) 832–5000.
Honolulu: Kalanianaole Federal Office Building, 300 Ala Moana Boulevard, Room 4–230, Honolulu, HI 96850 (808) 566–4300.
Houston: 2500 East T.C. Jester, Suite 200, Houston, TX 77008 (713) 693–5000.
Indianapolis: Federal Office Building, 575 North Pennsylvania Street, Room 679, Indianapolis, IN 46204 (371) 639–3301.
Jackson: Federal Office Building, 100 West Capitol Street, Suite 1553, Jackson, MS 39269 (601) 948–5000.
Jacksonville: 7820 Arlington Expressway, Suite 200, Jacksonville, FL 32211 (904) 721–1211.
Kansas City: 1300 Summit, Kansas City, MO 64105 (816) 512–8200.
Knoxville: John J. Duncan Federal Office Building, 710 Locust Street, Room 600, Knoxville, TN 37902 (423) 544–0751.
Las Vegas: John Lawrence Bailey Building, 1787 West Lake Mead Boulevard, Las Vegas, NV 89106–2135 (702) 385–1281.
Little Rock: #24 Shackleford West Boulevard, Little Rock, AR 72211 (501) 221–9100.
Los Angeles: Federal Office Building, 11000 Wilshire Boulevard, Suite 1700, Los Angeles, CA 90024 (310) 477–6565.
Louisville: 600 Martin Luther King, Jr. Place, Room 500, Louisville, KY 40202 (502) 583–2941.
Memphis: Eagle Crest Building, 225 North Humphreys Boulevard, Suite 3000, Memphis, TN 38120 (901) 747–4300.
Miami: 16320 Northwest Second Avenue, Miami, FL 33169 (305) 944–9101.
Milwaukee: 330 East Kilbourn Avenue, Suite 600, Milwaukee, WI 53202 (414) 276–4684.
Minneapolis: 111 Washington Avenue South, Suite 100, Minneapolis, MN 55401 (612) 376–3200.
Mobile: 200 North Royal Street, Mobile, AL 36602 (334) 438–3674.
New Haven: 600 State Street, New Haven, CT 06511 (203) 777–6311.
New Orleans: 2901 Leon C. Simon Boulevard, New Orleans, LA 70126 (504) 816–3122.
New York: 26 Federal Plaza, 23rd Floor, New York, NY 10278 (212) 384–1000.
Newark: Claremont Tower Building, 11 Centre Place, Newark, NJ 07102 (973) 792–3000.
Norfolk: 150 Corporate Boulevard, Norfolk, VA 23502 (757) 455–0100.
Oklahoma City: 3301 West Memorial, Oklahoma City, OK 73134 (405) 290–7770.
Omaha: 10755 Burt Street, Omaha, NE 68114 (402) 493–8688.
Philadelphia: William J. Green, Jr., Federal Office Building, 600 Arch Street, Eighth Floor, Philadelphia, PA 19106 (215) 418–4000.
Phoenix: 201 East Indianola Avenue, Suite 400, Phoenix, AZ 85012 (602) 279–5511.
Pittsburgh: Martha Dixon Building, 3311 East Carson Street, Pittsburgh, PA 15203 (412) 432–4000.

Portland: Crown Plaza Building, 1500 Southwest First Avenue, Suite 401, Portland, OR 97201 (503) 224–4181.
Richmond: 1970 East Parham Road, Richmond, VA 23228 (804) 261–1044.
Sacramento: 4500 Orange Grove Avenue, Sacramento, CA 95841 (916) 481–9110.
Salt Lake City: 257 Towers Building, 257 East, 200 South, Suite 1200, Salt Lake City, UT 84111 (801) 579–1400.
San Antonio: 5740 University Heights Boulevard, San Antonio, TX 78249 (210) 225–6741.
San Diego: Federal Office Building, 9797 Aero Drive, San Diego, CA 92123 (858) 565–1255.
San Francisco: 450 Golden Gate Avenue, 13th Floor, San Francisco, CA 64102 (415) 553–7400.
San Juan: U.S. Federal Office Building, 150 Chardon Avenue, Room 526, Hato Rey, PR 00918 (787) 754–6000.
Seattle: 1110 Third Avenue, Seattle, WA 98101 (206) 622–0460.
Springfield: 900 East Linton Avenue, Springfield, IL 62703 (217) 522–9675.
St. Louis: 2222 Market Street, St. Louis, MO 63103 (314) 241–5357.
Tampa: 5525 West Gray Street, Tampa, FL 33609 (813) 273–4566.
Washington, DC: 601 Fourth Street, NW., Washington, DC 20535 (202) 278–3400.

FEDERAL BUREAU OF PRISONS (BOP)

320 First Street, NW., 20534

General Information Number (202) 307–3198

Director.—Charles E. Samuels, Jr., room 654, HOLC, 307–3250.
Deputy Director.—Thomas R. Kane, Ph.D., room 654, HOLC, 307–3250.
Director, National Institute of Corrections.—Robert Brown, Sr. (acting), 7th floor, 500 FRST, 307–3106.
Assistant Director of:
Administration.—William Dalius, 9th floor, 500 FRST, 307–3230.
Correctional Programs.—Blake R. Davis, room 554, HOLC, 307–3226.
General Counsel.—Kathleen M. Kenney, room 958C, HOLC, 307–3062.
Health Services.—Newton Kendig, M.D., room 1054, HOLC, 307–3055.
Human Resources Management.—Dan Joslin, room 754, HOLC, 307–3082.
Industries, Education, and Vocational Training.—Mary Mitchell, 8th floor, 400 FRST, 305–3501.
Information, Policy and Public Affairs.—Judi S. Garrett, room 641, HOLC, 514–6537.
Program Review.—Sara Revell, room 1054, HOLC, 307–1076.
Regional Director for—
Mid-Atlantic.—Louis Eichenlaub (301) 317–3101.
North Central.—Paul Laird (913) 621–3939.
Northeast.—Joseph Norwood (215) 521–7300.
South Central.—Jeffery Keller (214) 224–3389.
Southeast.—Helen Marberry (678) 686–1200.
Western.—Juan Castillo (209) 956–9700.
Telephone Directory Coordinator.—Marla Clayton, 307–3250.

FOREIGN CLAIMS SETTLEMENT COMMISSION

Bicentennial Building (BICN), 600 E Street, NW., Suite 6002, 20579

phone (202) 616–6975

Chairman.—Vacant.
Commissioners: Anuj C. Desai, Rafael E. Martinez.
Chief Counsel.—Brian M. Simkin.
Executive Officer.—Judith H. Lock.

OFFICE OF INFORMATION POLICY

1425 New York Avenue, NW., Suite 11050, 20530, phone (202) 514–3642

Director.—Melanie Ann Pustay.
Chief of Staff.—Carmen L. Mallon.

OFFICE OF THE INSPECTOR GENERAL

RFK Main Justice Building, Room 4706, phone (202) 514–3435
950 Pennsylvania Avenue, NW., 20530

Inspector General.—Michael E. Horowith.
Deputy Inspector General.—Cynthia A. Schnedar.
Chief of Staff/Senior Counsel.—Jay Lerner.
Counselors to the IG: Harold Damelin, Robert Storch.
General Counsel.—William Blier, RFK, Suite 4726, 616–0646.
Assistant Inspectors General:
Audit.—Raymond Beaudet (NYAV), Suite 13000, 616–1697.
Evaluations and Inspections.—Jason Higley (acting), (NYAV), Suite 6100, 616–4620.
Investigations.—George Dorsett (NYAV), Suite 7100, 616–4760.
Management and Planning.—Gregory T. Peters (NYAV), Suite 7000, 616–4550.
Oversight and Review.—Carol F. Ochoa (NYAV), Suite 13000, 616–0645.

REGIONAL AUDIT OFFICES

Atlanta: Ferris B. Polk, Suite 1130, 75 Spring Street, Atlanta, GA 30303 (404) 331–5928.
Chicago: Carol S. Taraszka, Suite 3510, Citicorp Center, 500 West Madison Street, Chicago, IL 60661 (312) 353–1203.
Dallas: Robert J. Kaufman, Room 575, Box 4, 207 South Houston Street, Dallas, TX 75202–4724 (214) 655–5000.
Denver: David M. Sheeren, Suite 1500, Chancery Building, 1120 Lincoln Street, Denver, CO 80203 (303) 864–2000.
Philadelphia: Thomas O. Puerzer, Suite 201, 701 Market Street, Philadelphia, PA 19106 (215) 580–2111.
San Francisco: David J. Gaschke, Suite 201, 1200 Bayhill Drive, San Bruno, CA 94066 (650) 876–9220.
Washington: Troy M. Meyer, 1300 North 17th Street, Suite 3400, Arlington, VA 22209 (202) 616–4688.
Computer Security and Information Technology Audit Office: Reginald Allen, room 5000 (202) 616–3801.
Financial Statement Audit Office: Mark L. Hayes, 1425 New York Avenue, NW., #13000, Washington, DC 20530 (202) 616–4660.

REGIONAL INVESTIGATIONS OFFICES

Atlanta: Eddie D. Davis, 60 Forsyth Street, SW., Room 8M45, Atlanta, GA 30303 (404) 562–1980.
Boston: Thomas M. Hopkins, U.S. Courthouse, 1 Courthouse Way, Room 9200, Boston, MA 02210 (617) 748–3218.
Chicago: John F. Oleskowicz, P.O. Box 1802, Chicago, IL 60690 (312) 886–7050.
Denver: Norman K. Lau, Suite 1501, 1120 Lincoln Street, Denver, CO 80203 (303) 335–4201.
Dallas: James H. Mahon, 2505 State Highway 360, Room 410, Grand Prairie, TX 75050 (817) 385–5200.
Detroit: Nicholas V. Candela, Suite 1402, 211 West Fort Street, Detroit, MI 48226 (313) 226–4005.
El Paso: Eric Benn, Suite 135, 4050 Rio Bravo, El Paso, TX 79902 (915) 577–0102.
Houston: Carlos Capano, P.O. Box 53509, Houston, TX 77052 (713) 718–4888.
Los Angeles: Kenneth R. Strange, Jr., Suite 655, 330 North Brand Street, Glendale, CA 91203 (818) 543–1172.
Miami: Teresa M. Gulotta Powers, Suite 200, 510 Shotgun Road, Sunrise, FL 33326 (954) 370–8300.
New York: Eric J. Blachman, One Battery Park Plaza, 29th floor, New York, NY 10004 (212) 824–3650.
New Jersey: Kenneth R. Connaughton, Jr., 361 Scotch Road, West Trenton, NJ 08628 (609) 883–5423.
San Francisco: Michael Barranti, Suite 220, 1200 Bayhill Drive, San Bruno, CA 94066 (650) 876–9058.
Seattle: Wayne Hawney, Suite 104, 620 Kirkland Way, Kirkland, WA 98033 (253) 852–0194.
Tucson: Joseph V. Cuffari, 405 West Congress, Room 3600, Tucson, AZ 85701 (520) 620–7389.

Washington: Scott Barden, 1425 New York Avenue, NW., Suite 7100, Washington, DC 20530 (202) 616–4760.

Fraud Detection Office.—Joseph Barlow, room 7100 (202) 353–2975.

INTERPOL—U.S. NATIONAL CENTRAL BUREAU

phone (202) 616–9000

Director.—Shawn A. Bray, 616–4239.

Deputy Director.—Geoffrey Shank, 616–4239.

Executive Office.—Warren A. Lewis, 616–8810.

General Counsel.—Kevin Smith, 616–4103.

Assistant Director, Division of:

Alien/Fugitive.—Mark Shealey, 616–0310.

Counterterrorism.—Robert Meadows, 616–7258.

Drug.—Richard Joyce, 616–3379.

Economic Crimes.—Robert Montemorra, 616–5466.

Human Trafficking and Child Protection.—George Guzman, 616–1753.

INTERPOL Operations and Command Center.—Vacant, 616–3459, (24/7 Command Center).

State and Local Liaison.—Michael D. Muth, 616–8272.

Violent Crimes.—Monique Randall, 616–7258.

Deputy Assistant Director, Division of:

INTERPOL Operations and Command Center.—Edwin Quall, 616–7589, (24/7 Command Center).

JUSTICE MANAGEMENT DIVISION

RFK Main Justice Building, 950 Pennsylvania Avenue, NW., 20530

2CON—145 N Street, NE., 20530

LSB—Liberty Square Building, 450 5th Street, NW., 20530

Assistant Attorney General for Administration.—Lee J. Lofthus, room 1111 (202) 514–3101.

Deputy Assistant Attorney General, Policy, Management and Planning.—Michael H. Allen, room 1113 (202) 514–3101.

Staff Directors:

Department Ethics Office.—Janice Rodgers (2CON), room 8E310 (202) 514–8196.

Facilities and Administrative Services Staff.—Christine Schwartz (acting), (2CON), room 9E.408 (202) 616–2995.

General Counsel Office.—Arthur Gary, General Counsel (2CON), room 8E528 (202) 514–3452.

Internal Review and Evaluation Office.—Neil Ryder, (2CON), room 8W1419 (202) 616–5499.

Senior Procurement Executive.—Michael H. Allen, room 1113 (202) 514–3101.

Office of Small and Disadvantaged Business Utilization.—Robert Connolly (2CON), room 8E1009 (202) 616–0521.

Procurement Services Staff.—James Johnston (2CON), room 8E202 (202) 307–2000.

Records Management Policy Office.—Jeanette Plante (2CON), room 8W1401 (202) 514–3528.

Deputy Assistant Attorney General/Controller.—Jolene Lauria Sullens, room 1117 (202) 514–1843.

Staff Directors:

Asset Forfeiture Management.—Candace Olds (2CON), room 5W725 (202) 616–8000.

Budget Staff.—Karin O'Leary, room 7601 (202) 514–4082.

Debt Collection Management.—Dennis Dauphin (acting) (2CON), room 5E103 (202) 514–5343.

Finance.—Melinda Morgan (2CON), room 7E202 (202) 616–5800.

Unified Financial System Project Management Office.—Kay Clarey (2CON), room 6W102 (202) 305–3651.

Deputy Assistant Attorney General, Human Resources and Administration.—Mari Santangelo, room 1112 (202) 514–5501.

Staff Directors:

Attorney Recruitment and Management Office.—Louis DeFalaise, Suite 10200, 450 5th Street, NW. (Liberty Square), (202)514–8900.

Consolidated Executive Office.—Cyntoria Carter, room 7113(202) 514–5537.
DOJ Executive Secretariat.—Dana Paige, room 4412 (202) 514–2063.
Equal Employment Opportunity.—Richard Toscano (2CON), room 1W102, 616–4800.
Library.—Dennis Feldt, room 7535 (202) 514–2133.
Human Resources Staff.—Terry Cook (2CON), room 9W102 (202) 514–6788.
Security and Emergency Planning Staff.—James Dunlap, room 6217 (202) 514–2094.

Deputy Assistant Attorney General, Information Resources Management/CIO.—Luke McCormack, room 1310–A, 514–0507.

Staff Directors:
Enterprise Solutions.—John Murray (2CON), room 3E202 (202) 305–9635.
IT Security.—Melinda Rogers (acting), (2CON), room 4E1407 (202) 353–2421.
Operation Services.—Joan Crum (acting), (RDC), room 203 (202) 307–6944.
Policy and Planning.—Kevin Deeley (acting), (2CON), room 4E202 (202) 353–2421.
Systems Engineering.—Eric Olson (2CON), room 3W701 (202) 353–2355.

OFFICE OF JUSTICE PROGRAMS (OJP)

810 7th Street, NW., 20531

OFFICE OF THE ASSISTANT ATTORNEY GENERAL

Assistant Attorney General.—Mary Lou Leary (acting), (202) 307–5933.
Principal Deputy Assistant General.—Mary Lou Leary, 307–5933.
Deputy Assistant Attorney General.—James H. Burch II, 307–5933.
Manager, Equal Employment Opportunity.—Vacant.

BUREAU OF JUSTICE ASSISTANCE

Director.—Denise O'Donnell, 616–6500.
Deputy Directors of:
Planning.—Eileen Garry, 307–6226.
Policy.—Pamela Cammarata (acting), 514–9193.
Programs.—Tracey Trautman, 305–1491.

BUREAU OF JUSTICE STATISTICS

Director.—William Sabol (acting), 307–0765.
Deputy Directors of:
Statistical Collections and Analysis: Victimization, Corrections, and Special Projects Division.—William Sabol, 514–1062.
Statistical Collections and Analysis: Law Enforcement, Prosecution, and Courts Division.—Vacant, 307–0765.
Statistical Planning, Policy and Operations.—Gerard Ramker, 307–0759.

NATIONAL INSTITUTE OF JUSTICE

Director.—Greg Ridgeway (acting), 307–2942.
Deputy Directors: Kristina Rose, 307–0466; Ellen Scrivner, 514–4693.
Investigative and Forensic Sciences.—Michael Sheppo, 353–3756.
Research and Evaluation.—Phyllis Newton, 305–2457.
Science and Technology.—George Tillery, 305–9829.

OFFICE OF JUVENILE JUSTICE AND DELINQUENCY PREVENTION

Administrator.—Robert Listenbee, Jr., 307–5911.
Deputy Administrator of:
Policy.—Melodee Hanes (acting), 305–1973.
Programs.—Marilyn Roberts, 616–9055.

OFFICE FOR VICTIMS OF CRIME

Director.—Joye E. Frost (acting), 307–5983.
Deputy Director.—Barbara Walker, 305–2172.

OFFICE OF ADMINISTRATION

Director.—Phillip K. Merkle, 307–0087.
Deputy Director, Division of:
Acquisition Management.—Nichele C. Robinson, 514–9497.
Human Resources.—Jennifer McCarthy, 616–0389.
Support Services.—Cheryl Leleck.

OFFICE OF THE CHIEF FINANCIAL OFFICER

Chief Financial Officer.—Leigh Benda, 353–8153.
Deputy Chief Financial Officer.—Ralph Martin, 305–1802.

OFFICE OF THE CHIEF INFORMATION OFFICER

Chief Information Officer.—Walter Iwanow, 305–9071.
Deputy Chief Information Officer.—Angel Santa, 514–9089.

OFFICE FOR CIVIL RIGHTS

Director.—Michael Alston, 307–0690.

OFFICE OF COMMUNICATION

Director.—Sabra Horne, 353–0798.
Deputy Director.—Vacant.

OFFICE OF THE GENERAL COUNSEL

General Counsel.—Rafael A. Madan, 307–6235.

OFFICE OF SEX OFFENDER SENTENCING, MONITORING, APPREHENDING, REGISTERING, AND TRACKING

Director.—Linda M. Baldwin, 305–2463.
Deputy Director.—Dawn Doran, 353–3040.

OFFICE OF LEGAL COUNSEL

RFK Main Justice Building, Room 5218, phone (202) 514–2051

Assistant Attorney General.—Virginia Seitz, room 5218, 514–2051.
Principal Deputy Assistant Attorney General.—Caroline Krass, room 5218, 514–4132.
Deputy Assistant Attorneys General: John Bies, room 5237, 305–8521; Daniel Koffsky, room 5238, 514–2030; Leondra Kruger, room 5229, 514–4038; Ben Mizer, room 5235, 514–9700.
Special Counsels: Paul P. Colborn, room 5240, 514–2048; Rosemary Hart, room 5242, 514–2027.
Senior Counsel.—Jeffrey Singdahlsen, room 5262, 514–4174.

OFFICE OF LEGAL POLICY

RFK Main Justice Building, Room 4234, phone (202) 514–4601

Assistant Attorney General.—Elana Tyrangiel (acting), room 4238, 514–5651.
Principal Deputy Assistant Attorney General.—Elana Tyrangiel, room 4238, 514–5651.
Deputy Assistant Attorneys General: Kevin Jones, room 4248, 514–4604; Robyn Thiemann, room 4237, 514–8356; Michael Zubrensky, room 4229, 514–4606.
Chief of Staff.—Steven Siger (acting), room 4228, 305–0071.
Executive Officer.—Matrina Matthews, room 4517, 616–0040.

OFFICE OF LEGISLATIVE AFFAIRS (OLA)

RFK Main Justice Building, Room 1145, phone (202) 514–2141

Assistant Attorney General.—Vacant.
Principal Deputy Assistant Attorney General.—Peter J. Kadzik.
Deputy Assistant Attorney General.—Mark D. Agrast.

NATIONAL SECURITY DIVISION

RFK Main Justice Building, Room 7339, phone (202) 514–1057

Assistant Attorney General.—John P. Carlin (acting).
Deputy Assistant Attorneys General: Tashina Gauhar, George Toscas, Brad Wiegmann.
Chief of Staff.—Anita Singh (acting).
Deputy Chief of Staff.—James Rybicki (acting).
Senior Counsel to the Assistant Attorney General.—James Walsh.
Counsels to the Assistant Attorney General: Alexis Collins, Kate Heinzelman, David Newman.
Executive Officer.—Mark A. Jenkins.
Special Assistant to the Assistant Attorney General.—Jacqueline Prim.

COUNTERESPIONAGE SECTION

600 E Street, NW., Room 10100, phone (202) 233–0986

Chief.—Vacant.

COUNTERTERRORISM SECTION

RFK Main Justice Building, Room 2643, phone (202) 514–0849

Chief.—Michael J. Mullaney.
Principal Deputy Chief.—Jennifer Smith (acting).
International Terrorism Unit I.—Alamdar Hamdani.
International Terrorism Unit II.—Stephen Ponticiello.
Terrorist Financing Unit.—Michael Taxay.

FOREIGN INVESTMENT REVIEW STAFF

600 E Street, NW., Room 10000

Director.—Richard Sofield.

OFFICE OF INTELLIGENCE

RFK Main Justice Building, Room 6150, phone (202) 514–5600

Section Chief for—
Litigation.—Nancy Newcomb.
Operations.—Gabrielle Sanz-Rexach.
Oversight.—Kevin O'Connor.

OFFICE OF JUSTICE FOR VICTIMS OF OVERSEAS TERRORISM

600 E Street, NW., Room 10102, phone (202) 233–0701

Director.—Heather Cartwright.

OFFICE OF THE PARDON ATTORNEY

1425 New York Avenue, NW., 20530, phone (202) 616–6070

Pardon Attorney.—Ronald L. Rodgers.
Deputy Pardon Attorney.—Helen M. Bollwerk.

OFFICE OF PROFESSIONAL RESPONSIBILITY

RFK Main Justice Building, Room 3266, phone (202) 514–3365

Counsel.—Robin C. Ashton.
Deputy Counsel.—G. Bradley Weinsheimer.
Senior Associate Counsel.—William J. Birney.
Associate Counsels: Raymond C. "Neil" Hurley, Margaret McCarty.
Senior Counsel.— Lyn Hardy.
Senior Assistant Counsels: Suzanne Drouet, Frederick Leiner, Mark Masling.
Assistant Counsels: Allison Barlotta, Sarah Cable, Paul Colby, Mark G. Fraase, Amy Goldfrank, Gregory Gonzalez, Albert Herring, Cathleen Mahoney, Noreen McCarthy, John Sciortino, James Vargason, Barbara Ward.

PROFESSIONAL RESPONSIBILITY ADVISORY OFFICE

1425 New York Avenue, NW., 20530, phone (202) 514–0458

Director.—Jerri Dunston.
Deputy Director.—Stacy Ludwig.

OFFICE OF PUBLIC AFFAIRS

RFK Main Justice Building, Room 1220, phone (202) 514–2007

Director.—Nanda Chitre (acting).
Deputy Director.—Gina M. Talamona.

TAX DIVISION

RFK Main Justice Building, 950 Pennsylvania Avenue, NW., 20530

Judiciary Center Building, 555 Fourth Street, NW., 20001 (JCB)

Maxus Energy Tower, 7717 North Harwood Street, Suite 400, Dallas, TX 75242 (MAX)

Patrick Henry Building, 601 D Street, NW., 20004 (PHB)

Assistant Attorney General.—Kathryn Keneally, room 4141 (202) 514–2901.
Deputy Assistant Attorneys General: Ronald A. Cimino, room 4603 (Main) 514–2915 (Criminal Matters); David A. Hubbert, room 4137 (Main), 514–5109 (Civil Trial Matters); Tamara W. Ashford, room 4609 (Main), 514–3361 (Appellate and Review, Principal/ Policy and Planning).
Senior Legislative Counsel.—Eileen M. Shatz, room 4134 (Main), 307–6419.
Civil Trial Section Chiefs:
Central Region.—Seth Heald (JCB), room 8921–B, 514–6502.
Eastern Region.—Deborah S. Meland (JCB), room 6126, 307–6426.
Northern Region.—D. Patrick Mullarkey, (JCB), room 7804–A, 307–6490.
Southern Region.—Michael Kearns (JCB), room 6243–A, 514–5905.
Southwestern Region.—Louise P. Hytken (MAX), room 4100 (214) 880–9725.
Western Region.—Richard R. Ward (JCB), room 7907–B, 307–6413.
Criminal Enforcement Section Chiefs:
Northern Region.—Rosemary E. Paguni (PHB), room 7334, 514–2323.
Southern Region.—Bruce Salad (PHB), room 7640, 514–5145.
Western Region.—Mitchell J. Ballweg (PHB), room 7038, 514–5762.
Section Chiefs:
Appellate.—Gilbert S. Rothenberg, room 4326, 514–3361.
Court of Federal Claims.—David I. Pincus (JCB), room 8804–A, 307–6440.
Criminal Appeals and Tax Enforcement Policy.—Frank Cihlar (PHB), room 7002, 514–2839.
Office of Review.—Ann Carroll Reid (acting), (JCB), room 8921–D, 514–6636.
Executive Officer.—Robert Bruffy (PHB), room 10002, (202) 616–8412.

UNITED STATES MARSHALS SERVICE (USMS)

2604 Jefferson Davis Highway, Alexandria, VA 20022

[Use (202) for 307 and 305 exchanges]

Communications Center (202) 307–9100

Director.—Stacia A. Hylton (202) 307–9000, fax (703) 603–7021.
Deputy Director.—James Thompson (acting), 307–9005.
Chief of Staff.—Donald O'Hearn, 307–9841.
Associate Director for Administration.—Steve Mertens, 305–8572.
Associate Director for Operations.—David Harlow, 307–9001.
Chief, Congressional Affairs.—Jennifer Eskra (acting), 307–9220, fax (703) 603–2819.
Chief, Public Affairs.—Drew Wade, 307–9065.

OFFICE OF EQUAL EMPLOYMENT OPPORTUNITY

Equal Employment Opportunity Officer.—Marcus Williams, 307–9048, fax (703) 603–7005.

OFFICE OF THE GENERAL COUNSEL

General Counsel.—Gerald M. Auerbach, 307–9054, fax (703) 603–7022.

OFFICE OF INSPECTION

Assistant Director.—Michael Prout, 307–9155.

ASSET FORFEITURE DIVISION

Assistant Director.—Kim Beal (acting), 305–8572, fax (703) 308–0374.

FINANCIAL SERVICES DIVISION

Assistant Director.—Holley O'Brien, 307–9037, fax (703) 603–2033.

HUMAN RESOURCES DIVISION

Assistant Director.—Katherine Mohan, 307–9625, fax (703) 603–7023.

INFORMATION TECHNOLOGY DIVISION

Assistant Director.—Shannon Brown (703) 604–2054, fax (703) 603–7003.

MANAGEMENT SUPPORT DIVISION

Assistant Director.—Aldean Lee, 307–9011, fax (703) 603–2032.

TRAINING DIVISION

Federal Law Enforcement Training Center, Building 20, Glynco, GA 31524

Assistant Director.—William Fallon (912) 267–2505, fax (912) 267–2882.

INVESTIGATIVE OPERATIONS DIVISION

Assistant Director.—William Snelson, 307–9110, fax (703) 603–7006.

JUSTICE PRISONER AND ALIEN TRANSPORTATION SYSTEM (JPATS)

1251 Northwest Briar Cliff Parkway, Suite 300, Kansas City, MO 64116

Assistant Director.—David Musel (816) 467–1900, fax (816) 467–1980.

JUDICIAL SECURITY DIVISION

Assistant Director.—Carl Caulk, 307–9500, fax (703) 307–5206.
Deputy Assistant Director, Judicial Operations.—Thomas Wight.
Deputy Assistant Director, Judicial Services.—Noelle Douglas.

PRISONER OPERATIONS DIVISION

Assistant Director.—David Musel (acting), 307–5100, fax (703) 603–7008.
Deputy Assistant Director, Office of the Federal Detention Trustee (OFDT).—Bruce Vargo.
Deputy Assistant Director, Prisoner Operations.—Joseph Johnson (acting).

TACTICAL OPERATIONS DIVISION

Assistant Director.—Derrick Driscoll (acting), 307–3437, fax 307–3446.

WITNESS SECURITY DIVISION

Assistant Director.—Sylvester Jones, 307–9150.

U.S. PAROLE COMMISSION

90 K Street, NE., 3rd Floor, 20530, phone (202) 346–7000, fax (202) 357–1085

Chairman.—Isaac Fulwood, Jr.
Vice Chairman.—Cranston J. Mitchell.
Commissioners: Patricia K. Cushwa, Charles T. Massarone, J. Patricia Wilson Smoot.
Case Operations Administrator.—Stephen J. Husk.
Case Services Administrator.—Deirdre M. McDaniel.
General Counsel.—Rockne J. Chickinell.
Chief Information Officer.—Jonathan H. Pinkerton.
Executive Officer.—Judy I. Carter.
Staff Assistant to the Chairman.—Patricia W. Moore.

OFFICE ON VIOLENCE AGAINST WOMEN

145 N Street, NE., Suites 10W.121, 20530

Director.—Bea Hanson (acting), (202) 307–6026.
Principal Deputy Director.—Bea Hanson (202) 307–6026.
Deputy Director for—
Grants Development and Management.—Nadine Neufville, 305–2590.
Policy, Communication and Evaluation.—Virginia Davis, 305–9660.
Tribal Affairs.—Lorraine Edmo, 514–8804.
Senior Attorney-Advisor.—Jennifer Kaplan.

DEPARTMENT OF THE INTERIOR

Interior Building, 1849 C Street, NW., 20240, phone (202) 208–3100, http://www.doi.gov

SALLY JEWELL, Secretary of the Interior; born in England, UK, 1955; education: graduate of the University of Washington, Seattle; professional: served in the private sector, most recently as President and Chief Executive Officer of Recreation Equipment, Inc. (REI); joined REI as Chief Operating Officer in 2000 and was named CEO in 2005; before joining REI, spent 19 years as a commercial banker; first as an energy and natural resources expert and later working with a diverse array of businesses that drive our nation's economy; trained as a petroleum engineer, started her career with Mobil Oil Corp. in the oil and gas fields of Oklahoma and the exploration and production office in Denver, CO, where she was exposed to the remarkable diversity of our nation's oil and gas resources; nominated by President Barack Obama to become the 51th Secretary of the Interior, and was confirmed by the U.S. Senate on April 10, 2013.

OFFICE OF THE SECRETARY

Secretary of the Interior.—Sally Jewell, room 6156, 208–7351.
Special Assistant/Director, Scheduling and Advance.—Francis Iacobucci, room 6243.
Special Assistant.—Erin Walls.
Chief of Staff.—Laura Davis, room 6144.
Deputy Chief of Staff.—Nicole ''Nikki'' Buffa, room 6140.
Senior Advisors to the Secretary: Sarah Greenberger, room 6128; Joan Padilla, room 6142.
Director of External and Intergovernmental Affairs.—Gail Adams, room 6311, 208–1923.
Senior Advisor for Alaska Affairs.—Vacant, room 6020, 208–4177.
Counselor to the Secretary.—Steve Black, room 6130, 208–4123.

EXECUTIVE SECRETARIAT

Director.—Fay Iudicello, room 7314, 208–3181.

CONGRESSIONAL AND LEGISLATIVE AFFAIRS

Director.—Vacant, room 6256, 208–7264.
Deputy Directors: Jason Buckner, room 6254; Stephenne Harding, room 6252.
Legislative Counsel.—Chris Salotti, room 6259.

OFFICE OF COMMUNICATIONS

Director.—Kate Kelly, room 6210, 208–6416.
Deputy Director.—Blake Androff, room 6212.
Press Secretary.—Vacant.
Director of Digital Strategy.—Tim Fullerton.
Information Officers: Joan Moody, Frank Quimby, Hugh Vickery.

OFFICE OF THE DEPUTY SECRETARY

Deputy Secretary.—David Hayes, room 6117, 208–6291.
Associate Deputy Secretary.—Elizabeth Klein, room 6117, 208–6291.
Counselor to Deputy Secretary.—Letty Belin, 208–6291, room 6116.
Special Assistant to the Deputy Secretary.—James Anderson, room 6125, 208–4591.
Chief of Staff.—Lizzie Marsters, 208–6291, room 6118.

ASSISTANT SECRETARY FOR FISH AND WILDLIFE AND PARKS

Assistant Secretary.—Vacant, room 3160 (202) 208–5347.
Principal Deputy Assistant Secretary.—Rachel Jacobson, room 3160, 208–5347.
Deputy Assistant Secretary.—Eileen Sobeck, room 3151, 208–4416.
Chief of Staff.—Vacant.

U.S. FISH AND WILDLIFE SERVICE

Director.—Dan Ashe (202) 208–4717.
Deputy Directors: Rowan Gould, 208–4545; Steve Guertin, 208–4545.
Counsel to Assistant Secretary.—Michael Bean, room 3152, 508–4416.
Chief, Office of Law Enforcement.—William Woody, 208–3809.
Assistant Director for External Affairs.—Vacant, 208–6541.
Chief, Division of:
Congressional and Legislative Affairs.—Matt Huggler (703) 358–2243.
Public Affairs.—Chris Tollefson (703) 358–2222.
Assistant Director for—
Migratory Birds.—Paul Schmidt, 208–1050.
Budget, Planning, and Human Capital.—Denise Sheehan (703) 358–2400.
Business Management and Operations.—Vacant (703) 358–1822.
Endangered Species.—Gary Frazer, 208–4646.
Fisheries and Habitat Conservation.—Vacant, 208–6394.
Information Resources and Technology Management.—Kenneth Taylor (703) 358–1729.
International Affairs.—Bryan Arroyo, 208–6393.
Wildlife and Sport Fish Restoration.—Hannibal Bolton, 208–7337.
Chief, National Wildlife Refuge System.—Jim Kurth, 208–5333.

Regional Directors:
Region 1.—Robyn Thorson, Eastside Federal Complex, 911 Northeast 11th Avenue, Portland, OR 97232 (503) 231–6118, fax 872–2716.
Region 2.—Benjamin Tuggle, Room 1306, 500 Gold Avenue, SW., Albuquerque, NM 87103 (505) 248–6845, fax (503) 872–2716.
Region 3.—Thomas Melius, Federal Building, Fort Snelling, Twin Cities, MN 55111 (612) 713–5301, fax 713–5284.
Region 4.—Cynthia Dohner, 1875 Century Boulevard, Atlanta, GA 30345 (404) 679–4000, fax 679–4006.
Region 5.—Wendi Weber, 300 Westgate Center Drive, Hadley, MA 01035 (413) 253–8300, fax 253–8308.
Region 6.—Noreen Walsh, 134 Union Boulevard, #400, Lakewood, CO 80228 (303) 236–7920, fax 236–8295.
Region 7.—Geoff Hasketts, 1011 East Tudor Road, Anchorage, AK 99503 (907) 786–3542, fax 786–3306.
Region 8.—Renne Lohoefener, 2800 Cottage Way, #W2606, Sacramento, CA 95825 (916) 414–6464, fax 414–6484.

NATIONAL PARK SERVICE

Director.—Jon Jarvis, room 3112 (202) 208–4621.
Deputy Director, Operations.—Peggy O'Dell, room 3113, 208–3818.
Deputy Director, Communications and Community Assistance.—Vacant.
Chief of Staff.—Maureen Foster, room 3114, 208–3818.
Associate Director for—
Business Services.—Lena McDowall, room 2274, 208–5651.
Cultural Resources.—Stephanie Toothman, room 3128, 208–7625.
Information Resources.—Shane Compton, Eye Street (202) 354–1478.
Interpretation and Education.—Julia Washburn, room 3129, 208–4829.
Natural Resource Stewardship and Science.—Bert Frost, room 3130, 208–3884.
Park Planning, Facilities, and Lands.—Victor Knox, room3124, 208–3264.
Visitor and Resource Protection.—Cam Sholly, room 3120, 565–1020.
Workforce Management.—David Vela, room 3129, 208–5587.
Comptroller.—Bruce Sheaffer, room 2280, 208–4566.
Assistant Director for—
Communications.—Sue Waldron, room 3320, 208–3046.
Legislative and Congressional Affairs.—Don Hellmann, room 3309, 208–5656.
Partnerships and Civic Engagement.—Rich Weideman, Eye Street (202) 354–2150.

Regional Directors:
Alaska.—Sue Masica, 240 West Fifth Avenue, Room 114, Anchorage, AK 99501 (907) 644–3510, fax 644–3816.
Intermountain.—John Wessels, P.O. Box 25287, 12795 West Alameda Parkway, Denver, CO 80225 (303) 969–2500, fax 969–2785.
Midwest.—Michael Reynolds, 601 Riverfront Drive, Omaha, NE 68102 (402) 661–1736, fax 661–1737.
National Capital.—Steve Whitesell, 1100 Ohio Drive, SW., Washington, DC 20242 (202) 619–7000, fax 619–7220.
Northeast.—Dennis Reidenbach, U.S. Custom House, 200 Chestnut Street, Suite 306, Philadelphia, PA 19106 (215) 597–7013, fax 597–0815.
Southeast.—Vacant, 100 Alabama Street, NW., 1924 Building, Atlanta, GA 30303 (404) 562–3327, fax 562–3216.
Pacific West.—Christine Lehnertz, 333 Bush Street, Suite 500, San Francisco, CA 94104–2828, fax (415) 623–2101.

ASSISTANT SECRETARY FOR INDIAN AFFAIRS

Assistant Secretary.—Kevin K. Washburn, room 4160, 208–7163.
Principal Deputy Assistant Secretary.—Lawrence Roberts (acting), 208–7163.
Deputy Assistant Secretary for—
Management.—Thomas Thompson, 208–3508.
Chief of Staff.—Sarah E. Harris, 208–7163.
Director of:
Congressional Affairs.—Darren Pete, 208–5610.
Public Affairs.—Nedra Darling, 219–4150.

BUREAU OF INDIAN AFFAIRS

Director.—Mike Black (202) 208–5116.
Deputy Director of:
Field Operations.—Michael Smith, 208–5116.
Justice Services.—Darren Cruzan, 208–5787.
Tribal Services.—Hankie Ortiz (202) 513–7640.
Trust Services.—Bryan Rice, 208–5831.

BUREAU OF INDIAN EDUCATION

Director.—Charles ''Monty'' Roessel (acting), (202) 208–6123.
Assistant Deputy Director:
Administration.—David Talayumptewa (505) 563–5227.
Associate Deputy Director:
East.—Roxanne Brown (952) 851–5420.
Division of Performance and Accountability.—Jeff Hamley (505) 563–5260.
Navajo.—Charles ''Monty'' Roessel (928) 871–5961.
West.—Bart Stevens (505) 563–5227.

ASSISTANT SECRETARY FOR LAND AND MINERALS MANAGEMENT

Assistant Secretary.—Tommy Beaudreau (acting), room 6612 (202) 208–6734.
Deputy Assistant Secretary.—Ned Farquhar, room 6614.

BUREAU OF LAND MANAGEMENT

Director.—Neil Kornze (acting), room 5661 (202) 208–3801.
Principal Deputy Director.—Neil Kornze, room 5661 (202) 208–3801.
Deputy Director of:
Operations.—Jamie Connell.
Programs and Policy.—Vacant.
Division Chief, Legislative Affairs and Correspondence.—Patrick Wilkerson (202) 912–7429.
Deputy Division Chief.—Andrea Nelson (202) 912–7431.
State Directors:
Alaska.—Bud Cribley, 222 West Seventh Avenue, No. 13, Anchorage, AK 99513 (907) 271–5080, fax 271–4596.

Arizona.—Ray Suazo, One North Central Avenue, Phoenix, AZ 85004 (602) 417–9500, fax 417–9398.

California.—Jim Kenna, 2800 Cottage Way, Suite W1834, Sacramento, CA 95825 (916) 978–4600, fax 978–4699.

Colorado.—Helen Hankins, 2850 Youngfield Street, Lakewood, CO 80215 (303) 239–3700, fax 239–3934.

Eastern States.—Dr. John Lyon, 7450 Boston Boulevard, Springfield, VA 22153 (703) 440–1700, fax 440–1701.

Idaho.—Steven Ellis, 1387 South Vinnell Way, Boise, ID 83709 (208) 373–4000, fax 373–3919.

Montana.—Jamie Connell, 5001 Southgate Drive, Billings, MT 59101 (406) 896–5012, fax 896–5004.

Nevada.—Amy Lueders, 1340 Financial Boulevard, Reno, NV 89502 (775) 861–6590, fax 861–6601.

New Mexico.—Jesse Juen, 1474 Rodeo Road, P.O. Box 27115, Sante Fe, NM 87505 (505) 438–7501, fax 438–7452.

Oregon.—Jerome Perez, 333 Southwest 1st Avenue, P.O. Box 2965, Portland, OR 97204 (503) 808–6024, fax 808–6308.

Utah.—Juan Palma, 440 West 200 South, Suite 500, P.O. Box 45155, Salt Lake City, UT 84101 (801) 539–4010, fax 539–4013.

Wyoming.—Don Simpson, 5353 Yellowstone Road, P.O. Box 1828, Cheyenne, WY 82003 (307) 775-6001, fax 775–6028.

BUREAU OF OCEAN ENERGY MANAGEMENT, REGULATION AND ENFORCEMENT

Director.—James A. Watson (202) 208–3500.

Deputy Director.—Margaret N. Schneider.

Chief of Administration.—Scott Mabry (202) 208–3220.

Budget.—Eric Modrow (703) 787–1694.

Offshore Regulatory Programs.—Doug Morris (202) 208–3974.

Policy and Analysis.—John Keith (202) 208–3236.

Congressional Affairs.—Julie Fleming (202) 208–3827.

Outer Continental Shelf Regional Directors:

Alaska.—Mark Fesmire, 3801 Centerpoint Drive, Suite 500, Anchorage, AK 99503 (907) 334–5300.

Gulf of Mexico.—Lars T. Herbst, 1201 Elmwood Park Boulevard, New Orleans, LA 70123 (504) 736–2589.

Pacific.—Jaron Ming, 770 Paseo Camarillo, Camarillo, CA 93010 (805) 389–7514.

OFFICE OF SURFACE MINING RECLAMATION AND ENFORCEMENT

Director.—Joseph G. Pizarchik, room 233 (202) 208–4006.

Deputy Director.—Glenda Owens, 208–4006.

Assistant Director for Finance and Administration.—Ted Woronka, 208–2546.

Congressional Contact.—Peter Mali, 208–2566.

Regional Director for—

Appalachian Region.—Thomas D. Shope, Three Parkway Center, Pittsburgh, PA 15220 (412) 937–2828, fax 937–2903.

Mid-Continent Region.—Ervin Barchenger, 501 Belle Street, Room 216, Alton, IL 62002 (618) 463–6460, fax 463–6470.

Western Region.—Allen D. Klein, 1999 Broadway, Suite 3320, Denver, CO 80202 (303) 293–5001, fax 293–5006.

ASSISTANT SECRETARY FOR POLICY, MANAGEMENT AND BUDGET

Assistant Secretary.—Rhea Suh, room 5113 (202) 208–1927.

Deputy Assistant Secretary for—

Budget, Finance, Performance and Acquisition.—Pam Haze, 208–4775.

Human Capital and Diversity.—Pam Malam, 208–1738.

Natural Resources Revenue Management.—Paui Mussenden, 208–2842.

Policy and International Affairs.—Lori Faeth, 208–4852.

Public Safety, Resource Protection, and Emergency Services.—Kim Thorsen, 208–5773.

Technology, Information and Business Services.—Andrew Jackson, 208–7966.

Youth, Partnership and Service.—Michael Gale, 208–1508.

ASSISTANT SECRETARY FOR WATER AND SCIENCE

Assistant Secretary.—Anne J. Castle, room 6657 (202) 208–3186.
Principal Deputy Assistant Secretary.—Lori Caramanian.
Deputy Assistant Secretary.—Tom Iseman.
Chief of Staff.—Kerry Rae, room 6645 (202) 513–0535.

U.S. GEOLOGICAL SURVEY

The National Center, 12201 Sunrise Valley Drive, Reston, VA 20192
phone (703) 648–7411, fax 648–4454

Director.—Suzette M. Kimball (acting), 648–7412.
Deputy Director.—William Werkheiser (acting), 648–4557.
Chief of Staff.—Judy Nowakowski (703) 648–4411.
Office of:
Administrative Policy and Services.—Diane Wade, 648–7200.
Budget and Performance.—Carla Burzyk, 648–4443.
Communications and Outreach.—Barbara Wainman, 648–5750.
Congressional Liaison Officer.—Timothy J. West, 648–4300.
Human Capital.—Diane Wade, 648–7200.
Public Affairs Officer.—Anne-Berry Wade, 648–4483.
Associate Directors for—
Climate and Land Use Change.—Matthew Larsen (703) 648–5212.
Core Science Systems.—Kevin Gallagher, 648–5747.
Ecosystems.—Anne Kinsinger, 648–4050.
Energy and Minerals, and Environmental Health.—Ione Taylor, 648–6403.
Natural Hazards.—David Applegate, 648–6600.
Water Resources.—Jared Bales, 648–5044.
Regional Directors for—
Northeast Area.—David Russ, 12201 Sunrise Valley Drive, Reston, VA 20192 (703) 648–6600.
Southeast Area.—Jess Weaver, 3850 Holcomb Bridge Road, Suite 160, Norcross, GA 30092 (770) 409–7701.
Midwest Area.—Leon Carl, 1451 Green Road, Anne Arbor, MI 48105 (734) 214–7201.
Southwest Area.—Randall Updike, P.O. Box 25046, Denver Federal Center, Building 810, Denver, CO 80225 (303) 236–5438.
Northwest Area.—Max Ethridge, Federal Office Building, 909 First Avenue, 8th Floor, Seattle, WA 98104 (206) 220–4600.
Pacific Area.—Richard Ferrero (acting), Modoc Hall, 3020 State University Drive East, Sacramento, CA 95819 (206) 795–4527.
Alaska.—Leslie Holland-Bartels, 4230 University Drive, Suite 201, Anchorage, AK 99508 (907) 786–7055.

BUREAU OF RECLAMATION

Commissioner.—Michael Connor, room 7657 (202) 513–0501.
Deputy Commissioner for—
External and Intergovernmental Affairs.—Vacant, room 7645, 513–0615.
Operations.—Lowell Pimley, room 7653, 513–0615.
Policy, Administration, and Budget.—Grayford Payne, room 7650, 513–0542.
Chief of Staff.—Robert Quint, room 7641.
Chief of:
Congressional and Legislative Affairs.—Dionne Thompson, room 7643, 513–0570.
Public Affairs.—Daniel J. DuBray, room 7644, 513–0574.
Regional Directors:
Great Plains.—Michael J. Ryan, P.O. Box 36900, Billings, MT 59107 (406) 247–7795, fax 247–7793.
Lower Colorado.—Terrance Fulp, P.O. Box 61470, Boulder City, NV 89006 (702) 293–8000, fax 293–8333.
Mid-Pacific.—David Murillo, 2800 Cottage Way, Sacramento, CA 95825 (916) 978–5000, fax 978–5005.
Pacific Northwest.—Lorri Lee, 1150 North Curtis Road, Suite 100, Boise, ID 83706 (208) 378–5012, fax 378–5019.
Upper Colorado.—Larry Walkoviak, 125 South State Street, room 6107, Salt Lake City, UT 84138 (801) 524–3600, fax 524–3855.

OFFICE OF INSPECTOR GENERAL

Inspector General.—Vacant, room 4411 (202) 208–5745.
Deputy Inspector General.—Mary Kendall, room 4411 (202) 208–5745.
Chief of Staff.—Stephen Hardgrove, room 4410 (202) 208–5745.
Associate Inspector General for Whistleblower Protection.—Laurie Larson-Jackson, room 4429.
Associate Inspector General for External Affairs.—Kris Kolesnik, room 4422.

OFFICE OF THE SOLICITOR

Solicitor.—Hilary C. Tompkins, room 6415 (202) 208–4423.
Principal Deputy Solicitor.—K. Jack Haugrud (acting).
Deputy Solicitors for—
General Law.—Ed Keable.
Indian Affairs.—Patrice Kunesh.
Land Resources.—Ted Boling.
Mineral Resources.—K. Jack Haugrud.
Parks and Wildlife.—Vacant.
Water.—Fritz Holleman.
Deputy Solicitors for—
General Law.—Mark Teskey.
Indian Affairs.—Michael Berrigan.
Land and Water.—Laura Brown.
Mineral Resources.—Karen Hawbecker.
Parks and Wildlife.—Barry Roth.
Senior Counsel CADR.—Shayla Simmons.
Designated Agency Ethics Official.—Melinda Loftin, 208–5295.

OFFICE OF THE SPECIAL TRUSTEE FOR AMERICAN INDIANS

Principal Deputy Special Trustee.—Michele Singer (acting), (202) 208–3946.

DEPARTMENT OF AGRICULTURE

Jamie L. Whitten Building, 1400 Independence Avenue, SW., 20250
phone (202) 720–3631, http://www.usda.gov

TOM VILSACK, Secretary of Agriculture; education: B.A., Hamilton College; J.D., Albany Law School; professional: Governor, Iowa, 1999–2007; nominated by President Barack Obama to become the 30th Secretary of Agriculture, and was confirmed by the U.S. Senate on January 20, 2009.

OFFICE OF THE SECRETARY

Secretary of Agriculture.—Tom Vilsack, room 200–A (202) 720–3631.
Deputy Secretary.—Michael Scuse (acting).
Chief of Staff.—Krysta Harden.
Deputy Chief of Staff for Operations.—Oscar Gonzales.
Deputy Chief of Staff for Policy.—Anne MacMillan.

ASSISTANT SECRETARY FOR ADMINISTRATION

Jamie L. Whitten Building, Room 240–W, phone (202) 720–3291

Assistant Secretary.—Dr. Gregory Parham.
Deputy Assistant Secretaries: Robin Heard, Curtis Wiley (acting).
Executive Assistant.—Francesca Yabraian.
Senior Advisor.—Elizabeth Reiter.
Special Assistant.—Carlissia Graham.

OFFICE OF ADMINISTRATIVE LAW JUDGES

South Agriculture Building, Room 1070–S, phone (202) 720–6383

Chief Administrative Law Judge.—Peter Davenport.
Secretary to the Chief Administrative Law Judge.—Diane Green.
Administrative Law Judges: Jill S. Clifton, Victor W. Palmer, 720–8161.
Hearing Clerk.—Leslie E. Whitfield, 720–4443.

OFFICE OF HUMAN RESOURCES MANAGEMENT

Jamie L. Whitten Building, Room 302–W, phone (202) 720–3585

Director.—William Milton.
Secretary.—Melanie Clemons.
Deputy Director.—Bobbi Jeanquart.
Division Director for—
Departmental Human Resources and Executive Resources.—Rhonda Carr, 720–2101.
Employee Recruitment/Development.—Monshi Radass, 720–5618.

OFFICE OF THE JUDICIAL OFFICER

South Agriculture Building, Room 1449–S, phone (202) 720–4764

Judicial Officer.—William G. Jenson.
Attorney.—Stephen Reilly.
Legal Technician.—Gloria Derobertis.

OFFICE OF MANAGEMENT SERVICES

Office of Management Services.—Rick Swenson (202) 720–9824.

Secretary.—Nanette McGraw.
Director of:
Budget Formulation Division.—Telora Dean, 690–1331.

OFFICE OF OPERATIONS

South Agriculture Building, Room 1456–S, phone (202) 720–3937

Director.—Curtis Wilburn.
Director, Office of:
Facilities.—Valencia Winstead, 720–2804.
Management Services.—Morris Tate.
Director for—
Beltsville Service Center.—Randall Carter (301) 394–0410.
Mail and Reproduction.—Michele Lambert, 720–8393.
Washington Area Service Center.—Steve Law, 720–2777.

OFFICE OF PROCUREMENT AND PROPERTY MANAGEMENT

Reporters Building, Room 302, phone (202) 720–9448

Director.—Lisa Wilusz.
Division Director for—
Procurement Operations.—Shawn Kerkes, 690–0142.
Procurement Policy.—Dorothy Lilly, 690–1060.
Procurement Systems.—Vacant, 401–1023.
Property Management.—Vacant, 720–7283.
Radiation Safety.—John Jensen (301) 504–2440.

OFFICE OF HOMELAND SECURITY

Director.—Todd Repass, room S–310 (202) 720–0272.
Division Chief for—
Continuity of Operations Planning.—Jessica Pulz, 720–2667.
Personnel and Document Security.—Cody Allers, 720–7373.
Physical Security.—Richard Holman, 720–3901.
Director, Office of:
Emergency Programs.—Todd Barrett, 690–3191.
Protective Operations.—Daniel Downy, 720–6270.

OFFICE OF SMALL AND DISADVANTAGED BUSINESS UTILIZATION

South Agriculture Building, Room 1085–S, phone (202) 720–7117

Director.—Carmen Jones.

ASSISTANT SECRETARY FOR CIVIL RIGHTS

Jamie L. Whitten Building, Room 240–W, phone (202) 720–3808

Assistant Secretary.—Joe Leonard, Jr., Ph.D.
Deputy Assistant Secretary.—Lisa Pino.

OFFICE OF BUDGET AND PROGRAM ANALYSIS

Jamie L. Whitten Building, Room 101–A, phone (202) 720–3323

Director.—Michael L. Young.
Associate Director.—Don Bice, 720–5303.
Deputy Director for—
Budget, Legislative and Regulatory Systems.—Diem-Linh Jones, room 102–E, 720–6667.
Program Analysis.—Christopher Zehren, room 126–W, 720–3396.

OFFICE OF THE CHIEF ECONOMIST

Jamie L. Whitten Building, Room 112–A, phone (202) 720–4164

Chief Economist.—Joseph W. Glauber.
Deputy Chief Economist.—James Hrubovcak, room 112–A, 720–4737.
Chairperson, World Agricultural Outlook Board.—Gerald A. Bange, room 4419–S, 720–6030.
Chief Meteorologist.—Ray Motha, room 4441–S, 720–8651.
Global Change Program Office.—William Hohenstein, room 4407–S, 720–6698.
Office of:
Energy Policy and New Uses.—Harry Baumes, room 4059–S, 401–0461.
Risk Assessment and Cost Benefit Analysis.—James D. Schaub, room 4032–S, 720–8022.
Sustainable Development.—Elise Golan, room 112–A, 720–2456.
Supervisory Meteorologist, National Weather Service.—Mark Brusberg, room 4443–S, 720–6030.

OFFICE OF THE CHIEF FINANCIAL OFFICER

Jamie L. Whitten Building, Room 143–W, phone (202) 720–5539

Chief Financial Officer.—Jon Holladay (acting).
Deputy Chief Financial Officer.—Jon M. Holladay, room 143–W, 720–0727.
Associate Chief Financial Officers for—
Financial Operations.—John Brewer, room 3053–S, 720–9427.
Financial Policy and Planning.—Kim Farington.
Financial Systems.—Michael Clanton, room 3057–S, 690–3068.
Director, National Finance Center.—John White, P.O. Box 60000, New Orleans, LA 70160 (504) 426–0120.

OFFICE OF THE CHIEF INFORMATION OFFICER

Jamie L. Whitten Building, Room 414–W, phone (202) 720–8833

Chief Information Officer.—Cheryl Cook.
Deputy Chief Information Officer for—
Policy and Architecture.—Charles McClam, 720–8833.
Policy and Planning.—Joyce Hunter.
Associate Chief Information Officer for—
Cyber and Privacy Policy and Oversight.—Richard Coffee, 690–0048.
Data Center Operations (National Information Technology Center).—Kent Armstrong, 8930 Ward Parkway, Kansas City, MO 64114 (816) 926–6501.
International Security Operations Center.—Chris Lowe, 720–5939.
International Technology Services.—David Shearer, 2150 Centre Avenue, Building A, Fort Collins, CO 80526 (970) 295–5020.
Director for—
Distance Learning Program.—Jerome Davin, 694–0006.
Innovations and Operational Architecture.—Owen Unangst, 2150 Centre Avenue, Building A, Fort Collins, CO 80526 (970) 295–5538.
Resource Management.—Lisa Keeter, 720–4109.
Telecommunications Services and Operations.—John Donovan, 720–8695.

OFFICE OF COMMUNICATIONS

Jamie L. Whitten Building, Room 402–A, phone (202) 720–4623

Director.—Matt Paul.
Deputy Director for—
Creative Development.—David Black.
Public Affairs.—Justin DeJong.
Press Secretary.—Courtney Rowe.
Center Director for—
Brand Review.—Carolyn O'Connor.
Broadcast Media and Technology.—Garth Clark.
Constituent Affairs.—Vacant.

Information Technology.—Wayne Moore.
Web Communication.—Amanda Eamich.

OFFICE OF CONGRESSIONAL RELATIONS

Jamie L. Whitten Building, Room 212–A, phone (202) 720–7095

Assistant Secretary.—Brian Baenig.
Deputy Assistant Secretary.—Ann Wright.
Congressional Liaisons:
Farm and Foreign Agricultural Service.—Ashley Martin.
Food Safety.—Ashley Martin.
Food, Nutrition and Consumer Services.—Callie Varner.
Marketing and Regulatory Programs.—Ann Wright.
Forest Service.—Kevin Bailey.
Natural Resources Conservation Service.—Callie Varner.
Research, Education and Economics.—Ashley Martin.
Rural Development.—Kevin Bailey.

EXTERNAL AND INTERGOVERNMENTAL AFFAIRS

Room 216–A, phone (202) 720–6643

Director.—Jennifer Yezak.
Deputy Director.—Sarah Scanlon.

OFFICE OF TRIBAL AFFAIRS

Room 544–A, phone (202) 690–1615

Director.—Leslie Wheelock.

OFFICE OF THE EXECUTIVE SECRETARIAT

Jamie L. Whitten Building, Room 116–A, phone (202) 720–7100

Director.—Sally Liska.
Deputy Director.—Maureen Wood.

OFFICE OF THE GENERAL COUNSEL

Jamie L. Whitten Building, Room 107–W, phone (202) 720–3351

General Counsel.—Ramona Romero.
Principal Deputy General Counsel.—Fred Pfaeffle.
Deputy General Counsel.—Inga Bumbary-Langston.
Associate General Counsel for—
Civil Rights, Labor and Employment Law.—Arlean Leland, 720–1760.
International Affairs, Food Assistance, and Farm and Rural Programs.—David P. Grahn, 720–8063.
General Law and Research.—Benjamin Young, 720–4814.
Marketing, Regulatory and Food Safety Programs.—Vacant, 720–9014.
Natural Resources and Environment.—Ralph Linden, 720–6883.
Assistant General Counsel, Division of:
Civil Rights Litigation.—Steven Brammer, 720–4375.
Civil Rights Policy, Compliance, and Counsel.—Tami Trost, 690–3993.
General Law and Research.—Shawn McGruder, 720–5565.
International Affairs, Food Assistance, and Farm and Rural Programs: Peter Bonner, 720–3569; Terence M. Brady, 720–8103.
Marketing, Regulatory and Food Safety.—James Booth, 720–3461; Carrie Ricci, 720–5935.
Natural Resources and Environment.—Vacant, 720–6716.
Director, Administration and Resource Management.—Charlene Buckner, 720–6324.
Resource Management Specialist.—Robyn Davis, 720–4861.

INSPECTOR GENERAL

Jamie L. Whitten Building, Room 117–W, phone (202) 720–8001, fax 690–1278

Inspector General.—Phyllis K. Fong.
Deputy Inspector General.—David Gray.
Assistant Inspector General for—
Audit.—Gil Harden, room 403–E, 720–6945.
Investigations.—Karen Ellis, room 507–A, 720–3306.
Management.—Suzanne Murrin, room 5–E, 720–6979.

NATIONAL APPEALS DIVISION

3101 Park Center Drive, Suite 1100, Alexandria, VA 22302

Director.—Roger J. Klurfeld (703) 305–2708.

UNDER SECRETARY FOR NATURAL RESOURCES AND ENVIRONMENT

Jamie L. Whitten Building, Room 217–E, phone (202) 720–7173

Under Secretary.—Michael Scuse.
Deputy Under Secretaries: Arthur Butch Blazer, Ann Mills.

FOREST SERVICE

Sydney R. Yates Building, 201 14th Street, SW., 20250, phone (202) 205–1661

Chief.—Thomas Tidwell.
Associate Chief.—Mary Wagner, 205–1779.
Director for—
International Programs.—Valdis E. Mezainis, 205–1650.
Law Enforcement and Investigations.—David Ferrell (703) 605–4690.
Legislative Affairs.—Douglas Crandall, 205–1637.

BUSINESS OPERATIONS

Sydney R. Yates Building, Fifth Floor, phone (202) 205–1707

Deputy Chief.—Charles L. Myers.
Associate Deputy Chiefs: Barbara Cooper, Jacqueline Myers, 205–1709.
Senior Staff Assistant.—Vacant, 401–4470.
Director for—
Acquisition Management.—Melissa Dyniec (703) 605–4744.
Budget and Financial Management.—Michael Clonts (505) 563–7103.
Civil Rights.—Debra Muse, 205–0827.
Freedom of Information/Privacy Act.—George Vargas (acting), 205–0444.
Homeland Security.—Arthur Bryant, 205–0942.
Human Resources Management.—Robin Bailey (503) 563–9700.
Information Resources Management.—Douglas Nash (505) 563–7978.
Job Corps.—Larry Dawson (303) 236–9939.
Regulatory and Management Services.—Thelma Strong, 205–5102.
Safety and Occupational Health.—Gary Helmer (703) 605–4482.
Strategic Program and Budget Analysis.—Kathleen Atkinson, 205–1088.

NATIONAL FOREST SYSTEM

Sydney R. Yates Building, Third Floor, phone (202) 205–1523

Deputy Chief.—Joel Holtrop.
Associate Deputy Chief.—Joe Meade.
Staff Director of:
Ecosystem Management Coordination.—Tony Tooke, 205–0895.
Engineering.—Lou Leibbrand (703) 605–4646.
Forest Management.—Nora Rasure, 205–0893.

Lands and Realty Staff.—Greg Smith, 205–1248.
Minerals and Geology Management.—Tony Ferguson (703) 605–4545.
Range Management.—Janette Kaiser, 205–0893.
Recreation and Heritage Resources.—Jim Bedwell, 205–0900.
Watershed, Fish, Wildlife, Air and Rare Plants.—Anne Zimmermann, 205–1671.
Wilderness, Wild and Scenic Resources.—Jeff Vail, 205–0925.

RESEARCH AND DEVELOPMENT

Sydney R. Yates Building, First Floor, phone (202) 205–1665

Deputy Chief.—Dr. Jim Reapes, 205–1665.
Associate Deputy Chief.—Angela Coleman, 205–1702.
Staff Assistants: Daina Apple, 205–1452; John Kusano, 205–1105.
Staff Director of:
Environmental Sciences.—Vacant (703) 605–5277.
Forest Management Sciences.—Carlos Rodriguez-Franco (703) 605–5252.
Policy Analysis.—William Lange, 205–1775.
Quantitative Sciences.—Richard W. Guldin (703) 605–4177.
Resource Use Sciences.—Vacant (703) 605–4880.
Science Quality Services.—John Sebelius (703) 605–5294.

STATE AND PRIVATE FORESTRY

Sydney R. Yates Building, Second Floor, phone (202) 205–1657

Deputy Chief.—James E. Hubbard, 205–1606.
Associate Deputy Chief.—Paul Ries.
Senior Advisor.—John Phipps.
Chief of Staff.—Debbie Pressman.
Director of:
Conservation Education.—Safiya Samman, 205–5681.
Cooperative Forestry.—Paul Ries, 205–1389.
Fire and Aviation Management.—Tom Harbour, 205–1483.
Forest Health Protection.—Rob Mangold (703) 605–5334.
Office of Tribal Relations.—Fred Clark, 205–1514.

NATURAL RESOURCES CONSERVATION SERVICE

South Building, Room 5105–A, phone (202) 720–7246

Chief.—Jason Weller (acting).
Associate Chiefs: James Gore; Virginia ''Ginger'' Murphy, 720–4531.
Director, Division of:
Civil Rights.—Gregory Singleton (301) 504–2181.
Legislative.—Keira Franz, 720–3210.
Public Affairs.—Patty Lawrence, 720–3210.

DEPUTY CHIEF FOR FINANCIAL MANAGEMENT

Chief Financial Officer.—David Morris, 720–5904, 720–4251.
Director Civil Rights.—Gregory Singleton.
Director Outreach.—Frank Clearfield.
Team Leaders:
Accounting Team.—Robin Aldridge, 205–5415.
Budget Team.—Selena Miller, 205–6134.
Fiscal Team.—Robin Kelly, 205–0113.

DEPUTY CHIEF OF MANAGEMENT

Deputy Chief.—Eloris Speight (acting), (202) 720–7847.
Ethics Officer.—Ellen Pearson (301) 205–1826.
Director, Division of:
Human Resources Management.—Yvette Gray, 720–2227.

Management Services.—Tim Beard, 720–4102.
National Employee Development Center.—Sandra Detter (817) 509–3242.
Chief Information Officer.—Gary Washington (970) 217–8185.
Supervisory Agency Representative.—Lauren Ruby (301) 504–2176.

DEPUTY CHIEF OF PROGRAMS

Deputy Chiefs: Diane Gilbert, 205–7704; Anthony Kramer (202) 720–4527.
Director, Division of:
Conservation Technical Assistance Division.—Andree DuVarney, 720–1854.
Financial Assistance Programs.—Gregory Johnson, 720–1845.
Watershed.—Keith Admire, 720–1510.

DEPUTY CHIEF OF SCIENCE AND TECHNOLOGY

Deputy Chief.—C. Wayne Honeycutt (202) 720–4630.
Director, Division of:
Conservation Engineering.—Noller Herbert, 720–2520.
Ecological Sciences.—Terrell Erickson, 720–5992.

DEPUTY CHIEF OF SOIL SURVEY AND RESOURCE ASSESSMENT

Deputy Chief.—Doug Lawrence (202) 690–4616.
Director, Division of:
International Programs.—Melvin Westbrook (301) 504–2271.
Resources Assessment.—Michele Laur.
Resources Inventory and Assessment.—Jeff Gobel (acting), (301) 504–2300.
Soil Survey.—Michael L. Golden, 720–1820.

DEPUTY CHIEF OF STRATEGIC PLANNING AND ACCOUNTABILITY

Deputy Chief.—Lesia Reed (202) 720–6297.
Director, Division of:
Budget Planning and Analysis.—Mary Koskinen, 720–4533.
Strategic and Performance Planning.—Craig Aiello, 720–8388.

UNDER SECRETARY FOR FARM AND FOREIGN AGRICULTURAL SERVICES

Under Secretary.—Michael Scuse.
Deputy Under Secretaries: Karis Gutter, 720–7107; Darci Vetter (202) 720–3111.
Special Assistant.—Jillian Semaan.
Administrative Assistants: Debra Anderson, Robin Anderson.

FARM SERVICE AGENCY

South Building, Room 3086–S, phone (202) 720–3467

Administrator.—Juan Garcia.
Associate Administrator for Operations and Management.—Carolyn Cooksie.
Civil Rights.—Johnny Toles, 410–7197.
Economic and Policy Analysis Staff.—Joy Harwood (acting), room 3741–S, 720–3451.
Deputy Administrator for Farm Programs.—Brandon Willis, room 3612–S, 720–3175.
Assistant Deputy Administrator.—Vacant, 720–2070.
Conservation and Environmental Programs Division.—Robert Stephenson, room 4714–S, 720–6221.
Price Support Division.—Soloman Whitfield, room 4095–S, 720–7901.
Production, Emergencies and Compliance Division.—Candice Thompson, room 4754, 720–7641.
Deputy Administrator for Farm Loan Programs.—Chris Beyerhelm, 720–4671.
Program Development and Economic Enhancement Division.—Nancy New, room 4919–S, 720–3647.
Loan Making Division.—Vacant, room 5438–S, 720–1632.
Loan Servicing and Property Management Division.—Michael Hinton, room 5449–S, 720–4572.

Deputy Administrator for Field Operations.—Michael Wooden, room 3092, 690–2807.
Assistant Deputy Administrator.—John W. Chott, Jr., room 8092, 690–2807.
Operations Review and Analysis Staff.—Phillip Sharp, room 2720–S, 690–2532.
Deputy Administrator for Commodity Operations.—James Monahan, room 3080–S, 720–3217.
Kansas City Commodity Office.—Vacant (816) 926–6301.
Deputy Administrator for Management.—Phil Short, room 3095–S, 720–3438.
Budget Division.—Ricky Valentine, room 4720–S.
Human Resources Division.—Jacqueline Whitaker, room 5200 (L–St), 418–8950.
Information Technology Services Division.—Jim Gwinn, room 5768–S, 720–5320.
Management Services Division.—Ezekiel Dennison, room 520–PRTL, 720–3438.

FOREIGN AGRICULTURAL SERVICE

South Building, Room 5071, phone (202) 720–3935, fax 690–2159

Administrator.—Phil Karsting.
Associate Administrator.—Janet Nuzum, 690–8108.
Director of:
Civil Rights Staff.—Daniel Whitley, 720–7061.
Legislative and Public Affairs.—Christopher Church, 720–6830.
Public Affairs and Executive Correspondence.—Sally Klusaritz, 720–4064.

OFFICE OF ADMINISTRATIVE OPERATIONS

Assistant Deputy Administrator.—Larry Bevan (202) 720–0690.
Senior Advisor.—David Pendlum, 720–1293.
Director, Division of:
Budget.—Scott Redman, 690–4052.
Information Technology.—Swarnali Haldar, 690–2936.
Knowledge Management.—Ted Goldammer, 720–3241.

OFFICE OF CAPACITY BUILDING AND DEVELOPMENT

Deputy Administrator.—Patricia R. Sheikh (202) 720–6887.
Assistant Deputy Administrator.—Roger Mireles, 690–1791.
Policy Coordination and Planning Staff.—Vacant, 720–1314.
Director, Division of:
Development Resources and Disaster Assistance.—Robert Curtis, 690–1924.
Food Assistance.—Ronald Croushorn, 720–4221.
Trade and Scientific Capacity Building.—Vacant, 690–4872.
Trade and Scientific Exchanges.—Ali Abdi, 690–1821.

OFFICE OF COUNTRY AND REGIONAL AFFAIRS

Deputy Administrator.—Lloyd Harbert (202) 720–7562.
Assistant Deputy Administrators: Jocelyn Brown, 690–1779; Mark Dries, 720–1134.
Director, Division of:
Africa and Middle East.—Stan Phillips, 720–1326.
Asia.—Cina Radler, 720–3403.
Europe.—Sharynne Nenon, 720–1330.
Western Hemisphere.—John Passino, 720–5219.

OFFICE OF FOREIGN SERVICE OPERATIONS

Deputy Administrator.—James Higgiston (202) 720–8322.
Assistant Deputy Administrator.—Bonnie Borris, 690–4062.
Director for—
Africa and Middle East Area.—Kim Svec, 690–4066.
Asia Area.—Susan Phillips, 690–4053.
Europe Area.—Michael Conlon, 690–4057.
Planning and Global Resources Staff.—Pamela Sherard, 720–1346.
Western Hemisphere Area.—Hugh Maginnis, 720–3223.

OFFICE OF GLOBAL ANALYSIS

Deputy Administrator.—Robert Riemenschneider (202) 720–6301.
Assistant Deputy Administrators: Ralph Gifford, 690–1198; Patrick Packnett, 720–1590.
Director, Division of:
Industry and Sector Analysis Division.—Tim Rocke, 690–0292.
International Production Assessment Division.—Derrick Williams, 720–2974.
Trade and Biofuels Analysis Division.—Mike Dwyer, 720–3124.

OFFICE OF AGREEMENTS AND SCIENTIFIC AFFAIRS

Assistant Deputy Administrators: Robert Macke, Gary Meyer, 720–4434.
Policy Formulation Staff:
Senior Trade Negotiator.—David Miller, 720–1324.
Planning and Operations Group:
Assistant to the Deputy Administrator: Barbara Wolff.
Animal Division:
Division Director.—Casey Bean, 720–1353.
Deputy Director.—Catherine Fulton, 720–2461.
Multilateral Affairs:
Division Director.—Andrew Burst, 720–9519.
Bilateral Agreements and Enforcement Division:
Division Director.—Charles Bertsch, 720–6278.
International Regulations and Standards Division:
Division Director.—Cathy McKinnell, 690–0929.
New Technologies and Production Methods Division:
Director.—Ed Porter, 720–2502.
Plant Division:
Division Director.—Peter Tabor, 720–0765.
Processed Products and Technical Regulations Division:
Division Director.—Marianne McElroy, 720–7227.

OFFICE OF TRADE PROGRAMS

Deputy Administrator.—Christian Foster (202) 401–0015.
Assistant Deputy Administrator.—Lynne Reich, 401–0023.
Director, Division of:
Cooperator Programs Division.—Eric Wenberg, 690–0159.
Credit Programs.—Mark Rowse, 720–0624.
Import Policies and Export Reporting Division.—Ronald Lord, 720–0638.
Program Operations Division.—Mark Slupek, 720–4327.

RISK MANAGEMENT AGENCY

South Building, Room 6092–S, phone (202) 690–2803

Administrator.—Brandon Willis.
Associate Administrator.—Barbara Leach.
Deputy Administrator for—
Compliance.—Michael Hand, room 4619–S, 720–0642.
Insurance Services.—Michael Ofton, room 6709–S, 690–4494.
Product Management.—Timothy Witt, Kansas City (816) 926–7394 / 7822.

UNDER SECRETARY FOR RURAL DEVELOPMENT

Jamie L. Whitten Building, phone (202) 720–4581

Under Secretary.—Doug O'Brien (acting).
Deputy Under Secretaries: Doug O'Brien, Judith Canales (acting).
Chief of Staff.—Todd Campbell (acting).
Deputy Chief of Staff.—Johnie Jones.
Director, Legislative and Public Affairs.—David Sandretti, 720–1019.

BUSINESS AND COOPERATIVE PROGRAMS

South Building, Room 5801–S, phone (202) 690–4730

Administrator.—Lillian Salerno.
Associate Administrator.—Curtis A. Wiley, 720–6165.
Oversight/Resource Coordination Staff (OCS).—Nannie Hill-Midgett, 690–4100.
Deputy Administrator for Business Programs.—Pandor H. Hadjy, 720–7287.
Director of:
Business and Industry Division.—Vacant, 690–4103.
Specialty Lenders Division.—Mark Brodzinski, 720–1400.
Deputy Administrator for Cooperative Programs.—Andrew Jermolowizc (acting), 720–7558.
Assistant Deputy Administrator.—Andy Jermolowizc, 720–8460.
Director of:
Cooperative Development Division.—John H. Wells, 720–3350.
Cooperative Marketing Division.—David Sears, 690–0368.
Cooperative Resources Management Division.—Bruce Reynolds (acting), 690–1374.

RURAL HOUSING SERVICE

South Building, Room 5014–S, phone (202) 690–1533

Administrator.—Tammye Trevino.
Director, Program Support Staff.—Rich Davis, 720–9619.
Deputy Administrator for Single Family.—Chadwick Parker (acting), 720–5177.
Director of:
Family Housing Direct Loan Division.—Carolyn Bell (acting), 720–1474.
Family Housing Guaranteed Loan Division.—Joaquin Tremols, 720–1452.
Deputy Administrator for Multi-Family Housing.—Bryan Hooper, 720–3773.
Deputy Director.—Sue Harris-Green, 720–1606.
Director of:
Direct Loan and Grant Processing Division.—Chadwick Parker, 720–1502.
Multi-Family Housing Portfolio Management Division, Direct Housing.—Stephanie White, 720–1600.

RURAL UTILITIES SERVICE

South Building, Room 5135, phone (202) 720–9540

Administrator.—John Padalino (acting).
Deputy Administrator.—Jessica Zufolo.
Assistant Administrator for—
Electric Division.—Nivin Elgohary (acting), room 5165, 720–9505.
Program Accounting and Regulatory Analysis.—Kenneth M. Ackerman, room 5159, 720–9450.
Telecommunications.—Jon Claffey, room 5151, 720–9554.
Water and Environmental Programs.—Jacqueline Ponti-Lazaruk, room 5145, 690–2670.
Director of:
Advanced Services Division.—Norberto Esteves, room 2845–S, 690–4493.
Broadband Division.—Kenneth Kuchno, room 2846–S, 690–4673.
Electric Staff Division.—Donald Junta (acting), room 1246–S, 720–1900.
Northern Regional Electric Division.—Joseph Badin, room 0243–S, 720–1420.
Northern Area, Telecommunications Program.—Shawn Arner (acting), room 2835–S, 720–1025.
Power Supply Division.—Victor T. Vu, room 270–S, 720–6436.
Southern Regional Electric Division.—Doris Nolte, room 221–S, 720–0848.
Southern Area, Telecommunications Program.—Ken B. Chandler, room 2808–S, 720–0800.
Telecommunications Standards Division.—John Schnell (acting), room 2868–S, 720–8663.
Chief, Portfolio Management Branch.—Steve Saulnier, room 2231–S, 720–9631.
Engineering and Environmental Staff.—Mark Plank, room 2237, 720–1649.

FOOD, NUTRITION, AND CONSUMER SERVICES

1400 Independence Avenue, SW., Room 216–E, Whitten Building, 20250

Under Secretary.—Kevin Concannon (202) 720–7711.

Deputy Under Secretary.—Janey Thornton.
Chief of Staff.—Dan Christenson.

FOOD AND NUTRITION SERVICE

3101 Park Center Drive, Room 906, Alexandria, VA 22302 (703) 305–2062

OFFICE OF THE ADMINISTRATOR

Administrator.—Audrey Rowe.
Deputy Associate Administrators:
Supplemental Nutrition Assistance Program.—Jeff Cohen (703) 305–2064.
Special Nutrition Programs.—Diane Kriviski, 305–2060.

OFFICE OF RESEARCH AND ANALYSIS

Association Administration (ORA) Communication and Strategic.—Steven Carlson, room 1014 (703) 305–2017.
Assistant Director.—Rich Lucas, room 1002, 605–0707.
Division, Director of:
Family Program Staff.—Carol Olander, room 1030, 305–2134.
Special Nutrition Staff.—Jay Hirschman, room 1010, 305–2117.

OFFICE OF COMMUNICATIONS AND GOVERNMENTAL AFFAIRS

Director.—Bruce C. Alexander, room 926–A (703) 305–2281.
Deputy Director.—Susan Siemietkowski, room 926–B, 305–2281.
Division, Director of:
Controlled Correspondence Officer.—Twanda Rodgers, room 918, 305–2066.
Governmental Affairs.—Scott A. Carter, room 918, 305–2010.
Public Affairs.—Jean Daniel, room 912, 305–2286.

OFFICE OF MANAGEMENT TECHNOLOGY AND FINANCE

Associate Administrator.—Jeffery Tribiano, room 906 (703) 305–2064.
Director of Civil Rights.—Deborah Minor, room 942, 305–2195.

MANAGEMENT

Deputy Administrator.—Mark Rucker, room 400 (703) 305–2030.
Division, Director of:
Contracts Management.—Lance Patterway (acting), room 220, 305–2251.
Human Resources.—Frank McDonna, room 404, 305–2326.
Logistics and Facility Management.—Mark Rucker, room 222, 305–2220.

FINANCIAL MANAGEMENT

Deputy Administrator (CFO).—Steven Butler, room 712 (703) 305–2046.
Division, Director of:
Accounting.—Linda Washington, room 724, 305–2850.
Administrative Operations.—Larry Blim, room 716, 305–2240.
Budget.—Lisa Greenwood, room 708, 305–2172.
Grants and Fiscal Policy.—Lael Lubing, room 732, 305–2048.
Internal Controls, Audits, and Investigations Liaison.—Katherine Day, room 732, 305–2493.

INFORMATION TECHNOLOGY

Deputy Administrator.—Jonathan Alboum, room 314 (703) 605–4318.
Information Security Office Chief.—Brad Nix, room 314, 305–2242.
Division, Director of:
Financial Systems.—Rich Platt, room 314, 305–2346.

Portfolio Management.—Jacquie Butler, room 314, 605–4318.
Technology.—Rory Schultz, room 316, 305–2244.

REGIONAL OPERATIONS AND SUPPORT

Associate Administrator.—Yvette Jackson, room 906 (703) 305–2060.
Division, Director of:
Office of Emergency Management and Food Safety.—Brenda Lisi, room 1441, 305–1504.
Office of Strategic Initiatives Partnership and Outreach.—Duke Storen, room 1441, 305–1504.

OFFICE OF SUPPLEMENTAL NUTRITION ASSISTANCE PROGRAM

Associate Administrator.—Jessica Shahin, room 808 (703) 305–2026.
Division, Director of:
Benefit Redemption.—Andrea Gold, room 408, 305–2434.
Program Accountability and Administration.—David Burr, room 816, 305–2413.
Program Development.—Liz Beth Silbernan, room 814, 305–2494.

OFFICE OF SPECIAL NUTRITION PROGRAMS

Associate Administrator.—Tim O'Connor, room 628 (703) 305–2052.
Division, Director of:
Child Nutrition.—Cindy Long, room 640, 305–2590.
Food Distribution.—Cathie McCullough (acting), room 500, 305–2680.
Supplemental Food Program.—Debra Whitford, room 520, 305–2746.

CENTER FOR NUTRITION POLICY AND PROMOTION

Executive Director.—Dr. Raj Anand, room 1034 (703) 305–7600.
Deputy Director.—Robert Post, room 1034, 305–7600.
Division, Director of:
Evidence Analysis Library.—Joanne Spahn, room 1034, 305–2870.
Nutrition Guidance and Analysis.—Carole Davis, room 1034, 605–4265.
Nutrition Marketing and Communication Division.—Jackie Haven, room 1034, 605–4434.
Public Affairs and FNS Liaison.—John Webster, room 1034, 605–4270.

UNDER SECRETARY FOR FOOD SAFETY

Under Secretary.—Elisabeth Hagen (202) 720–0350.
Deputy Under Secretary.—Brian Ronholm.
Special Assistant to the Under Secretary.—Katie Naessens.

FOOD SAFETY AND INSPECTION SERVICE

Jamie L. Whitten Building, Room 331–E, phone (202) 720–7025, fax 690–0550

Administrator.—Alfred V. Almanza.
Deputy Administrator.—Phil Derfler, 692–4207.
U.S. Manager for Codex.—Karen Stuck, room 4861–S, 720–2057.

OFFICE OF FIELD OPERATIONS (OFO)

Assistant Administrator.—Dr. Daniel Engeljohn, room 344–E (202) 720–8803.
Deputy Assistant Administrator.—Judy Riggins, 720–5190.
Executive Associates, Regulatory Operations: Cheryl Hicks, room 3159–S, 690–2709; Dr. William James, room 3153–S, 720–9521; Dr. Armia Tawadrous, room 3161–S, 720–5714.
Director of:
Recall Management Staff.—Dr. Lisa Volk, room 0010–S, 690–6536.

OFFICE OF DATA INTEGRATION AND FOOD PROTECTION (ODIFP)

Assistant Administrator.—Terri Nintemann, room 3130–S (202) 720–5643.
Deputy Assistant Administrator.—Christopher Alvares (acting), 205–0452.
Director of:
Biosurveillance and Emergency Response Staff.—Mary K. Cutshall, 414 Aero Building, 690–6523.

OFFICE OF INTERNATIONAL AFFAIRS (OIA)

Assistant Administrator.—Dr. Ronald Jones, room 3143–S (202) 720–3473.
Deputy Assistant Administrator.—Vacant, 720–5362.
Director, Import Inspection Division.—Jerry Elliott, room 1–2288B (301) 504–2153.

OFFICE OF MANAGEMENT (OM)

Assistant Administrator.—Anthony Thompson, room 347–E (202) 720–4425.
Deputy Assistant Administrator.—Lorrena Carraco, 720–4744.

OFFICE OF POLICY AND PROGRAM DEVELOPMENT (OPPD)

Assistant Administrator.—Daniel Engeljohn, room 350–E (202) 720–2709.
Deputy Assistant Administrator.—Vacant, 205–0495.

OFFICE OF PROGRAM EVALUATION, ENFORCEMENT AND REVIEW (OPEER)

Assistant Administrator.—William C. "Bill" Smith, room 3133–S (202) 720–8609.
Deputy Assistant Administrator.—Dr. Jane Roth, room 3133–S, 720–8609.
Director of:
Compliance and Investigations Division.—Randy Robertson, room 300B–CQ, WEC, 418–8874.
Program Evaluation and Improvement Staff.—Matthew Michael, room 3831–S, 720–6735.

OFFICE OF PUBLIC AFFAIRS AND CONSUMER EDUCATION (OPACE)

Assistant Administrator.—Lisa Picard, room 339–E (202) 720–8217.
Deputy Assistant Administrator.—Vacant, room 3137–S, 720–3884.
Director of:
Congressional and Public Affairs Staff.—Carol Blake, room 1175–S, 720–9891 or 9113.
Executive Correspondence and Issues Management Staff.—Alicemary Leach, room 1167–S, 690–3882.

OFFICE OF PUBLIC HEALTH SCIENCE (OPHS)

Assistant Administrator.—Dr. David Goldman, room 341–E (202) 720–2644.
Deputy Assistant Administrator.—Dr. Vivian Chen, room 341–E, 205–0293.

OFFICE OF OUTREACH, EMPLOYEE EDUCATION AND TRAINING (OOEET)

Assistant Administrator.—Lisa Picard, room 4862–S, 205–0194.

UNDER SECRETARY FOR RESEARCH, EDUCATION, AND ECONOMICS

Under Secretary.—Dr. Cathie Woteki (202) 720–5923.
Deputy Under Secretary.—Ann Bartuska.
Chief of Staff.—Yeshi Abebe.
Confidential Assistant to the Under Secretary.—Franz Hochstrasser.

AGRICULTURAL RESEARCH SERVICE

Administration Building, Room 302–A, phone (202) 720–3656, fax 720–5427

Administrator.—Edward B. Knipling.
Associate Administrator for—
Research Operations.—Dr. Caird E. Rexroad, 720–3658.
Research Programs.—Judy St. John (301) 504–5084.
Director of:
Budget and Program Management Staff.—Michael Arnold, room 358–A, 720–4421.
Legislative Affairs.—David Kelly, 720–3173.
Information Staff.—Sandy Miller-Hays (301) 504–1638.
Assistant Administrator, Research Operations and Management, Office of Technology Transfer.—Richard J. Brenner (301) 504–6905.
Deputy Administrator, Administrative and Financial Management.—James H. Bradley, 690–2575.
National Agricultural Library.—Vacant (301) 504–5248.

AREA OFFICES

Director of:
Beltsville Area.—Joseph Spence, 10300 Baltimore Boulevard, Building 2003, Room 223, BARC–West, Beltsville, MD 20705 (301) 504–6078.
Mid South Area.—Edgar King, Jr., 141 Experiment Station Road, Stoneville, MS 38776 (662) 686–5265.
Midwest Area.—Larry Chandler, 1815 North University Street, Room 2004, Peoria, IL 61604–0000 (309) 681–6602.
North Atlantic Area.—Dariusz Swietlik, 600 East Mermaid Lane, Room 2031, Wyndmoor, PA 19038 (215) 233–6593.
Northern Plains Area.—Wilbert H. Blackburn, 2150 Centre Avenue, Building D, Ft. Collins, CO 80525–8119 (970) 492–7057.
Pacific West Area.—Andrew Hammond, 800 Buchanan Street, Room 2030, Albany, CA 94710 (510) 559–6060.
South Atlantic Area.—Deborah Brennan, P.O. Box 5677, College Station Road, Room 201, Athens, GA 30605 (706) 546–3311.
Southern Plains Area.—Dan Upchurch, 1001 Holleman Drive East, College Station, TX 77845 (979) 260–9346.

COOPERATIVE STATE RESEARCH, EDUCATION AND EXTENSION SERVICE

Jamie L. Whitten Building, Room 305–A, phone (202) 720–4423, fax 720–8987

Administrator.—Roger N. Beachy.
Deputy Director.—Meryl Broussard, 720–7441.
Assistant Administrator/Legislative Liaison.—Betty Lou Gilliland, room 305–A, 720–8187.
Directors, Office of:
Budget.—Vacant, room 332–A, 720–2675.
Communications.—Ellen Frank, room 4231, 720–2677.
Equal Opportunity Staff.—Curt DeVille, room 1230, 720–2700.
Planning and Accountability.—Bart Hewitt (acting), room 1315, 720–5623.
Deputy Administrator for—
Bioenergy, Climate, Environment/Science and Education Resources Development.—Frank Boteler, room 4343, 720–7947.
Extramural Programs.—Andrea Brandon, room 2256, 401–6021.
Information Systems and Technology Management.—Michel Desbois, room 4122, 401–0117.
Institute of Food/Production and Sustainability.—Deborah Sheely (acting), room 2334, 401–5024.
Youth Families Community.—Vacant, room 3231, 401–4555.

ECONOMIC RESEARCH SERVICE

1800 M Street, NW., 20036–5831, phone (202) 694–5000

Administrator.—Mary Bohman, room N4145.

Associate Administrators: Stephen Crutchfield, room N4149; John Kort, room N4150.
Special Assistant to Administrator.—Leslee Lowstutter, room N4151.
Civil Rights Director.—Vacant, room N4152.
Division Directors:
Food Economics.—Laurian Unnevehr, room N2168, 694–5400.
Information Services.—Ron Bianchi, room S2032, 694–5100.
Market Trade and Economics.—Sally Thompson, room N5119, 694–5200.
Resource and Rural Economics.—Mary Bohman, room S4182, 694–5500.

NATIONAL AGRICULTURAL STATISTICS SERVICE

South Agriculture Building, Room 5041A–S, phone (202) 720–2707, fax 720–9013

Administrator.—Cynthia Clark.
Associate Administrator.—Joseph T. Reilly, 720–4333.
Deputy Administrator for—
Eastern Field Operations.—Norman Bennett, room 5053, 720–3638.
Programs and Products.—Hubert Hamer, room 5029, 690–8141.
Division Directors for—
Census and Survey.—Renee Picanso, room 6306, 720–4557.
Information Technology.—Michael Valivullah, room 5847, 720–2984.
Research and Development.—James M. Harris, Fairfax (703) 877–8000, ext. 100.
Statistics.—Joseph Prusacki, room 5433, 720–3896.

UNDER SECRETARY FOR MARKETING AND REGULATORY PROGRAMS

Jamie L. Whitten Building, Room 228–W, phone (202) 720–4256, fax 720–5775

Under Secretary.—Edward Avalos.
Deputy Under Secretary.—Joani Walsh.
Special Assistant to the Under Secretary.—Vacant.

AGRICULTURAL MARKETING SERVICE

South Agriculture Building, Room 3064–S, phone (202) 720–5115, fax 720–8477

Administrator.—Anne Alonzo.
Associate Administrator.—David R. Shipman, 720–4276.
Deputy Associate Administrator.—Erin Morris, 720–4024.
Deputy Administrator for—
Compliance and Analysis Programs.—Ellen King, room 3507–S, 720–6766.
Cotton and Tobacco Programs.—Darryl Earnest, room 2639–S, 720–3193.
Dairy Programs.—Dana Cole, room 2968–S, 720–4392.
Fruit and Vegetable Programs.—Robert C. Keeney, room 2077–S, 720–4722.
Poultry Programs.—Craig Morse, room 2902–S, 720–5705.
Science and Technology.—Robert L. Epstein, room 1090–S, 720–5231.
Transportation and Marketing.—Barbara C. Robinson, room 1098, 690–1300.
Director, Legislative and Review Staff.—Chris Sarcone, room 2625–S, 720–3203.

ANIMAL AND PLANT HEALTH INSPECTION SERVICE (APHIS)

Jamie L. Whitten Building, Room 312–E, phone (202) 720–3668, fax 720–3054

OFFICE OF THE ADMINISTRATOR

Administrator.—Kevin Shea (acting).
Associate Administrator.—Kevin Shea.
Director of Civil Rights Enforcement and Compliance.—Myra Young, room 1137–S, 720–6312, fax 720–2365.

ANIMAL CARE

4700 River Road, Riverdale, MD 20737, phone (301) 734–4980, fax 734–4328

Deputy Administrator.—Chester Gipson.

Associate Deputy Administrator.—Andrea Morgan.

BIOTECHNOLOGY REGULATORY SERVICES

4700 River Road, Riverdale, MD 20737, phone (301) 734–7324, fax 734–8724

Deputy Administrator.—Michael Gregoire.
Assistant Deputy Administrator.—Sidney Abel, 734–5716.

INTERNATIONAL SERVICES

Jamie L. Whitten Building, Room 324–E, phone (202) 720–7593, fax 690–1484

Deputy Administrator.—Ronald Hicks.
Active Deputy Administrator.—Karen Sliter, 720–7021.
Division Directors: Freida Skaggs (301) 734–5214; John Wyss, 734–3779.
Trade Support Team.—John Greifer, room 1128, 720–7677.

LEGISLATIVE AND PUBLIC AFFAIRS

South Building, Room 1147–S, phone (202) 720–2511, fax 720–3982

Deputy Administrator.—Bethany Jones.
Associate Deputy Administrator.—James Ivy.
Assistant Director of:
Executive Correspondence.—Christina Myers (301) 734–7776.
Freedom of Information.—Tonya Woods (301) 734–8296.
Public Affairs.—Ed Curlett (301) 734–7799.

MARKETING AND REGULATORY PROGRAMS BUSINESS SERVICES

Jamie L. Whitten Building, Room 308–E, phone (202) 720–5213, fax 690–0686

Deputy Administrator.—Joanne Munno, 720–5214 (301) 734–3768.
Associate Deputy Administrator.—Vacant.

PLANT PROTECTION AND QUARANTINE

Jamie L. Whitten Building, Room 302–E, phone (202) 720–5601, fax 690–0472

Deputy Administrator.—Rebecca Bech.
Associate Deputy Administrator.—Paul Eggert, 720–4441.
Assistant to the Deputy Administrator.—John H. Payne, 720–5601.
Director of:
Biocontrol.—Dr. Alan Dowdy (301) 734–5667.
Center for Plant Health Science and Technology.—Gordon Gordh (919) 513–2400.
Resource Management Support.—Terri Burrell (301) 734–7764.
Technical Information Systems.—Allison Young (301) 734–5518.

POLICY AND PROGRAM DEVELOPMENT

4700 River Road, Riverdale, MD 20737, phone (301) 734–5136, fax 734–5899

Deputy Administrator.—Christine Zakarka.
Associate Deputy Administrator.—Shannon Hamm.
Unit Chiefs:
Environmental and Risk Analysis Service.—Ken Seeley, 734–3634.
Planning, Evaluation and Monitoring.—Connie Williams, 734–8512.
Policy Analysis and Development.—Parveen Sepia, 734–8667.
Regulatory Analysis and Development.—Stephen O'Neil, 734–0682.

VETERINARY SERVICES

Jamie L. Whitten Building, Room 317–E, phone (202) 720–5193, fax 690–4171

Deputy Administrator.—John Clifford.

Administrative Assistant.—Paula Lee, 720–5793.
Associate Deputy Administrator for Regional Operations.—Jere Dick, 720–5193.
Assistant Deputy Administrators: India Wilson, David Zimmerman (301) 734–3754.
Director for—
Emergency Programs.—Jose Diez (301) 734–8073.
Inspection and Compliance.—Steven A. ''Ames'' Karli (515) 232–5785.
National Center of Import and Export.—Gary S. Colgrave (301) 734–4356.
Outreach Liaison.—Joseph Annelli (301) 794–8073.
Policy, Evaluation and Licensing.—Richard E. Hill, Jr. (515) 232–5785.

WILDLIFE SERVICES

South Building, Room 1624, phone (202) 720–2054, fax 690–0053

Deputy Administrator.—William H. Clay.
Assistant Deputy Administrator.—Vacant.
Director for Operational Support.—Joanne Garrett (301) 734–7921.

GRAIN INSPECTION, PACKERS AND STOCKYARDS ADMINISTRATION

South Building, Room 2055, phone (202) 720–0219, fax 205–9237

Administrator.—Larry Mitchell.
Director of:
Budget and Planning Staff.—Marianne Plaus, room 2045–S, 720–0231.
Civil Rights Staff.—Eugene Bass, room 0623–S, 720–0218.
Management and Budget Services: Frieda Achtentuch, Albert Conerly, room 2446–S, 720–1741.
Deputy Administrator for Federal Grain Inspection Service.—Randall Jones, room 2063–S, 720–9170.
Director of:
Compliance.—Thomas O'Connor, room 1647–S, 720–8262.
Departmental and International Affairs.—John Pitchford, room 1629–S, 720–0226.
Field Management Division.—Robert Lijewski, room 2409–S, 720–0228.
Technical Services Division.—Donald Kendall (acting), Kansas City, MO (816) 891–0463.
Deputy Administrator for Packers and Stockyards Programs.—Susan Keith, room 2055–S, 720–7051.
Director of:
Business and Economic Analysis Division.—Gary McBryde, room 2430–S, 720–7455.
Regional Supervisors:
Atlanta, GA.—Elkin Parker (404) 562–5840.
Aurora, CO.—John Barthel (303) 375–4240.
Des Moines, IA.—Jay Johnson (515) 323–2579.

DEPARTMENT OF COMMERCE

Herbert C. Hoover Building

14th Street between Pennsylvania and Constitution Avenues, NW., 20230

phone (202) 482–2000, http://www.doc.gov

PENNY PRITZKER, Secretary of Commerce; born in Chicago, Illinois, 1959; education: graduated, Castilleja School, Palo Alto, California, 1977; A.B., economics, Harvard University, 1981; J.D., M.B.A., Stanford University, 1984; professional: founder of Vi (formerly Classic Resident by Hyatt), 1987; founder of Pritzker Realty Group, 1991; chairman of Superior Bank, 1991–1994; co-founder of The Parking Spot, 1998; Executive Chairman of the Board of TransUnion, LLC, 2005–2012; co-founder of Artemis Real Estate Partners, 2010; founder and CEO of PSP Capital Partners, 2012; married: Dr. Bryan Traubert; two children: Donald Pritzker Traubert, Rose Pritzker Traubert; nominated by President Barack Obama to become the 38th Secretary of Commerce, and was confirmed by the U.S. Senate on June 16, 2013.

OFFICE OF THE SECRETARY

Secretary of Commerce.—Penny Pritzker, room 5858 (202) 482–9043.
Deputy Secretary.—Vacant, room 5838, 482–2112.
Chief of Staff.—Bruce Andrews, room 5858, 482–4246.
Deputy Chief of Staff.—Vacant.
Senior Advisor to the Secretary.—Kate McAdams, room 5854, 482–3539.
Chief Protocol Officer.—Amy Rosenfield, room 5847, 482–8011.
Director, Office of:
Business Liaison.—Matthew McGuire, room 5062, 482–1360.
Executive Secretariat.—Christine Turner, room 5516, 482–3934.
Policy and Strategic Planning.—Vacant, room 5865, 482–4127.
Public Affairs.—Jim Hock, room 5413, 482–4883.
Scheduling and Advance.—Lisa Kohnke, room 5883, 482–5129.
White House Liaison.—Theodore Johnston, room 5835, 482–1684.

GENERAL COUNSEL

General Counsel.—Vacant, room 5870 (202) 482–4772.
Deputy General Counsel.—Justin Antonipillai.

ASSISTANT SECRETARY FOR LEGISLATIVE AND INTERGOVERNMENTAL AFFAIRS

Deputy Assistant Secretary.—Jim Stowers, room 5421 (202) 482–3663, fax 482–4420.
Senior Adviosr.—Ryan Hedgepeth, room 5421, 482–3663.
Director for—
Intergovernmental Affairs.—William Ramos, room 5422, 482–3663, fax 482–4420.
Associate Directors for—
Census, EDA, ESA, MBDA.—Victoria Tung, room 5422, 482–3663.
NOAA.—Jen Costanza, room 5422, 482–3663.
NTIA, NIST, NTIS, USPTO, BIS.—Andrew Su, room 5422, 482–3663.
Oversight.—Brian Eiler, room 5422, 482–3663.
Senior Advisor for Native American Affairs.—Dee Alexander, room 5422, 482–3663.

CHIEF FINANCIAL OFFICER (CFO) AND ASSISTANT SECRETARY FOR ADMINISTRATION

Chief Financial Officer and Assistant Secretary.—Ellen Herbst, room 5830 (202) 482–4951, fax 482–3592.
Deputy Assistant Secretary for Administration.—Fred Stephens, room 5830.
Deputy Chief Financial Officer/Director for Financial Management.—Lisa Casias, room 6827, 482–1207, fax 482–5070.

Director for—

Acquisition Management.—Berry Berkowitz, room 6422, 482–4248, fax 482–1711.

Administrative Services.—Vacant, room 6316, 482–1200, fax 482–8890.

Budget.—Michael Phelps, room 6317, 482–5969, fax 482–3361.

Civil Rights.—Suzan J. Aramaki, room 6010, 482–0625, fax 482–3364.

Human Resources Management.—Kevin Mahoney, room 5001, 482–4807, fax 482–0249.

Program Evaluation and Risk Management.—Vacant, room 5327, 482–3707, fax 482–1423.

Security.—Tom Predmore, room 1069, 482–4371, fax 501–6355.

Small and Disadvantaged Business Utilization.—LaJuene Desmukes, room 6411, 482–1472, fax 482–0501.

CHIEF INFORMATION OFFICER

Chief Information Officer.—Simon Szykman, room 5029B (202) 482–4797.

Deputy Chief Information Officer.—Izella Dornell, room 5027.

Office of:

IT Policy and Planning, Deputy Chief Information Officer and Chief Technology Officer.—Kirit Amin, room 6612, 482–4444.

IT Security, Infrastructure and Technology, Chief Information Security Officer.—Rod Turk, room 6895, 482–4708.

Networking and Telecommunications Operations.—Ricardo Farraj-Feijoo, room 6625, 482–4444.

INSPECTOR GENERAL

Inspector General.—Todd J. Zinser, room 7898C, (202) 482–4661.

Deputy Inspector General.—David P. Smith, room 7898C, 482–4661.

Special Assistant to the Inspector General.—Sonia D. Brown, room 7898C, 482–5363.

Principal Assistant Inspector General for Investigations and Whistleblower Protection.—Rick Beitel, 482–2558.

Counsel to Inspector General.—Wade Green, Jr., room 7892, 482–1577.

Principal Assistant Inspector General Audit and Evaluation.—Anne Eilers, room 7886B, 482–2754.

Assistant Inspector General, Office of:

Administration.—Kathy Hammer, room 7099C, 482–2877.

Auditing.—Andrew Katsaros, room 7886B, 482–2600.

Economic and Statistical Program Assessment.—Ron Prevost, room 7520, 482–3052.

Investigations.—C. Morgan Kim, room 7614, 482–3486.

Systems Acquisition and IT Security.—Allen Crawley, room 7876, 482–1855.

ECONOMICS AND STATISTICS ADMINISTRATION

1401 Constitution Avenue, NW., 20230, phone (202) 482–6607

Under Secretary for Economic Affairs.—Mark E. Doms, room 4848 (202) 482–3727.

Deputy Under Secretary for Economic Affairs.—Vacant, room 4848, 482–3727.

Chief Counsel.—Barry K. Robinson, room 4877, 482–5394.

Chief Economist.—Vacant, room 4850, 482–3523.

Deputy Chief Economist.—Robert N. Rubinovitz, room 4861, 482–4871.

Associate Under Secretary for—

Communications.—Joanne Caldwell, room 4836, 482–2760.

Management.—Kenneth A. Arnold, room 4836, 482–2405.

Chief Financial Officer.—Vacant, room 4842, 482–3038.

BUREAU OF ECONOMIC ANALYSIS

1441 L Street, NW., 20230 (USPS) / 20005 (physical), phone (202) 606–9900

Director.—J. Steven Landefeld, room 6006, 606–9600.

Deputy Director.—Brian Moyer, room 6005, 606–9602.

Chief Economist.—Ana Aizcorbe, room 6060, 606–9603.

Chief Information Officer.—Brian Callahan, room 6052, 606–9906.

Chief Statistician.—Dennis J. Fixler, room 6060, 606–9607.

Associate Director for—
Industry Economics.—Carol Moylan, room 6062, 606–9612.
International Economics.—Sally Thompson, room 6004, 606–9604.
National Economic Accounts.—Brent R. Moulton, room 6064, 606–9606.
Regional Economics.—Joel Platt, room 6065, 606–9605.
Chief Administrative Officer.—Kathy James, room 6027, 606–9616.
Division Chiefs:
Administrative Services.—Spence Burton, room 2025, 606–9967.
Balance of Payments.—Paul Farello, room 8024, 606–9561.
Communications.—H. Lucas Hitt, room 3029, 606–9223.
Direct Investment Division.—David Galler, room 7005, 606–9835.
Government Division.—Pamela Kelly, room 4067, 606–9781.
Industry Applications Division.—Erich Strassner, room 4006, 606–9539.
Industry Sector Division.—Dave Wasshausen, room 4028, 606–9752.
National Income and Wealth.—Nicole Mayerhauser, room 5006, 606–9742.
Regional Income Division.—Mauricio Ortiz, room 8057, 606–9629.
Regional Product Division.—C. Ian Mead, room 9018, 606–9661.

THE BUREAU OF THE CENSUS
4600 Silver Hill Road, Suitland, MD 20746

Director.—Vacant.
Senior Advisor Performing the Duties of the Director.—Thomas Mesenbourg, Jr. (A), room 8H002, 763–2135.
Deputy Director and Chief Operating Officer.—Nancy Potok, room 8H006, 763–2138.
Associate Director for Administration and Chief Financial Officer.—Carol M. Rose (A), room 2K122, 763–5818.
Associate Director for Performance Improvement.—Ted A. Johnson, room 8H144, 763–3464.
Communications.—Stephen Buckner (A), room 8H062, 763–3586.
Decennial Census.—Frank A. Vitrano (A), room 8H122, 763–3961.
Demographic Programs.—Enrique Lamas, room 8H134, 763–2160.
Economic Programs.—Shirin A. Ahmed, room 8K108, 763–2558.
Field Operations.—William W. Hatcher, Jr., room 8H126, 763–2074.
Information Technology and CIO.—Brian McGrath, room 8H140, 763–2117.
Chief Technology Officer.—Avi Bender, room 5K030, 763–7807.
Assistant Director for—
Acquisition Division.—Michael L. Palensky, room 3J438, 763–1818.
American Community Survey.—James B. Treat, room 3K276, 763–3609.
Economic Programs.—Samuel C. Jones, room 7K108, 763–7600.
Division and Office Chiefs for—
Administrative and Customer Services.—F. Grailand Hall, room 3J436, 763–1629.
Administrative and Management Systems Division.—James Aikman, room 3K138, 763–3149.
Budget Division.—Carol Rose, room 2K122, 763–5818.
Center for New Media and Promotion.—Stanley J. Rolark, room 8H484, 763–3100.
Center for Economic Studies.—Lucia S. Foster, room 2K124, 763–1858.
Company Statistics Division.—Jeffrey L. Mayer, room 6K064, 763–2905.
Computer Services Division.—Thomas J. Berti, Bowie 28, 763–4341.
Customer Liaison and Marketing Services Office.—Kendall B. Johnson, room 8H180, 763–1911.
Decennial Systems and Contract Management Office.—Frank A. Vitrano (A), room 3H162, 763–9062.
Decennial Management Division.—Burton Reist (A), room 8H122, 763–8626.
Decennial Statistical Studies Division.—Frank A. Vitrano (A), room 3H162, 763–4035.
Demographic Statistical Methods Division.—Ruth Ann Killion, room 7H162, 763–2048.
Demographic Surveys Division.—Enrique Lamas (A), room 5H174, 763–2071.
Economic Planning and Coordination Division.—Deborah Stempowski, room 8K119, 763–1417.
Economic Statistical Methods and Programming Division.—Samuel C. Jones, room 7K108, 763–7600.
Equal Employment Opportunity Office.—Roy P. Castro, room 3K106, 763–5120.
Field Division.—Brian Monaghan, room 5H128, 763–2011.
Finance Division.—Sandi Walters, room 2K106, 763–9398.
Foreign Trade Division.—Nick Orsini, room 6K032, 763–2255.

Geography Division.—Timothy F. Trainor, room 4H174, 763–2131.
Governments Division.—Lisa Blumerman, room 5K156, 763–8050.
Human Resources Division.—Cynthia M. Vaughan, room 2J436, 763–3721.
Information Systems Support and Review Office.—Terryne F. Murphy, room 4K030, 763–6846.
LAN Technology Support Office.—Patricia T. Musselman, room 4K108, 763–5632.
Manufacturing and Construction.—Mendel D. Gayle, room 7K154, 763–4587.
National Processing Center.—David Hackbarth (812) 218–3344.
Office of Congressional Intergovermental Affairs.—Angela M. Manso, room 8H166, 763–6100.
Office of External Engagement.—Jeri Green, room 8H182, 763–6590.
Policy Office.—Christa D. Jones, room 8H028.
Population.—Enrique J. Lamas (A), room 5H174, 763–2071.
Public Information Office.—Seth L. Amgott, room 8H160, 763–7610.
Security Office.—Harold L. Washington, Jr., room 2J438, 763–1716.
Service Sector Statistics.—Shirin A. Ahmed, room 8K108, 763–2558.
Social, Economic and Housing Services.—David S. Johnson, room 7H174, 763–3234.
Technologies Management Office.—Barbara M. LoPresti, room 5H160, 763–7765.
Telecommunications Office.—Scott D. Williams, room 4K032, 763–1793.
2020 Research and Planning Office.—Burton H. Reist, room 3H174, 763–3949.

BUREAU OF INDUSTRY AND SECURITY

Under Secretary.—Eric L. Hirschhorn, room 3898B (202) 482–1455.
Deputy Under Secretary.—Daniel O. Hill, room 3892, 482–1427.
Chief Counsel.—John T. Masterson, Jr., room 3839, 482–2315.
Office of Congressional and Public Affairs.—Charles Sean Foertsch, room 3897, 482–0097.
Director, Office of Administration.—Gay Shrum, room 6622, 482–1058.
Chief Information Officer.—Eddie Donnell, room 6092, 482–4296.
Assistant Secretary for Export Administration.—Kevin Wolf, room 3886C, 482–5491.
Deputy Assistant Secretary.—Matthew Borman, room 3886C, 482–5711.
Operating Committee Chair.—Eric Longnecker, room 3889, 482–5537.
End-User Review Committee Chair.—Karen Nies-Vogel, room 2625, 482–3811.
Office of:
Exporter Services.—Bernard Kritzer, room 1093, 482–4196.
National Security and Technology Transfer Controls.—Eileen M. Albanese, room 2616, 482–8179.
Nonproliferation and Treaty Compliance.—Alexander Lopes, room 2093, 482–3825.
Strategic Industries and Economic Security.—Michael Vaccaro, room 3878, 482–4506.
Technology Evaluation.—Gerald Horner, room 3886, 482–2078.
Assistant Secretary for Export Enforcement.—David W. Mills (acting), room 3730, 482–3618.
Deputy Assistant Secretary.—Douglas Hassebrock (acting), room 3723, 482–6119.
Office of:
Antiboycott Compliance.—Edward Weant, room 6098, 482–2209.
Enforcement Analysis.—Kevin Kurland, room 4065, 482–4255.
Export Enforcement.—Douglas Hassebrock, room 4508, 482–6119.

ECONOMIC DEVELOPMENT ADMINISTRATION

Assistant Secretary.—John R. Fernandez, room 7300, (202) 482–5081.
Deputy Assistant Secretary for—
EDA and Chief Operating Officer.—Brian McGowan, room 7300, 482–5081.
Regional Affairs.—Thomas Guevara, room 7800, 482–5891.
Chief Counsel.—Barry Bird, room D–100, 482–4687.
Chief Information Officer.—Brian McGowan (acting), room 7300, 482–5081.
Chief Financial Officer and Chief Administrative Officer.—Sandra R. Walters, room 7231, 482–5892.
Director, Office of:
Budget and Finance Division.—James LeDuc, room 7217, 482–0547.
External Affairs.—Angela Martinez, room 7814, 482–2900.
Innovation and Entrepreneurship.—Esther Lee, room 7019, 482–2042.
Legislative Affairs.—Angela Ewell-Madison (acting), room 7816, 482–2900.
Public Affairs.—Cleve Mesidor, room 7814, 482–4085.

Trade Adjustment Assistance.—Bryan Borlik, room D–100, 482–0556.

INTERNATIONAL TRADE ADMINISTRATION

Under Secretary.—Francisco Sanchez, room 3850 (202) 482–2867.
Deputy Under Secretary.—Vacant, room 3842, 482–3917.
Chief of Staff.—Adam Wilczewski, room 3850, 482–2867.
Legislative and Intergovernmental Affairs.—Vacant, room 3424, 482–3015.
Public Affairs.—Mary Trupo, room 3416, 482–3809.
Chief Counsel for International Commerce.—John Cobau, room 5624, 482–0937.

ADMINISTRATION

Director and Chief Financial Officer.—Patricia M. Sefcik, room 3827 (202) 482–5855.
Deputy Chief Administrative Officer.—Kurt Bersani, room 41012, 482–8026.
Office of Financial Management and Administrative Oversight.—Anne McDonagh, room 41018, 482–2136.
Chief Information Officer.—Renee Macklin, room 4800, 482–3801.
Director, Office of:
Management and Operations.—Victor E. Powers, Suite 40001R, 482–5436.
Strategic Resources.—Blanche Ziv, room 41017, 482–3302.
Office of Budget.—Michael House, room 41028, 482–5739.

TRADE PROMOTION AND U.S. AND FOREIGN COMMERCIAL SERVICE

Assistant Secretary for Trade Promotion and Director General of the Commercial Service.—Vacant, room 38006 (202) 482–5777.
Deputy Director General.—Charles A. Ford, HCH 38006, 482–5777.
Deputy Assistant Secretary for:
Domestic Operations.—Antwaun Griffin, RRB STE 800–M, 482–4767.
International Operations.—Thomas Moore, HCH 31032, 482–6228.
Regional Director, Office of:
Africa, Near East and South Asia.—Janice Corbett, HCH 200–A, 482–1209.
East Asia and Pacific.—Dan Harris, HCH 31018, 482–0423.
Europe.—Danny Devito, HCH 200–A, 482–5402.
National Field.—Thomas McGinty, RRB STE 800–M, 482–2732.
Western Hemisphere.—Cynthia Griffin, RMC 300, 482–3484.
Director, Office of:
Advocacy Center.—Bryan Erwin, HCH 3814–A, 482–3896.
Budget.—Barbara Gilchrist, HCH 21010, 482–0823.
Business Information and Technology.—Ed Howard, HCH 11013, 482–3261.
Foreign Service Human Capital.—Joseph Winiarz, HCH 1842, 482–4938.
Global Knowledge Center.—Anand Basu, RRB STE 800–M, 482–1489.
Trade Promotion Coordinating Committee.—Pat Kirwan, HCH 31027, 482–5455.
SelectUSA.—Aaron Brickman (acting), HCH 1235, 482–1889.
Strategic Partnership Program.—Robert McEntire (acting), RRB STE 800–M, 482–5226.
Strategic Planning and Resource Management.—Debra Delay, HCH 21022, 482–8003.

ASSISTANT SECRETARY FOR IMPORT ADMINISTRATION

Assistant Secretary.—Paul Piquado, room 3099B (202) 482–1780.
Deputy Assistant Secretary.—Ronald Lorentzen, room 3705, 482–2104.
Chief Counsel.—John D. McInerney, room 3622, 482–5589.
Director for—
Office of Accounting.—Neal Halper, room 3087B, 482–2210.
Office of Policy.—Carole Showers, room 3713, 482–4412.
Executive Secretary for Foreign Trade Zones Board.—Andrew McGilvray, room 21013, 482–2862.
Deputy Assistant Secretary for—
Antidumping Countervailing Duty Operations.—Christian Marsh, room 3095, 482–5497.
Antidumping Countervailing Duty Policy and Negotiations.—Lynn Fischer Fox, room 3089, 482–6199.
Textiles and Apparel.—Kimberly Thompson Glas, room 30003, 482–3737.

ASSISTANT SECRETARY FOR MARKET ACCESS AND COMPLIANCE

Assistant Secretary.—Michael C. Camunez, room 3868A (202) 482–3022.
Deputy Assistant Secretary.—John Andersen, room 3868A, 482–3022.
Deputy Assistant Secretary for—
Africa, the Middle East and South Asia.—Holly Vineyard, room 2329, 482–4651.
Asia.—Craig Allen, room 2038, 482–4527.
Europe.—Matthew Murray, room 3863, 482–5638.
Trade Agreements Compliance.—Skip Jones, room 3043, 482–5767.
Western Hemisphere.—Walter Bastian, room 3826, 482–5324.
Director, Office of:
Africa.—Kevin Boyd, room 2037, 482–4227.
China Economic Area.—Nicole Melcher, room 3204, 428–2515.
European Country Affairs.—Jay Burgess, room 3319, 482–2630.
European Union.—David DeFalco, room 3513, 482–2178.
Intellectual Property Rights.—Susan Wilson, room 3043, 482–0781.
Japan.—Keith Roth, room 2320, 482–5012.
Middle East.—Susan Hamrock (acting), room 2031, 482–4442.
Multilateral Affairs.—Christopher Rosettie, room 3033, 482–3227.
North and Central America and the Caribbean.—Geri Word, room 3024, 482–6452.
Pacific Basin.—Jeffrey Dutton, room 2319, 482–0358.
Russia, Ukraine, and Eurasia.—Matt Edwards, room 3318, 482–4365.
South Asia and Oceania.—Valerie Dees, room 2312, 482–2955.
South America.—Alexander Peacher (acting), room 3203, 482–3872.
Trade Compliance Center.—Beverly Vaughan, room 3043, 482–1191.

ASSISTANT SECRETARY FOR MANUFACTURING AND SERVICES

Assistant Secretary.—Nicole Y. Lamb-Hale, room 3832 (202) 482–1461.
Deputy Assistant Secretary.—Vacant, room 3832.
Deputy Assistant Secretary for—
Industry Analysis.—Praveen Dixit, room 21028, 482–3177.
Director for Office of:
Advisory Committees.—Jennifer Pilat, room 4043 (202) 482–4501.
Competition and Economic Analysis.—Joseph Flynn, room 7025R, 482–1606.
Energy and Environmental Industries.—Adam O'Malley, room 4055, 482–4850.
Manufacturing.—Chandra Brown, room 28004, 482–1872.
Planning, Coordination and Management.—J. Slade Broom, room 4324 (202) 482–4921.
Services.—Joel Secundy, room 1128, 482–5261.
Technology and Electronic Commerce.—Robin Roark (acting), room 28008R, 482–3090.
Trade Industry Information.—Wassel Mashagbeh, room A211, 482–4691.
Trade Policy Analysis.—Jean Janicke, room C126, 482–5947.

PRESIDENT'S EXPORT COUNCIL

[Authorized by Executive Orders 12131, 12534, 12551, 12610, 12692, 12774, 12869, and 12974 (May through September 1995)]

Executive Director, Under Secretary of International Trade.—Francisco Sanchez, room 3850 (202) 482–1124.
Executive Secretary and Staff Director.—Tricia Van Orden, room 4043.

MINORITY BUSINESS DEVELOPMENT AGENCY

Director.—David Hinson, room 5051, (202) 482–2332.
National Deputy Director.—Alejandra Castillo, room 5051, 482–2332.
Associate Directors for—
Business Development.—Vacant, room 5079, 482–6045.
Legislative, Education, and Intergovernmental Affairs.—Kimberly R. Marcus, room 5067, 482–6272.
Management.—Edith McCloud, room 5092, 482–6224.
Senior Advisor on Native American Affairs.—Dee Alexander, room 5093, 482–5644.
Chief Counsel.—Josephine Arnold, room 5069, 482–5045.
Chief Financial Officer.—Ronald Marin, room 5089, 482–1621.

Chief Information Officer.—Vacant, room 5082, 482–3831.
Chief of Legislative, Educational and Intergovernmental Affairs.—Bridget Gonzales, room 5069A, 482–3774.

NATIONAL OCEANIC AND ATMOSPHERIC ADMINISTRATION

Under Secretary of Commerce for Oceans and Atmosphere.—Kathy D. Sullivan, Ph.D. (acting), room 51030 (202) 482–3436.
Assistant Secretary for Conservation and Management/Deputy Administrator.—Eric C. Schwaab, (assuming duties of AS/CM), room 51027, 482–6255.
Assistant Secretary for Environmental Observation and Prediction/Deputy Administrator.—Kathy D. Sullivan, Ph.D.
Chief Scientist.—Vacant, room 6807, 482–9049.
Principal Deputy Under Secretary for Oceans and Atmosphere.—Vacant, room 7324, 482–3567.
Deputy Under Secretary for Operations.—David M. Kennedy, room 7316, 482–4569.
Chief of Staff.—Renee Stone, room 51030, 482–3436.
Deputy Assistant Secretary for International Fisheries.—Russell Smith, room 61013, 482–5682.
Senior Advisor for International Affairs.—Dr. James Turner, room A301, 482–6076.
Director, Office of:
Communications and External Affairs.—Ciaran Clayton, room A100, 482–6090.
Education.—Louisa Koch, room 6869, 482–3384.
Federal Coordinator for Meteorology.—Samuel P. Williamson, SSMC1, room 1500, (301) 427–2002.
General Counsel.—Lois Schiffer, room A100, 482–4080.
Legislative and Intergovernmental Affairs.—Amanda Hallberg Greenwell, room A100, 482–4981.
Marine and Aviation Operations.—RADM Michael S. Devany, 8403 Colesville Road, Suite 500, Silver Spring, MD 20910 (301) 713–7600.
Policy and Senior Advisor to Under Secretary.—Sally Yozell, room 51027, 482–3567.
Strategic Initiatives and Partnerships.—Vacant.
Chief Financial Officer.—Maureen Wylie, room D200, 482–0917.
Chief Administrative Officer.—Vacant, SSMC4, room 8431, 713–0836, ext. 105.
Chief Information Officer/High Performance Computing and Communications.—Joseph Klimavicz, SSMC3, room 9651, 713–9600.
Acquisition and Grants.—Mitchell Ross, SSMC1, room 6300, 713–0325.
Decision Coordination and Executive Secretariat.—Kelly Quickle, room 5230, 482–2985.
Workforce Management.—Sandra Manning, SSMC4, room 12520, 713–6300.

NATIONAL MARINE FISHERIES SERVICE

1315 East-West Highway, Silver Spring, MD 20910

Assistant Administrator.—Eric Schwaab, room 14636 (301) 427–8000.
Deputy Assistant Administrator for—
Operations.—Paul Doremus, room 14743, 427–8000.
Regulatory Programs.—Samuel Rauch, room 14657, 427–8000.
Director, Office of:
Habitat Conservation.—Buck Sutter, room 14828, 427–8600.
International Affairs.—Jean-Pierre Ple (acting), room 12659, 427–8350.
Law Enforcement.—Bruce Buckson, 427–2300.
Management and Budget.—Gary Reisner, room 14450, 713–2259.
Protected Resources.—Helen Golde (acting), room 13821, 427–8400.
Science and Technology.—Ned Cyr, Ph.D., room 12450, 427–8100.
Scientific Programs and Chief Science Advisor.—Richard Merrick, Ph.D., room 14659, 427–8000.
Seafood Inspection Program.—Tim Hansen, room 10837, 427–8300.
Sustainable Fisheries.—Emily Menashes (acting), room 13362, 427–8500.
Chief Information Officer.—Larry Tyminski, room 3657, 427–8800.
Aquaculture Program.—Michael Rubino, room 13117, 427–8325.
Policy.—Mark Holliday, Ph.D., room 14451, 427–8004.

NATIONAL OCEAN SERVICE

Assistant Administrator.—Holly A. Bamford, room 13632 (301) 713–3074.

Deputy Assistant Administrator.—Russell Callender (acting), room 13635, 713–3074.
Director, Center for Operational Oceanographic Products and Services.—Richard Edwing, room 6650, 713–2981.
Deputy Director.—Ellen Clark, room 6633, 713–2981.
Chief Financial Officer.—Christopher Cartwright, room 13442, 713–3056.
Director, Office of:
Coast Survey.—RADM Gerd Glang, room 6147, 713–2770.
International Programs.—Clement Lewsey, room 5652, 713–3078.
National Centers for Coastal Ocean Science.—Mary Erickson (acting), room 8211, 713–3020.
National Geodetic Survey.—Juliana Blackwell, room 8657, 713–3222.
National Marine Sanctuaries.—Daniel Basta, room 11523, 713–7235.
NOAA Coastal Services.—Jeff Payne (acting), (843) 740–1207.
Ocean and Coastal Resource Management.—Margaret Davidson (acting), room 10413 (843) 740–1220.
Response and Restoration.—Dave Westerholm, room 10102, 713–2989.

NATIONAL ENVIRONMENTAL SATELLITE, DATA AND INFORMATION SERVICE

1315 East-West Highway, Silver Spring, MD 20910

Assistant Administrator.—Mary E. Kicza, room 8268 (301) 713–3578.
Deputy Assistant Administrator.—Charles S. Baker, room 8300, 713–2010.
Deputy Assistant Administrator, Systems.—Vacant, room 8338, 713–2005.
Chief Information Officer.—Irene Parker (acting), room 7103, 713–1283.
Chief Financial Officer.—Michael H. Abreu, room 8338, 713–9476.
Deputy Chief Financial Officer.—Cherish Johnson, room 8340, 713–9228.
International and Interagency Affairs Chief.—D. Brent Smith, room 7315, 713–2024.
Director, Office of:
Marine Data Stewardship Division.—Dr. Krisa Arzayus, room 4651, 713–3272.
Commercial Remote Sensing Regulatory Affairs.—Tahara Dawkins, Director, room 8260, 713–3385.
GOES–R Program.—Gregory A. Mandt, NASA GSFC, room C100D, 286–1355.
Joint Polar Satellite System.—Harry Cikanek, Greentec, room 3301, (240) 684–0900.
National Climatic Data Center.—Thomas Karl, room 557–C (828) 271–4476.
National Geophysical Data Center.—Eric Kihn (acting), room 1B148 (303) 497–6215.
National Oceanographic Data Center.—Margarita Gregg, room 4820, 713–3270.
Satellite and Product Operations.—Vanessa Griffin, room 1605, 817–4000.
Satellite Applications and Research.—Al Powell, NCWCP 2600, 683–3487.
Space Commercialization.—Charles S. Baker (acting), HCHB room 2518 (202) 482–6125.
Systems Development.—Susanne Hilding, room 6234, 713–0100.

NATIONAL WEATHER SERVICE

1315 East-West Highway, Silver Spring, MD 20910

Assistant Administrator.—Louis W. Uccelini, Ph.D., room 18150 (301) 713–9095.
Deputy Assistant Administrator.—Laura Furgione, room 18130, 713–0711.
Chief Financial Officer.—Vacant, room 18176, 713–0397.
Deputy Chief Financial Officer.—John K. Longenecker, room 18212, 713–0397.
NOAA Assistant Chief Information Officer.—Iftikhar Jamil, room 17424, 713–1360.
Director, Office of:
Climate, Water and Weather Services.—Christopher Strage (acting), room 14348, 713–0700.
Hydrologic Development.—Capt. Barry Choy (acting), room 8212, 713–1658.
National Centers for Environmental Prediction.—Wayne Higgings (acting), room 101, 763–8016.
Operational Systems.—Mark Paese, room 16212, 713–0165.
Science and Technology.—John D. Murphy, room 15300, 713–1746.

OCEANIC AND ATMOSPHERIC RESEARCH

1315 East-West Highway, Silver Spring, MD 20910

Assistant Administrator.—Robert Detrick, Ph.D. (301) 713–2458.

Deputy Assistant Administrator for—
Labs and Cooperative Institutes.—Steven Fine, Ph.D. (303) 497–6005.
Programs and Administration.—Craig McLean.
Director of:
Earth System Research Laboratory.—Alexander MacDonald, Ph.D. (303) 497–6005.
Division of:
Chemical Sciences.—A.R. "Ravi" Ravishankara, Ph.D. (303) 497–5821.
Global Monitoring.—Jim Butler, Ph.D. (303) 497–6898.
Global Systems.—Scott Hausman, Ph.D.
Physical Science.—William Neff, Ph.D. (303) 497–6265.
Air Resources Laboratory.—Michael Uhart, Ph.D. (301) 734–1177.
Atlantic Oceanographic and Meteorological Laboratory.—Robert Atlas (305) 361–4300.
Geophysical Fluid Dynamics Laboratory.—Ram Ramaswamy, Ph.D. (609) 452–6510.
Great Lakes Environmental Research Laboratory.—Mare Colton, Ph.D. (734) 741–2254.
National Sea Grant College Program.—Leon Cammen, room 11716, 713–1088.
National Severe Storms Laboratory.—Steve Koch, Ph.D. (405) 325–6900.
Pacific Marine Environmental Laboratory.—Chris Sabine (206) 526–6800.
Director, Office of:
Arctic Research.—Janet Intrieri, Ph.D. (acting), (301) 427–2470.
Climate Program.—Richard Rosen, Ph.D. (acting), 427–1263.
Oceanic Exploration and Research.—Joseph "Tim" Arcano, Ph.D., 734–1145.

PROGRAM PLANNING AND INTEGRATION

Assistant Administrator.—Pat Montanio, room 15628 (301) 713–1632.
Deputy Assistant Administrator.—Vacant, room 15629, 713–3318.

UNITED STATES PATENT AND TRADEMARK OFFICE

P.O. Box 1450, 600 Dulany Street, Arlington, VA 22313–1450

Phone (571) 272–8600

Under Secretary of Commerce for Intellectual Property and Director of U.S. Patent and Trademark Office.—Vacant.
Deputy Under Secretary of Commerce for Intellectual Property and Deputy Director of the U.S. Patent and Trademark Office.—Michelle Lee.
Chief of Staff.—Andrew Byrnes, 272–8600.
Deputy Chief of Staff.—Vikrum Aiyer.
Chief Communications Officer.—Todd Elmer, 272–3500.
Chief Administrative Patent Judge, Board of Patent Appeals and Interferences.—James Donald Smith, 272–9797.
Deputy Chief Administrative Patent Judge.—Vacant, 272–9797.
Chief Administrative Trademark Judge, Trademark Trial and Appeal Board.—Gerard Rogers, 272–8500.
Director, Office of Enrollment and Discipline.—William Covey, 272–4097.

COMMISSIONER FOR PATENTS

Commissioner.—Margaret A. Focarino (571) 272–8800.
Deputy Commissioner for Patent Examination Policy.—Andrew Hirshfeld.
Deputy Commissioner for Patent Operations.—Andrew Faile.
Deputy Commissioner for Patent Administration..—Bruce Kisliuk.
Deputy Commissioner, International Patent Classification.—Mark Powell.
Associate Commissioner for—
Patent Examination Policy.—Janet Gongola.
Patent Information Management.—Deborah Stephens.
Patent Resources and Planning.—Vacant.
Innovation Development.—Anthony Knight (acting).
Director, Office of:
Patent Cooperation Treaty Legal Administration.—Charles A. Pearson, 272–3224.
Patent Legal Administration.—Brian Hanlon, 272–7735.
Assistant Deputy Commissioner for Patent Operations:
Chemical and Design Discipline.—Jacqueline Stone (TC 1600, 1700, and 2900).
Electrical I Discipline.—Valencia Martin-Wallace (TC 2100 and 2400).
Electrical II Discipline.—James Dwyer (TC 2600 and Office of Patent Training).

Electrical III Discipline.—Robert Oberleitner (TC 2800 and Central Re-Exam Unit).
Mechanical Discipline.—Richard Seidel (TC 3600 and 3700).
Patent Examining Group Directors:
Technology Center 1600 (biotechnology and organic chemistry): Jerry Lorengo, 272–0600; Wanda Walker, 272–0500.
Technology Center 1700 (chemical and materials engineering): Yvonne Eyler, 272–1200; Karen Young, 272–1100; Gladys Corcoran, 272–1300.
Technology Center 2100 (computer architecture and software): Wendy Garber, 272–0800; Seema Rao, 272–2168; David Talbott, 272–4150.
Technology Center 2400 (networking, multiplexing, cable, and security): Timothy Callahan, 272–4066; Nancy Le, 272–4056; Nester Ramirez, 272–3174.
Technology Center 2600 (communications): Derris Banks, 272–2560; Tariq Hafiz, 272–4550; John LeGuyader, 272–4650; David Wiley, 272–4750.
Technology Center 2800 (semiconductor, electrical mechanical and physics/optical systems and components): Wynn Coggins, 272–1850; Jack Harvey, 272–1850; Joseph Thomas, 272–1550.
Technology Center 2900 (Designs): Robert Olszewski, 272–6788.
Technology Center 3600 (transportation, construction, electronic commerce, agriculture, national security, and license and review): Greg Vidovich, 272–5350; Katherine Matecki, 272–5250; Edward Lefkowitz, 272–5150.
Technology Center 3700 (mechanical engineering, manufacturing, and products): Donald Hajec, 272–2975; Angela Sykes, 272–4390; Andrew Wang, 272–3750; Diego Gutierrez, 272–3680.
Technology Center 3900 (Central Reexamination Unit): Irem Yucel, 272–7403.
Technology Center 4100 (Patent Training): Gary Jones, 272–8320.
Director, Office of:
Central Reexamination Unit.—Irem Yucel, 272–7403.
Data Management (PUBS).—Thomas Koontz (703) 756–1492.
Legal Administration and Petitions (PCT).—Charles Pearson, 272–3224.
Patent Application Processing (PCT Operations).—Kevin Little (703) 756–1451.
Patent Classification.—John Salotto (acting), (703) 756–1850.
Patent Financial Management.—John Buie, 272–6283.
Patent Legal Administration.—Brian Hanlon, 272–7735.
Patent Processing Services (OPPS).—Thomas Koontz (acting), (703) 756–1490.
Patent Quality Assurance.—Paula Hutzell, 272–0531.
Patent Training.—Gary Jones, 272–8320.

COMMISSIONER FOR TRADEMARKS

Commissioner.—Deborah Cohn (571) 272–8901.
Deputy Commissioner for Trademark Operations.—Mary Boney (571) 272–8901.
Trademark Examination Law Office Managing Attorneys:
Law Office 101.—Ron Sussman, 272–9696.
Law Office 102.—Mitchell Front, 272–9382.
Law Office 103.—Michael Hamilton, 272–9278.
Law Office 104.—Chris Doninger, 272–9297.
Law Office 105.—Susan Hayash, 272–9692
Law Office 106.—Mary Sparrow, 272–9332.
Law Office 107.—Leslie Bishop, 272–9445.
Law Office 108.—Andrew Lawrence, 272–9342.
Law Office 109.—Dan Vavonese, 272–9288.
Law Office 110.—Chris Pedersen, 272–9371.
Law Office 111.—Robert Lorenzo, 272–9387.
Law Office 112.—Angela Wilson, 272–9443.
Law Office 113.—Odette Bonnet, 272–9426.
Law Office 114.—Margaret Le, 272–9456.
Law Office 115.—John Lincoski, 272–9436.
Law Office 116.—Michael Baird, 272–9487.
Law Office 117.—Hellen Bryan-Johnson, 272–9446.
Virtual Law Office - Pilot Sometime in January 2014.
Law Office 118.—Tomas Howell (571) 272–9302.
Law Office 119.—Brett Golden (571) 272–9257.
Director, Office of Trademark Program Control.—Betty Andrews, 272–9666.
Deputy Commissioner for Trademark Examination Policy.—Sharon Marsh, 272–8901.
Director, Office of Trademark Quality Review.—Kevin Peska, 272–9658.

POLICY AND EXTERNAL AFFAIRS

Chief Policy Officer and Director for International Affairs.—Shira Perlmutter.
Deputy Chief Policy Officer for Operations.—George Elliott (571) 272–9300.
Director, Office of:
Governmental Affairs.—Dana Colarulli, 272–7300.
Copyright.—Michael Shapiro, 272–9300.
Enforcement.—Michael Smith, 272–9300.
International Trade.—Paul Salmon, 272–9300.
Patents.—Chuck Eloshway, 272–9300.
Trademarks.—Amy Cotton, 272–9300.
Director of Global Intellectual Property Academy.—Rachel Wallace, 272–1500.

CHIEF FINANCIAL OFFICER

Chief Financial Officer.—Anthony Scardino (571) 272–9200.
Deputy Chief Financial Officer.—Frank Murphy.
Senior Financial Manager.—Michelle Picard.
Director, Office of Planning and Budget.—Timothy Rosado (571) 272–6538.
Finance.—Mark Krieger, 272–6339.
Financial Management Systems.—Gita Zoks, 272–6363.
Procurement.—Michelle Picard (acting).

CHIEF PERFORMANCE IMPROVEMENT OFFICER

Chief Performance Improvement Officer.—Vacant (571) 272–9200.

CHIEF ADMINISTRATIVE OFFICER

Chief Administrative Officer.—Frederick Steckler (571) 272–9600.
Deputy Chief Administrative Officer.—Wynn Coggins (acting).
Director of:
Corporate Services.—John Hassett, 272–6250.
Director of the Office of Equal Employment Opportunity and Diversity.—Bismarck Myrick, 272–6315.
Human Resources.—Karen Karlinchak, 272–6200.

OFFICE OF GENERAL COUNSEL

General Counsel.—William Covey (acting), (571) 272–7000.
Deputy General Counsel for—
General Law.—James O. Payne Jr., 272–3000.
Intellectual Property Law and Solicitor.—Nathan Kelley, 272–9035.

CHIEF INFORMATION OFFICER

Chief Information Officer.—John B. Owens II (571) 272–9400.
Deputy Chief Information Officer.—Vacant.
Chief of Staff.—John S. Williams, 272–5664.
Director of Infrastructure Engineering and Operations.—Robert Cobert (571) 272–5481.
Director of:
Budget and Finance.—Keith M. VanderBrink, 272–5662.
Program Administration Organization.—Toby Bennett, 272–6205.
Customer Information Services.—Tom Kenton (571) 272–8998.
Manager, Office of:
Electronic Information Products.—James Thompson (571) 756–1422.
Public Information Services.—Ted L. Parr (703) 756–1267.
Public Records Division.—Donna Cooper (703) 756–1893.
Customer Support Services.—Thomas Kenton, 272–8998.
Enterprise Systems Services.—Carol R. Eakins, 272–5426.
Network and Telecommunications.—Vacant.
Director of:
Application Engineering and Development.—David Chiles (571) 272–7001.

Information Management Services.—Rhonda Foltz (571) 272–6147.
Organizational Policy and Governance.—Kevin Smith (571) 272–3200.
Quality Management.—Brain R. Jones, 272–1659.
Systems Development and Maintenance.—Patsy Riley, 272–3925.

NATIONAL INSTITUTE OF STANDARDS AND TECHNOLOGY

100 Bureau Drive Gaithersburg, MD 20899 (301) 975–6478

Under Secretary of Standards and Technology and Director.—Dr. Patrick Gallagher (301) 975–2300.
Associate Director for Laboratory Programs.—Dr. Willie E. May (301) 975–2300.
Chief Safety Officer.—Dr. Richard Kayser, 975–4502.
Baldrige Performance Excellence Program.—Dr. Robert Fangmeyer, 975–2360.
International and Academic Affairs.—Dr. Claire M. Saundry, 975–2386.
NIST/Boulder Laboratories.—Dr. Mike Kelley (acting), (303) 497–5285.
Chief of Staff.—Kevin Kimball, 975–3070.
Congressional and Legislative Affairs.—Jim Schufreider, 975–5675.
Program Coordination Office.—Dr. Jason Boehm, 975–8678.
Public and Business Affairs.—Gail J. Porter, 975–3392.
Chief Financial Officer.—George Jenkins, 975–5080.
Budget.—Eddie Rivera, 975–2670.
Business Systems.—Fred Lehnhoff, 975–2290.
Finance.—Marvin Washington, 975–6897.
Grants and Agreements Management.—Cecelia Royster (acting), 975–6336.
Chief Human Capital Officer.—Susanne Porch, 975–2487.
Human Resources Management.—Janet Hoffman, 975–3185.
Management and Organization.—Catherine S. Fletcher, 975–4054.
Safety, Health and Environment.—Jeffrey Good, 975–6114.
Civil Rights and Diversity Office.—Mirta-Marie M. Keys, 975–2042.
Applications Systems.—L. Dale Little, 975–8982.
Customer Access and Support.—Tim Halton, 975–8920.
Enterprise Systems.—James E. Fowler, 975–6888.
Information Technology Security and Networking.—Robert Glenn, 975–3667.
Chief Facilities Management Officer.—Stephen Salber, 975–8836.
Emergency Services.—Dr. Benjamin Overbey, 975–8247.
Engineering, Maintenance and Support Services.—Donald Archibald (301) 975–5680.
Plant.—David Henry, 975–6901.
Associate Director for Industry and Innovation Services.—Dr. Phillip Singerman, 975–2340.
Research Support Information Services.—Mary-Deirdre Coraggio, 975–5158.
Reference Materials.—Robert L. Watters, Jr., 975–4122.
Standards Coordination Office.—George Arnold, 975–5627.
Weights and Measures.—Carol Hockert, 975–5507.
Director, Technology Innovation Program.—Thomas Wiggins, 975–2162.
Project Management Office.—Linda Beth Schilling, 975–2887.
Selection Management Office.—Thomas Wiggins, 975–5416.
Director, Hollings Manufacturing Extension Partnership Program.—Dr. Phillip Singerman (acting), 975–4676.
Program Development Office.—Alex Folk, 975–8089.
Systems Operations Office.—Michael J. Simpson, 975–6147.
Director, Engineering Laboratory.—Dr. Howard Harary (acting), (301) 975–5900.
Deputy Director.—Dr. Joannie Chin, 975–6815.
Electromagnetics.—Dr. Perry Wilson (acting), (303) 497–3406.
Quantum Electronics and Photonics.—Dr. Robert Hickernell (acting), (303) 497–3455.
Semiconductor Electronics.—Dr. David G. Seiler, 975–2054.
Director, Center for Nanoscale Science and Technology.—Dr. Robert Celotta, 975–8001.
Intelligent Systems.—Dr. Al Wavering, 975–3401.
Fabrication Technology.—Mark E. Luce, 975–2159.
Systems Integration.—Vijay Srinivasan, 975–3524.
Semiconductor and Dimensional Metrology Division.—Dr. Michael Postek, 975–2299.
Chief, Chemical Science and Technology Laboratory.—Dr. Carlos Gonzalez, 975–2483.
Deputy Chief.—Dr. Roger D. Van Zee, 975–8301.
Director, Material Measurement Laboratory.—Dr. Laurie E. Locascio, 975–3130.
Greenhouse Gas and Climate Science Measurements.—Dr. James R. Whetstone, 975–2609.
Materials Measurement Science.—Dr. John Small, 975–3900.
Energy Research.—Dr. Daniel G. Friend (303) 497–5424.

Director, Physical Measurement Laboratory.—Dr. Joseph Dehmer, 975–4200.
Deputy Director.—Dr. James Olthoff, 975–2220.
Quantum Measurement.—Dr. Carl J. Williams, 975–3531.
Radiation Physics.—Dr. Lisa R. Karam, 975–5561.
Sensor Science.—Dr. Gerald Fraser, 975–3797.
Quantum Physics.—Dr. Thomas O'Brian (303) 497–4570.
Time and Frequency.—Dr. Thomas R. O'Brian (303) 497–4570.
Applied Chemicals and Materials.—Dr. Stephanie Hooker (303) 497–4326.
Materials Science and Engineering.—Dr. Frank W. Gayle, 975–6161.
Chief, Materials Science.—Dr. Eric Lin, 975–6743.
Director, NIST Center for Neutron Research.—Dr. Robert Dimeo, 975–6210.
Chief, Fire Research.—Dr. Anthony Hamins, 975–6598.
Energy and Environment.—Dr. Hunter Fanney, 975–5864.
Materials and Structural Systems.—Jason Averill (acting), 975–6051.
Director, Information Technology Laboratory.—Dr. Charles Romine, 975–2900.
Deputy Director.—James A. St. Pierre, 975–2900.
Advanced Network Technologies.—Dr. Abdelila Battou, 975–5247.
Computer Security.—Donna Dodson, 975–3669.
Information Access.—Dr. Ashit Talukder, 975–3889.
Applied and Computational Mathematics.—Dr. Ronald F. Boisvert, 975–3800.
Software and Systems.—Dr. Ram Sriram, 975–3507.
Statistical Engineering.—Dr. Antonio Possolo (acting), 975–2853.

NATIONAL TECHNICAL INFORMATION SERVICE

5285 Port Royal Road, Springfield, VA 22161

Director.—Bruce Borzino (703) 605–6400.

NATIONAL TELECOMMUNICATIONS AND INFORMATION ADMINISTRATION

1401 Constitution Avenue, NW., 20230

Assistant Secretary and Administrator.—Lawrence E. Stickling, room 4898 (202) 482–1840.
Deputy Assistant Secretary.—Angela Simpson (acting) 482–1840.
Chief of Staff.—Angela Simpson (acting) 482–1840.
Deputy Chief of Staff and Congressional Affairs Director.—James Wasilewski.
Senior Advisors: Jennifer Duane, Jade Nester, Peter Tenhula.
Chief Counsel.—Kathy Smith.
Director, Office of:
Institute for Telecommunication Sciences.—Al Vincent (303) 497–3500.
International Affairs.—Fiona Alexander.
Policy Analysis and Development.—John B. Morris, Jr.
Public Affairs Director.—Heather Phillips.
Public Safety Communications.—Stephen Fletcher.
Spectrum Management.—Karl Nebbia.
Telecommunications and Information Applications.—Anthony Wilhelm.

DEPARTMENT OF LABOR

Frances Perkins Building, Third Street and Constitution Avenue, NW., 20210

phone (202) 693–5000, http://www.dol.gov

THOMAS E. PEREZ, Secretary of Labor; education: B.A., Brown University, 1983; J.D., Harvard Law School, 1987; M.P.P, Harvard University John F. Kennedy School of Government, 1987; professional: Law Clerk, U.S. District Court for the District of Colorado, 1987–89; Federal Prosecutor, Civil Rights Division, Department of Justice, 1989–95; Special Counsel, Senator Edward Kennedy, 1995–98; Deputy Assistant Attorney General for Civil Rights, Department of Justice, 1998–99; Director, Office for Civil Rights, Department of Health and Human Services, 1999–01; Professor, University of Maryland School of Law, 2001–07; Secretary, Maryland Department of Labor, Licensing and Regulation, 2007–09; Assistant United States Attorney General for the Civil Rights Division, 2009–13; Member, Montgomery County (MD) Council, 2002–06; President, Montgomery County (MD) Council, 2004–05; married: Ann Marie Staudenmaier; nominated by President Barack Obama to become the 26th Secretary of Labor, and was confirmed by the U.S. Senate on July 18, 2013.

OFFICE OF THE SECRETARY

phone (202) 693–6000

Secretary of Labor.—Thomas E. Perez.
Deputy Secretary.—Seth Harris.
Associate Deputy Secretaries: Laura McClintock; Nancy Rooney.
Executive Secretariat Director.—Elizabeth Kim.
Chief of Staff.—Matthew Colangelo.
Director of Advance and Scheduling.—C. Wayne Skinner.

OFFICE OF PUBLIC ENGAGEMENT

Senior Advisor and Director.—Dr. Gabriela Lemus (202) 693–6000, fax (202) 693–6145.

ADMINISTRATIVE LAW JUDGES

Techworld, 800 K Street, NW., Suite 400–N, 20001–8002

Chief Administrative Law Judge.—Stephen L. Purcell (202) 693–7542.
Associate Chief Judges: William S. Colwell, Paul C. Johnson, Jr. (acting).

ADMINISTRATIVE REVIEW BOARD

Chief and Chair.—Paul M. Igasaki, room N–5404 (202) 693–6200.
Vice Chair.—E. Cooper Brown, room N–5404, 693–6200.

OFFICE OF THE ASSISTANT SECRETARY FOR ADMINISTRATION AND MANAGEMENT (OASAM)

Assistant Secretary.—T. Michael Kerr, room S–2203 (202) 693–4040.
Deputy Assistant Secretary for—
Operations.—Edward C. Hugler, room S–2203 (202) 693–4040.
Policy.—Charlotte Hayes, room S–2203 (202) 693–4040.
Special Assistants: Douglas Robins, Traci Smith (202) 693–4040.
Administrative Officer.—Christopher Yerxa (202) 693–4040.
Staff Assistants: Vacant.

BUSINESS OPERATIONS CENTER

Director.—Al Stewart, room S–1524 (202) 693–4028.
Deputy Director.—Catherine Breitenbach (202) 693–7273.
Office of:
Acquisition Management Services.—Carl V. Campbell, room S–1510–C, 693–7246.
Administrative Services.—Phil Puckett, room S–1521, 693–6650.
Management Support Services.—Vacant, room S–1519B, 693–7272.
Office of Asset and Resource Management.—Bill Keisler, room S–1519B, 693–4020.
Procurement Services.—Sandra Foster, room S–4307, 693–4570.
Worker Safety and Health Services.—Stephanie Semmer, room S–1321, 693–6678.

PERFORMANCE MANAGEMENT CENTER

Director.—Holly Donnelly, room S–3317 (202) 693–7125.
Office of:
Performance Monitoring.—David Frederickson, room S–3317, 693–7123.
Planning.—Lissette Gean, room S–3317, 693–7951.

CIVIL RIGHTS CENTER

Director.—Naomi Barry-Perez, room N–4123 (202) 693–6500.
Staff Assistant.—Katrina Creek, room N–4123 (202) 693–6549.
Office of:
Compliance Assistance and Planning.—Roger Ocampo, 693–6562.
Enforcement/External.—Denise Sudell (acting), 693–6519.
Enforcement/Internal.—Samuel Rhames, 693–6500.
Reasonable Accommodation Hotline.—Dawn Johnson, room N–4123, 693–6527.

DEPARTMENTAL BUDGET CENTER

Director.—Geoff Kenyon, room S–4020 (202) 693–4090.
Deputy Director.—Mark P. Wichlin (202) 693–4090.
Administrative Officer.—Patricia Smith (202) 693–4067.
Office of:
Budget Programs.—James Martin, 693–4077.
Budget Policy and Systems.—Sandra Mulcahy, 693–4078.

EMERGENCY MANAGEMENT CENTER

800 K Street, NW., Suite 450 North, 20001–8002

Director.—Greg Rize (202) 693–7514.
Deputy Director.—Mary Jo Hogan (202) 693–7504.

GOVBENEFITS.GOV

Program Manager.—Al Sloane, room N–4309 (202) 693–8067.

HUMAN RESOURCES CENTER

Director.—Sydney Rose, room C–5526 (202) 693–7600.
Deputy Director.—Vacant.
Office of:
Administration and Management Services.—Donna Childs Speight, room C–5517, 693–7773.
Departmental Labor Relations and Negotiations.—Earsie Johnson (acting), room N–5476, 693–7670.
Executive Resources.—Kim Green (acting), room N–2453, 693–7800.
Human Resources Consulting and Operations.—Donna Kramer, room C–5516, 693–7690.
Human Resources Policy and Accountability.—Kim Sasajima, room N–5464, 693–7720.
Human Resources Systems (OHRS).—Alvin Black, room S–3314, 693–7740.
Training and Development.—LaVeen Thompson, room S–3308, 693–7623.

Worklife, Leave, Benefits Policy and Programs.—Deborah Dudley, room N–5454, 693–7610.

OFFICE OF THE CHIEF INFORMATION OFFICER

Deputy CIO.—Dawn Leaf, room N–1301 (202) 693–4200.
Associate Deputy CIO.—Curtis Turner (acting).
IT Administration Director.—Kathy Fox, 693–4215.
Director, Office of:
Enterprise Services.—Louis Charlier, 693–4147.
IT Governance.—Peter Sullivan, 693–4211.
IT Help Desk.—(8 a.m. to 6:30 p.m.), room N–1505, 693–4444.

SECURITY CENTER

Director.—Kenneth McCreless, room S–1229G (202) 693–7994.
Deputy Director.—Stacey Thompson (202) 693–7210.
Staff Assistant.—Dianna Cornish (202) 693–7991.

ASSISTANT SECRETARY FOR POLICY

Assistant Secretary.—Vacant, room S–2312 (202) 693–5959.
Deputy Assistant Secretary.—Megan Uzzell.
Career Deputy Assistant Secretary.—James H. Moore.
Chief of Staff.—Vacant.
Staff Assistant.—Vacant.
Director, Office of:
Compliance Assistance Policy.—Vacant.
Economic Policy and Analysis.—Vacant.
Regulatory and Programmatic Policy.—Kathleen Franks, 693–5072.
Chief Evaluation Officer.—Demetra Nightingale, room S–2312 (202) 693–5959.
Deputy Chief Evaluation Officer.—Jonathan Simonetta.

BENEFITS REVIEW BOARD

Chair.—Nancy S. Dolder, room N5101 (202) 693–6300.

BUREAU OF LABOR STATISTICS

Postal Square Building, Suite 4040, 2 Massachusetts Avenue, NE., 20212

phone (202) 691–7800

Commissioner.—Erica L. Groshen.
Deputy Commissioner.—John M. Galvin, 691–7802.
Associate Commissioner, Office of:
Administration.—Daniel J. Lacey, suite 4060, 691–7777.
Compensation and Working Conditions.—William Wiatrowski, suite 4130, 691–6300.
Employment and Unemployment Statistics.—Thomas J. Nardone, suite 4945, 691–6400.
Field Operations.—Jay Mousa, suite 2935, 691–5800.
Prices and Living Conditions.—Michael Horrigan, suite 3120, 691–6960.
Productivity and Technology.—John Ruser, suite 2150, 691–5600.
Publications and Special Studies.—Michael Levi, suite 4110, 691–5900.
Survey Methods Research.—John Eltinge, suite 1950, 691–7404.
Technology and Survey Processing.—Richard Schroeder (acting), suite 5025, 691–7600.
Assistant Commissioner, Office of:
Compensation Levels and Trends.—Phil Doyle, suite 4130, 691–6200.
Consumer Prices and Price Indexes.—John Layng, suite 3130, 691–6955.
Current Employment Analysis.—Vacant, suite 4675, 691–6378.
Industrial Prices and Price Indexes.—David Friedman, suite 4170, 691–7700.
Industry Employment Statistics.—Kenneth W. Robertson, suite 4840, 691–6521.
Occupational Statistics and Employment Projections.—Dixie Sommers, suite 2135, 691–5701.

Director of:
Survey Processing.—Richard L. Schroeder, suite 5025, 691–6730.
Technology and Computing Services.—Rick Kryger, suite 5025, 691–7562.

BUREAU OF INTERNATIONAL LABOR AFFAIRS

Deputy Undersecretary.—Carol Pier (acting), room S–2235 (202) 693–4770.
Associate Deputy Undersecretary.—Mark Mittelhauser, room S–2235 (202) 693–4770.
Associate Deputy Undersecretary.—Eric Biel (acting), room S–2235 (202) 693–4770.
Special Assistant.—Kathleen Schalch, room S–2235 (202) 693–4770.
Chief of Staff.—Amit Pandya, room S–2235, 693–4770.
Administrative Officer.—Ralph Cox, room S–2235 (202) 693–4770.
Executive Assistant.—Diane Ward, room S–2235 (202) 693–4770.
Program Analyst.—Candice Streeter, room S–2235 (202) 693–4770.

OFFICE OF TRADE AND LABOR AFFAIRS

Director.—Gregory Schoepfle, room S–5303 (202) 693–4887.
Deputy Director.—Sueryun Hahn, room S–5303, 693–4800.

OFFICE OF CHILD LABOR, FORCED LABOR, AND HUMAN TRAFFICKING

Director.—Marcia Eugenio, room S–5317 (202) 693–4849.
Deputy Director.—Kevin Willcutts, room S–5317, 693–4832.

OFFICE OF INTERNATIONAL RELATIONS

Director.—Robert B. Shepard, room S–5004 (202) 693–4808
Deputy Director.—Zhao Li, room S–5004, 693–4803.
Chief, Division of Multilateral Issues.—Joan Barrett, room S–5004, 693–4857.

OFFICE OF THE CHIEF FINANCIAL OFFICER

Chief Financial Officer.—James Taylor, room S–4030 (202) 693–6800.
Deputy Chief Financial Officer.—Karen Tekleberhan.
Associate Deputy CFO for—
Financial Systems.—Myrian Myer, room N–2719.
Fiscal Integrity.—Karen Tekleberhan (acting), room S–4030.
Administrative Officer.—Marella Turner.
Business Process Improvement.—Robert Beckman, room S–4030.

OFFICE OF FISCAL INTEGRITY

Division of:
Internal Control.—Naresh Chopra, room S–4502.
Financial Policy.—Robert Balin (acting), room S–4030.
Travel.—Madhuri Edwards, room N–2719.

OFFICE OF FINANCIAL REPORTING AND COMPLIANCE

Division of:
Financial Reporting and Compliance.—Stanley Karczewski, room S–4030.
Financial Compliance.—Robert Balin, room S–4030.
Financial Reporting.—Kevin Brown, room S–4502.

OFFICE OF FINANCIAL MANAGEMENT

Division of:
Central Accounting Operations.—Sahra Torres-Rivera, room S–4502.
Client Financial Management Services.—Adrienne Young, room S–5526.
Client Accounting Services.—Janice Blake-Green, room S–5526.

OFFICE OF FINANCIAL SYSTEMS

Division of:
Payroll Systems Support.—Roy Abreu, room S–4214.
Quality Assurance and Customer Support.—Patrice Clement, room N–2719.
Security and Technology.—Richard Westmark, room N–2719.

OFFICE OF CONGRESSIONAL AND INTERGOVERNMENTAL AFFAIRS

Assistant Secretary.—Brian Kennedy, room S–2006 (202) 693–4601.
Chief of Staff.—Nikki McKinney, room S–2006, 693–4601.
Staff Assistant.—Glenda Manning, room S–2006, 693–4601.
Deputy Assistant Secretary for Policy for Congressional and Intergovernmental Affairs.—Adri Jayaratne, room S–2220, 693–4600.
Director for Intergovernmental Affairs.—Elmy A. Bermejo, S–2220, 693–6400.
Deputy Director for Intergovernmental Affairs.—Carrianna Suiter, S–2220.
Deputy Assistant Secretary for Operations for Budget and Appropriations.—Teri Bergman, room S–2220, 693–4600.
Senior Legislative Officers:
Appropriations / Budget.—Stephen Steigledger, room S–2220, 693–4600.
Employee Benefits.—Vacant, room S–2220, 693–4600.
Employment and Training.—Laura MacDonald, room S–2220, 693–4600.
VETS.—Margaret Cantrell, S–2220, 693–4600.
Foreign Labor Certification / Wage and Hour Division.—Tony Zaffirini, room–2220, 693–4600; Nikki McKinney, room S–2220, 693–4600.
ILAB / International Affairs.—Laura de la Torre.
Senior Legislative Counsel for Oversight / Investigation and Labor Management Standards.—Kate Ahlgren room S–2220, 693–4600.
Legislative Officers: Brittany Diegel, Andria Oliver, Michelle Rose, Carmen Torres, Rahsheim Wright, room S–2220, 693–4600.
Senior Legislative Assistant.—Laura de la Torre.
Senior Intergovernmental Officer.—Vacant.
Administrative Officer.—Joycelyn Daniels, room S1204, 693–4600.

SECRETARY'S REPRESENTATIVES IN THE REGIONAL OFFICES

Region II, New York.—Robert Angelo, Connecticut, Delaware, District of Columbia, New Hampshire, New Jersey, New York, Pennsylvania, Vermont, Virginia, West Virginia.
Region IV, Miami.—Millie Herrera, Alabama, Arkansas, Florida, Georgia, Louisiana, Mississippi, North Carolina, South Carolina, Tennessee.
Region V, Chicago.—Ken Williams-Bennett, Illinois, Indiana, Iowa, Kentucky, Michigan, Minnesota, Missouri, Ohio, Wisconsin.
Region VIII, Denver.—Dusti Gurule, Colorado, Kansas, Nebraska, New Mexico, Oklahoma, Texas.
Region IX, Los Angeles.—Alicia Villarreal, Arizona, California, Hawaii, Nevada, Utah.
Region X, Seattle.—Vacant, Alaska, Idaho, Montana, North Dakota, Oregon, South Dakota, Washington, Wyoming.

OFFICE OF DISABILITY EMPLOYMENT POLICY

Assistant Secretary.—Kathleen Martinez, room S–1303 (202) 693–7880, TTY 693–7881.
Deputy Assistant Secretary.—Jennifer Sheehy.
Chief of Staff.—Rhonda Basha.
Special Assistant.—Dylan Orr.
Director of Policy Development.—Vacant.

EMPLOYEE BENEFITS SECURITY ADMINISTRATION

Assistant Secretary.—Phyllis C. Borzi, room S–2524 (202) 693–8300.
Deputy Assistant Secretary.—Vacant (202) 693–8300.
Special Assistants: Ali Khawar, Meredith Regine, 693–8300.
Confidential Assistant.—Michelle S. Brown.
Deputy Assistant Secretary for Program Operations.—Alan D. Lebowitz, room N–5677, 693–8315.

Executive Assistant.—Becki Marchand, 693–8315.
Director of:
Program, Planning, Evaluation and Management.—Joel Lovelace, room N–5668, 693–8480.
Chief Accountant.—Ian Dingwall, 122 C Street, suite 400, 693–8360.
Enforcement.—Mable Capolongo, 122 C Street, suite 600, 693–8440.
Exemption Determinations.—Lyssa Hall, room N–5649, 693–8540.
Technology and Information Services.—Diane Schweizer, room N–5459, 693–8600.
Particiapnt Assistance.—Sharon Watson, room N–5625, 693–8630.
Regulations and Interpretations.—Joe Canary, room N–5669, 693–8500.
Policy and Research.—Joseph Piacentini, room N–5718, 693–8410.
Health Plan Standards and Compliance Assistance.—Daniel Maguire, room 5653, 693–8335.

EMPLOYEES' COMPENSATION APPEALS BOARD

Chairman.—Richard J. Daschbach, room N–5416 (202) 693–6374.

EMPLOYMENT AND TRAINING ADMINISTRATION

Assistant Secretary.—Jane Oates, room S–2307 (202) 693–2700.
Deputy Assistant Secretary.—Gerri Fiala, room S–2307, 693–2700.
Administrator, Office of:
Apprenticeship.—John Ladd, room N–5311, 693–2796.
Contracts Management.—Linda Heartley, room N–4702, 693–2800.
Financial Administration.—Gary Maupin, room N–4702, 693–2866.
Foreign Labor Certification.—William Carlson, room C–4312, 693–3010.
Job Corps.—Robert Pitulej (acting), room N–4463, 693–3000.
Management and Administrative Services.—William W. Thompson II, room N–4655, 693–2800.
National Response.—Erica Cantor, room C–5321, 693–3500.
Policy Development and Research.—Mike Jones (acting), room N-5637, 693–3700.
Trade Adjustment Assistance.—Norris Tyler (acting), room C–5321, 693–3560.
Unemployment Insurance.—Gay Gilbert, room S–4231, 693–3029.
Workforce Investment.—Amanda Ahlstrand (acting), room S–4231, 693–3980.

DOL CENTER FOR FAITH-BASED AND NEIGHBORHOOD PARTNERSHIPS

Director.—Philip Tom (202) 693–6030.
Deputy Director.—Benjamin Seigel, 693–6032.

OFFICE OF THE INSPECTOR GENERAL

Inspector General.—Vacant, room S–5502 (202) 693–5100.
Deputy Inspector General.—Daniel R. Petrole.
Assistant Inspector General for—
Audit.—Elliot P. Lewis, room S–5518, 693–5170.
Inspections and Special Investigations.—Asa "Gene" Cunningham, room S–5021, 693–5124.
Labor Racketeering and Fraud Investigations.—Thomas F. Farrell, room S–5014, 693–7034.
Legal Services.—Howard L. Shapiro, room S–5506, 693–5116.
Management and Policy.—Nancy Ruiz de Gamboa, room S–5028, 693–5191.

MINE SAFETY AND HEALTH ADMINISTRATION

1100 Wilson Boulevard, Arlington, VA 22209–3939, phone (202) 693–9414

fax 693–9401, http://www.msha.gov

Assistant Secretary.—Joseph A. Main, room 2322, 693–9402.
Deputy Assistant Secretary for Policy.—Stephen R. Weatherford, room 2321, 693–9407.
Deputy Assistant Secretary for Operations.—Patricia W. Silvey, room 2324, 693–9642.
Director, Office of:
Assessments, Accountability, Special Enforcement and Investigations.—Jay P. Mattos, room 2518, 693–9702.

Diversity and Equal Opportunity.—Darlene Farrar-Warren, room 2407, 693–9885.
Program Education and Outreach Services.—Layne Lathram, room 2317, 693–9422.
Program Evaluation and Information Resources.—Syed Hafeez (acting), room 2300, 693–9750.
Standards, Regulations and Variances (OSRV).—George Triebsch, room 2313, 693–9440.
Technical Support.—George M. Fesak, room 2330, 693–9470.

COAL MINE SAFETY AND HEALTH

Administrator.—Kevin Stricklin, room 2424, 693–9500.
Deputy Administrator.—Charles J. Thomas (acting), room 2426, 693–9503.

METAL AND NONMETAL MINE SAFETY AND HEALTH

Administrator.—Neal H. Merrifield, room 2436, 693–9600.
Deputy Administrator for Metal and Nonmetal.—Marvin Lichtenfels, room 2437, 693–9645.

EDUCATIONAL POLICY AND DEVELOPMENT

Director.—Jeffrey A. Duncan, room 2148, 693–9570.
Administration and Management (A&M).—Ernest A. Cameron, room 2125, 693–9802.

OCCUPATIONAL SAFETY AND HEALTH ADMINISTRATION

Assistant Secretary.—David Michaels, room S–2315 (202) 693–2000.
Deputy Assistant Secretaries: Jordan Barab, Greg Baxter (acting), 693–2000.
Chief of Staff.—Deborah Berkowitz, 693–2000.
Director, Office of:
Communications.—Frank Meilinger, 693–1999.
Director of:
Administrative Programs.—Kimberly A. Locey, 693–1600.
Construction.—Jim Maddux, 693–2100.
Cooperative and State Programs.—Doug Kalinowski, 693–2200.
Enforcement Programs.—Thomas Galassi, 693–2100.
Evaluation and Analysis.—Jens Svenson (acting), 693–2400.
Technology Support and Emergency Management.—Amanda Edens, 693–2300.
Standards and Guidance.—Dorothy Dougherty, 693–1950.
Whistleblower Protection Programs.—Beth Slavet, 693–2199.

OFFICE OF PUBLIC AFFAIRS

Senior Advisor for Communications and Public Affairs.—Carl Fillichio, room S–2514 (202) 693–4676.
Senior Managing Directors: Elizabeth Alexander, G. Stephen Barr.

REGIONAL OFFICES

Region I.—Boston.
Regional Director.—Ted Fitzgerald, JFK Federal Building, Government Center, 25 New Sudbury Street, Boston, MA 02203 (617) 565–2075.
Region III.—Philadelphia.
Regional Director.—Leni Uddyback-Fortson, Curtis Center, 170 South Independence Mall West, Suite 633–East, Philadelphia, PA 19106–3306 (215) 861–5102.
Region IV.—Atlanta.
Regional Director.—Michael D'Aquino, Atlanta Federal Center, 61 Forsyth, SW., Suite 6B75, Atlanta, GA 30303 (404) 562–2078.
Region V.—Chicago.
Regional Director.—Scott Allen, 230 South Dearborn Street, Room 3192 or Room 3194, Chicago, IL 60604 (312) 353–4727.
Region VI.—Dallas.
Regional Director.—Diana Petterson, 525 Griffin Street, Room 734, Dallas, TX 75202 (972) 850–4710.

Region IX.—California.
Regional Director.—Deanne Amaden, 90 7th Street, Suite 2–650, San Francisco, CA 94103–1516 (415) 625–2630.

OFFICE OF SMALL AND DISADVANTAGED BUSINESS UTILIZATION

Director.—Sonya Carrion, N–6432 (202) 693–7299.

OFFICE OF THE SOLICITOR

Solicitor.—M. Patricia Smith, room S–2002 (202) 693–5260.
Deputy Solicitor.—Deborah Greenfield.
Deputy Solicitor for—
National Operations.—Steven J. Mandel, 693–5260.
Regional Enforcement.—Katherine Bissell, 693–5260.
Senior Advisors.—Craig Hukill, Edward Sieger, Myron Zeitz.
Special Assistant.—Rajesh Nayak.

DIVISION OF BLACK LUNG AND LONGSHORE LEGAL SERVICES

Associate Solicitor.—Rae Ellen James, room N–2117 (202) 693–5660.
Deputy Associate Solicitor.—M. Elizabeth Medaglia.
Counsel for—
Administrative Litigation and Legal Advice.—Michael J. Rutledge.
Appellate Litigation.—Gary K. Stearman.
Enforcement and Appellate Litigation.—Sean G. Bajkowski.
Longshore.—Mark A. Reinhalter.
Regulations and Legislation.—Patricia M. Nece.

DIVISION OF CIVIL RIGHTS AND LABOR-MANAGEMENT

Associate Solicitor.—Christopher B. Wilkinson, room N–2474 (202) 693–5740.
Deputy Associate Solicitor.—Beverly Dankowitz.
Counsel for—
Civil Rights and Appellate Litigation.—Radine Legum.
Interpretation and Advice.—Suzan Chastain.
Litigation and Regional Coordination.—Consuela Pinto.
LMRDA Advice.—Clinton Wolcott.
LMRDA Programs.—Sharon E. Hanley.

DIVISION OF EMPLOYMENT AND TRAINING LEGAL SERVICES

Associate Solicitor.—Gary M. Buff, room N–2101 (202) 693–5710.
Deputy Associate Solicitor.—Jonathan H. Waxman, 693–5730.
Counsel for—
Employment and Training Advice: Robert P. Hines, Michael N. Apfelbaum.
Immigration Programs.—Nora Carroll.
International Affairs and USERRA.—Matthew P. Levin.
Litigation.—Harry L. Sheinfeld.

DIVISION OF FAIR LABOR STANDARDS

Associate Solicitor.—Jennifer S. Brand, room N–2716 (202) 693–5555.
Deputy Associate Solicitor.—William C. Lesser.
Counsel for—
Appellate Litigation.—Paul L. Frieden.
Contract Labor Standards.—Jonathan T. Rees.
Legal Advice.—Lynn McIntosh.
Trial Litigation: Jonathan M. Kronheim.
Whistleblower Programs.—Megan E. Guenther.

DIVISION OF FEDERAL EMPLOYEE AND ENERGY WORKERS COMPENSATION

Associate Solicitor.—Jeffrey L. Nesvet, room S–4325 (202) 693–5320.
Deputy Associate Solicitor.—Thomas G. Giblin.
Counsel for—
Claims and Compensation.—Catherine P. Carter.
Energy Employees Compensation.—Sheldon O. Turley, Jr.
FECA Subrogation.—Alexandra Tsiros.

DIVISION OF MANAGEMENT AND ADMINISTRATIVE LEGAL SERVICES

Associate Solicitor.—Rose Marie L. Audette, room N–2420 (202) 693–5405.
Deputy Associate Solicitors: Susan E. Howe, Allen K. Goshi.
Counsel for—
Appropriations.—Eileen McCarthy.
Employment Law.—James V. Blair.
FOIA and Information Law.—Joseph J. Plick.
FOIA Appeals, Paperwork Reduction Act and Federal Records Act.—Ray Mitten, Jr.
Procurement and Contracts.—David Koeppel.
Chief, Human Resources Office.—Michael Parrish.
Chief, Financial Management Office.—James Taylor.
Chief, Legal Technology Unit.—Donald Knickerbocker.
Director, Office of Information Services.—Ramona Oliver.

DIVISION OF MINE SAFETY AND HEALTH

1100 Wilson Boulevard, 22nd Floor, Arlington, VA 22209

Associate Solicitor.—Heidi W. Strassler, room 2222 (202) 693–9333.
Deputy Associate Solicitor.—Thomas A. Paige.
Counsel for—
Appellate Litigation.—W. Christian Schumann.
Standards and Legal Advice.—April E. Nelson.
Trial Litigation: Derek Baxter, Jason Grover.

DIVISION OF OCCUPATIONAL SAFETY AND HEALTH

Associate Solicitor.—Joseph M. Woodward, room S–4004 (202) 693–5452.
Deputy Associate Solicitor.—Ann S. Rosenthal.
Counsel for—
Appellate Litigation: Charles F. James, Heather Phillips.
Health Standards.—Ian J. Moar.
Regional Litigation and Legal Advice: Orlando J. Pannocchia, Robert W. Swain.
Safety Standards.—Robert J. Biersner.
Special Litigation.—Kenneth A. Hellman.

DIVISION OF PLAN BENEFITS SECURITY

Associate Solicitor.—Timothy D. Hauser, room N–4611 (202) 693–5600.
Deputy Associate Solicitor.—William Scott.
Counsel for—
Appellate and Special Litigation: Elizabeth Hopkins, Nathaniel I. Spiller.
Fiduciary Litigation.—Risa D. Sandler.
Financial Litigation.—Michael Schloss.
General Litigation.—Leslie Canfield Perlman.
Regulations.—William White Taylor.

OFFICE OF LEGAL COUNSEL

Associate Solicitor.—Robert A. Shapiro, room N–2700 (202) 693–5500.
Counsel for—
Ethics.—Robert M. Sadler.
Legislative Affairs.—Jill M. Otte.
Honors Program Director.—Susan Hutton.

VETERANS' EMPLOYMENT AND TRAINING SERVICE

Assistant Secretary.—Keith Kelly, room S–1312 (202) 693–4700.
Deputy Assistant Secretary for Operations and Management.—John Moran (202) 693–4700.
Chief of Staff.—Brian Ketz (acting), (202) 693–4721.
Executive Assistant.—Andrea Kyle (202) 693–4710.
Staff Assistant.—Dixi Belin (202) 693–4739.
Senior Advisor.—Gordon Burke (202) 693–4707.
Senior Advisor.—Jenny Erwin, Women Veteran Initiative (202) 693–4712.
Director for—
Office of National Programs.—Ruth Samardick (202) 693–4749.
Office of Strategic Outreach.—Tim Green (202) 693–4723.
Office of Agency Management and Budget.—Maria Temiquel (202) 693–4706.

REGIONAL OFFICES

Atlanta:
Administrator.—Vacant (404) 665–4330.
Boston:
Administrator.—Vacant (617) 565–2080.
Chicago:
Administrator.—Heather Higgins (312) 353–4932.
Dallas:
Administrator.—Robert Creel (972) 850–4718.
Philadelphia:
Administrator.—Joseph W. Hortiz, Jr. (215) 861–5385.
San Francisco:
Administrator.—Vacant (415) 625–7670.

WOMEN'S BUREAU

Director.—Latifa Lyles (acting), room S–3002 (202) 693–6719.
Deputy Director.—Joan Harrigan-Farrelly, room S–3002 (202) 693–6712.
Deputy Director.—Vacant, room S–3002 (202) 693–6762.
Chief of Staff.—Sandra Vega, room S–3002 (202) 693–6711.
National Office Coordinator.—Karen Furia, room S–3002 (202) 693–6753.
Field Coordinator.—Vacant.
Chief, Office of:
Information and Support Services.—Paris M. Mack, room S–3002 (202) 693–6754.
Policy and Programs.—Vacant, room S–3002 (202) 693–6762.

OFFICE OF WORKERS' COMPENSATION PROGRAMS

Director.—Gary Steinberg (acting), room S–3522, (202) 693–0031.
Special Assistant.—Judith Binder (202) 693–0032.
Director, Division of Financial Administration.—Joseph "Sam" Shellenberger (202) 693–0032.
Deputy Director.—Jose Moreno (202) 693–0032.
Director, Division of Administration and Operations.—Michael A. Tyllas (202) 693–0032.
Deputy Director.—Vincent Alvarez (202) 693–0032.
Director, Division of Federal Employees' Compensation.—Douglas Fitzgerald, room C–3514 (202) 693–0040.
Director, Division of Longshore and Harbor Workers' Compensation.—Antonio Rios (acting), room C–4315 (202) 693–0038.
Director, Division of Coal Mine Workers' Compensation.—Stephen Breeskin, room C–3520 (202) 693–0824.
Director, Division of Energy Employees Occupational Illness Compensation.—Rachel Leiton, room C–3321 (202) 693–0081.
Regional Director, Northeast Region.—Zev Sapir (212) 868–0844.
Regional Director, Mid-Atlantic Region.—John McKenna (acting), (267) 687–4089
Regional Director, Southeast Region.—Richard Brettell (acting), (904) 357–4776
Regional Director, Midwest Region.—Robert Sullivan (312) 789–2800.
Regional Director, Southwest Region.—Magdalena Fernandez (acting), (972) 850–2409.
Regional Director, Pacific Region.—Sharon Tyler (972) 850–2409.

OFFICE OF LABOR-MANAGEMENT STANDARDS

Director.—Vacant.

Deputy Director.—Andrew Auerbach, room N–5603 (202) 693–1203.
Director of Field Operations.—Stephen Willertz, room N–5119 (202) 693–1182.
Regional Director, Northeastern Region.—Peter Papinchak (215) 861–4822.
Regional Director, Central Region.—Ronald Lehman (312) 596–7161.
Regional Director, Southern Region.—Daniel Cherry (504) 589–6174.
Regional Director, Western Region.—Jena de Mers Raney (720) 264–3122.
Division of:
Planning, Management and Technology.—Deborah Becker, room N–5613 (202) 693–0605.
Enforcement.—Patricia Fox, room N–5119 (202) 693–1204.
Interpretations and Standards.—Andrew Davis, room N–5609 (202) 693–1254.
Reports, Disclosure and Audits.—Larry King, room N–5616 (202) 693–1259.
Statutory Programs.—Ann Comer, room N–5112 (202) 693–1193.

WAGE AND HOUR DIVISION

Administrator.—Vacant, room S–3202 (202) 693–0051.
Deputy Administrator.—Mary Beth Maxwell (acting), room S–3502, 693–0051.
Chief of Staff.—Tony Martinez, room S–3502, 693–0686.
Senior Advisor.—Melvina Ford, room S–3502, 693–1074.
Special Assistant.—Tania Mejia, room S–3502, 693–0527.
Deputy Administrator for Program Operations.—Patricia Davidson, room S–3502, 693–0663.
Assistant Administrators, Office of:
Planning, Performance, Evaluation and Communications.—Janice Hendrix, room S–3502, 693–0069.
Policy.—Michael Hancock, room S–3502, 693–0597.
Director, Division of:
Administrative Operations.—Denise Huttenlocker, room S–3502, 693–1077.
Communications.—Michael Kravitz, room S–3502, 693–0185.
Enforcement Policy and Procedures.—Michael Lazzeri, room S–3502, 693–1950.
Enforcement Strategy and Support.—Bruce Clark, room S–3502, 693–2520.
Information Technology.—Randell Dofat, room S–3006, 693–0015.
Regulations, Legislation and Interpretation.—Mary Ziegler, room S–3502, 693–5951.
Strategic Planning and Performance.—Karen Livingston, room S–3502, 693–0271.
Wage Determinations.—Bezarah Gaither (acting), room S–3502, 693–0514.

OFFICE OF FEDERAL CONTRACT COMPLIANCE PROGRAMS

Director.—Patricia A. Shiu, room C3325, 693–0205.
Deputy Director.—Leslie Jin, room C3325, 693–1120.
Senior Policy Advisor.—Donna R. Lenhoff, room C3325, 693–1115.
Program Advisor.—Pamela Couukos, room C3325, 693–0101.
Special Assistants: Claudia Gordon, 693–0101; Parag V. Mehta, room C3325, 693–0101; Claudia Montelongo, room N3422, 693–0352; Renee Tajudeen, room N3422, 693–0078.
Director of Statistical Analysis.—Javaid Kaiser, room C3325, 693–2253.
Division of Policy, Planning and Program Development.—Debra A. Carr, room N3325, 693–1159.
Division of Program Operations.—Thomas M. Dowd, room N3402, 693–1106.
Deputy Director.—James C. Pierce, room N3402, 693–1158.
Functional Affirmative Action Program Unit.—Nakisha Pugh, room N3402, 693–1083.
Division of Management and Administrative Programs.—Rachel Torres, room C3315, 693–1143.
Deputy Director.—Cynthia Spishak, room C3315, 693–0357.
Administrative Officer.—Patricia A. Cheeks, room C3311, 693–1112.

DEPARTMENT OF HEALTH AND HUMAN SERVICES

200 Independence Avenue, SW., 20201, http://www.hhs.gov

KATHLEEN G. SEBELIUS, Secretary of Health and Human Services; born in Cincinnati, OH, May 15, 1948; education: B.S., Trinity University, 1970; M.P.A., University of Kansas, 1977; professional: elected Governor of Kansas, 2002 and re-elected, 2006; before tenure as Governor, served as the Kansas State Insurance Commissioner for 8 years; served as a member of the Kansas House of Representatives, 1986–94; married: Gary, a federal magistrate judge; children: two sons, Ned and John; nominated by President Barack Obama to become the 21st Secretary of Health and Human Services, confirmed by the U.S. Senate and sworn in, both on April 28, 2009.

OFFICE OF THE SECRETARY

Secretary of Health and Human Services.—Kathleen G. Sebelius (202) 690–7000.
Executive Assistant to the Secretary.—Lynda M. Gyles.

OFFICE OF THE DEPUTY SECRETARY

Chief of Staff.—Andrea Palm (202) 690–8157.
Deputy Chief of Staff.—Dawn O'Connell, 690–8157.
Deputy Secretary.—Williams V. Corr, 690–6133.
Executive Secretary.—Jennifer Cannistra, 690–5627.
Deputy Executive Secretary.—Oliver Potts, 690–5627.
Director, Intergovernmental Affairs.—Paul Dioguardi, 690–6060.
Chair, Departmental Appeals Board.—Constance Tobias, 565–0220.

ASSISTANT SECRETARY FOR ADMINISTRATION AND MANAGEMENT

Assistant Secretary.—E.J. ''Ned'' Holland Jr., 690–7431.
Deputy Assistant Secretary for—
Business Transformation.—Micheal Yea, 690–7431.
Chief Information Officer.—Frank Baitman, 690–6162.
Human Resources.—Heidi Sheaffer (acting), 690–6191.
Program Support Center.—Paul Bartley (301) 492–4600.
Security and Strategic Information.—Dr. Joy Miller, 690–5756.
Director, Office of Equal Employment Opportunity.—Cynthia Richardson-Crooks, 690–7431.

PROGRAM SUPPORT CENTER

5600 Fishers Lane, Rockville, MD 20857

Director.—Paul S. Bartley (301) 492–4600.
Federal Operational Health.—Gene Migliaccio, Ph.D., (301) 492–5405.
Financial Management Service.—William McCabe (301) 492–4949.
Administrative Operations Service.—Suzi Casas (301) 443–2516.
Strategic Acquisitions Service.—Christie Goodman (301) 443–6557.
Facilities and Logistics Services.—Howard Kelsey, 401–1437.

ASSISTANT SECRETARY FOR LEGISLATION

Assistant Secretary.—Jim Esquea (202) 690–7627.
Deputy Assistant Secretary for—
Congressional Liaison.—Fatima Cuevas, 690–6786.
Discretionary Health Programs.—Jeremy Sharp, 690–7450.
Human Services Programs.—Sonja Nesbit, 690–6311.
Mandatory Health Programs.—Bridgett Taylor, 690–7450.

ASSISTANT SECRETARY FOR PLANNING AND EVALUATION

Assistant Secretary for Planning and Evaluation.—Donald Moulds (acting), (202) 690–7858.

Principal Deputy Assistant Secretary.—Donald Moulds, 690–7858.
Deputy Assistant Secretary for—
Disability and Long Term Care.—Peter Kemper, 690–6443.
Health Policy.—Richard Kronick, 690–6870.
Human Services Policy.—Ajay Chaudry, 690–7409.
Science and Data Policy.—Jim Scanlon, 690–7100.

ASSISTANT SECRETARY FOR PUBLIC AFFAIRS

Assistant Secretary.—Dori Salcido (acting), (202) 690–7850.
Deputy Assistant Secretary for—
Health Care.—Jason Young, 690–7850, fax 690–6247.
Public Health.—Tait Sye, 690–7850, fax 690–6247.
Human Services.—Mark Weber, 690–7850, fax 690–6247.
Director, Division of Freedom of Information/Privacy.—Robert Eckert, 690–7453.

ASSISTANT SECRETARY FOR PREPAREDNESS AND RESPONSE

Assistant Secretary.—Dr. Nicole Lurie (202) 205–2882.
Principal Deputy Assistant Secretary.—Edward Gabriel, 205–2882.
Deputy Assistant Secretary and Director, Office of:
Biomedical Advanced Research and Development Authority.—Dr. Robin Robinson, 260–1200.
Emergency Management.—Don Boyce, 205–8387.
Policy and Planning.—Dr. Lisa Kaplowitz, 260–1202.

ASSISTANT SECRETARY FOR FINANCIAL RESOURCES

Assistant Secretary.—Ellen G. Murray (202) 690–6396.
Principal Deputy Assistant Secretary.—Vacant, 690–6061.
Deputy Assistant Secretary for—
Budget.—Norris Cochran, 690–7393.
Finance.—Shelia Conley, 690–7084.
Grants.—Nancy Gunderson, 690–6377.

OFFICE FOR CIVIL RIGHTS

Director.—Leon Rodriguez (202) 619–0403.
Chief of Staff and Senior Advisor.—Juliet K. Choi, 619–0403.
Deputy Directors for—
Civil Rights Division.—Robinsue Frohboese, 619–0403.
Enforcement and Regional Operations.—Valerie Morgan-Alston, 619–0403.
Health Information Privacy.—Susan McAndrew, J.D., 619–0403.
Planning and Business Administration Management Division.—Steve Novy, 619–0403.
Toll Free Voice Number (Nationwide).—1–800–368–1019.
Toll Free TDD Number (Nationwide).—1–800–527–7697.

OFFICE OF THE GENERAL COUNSEL

fax [Immediate Office] 690–7998

General Counsel.—William B. Schultz.
Deputy General Counsels: David S. Cade, Ken Choe, David Horowitz, Peggy Dotzel, Gia Lee, 690–7741.
Senior Advisors to the General Counsel: Gemma Flamberg, Elizabeth Gianturco (202) 690–7741.
Associate General Counsel for—
Centers for Medicare and Medicaid Division.—Janice Hoffman, 619–0150.
Children, Family and Aging Division.—Robert Keith, 690–8005.
Civil Rights Division.—Edwin Woo, 619–2777.
Ethics Division/Special Counsel for Ethics.—Edgar Swindell, 690–7258.
Food and Drug Division.—Elizabeth Dickinson (301) 796–3978.
General Law Division.—Jeffrey Davis, 619–0150.
Legislation Division.—Edith Blackwell, 690–7773.
Public Health Division.—David Benor (301) 443–2644.

OFFICE OF GLOBAL HEALTH AFFAIRS

Director.—Nils Daulaire (202) 690–6174.

OFFICE OF THE INSPECTOR GENERAL

330 Independence Avenue, SW., 20201

Principal Deputy Inspector General.—Joanne M. Chiedi (202) 619–3148.
Chief Counsel to the Inspector General.—Gregory E. Demske, 619–0568.
Deputy Inspector General for Audit Services.—Gloria L. Jarmon, 619–3155.
Deputy Inspector for—
Evaluation and Inspections.—Stuart Wright, 619–0480.
Investigations.—Gary L. Cantrell, 205–4081.
Management and Policy.—Paul R. Johnson, 205–9117.
Director, External Affairs.—Erin C. Bliss, 205–9523.

OFFICE OF MEDICARE HEARINGS AND APPEALS

Chief Administrative Law Judge.—Nancy J. Griswold (703) 235–0635.
Deputy Chief Administrative Law Judge.—C. F. Moore (703) 235–0635.
Directors:
Operations.—Segundo Pereira (703) 235–0256.
Programs.—Eileen McDaniel (703) 235–0635.

OFFICE OF THE NATIONAL COORDINATOR FOR HEALTH INFORMATION TECHNOLOGY

National Coordinator for Health Information Technology.—Farzad Mostashari, M.D., ScM, M.P.P. (202) 690–7151.

OFFICE OF THE ASSISTANT SECRETARY FOR HEALTH

Assistant Secretary for Health.—Howard K. Koh, M.D., M.P.H. (202) 690–7694.
Senior Executive Assistant to the Assistant Secretary for Health.—Dinah Bembo, 690–7694.
Principal Deputy Assistant Secretary for Health.—Wanda K. Jones, DrPH, 401–8034.
The Surgeon General.—VADM Regina Benjamin, M.D., M.B. (301) 443–4000.
Deputy Assistant Secretary, Office of:
Disease Prevention and Health Promotion.—Don Wright, M.D., M.P.H. (240) 453–8280.
HIV/AIDS and Infectious Disease Policy.—Ronald O. Valdiserri, M.D., M.P.H. (202) 690–5560.
Minority Health.—J. Nadine Gracia, M.D. (240) 453–6179.
National Vaccine Program.—Bruce Gellin, M.D., M.P.H. (202) 205–5294.
Population Affairs.—Marilyn Keefe, M.P.H. (240) 453–2805.
Science and Medicine.—Anand K. Parekh, M.D., M.P.H. (202) 260–2873.
Women's Health.—Nancy C. Lee, M.D. (202) 690–7650.
Directors Office of:
Adolescent Health.—Evelyn Kappeler (240) 453–2837.
Communications.—Tara Broido (acting), (202) 205–0143.
Human Research Protections.—Jerry Menikoff, M.D., J.D. (240) 453–6900.
Research Integrity.—David Wright, M.D., M.P.H. (301) 443–3400.
Executive Directors of:
President's Council on Fitness, Sports and Nutrition.—Shellie Pfohl (240) 276–9567.
Presidential Commission for the Study of Bioethical Issues.—Dr. Lisa Lee (202) 233–3960.
Regional Administrators for—
Region I: CT, ME, MA, NH, RI, VT.—Betsy Rosenfeld, JD–C (617) 565–1505.
Region II: NJ, NY, PR, VI.—Michelle Davis, Ph.D. (212) 742–7036.
Region III: DE, DC, MD, PA, VA, WV.—Dalton G. Paxman, Ph.D. (215) 861–4631.
Region IV: AL, FL, GA, KY, MS, NC, SC, TN.—RADM Clara H. Cobb, M.S., R.N. (404) 562–7894.
Region V: IL, IN, MI, MN, OH, WI.—Robert Herskovitz, JD (acting), (312) 886–3880.
Region VI: AR, LA, NM, OK, TX.—RADM Epi Elizondo, Ph.D., PA–C (214) 767–3879.
Region VII: IA, KS, MO, NE.—CAPT Jose Belardo, JD, MSW (816) 426–3294.

Region VIII: CO, MT, ND, SD, UT, WY.—CAPT Zachery Taylor, M.D., M.S. (303) 844–7680.

Region IX: AZ, CA, HI, NV, Guam, American Samoa, CNMI, FSMI, RMI, Palau.—CAPT Nadine Simons, MS, RN (415) 437–8102.

Region X: AK, ID, OR, WA.—RADM Patrick O'Carroll, M.D., M.P.H., FACPM (206) 615–2469.

ADMINISTRATION FOR COMMUNITY LIVING

1 Massachusetts Avenue, NW., 20001

Assistant Secretary for Aging and Administrator, Administration for Community Living.—Kathy Greenlee (202) 401–4541.

Deputy Assistant Secretary for Aging.—Edwin L. Walker (202) 401–4634.

Principal Deputy Administrator, Administration for Community Living Commissioner, Administration on Intellectual and Developmental Disabilities.—Sharon Lewis (acting), (202) 690–6590.

Legislative Affairs.—Brian Lutz (202) 357–3530.

Chief of Staff.—Jason Bennett (202) 357–3408.

ADMINISTRATION FOR CHILDREN AND FAMILIES

370 L'Enfant Promenade, SW., 20447 (202) 401–9200

Assistant Secretary.—George H. Sheldon (acting), (202) 401–5383.

Chief of Staff.—Mike McCauley.

Deputy Assistant Secretary for Administration.—Robert Noonan, 401–9238.

Deputy Assistant Secretary for Policy.—Mark Greenberg, 401–6781.

Senior Advisor to the Assistant Secretary.—Laura Irizzary, 401–6947.

Director, Regional Operations Staff.—James Murray (acting), 401–4802.

Commissioner for Administration on Children, Youth and Families.—Bryan Samuels, 205–8347.

Commissioner, Administration for Native Americans.—Lillian Sparks.

Deputy Commissioner, Office of Child Support Enforcement.—Vicki Turteski, 401–9369.

Associate Commissioner for Children's Bureau.—Shannon Rudisill, 690–5780.

Family and Youth Services Bureau.—Debbie Powell, 205–8102.

Director, Office of:

Community Services.—Jeannie Chaffin, 401–9333.

Head Start.—Yvette Sanchez Fuentes, 205–8573.

Family Assistance.—Earl Johnson, 401–9275.

Legislative Affairs and Budget.—Matthew McKearn, 401–9223.

Planning, Research and Evaluation.—Noami Goldstein, 401–9220.

Public Affairs.—Marrianne McMullen, 401–9215.

Refugee Resettlement.—Eskinder Negash, 401–9246.

AGENCY FOR HEALTHCARE RESEARCH AND QUALITY (AHRQ)

Director.—Carolyn Clancy, M.D. (301) 427–1200.

Deputy Director.—Dr. Boyce Ginieczki (acting), 427–1200.

AGENCY FOR TOXIC SUBSTANCES AND DISEASE REGISTRY

1600 Clifton Road, NE., Atlanta, GA 30333

Director.—Thomas R. Frieden, M.D., M.P.H. (404) 639–7000.

Principal Deputy Director.—Ileana Arias, Ph.D.

CENTER FOR DISEASE CONTROL AND PREVENTION

1600 Clifton Road, NE., Atlanta, GA 30333, phone (404) 639–7000

Director.—Thomas R. Frieden, M.D., M.P.H.

Principal Deputy Director.—Ileana Arias, Ph.D.

Chief Operating Officer.—Sherri A. Berger, M.SP.H.

Chief of Staff.—Carmen Villar, M.S.W.

Office of:

Diversity Management and Equal Employment Opportunity.—Reginald R. Mebane, M.S.

Minority Health and Health Equity.—Leandris Liburd, Ph.D., M.P.H., M.A.

Associate Director for—

Communication.—Katherine Lyon Daniel, Ph.D. (acting).

Program.—Kathleen Ethier, Ph.D. (acting).

Science.—Harold W. Jaffe, M.D., M.A.

Policy.—Andrew S. Rein, M.S. (202) 245–0600.

Office of Public Health Preparedness and Response.—Ali Khan, M.D. M.P.H. (404) 639–7405.

Deputy Director:

Office for State, Tribal, Local and Territorial Support.—Judith A. Monroe, M.D., F.A.A.F.P. (404) 498–0300.

Director:

Center for Global Health.—Thomas Kenyon, M.D., M.P.H. (404) 639–7420.

National Institute for Occupational Safety and Health.—John Howard, M.D., M.P.H., J.D. (202) 245–0625.

Deputy Director Office of:

Infectious Diseases.—Rima Khabbaz, M.D. (404) 639–2100.

Noncommunicable Diseases, Injury and Environmental Health.—Robin Ikeda, M.D., M.P.H. (770) 488–0608.

Surveillance, Epidemiology and Laboratory Services.—Denise Cardo, M.D. (acting), (404) 498–6010.

Director of the National Centers:

Birth Defects and Developmental Disabilities.—Coleen Boyle, Ph.D. (404) 498–3800.

Chronic Disease Prevention and Health Promotion.—Ursula Bauer, Ph.D., M.P.H. (acting) (770) 488–5401.

Emerging and Zoonotic Infectious Diseases.—Beth P. Bell, M.D., M.P.H. (404) 639–3967.

Environmental Health/Agency for Toxic Substances and Disease Registry.—Robin Ikeda, M.D., M.P.H. (acting), (770) 488–0604.

HIV/AIDS, Viral Hepatitis, STD and TB Prevention.—Rima Khabbaz, M.D. (acting), (404) 639–8000.

Immunization and Respiratory Diseases.—Anne Schuchat, M.D. (404) 639–1540.

Injury Prevention and Control.—Linda C. Degutis, Dr.P.H., M.S.N. (770) 488–4696.

CENTER FOR FAITH-BASED AND NEIGHBORHOOD PARTNERSHIPS

Director.—Acacia Bamberg Salatti (acting), (202) 358–3595.

CENTERS FOR MEDICARE & MEDICAID SERVICES

200 Independence Avenue, SW., 20201, phone (202) 690–6726

Administrator.—Marilyn Tavenner.

Principal Deputy Administrator.—Jonathan Blum (acting).

Chief Operating Officer.—Marilyn Tavenner.

Deputy Chief Operating Officer.—Michelle Snyder (410) 786–3151.

Chief Actuary, Office of the Actuary.—Paul Spitalnic (acting), (410) 786–6374.

Deputy Administrator and Director, Center for—

Consumer Information and Insurance Oversight.—Gary Cohen (202) 260–6085.

Medicaid and CHIP Services.—Cindy Mann (202) 690–7428.

Medicare.—Jonathan Blum (202) 690–6301.

Program Integrity.—Peter Budetti (410) 786–3336.

Strategic Planning.—Michelle Snyder (acting), (410) 786–3151.

Director, Center for Medicare and Medicaid Innovation.—Richard Gilfillan (410) 786–3316.

Director and CMS Chief Medical Officer, Center for Clinical Standards and Quality.—Patrick Conway, M.D. (410) 786–6841.

Director and Chief Information Officer, Office of Information Services.—Tony Trenkle (410) 786–1800.

Director and Chief Administrative Officer, Office of Operations Management.—James Weber (410) 786–1051.

Director, Office of:

Acquisition and Grants Management.—Daniel Kane (410) 786–1391.

Communications.—Julie Bataille (202) 205–9450.

Enterprise Management.—David Nelson (acting), (410) 786–5246.
Equal Opportunity and Civil Rights.—Arlene Austin (410) 786–5110.
Federal Coordinated Health Care.—Melanie Bella (202) 260–1291.
Financial Management.—Deborah Taylor (410) 786–5448.
Legislation.—Lauren Aronson (202) 690–5960.
Minority Health.—Cara James (410) 786–2773.
Public Engagement.—Teresa Nino (202) 401–3135.
Strategic Operations and Regulatory Affairs.—Kathleen Cantwell (202) 690–8390.
Consortium Administrator for—
Financial Management and FFS Operations.—Nanette Foster Reilly (816) 426–5233.
Medicaid and Children's Health Operations.—Jackie Garner (312) 886–6432.
Medicare Health Plans Operations.—James T. Kerr (212) 616–2205.
Quality Improvement and Survey and Certification Operations.—James R. Farris, M.D. (214) 767–6427.

FOOD AND DRUG ADMINISTRATION

10903 New Hampshire Avenue, Silver Spring, MD 20993

Commissioner.—Margaret A. Hamburg, M.D. (301) 796–5000.
Chief of Staff.—Lisa Barclay, J.D., 796–5020.
The Executive Secretariat.—Martina Varnado, 796–4520.
Counselor to the Commissioner.—John Taylor, J.D., 796–7460.
Deputy Commissioner for—
Foods and Veterinary Medicine.—Michael Taylor, J.D., 796–4500.
Global Regulatory Operations and Policy.—John Taylor, J.D. (acting), 796–7460.
Medical Products and Tobacco.—Vacant, 796–4930.
Policy, Planning, and Legislation.—Sally Howard, 796–3011.
Chiefs:
Counsel.—Liz Dickinson, J.D., 796–8540.
Information Officer and Chief Scientist (Informatics).—Vacant, 796–6700.
Operating Officer.—Walter Harris, 796–4700.
Scientist.—Jesse Goodman, M.D., M.P.H., 796–4880.
Associate Commissioner for—
External Affairs.—Virginia Cox, 796–4631.
International Programs.—Mary Lou Valdez, 796–8400.
Legislation.—Michele Mital (acting), 796–8900.
Policy and Planning.—Peter Lurie (acting), 796–4800.
Regulatory Affairs.—Melinda Plaisier (acting), 796–8800.
Special Medical Programs.—Jill Warner, J.D. (acting), 796–4810.
Director, Center for—
Biologics Evaluation and Research.—Karen Midthun, M.D., 827–0372.
Center for Drug Evaluation and Research.—Janet Woodcock, M.D., 796–5400.
Devices and Radiological Health.—Jeffrey Shuren, M.D., J.D., 796–5900.
Food Safety and Applied Nutrition.—Michael Landa, J.D. (240) 402–1600.
Office of Crisis Management.—Mark Russo (acting), 796–8250.
Office of Minority Health.—Jonca Bull, M.D., 796–4649.
Tobacco Products.—Mitch Zeller, J.D., 796–9200.
Veterinary Medicine.—Bernadette Dunham, D.V.M., Ph.D., (240) 276–9000.
Director, National Center for Toxicological Research.—William Slikker, Jr., Ph.D. (870) 543–7517.
Senior Advisor and Representative for Global Issues.—Murray M. Lumpkin, M.D., M.Sc., 796–4804.
Senior Advisor for Science, Innovation and Policy.—Vacant, 796–5307.
Senior Advisor to the Commissioner.—Jeanne Ireland, 796–4618.

HEALTH RESOURCES AND SERVICES ADMINISTRATION

5600 Fishers Lane, Rockville, MD 20857

Administrator.—Mary K. Wakefield, Ph.D., RN (301) 443–2216.
Deputy Administrator.—Marcia K. Brand, Ph.D., 443–2216.
Senior Advisor.—Diana Espinosa, 443–2216.
Senior Advisor for HIV/AIDS Policy.—Deborah Parham-Hopson, RN, RADM, USPHS, 443–2216.
Chief Public Health Officer.—Sarah Linde, M.D., RADM, USPHS, 443–2216.

Chief Operating Officer.—Thomas G. Morford, 443–4244.
Associate Administrator for—
Clinician Recruitment and Service.—Rebecca Spitzgo, 594–4130.
Federal Assistance Management.—Michael Nelson, 443–5877.
Health Professions.—Janet Heinrich, Ph.D., RN, 443–5794.
Healthcare Systems.—Cheryl Dammons, 443–3300.
HIV/AIDS.—Laura Cheever, M.D. (acting), 443–1993.
Maternal and Child Health.—Michael Lu, M.D., 443–2170.
Primary Health Care.—James Macrae, 594–4110.
Regional Operations.—Dennis Malcomson, 443–7070.
Rural Health Policy.—Tom Morris, 443–0835.
Director, Office of:
Communications.—Martin Kramer, 443–3376.
Equal Opportunity, Civil Rights and Diversity Management.—M. June Horner, 443–5636.
Health Equity.—Michelle Allender-Smith, RN, 443–5323.
Legislation.—Leslie Atkinson, 443–1890.
Planning, Evaluation and Analysis.—Rebecca Slifkin, Ph.D., 443–3983.
Women's Health.—Sabrina Matoff-Stepp, Ph.D., 443–8664.

INDIAN HEALTH SERVICE

801 Thompson Avenue, Rockville, MD 20852

Director.—Yvette Roubideaux, M.D., M.P.H. (301) 443–1083.
Deputy Director.—Vacant.
Deputy Director for—
Field Operations.—Randy Grinnell.
Intergovernmental Affairs.—Sandra Pattea.
Management Operations.—Robert McSwain.
Chief Medical Officer.—Susan V. Karol, M.D.
Senior Advisor.—Geoffrey Roth.
Director of:
Clinical and Preventative Services.—Charlene Avery, 443–4644.
Direct Service and Contracting Tribes.—Chris Buchanan, 443–1104.
Environmental Health and Engineering.—Gary Hartz, 443–1247.
Equal Employment Opportunity.—Pauline Bruce, 443–1108.
Executive Secretariat.—Julie Czajkowski, 443–1011.
Finance and Accounting.—Elizabeth Fowler, 443–1270.
Information Technology.—Howard Hays (acting), 443–0750.
Legislative and Congressional Affairs.—Michael Mahsetky, 443–7261.
Management Services.—Athena Elliott, 443–6290.
Public Affairs.—Constance James, 443–3593.
Public Health Support.—Richard Church, 443–0222.
Resource Access and Partnerships.—Carl Harper, 443–2694.
Tribal Self-Governance.—Benjamin Smith, 443–7821.
Urban Indian Health Programs.—Phyllis Wolfe, 443–4680.

NATIONAL INSTITUTES OF HEALTH

9000 Rockville Pike, Bethesda, MD 20892

Director.—Francis S. Collins, M.D., Ph.D. (301) 496–2433.
Deputy Director.—Lawrence Tabak, D.D.S., Ph.D., 496–7322.
Deputy Director for Science, Outreach, and Policy.—Kathy Hudson, Ph.D., 496–1455.
Director, Executive Secretariat.—Ann Brewer, RN, 496–1461.
Director, Office of Federal Advisory Committee Policy.—Jennifer Spaeth, 496–2123.
Executive Officer, Office of the Director.—LaVerne Y. Stringfield, 594–8231.
Chief Information Officer.—Andrea Norris, 496–5703.
Legal Advisor, Office of the General Counsel.—Barbara M. McGarey, J.D., 496–6043.
Deputy Director for—
Extramural Research.—Sally J. Rockey, Ph.D., 496–1096.
Intramural Research.—Michael M. Gottesman, M.D., 496–1921.
Management.—Colleen Barros, 496–3271.
Director, Division of Program Coordination, Planning, and Strategic Initiatives.—James Anderson, M.D., Ph.D., 402–9852.

Associate Director for—
Administration.—Diane Frasier, 496–4422.
AIDS Research.—Jack E. Whitescarver, Ph.D., 496–0357.
Behavioral and Social Sciences Research.—Robert Kaplan, Ph.D., 496–9485.
Budget.—Neil Shapiro, 496–4477.
Communications and Public Liaison.—John T. Burklow, 496–4461.
Disease Prevention.—David Murray, Ph.D., 496–1508.
Research on Women's Health.—Janine Clayton, M.D., 402–1770.
Research Services.—Alfred C. Johnson, Ph.D., 496–2215.
Science Policy.—Amy Patterson, M.D., 496–2122.
Director, Office of:
Ethics.—Holli Beckerman Jaffe, J.D., 402–6628.
Equal Opportunity and Diversity Management.—Debra Chew, Esq., 496–6301.
Financial Management.—Kenneth Stith, 402–8831.
Human Resources.—Chris Major, 496–3592.
Legislative Policy and Analysis.—F. Patrick White, 496–3471.
Management Assessment.—Suzanne J. Servis, 496–1873.
Research Facilities Development and Operations.—Daniel Wheeland, 594–0999.
Technology Transfer.—Mark L. Rohrbaugh, Ph.D., J.D., 594–7700.
Directors:
Eunice Kennedy Shriver National Institute of Child Health and Human Development.—Alan Guttmacher, M.D., 496–3454.
Fogarty International Center.—Roger I. Glass, M.D., Ph.D., 496–1415.
National Institute on Minority Health and Health Disparities.—John Ruffin, Ph.D., 402–1366.
National Library of Medicine.—Donald A. B. Lindberg, M.D., 496–6221.
Warren Grant Magnuson Clinical Center.—John I. Gallin, M.D., 496–4114.
Center for—
Complementary and Alternative Medicine.—Josephine P. Briggs, M.D., 435–6826.
Information Technology.—Andrea T. Norris, 496–5703.
Scientific Review.—Richard Nakamura, Ph.D., 435–1114.
National Center for Advancing Translational Sciences.—Christopher Austin, M.D., 496–5793.
Director, National Institute on:
Aging.—Richard J. Hodes, M.D., 496–9265.
Alcohol Abuse and Alcoholism.—Kenneth R. Warren, Ph.D. (acting), 443–3885.
Drug Abuse.—Nora D. Volkow, M.D., 443–6480.
Deafness and Other Communication Disorders.—James F. Battey, Jr., M.D., Ph.D., 402–0900.
Director, National Institute of:
Allergy and Infectious Diseases.—Anthony S. Fauci, M.D., 496–2263.
Arthritis and Musculoskeletal and Skin Diseases.—Stephen I. Katz, M.D., Ph.D., 496–4353.
Biomedical Imaging and Bioengineering.—Roderic I. Pettigrew, Ph.D., M.D., 496–8859.
Dental and Craniofacial Research.—Martha Somerman, D.D.S., Ph.D., 496–3571.
Diabetes and Digestive and Kidney Diseases.—Griffin P. Rodgers, M.D., M.A.C.P., 496–5877.
Environmental Health Sciences.—Linda S. Birnbaum, Ph.D., D.A.B.T., A.T.S. (919) 541–3201.
General Medical Sciences.—Judith Greenberg, Ph.D. (acting), 594–2172.
Mental Health.—Thomas Insel, M.D., 443–3673.
Neurological Disorders and Stroke.—Story C. Landis, Ph.D., 496–9746.
Nursing Research.—Patricia A. Grady, Ph.D., RN, 496–8230.
Director, National:
Cancer Institute.—Harold Varmus, M.D., 496–5615.
Eye Institute.—Paul A. Sieving, M.D., Ph.D., 496–2234.
Heart, Lung and Blood Institute.—Gary Gibbons, M.D., 496–5166.
Human Genome Research Institute.—Eric Green, M.D., Ph.D., 496–0844.

SUBSTANCE ABUSE AND MENTAL HEALTH SERVICES ADMINISTRATION (SAMHSA)

1 Choke Cherry Road, Rockville, MD 20857

www.samhsa.gov

Administrator.—Pamela Hyde, room 8–1061 (240) 276–2000.
Principal Deputy Administrator.—Kana Enomoto, room 8–1059, 276–2000.
Deputy Administrator for Operations.—Mirtha Beadle, room 8–1069, 276–2000
Director, Office of:
Behavioral Health Equity.—Larke Huang, room 8–1051, 276–2014
Communications.—Marla Hendriksson, room 8–1033, 276–2130.
Financial Resources.—Daryl Kade, room 8–1083, 276–2200.
Management, Technology, and Operations.—Mike Etzinger, room 7–1073, 276–1110.
Policy, Planning, and Innovation.—Anne Herron (acting), room 8–1015, 276–2856.
Director, Center for—
Behavioral Health Statistics and Quality.—Peter Delany, Ph.D., LCSW–C, room 2–1049, 276–1250.
Mental Health Services.—Paolo del Vecchio, room 6–1057, 276–1310.
Substance Abuse Prevention.—Frances M. Harding, room 4–1057, 276–2420.
Substance Abuse Treatment.—H. Westley Clark, M.D., J.D., M.P.H., CAS, FASAM, room 5–1015, 276–1660.

DEPARTMENT OF HOUSING AND URBAN DEVELOPMENT

Robert C. Weaver Federal Building, 451 Seventh Street, SW., 20410
phone (202) 708–1112, http://www.hud.gov

SHAUN DONOVAN, Democrat, of Washington, DC; born in New York, NY, January 24, 1966; undergraduate and graduate degrees from Harvard University, graduating from Harvard College in 1987, Master of Public Administration from the John F. Kennedy School of Government and a master's in architecture at the Graduate School of Design in 1995. Commissioner of the New York City Department of Housing Preservation and Development (HPD); visiting scholar, New York University; consultant to the Millennial Housing Commission; Deputy Assistant Secretary for Multifamily Housing and acting FHA commissioner (HUD); Community Preservation Corporation (CPC), a non-profit lender and developer of affordable housing. Married to Liza Gilbert; two sons; nominated by President-elect Barack Obama on December 13, 2008; confirmed by the U.S. Senate through unanimous consent on January 22, 2009; sworn-in on January 26.

OFFICE OF THE SECRETARY

Secretary of Housing and Urban Development.—Shaun Donovan, room 10000 (202) 708–0417.
  Chief of Staff.—C. Brent Colburn, 708–2713.
  Deputy Chief of Staff.—Vacant, 708–1781.
  Executive Operations Officer.—Tawanna Preston, 708–3750.
  Administrative Officer.—Karen Lake, 708–3750.

OFFICE OF THE DEPUTY SECRETARY

Deputy Secretary.—Maurice A. Jones, room 10100 (202) 708–0123.
  Chief of Staff for the Deputy Secretary.—Vacant, room 10100, 708–0123.

ASSISTANT SECRETARY FOR COMMUNITY PLANNING AND DEVELOPMENT

Assistant Secretary.—Vacant.
  General Deputy Assistant Secretary.—Clifford Taffet, room 7100 (202) 708–2690.
  Deputy Assistant Secretary for—
    Economic Development.—Valerie Piper, room 7136, 708–2690.
    Grant Programs.—Yolanda Chavez, room 7204, 708–2111.
    Operations.—Frances Bush, room 7128, 402–7515.
    Special Needs.—Mark Johnston, room 7100, 708–2690.

ASSISTANT SECRETARY FOR CONGRESSIONAL AND INTERGOVERNMENTAL RELATIONS

Assistant Secretary.—Vacant, room 10120 (202) 708–0005.
  General Deputy Assistant Secretary.—Elliot M. Mincberg, room 10120, 708–0005.
  Deputy Assistant Secretary for—
    Congressional Relations.—Bernard Fulton, room 10120, 708–0005.
    Intergovernmental Relations.—Jennifer Leigh Szubrowski, room 10148, 708–0005.

ASSISTANT SECRETARY FOR FAIR HOUSING AND EQUAL OPPORTUNITY

Assistant Secretary.—Bryan Greene (acting), room 5100 (202) 708–4252.
  General Deputy Assistant Secretary.—Bryan Greene, 708–4211.
  Deputy Assistant Secretary for—

Enforcement and Programs.—Sara Pratt, 619–8046.
Operations and Management.—David Ziaya, 708–0768.

ASSISTANT SECRETARY FOR HOUSING

Assistant Secretary/Federal Housing Commissioner.—Carol J. Galante, room 9100 (202) 708–2601.
General Deputy Assistant Secretary.—Laura Marin (acting).
Associated General Deputy Assistant Secretary.—Laura Marin.
Deputy Assistant Secretary for—
Finance and Budget.—Monica Clarke (acting), (202) 401–8975.
Healthcare Programs.—Roger Miller, 708–0599.
Housing Counseling.—Sarah Gerecke, 708–0317.
Housing Operations.—Lori Michalski, 708–1104.
Multifamily Housing Programs.—Marie Head, 708–2495.
Risk Management and Regulatory Affairs.—Frank Vetrano, 708–6401.
Single Family Housing.—Charles Coulter, 708–3175.

ASSISTANT SECRETARY FOR POLICY DEVELOPMENT AND RESEARCH

Assistant Secretary.—Vacant.
General Deputy Assistant Secretary.—Jean Lin Pao, room 8100, 708–1600.
Deputy Assistant Secretary for the Office of:
Economic Affairs.—Kurt G. Usowski, room 8204, 708–3080.
International and Philanthropic Innovation.—Ana Marie Argilagos, room 8138, 708–0770.
Research, Evaluation, and Monitoring.—Calvin C. Johnson, room 8124, 708–4230.
Associate Deputy Assistent Secretary, Policy Development.—Todd Richardson, room 8106, 708–1537.

ASSISTANT SECRETARY FOR PUBLIC AFFAIRS

Assistant Secretary for Public Affairs.—Melanie Roussell (202) 708–0980.
General Deputy Assistant Secretary.—Vacant.
Deputy Assistant Secretary.—Jereon M. Brown.
Press Secretary.—Addie Whisenant.

ASSISTANT SECRETARY FOR PUBLIC AND INDIAN HOUSING

Assistant Secretary.—Sandra B. Henriquez, room 4100 (202) 708–0950.
General Deputy Assistant Secretary.—Deborah Hernandez.
Office of Field Operations.—Lindsey Reames (acting), 708–4016.
Policy, Programs and Legislative Initiatives.—Debra Gross, 708–0713.
Real Estate Assessment Center.—Donald Lavoy, 475–8906.

OFFICE OF FIELD POLICY AND MANAGEMENT

Assistant Deputy Secretary.—Patricia A. Hoban-Moore, room 7108 (202) 708–2426.

GOVERNMENT NATIONAL MORTGAGE ASSOCIATION

President.—Theodore W. Tozer (202) 708–0926.
Executive Vice President.—Mary K. Kinney, 708–0926.
Senior Vice President, Office of:
Capital Markets.—John Getchis, 401–8970.
Finance.—Michael J. Najjum, 401–2064.
Issuer and Portfolio Management.—Michael Drayne, 708–4141.
Securities Operations.—Thomas R. Weakland, 708–2884.
Senior Vice President and Chief Risk Officer.—Gregory A. Keith, 708–0926.
Enterprise Data and Technology Solutions.—Barbara Cooper-Jones, 708–0926.

CHIEF FINANCIAL OFFICER

Chief Financial Officer.—Vacant.

Deputy Chief Financial Officer.—David P. Sidari, room 3126, 708–1946.
Assistant Chief Financial Officer for—
Accounting.—Nita Nigam, 708–1946.
Budget.—Jessica K. Lee (acting), 708–1946.
Financial Management.—Jerome A. Vaiana (acting), 708–1946.
Systems.—Nita Nigam (acting), 708–1946.

CHIEF INFORMATION OFFICER

Chief Information Officer.—Barbara A. Elliott (acting), room 4160 (202) 708–0306.
Deputy Chief Information Officer.—Kevin R. Cooke, Jr., room 4158, 708–0306.
Deputy Chief Information Officer for—
IT Operations.—Mike Milazzo, room 4178, 708–4562, ext. 6098.
Chief Information Security Officer.—Harold E. Williams (acting), room 4282 (202) 402–8087.

CHIEF PROCUREMENT OFFICER

Chief Procurement Officer.—Jemine A. Bryon, room 5280 (202) 708–0600.
Deputy Chief Procurement Officer.—Keith Surber, room 5256, 708–1290.
Associate Chief Procurement Officer.—Vacant.

GENERAL COUNSEL

General Counsel.—Helen R. Kanovsky, room 10110 (202) 708–2244.
Principal Deputy General Counsel.—Damon Y. Smith (acting), (202) 708–2244.
Deputy General Counsel for—
Housing Programs.—Elton Lester, room 10238, 402–5280.
Operations.—Linda M. Cruciani, room 10240, 402–5108.
Associate General Counsel for—
Assisted Housing and Community Development.—Althea Forrester, room 8166, 708–0470.
Ethics.—Peter J. Constantine, room 10164, 708–2864.
Fair Housing.—Jeanine Worden, room 10270, 708–2787.
Finance and Regulatory Compliance.—Kevin M. Simpson, room 8150, 708–2203.
Insured Housing.—Millicent Potts, room 9226, 708–1274.
Legislation and Regulations.—Camille E. Acevedo, room 10282, 708–1793.
Litigation.—Nancy Christopher, room 10258, 708–0300.
Program Enforcement.—Dane M. Narode, PORTALS, 245–4141.
Deputy Director, Departmental Enforcement Center.—Craig Clemmensen, PORTALS, 245–4195.

INSPECTOR GENERAL

Inspector General.—David A. Montoya, room 8256 (202) 708–0430.
Deputy Inspector General.—Helen Albert.
Counsel to the Inspector General, Office of Legal Counsel.—J. Bryan Howell, 708–1613.
Assistant Inspector General, Office of:
Audit.—Randy McGinnis, 708–0364.
Investigation.—Vacant, 708–0390.
Management and Policy.—Eddie Saffarinia, 708–0006.

OFFICE OF DEPARTMENTAL EQUAL EMPLOYMENT OPPORTUNITY

Director.—John P. Benison, room 2134 (202) 708–3362.

OFFICE OF THE HUMAN CAPITAL OFFICER

Chief Human Capital Officer.—Michael Anderson (202) 708–0940.
Deputy Chief Human Capital Officers:—Towanda Brooks (202) 708–0940, Karen Newton Cole (202) 402–5520.
Director:
Administration.—Patricia Hoban-Moore (202) 402–5458.
Executive Resources.—Juliette Middleton (202) 402–3058.
Executive Scheduling and Operations.—Melissa Bruns (202) 402–6457.

Executive Secretariat.—Dolores Cole (202) 402–2671.
Office of Human Capital Field Support.—Kathy Brantley (219) 794–5353.
Project Management Office.—Charles Butler (202) 402–6310.

Deputy Director, Office of:
Chief Human Capital Officer Support Services.—Michelle Gaston (202) 402–4107.
Facilities Management Services.—Michael Schimmenti (202) 402–7325.
Human Capital Services.—Kathy Brantley (acting), (202) 402–5746.

Chief:
Broadcasting Operations Officer.—Williams Amos (202) 402–2628.
Disaster Management and National Security Officer.—Mark Carr (202) 402–6281.
Learning Officer.—Sheila Wright (202) 402–2355.
Performance Officer.—Joseph Smith (202) 402–2808.

OFFICE OF DEPARTMENTAL OPERATIONS AND COORDINATION

Director.—Inez Banks-Dubose, room 2124 (202) 708–2806.
Deputy Director.—Vacant.

OFFICE OF LABOR RELATIONS

Director.—Jacqueline W. Roundtree.

OFFICE OF HEALTHY HOMES AND LEAD HAZARD CONTROL

Director.—Jon L. Gant, room 8236 (202) 708–0310.
Deputy Director.—Matthew Ammon.

SMALL AND DISADVANTAGED BUSINESS UTILIZATION

Director.—Vacant, room 2200 (202) 402–5477.

HUD REGIONAL ADMINISTRATORS

Region I.—Connecticut, Maine, Massachusetts, New Hampshire, Rhode Island, Vermont.
Regional Administrator.—Barbara G. Fields, Federal Building, 10 Causeway Street, Room 301, Boston, MA 02222–1092 (617) 994–8200.

Region II.—New Jersey, New York.
Regional Administrator.—Mirza Orriols (acting), 26 Federal Plaza, Suite 3541, New York, NY 10278–0068 (212) 542–7109.

Region III.—Delaware, District of Columbia, Maryland, Pennsylvania, Virginia, West Virginia.
Regional Administrator.—Jane C.W. Vincent, The Wanamaker Building, 100 Penn Square East, Philadelphia, PA 19107–3380 (215) 656–0600.

Region IV.—Alabama, Florida, Georgia, Kentucky, Mississippi, North Carolina, Puerto Rico, South Carolina, Tennessee.
Regional Administrator.—Edward Jennings, Jr., Five Points Plaza, 40 Marietta Street, NW., 2nd Floor, Atlanta, GA 30303–2806 (687) 732–2009.

Region V.—Illinois, Indiana, Michigan, Minnesota, Ohio, Wisconsin.
Regional Administrator.—Antonio Riley, Ralph Metcalfe Federal Building, 77 West Jackson Boulevard, Chicago, IL 60604–3507 (312) 353–5680.

Region VI.—Arkansas, Louisiana, New Mexico, Oklahoma, Texas.
Regional Administrator.—Mark J. Brezina (acting), 801 Cherry Street, Fort Worth, TX 76113–2905 (817) 978–5542.

Region VII.—Iowa, Kansas, Missouri, Nebraska.
Regional Administrator.—Vacant, Gateway Tower II, 400 State Avenue, Room 507, Kansas City, KS 66101–2406 (913) 551–5462.

Region VIII.—Colorado, Montana, North Dakota, South Dakota, Utah, Wyoming.
Regional Administrator.—Rick M. Garcia, 1670 Broadway, Denver, CO 80202–4801 (303) 672–5440.

Region IX.—Arizona, California, Hawaii, Nevada.
Regional Administrator.—Ophelia Basgal, 600 Harrison Street, 3rd Floor, San Francisco, CA 94107–1300 (415) 489–6401.

Region X.—Alaska, Idaho, Oregon, Washington.
Regional Administrator.—Mary McBride, Seattle Federal Office Building, 909 First Avenue, Suite 200, Seattle, WA 98104–1000 (206) 220–5101.

DEPARTMENT OF TRANSPORTATION

1200 New Jersey Avenue, SE., Washington, DC 20590

phone (202) 366–4000, http://www.dot.gov

ANTHONY R. FOXX, Secretary of Transportation; born in Charlotte, NC, April 30, 1971; education: J.D., New York University School of Law, B.A. Davidson College, Davidson, NC; professional: Mayor of Charlotte, NC from 2009–13; Deputy General Counsel, DesignLine, from 2009–13; Charlotte City Council At-Large Representative from 2005–09; Litigator, Hunton & Williams, from 2001–09; Staff Counsel to the U.S. House of Representatives Committee on the Judiciary from 1999–2001; Trial Attorney for the Civil Rights Division of the U.S. Department of Justice from 1997–99; Law Clerk for the U.S. Sixth Circuit Court of Appeals, 1997; family: married to Samara Foxx; two children: Hillary and Zachary; nominated by President Barack H. Obama to become the 17th Secretary of Transportation, and was confirmed by the U.S. Senate on June 27, 2013.

OFFICE OF THE SECRETARY

[Created by the act of October 15, 1966; codified under U.S.C. 49]

Secretary of Transportation.—Anthony R. Foxx, room W91–317 (202) 366–1111.
Deputy Secretary.—John D. Porcari, 366–2222.
Chief of Staff.—Kathryn Thomson (acting), 366–1103.
Deputy Chief of Staff.—Vacant, 366–1103.
Under Secretary of Transportation for Policy.—Polly Trottenberg, 366–4540.
Director, Office of:
Civil Rights.—Camille Hazeur (acting), room W78–318, 366–4648.
Executive Secretariat.—Carol C. Darr, room W93–324, 366–4277.
Intelligence and Security.—Michael Lowder, room W56–302, 366–6525.
Small and Disadvantaged Business Utilization.—Brandon Neal, room W56–308, 366–1930.

ASSISTANT SECRETARY FOR ADMINISTRATION

Assistant Secretary.—Vacant, room W80–322 (202) 366–2332.
Deputy Assistant Secretary.—Brodi Fontenot, W80–320, 366–2332.
Director, Office of:
Facilities, Information and Asset Management.—George Fields, room W58–334, 366–9756.
Financial Management.—Marie Petrosino, room W81–306, 366–3967.
Hearings, Chief Administrative Law Judge.—Judge Ronnie A. Yoder, room E12–356, 366–2142.
Human Resource Management.—Nancy Mowry, room W81–302, 366–4088.
Security.—Rob Lee (acting), room W54–336, 366–4677.
Senior Procurement Executive.—Willie Smith, room W83–306, 366–4212.

ASSISTANT SECRETARY FOR AVIATION AND INTERNATIONAL AFFAIRS

Assistant Secretary.—Susan Kurland, room W88–314 (202) 366–8822.
Deputy Assistant Secretaries: Robert Letteney, room W88–324; Susan McDermott, room W88–326, 366–4551.
Director, Office of:
Aviation Analysis.—Todd Homan, room W86–481, 366–5903.
International Aviation.—Paul Gretch, room W86–406, 366–2423.

International Transportation and Trade.—Julie Abraham, room W88–306, 366–4398.

ASSISTANT SECRETARY FOR BUDGET AND PROGRAMS

Assistant Secretary/Chief Financial Officer.—Sylvia Garcia (acting), room W95–330 (202) 366–9191.
Deputy Assistant Secretary.—Lana Hurdle, room W95–316, 366–9192.
Deputy Chief Financial Officer.—David Rivait, room W95–320, 366–9192.
Director, Office of:
Budget and Program Performance.—Laura Ziff, room W93–308, 366–4594.
Financial Management.—Vacant, room W93–322, 366–1306.

ASSISTANT SECRETARY FOR GOVERNMENTAL AFFAIRS

Assistant Secretary.—Dana Gresham, room W85–326 (202) 366–4573.
Deputy Assistant Secretaries: Amit Bose, Patricia Readinger, Joanna Turner.
Associate Directors: Natalie Angelo, Alexander Friendly, Maria Elena Juarez, Peter Gould, Michael Daley.

OFFICE OF THE UNDER SECRETARY OF TRANSPORTATION FOR POLICY

Under Secretary of Transportation for Policy.—Polly Trottenberg, room W80–308 (202) 366–4540.
Assistant Secretary for Policy.—Vacant.
Deputy Assistant Secretaries for Policy: Elizabeth Osborne, room W82–308, 366–8979; Amy Scarton, room W82–310, 366–4005.

GENERAL COUNSEL

General Counsel.—Kathryn Thomson (acting), room W92–300, 366–4702.
Deputy General Counsel: James Cole, Jr., room W92–312, 366–4702; Judith Kaleta, room W92–318, 366–4713.
Associate General Counsel.—Amy Tovar, room W92–320, 366–4702.
General Law.—Terence Carlson, room W94–306, 366–9152.
Assistant General Counsel for—
Aviation Enforcement and Proceedings.—Samuel Podberesky, room W96–322, 366–9342.
International Law.—Donald H. Horn, room W98–324, 366–2972.
Legislation.—Thomas W. Herlihy, room W96–326, 366–4687.
Litigation.—Paul M. Geier, room W94–310, 366–4731.
Regulation and Enforcement.—Vacant, room W96–302, 366–4723.
Operations.—Ronald Jackson, room W96–304, 366–4710.

INSPECTOR GENERAL

Inspector General.—Calvin L. Scovel III, room W70–300 (202) 366–1959.
Deputy Inspector General.—Ann Calvaresi Barr (202) 366–6767.
Principal Assistant Inspector General for Auditing and Evaluation.—Lou Dixon (202) 366–8751.
Assistant Inspector General for—
Administration.—Susan Dailey (202) 366–1748.
Acquisition and Procurement Audits.—Mary Kay Langan Feirson (202) 366–9158.
Aviation Audits.—Jeff Guzzetti (202) 366–0500.
Financial and Information Technology Audits.—Louis King (202) 366–1407.
Highway and Transit Audits.—Joe Come (202) 366–5630.
Investigations.—Tim Barry (202) 366–1967.
Legal, Legislative and External Affairs.—Brian A. Dettelbach (202) 366–8751.
Rail, Maritime, and Hazmat Transport Audits, and Economic Analysis.—Mitch Behm (202) 366–9970.
Deputy Assistant Inspector General for—
Aviation Audits.—Matt Hampton (202) 366–0500.
Highway and Transit Audits.—Tom Yatsco (202) 366–5630.

REGIONAL AUDIT OFFICES

Regional Program Directors:
Tina Nysted, 61 Forsyth Street, SW., Suite 17T60, Atlanta, GA 30303 (404) 562–3770.
Robin Koch, 61 Forsyth Street, SW., Suite 17T60, Atlanta, GA 30303 (404) 562–3770.
Scott Macey, 201 Mission Street, Suite 1750, San Francisco, CA 94105 (415) 744–3090.
Barry DeWeese, 201 Mission Street, Suite 1750, San Francisco, CA 94105 (415) 744–3090.
Darren Murphy, 915 Second Avenue, Room 644, Seattle, WA 98174 (206) 220–7754.
George Banks, 10 South Howard Street, Suite 4500, Baltimore, MD 21201 (410) 962–3612.
Kerry Barras, 819 Taylor Street, Room 13A42, Fort Worth, TX 76102 (817) 978–3545.

REGIONAL INVESTIGATIONS OFFICES

Special Agents-In-Charge:
Region I.—Ted Doherty, 55 Broadway, Room 1055, Cambridge, MA 02142 (617) 494–2701.
Region II.—Douglas Shoemaker, 201 Varick Street, Room 1161, New York, NY 10014 (212) 337–1250.
Region III.—Kathryn Jones, 409 3rd Street, SW., Room 301, Washington, DC 20024 (202) 260–8580.
Region IV.—Marlies Gonzalez, 510 Shotgun Road, Suite 220, Sunrise, FL 33326 (954) 382–6645.
Region V.—Michelle McVicker, 200 West Adams Street, Suite 300, Chicago, IL 60606 (312) 353–0106.
Region VI.—Max Smith, 819 Taylor Street, Room 13A42, Fort Worth, TX 76102 (817) 978–3236.
Region IX.—Bill Swallow, 17785 Center Court Drive, Suite 350, Cerritos, CA 90703 (562) 467–5360.

OFFICE OF PUBLIC AFFAIRS

Assistant to the Secretary and Director of Public Affairs.—Meghan Keck, room W93–310 (202) 366–4312.
Deputy Director.—Casey Hernandez, 366–1621.
Associate Director of Media Relations.—William S. ''Bill'' Adams, 366–4570.
Director of Speechwriting and Research Division.—Ashley Nash-Hahn, room W93–319, 366–0679.

FEDERAL AVIATION ADMINISTRATION

800 Independence Avenue, SW., 20591 (202) 267–3484

Administrator.—Michael Huerta, 267–3111.
Chief of Staff.—Sasha Johnson, 267–7416.
Counselor to the Administrator.—Christopher Rocheleau, 267–3180.
Special Assistant to the Administrator.—Trish Fritz, 267–8208.
Executive Assistant to the Administrator.—Sharon Harrison, 267–3111.
Deputy Administrator.—Michael Whitaker, 267–8111.
Executive Assistant to the Administrator.—Nicole Harrison (A), 267–8111.
Senior Advisor to the Deputy Administrator.—Vacant, 267–8111.
Assistant Administrator for Finance and Management.—Victoria Wassmer, 267–8627.
Deputy Assistant Administrator for—
Acquisitions and Business Services.—Patricia McNall, 267–7222.
Financial Services / CFO.—Mark House, 267–9105.
Information Services / CIO.—Tina Amereihn, 493–4570.
Regions and Center Operations.—Ray Towles, 267–7369.
Regional Administrators:
Alaskan.—Robert N. Lewis (907) 271–5645.
Central.—Joseph N. Miniace (818) 329–3050.
Eastern.—Carmine Gallo (718) 553–3000.
Great Lakes.—Barry D. Cooper (847) 294–7294.
New England.—Amy Lind Corbett (781) 238–7020.

Northwest Mountain.—Kathryn Vernon (425) 227–2001.
Southern.—Doug Murphy (404) 305–5000.
Southwest.—Teresa Bruner (817) 222–5001.
Western-Pacific.—David Suomi (A), (310) 725–3550.

Director, Aviation Logistics.—David Foley 267–9011.

Director, Mike Monroney Aeronautical Center.—Michelle Coppedge (405) 954–4521.

Director of:
Budget and Programs.—Carl Burrus, 267–8010.
Financial Analysis.—David Rickard, 267–7140.
Financial Reporting and Accountability.—Allison Ritman, 267–3018.
Financial Operations.—Peter Basso, 267–8242.
Investment Planning and Analysis.—Kristen Burnham, 493–5672.
Labor Analysis.—Rich McCormick, 267–5943.

Assistant Administrator for Civil Rights.—Mamie Mallory, 267–3254.
Deputy Assistant Administrator for Civil Rights.—Courtney Wilkerson, 267–3254.

Assistant Administrator for Policy, International Affairs and Environment.—Julie Oettinger, 267–3927.
Deputy Assistant Administrator.—Carl Burleson, 267–7954.
Executive Director of:
Aviation Policy and Plans.—Nan Shellabarger, 267–3274.
Environment and Energy.—Lourdes Maurice, 267–7954.
International Affairs.—Carey Fagan, 385–8900.
Director of:
Asia-Pacific.—Mark Reeves, 011–65–6575–9475.
Europe, Africa, and Middle East.—Steve Creamer, 011–322–811–5159.
Western Hemisphere.—Christopher Banks (acting), 385–8900.

Chief Counsel.—Marc Warren (acting), 267–3222.
Deputy Chief Counsel.—Marc Warren, 267–3773.

Director of Audit and Evaluation.—H. Clayton Foushee, 267–9440.

Assistant Administrator for Government and Industry Affairs.—Roderick Hall, 267–3277.
Deputy Assistant Administrator.—Molly Harris, 267–8211.

Assistant Administrator for Human Resource Management.—Carrolyn Bostick, 267–3456.
Deputy Assistant Administrator.—Kimberly Moseley, 267–3850.
Executive Director of:
Accountability Board.—Maria Fernandez-Greczmiel, 267–3065.
Employee and Labor Relations.—Ronald James, 493–4291.
Human Resources Management Programs and Policies.—Angela Wilson (A), 267–3850.
Regional Human Resource (HR) Services.—Rickie Cannon, 267–4028.

Director, Talent Development and Chief Learning Officer.—Melissa King, 267–9041.

Assistant Administrator for Communications.—Kristie Greco, 267–3883.
Deputy Assistant Administrator for Public Affairs.—Laura Brown, 267–3883.
Deputy Assistant Administrator for Corporate Communications.—Deborah Green, 267–8859.

Assistant Administrator for Security and Hazardous Material.—Claudio Manno, 267–7211.
Deputy Assistant Administrator.—Thomas D. Ryan, 267–7211.
Director Office of:
Emergency Operations, Communications, and Investigations.—Angela Stubblefield, 267–7576.
Executive and Center Operations.—Victor Kemens, 267–3538.
Hazardous Materials Safety.—Chris Glasow, 385–4904.
Director of:
Joint Security and Hazardous Material Safety, Central.—Mary Alford (817) 222–5700.
Joint Security and Hazardous Material Safety, East.—Wilie Gripper (404) 305–6750.
Joint Security and Hazardous Material Safety, West.—Patricia Pausch (425) 227–2705.
Office of Security.—Bruce Herron, 493–5405.
Chief Operating Officer for Air Traffic Organization.—J. David Grizzle, 493–5602.
Deputy Chief Operating Officer.—Teri Bristol, 267–7224.
Vice President for—
En Route and Oceanic Services.—Gregory Burke, 385–8501.
Management Services.—Michael McCormick, 267–5724.
Mission Support.—Elizabeth Ray, 367–8261.
Program Management.—Chris Metts, 385–8343.
Safety and Technical Training.—Joseph Teixeira, 267–3341.
System Operations.—Nancy Kalinowski, 385–8704.
Technical Operations.—Vaughn Turner, 267–3366.
Terminal.—Walt Cochran, 385–8802.

Assistant Administrator for NextGen.—Pamela Whitley (A), 267–7111.
Deputy Assistant Administrator.—Pamela Whitley 267–7111.
Office of the Chief Scientist.—Steve Bradford, 267–7111.
Office of the Chief Scientist for Software.—Natesh Manikoth, 267–3250.
Director of:
Advanced Concepts and Technology Development.—Paul Fontaine, 267–9250.
Engineering Services.—Michele Merkle, 385–7100.
Management Services.—Jaime Figueroa, 267–3837.
NAS Lifecycle Integration.—J.C. Johns, 385–6724.
NextGen Performance and Outreach.—Gisele Mohler, 385–7257.
Systems Analysis and Modeling.—Joseph Post, 385–7305.
William J. Hughes Technical Center.—Dennis Filler (609) 485–6641.
Associate Administrator for Airports.—Christa Fornarotto, 267–9471.
Deputy Associate Administrator.—Catherine Lang, 267–9471.
Director of:
Airport Compliance and Management Analysis.—Randall Fiertz, 267–3085.
Airport Planning and Programming.—Ben DeLeon, 267–8775.
Airport Safety and Standards.—Michael J. O'Donnell, 267–3053.
Associate Administrator for Commercial Space Transportation.—Dr. George C. Nield, 267–7793.
Deputy Associate Administrator.—George Zamka, 267–7848.
Associate Administrator for Aviation Safety.—Peggy Gilligan, 267–3131.
Deputy Associate Administrator.—John J. Hickey, 267–7804.
Federal Air Surgeon.—Dr. Fred Tilton, 267–3535.
Director of:
Accident Investigation and Prevention.—Tony Fazio, 267–9612.
Aircraft Certification Service.—Dorenda Baker, 267–8235.
Flight Standards Service.—John Allen, 267–8237.
Office of Air Traffic Oversight.—Anthony Ferrante, 267–5202.
Quality, Integration and Executive Service.—Pamela Hamilton, 493–5717.
Rulemaking.—Lirio Liu (A), 267–9677.

FEDERAL HIGHWAY ADMINISTRATION

Washington Headquarters, 1200 New Jersey Avenue, SE., 20590–9898
Turner-Fairbank Highway Research Center (TFHRC)
6300 Georgetown Pike, McLean, VA 22201

Administrator.—Victor Mendez (202) 366–0650.
Deputy Administrator.—Greg Nadeau, 366–0650.
Associate Administrator/Director of TFHRC.—Michael F. Trentacoste, 493–3259.
Associate Administrator for Administration.—Sarah J. Shores, 366–0604.
Executive Director.—Jeffrey F. Paniati, 366–2242.
Chief Counsel.—Fred Wagner, 366–0740.
Chief Financial Officer.—Elissa K. Konove, 366–0622.
Associate Administrator for—
Civil Rights.—Warren S. Whitlock, 366–0693.
Federal Lands.—Joyce A. Curtis, 366–9472.
Infrastructure.—Walter Waidelich, 366–0116.
Operations.—Jeffrey A. Lindley, 366–9210.
Planning, Environment, and Realty.—Gloria M. Shepherd, 366–0116.
Policy.—David Kim, 366–8169.
Public Affairs.—Cathy St. Denis, 366–0660.
Safety.—Tony T. Furst, 366–2288.

FIELD SERVICES

Organizationally report to Executive Director (HOA–3), Washington, DC

Director of Technical Services.—Amy Lucero, 12300 West Dakota Avenue, Suite 340, Lakewood, CO 80228 (720) 963–3246.
Director of:
Field Services-North.—Martin C. Knopp, 10 South Howard Street, Baltimore, MD 21201–2819 (410) 962–0739.
Field Services-South.—Janice W. Brown, 61 Forsyth Street, SW., Suite 17T26, Atlanta, GA 30303–3104 (512) 406–1831.

Field Services-West.—Walter Waidelich, 2520 West 4700 South, Suite 9C, Salt Lake City, UT 84118–1847 (801) 955–3530.

Field Services-Mid America.—Vacant, 4749 Lincoln Mall Drive, Suite 600, Matteson, IL 60443 (708) 283–3500.

FEDERAL MOTOR CARRIER SAFETY ADMINISTRATION

Administrator.—Anne S. Ferro, room W60–308 (202) 366–1927.

Deputy Administrator.—William A. Bronrott.

Chief Safety Officer.—John Van Steenburg.

Chief Counsel.—Scott Darling, 366–0349.

Associate Administrator for Field Operation.—Anne L. Collins, 366–2027.

Director, Office of Communications.—Marissa Padilla, 366–8810.

FIELD OFFICES

Eastern Service Center (CT, DC, DE, MA, MD, ME, NJ, NH, NY, PA, PR, RI, VA, VT, WV).—802 Cromwell Park Drive, Suite N, Glen Burnie, MD 21061 (443) 703–2240.

Midwestern Service Center (IA, IL, IN, KS, MI, MO, MN, NE, OH, WI).—4749 Lincoln Mall Drive, Suite 300A, Matteson, IL 60443 (708) 283–3577.

Southern Service Center (AL, AR, FL, GA, KY, LA, MS, NC, NM, OK, SC, TN, TX).—1800 Century Boulevard, Suite 1700, Atlanta, GA 30345 (404) 327–7400.

Western Service Center (American Samoa, AK, AZ, CA, CO, Guam, HI, ID, Mariana Islands, MT, ND, NV, NM, OR, SD, UT, WA, WY).—Golden Hills Office Centre, 12600 W. Colfax Avenue, Suite B–300, Lakewood, CO 80215 (303) 407–2350.

FEDERAL RAILROAD ADMINISTRATION

1200 New Jersey Avenue, SE., Washington, DC 20590

http://www.fra.dot.gov

Administrator.—Joseph C. Szabo, room W30–308, 493–6014.

Deputy Administrator.—Karen Hedlund, room W32–308, 493–6015.

Executive Director.—Stacy Cummings, room W30–310, 493–6194.

Associate Administrator for—

Planning, Administration and Financial Management.—Rebecca Pennington, room W36–306, 440–2870.

Railroad Policy and Development.—Paul Nissenbaum, room W38–328, 493–6312.

Safety.—Robert Lauby (acting), room W35–306, 493–6474.

Chief Counsel.—Melissa Porter, room W31–320, 493–6034.

Communications and Legislative Affairs.—Kevin Thompson, room W31–326, 366–1299.

Director of:

Budget.—Erin McCartney, room W36–306, 493–6454.

Civil Rights.—Calvin Gibson, room W33–316, 493–6010.

Financial Management.—Tiwalade Bello, room W34–308, 493–6163.

Public Engagement.—Timothy Barkley, room W33–320, 493–1305.

REGIONAL OFFICES (RAILROAD SAFETY)

Region 1 (Northeastern).—Connecticut, Maine, Massachusetts, New Hampshire, New Jersey, New York, Rhode Island, Vermont.

Regional Administrator.—Les Fiorenzo, Room 1077, 55 Broadway, Cambridge, MA 02142 (617) 494–3484.

Region 2 (Eastern).—Delaware, District of Columbia, Maryland, Pennsylvania, Virginia, West Virginia, Ohio.

Regional Administrator.—Brian Hontz, 1510 Chester Pike, Baldwin Tower, Suite 660, Crum Lynne, PA 19022 (610) 521–8200.

Region 3 (Southern).—Kentucky, Tennessee, Mississippi, North Carolina, South Carolina, Georgia, Alabama, Florida.

Regional Administrator.—Patrick Plum, 61 Forsyth Street, NW., Suite 16T20, Atlanta, GA 30303 (404) 562–3809.

Region 4 (Central).—Minnesota, Illinois, Indiana, Michigan, Wisconsin.

Regional Administrator.—Michael Long, 200 W. Adams Street, Chicago, IL 60606 (312) 353–6203.

Region 5 (Southwestern).—Arkansas, Louisiana, New Mexico, Oklahoma, Texas.
Regional Administrator.—Vence Haggard, 4100 International Plaza, Suite 450, Ft. Worth, TX 96109 (817) 862–2220.
Region 6 (Midwestern).—Iowa, Missouri, Kansas, Nebraska, Colorado.
Regional Administrator.—Steven Fender, DOT Building, 901 Locust Street, Suite 464, Kansas City, MO 64106 (816) 329–3840.
Region 7 (Western).—Arizona, California, Nevada, Utah.
Regional Administrator.—James Jordan, 801 I Street, Suite 466, Sacramento, CA 95814 (916) 498–6547.
Region 8 (Northwestern).—Idaho, Oregon, Wyoming, Montana, North Dakota, South Dakota, Washington, Alaska.
Regional Administrator.—Mark Daniels, 500 Broadway, Murdock Executive Plaza, Suite 240, Vancouver, WA 98660 (360) 696–7536.

FEDERAL TRANSIT ADMINISTRATION

Administrator.—Peter Rogoff, 366–4040.
Deputy Administrator.—Therese McMillan, 366–4040.
Chief Counsel.—Dorval Carter, 366–1936.
Director, Office of Civil Rights.—Linda C. Ford (acting), 366–4018.
Planning and Environment.—Lucy Garliauskas, 366–4033.
Associate Administrator for—
Administration.—Matt Crouch (acting), 366–4007.
Budget and Policy.—Robert Tuccillo, 366–4050.
Communications and Congressional Affairs.—Brian Farber, 366–4043.
Program Management.—Henrika Buchanan-Smith, 366–4020.
Research, Demonstration and Innovation.—Walt Kulyk (acting), 366–4052.
Safety and Oversight.—Vince Valdes (acting), 366–3052.

MARITIME ADMINISTRATION

Administrator and Chairman, Maritime Subsidy Board.—Paul Jaenichen (acting), room W22–318 (202) 366–1719.
Deputy Administrator.—Paul Jaenichen, room W22–314, 366–5823.
Secretary, Maritime Administration and Maritime Subsidy Board.—Vacant, 366–5746.
Chief Counsel and Member, Maritime Subsidy Board.—Franklin Parker, room W24–310, 366–0709.
Director, Office of Congressional and Public Affairs.—Michael Novak, room W22–324, 366–9407.
Public Affairs Officer.—Kim Strong, room W22–324, 366–5067.
Executive Director.—Joel Szabat, room W28–316, 366–3907.
Director of:
International Activities.—Gregory Hall, room W28–314, 366–2765.
Policy and Plans.—Janice G. Weaver, room W28–312, 366–5493.
Associate Administrator for Budget and Programs/Chief Financial Officer.—Lydia Moschkin, room W21–334, 366–3071.
Director, Office of:
Accounting.—Jim Chen, room W24–301, 366–5103.
Budget.—James Lampert, room W26–310, 366–1369.
National Security Program/Funds Control.—Jennifer Fallis, room W25–333, 366–1947.
Resources.—Vacant, room W26–309, 366–5110.
Associate Administrator for Administration.—Keith Washington, room W26–312, 366–2181.
Director, Office of:
Acquisition.—Wayne Leon, room W26–324, 366–5620.
Information Technology.—Robert Ellington, room W26–320, 366–2531.
Management and Information Services.—Steve Snipes, room W26–302, 366–2811.
Personnel.—Kim Norris, room W28–304, 366–4141.
Associate Administrator for Environment and Compliance.—John Quinn, room W21–326, 366–1931.
Director, Office of:
Environment.—Michael C. Carter, room W25–302, 366–9431.
Safety.—Christopher McMahon, room W28–342, 366–7018.
Security.—Robert Ford (acting), room W25–308, 366–1883.
Associate Administrator for Intermodal System Development.—Keith Lesnick, room W21–320, 366–1624.

Deputy.—Roger V. Bohnert, room W21–324, 366–0720.
Director, Office of:
Deepwater Ports and Offshore Activities.—Yvette Fields, room W21–309, 366–0926.
Gateway Offices.—Christopher Moore, room W21–307, 366–5005.
Infrastructure Development and Congestion Mitigation.—Robert Bouchard, room W21–308, 366–5076.
Marine Highways and Passenger Services.—Lauren Brand, room W23–311, 366–7057.
Shipper and Carrier Outreach.—Richard J. Lolich, room W21–310, 366–0704.
Associate Administrator for National Security.—Kevin M. Tokarski, room W25–330, 366–5400.
Director, Office of:
Emergency Preparedness.—Thomas M.P. Christensen, room W23–304, 366–5909.
Sealift Support.—Jerome D. Davis, room W25–310, 366–0688.
Ship Disposal.—Curt J. Michanczyk, room W25–334, 366–6467.
Ship Operations.—William H. Cahill, room W25–336, 366–1875.
Associate Administrator for Business and Workforce Development.—Owen Doherty (acting), room W21–318, 366–5737.
Director, Office of:
Cargo Preference and Domestic Trade.—Dennis Brennan, room W23–316, 366–1029.
Financial Approvals and Marine Insurance.—Vacant, room W23–322, 366–2279.
Chief, Division of:
Business Finance.—Vacant, room W23–321, 366–1908.
Director, Office of:
Maritime Workforce Development.—Anne Wehde, room W23–314, 366–5469.
Shipyards and Marine Finance.—David Heller, room W23–234, 366–1850.

FIELD ACTIVITIES

Director for:
Great Lakes and Upper Inland Waterways Region.—Floyd Miras, Suite 185, 2860 South River Road, Des Plaines, IL 60018 (847) 905–0122.
North Atlantic Region.—Jeffrey Flumignan, 1 Bowling Green, Room 418, New York, NY 10004 (212) 668–2064.
Northern California/Hawaii Region.—John Hummer, Suite 2200, 201 Mission Street, San Francisco, CA 94105 (415) 744–3125.
South Atlantic Region.—Frances Bohnsack, Building 4D, Room 211, 7737 Hampton Boulevard, Norfolk, VA 23505 (757) 441–6393.

U.S. MERCHANT MARINE ACADEMY

Superintendent.—RADM Philip H. Greene, Jr., Kings Point, NY 11024 (516) 773–5000.
Assistant Superintendent for Academic Affairs (Academic Dean).—Shashi N. Kumar.

NATIONAL HIGHWAY TRAFFIC SAFETY ADMINISTRATION

Administrator.—David Strickland, room W42–302 (202) 366–1836.
Deputy Administrator.—Ronald L. Medford, 366–1836.
Director, Communications.—Vacant.
Director, Governmental Affairs, Policy and Strategic Planning.—Chan Lieu, 366–1836.
Senior Associate Administrator for—
Policy and Operation.—Gregory Walter, 366–2330.
Traffic Injury Control.—Brian McLaughlin, 366–1755.
Vehicle Safety.—Daniel Smith, 366–9700.
Associate Administrator for—
Communications and Consumer Information.—Susan Gorcowski, 366–9550.
Enforcement.—Claude Harris (acting), 366–2669.
National Center for Statistics and Analysis.—Jeff Michael (acting), 366–1503.
Planning, Administrative and Financial Management.—Rebecca Pennington, 366–2550.
Regional Operations and Program Delivery.—Maggi Gunnels, 366–2121.
Research and Program Development.—Michael Brown (acting), 366–1755.
Rulemaking.—Chris Bonanati, 366–1810.
Vehicle Safety Research Program.—John Maddox, 366–4862.
Chief Information Officer.—Colleen Coggins, 366–4878.
Director, Office of Civil Rights.—Philip Newby, 366–0972.

Chief Counsel.—O. Kevin Vincent, 366–9511.
Director, Executive Correspondence.—Gregory Walter, 366–2330.
Supervisor, Executive Correspondence.—Bernadette Millings, 366–5470.

REGIONAL OFFICES

Region 1.—Connecticut, Maine, Massachusetts, New Hampshire, Rhode Island, Vermont.
Regional Administrator.—Philip J. Weiser, Volpe National Transportation Center, 55 Broadway, Kendall Square, Code RTV–8E, Cambridge, MA 02142 (617) 494–3427.
Region 2.—Pennsylvania, New York, New Jersey, Puerto Rico, Virgin Islands.
Regional Administrator.—Thomas M. Louizou, 222 Mamaroneck Avenue, Suite 204, White Plains, NY 10605 (914) 682–6162.
Region 3.—Delaware, District of Columbia, Maryland, Kentucky, North Carolina, Virginia, West Virginia.
Regional Administrator.—Elizabeth Baker, 10 South Howard Street, Suite 6700, Baltimore, MD 21201 (410) 962–0090.
Region 4.—Alabama, Florida, Georgia, South Carolina, Tennessee.
Regional Administrator.—Terrance D. Schiavone, Atlanta Federal Center, 61 Forsyth Street, SW., Suite 17T30, Atlanta, GA 30303–3106 (404) 562–3739.
Region 5.—Illinois, Indiana, Michigan, Minnesota, Ohio, Wisconsin.
Regional Administrator.—Michael Witter, 19900 Governors Drive, Suite 201, Olympia Fields, IL 60461 (708) 503–8892.
Region 6.—Louisiana, Mississippi, New Mexico, Oklahoma, Texas, Indian Nations.
Regional Administrator.—George S. Chakiris, 819 Taylor Street, Room 8A38, Fort Worth, TX 76102–6177 (817) 978–3653.
Region 7.—Arkansas, Iowa, Kansas, Missouri, Nebraska.
Regional Administrator.—Romell Cooks, 901 Locust Street, Room 466, Kansas City, MO 64106 (816) 329–3900.
Region 8.—Colorado, North Dakota, Nevada, South Dakota, Utah, Wyoming.
Regional Administrator.—Bill Watada, 12300 West Dakota Avenue, Suite 140, Lakewood, CO 80228–2583 (720) 963–3100.
Region 9.—American Samoa, Arizona, California, Guam, Mariana Islands, Hawaii.
Regional Administrator.—David Manning, 201 Mission Street, Suite 1600, San Francisco, CA 94105 (415) 744–3089.
Region 10.—Alaska, Idaho, Montana, Oregon, Washington.
Regional Administrator.—John Moffat, Federal Building, 915 Second Avenue, Suite 3140, Seattle, WA 98174 (206) 220–7640.

PIPELINE AND HAZARDOUS MATERIALS SAFETY ADMINISTRATION

Administrator.—Cynthia Quarterman, room E27–300 (202) 366–4433.
Deputy Administrator.—Timothy Butters, room E27–300, 366–4461.
Assistant Administrator/Chief Safety Officer.—Vacant.
Chief Counsel.—Vanessa Sutherland, room E26–320, 366–4400.
Director, Office of Civil Rights.—Rosanne Goodwill, room E27–334, 366–9638.
Chief Financial Officer.—Monica Summitt, room E32–330, 366–5608.
Associate Administrator for—
Governmental, International and Public Affairs.—Jeannie Layson, room E27–300, 366–4831.
Hazardous Materials Safety.—Dr. Magdy El-Sibaie, room E21–316, 366–0656.
Management and Administration.—Scott Poyer, room E22–312, 366–5608.
Pipeline Safety.—Jeffrey Wiese, room E22–321, 366–4595.

HAZARDOUS MATERIALS SAFETY OFFICES

Chief of:
Eastern Region.—Colleen D. Abbenhaus, 820 Bear Tavern Road, Suite 306, West Trenton, NJ 08628 (609) 989–2256.
Central Region.—Kipton Wills, Suite 478, 2350 East Devon Avenue, Des Plaines, IL 60018 (847) 294–8580.
Western Region.—Sean Lynum, 3401 Centre Lake Drive, Suite 550–B, Ontario, CA 91761 (909) 937–3279.
Southern Region.—John Heneghan, 233 Peachtree Street, NE., Suite 602, Atlanta, GA 30303 (404) 832–1140.

Southwest Region.—Billy Hines, 8701 South Gessner Road, Suite 1110, Houston, TX 77004 (713) 272–2820.

PIPELINE SAFETY OFFICES

Director of:

Eastern Region.—Byron Coy, 820 Bear Tavern Road, Suite 103, West Trenton, NJ 08628 (609) 989–2171.

Central Region.—David Barrett, 901 Locust Street, Room 462, Kansas City, MO 64106 (816) 329–3800.

Western Region.—Chris Hoidal, 12300 West Dakota Avenue, Suite 110, Lakewood, CO 80228 (720) 963–3160.

Southwest Region.—Rodrick M. Seeley, 8701 South Gessner, Suite 1110, Houston, TX 77074 (713) 272–2859.

Southern Region.—Wayne Lemoi, 233 Peachtree Street, NE., Suite 600, Atlanta, GA 30303 (404) 832–1140.

RESEARCH AND INNOVATIVE TECHNOLOGY ADMINISTRATION (RITA)

http://www.rita.dot.gov

Deputy Administrator.—Gregory Winfree (202) 366–4412.

Chief Counsel.—Ellen Partridge, room E35–326, 366–1580.

Chief Financial Officer.—Nelson Torres (acting), room E37–315, 366–0314.

Public Affairs Contact, Bureau of Transportation Statistics.—David Smallen, room E36–328, 366–5568.

Director for—

Governmental, International and Public Affairs.—Jane Mellow, room E36–334, 366–4792.

Intelligent Transportation Systems.—Kenneth M. Leonard, room E31–301, 366–9536.

Transportation Safety Institute.—Christine Lawrence, 6500 South MacArthur Boulevard MPB–343, Oklahoma City, OK 73169 (405) 954–3153.

Volpe National Transportation Systems Center.—Robert Johns, room 1240, 55 Broadway, Kendall Square, Cambridge, MA 02142 (617) 494–2222.

SAINT LAWRENCE SEAWAY DEVELOPMENT CORPORATION-U.S. DOT

www.greatlakes-seaway.com/en

Administrator.—Vacant (202) 366–0091, fax 366–7147.

Deputy Administrator.—Craig H. Middlebrook (acting), (202) 366–0105.

Senior Advisor to the Administrator.—Anita K. Blackman, 366–0107.

Director, Office of:

Budget and Programs.—Kevin P. O'Malley.

Congressional and Public Relations.—Nancy T. Alcalde.

Trade Development.—Rebecca Spruill.

SEAWAY OPERATIONS

180 Andrews Street, P.O. Box 520, Massena, NY 13662–0520

phone (315) 764–3200, fax (315) 764–3235

Associate Administrator.—Salvatore Pisani.

Deputy Associate Administrator.—Vacant.

Assistant.—Vacant.

Chief Counsel.—Carrie Mann Lavigne.

Director, Office of:

Engineering and Maintenance.—Thomas A. Lavigne.

Financial Management and Administration and CFO.—Marsha Sienkiewicz.

Lock Operations and Marine Services.—Lori K. Curran.

SURFACE TRANSPORTATION BOARD

395 E Street, SW., 20423–0001, phone (202) 245–0245

http://www.stb.dot.gov

Chairman.—Daniel R. Elliott III, 245–0220.
Vice Chairman.—Ann Begeman, 245–0203.
Commissioner.—Francis P. Mulvey, 245–0213.
Office of:
Economics, Environmental Analysis, and Administration.—Leland L. Gardner, 245–0291.
General Counsel.—Ray Atkins, 245–0261.
Director, Office of:
Proceedings.—Rachel D. Campbell, 245–0352.
Public Assistance, Governmental Affairs, and Compliance.—Lucille Marvin, 245–0238.

DEPARTMENT OF ENERGY

James Forrestal Building, 1000 Independence Avenue, SW., 20585

phone (202) 586–5000, http://www.energy.gov

ERNEST MONIZ, Secretary of Energy; born on December 22, 1944, in Fall River MA; education: B.S., physics, Boston College, 1966; Ph.D., theorectical physics, Stanford University, 1972; honorary degrees from three universities; professional: Under Secretary, Department of Energy; Associate Director for Science, Office of Science and Technology Policy; professor, Massachusetts Institute of Technology; organizations: President Obama's Council of Advisors on Science and Technology; Department of Defense Threat Reduction Advisory Committee; Blue Ribbon Commission on America's Nuclear Future; Council on Foreign Relations; Fellow of the American Association for the Advancement of Science, the Humboldt Foundation, and the American Physical Society; and a member of numerous other civic and professional organizations; married: Dr. Naoimi; one child, two grandchildren; nominated by President Barack Obama to become the 13th Secretary of Energy, and confirmed by the U.S. Senate on May 16, 2013.

OFFICE OF THE SECRETARY

Secretary of Energy.—Ernest Moniz (202) 586–6210.
Deputy Secretary.—Daniel B. Poneman, 586–5500.
Associate Deputy Secretary.—Bruce Held, 586–6210.
Chief of Staff.—Jonathan Levy (acting), 586–6210.
Inspector General.—Gregory H. Friedman, 586–4393.
Assistant Secretary for—
Congressional and Intergovernmental Affairs.—Brad Crowell, 586–5450.
Policy and International Affairs.—Jon Elkind, 586–5800.
General Counsel.—Greg Woods, 586–5281.
Chief Information Officer.—Bob Brese, 586–0166.
Chief Human Capital Officer.—Bob Gibbs, 586–1234.
Chief Financial Officer.—Vacant.
Chief Health Safety and Security Officer.—Glenn Podonsky, 586–9275.
Executive Director of the Loan Programs Office.—Peter Davidson, 287–5854.
Director, Office of:
Economic Impact and Diversity.—Dot Harris, 586–8383.
Hearings and Appeals.—Poli Marmolejos, 287–1566.
Intelligence and Counterintelligence.—Steve Black, 586–1352.
Management.—Ingrid Kolb, 586–2550.
Public Affairs.—Dan Leistikow, 586–4940.
Director for Advanced Research Projects Agency-Energy.—Cheryl Martin (acting), 287–1004.
Administrator for Energy Information Administration.—Adam Sieminski, 586–4361.

UNDER SECRETARY OF ENERGY

Under Secretary of Energy.—Vacant (202) 586–7700.
Assistant Secretary for—
Electricity Delivery and Energy Reliability.—Patricia Hoffman, 586–1411.
Energy Efficiency and Renewable Energy.—David Danielson, 586–9220.
Environmental Management.—David Huizenga (acting), 586–7709.
Fossil Energy.—Christopher Smith (acting), 586–6660.
Nuclear Energy.—Peter Lyons (acting), 586–6630.
Director, Office of:
Legacy Management.—David Geiser, 586–7550.

UNDER SECRETARY FOR SCIENCE

Under Secretary for Science.—Vacant, (202) 586–0505.
Director, Office of Science.—Patricia Dehmer (acting), 586–0505.

NATIONAL NUCLEAR SECURITY ADMINISTRATION

Administrator for National Nuclear Security Administration/Under Secretary for Nuclear Security.—Vacant (202) 586–5555.
Principal Deputy Administrator.—Vacant, 586–5555.
Deputy Administrator for—
Defense Programs.—Donald Cook, 586–2179.
Defense Nuclear Nonproliferation.—Anne Harrington, 586–0645.
Naval Reactors.—Admiral John M. Richardson, USN, 781–6174.
Deputy Under Secretary for Counterterrorism.—Dr. Steven Aoki, 586–1734.
Associate Administrator for—
Defense Nuclear Security.—Steve Asher (acting), 586–8900.
Emergency Operations.—Rear Admiral Joseph Krol, USN (Ret.), 586–9892.
Infrastructure and Operations.—Michael Lempke, 586–8115.

MAJOR FIELD ORGANIZATIONS

OPERATIONS OFFICES

Managers:
Idaho.—Richard Provencher (208) 526–7300, fax (208) 526–0542.
Oak Ridge.—Larry Kelly (865) 576–4444, fax (865) 576–0006.
Richland.—Matt McCormick (509) 376–7395, fax (509) 376–4789.
Savannah River.—David Moody (803) 952–8725, fax (803) 952–8144.

INTEGRATED SUPPORT/BUSINESS CENTERS

Managers:
Chicago Office.—Roxanne E. Purucker (630) 252–2110.
EM Consolidated Business Center.—Jack Craig (513) 246–0460.
NNSA Service Center.—Gregory Beausoleil (505) 845–4392.

POWER MARKETING ADMINISTRATIONS

Administrator, Power Administration:
Bonneville.—Elliott Mainzer (acting), (503) 230–5101, fax (503) 230–4018.
Southeastern Area.—Kenneth Legg (706) 213–3800, fax (706) 213–3884.
Southwestern Area.—Christopher M. Turner (918) 595–6601, fax (918) 595–6755.
Western Area.—Mark Gabriel (720) 962–7077, fax (720) 962–7083.

PETROLEUM RESERVES

Deputy Assistant Secretary for Petroleum Reserves.—David Johnson (202) 586–4733.

FEDERAL ENERGY REGULATORY COMMISSION

888 First Street, NE., 20426

Chair.—Jon Wellinghoff (202) 502–6580.
Commissioners:
Cheryl A. LaFleur, 502–8961.
Philip D. Moeller, 502–8852.
John R. Norris, 502–6530.
Tony Clark, 502–6501.
Chief Administrative Law Judge.—Curtis L. Wagner, Jr., 502–8500.
Executive Director.—Anton C. Porter, 502–8300.

General Counsel.—David L. Morenoff (acting), 502–6000.
Secretary, Office of the Secretary.—Kimberly Bose, 502–8400.
Director, Office of:
Administrative Litigation.—Ted Gerarden, 502–6100.
Electric Reliability.—Michael Bardee, 502–8600.
Energy Infrastructure Security.—Joseph McClelland, 502–8867.
Energy Market Regulation.—Michael C. McLaughlin, 502–6700.
Energy Policy and Innovation.—Jamie L. Simler, 502–8934.
Energy Projects.—Jeff C. Wright, 502–8700.
Enforcement.—Norman C. Bay, 502–8100.
External Affairs.—Leonard Tao, 502–8004.

DEPARTMENT OF EDUCATION

400 Maryland Avenue, SW., 20202

phone (202) 401–3000, fax 401–0596, http://www.ed.gov

ARNE DUNCAN, Secretary of Education; born in Chicago, IL, November 6, 1964; children: Clare and Ryan; education: B.A., Harvard University, *magna cum laude*, 1987; professional: professional basketball player in Australia, 1987–91; Director of Ariel Education Initiative, 1992–98; Deputy Chief of Staff to the Chief Executive Officer of the Chicago Public Schools, 1999–2001; Chief Executive Officer of the Chicago Public Schools, 2001–09; nominated by President Barack Obama to become the 9th Secretary of Education on December 16, 2008; confirmed on January 20, 2009.

OFFICE OF THE SECRETARY

Room 7W301, phone (202) 401–3000, fax 260–7867

Secretary of Education.—Arne Duncan.
Chief of Staff.—Joanne Weiss.
Deputy Chief of Staff.—Eric Waldo.

OFFICE OF THE DEPUTY SECRETARY

Room 7W308, phone 401–1000

Deputy Secretary.—James H. Shelton III (acting).
Chief of Staff.—Tyra Mariani (acting).

OFFICE OF THE UNDER SECRETARY

Room 7E307, phone (202) 401–0429

Under Secretary.—Martha J. Kanter.
Deputy Under Secretary.—Vacant.
Chief of Staff.—Jon O'Berg.

OFFICE OF THE CHIEF FINANCIAL OFFICER

PCP 550 12th Street, SW., phone (202) 245–8144, fax 485–0160

Chief Financial Officer.—Thomas Skelly (acting), LBJ, 400 Maryland Avenue, SW., room 5W313, 401–0287.
Deputy Chief Financial Officers: James Ropelewski, PCP, room 6095, 245–6221; Timothy Soltis, PCP, room 6124, 245–6555.
Executive Officer.—Michael Holloway, PCP, room 6090, 245–8150.
Director of:
Contracts and Acquisitions Management.—James Hairfield, PCP, room 7173, 245–6219.
Financial Improvement and Post Audit Operations.—Craig Stanton, PCP, room 6056, 245–8102.
Financial Management Operations.—Gary Wood, PCP, room 6089, 245–8118.

OFFICE OF THE CHIEF INFORMATION OFFICER

PCP 550 12th Street, SW., phone (202) 245–6400, fax 245–6621

Chief Information Officer.—Danny Harris, PCP, room 9112, 245–6252.

Deputy Chief Information Officer.—Shawn Wang, PCP, room 9149, 245–6338.
Executive Officer.—Michael Holloway, PCP, room 6090, 245–8150.
Director of:
Financial Systems Services.—Constance Davis, PCP, room 9150, 245–7173.
Information Assurance Services.—Steven Grewal, PCP, room 10057, 245–6316.
Information Technology Program Services.—Ken Moore, PCP, room 9109, 245–6908.
Information Technology Services.—Tony Wood, PCP, room 9151, 245–7214.

OFFICE OF MANAGEMENT

Room 2W301, phone (202) 401–5848, fax 260–3761

Assistant Secretary.—Denise L. Carter (acting), room 2W311, 401–1583, fax 260–3761.
Principal Deputy Assistant Secretary.—Denise L. Carter, room 2W311, 401–1583, fax 260–3761.
Chief of Staff.—Richard Smith, room 2W309, 401–8530, fax 260–3761.
Executive Officer.—David Cogdill, room 2W227, 401–0695, fax 401–3513.
Director, Alternative Dispute Resolution Center.—Debra Bennett, room 408–C, 80 F Street, NW., 219–0955, fax 219–2217.
Service Director of:
Equal Employment Opportunity Services.—Selina Lee, room 2W236, 205–0518, fax 205–5760.
Facilities Services.—Scott Taylor, room 2C106, 401–9496, fax 453–5579.
Human Capital and Client Services.—Pam Malam, room 2E314, fax 401–0520.
Management Services.—Wanda Davis, room 2W119, 401–5931, fax 205–1866.
Office of Hearings and Appeals.—Frank J. Furey, L'Enfant Plaza–2134, 619–9701, fax 619–9726.
Privacy, Information and Records Management Services.—Kathleen Styles, room 2E315, 453–5587, fax 401–0920.
Security Services.—Ronald Luczak, room 2W314, 260–7727, fax 260–3761.

OFFICE FOR CIVIL RIGHTS

400 Maryland Avenue, SW., Room 4E319, 20202–1100, phone (202) 423–5900,

fax 423–6010

Assistant Secretary.—Catherine Lhamon, room 4E313, 453–7240.
Confidential Assistant.—Helen Boyer, room 4E317, 453–6048.
Principal Deputy Assistant Secretary.—Seth Galanter, room 4E329, 453–6048.
Deputy Assistant Secretary for—
Enforcement.—Sandra Battle, room 4E314, 453–5958.
Policy.—John DiPaolo, room 4E348, 453–6594.
Strategic Operations and Outreach.—Robert Kim, room 4E311, 453–6053.
Directors of Enforcement: Debbie Osgood, room 4E330, (202) 730–1598; Randolph Wills, room 4E332, 453–5956.
Executive Officer and Director, Resource Management.—Diedre Windsor, room 4E305, 453–5512.
Senior Counsel: Saba Bireda, room 4E307, 453–6025; Lillian Dorka, room 4E306, 453–6035.
Special Assistant.—Andrew Amore, room 4E319, 453–6359.

OFFICE OF COMMUNICATIONS AND OUTREACH

Information Resource Center (202) 401–8964

Room 5E300, phone (202) 401–8964

Assistant Secretary.—Massie Ritsch (acting), room 7W101, LBJ, 260–2671.
Press Secretary.—Vacant, LBJ, press@ed.gov.
Deputy Assistant Secretaries:
Communication Development.—Jonathan Schorr, room 7W103, LBJ, 401–6359.
Operations.—Cynthia Dorfman, room 5E231, LBJ, 205–2604.
National Engagement.—Karen Stratman-Krusemark (acting), room 316, LBJ, 401–2559.

OFFICE OF ELEMENTARY AND SECONDARY EDUCATION

Room 3W300, phone (202) 401–0113, fax 205–0303

Assistant Secretary.—Deb Delisle, room 3W315, 401–0113.
Deputy Assistant Secretary.—Scott Sargrad, room 3W307, 453–7254.
Chief of Staff.—Elizabeth Grant, room 3W313, 453–6037.
Deputy Assistant Secretary for—
Management.—Alex Goniprow, room 3W314, 401–9090.
Program Directors:
Academic Improvement and Teacher Quality Programs.—Sylvia Lyles, room 3E314, 260–8228, fax 260–8969.
Impact Aid Programs.—Alfred Lott, room 3E105, 260–3858, fax 205–0088.
Office of Indian Education.—Joyce Silverthorne, room 3E201, 401–0767.
Office of Migrant Education.—Lisa Ramirez, room 3E317, 260–1127, fax 205–0089.
School Support and Technology Programs.—Jenelle Leonard, room 3W203, 401–3641.
Student Achievement and School Accountability Programs.—Monique Chism, room 3W224, 260–0826.

OFFICE OF ENGLISH LANGUAGE ACQUISITION

400 Maryland Avenue, SW., 5C–132, 20202, phone (202) 401–4300, fax 401–8452

Assistant Deputy Secretary and Director.—Joseph Conaty (acting).
Deputy Director.—Vacant.

OFFICE OF FEDERAL STUDENT AID

830 First Street, NE., 20202, phone (202) 377–3000, fax 275–5000

Chief Operating Officer.—Jim Runcie.
Deputy Chief Operating Officer.—Vacant.
Chief of Staff.—Jim Manning, 377–3007.
Ombudsman.—Joyce DeMoss, room 41I1, 377–3992.
Chief:
Business Operations Officer.—Bill Leith, room 111I1, 377–3676.
Communications Officer.—Christopher B. Greene, room 22C7, 377–4003.
Compliance Officer.—Robin Minor, room 81K2, 377–4273.
Financial Officer.—Jay Hurt, room 54E1, 377–3453.
Information Officer.—Jerry Williams, room 102E3, 377–3101.
Director, Policy Liaison and Implementation Staff.—Jeff Baker, room 113C1, 377–4009.
Chief of Administration Services.—Irma Blanchett, room 21A5, 377–4165.
Chief Customer Experience Officer.—Brenda Wensil, room 114F1, 377–4671.

OFFICE OF THE GENERAL COUNSEL

Room 6E313, phone (202) 401–6000, fax 205–2689

General Counsel.—Vacant.
Chief of Staff.—Lauren Thompson Starks.
Senior Counsel: Ron Petracca, Robert Wexler.
Senior Counsel for Information and Technology.—''Bucky'' Methfessel.
Executive Officer.—LaVerne Chester, 401–5937.
Deputy General Counsel for—
Postsecondary and Business Administrative Law Service.—Julie Miceli.
Ethics, Legislative Counsel and Regulatory Service.—Elizabeth McFadden.
Program Service.—Philip H. Rosenfelt.

OFFICE OF INNOVATION AND IMPROVEMENT

phone (202) 205–4500

Assistant Deputy Secretary.—Nadya Chinoy Dabby (acting), 401–8532.
Associate Assistant Deputy Secretary for—
Innovation and Reform.—Margo Anderson.

Special Projects.—Vacant.
Chief of Staff.—Marisa Bold.

OFFICE OF INSPECTOR GENERAL

Potomac Center Plaza (PCP), 8th Floor, 20024, phone (202) 245–6900, fax 245–6993

Inspector General.—Kathleen Tighe.
Deputy Inspector General.—Vacant.
Counsel to the Inspector General.—Marta Erceg, 245–7015.
Assistant Inspector General for—
Audit Services.—Patrick Howard, 245–6949.
Management Services.—Wanda Scott, 245–6065.
Investigations.—William Hamel, 245–6922.
IT Audit and Computer Crimes Investigations.—Charles Coe, 245–7033.

INTERNATIONAL AFFAIRS OFFICE

Room 6W108, phone (202) 401–0430, fax 401–2508

Senior Advisor to the Secretary and Director.—Maureen McLaughlin.
Deputy Director.—JoAnne Livingston.
International Visitors.—Sambia Shivers-Barclay.
Western Hemisphere and Oceania Affairs, Organization of American States (OAS).—Rafael Nevarez.
Staff Assistant.—Ashley Patillo.

INSTITUTE OF EDUCATION SCIENCES

555 New Jersey Avenue, NW., Room 600, 20208, phone (202) 219–1385, fax 219–1466

Director.—John Q. Easton, 219–1385.
Deputy Director for—
Administration and Policy.—Sue Betka, 219–1385.
Science.—Anne Riccuiti, 219–2247.
National Center for—
Education Evaluation and Regional Assistance.—Ruth C. Neild, 208–1200.
Education Research.—Thomas W. Brock, 219–2006.
Education Statistics.—Jack Buckley, 219–7001.
Special Education Research.—Joan McLaughlin (acting), 219–1309.

OFFICE OF LEGISLATION AND CONGRESSIONAL AFFAIRS

Room 6W301, phone (202) 401–0020, fax 401–1438

Assistant Secretary.—Gabriella Gomez, 401–0020.
Deputy Assistant Secretaries: Jodie Fingland, 401–1043; J. Lloyd Horwich, 205–0490.
Chief of Staff.—Ruthanne Buck, 401–1036.

OFFICE OF PLANNING, EVALUATION AND POLICY DEVELOPMENT

Room 5E301, phone (202) 401–0831, fax 401–8607

Assistant Secretary.—Denise Forte (acting), room 5E313.
Executive Officer.—Brenda Long, room 7E201.
Director of:
Budget Service.—Thomas Skelly, room 5W313, 401–7888.
Performance Information Management Service.—Ross C. Santy, room 6W231, 401–1959.
Policy and Program Studies Service.—Tom Weko, room 6W231, 401–1270.

OFFICE OF POSTSECONDARY EDUCATION

1990 K Street, NW., 20006, phone (202) 502–7750, fax 502–7677

Assistant Secretary.—Brenda Dann-Messier (acting).

Chief of Staff.—Vacant.
Deputy Assistant Secretary for—
Higher Education Programs.—Linda Byrd-Johnson (acting), 502–7729.
International and Foreign Language Education.—Clay Pell, 502–7697.
Policy, Planning and Innovation.—Lynn Mahaffie (acting), 502–7903.

OFFICE OF SAFE AND HEALTHY STUDENTS

400 Maryland Avenue SW., 20202–6450, phone (202) 453–6777

Program Director.—David Esquith, room 3E328, 453–6722.

OFFICE OF SPECIAL EDUCATION AND REHABILITATIVE SERVICES

Potomac Center Plaza (PCP), 550 12th Street, SW., 5th Floor, 20202

phone (202) 245–7468, fax 245–7638

Assistant Secretary.—Michael K. Yudin, delegated the authority to perform the functions and duties of the Assistant Secretary for Special Education and Rehabilitative Services, room 5107, 245–6496.
Executive Administrator.—Andrew J. Pepin, room 5106, 245–7632.
Deputy Assistant Secretary.—Sue Swenson, room 5138, 245–8021.
Director of:
National Institute on Disability and Rehabilitation Research.—Charlie Lakin.
Office of Special Education Programs.—Melody Musgrove.
Commissioner of the Rehabilitation Services Administration.—Edward Anthony (acting).

OFFICE OF VOCATIONAL AND ADULT EDUCATION

550 12th Street, SW., 11th Floor, 20202, phone (202) 245–7700, fax 245–7171

Assistant Secretary.—Brenda Dann-Messier, brenda.dann-messier@ed.gov.
Chief of Staff.—George Smith, george.smith@ed.gov.
Deputy Assistant Secretaries: Mark Mitsui, mark.mitsui@ed.gov; Johan Uvin, johan.uvin@ed.gov.
Staff Assistants: Russella Davis-Rogers, russella.davis@ed.gov; Francine Sinclair, francine.sinclair@ed.gov.

DEPARTMENT OF VETERANS AFFAIRS

Mail should be addressed to 810 Vermont Avenue, NW.,Washington, DC 20420
http://www.va.gov

ERIC K. SHINSEKI, Secretary of Veterans Affairs; education: graduated, U.S. Military Academy, West Point, NY, 1965; M.A., Duke University; graduated, National War College; military service: Chief of Staff, U.S. Army, 1999–2003; Vice Chief of Staff, U.S. Army, 1998–99; Commanding General, United States Army, Europe and Seventh Army; Commanding General NATO Land Forces, Central Europe; Commander NATO-led Stabilization Force, Bosnia-Herzegovina; Vietnam War Veteran; military awards: Defense Distinguished Service Medal, Distinguished Service Medal, Legion of Merit (with Oak Leaf Clusters), Bronze Star Medal with "V" Device (with 2 Oak Leaf Clusters), Purple Heart (with Oak Leaf Cluster), Defense Meritorious Service Medal, Meritorious Service Medal (with 2 Oak Leaf Clusters), Air Medal, Parachutist Badge, Ranger Tab, Joint Chiefs of Staff Identification Badge, and Army Staff Identification Badge; married: Patricia; two children; nominated by President Barack Obama to become 7th Secretary of Veterans Affairs, and was confirmed by the U.S. Senate on January 21, 2009.

OFFICE OF THE SECRETARY

Secretary of Veterans Affairs.—Eric K. Shinseki (202) 461–4800.
Deputy Secretary of Veterans Affairs.—Vacant, 461–4817.
Chief of Staff.—Jose D. Riojas (acting), 461–4808.
Deputy Chief of Staff.—Hughes Turner, 461–4808.
Senior Advisor to the Secretary.—John Spinelli, 461–4874.
Special Assistant for Veterans Service Organizations Liaison.—Kevin S. Secor, 461–4835.
Executive Secretary.—Bonnie Miranda, 461–4869.
Director, Center for—
Faith-Based Community Initiative.—Rev. E. Terri LaVelle, 461–7611.
Minority Veterans.—Barbara Ward, 461–6191.
Women Veterans.—Irene Trowell-Harris, Ed.D., RN, 461–6193.
Employment Discrimination Complaint Adjudication.—Maxanne R. Witkin, 1722 I Street, NW., 461–1650.
Small and Disadvantaged Business Utilization.—Tom Leney, 801 I Street, NW., 461–4300.

BOARD OF VETERANS' APPEALS

Chairman.—Vacant, 425 I Street (202) 632–4603.
Executive in Charge.—Laura H. Eskenazi (202) 632–4603.
Vice Chairman.—Vacant.

OFFICE OF GENERAL COUNSEL

General Counsel.—Will A. Gunn (202) 461–4995.
Deputy General Counsel.—John "Jack" Thompson, 461–4995.

OFFICE OF INSPECTOR GENERAL

Inspector General.—George J. Opfer, 801 I Street, NW. (202) 461–4720.
Deputy Inspector General.—Richard J. Griffin.

OFFICE OF ACQUISITIONS, LOGISTICS, AND CONSTRUCTION

Executive Director.—Glenn D. Haggstrom, 425 I Street, NW. (202) 461–8007.
Deputy Assistant Secretary, Office of Acquisition and Logistics.—Jan R. Frye, 810 Vermont Avenue, NW., 461–6920.

Director, Office of Construction and Facilities Management.—Stella Fiotes, 425 I Street, NW., 461–8197.

ASSISTANT SECRETARY FOR CONGRESSIONAL AND LEGISLATIVE AFFAIRS

Assistant Secretary.—Joan M. Mooney (202) 461–6490.
Director of Operations.—Lawrence W. Hinkin, 461–5914.
Director of Congressional Affairs.—Vacant.
Associate Deputy Assistant Secretary.—Christopher E. O'Connor, 461–6456.
Director for—
Benefits Legislative Affairs Service.—John Kruse, 461–6467.
Congressional Liaison Service.—Ronald Maurer, 461–0398.
Corporate Enterprise Legislative Affairs Service.—Lesia Mandzia, 461–6177.
Health Legislative Affairs Service.—Jeffrey Gall, 461–7339.
Legislative Affairs Service.—David Ballenger, 461–6464.

ASSISTANT SECRETARY FOR PUBLIC AND INTERGOVERNMENTAL AFFAIRS

Assistant Secretary.—Dr. Tommy Sowers (202) 461–7500.
Deputy Assistant Secretary for—
Intergovernmental and International Affairs.—John Garcia, 461–7400.
Public Affairs.—Josh Taylor (acting), 461–7700.

ASSISTANT SECRETARY FOR POLICY AND PLANNING

Assistant Secretary.—Robert Snyder (acting), 461–5800.
Principal Deputy Assistant Secretary.—Robert Snyder, 461–5800.
Deputy Assistant Secretary for—
Data Governance and Analysis.—Dat Tran, 461–5788.
Policy.—Susan Sullivan (acting), 461–5831.
Executive Director for—
Corporate Analysis and Evaluation.—Subhi Mehdii, 461–5752.
Enterprise Program Management Office.—Greg L. Giddens, 461–6986.
Office of Interagency Collaboration and Integration (VA/DoD Collaboration).—John P. Medve, 461–5626.

ASSISTANT SECRETARY FOR OPERATIONS, SECURITY AND PREPAREDNESS

Assistant Secretary.—Jose D. Riojas (202) 461–4980.
Deputy Assistant Secretary for—
Emergency Management.—Kevin Hanretta, 461–4985.
Security and Law Enforcement.—Frederick R. Jackson, 461–5544.

ASSISTANT SECRETARY FOR MANAGEMENT

Executive in Charge/Chief Financial Officer.—Helen Tierney (202) 461–6703.
Executive Director of Operations.—Vacant, 461–6703.
Deputy Assistant Secretary for—
Budget.—Maureen Walsh, 461–6654.
Finance.—Edward J. Murray, 461–6180.
Director for—
Asset Enterprise Management.—James Sullivan, 461–6671.
Business Oversight.—Rodney Wood (512) 981–4202.
Performance Management.—Dave Zlowe, 461–6608.

ASSISTANT SECRETARY FOR INFORMATION AND TECHNOLOGY

Assistant Secretary.—Stephen W. Warren (acting), (202) 461–6911.
Principal Deputy Assistant Secretary.—Stephen W. Warren, 461–6910.

ASSISTANT SECRETARY FOR HUMAN RESOURCES AND ADMINISTRATION

Assistant Secretary.—Ralph Torres (acting), (202) 461–7750.

Principal Deputy Assistant Secretary.—Rafael Torres, 501–2662.
Deputy Assistant Secretary for—
Administration.—Roy Hurndon, 461–5500
Diversity and Inclusion.—Georgia Coffey, 461–4131, 1575 I Street.
Human Resources Management.—Vacant.
Labor Management Relations.—Leslie Wiggins, 461–4119, 1575 I Street.
Resolution Management.—Rosa Franco, 501–2800, 1575 I Street.

NATIONAL CEMETERY ADMINISTRATION

Under Secretary for Memorial Affairs.—Steve L. Muro, (202) 461–6112.
Executive Assistants: Sharon Stevens, 461–6368; George D. Eisenbach, Jr., 461–6014.
Principal Deputy Under Secretary.—Ronald Walters (acting), 461–6510.
Executive Assistant.—Jacqueline Hillian-Craig, 461–0977.
Deputy Under Secretary for—
Field Programs.—Glenn Powers, 461-6071.
Finance and Planning/CFO.—Ronald Walters, 461–6738.
Management.—Thomas Muir, 461–6234.
Director of:
Budget Service.—Joan Jefferies, 461–6742.
Design and Construction Service.—Thomas Basham, 632–4874.
Field Programs.—Kimberly Wright, 461–6748.
IT Business Requirements and Administrative Service.—Timothy Godlove, 632–7209.
Management and Communications Service.—Patricia ''Tish'' Tyson, 461–6307.
Memorial Programs Service.—Anita Hanson, 501–3060.
Veterans Cemetery Grants Program.—Joshua de Leon, 632–7369.

VETERANS BENEFITS ADMINISTRATION

Under Secretary.—Allison A. Hickey, 1800 G Street, NW. (202) 461–9300.
Principal Deputy Under Secretary.—Danny Pummill.
Chief of Staff.—Lois Mittelstaedt.
Deputy Under Secretary for—
Disability Assistance.—Janice Jacobs, 461–9320.
Economic Opportunity.—Curtis L. Coy, 443–6080.
Field Operations.—Diana Rubens, 461–9340.
Chief Financial Officer.—Jamie Manker, 461–9900.
Director of:
Business Process Integration.—Brad Houston, 461–9797.
Compensation.—Thomas Murphy, 461–9700.
Education.—Robert M. Worley II, 461–9800.
Employee Development and Training.—Terence Meehan, 461–9860.
Insurance.—Vincent E. Markey (215) 381–3100.
Loan Guaranty.—Mike Frueh, 632–8862.
Management.—Ezra Safdie (acting), 461–9412.
Pension and Fiduciary.—David McLenachen, 461–9700.
Performance Analysis and Integrity.—Mark Seastrom, 461–9040.
Strategic Planning.—Richard Buchanan, 461–9222.
Veterans Benefits Management System.—Alan Bozeman, 461–9640.
Veterans Relationship Management.—Maureen Ellenberger, 632–9103.
Vocational Rehabilitation and Employment.—Margarita Cocker (acting), 461–9333.

VETERANS HEALTH ADMINISTRATION

Under Secretary for Health.—Robert A. Petzel, M.D. (202) 461–7000.
Principal Deputy Under Secretary for Health.—Robert L. Jesse, M.D., Ph.D., 461–7008.
Deputy Under Secretary for Health for Operations and Management.—William C. Schoenhard, FACHE, 461–7026.
Deputy Under Secretary for Health for Policy and Services.—Madhulika Agarwal, M.D., M.P.H., 461–7590.
Chief of Staff.—Lisa Thomas, Ph.D., 461–7016.
Deputy Chief of Staff.—Ann C. Patterson, 461–7016.
Assistant Deputy Under Secretary for Health for—
Administrative Operations.—Philip Matkovsky, 461–7029.
Clinical Operations and Management.—Thomas Lynch, M.D., 461–7046.

Health for Quality, Safety and Value.—Robin Hemphill, M.D., M.P.H (acting), 461–1994.
Informatics and Analytics.—Gail Graham, 461–5874.
Organizational Integration.—Catherine Dischner, MSN, RN, CEN, 461–7008.
Policy and Service.—Stanlie Daniels, 461–7590.
Policy and Planning.—Patricia Vandenberg, M.H.A., B.S.N., 461–7100.
Patient Care Services.—Rajiv Jain, M.D., 461–7800.
Workforce Services.—Annie Spiczak, 461–4076.

Medical Inspector.—John Pierce, M.D., 266–4676.

Chief Officer for—
Academic Affiliations.—Malcolm Cox, M.D., 461–9490.
Business.—Katie Shebesh, 461–1600.
Communications.—John S. Hale, 461–7070.
Compliance and Business Integrity.—Robert Criscuolo (201) 643–1101.
Employee Education System.—Jim Warner, 461–4076.
Ethics in Health Care.—Ellen Fox, M.D., 1575 I Street, NW., 501–0364.
Financial.—Kathleen Turco, M.B.A., 266–4513.
Nursing.—James Harris, DSN, M.B.A., FAAN (acting), 461–6962.
Procurement and Logistics.—Norbert Doyle, 632–7942.
Public Health and Environmental Hazards.—Victoria Davey, Ph.D., 461–1000.
Readjustment Counseling.—Donald Smith (acting), 461–6525.
Research and Development.—Tim O'Leary, M.D. (acting), 461–1700.
Research Oversight.—J. Thomas Puglisi, Ph.D., CIP, 1717 H Street, NW., 266–4580.
Workforce Management and Consulting.—Michael Culpepper, 461–7337.

Director, Office of Patient Centered Care.—Tracy Gaudet, M.D., 461–1719.

DEPARTMENT OF HOMELAND SECURITY

U.S. Naval Security Station, 3801 Nebraska Avenue, NW., 20016

Phone (202) 282–8000

JEH CHARLES JOHNSON, Secretary of Homeland Security was sworn in on December 23, 2013 as the fourth Secretary of Homeland Security. Prior to joining DHS, Secretary Johnson served as General Counsel for the Department of Defense, where he was part of the senior management team and led the more than 10,000 military and civilian lawyers across the Department. As General Counsel of the Defense Department, Secretary Johnson oversaw the development of the legal aspects of many of our nation's counterterrorism policies, spearheaded reforms to the military commissions system at Guantanamo Bay in 2009, and co-authored the 250-page report that paved the way for the repeal of "Don't Ask, Don't Tell" in 2010.

Secretary Johnson's overall career has included extensive service in national security, law enforcement, and as an attorney in private corporate law practice. Secretary Johnson was General Counsel of the Department of the Air Force in 1998 to 2001, and he served as an Assistant U.S Attorney in the Southern District of New York in 1989 to 1991.

In private law practice, Secretary Johnson was a partner with the New York City-based law firm of Paul, Weiss, Rifkind, Wharton and Garrison, LLP. In 2004, Secretary Johnson was elected a Fellow in the prestigious American College of Trial Lawyers, and he is a member of the Council on Foreign Relations.

Secretary Johnson graduated from Morehouse College in 1979 and received his law degree from Columbia Law School in 1982.

OFFICE OF THE SECRETARY

Secretary of Homeland Security.—Jeh Charles Johnson.
Deputy Secretary of Homeland Security.—Alejandro Mayorkas.
Chief of Staff.—Philip A. McNamara (acting).

CITIZENSHIP AND IMMIGRATION SERVICES OMBUDSMAN

Phone (202) 357–8100

Ombudsman.—Maria Odom.

CIVIL RIGHTS AND CIVIL LIBERTIES

Phone (202) 401–1474, Toll Free: 1–866–644–8360

Officer for Civil Rights and Civil Liberties.—Megan H. Mack.

EXECUTIVE SECRETARIAT

Phone (202) 282–8221

Executive Secretary.—Elisa Montoya.

OFFICE OF THE GENERAL COUNSEL

Phone (202) 282–9822

General Counsel.—Stevan Bunnell.

OFFICE OF INSPECTOR GENERAL

Phone (202) 254–4100

Inspector General.—Carlton Mann (acting).

Deputy Inspector General.—Anne Richards (acting).
Chief Operating Officer.—Carlton Mann.
Deputy Counsel to the Inspector General.—Michael Mobbs.
Assistant Inspector General for—
Audits.—Mark Bell (acting).
Emergency Management Oversight.—John V. Kelly.
Information Technology Audits.—Frank Deffer.
Inspections.—Deborah Outten-Mills (acting).
Integrity and Quality Oversight.—Michael Beard.
Investigations.—John Dupuy.
Management.—Russell H. Barbee.
Director, External Affairs (Legislative and Public).—Vacant.
Chief of Staff.—Yvonne Manino (acting).
Special Assistant to the Inspector General.—Dorothy Balaban.

OFFICE OF INTELLIGENCE AND ANALYSIS

Phone (202) 282–8353

Under Secretary and Chief Intelligence Officer.—Vacant.
Principal Deputy Under Secretary.—John Cohen.
Chief of Staff.—Philip Groven (acting).
Deputy Under Secretaries for—
Analysis.—Jennifer Lasley.
Enterprise and Mission Support.—Michael Potts.
Plans, Policy, and Performance Management.—Glenn Krizay.
State and Local Program Office.—Scott McAllister.

OFFICE OF INTERGOVERNMENTAL AFFAIRS

Phone (202) 282–9310

Assistant Secretary.—Philip A. McNamara.
Deputy Assistant Secretary.—Alaina Clark.

OFFICE OF LEGISLATIVE AFFAIRS

Phone (202) 447–5890

Assistant Secretary.—Brian de Vallance (acting).
Deputy Assistant Secretaries: Sue Ramanathan (acting), Alexandra Veitch (acting).

MILITARY ADVISOR'S OFFICE

Phone (202) 282–8239

Military Advisor to the Secretary.—RDML June Ryan.

PRIVACY OFFICE

Phone (703) 235–0780

Chief Privacy Officer.—Karen Neuman.

OFFICE OF PUBLIC AFFAIRS

Phone (202) 282–8069

Assistant Secretary.—Clark Stevens.
Principal Deputy Assistant Secretary.—Bob Jensen.

NATIONAL PROTECTION AND PROGRAMS DIRECTORATE

Phone (202) 282–8400

Under Secretary.—Suzanne E. Spaulding (acting).

Deputy Under Secretary.—Suzanne E. Spaulding.
Deputy Under Secretary for Cybersecurity.—Phyllis Schneck.
Chief of Staff.—David Hess.
Assistant Secretary for—
Cybersecurity and Communications.—Roberta Stempfley (acting).
Infrastructure Protection.—Caitlin Durkovich.
Director for—
Federal Protective Service.—L. Eric Patterson.
Office of Biometric Identity Management.—Shonnie Lyon (acting).

SCIENCE AND TECHNOLOGY DIRECTORATE

Phone (202) 254–6033

Under Secretary.—Daniel Gerstein (acting).
Deputy Under Secretary.—Daniel Gerstein.
Chief of Staff.—Christina Murata.
Deputy Chief of Staff.—Tod Companion (acting).
Director of—
Acquisition Support and Operations Analysis.—Debra Durham.
Finance and Budget.—Richard Williams.
Homeland Security Advanced Research Projects Agency.—Adam Cox (acting).
Research and Development Partnerships.—Keith Holtermann.
Support to the Homeland Security Enterprise and First Responders.—Robert Griffin.

MANAGEMENT DIRECTORATE

Phone (202) 447–3400

Under Secretary.—Rafael Borras.
Deputy Under Secretary.—Chris Cummiskey.
Chief of Staff.—Vince Micone.
Chief Readiness Support Officer.—Jeffrey Orner.
Chief Financial Officer.—Chip Fulghum (acting).
Chief Human Capital Officer.—Catherine Emerson.
Chief Information Officer.—Luke McCormack.
Chief Procurement Officer.—Nick Nayak.
Chief Security Officer.—Greg Marshall.
Executive Director, Office of Program Accountability and Risk Management.—Gary Carter.

OFFICE OF POLICY

Phone (202) 282–9708

Assistant Secretary.—David Heyman.
Principal Deputy Assistant Secretary.—Leonard P. Joseph.
Chief of Staff.—Holly Canevari.
Deputy Chief of Staff.—Gail Kaufman.
Chemical, Biological, Radiological and Nuclear Office.—Deputy Assistant Secretary, Gerald Epstein.
Counterterrorism Policy.—Deputy Assistant Secretary, Thomas Warrick.
Homeland Security Advisory Council.—Executive Director, Erin O'Connor.
Immigration and Border Security.—Deputy Assistant Secretary, Molly Groom (acting).
Immigration and Border Security.—Senior Advisor for Immigration Policy, Esther Olavarria.
Immigration Statistics.—Director, Nancy Rytina.
International Affairs.—Deputy Assistant Secretary, Mark Koumans.
Office for State and Local Law Enforcement.—Vacant.
Office of International Affairs.—Assistant Secretary, and Chief Diplomatic Officer, Alan Bersin.
Policy Integration and Implementation.—Assistant Secretary, Patricia Cogswell (acting).
Private Sector Office.—Assistant Secretary, Michael Stroud.
Screening Coordination.—Deputy Assistant Secretary, Kelli Walther (acting).
Strategy, Planning, Analysis, and Risk.—Assistant Secretary, Alan Cohn.
Strategy, Planning, and Long Term Assessment.—Deputy Assistant Secretary, Ronald Salazar.
Strategy, Risk and Decision Analysis.—Deputy Assistant Secretary, Caryl Brzymialkiewicz.
Transborder Policy.—Deputy Assistant Secretary, Ellen McClain.

FEDERAL EMERGENCY MANAGEMENT AGENCY (FEMA) DIRECTORATE

500 C Street, SW., 20472, phone (202) 646–2500

Administrator.—W. Craig Fugate.
Deputy Administrator.—Richard Serino.
Chief of Staff.—Michael Coen (acting).
Director, Office of:
Disability Integration and Coordination.—Marcie Roth.
Executive Secretariat.—Alyson Vert.
Equal Rights.—Pauline Campbell.
External Affairs.—Joshua C. Batkin.
National Advisory Council.—Charlotte Hyams Porter.
Regional Operations.—Elizabeth Edge.
Chief Financial Officer.—Edward H. Johnson.
Chief Counsel.—Brad Kieserman.
Senior Law Enforcement Advisor.—Roberto L. Hylton.
Associate Administrator, Office of Policy and Program Analysis.—David J. Kaufman.
Director, DHS Center for Faith-Based and Neighborhood Partnerships.—David L. Myers.
Deputy Administrator, Protection and National Preparedness.—Timothy W. Manning.
Assistant Deputy Administrator, National Preparedness.—Corey Gruber.
Assistant Administrators:
Grant Programs.—Brian Kamoie.
National Continuity Programs.—Damon Penn.
Director, Office of National Capital Region Coordination.—Steward D. Beckham.
Administrator, U.S. Fire Administration.—Ernest Mitchell, Jr.
Associate Administrator, Mission Support Bureau.—David Robinson.
Deputy Associate Administrator, Mission Support Bureau.—Carla Gammon.
Chief:
Administrative Officer, Mission Support Bureau.—Dwight Williams (acting).
Component Human Capital Officer, Mission Support Bureau.—Corey J. Coleman.
Information Officer, Mission Support Bureau.—Rob C. Thomas II.
Procurement Officer, Mission Support Bureau.—Francis Spaminato.
Security Officer, Mission Support Bureau.—Michael Apodaca.
Associate Administrator, Response and Recovery.—Joseph L. Nimmich.
Deputy Associate Administrator, Response and Recovery.—Elizabeth A. Zimmerman.
Assistant Administrators:
Logistics.—Eric Smith.
Recovery.—Deborah Ingram.
Response.—Robert J. Fenton, Jr.
Director, Office of Federal Coordinating Officer Operations.—Jeff Dorko.
Administrator, Federal Insurance and Mitigation Administration.—David L. Miller.
Deputy Administrator for Insurance, Federal Insurance and Mitigation Administration.—Edward L. Connor.
Deputy Administrator for Mitigation, Federal Insurance and Mitigation Administration.—Roy E. Wright.

OFFICE OF OPERATIONS COORDINATION AND PLANNING

phone (202) 282–9580

Director.—Richard Chávez.
Deputy Director.—Frank DiFalco.
Chief of Staff.—Mary Kruger.

DOMESTIC NUCLEAR DETECTION OFFICE

phone (202) 254–7300

Director.—Huban A. Gowadia, Ph.D.
Deputy Director.—*Vacant.*
Chief of Staff.—Patrick Philbin.
Assistant Director, Office of:
Architecture and Plans.—John Zabko.
National Technical Nuclear Forensics Center.—William Daitch.
Operations Support.—Paul Ryan.
Product Acquisition and Deployment.—Stephen Karoly (acting).

Red Team/Net Assessments.—Kevin McCarthy.
Systems Engineering and Evaluation.—Julian Hill.
Transformational Research and Development.—Joel Rynes.

TRANSPORTATION SECURITY ADMINISTRATION (TSA)

601 South 12th Street, Arlington, VA 20598–6001

Administrator/Assistant Secretary.—John S. Pistole.
Deputy Administrator.—John W. Halinski.
Chief of Staff.—Thomas C. McDaniels, Jr.

UNITED STATES CUSTOMS AND BORDER PROTECTION (CBP)

1300 Pennsylvania Avenue, NW., 20229

Commissioner.—Thomas S. Winkowski (acting), (202) 344–1010/344–2001.
Deputy Commissioner.—Kevin McAleenan (acting), 344–1010/2001.
Chief of Staff.—Kimberly O'Connor, 344–1080/1001.
Deputy Chief of Staff.—Stephen Schorr, 344–2568.
Chief Counsel.—Scott Falk (acting), 344–2990.
Assistant Commissioner, Office of:
Administration.—Eugene H. Schied, 344–2300.
Air and Marine.—Randolph Alles, 344–3950.
Congressional Affairs.—Michael Yeager, 344–1760.
Field Operations.—David Murphy (acting), 344–1620.
Human Resources Management.—Katherine Coffman, 863–6100.
Information and Technology.—Charles R. Armstrong, 344–1680.
Intelligence and Operations Coordination.—Troy Miller (acting), 344–1150.
Internal Affairs.—James F. Tomsheck, 344–1800.
International Affairs and Trade Relations.—Charles Stallworth, 344–3000.
International Trade.—Allen Gina, 863–6000.
Public Affairs.—Melanie Roe, 344–1700.
Technology Innovation and Acquisition.—Mark Borkowski, 344–2450.
Training and Development.—Christopher Hall, 344–1130.
Chief, Office of Border Patrol.—Michael Fisher, 344–2050.
Executive Director, Office of:
Diversity and Civil Rights.—Franklin C. Jones, 344–1610.
Policy and Planning.—Lewis Roach (acting), 344–2700.
Director, State, Local and Tribal Governments.—Bonnie Arellano (acting), 344–1619.
Director, Executive Secretariat.—Joseph E. Tezak, 344–1040.
Senior Advisor Trade Relations.—Maria Luisa Boyce, 325–4290.

UNITED STATES IMMIGRATION AND CUSTOMS ENFORCEMENT (ICE)

Director.—John Morton (202) 732–3000.
Chief of Staff.—Paul Rosen, 732–3000.
Executive Secretariat.—Cynthia O'Connor, 732–5580.
Deputy Director.—Daniel Ragsdale, 732–3000.
Detention Policy and Planning.—Kevin Landy, 732–5500.
Professional Responsibility.—Timothy Moynihan, 732–8300.
Principal Legal Advisor.—Peter S. Vincent, 732–5000.
Congressional Relations.—Elliot Williams, 732–6171.
Public Affairs.—Brian P. Hale, 732–4250.
State, Local and Tribal Coordination.—Harold Hurtt, 732–5060.
Executive Associate Director, Enforcement and Removal Operations.—Thomas Homan, 732–5545.
Custody Management.—Tae D. Johnson, 732–3110.
Law Enforcement Systems and Analysis.—Marc Rapp, 732–3915.
Field Operations.—Philip T. Miller, 732–3941.
ICE Health Service Corps.—Dr. John Krohmer, 732–3047.
Operational Support.—William C. Randolph, 732–3090.
Repatriation.—John P. Longshore (acting), 732–4511.
Secure Communities and Enforcement.—Matthew Albence, 732–5513.
Executive Associate Director, Homeland Security Investigations.—James Dinkins, 732–5100.

Deputy Executive Associate Director, Homeland Security Investigations.—Peter Edge, 732–5100.
Assistant Director of:
Domestic Operations.—Leigh H. Winchell, 732–5116.
Intelligence.—Frank Reeder (acting), 732–3624.
International Affairs.—John Connolly, 732–5808.
Law Enforcement Information Sharing Initiative.—Steven Cooper, 732–3708.
Mission Support.—Staci Barrera, 732–5702.
National Intellectual Property Rights Coordination Center.—Lev Kubiak (703) 603–3900.
National Security.—John Woods (703) 287–6853.
Programs.—Traci Lembke, 732–5852.
Executive Associate Director, Management and Administration.—Radha Sekar (acting), 732–3000.
Acquisition Management.—Cheri Tyner (acting), 732–2398.
Diversity Officer and Civil Rights.—Scott Lanum, 732–0190.
Chief Financial Officer.—Radha Sekar, 732–3077.
Chief Information Officer.—Thomas P. Michelli, 732–2000.
Freedom of Information Act.—Catrina Pavlik Keenan, 732–0300.
Human Capital Officer.—Kimberlyn J. Bauhs, 732–7770.
National Firearms and Tactical Training Unit.—Humberto Medina, 732–3937.
Office of Policy.—Tracey Bardorf, 732–3009.
Privacy Officer.—Lyn Rahilly, 732–3301.
Training and Development.—Donato W. Coyer (acting), 732–7800.

FEDERAL LAW ENFORCEMENT TRAINING CENTER

1131 Chapel Crossing Road, Glynco, GA 31524

Director.—Connie L. Patrick (912) 267–2070.
Deputy Director.—Ken Keene, 267–2680.
Chief of Staff.—Woody Wright (acting), 267–2070.
Assistant Director for—
Administration.—Marcus Hill, 267–2231.
Washington Operations.—Woody Wright (acting), (202) 233–0260.
Assistant Director/Chief Financial Officer.—Don Lewis, 267–2999.
Assistant Director/Innovation and Technology.—Sandy Peavy, 267–2014.
Assistant Director for—
Field Training.—Woody Wright (575) 746–5712.
Glynco Training.—Dominick Braccio, 267–3373.
Centralized Training Management.—Cindy Atwood, 267–2451.
Chief for—
Office of Organizational Health.—Brenda Lloyd, 267–2280.
Protocol and Communications Office.—Dana O'Quinn, 267–2447.
Chief Counsel.—Dave Brunjes, 267–2441.

UNITED STATES CITIZENSHIP AND IMMIGRATION SERVICES

20 Massachusetts Avenue, NW., Washington, DC 20529, phone (202) 272–1000

Director.—Alejandro Mayorkas.
Deputy Director.—Lori Scialabba.
Chief of Staff.—Adam Hunter (acting).
Chief Information Officer.—Mark Schwartz.
Associate Director for—
Fraud Detection and National Security Directorate.—Sarah Kendall.
Refugee, Asylum and International Operations Directorate.—Joseph Langlois.
Service Center Operations Directorate.—Donald Neufeld.
Chief, Office of:
Administration.—Renee Downs (acting).
Administrative Appeals.—Ron Rosenberg (acting).
Chief Counsel.—Stephen Legomsky.
Chief Financial Officer.—Joseph Moore.
Citizenship.—Laura Patching (acting).
Communications.—Angie Alfonso-Royals (acting).
Legislative Affairs.—James McCament.
Policy and Strategy.—Denise Vanison.

UNITED STATES COAST GUARD

2100 Second Street, SW., 20593, phone (202) 372–4400

Commandant.—ADM Robert J. Papp, Jr.
Vice Commandant.—VADM John P. Currier.
Deputy Commandant for—
Mission Support.—VADM Manson Brown.
Operations.—VADM Peter Neffenger.
Chief Administrative Law Judge.—Hon. Walter Brudzinski.
Judge Advocate General/Chief Counsel.—RADM Fred Kenney.
Deputy Judge Advocate General/Deputy Chief Counsel.—Calvin Lederer.
Director of Governmental and Public Affairs.—RDML Steven Poulin.
Senior Military Advisor to the Secretary of Homeland Security.—RDML June Ryan.

UNITED STATES SECRET SERVICE

245 Murray Drive, SW., Building 410, 20223

Director.—Julia A. Pierson.
Deputy Director.—A.T. Smith.
Deputy Assistant Director, Congressional Affairs Program.—Faron Paramore (202) 406–5676, fax 406–5740.

INDEPENDENT AGENCIES, COMMISSIONS, BOARDS

ADVISORY COUNCIL ON HISTORIC PRESERVATION

1100 Pennsylvania Avenue, NW., Suite 803, 20004

phone (202) 606–8503, http://www.achp.gov

[Created by Public Law 89–665, as amended]

Chairman.—Milford Wayne Donaldson, Sacramento, California.
Vice Chairman.—Clement A. Price, Newark, New Jersey.
Expert Members:
Lynne Sebastian, Rio Rancho, New Mexico.
Terry Guen-Murray, Chicago, Illinois.
Dorothy Lippert, Washington, District of Columbia.
Horace H. Foxall, Jr., Seattle, Washington.
Citizen Members:
Bradford J. White, Evanston, Illinois.
Teresa Isabel Leger, Santa Fe, New Mexico.
Native American Member.—John L. Berrey, Quapaw, Oklahoma.
Governor.—Vacant.
Mayor.—Hon. Michael B. Coleman, Columbus, Ohio.
Architect of the Capitol.—Hon. Stephen T. Ayers, FAIA.
Secretary, Department of:
Agriculture.—Hon. Thomas J. Vilsack.
Commerce.—Rebecca M. Blank (acting).
Defense.—Hon. Charles T. ''Chuck'' Hagel.
Education.—Hon. Arne Duncan.
Housing and Urban Development.—Hon. Shaun Donovan.
Interior.—Hon. Kenneth L. Salazar.
Transportation.—Hon. Ray LaHood.
Veterans' Affairs.—Hon. Eric K. Shinseki.
Administrator of General Services Administration.—Daniel M. Tangherlini (acting).
National Conference of State Historic Preservation Officer.—Elizabeth A. Hughes, Crownsville, Maryland.
National Trust for Historic Preservation.—Carolyn Brody, Chairman, Washington, DC.
Executive Director.—John M. Fowler.
Directors for:
Office of Administration.—Ralston Cox.
Office of Communications, Education, and Outreach.—Susan A. Glimcher.
Office of Federal Agency Programs.—Reid J. Nelson.
Office of Native American Affairs.—Valerie Hauser.
Office of Preservation Initiatives.—Ronald D. Anzalone.

AMERICAN BATTLE MONUMENTS COMMISSION

Courthouse Plaza II, Suite 500, 2300 Clarendon Boulevard, Arlington, VA 22201–3367

phone (703) 696–6902

[Created by Public Law 105–225]

Chairman.—Merrill A. McPeak appointed as of 6/3/11.
Commissioners:
Hon. Barbaralee Diamonstein-Spielvogel.
Hon. Darrell Dorgan.
Hon. John Estrada.
Hon. Rolland Kidder.
Hon. Richard Klass.
Hon. Constance Morella.
Hon. Maura Sullivan.
Secretary.—Joseph Maxwell Cleland.
Deputy Secretary.—Raymond J. Wollman.

Chief of Staff.—Mike Conley.
CIO.—Monique Ceruti.
Director for—
Finance.—Christine Fant.
Human Resources and Administration.—Frank Manies.
Public Affairs.—Tim Nosal.
U.S. Memorials.—Thomas R. Sole.
(Note: Public law changed to 105–225, August 1998; H.R. 1085).

AMERICAN NATIONAL RED CROSS

National Headquarters, 430 17th Street, 20006, phone (202) 303–5000

Government Relations, phone (202) 303–4371, fax 638–3960

HONORARY OFFICERS

Honorary Chair.—Barack H. Obama, President of the United States.

CORPORATE OFFICERS

Chairman.—Bonnie McElveen-Hunter.
President/CEO.—Gail J. McGovern.
Chief Audit Executive.—Dale P. Bateman.
General Counsel/Chief International Officer.—David Meltzer.
Chief Financial Officer.—Brian Rhoa.

BOARD OF GOVERNORS

Cesar A. Aristeiguieta
Paula E. Boggs
Richard K. Davis
Allan I. Goldberg
James W. Keyes
Bonnie McElveen-Hunter
Gail J. McGovern
Judith A. McGrath
Suzanne Nora Johnson
Richard C. Patton
Laurence E. Paul
Joseph B. Pereles
Josue Robles, Jr.
Melanie R. Sabelhaus
H. Marshall Schwarz
Steven H. Wunning

EXECUTIVE LEADERSHIP

Chief Development Officer.—Neal Litvack.
Chief Diversity Officer.—Floyd Pitts.
Chief Human Resources Officer.—Melissa Hurst.
Chief Information Officer.—John Crary.
Chief Marketing Officer.—Peggy Dyer.
Chief Public Affairs Officer.—Suzanne DeFrancis.
Corporate Ombudsman.—Kevin Jessar.
President Biomedical Services.—Shaun P. Gilmore.
President Humanitarian Services.—Gerald DeFrancisco.
President Preparedness and Health and Safety Services.—Jack McMaster.

GOVERNMENTAL RELATIONS

Senior Vice President for Government Relations.—Cherae L. Bishop.
Senior Policy Advisor.—Dawn P. Latham.
Federal Relations Director.—Karen Quarles.
State Relations Manager.—Christy Foertsch.
Legislative Specialists: Jan Michael DeJesus, Jacqui Godfrey, Marvin Steele.

APPALACHIAN REGIONAL COMMISSION

1666 Connecticut Avenue, NW., 20009, phone (202) 884–7660, fax 884–7693

Federal Co-Chair.—Earl F. Gohl.
Alternate Federal Co-Chair.—Vacant.
States' Washington Representative.—Cameron Whitman.
Executive Director.—Thomas M. Hunter.
Chief of Staff.—Guy Land.

ARMED FORCES RETIREMENT HOME

3700 North Capitol Street, NW., Box 1303, Washington, DC 20011–8400
phone (202) 541–7532, fax 541–7506

Chief Operating Officer.—Steven G. McManus.
Chief Information Officer.—Maurice Swinton.

ARMED FORCES RETIREMENT HOME—WASHINGTON

phone (202) 541–7536, fax 541–7588 or 7615

Administrator.—David Watkins.

ARMED FORCES RETIREMENT HOME—GULFPORT

1800 Beach Drive, Gulfport, MS 39507
phone (202) 897–4408, fax 897–4488

Administrator.—Charles Dickerson.

BOARD OF GOVERNORS OF THE FEDERAL RESERVE SYSTEM

Constitution Avenue and 20th Street, NW., 20551, phone (202) 452–3000

Chair.—Janet L. Yellen.
Members: Jerome H. Powell, Sarah Bloom Raskin, Jeremy C. Stein, Daniel K. Tarullo.
Assistant to the Board and Division Director.—Michelle A. Smith.
Assistants to the Board: Rosanna Pianalto Cameron, Linda L. Robertson, David W. Skidmore.
Special Adviser to the Board.—Jon Faust.
Special Assistants to the Board: Lucretia M. Boyer, Brian J. Gross.
Senior Adviser.—Winthrop P. Hambley.
Adviser.—Adrienne D. Hurt.

DIVISION OF BANKING SUPERVISION AND REGULATION

Director.—Michael S. Gibson.
Deputy Directors: Maryann F. Hunter, Mark E. Van Der Weide.
Senior Associate Directors: Barbara J. Bouchard, Timothy P. Clark, Jack P. Jennings, Arthur W. Lindo, Peter J. Purcell, William G. Spaniel, Todd Vermilyea.
Associate Directors: Kevin M. Bertsch, Nida Davis, Ann E. Misback, Richard A. Naylor II, Michael D. Solomon.
Deputy Associate Director: Anna Lee Hewko, Steven P. Merriett, Lisa H. Ryu, Michael J. Sexton.
Assistant Directors: Mary L. Aiken, Robert T. Ashman, Adrienne T. Haden, Michael J. Hsu, Michael J. Kraemer, David K. Lynch, Robert T. Maahs, T. Kirk Odegard, Nancy J. Perkins, Tameika Pope, Laurie Priest, Richard C. Watkins, Suzanne L. Williams, Sarkis D. Yoghourtdjian.
Senior Advisers: Norah M. Barger, Gerald A Edwards, David S. Jones.
Advisers: Molly E. Mahar, William F. Treacy.

DIVISION OF CONSUMER AND COMMUNITY AFFAIRS

Director.—Sandra F. Braunstein.

Deputy Director.—Tonda Price.
Senior Associate Directors: Anna Alvarez Boyd, Suzanne G. Killian.
Associate Directors: Allen J. Fishbein, James A. Michaels.
Deputy Associate Director.—Joseph Firschein.
Assistant Directors: David E. Buchholz, Carol A. Evans, Phyllis L. Harwell, Marisa A. Reid.

DIVISION OF FEDERAL RESERVE BANK OPERATIONS AND PAYMENT SYSTEMS

Director.—Louise L. Roseman.
Deputy Director.—Jeffrey C. Marquardt.
Senior Associate Directors: Susan V. Foley, Jeff J. Stehm.
Associate Directors: Kenneth D. Buckley, Gregory L. Evans, Dorothy B. LaChapelle, Michael J. Lambert.
Deputy Associate Directors: Lisa K. Hoskins, Jennifer A. Lucier, Stuart E. Sperry.
Assistant Directors: Timothy W. Maas, Jeffrey Douglas Walker, David Mills, Lorelei Pagano, Shaun Ferrari, Marybeth Traverso, Lawrence Mize.
Senior Adviser.—Paul W. Bettge.
Adviser.—Michael J. Stan.

DIVISION OF INFORMATION TECHNOLOGY

Director.—Sharon L. Mowry.
Deputy Directors: Geary L. Cunningham, Wayne A. Edmondson.
Associate Directors: Lisa M. Bell, Raymond Romero, Kofi A. Sapong.
Deputy Associate Directors: William K. Dennison, Glenn S. Eskow, Marietta Murphy, Kassandra A. Quimby, Sheryl L. Warren, Rajasekhar R. Yelisetty.
Assistant Directors: Theresa C. Palya, Virginia M. Wall, Edgar Wang, Charles B. Young.
Advisers: Tillena G. Clark, Can Xuan Nguyen.

DIVISION OF INTERNATIONAL FINANCE

Director.—Steve B. Kamin.
Deputy Directors: Thomas A. Connors, Michael P. Leahy.
Senior Associate Director.—Trevor A. Reeve.
Associate Directors: Christopher J. Erceg.
Deputy Associate Directors: David H. Bowman, Charles P. Thomas, Beth Anne Wilson.
Assistant Directors: Shaghil Ahmed, Joseph W. Gruber.
Senior Advisers: Mark S. Carey, Sally M. Davies, Jane Haltmaier, John H. Rogers.
Adviser.—Brian M. Doyle.

DIVISION OF MONETARY AFFAIRS

Director.—William B. English.
Deputy Directors: James Clouse, Deborah Danker, Stephen A. Meyer, William R. Nelson, Janice Shack-Marquez.
Senior Associate Director: Seth B. Carpenter.
Associate Directors: Fabio M. Natalucci, Gretchen C. Weinbach, Egon Zakrajsek.
Deputy Associate Directors: William F. Bassett, Margaret DeBoer, Jane E. Ihrig, J. David Lopez-Salido.
Assistant Directors: Matthew M. Luecke, Edward M. Nelson, Min Wei.
Senior Advisers: Ellen Meade, Joyce K. Zickler.
Adviser.—Mary T. Hoffman.

DIVISION OF RESEARCH AND STATISTICS

Director.—David Wilcox.
Deputy Directors: Matthew J. Eichner, Janice Shack-Marquez, William L. Wascher III.
Associate Directors: Daniel M. Covitz, Michael S. Cringoli, Eric M. Engen, Heinrich T. Laubach, David E. Lebow, Michael G. Palumbo, S. Wayne Passmore.
Deputy Associate Directors: Sean D. Campbell, Jeffrey C. Campione, Joshua H. Gallin, Diana Hancock.

Assistant Directors: Arthur Kennickell, Elizabeth K. Kiser, Steven A. Sharpe, John J. Stevens, Stacey M. Tevlin.
Senior Advisers: Glenn B. Canner, Michael Kiley.
Adviser.—Karen M. Pence, Jeremy Rudd.

INSPECTOR GENERAL

Inspector General.—Mark Bialek.
Deputy Inspector General.—J. Anthony Ogden.
Associate Inspector Generals: Jacqueline M. Becker, Anthony J. Castaldo, Elise M. Ennis, Andrew Patchan, Jr., Harvey Witherspoon.

LEGAL DIVISION

General Counsel.—Scott G. Alvarez.
Deputy General Counsels: Richard M. Ashton, Kathleen M. O'Day.
Associate General Counsels: Stephanie Martin, Laurie S. Schaffer, Katherine H. Wheatley.
Assistant General Counsels: Jean C. Anderson, Alison M. Thro, Cary K. Williams.

MANAGEMENT DIVISION

Director.—Michell C. Clark.
Deputy Directors: David J. Capp, David J. Harmon.
Associate Directors: Tara Tinsley Pelitere, Marie S. Savoy.
Assistant Directors: Keith F. Bates, Curtis Eldridge, Reginald V. Roach, Theresa A. Trimble.
Special Advisers: Todd A. Glissman, Carol A. Sanders, Christopher J. Suma.

OFFICE OF THE SECRETARY

Secretary.—Robert deV. Frierson.
Deputy Secretary.—Margaret M. Shanks.
Associate Secretary.—Michael J. Lewandowski.

OFFICE OF FINANCIAL STABILITY POLICY AND RESEARCH

Director.—J. Nellie Liang.
Deputy Director.—Andreas W. Lehnert.
Associate Director.—David Bowman, Michael T. Kiley.
Adviser.—David Aikman.

OFFICE OF THE CHIEF OPERATING OFFICER

Chief Operating Officer.—Donald V. Hammond.
ODI Program Director.—Sheila Clark.

BROADCASTING BOARD OF GOVERNORS

330 Independence Avenue, SW., Suite 3360, 20237

phone (202) 203–4545, fax 203–4568

The Broadcasting Board of Governors oversees the operation of the IBB and provides yearly funding grants approved by Congress to three non-profit grantee corporations, Radio Free Europe/Radio Liberty, Radio Free Asia, and the Middle East Broadcasting Networks.

Chairman.—Vacant.

INTERNATIONAL BROADCASTING BUREAU

[Created by Public Law 103–236]

The International Broadcasting Bureau (IBB) is composed of the Voice of America, and Radio and TV Marti.

International Broadcasting Bureau.—Richard M. Lobo, (202) 203–4515, fax 203–4587.
Director of:
Cuba Broadcasting.—Carlos Garcia-Perez (305) 437–7012, fax 437–7016.
Voice of America.—David B. Ensor (202) 203–4500, fax 203–4513.
President, Radio Free Asia.—Libby Liu (202) 530–4900, fax 530–7795.
President, Radio Free Europe.—Kevin Klose (202) 457–6900, fax 457–6933.
President, Middle East Broadcasting Networks.—Brian Conniff (703) 852–9000, fax 991–1250.

GOVERNORS

Victor Ashe
Michael Lynton
Susan McCue
Michael Meehan
Dennis Mulhaupt
John F. Kerry (ex officio)

STAFF

Deputy Director.—Jeffrey Trimble.
Director of Strategic Planning.—Bruce Sherman.
Chief Financial Officer.—Vacant.
Deputy General Counsel.—Paul Kollmer-Dorsey.
Director Board Operations.—Hoang-Oanh Tran.

CENTRAL INTELLIGENCE AGENCY

phone (703) 482–1100

Director.—John O. Brennan.
Deputy Director.—Michael J. Morell.
Associate Deputy Director.—V. Sue Bromley.
General Counsel.—Stephen W. Preston.
Director of:
Intelligence.—Fran Moore.
Public Affairs.—Cynthia L. ''Didi'' Rapp.
Science and Technology.—Glenn Gaffney.
Support.—Sue Gordon.
Congressional Affairs.—Tim Ireland (acting).

COMMISSION OF FINE ARTS

National Building Museum, 401 F Street, NW., Suite 312, 20001–2728

phone (202) 504–2200, fax 504–2195, http://www.cfa.gov

Commissioners:
Earl A. Powell III, Washington, DC, Chair.
Elizabeth Plater-Zyberk, Miami, FL, Vice Chair.
Edwin Schlossberg, New York, NY.
Teresita Fernandez, Brooklyn, NY.
Philip Freelon, FAIA, Durham, NC.
Beth Meyer, Charlottesville, VA.
Alex Krieger, Boston, MA.

Secretary.—Thomas Luebke, FAIA.
Assistant Secretary.—Frederick J. Lindstrom.

BOARD OF ARCHITECTURAL CONSULTANTS FOR THE OLD GEORGETOWN ACT

David Cox, FAIA, Chair.
Anne Lewis, FAIA.
Stephen Muse, FAIA.

COMMITTEE FOR PURCHASE FROM PEOPLE WHO ARE BLIND OR SEVERELY DISABLED

1421 Jefferson Davis Highway, Jefferson Plaza 2, Suite 10800

Arlington, VA 22202–3259, phone (703) 603–7740, fax 603–0655

Chairperson.—J. Anthony ''Tony'' Poleo.
Vice Chairperson.—James M. Kesteloot.
Executive Director.—Tina Ballard.
Members:
Perry Edward ''Ed'' Anthony, Department of Education.
Jan R. Frye, Department of Veterans Affairs.
Admiral Mark F. Heinrich, Department of the Navy.
Paul Laird, Department of Justice.
Kathleen Martinez, Department of Labor.
J. Anthony ''Tony'' Poleo, Department of Defense.
William Sisk, General Services Administration.
Lisa M. Wilusz, Department of Agriculture.
James M. Kesteloot, Private Citizen (Obstacles to Employment of People Who Are Blind).
Anil Lewis, Private Citizen (Nonprofit Agency Employees Who Are Blind).
Karen J. McCulloh, Private Citizen (Nonprofit Agency Employees with Other Severe Disabilities).
Robert T. Kelly, Jr., Private Citizen (Obstacles to Employment of People with Other Severe Disabilities).
Vacant, Department of Commerce.
Vacant, Department of the Army.
Vacant, Department of the Air Force.

COMMODITY FUTURES TRADING COMMISSION

Three Lafayette Centre, 1155 21st Street, NW., 20581, phone (202) 418–5000

fax 418–5521, http://www.cftc.gov

Chairman.—Gary Gensler, 418–5150.
Senior Counsel to the Chairman.—Eric Juzenas, 418–5050.
Commissioners:
Jill Sommers, 418–5030.
Bart Chilton, 418–5060.
Scott O'Malia, 418–5870.
Mark Wetjen, 418–5010.
Executive Director.—Tony Thompson, 418–5160.
General Counsel.—Vacant, 418–5120.
Chief Economist.—Scott Mixon (acting), 418–5000.
Director, Division of:
Clearing and Intermediary Oversight.—Ananda Radhakrishnan, 418–5430.
Enforcement.—David Meister, 418–5000.
Market Oversight.—Rick Shilts, 418–5260.
Director, Office of:
Diversity and Inclusion.—Lorena Carrasco, 418–5400.
Inspector General.—A. Roy Lavik, 418–5110.
International Affairs.—Jacqueline H. Mesa, 418–5645.
Legislative Affairs.—John Riley, 418–5075.
Secretary.—Melissa Jurgens, 418–5100.

REGIONAL OFFICES

Chicago: 525 West Monroe Street, Suite 1100, Chicago, IL 60601 (312) 596–0700, fax 596–0716.
Kansas City: 4900 Main Street, Suite 500, Kansas City, MO 64112 (816) 960–7700, fax 960–7750.
New York: 140 Broadway, Nineteenth floor, New York, NY 10005 (646) 746–9700, fax 746–9938.

CONSUMER PRODUCT SAFETY COMMISSION

4330 East West Highway, Bethesda, MD 20814, phone (301) 504–7923

fax 504–0124, http://www.cpsc.gov

[Created by Public Law 92–573]

Chairperson.—Inez Tenenbaum, 504–7900.
Commissioners:
Robert ''Bob'' Adler, 504–7731.
Vacant, 504–7902.
Nancy Nord, 504–7901.
Vacant, 504–7780.
Executive Director.—Kenneth R. Hinson, 504–7625.
Deputy Executive Director.—Robert J. Howell, 504–7621.
Director, Office of:
The Secretary.—Todd A. Stevenson, 504–7923.
Congressional Relations.—Christopher Day, 504–7853.
General Counsel.—Stephanie Tsacoumis, 504–7612.

CORPORATION FOR NATIONAL AND COMMUNITY SERVICE

1201 New York Avenue, NW., 20525, phone (202) 606–5000
http://www.cns.gov

[Executive Order 11603, June 30, 1971; codified in 42 U.S.C., section 4951]

Chief Executive Officer.—Wendy Spencer.
Chief of Staff.—Asim Mishra.
Chief Financial Officer.—David Rebich, 606–6694.
Inspector General.—Deborah Jeffrey.
Director of:
AmeriCorps/National Civilian Community Corps.—Kate Raftery, 606–6706.
AmeriCorps/State and National.—Bill Basl, 606–6790.
AmeriCorps/VISTA.—Mary Strasser, 606–6943.
Senior Corps.—Erwin Tan, 606–3237.
Office of Government Relations.—Kim Allman (acting), 606–6707.
General Counsel.—Valerie Green, 606–6677.

DEFENSE NUCLEAR FACILITIES SAFETY BOARD

625 Indiana Avenue, NW., Suite 700, 20004, phone (202) 694–7000

fax 208–6518, http://www.dnfsb.gov

Chairman.—Peter S. Winokur.
Vice Chairman.—Jessie Hill-Roberson.
Members: Joseph F. Bader, John E. Mansfield, Sean Sullivan.
General Counsel.—Dave Jonas.
General Manager.—Marcy Atwood.
Technical Director.—Timothy J. Dwyer.

DELAWARE RIVER BASIN COMMISSION

25 State Police Drive, P.O. Box 7360, West Trenton, NJ 08628–0360

phone (609) 883–9500, fax 883–9522, http://www.drbc.net

[Created by Public Law 87–328]

FEDERAL REPRESENTATIVES

Federal Commissioner.—COL Kent D. Savre, Commander, U.S. Army Corps of Engineers, North Atlantic Division (718) 765–7000.

First Alternate.—LTC Chris Becking, District Engineer, U.S. Army Corps of Engineers, Philadelphia (215) 656–6501.

Second Alternate.—David J. Leach, Director of Programs, U.S. Army Corps of Engineers, North Atlantic Division (718) 765–7129.

Third Alternate.—Erik J. Rourke, Strategic Planner, U.S. Army Corps of Engineers, Philadelphia (215) 656–6616.

STAFF

Executive Director.—Carol R. Collier, ext. 200.

Deputy Executive Director.—Robert Tudor, ext. 208.

Commission Secretary/Assistant General Counsel.—Pamela M. Bush, Esq., ext. 203.

Communications Manager.—Clarke Rupert, ext. 260.

DELAWARE REPRESENTATIVES

State Commissioner.—Jack A. Markell, Governor (302) 577–3210.

First Alternate.—Collin P. O'Mara, Secretary, Delaware Department of Natural Resources and Environmental Control (DNREC), (302) 739–9000.

Second Alternate.—Kathleen M. Stiller, Director, Division of Water Resources (DNREC), (302) 739–9949.

NEW JERSEY REPRESENTATIVES

State Commissioner.—Chris Christie, Governor (609) 292–6000.

First Alternate.—Bob Martin, Commissioner, New Jersey Department of Environmental Protection (NJDEP), (609) 292–2885.

Second Alternate.—Michele N. Siekerka, Esq., Assistant Commissioner, Water Resource Management, (NJDEP), (609) 292–4543.

Third Alternate.—Fred Sickels, Assistant Director, Water Supply Permitting Element (NJDEP), (609) 292–2957.

Fourth Alternate.—Dr. Karl W. Muessig, State Geologist, New Jersey Geological Survey (609) 292–1185.

NEW YORK REPRESENTATIVES

State Commissioner.—Andrew M. Cuomo, Governor (518) 474–8390.

First Alternate.—Joe Martens, Commissioner, New York State Department of Environmental Conservation (NYSDEC), (518) 402–8545.

Second Alternate.—Mark Klotz, P.E., Director, Division of Water (NYSDEC), (518) 402–8233.

Third Alternate.—Tom Cullen, Assistant Director, Division of Water (NYSDEC), (518) 402–8233.

Fourth Alternate.—Angus Eaton, Director, Bureau of Water Resource Management (NYSDEC), (518) 402–8132.

PENNSYLVANIA REPRESENTATIVES

State Commissioner.—Thomas W. Corbett, Governor (717) 787–2500.

First Alternate.—Michael L. Krancer, Secretary, Pennsylvania Department of Environmental Protection (PADEP), (717) 787–2814.

Second Alternate.—Kelly J. Heffner, Deputy Secretary for Water Management, (PADEP), (717) 783–4693.

Third Alternate.—Andrew Zemba, Director of Interstate Waters (PADEP), (717) 772–5633.

Fourth Alternate.—Charles W. Kirkwood (570) 421–6513.

Fifth Alternate.—Randal Adams, Executive Assistant (PADEP), (717) 783–7404.

ENVIRONMENTAL PROTECTION AGENCY

1200 Pennsylvania Avenue, NW., 20460, phone (202) 564–4700, http://www.epa.gov

Administrator.—Gina McCarthy

Deputy Administrator.—Bob Perciasepa, 564–4711.

Chief of Staff.—Gwendolyn Keyes-Fleming, 564–6999.

Deputy Chief of Staff.—John Reeder, 564–4715.

Agriculture Counsel.—Sarah Bittleman, 564–7719.

White House Liaison.—Luseni Pieh, 564–7960.

Environmental Appeals Board: Annette Duncan, Lesley Fraser, Catherine McCabe, 233–0122.

Associate Administrator for—

Congressional and Intergovernmental Relations.—Laura Vaught, 564–5200.

Homeland Security.—Juan Reyes (acting), 564–6978.

Policy, Economics, and Innovation.—Michael Goo, 564–4332.

Public Affairs.—Tom Reynolds, 564–8368.

Director, Office of:

Children's Health Protection.—Jackie Mosby, 564–2188.

Civil Rights.—Vicki Simons (acting), 564–7272.

Cooperative Environmental Management.—Vacant, 233–0090.

Executive Secretariat.—Eric Wachter, 564–7311.

Executive Services.—Diane Bazzle, 564–0444.

Science Advisory Board.—Christopher Zarba, 343–9999.

Small and Disadvantaged Business Utilization.—Jeanette L. Brown, 564–4100.

Director of Management, Office of Administrative Law Judges.—Susan Biro, 564–6255.

ADMINISTRATION AND RESOURCES MANAGEMENT

Assistant Administrator.—Craig Hooks, 564–4600.

Deputy Assistant Administrator.—Nancy Gelb (acting), 564–4600.

AIR AND RADIATION

Assistant Administrator.—Janet McCabe (acting), 564–7404.

Principle Deputy Assistant Administrator.—Janet McCabe, 564–7400.

ENFORCEMENT AND COMPLIANCE ASSURANCE

Assistant Administrator.—Cynthia Giles, 564–2440.

Principal Deputy Assistant Administrator.—Lawrence Starfield.

OFFICE OF ENVIRONMENTAL INFORMATION

Assistant Administrator.—Malcom Jackson, 564–6665.

Deputy Assistant Administrator.—Renee Wynn.

CHIEF FINANCIAL OFFICER

Chief Financial Officer.—Maryann Froehlich (acting), 564–1151.

Deputy Chief Financial Officer.—David Bloom (acting).

GENERAL COUNSEL

General Counsel.—Avi Garbow, 564–8064.

Principal Deputy General Counsel.—Brenda Mallory, 564–8064.

Deputy General Counsels: Bicky Corman; Kevin Minolo (acting), 564–8040.

INSPECTOR GENERAL

Inspector General.—Arthur Elkins, Jr., 566–0847.

Deputy Inspector General.—Charles Sheehan.

INTERNATIONAL AFFAIRS

Assistant Administrator.—Michelle DePass, 564–6600.

Deputy Assistant Administrator.—Michael Stahl.

CHEMICAL SAFETY AND POLLUTION PREVENTION

Assistant Administrator.—James Jones (acting), 564–2902.

Principal Deputy Assistant Administrator.—Louise Wise.

RESEARCH AND DEVELOPMENT

Assistant Administrator.—Vacant, 564–6620.
Deputy Assistant Administrator of:
Management.—Lek Kadeli.
Science.—Bob Kavlock.

SOLID WASTE AND EMERGENCY RESPONSE

Assistant Administrator.—Mathy Stanislaus, 566–0200.
Principal Deputy Assistant Administrator.—Barry Breen.

WATER

Assistant Administrator.—Nancy Stoner (acting), 564–5700.
Director of Emergency Management.—Jim Wheeler.

REGIONAL ADMINISTRATION

Region I, Boston.—Connecticut, Maine, New Hampshire, Rhode Island, Vermont.
Regional Administrator.—Curt Spalding, One Congress Street, Suite 1100, Boston, MA 02114 (617) 918–1010.
Public Affairs.—Nancy Grantham.
Region II, New York City.—New Jersey, New York, Puerto Rico, Virgin Islands.
Regional Administrator.—Judith Enck, 290 Broadway, New York, NY 10007 (212) 637–5000.
Public Affairs.—Bonnie Bellow (212) 637–3660.
Region III, Philadelphia.—Delaware, Washington, DC, Maryland, Pennsylvania, Virginia, West Virginia.
Regional Administrator.—Shawn Garvin, 1650 Arch Street, Philadelphia, PA 19103–2029 (215) 814–2900.
Public Affairs.—Richard Sumter (215) 814–5100.
Region IV, Atlanta.—Alabama, Florida, Georgia, Kentucky, Mississippi, North Carolina, South Carolina, Tennessee.
Regional Administrator.—Stan Meiburg (acting), 61 Forsyth Street, SW., Atlanta, GA 30303–8960 (404) 562–8357.
Public Affairs.—Larry Lincoln (404) 562–8327.
Region V, Chicago.—Illinois, Indiana, Michigan, Minnesota, Ohio, Wisconsin.
Regional Administrator.—Susan Hedman, 77 West Jackson Boulevard, Chicago, IL 60604–3507 (312) 886–3000.
Public Affairs.—Anne Rowan.
Region VI, Dallas.—Arkansas, Louisiana, New Mexico, Oklahoma, Texas.
Regional Administrator.—Ron Curry, Fountain Place, 1445 Ross Avenue, 12th Floor, Suite 1200, Dallas, TX 75202–2733 (214) 665–2100.
Public Affairs.—David W. Gray.
Region VII, Kansas City.—Iowa, Kansas, Missouri, Nebraska.
Regional Administrator.—Karl Brooks, 901 North 5th Street, Kansas City, MO 66101 (913) 551–7006.
Public Affairs.—Rich Hood (913) 551–7305.
Region VIII, Denver.—Colorado, Montana, North Dakota, South Dakota, Utah, Wyoming.
Regional Administrator.—Shaun McGrath, 999 18th Street, Suite 300, Denver, CO 80202–2466 (303) 312–6308.
Public Affairs.—Paula Smith (303) 312–6599.
Region IX, San Francisco.—Arizona, California, Hawaii, Nevada, American Samoa, Guam.
Regional Administrator.—Jared Blumenfeld, 75 Hawthorne Street, San Francisco, CA 94105 (415) 947–8702.
Public Affairs.—Kelly Zito.
Region X, Seattle.—Alaska, Idaho, Oregon, Washington.
Regional Administrator.—Dennis McLerran, 1200 Sixth Avenue, Seattle, WA 98101 (206) 553–1234.
Public Affairs.—Kendra Tyler (206) 553–1234.

EQUAL EMPLOYMENT OPPORTUNITY COMMISSION

131 M Street, NE., 20507, phone (202) 663–4900

Chairman.—Jacqueline A. Berrien, suite 6NW08F, 663–4001, fax 663–4110.

Chief Operating Officer.—Claudia Withers, suite 6NW08F.
Deputy Chief Operating Officer.—Vacant.
Confidential Assistant.—Michelle Waldron Patterson, suite 6NW08F, 663–4002.
Commissioners: Constance Barker, suite 6NE25F, 663–4027, fax 663–7121; Chai R. Feldblum, suite 6NE07F, 663–4090, fax 663–7101; Victoria Lipnic, suite 6NE19F, 663–4099, fax 663–7086; Vacant, suite 6NE37F, 663–4052, fax 663–4108.
General Counsel.—P. David Lopez, 5th floor, 663–7034, fax 663–4196.
Legal Counsel.—Peggy Mastroianni, 5th floor, 663–4327, fax 663–4639.
Director, Office of:
Chief Financial Officer.—Germaine Roseboro, 4th floor, 663–4200, fax 663–7068.
Communications and Legislative Affairs.—Todd A. Cox, 6th floor, 663–4191, fax 663–4912.
Equal Opportunity.—Matthew Murphy (acting), 6th floor, 663–7081, fax 663–7003.
Executive Secretariat/Executive Secretary.—Bernadette Wilson (acting), 6th floor, 663–4070, fax 663–4114.
Field Operations.—Carlton Hadden, 5th floor, 663–4599, fax 633–7022.
Field Programs.—Nicholas Inzeo, 5th floor, 663–4801, fax 663–7190.
Human Resources.—Lisa Williams, 4th floor, 663–4306, fax 663–4324.
Information Technology.—Kimberly Hancher, 4th floor, 663–4447, fax 663–4451.
Inspector General.—Milton Mayo, 6th floor, 663–4327, fax 663–7204.
Research, Information and Planning.—Deidre Flippen, 4th floor, 663–4853, fax 663–4093.

EXPORT–IMPORT BANK OF THE UNITED STATES

811 Vermont Avenue, NW., 20571, phone (800) 565–EXIM, fax 565–3380

President and Chairman.—Fred Hochberg, 565–3500.
First Vice President and Vice Chair.—Wanda Felton, 565–3546.
Directors: Patricia Loui, 565–3520; Sean Mulvaney, room 1241, 565–3530; Larry Walther, 565–3540.
Chief of Staff.—Vacant.
Chief Operating Officer.—Vacant.
General Counsel.—Angela Freye, 565–3430.
Chief Financial Officer.—David Sena, 565–3272.
Chief Information Officer.—Fernanda Young, 565–3798.
Senior Vice President of:
Communications.—Dan Reilly, 565–3201.
Congressional Affairs.—Scott Schloegel, 565–3502.
Credit Risk Management.—Kenneth Tinsley, 565–3222.
Export Finance.—John McAdams, 565–3222.
Policy and Planning.—James C. Cruse, 565–3761.
Resource Management.—Michael Cushing, 565–3561.
Small Business.—Charles Tansey, 565–3701.
Vice President of:
Business Credit.—Pamela Bowers, 565–3792.
Communications.—Phil Cogan, room 1264, 565–3203.
Congressional Affairs.—Vacant, 565–3233.
Controller.—Joseph Sorbera, 565–3241.
Country Risk and Economic Analysis.—William Marsteller, 565–3739.
Credit Review and Compliance.—Walter Hill, Jr., 565–3672.
Credit Underwriting.—David Carter, 565–3667.
Domestic Business Development.—Vacant, 565–3787.
Engineering and Environment.—James Mahoney, 565–3573.
Office of Industry Sector Development.—C. Michael Forgione, 565–3224.
Operation and Data Quality.—Michele Kuester, 565–3221.
Policy Analysis.—Helene Walsh, room 1238, 565–3768.
Project and Corporate Portfolio Management.—Richard Park, 565–3631.
Short-Term Trade Finance.—Walter Kosciow, 565–3649.
Structured Finance.—John Schuster, 565–3691.
Strategic Initiatives.—Raymond Ellis, 565–3674.
Trade Finance and Insurance.—Jeffrey Abramson, room 931, 565–3633.
Transportation.—Robert A. Morin, 565–3453.
Transportation Portfolio Management.—Michele Dixey, 565–3554.
Treasurer.—Nathalie Herman, 565–3881.

Directors of:
Contracting Services.—William Boyd, 565–3388.
Human Resources.—Natasha McCarthy, 565–3592.
Inspector General.—Osvaldo Gratacos, 565–3923.
Security.—Selma Hamilton, 565–3313.

FARM CREDIT ADMINISTRATION

1501 Farm Credit Drive, McLean, VA 22102–5090

phone (703) 883–4000, fax 734–5784

[Reorganization pursuant to Public Law 99–205, December 23, 1985]

Board Chair and Chief Executive Officer.—Jill Long Thompson.
Board Members:
Kenneth A. Spearman.
Leland A. Strom.
Secretary to the Board.—Dale L. Aultman, 883–4009, fax 790–5241.
Chief Operating Officer.—William J. Hoffman, 883–4340, fax 790–5241.
Director, Office of:
Congressional and Public Affairs.—Michael A. Stokke, 883–4056, fax 790–3260.
Examination.—S. Robert Coleman, 883–4160, fax 893–2978.
General Counsel.—Charles R. Rawls, 883–4020, fax 790–0052.
Inspector General.—Elizabeth M. Dean (acting), 883–4030, fax 883–4059.
Management Services.—Stephen G. Smith, 883–4200, fax 883–4151.
Regulatory Policy.—Gary K. Van Meter, 883–4414, fax 883–4477.
Secondary Market Oversight.—Laurie Rea, 883–4280, fax 883–4478.
Chief Human Capital Officer.—Stephen G. Smith (acting), 883–4200, fax 883–4151.
Chief Information Officer.—Doug Valcour, 883–4200, fax 883–4151.
Director, Equal Employment Opportunity and Inclusion.—Thais Burlew, 883–4290, fax 883–4351.

FEDERAL COMMUNICATIONS COMMISSION

445 12th Street, SW., 20554, phone (202) 418–0200, http: / / www.fcc.gov

FCC National Consumer Center: 1–888–225–5322 / 1–888–835–5322 (TTY)

Chairman.—Julius Genachowski, room 8–B201, 418–1000.
Confidential Assistant.—Maria Gaglio.
Chief of Staff.—Zachary Katz.
Chief Counsel and Senior Legal Advisor.—Elizabeth Andrion.
Senior Counselor.—Charles Mathias.
Wireline Legal Advisor.—Michael Steffen.
Wireless Legal Advisor.—Renee Gregory.
Special Assistant.—Russell Caditz-Peck.
Commissioner.—Robert McDowell, room 8–C302, 418–2200.
Confidential Advisor.—Brigid Calamis.
Media Advisor.—Erin A. McGrath
Chief of Staff.—Erin A. McGrath (acting).
Wireline Advisor.—Christine Kurth.
Commissioner.—Mignon Clyburn, room 8–A302, 418–2100.
Chief of Staff/Media Legal Advisor.—Dave Grimaldi.
Deputy Chief of Staff.—Drema Johnson.
Legal Advisor (Wireline).—Angela Kronenberg.
Legal Advisor (Wireless).—Louis Peraertz.

OFFICE OF ADMINISTRATIVE LAW JUDGES

Administrative Law Judge.—Richard L. Sippel, room 1–C768, 418–2280.

OFFICE OF COMMUNICATIONS BUSINESS OPPORTUNITIES

Director.—Thomas Reed, room 4–A760, 418–0531.

CONSUMER AND GOVERNMENTAL AFFAIRS BUREAU

Chief.—Kris Monteith (acting), room 5–C758, 418–1400.

Deputy Bureau Chiefs: Karen Peltz-Strauss, room 5–C755; Mark Stone, room 5–C754, 418–0816.

Chief of Staff.—Michael Carowitz (acting), room 5–C739, 418–0651.

Associate Bureau Chief.—D'Wana Terry, room 5–C831, 418–0643.

Associate Bureau Chief for Management.—Tamika Jackson, room 5–A847, 418–0159.

Consumer Information.—Bill Cline, room 5–A729, 418–0267.

Education and Outreach.—Roger Goldblatt, room 5–A848, 418–1035.

Division Chief of:

Consumer Affairs and Outreach.—Susan McLean, room 3–A644, 418–7868.

Consumer Inquiries and Complaints.—Sharon Bowers (Gettysburg), (717) 338–2533.

Consumer Policy.—Kurt Schroeder (acting), room 5–A812, 418–0966.

Web and Print Publishing.—Howard Parnell, room 1–B115, 418–7280.

Office Chief of:

Disability Rights.—Gregory Hlibok, room 3–C341, 559–5158.

Intergovernmental Affairs.—Gregory Vadas, room 5–A660, 418–1798.

Office of Native Affairs and Policy.—Geoffrey Blackwell, room 4–C763, 418–3629.

Reference Information Center.—Vacant.

ENFORCEMENT BUREAU

Chief.—P. Michelle Ellison, room 3–C252, 418–7450.

Deputy Bureau Chiefs: William Davenport, room 3–C255, 418–7450; David Kolker, room 3–C250, 418–1309.

Associate Chiefs: Ben Bartolome, (770) 935–3383; Eric Bash, room 3–C204, 418–2057; Charles "Chad" Breckinridge, room 3–C220, 418–2035; Eloise Gore, room 3–A465, 418–1066; Christopher Killion, room 3–C222, 418–1711; Karen Onyeije, room 3–C365, 418–1757; Priya Shrinivasan, room 3–C163, 418–7005.

Chief, Division of:

Investigations and Hearings.—Theresa Cavanaugh, room 4–C322, 418–1573.

Market Disputes Resolutions.—Alex Starr, room 4–C342, 418–0662.

Spectrum Enforcement.—John Poutasse, room 3–C366, 418–2172.

Telecommunications.—Richard Hindman, room 4–C224, 418–3613.

Director of:

North East Region: Chicago, IL.—Michael Moffitt.

South Central Region: Kansas City, MO.—Denny Carlton.

Western Region: San Diego, CA.—Rebecca Dorch.

OFFICE OF ENGINEERING AND TECHNOLOGY

Chief.—Julius P. Knapp, room 7–C155, 418–2470.

OFFICE OF GENERAL COUNSEL

General Counsel.—Sean Lev, room 8–C750, 418–0980.

Deputy General Counsels: Peter Karanjia, room 8–C758, 418–1700; Suzanne Tetreault, room 8–C758, 418–1769.

Associate General Counsel and Chief Diversity Officer.—Mark Lloyd, room 8–C860, 418–7390.

Associate General Counsel.—Jennifer Tatel, room 8–C833, 418–1700.

OFFICE OF INSPECTOR GENERAL

Inspector General.—David L. Hunt, room 2–C327, 418–0470.

INTERNATIONAL BUREAU

Chief.—Mindel De La Torre, room 6–C750, 418–0437.

Deputy Chiefs: Roderick Porter, room 6–C752, 418–0423; Troy Tanner, room 6–C475, 418–1475.

Chief, Division of:
Policy.—James Ball, room 7–A760, 418–0427.
Satellite.—Fern Jarmulnek, room 6–A760, 418–0751.
Strategic Analysis and Negotiations.—Narda Jones, room 6–A763, 418–2489.

OFFICE OF LEGISLATIVE AFFAIRS

Director.—Greg Guice, room 8–C464, 418–0095.
Deputy Director.—Christopher Lewis, room 8–C457, 418–7285.

OFFICE OF MANAGING DIRECTOR

Managing Director.—David Robbins, room 1–C152, 418–1919.
Deputy Managing Directors: Mindy Ginsburg, room 1–C154, 418–0983; Joseph Hall, room 1–C150, 216–4024; Dana Shaffer, room 1–C155, 418–0832.
Secretary.—Marlene Dortch, room TW–B204, 418–0300.
Chief Human Capital Office.—Bonita Tinley, room 1–A100, 418–0293, TTY 481–0150 (employment verification).
Associate Managing Directors:
Administrative Operations.—Wanda Sims, room 1–C402, 418–2990.
Financial Operations.—Mark Stephens, 418–0817.
Information Technology.—Joseph Hall (acting), room 1–C150, 216–4024.
Performance Evaluations and Records Management.—Walter Boswell, room 1–A105, 418–2178.
Assistant Chief for Management.—Marie Davis, room CY–C428, 418–2111.

MEDIA BUREAU

Chief.—Williams Lake, room 3–C740, 418–7200.
Deputy Bureau Chiefs: Michelle Carey, room 3–C830, 418–7200; Kris Monteith, room 3–C486, 418–7200; Robert Ratcliffe, room 3–C742, 418–7200; Sarah Whitesell, room 3–C458, 418–7200.
Chief of Staff.—Thomas Horan, room 3–C478, 418–7200.
Chief, Division of:
Audio Division.—Peter Doyle, room 2–A360, 418–2700.
Engineering Division.—John Wong, room 4–A838, 418–7012.
Industry Analysis Division.—Hillary DeNigro, room 2–C360, 418–2330.
Policy Division.—Mary Beth Murphy, room 4–A766, 418–2120.
Video Division.—Barbara A. Kreisman, room 2–A666, 418–1600.

OFFICE OF MEDIA RELATIONS

Director.—Tammy Sun, room CY–C314B, 418–0505.
Deputy Director.—Mark Wigfield, room CY–C314C, 418–0253.

OFFICE OF STRATEGIC PLANNING AND POLICY ANALYSIS

Chief.—Jonathan Chambers (acting), room 7–C452, 418–2007.
Deputy Chief.—Elizabeth Andrion, room 7–C450, 418–2030.
Chief Economist.—Steve Wildman, room 7–C769–1, 418–2031.
Chief Technologist.—Henning Schulzrinne, room 7–C252, 418–1544.
Chief of Incentive Auctions/Senior Advisor to the Chairman.—Gary Epstein, room 7–C357, 418–2030.

WIRELESS TELECOMMUNICATIONS BUREAU

Chief.—Ruth Milkman, room 6411, 418–0600.
Deputy Bureau Chiefs: John Leibovitz, room 6417, 418–0600; Jim Schlichting, room 6413, 418–0600.
Associate Bureau Chiefs: Jane Jackson, room 6419, 418–1545; Paul Murray, room 6405, 418–0688.
Assistant Bureau Chief for Management.—Stephen Ebner, room 6442, 418–2147.

Chiefs, Division of:
Action and Spectrum Access.—Margaret Wiener, room 6419, 418–0660.
Broadband.—Blaise Scinto, room 3–C124, 418–BITS.
Mobility.—Roger Noel, room 6411, 418–0620.
Spectrum and Competition Policy.—Nese Guendelsberger, room 6405, 418–0634.
Technology, Systems and Innovation.—Mary Bucher (Gettysburg), (717) 338–2656.

WIRELINE COMPETITION BUREAU

Chief.—Julie Veach, room 5–C354, 418–1500.
Deputy Bureau Chiefs: Lisa Gelb, room 5–C413; Carol Mattey, room 5–C352, 418–1500.
Associate Bureau Chiefs: Denna Shetler, room 5–A221, 418–1500; Trent Harkrader, room 5–A526, 418–2995.
Chief Economist.—Eric Ralph, room 5–C450, 418–1500.
Chief Data Officer.—Steven Rosenberg, room 6–A363, 418–1500.

OFFICE WORKPLACE DIVERSITY

Director.—Thomas Wyatt, room 5–C750, 418–1799.

REGIONAL AND FIELD OFFICES

NORTHEAST REGION

Regional Director of:
Chicago: G. Michael Moffitt, Park Ridge Office Center, Room 306, 1550 Northwest Highway, Park Ridge, IL 60068 (847) 813–4671.

FIELD OFFICES–NORTHEAST REGION

Director of:
Boston: Dennis V. Loria, One Batterymarch Park, Quincy, MA 02169 (617) 786–1154.

Columbia: James T. Higgins, 9200 Farm House Lane, Columbia, MD 21046 (301) 725–0019.

Detroit: James A. Bridgewater, 24897 Hathaway Street, Farmington Hills, MI 48335 (248) 471–5661.

New York: Dan Noel, 201 Varick Street, Room 1151, New York, NY 10014 (212) 337–1865.

Philadelphia: Gene J. Stanbro, One Oxford Valley Office Building, Room 404, 2300 East Lincoln Highway, Langhorne, PA 19047 (215) 741–3022.

SOUTH CENTRAL REGION

Regional Director of:
Kansas City: Ronald Ramage, 520 NE Colbern Road, Second Floor, Lee's Summit, MO 64086 (816) 316–1243.

FIELD OFFICES–SOUTH CENTRAL REGION

Director of:
Atlanta: Doug Miller, Koger Center, 3575 Koger Boulevard, Suite 320, Duluth, GA 30096 (770) 935–3372.

Dallas: James D. Wells, 9330 LBJ Freeway, Room 1170, Dallas, TX 75243 (214) 575–6361.

Kansas City: Robert C. McKinney, 520 Northeast Colbern Road, Second Floor, Lee's Summit, MO 64086 (816) 316–1248.

New Orleans: Walter Gernon, 2424 Edenborn Avenue, Room 460, Metarie, LA 70001 (504) 219–8989.

Tampa: Ralph M. Barlow, 4010 W. Boy Scout Boulevard, Suite 425, Tampa, FL 33607 (813) 348–1741.

WESTERN REGION

Regional Director of:
Denver: Rebecca Dorch, 215 South Wadsworth Boulevard, Suite 303, Lakewood, CO 80226 (303) 407–8708.

FIELD OFFICES–WESTERN REGION

Director of:
Denver: Nikki Shears, 215 South Wadsworth Boulevard, Suite 303, Lakewood, CO 80226 (303) 231–5212.

Los Angeles: Nader Haghighat, Cerritos Corporate Towers, 18000 Studebaker Road, Room 660, Cerritos, CA 90701 (562) 865–0235.

San Diego: James Lyons, Interstate Office Park, 4542 Ruffner Street, Room 370, San Diego, CA 92111 (858) 496–5125.

San Francisco: Thomas N. Van Stavern, 5653 Stoneridge Drive, Suite 105, Pleasanton, CA 94588 (925) 416–9777.

Seattle: Kris McGowan, 11410 Northeast 122nd Way, Room 312, Kirkland, WA 98034 (425) 820–6271.

FEDERAL DEPOSIT INSURANCE CORPORATION

550 17th Street, NW., 20429

phone (877) 275–3342, http://www.fdic.gov

Chairman.—Martin J. Gruenberg, 898–3888.
Chief of Staff to the Chairman.—Barbara Ryan, 898–3841.
Deputy to the Chairman and Chief Financial Officer.—Steve App, 898–8732.
Vice Chairman.—Thomas M. Hoenig, 898–6616.
Deputy to the Vice Chairman.—Diane Ellis (acting), 898–8978.
Director.—Jeremiah O. Norton, 898–3964.
Deputy to the Director.—Marianne Hatheway, 898–6548.
Director (OCC).—Thomas Curry, 874–4900.
Deputy.—William Rowe, 898–6960.
Director (CFPB).—Richard Cordray, 435–9637.
Deputy.—Elizabeth Brennan, 435–7259.
Director, Office of Legislative Affairs.—Eric Spitler, 898–7140, fax 898–3745.

FEDERAL ELECTION COMMISSION

999 E Street, NW., 20463

phone (202) 694–1000, Toll Free (800) 424–9530, fax 219–3880, http://www.fec.gov

Chair.—Ellen L. Weintraub, 694–1035.
Vice Chairman.—Donald F. McGahn II, 694–1050.
Commissioners:
Caroline C. Hunter, 694–1045
Matthew S. Petersen, 694–1011.
Steven T. Walther, 694–1055.
Staff Director.—D. Alec Palmer, 694–1007, fax 219–2338.
Deputy Staff Director for—
Compliance/Chief Compliance Officer.—Patricia C. Orrock, 694–1150.
Information Technology/Chief Information Officer.—D. Alec Palmer, 694–1250.
Management and Administration.—Mitra Nejad-Guerin, 694–1007.
Assistant Staff Director for—
Information Division.—Greg J. Scott, 694–1100.
Disclosure.—Patricia Klein Young, 694–1120.
Director for Congressional Affairs.—J. Duane Pugh, 694–1006.
Press Officer.—Judith Ingram, 694–1220.
Director Human Resources.—Judy McLaughlin, 694–1080.
Administrative Officer.—India K. Robinson, 694–1240.
EEO Director.—Kevin Salley, 694–1229.

General Counsel.—Anthony Herman, 694–1650.
Deputy General Counsel for—
Law.—Lisa J. Stevenson, 694–1650.
Administration.—Gregory R. Baker, 694–1650.
Associate General Counsel for—
Enforcement.—Daniel A. Petalas.
Litigation.—David Kolker.
Policy.—Kevin Deeley (acting).
Library Director (Law).—Leta L. Holley.
Chief Financial Officer.—Judy Berning (acting), 694–1217.
Deputy Chief Financial Officer/Budget Director.—Gilbert Ford, 694–1216.
Director of Accounting.—Judy Berning, 694–1230.
Inspector General.—Lynne A. McFarland, 694–1015.
Deputy Inspector General.—Jonathon A. Hatfield.

FEDERAL HOUSING FINANCE AGENCY *

400 7th Street, NW., 20024

phone (202) 649–3800, fax 649–1017, http://www.fhfa.gov

[Created by Housing and Economic Recovery Act of 2008, 122 Stat. 2654, Public Law 110–289—July 30, 2008]

Director.—Edward J. DeMarco (acting), 649–3801.
Deputy Director, Division of:
Federal Home Loan Bank Regulation.—Vacant.
Enterprise Regulation.—Jon Greenlee, 649–3247.
Examination Programs and Support.—Wanda DeLeo, 649–3400.
Housing, Mission and Goals.—Sandra Thompson, 649–3384.
General Counsel.—Alfred Pollard, 649–3050.
Senior Deputy General Counsel.—Christopher T. Curtis, 649–3051.

OFFICE OF CONGRESSIONAL AFFAIRS AND COMMUNICATIONS

Senior Associate Director.—Denise Dunckel, 649–3034.
Associate Director for Congressional Affairs.—Peter Brereton, 649–3022.
Congressional Affairs Staff: Jennifer Cowell, 649–3025; Patricia Driver, 649–3027; Jeannine Schroeder, 649–3029.
Director of Communications.—Peter Garuccio, 649–3036.
Public Affairs Staff: Stefanie Johnson, 649–3030; Corinne Russell, 649–3032.
Executive Advisor for Consumer Communications.—Owen Highfill (acting), 649–3042.
Senior Associate Director for Conservatorship.—Jeff Spohn, 649–3040.
Ombudsman.—Michael Powers, 649–3010.
Associate Director for the Office of Minority and Women Inclusion.—Lee Bowman, 649–3008.
Chief Operating Officer.—Rick Hornsby, 649–3709.
Chief Information Officer.—Kevin Winkler, 649–3600.
Associate Director for the Office of Quality Assurance.—Edward Stolle, 649–3717.
Inspector General.—Steve Linick (800) 793–7724.

FEDERAL LABOR RELATIONS AUTHORITY

1400 K Street, NW., 20424–0001, phone (202) 218–7770, fax 482–6635

FLRA Agency Head.—Ernest DuBester, 218–7920.
Executive Director.—Sarah Whittle Spooner, 218–7791.
Counsel for Regulatory and External Affairs.—Vacant.
Solicitor.—Rosa Koppel, 218–7999.
Inspector General.—Dana Rooney-Fisher, 218–7744.
Collaboration and Alternative Dispute Resolution Program.—Michael Wolf, 218–7933.
Foreign Service Impasse Disputes Panel.—Chairman Mary Jacksteit, 218–7790.
Foreign Service Labor Relations Board.—Ernest DuBester, 218–7920.

AUTHORITY

Chairman.—Ernest DuBester, 218–7920.
Chief Counsel.—William Tobey, 218–7920.
Member.—Vacant, 218–7930.
Chief Counsel.—James Abbott, 218–7930.
Member.—Vacant, 218–7900.
Chief Counsel.—Susan D. McCluskey, 218–7900.
Chief, Case Intake and Publication.—Gina Grippando, 218–7740.

GENERAL COUNSEL OF THE FLRA

General Counsel.—Julia A. Clark, 218–7910.
Deputy General Counsel.—Peter Sutton (acting), 218–7910.
Assistant General Counsel for Appeals.—Richard Zorn, 218–7910.

OFFICE OF ADMINISTRATIVE LAW JUDGES

Chief Judge.—Charles Center, 218–7950.

FEDERAL SERVICE IMPASSES PANEL (FSIP)

FSIP Chairman.—Mary Jacksteit, 218–7790.
Executive Director.—H. Joseph Schimansky, 218–7790.

REGIONAL OFFICES

Regional Directors:
Atlanta.—Richard S. Jones, Marquis Two Tower, Suite 701, 285 Peachtree Center Avenue, Atlanta, GA 30303 (404) 331–5300, fax (404) 331–5280.
Boston.—Philip T. Roberts, 10 Causeway Street, Suite 472, Boston, MA 02222 (617) 565–5100, fax 565–6262.
Chicago.—Peter A. Sutton, 224 South Michigan Avenue, Suite 445, Chicago, IL 60604 (312) 886–3465, fax 886–5977.
Dallas.—James E. Petrucci, 525 Griffin Street, Suite 926, LB 107, Dallas, TX 75202 (214) 767–6266, fax 767–0156.
Denver.—Matthew Jarvinen, 1244 Speer Boulevard, Suite 446, Denver, CO 80204 (303) 844–5224, fax 844–2774.
San Francisco.—Jean Perata, 901 Market Street, Suite 470, San Francisco, CA 94103 (415) 356–5000, fax 356–5017.
Washington, DC.—Barbara Kraft, 1400 K Street, NW., Suite 200, Washington, DC 20005 (202) 357–6029, fax (202) 482–6724.

FEDERAL MARITIME COMMISSION
800 North Capitol Street, NW., 20573
phone (202) 523–5725, fax 523–0014

OFFICE OF THE CHAIRMAN

Chairman.—Mario Cordero, room 1000, 523–5911.
Counsel.—Mary T. Hoang.
Commissioner.—Rebecca F. Dye, room 1038, 523–5715.
Counsel.—Edward L. Lee, Jr.
Commissioner.—Richard A. Lidinsky, room 1032, 523–5721.
Counsel.—Michael J. Gordon.
Commissioner.—Michael A. Khouri, room 1044, 523–5712.
Counsel.—John A. Moran.
Commissioner.—William P. Doyle, room 1026, 523–5723.
Counsel.—David J. Tubman, Jr.

OFFICE OF THE SECRETARY

Secretary.—Karen V. Gregory, room 1046, 523–5725.

Assistant Secretary.—Rachel E. Dickon.
Librarian.—Charlotte C. White, room 1085, 523–5762.

OFFICE OF EQUAL EMPLOYMENT OPPORTUNITY

Director.—Keith I. Gilmore, room 1052, 523–5859.

OFFICE OF THE GENERAL COUNSEL

General Counsel.—Rebecca A. Fenneman, room 1018, 523–5740.
Deputy General Counsel.—Tyler J. Wood.

OFFICE OF CONSUMER AFFAIRS AND DISPUTE RESOLUTION

Director.—Vacant, room 932, 523–5807.
Deputy Director.—Jennifer M. Gartlan.

OFFICE OF ADMINISTRATIVE LAW JUDGES

Chief Judge.—Clay G. Guthridge, room 1088, 523–5750.
Administrative Law Judge.—Erin M. Wirth, room 1088, 523–5750.

OFFICE OF THE INSPECTOR GENERAL

Inspector General.—Vacant, room 1054, 523–5863.

OFFICE OF THE MANAGING DIRECTOR

Director.—Vern W. Hill, room 1082, 523–5800.
Deputy Director.—Florence A. Carr.
Area Representatives:
Houston.—Debra A. Zezima (281) 591–6088.
Los Angeles.—Oliver E. Clark (310) 514–4905.
New Orleans.—Bruce N. Johnson, Sr. (504) 589–6662.
New York: Joseph A. Castellano (718) 553–2223; Ron Podlaskowich (718) 553–2228.
Seattle.—Michael A. Moneck (206) 553–0221.
South Florida.—Andrew Margolis (954) 963–5362; Eric O. Mintz (954) 963–5284.
Director, Office of:
Budget and Finance.—Karon E. Douglass, room 916, 523–5770.
Human Resources.—Vacant, room 924, 523–5773.
Information Technology.—Vacant, room 904, 523–5835.
Management Services.—Michael H. Kilby, room 926, 523–5900.

BUREAU OF CERTIFICATION AND LICENSING

Director.—Vern W. Hill, room 970, 523–5787.
Deputy Director.—James A. Nussbaumer.
Director, Office of:
Passenger Vessels and Information Processing.—Vacant, 523–5818.
Transportation Intermediaries.—Jeremiah D. Hospital, 523–5843.

BUREAU OF ENFORCEMENT

Director.—Peter J. King, room 900, 523–5783 or 523–5860.
Deputy Director.—Brian L. Troiano.

BUREAU OF TRADE ANALYSIS

Director.—Sandra L. Kusumoto, room 940, 523–5796.
Deputy Director.—Tanga S. FitzGibbon.

Director, Office of:
Agreements.—Jason W. Guthrie, 523–5793.
Economics and Competition Analysis.—Roy J. Pearson, 523–5845.
Service Contracts and Tariffs.—F. Gary Kardian, room 940, 523–5856.

FEDERAL MEDIATION AND CONCILIATION SERVICE

2100 K Street, NW., 20427, phone (202) 606–8100, fax 606–4251

[Codified under 29 U.S.C. 172]

Director.—George Cohen.
Deputy Director.—Scot L. Beckenbaugh.
Chief of Staff.—Fran L. Leonard, 606–3661.
General Counsel.—Dawn Starr, 606–8090.
Director for—
ADR/International/FMCS Institute.—Allison Beck, 606–8100.
Arbitration Services.—Vella M. Traynham, 606–5111.
Budget and Finance.—Fran L. Leonard, 606–3661.
Grants.—Linda Gray-Broughton, 606–8181.
Human Resources.—Adam Ramsey, 606–5460.
Information Systems.—Doug Jones, 606–5483.
Administrative Services.—Cynthia Washington, 606–5477.
Regional Director (Eastern/Western).—Vacant.

FEDERAL MINE SAFETY AND HEALTH REVIEW COMMISSION

1331 Pennsylvania Avenue, NW., Suite 9500, 20004

phone (202) 434–9900, fax 434–9944

[Created by Public Law 95–164]

Chairperson.—Mary Lu Jordan, room 9527, 434–9900.
Commissioners: Patrick K. Nakamura, room 541; Michael G. Young, room 543, 434–9900.
Executive Director.—Lisa M. Boyd, room 553, 434–9905.
Chief Administrative Law Judge.—Robert J. Lesnick, room 8515, 434–9958.
General Counsel.—Michael McCord, room 9547, 434–9935.

FEDERAL RETIREMENT THRIFT INVESTMENT BOARD

77 K Street, NW., 20002, phone (202) 942–1600, fax 942–1676

[Authorized by 5 U.S.C. 8472]

Executive Director.—Gregory T. Long, 942–1601.
General Counsel.—James B. Petrick, 942–1660.
Director, Office of:
Benefits.—Thomas K. Emswiler, 942–1460.
Communications and Education.—Sophie Dmuchowski (acting), 942–1630.
Enterprise Planning.—Renee Wilder, 942–1630.
Enterprise Risk Management.—Jay Ahuja, 942–1630.
External Affairs.—Kimberly Weaver, 942–1640.
Financial Management.—Susan Crowder, 942–1620.
Investments.—Theresa Ray, 942–1630.
Resource Management.—Gisile Goethe (acting), 942–1630.
Technology Services.—Mark Walther, 942–1440.
Chairman.—Michael Kennedy, 942–1660.
Board Members:
Terrence A. Duffy.
Dana K. Bilyeu.
Ronald D. McCray.
David A. Jones.

FEDERAL TRADE COMMISSION

600 Pennsylvania Avenue, NW., 20580

phone (202) 326–2222, http://www.ftc.gov

Chairman.—Edith Ramirez, room 438, 326–2856.
Staff Assistant.—Monica Etheridge-Pyos, room 440, 326–2666.
Chief of Staff.—Vacant.
Commissioners: Julie Brill, room 328, 326–2626; Maureen Ohlhausen, room 538, 326–2150; Joshua Wright, room 528, 326–2229.
Director, Office of:
Competition.—Richard A. Feinstein, room 370, 326–3658.
Congressional Relations.—Jeanne Bumpus, room 408, 326–2195.
Consumer Protection.—Chuck Harwood (acting), room 470, 326–3240.
Economics.—Howard Shelanski, room 270, 326–2784.
Policy Planning.—Andrew Gavil, room 392, 326–3620.
Public Affairs.—Peter Kaplan (acting), 326–2180.
Executive Director.—Pat Bak (acting), room 426, 326–3127.
General Counsel.—David Shonka (acting), room 584, 326–2436.
Secretary.—Donald S. Clark, room 172, 326–2514.
Inspector General.—Scott E. Wilson, room 1119NJ, 326–2800.
Chief Administrative Law Judge.—D. Michael Chappell, room 106, 326–3637.

REGIONAL DIRECTORS

East Central Region: Jonathan M. Steiger, Eaton Center, Suite 200, 1111 Superior Avenue, Cleveland, OH 44114 (216) 263–3455.
Midwest Region: C. Steve Baker, 55 East Monroe Street, Suite 1825, Chicago, IL 60603 (312) 960–5634.
Northeast Region: William Efron, One Bowling Green, Suite 318, New York, NY 10004 (212) 607–2829.
Northwest Region: Robert J. Schroeder, 915 Second Avenue, Suite 2896, Seattle, WA 98174 (206) 220–6350.
Southeast Region: Cindy A. Liebes, 225 Peachtree Street, NE., Suite 1500, Atlanta, GA 30303 (404) 656–1390.
Southwest Region: Deanya T. Kueckelhan, 1999 Bryan Street, Suite 2150, Dallas, TX 75201 (214) 979–9350.
Western Region—Los Angeles: Jeffrey Klurfeld, 18077 Wilshire Boulevard, Suite 700, Los Angeles, CA 90024–3679 (310) 824–4343.
Western Region—San Francisco: Jeffrey Klurfeld, 901 Market Street, Suite 570, San Francisco, CA 94103 (415) 848–5100.

FOREIGN–TRADE ZONES BOARD

1401 Constitution Avenue, NW., Room 2113, 20230

phone (202) 482–2862, fax 482–0002

Chairman.—Vacant, Secretary of Commerce.
Member.—Jacob J. Lew, Secretary of the Treasury.
Executive Secretary.—Andrew McGilvray.

GENERAL SERVICES ADMINISTRATION

1800 F Street, NE., 20405 phone (202) 501–0800, http://www.gsa.gov

OFFICE OF THE ADMINISTRATOR

Administrator.—Daniel M. Tangherlini.
Deputy Administrator.—Susan F. Brita.
Chief of Staff.—Adam Neufeld.
Associate Administrator for Communications Marketing.—Betsaida Alcantara.
White House Liaison.—Reginald H. Cardozo, Jr.

OFFICE OF CONGRESSIONAL AND INTERGOVERNMENTAL AFFAIRS

Associate Administrator.—Lisa A. Austin (202) 501–0563.

Deputy Associate Administrator.—Brett Prather.
Director of:
Congressional Operations.—Erin Mewhirter.
Congressional Support Services.—Michael Gurgo.
Senior Advisor of Appropriations.—Saul Japson.

OFFICE OF THE CHIEF FINANCIAL OFFICER

Chief Financial Officer.—Michael Casella (202) 501–1721.
Director of:
Budget.—Amy Hay (acting).
Financial Operations.—Edward Gramp (acting).
Financial Services Federal Acquisition.—Agnes Leung.
Financial Services Public Buildings.—William Strickland (acting).

OFFICE OF THE CHIEF PEOPLE OFFICER

Chief People Officer.—Anthony ''Tony'' Costa (202) 501–0398.
Chief of Staff.—Peter Russelburg.

OFFICE OF THE GENERAL COUNSEL

General Counsel.—Kris Durmer (202) 501–2200.
Deputy General Counsel.—Lennard S. Loewentritt.
Associate General Counsel for—
General Law.—Eugenia D. Ellison, 501–1460.
Personal Property.—Janet Harney, 501–1156.
Real Property.—Berry Segal, 501–0430.

OFFICE OF THE CHIEF INFORMATION OFFICER

Chief Information Officer.—Casey Coleman (202) 501–1000.
Deputy Chief Information Officer.—Sonny Hashmi.
Director, Office of:
Enterprise Infrastructure.—David Shive.
Enterprise Management Service.—Daryle ''Mike'' Seckar.

OFFICE OF GOVERNMENTWIDE POLICY

Associate Administrator.—Anne Rung (acting), (202) 501–8880.
Chief Acquisition Officer.—Anne Rung.
Senior Procurement Executive.—Vacant.
Chief of Staff.—Stephanie Rivera.
Executive Officer.—Teresa Tippins.
Deputy Associate Administrators, Office of:
Travel Transportation and Asset Management.—Carolyn Austin-Diggs.

OFFICE OF CITIZEN SERVICES AND INNOVATIVE TECHNOLOGIES

Associate Administrator.—David L. McClure (202) 501–0705.
Principal Deputy Associate Administrator.—Kathy Conrad.

OFFICE OF CIVIL RIGHTS

Associate Administrator.—Madeline Caliendo (202) 501–0767.

OFFICE OF SMALL BUSINESS UTILIZATION

Associate Administrator.—Jiyoung Park (202) 501–1021.

OFFICE OF THE INSPECTOR GENERAL

Inspector General.—Brian D. Miller (202) 501–0450.

Deputy Inspector General.—Robert C. Erickson, Jr. 501–3105.
Director of Communications and Congressional Affairs.—Dave Farley, 219–1062.
Director, Office of Internal Evaluation and Analysis.—Patricia Sheenan, 273–4989.
Counsel to the Inspector General.—Richard Levi, 501–1932.
Assistant Inspector General for—
Administration.—Larry Gregg, 219–1041.
Auditing.—Theodore R. Stehney, 501–0374.
Investigations.—Jeff Seherrngton, 501–0035.

CIVILIAN BOARD OF CONTRACT APPEALS

Chairman.—Stephen M. Daniels (202) 606–8820.
Vice Chairman.—Jeri K. Somers, 606–8831.
Chief Counsel.—James G. Parks, 606–8787.
Clerk.—Cheryl L. Hilton, 606–8800.
Board Judges, 606–8820: Anthony S. Borwick, Stephen M. Daniels, Jerome Drummond, Allan H. Goodman, Catherine B. Hyatt, H. Chuck Kullberg, R. Anthony McCann, Howard Pollack, Patricia Sheridan, Jeri Somers, Candida Steel, James Stern, Joseph Vergilio, Jonathan D. Zischkau.

NATIONAL SERVICES

FEDERAL ACQUISITION SERVICE

Commissioner.—Thomas A. Sharpe, Jr. (703) 605–5400.
Deputy Commissioner.—William Sisk.
Chief of Staff.—Christopher Bennethum.
Chief Information Officer.—Elizabeth F. DelNegro.
Assistant Commissioners for Office of:
Acquisition Management.—Houston W. Taylor.
Assisted Acquisition Services.—Timothy E. Fleming.
Customer Accounts and Research.—Tamela L. Riggs.
General Supplies and Services.—Marty Jennings (acting).
Strategic Business Planning and Process Improvement.—Amanda Fredriksen, 601–5513.
Travel, Motor Vehicle and Card Services.—Bill Webster (703) 605–5500.

PUBLIC BUILDING SERVICE

Commissioner.—Dorothy Robyn (202) 501–1100.
Deputy Commissioner.—Michael Gelber.
Chief of Staff.—Chelsea Waliser.
Associate Commissioner.—Desa Sealy.
Chief Architect.—Leslie Shepherd, 501–1888.

REGIONAL OFFICES

National Capital Region (NCR 11): 7th and D Street, SW., Washington, DC 20407 (202) 708–9100.
Regional Administrator.—Julia E. Hudson.
Regional Commissioner for Federal Acquisition Service.—Alfonso Finley.
Regional Commissioner for Public Buildings Service.—Thomas James (acting).
Regional Counsel.—Paula DeMuth.

New England Region I: Thomas P. O'Neill Federal Building, 10 Causeway Street, Boston, MA 02222 (617) 565–5860.
Regional Administrator.—Robert Zarnetske.
Regional Commissioner for Federal Acquisition Service.—Sharon Wall.
Regional Commissioner for Public Buildings Service.—Glenn Rotondo.

Northeast and Caribbean Region 2: 26 Federal Plaza, New York, NY 10278 (212) 264–2600.
Regional Administrator.—Denise L. Pease.
Regional Commissioner for Federal Acquisition Service.—Frank Mayer (acting).
Regional Commissioner for Public Building Service.—Joanna Rosato.

Mid-Atlantic Region 3: The Strawbridge's Building, 20 North Eight Street, Philadelphia, PA 19107 (215) 446–4900.
Regional Administrator.—Sara Manzano-Diaz.

Regional Commissioner for Federal Acquisition Service.—Linda Chero.
Regional Commissioner for Public Buildings Service.—Rob Hewell.

Southeast Sunbelt Region 4: 77 Forsyth Street, Suite 600, Atlanta, GA 30303 (404) 331–3200.
Regional Administrator.—Sara Manzano-Diaz (acting).
Regional Commissioner for Federal Acquisition Service.—Erville Koehler.
Regional Commissioner for Public Buildings Service.—John Smith.

Great Lakes Region 5: 230 South Dearborn, Chicago, IL 60604 (312) 353–5395.
Regional Administrator.—Ann P. Kalayil.
Regional Commissioner for Federal Acquisition Service.—Kim Brown.
Regional Commissioner for Public Buildings Service.—Allison Azevedo.

Heartland Region 6: 1500 East Bannister Road, Kansas City, MO 64131 (816) 926–7201.
Regional Administrator.—Jason O. Klumb.
Regional Commissioner for Federal Acquisition Service.—Mary Ruwwe.
Regional Commissioner for Public Buildings Service.—Cy Houston (acting).

Great Southwest Region 7: 819 Taylor Street, Fort Worth, TX 76102 (817) 978–2321.
Regional Administrator.—Sylvia Hernandez (acting).
Regional Commissioner for Federal Acquisition Service.—Kathy Colomo (acting).
Regional Commissioner for Public Buildings Service.—James Serracci (acting).

Rocky Mountain Region 8: Building 41, Denver Federal Center, Denver, CO 80225 (303) 236–7329.
Regional Administrator.—Susan B. Damour.
Regional Commissioner for Federal Acquisition Service.—Timothy Horne.
Regional Commissioner for Public Buildings Service.—Scott Conner (acting).

Pacific Mountain Region 9: 450 Golden Gate Avenue, Room 5–2690, San Francisco, CA 94102 (415) 522–3001.
Regional Administrator.—Ruth Cox.
Regional Commissioner for Federal Acquisition Service.—Kathryn Pamiroyan (acting).
Regional Commissioner for Public Buildings Service.—Sam Mazzola (acting).

Northwest/Arctic Region 10: GSA Center, 400 15th Street, SW., Auburn, WA 98001 (253) 931–7000.
Regional Administrator.—George Northcroft.
Regional Commissioner for Federal Acquisition Service.—Tiffany Hixson.
Regional Commissioner for Public Buildings Service.—Benjamin Chaun (acting).

HARRY S. TRUMAN SCHOLARSHIP FOUNDATION

712 Jackson Place, NW., 20006

phone (202) 395–4831, fax 395–6995

[Created by Public Law 93–642]

BOARD OF TRUSTEES

President.—Madeleine K. Albright.
Vice President.—Max Sherman.
Treasurer.—Frederick Slabach.
General Counsel.—C. Westbrook Murphy.
Members:
Javaid Anwar, CEO, Quality Care Consultants, LLC.
Mark Begich, Senator from Alaska.
Roy Blunt, Senator from Missouri.
Steven Cohen, Attorney, Cohen Law Group.
Hon. Laura Cordero, Judge, DC Superior Court.
Hon. Arne Duncan, Secretary of Education.
Ingrid Gregg, President, Earhart Foundation.
Hon. Dave Heineman, Governor, State of Nebraska.
Hon. James Henderson, Judge, Simpson County, KY.
Roger Hunt, U.S. District Judge.
Sharon ''Nyota'' Tucker, Assistant Professor, Albany State University.
Executive Secretary.—Andrew Rich.
Deputy Executive Secretary.—Tara Yglesias.
Chief Information Officer.—Tonji Wade.
Education Officer.—Ruth Keen.
Program Manager.—Andrew Kirk.

JAMES MADISON MEMORIAL FELLOWSHIP FOUNDATION

1613 Duke Street, Alexandria, VA 22314

phone (571) 858–4200, fax (703) 838–2180

[Created by Public Law 99–591]

BOARD OF TRUSTEES

Members Appointed by the President of the United States:

John Cornyn, Senator from Texas, Chairman.
Catherine Allgor, Nadine Skotheim, Robert A. Skotheim, Director of Education Huntington Library, Art Collections, and Botanical Gardens.
Benjamin L. Cardin, Senator from Maryland.
Steven M. Colloton, U.S. Circuit Judge, U.S. Court of Appeals, 8th Circuit, Des Moines, Iowa.
John J. Faso, Attorney, Manatt, Phelps and Phillips, Albany, New York.
William Terrell Hodges, Senior U.S. District Judge, Middle District, Florida.
Pauline Maier, William R. Kenan, Jr., Professor of American History, Massachusetts Institute of Technology.
Drew R. McCoy, Department of History, Clark University.
Harvey M. Tettlebaum, Partner, Husch Blackwell LLP, Jefferson City, Missouri.
Arne Duncan, U.S. Secretary of Education (ex officio).

Foundation Staff:
President Emeritus.—Admiral Paul A. Yost, Jr.
President.—Lewis F. Larsen.
Academic Advisor to the President.—Herman Belz.
Administrative Assistant.—Colin Bornmann.
Director of Special Programs.—Claire Griffin.
Special Assistant/Office Manager.—Anne Marie Kanakkanatt.
Academic Assistant.—Sheila Osbourne.
Management and Program Analysis Officer.—Elizabeth G. Ray.

INTER-AMERICAN FOUNDATION

1331 Pennsylvania Avenue, NW., 1200 North, Washington, DC, phone (202) 360–4530

Chair, Board of Directors.—John P. Salazar (acting).
Vice Chair, Board of Directors.—Thomas J. Dodd (acting).
President and Chief Executive Officer.—Robert N. Kaplan.
Chief Operating Officer.—Jacob Sgambati.
Vice President for Programs.—Stephen Cox.
General Counsel.—Paul Zimmerman.
Director of:
Evaluation and Audit.—Emilia Rodríguez-Stein.
External and Government Affairs.—Manuel Nuñez.

JOHN F. KENNEDY CENTER FOR THE PERFORMING ARTS

2700 F Street, NW., 20566, phone (202) 416–8000, fax 416–8205

BOARD OF TRUSTEES

Honorary Chairs:
Mrs. Michelle Obama
Mrs. Laura Bush
Mrs. Hillary Rodham Clinton
Mrs. George Bush
Mrs. Ronald Reagan
Mrs. Jimmy Carter

Officers:
Chairman.—David M. Rubenstein.
President.—Michael M. Kaiser.
Secretary.—Helen Lee Henderson.
Treasurer.—Michael F. Neidorff.
General Counsel.—Maria C. Kersten.
Assistant Secretary.—Kathy Kruse.

Members Appointed by the President of the United States:

Adrienne Arsht
Colleen Bell
David C. Bohnett
Nancy Goodman Brinker
Gordon J. Davis
Judith Ann Eisenberg
Fred Eychaner
Giselle Fernandez
Norma Lee Funger
Donald J. Hall, Jr.
Joan E. Hotchkis
Caroline Kennedy
Victoria Reggie Kennedy
Herbert V. Kohler, Jr.
C. Michael Kojaian
Carl H. Lindner III
Donna G. Marriott
Cappy R. McGarr
Marilyn Carlson Nelson
Charles B. Ortner
Robert Frank Pence
Rebecca Pohlad
William Charles Powers
Penny Pritzker
Duane R. Roberts
David M. Rubenstein
Shirley W. Ryan
Leonard Sands
Marc I. Stern
Romesh Wadhwani
Anthony Welters
Elaine Wynn

Ex Officio Members Designated by Act of Congress
(Note: The names of Senators and Representatives appear in order of their years of service)

John F. Kerry, Secretary of State.
Kathleen Sebelius, Secretary of Health and Human Services.
Arne Duncan, Secretary of Education.
Harry Reid, Senate Majority Leader from Nevada.
Thad Cochran, Senator from Mississippi.
Mitch McConnell, Senate Republican Leader from Kentucky.
Barbara Boxer, Senator from California.
Dianne Feinstein, Senator from California.
David Vitter, Senator from Louisiana.
Nancy Pelosi, Democratic Leader of the House of Representatives from California.
John Boehner, Speaker of the House of Representatives from Ohio.
Rosa L. DeLauro, Representative from Connecticut.
Nick J. Rahall II, Representative from West Virginia.
Bill Shuster, Representative from Pennsylvania.
Vincent C. Gray, Mayor, District of Columbia.
James H. Billington, Librarian of Congress.
Dr. G. Wayne Clough, Secretary, Smithsonian Institution.
Jonathan Jarvis, Director, National Park Service.
Kaya Henderson, Chancellor, DC Public Schools.
Earl A. Powell III, Chairman of the Commission of Fine Arts.

Senior Counsel.—Robert Barnett.
Founding Chairman.—Roger L. Stevens (deceased).
Chairmen Emeriti: James A. Johnson, Stephen A. Schwarzman, James D. Wolfensohn.

Honorary Trustees:

Buffy Cafritz
Kenneth M. Duberstein
James H. Evans
Alma Gildenhorn
Melvin R. Laird
Leonard L. Silverstein
Jean Kennedy Smith

LEGAL SERVICES CORPORATION

3333 K Street, NW., 3rd Floor, 20007–3522

phone (202) 295–1500, fax 337–6797

BOARD OF DIRECTORS

John G. Levi, Board *Chair*
Martha L. Minow, Board *Vice Chair*
Sharon L. Browne
Robert J. Grey, Jr.
Charles N.W. Keckler
Harry Korrell
Victor B. Maddox
Laurie I. Mikva
Rev. Joseph Pius Pietrzyk
Julie A. Reiskin
Gloria Valencia-Weber

President.—James J. Sandman.
Vice President, Legal Affairs, General Counsel and Corporate Secretary.—Vacant.
Comptroller and Treasurer.—David L. Richardson.
Inspector General.—Jeffrey E. Schanz.
Director, Government Relations and Public Affairs.—Carol Bergman.
Media Director.—Carl Rauscher.

NATIONAL AERONAUTICS AND SPACE ADMINISTRATION

300 E Street, SW., 20546, phone (202) 358–0000, http://www.nasa.gov

OFFICE OF THE ADMINISTRATOR

Code AA000, Room 9F44, phone 358–1010

Administrator.—Charles F. Bolden, Jr.
Executive Assistant.—Kathryn Manuel, 358–1010.
Deputy Administrator.—Lori Garver, 358–1020.
Associate Administrator.—Robert Lightfoot.
Chief of Staff.—David Radzanowski, 358–1827.
Director for Office of Evaluation.—Vacant.
Director for Council Staff.—Vacant.
Associate Deputy Administrator.—Richard Keegan, 358–2810.
Associate Deputy Administrator for Strategy and Policy.—Dr. Rebecca Keiser, 358–0286.
Assistant Associate Administrator.—Arthur Maples (acting), 358–1423.
Deputy Chief of Staff.—Michael French, 358–1441.
White House Liaison.—Jonathan Herczeg, 358–2198.
Chiefs:
Financial Officer.—Dr. Elizabeth Robinson, 358–0978.
Information Officer.—Keegan (acting), 358–2810.
Engineer.—Dr. Mike Ryschkewitsch, 358–1823.
Health and Medical Officer.—Dr. Richard S. Williams, 358–2390.
Safety and Mission Assurance.—Wilcutt.
Scientist.—Vacant, 358–1163.
Technologist.—Dr. Mason Peck, 358–1909.

OFFICE OF THE GENERAL COUNSEL

Code MA000, Room 9V39, phone 358–2450

General Counsel.—Michael Wholley.

OFFICE OF INSPECTOR GENERAL

Code WAH10, Room 8U79, phone 358–1220

Inspector General.—Paul K. Martin.
Deputy Inspector General.—Gail A. Robinson.

OFFICE OF COMMUNICATIONS

Code NA000, Room 9P39, phone 358–1898

Associate Administrator.—David Weaver.
Deputy Associate Administrator, News and Multimedia.—Robert Jacobs, 358–1600.
Deputy Associate Administrator, Public Outreach.—Alan Ladwig, 358–1410.

OFFICE OF DIVERSITY AND EQUAL OPPORTUNITY PROGRAMS

Code YA000, Room 6J81, phone 358–2167

Associate Administrator.—Brenda R. Manuel.

OFFICE OF EDUCATION

Code HA000, Room 4V76, phone 358–0100

Associate Administrator.—Leland Melvin.

OFFICE OF INTERNATIONAL AND INTERAGENCY RELATIONS

Code TA000, Room 2V39, phone 358–0450

Associate Administrator.—Michael F. O'Brien.
Deputy Associate Administrator.—Al Condes.

OFFICE OF LEGISLATIVE AND INTERGOVERNMENTAL AFFAIRS

Code VA000, Room 9K39, phone 358–1948

Associate Administrator.—Seth Statler.
Deputy Assistant Administrator.—Mary D. Kerwin.

OFFICE OF SMALL BUSINESS PROGRAMS

Code ZA000, Room 2K39, phone 358–2088

Associate Administrator.—Glenn A. Delgado.

AERONAUTICS RESEARCH MISSION DIRECTORATE

Code EA000, Room 6J39–A, phone 358–4700

Associate Administrator.—Jaiwon Shin.
Deputy Associate Administrator.—Thomas B. Irvine.

HUMAN EXPLORATION AND OPERATIONS MISSION DIRECTORATE

Code CA000, Room 7K39, phone 358–2015

Associate Administrator.—William H. Gerstenmaier.

SCIENCE MISSION DIRECTORATE

Code DA000, room 3C26, phone 358–3889

Associate Administrator.—Dr. John Grunsfeld.
Deputy Associate Administrator.—Chuck Gay, 358–2165.

SPACE TECHNOLOGY MISSION DIRECTORATE

Associate Administrator.—Dr. Gazarik.

MISSION SUPPORT DIRECTORATE

Code LA000, Room 4K39, phone 358–0227

Associate Administrator.—Woodrow Whitlow, Jr.
Executive Director Headquarters Operations.—Jay Henn.

OFFICE OF HUMAN CAPITAL MANAGEMENT

Code LE000, Room 4V76, phone 358–0100

Assistant Administrator.—Jeri Buchholz.

OFFICE OF PROCUREMENT

Code LP010, Room 2P40, phone 358–2090

Assistant Administrator.—Bill McNally.

OFFICE OF PROTECTIVE SERVICES

Code LP020, Room 6T26, phone 358–3752

Assistant Administrator.—Joseph Mahaley.
Deputy Associate Administrator.—Charles Lombard.

OFFICE OF STRATEGIC INFRASTRUCTURE

Code LD000, Room 4G74, phone 358–2800

Assistant Administrator.—Dominguez.

INTERNAL CONTROLS AND MANAGEMENT SYSTEMS

Code LPO30, Room 5A70, phone 358–1061

Director.—Nancy Baugher.

NASA MANAGEMENT OFFICE

Code LA000, Room 4K39, phone 358–0227

Director.—Dr. Whitlow (acting).

NASA NATIONAL OFFICES

Air Force Space Command / XPX (NASA): Peterson Air Force Base, CO 80914.
NASA Senior Representative.—B. Alvin Drew (719) 554–4900.

Ames Research Center: Moffett Field, CA 94035.
Director.—Dr. Simon P. Worden (650) 604–5000.

Dryden Flight Research Center: P.O. Box 273, Edwards, CA 93523.
Director.—David McBride (661) 276–3101.

Glenn Research Center at Lewisfield: 21000 Brookpark Road, Cleveland, OH 44135.
Director.—Chris Free (216) 433–4000.

Goddard Institute for Space Studies: Goddard Space Flight Center, 2880 Broadway, New York, NY 10025.
Head.—Vacant (212) 678–5500.

Goddard Space Flight Center: 8800 Greenbelt Road, Greenbelt, MD 20771.
Director.—Christopher Scolese (301) 286–2000.

Jet Propulsion Laboratory: 4800 Oak Grove Drive, Pasadena, CA 91109.
Director.—Dr. Charles Elachi (818) 354–4321.

Lyndon B. Johnson Space Center: 2101 NASA Parkway Houston, TX 77058–3696.
Director.—Dr. Ellen Ochoa (281) 483–5000.

John F. Kennedy Space Center: Kennedy Space Center, FL 32899.
Director.—Robert Cabana (321) 867–5000.

Langley Research Center: Hampton, VA 23681.
Director.—Lesa Roe (757) 864–1000.

George C. Marshall Space Flight Center: Marshall Space Flight Center, AL 35812.
Director.—Patrick Scheuermann (256) 544–1910.

Michoud Assembly Facility: P.O. Box 29300, New Orleans, LA 70189.
Manager.—Stephen C. Doering (504) 257–3311.

NASA IV and V Facility: NASA Independent Verification and Validation Facility, 100 University Drive, Fairmont, WV 26554.
Director.—Gregory D. Blaney (304) 367–8200.

NASA Management Office: Jet Propulsion Laboratory, 4800 Oak Grove Drive, Pasadena, CA 91109.
Director.—Eugene Trinh (818) 354–5359.

John C. Stennis Space Center: Stennis Space Center, MS 39529.
Director.—Dr. Richard Gilbrech (228) 688–2121.

Vandenberg AFB: P.O. Box 425, Lompoc, CA 93438.
Manager.—Ted L. Oglesby (805) 866–5859.

Wallops Flight Facility: Goddard Space Flight Center, Wallops Island, VA 23337.
Director.—William Wrobel (757) 824–1000.

White Sands Test Facility: Johnson Space Center, P.O. Drawer MM, Las Cruces, NM 88004.
Manager.—Frank J. Benz (505) 524–5771.

NASA OVERSEAS REPRESENTATIVES

Europe: U.S. Embassy-Paris, Unit 9200, Box 1653, DPO, AE 09777, 011–33–1–4312–7070.
NASA Representative.—Gilbert Kirkham.

Japan: U.S. Embassy, Tokyo, 1–10–5 Akasaka, Minato-ku, Tokyo, Japan 107–8420 81–3–3224–5000.
NASA Representative.—Christopher Blackerby.

Russia: U.S. Embassy, Moscow, NASA, DPO AE 09721, (256) 961–6333.
NASA Representative.—Thomas Plumb.

NATIONAL ARCHIVES AND RECORDS ADMINISTRATION

700 Pennsylvania Avenue, NW., 20408–0001

8601 Adelphi Road, College Park, MD 20740–6001

http://www.archives.gov

[Created by Public Law 98–497]

Archivist of the United States.—David S. Ferriero (202) 357–5900, (301) 837–1600, fax (202) 357–5901.
Deputy Archivist of the United States.—Debra S. Wall (202) 357–5900, (301) 837–1600, fax (202) 357–5901.
Chief Officers:
Financial.—Micah Cheatham (301) 837–2992, fax 837–3224.
Human Capital.—Deborah Dodson (acting), (301) 837–0366, fax 837–3195.
Innovation.—Pamela Wright (301) 837–2029, fax 837–0312.
Operating.—William J. Bosanko (301) 837–3604, fax 837–3217.
Records.—Paul Wester (301) 837–3120, fax 837–3697.
Strategy and Communications.—Donna Garland (202) 357–7464, fax 357–5901.
Executive for—
Agency Services.—Carla Riner (acting), (301) 837–0643, fax 837–1617.
Business Support Services.—Charles Piercy (301) 837–1973, fax 837–3191.
Information Services.—Michael Wash (301) 837–1992, fax 713–7409.
Legislative Archives, Presidential Libraries, and Museum Services.—Jim Gardner (202) 357–5472, fax 357–5939.
Research Services.—William Mayer (301) 837–3110, fax 837–3633.
Director for—
Federal Register.—Charley Barth (202) 741–6100, fax 741–6012.
Congressional Affairs.—John O. Hamilton (202) 357–5100, fax 357–5959.
National Historical Publications and Records Commission.—Kathleen Williams (202) 357–5263, fax 357–5914.
Equal Employment Opportunity and Diversity Office.—Ismael Martinez (301) 837–1849, fax 837–0869.
Information Security Oversight Office.—John Fitzpatrick (202) 357–5205, fax 357–5907.
General Counsel.—Gary M. Stern (301) 837–3025, fax 837–0293.
Inspector General.—Paul Brachfeld (301) 837–3000, fax 837–3197.
Communications and Marketing Division.—Chris Isleib (202) 357–5300, fax 357–5999.
Strategy Division.—Paula Jonak (301) 837–3534, fax 837–0319.

ADMINISTRATIVE COMMITTEE OF THE FEDERAL REGISTER

800 North Capitol Street, NW., Suite 700, 20001, phone (202) 741–6100

Mailing Address: 8601 Adelphi Road, College Park, MD 20740

Members:
David Ferriero, Archivist of the United States, *Chair.*
Davita Vance-Cooks, Public Printer of the United States.
Rosemary Hart, Senior Counsel, Department of Justice.
Secretary.—Charley Barth, Director of the Federal Register, National Archives and Records Administration.

NATIONAL ARCHIVES TRUST FUND BOARD

phone (301) 837–3550, fax 837–3191

Members:
David Ferriero, Archivist of the United States, *Chair.*
Jim Leach, Chairman, National Endowment for the Humanities.
Richard Gregg, Fiscal Assistant Secretary, Department of the Treasury.
Secretary.—Lawrence Post.

NATIONAL HISTORICAL PUBLICATIONS AND RECORDS COMMISSION

700 Pennsylvania Avenue, NW., 20408

phone (202) 357–5010, fax 357–5914

http://www.archives.gov/nhprc

Members:

David S. Ferriero Chairman, Archivist of the United States, National Archives and Records Administration.

Jeremy D. Fogel, Director, Federal Judicial Center, Judicial Branch.

Vacant, member of U.S. Senate.

Vacant, member of U.S. House.

James W. Ceaser, Department of Politics, University of Virginia, Presidential Appointee.

Karen L. Jefferson, Woodruff Library, Atlanta University Center, Presidential Appointee.

Erin Mahan, Chief Historian, Office of the Secretary, Department of Defense.

Nicole Saylor, Head, American Folklife Center Archive, Library of Congress.

Stephen P. Randolph, Chief Historian, Office of the Historian, Department of State.

Raymond Smock, Director, Robert C. Byrd Center for Legislative Studies, Shepherd University, Association for Documentary Editing.

Rodger E. Stroup, Curator, South Carolina Railroad Museum, American Association for State and Local History.

William G. Thomas III, Department of History, American Historical Association.

F. Gerald Handfield, National Association of Government Archives and Records Administrators.

George A. Miles, Curator of Western Americana, Bienecke Rare Book and Manuscript Library, Yale University, Organization of American Historians.

Peter Gottlieb, Society of American Archivists.

Executive Director.—Kathleen Williams (202) 357–5010.

Presidential Libraries.—Susan K. Donius (301) 837–3250, fax (301) 837–3199.

Director for—

Herbert Hoover Library.—Thomas Schwartz, West Branch, IA 52358–0488 (319) 643–5301.

Franklin D. Roosevelt Library.—Lynn Bassanese, Hyde Park, NY 12538–1999 (845) 486–7770.

Harry S. Truman Library.—Michael Devine, Independence, MO 64050–1798 (816) 268–8200.

Dwight D. Eisenhower Library.—Karl Weissenbach, Abilene, KS 67410–2900 (785) 263–6700.

John F. Kennedy Library.—Thomas Putnam, Boston, MA 02125–3398 (617) 514–1600.

Lyndon Baines Johnson Library.—Mark Updegrove, Austin, TX 78705–5737 (512) 721–0200.

Richard Nixon Library.—Susan K. Donius (acting), Yorba Linda, CA 92886 (714) 983–9120.

Gerald R. Ford Library.—Elaine K. Didier, Ann Arbor, MI 48109–2114 (734) 205–0555.

Gerald R. Ford Museum.—Elaine K. Didier, Grand Rapids, MI 49504–5353 (616) 254–0400.

Jimmy Carter Library.—Jay E. Hakes, Atlanta, GA 30307–1498 (404) 865–7100.

Ronald Reagan Library.—R. Duke Blackwood, Simi Valley, CA 93065–0699 (800) 410–8354.

George Bush Library.—Warren Finch, College Station, TX 77845 (979) 691–4000.

William J. Clinton Library.—Terri Garner, Little Rock, AR 72201 (501) 374–4242.

George W. Bush Library.—Alan Lowe, Dallas, TX 75205–2300 (972) 353–0545.

NATIONAL CAPITAL PLANNING COMMISSION

401 9th Street, NW., North Lobby, Suite 500, 20004, phone (202) 482–7200

fax 482–7272, info@ncpc.gov, http://www.ncpc.gov

APPOINTIVE MEMBERS

Presidential Appointees:
L. Preston Bryant, Jr., *Chair.*
Elizabeth Ann White.
John M. Hart.
Mayoral Appointees:
Arrington Dixon.
Robert E. Miller, NCPC Vice Chairman.
Ex Officio Members:
Chuck Hagel, Secretary of Defense.
First Alternate.—Michael L. Rhodes.
Second Alternate.—Bradley Provancha.
Ken Salazar, Secretary of the Interior.
First Alternate.—Jonathan B. Jarvis.
Second Alternate.—Vacant.
Third Alternate.—Woody Smeck.
Fourth Alternate.—Peter May.
Daniel M. Tangherlini (acting), Administrator of General Services.
First Alternate.—Julia E. Hudson.
Second Alternate.—Vacant.
Third Alternate.—Mina Wright.
Fourth Alternate.—Michael S. McGill.
Thomas R. Carper, Chairman, Senate Committee on Homeland Security and Governmental Affairs.
Alternate.—Elyse Greenwald.
Alternate.—Garth Spencer.
Alternate.—Holly Idelson.
Darrell E. Issa, Chairman, House Committee on Oversight and Government Reform.
First Alternate.—John Cuaderes.
Second Alternate.—Howard A. Denis.
Third Alternate.—Mary Pritschau.
Vincent C. Gray, Mayor of the District of Columbia.
First Alternate.—Harriet Tregoning.
Second Alternate.—Jennifer Steingasser.
Phil Mendelson, Chairman, Council of the District of Columbia.
First Alternate.—Tommy Wells.

EXECUTIVE STAFF

Executive Director.—Marcel C. Acosta, 482–7221.
Chief Operating Officer.—Barry S. Socks, 482–7209.
Secretariat.—Deborah B. Young, 482–7228.
General Counsel.—Anne R. Schuyler, 482–7223.
Director, Office of:
Administration.—Deborah B. Young, 482–7228.
Physical Planning.—William G. Dowd, 482–7240.
Policy and Research.—Michael A. Sherman, 482–7254.
Public Engagement.—Julia A. Koster, 482–7211.
Urban Design and Plan Review.—Christine Saun, 482–7245.

NATIONAL COUNCIL ON DISABILITY

1331 F Street, NW., Suite 850, 20004, phone (202) 272–2004, TTY (202) 272–2074

fax 272–2022

Chairman.—Jeff Rosen, Rockville, MD.
Co-Vice Chairs: Kamilah Oni Martin-Proctor, Washington, DC; Lynnae Ruttledge Vancouver, WA.

Members:

Gary Blumenthal, Sudbury, MA.
Chester Finn, Albany, NY.
Sara Gelser, Corvalis, OR.
Matan Aryeh Koch, New York, NY.
Captain Jonathan F. Kuniholm, USMC (Ret.), Durham, NC.
Janice Lehrer-Stein, San Francisco, CA.
Ari Ne'eman, Silver Spring, MD.
Stephanie Orlando, Albany, NY.
Clyde Terry, Concord, NH.
Fernando Torres-Gil, Los Angeles, CA.
Alice Wong, San Francisco, CA.
Pamela Young-Holmes, Madison, WI.

NATIONAL CREDIT UNION ADMINISTRATION

1775 Duke Street, Alexandria, VA 22314–3428, phone (703) 518–6300, fax 518–6319

Chairman.—Debbie Matz.
Board Member.—Michael E. Fryzel.
Secretary to the Board.—Mary Rupp.
Executive Director.—Mark Treichel, 518–6320, fax 518–6661.
Deputy Executive Director.—John Kutchey, 518–6320.
Inspector General.—William DeSarno, 518–6350.
Director, Office of:
Capital Markets.—Owen Cole, 518–6620, fax 518–6663.
Chief Financial Officer.—Mary Ann Woodson, 518–6570, fax 518–6664.
Chief Information Officer.—Ronnie Levine, 518–6440, fax 518–6669.
National Examinations and Supervision.—Scott Hunt, 518–6640, fax 518–6665.
EEO.—S. Denise Hendricks, 518–6325.
Examination and Insurance.—Larry Fazio, 518–6360, fax 518–6666.
General Counsel.—Michael McKenna, 518–6540, fax 518–6667.
Deputy General Counsel.—Lara Rodriguez.
Human Resources.—Cheryl Eyre, 518–6510, fax 518–6668.
Public and Congressional Affairs.—Todd M. Harper, 518–6330.
Small Credit Union Initiatives.—William Myers, 518–6610.

REGIONAL OFFICES

Director, Office of:

Region I (Albany).—L.J. Blankenberger, 9 Washington Square, Washington Avenue Extension, Albany, NY 12205 (518) 862–7400, fax 862–7420.

Region II (National Capital Region).—Jane A. Walters, 1775 Duke Street, Suite 4206, Alexandria, VA 22314 (703) 519–4600, fax 519–4620.

Region III (Atlanta).—Herbert Yolles, 7000 Central Parkway, Suite 1600, Atlanta, GA 30328 (678) 443–3000, fax 443–3020.

Region IV (Austin).—Keith Morton, 4807 Spicewood Springs Road, Suite 5200, Austin, TX 78759–8490 (512) 342–5600, fax 342–5620.

Region V (Tempe).—Elizabeth Whitehead, 1230 West Washington Street, Suite 301, Tempe, AZ 85281 (602) 302–6000, fax 302–6024.

President, Asset Management and Assistance Center (Austin).—Mike Barton, 4807 Spicewood Springs Road, Suite 5100, Austin, TX 78759–8490 (512) 231–7900, fax 231–7920.

NATIONAL FOUNDATION ON THE ARTS AND THE HUMANITIES

Old Post Office Building, 1100 Pennsylvania Avenue, NW., 20506

NATIONAL ENDOWMENT FOR THE ARTS

http://www.arts.gov

Chairman.—Vacant.
Chairman.—Joan Shigekawa (acting), 682–5414.
Senior Deputy Chairman.—Joan Shigekawa, 682–5414.
Deputy Chairman for Management and Budget.—Vacant, 682–5408.
Chief of Staff.—Jamie Bennett, 682–5434.
Congressional Liaison.—Mike Griffin, 682–5773.
Senior Adviser for Program Innovation.—Bill O'Brien, 682–5550.
Director of Research and Analysis.—Sunil Iyengar, 682–5424.

General Counsel.—India Pinkney, 682–5418.
Inspector General.—Toni Jones, 682–5402.

THE NATIONAL COUNCIL ON THE ARTS

Chairman.—Vacant.
Chairman.—Joan Shigekawa (acting).

Members:

Miguel Campaneria
Bruce Carter, Ph.D.
Aaron Dworkin
JoAnn Falletta
Lee Greenwood
Deepa Gupta
Paul Hodes
Joan Israelite
Maria Rosario Jackson, Ph.D.
Emil J. Kang
Charlotte Kessler
María López De León
David "Mas" Masumoto
Irvin Mayfield
Barbara Ernst Prey
Frank Price

Ex Officio Members:

Tammy Baldwin, Senator
Sheldon Whitehouse, Senator
Betty McCollum, Representative
Patrick J. Tiberi, Representative

NATIONAL ENDOWMENT FOR THE HUMANITIES

phone 1–800–NEH–1121, or (202) 606–8446, info@neh.gov, http://www.neh.gov

Chairman.—James A. Leach, 606–8310.
Deputy Chairman.—Carole Watson, 606–8572.
Director, Communications.—Judy Havemann, 606–8446.
Director, White House and Congressional Affairs.—Courtney Chapin, 606–8298.
General Counsel.—Michael McDonald, 606–8322.
Inspector General.—Laura M.H. Davis, 606–8574.
Public Information Officer.—Christopher Flynn, 606–8440.
Director, Planning and Budget.—Larry Myers, 606–8428.

NATIONAL COUNCIL ON THE HUMANITIES

Members:

Rolena K. Adorno
Adele L. Alexander
Camila A. Alire
Albert J. Beveridge III
Allison Blakely
Constance M. Carroll
Jamsheed K. Choksy
Cathy N. Davidson
Dawn H. Delbanco
Jane M. Doggett
Paula B. Duffy
Jean B. Elshtain
Gary D. Glenn
Mary Habeck
David M. Hertz
Marvin Krislov
Robert S. Martin
Christopher Merrill
Ricardo J. Quinones
Ramón Saldívar
Bruce R. Sievers
Carol M. Swain
Martha W. Weinberg
Jay Winik

FEDERAL COUNCIL ON THE ARTS AND THE HUMANITIES

Federal Council Members:

Joan Shigekawa (acting) Chairman, National Endowment for the Arts.
James A. Leach, Chairman, National Endowment for the Humanities.
Arne Duncan, Secretary, Department of Education.
G. Wayne Clough, Secretary, Smithsonian Institution.
Subra Suresh, Director, National Science Foundation.
James H. Billington, Librarian of Congress, Library of Congress.
Earl A. Powell III, Director, National Gallery of Art, Chairman, Commission of Fine Arts.
David S. Ferriero, Archivist of the United States, National Archives and Records Administration.
Dorothy Robyn, Commissioner, Public Buildings Service, General Services Administration.
Ann Stock, Assistant Secretary of State, Bureau of Educational and Cultural Affairs, Department of State.
Nancy Erickson, Secretary, United States Senate.
Rebecca Blank (acting), Secretary, Department of Commerce.

Ray H. LaHood, Secretary, Department of Transportation.
Susan Hildreth, Chairman, National Museum and Library Services Board, Director, Institute of Museum and Library Services.
Shaun L.S. Donovan, Secretary, Department of Housing and Urban Development.
Daniel M. Tangherlini (acting), Administrator, General Services Administration.
Seth D. Harris (acting), Secretary, Department of Labor.
Eric K. Shinseki, Secretary, Department of Veterans Affairs.
Kathy Greenlee, Assistant Secretary for Aging, Department of Health and Human Services.

INSTITUTE OF MUSEUM AND LIBRARY SERVICES

phone (202) 653–4657, fax 653–4625, http://www.imls.gov

[The Institute of Museum and Library Services was created by the Museum and Library Services Act of 1996, Public Law 104–208]

Director.—Susan Hildreth, 653–4711.
Deputy Director for Library Services.—Maura Marx.
Deputy Director for Museum Services.—Claudia French, 653–4717.
Director, Office of:
Communications and Government Affairs.—Mamie Bittner, 653–4757.
Chief Operating Officer.—Michael Jerger, 653–4721.
General Counsel.—Nancy Weiss, 653–4640.
Planning, Research and Evaluation.—Carlos Manjarrez, 653–4671.
Associate Deputy Director for—
Library Services, State Programs.—Laurie Brooks, 653–4650.
Associate Deputy Director for—
Library Services, Discretionary Programs.—Robert Horton, 653–4660.

NATIONAL MUSEUM AND LIBRARY SERVICES BOARD

Members:
Althemese Pemberton Barnes
Charles Benton
Julia W. Bland
Christie Pearson Brandau
Bert Castro
Jan Cellucci
John Coppola
Vishakha N. Desai
Paula Gangopadhyay
William J. Hagenah
Carla Hayden
Luis Herrera
Mark Y. Herring
Eric Jolly
Susana Torruella Leval
Mary Minow
Lawrence J. Pijeaux, Jr.
Winston Tabb
Suzanne Thorin
Robert Wedgeworth

NATIONAL GALLERY OF ART

Sixth Street and Constitution Avenue, NW., 20565

phone (202) 737–4215, http://www.nga.gov

[Under the direction of the Board of Trustees of the National Gallery of Art]

BOARD OF TRUSTEES

General Trustees:
John Wilmerding, Chairman.
Victoria P. Sant, President.
Frederick W. Beinecke.
Mitchell P. Rales.
Sharon Percy Rockefeller.
Trustees Emeriti:
Robert F. Erburu.
Julian Ganz, Jr.
Alexander M. Laughlin.
David O. Maxwell.
Ruth Carter Stevenson.
Ex Officio Trustees:
John G. Roberts, Jr., Chief Justice of the United States.
Hillary Rodham Clinton, Secretary of State.
Timothy F. Geithner, Secretary of the Treasury.
G. Wayne Clough, Secretary of the Smithsonian Institution.

Director.—Earl A. Powell III.
Deputy Director.—Franklin Kelly.
Dean, Center for Advanced Study in the Visual Arts.—Elizabeth Cropper.
Administrator.—Darrell Willson.
Treasurer.—William W. McClure.
Secretary-General Counsel.—Elizabeth A. Croog.
Executive Officer, Development and External Affairs.—Joseph J. Krakora.

NATIONAL LABOR RELATIONS BOARD

1099 14th Street, NW., 20570–0001

Personnel Locator (202) 273–1000

Chairman.—Mark Gaston Pearce, 273–1070, fax 273–4270. (Term expires August 27, 2013).
Chief Counsel.—Kent Y. Hirozawa.
Deputy Chief Counsel.—Kathleen Nixon.
Members:
Board Member.—Richard F. Griffin, Jr., 273–2986.
Chief Counsel.—Peter D. Winkler.
Deputy Chief Counsel.—Rachel G. Lennie.
Board Member.—Vacant, 273–1770.
Chief Counsel.—James R. Murphy.
Deputy Chief Counsel.—David P. Martin.
Board Member.—Vacant, 273–1790.
Chief Counsel.—Peter Carlton.
Deputy Chief Counsel.—Robert F. Kane.
Board Member.—Sharon Block, 273–1070.
Chief Counsel.—John F. Colwell.
Deputy Chief Counsel.—Andrew Krafts.
Executive Secretary.—Gary W. Shinners (acting), 273–1940, fax 273–4270.
Deputy Executive Secretary.—Gary W. Shinners, 272–3737.
Associate Executive Secretaries: Henry S. Breiteneicher, 273–2917; Farah Qureshi, 273–1949; Roxanne L. Rothschild, 273–1746.
Solicitor.—William B. Cowen, 273–2914, fax 273–1962.
Inspector General.—David P. Berry, 273–1960, fax 273–2344.
Director, Representation Appeals.—Vacant, 273–1975, fax 273–1962.
Director, Office of Public Affairs.—Nancy Cleeland, 273–1991, fax 273–1789.
Office of the Chief Information Officer, Chief Information Officer.—Bryan Burnett, 273–1450, fax 273–2850.

DIVISION OF JUDGES

Chief Administrative Law Judge.—Robert A. Giannasi, 501–8800, fax 501–8686.
Deputy Chief Administrative Law Judge.—Arthur Amchan, 501–8800.
Associate Chief Administrative Law Judge.—Vacant.
Associate Chief Administrative Law Judges:
Joel P. Biblowitz, 120 West 45th Street, 11th Floor, New York, NY 10036–5503 (212) 944–2943, fax 944–4904.
William N. Cates, 401 West Peachtree Street, NW., Suite 1708, Atlanta, GA 30308–3510 (404) 331–6654, fax 331–2061.
Gerald M. Etchingham, 901 Market Street, Suite 300, San Francisco, CA 94103–1779 (415) 356–5255, fax 356–5254.
General Counsel.—Lafe E. Solomon (acting), 273–3700, fax 273–4483.
Deputy General Counsel.—Celeste Mattina.
Director, Division of Administration.—Thomas J. Christman (acting), 273–3890, fax 273–2928.
Office of the Chief Financial Officer, Chief Financial Officer.—Ronald E. Crupi, 273–3000, fax 273–2928.

DIVISION OF OPERATIONS MANAGEMENT

Associate General Counsel.—Anne G. Purcell, 273–2900, fax 273–4274.
Deputy Associate General Counsel.—Nelson Levin.
Assistant General Counsels: Elizabeth Kilpatrick, 273–0058; Charles Posner, 273–2877; Beth Tursell, 273–2888; Dottie Wilson, 273–3781.

DIVISION OF ADVICE

Associate General Counsel.—Barry J. Kearney, 273–3800, fax 273–4275.
Deputy Associate General Counsel.—Jayme Sophir.
Assistant General Counsels:
Injunction Litigation Branch.—Elinor Merberg, 273–3833.
Regional Advice Branch.—Vacant.
Research and Policy Planning Branch.—Jacqueline A. Young, 273–3825.

DIVISION OF ENFORCEMENT LITIGATION

Associate General Counsel.—John H. Ferguson, 273–2950, fax 273–4244.
Deputy Associate General Counsel.—Margery E. Lieber, 273–2950.
Appellate and Supreme Court Litigation Branch:
Deputy Associate General Counsel.—Linda J. Dreeben, 273–2960.
Assistant General Counsel.—David Habenstreit, 273–0979.
Deputy Assistant General Counsels: Fred Jacob, 273–2971; Meredith Jason, 273–2945.
Special Litigation Branch:
Assistant General Counsel.—Abby P. Simms (acting), 273–2934, fax 273–1799.
Deputy Assistant General Counsel.—Abby P. Simms, 273–2934.
Contempt Litigation and Compliance Branch:
Assistant General Counsel.—Barbara O'Neill (acting), 273–3739, fax 273–4244.
Deputy Assistant General Counsel.—Kenneth J. Shapiro,273–3741.
Director, Office of Appeals.—Deborah M.P. Yaffe, 273–3760, 273–4283.
Deputy Director.—Vacant.

NATIONAL MEDIATION BOARD

1301 K Street, NW., Suite 250 East, 20005, phone (202) 692–5000, fax 692–5080

Chairman.—Linda Puchala, 692–5016.
Board Member.—Harry Hoglander, 692–5021.
Director, Office of:
Administration.—June D.W. King, 692–5010.
Chief of Staff.—Daniel Rainey, 692–5051.
Arbitration Services.—Roland Watkins, 692–5055.
Legal Affairs.—Mary L. Johnson, 692–5040.
Mediation Services.—Larry Gibbons, 692–5040.

NATIONAL RESEARCH COUNCIL—NATIONAL ACADEMY OF SCIENCES NATIONAL ACADEMY OF ENGINEERING—INSTITUTE OF MEDICINE

2101 Constitution Avenue, NW., 20418, phone (202) 334–2000

(Mailing address: 500 Fifth Street, NW., 20001)

The National Research Council, National Academy of Sciences, National Academy of Engineering, and Institute of Medicine, serves as an independent adviser to the Federal Government on scientific and technical questions of national importance. Although operating under a congressional charter granted the National Academy of Sciences in 1863, the National Research Council and its three parent organizations are private organizations, not agencies of the Federal Government, and receive no appropriations from Congress.

NATIONAL RESEARCH COUNCIL

Chairman.—Ralph J. Cicerone, President, National Academy of Sciences, 334–2000.
Vice Chairman.—C.D. ''Dan'' Mote, Jr., President, National Academy of Engineering, 334–3200.
Executive Officer.—Bruce B. Darling, 334–3000.
Executive Director, Office of Congressional and Government Affairs.—James E. Jensen, 334–1601.

NATIONAL ACADEMY OF SCIENCES

President.—Ralph J. Cicerone, 334–2100.

Vice President.—Diane E. Griffin, Johns Hopkins Bloomberg School of Public Health.
Home Secretary.—Susan R. Wessler, University of California, Riverside.
Foreign Secretary.—M.T. Clegg, University of California, Irvine.
Treasurer.—Jeremiah P. Ostriker, Princeton University.
Executive Officer.—Bruce B. Darling, 334–3000.

NATIONAL ACADEMY OF ENGINEERING

President.—C.D. ''Dan'' Mote, Jr., 334–3200.
Chairman.—Charles O. Holliday, Jr. (Ret.), Chairman and CEO of DuPont.
Vice President.—Maxine L. Savitz (Ret.), Honeywell, Inc.
Home Secretary.—Thomas F. Budinger, Lawrence Berkeley National Laboratory.
Foreign Secretary.—Venkatesh Narayanamurti, Harvard University.
Executive Officer.—Lance Davis, 334–3677.
Treasurer.—Martin B. Sherwin (Ret.), W.R. Grace.

INSTITUTE OF MEDICINE

President.—Harvey V. Fineberg, M.D., 334–3300.
The Leonard D. Schaeffer Executive Officer.—Clyde Behney (acting).

NATIONAL SCIENCE FOUNDATION

4201 Wilson Boulevard, Suite 1245, Arlington, VA 22230

phone (703) 292–5111, http://www.nsf.gov

Director.—Dr. Cora Marrett (acting), 292–8000.
Deputy Director.—Cora Marrett, 292–8001.
Inspector General.—Allison C. Lerner, 292–7100.
Equal Opportunity Programs.—Claudia Postell, 292–8020.
Director, Office of:
General Counsel.—Lawrence Rudolph, 292–8060.
Office of International and Integrative Activities.—Dr. Wanda Ward, 292–8040.
Office of Legislative and Public Affairs.—Judith Gan, 292–8070.
Office of Polar Programs.—Dr. Kelly Falkner, 292–8030.
Assistant Director for—
Biological Sciences.—Dr. John C. Wingfield, 292–8400.
Computer and Information Science and Engineering.—Dr. Farnam Jahanian, 292–8900.
Education and Human Resources.—Dr. Joan Ferrini-Mundy, 292–8300.
Engineering.—Dr. Pramod Khargonekar, 292–8300.
Geosciences.—Dr. Roger Wakimoto, 292–8500.
Mathematical and Physical Sciences.—Dr. F. Fleming Crim, 292–8800.
Social, Behavorial, and Economic Sciences.—Dr. Myron Gutmann, 292–8700.
Director, Office of:
Budget, Finance, and Award Management.—Martha Rubenstein, 292–8200.
Information and Resource Management.—Gene Hubbert, 292–8100.

NATIONAL SCIENCE BOARD

Chairman.—Dan E. Arizu (703) 292–7000.
Vice Chairman.—Kelvin K. Droegemier.
Executive Officer.—Dr. Michael Van Woert.

MEMBERS

Dr. Dan E. Arvizu
Dr. Deborah L. Ball
Dr. Bonnie Bassler
Dr. Arthur Bienenstock
Dr. Ray M. Bowen
Dr. Vinton G. Cerf
Dr. France A. Cordova
Dr. Ruth David
Dr. Kelvin K. Droegemier
Dr. Inez Fung
Dr. Esin Gulari
Dr. G. Peter LePage
Dr. Alan I. Leshner
Dr. W. Carl Lineberger
Dr. Steven L. Mayo
Dr. G.P. Peterson
Dr. Douglas D. Randall
Dr. Geraldine Richmond
Dr. Annelia Sargent
Dr. Diane L. Souvaine
Dr. Arnold F. Stancell
Dr. Claude M. Steele
Dr. Robert J. Zimmer
Dr. Maria Zuber
Dr. Cora Marrett

NATIONAL TRANSPORTATION SAFETY BOARD

490 L'Enfant Plaza, SW., 20594, phone (202) 314–6000

Chairman.—Deborah A.P. Hersman, 314–6662.
Vice Chairman.—Christopher A. Hart, 314–6149.
Member.—Robert L. Sumwalt III, 314–6021.
Managing Director.—David Mayer, 314–6318.
General Counsel.—David Tochen, 314–6616.
Chief Administrative Law Judge.—Alfonso Montano, Jr., 314–6150.
Chief Financial Officer.—Steven Goldberg, 314–6212.
Director, Office of:
Aviation Safety.—John Delisi, 314–6302.
Communications.—Thomas Zoeller, 314–6690.
Government Affairs.—Jane Terry, 314–6218.
Highway Safety.—Donald Karol, 314–6419.
Marine Safety.—Tracy Muurell, 314–6450.
Public Affairs.—Kelly Nantel, 314–6100.
Railroad, Pipeline and Hazardous Materials Investigations.—Stephen Klejst, 314–6098.
Research and Engineering.—Joseph Kolly, 314–6501.
Safety Advocacy.—Danielle Roeber, 314–6436.
Transportation Disaster Assistance.—Paul Sledzik, 314–6134.

NEIGHBORHOOD REINVESTMENT CORPORATION

(Doing business as NeighborWorks America)

1325 G Street, NW., Suite 800, 20005, phone (202) 220–2300, fax 376–2600

BOARD OF DIRECTORS

Chair.—Hon. Sarah Bloom Raskin, Member, Board of Governors, Federal Reserve System.
Vice Chair.—Hon. Debbie Matz, Chairman, National Credit Union Administration.
Members:
Hon. Thomas J. Curry, Comptroller of the Currency.
Hon. Carol Galante, FHA Commissioner and Assistant Secretary for Housing, HUD.
Hon. Jeremiah O. Norton, Member, Board of Directors, Federal Deposit Insurance Corporation.
Chief Executive Officer.—Eileen Fitzgerald, 220–2452.
General Counsel/Secretary.—Jeffrey T. Bryson, 220–2372.
Chief Operating Officer.—Chuck Wehrwein, 220–2410.
Chief Financial Officer.—Michael Forster, 220–2374.
Director for—
Development and Communications.—Christina McHenry, 220–7076.
Field Operations.—Don Phoenix (acting), 220–2313.
Finance and Administration.—Michael Forster, 220–2374.
Internal Audit.—Frederick Udochi, 220–2409.
Public Policy and Legislative Affairs.—Steven J. Tuminaro, 220–2415.
Training.—Paul Kealey, 220–2375.

NUCLEAR REGULATORY COMMISSION

Washington, DC 20555–0001, phone (301) 415–7000, http//www.nrc.gov

[Authorized by 42 U.S.C. 5801 and U.S.C. 1201]

OFFICE OF THE CHAIRMAN

Chairman.—Allison M. Macfarlane, 415–1820.
Chief of Staff.—Philip Niedzielski-Eichner, 415–1820.
Administrative Assistant.—Catina Gibbs, 415–1820.

COMMISSIONERS

Kristine L. Svinick, 415–1855.
Chief of Staff.—Jeffry Sharkey.

Administrative Assistant.—Janet L. Lepre.

William D. Magwood IV, 415–8430.

Chief of Staff.—Patrice Bubar.

Administrative Assistant.—Renee Taylor.

George Apostolaki, 415–1810.

Chief of Staff.—Belkys Sosa.

Administrative Assistant.—Kathleen Blake.

William C. Ostendorf, 415–1759.

Chief of Staff.—John Tappert.

Administrative Assistant.—Linda S. Herr.

STAFF OFFICES OF THE COMMISSION

Secretary.—Annette L. Vietti-Cook, 415–1969, fax 415–1672.

Chief Financial Officer.—James E. Dyer, 415–7322, fax 415–4236.

Commission Appellate Adjudication.—Brooke D. Poole, 415–2653, fax 415–3200.

Congressional Affairs.—Rebecca L. Schmidt, 415–1776, fax 415–8571.

General Counsel.—Margaret M. Doane, 415–1743, fax 415–3086.

Inspector General.—Hubert T. Bell, 415–5930, fax 415–5091.

International Programs.—Nader L. Mamish, 415–1780, fax 415–2400.

Public Affairs.—Eliot B. Brenner, 415–8200, fax 415–2234.

ADVISORY COMMITTEE ON MEDICAL USES OF ISOTOPES

Chairman.—Said Abdel-Khalik.

Committee Coordinator.—Ashley Cockerham (240) 888–7129.

ADVISORY COMMITTEE ON REACTOR SAFEGUARDS

Chairman.—Said Abdel-Khalik.

Executive Director.—Edwin M. Hackett, 415–7360, fax 415–5589.

ATOMIC SAFETY AND LICENSING BOARD PANEL

Chief Administrative Judge.—E. Roy Hawkens, 415–7454, fax 415–5599.

OFFICE OF THE EXECUTIVE DIRECTOR FOR OPERATIONS

Executive Director for Operations.—R. William Borchardt, 415–1700, fax 415–2700.

Deputy Executive Director for—

Corporate Management.—Darren Ash, 415–7443, fax 415–2700.

Materials, Waste, Research, State, Tribal and Compliance Programs.—Michael F. Weber, 415–1705, fax 415–2700.

Reactor and Preparedness Programs.—Michael R. Johnson, 415–1714, fax 415–2700.

Director, Office of:

Administration.—Cynthia A. Carpenter, 492–3500, fax 492–5400.

Enforcement.—Roy Zimmerman, 415–2741, fax 415–3431.

Federal and State Materials and Environmental Management Programs.—Mark A. Satorius, 415–7197, fax 415–6680.

Human Resources.—Miriam L. Cohen, 492–2076, fax 492–2247.

Information Services.—James P. Flanagan, 415–8700, fax 415–4246.

Investigations.—Cheryl L. McCrary, 415–2373, fax 415–2370.

New Reactors.—Glenn M. Tracy, 415–1897, fax 415–2700.

Nuclear Material Safety and Safeguards.—Catherine Haney, 492–3557, fax 492–3360.

Nuclear Reactor Regulation.—Eric J. Leeds, 415–1270, fax 415–8333.

Nuclear Regulatory Research.—Brian W. Sheron, 251–7400, fax 251–7426.

Nuclear Security and Incident Response.—James Wiggins, 415–8003, fax 415–6382.

Small Business and Civil Rights.—Vonna L. Ordaz, 415–7380, fax 415–5953.

REGIONAL OFFICES

Region I: William M. Dean, 2100 Renaissance Boulevard, Suite 100, King of Prussia, PA 19406 (610) 337–5299, fax 337–5241.

Region II: Victor McCree, 245 Peachtree Center Avenue, NE., Suite 1200, Atlanta, GA 30303 (404) 562–4410, fax 562–4766.
Region III: Charles A. Casto, 2443 Warrensville Road, Suite 210, Lisle, IL 60532 (630) 829–9657, fax 515–1096.
Region IV: Arthur T. Howell, 1600 East Lamar Boulevard, Arlington, TX 76011 (817) 860–8225, fax 860–8122.

OCCUPATIONAL SAFETY AND HEALTH REVIEW COMMISSION

1120 20th Street, NW., 20036–3457, phone (202) 606–5100

[Created by Public Law 91–596]

Chairman.—Thomasina V. Rogers, 606–5370.
Chief of Staff and Legal Counsel to the Chairman.—Richard L. Huberman, 606–5723.
Confidential Assistant to the Chairman (Public Affairs Officer).—Melik Ahmir-abdul.
Commissioner.—Cynthia L. Attwood, 606–5377.
Chief Counsel to the Commissioner.—Janice L. Glick, 606–5703.
Administrative Law Judges:
Patrick B. Augustine, U.S. Customs House, 721 19th Street, Room 407, Denver, CO 80202–2517.
Carol A. Baumerich, 1120 20th Street, NW., 9th Floor, Washington, DC 20036–3457.
Keith E. Bell, 1120 20th Street, NW., 9th Floor, Washington, DC 20036–3457.
Sharon D. Calhoun, 100 Alabama Street, SW., Building 1924, Room 2R90, Atlanta, GA 30303–3104.
William S. Coleman, 1120 20th Street, NW., 9th Floor, Washington, DC 20036–3457.
Brian A. Duncan, U.S. Customs House, 721 19th Street, Room 407, Denver, CO 80202–2517.
Dennis L. Phillips, 1120 20th Street, NW., 9th Floor, Washington, DC 20036–3457.
Covette Rooney, 1120 20th Street, NW., 9th Floor, Washington, DC 20036–3457.
John H. Schumacher, U.S. Customs House, 721 19th Street, Room 407, Denver, CO 80202–2517.
Stephen J. Simko, 100 Alabama Street, SW., Building 1924, Room 2R90, Atlanta, GA 30303–3104.
Horace A. Thompson III, U.S. Customs House, 721 19th Street, Room 407, Denver, CO 80202–2517.
Ken S. Welsch, 100 Alabama Street, SW., Building 1924, Room 2R90, Atlanta, GA 30303–3104.
General Counsel.—Nadine N. Mancini.
Executive Secretary.—Ray H. Darling, Jr.
Executive Director.—Debra A. Hall.

OFFICE OF GOVERNMENT ETHICS

1201 New York Avenue, NW., Suite 500, 20005, phone (202) 482–9300, fax 482–9238

[Created by Act of October 1, 1989; codified in 5 U.S.C. app., section 401]

Director.—Walter M. Shaub, Jr.
Assistant to the Director.—Teresa Weakley.
Principal Deputy Director and General Counsel.—Don W. Fox.
Program Counsel.—Shelley K. Finlayson.
Deputy Director for Compliance.—Joseph E. Gangloff.
Assistant Director for Compliance.—Barbara A. Mullen-Roth.
Deputy Director for International Assistance and Internal Operations.—Jane S. Ley.

OFFICE OF PERSONNEL MANAGEMENT

Theodore Roosevelt Building, 1900 E Street, NW., 20415–0001

phone (202) 606–1800, http://www.opm.gov

OFFICE OF THE DIRECTOR

Director.—Elaine Kaplan (acting), 606–1000.
Senior Executive Assistant.—Demetriss Williams.

Deputy Director.—Vacant.
Executive Assistant.—Vacant.
Senior Advisor.—Vacant.
Chief of Staff.—Elizabeth Montoya.
Deputy Chiefs of Staff: Justin Johnson, Jennifer I. Mason.
Executive Assistant.—Torlanda Young.
Counselors to the Director: Vic Basile, Michael A. Grant.
Executive Assistant.—Leroy Moore.
Chief Operating Officer.—Chuck Grimes.
Executive Assistant.—Vannessa Brown.
Special Assistant to the Director.—Matthew W. Collier.
White House Fellow.—Amen Mashariki.
CHCO Executive Director.—Kathryn M. Medina.

EXECUTIVE SECRETARIAT AND OMBUDSMAN

Director.—Chris Hammond, 606–1100.
Ombudsman.—Barbara Malebranche, 606–3132.
Resource Management.—Jozetta R. Robinson, 606–8004.
Executive Correspondence.—Joann C. Rockwell, 606–1000
International Affairs.—Jill Feldman, 606–5099.
Regulatory Affairs.—Stephen D. Hickman, 606–1941.

CHIEF FINANCIAL OFFICER

Chief Financial Officer.—Dennis D. Coleman, 606–1918.
Deputy Chief Financial Officer.—Daniel K. Marella, 606–2638.
Executive Officer/Resource Management.—Katina P. Cotton, 606–4725.
OPM Projects and Initiatives.—Teresa F. Williams, 606–1414.
Policy and Internal Control.—Robert T. Wurster, 606–5220.
Travel Operations.—Michael Divittorio, 606–9318.
Associate CFO:
Budget and Performance.—Margaret P. Pearson, 606–1491.
Financial Services.—Kolo Babagana (acting), 606–1676.
Financial Systems Management.—Rochelle S. Bayard, 606–4366.

COMMUNICATIONS AND PUBLIC LIAISON

Director.—Thomas J. Richards, 606–2402.
Deputy Director.—Catherine Hand.
Press Secretary.—Sedelta Verble.
Director, External Communications.—Edmund D. Byrnes.
Web Presence.—Vivian Mackey.
Creative Services.—Jay Porter.
Speechwriting and Editorial.—John A. LaRue.
Administrative Assistant.—Jean A. Smith.

CONGRESSIONAL, LEGISLATIVE AND INTERGOVERNMENTAL AFFAIRS

Director.—Tania A. Shand, 606–1300.
Executive Assistant.—Vacant.
Deputy Director.—Jennifer Tyree.
Congressional Relations Officers: Jill L. Crissman, Christopher Medley.
Chief, Legislative Analysis.—Christopher Wallace, 606–1424.
Legislative Analysts: John Barone, Steven J. Driscoll, Janell Fitzhugh.
Administrative Assistant.—Vacant.
Chief, Constituent Services, Capitol Hill.—Jennifer Tyree (acting), B332 Rayburn House Office Building, 225–4955, fax 225–4974.
Constituent Services Representatives: Moshafa ''Fatima'' Moghis, Kristen Soper, Carlos E. Tingle.
Administrative Assistant.—Kirk H. Brightman.

FEDERAL INVESTIGATIVE SERVICES

Associate Director.—Merton Miller (724) 794–5612.
Deputy Associate Director.—Vacant.
Executive Assistant.—Jody L. Montgomery.
Deputy Associate Directors:
External Affairs.—M. Colleen Crowley, 606–1042.
Management Services.—Thomas L. Forman, 606–1042.
Operations.—Mark P. Sherwin (acting), (724) 794–5612.
Quality.—Jeffrey C. Flora (443) 698–9400.

MERIT SYSTEM AUDIT AND COMPLIANCE

Associate Director.—Mark W. Lambert, 606–2980.
Deputy Associate Director.—Ana Mazzi.
Directors:
CFC Operations.—Keith Willingham, 606–2564.
Internal Oversight and Compliance.—Janet L. Barnes, 606–3207.
Voting Rights and Resource Management.—Vacant.
Administrative Assistant.—Kimberlin C. Clark.

CHIEF INFORMATION OFFICER

Chief Information Officer.—Chuck Simpson (acting), 606–2150.
Deputy Chief Information Officer.—Chuck Simpson.
Management Assistant.—Latisha Jones.
Deputy CIO for Operations.—Joy S. Fairtile.
Chief Technology Officer.—Vacant.

HUMAN RESOURCES SOLUTIONS

Associate Director.—Joseph S. Kennedy, 606–0900.
Principal Deputy Associate Director.—Kathleen McGettigan, 606–1594.
Executive Assistant.—Shirl Sibley, 606–0900.
Resource Management.—Curt Marshall, 606–2010.
Administrative Law Judge.—Juanita Howard Love, 606–3822.
Deputy Associate Directors:
Center for Leadership Development, Assistant Director.—Maureen B. Higgins, 606–2855.
Center for Leadership Development, Federal Executive Institute Director.—Suzanne G. Logan (434) 980–6220.
Center for Management Services.—Reginald M. Brown, 606–1332.
Eastern Center/Training Delivery.—Teresa Trainor (304) 870–8038.
Federal Staffing Group.—Dianna Saxman (215) 362–3154.
HR Strategy and Evaluation Solutions.—Leslie Pollack, 606–1426.
Training and Management Assistance Program.—George Price, 606–8614.
Western Center/Custom Solutions.—William Bonds (303) 671–1027.

RETIREMENT SERVICES

Associate Director.—Kenneth Zawodny, Jr. 606–3502.
Deputy Associate Director for—
Retirement Operations.—Nicholas Ashenden (724) 794–2005.
Retirement Services.—Linda Bradford, 606–4168.

OFFICE OF THE GENERAL COUNSEL

General Counsel.—Sharon McGowan (acting), 606–1700.
Deputy General Counsel.—Kathie Ann Whipple.
Deputy General Counsel for Policy.—Vacant.
Associate General Counsel (Compensation, Benefits, Products and Services).—R. Alan Miller.
Assistant General Counsel (Merit Systems and Accountability).—Steven E. Abow.
Chief, Administration (Administrative Officer).—Gloria V. Clark.

OFFICE OF THE INSPECTOR GENERAL

Inspector General.—Patrick E. McFarland, 606–1200.
Deputy Inspector General.—Norbert E. Vint.
Executive Assistant.—A. Paulette Berry.
Assistant Inspector General for Legal Affairs.—J. David Cope.
Counsel to the Inspector General.—Timothy C. Watkins, 606–2030.
Assistant Inspector General for Management.—Terri H. Fazio, 606–0846.
Deputy Assistant Inspector General for Management.—Joyce D. Price, 606–2156.
Assistant Inspector General for Audits.—Michael R. Esser, 606–1200.
Deputy Assistant Inspector General for Audits.—Vacant, Melissa D. Brown, 606–4714.
Assistant Inspector General for Investigations.—Michelle B. Schmitz, 606–1200.
Deputy Assistant Inspector General for Investigations.—Kimberly A. Howell.

FACILITIES, SECURITY AND CONTRACTING

Director.—Dean Hunter, 606–2200.
Resource Management.—James S. Connors, 606–1047.
Small and Disadvantaged Business Utilization and Policy.—Desmond Brown, 606–2083.
Contracting.—W. Neal Patterson, 606–1984.
Facilities Management.—Mariano S. Aquino, 606–4590.
Publications Management.—Ray J. Theriault, 606–1822.
Security Services.—Kevin McCombs (acting), 418–0201.
Personnel Security.—Melinda M. Davis (724) 794–7112.
Emergency Actions.—Sandra L. Hawthorne, 606–5068.

EQUAL EMPLOYMENT OPPORTUNITY

Director.—Lorna Lewis, 606–2460.
Lead EEO Specialist: Nicole Lassiter, LaShonn Woodland.

DIVERSITY AND INCLUSION

Director.—Veronica E. Villalobos, 606–0020.
Senior Diversity Program Managers: Bruce Stewart, Sharon Wong.

HEALTHCARE AND INSURANCE

Director.—John O'Brien, 606–2634.
Deputy Director.—Vacant.
Chief Medical Officer.—Christine Hunter, 606–4653.
Resource Management.—Danny A. Cieslicki, 606–0067.
Assistant Director for—
Federal Employee Insurance Operations.—Shirley Patterson, 606–1234.
National Healthcare Operations.—Robert H. Shriver, 606–2044.

PLANNING AND POLICY ANALYSIS

Director.—Jonathan Foley, 606–4794.
Deputy Director.—Anne Easton, 606–2213.
Chief Actuary.—Steve Niu, 606–1578.

EMPLOYEE SERVICES

Associate Director and Chief Human Capital Officer.—Angela Bailey, 606–0388.
Principal Deputy Associate Director.—Vacant, 606–1575.
Deputy Associate Directors:
Partnership and Labor Relations.—Tim F. Curry, 606–2584.
Pay and Leave.—Jeanne Jacobson (acting), 606–2858.
Recruitment and Hiring.—Kimberly Holden, 418–3218.
Senior Executive Service and Performance Management.—Stephen T. Shih, 606–8046.
Strategic Workforce Planning.—Sydney Smith-Heimbrock, 606–2762.
Veterans Services.—Ray Decker, 606–2511.

Deputy Associate Director, OPM Human Resources and Deputy Chief Human Capital Officer.—Mark D. Reinhold, 606–1402.
Human Resources Deputy Director.—Andrea Bright, 606–3590.

OFFICE OF THE SPECIAL COUNSEL

1730 M Street, NW., Suite 300, 20036–4505, phone (202) 254–2000

[Authorized by 5 U.S.C 1101 and 5 U.S.C 1211]

Special Counsel.—Carolyn Lerner.
Deputy Special Counsel.—Mark Cohen.
Policy and Congressional Affairs Division.—Adam Miles.
Senior Legal Counsel.—Jason Zuckerman.

THE PEACE CORPS

1111 20th Street, NW., 20526, phone (202) 692–2000

Toll-Free Number (855) 855–1961, http://www.peacecorps.gov

[Created by Public Law 97–113]

OFFICE OF THE DIRECTOR

phone (202) 962–2100, fax 692–2101

Director.—Carrie Hessler-Radelet (acting).
Deputy Director.—Carrie Hessler-Radelet.
Chief of Staff.—W. Stacy Rhodes.
White House Liaison/Counselor to the Director.—Elisa Montoya.
Senior Advisor to the Director.—Carl Sosebee.
Senior Advisor.—Maryann Minutillo.
Expert Consultant.—James Cuffe.
Administrative Officer.—Nina Basiliko.

OFFICE OF VICTIM ADVOCACY

Director.—Kellie Greene.
Chief Compliance Officer.—Daljit Bains.

OFFICE OF INNOVATION

Director.—Patrick Choquette (acting).

OFFICE OF CIVIL RIGHTS AND DIVERSITY

Director.—David King.

OFFICE OF COMMUNICATIONS

Director.—Maureen Knightly.
Deputy Director.—Kristen Fernekes (acting).
Director of Press Relations.—Vacant.

OFFICE OF CONGRESSIONAL RELATIONS

Director.—Alyson Hatchett (acting).
Deputy Director.—Jeremy Haldeman.

OFFICE OF THE GENERAL COUNSEL

General Counsel.—Bill Rubin.

OFFICE OF STRATEGIC PARTNERSHIPS

Associate Director.—Corey Griffin.

OFFICE OF INTERGOVERNMENTAL AFFAIRS AND GLOBAL PARTNERSHIPS

Director.—Nicole Mlade.

OFFICE OF GIFTS AND GRANTS MANAGEMENT

Director.—Jennifer Chavez Rubio.

OFFICE OF UNIVERSITY AND DOMESTIC PARTNERSHIPS

Director.—Rebecca Sharp.

OFFICE OF STRATEGIC INFORMATION RESEARCH AND PLANNING

Director.—Cathryn Thorup.
Deputy Director.—Jamie Loughridge.

OFFICE OF THIRD GOAL AND RETURNED VOLUNTEER SERVICE

Director.—Eileen Conoboy.

OFFICE OF GLOBAL OPERATIONS

Associate Director.—Carlos Torres (acting).
Senior Advisors: Peter Redmond, Diana Schmidt.

Africa Operations:

Regional Director.—Dick Day.
Chief of Operations.—Michael Simsik.

Europe / Mediterranean / Asia Region:

Regional Director.—Helen Lowman.
Chief of Operations.—David Burgess.

Inter-America and Pacific Region:

Regional Director.—Nina Favor (acting).
Chief of Operations.—Shelley Swediman (acting).

Office of Overseas Programming and Training Support:

Director.—Sonia Stines Derenoncourt.

Peace Corps Response:

Director.—Sarah Morgenthau.
Chief of Operations.—Tom Ross.

Office of Global Health and HIV:

Director.—Kathy Rulon (acting).

Office of Management:

Associate Director.—Garry Stanberry (acting).

Management / Administrative Services:

Chief of Administrative Services.—James Pimpedly.

Transportation:

Chief of Transportation.—Pat Kreamer.

Office of Human Resource Management:

Director.—Karen Bickle.

Overseas Recruitment, Selection, and Support:

Manager.—Peter Loan.

FOIA / Privacy Act:

FOIA / Privacy Act Officer.—Denora Miller.

OFFICE OF THE INSPECTOR GENERAL

Inspector General.—Kathy Buller.
Deputy Inspector General.—Joaquin Ferrao.

OFFICE OF ACQUISITIONS AND CONTRACT MANAGEMENT

Chief Acquisition Officer.—Lisa Bilder.

OFFICE OF THE CHIEF FINANCIAL OFFICER

Chief Financial Officer.—Joe Hepp.
Deputy Chief Financial Officer.—Paul Shea.

OFFICE OF THE CHIEF INFORMATION OFFICER

Chief Information Officer.—Dorine Andrews.

OFFICE OF VOLUNTEER RECRUITMENT AND SELECTION

Associate Director.—Earl Yates.
Chief of Operations.—Amy Drader.
Director of Placement and Staging.—Nicholas Bassey.
Director of Recruitment.—Vacant.

REGIONAL OFFICES

Atlanta (FL, GA, TN, MS, AL, SC, PR): 60 Forsyth Street, Suite 3M40, Atlanta, GA 30303 (404) 562–3451, fax 562–3455.
Manager.—Eric Zdanowicz.
Public Affairs Specialist.—Alethea Parker.
Chicago (IL, IN, KY, MI, MO, OH, IA, MN, ND, SD, WI): 55 West Monroe Street, Suite 450, Chicago, IL 60603 (312) 353–4990, fax 353–4192.
Manager.—Brad Merryman.
Public Affairs Specialist.—Christine Torres.
Dallas (AR, LA, NM, OK, TX, CO, KS, NE, UT, WY): 1100 Commerce Street, Suite 427, Dallas, TX 75242 (214) 253–5400, fax 253–5401.
Manager.—Michael McKay.
Public Affairs Specialist.—LaShonda Walker.
Los Angeles (Southern CA, AZ): 2361 Rosecrans Avenue, Suite 155, El Segundo, CA 90245 (310) 356–1100, fax 356–1125.
Recruitment Supervisor.—Johann D'Agostino.
Public Affairs Coordinator.—Bruno Veselic.
New York (NY, NJ, CT, PA, MA, VT, NH, RI, ME): 201 Varick Street, Suite 1025, New York, NY 10014 (212) 352–5440, fax 352–5442.
Manager.—Brian Melman.
Public Affairs Coordinator.—Margaret Rusek.
San Francisco (Northern CA, NV, HI): 1301 Clay Street, Suite 620N, Oakland, CA 94612 (510) 452–8444, fax 452–8441.
Manager.—Janet Allen.
Public Affairs Specialist.—Vacant.
Seattle (WA, OR, ID, AK, MT): Westlake Building, 1601 5th Avenue, Suite 605, Seattle, WA 98101 (206) 553–5490, fax 553–2343.
Recruitment Supervisor.—Erin Carlson.
Public Affairs Specialist.—Vacant.
Washington, DC (DC, MD, NC, WV, DE, VA): 1111 20th Street, NW., Washington, DC 20526 (202) 692–1040, fax 692–1041.
Manager.—Christopher Gilson.
Public Affairs Specialist.—Kelly McCormack.

OFFICE OF SAFETY AND SECURITY

Associate Director.—Ed Hobson.

PHYSICAL SECURITY

Physical Security Specialist.—John McIntire.

OFFICE OF HEALTH SERVICES

Associate Director.—Jules Delaune.
Deputy Associate Director.—Brenda Goodman.

Office of Medical Services:

Director.—Barry Simon.

Counseling and Outreach Unit:

Director.—Tim Lawler.

PENSION BENEFIT GUARANTY CORPORATION

1200 K Street, 20005–4026, (202) 326–4000

BOARD OF DIRECTORS

Chairman.—Thomas Perez, Secretary of Labor.
Members:
Jack Lew, Secretary of the Treasury.
Penny Pritzker, Deputy Secretary of Commerce.

OFFICIALS

Director.—Josh Gotbaum, 326–4010.
Deputy Chief Policy Officer.—Leslie Kramerich.
Chief Officer for—
Finance.—Patricia Kelly, 326–4060.
Information Technology.—Barry West, 326–4000.
Negotiations and Restructuring.—Sandy Rich, 326–4000.
Management.—Alice Maroni, 326–4000.
Department Director for—
Benefits Administration and Payment.—Phillip Langham, 326–4050.
Budget and Organizational Performance.—Edgar Bennett, 326–4120.
Communications and Public Affairs.—Jioni Palmer, 326–4040.
Contracts and Controls Review.—Martin Boehm, 326–4161.
Facilities and Services.—Cathleen Kronopolus, 326–4150.
Financial Operations.—Theodore Winter, 326–4060.
General Counsel.—Judith Starr, 326–4020.
Human Resources.—Arrie Etheridge, 326–4110.
Information Technology Infrastructure Operations.—Deborah Herald, 326–4130.
Information Technology and Business Modernization.—Srividhya Shyamsunder, 326–4000.
Corporate Finance and Restructuring.—Kristina Archeval, 326–4070.
Legislative and Regulatory Affairs.—John Hanley, 326–4000.
Policy, Research and Analysis.—Salil Mehta, 326–4080.

POSTAL REGULATORY COMMISSION

901 New York Avenue, NW., Suite 200, 20268–0001

phone (202) 789–6800, fax 789–6891

Chairman.—Ruth Y. Goldway, 202–789–6810.
Vice Chairman.—Robert Taub, 202–789–6897.
Commissioners:
Mark Acton, 202–789–6866.
Tony Hammond, 202–789–6805.
Nanci Langley, 202–789–6887.
Chief Administrative Officer and Secretary.—Shoshana Grove, 202–789–6842.
Director, Public Affairs and Government Relations.—Ann Fisher, 202–789–6803.
General Counsel.—Stephen L. Sharfman, 202–789–6818.
Director, Office of Accountability and Compliance.—Margaret Cigno, 202–789–6855.

SECURITIES AND EXCHANGE COMMISSION

100 F Street, NE., 20549, phone (202) 551–7500

TTY Relay Service 1–800–877–8339 http://www.sec.gov

THE COMMISSION

Chairman.—Mary Jo White, 551–2100, fax 772–9200.
Chief of Staff.—Lona Nallengara.
Deputy Chiefs of Staff: Nathaniel Stankard, Erica Williams.
Special Counsel.—Geoffrey Aronow.
Senior Advisors to the Chairman: Tamara Brightwell, Christian Broadbent, Michael Liftik, Cristie March, Jennifer McHugh.
Commissioners:
Elisse Walter, 551–2800, fax 772–9340.
Counsels to the Commissioner: Sara Cortes, Cyndi Rodriguez.
Luis A. Aguilar, 551–2500, fax 772–9335.
Counsels to the Commissioner: Paul Gumagay, Liban Jama, Marc Leaf, Smeeta Ramarathnam.
Troy A. Paredes, 551–2700, fax 772–9330.
Counsels to the Commissioner: Michael Diduk, Jaime Klima, Saurabh Shah.
Daniel M. Gallagher, 551–2600, fax 772–9345.
Counsels to the Commissioner: Anil Abraham, Stephen Devine, Joseph I. Levinson, Elad Roisman.

OFFICE OF THE SECRETARY

Secretary.—Elizabeth Murphy, 551–5400, fax 772–9324.
Deputy Secretaries: Kevin O'Neill, 551–5472; Lynn Powalski, 551–4927.
Assistant Secretary.—Jill Peterson, 551–5458.

OFFICE OF LEGISLATIVE AND INTERGOVERNMENTAL AFFAIRS

Director.—Timothy Henseler, 551–2010, fax 772–9250.
Deputy Directors: Keith Cassidy, 551–2096; Julie Z. Davis, 551–2233.

OFFICE OF THE CHIEF OPERATING OFFICER

Chief Operating Officer.—Jeff Heslop, 551–2200.

OFFICE OF INVESTOR EDUCATION AND ADVOCACY

Director.—Lori J. Schock, 551–6500, fax 772–9295.
Deputy Director.—Mary S. Head, 551–6351.

OFFICE OF SUPPORT OPERATIONS

Director/Chief FOIA Officer.—Barry Walters, 551–8400.
FOIA Officer.—John Livornese, 551–8400, fax 772–9336.

OFFICE OF EQUAL EMPLOYMENT OPPORTUNITY

Director.—Alta Rodriguez, 551–6040, fax 772–9316.

OFFICE OF MINORITY AND WOMEN INCLUSION

Director.—Pamela Gibbs, 551–6503.
Deputy Director.—Laura Stomski, 551–4102.

OFFICE OF THE CHIEF ACCOUNTANT

Chief Accountant.—Paul Beswick, 551–5300, fax 772–9253.
Chief Counsel.—Jeff Minton, 551–5342.

OFFICE OF COMPLIANCE INSPECTIONS AND EXAMINATIONS

Director.—Andrew Bowden, 551–6200, fax 772–9179.
Deputy Director.—Vacant.
Associate Director/Chief Counsel.—Paula Drake, 551–6460.
Associate Directors: Vacant (Broker/Dealer); Dawn Patterson (Clearance and Settlement), (212) 336–0047; John Polise (Market Oversight), 551–4981; Vacant (Investment Adviser/ Investment Company).

DIVISION OF RISK, STRATEGY, AND FINANCIAL INNOVATION

Director and Chief Economist.—Craig Lewis, 551–6646, fax 756–0505.
Deputy Directors.—Kathleen Hanley, 551–6255; Jennifer Marietta-Westberg, 551–6659.

OFFICE OF THE GENERAL COUNSEL

General Counsel.—Ann K. Small, 551–5100, fax 772–9260.
Deputy General Counsels: Michael Conley, 551–5100; Meredith Mitchell, 551–5184.
Associate General Counsel for Litigation and Adjudication.—Vacant, 551–5169.
Solicitor, Appellate Litigation and Bankruptcy.—Jacob Stillman, 551–5130.
Deputy Solicitor.—John Avery, 551–5127.
Associate General Counsel for Legal Policy 1.—Vacant.
Associate General Counsel for Legal Policy 2.—Richard Levine, 551–5168.
Associate General Counsel for Litigation and Administrative Practice.—Richard M. Humes, 551–5140.

OFFICE OF ETHICS COUNSEL

Ethics Counsel and Designated Ethics Officer.—Shira Minton, 551–7938.

DIVISION OF INVESTMENT MANAGEMENT

Director.—Norm Champ (212) 336–0446, fax 772–7234.
Deputy Director.—David Grim, 551–6767.
Associate Director, Chief Counsel.—Douglas J. Scheidt, 551–6701.
Enforcement Liaison.—Barbara Chretien-Dar, 551–6785.
Associate Director, Office of:
Exemptive Application.—Elizabeth G. Osterman, 551–6746.
Disclosure Review and Accounting.—Barry D. Miller, 551–6725.
Insured Investments.—Susan Nash, 551–6742.
Regulatory Policy and Investment Adviser Regulation.—Vacant.
Rulemaking.—Diane Blizzard, 551–6864.
Chief Accountant, Office of Chief Accountant.—Jaime Eichen, 551–6918.

DIVISION OF CORPORATION FINANCE

Director.—Keith Higgins, 551–3100, fax 772–9215.
Deputy Director of:
Disclosure Operations.—Shelley E. Parratt, 551–3130.
Legal and Regulatory.—Vacant.
Policy and Capital Markets.—Paula Dubberly, 551–3180.
Associate Director, Regulatory Policy.—Mauri L. Osheroff, 551–3190.
Chief Accountant.—Vacant, 551–3400.
Disclosure Operations: Paul Belvin, 551–3150; James Daly, 551–3140; Karen Garnett, 551–3780; Mark Kronforst, 551–3870; Kyle Moffatt, 551–3836; Barry Summer, 551–3160.
Chief Counsel.—Thomas Kim, 551–3520.

DIVISION OF ENFORCEMENT

Directors: George Canellos, Andrew Ceresney, 551–4500, fax 772–9279.
Deputy Director.—David Bergers (acting), 551–4787.
Managing Executive.—Adam Storch, 551–4625.
Associate Directors: Kara Brockmeyer, 551–4767; Stephen Cohen, 551–4834; Scott Friestad, 551–4962; Gerald Hodgkins, 551–4719.

Chief, Market Surveillance.—Vincente Martinez, 551–4541.
Associate Directors: Antonia Chion, 551–4842; Kenneth Lench, 551–4938; Reid Muoio, 551–4488.
Chief Counsel.—Joseph Brenner, 551–4933.
Chief Litigation Counsel.—Matthew Martens, 551–4481.
Deputy Chief Litigation Counsel.—Vacant.
Chief Accountant.—Howard Scheck.
Deputy Chief Accountant.—Jason Flemmons.
Office of Collections: Gordon Brumback, 551–4424; Marsha Massey, 551–4452.
Office of Whistleblower, Chief.—Sean McKessey, 551–4786.

DIVISION OF TRADING AND MARKETS

Director.—John Ramsay (acting), 551–5500, fax 772–9273.
Deputy Directors: James Burns, 551–5733, Vacant.
Associate Director, Chief Counsel.—David Blass, 551–5165.
Associate Directors:
Broker Dealer Finances.—Michael Macchiaroli, 551–5525.
Clearance and Settlement.—Peter Curley, 551–5696.
Trading Practices.—Brian Bussey, 551–5571.
Market Supervision: Heather Seidel, 551–5608; David Shillman, 551–5685.

OFFICE OF CREDIT RATINGS

Director.—Tom Butler (212) 336–9080.

OFFICE OF MUNICIPAL SECURITIES

Director.—John Cross, 551–5839.

OFFICE OF ADMINISTRATIVE LAW JUDGES

Chief Administrative Law Judge.—Brenda Murray, 551–6030, fax 777–1031.
Administrative Law Judges: Cameron Elliot, Carol Fox Foelak, Robert Mahony.

OFFICE OF INTERNATIONAL AFFAIRS

Director.—Robert Fisher (acting), 551–6690, fax 772–9280.
Deputy Director.—Elizabeth Jacobs, 551–6676.

OFFICE OF THE INSPECTOR GENERAL

Inspector General.—Carle Hoecker, 551–6060, fax 772–9265.
Deputy Inspector General.—Vacant, 551–6035.

OFFICE OF PUBLIC AFFAIRS

Director.—John Nester, 551–4120, fax 777–1026.
Deputy Director.—Florence Harmon, 551–5604.

OFFICE OF FINANCIAL MANAGEMENT

Chief Financial Officer.—Kenneth Johnson, 551–7840, fax 756–0473.
Chief Accounting Officer.—Caryn Kauffman, 551–8834.

OFFICE OF INFORMATION TECHNOLOGY

Director/Chief Information Officer.—Thomas A. Bayer, 551–8800, fax (703) 914–2621.
Deputy Director/Deputy Chief Information Officer.—Pam Dyson.

OFFICE OF ADMINISTRATIVE SERVICES

Associate Executive Director.—Vance Cathrell, 551–7400, fax (703) 914–4459.

OFFICE OF HUMAN RESOURCES

Executive Director.—Lacey Dingman, 551–7500, fax 777–1028.

REGIONAL OFFICES

Atlanta Regional Office: 3475 Lenox Road, NE., Suite 1000, Atlanta, GA 30326 (404) 842–7600, fax (404) 842–7633.
Regional Director.—Rhea Kemble Dignam, 842–7610.
Associate Regional Director.—William P. Hicks, 842–7675.
Boston Regional Office: 33 Arch Street, 23rd Floor, Boston, MA 02110 (617) 573–8900, fax (617) 573–4590.
Regional Director.—David Bergers, 573–8927.
Associate District Director, Enforcement.—John Dugan, 573–8936.
Associate Regional Director, Examinations.—Lucile Corkery, 573–8932.
Chicago Regional Office: 175 West Jackson Boulevard, Suite 900, Chicago, IL 60604 (312) 353–7390, fax 353–7398.
Regional Director.—Merri Jo Gillette, 353–9338.
Senior Associate Regional Director, Enforcement.—Robert J. Burson, 353–7428.
Associate Regional Director, Enforcement.—Timothy L. Warren, 353–7394.
Associate Regional Directors, Examinations: Jane E. Jarcho, 353–5479; Barbara S. Lorenzen, 353–7436.
Denver Regional Office: 1801 California Street, Suite 1500, Denver, CO 80202 (303) 844–1000, fax (303) 844–1010.
Regional Director.—Donald M. Hoerl, 844–1060.
Associate Regional Director.—Julie K. Lutz, 844–1056.
Supervisory Trial Counsel.—Thomas J. Krysa, 844–1118.
Associate Regional Director, Office of the Regulator.—Kevin Goodman, 844–1040.
Fort Worth Regional Office: 801 Cherry Street, Unit #18, Fort Worth, TX 76102 (817) 978–3821, fax 978–2700.
Regional Director.—David Woodcock, 900–2623.
Associate Regional Director, Enforcement.—David Peavler, 978–1417.
Regional Trial Counsel.—Toby Galloway, 978–6447.
Associate Regional Director, Examinations.—Marshall Gandy, 900–2622.
Los Angeles Regional Office: 5670 Wilshire Boulevard, 11th Floor, Los Angeles, CA 90036 (323) 965–3998, fax 965–3816.
Regional Director.—Michelle Wein Layne, 965–3850.
Associate Regional Directors, Enforcement: Lorraine Echavarria, 965–3914; John McCoy III, 965–3864.
Senior Regional Trial Counsel, Enforcement.—Kelly C. Bowers, 965–3924.
Associate Regional Director, Regulation.—Martin J. Murphy, 965–3859.
Miami Regional Office: 801 Brickell Avenue, Suite 1800, Miami, FL 33131 (305) 982–6300, fax (305) 536–4120.
Regional Director.—Eric Bustillo, 982–6332.
Associate Regional Directors:
Enforcement.—Glenn S. Gordon, 536–6360.
Examination.—John C. Mattimore, 982–6357.
New York Regional Office: 3 World Financial Center, Suite 400, New York, NY 10281–1022, (212) 336–1100, fax (212) 336–1323.
Regional Director.—Andrew Calamari, 336–0042.
Associate Regional Directors, Enforcement: Robert B. Blackburn, 336–1050; Robert Keyes, 336–0109; David Rosenfeld, 336–0153; Sanjay Wadhwa, 336–0181.
Associate Regional Directors:
Broker/Dealer.—Robert A. Sollazzo, 336–1070.
Investment Adviser/Investment Company.—Ken Joseph, 336–0097.
Philadelphia Regional Office: Mellon Independence Center, 701 Market Street, Suite 2000, Philadelphia, PA 19106 (215) 597–3100, fax 597–3194.
Regional Director.—Daniel Hawke, 597–3191.
Associate Regional Directors:
Enforcement.—Elaine C. Greenberg, 597–3107.
Regulation.—Joy G. Thompson, 597–6135.
Salt Lake Regional Office: 15 West South Temple Street, Suite 1800, Salt Lake City, UT 84101 (801) 524–5796, fax 524–3558.
Regional Director.—Kenneth D. Israel, 524–6745.
San Francisco Regional Office: 44 Montgomery Street, Suite 2600, San Francisco, CA 94104 (415) 705–2500, fax 705–2501.

Regional Directors: Michael S. Dicke (acting), 705–2458; Kristin A. Snyder (acting), 705–2373.
Associate Regional Directors:
Enforcement.—Michael S. Dicke, 705–2458.
Examinations.—Kristin A. Snyder, 705–2373.

SELECTIVE SERVICE SYSTEM

1515 Wilson Boulevard, 5th Floor, Arlington, VA 22209–2425

phone (703) 605–4100, fax 605–4106, http://www.sss.gov

Director.—Lawrence G. Romo, 605–4010.
Inspector General.—Mariano Campos (acting), 605–4111.
Director for—
Operations.—Mariano Campos, 605–4111.
Public and Intergovernmental Affairs.—Richard S. Flahavan, 605–4017, fax 605–4106.
Financial Management.—Roderick R. Hubbard, 605–4022.
Registration Information Office, P.O. Box 94638, Palatine, IL 60094–4638, phone (847) 688–6888, fax (847) 688–2860.

SMALL BUSINESS ADMINISTRATION

409 Third Street, SW., 20416

phone (202) 205–6600, fax 205–7064, http://www.sbaonline.sba.gov

Administrator.—Maria Contreras-Sweet, 205–6605.
Deputy Administrator.—Marie Johns, 205–6605.
Chief of Staff (A).—Jonathan Swain, 205–6605
Director of Executive Secretariat.—Kim Bradley, 205–6608.
General Counsel.—Sara Lipscomb, 205–6642.
Chief Counsel for Advocacy.—Winslow Sargeant, 205–6533.
Inspector General.—Peg Gustafson, 205–6580.
Chief Financial Officer.—Jonathan Carver, 205–6449.
Associate Administrator for—
Disaster Assistant.—James Rivera, 205–6734.
Field Operations.—Robert Hill, 205–6808.
Assistant Administrator for—
Communications and Public Liaison.—Fred Baldassaro, 205–6740.
Associate Administrator for—
Congressional and Legislative Affairs.—Nicholas Coutsos, 205–6700.
Equal Employment Opportunity and Civil Rights Compliance.—Vacant, 205–6750.
Hearings and Appeals.—Delorice Ford, 205–7340.
Chief Operating Officer.—Paul Christy, 205–6610.
(A) Chief Information Officer.—Chase Garwood, 205–6706.
(A) Chief, Human Capital Management.—Bridget Bean, 205–6784.
(A) Associate Administrator for Capital Access.—Pravina Raghavan, 205–2227.
Associate Administrator for Business and Community Initiatives.—Ellen Thrasher, 205–6665.
Director, Financial Assistance.—Grady Hedgespeth, 205–6490.
Director, Investment.—Tom Morris, 205–6510.
Technology.—Edsel Brown, 205–6450.
Director (A), Credit Risk Management.—Eugene Stewman, 205–3049.
Associate Administrator for Small Business Development Centers.—Carol Thomas, 205–6766.
Director, Surety Guarantees.—Frank Lalumiere, 205–6540.
Associate Administrator for International Trade.—Dario Gomez, 205–6720.
Assistant Administrator for Veterans' Affairs.—Rhett Jeppson, 205–6773.
Assistant Administrator (A), Women's Business Ownership.—Ana Harvey, 205–6673.
Associate Administrator for Government Contracting and Business Development.—John Shoraka, 205–6459.
Assistant Administrator for—
Business Development.—Darryl Hairston, 205–5852.
Government Contracting (A).—John Klein, 205–6460.
Size Standard.—Khem Sharma, 205–6618.

SMITHSONIAN INSTITUTION

Smithsonian Institution Building—The Castle (SIB), 1000 Jefferson Drive, SW., 20560

phone (202) 633–1000, http://www.si.edu

The Smithsonian Institution is an independent trust instrumentality created in accordance with the terms of the will of James Smithson of England who in 1826 bequeathed his property to the United States of America ''to found at Washington under the name of the Smithsonian Institution an establishment for the increase and diffusion of knowledge among men.'' Congress pledged the faith of the United States to carry out the trust in 1836 (Act of July 1, 1836, C. 252, 5 Stat. 64), and established the Institution in its present form in 1846 (August 10, 1846, C. 178, 9 Stat. 102), entrusting the management of the institution to its independent Board of Regents.

THE BOARD OF REGENTS

ex officio

Chief Justice of the United States.—John G. Roberts, Jr., Chancellor.
Vice President of the United States.—Joseph R. Biden, Jr.

Appointed by the President of the Senate	*Appointed by the Speaker of the House*
Hon. Thad Cochran	Hon. Sam Johnson
Hon. Jack Reed	Hon. Tom Cole
Hon. Patrick J. Leahy	Hon. Xavier Becerra

Appointed by Joint Resolution of Congress

France Córdova	David Rubenstein	John McCarter
Shirley Ann Jackson	Dr. Patty Stonesifer	Steve Case
Robert Kogod	Roger Sant	Barbara Barrett

Chief of Staff to the Regents.—John K. Lapiana, 633–5230.

OFFICE OF THE SECRETARY

Secretary.—G. Wayne Clough, 633–1846.
Chief of Staff.—Patricia Bartlett, 633–1869.
Inspector General.—Scott Dahl, 633–7050.
General Counsel.—Judith Leonard, 633–5099.
Director of:
Communications and Public Affairs.—Evelyn Lieberman, 633–5190.
External Affairs.—Virginia Clark, 633–5021.
Government Relations.—Nell Payne, 633–5125.
Assistant Secretary for Education and Access.—Claudine Brown, 633–0077.
Smithsonian Affiliations Program.—Harold Closter, 633–5321.
Smithsonian Associates Program.—Vacant, 633–8880.
Smithsonian Center for Education and Museum Studies.—Stephanie L. Norby, 633–5297.
Smithsonian Institution Traveling Exhibition Service.—Anna Chon, 633–3136.
Smithsonian Science Education Center.—Thomas Emrick, 633–2972.

OFFICE OF THE UNDER SECRETARY FOR FINANCE AND ADMINISTRATION

Under Secretary and CFO.—Albert G. Horvath, 633–5240.
Director of:
Accessibility Program.—Elizabeth Ziebarth, 633–2946.
Special Events and Protocol.—Karen Keller, 633–2020.
Director, Office of:
Equal Employment and Minority Affairs.—Era Marshall, 633–6414.
Facilities Engineering and Operations.—Nancy Bechtol, 633–1873.
Human Resources.—James Douglas, 633–6301.
Information Technology and CIO.—Deron Burba, 633–4901.
Ombudsman.—Chandra Heilman, 633–2010.

OFFICE OF THE UNDER SECRETARY FOR HISTORY, ART, AND CULTURE

Under Secretary.—Richard Kurin, 633–5240.
Director of:
Anacostia Community Museum.—Camille Akeju, 633–4839.
Archives of American Art.—Kate Haw, 633–7969.
Asian Pacific American Program.—Konrad Ng, 786–2963.
Center for Folklife and Cultural Heritage.—Michael Mason, 633–6440.
Cooper Hewitt, National Design Museum.—Caroline Baumann (acting), (212) 849–8320.
Freer and Sackler Galleries.—Julian Raby, 633–0456.
Hirshhorn Museum and Sculpture Garden.—Richard Koshalek, 633–2824.
National Museum of African American History and Culture.—Lonnie Bunch, 633–4751.
National Museum of African Art.—Johnnetta Cole, 633–4610.
National Museum of American History.—John L. Gray, 633–3435.
National Museum of the American Indian.—Kevin Gover, 633–6700.
National Portrait Gallery.—Kim Sajet, 275–1740.
National Postal Museum.—Allen Kane, 633–5500.
Smithsonian American Art Museum.—Elizabeth Broun, 275–1515.
Smithsonian Latino Center.—Eduardo Diaz, 633–1240.
Smithsonian Institution Archives.—Anne Van Camp, 633–5908.
Smithsonian Institution Libraries.—Nancy Gwinn, 633–2240.

OFFICE OF THE UNDER SECRETARY FOR SCIENCE

Under Secretary.—Eva Pell, 633–5127.
Director of:
International Relations.—Molly Fannon, 633–4795.
National Air and Space Museum.—Jack Dailey, 633–2350.
National Museum of Natural History.—Kirk Johnson, 633–2664.
National Zoological Park.—Dennis Kelly, 633–4442.
Office of Research and Training Services.—Catherine Harris, 633–7070.
Smithsonian Astrophysical Observatory.—Charles Alcock (617) 495–7100.
Smithsonian Environmental Research Center.—Anson Hines (443) 482–2208.
Smithsonian Museum Conservation Institute.—Robert Koestler (301) 238–1205.
Smithsonian Tropical Research Institute.—Eldredge Bermingham, 011–507–212–8110.

SMITHSONIAN ENTERPRISES

President.—Chris Liedel, 633–5169.
Publisher, Smithsonian Magazine.—Kerry Bianchi, 633–6090.
Editor, Smithsonian Magazine.—Michael Caruso, 633–6072.

SOCIAL SECURITY ADMINISTRATION

Altmeyer Building, 6401 Security Boulevard, Baltimore, MD 21235 (ALTMB)

Annex Building, 6401 Security Boulevard, Baltimore, MD 21235 (ANXB)

East High Rise Building, 6401 Security Boulevard, Baltimore, MD 21235 (EHRB)

International Trade Commission Building, 500 E Street, SW., Washington, DC 20024 (ITCB)

Meadows East Building, 6300 Security Boulevard, Baltimore, MD 21235 (MEB)

National Computer Center, 6201 Security Boulevard, Baltimore, MD 21235 (NCC)

Oak Meadows Building, 6340 Security Boulevard, Baltimore, MD 21235 (OMB)

One Skyline Tower, 5107 Leesburg Pike, Falls Church, VA 22041 (SKY)

Robert M. Ball Building, 6401 Security Boulevard, Baltimore, MD 21235 (RMBB)

Rolling Road Commerce Center, 2709 Rolling Road, Baltimore, MD 21244 (RRCC)

Security West Tower, 1500 Woodlawn Drive, Baltimore, MD 21241 (SWTB)

West High Rise Building, 6401 Security Boulevard, Baltimore, MD 21235 (WHRB)

West Low Rise Building, 6401 Security Boulevard, Baltimore, MD 21235 (WLRB)

http://www.socialsecurity.gov

OFFICE OF THE COMMISSIONER

Commissioner.—Carolyn W. Colvin (acting), ALTMB, suite 900 (410) 965–3120 or ITCB, room 850 (202) 358–6000.
Deputy Commissioner.—Vacant.
Chief of Staff.—James A. Kissko, ALTMB, suite 900 (410) 965–28500 or ITCB, room 858 (202) 358–6000.
Deputy Chief of Staff.—Katherine A. Thornton, ALTMB, suite 900 (410) 966–9014.
Executive Counselor to the Commissioner.—Vacant.
Executive Secretary.—Karie L. Kilgore, ALTMB, suite 900 (410) 966–1127.
Chief Strategic Officer/Performance Improvement Officer.—Ruby D. Burrell, ALTMB, suite 960 (410) 965–1250.

OFFICE OF THE CHIEF ACTUARY

Chief Actuary.—Stephen C. Goss, ALTMB, room 700 (410) 965–3000.
Deputy Chief Actuary for—
Long Range.—Alice H. Wade, ALTMB, room 700 (410) 965–3002.
Short Range.—Eli N. Donkar, ALTMB, room 760 (410) 965–3004.

OFFICE OF COMMUNICATIONS

Deputy Commissioner.—Philip A. Gambino, ALTMB, room 460 (410) 966–2030, or ITCB, room 866 (202) 358–6131.
Assistant Deputy Commissioner.—Vacant.
Associate Commissioner, Office of:
Communications Planning and Technology.—Laura N. Train, ANXB, room 3165 (410) 965–4029.
External Affairs.—Kojuan L. Almond, ANXB, room 3505 (410) 965–1804.
Open Government.—Alan H. Lane, WHRB, room 1126 (410) 965–4331.
Public Inquiries.—Steven L. Patrick, Windsor Park Building, 2555 Lord Baltimore Drive, Baltimore, MD 21244 (410) 965–0709.
Press Officer.—Mark Hinkle (acting), ALTMB, room 440 (410) 965–8904.
Director, Office of Publications Management.—Mark E. Graydon, ANXB, room 1408 (410) 965–4121.

OFFICE OF DISABILITY ADJUDICATION AND REVIEW

Deputy Commissioner.—Glenn E. Sklar, SKY, suite 1600 (703) 605–8200, or ALTMB, room 560 (410) 965–6006.

Assistant Deputy Commissioner.—James C. Borland, SKY, suite 1600 (703) 605–8200, or ALTMB, room 560 (410) 965–5200.

Executive Director, Office of Appellate Operations.—Patricia A. Jonas, SKY, suite 1400 (703) 605–7100.

Chief Administrative Law Judge.—Debra Bice, SKY, suite 1608 (703) 605–8500.

Associate Commissioner, Office of:

Executive Operations and Human Resources.—James R. Julian, SKY, suite 1700 (703) 605–8700.

Budget, Facilities and Security.—Frank Biro, SKY, suite 1500 (703) 605–8989.

Electronic Services and Strategic Information.—Vacant, SKY, suite 1604 (703) 605–8970.

Regional Chief Administrative Law Judges:

Atlanta.—Ollie L. Garmon III, 61 Forsyth Street, SW., Suite 20T10, Atlanta, GA 30303 (404) 562–1182.

Boston.—Carol Sax, One Bowdoin Square, 10th Floor, Boston, MA 02114 (888) 870–7578.

Chicago.—Sherry Thompson, 200 West Adams Street, Suite 2901, Chicago, IL 60606 (877) 800–7576.

Dallas.—Joan Parks Saunders, 1301 Young Street, Suite 460, Dallas, TX 75202 (214) 767–9401.

Denver.—Lyle Olson (acting), 1244 North Speer Boulevard, Suite 600, Denver, CO 80204 (888) 397–9803.

Kansas City.—Sherianne Laba, 1100 Main Street, Suite 1700, Kansas City, MO 64105 (888) 238–7975.

New York.—Mark Sochaczewsky, 26 Federal Plaza, Room 34–102, New York, NY 10278 (212) 264–4036.

Philadelphia.—Jasper J. Bede, 300 Spring Garden Street, 4th Floor, Philadelphia, PA 19123 (215) 597–1700.

San Francisco.—William J. King, Jr., 555 Battery Street, 5th Floor, San Francisco, CA 94111 (866) 964–7584.

Seattle.—David J. DeLaittre, 701 5th Avenue, Suite 2900 M/S 904, Seattle, WA 98104 (206) 615–2236.

OFFICE OF RETIREMENT AND DISABILITY POLICY

Deputy Commissioner.—Marianna E. LaCanfora (acting), ALTMB, room 100 (410) 965–0100.

Assistant Deputy Commissioner.—LaTina Burse Greene, ALTMB, room 100 (410) 965–4507.

Associate Commissioner, Office of:

Income Security Programs.—Gina Clemons (acting), ALTMB, room 250 (410) 966–9897.

Disability Programs.—Arthur R. Spencer, ANXB, room 4550 (410) 966–5766.

Employment Support Programs.—Robert R. Williams, OPRB, room 2607 (410) 597–1352 or ITCB, room 830 (202) 358–6921.

International Programs.—Vance N. Teel, RMBB, room 3700 (410) 597–1649 or ITCB, room 869 (202) 358–6177.

Medical and Vocational Expertise.—Vacant.

Program Development and Research.—David A. Weaver, ITCB, room 822 (202) 358–6252.

Research, Evaluation and Statistics.—Manuel de la Puente, ITCB, room 828 (202) 358–6020.

Retirement Policy.—Natalie Lu, ALTB, room 118 (410) 965–3327.

Data Exchange and Policy Publications.—Stephen Evangelista, RRCC, room 1910 (410) 965–6522.

Director, Office of Regulations and Reports Clearance.—Paul Kryglik, WHRB, room 4400 (410) 965–3735.

OFFICE OF BUDGET, FINANCE AND MANAGEMENT

Deputy Commissioner.—Pete D. Spencer, ALTMB, room 800 (410) 965–2475.

Assistant Deputy Commissioner.—Tina M. Waddell, ALTMB, room 800 (410) 965–5288.

Associate Commissioner, Office of:

Acquisition and Grants.—Seth P. Binstock, 7111 Security Boulevard (rear entrance), room 120 (410) 965–9538.

Budget.—Bonnie Kind, WHRB, room 2126 (410) 965–3501.

Facilities and Supply Management.—Michael J. Keegan, RMBB, room 2710 (410) 965–4272.

Financial Policy and Operations.—Carla A. Krabbe, EHRB, room 200 (410) 965–0759.
Security and Emergency Preparedness.—Jonas M. Garland, RMBB, room 1500 (410) 965–6660.
Senior Advisor, Records Management and Audit Liaison Staff.—Gary S. Hatcher, ALTMB, room 807 (410) 965–0680.

OFFICE OF THE GENERAL COUNSEL

General Counsel.—David F. Black, ALTMB, room 600 (410) 965–0600.
Deputy General Counsel.—Gwen Jones Kelley, ALTMB, room 600 (410) 965–0495.
Associate General Counsel for—
General Law.—Mitchell R. Chitwood, WLRB, room G300c (410) 965–4660.
Program Law.—Jeffrey C. Blair, ALTMB, room 624 (410) 965–3157.
Executive Director, Office of Privacy and Disclosure.—Kirsten J. Moncada, WLRB, G400-F (410) 965–0205.
Regional Chief Counsel for—
Atlanta.—Mary Ann Sloan, Atlanta Federal Center, 61 Forsyth Street, SW., Suite 20T45, Atlanta, GA 30303 (404) 562–1010.
Boston.—Frank Cristaudo, JFK Federal Building, 15 Sudbury Street, Room 625, Boston, MA 02203 (617) 565–2386.
Chicago.—Donna Calvert, 200 West Adams Street, 30th Floor, Chicago, IL 60606, 1 (877) 800–7578, ext. 19111.
Dallas.—Mike McGaughran, 1301 Young Street, Room A–702, Dallas, TX 75202–5433 (214) 767–4660.
Denver.—John J. Lee, 1001 17th Street, 6th Floor, Denver, CO 80202 (303) 844–0013.
Kansas City.—Kristi A. Schmidt, Richard Bolling Federal Building, 601 East 12th Street, Room 965, Kansas City, MO 64106 (816) 936–5756.
New York.—Stephen P. Conte, 26 Federal Plaza, Suite 3904, New York, NY 12078 (212) 264–2216.
Philadelphia.—Vacant, 300 Spring Garden Street, 6th Floor, Philadelphia, PA 19123 (215) 597–1847.
San Francisco.—Grace Kim, 160 Spear Street, Suite 800, San Francisco, CA 94105 (415) 977–8971.
Seattle.—David F. Morado, 701 Fifth Avenue, Suite 2900, M/S 221A, Seattle, WA 98104 (206) 615–2662.

OFFICE OF HUMAN RESOURCES

Deputy Commissioner.—Dr. Reginald F. Wells, ALTMB, room 200 (410) 965–1900.
Assistant Deputy Commissioner.—Donna L. Siegel, ALTMB, room 200 (410) 965–7642.
Associate Commissioner, Office of:
Civil Rights and Equal Opportunity.—Alan S. Frank, ANXB, room 2570 (410) 966–0941.
Labor Management and Employee Relations.—Ralph A. Patinella (acting), ANXB, room 2170 (410) 966–7860.
Learning.—Lydia C. Marshall, EHRB, room 100 (410) 966–9916.
Personnel.—Bonnie L. Doyle, ANXB, room 2510 (410) 965–4463.
Director, Executive and Special Services.—Bonnie L. Doyle, ANXB, room 2510 (410) 965–4463.

OFFICE OF THE INSPECTOR GENERAL

Inspector General.—Patrick P. O'Carroll, ALTMB, suite 300 (410) 966–8385.
Deputy Inspector General.—Gale Stallworth Stone, ALTMB, suite 300 (410) 966–8385.
Counsel to the Inspector General.—B. Chad Bungard, MEB, room 3–ME–1 (410) 966–2323.
Assistant Inspector General for—
Audit.—Steven L. Schaeffer, MEB, room 3–ME–2 (410) 965–9701.
External Relations.—Jonathan L. Lasher, MEB, room 3–ME–4 (410) 965–7178.
Investigations.—Richard A. Rohde, MEB, room 3–ME–3 (410) 966–2436.
Technology and Resource Management.—Michael D. Robinson, MEB, room 2–ME–4 (410) 965–8240.

OFFICE OF LEGISLATION AND CONGRESSIONAL AFFAIRS

Deputy Commissioner.—Scott L. Frey, ITCB, room 816 (202) 358–6030, or ALTMB, room 500 (410) 966–8088.

Assistant Deputy Commissioner.—Thomas M. Parrott, ITCB, room 819 (202) 358–6013 or ALTMB, room 500 (410) 965–3737.

Associate Commissioner, Office of:

Legislative Development and Operations.—Royce B. Min, WHRB, room 3103–B (410) 965–4511.

Congressional Affairs.—Ken Mannella, ITC, room 818 (202) 358–6083.

Director for—

Legislative and Constituent Relations.—Sharon A. Wilson, WHRB, room 3105 (410) 965–3931.

Disability Insurance.—John Brzostowski, WHRB, room 3109 (410) 965–1472.

Immigration, Data Exchange and Enumeration.—Elizabeth Tino, WHRB, room 3104 (410) 965–2871.

Retirement and Survivors Insurance Benefits.—Susan Bussman, WHRB, room 3102 (410) 965–3313.

Supplemental Security Income and Health.—Erik Hansen, WHRB, room 3107 (410) 965–1734.

OFFICE OF OPERATIONS

Deputy Commissioner.—Nancy A. Berryhill (acting), WHRB, room 1204 (410) 965–3145.

Assistant Deputy Commissioners: Theresa L. Gruber, WHRB, room 1204 (410) 965–7842; Martha J. Lambie, WHRB, room 1204 (410) 966–1751.

Associate Commissioner, Office of:

Automation Support.—Sylviane D. Haldiman, ANXB, room 4705 (410) 965–7166.

Central Operations.—Van T. Nguyen, SWTB, room 7000 (410) 966–7000.

Disability Determinations.—Ann P. Robert (acting), ANXB, room 3570 (410) 965–1170.

Electronic Services.—Roy A. Snyder (acting), WHRB, room 4200 (410) 965–1111.

Public Service and Operations Support.—Eric N. D. Jones, WHRB, room 1224 (410) 965–5514.

Telephone Services.—Kenneth H. Rivers (acting), ANXB, room 4845 (410) 597–0615.

Regional Commissioner for—

Atlanta.—Michael W. Grochowski, 61 Forsyth Street, Suite 23T30, Atlanta, GA 30303 (404) 562–5600.

Boston.—Michael F. Bertrand, JFK Federal Building, Room 1900, Boston, MA 02203 (617) 565–2870.

Chicago.—Marcia R. Mosley (acting), Harold Washington Social Security Center, 600 West Madison Street, Chicago, IL 60661 (312) 575–4000.

Dallas.—Sheila Everett, 1301 Young Street, Suite 130, Dallas, TX 75202–5433 (214) 767–4207.

Denver.—Sean P. Brune, Federal Office Building, 1961 Stout Street, Suite 07–115, Denver, CO 80294 (303) 844–2388.

Kansas City.—W. Kenneth Powell, Federal Office Building, 601 East 12th Street, Room 1016, Kansas City, MO 64106 (816) 936–5700.

New York.—Beatrice M. Disman, 26 Federal Plaza, Room 40–102, New York, NY 10278 (212) 264–3915.

Philadelphia.—Terry M. Stradtman, 300 Spring Garden Street, Philadelphia, PA 19123 (215) 597–5157.

San Francisco.—William Zielinski, 1221 Nevin Avenue, Richmond, CA 94801 (510) 970–8400.

Seattle.—Stanley C. Friendship, 701 5th Avenue, Seattle, Suite 2900, M/S 301, WA 98104–7075 (206) 615–2107.

OFFICE OF SYSTEMS/OFFICE OF THE CHIEF INFORMATION OFFICER

Deputy Commissioner and Chief Information Officer.—Debbi Russell (acting), ALTMB, room 400 (410) 965–1345.

Assistant Deputy Commissioner and Deputy Chief Information Officer.—John W. Simermeyer (acting), ALTMB, room 400 (410) 965–5789.

Associate Commissioner, Office of:

Applications and Supplemental Security Income Systems.—Debby S. Ellis, RMBB, room 2100 (410) 965–3072.

Disability Systems.—Roderick O. Hairston, RMBB, room 3606 (410) 965–8227.

Earnings, Enumeration and Administrative Systems.—Karen R. Martin, RMBB, room 3103 (410) 965–5069.

Enterprise Support, Architecture and Engineering.—John C. Morenz, RMBB, room 4100 (410) 966–4205.

Information Security.—Marti A. Eckert (acting), ANXB, room 3100 (410) 965–0445.

Retirement and Survivors Insurance Systems.—Frank Sotaski (acting), RMBB, room 4700 (410) 965–6546.

Systems Electronic Services.—Diana E. Andrews, RMBB, room 3003 (410) 965–7641.

Telecommunications and Systems Operations.—Thomas G. Grzymski, NCC, room 550 (410) 965–7626.

OFFICE OF QUALITY PERFORMANCE

Deputy Commissioner.—Stephanie J. Hall, ALTMB, room 860 (410) 965–9704.

Assistant Deputy Commissioner.—David V. Foster, ALTMB, room 860 (410) 965–8804.

Associate Commissioner, Office of:

Field Site Operations.—Avis H. Payne (acting), EHRB, room 7160B (410) 965–2518.

Quality Improvement.—Daryl X. Wise, EHRB, room 4138 (410) 965–4557.

Quality Review.—Amy G. Thompson (acting), EHRB, room 6145 (410) 966–0569.

Field Directors—

Atlanta.—Robert L. Raines, 61 Forsyth Street, SW., Suite 21T50, Atlanta, GA 30303 (404) 562–5676.

Baltimore.—Patricia A. Biggers, OMB, room 216 (410) 966–9230.

Boston.—Christine D. Tebbetts, 99 High Street, Suite 400, Boston, MA 02110 (866) 716–7420 x14902.

Chicago.—Mary T. Byrns, 600 West Madison Street, 5th Floor, Chicago, IL 60661 (312) 575–6000.

Dallas.—Sheena Hayes, 1301 Young Street, Room 300, Dallas, TX 75202 (214) 767–3164.

Denver.—Cathy Horiuchi, 1961 Stout Street, Room 1126, Denver, CO 80202 (303) 844–3694.

Kansas City.—Carrie Taber, 601 East 12th Street, Room 1200 South, Kansas City, MO 64106 (816) 936–5151.

New York.—Vera Bostick-Borden, 26 Federal Plaza, Room 39–100, New York, NY 10278 (212) 264–2827.

Philadelphia.—Diane Graboyes, 300 Spring Garden, 2nd Floor East, Philadelphia, PA 19123 (215) 597–1188.

San Francisco.—Darryl Moore, 1301 Clay Street, Suite 900 North, Oakland, CA 94612 (877) 700–4841 x18047.

Seattle.—Rubie J. Toney, 701 5th Avenue, Suite 2900, M/S 103, Seattle, WA 98104 (206) 615–2146.

STATE JUSTICE INSTITUTE

11951 Freedom Drive, Suite 1020, Reston, VA 20190, phone (571) 313–8843

http://www.sji.gov

BOARD OF DIRECTORS

Chairman.—James R. Hannah.

Vice Chairman.—Daniel J. Becker.

Secretary.—Gayle A. Nachtigal.

Treasurer.—Hernan D. Vera.

Members:

Chase T. Rogers
Jonathan Lippman
David V. Brewer
Wilfredo Martinez
Marsha J. Rabiteau
John B. Nalbandian
Isabel Framer

Officer:

Executive Director.—Jonathan D. Mattiello.

SUSQUEHANNA RIVER BASIN COMMISSION

COMMISSIONERS AND ALTERNATES

Federal Government.—BG Kent D. Savre (Commissioner); COL J. Richard Jordan III (Alternate); David J. Leach (2nd Alternate); Amy M. Guise (3rd Alternate).

New York.—James M. Tierney (Commissioner); Kenneth P. Lynch (Alternate); Peter Freehafer (2nd Alternate).

Pennsylvania.—Vacant (Commissioner); Kelly J. Heffner (Alternate); Andrew C. Zemba (2nd Alternate); Randal D. Adams (3rd Alternate).

Maryland.—Dr. Robert Summers (Commissioner); Jay Sakai (Alternate); Saeid Kasraei (2nd Alternate).

STAFF

1721 North Front Street, Harrisburg, PA 17102, phone (717) 238–0423

srbc@srbc.net, http://www.srbc.net

Executive Director.—Paul O. Swartz.

Deputy Executive Director.—Thomas W. Beauduy.

Director of Administration and Finance.—Marcia E. Rynearson.

Director of Technical Programs.—Dr. James Richenderfer.

Secretary to the Commission.—Stephanie L. Richardson.

Director of Communications.—Susan S. Obleski.

TENNESSEE VALLEY AUTHORITY

One Massachusetts Avenue, NW., 20444, Suite 300, phone (202) 898–2999

Knoxville, TN 37902, phone (865) 632–2101

Chattanooga, TN 37401, phone (423) 751–0011

BOARD OF DIRECTORS

Chairman.—William B. Sansom (Knoxville).

Directors: V. Lynn Evans (Knoxville), Barbara S. Haskew (Knoxville), Richard C. Howorth (Knoxville), Pete Mahurin (Knoxville), Neil G. McBride (Knoxville), Michael R. McWherter (Knoxville), Joe H. Ritch (Knoxville).

EXECUTIVE OFFICERS

President and Chief Executive Officer.—William D. Johnson (865) 632–2366 (Knoxville).

Vice President and Chief of Staff.—Justin C. Maierhofer (865) 632–2095 (Knoxville).

Executive Vice Presidents:

Chief Administration Officer.—Janet C. Herrin (865) 632–6770 (Knoxville).

Chief Energy Delivery Officer.—Robin E. Manning (423) 751–6000 (Chattanooga).

Chief Financial Officer.—John M. Thomas III (423) 751–8919 (Chattanooga).

Chief Generation Officer.—Charles G. Pardee (865) 632–4049 (Knoxville).

Chief Nuclear Officer.—Preston D. Swafford (423) 751–8682 (Chattanooga).

General Counsel.—Ralph E. Rodgers (865) 632–4131 (Knoxville).

Senior Vice Presidents:

Nuclear Construction.—Michael D. Skaggs (423) 751–6506 (Chattanooga).

Policy and Oversight.—Dr. Joseph J. Hoagland (865) 632–3575 (Knoxville).

WASHINGTON OFFICE

Senior Vice President, Government Relations.—Emily J. Reynolds (202) 898–2999, fax: (202) 898–2998.

U.S. ADVISORY COMMISSION ON PUBLIC DIPLOMACY

301 4th Street, SW., SA–44, M–21, 20547

phone (202) 203–7880, fax 203–7886

[Created by Executive Order 12048 and Public Law 96–60]

Chair.—William J. Hybl.

Members: Vice-Chairman, Sim Farar, Vice-Chairman, Amb. Lyndon Olson, Jr., Amb. Penne K. Peacock, Anne Terman Wedner, Lezlee Westine.

Executive Director.—Katherine Brown.

U.S. AGENCY FOR INTERNATIONAL DEVELOPMENT

1300 Pennsylvania Avenue, NW., 20523, phone (202) 712–0000

http://www.usaid.gov

Administrator.—Rajiv Shah, room 6.09, 712–4040, fax 216–3445.
Deputy Administrator.—Donald Steinberg, room 6.09, 712–4040, fax 216–3445.
Counselor.—David Eckerson, room 6.08, 712–5010.
Executive Secretary.—Bob Leavitt, room 6.08–032, 712–0700.
Assistant Administrator for—
Africa.—Earl Gast, room 4.08–031, 712–0500.
Asia.—Nisha Biswal, room 4.09, 712–0200.
Democracy, Conflict and Humanitarian Assistance.—Nancy Lindborg, room 8.06–084, 712–0100.
Economic Growth, Agriculture, and Trade.—Eric Postel, room 3.09–008, 712–0670.
Europe and Eurasia.—Paige Alexander, room 5.06, 567–4001.
Global Health.—Ariel Pablos-Mendez, room 3.06, 712–4120.
Latin America and the Caribbean.—Mark Feierstein, room 5.09–012, 712–4800.
Legislative and Public Affairs.—Chuck Cooper, room 6.10–107, 712–4300.
Management.—Angelique Crumbly, room 6.08, 712–1200.
Middle East.—Alina Romanowski (acting), room 4.09–005, 712–0300.
Director, Office of:
Senior Counselor to the Administrator and Chief Innovation Officer.—Maura O'Neill, room 6.08–025, 712–4190.
Office of Civil Rights and Diversity.—Patricia Lamond (acting), room 4.06–143, 712–1110.
Security.—Mark Webb (acting), room 2.06, 712–0990.
Small and Disadvantaged Business Utilization.—Mauricio Vera, room 848–E, 567–4735, SA–44.
General Counsel.—Susan Pascocello (acting), room 6.06–125, 712–0900.
Inspector General.—Michael Carroll (acting), room 6.06D, 712–1150.

U.S. COMMISSION ON CIVIL RIGHTS

1331 Pennsylvania Avenue, NW., Suite 1150, 20425

phone (202) 376–8591, fax 376–7672

(Codified in 42 U.S.C., section 1975)

Chairman.—Martin Castro.
Vice Chairperson.—Abigail Thernstrom.
Commissioners: Roberta Achtenberg, Todd Gaziano, Gail Heriot, Peter N. Kirsanow, David Kladney, Michael Yaki.
Staff Director.—Vacant.

U.S. ELECTION ASSISTANCE COMMISSION

1201 New York Avenue, NW., Suite 300, Washington, DC 20005

phone (202) 566–3100, (866) 747–1471, fax 566–3127, http://www.eac.gov

[Created by Public Law 107–252]

Commissioner.—Vacant.
Commissioner.—Vacant.
Commissioner.—Vacant.
Commissioner.—Vacant.

OFFICE OF THE EXECUTIVE DIRECTOR

Executive Director.—Alice P. Miller (acting), (202) 566–3100.
Chief Operating Officer.—Alice P. Miller.
Chief Financial Officer.—Annette Lafferty.

OFFICE OF COMMUNICATIONS AND CONGRESSIONAL AFFAIRS

Director of Communications and Clearinghouse.—Bryan Whitener (202) 566–3118.

OFFICE OF THE GENERAL COUNSEL

General Counsel.—Vacant.

OFFICE OF THE INSPECTOR GENERAL

Inspector General.—Curtis Crider (202) 566–3125.

U.S. HOLOCAUST MEMORIAL COUNCIL

The United States Holocaust Memorial Museum

100 Raoul Wallenberg Place, SW., 20024, phones (202) 488–0400 / (202) 314–7881

fax 488–2690

Officials:
Chair.—Tom A. Bernstein, New York, NY.
Vice Chair.—Joshua B. Bolten, Washington, DC.
Director.—Sara J. Bloomfield, Washington, DC.

Members:
Elliott Abrams, Great Falls, VA.
Matthew L. Adler, Miami Beach, FL.
Norman R. Bobins, Chicago, IL.
Joseph M. Brodecki, Washington, DC.
Michael Chertoff, Potomac, MD.
Diana Shaw Clark, London, England.
William J. Danhof, Lansing, MI.
Kitty Dukakis, Brookline, MA.
Michael David Epstein, Rockville, MD.
Donald Etra, Los Angeles, CA.
Todd A. Fisher, New York, NY.
David M. Flaum, Rochester, NY.
Jonathan Safran Foer, Brooklyn, NY.
Amy R. Friedkin, San Francisco, CA.
K. Chaya Friedman, Baltimore, MD.
Nancy B. Gilbert, Boca Raton, FL.
Constance B. Girard-diCarlo, Philadelphia, PA.
Mark D. Goodman, Cambridge, MA.
Sanford L. Gottesman, Austin, TX.
Joseph D. Gutman, Chicago, IL.
Cheryl F. Halpern, Livingston, NJ.
J. David Heller, Cleveland, OH.
Andrew S. Hochberg, Northbrook, IL.
Amy Kaslow, Potomac, MD.
Ezra Katz, Coconut Grove, FL.
Roman R. Kent, New York, NY.
Howard E. Konar, West Henrietta, NY.
Douglas R. Korn, New York, NY.
M. Ronald Krongold, Miami, FL.
Hadassah F. Lieberman, New Haven, CT.
Deborah E. Lipstadt, Atlanta, GA.
Susan E. Lowenberg, San Francisco, CA.
Kenneth B. Mehlman, Washington, DC.
Michael B. Mukasey, New York, NY.
Deborah A. Oppenheimer, Los Angeles, CA.
Cheryl Peisach, Golden Beach, FL.
Richard S. Price, Chicago, IL.
Pierre-Richard Prosper, Salt Lake City, UT.
Ronald Ratner, Cleveland, OH.
Greg A. Rosenbaum, Bethesda, MD.
Menachem Z. Rosensaft, New York, NY.
Kirk A. Rudy, Austin, TX.
Elliot J. Schrage, Menlo Park, CA.
Robert A. Sherman, Boston, MA.
Daniel J. Silva, Washington, DC.
Andrea Slavin Solow, Chicago, IL.
Marc R. Stanley, Dallas, TX.
Michael A. Stein, Cambridge, MA.
Howard D. Unger, Briarcliff Manor, NY.
Clemantine Wamariya, Kenilworth, IL.
Elie Wiesel, Boston, MA.
Jeffrey S. Wilpon, Flushing, NY.
Fred S. Zeidman, Houston, TX.

Former Chairs:
Fred S. Zeidman, 2002–2010.
Irving Greenberg, 2000–2002.
*Miles Lerman, 1993–2000.
Harvey M. Meyerhoff, 1987–1993.
Elie Wiesel, 1980–1986.

Fomer Vice Chairs:
Joel M. Geiderman, 2005–2010.
Ruth B. Mandel, 1993–2005.
*William J. Lowenberg, 1986–1993.
Mark E. Talisman, 1980–1986.

Congressional Members:

U.S. House of Representatives:
Michael G. Grimm, from New York.
Steve Israel, from New York.
Patrick Meehan, from Pennsylvania.
Henry A. Waxman, from California.

U.S. Senate:
Al Franken, from Minnesota.
Orrin G. Hatch, from Utah.
BERNARD SANDERS, from Vermont.

Ex Officio Members:
U.S. Department of:
Education.—Philip H. Rosenfelt.
Interior.—Vacant.
State.—Douglas A. Davidson.

**Deceased*

Council Staff:
General Counsel.—Gerard Leval.
Secretary of the Council.—Jane M. Miller.

U.S. INSTITUTE OF PEACE

2301 Constitution Avenue, NW., 20037

phone (202) 457–1700, fax 429–6063

BOARD OF DIRECTORS

Public Members:
Chairman.—J. Robinson West.
Vice Chairman.—George E. Moose.
Members:
Judith A. Ansley
Eric Edelman
Joseph Eldridge
Kerry Kennedy
Ikram U. Khan
Stephen D. Krasner
John A. Lancaster
Jeremy A. Rabkin
Judy Van Rest
Nancy Zirkin
Ex Officio:
Department of Defense.—Secretary Chuck Hagel (or his designee).
Department of State.—Secretary John F. Kerry (or his designee).
National Defense University.—Major General Gregg F. Martin.
United States Institute of Peace.—President Jim Marshall.
Officials:
President.—Jim Marshall.
Executive Vice President.—Kristin Lord.
Congressional Relations.—Laurie Schultz Heim.
Intergovernmental Affairs.—Marcia Wong.
Public Affairs and Communication.—P. David Early.

U.S. INTERNATIONAL TRADE COMMISSION

500 E Street, SW., 20436

phone (202) 205–2000, fax 205–2798, http://www.usitc.gov

COMMISSIONERS

Chairman.—Irving A. Williamson.
Vice Chairman.—Vacant.
Commissioners:
Daniel R. Pearson.
Shara L. Aranoff.
Dean A. Pinkert.
David S. Johanson.
Meredith Broadbent.
Congressional Relations Officer.—Joshua Levy, 205–3151.
External Relations.—Lyn M. Schlitt, 205–3141.
General Counsel.—Paul Bardos (acting).
Secretary to the Commission.—Lisa Barton (acting).
Inspector General.—Philip M. Heneghan.
Director, Office of:
Economics.—Robert B. Koopman.
Industries.—Karen Laney.
Tariff Affairs and Trade Agreements.—David Michels (acting).

U.S. MERIT SYSTEMS PROTECTION BOARD

1615 M Street, NW., 20419

phone (202) 653–7200, toll-free (800) 209–8960, fax 653–7130

[Created by Public Law 95–454]

Chairman.—Susan Tsui Grundmann.
Vice Chairman.—Anne M. Wagner.
Member.—Mark A. Robbins.
Executive Director.—James M. Eisenmann.
General Counsel.—Bryan Polisuk.
Appeals Counsel.—Susan Swafford.
Legislative Counsel.—Rosalyn L. Coates, 653–7171.

REGIONAL OFFICES

Regional Directors:

Atlanta Regional Office: Covering Alabama, Florida, Georgia, Mississippi, South Carolina, Tennessee.—Thomas J. Lanphear, 10th Floor, 401 West Peachtree Street, NW., Atlanta, GA 30308–3519 (404) 730–2751, fax 730–2767.

Central Regional Office: Covering Illinois, Iowa, Kansas City, Kansas, Kentucky, Indiana, Michigan, Minnesota, Missouri, Ohio, Wisconsin.—Martin Baumgaertner, 31st Floor, 230 South Dearborn Street, Chicago, IL 60604–1669 (312) 353–2923, fax 886–4231.

Dallas Regional Office: Covering Arkansas, Louisiana, Oklahoma, Texas.—Sharon F. Jackson, Room 620, 1100 Commerce Street, Dallas, TX 75242–9979 (214) 767–0555, fax 767–0102.

Northeastern Regional Office: Covering Connecticut, Delaware, Maine, Maryland (except Montgomery and Prince Georges counties), Massachusetts, New Hampshire, New Jersey (except the counties of Bergen, Essex, Hudson, and Union), Pennsylvania, Rhode Island, Vermont, West Virginia.—William L. Boulden, 1601 Market Street, Suite 1700, Philadelphia, PA 19103–2310 (215) 597–9960, fax 597–3456.

Western Regional Office: Covering Alaska, California, Hawaii, Idaho, Nevada, Oregon, Washington, and Pacific Overseas.—Amy Dunning, 201 Mission Street, Suite 2310, San Francisco, CA 94105–1831 (415) 904–6772, fax 904–0580.

Washington Regional Office: Covering Washington, DC; Maryland (counties of Montgomery and Prince Georges), North Carolina; Virginia; all overseas areas not otherwise covered.—Jeremiah Cassidy, 1811 Diagonal Road, Suite 205, Alexandria, VA 22314–2840 (703) 756–6250, fax 756–7112.

New York Field Office: Covering New York, Puerto Rico, Virgin Islands, the following counties in New Jersey: Bergen, Essex, Hudson, Union.—Arthur Joseph, Chief Administrative Judge, Room 3137–A, 26 Federal Plaza, New York, NY 10278–0022 (212) 264–9372, fax 264–1417.

Denver Field Office: Covering Arizona, Colorado, Kansas (except Kansas City), Montana, Nebraska, New Mexico, North Dakota, South Dakota, Utah, Wyoming.—Laura M. Albornoz, Chief Administrative Judge, 165 South Union Boulevard, Suite 318, Lakewood, CO 80228–2211 (303) 969–5101, fax 969–5109.

U.S. OVERSEAS PRIVATE INVESTMENT CORPORATION

1100 New York Avenue, NW., 20527, phone (202) 336–8400

President and CEO.—Elizabeth L. Littlefield.
Executive Vice President.—Mimi Alemayehou.
Chief of Staff.—John Morton.
Vice President and General Counsel.—Don De Amicis.
Head of Investment Funds and Chief Investment Strategist.—William R. Pearce (acting).
Vice President for Investment Policy.—Margaret Kuhlow.
Deputy Chief of Staff.—Paula Tufro.
Vice President of:
External Affairs.—Judith Pryor.
Insurance.—John Moran.
Small and Medium Enterprise Finance.—James Polan.
Structured Finance.—Vacant.
Chief Financial Officer.—Allan Villabroza.
Special Assistant for Congressional and Intergovernmental Affairs.—James W. Morrison,

BOARD OF DIRECTORS

Government Directors:
Dr. Rajiv Shah, Administrator, U.S. Agency for International Development.
Demetrios Marantis, Deputy U.S. Trade Representative.
Elizabeth L. Littlefield, President and Chief Executive Officer, OPIC.
Francisco J. Sanchez, U.S. Department of Commerce.
Seth D. Harris, Deputy Secretary, U.S. Department of Labor.
Robert Hormats, Under Secretary for Economic, Energy and Agricultural Affairs, U.S. Department of State.
Lael Brainard, Under Secretary for International Affairs, U.S. Department of the Treasury.
Private Sector Directors:
Matthew Maxwell Taylor Kennedy, Director, Kennedy Enterprises.
Katherine Gehl, President and CEO, Gehl Foods, Inc.
Michael J. Warren, Principal, Albright Stonebridge Group, LLC.
Terry Lewis, Principal, LIA Advisors, LLC.
James Demers, President, Demers and Blaisdell, Inc.
James Torrey, Director, The Torrey Family Office
Roberto Herencia, President and CEO, BXM Holdings, Inc.
Naomi Walker, Assistant to the President, AFL/CIO.

U.S. POSTAL SERVICE

475 L'Enfant Plaza, SW., 20260–0010, phone (202) 268–2000

BOARD OF GOVERNORS

Chairman.—Mickey D. Barnett.
Vice Chairman.—James H. Bilbray.
Postmaster General/CEO.—Patrick R. Donahoe.
Deputy Postmaster General.—Ronald A. Stroman.

MEMBERS

Louis J. Giuliano
Dennis J. Toner
Ellen C. Williams

OFFICERS OF THE BOARD OF GOVERNORS

Secretary to the Board of Governors.—Julie S. Moore.

OFFICERS OF THE POSTAL SERVICE

Postmaster General, Chief Executive Officer.—Patrick R. Donahoe, 268–2550.
Deputy Postmaster General.—Ronald A. Stroman, 268–4290.
Chief Postal Inspector.—Guy J. Cottrell, 268–5615.
Judicial Officer.—William A. Campbell (703) 812–1902, 2101 Wilson Boulevard, Suite 600, Arlington, VA 22201–3078.
Vice President of:
Consumer and Industry Affairs.—Maura Robinson, 268–7319.
Corporate Communications.—Samuel M. Pulcrano, 268–2143.
Government Relations and Public Policy.—Marie Therese Dominguez, 268–2506.
Chief Operating Officer and Executive Vice President.—Megan J. Brennan, 268–4842.
Vice President of:
Delivery and Post Office Operations.—Edward F. Phelan, Jr., 268–6500.
Facilities.—Tom A. Samra, 268–3389.
Network Operations.—David E. Williams, Jr. 268–4305.
Chief Information Officer and Executive Vice President.—Ellis A. Burgoyne, 268–6900.
Vice President of:
Engineering Systems.—Michael J. Amato (703) 280–7001, 8403 Lee Highway, 4th Floor, Merrifield, VA 22082–8101.
Information Technology.—John T. Edgar, 268–3977.
Mail Entry and Payment Technology.—Pritha Mehra, 268–8049.
Product Information.—James P. Cochrane, 268–7536.

Chief Financial Officer and Executive Vice President.—Joseph Corbett, 268–5272.
Vice President of:
Controller.—Timothy F. O'Reilly, 268–5521.
Finance and Planning.—Stephen J. Masse, 268–7645.
Supply Management.—Susan M. Brownell, 268–4040.
General Counsel and Executive Vice President.—Mary Anne Gibbons, 268–2950.
Chief Human Resources Officer and Executive Vice President.—Jeffrey Williamson, 268–2028.
Vice President of:
Employee Resource Management.—Deborah Giannoni-Jackson, 268–3783.
Labor Relations.—Douglas A. Tulino, 268–7447.
Chief Marketing and Sales Officer and Executive Vice President.—Nagisa Manabe, 268–4900.
Vice President of:
Channel Access.—Kelly M. Sigmon, 268–2252.
Global Business.—Giselle E. Valera, 268–5931.
New Products and Innovation.—Gary C. Reblin, 268–6078.
Pricing.—Cynthia Sanchez-Hernandez, 268–4897.
Sales.—Cliff Rucker, 268–8800.
Secure Digital Solutions.—Randy Miskanic, 268–7666.

U.S. RAILROAD RETIREMENT BOARD

844 North Rush Street, Chicago, IL 60611, phone (312) 751–4777, fax 751–7154
Office of Legislative Affairs, 1310 G Street, NW., Suite 500, 20005
phone (202) 272–7742, fax 272–7728, e-mail: ola@rrb.gov
http://www.rrb.gov

Chairman.—Michael S. Schwartz (312) 751–4900, fax 751–7193.
Assistant to the Chairman.—Nancy S. Pittman.
Counsel to the Chairman.—Stephen W. Seiple.
Labor Member.—Walter A. Barrows, 751–4905, fax 751–7194.
Assistants to the Labor Member: James C. Boehner, Geraldine L. Clark, Michael J. Collins.
Counsel to the Labor Member.—Nancy V. Russell.
Management Member.—Jerome F. Kever, 751–4910, fax 751–7189.
Assistant to the Management Member.—Joseph M. Waechter.
Counsel to the Management Member.—Robert M. Perbohner.
Inspector General.—Martin J. Dickman, 751–4690, fax 751–4342.
General Counsel.—Karl T. Blank, 751–4941, fax 751–7102.
Assistant General Counsel.—Marguerite P. Dadabo, 751–4945, fax 751–7102.
Secretary to the Board.—Martha P. ''Pat'' Rico, 751–4920, fax 751–4923.
Director of:
Disability Benefits.—John A. Bognar, 751–4801, fax 751–7167.
Equal Opportunity.—Lynn E. Cousins, 751–4942, fax 751–7179.
Field Service.—Daniel J. Fadden, 751–4627, fax 751–3360.
Hearings and Appeals.—Rachel L. Simmons, 751–4946, fax 751–7159.
Human Resources.—Marguerite V. Daniels, 751–4384, fax 751–7164.
Legislative Affairs.—Margaret A. Lindsley (202) 272–7742, fax 272–7728.
Policy and Systems.—Ronald Russo, 751–4984, fax 751–4650.
Program Evaluation and Management Services.—Janet M. Hallman, 751–4543, fax 751–7190.
Programs.—Martha M. Barringer, 751–4515, fax 751–4333.
Retirement Benefits.—Cecilia A. Freeman, 751–4576, fax 751–7192.
Survivor Benefits.—Valerie F. Allen, 751–3323, fax 751–7104.
Unemployment and Programs Support.—Micheal T. Pawlak, 751–4708, fax 751–7157.
Supervisor of:
Congressional Inquiry.—Carl D. Mende, 751–4970, fax 751–7154.
Public Affairs.—Michael P. Freeman, 751–4777, fax 751–7154.
Chief of:
Acquisition Management.—Paul T. Ahern, 751–7130, fax 751–4923.
Actuary.—Frank J. Buzzi, 751–4915, fax 751–7129.
Benefit and Employment Analysis.—Marla L. Huddleston, 751–4779, fax 751–7129.
Information.—Terri S. Morgan, 751–4851, fax 751–7169.
Librarian.—Katherine Tsang, 751–4926, fax 751–4924.
SEO/Finance.—George V. Govan, 751–4930, fax 751–4931.

U.S. SENTENCING COMMISSION

One Columbus Circle, NE., Suite 2–500, South Lobby, 20002–8002

phone (202) 502–4500, fax 502–4699

Chair.—Patti B. Saris.
Vice Chair.—Ketanji B. Jackson.
Commissioners: Ricardo H. Hinojosa, Dabney L. Friedrich.
Commissioners, ex officio: Isaac Fulwood, Jr., Jonathan J. Wroblewski.
Staff Director.—Judith W. Sheon, 502–4510.
General Counsel.—Kenneth P. Cohen, 502–4520.
Director of Legislative and Governmental Affairs.—Noah Bookbinder, 502–4519.
Director of:
Administration.—Susan Brazel, 502–4610.
Research and Data Collection.—Glenn R. Schmitt, 502–4530.
Director and Chief Counsel of Office of Training.—Pamela G. Montgomery, 502–4540.
Public Affairs Officer.—Jeanne Doherty, 502–4502.

U.S. TRADE AND DEVELOPMENT AGENCY

1000 Wilson Boulevard, Suite 1600, Arlington, VA 22209,phone (703) 875–4357

Director.—Leocadia I. Zak.
Deputy Director.—Peggy Philbin.
Chief of Staff.—Jonathan Wright.
Administrative Officer.—Carolyn Hum.
Director for Congressional Affairs and Public Relations.—Thomas R. Hardy.
Director for Export Promotion.—Leila A. Afas.
Contracting Officer.—Lori Donovan.
Evaluations Officer.—Diana Rossiter.
Financial Manager.—Liz Gustafson.
General Counsel.—Enoh T. Ebong.
Grants Administrator.—Patricia Daughetee.
Director for Policy and Program.—Geoffrey Jackson.
Resource Advisor.—Micheal Hillier.
Regional Director for—
East Asia and Eurasia.—Geoffrey Jackson.
Latin America and the Caribbean.—Nathan Younge.
Middle East, North Africa and Europe.—Carl B. Kress.
South and Southeast Asia.—Henry Steingass.
Sub-Saharan Africa.—Paul Marin.

WASHINGTON METROPOLITAN AREA TRANSIT AUTHORITY

600 Fifth Street, NW., 20001, phone (202) 637–1234

General Manager and Chief Executive Officer.—Richard Sarles.
General Counsel.—Carol A. O'Keeffe.
Deputy General Manager, Administration/Chief Financial Officer.—Carol D. Kissal.
Assistant General Manager for—
Bus Service.—Jack Requa.
Customer Service, Communications and Marketing.—Lynn Bowersox.
Deputy General Manager, Operations.—Robert Troup.
Chief Safety Officer.—James Dougherty.
Managing Director, Office of Government Relations.—Regina Sullivan.
Managing Director, Public Relations.—Dan Stessel.
Chief, Metro Transit Police Department.—Ronald Pavlik.

WASHINGTON NATIONAL MONUMENT SOCIETY

[Organized 1833; chartered 1859; amended by Acts of August 2, 1876, October, 1888]

President Ex Officio.—Barack H. Obama, President of the United States.
First Vice President.—James W. Symington, 1666 K Street, NW., Suite 500, Washington, DC 20006–2107 (202) 778–2107.
Treasurer.—Henry Ravenel, Jr.
Secretary.—Robert Vogel, Superintendent, National Mall and Memorial Parks, 900 Ohio Drive, SW., Washington, DC 20024–2000, 485–9875.

Members:
Christopher Addison
Neil C. Folger
James M. Goode
Gilbert M. Grosvenor
Outerbridge Horsey
Steve Lorenzetti, Deputy Superintendent, National Park Service.
Henry Ravenel, Jr.
Hon. James W. Symington
John A. Washington

Member Emeritus:
Harry F. Byrd, Jr.

WOODROW WILSON INTERNATIONAL CENTER FOR SCHOLARS
One Woodrow Wilson Plaza, 1300 Pennsylvania Avenue, NW., 20004–3027
phone (202) 691–4000, fax 691–4001
(Under the direction of the Board of Trustees of
Woodrow Wilson International Center for Scholars)

Director/President/CEO.—Jane Harman, 691–4202.
Executive Vice President.—Michael Van Dusen, 691–4055.
Vice President for—
Administration and Resource Management.—Leslie Johnson, 691–4103.
Communications and Media Relations.—Peter Reid, 691–4122.
Programs.—Andrew Selee, 691–4088.
Scholar and Academic Relations.—Robert Litwak, 691–4179.
Chief Financial Officer.—John Dysland, 691–4096.
Board of Trustees:
Chairman.—Joseph B. Gildenhorn.
Vice Chairman.—Sander R. Gerber.

Private Members:
Timothy Broas
John T. Casteen III
Charles E. Cobb, Jr.
Thelma Duggin
Carlos M. Gutierrez
Susan Hutchison
Barry S. Jackson

Public Members:
James H. Billington, Librarian of Congress.
John F. Kerry, Secretary of State.
G. Wayne Clough, Secretary of the Smithsonian Institution.
Arne Duncan, Secretary of Education.
David S. Ferriero, Archivist of the United States.
James Leach, Chairman of the National Endowment for the Humanities.
Kathleen Sebelius, Secretary of Health and Human Services.
Designated Appointee of the President of the United States from within the Federal Government:
Fred P. Hochberg, Chairman and President, Export-Import Bank of the United States.

JUDICIARY

SUPREME COURT OF THE UNITED STATES

One First Street, NE., 20543, phone (202) 479–3000

JOHN G. ROBERTS, JR., Chief Justice of the United States, was born in Buffalo, NY, January 27, 1955. He married Jane Marie Sullivan in 1996 and they have two children, Josephine and John. He received an A.B. from Harvard College in 1976 and a J.D. from Harvard Law School in 1979. He served as a law clerk for Judge Henry J. Friendly of the United States Court of Appeals for the Second Circuit from 1979–80 and as a law clerk for then Associate Justice William H. Rehnquist of the Supreme Court of the United States during the 1980 term. He was Special Assistant to the Attorney General, U.S. Department of Justice from 1981–82, Associate Counsel to President Ronald Reagan, White House Counsel's Office from 1982–86, and Principal Deputy Solicitor General, U.S. Department of Justice from 1989–93. From 1986–89 and 1993–2003, he practiced law in Washington, DC. He was appointed to the United States Court of Appeals for the District of Columbia Circuit in 2003. President George W. Bush nominated him as Chief Justice of the United States, and he took his seat September 29, 2005.

ANTONIN SCALIA, Associate Justice, was born in Trenton, NJ, March 11, 1936. He married Maureen McCarthy and has nine children, Ann Forrest, Eugene, John Francis, Catherine Elisabeth, Mary Clare, Paul David, Matthew, Christopher James, and Margaret Jane. He received his A.B. from Georgetown University and the University of Fribourg, Switzerland, and his LL.B. from Harvard Law School, and was a Sheldon Fellow of Harvard University from 1960–61. He was in private practice in Cleveland, OH from 1961–67, a Professor of Law at the University of Virginia from 1967–71, and a Professor of Law at the University of Chicago from 1977–82, and a Visiting Professor of Law at Georgetown University and Stanford University. He was chairman of the American Bar Association's Section of Administrative Law, 1981–82, and its Conference of Section Chairmen, 1982–83. He served the Federal Government as General Counsel of the Office of Telecommunications Policy from 1971–72, Chairman of the Administrative Conference of the United States from 1972–74, and Assistant Attorney General for the Office of Legal Counsel from 1974–77. He was appointed Judge of the United States Court of Appeals for the District of Columbia Circuit in 1982. President Reagan nominated him as an Associate Justice of the Supreme Court, and he took his seat September 26, 1986.

ANTHONY M. KENNEDY, Associate Justice, was born in Sacramento, CA, July 23, 1936. He married Mary Davis and has three children. He received his B.A. from Stanford University and the London School of Economics, and his LL.B. from Harvard Law School. He was in private practice in San Francisco, CA from 1961–63, as well as in Sacramento, CA from 1963–75. From 1965 to 1988, he was a Professor of Constitutional Law at the McGeorge School of Law, University of the Pacific. He has served in numerous positions during his career, including a member of the California Army National Guard in 1961, the board of the Federal Judicial Center from 1987–88, and two committees of the Judicial Conference of the United States: the Advisory Panel on Financial Disclosure Reports and Judicial Activities, subsequently renamed the Advisory Committee on Codes of Conduct, from 1979–87, and the Committee on Pacific Territories from 1979–90, which he chaired from 1982–90. He was appointed to the United States Court of Appeals for the Ninth Circuit in 1975. President Reagan nominated him as an Associate Justice of the Supreme Court, and he took his seat February 18, 1988.

CLARENCE THOMAS, Associate Justice, was born in the Pin Point community of Georgia near Savannah June 23, 1948. He married Virginia Lamp in 1987 and has one child, Jamal

Adeen, by a previous marriage. He attended Conception Seminary and received an A.B., *cum laude,* from Holy Cross College, and a J.D. from Yale Law School in 1974. He was admitted to law practice in Missouri in 1974, and served as an Assistant Attorney General of Missouri from 1974–77, an attorney with the Monsanto Company from 1977–79, and Legislative Assistant to Senator John Danforth from 1979–81. From 1981–82, he served as Assistant Secretary for Civil Rights, U.S. Department of Education, and as Chairman of the U.S. Equal Employment Opportunity Commission from 1982–90. He became a Judge of the United States Court of Appeals for the District of Columbia Circuit in 1990. President George W. Bush nominated him as an Associate Justice of the Supreme Court, and he took his seat October 23, 1991.

RUTH BADER GINSBURG, Associate Justice, was born in Brooklyn, NY, March 15, 1933. She married Martin D. Ginsburg in 1954, and has a daughter, Jane, and a son, James. She received her B.A. from Cornell University, attended Harvard Law School, and received her LL.B. from Columbia Law School. She served as a law clerk to the Honorable Edmund L. Palmieri, Judge of the United States District Court for the Southern District of New York, from 1959–61. From 1961–63, she was a research associate and then associate director of the Columbia Law School Project on International Procedure. She was a Professor of Law at Rutgers University School of Law from 1963–72, and Columbia Law School from 1972–80, and a fellow at the Center for Advanced Study in the Behavioral Sciences in Stanford, CA from 1977–78. In 1971, she was instrumental in launching the Women's Rights Project of the American Civil Liberties Union, and served as the ACLU's General Counsel from 1973–80, and on the National Board of Directors from 1974–80. She was appointed a Judge of the United States Court of Appeals for the District of Columbia Circuit in 1980. President Clinton nominated her as an Associate Justice of the Supreme Court, and she took her seat August 10, 1993.

STEPHEN G. BREYER, Associate Justice, was born in San Francisco, CA, August 15, 1938. He married Joanna Hare in 1967, and has three children, Chloe, Nell, and Michael. He received an A.B. from Stanford University, a B.A. from Magdalen College, Oxford, and an LL.B. from Harvard Law School. He served as a law clerk to Justice Arthur Goldberg of the Supreme Court of the United States during the 1964 term, as a Special Assistant to the Assistant U.S. Attorney General for Antitrust, 1965–67, as an Assistant Special Prosecutor of the Watergate Special Prosecution Force, 1973, as Special Counsel of the U.S. Senate Judiciary Committee, 1974–75, and as Chief Counsel of the committee, 1979–80. He was an Assistant Professor, Professor of Law, and Lecturer at Harvard Law School, 1967–94, a Professor at the Harvard University Kennedy School of Government, 1977–80, and a Visiting Professor at the College of Law, Sydney, Australia and at the University of Rome. From 1980–90, he served as a Judge of the United States Court of Appeals for the First Circuit, and as its Chief Judge, 1990–94. He also served as a member of the Judicial Conference of the United States, 1990–94, and of the United States Sentencing Commission, 1985–89. President Clinton nominated him as an Associate Justice of the Supreme Court, and he took his seat August 3, 1994.

SAMUEL ANTHONY ALITO, JR., Associate Justice, was born in Trenton, NJ, April 1, 1950. He married Martha-Ann Bomgardner in 1985, and has two children, Philip and Laura. He served as a law clerk for Leonard I. Garth of the United States Court of Appeals for the Third Circuit from 1976–77. He was Assistant U.S. Attorney, District of New Jersey, 1977–81, Assistant to the Solicitor General, U.S. Department of Justice, 1981–85, Deputy Assistant Attorney General, U.S. Department of Justice, 1985–87, and U.S. Attorney, District of New Jersey, 1987–90. He was appointed to the United States Court of Appeals for the Third Circuit in 1990. President George W. Bush nominated him as an Associate Justice of the Supreme Court, and he took his seat January 31, 2006.

SONIA SOTOMAYOR, Associate Justice of the United States Supreme Court, was born in Bronx, NY, June 25, 1954. She earned a B.A. in 1976 from Princeton University, graduating *summa cum laude* and receiving the university's highest academic honor. In 1979, she earned a J.D. from Yale Law School where she served as an editor of the *Yale Law Journal.* She served as Assistant District Attorney in the New York County District Attorney's Office from 1979–84. She then litigated international commercial matters in New York City at Pavia & Harcourt, where she served as an associate and then partner from 1984–92. In 1991, President George H.W. Bush nominated her to the U.S. District Court Southern District of New York, and she served in that role from 1992–98. She served as a judge on the United States Court of Appeals for the Second Circuit from 1998–2009. President Barack Obama nominated her as an Associate Justice of the Supreme Court on May 26, 2009, and she assumed this role August 8, 2009.

ELENA KAGAN, Associate Justice, was born in New York, NY, on April 28, 1960. She received an A.B., *summa cum laude,* in 1981 from Princeton University. She attended Worcester College, Oxford University, as Princeton's Daniel M. Sachs Graduating Fellow, and received an M.Phil. in 1983. In 1986, she earned a J.D. from Harvard Law School, graduating *magna cum laude,* where she was supervising editor of the *Harvard Law Review.* She served as a law clerk to Judge Abner Mikva of the U.S. Court of Appeals for the District of Columbia Circuit from 1986–87. She served as a law clerk to Justice Thurgood Marshall of the Supreme Court of the United States during the 1987 term. She worked as an associate in the Washington, DC, law firm of Williams & Connolly, LLP, from 1989–91. She became an assistant professor at the University of Chicago Law School in 1991 and a tenured professor of law in 1995. From 1995–99, she was associate counsel to President Clinton and then served as deputy assistant to the President for Domestic Policy and Deputy Director of the Domestic Policy Council. She joined Harvard Law School as a visiting professor in 1999 and became professor of law in 2001. She was the Charles Hamilton Houston Professor of Law and was appointed the 11th Dean of Harvard Law School in 2003. President Obama nominated her to serve as the 45th Solicitor General of the United States and she was confirmed on March 19, 2009. President Obama nominated her as an Associate Justice of the Supreme Court on May 10, 2010, and she assumed this role on August 7, 2010.

RETIRED ASSOCIATE JUSTICE

SANDRA DAY O'CONNOR (Retired), Associate Justice, was born in El Paso, TX, March 26, 1930. She married John Jay O'Connor III in 1952 and has three sons, Scott, Brian, and Jay. She received her B.A. and LL.B. from Stanford University. She served as Deputy County Attorney of San Mateo County, CA from 1952–53 and as a civilian attorney for Quartermaster Market Center, Frankfurt, Germany from 1954–57. From 1958–60, she practiced law in Maryvale, AZ, and served as Assistant Attorney General of Arizona from 1965–69. She was appointed to the Arizona State Senate in 1969 and was subsequently reelected to two two-year terms. In 1975 she was elected Judge of the Maricopa County Superior Court and served until 1979, when she was appointed to the Arizona Court of Appeals. President Reagan nominated her as an Associate Justice of the Supreme Court, and she took her seat September 25, 1981. Justice O'Connor retired from the Supreme Court on January 31, 2006.

DAVID H. SOUTER (Retired), Associate Justice, was born in Melrose, MA, September 17, 1939. He graduated from Harvard College, from which he received his A.B. After two years as a Rhodes Scholar at Magdalen College, Oxford, he received an A.B. in Jurisprudence from Oxford University and an M.A. in 1989. After receiving an LL.B. from Harvard Law School, he was an associate at Orr and Reno in Concord, NH from 1966 to 1968, when he became an Assistant Attorney General of New Hampshire. In 1971 he became Deputy Attorney General and in 1976, Attorney General of New Hampshire. In 1978 he was named an Associate Justice of the Superior Court of New Hampshire, and was appointed to the Supreme Court of New Hampshire as an Associate Justice in 1983. He became a Judge of the United States Court of Appeals for the First Circuit on May 25, 1990. President Bush nominated him as an Associate Justice of the Supreme Court, and he took his seat October 9, 1990. Justice Souter retired from the Supreme Court on June 29, 2009.

JOHN PAUL STEVENS (Retired), Associate Justice, was born in Chicago, IL, April 20, 1920. He married Maryan Mulholland, and has four children, John Joseph (deceased), Kathryn, Elizabeth Jane, and Susan Roberta. He received an A.B. from the University of Chicago, and a J.D. from Northwestern University School of Law. He served in the United States Navy from 1942–45, and was a law clerk to Justice Wiley Rutledge of the Supreme Court of the United States during the 1947 term. He was admitted to law practice in Illinois in 1949. He was Associate Counsel to the Subcommittee on the Study of Monopoly Power of the Judiciary Committee of the U.S. House of Representatives, 1951–52, and a member of the Attorney General's National Committee to Study Antitrust Law, 1953–55. He was Second Vice President of the Chicago Bar Association in 1970. From 1970–75, he served as a Judge of the United States Court of Appeals for the Seventh Circuit. President Ford nominated him as an Associate Justice of the Supreme Court, and he took his seat December 19, 1975. Justice Stevens retired from the Supreme Court on June 29, 2010.

Officers of the Supreme Court

Counselor to the Chief Justice.—Jeffrey P. Minear.
Clerk.—William K. Suter.
Librarian.—Judith A. Gaskell.
Marshal.—Pamela Talkin.
Reporter of Decisions.—Christine L. Fallon.
Court Counsel.—Scott Harris.
Curator.—Catherine E. Fitts.
Director of Information Technology.—Robert J. Hawkins.
Public Information Officer.—Kathleen L. Arberg.

UNITED STATES COURTS OF APPEALS

First Judicial Circuit (Districts of Maine, Massachusetts, New Hampshire, Puerto Rico, and Rhode Island).—*Chief Judge:* Sandra L. Lynch. *Circuit Judges:* Juan R. Torruella; Jeffrey R. Howard; O. Rogeriee Thompson; William J. Kayatta, Jr. *Senior Circuit Judges:* Bruce M. Selya; Michael Boudin; Norman H. Stahl; Kermit V. Lipez. *Circuit Executive:* Gary H. Wente (617) 748–9613. *Clerk:* Margaret Carter (617) 748–9057, John Joseph Moakley U.S. Courthouse, One Courthouse Way, Suite 2500, Boston, MA 02210.

Second Judicial Circuit (Districts of Connecticut, New York, and Vermont).—*Chief Judge:* Robert A. Katzmann. *Circuit Judges:* José A. Cabranes; Susan L. Carney; Denny Chin; Christopher F. Droney; Peter W. Hall; Dennis Jacobs; Robert A. Katzmann; Debra A. Livingston; Raymond J. Lohier; Gerard E. Lynch; Rosemary S. Pooler; Reena Raggi; Richard C. Wesley. *Senior Judges:* Giudo Calabresi; Amalya L. Kearse; Pierre N. Leval; Jon O. Newman; Barrington D. Parker, Jr.; Robert D. Sack; Chester J. Straub; John M. Walker, Jr.; Ralph K. Winter. *Circuit Executive:* Karen Greve Milton. *Clerk:* Catherine O'Hagan Wolfe (212) 857–8700, Thurgood Marshall United States Courthouse, 40 Foley Square, New York, NY 10007–1581.

Third Judicial Circuit (Districts of Delaware, New Jersey, Pennsylvania, and Virgin Islands).—*Chief Judge:* Theodore A. McKee. *Circuit Judges:* Marjorie O. Rendell; Thomas L. Ambro; Julio M. Fuentes; D. Brooks Smith; D. Michael Fisher; Michael A. Chagares; Kent A. Jordan; Thomas M. Hardiman; Joseph A. Greenaway, Jr.; Thomas I. Vanaskie; Patty Shwartz. *Senior Circuit Judges:* Ruggero J. Aldisert; Maryanne Trump Barry; Joseph F. Weis, Jr.; Leonard I. Garth; Dolores K. Sloviter; Walter K. Stapleton; Morton I. Greenberg; Anthony J. Scirica; Robert E. Cowen; Richard L. Nygaard; Jane R. Roth; Franklin S. VanAntwerpen. *Circuit Executive:* Margaret A. Wiegand (215) 597–0718. *Clerk:* Marcia M. Waldron (215) 597–2995, U.S. Courthouse, 601 Market Street, Philadelphia, PA 19106.

Fourth Judicial Circuit (Districts of Maryland, North Carolina, South Carolina, Virginia, and West Virginia).—*Chief Judge:* William B. Traxler, Jr. *Circuit Judges:* J. Harvie Wilkinson III; Paul V. Niemeyer; Diana Gribbon Motz; Robert B. King; Roger L. Gregory; Dennis W. Shedd; Allyson K. Duncan; G. Steven Agee; Andre M. Davis; Barbara Milano Keenan; James A. Wynn, Jr.; Albert Diaz; Henry F. Floyd; Stephanie D. Thacker. *Senior Circuit Judge*: Clyde H. Hamilton. *Circuit Executive:* Samuel W. Phillips (804) 916–2184. *Clerk:* Patricia S. Connor (804) 916–2700, Lewis F. Powell, Jr. U.S. Courthouse Annex, 1100 E. Main Street, Richmond, VA 23219.

Fifth Judicial Circuit (Districts of Louisiana, Mississippi, and Texas).—*Chief Judge:* Carl E. Stewart. *Circuit Judges:* Carolyn Dineen King; E. Grady Jolly; W. Eugene Davis; Edith H. Jones; Jerry E. Smith; James L. Dennis; Edith Brown Clement; Edward C. Prado; Priscilla R. Owen; Jennifer Walker Elrod; Leslie H. Southwick; Catharina Haynes; James E. Graves, Jr.; Stephen A. Higginson. *Senior Circuit Judges:* Thomas M. Reavley; Patrick E. Higginbotham; John M. Duhé, Jr.; Jacques L. Wiener, Jr.; Rhesa H. Barksdale; Emilio M. Garza; Harold R. DeMoss, Jr.; Fortunato P. Benavides. *Circuit Executive:* Gregory A. Nussel (504) 310–7777. *Clerk:* Lyle W. Cayce (504) 310–7700, John Minor Wisdom, U.S. Court of Appeals Building, 600 Camp Street, New Orleans, LA 70130–3425.

Sixth Judicial Circuit (Districts of Kentucky, Michigan, Ohio, and Tennessee).—*Chief Judge:* Alice M. Batchelder. *Circuit Judges:* Danny J. Boggs; Karen Nelson Moore; R. Guy Cole, Jr.; Eric Lee Clay; Julia Smith Gibbons; John M. Rogers; Jeffrey S. Sutton; Deborah L. Cook; David W. McKeague; Richard Allen Griffin; Raymond M. Kethledge; Helene N. White; Jane B. Stranch; Bernice Bouie Donal. *Senior Circuit Judges:* Damon J. Keith; Gilbert S. Merritt; Cornelius G. Kennedy; Ralph B. Guy; Alan E. Norris; Richard F. Suhrheinrich; Eugene E. Siler, Jr.; Martha Craig Daughtrey; Ronald Lee Gilman. *Circuit Executive:* Clarence Maddox (513) 564–7200. *Clerk:* Deborah Hunt (513) 564–7000, Potter Stewart U.S. Courthouse, 100 E. Fifth Street, Cincinnati, OH 45202.

Seventh Judicial Circuit (Districts of Illinois, Indiana, and Wisconsin).—*Chief Judge:* Frank H. Easterbrook. *Circuit Judges:* Richard A. Posner; Joel M. Flaum; Michael S. Kanne; Ilana Diamond Rovner; Diane P. Wood; Ann Claire Williams; Diane S. Sykes; John Daniel Tinder; David F. Hamilton. *Senior Circuit Judges:* William J. Bauer; Richard D. Cudahy; Kenneth F. Ripple; Daniel A. Manion. *Circuit Executive:* Collins T. Fitzpatrick (312) 435–

5803. *Clerk:* Gino J. Agnello (312) 435–5850, 2722 U.S. Courthouse, 219 S. Dearborn Street, Chicago, IL 60604.

Eighth Judicial Circuit (Districts of Arkansas, Iowa, Minnesota, Missouri, Nebraska, North Dakota, and South Dakota).—*Chief Judge:* William Jay Riley. *Circuit Judges:* Roger L. Wollman; James B. Loken; Diana E. Murphy; Kermit E. Bye; Lavenski R. Smith; Steven M. Colloton; Raymond W. Gruender; Duane Benton; Bobby E. Shepherd; Jane L. Kelly. *Senior Circuit Judges:* Myron H. Bright; Pasco M. Bowman II; C. Arlen Beam; Michael J. Melloy. *Circuit Executive:* Millie Adams (314) 244–2600. *Clerk:* Michael E. Gans (314) 244–2400, 111 S. Tenth Street, Suite 24.329, St. Louis, MO 63102.

Ninth Judicial Circuit (Districts of Alaska, Arizona, Central California, Eastern California, Northern California, Southern California, Guam, Hawaii, Idaho, Montana, Nevada, Northern Mariana Islands, Oregon, Eastern Washington, Western Washington).—*Chief Judge:* Alex Kozinski. *Circuit Judges:* Harry Pregerson; Stephen R. Reinhardt; Diarmuid F. O'Scannlain; Pamela A. Rymer; Sidney R. Thomas; Barry G. Silverman; Susan P. Graber; M. Margaret McKeown; Kim McLane Wardlaw; William A. Fletcher; Ronald M. Gould; Richard A. Paez; Marsha L. Berzon; Richard C. Tallman; Johnnie B. Rawlinson; Richard R. Clifton; Consuelo M. Callahan; Carlos T. Bea; Milan D. Smith, Jr.; Sandra S. Ikuta; N. Randy Smith; Mary H. Murguia; Morgan Christen; Jacqueline H. Nguyen; Paul J. Watford; Andrew D. Hurwitz. *Senior Circuit Judges:* Alfred T. Goodwin; J. Clifford Wallace; Procter R. Hug, Jr.; Mary M. Schroeder; J. Jerome Farris; Arthur L. Alarcón; Dorothy W. Nelson; William C. Canby, Jr.; John T. Noonan, Jr.; Edward Leavy; Stephen S. Trott; Ferdinand F. Fernandez; Andrew J. Kleinfeld; Michael D. Hawkins; A. Wallace Tashima; Raymond C. Fisher. *Circuit and Court of Appeals Executive:* Cathy A. Catterson (415) 355–8800. *Clerk:* Molly C. Dwyer (415) 355–8000. P.O. Box 193939, San Francisco, CA 94119–3939.

Tenth Judicial Circuit (Districts of Colorado, Kansas, New Mexico, Oklahoma, Utah, and Wyoming).—*Chief Judge:* Mary Beck Briscoe. *Circuit Judges:* Paul J. Kelly, Jr.; Carlos F. Lucero; Harris L. Hartz; Timothy M. Tymkovich; Neil M. Gorsuch; Jerome A. Holmes; Scott M. Matheson, Jr.; Robert E. Bacharach; Gregory A. Phillips. *Senior Circuit Judges:* William J. Holloway, Jr.; Monroe G. McKay; Stephanie K. Seymour; John C. Porfilio; Stephen H. Anderson; Bobby R. Baldock; Wade Brorby; David M. Ebel; Michael R. Murphy; Terrence L. O'Brien. *Circuit Executive:* David Tighe (303) 844–2067. *Clerk:* Betsy Shumaker (303) 844–3157, Byron White United States Courthouse, 1823 Stout Street, Denver, CO 80257.

Eleventh Judicial Circuit (Districts of Alabama, Florida, and Georgia).—*Chief Judge:* Joel F. Dubina. *Circuit Judges:* Gerald Bard Tjoflat; Ed Carnes; Rosemary Barkett; Frank M. Hull; Stanley Marcus; Charles R. Wilson; William H. Pryor Jr.; Beverly B. Martin; Adalberto Jordán. *Senior Circuit Judges:* James C. Hill; Peter T. Fay; Phyllis A. Kravitch; Emmett R. Cox; R. Lanier Anderson III; Susan H. Black; J. L. Edmondson. *Circuit Executive:* James P. Gerstenlauer (404) 335–6535. Clerk: John P. Ley (404) 335–6100, 56 Forsyth Street, NW., Atlanta, GA 30303.

UNITED STATES COURT OF APPEALS

FOR THE DISTRICT OF COLUMBIA CIRCUIT

333 Constitution Avenue, NW., 20001, phone (202) 216–7300

MERRICK BRIAN GARLAND, chief circuit judge; born in Chicago, IL, 1952; A.B., Harvard University, 1974, *summa cum laude*, Phi Beta Kappa, Paul Revere Frothingham and Richard Perkins Parker Award; J.D., Harvard Law School, 1977, *magna cum laude*, articles editor, Harvard Law Review; law clerk to Judge Henry J. Friendly, U.S. Court of Appeals for the 2d Circuit, 1977–78; law clerk to Justice William J. Brennan, Jr., U.S. Supreme Court, 1978–79; Special Assistant to the Attorney General, 1979–81; associate then partner, Arnold and Porter, Washington, DC, 1981–89; Assistant U.S. Attorney, Washington, DC, 1989–92; partner, Arnold and Porter, 1992–93; Deputy Assistant Attorney General, Criminal Division, U.S. Department of Justice, 1993–94; Principal Associate Deputy Attorney General, 1994–97; Lecturer on Law, Harvard Law School, 1985–86; Associate Independent Counsel, 1987–88. Edmund J. Randolph Award, U.S. Department of Justice, 1997. Admitted to the bars of the District of Columbia; U.S. District Court; Court of Appeals, District of Columbia Circuit; U.S. Courts of Appeals for the 4th, 9th, and 10th Circuits; and U.S. Supreme Court. Author: *Antitrust and State Action*, 96 *Yale Law Journal* 486 (1987); *Antitrust and Federalism*, 96 *Yale Law Journal* 1291 (1987); *Deregulation and Judicial Review*, 98 *Harvard Law Review* 505 (1985); co-chair, Administrative Law Section, District of Columbia Bar, 1991–94; President, Board of Overseers, Harvard University, 2009–10, member, 2003–09; American Law Institute; U.S. Judiciary Conference Committee on Judicial Security, 2008–present, Committee on the Judicial Branch, 2001–05; appointed to the U.S. Court of Appeals for the District of Columbia Circuit on April 9, 1997.

KAREN LECRAFT HENDERSON, circuit judge. [Biographical information not supplied, per Judge Henderson's request.]

JUDITH W. ROGERS, circuit judge; born in New York, NY; A.B. (with honors), Radcliffe College, 1961; Phi Beta Kappa honors member; LL.B., Harvard Law School, 1964; LL.M., University of Virginia School of Law, 1988; law clerk, D.C. Juvenile Court, 1964–65; assistant U.S. Attorney for the District of Columbia, 1965–68; trial attorney, San Francisco Neighborhood Legal Assistance Foundation, 1968–69; Attorney, U.S. Department of Justice, Office of the Associate Deputy Attorney General and Criminal Division, 1969–71; General Counsel, Congressional Commission on the Organization of the D.C. Government, 1971–72; legislative assistant to D.C. Mayor Walter E. Washington, 1972–79; Corporation Counsel for the District of Columbia, 1979–83; trustee, Radcliffe College, 1982–90; member of Visiting Committee to Harvard Law School, 1984–90 and 2006–11; appointed by President Reagan to the District of Columbia Court of Appeals as an Associate Judge on September 15, 1983; served as Chief Judge, November 1, 1988 to March 17, 1994; appointed by President Clinton to the U.S. Court of Appeals for the District of Columbia Circuit on March 18, 1994, and entered on duty March 21, 1994; member of Executive Committee, Conference of Chief Justices, 1993–94; member, U.S. Judicial Conference Committee on the Codes of Conduct, 1998–2004.

DAVID S. TATEL, circuit judge; born in Washington, DC, March 16, 1942; son of Molly and Dr. Howard Tatel (both deceased); married to the former Edith Bassichis, 1965; children: Rebecca, Stephanie, Joshua, and Emily; grandchildren: Olivia, Maya, Olin, Reuben, Rae, Cameron, Ozzie, and Daria; B.A., University of Michigan, 1963; J.D., University of Chicago Law School, 1966; instructor, University of Michigan Law School, 1966–67; associate, Sidley and Austin, 1967–69, 1970–72; director, Chicago Lawyers' Committee for Civil Rights Under Law, 1969–70; director, National Lawyers' Committee for Civil Rights Under Law, 1972–74; director, Office for Civil Rights, U.S. Department of Health, Education and Welfare, 1977–79; associate and partner, Hogan and Hartson, 1974–77, 1979–94; lecturer, Stanford University Law School, 1991–92; board of directors, Spencer Foundation, 1987–97 (chair, 1990–97); board of directors, National Board for Professional Teaching Standards, 1997–

2000; National Lawyers' Committee for Civil Rights Under Law, co-chair, 1989–91; board of directors, Carnegie Foundation for the Advancement of Teaching, (chair, 2005–09); member of the American Philosophical Society, the National Academy of Education, and the National Academy of Sciences Committee on Science, Technology and Law; admitted to practice law in Illinois in 1966 and the District Columbia in 1970; appointed to the U.S. Court of Appeals for the District of Columbia Circuit by President Clinton on October 7, 1994, and entered on duty October 11, 1994.

JANICE ROGERS BROWN, circuit judge; born in Greenville, AL; B.A., California State University, 1974; J.D., University of California School of Law, 1977; LL.M., University of Virginia School of Law, 2004; Deputy Legislative Counsel, Legislative Counsel Bureau, 1977–79; Deputy Attorney General, California Department of Justice, 1979–87; Deputy Secretary and General Counsel, California Business, Transportation, and Housing Agency, 1987–90; Senior Associate, Nielsen, Merksamer, Parinello, Mueller and Naylor, 1990–91; Legal Affairs Secretary for Governor Pete Wilson, 1991–94; Associate Justice, California Court of Appeals for the Third District, 1994–96; Associate Justice, California Supreme Court, 1996–2005; appointed to the U.S. Court of Appeals for the District of Columbia Circuit by President George W. Bush on June 10, 2005 and sworn in on July 1, 2005.

THOMAS B. GRIFFITH, circuit judge; born in Yokohama, Japan, July 5, 1954; B.A., Brigham Young University, 1978; J.D., University of Virginia School of Law, 1985; editor, Virginia Law Review; associate, Robinson, Bradshaw and Hinson, Charlotte, NC, 1985–89; associate and then a partner, Wiley, Rein and Fielding, Washington, DC, 1989–95 and 1999–2000; Senate Legal Counsel of the United States, 1995–99; Assistant to the President and General Counsel, Brigham Young University, Provo, UT, 2000–05; member, Executive Committee of the American Bar Association's Central European and Eurasian Law Initiative; appointed to the United States Court of Appeals for the District of Columbia Circuit on June 14, 2005 and sworn in on June 29, 2005.

BRETT M. KAVANAUGH, circuit judge; born in Washington, DC, February 12, 1965; son of Edward and Martha Kavanaugh; married to Ashley Estes; two daughters; B.A., *cum laude*, Yale College, 1987; J.D., Yale Law School, 1990; law clerk to Judge Walter Stapleton of the U.S. Court of Appeals for the Third Circuit, 1990–91; law clerk for Judge Alex Kozinski of the U.S. Court of Appeals for the Ninth Circuit, 1991–92; attorney, Office of the Solicitor General of the United States, 1992–93; law clerk to Associate Justice Anthony Kennedy of the U.S. Supreme Court, 1993–94; Associate Counsel, Office of Independent Counsel, 1994–97; partner, Kirkland & Ellis LLP, 1997–98, 1999–2001; Associate Counsel and then Senior Associate Counsel to President George W. Bush, 2001–03; Assistant to the President and Staff Secretary to President Bush, 2003–06; Adjunct Professor of Law, Georgetown University Law Center, 2007; Lecturer on Law, Harvard Law School, 2008–14; appointed to the U.S. Court of Appeals for the District of Columbia Circuit on May 30, 2006.

SRI SRINIVASAN, circuit judge; born in Chandigarh, India, February 23, 1967; son of Saroja and T.P. Srinivasan; two children; B.A. Stanford University, 1989; J.D. Stanford Law School, 1995; M.B.A. Stanford Graduate School of Business, 1995; law clerk to Judge J. Harvie Wilkinson III of the U.S. Court of Appeals for the Fourth Circuit, 1995–96; Bristow Fellow, Office of the Solicitor General of the United States, 1996–97; law clerk to Associate Justice Sandra Day O'Connor of the U.S. Supreme Court, 1997–98; associate, O'Melveny & Myers LLP, 1998–2002; Assistant to the Solicitor General, 2002–07; partner, O'Melveny & Myers LLP, 2007–11; Lecturer on Law, Harvard Law School, 2009–10; Principal Deputy Solicitor General, 2011–13; appointed to the U.S. Court of Appeals for the District of Columbia Circuit on May 24, 2013.

SENIOR CIRCUIT JUDGES

HARRY T. EDWARDS, senior circuit judge; born in New York, NY, November 3, 1940; son of George H. Edwards and Arline (Ross) Lyle; married to Pamela Carrington-Edwards; children: Brent and Michelle; B.S., Cornell University, 1962; J.D. (with distinction), University of Michigan Law School, 1965; associate with Seyfarth, Shaw, Fairweather and Geraldson, 1965–70; professor of law, University of Michigan, 1970–75 and 1977–80; professor of law, Harvard University, 1975–77; visiting professor of law, Free University of Brussels, 1974; arbitrator of labor/management disputes, 1970–80; vice president, National Academy of Arbitrators, 1978–80; member (1977–79) and chairman (1979–80), National Railroad Passenger Corporation (Amtrak); Executive Committee of the Association of American Law Schools, 1979–80; public member of the Administrative Conference of the United States, 1976–80;

International Women's Year Commission, 1976–77; American Bar Association Commission of Law and the Economy; co-author of five books: *Labor Relations Law in the Public Sector, The Lawyer as a Negotiator, Higher Education and the Law*, and *Collective Bargaining and Labor Arbitration*; and, most recently, Edwards, Ellliot, & Levy, *Federal Standards of Review*, recipient of the Judge William B. Groat Alumni Award, 1978, given by Cornell University; the Society of American Law Teachers Award (for ''distinguished contributions to teaching and public service''); the Whitney North Seymour Medal presented by the American Arbitration Association for outstanding contributions to the use of arbitration; Recipient of the 2004 Robert J. Kutak Award, presented by the American Bar Association Selection of Legal Education and Admission to the Bar ''to a person who meets the highest standards of professional responsibility and demonstrates substantial achievement toward increased understanding between legal education and the active practice of law'', and several Honorary Doctor of Laws degrees; Professor of Law at NYU School of Law (member of faculty since 1990); has also taught part-time at Duke, Georgetown, Michigan, and Harvard Law Schools; co-chair of the Forensics Science Committee established by the National Academy of Sciences, 2006–09; member of the Committee on Science, Technology, and Law at the National Academy of Sciences; appointed to the U.S. Court of Appeals, February 20, 1980; served as chief judge September 15, 1994 to July 16, 2001.

LAURENCE HIRSCH SILBERMAN, senior circuit judge; recipient of the Presidential Medal of Freedom, June 19, 2008; born in York, PA, October 12, 1935; son of William Silberman and Anna (Hirsch); married to Rosalie G. Gaull on April 28, 1957 (deceased), married Patricia Winn on January 5, 2008; children: Robert Stephen Silberman, Katherine DeBoer Balaban, and Anne Gaull Otis; B.A., Dartmouth College, 1957; LL.B., Harvard Law School, 1961; admitted to Hawaii Bar, 1962; District of Columbia Bar, 1973; associate, Moore, Torkildson and Rice, 1961–64; partner (Moore, Silberman and Schulze), Honolulu, 1964–67; attorney, National Labor Relations Board, Office of General Counsel, Appellate Division, 1967–69; Solicitor, Department of Labor, 1969–70; Under Secretary of Labor, 1970–73; partner, Steptoe and Johnson, 1973–74; Deputy Attorney General of the United States, 1974–75; Ambassador to Yugoslavia, 1975–77; President's Special Envoy on ILO Affairs, 1976; senior fellow, American Enterprise Institute, 1977–78; visiting fellow, 1978–85; managing partner, Morrison and Foerster, 1978–79 and 1983–85; executive vice president, Crocker National Bank, 1979–83; lecturer, University of Hawaii, 1962–63; board of directors, Commission on Present Danger, 1978–85, Institute for Educational Affairs, New York, NY, 1981–85, member: General Advisory Committee on Arms Control and Disarmament, 1981–85; Defense Policy Board, 1981–85; vice chairman, State Department's Commission on Security and Economic Assistance, 1983–84; American Bar Association (Labor Law Committee, 1965–72, Corporations and Banking Committee, 1973, Law and National Security Advisory Committee, 1981–85); Hawaii Bar Association Ethics Committee, 1965–67; Council on Foreign Relations, 1977–present; Judicial Conference Committee on Court Administration and Case Management, 1994; member, U.S. Foreign Intelligence Surveillance Act Court of Review, 1996–2003; Adjunct Professor of Law (Administrative Law and Labor Law) Georgetown Law Center, 1987–94; 1997; Adjunct Professor of Law, New York University Law School, 1995–96; Distinguished Visitor from the Judiciary, Georgetown Law Center, 2003–present; co-chairman of the President's Commission on The Intelligence Capabilities of the United States Regarding Weapons of Mass Destruction, 2004–05; appointed to the U.S. Court of Appeals for the District of Columbia Circuit by President Reagan on October 28, 1985.

STEPHEN F. WILLIAMS, senior circuit judge; born in New York, NY, September 23, 1936; son of Charles Dickerman Williams and Virginia (Fain); married to Faith Morrow, 1966; children: Susan, Geoffrey, Sarah, Timothy, and Nicholas; B.A., Yale, 1958, J.D., Harvard Law School, 1961; U.S. Army Reserves, 1961–62; associate, Debevoise, Plimpton, Lyons and Gates, 1962–66; Assistant U.S. Attorney, Southern District of New York, 1966–69; associate professor and professor of law, University of Colorado School of Law, 1969–86; visiting professor of law, UCLA, 1975–76; visiting professor of law and fellow in law and economics, University Chicago Law School, 1979–80; visiting George W. Hutchison Professor of Energy Law, SMU, 1983–84; consultant to: Administrative Conference of the United States, 1974–76; Federal Trade Commission on energy-related issues, 1983–85; member, American Law Institute; appointed to the U.S. Court of Appeals for the District of Columbia Circuit by President Reagan, June 16, 1986.

DAVID BRYAN SENTELLE, circuit judge, born in Canton, NC, February 12, 1943; son of Horace and Maude Sentelle; married to Jane LaRue Oldham; three daughters and four granddaughters; B.A., University of North Carolina at Chapel Hill, 1965; J.D. with honors, University of North Carolina School of Law, 1968; associate, Uzzell and Dumont, Charlotte, 1968–79; Assistant U.S. Attorney, Charlotte, 1970–74; North Carolina State District Judge, 1974–77; partner, Tucker, Hicks, Sentelle, Moon and Hodge, Charlotte, 1977–85; U.S. District

Judge for the Western District of North Carolina, 1985–87; appointed to the U.S. Court of Appeals by President Reagan in October 1987; assumed the position of Chief Judge on February 11, 2008.

DOUGLAS HOWARD GINSBURG, circuit judge; born in Chicago, IL, May 25, 1946; diploma, Latin School of Chicago, 1963; B.S., Cornell University, 1970 (Phi Kappa Phi, Ives Award); J.D., University of Chicago, 1973 (Mecham Prize Scholarship 1970–73, Casper Platt Award, 1973, Order of Coif, Articles and Book Rev. Ed., 40 U. Chi. L. Rev.); bar admissions: Illinois (1973), Massachusetts (1982), U.S. Supreme Court (1984), U.S. Court of Appeals for the Ninth Circuit (1986); member: Mont Pelerin Society, American Economic Association, American Law and Economics Association, Honor Society of Phi Kappa Phi, American Bar Association, Antitrust Section, Council, 1985–86 (ex officio), judicial liaison (2000–03 and 2009–12); advisory boards: Competition Policy International; Harvard Journal of Law and Public Policy; Journal of Competition Law and Economics; Law and Economics Center, George Mason University School of Law; Supreme Court Economic Review; University of Chicago Law Review; Board of Directors: Foundation for Research in Economics and the Environment, 1991–2004; Rappahannock County Conservation Alliance, 1998–2004; Rappahannock Association for Arts and Community, 1997–99; Committees: Judicial Conference of the United States, 2002–08, Budget Committee, 1997–2001, Committee on Judicial Resources, 1987–96; Boston University Law School, Visiting Committee, 1994–97; University of Chicago Law School, Visiting Committee, 1985–88; law clerk to: Judge Carl McGowan, U.S. Court of Appeals for the District of Columbia Circuit, 1973–74; Associate Justice Thurgood Marshall, U.S. Supreme Court, 1974–75; previous positions: assistant professor, Harvard University Law School, 1975–81; Professor 1981–83; Deputy Assistant Attorney General, Antitrust Division, U.S. Department of Justice, 1983–84; Administrator for Information and Regulatory Affairs, Executive Office of the President, Office of Management and Budget, 1984–85; Assistant Attorney General, Antitrust Division, U.S. Department of Justice, 1985–86; lecturer in law, Columbia University, New York City, 1987–88, 2009–11; lecturer in law, Harvard University, Cambridge, MA, 1988–89; distinguished professor of law, George Mason University, Arlington, VA, 1988–present; senior lecturer, University of Chicago Law School, 1990–present; lecturer on law, New York Law School, 2005–09; Visiting Professor, Faculty of Laws, University College, London, 2010–15; appointed to U.S. Court of Appeals for the District of Columbia Circuit by President Reagan on October 14, 1986, taking the oath of office on November 10, 1986, Chief Judge, 2001–08.

A. RAYMOND RANDOLPH, senior circuit judge; born in Riverside, NJ, November 1, 1943; son of Arthur Raymond Randolph, Sr. and Marile (Kelly); two children: John Trevor and Cynthia Lee Randolph; married to Eileen Janette O'Connor, May 18, 1984. B.S., Drexel University, 1966; J.D., University of Pennsylvania Law School, 1969, *summa cum laude;* managing editor, University of Pennsylvania Law Review; Order of the Coif. Admitted to Supreme Court of the United States; Supreme Court of California; District of Columbia Court of Appeals; U.S. Courts of Appeals for the First, Second, Fourth, Fifth, Sixth, Seventh, Ninth, Eleventh, and District of Columbia Circuits. Memberships: American Law Institute. Law clerk to Judge Henry J. Friendly, U.S. Court of Appeals for the Second Circuit, 1969–70; Assistant to the Solicitor General, 1970–73; adjunct professor of law, Georgetown University Law Center, 1974–78; George Mason School of Law, 1992; Deputy Solicitor General, 1975–77; Special Counsel, Committee on Standards of Official Conduct, House of Representatives, 1979–80; special assistant attorney general, State of Montana (honorary), 1983–July 1990; special assistant attorney general, State of New Mexico, 1985–July 1990; special assistant attorney general, State of Utah, 1986–July 1990; advisory panel, Federal Courts Study Committee, 1989–July 1990; partner, Pepper, Hamilton and Scheetz, 1987–July 1990; chairman, Committee on Codes of Conduct, U.S. Judicial Conference, 1995–98; distinguished professor of law, George Mason Law School, 1999–present; recipient, Distinguished Alumnus Award, University of Pennsylvania Law School, 2002; appointed to the U.S. Court of Appeals for the District of Columbia Circuit by President George H.W. Bush on July 16, 1990, and took oath of office on July 20, 1990.

OFFICERS OF THE UNITED STATES COURT OF APPEALS FOR THE DISTRICT OF COLUMBIA CIRCUIT

Circuit Executive.—Betsy Paret (202) 216–7340.
Clerk.—Mark J. Langer, 216–7000.
Chief Deputy Clerk.—Marilyn R. Sargent, 216–7000.
Chief, Legal Division.—Martha Tomich, 216–7500.

UNITED STATES COURT OF APPEALS

FEDERAL CIRCUIT

717 Madison Place, NW., 20439, phone (202) 275–8000

RANDALL R. RADER, chief circuit judge; born in Hastings, NE, April 21, 1949; son of Raymond A. and Gloria R. Rader; B.A., Brigham Young University, 1971–74, (*magna cum laude*), Phi Beta Kappa; J.D., George Washington University Law Center, 1974–78; legislative assistant to Representative Virginia Smith; legislative director, counsel, House Committee on Ways and Means to Representative Philip M. Crane, 1978–81; General Counsel, Chief Counsel, Subcommittee on the Constitution, 1981–86; Minority Chief Counsel, Staff Director, Subcommittee on Patents, Trademarks and Copyrights, Senate Committee on Judiciary, 1987–88; Judge, U.S. Claims Court, 1988–90, nominated by President Ronald Reagan; recipient: Outstanding Young Federal Lawyer Award by Federal Bar Association, 1983; Jefferson Medal Award, 2003; bar member: District of Columbia, 1978; Supreme Court of the United States, 1984; nominated to the U.S Court of Appeals for the Federal Circuit by President George H.W. Bush on June 12, 1990; confirmed by Senate August 3, 1990, sworn in August 14, 1990.

PAULINE NEWMAN, circuit judge; born in New York, NY, June 20, 1927; daughter of Maxwell H. and Rosella G. Newman; B.A., Vassar College, 1947; M.A. in pure science, Columbia University, 1948; Ph.D. degree in chemistry, Yale University, 1952; LL.B., New York University School of Law, 1958; Doctor of Laws (honorary), Franklin Pierce School of Law, 1991; admitted to the New York bar in 1958 and to the Pennsylvania bar in 1979; worked as research scientist for the American Cyanamid Co. from 1951–54; worked for the FMC Corp. from 1954–84 as patent attorney and house counsel and, since 1969, as director of the Patent, Trademark, and Licensing Department; on leave from FMC Corp. worked for the United Nations Educational, Scientific and Cultural Organization as a science policy specialist in the Department of Natural Sciences, 1961–62; offices in scientific and professional organizations include: member of Council of the Patent, Trademark and Copyright Section of the American Bar Association, 1982–84; board of directors of the American Patent Law Association, 1981–84; vice president of the United States Trademark Association, 1978–79, and member of the board of directors, 1975–76, 1977–79; board of governors of the New York Patent Law Association, 1970–74; president of the Pacific Industrial Property Association, 1978–80; executive committee of the International Patent and Trademark Association, 1982–84; board of directors: the American Chemical Society, 1973–75, 1976–78, 1979–81; American Institute of Chemists, 1960–66, 1970–76; Research Corp., 1982–84; member: board of trustees of Philadelphia College of Pharmacy and Science, 1983–84; patent policy board of State University of New York, 1983–84; national board of Medical College of Pennsylvania, 1975–84; governmental committees include: State Department Advisory Committee on International Intellectual Property, 1974–84; advisory committee to the Domestic Policy Review of Industrial Innovation, 1978–79; special advisory committee on Patent Office Procedure and Practice, 1972–74; member of the U.S. Delegation to the Diplomatic Conference on the Revision of the Paris Convention for the Protection of Industrial Property, 1982–84; awarded Wilbur Cross Medal of Yale University Graduate School, 1989, the Jefferson Medal of the New Jersey Intellectual Property Law Association, 1988; the Eli Whitney Award of the Connecticut Patent Law Association, 1999; Lifetime Achievement Award; Managing Intellectual Property, 2008; AIPLA Present's Outstanding Service Award, 2007; Outstanding Public Service Award; New York Intellectual Property Law Association, 2005; Lifetime Achievement Award; Sedona Conference, 2006; the Award for Outstanding Contributions in the Intellectual Property Field of the Pacific Industrial Property Association, 1987; Vanderbilt Medal of New York University School of Law, 1995; Vasser College Distinguished Achievement Award, 2002; Distinguished Professor of Law, George Mason University School of Law (adjunct faculty); Council on Foreign Relations; appointed judge of the U.S. Court of Appeals for the Federal Circuit by President Reagan and entered upon duties of that office on May 7, 1984.

ALAN D. LOURIE, circuit judge; born in Boston, MA, January 13, 1935; son of Joseph Lourie and Rose; educated in public schools in Brookline, MA; A.B., Harvard University, 1956; M.S., University of Wisconsin, 1958; Ph.D., University of Pennsylvania, 1965; J.D., Temple University, 1970; married; two children; four grandchildren; employed at Monsanto Company (chemist, 1957–59); Wyeth Laboratories (chemist, literature scientist, patent liaison specialist, 1959–64); SmithKline Beecham Corporation, (Patent Agent, 1964–70; assistant director, Corporate Patents, 1970–76; director, Corporate Patents, 1976–77; vice president, Corporate Patents and Trademarks and Associate General Counsel, 1977–90); vice chairman of the Industry Functional Advisory Committee on Intellectual Property Rights for Trade Policy Matters (IFAC 3) for the Department of Commerce and the Office of the U.S. Trade Representative, 1987–90; Treasurer of the Association of Corporate Patent Counsel, 1987–89; President of the Philadelphia Patent Law Association, 1984–85; member of the board of directors of the American Intellectual Property Law Association (formerly American Patent Law Association), 1982–85; member of the U.S. delegation to the Diplomatic Conference on the Revision of the Paris Convention for the Protection of Industrial Property, October–November 1982, March 1984; chairman of the Patent Committee of the Law Section of the Pharmaceutical Manufacturers Association, 1980–85; member of the Judicial Conference Committee on Financial Disclosure, 1990–98; member of the Judicial Conference Committee on Codes of Conduct, 2005; member of the American Bar Association, the American Chemical Society, the Cosmos Club, and the Harvard Club of Washington; recipient of the Jefferson Medal of the New Jersey Intellectual Property Law Association for outstanding contributions to intellectual property law, 1998; recipient of the first Distinguished Intellectual Property Professional Award of the Intellectual Property Owners Education Foundation, 2008; admitted to: Supreme Court of Pennsylvania, U.S. District Court for the Eastern District of Pennsylvania, U.S. Court of Appeals for the Third Circuit, U.S. Court of Appeals for the Federal Circuit, U.S. Supreme Court; nominated January 25, 1990, by President George H.W. Bush to be circuit judge, U.S. Court of Appeals for the Federal Circuit, confirmed by the Senate on April 5, 1990, and assumed duties of the office on April 11, 1990.

TIMOTHY B. DYK, circuit judge; A.B., Harvard College (*cum laude*), 1958; LL.B. (*magna cum laude*), Harvard Law School, 1961; law clerk to Justices Reed and Burton (retired), 1961–62; law clerk to Chief Justice Warren, 1962–63; special assistant to Assistant Attorney General, Louis F. Oberdorfer, 1963–64; associate and partner, Wilmer, Cutler & Pickering, 1964–90; partner, and chair, of Issues & Appeals Practice area (until nomination) with Jones, Day, Reavis and Pogue, 1990–2000; and Adjunct Professor at Yale, University of Virginia and Georgetown Law Schools; nominated for appointment to the U.S. Court of Appeals for the Federal Circuit on April 1, 1998 by President Clinton; confirmed by the Senate on May 24, 2000; entered on duty June 9, 2000.

SHARON PROST, circuit judge; born in Newburyport, MA; daughter of Zyskind and Ester Prost; two sons, Matthew and Jeffrey; educated in Hartford, CT; B.S., Cornell University, 1973; M.B.A., George Washington University, 1975; J.D., Washington College of Law, American University, 1979; admitted to practice in Washington, DC, 1979; LL.M., George Washington University School of Law, 1984; Labor Relations Specialist, U.S. Civil Service Commission, 1973–76; Labor Relations Specialist/Auditor, U.S. General Accounting Office, 1976–79; Trial Attorney, Federal Labor Relations Authority, 1979–82; Chief Counsel's Office, Department of Treasury, 1982–84; Assistant Solicitor, Associate Solicitor, and then Acting Solicitor, National Labor Relations Board, 1984–89; Adjunct Professor of Labor Law, George Mason University School of Law, 1986–87; Chief Labor Counsel, Senate Labor Committee—minority, 1989–93; Chief Counsel, Senate Judiciary Committee—minority, 1993–95; Deputy Chief Counsel, Senate Judiciary Committee—majority, 1995–2001; Chief Counsel, Senate Judiciary Committee—majority, 2001; appointed by President George W. Bush to the U.S. Court of Appeals for the Federal Circuit, September 21, 2001; assumed duties of the office on October 3, 2001.

KIMBERLY A. MOORE, circuit judge; born in Baltimore, MD; married to Matthew J. Moore; four children; B.S.E.E., Massachusetts Institute of Technology, 1990; M.S., Massachusetts Institute of Technology, 1991; J.D. (*cum laude*), Georgetown University Law Center, 1994; Electrical Engineer, Naval Surface Warfare Center, 1988–92; Associate, Kirkland & Ellis, 1994–95; Judicial Clerk, Hon. Glenn L. Archer, Jr., Chief Judge, United States Court of Appeals for the Federal Circuit, 1995–97; Assistant Professor of Law, Chicago-Kent College of Law, 1997–99; Associate Director of the Intellectual Property Law Program, Chicago-Kent College of Law, 1998–99; Assistant Professor of Law, University of Maryland School of Law, 1999–2000; Associate Professor of Law, George Mason University School of Law, 2000–04; Professor of Law, George Mason University School of Law, 2004–06; nominated to the United States Court of Appeals for the Federal Circuit by President George W. Bush on May 18, 2006; confirmed by the Senate on September 5, 2006 and assumed the duties of office on September 8, 2006.

KATHLEEN M. O'MALLEY, prior to her elevation to the Federal Circuit, Judge O'Malley was appointed to the United States District Court for the Northern District of Ohio by President William J. Clinton on October 12, 1994. Judge O'Malley served as First Assistant Attorney General and Chief of Staff for Ohio Attorney General Lee Fisher from 1992–94, and Chief Counsel to Attorney General Fisher from 1991–92. From 1985–91, she worked for Porter, Wright, Morris & Arthur, where she became a partner. From 1983–84, she was an associate at Jones, Day, Reavis and Pogue. During her sixteen years on the district court bench, Judge O'Malley presided over in excess of 100 patent and trademark cases and sat by designation on the United States Circuit Court for the Federal Circuit. As an educator, Judge O'Malley has regularly taught a course on Patent Litigation at Case Western Reserve University Law School; she is a member of the faculty of the Berkeley Center for Law & Technology's program designed to educate Federal Judges regarding the handling of intellectual property cases. Judge O'Malley serves as a board member of the Sedona Conference; as the judicial liaison to the Local Patent Rules Committee for the Northern District of Ohio; and as an advisor to national organizations publishing treatises on patent litigation (Anatomy of a Patent Case, Complex Litigation Committee of the American College of Trial Lawyers; Patent Case Management Judicial Guide, Berkeley Center for Law & Technology). Judge O'Malley began her legal career as a law clerk to the Honorable Nathaniel R. Jones, Sixth Circuit Court of Appeals in 1982–83. She received her J.D. degree from Case Western Reserve University School of Law, Order of the Coif, in 1982, where she served on *Law Review* and was a member of the National Mock Trial Team. Judge O'Malley attended Kenyon College in Gambier, Ohio where she graduated *magna cum laude* and Phi Beta Kappa in 1979; was appointed to the United States Court of Appeals for the Federal Circuit by President Barack Obama in 2010.

JIMMIE V. REYNA, prior to his appointment, Judge Reyna was an international trade attorney and shareholder at Williams Mullen, where, from 1998 to 2011, he directed the firm's Trade and Customs Practice Group and its Latin America Task Force, and served on its board of directors (2006–08, 2009–11). He was an associate and partner at the law firm of Stewart and Stewart (1986–98). From 1981 to 1986, Judge Reyna was a solo practitioner in Albuquerque, New Mexico and, prior to that, an associate at Shaffer, Butt, Thornton & Baehr, also in Albuquerque, New Mexico. Judge Reyna served on the U.S. roster of dispute settlement panelists for trade disputes under Chapter 19 of the North American Free Trade Agreement, and the U.S. Indicative List of Non-Governmental Panelists for the World Trade Organization, Dispute Settlement Mechanism, for both trade in goods and trade in services. Judge Reyna is the author of two books, *Passport to North American Trade: Rules of Origin and Customs Procedures Under the NAFTA* (Shepards 1995), and *The GATT Uruguay Round, A Negotiating History: Services, 1986–92* (Kluwer 1993) and numerous articles on international trade and customs issues. He was the founder and Senior Co-Editor of the Hispanic National Bar Association *Journal of Law and Policy*. Judge Reyna is a recipient of the Ohtli Award (the highest honor bestowed by the Mexican Government for non-Mexican citizens). Other awards include: 100 Influentials, *Hispanic Business Magazine* (2011); 101 Latino Leaders in America, *Latino Leaders Magazine* 2011, 2012, and 2013; Minority Business Leader, *Washington Business Journal;* Extraordinary Leadership, Hispanic National Bar Association (HNBA); Lifetime Honorary Membership, Society of Hispanic Professional Engineers; Distinguished Citizen Award, Military Airlift Command, U.S. Air Force; Spirit of Excellence Award, Albuquerque Hispano Chamber of Commerce. Judge Reyna served over a decade of leadership in the HNBA, including as National President (2006–07). He served in various leadership positions in the ABA Sections on International Law and Dispute Settlement. He was a founder and member of the board of directors of the U.S.-Mexico Law Institute, and the Community Services for Autistic Adults and Children Foundation. He currently serves on the Nationwide Hispanic Advisory Council of Big Brothers Big Sisters of America. He received a B.A. from the University of Rochester in 1975 and a J.D. from the University of New Mexico School of Law in 1978; was appointed to the United States Court of Appeals for the Federal Circuit by President Barack Obama in 2011.

EVAN J. WALLACH, prior to his appointment, he served for 16 years as a judge of the United States Court of International Trade, having been appointed to that court by President William J. Clinton in 1995. Judge Wallach worked as a general litigation partner with an emphasis on media representation at the law firm of Lionel Sawyer & Collins in Las Vegas, Nevada from 1982 to 1995. He was an associate at the same firm from 1976 to 1982. While working with the firm, Judge Wallach took a leave of absence to serve as General Counsel and Public Policy Advisor to Senator Harry Reid from 1987 to 1988. From 1989 to 1995, he served in the Nevada National Guard as a Judge Advocate. In 1991, while on leave from his firm, he served as an Attorney/Advisor in the International Affairs Division of the Judge Advocate of the Army at the Pentagon. Judge Wallach, a recognized expert in the law of war, has taught at a number of law schools, including Brooklyn Law School, New York Law School, George Mason University School of Law, and the University of Müenster in Münster, Germany. Judge Wallach has received a number of awards, including: the ABA Liberty Bell Award in 1993; the Nevada Press Association President's Award in 1994; and the Clark County School Librarians Intellectual Freedom Award in 1995. Judge Wallach served on active duty in the Army of the United States from 1969 to 1971. During his military career, he was awarded the Bronze Star, the Air Medal, the Good Conduct Medal, the Meritorious Service Medal, the Nevada Medal of Merit, the Valorous Unit Citation, a Vietnam Campaign Medal, and the RVN Cross of Gallantry with Palm. Judge Wallach received his B.A. in journalism from the University of Arizona in 1973, his J.D. from the University of California, Berkeley in 1976, and an LLB with honors in International Law from Cambridge University in 1981; was appointed to the United States Court of Appeals for the Federal Circuit by President Barack Obama in 2011, confirmed by the Senate on November 9, 2011, and assumed the duties of his office on November 18, 2011.

RICHARD G. TARANTO, practiced law with the firm of Farr & Taranto from 1989 to 2013, where he specialized in appellate litigation. From 1986 to 1989, he served as an Assistant to the Solicitor General, representing the United States in the Supreme Court. He was in private practice from 1984 to 1986 with the law firm of Onek, Klein & Farr. Judge Taranto served as a law clerk at all three levels of the federal court system. He clerked for Justice Sandra Day O'Connor of the Supreme Court of the United States from 1983 to 1984; for Judge Robert Bork of the United States Court of Appeals for the District of Columbia Circuit from 1982 to 1983; and for Judge Abraham Sofaer of the United States District Court for the Southern District of New York from 1981 to 1982. Judge Taranto received a J.D. from Yale Law School in 1981 and a B.A. from Pomona College in 1977; was appointed to the United States Court of Appeals for the Federal Circuit by President Barack H. Obama, in 2013, confirmed by the Senate on March 11, 2013 and assumed the duties of his office on March 15, 2013.

RAYMOND T. CHEN, served as Deputy General Counsel for Intellectual Property Law and Solicitor at the United States Patent and Trademark Office from 2008 to 2013. He was an Associate Solicitor in that office from 1998 to 2008. From 1996 to 1998, Judge Chen served as a Technical Assistant at the United States Court of Appeals for the Federal Circuit. Before joining the court staff, Judge Chen was an associate with Knobbe, Martens, Olson & Bear from 1994 to 1996. Before entering law school, Judge Chen worked as a scientist at the law firm of Hecker & Harriman from 1989 to 1991. Judge Chen received his J.D. from the New York University School of Law in 1994 and his B.S. in electrical engineering from the University of California, Los Angeles in 1990; was appointed to the United States Court of Appeals for the Federal Circuit by President Barack H. Obama in 2013, confirmed by the Senate on August 1, 2013 and assumed his office on August 5, 2013.

TODD M. HUGHES, served as Deputy Director of the Commercial Litigation Branch of the Civil Division of the United States Department of Justice from 2007 to 2013. He was the Assistant Director in that office from 1999 to 2007 and a Trial Attorney from 1994 to 1999. From 1992 to 1994, Judge Hughes served as a Law Clerk to Circuit Judge Robert Krupansky of the United States Court of Appeals for the Sixth Circuit. He was an Adjunct Lecturer in Law at Cleveland-Marshall College of Law during the Spring, 1994 semester. Judge Hughes received a J.D. from Duke Law School in 1992, an M.A. from Duke University in 1992, and an A.B. from Harvard College in 1989; was appointed to the United States Court of Appeals for the Federal Circuit by President Barack H. Obama in 2013, confirmed by the Senate on September 24, 2013 and assumed the duties of his office on September 30, 2013.

SENIOR CIRCUIT JUDGES

HALDANE ROBERT MAYER, senior circuit judge; born in Buffalo, NY, February 21, 1941; educated in the public schools of Lockport, NY; B.S., U.S. Military Academy, West Point, NY, 1963; J.D., Marshall-Wythe School of Law, The College of William and Mary in Virginia, 1971; editor-in-chief, *William and Mary Law Review,* Omicron Delta Kappa; admitted to practice in Virginia and the District of Columbia; board of directors, William and Mary Law School Association, 1979–85; served in the U.S. Army, 1963–75, in the Infantry and the Judge Advocate General's Corps; awarded the Bronze Star Medal, Meritorious Service Medal, Army Commendation Medal with Oak Leaf Cluster, Combat Infantryman Badge, Parachutist Badge, Ranger Tab, Ranger Combat Badge (RVN), Campaign and Service Ribbons; resigned from Regular Army and was commissioned in the U.S. Army Reserve, currently Lieutenant Colonel, retired; law clerk for Judge John D. Butzner, Jr., U.S. Court of Appeals for the Fourth Circuit, 1971–72; private practice with McGuire, Woods and Battle in Charlottesville, VA, 1975–77; adjunct professor, University of Virginia School of Law, 1975–77, 1992–94, George Washington University National Law Center, 1992–96; Special Assistant to the Chief Justice of the United States, Warren E. Burger, 1977–80; private practice with Baker and McKenzie in Washington, DC, 1980–81; Deputy and Acting Special Counsel (by designation of the President), 1981–82; appointed by President Reagan to the U.S. Claims Court, 1982; appointed by President Reagan to the U.S. Court of Appeals for the Federal Circuit, June 15, 1987; assumed duties of the office, June 19, 1987; elevated to the position of Chief Judge on December 25, 1997; relinquished that position on December 24, 2004, after having held it for seven years; Judicial Conference of the U.S. Committee on the International Appellate Judges Conference, 1988–91, Committee on Judicial Resources, 1990–97 and 2007–present; member of the Judicial Conference of the United States, 1997–2004.

S. JAY PLAGER, senior circuit judge; born May 16, 1931; son of A.L. and Clara Plager; three children; educated public schools, Long Branch, NJ; A.B., University of North Carolina, 1952; J.D., University of Florida, with high honors, 1958; LL.M., Columbia University, 1961; Phi Beta Kappa, Phi Kappa Phi, Order of the Coif, Holloway Fellow, University of North Carolina; Editor-in-Chief, University of Florida Law Review; Charles Evans Hughes Fellow, Columbia University; commissioned, Ensign U.S. Navy, 1952; active duty Korean conflict; honorable discharge as Commander, USNR, 1971; professor, Faculty of Law, University of Florida, 1958–64; University of Illinois, 1964–77; Indiana University School of Law, Bloomington, 1977–89; visiting research professor of law, University of Wisconsin, 1967–68; visiting fellow, Trinity College and visiting professor, Cambridge University, 1980; visiting scholar, Stanford University Law School, 1984–85; dean, Indiana University School of Law, Bloomington, 1977–84; counselor to the Under Secretary, U.S. Department of Health and Human Services, 1986–87; Associate Director, Office of Management and Budget; Executive Office of the President of the United States, 1987–88; Administrator, Office of Information and Regulatory Affairs; Office of Management and Budget; Executive Office of the President of the United States, 1988–89; appointed by President George H.W. Bush to the U.S. Court of Appeals for the Federal Circuit in November 1989; assumed senior status November 2000.

RAYMOND C. CLEVENGER III, senior circuit judge; born in Topeka, KS, August 27, 1937; son of R. Charles and Mary Margaret Clevenger; educated in the public schools in Topeka, Kansas, and at Phillips Academy, Andover, MA; B.A., Yale University, 1959; LL.B., Yale University, 1966; law clerk to Justice White, October term, 1966; practice of law at Wilmer, Cutler and Pickering, Washington, DC, 1967–90; nominated to the U.S. Court of Appeals for the Federal Circuit by President George H.W. Bush on January 24, 1990, confirmed on April 27, 1990 and assumed duties on May 3, 1990.

ALVIN A. SCHALL, senior circuit judge; born in New York City, NY, April 4, 1944; son of Gordon W. Schall and Helen D. Schall; preparatory education: St. Paul's School, Concord, NH, 1956–62, graduated *cum laude*; higher education: B.A., Princeton University, 1962–66; J.D., Tulane Law School, 1966–69; married to the former Sharon Frances LeBlanc, children: Amanda and Anthony; associate with the law firm of Shearman and Sterling in New York City, 1969–73; Assistant United States Attorney, Office of the United States Attorney for the Eastern District of New York, 1973–78; Chief of the Appeals Division, 1977–78; Trial Attorney, Senior Trial Counsel, Civil Division, United States Department of Justice, Washington, DC, 1978–87; member of the Washington, DC law firm of Perlman and Partners, 1987–88; Assistant to the Attorney General of the United States, 1988–92; author, *Federal Contract Disputes and Forums, Chapter 9 in Construction Litigation: Strategies and Techniques*, published by John Wiley and Sons (Wiley Law Publications), 1989; bar memberships: State of New York (1970), U.S. District Courts for the Eastern and Southern Districts of New York (1973), U.S. Court of Appeals for the Second Circuit (1974), U.S. Court of Federal Claims, formerly the U.S. Claims Court (1978), District of Columbia (1980), U.S. Court of Appeals for the Federal Circuit (1982), Supreme Court of the United States (1989), U.S. Court of Appeals for the District of Columbia Circuit (1991), and United States District Court for the District of Columbia (1991); appointed U.S. Court of Appeals for the Federal Circuit by President George H.W. Bush on August 17, 1992, sworn in on August 19, 1992.

WILLIAM CURTIS BRYSON, senior circuit judge; born in Houston, TX, August 19, 1945; A.B., Harvard University, 1969; J.D., University of Texas School of Law, 1973; married with two children; law clerk to Hon. Henry J. Friendly, circuit judge, U.S. Court of Appeals for the Second Circuit, 1973–74, and Hon. Thurgood Marshall, associate justice, U.S. Supreme Court, 1974–75; associate, Miller, Cassidy, Larroca and Lewin, Washington, DC, 1975–78; Department of Justice, Criminal Division, 1979–86, Office of Solicitor General, 1978–79 and 1986–94; Office of the Associate Attorney General, 1994; nominated in June 1994 by President Clinton to be circuit judge, U.S. Court of Appeals for the Federal Circuit, and assumed duties of the office on October 7, 1994.

RICHARD LINN, senior circuit judge; Polytechnic Preparatory County Day School, Brooklyn, NY, Bachelor of Electrical Engineering degree, Rensselaer Polytechnic Institute; J.D., Georgetown University Law Center; served as patent examiner at the U.S. Patent and Trademark Office, 1965–68; member of the founding Board of Governors of the Virginia State Bar Section on Patent, Trademark and Copyright Law, chairman, 1975; member of the American Intellectual Property Law Association; the Virginia Bar Intellectual Property Law Section; and the Federal Circuit Bar Association; admitted to the Virginia bar in 1969, the District of Columbia bar in 1970, and the New York bar in 1994; admitted to practice before the U.S. Supreme Court, the U.S. Courts of Appeals for the Fourth, Sixth, District of Columbia, and Federal Circuits, and the U.S. District Courts for the Eastern District of Virginia and the District of Columbia; partner, Marks and Murase, L.L.P., 1977–97, and member of the Executive Committee, 1987–97; partner, Foley and Lardner, 1997–99, Practice Group Leader, Electronics Practice Group, and Intellectual Property Department, 1997–99; recipient, Rensselaer Alumni Association Fellows Award for 2000; adjunct professor of law and professional lecturer, George Washington University Law School, 2001–03; member, Advisory Board of the George Washington University Law School, 2001–present; Master, Giles S. Rich American Inn of Court, 2000–present, president, 2004–05; member, Richard Linn American Inn of Court, 2007–present; visiting member, Hon. William C. Conner American Inn of Court, 2008–present; nominated to be Circuit Judge by President Clinton on September 28, 1999, and confirmed by the Senate on November 19, 1999; assumed duties of the office on January 1, 2000.

RETIRED CIRCUIT JUDGE

ARTHUR J. GAJARSA (Retired), circuit judge; born in Norcia (Pro. Perugia), Italy, March 1, 1941; married to Melanie Gajarsa; five children; Rensselaer Polytechnic Institute, Troy, NY, 1958–62, B.S.E.E., Bausçh and Lomb Medal, 1958, Benjamin Franklin Award, 1958; Catholic University of America, Washington, DC, 1968; M.A. in economics, graduate studies; J.D., Georgetown University Law Center, Washington, DC, 1967; patent examiner, U.S. Patent Office, Department of Commerce, 1962–63; patent adviser, U.S. Air Force, Department of Defense, 1963–64; patent adviser, Cushman, Darby and Cushman, 1964–67; law clerk to Judge Joseph McGarraghy, U.S. District Court for the District of Columbia, Washington, DC, 1967–68; attorney, Office of General Counsel, Aetna Life and Casualty Co., 1968–69; special counsel and assistant to the Commissioner of Indian Affairs, Bureau of Indian Affairs, Department of Interior, 1969–71; associate, Duncan and Brown, 1971–72; partner, Gajarsa, Liss and Sterenbuch, 1972–78; partner, Garjarsa, Liss and Conroy, 1978–80; partner, Wender, Murase and White, 1980–86; partner and officer, Joseph Gajarsa, McDermott and Reiner, P.C., 1987–97; registered patent agent, registered patent attorney, 1963; admitted to the D.C. bar, U.S. District Court for the District of Columbia, and U.S. Court of Appeals for the District of Columbia, 1968; Connecticut State Bar, 1969; U.S. Supreme Court, 1971; Superior Court for D.C., Court of Appeals for D.C., 1972; U.S. Courts of Appeals for the Ninth and Federal Circuits, 1974; U.S. District Court for the Northern District of New York, 1980; awards: Sun and Balance Medal, Rensselaer Polytechnic Institute, 1990; Gigi Pieri Award, Camp Hale Association, Boston, MA, 1992; Rensselaer Key Alumni Award, 1992; 125th Anniversary Medal, Georgetown University Law Center, 1995; Order of Commendatore, Republic of Italy, 1995; Alumni Fellow Award, Rensselaer Alumni Association, 1996; Board of Directors, National Italian American Foundation, 1976–97, serving as general counsel, 1976–89, president, 1989–92, and vice chair, 1993–96; Rensselaer Neuman Foundation, trustee, 1973–present; Foundation for Improving Understanding of the Arts, trustee, 1982–96; Outward Bound, U.S.A., trustee, 1987–2002; John Carroll Society, Board of Governors, 1992–96; Rensselaer Polytechnic Institute, trustee, 1994–present; Georgetown University, regent, 1995–2001; Georgetown University Board of Directors, 2001–present; member: Federal, American, Federal Circuit, and D.C. Bar Associations; American Judicature Association; nominated for appointment to the U.S. Court of Appeals for the Federal Circuit on April 18, 1996 by President Clinton; confirmed by the Senate on July 31, 1997; entered service September 12, 1997.

OFFICERS OF THE UNITED STATES COURT OF APPEALS FOR THE FEDERAL CIRCUIT

Circuit Executive and Clerk of Court.—Daniel E. O'Toole (202) 275–8020.
Senior Staff Attorney.—J. Douglas Steere, 275–8061.
Circuit Librarian.—Patricia M. McDermott, 275–8400.
Information Technology Office.—Mona Harrington, 275–8422.
Administrative Services Office.—Dale Bosley, 275–8141.
Mediation Office.—James Amend, 275–8120.

UNITED STATES DISTRICT COURT FOR THE DISTRICT OF COLUMBIA

E. Barrett Prettyman U.S. Courthouse, 333 Constitution Avenue, NW., 20001 room 2002, phone (202) 354–3320, fax 354–3412

RICHARD W. ROBERTS, chief judge; born in New York, NY; son of Beverly N. Roberts and Angeline T. Roberts; graduate of the High School of Music and Art, 1970; A.B. Vassar College, 1974; M.I.A. School for International Training, 1978; J.D., Columbia Law School, 1978; Honors Program Trial Attorney, Criminal Section, Civil Rights Division, U.S. Department of Justice, Washington, DC, 1978–82; Associate, Covington and Burling, Washington, DC, 1982–86; Assistant U.S. Attorney, Southern District of NY, 1986–88; Assistant U.S. Attorney, 1988–93, then Principal Assistant U.S. Attorney, District of Columbia, 1993–95; Chief, Criminal Section, Civil Rights Division, U.S. Department of Justice, Washington, DC, 1995–98; adjunct professor of trial practice, Georgetown University Law Center, Washington, DC, 1983–84; Guest faculty, Harvard Law School, Trial Advocacy Workshop, 1984–present; admitted to bars of NY (1979) and DC (1983); U.S. District Court for District of Columbia, 1983; U.S. Court of Appeals for the D.C. Circuit, 1984; U.S. Supreme Court, 1985; U.S. District Court for the Southern District of NY and U.S. Court of Appeals for the Second Circuit, 1986; past or present member or officer of National Black Prosecutors Association; Washington Bar Association; National Conference of Black Lawyers; Department of Justice Association of Black Attorneys; Department of Justice Association of Hispanic Employees for Advancement and Development; DC Bar, Committee on Professionalism and Public Understanding About the Law; American Bar Association Criminal Justice Section Committees on Continuing Legal Education, and Race and Racism in the Criminal Justice System; ABA Task Force on the Judiciary; DC Circuit Judicial Conference Arrangements Committee; D.C. Judicial Conference Planning Committee; Edward Bennett Williams Inn of Court, Washington, DC, master; board of directors, Alumnae and Alumni of Vassar College; African American Alumni of Vassar College; Vassar Club of Washington, DC; Concerned Black Men, Inc., Washington, DC Chapter; Sigma Pi Phi, Epsilon Boule; Council on Foreign Relations; DC Coalition Against Drugs and Violence; Murch Elementary School Restructuring Team; nominated as U.S. District Judge for the District of Columbia by President Clinton on January 27, 1998 and confirmed by the Senate on June 5, 1998; took oath of office on July 31, 1998.

EMMET G. SULLIVAN, judge; born in Washington, DC; graduated McKinley High School, 1964; B.A., Howard University, 1968; J.D., Howard University Law School, 1971; law clerk to Judge James A. Washington, Jr.; joined the law firm of Houston and Gardner, 1973–80, became a partner; thereafter was a partner with Houston, Sullivan and Gardner; board of directors of the D.C. Law Students in Court Program; D.C. Judicial Conference Voluntary Arbitration Committee; Nominating Committee of the Bar Association of the District of Columbia; U.S. District Court Committee on Grievances; adjunct professor at Howard University School of Law; member: National Bar Association, Washington Bar Association, Bar Association of the District of Columbia; appointed by President Reagan to the Superior Court of the District of Columbia as an associate judge, 1984; deputy presiding judge and presiding judge of the probate and tax division; chairperson of the rules committees for the probate and tax divisions; member: Court Rules Committee and the Jury Plan Committee; appointed by President George H.W. Bush to serve as an associate judge of the District of Columbia Court of Appeals, 1991; chairperson for the nineteenth annual judicial conference of the District of Columbia, 1994 (the Conference theme was "Rejuvenating Juvenile Justice-Responses to the Problems of Juvenile Violence in the District of Columbia"); appointed by chief judge Wagner to chair the "Task Force on Families and Violence for the District of Columbia Courts"; nominated to the U.S. District Court by President Clinton on March 22, 1994; and confirmed by the U.S. Senate on June 15, 1994; appointed by Chief Justice Rehnquist to serve on the Federal Judicial Conference Committee on Criminal Law, 1998; District of Columbia Judicial Disabilities and Tenure Commission, 1996–2001; presently serving on the District of Columbia Judicial Nomination Commission; first person in the District of Columbia to have been appointed to three judicial positions by three different U.S. Presidents.

COLLEEN KOLLAR-KOTELLY, judge; born in New York, NY; daughter of Konstantine and Irene Kollar; attended bilingual schools in Mexico, Ecuador and Venezuela, and Georgetown Visitation Preparatory School in Washington, DC; received B.A. degree in English at Catholic University (Delta Epsilon Honor Society); received J.D. at Catholic University's Columbus School of Law (Moot Court Board of Governors); law clerk to Hon. Catherine B. Kelly, District of Columbia Court of Appeals, 1968–69; attorney, United States Department of Justice, Criminal Division, Appellate Section, 1969–72; chief legal counsel, Saint Elizabeths Hospital, Department of Health and Human Services, 1972–84; received Saint Elizabeths Hospital Certificate of Appreciation, 1981; Meritorious Achievement Award from Alcohol, Drug Abuse and Mental Health Administration (ADAMHA), Department of Health and Human Services, 1981; appointed judge, Superior Court of the District of Columbia by President Reagan, October 3, 1984, took oath of office October 21, 1984; served as Deputy Presiding Judge, Criminal Division, January 1996–April 1997; received Achievement Recognition Award, Hispanic Heritage CORO Awards Celebration, 1996; appointed judge, U.S. District Court for the District of Columbia by President Clinton on March 26, 1997, took oath of office May 12, 1997; appointed by Chief Justice Rehnquist to serve on the Financial Disclosure Committee, 2000–02; presiding judge of the United States Foreign Intelligence Surveillance Court, 2002–09.

ELLEN SEGAL HUVELLE, judge; born in Boston, MA, 1948; daughter of Robert M. Segal, Esq. and Sharlee Segal; B.A., Wellesley College, 1970; Masters in City Planning, Yale University, 1972; J.D., magna cum laude, Boston College Law School, 1975 (Order of the Coif; Articles Editor of the law review); law clerk to Chief Justice Edward F. Hennessey, Massachusetts Supreme Judicial Court, 1975–76; associate, Williams & Connolly, 1976–84; partner, Williams & Connolly, 1984–90; associate judge, Superior Court of the District of Columbia, 1990–99; member: American Bar Association, District of Columbia Bar, Women's Bar Association; Fellow of the American Bar Foundation; Master in the Edward Bennett Williams Inn of Court and member of the Inn's Executive Committee; instructor of Trial Advocacy at the University of Virginia Law School; member of Visiting Faculty at Harvard Law School's Trial Advocacy Workshop; Boston College Law School Board of Overseers; appointed judge, U.S. District Court for the District of Columbia by President Clinton in October 1999, and took oath of office on February 25, 2000.

REGGIE B. WALTON, judge; born in Donora, PA, 1949; son of the late Theodore and Ruth (Garard) Walton; B.A., West Virginia State College, 1971; J.D., American University, Washington College of Law, 1974; admitted to the bars of the Supreme Court of Pennsylvania, 1974; United States District Court for the Eastern District of Pennsylvania, 1975; District of Columbia Court of Appeals, 1976; United States Court of Appeals for the District of Columbia Circuit, 1977; Supreme Court of the United States, 1980; United States District Court for the District of Columbia; Staff Attorney, Defender Association of Philadelphia, 1974–76; Assistant United States Attorney for the District of Columbia, 1976–80; Chief, Career Criminal Unit, Assistant United States Attorney for the District of Columbia, 1979–80; Executive Assistant United States Attorney for the District of Columbia, 1980–81; Associate Judge, Superior Court of the District of Columbia, 1981–89; deputy presiding judge of the Criminal Division, Superior Court of the District of Columbia, 1986–89; Associate Director, Office of National Drug Control Policy, Executive Office of the President, 1989–91; Senior White House Advisor for Crime, The White House, 1991; Associate Judge, Superior Court of the District of Columbia, 1991–2001; Presiding Judge of the Domestic Violence Unit, Superior Court of the District of Columbia, 2000; Presiding Judge of the Family Division, Superior Court of the District of Columbia, 2001; Instructor: National Judicial College, Reno, Nevada, 1999–present; Harvard University Law School, Trial Advocacy Workshop, 1994–present; National Institute of Trial Advocacy, Georgetown University Law School, 1983-present; Co-author, Pretrial Drug Testing-An Essential Component of the National Drug Control Strategy, Brigham Young University Law Journal of Public Law (1991); Distinguished Alumnus Award, American University, Washington College of Law (1991); The William H. Hastie Award, The Judicial Council of the National Bar Association (1993); Commissioned as a Kentucky Colonel by the Governor (1990, 1991); Governor's Proclamation declaring April 9, 1991, Judge Reggie B. Walton Day in the State of Louisiana; The West Virginia State College National Alumni Association James R. Waddy Meritorious Service Award (1990); Secretary's Award, United States Department of Veterans Affairs (1990); Outstanding Alumnus Award, Ringgold High School (1987); Director's Award for Superior Performance as an Assistant United States Attorney (1980); Profiled in book entitled "Black Judges on Justice: Prospectives From The Bench" by Linn Washington (1995); appointed district judge, United States District Court for the District of Columbia by President George W. Bush, September 24, 2001, and took oath of office October 29, 2001; appointed by President Bush in June of 2004 to serve as the Chairperson of the National Prison Rape Reduction Commission, a two-year commission created by the United States Congress that is tasked with the mission of identifying methods to curb the incidents of prison rape; member, United States Foreign Intelligence Surveillance Court, 2007–present; Presiding Judge, 2013–present.

JOHN D. BATES, judge; born in Elizabeth, NJ, 1946; son of Richard D. and Sarah (Deacon) Bates; B.A., Wesleyan University, 1968; J.D., University of Maryland School of Law, 1976; U.S. Army (1968–71, 1st Lt., Vietnam Service Medal, Bronze Star); law clerk to Hon. Roszel Thomsen, U.S. District Court for the District of Maryland, 1976–77; Assistant U.S. Attorney, District of Columbia, 1980–97 (Chief, Civil Division, 1987–97); Director's Award for Superior Performance (1983); Attorney General's Special commendation Award (1986); Deputy Independent Counsel, Whitewater Investigation, 1995–97; private practice of law, Miller & Chevalier (partner, 1998–2001), Chair of Government Contracts Litigation Department and member of Executive Committee), Steptoe & Johnson (associate, 1977–80); District of Columbia Circuit Advisory Committee for Procedures, 1989–93; Civil Justice Reform Committee of the U.S. District Court for the District of Columbia, 1996–2001; Treasurer, D.C. Bar, 1992–93; Publications Committee, D.C. Bar (1991–97, Chair 1994–97); D.C. Bar Special Committee on Government Lawyers, 1990–91; D.C. Bar Task Force on Civility in the Profession, 1994–96; D.C. Bar Committee on Examination of Rule 49, 1995–96; Chairman, Litigation Section, Federal Bar Association, 1986–89; Board of Directors, Washington Lawyers Committee for Civil Rights and Urban Affairs, 1999–2001; appointed to the U.S. District Court for the District of Columbia in December, 2001; presiding judge, United States Foreign Intelligence Surveillance Court, 2009–2013.

RICHARD J. LEON, judge; born in South Natick, MA, 1949; son of Silvano B. Leon and Rita (O'Rorke) Leon; A.B., Holy Cross College, 1971, J.D., cum laude, Suffolk Law School, 1974; LL.M. Harvard Law School, 1981; Law Clerk to Chief Justice McLaughlin and the Associate Justices, Superior Court of Massachusetts, 1974–75; Law Clerk to Hon. Thomas F. Kelleher, Supreme Court of Rhode Island, 1975–76; admitted to bar, Rhode Island, 1975 and District of Columbia, 1991; Special Assistant U.S. Attorney, Southern District of New York, 1977–78; Assistant Professor of Law, St. John's Law School, New York, 1979–83; Senior Trial Attorney, Criminal Section, Tax Division, U.S. Department of Justice, 1983–87; Deputy Chief Minority Counsel, U.S. House Select "Iran-Contra" Committee, 1987–88; Deputy Assistant U.S. Attorney General, Environment Division, 1988–89; Partner, Baker & Hostetler, Washington, DC, 1989–99; Commissioner, The White House Fellows Commission, 1990–92; Chief Minority Counsel, U.S. House Foreign Affairs Committee "October Suprise" Task Force, 1992–93; Special Counsel, U.S. House Banking Committee "Whitewater" Investigation, 1994; Special Counsel, U.S. House Ethics Reform Task Force, 1997; Adjunct Professor, Georgetown University Law Center, 1997–present; Partner, Vorys, Sater, Seymourand Pease, Washington, DC, 1999–2002; Commissioner, Judicial Review Commission on Foreign Asset Control, 2000–01; Master, Edward Bennett Williams Inn of Court; appointed U.S. District Judge for the District of Columbia by President George W. Bush on February 19, 2002; took oath of office on March 20, 2002.

ROSEMARY M. COLLYER, judge; born in White Plains, NY, 1945; daughter of Thomas C. and Alice Henry Mayers; educated in parochial and public schools in Stamford, Connecticut; B.A., Trinity College, Washington, DC, 1968; J.D., University of Denver College of Law, 1977; practiced with Sherman & Howard, Denver, Colorado, 1977–81; Chairman, Federal Mine Safety and Health Review Commission, 1981–84 by appointment of President Reagan with Senate confirmation; General Counsel, National Labor Relations Board, 1984–89 by appointment of President Reagan with Senate confirmation; private practice with Crowell & Moring LLP, Washington, DC 1989–2003; member and chairman of the firm's Management Committee; appointed U.S. District Judge for the District of Columbia by President George W. Bush and took oath of office on January 2, 2003. Member, Foreign Intelligence Surveillance Court, 2013–Present.

BERYL A. HOWELL, judge; born in Fort Benning, GA; daughter of Col. (Ret.) Leamon and Ruth Howell; Killeen High School, 1974; B.A. with honors in philosophy, Bryn Mawr College (President and Member, Honor Board, 1976–78); J.D., Columbia University School of Law, 1983 (Harlan Fiske Stone Scholar, 1981–82; International Fellows Program, 1982–83, Transnational Law Journal, Notes Editor); law clerk to Hon. Dickinson R. Debevoise, District of New Jersey, 1983–84; litigation associate, Schulte, Roth & Zabel, 1985–87; Assistant United States Attorney, United States District Court for the Eastern District of New York, 1987–93; Deputy Chief, Narcotics Section, 1987–93; Senior Counsel, U.S. Senate Committee on the Judiciary Subcommittee on Technology and the Law, 1993–94; Senior Counsel, U.S Senate Committee on the Judiciary Subcommittee on Antitrust, Business Rights and Competition, 1995–96; General Counsel, U.S. Senate Committee on the Judiciary, 1997–2003; Executive Managing Director and General Counsel, Stroz Friedberg, 2003–09; Member, Commission on Cyber Security for the 44th Presidency, 2008; Adjunct Professor of Law, American University's Washington College of Law, 2010; Awards include U.S. Attorney's Special Achievement Award for Sustained Superior Performance, 1990, 1991; Drug Enforcement Administration Commendations, 1990, 1992, 1993; Attorney General's Director's Award for Superior Performance, 1991; Federal Bureau of Investigation Award and New York City Department of Investigation Award for public corruption investigation and prosecution, 1992; Freedom of Information Hall of Fame, 2001; First Amendment Award, Society of Professional Journalists, 2004; Federal Bureau of Investigation Director's Award, 2006; Book chapters and law review article publications include Seven Weeks: The Making of the USA PATRIOT Act, The George Washington Law Review, 2004; FISA's Fruits in Criminal Cases: An Opportunity for Improved Accountability, UCLA Journal of International Law and Foreign Affairs, 2007; Book Chapters include: Real World Problems of Virtual Crime, in Cybercrime: Digital Cops in a Networked Environment, 2007; Foreign Intelligence Surveillance Act: Has the Solution Become the Problem, in Protecting What Matters: Technology, Security, and Liberty Since 9/11, 2006 and articles in the New York Law Journal, Journal of Internet Law, the Vermont Bar Journal, and Yale Journal of Law and Technology; Appointed Commissioner, United States Sentencing Commission, 2004–11; appointed judge, U.S. District Court for the District of Columbia by President Obama on December 27, 2010, took oath of office on January 21, 2011.

ROBERT L. WILKINS, judge; born Muncie, Indiana; graduated cum laude from Rose-Hulman Institute of Technology in 1986 with a B.S. in chemical engineering; received J.D. from Harvard Law School in 1989 (Executive Editor and Comments Editor of the Civil Rights-Civil Liberties Law Review); law clerk to the Honorable Earl B. Gilliam of the United States District Court for the Southern District of California 1989–90; Staff Attorney for the District of Columbia Public Defender Service (PDS) 1990–95; PDS Chief of Special Litigation and Programs Division 1995–99; PDS Staff Attorney for special litigation and projects 1999–2000; President National African American Museum & Cultural Complex, Inc. (played key role in congressional legislation which authorized creation of the Smithsonian's National Museum of African American History and Culture slated to open on the National Mall in 2015) 2000–02; private law practice-partner, Venable LLP 2002–11; lead plaintiff in Wilkins, et al. v. State of Maryland, a civil rights lawsuit against the Maryland State Police which resulted in two landmark settlements that were the first to require statewide systematic compilation and publication by a police agency of data for all highway drug and weapons searches, including data regarding the race of the motorist involved, the justification for the search and the outcome of the search-these settlements inspired a June 1999 Executive Order by President Clinton, Congressional hearings and legislation that has been enacted in over half of the fifty states; named one of the 40 Under 40 Most Successful Young Litigators in America by the National Law Journal, 2002; Named one of the 90 Greatest Washington Lawyers of the Last 30 Years by the Legal Times, 2008; appointed judge, United States District Court for the District of Columbia by President Barack Obama December 27, 2010; took oath of office March 1, 2011.

JAMES E. BOASBERG, judge; born San Francisco, CA, 1963; son of Emanuel Boasberg III and Sarah Szold Boasberg; graduated St. Albans School, Washington, DC, 1981; B.A., magna cum laude in history from Yale College, 1985; M.St. in modern European history from Oxford University, 1986; J.D. from Yale Law School, 1990; law clerk to Judge Dorothy W. Nelson on the U.S. Court of Appeals for the Ninth Circuit, 1990–91; associate, Keker & Van Nest in San Francisco, CA, 1991–94; associate, Kellogg, Huber, Hansen, Todd & Evans in Washington, DC, 1995–96; Assistant United States Attorney for the District of Columbia, 1996–2002; visiting lecturer, George Washington Law School, 2003; Associate Judge, District of Columbia Superior Court, 2002–11; United States District Judge for the District of Columbia, 2011-present.

AMY BERMAN JACKSON, judge; appointed March of 2011; prior to joining the Court, engaged in private practice in Washington, DC as a member of Trout Cacheris, specializing in complex criminal and civil trials and appeals; earlier, partner at Venable, Baetjer, Howard, and Civiletti; Assistant United States Attorney for the District of Columbia, 1880–86; received Department of Justice Special Achievement Awards for work on murder and sexual assault cases; J.D., cum laude, Harvard Law School, 1979; A.B. cum laude, Harvard College, 1976; law clerk to the Honorable Harrison L. Winter of the United States Court of Appeals for the Fourth Circuit; lectured on corporate criminal investigations and has been a regular teacher at the National Institute of Trial Advocacy, the Georgetown University Law Center CLE Intensive Session in Trial Advocacy Skills, and the Harvard Law School Trial Advocacy workshop; while in private practice, was elected to serve as a DC Bar delegate to the ABA House of Delegates; active in the ABA Litigation Section, the ABA Criminal Justice Section White Collar Crime Committee, and DC Bar and Women's Bar Association committee activities; member of the Parent Steering Committee of the Interdisciplinary Council on Developmental and Learning Disorders; served on the Board of the DC Rape Crisis Center and other educational and community organizations.

RUDOLPH CONTRERAS, judge, appointed to the District Court in March 2012. Prior to joining the District Court, Judge Contreras served from 2006 to 2012 as the Chief of the Civil Division of the United States Attorney's Office of the District of Columbia. In that capacity, he supervised 39 Assistant United States Attorneys who defend and bring civil cases on behalf of the United States. Judge Contreras was awarded his Bachelor of Science degree from Florida State University in 1984 and his Juris Doctor degree, cum laude, from the University of Pennsylvania Law School in 1991, where he was a member of the Order of the Coif and Editor of the University of Pennsylvania Law Review. Following law school, Judge Contreras joined the law firm of Jones, Day, Reavis & Pogue, where he was an Associate in the General Litigation Group. In 1994, Judge Contreras joined the United States Attorney's Office for the District of Columbia as an Assistant United States Attorney in the Civil Division, where he was responsible for a wide array of cases, including employment, Federal Tort Claims Act, Administrative Procedure Act, Bivens and Affirmative Civil Enforcement matters. In 2003, Judge Contreras left the D.C. Office to become the Chief of the Civil Division for the United States Attorney's Office in Delaware, where he oversaw that civil program and personally handled a wide variety of matters, including environmental and health care fraud cases.

KETANJI BROWN JACKSON, judge, received her commission as a United States District Judge in March 2013. She also serves as a Vice Chair and Commissioner on the United States Sentencing Commission. Prior to her service on the Commission, Judge Jackson worked for three years as Of Counsel at Morrison & Foerster LLP, with a practice that focused on criminal and civil appellate litigation in both state and federal courts, as well as cases in the Supreme Court of the United States. From 2005 until 2007, prior to joining Morrison & Foerster LLP, Judge Jackson served as an assistant federal public defender in the Appeals Division of the Office of the Federal Public Defender in the District of Columbia. Before that appointment, Judge Jackson worked as an assistant special counsel at the United States Sentencing Commission and as an associate with two law firms, one specializing in white-collar criminal defense, the other focusing on the negotiated settlement of mass-tort claims. She also served as a law clerk to three federal judges: Associate Justice Stephen G. Breyer of the Supreme Court of the United States (October Term 1999), Judge Bruce M. Selya of the U.S. Court of Appeals for the First Circuit (1997–1998), and Judge Patti B. Saris of the U.S. District Court for the District of Massachusetts (1996–1997). Received an A.B., *magna cum laude,* in Government from Harvard-Radcliffe College in 1992, and, in 1996, a J.D., *cum laude,* from Harvard Law School, where she served as a supervising editor of the *Harvard Law Review.*

SENIOR JUDGES

THOMAS F. HOGAN, senior judge; born in Washington, DC, 1938; son of Adm. Bartholomew W. (MC) (USN) Surgeon Gen., USN, 1956–62, and Grace (Gloninger) Hogan; Georgetown Preparatory School, 1956; A.B., Georgetown University (classical), 1960; master's program, American and English literature, George Washington University, 1960–62; J.D., Georgetown University, 1965–66; Honorary Degree, Doctor of Laws, Georgetown University Law Center, May 1999; St. Thomas More Fellow, Georgetown University Law Center, 1965–66; American Jurisprudence Award: Corporation Law; member, bars of the District of Columbia and Maryland; law clerk to Hon. William B. Jones, U.S. District Court for the District of Columbia, 1966–67; counsel, Federal Commission on Reform of Federal Criminal Laws, 1967–68; private practice of law in the District of Columbia and Maryland, 1968–82; adjunct professor of law, Potomac School of Law, 1977–79; adjunct professor of law, Georgetown University Law Center, 1986–88; public member, officer evaluation board, U.S. Foreign Service, 1973; member: American Bar Association, State Chairman, Maryland Drug Abuse Education Program, Young Lawyers Section (1970–73), District of Columbia Bar Association, Bar Association of the District of Columbia, Maryland State Bar Association, Montgomery County Bar Association, National Institute for Trial Advocacy, Defense Research Institute, The Barristers, The Lawyers Club; chairman, board of directors, Christ Child Institute for Emotionally Ill Children, 1971–74; served on many committees; USDC Executive Committee; Conference Committee on Administration of Federal Magistrates System, 1988–91; chairman, Inter-Circuit Assignment Committee, 1990–present; appointed judge of the U.S. District Court for the District of Columbia by President Reagan on October 4, 1982; chief judge, June 19, 2001; member: Judicial Conference of the United States 2001–present; Executive Committee of the Judicial Conference, July 2001–08; member, Foreign Intelligence Surveillance Court, 2009–present.

ROYCE C. LAMBERTH, senior judge; born in San Antonio, TX, 1943; son of Nell Elizabeth Synder and Larimore S. Lamberth, Sr.; South San Antonio High School, 1961;

B.A., University of Texas at Austin, 1966; LL.B., University of Texas School of Law, 1967; permanent president, class of 1967, University of Texas School of Law; U.S. Army (Captain, Judge Advocate General's Corps, 1968–74; Vietnam Service Medal, Air Medal, Bronze Star with Oak Leaf Cluster, Meritorious Service Medal with Oak Leaf Cluster); assistant U.S. attorney, District of Columbia, 1974–87 (chief, civil division, 1978–87); President's Reorganization Project, Federal Legal Representation Study, 1978–79; honorary faculty, Army Judge Advocate General's School, 1976; Attorney General's Special Commendation Award; Attorney General's John Marshall Award, 1982; vice chairman, Armed Services and Veterans Affairs Committee, Section on Administrative Law, American Bar Association, 1979–82, chairman, 1983–84; chairman, Professional Ethics Committee, 1989–91; co-chairman, Committee of Article III Judges, Judiciary Section 1989–present; chairman, Federal Litigation Section, 1986–87; chairman, Federal Rules Committee, 1985–86; deputy chairman, Council of the Federal Lawyer, 1980–83; chairman, Career Service Committee, Federal Bar Association, 1978–80; appointed judge, U.S. District Court for the District of Columbia by President Reagan, November 16, 1987; appointed by Chief Justice Rehnquist to be presiding judge of the United States Foreign Intelligence Surveillance Court, May 1995–2002.

GLADYS KESSLER, senior judge; born in New York, NY, 1938; B.A., Cornell University, 1959; LL.B. Harvard Law School, 1962; member: American Judicature Society (board of directors, 1985–89); National Center for State Courts (board of directors, 1984–87); National Association of Women Judges (president, 1983–84); Women Judges' Fund for Justice, (president, 1980–82); Fellows of the American Bar Foundation; President's Council of Cornell Women; American Law Institute; American Bar Association-committees: Alternative Dispute Resolution, Bioethics and AIDS; Executive Committee, Conference of Federal Trial Judges; private law practice-partner, Roisman, Kessler and Cashdan, 1969–77; associate judge, Superior Court of the District of Columbia, 1977–94; court administrative activities: District of Columbia Courts Joint Committee on Judicial Administration, 1989–94; Domestic Violence Coordinating Council (chairperson, 1993–94); Multi-Door Dispute Resolution Program (supervising judge, 1985–90); family division, D.C. Superior Court (presiding judge, 1981–85); Einshac Institute Board of Directors; U.S. Judicial Conference Committee on Court Administration and Court Management; Frederick B. Abramson Memorial Foundation Board of Directors; Our Place Board of Directors; Vice Chair, District of Columbia Judicial Disabilities and Tenure Commission; appointed judge, U.S. District Court for the District of Columbia by President Clinton, June 16, 1994, and took oath of office, July 18, 1994.

PAUL L. FRIEDMAN, senior judge; born in Buffalo, NY, 1944; son of Cecil A. and Charlotte Wagner Friedman; B.A. (political science), Cornell University, 1965; J.D., cum laude, School of Law, State University of New York at Buffalo, 1968; admitted to the bars of the District of Columbia, New York, U.S. Supreme Court, and U.S. Courts of Appeals for the D.C., Federal, Fourth, Fifth, Sixth, Seventh, Ninth and Eleventh Circuits; Law Clerk to Judge Aubrey E. Robinson, Jr., U.S. district court for the District of Columbia, 1968–69; Law Clerk to Judge Roger Robb, U.S. Court of Appeals for the District of Columbia Circuit, 1969–70; Assistant U.S. Attorney for the District of Columbia, 1970–74; assistant to the Solicitor General of the United States, 1974–76; associate independent counsel, Iran-Contra investigation, 1987–88, private law practice, White and Case (partner, 1979–94; associate, 1976–79); member: American Bar Association, Commission on Multidisciplinary Practice (1998–2000), District of Columbia Bar (president, 1986–87), American Law Institute (1984) and ALI Council, 1998, American Academy of Appellate Lawyers, Bar Association of the District of Columbia, Women's Bar Association of the District of Columbia, Washington Bar Association, Hispanic Bar Association, Assistant United States Attorneys Association of the District of Columbia (president, 1976–77), Civil Justice Reform Act Advisory Group (chair, 1991–94), District of Columbia Judicial Nomination Commission (member, 1990–94; chair, 1992–94), Advisory Committee on Procedures, U.S. Court of Appeals for the D.C. Circuit (1982–88), Grievance Committee; U.S. District Court for the District of Columbia (member, 1981–87; chair, 1983–85); fellow, American College of Trial Lawyers; fellow, American Bar Foundation; board of directors: Frederick B. Abramson Memorial Foundation (president, 1991–94), Washington Area Lawyers for the Arts (1988–92), Washington Legal Clinic for the Homeless (member, 1987–92; vice-president 1988–91), Stuart Stiller Memorial Foundation (1980–94), American Judicature Society (1990–94), District of Columbia Public Defender Service (1989–92); member: Cosmos Club, Lawyers Club of Washington; appointed judge, U.S. District Court for the District of Columbia by President Clinton, June 16, 1994, and took oath of office August 1, 1994; U.S. Judicial Conference Advisory Committee on Federal Criminal Rules.

Officers of the United States District Court for the District of Columbia

Bankruptcy Judge.—S. Martin Teel, Jr.
United States Magistrate Judges: Alan Kay; John M. Facciola; Deborah A. Robinson.
Clerk of Court.—Angela Caesar.
Administrative Assistant to the Chief Judge.—Sheldon L. Snook.

UNITED STATES COURT OF INTERNATIONAL TRADE

One Federal Plaza, New York, NY 10278–0001, phone (212) 264–2800

DONALD C. POGUE, chief judge; graduated *magna cum laude,* Phi Beta Kappa from Dartmouth College; did graduate work at the University of Essex, England; J.D., Yale Law School and a Masters of Philosophy, Yale University; married 1971; served as judge in Connecticut's Superior Court; appointed to the bench in 1994; served as chairman of Connecticut's Commission on Hospitals and Health Care; practiced law in Hartford for 15 years; lectured on labor law at the University of Connecticut School of Law; assisted in teaching the Harvard Law School's program on negotiations and dispute resolution for lawyers; chaired the Connecticut Bar Association's Labor and Employment Law Section; appointed a judge of the United States Court of International Trade in 1995; prior to becoming chief judge, he chaired the Court's Long Range Planning Committee and Budget Committee; he also chaired the Judicial Conference's Committee on the Administrative Office; service by designation in the 2d, 3d, 5th, 9th, 11th and Federal Circuits and in the D.C. and New York Southern district courts. Chief Judge Pogue also serves as a member of the Judicial Conference.

GREGORY W. CARMAN, judge; born in Farmingdale, Long Island, NY; son of Nassau County District Court Judge Willis B. and Marjorie Sosa Carman; B.A., St. Lawrence University, Canton, NY, 1958; J.D., St. John's University School of Law (honors program), 1961; University of Virginia Law School, JAG (with honors), 1962; admitted to New York Bar, 1961; practiced law with firm of Carman, Callahan and Sabino, Farmingdale, NY; admitted to practice: U.S. Court of Military Appeals 1962, U.S. District Courts, Eastern and Southern Districts of New York 1965, Second Circuit Court of Appeals 1966, Supreme Court of the United States 1967, U.S. Court of Appeals, District of Columbia 1982; Councilman Town of Oyster Bay 1972–80; member U.S. House of Representatives, 97th Congress; member Banking, Finance and Urban Affairs Committee and Select Committee on Aging; member International Trade, Investment, and Monetary Policy Subcommittee; U.S. Congressional Delegate to International I.M.F. Conference; nominated by President Reagan, confirmed and appointed Judge of the U.S. Court of International Trade, March 2, 1983; Acting Chief Judge 1991; Chief Judge 1996–2003; Statutory Member, Judicial Conference of United States; member Executive Committee, Judicial Branch Committee, and Subcommittees on Long Range Planning, Benefits, Civic Education, and Seminars; Captain, U.S. Army, 1958–64; awarded Army Commendation Medal for Meritorious Service 1964; Member Rotary International 1964–present; named Paul Harris Fellow of the Rotary Foundation of Rotary International; member Holland Society, and recipient of its 1999 Gold Medal for Distinguished Achievement in Jurisprudence; member Federal Bar Association, American Bar Association, Fellow of American Bar Foundation, member New York State Bar Association, member and former chair New York State Bar Association's Committee on Courts and the Community, and recipient of its 1996 Special Recognition Award; Doctor of Laws, *honoris causa,* Nova Southeastern University, 1999; Distinguished Jurist in Residence, Touro College Law Center, 2000; Doctor of Laws, *honoris causa,* St. John's University, 2002; Inaugural Lecturer, DiCarlo U.S. Court of International Trade Lecture, John Marshall Law School 2003; Distinguished Alumni Citation, St. Lawrence University 2003; Italian Board of Guardians Public Service Award 2003; director and member Respect For Law Alliance, Inc.; Recipient of Respect For Law Alliance 2010 Judiciary Leader Award; Executive Committee member and past president Theodore Roosevelt American Inn of Court; past president Protestant Lawyers Association of Long Island; member Vestry, St. Thomas's Episcopal Church, Farmingdale, NY; married to Nancy Endruschat (deceased); children: Gregory Wright, Jr., John Frederick, James Matthew, and Mira Catherine; married to Judith L. Dennehy.

JANE A. RESTANI, judge; born in San Francisco, CA, 1948; parents: Emilia C. and Roy J. Restani; husband: Ira Bloom; B.A., University of California at Berkeley, 1969; J.D., University of California at Davis, 1973; law review staff writer, 1971–72; articles editor, 1972–73; member, Order of the Coif; elected to Phi Kappa Phi Honor Society; admitted to the bar of the Supreme Court of the State of California, 1973; joined the civil division of the Department of Justice under the Attorney General's Honor Program in 1973 as a trial attorney; assistant chief commercial litigation section, civil division, 1976–80; director, commercial litigation branch, civil division,1980–83; recipient of the John Marshall Award of outstanding legal achievement in 1983; Judicial Improvements Committee (now Committee on Court Administration and Case Management) of the Judicial Conference of the United States, 1987–94; Judicial Conference Advisory Committee on the Federal Rules of Bankruptcy Procedure, and liaison to the Advisory Committee on the Federal Rules of Civil Procedure, 1994–96; member Judicial Conference of the United States, 2003–10; Executive Committee of the Judicial Conference, 2010; ABA Standing Committee on Customs Laws, 1990–93; and the Board of Directors, New York State Association of Women Judges, 1992–present; nominated to the United States Court of International Trade on November 2, 1983 by President Reagan; entered upon the duties of that office on November 25, 1983; Chief Judge, 2003–10.

DELISSA A. RIDGWAY, judge; born in Kirksville, MO, June 28, 1955; B.A. (honors), University of Missouri-Columbia, 1975; graduate work, University of Missouri-Columbia, 1975–76; J.D., Northeastern University School of Law, 1979; Duke University School of Law, LL.M. in Judicial Studies (expected 2014); Shaw Pittman Potts and Trowbridge (Washington, DC), 1979–94; Chair, Foreign Claims Settlement Commission of the U.S., 1994–98; Adjunct Professor of Law, Cornell Law School, 1999–present; Adjunct Professor of Law/Lecturer, Washington College of Law / The American University, 1992–94; District of Columbia Bar, Secretary, 1991–92; Board of Governors, 1992–98; President, Women's Bar Association, 1992–93; American Bar Association, Standing Committee on Federal Judicial Improvements (2008–11); Co-Chair, Section of Litigation Task Force on Implicit Bias (2010–13); Commission on Women in the Profession, 2002–05; Federal Bar Association, National Council, 1993–2002, 2003–present; Government Relations Committee, 1996–2008, Public Relations Committee Chair, 1998–99; Board of Directors, Federal Bar Building Corporation; Executive Committee, National Conference of Federal Trial Judges, 2004–11; chair, National Conference of Federal Trial Judges, 2009–10; Board of Directors, American Judicature Society (2010–present); Founding Member of Board, D.C. Conference on Opportunities for Minorities in the Legal Profession, 1992–93; Chair, D.C. Bar Summit on Women in the Legal Profession, 1995–98; Fellow, American Bar Foundation; Member, American Law Institute; Fellow, Federal Bar Foundation; Earl W. Kintner Award of the Federal Bar Association (2000); Woman Lawyer of the Year, Washington, DC (2001); Distinguished Visiting Scholar-in-Residence, University of Missouri-Columbia (2003); sworn in as a judge to the U.S. Court of International Trade in May 1998.

RICHARD K. EATON, judge; born in Walton, NY; married to Susan Henshaw Jones; two children: Alice and Elizabeth; attended Walton public schools; B.A., Ithaca College, J.D., Union University Albany Law School, 1974; professional experience: Eaton & Eaton, partner; Mudge Rose Guthrie Alexander & Ferdon, New York, NY, associate and partner; Stroock & Stroock & Lavan, partner served on the staff of Senator Daniel Patrick Moynihan; confirmed by the United States Senate to the U.S. Court of International Trade on October 22, 1999.

TIMOTHY C. STANCEU, judge; born in Canton, OH; A.B., Colgate University, 1973; J.D., Georgetown University Law Center, 1979; appointed to the U.S. Court of International Trade by President George W. Bush and began serving on April 15, 2003; prior to appointment, private practice for 13 years in Washington, DC, with the law firm Hogan & Hartson, L.L.P., during which he represented clients in a variety of matters involving customs and international trade law; Deputy Director, Office of Trade and Tariff Affairs, U.S. Department of the Treasury; where his responsibilities involved the regulatory and enforcement matters of the U.S. Customs Service and other agencies; Special Assistant to the Assistant Secretary of the Office of Enforcement, U.S. Department of the Treasury; Program Analyst and Environmental Protection Specialist, U.S. Environmental Protection Agency, where he concentrated on the development and review of regulations on various environmental subjects.

LEO M. GORDON, judge; graduate of Newark Academy in Livingston, NJ; University of North Carolina–Chapel Hill, Phi Beta Kappa, 1973; J.D., Emory University School of Law, 1977; member of the Bars of New Jersey, Georgia and the District of Columbia; Assistant Counsel at the Subcommittee on Monopolies and Commercial Law, Committee on the Judiciary, U.S. House of Representatives, 1977–81; in that capacity, Judge Gordon was the principal attorney responsible for the Customs Courts Act of 1980 that created the U.S. Court of International Trade; for 25 years, Judge Gordon was on the staff at the Court, serving first as Assistant Clerk from 1981–99, and then Clerk of the Court from 1999–2006; appointed to the U.S. Court of International Trade in March 2006.

MARK A. BARNETT, judge; graduated *magna cum laude,* Phi Beta Kappa from Dickinson College; studied at the Dickinson Center for European Studies; J.D., *cum laude* from the University of Michigan Law School; member of the Bars of Pennsylvania and the District of Columbia and admitted to practice before the U.S. Court of International Trade and the U.S. Court of Appeals for the Federal Circuit; practiced in the international trade group at Steptoe & Johnson; joined the Office of Chief Counsel for Import Administration at the U.S. Department of Commerce as a staff attorney, served as a senior counsel, and subsequently served as the Deputy Chief Counsel for Import Administration; member of the U.S. negotiating teams for the U.S.-Morocco Free Trade Agreement, the World Trade Organization's Doha Round Rules Negotiating Group, and the Trans-Pacific Partnership; represented the United States before dispute settlement panels and the Appellate Body of the World Trade Organization and binational panels composed under the North American Free Trade Agreement; detailed to the U.S. House of Representatives, Committee on Ways and Means, Subcommittee on Trade as a Trade Counsel; served two terms as a member of the board of directors of the International Model United Nations Association, Inc., including Vice-Chairman and Chairman; nominated to the U.S. Court of International Trade by President Obama on July 12, 2012, and confirmed by the U.S. Senate on May 23, 2013.

CLAIRE R. KELLY, judge; born in New York, NY. Married to Joseph A DiBartolo. Child: Joseph J. DiBartolo. Attended Sacred Heart Academy, Hempstead NY; Barnard College, B.A. 1987 (*cum laude*); and Brooklyn Law School, J.D., 1993 (*magna cum laude*). Professional experience: Coudert Brothers (1993–97) associated; Brooklyn Law School (1997–2013), Legal Writing Instructor, Associate Professor of Law and Professor of Law and Co-Director of the Dennis J. Block Center for the Study of International Business Law. Elected Member of the American Law Institute 2011; nominated to the U.S. Court of International Trade by President Obama on November 14, 2012, and confirmed by the U.S. Senate on May 23, 2013.

SENIOR JUDGES

THOMAS J. AQUILINO, JR., senior judge; born in Mount Kisco, NY, December 7, 1939; son of Thomas J. and Virginia B. (Doughty) Aquilino; married to Edith Berndt Aquilino; children: Christopher Thomas, Philip Andrew, Alexander Berndt; attended Cornell University, 1957–59; B.A., Drew University, 1959–60, 1961–62; University of Munich, Germany, 1960–61; Free University of Berlin, Germany, 1965–66; J.D., Rutgers University School of Law, 1966–69; research assistant, Prof. L.F.E. Goldie (Resources for the Future-Ford Foundation), 1967–69; administrator, Northern Region, 1969 Jessup International Law Moot Court Competition; served in the U.S. Army, 1962–65; law clerk, Hon. John M. Cannella, U.S. District Court for the Southern District of New York, 1969–71; attorney with Davis Polk and Wardwell, New York, NY, 1971–85; admitted to practice New York, U.S. Supreme Court, U.S. Court of Appeals for Second and Third Circuits, U.S. Court of International Trade, U.S. Court of Claims, U.S. District Courts for Eastern, Southern and Northern Districts of New York, Interstate Commerce Commission; adjunct professor of law, Benjamin N. Cardozo School of Law, 1984–95; Mem., Drew University Board of Visitors, 1997–present; appointed to the U.S. Court of International Trade by President Reagan on February 22, 1985; confirmed by U.S. Senate, April 3, 1985.

NICHOLAS TSOUCALAS, senior judge; born in New York, NY, August 24, 1926; one of five children of George M. and Maria (Monogenis) Tsoucalas; married to Catherine Aravantinos; two daughters: Stephanie and Georgia; five grandchildren; B.S., Kent State University, 1949; LL.B., New York Law School, 1951; attended New York University Law School; entered U.S. Navy, 1944–46; served in the American and European Theaters of War on board the USS *Oden*, the USS *Monticello* and USS *Europa;* reentered Navy, 1951–52 and served on the carrier, USS *Wasp;* admitted to New York Bar, 1953; appointed Assistant U.S. Attorney for the Southern District of New York, 1955–59; appointed in 1959 as supervisor of 1960 census for the 17th and 18th Congressional Districts; appointed chairman, Board of Commissioners of Appraisal; appointed judge of Criminal Court of the City of New York, 1968; designated acting Supreme Court Justice, Kings and Queens Counties, 1975–82; resumed service as judge of the Criminal Court of the City of New York until June 1986; former chairman: Committee on Juvenile Delinquency, Federal Bar Association, and the Subcommittee on Public Order and Responsibility of the American Citizenship Committee of the New York County Lawyers' Association; member of the American Bar Association, New York State Bar Association; founder of Eastern Orthodox Lawyers' Association; former president: Greek-American Lawyers' Association, and Board of Directors of Greek Orthodox Church of "Evangelismos", St. John's Theologos Society, and Parthenon Foundation; member, Order of Ahepa, Parthenon Lodge, F.A.M.; appointed judge of the U.S. Court of International Trade by President Reagan on September 9, 1985, and confirmed by U.S. Senate on June 6, 1986; assumed senior status on September 30, 1996.

R. KENTON MUSGRAVE, senior judge; born in Clearwater, FL, September 7, 1927; married May 7, 1949 to former Ruth Shippen Hoppe, of Atlanta, GA; three children: Laura Marie Musgrave (deceased), Ruth Shippen Musgrave, Esq., and Forest Kenton Musgrave; attended Augusta Academy (Virginia); B.A., University of Washington, 1948; editorial staff, Journal of International Law, Emory University; J.D., with distinction, Emory University, 1953; assistant general counsel, Lockheed Aircraft and Lockheed International, 1953–62; vice president and general counsel, Mattel, Inc., 1963–71; director, Ringling Bros. and Barnum and Bailey Combined Shows, Inc., 1968–72; commissioner, BSA (Atlanta), 1952–55; partner, Musgrave, Welbourn and Fertman, 1972–75; assistant general counsel, Pacific Enterprises, 1975–81; vice president, general counsel and secretary, Vivitar Corporation, 1981–85; vice president and director, Santa Barbara Applied Research Corp., 1982–87; trustee, Morris Animal Foundation, 1981–94; director Emeritus, Pet Protection Society, 1981–present; director, Dolphins of Shark Bay (Australia) Foundation, 1985–present; trustee, The Dian Fossey Gorilla Fund, 1987–present; trustee, The Ocean Conservancy, 2000–present; vice president and director, South Bay Social Services Group, 1963–70; director, Palos Verdes Community Arts Association, 1973–79; member, Governor of Florida's Council of 100, 1970–73; director, Orlando Bank and Trust, 1970–73; counsel, League of Women Voters, 1964–66; member, State Bar of Georgia, 1953–present; State Bar of California, 1962–present; Los Angeles County Bar Association, 1962–87 and chairman, Corporate Law Departments Section, 1965–66; admitted to practice before the U.S. Supreme Court, 1962; Supreme Court of Georgia, 1953; California Supreme Court, 1962; U.S. Customs Court, 1967; U.S. Court of International Trade, 1980; nominated to the U.S. Court of International Trade by President Reagan on July 1, 1987; confirmed by the Senate on November 9, and took oath of office on November 13, 1987.

RICHARD W. GOLDBERG, senior judge; born in Fargo, ND, September 23, 1927; married; two children, a daughter and a son; J.D., University of Miami, 1952; served on active duty as an Air Force Judge Advocate, 1953–56; admitted to Washington, DC Bar, Florida Bar and North Dakota Bar; from 1959 to 1983, owned and operated a regional grain processing firm in North Dakota; served as State Senator from North Dakota for eight years; taught military law for the Army and Air Force ROTC at North Dakota State University; was vice-chairman of the board of Minneapolis Grain Exchange; joined the Reagan Administration in 1983 in Washington at the U.S. Department of Agriculture; served as Deputy Under Secretary for International Affairs and Commodity Programs and later as Acting Under Secretary; in 1990 joined the Washington, DC law firm of Anderson, Hibey and Blair; appointed judge of the U.S. Court of International Trade in 1991; assumed senior status in 2001.

JUDITH M. BARZILAY, senior judge; born in Russell, KS, January 3, 1944; husband, Sal (Doron) Barzilay; children, Ilan and Michael; parents, Arthur and Hilda Morgenstern; B.A., Wichita State University, 1965; M.L.S., Rutgers University School of Library and Information Science, 1971; J.D., Rutgers University School of Law, 1981, Moot Court Board, 1980–81; trial attorney, U.S. Department of Justice (International Trade Field Office), 1983–86; litigation associate, Siegel, Mandell and Davidson, New York, NY, 1986–88; Sony Corporation of America, 1988–98; customs and international trade counsel, 1988–89; vice-president for import and export operations, 1989–96; vice-president for government affairs, 1996–98; executive board of the American Association of Exporters and Importers, 1993–98; appointed by Treasury Secretary Robert Rubin to the Advisory Committee on Commercial Operations of the United States Customs Service, 1995–98; nominated for appointment on January 27, 1998 by President Clinton; sworn in as judge June 3, 1998.

OFFICERS OF THE UNITED STATES COURT OF INTERNATIONAL TRADE

Clerk.—Tina Potuto Kimble (212) 264–2814.

UNITED STATES COURT OF FEDERAL CLAIMS

Lafayette Square, 717 Madison Place, NW., 20005, phone (202) 357–6406

EMILY CLARK HEWITT, chief judge; born in Baltimore, MD, May 26, 1944; educated at the Roland Park Country School, Baltimore, MD, 1949–62; A.B., Cornell University, 1966; M. Phil., Union Theological Seminary, 1975; J.D. c.l., Harvard Law School, 1978; D. Min., Chicago Theological Seminary, 2011; ordained minister in the Episcopal Church (diaconate, 1972; priesthood, 1974); member, Bar of the Supreme Judicial Court of The Commonwealth of Massachusetts, 1978; administrator, Cornell / Hofstra Upward Bound Program, 1967–69; lecturer, Union Theological Seminary, 1972–73 and 1974–75; assistant professor, Andover Newton Theological School, 1973–75; private practice of law, Hill & Barlow, 1978–93; council member, Real Property Section, Massachusetts Bar Association, 1983–86; member, Executive Committee and chair, Practice Standards Committee, Massachusetts Conveyancers Association, 1990–92; General Counsel, U.S. General Services Administration, 1993–98; member, Administrative Conference of the United States, 1993–95; member, President's Interagency Council on Women, 1995–98; appointed by President Clinton to the U.S. Court of Federal Claims on October 22, 1998; entered duty on November 10, 1998; appointed by Chief Justice of the United States to serve on the Financial Disclosure Committee of the United States Judicial Conference, 2006–12; appointed chief judge on March 11, 2009.

MARIAN BLANK HORN, judge; born in New York, NY, 1943; daughter of Werner P. and Mady R. Blank; married to Robert Jack Horn; three daughters; attended Fieldston School, New York, NY, Barnard College, Columbia University and Fordham University School of Law; admitted to practice U.S. Supreme Court, 1973, Federal and State courts in New York, 1970, and Washington, DC, 1973; assistant district attorney, Deputy Chief Appeals Bureau, Bronx County, NY, 1969–72; attorney, Arent, Fox, Kintner, Plotkin and Kahn, 1972–73; adjunct professor of law, Washington College of Law, American University, 1973–76; litigation attorney, Federal Energy Administration, 1975–76; senior attorney, Office of General Counsel, Strategic Petroleum Reserve Branch, Department of Energy, 1976–79; deputy assistant general counsel for procurement and financial incentives, Department of Energy, 1979–81; deputy associate solicitor, Division of Surface Mining, Department of the Interior, 1981–83; associate solicitor, Division of General Law, Department of the Interior, 1983–85; principal deputy solicitor and acting solicitor, Department of Interior, 1985–86; adjunct professor of law, George Washington University National Law Center, 1991–present; Woodrow Wilson Visiting Fellow, 1994; assumed duties of judge, U.S. Court of Federal Claims in 1986 and confirmed for a second term in 2003.

FRANCIS M. ALLEGRA, judge; born in Cleveland, OH, October 14, 1957; married to Regina Allegra; one child (Domenic); B.A., Borromeo College of Ohio, 1978; J.D., Cleveland State University, 1981; judicial clerk to Chief Trial Judge Philip R. Miller, U.S. Court of Claims, 1981–82; associate, Squire, Sanders & Dempsey (Cleveland), 1982–84; line attorney, Appellate Section, then 1984–89, Counselor to the Assistant Attorney General, both with Tax Division, U.S. Department of Justice; Counselor to the Associate Attorney General (1994) then Deputy Associate Attorney General (1994–98), U.S. Department of Justice; appointed to the U.S. Court of Federal Claims on October 22, 1998.

LYNN J. BUSH, judge; born in Little Rock, AR, December 30, 1948; daughter of John E. Bush III and Alice (Saville) Bush; one son, Brian Bush Ferguson; B.A., Antioch College, 1970, Thomas J. Watson Fellow; J.D., Georgetown University Law Center, 1976; admitted to the Arkansas Bar in 1976 and to the District of Columbia Bar in 1977; trial attorney, Commercial Litigation Branch, Civil Division, U.S. Department of Justice, 1976–87; senior trial attorney, Naval Facilities Engineering Command, Department of the Navy, 1987–89; counsel, Engineering Field Activity Chesapeake, Naval Facilities Engineering Command, Department of the Navy, 1989–96; administrative judge, U.S. Department of Housing and Urban Development Board of Contract Appeals, 1996–98; nominated by President Clinton to the

U.S. Court of Federal Claims, June 22, 1998; and assumed duties of the office on October 26, 1998.

EDWARD J. DAMICH, judge; born in Pittsburgh, PA, June 19, 1948; son of John and Josephine (Lovrencic) Damich; A.B., St. Stephen's College, 1970; J.D., Catholic University, 1976; professor of law at Delaware School of Law of Widener University, 1976–84; served as a Law and Economics Fellow at Columbia University School of Law, where he earned his L.L.M. in 1983 and his J.S.D. in 1991; professor of law at George Mason University, 1984–98; appointed by President George H.W. Bush to be a Commissioner of the Copyright Royalty Tribunal, 1992–93; Chief Intellectual Property Counsel for the Senate Judiciary Committee, 1995–98; admitted to the Bars of the District of Columbia and Pennsylvania; member of the District of Columbia Bar Association, Pennsylvania Bar Association, American Bar Association, Supreme Court of the United States, the Federal Circuit and *Association litteraire et artistique internationale;* president of the National Federation of Croatian Americans, 1994–95; appointed by President Clinton as judge, U.S. Court of Federal Claims, October 22, 1998; served as chief judge May 13, 2002–March 11, 2009; adjunct professor of law, Catholic University and George Washington University.

NANCY B. FIRESTONE, judge; born in Manchester, NH, October 17, 1951; B.A., Washington University, 1973; J.D., University of Missouri, Kansas City, 1977; one child: Amanda Leigh; attorney, Appellate Section and Environmental Enforcement Section, U.S. Department of Justice, Washington, DC, 1977–84; assistant chief, Policy Legislation and Special Litigation, Environment and Natural Resources Division, Department of Justice, Washington, DC, 1984–85; Deputy Chief, Environmental Enforcement Section, Department of Justice, Washington, DC, 1985–89; associate deputy administrator, Environmental Protection Agency, Washington, DC, 1989–92; judge, Environmental Appeals Board, Environmental Protection Agency, Washington, DC, 1992–95; Deputy Assistant Attorney General, Environment and Natural Resources Division, Department of Justice, Washington, DC, 1995–98; adjunct professor, Georgetown University Law Center, 1985–present; appointed to the U.S. Court of Federal Claims by President Clinton on October 22, 1998.

LAWRENCE J. BLOCK, judge, born in New York City, March 15, 1951; son of Jerome Block and Eve Silver; B.A., magna cum laude, New York University, 1973; J.D., The John Marshall Law School, 1981; law clerk for Hon. Roger J. Miner, United States District Court Judge for Northern District of New York, 1981–83; associate, New York office of Skadden, Arps, Slate, Meagher and Flom, 1983–86; attorney, Commercial Litigation Branch, U.S. Department of Justice, 1986; senior attorney-advisor, Office of Legal Policy and Policy Development, U.S. Department of Justice, 1987–90; adjunct professor, George Mason University School of Law, 1990–91; acting general counsel for legal policy and deputy assistant general counsel for legal policy, U.S. Department of Energy, 1990–94; senior counsel, Senate Judiciary Committee, 1994–02; admitted to the bar of Connecticut; admitted to practice in the U.S. Supreme Court, 1982, the United States District Court for the northern district of New York, 1982, the U.S. Court of Appeals for the Eleventh Circuit, 1985, the United States District Court for the Eastern District of New York, 1985; appointed by President George W. Bush on October 3, 2002, to a 15-years term as judge, U.S. Court of Federal Claims.

SUSAN G. BRADEN, judge, born in Youngstown, OH, November 8, 1948; married to Thomas M. Susman; daughter (Daily); B.A., Case Western Reserve University, 1970; J.D., Case Western Reserve University School of Law, 1973; post graduate study Harvard Law School, Summer, 1979; private practice, 1985–2003 (1997–2003 Baker & McKenzie); Federal Trade Commission: special counsel to Chairman, 1984–85, senior attorney advisor to Commissioner and Acting Chairman, 1980–83; U.S. Department of Justice, Antitrust Division, Senior Trial Attorney, Energy Section, 1978–80; Cleveland Field Office, 1973–78; Special Assistant Attorney General for the State of Alabama, 1990; Consultant to the Administrative Conference of the United States, 1984–85; 2000 co-chair, Lawyers for Bush-Cheney; General Counsel Presidential Debate for Dole-Kemp Campaign, 1996; counsel to RNC Platform, 1996; coordinator for Regulatory Reform and Antitrust Policy, Dole Presidential Campaign, 1995–96; National Steering Committee, Lawyers for Bush-Quayle, 1992; Assistant General Counsel, Republican National Convention, 1988, 1992, 1996, 2000; elected At-Large Member, D.C. Republican National Committee, 2000–02; member of the American Bar Association (Council Member, Section on Administrative Law and Regulatory Practice, 1996–99), Federal Circuit Bar Association, District of Columbia Bar Association, Computer Law Bar Association; admitted to the Supreme Court of Ohio, 1973, U.S. District Court for the District of Columbia, 1980, U.S. Supreme Court, 1980; U.S. Court of Appeals for the District of Columbia, 1992; U.S. Court of Appeals for the Second Circuit, 1993, U.S. Court of Appeals for the Federal

Circuit, 2001; appointed to the U.S. Court of Federal Claims by President George W. Bush on July 14, 2003.

CHARLES F. LETTOW, judge, born in Iowa Falls, IA, 1941; son of Carl F. and Catherine Lettow; B.S.Ch.E., Iowa State University, 1962; LL.B., Stanford University, 1968, Order of the Coif; M.A., Brown University, 2001; Note Editor, Stanford Law Review; married to B. Sue Lettow; children: Renee Burnett, Carl Frederick II, John Stangland, and Paul Vorbeck; served U.S. Army, 1963–65; law clerk to Judge Ben C. Duniway, U.S. Court of Appeals for the Ninth Circuit, 1968–69, and Chief Justice Warren E. Burger, Supreme Court of the United States, 1969–70; counsel, Council on Environmental Quality, Executive Office of the President, 1970–73; associate (1973–76) and partner (1976–2003), Cleary, Gottlieb, Steen & Hamilton, Washington, DC; admitted to practice before the U.S. Supreme Court, the U.S. Courts of Appeals for the D.C., Second, Third, Fourth, Fifth, Sixth, Eighth, Ninth, Tenth, and Federal Circuits, the U.S. District Courts for the District of Columbia, the Northern District of California, and the District of Maryland, and the U.S. Court of Federal Claims; member: American Law Institute, he American Bar Association, the D.C. Bar, the California State Bar, the Iowa State Bar Association, and the Maryland State Bar; nominated by President George W. Bush to the U.S. Court of Federal Claims in 2001 and confirmed and took office in 2003.

MARY ELLEN COSTER WILLIAMS, judge; born in Flushing, NY, April 3, 1953; married to Mark Calhoun Williams; son: Justin; daughter: Jacquelyn; B.A. summa cum laude (Greek and Latin); M.A. (Latin), Catholic University, 1974; J.D. Duke University; Editorial Board, Duke Law Journal, 1976–77; admitted to the District of Columbia Bar; associate, Fulbright and Jaworski, 1977–79; associate, Schnader, Harrison, Segal and Lewis, 1979–83; Assistant U.S. Attorney, Civil Division, District of Columbia, 1983–87; partner-Janis, Schuelke and Wechsler, 1987–89; administrative judge, General Services Board of Contract Appeals March 1989–July 2003; secretary, District of Columbia Bar, 1988–89; Fellow, American Bar Foundation, elected, 1985; Board of Directors, Bar Association of District of Columbia, 1985–88; Chairman, Young Lawyers Section, Bar Association of District of Columbia, 1985–86; Chair, Public Contract Law Section of Amercan Bar Association, 2002–03, Chair-Elect, Vice-Chair, Secretary, Council, 1995–2002; Delegate, Section of Public Contract Law, ABA House of Delegates 2003–08; ABA Board of Governors, 2010–13; Lecturer, Government Contract Law, 1989–present; appointed to the U.S. Court of Federal Claims on July 21, 2003.

VICTOR JOHN WOLSKI, judge; born in New Brunswick, NJ, November 14, 1962; son of Vito and Eugenia Wolski; B.A., B.S., University of Pennsylvania, 1984; J.D., University of Virginia School of Law, 1991; married to Lisa Wolski; admitted to Supreme Court of the United States, 1995; California Supreme Court, 1992; Washington Supreme Court, 1994; Oregon Supreme Court, 1996; District of Columbia Court of Appeals, 2001; U.S. Court of Appeals for the Ninth Circuit, 1993; U.S. Court of Appeals for the Federal Circuit, 2001; U.S. District Court for the Eastern District of California, 1993; U.S. District Court for the Northern District of California, 1995; U.S. Court of Federal Claims, 2001; U.S. District Court for the District of Columbia, 2002; research assistant, Center for Strategic and International Studies, 1984–85; research associate, Institute for Political Economy, 1985–88; confidential assistant and speechwriter to the Secretary, U.S. Department of Agriculture, 1988; paralegal specialist, Office of the general counsel, U.S. Department of Energy, 1989; law clerk to Judge Vaughn R. Walker, U.S. District Court for the Northern District of California, 1991–92; attorney, Pacific Legal Foundation, 1992–97; general counsel, Sacramento County Republican Central Committee, 1995–97; counsel Senator Connie Mack, Vice-Chairman of the Joint Economic Committee, U.S. Congress, 1997–98; general counsel and chief tax adviser, Joint Economic Committee, U.S. Congress, 1999–2000; associate, Cooper, Carvin & Rosenthal, 2000–01; associate, Cooper & Kirk, 2001–03; associate editor, Public Contract Law Journal, 2006–present; appointed by President George W. Bush to the U.S. Court of Federal Claims on July 14, 2003.

GEORGE W. MILLER, judge, born in Schenectady, NY; married to Mary Katherine ''Kay'' Miller, three children; A.B., magna cum laude, Princeton University, 1963; J.D., Harvard Law School, 1966; L.L.M. in taxation, George Washington University Law School, 1968; law clerk to the late Judge Bruce M. Forrester of the United States Tax Court, 1966–67; officer, U.S. Navy Judge Advocate General Corps, 1967–70; trial attorney and partner at Hogan & Hartson (now Hogan Lovells), 1970–2004; District of Columbia Court of Appeals Board of Professional Responsibility, 1985 (Vice Chairman 1988-89, Chairman 1989–91); D.C. Court of Appeals Task Force on Racial and Ethnic Bias in the D.C. Courts, 1990–92; United States Court of Appeals for the District of Columbia Advisory Committee on Admissions and Grievances, 2002–04; United States Court of Federal Claims Advisory Council,

1994–2004; United States Court of Federal Claims Litigation Practice Task Force, 1995; member United States Court of Federal Claims Bar Association Board of Governors, 2004; admitted to the Bars of Virginia, District of Columbia, and New York; appointed to the United States Court of Federal Claims by President George W. Bush, 2004.

THOMAS C. WHEELER, judge; born in Chicago, IL, March 18, 1948; married; two grown children; B.A., Gettysburg College, 1970; J.D., Georgetown University Law School, 1973; private practice in Washington, DC, 1973–2005; associate and partner, Pettit & Martin until 1995; partner, Piper & Marbury (later Piper Marbury Rudnick & Wolfe, and then DLA Piper Rudnick Gray Cary); member of the District of Columbia Bar; American Bar Association's Public Contracts and Litigation Sections; appointed to the U.S. Court of Federal Claims on October 24, 2005.

MARGARET M. SWEENEY, judge; born in Baltimore, MD; B.A. in history, Notre Dame of Maryland, 1977; J.D., Delaware Law School, 1981; Delaware Family Court Master, 1981–83; litigation associate, Fedorko, Gilbert, & Lanctot, Morrisville, PA, 1983–85; law clerk to Hon. Loren A. Smith, Chief Judge of the U.S. Court of Federal Claims, 1985–87; trial attorney in the General Litigation Section of the Environment and Natural Resources Division of the United States Department of Justice, 1987–99; president, U.S. Court of Federal Claims Bar Association, 1999; attorney advisor, United States Department of Justice Office of Intelligence Policy and Review, 1999–2003; special master, U.S. Court of Federal Claims, 2003–05; member of the Bars of the Supreme Court of Pennsylvania and the District of Columbia Court of Appeals; appointed to the U.S. Court of Federal Claims by President George W. Bush on October 24, 2005, and entered duty on December 14, 2005.

SENIOR JUDGES

JAMES F. MEROW, senior judge; born in Salamanca, NY; educated in the public schools of Little Valley, NY and Alexandria, VA; A.B. (with distinction), George Washington University, 1953; J.D. (with distinction), George Washington University Law School, 1956; member: Phi Beta Kappa, Order of the Coif, Omicron Delta Kappa; married; officer, U.S. Army Judge Advocate General's Corps, 1956–59; trial attorney-branch director, Civil Division, U.S. Department of Justice, 1959–78; trial judge, U.S. Court of Claims,1978–82; member of Virginia State Bar, District of Columbia Bar, American Bar Association, and Federal Bar Association; judge, U.S. Court of Federal Claims since October 1, 1982 , reappointed by President Reagan to a 15-year term commencing August 5, 1983; assumed senior judge status on August 5, 1998.

ERIC G. BRUGGINK, senior judge; born in Kalidjati, Indonesia, September 11, 1949; naturalized U.S. citizen, 1961; married to Melinda Harris Bruggink; sons: John and David; B.A., cum laude (sociology), Auburn University, AL, 1971; M.A. (speech), 1972; J.D., University of Alabama, 1975; Hugo Black Scholar and Note and Comments Editor of Alabama Law Review; member, Alabama State Bar and District of Columbia Bar; served as law clerk to chief judge Frank H. McFadden, Northern District of Alabama, 1975–76; associate, Hardwick, Hause and Segrest, Dothan, AL, 1976–77; assistant director, Alabama Law Institute, 1977–79; director, Office of Energy and Environmental Law, 1977–79; associate, Steiner, Crum and Baker, Montgomery, AL, 1979–82; Director, Office of Appeals Counsel, Merit Systems Protection Board, 1982–86; appointed to the U.S. Court of Federal Claims on April 15, 1986.

UNITED STATES TAX COURT

400 Second Street, NW., 20217, phone (202) 521–0700

JOHN O. COLVIN, chief judge; born in Ohio, 1946; A.B., University of Missouri, 1968; J.D., 1971; LL.M., Taxation, Georgetown University Law Center, 1978; admitted to practice law in Missouri (1971) and District of Columbia (1974); Office of the Chief Counsel, U.S. Coast Guard, Washington, DC, 1971–75; served as Tax Counsel, Senator Bob Packwood, 1975–84; Chief Counsel (1985–87), and Chief Minority Counsel (1987–88), U.S. Senate Finance Committee; past Chair, Tax Section, Federal Bar Association and recipient of the FBA Tax Section's Liles Award; Adjunct Professor of Law, Georgetown University Law Center and recipient of Charles Fahy Distinguished Adjunct Professor Award; appointed by President Reagan as Judge, United States Tax Court, on September 1, 1988, for a term ending August 31, 2003; reappointed on August 12, 2004, for a term ending August 11, 2019; elected as Chief Judge for two-year terms beginning June 1, 2006, June 1, 2008, and June 1, 2010. Elected as Chief Judge for an interim period effective March 8, 2013.

JAMES S. HALPERN, judge; born in New York, 1945; Hackley School, Terrytown, NY, 1963; B.S., Wharton School, University of Pennsylvania, 1967; J.D., University of Pennsylvania Law School, 1972; LL.M., Taxation, New York University Law School, 1975; Associate Attorney, Mudge, Rose, Guthrie and Alexander, New York City, 1972–74; assistant professor of law, Washington and Lee University, 1975–76; assistant professor of law, St. John's University, New York City, 1976–78; visiting professor, Law School, New York University, 1978–79; associate attorney, Roberts and Holland, New York City, 1979–80; Principal Technical Advisor, Assistant Commissioner (Technical) and Associate Chief Counsel (Technical), Internal Revenue Service, Washington, DC, 1980–83; partner, Baker and Hostetler, Washington, DC, 1983–90; Adjunct Professor, Law School, George Washington University, Washington, DC, 1984–present; Colonel, U.S. Army Reserve (retired); appointed by President George H.W. Bush as Judge, United States Tax Court, on July 3, 1990, for a term ending July 2, 2005; reappointed on November 2, 2005, for a term ending November 1, 2020.

MAURICE B. FOLEY, judge; born in Illinois, 1960; B.A., Swarthmore College; J.D., Boalt Hall School of Law at the University of California at Berkeley; LL.M., Georgetown University Law Center; attorney for the Legislation and Regulations Division of the Internal Revenue Service, Tax Counsel for the United States Senate Committee on Finance; Deputy Tax Legislative Counsel in the U.S. Treasury's Office of Tax Policy; appointed by President Clinton as Judge, United States Tax Court, on April 9, 1995, for a term ending April 8, 2010; reappointed on November 25, 2011, for a term ending November 24, 2026.

JUAN F. VASQUEZ, judge; born in San Antonio, Texas, 1948; attended Fox Tech High School; A.D. (Data Processing), San Antonio Junior College; B.B.A. (Accounting), University of Texas, Austin, 1972; attended State University of New York, Buffalo in 1st year law school, 1975; J.D., University of Houston Law Center, 1977; LL.M., Taxation, New York University Law School of Law, 1978; Certified Public Accountant, Certificate from Texas, 1976; admitted to State Bar of Texas, 1977; admitted to the United States Tax Court, 1978; certified in tax law by Texas Board of Legal Specialization, 1984; admitted to the United States District Court, Southern District of Texas, 1982, Western District of Texas, 1985 and United States Court of Appeals for the Fifth Circuit, 1982; and the Supreme Court of the United States of America, 1996; private practice of tax law, in San Antonio, TX, 1987–April 1995; partner, Leighton, Hood and Vasquez, in San Antonio, TX, 1982–87; Trial Attorney, Office of Chief Counsel, Internal Revenue Service, Houston, TX, 1978–82; accountant, Coopers and Lybrand, Los Angeles, CA, 1972–74; member of American Bar Association, Tax Section; Texas State Bar, Tax Section; Fellow of Texas and San Antonio Bar Foundations; College of State Bar of Texas; National Hispanic Bar Association and Hispanic Bar Association of the District of Columbia; Mexican American Bar Association (MABA) of San Antonio 1982–95; Houston MABA 1978–82; Texas MABA 1986–88; National Association of Hispanic CPA's San Antonio Chapter (founding member) 1983–88; member of Greater Austin Tax

Litigation Association 1989–95; served on Austin Internal Revenue Service District Director's Practitioner Liaison Committee, 1990–91 (chairman, 1991); appointed by President Clinton as Judge, United States Tax Court, on May 1, 1995, for a term ending April 30, 2010; reappointed on October 13, 2011, for a term ending October 12, 2026.

JOSEPH H. GALE, judge; born in Virginia, 1953; A.B., Philosophy, Princeton University, 1976; J.D., University of Virginia School of Law, Dillard Fellow, 1980; practiced law as an Associate Attorney, Dewey Ballantine, Washington, DC, and New York, 1980–83; Dickstein, Shapiro and Morin, Washington, DC, 1983–85; served as Tax Legislative Counsel for Senator Daniel Patrick Moynihan (D–NY), 1985–88; Administrative Assistant and Tax Legislative Counsel, 1989; Chief Counsel, 1990–93; Chief Tax Counsel, Committee on Finance, U.S. Senate, 1993–95; minority Chief Tax Counsel, Senate Finance Committee, January 1995–July 1995; minority Staff Director and Chief Counsel, Senate Finance Committee, July 1995–January 1996; admitted to District of Columbia Bar; member of American Bar Association, Section of Taxation; appointed by President Clinton as Judge, United States Tax Court, February 6, 1996, for a term ending February 5, 2011; reappointed on October 18, 2011, for a term ending October 17, 2026.

JOSEPH ROBERT GOEKE, judge; born in Kentucky, 1950; B.S., *cum laude,* Xavier University, 1972; J.D., University of Kentucky College of Law, 1975 (Order of the Coif); admitted to Illinois and Kentucky Bar, U.S. District Court for the Northern District of Illinois (Trial Bar), U.S. Court of Federal Claims; Trial Attorney, Chief Counsel's Office, Internal Revenue Service, New Orleans, LA, 1975–80; Senior Trial Attorney, Chief Counsel's Office, Internal Revenue Service, Cincinnati, OH, 1980–85; Special International Trial Attorney, Chief Counsel's Office, Internal Revenue Service, Cincinnati, OH, 1985–88; partner, Law Firm of Mayer, Brown, Rowe and Maw, Chicago, IL, 1988–2003; appointed by President George W. Bush as Judge, United States Tax Court, on April 22, 2003, for a term ending April 21, 2018.

ROBERT A. WHERRY, Jr., judge; born in Virginia, 1944; B.S., and J.D., University of Colorado; LL.M., Taxation, New York University Law School; fellow and former Regent of the American College of Tax Counsel and former chairman of the Taxation Section of the Colorado Bar Association; served as chairman of the Small-Business Tax Committee of the Colorado Association of Commerce and Industry, as president of the Greater Denver Tax Counsel Association, is a past chairman of the Administrative Practice Committee of the American Bar Association Tax Section, a member of the Council, and a member of the Advisory Committee of the American Bar Association Section of Dispute Resolution; listed in *The Best Lawyers in America* (in tax litigation); his articles have appeared in ALI–ABA publications, *The Colorado Lawyer, Tax Notes, and State Tax Notes;* former Colorado correspondent for *State Tax Notes* and has spoken at numerous tax institutes, including the University of Denver Tax Institute, Tulane University Tax Institute, and American Bar Association Tax Section programs; was an instructor in Tax Court litigation for the National Institute for Trial Advocacy; appointed by President George W. Bush as Judge, United States Tax Court, on April 23, 2003, for a term ending April 22, 2018.

DIANE L. KROUPA, judge; born in South Dakota, 1955; B.S.F.S., Georgetown University School of Foreign Service, 1978; J.D., University of South Dakota Law School, 1981; practiced tax law at Faegre and Benson, LLP in Minneapolis, MN; Minnesota Tax Court Judge, 1995–2001 (Chief Judge, 1998–2001); attorney-advisor, Legislation and Regulations Division, Office of Chief Counsel (1981–84) and served as attorney-advisor to Judge Joel Gerber, United States Tax Court, 1984–85; admitted to practice law in South Dakota (1981), District of Columbia (1985) and Minnesota (1986); member: American Bar Association (Tax Section), Minnesota State Bar Association (Tax Section), National Association of Women Judges (1995–present), American Judicature Society (1995–present); Distinguished Service Award Recipient (2001), Minnesota State Bar Association (Tax Section); Volunteer of the Year Award, Junior League of Minneapolis (1993); Community Volunteer of the Year, Minnesota State Bar Association (1998); appointed by President George W. Bush as Judge, United States Tax Court, on June 13, 2003, for a term ending June 12, 2018.

MARK V. HOLMES, judge; born in New York, 1960; B.A., Harvard College, 1979; J.D., University of Chicago Law School, 1983; admitted to New York and District of Columbia Bars; U.S. Supreme Court; DC, Second, Fifth and Ninth Circuits; Southern and Eastern Districts of New York, Court of Federal Claims; practiced in New York as an Associate, Cahill Gordon and Reindel, 1983–85; Sullivan and Cromwell, 1987–91; served as clerk to the Hon. Alex Kozinski, Ninth Circuit, 1985–87; and in Washington as Counsel to Commissioners, United States International Trade Commission, 1991–96; Counsel, Miller and Chevalier, 1996–2001; Deputy Assistant Attorney General, Tax Division, 2001–03; member, American Bar Association (Litigation and Tax Sections); appointed by President George W. Bush as Judge, United States Tax Court, on June 30, 2003, for a term ending June 29, 2018.

DAVID GUSTAFSON, judge; born in Greenville, South Carolina, in 1956. Bob Jones University, B.A. *summa cum laude,* 1978. Duke University School of Law, J.D. with distinction, 1981. Order of the Coif (1981). Executive Editor of the *Duke Law Journal* (1980–81). Admitted to the District of Columbia Bar, 1981. Associate at the law firm of Sutherland, Asbill and Brennan, in Washington, DC, 1981–83. Trial Attorney (1983–89), Assistant Chief (1989–2005), and Chief (2005–08) in the Court of Federal Claims Section of the Tax Division in the U.S. Department of Justice; and Coordinator of Tax Shelter Litigation for the entire Tax Division (2002–06). Tax Division Outstanding Attorney Awards, 1985, 1989, 1997, 2001–05. Federal Bar Association's Younger Attorney Award, 1991. President of the Court of Federal Claims Bar Association (2001). Appointed by President George W. Bush as Judge, United States Tax Court, on July 29, 2008, for a term ending July 29, 2023.

ELIZABETH CREWSON PARIS, judge; born in Oklahoma, 1958; B.S., University of Tulsa, 1980; J.D., University of Tulsa College of Law, 1987; LL.M., Taxation, University of Denver College of Law, 1993. Admitted to the Supreme Court of Oklahoma and U.S. District Court for the District of Oklahoma, 1988; U.S. Tax Court, U.S. Court of Federal Claims, U.S. Court of Appeals for the Tenth Circuit, 1993; Supreme Court of Colorado, 1994. Former partner, Brumley Bishop and Paris, 1992; Senior Associate, McKenna and Cueno, 1994; Tax Partner, Reinhart, Boerner, Van Deuren, Norris and Rieselbach, 1998. Tax Counsel to the United States Senate Finance Committee, 2000–08. Member of the American Bar Association, Section of Taxation and Real Property and Probate Sections, formerly served as Vice Chair to both Agriculture and Entity Selection Committees. Member of Colorado and Oklahoma Bar Associations. Recognized as Distinguished Alumnus by the University of Tulsa School of law. Author of numerous tax, estate planning, real property, agriculture articles and chapters. Former adjunct professor, Georgetown University Law Center, LL.M. Taxation Program, and University of Tulsa College of Law. Appointed by President George W. Bush as Judge, United States Tax Court, on July 30, 2008, for a term ending July 29, 2023.

RICHARD T. MORRISON, judge; born in Hutchinson, Kansas 1967. B.A., B.S., University of Kansas, 1989; visiting student at Mansfield College, Oxford University, 1987–88; J.D., University of Chicago Law School, 1993; M.A., University of Chicago, 1994. Clerk to Judge Jerry E. Smith, United States Court of Appeals for the Fifth Circuit, 1993–94. Associate, Baker and McKenzie, Chicago, Illinois, 1994–96. Associate, Mayer Brown and Platt, Chicago, Illinois 1996–2001. Deputy Assistant Attorney General for Review and Appellate Matters, Tax Division, United States Department of Justice, from 2001 to 2008 (except for term as Acting Assistant Attorney General, from July 2007 to January 2008). Nominated by President George W. Bush as Judge, United States Tax Court, on November 15, 2007; confirmed by Senate, July 7, 2008.

KATHLEEN KERRIGAN, judge; born in Springfield, Massachusetts; B.S., Boston College 1985; J.D., University of Notre Dame Law School, 1990; admitted to Massachusetts Bar, 1991 and District Columbia Bar, 1992; Legislative Director for Congressman Richard E. Neal, Member of the Ways and Means Committee, 1990 to 1998; associate and partner at Baker & Hostetler LLP, Washington, DC, 1998–2005; tax counsel for Senator John F. Kerry, Member of Senate Finance Committee, 2005–12; appointed by President Barack Obama as Judge, United States, Tax Court, on May 4, 2012, for a term ending on May 3, 2027.

RONALD L. BUCH, judge; born in Flint, Michigan; B.B.A., Northwood Institute, 1987; J.D. with Taxation Concentration, Detroit College of Law, 1993; LL.M. in Taxation, Capital University Law School, 1994; Research Editor of the *Detroit College of Law Review,* 1992–93; Ohio Tax Review Fellow, 1993–94; admitted to the bars of Michigan, inactive (1993), Ohio, inactive (1994), Florida (1994), and the District of Columbia (1995); consultant at KPMG Washington National Tax (1995–97); Attorney-Advisor (1997–2000) and Senior Legal Counsel (2000–01) at the IRS Office of Chief Counsel; associate (2001–05) and partner (2005–09) at McKee Nelson LLP; partner at Bingham McCutchen LLP (2009–13); James E. Markham Attorney of the Year Award, 1999; Chair of the DC Bar Tax Audits and Litigation Committee, 2006–08; Chair of the ABA Tax Section's Administrative Practice

Committee, 2008–09; appointed by President Barack H. Obama as Judge, United States Tax Court, on January 14, 2013, for a term ending January 13, 2028.

ALBERT G. LAUBER, judge; born in Bronxville, New York. Education: Yale College (B.A., summa cum laude, 1971); Clare College, Cambridge University (M.A., Classics, 1974); Yale Law School (J.D., 1977). Phi Beta Kappa; Woodrow Wilson Fellow; Mellon Fellow; Note Editor, *Yale Law Journal;* Moot Court Prize Argument; Cardozo Prize, Best Moot Court Brief. Employment: Law Clerk to Malcolm R. Wilkey, U.S. Court of Appeals for the DC Circuit (1977–78); Law Clerk to Justice Harry A. Blackmun, U.S. Supreme Court (1978–79). Associate Attorney, Caplin & Drysdale, Chtd., Washington, DC (1979–83); Tax Assistant to the Solicitor General, U.S. Department of Justice (1983–86); Deputy Solicitor General, U.S. Department of Justice (1986–87); Partner, Caplin & Drysdale, Chtd., Washington, DC (1988–2005); Visiting Professor and Director, Graduate Tax & Securities Programs, Georgetown University Law Center (2006–13). Professorial Lecturer, George Washington University Law School (1983–84); Lecturer, University of Virginia Law School (1988–90); Adjunct Professor, Georgetown University Law Center (2013–present); Board of Trustees, the Studio Theatre (1993–present); Member, District of Columbia Alcoholic Beverage Control Board (2004–08). Admitted to the Bars of the District of Columbia (1978); U.S. Supreme Court (1983); U.S. Court of Appeals, DC Circuit (1983); U.S. Court of Appeals, Federal Circuit (1994); Connecticut (inactive); Member, American Bar Association, Section of Taxation; appointed by President Barack H. Obama as Judge, United States Tax Court, on January 31, 2013, for a term ending January 30, 2028.

SENIOR JUDGES

HOWARD A. DAWSON, Jr., senior judge; born in Arkansas, 1922; Woodrow Wilson High School, Washington, DC, 1940; B.S. in Commerce, University of North Carolina, 1946; J.D. with honors, George Washington University School of Law, 1949; President, Case Club; Secretary-Treasurer, Student Bar Association; private practice of law, Washington, DC, 1949–50; served with the United States Treasury Department, Internal Revenue Service, as follows: Attorney, Civil Division, Office of Chief Counsel, 1950–53; Civil Advisory Counsel, Atlanta Region, 1953–57; Regional Counsel, Atlanta Region, 1958; Personal Assistant to Chief Counsel, 1958–59, Assistant Chief Counsel (Administration), 1959–62; U.S. Army Finance Corps, 1943–45; two years in European Theater; Captain, Finance Corps, U.S. Army Reserve (Retired); member of District of Columbia Bar (1949), Georgia Bar (1958), American Bar Association (Section of Taxation), Federal Bar Association, Chi Psi, Delta Theta Phi, George Washington University Law Alumni Association; appointed by President Kennedy as Judge, Tax Court of the United States, on August 21, 1962, for a term ending June 1, 1970; reappointed by President Nixon on June 2, 1970, for a term ending June 1, 1985; served as Chief Judge from July 1, 1973 to June 30, 1977, during which time the United States Tax Court's Courthouse was built and dedicated; and served again as Chief Judge from July 1, 1983 to June 1, 1985; retired on June 2, 1985; David Brennan Distinguished Professor of Law, University of Akron Law School, Spring Term, 1986; Professor and Director, Graduate Tax Program, University of Baltimore Law School, 1986–89; Distinguished Visiting Professor of Law, University of San Diego, Winter 1991. Recalled as Senior Judge to perform judicial duties 1990–to–present. In 2009, the Court established the Howard A. Dawson, Jr. Award to honor exemplary service by Tax Court employees. On January 18, 2011, became the longest serving judge in Tax Court history.

HERBERT L. CHABOT, senior judge; born in New York, 1931; Stuyvesant High School, 1948; B.A., *cum laude,* C.C.N.Y., 1952; LL.B., Columbia University, 1957; LL.M. in Taxation, Georgetown University, 1964; served in United States Army, 2 years, and Army Reserves (civil affairs units), for 8 years; served on legal staff, American Jewish Congress, 1957–61; attorney-adviser to Judge Russell E. Train, 1961–65; Congressional Joint Committee on Taxation, 1965–78; elected Delegate, Maryland Constitutional Convention, 1967–68; adjunct professor, National Law Center, George Washington University, 1974–83; member of American Bar Association, Tax Section, and Federal Bar Association; appointed by President Carter as Judge, United States Tax Court, on April 3, 1978, for a term ending April 2, 1993; served as Senior Judge on recall performing judicial duties until reappointed on October 20, 1993, for a term ending October 19, 2008; retired on June 30, 2001, but recalled on July 1, 2001, as Senior Judge to perform judicial duties to the present time.

MARY ANN COHEN, senior judge; born in New Mexico, 1943; attended public schools in Los Angeles, CA; B.S., University of California, at Los Angeles, 1964; J.D., University of Southern California School of Law, 1967; practiced law in Los Angeles, member in law firm of Abbott and Cohen; American Bar Association, Section of Taxation, and Continuing Legal Education activities; received Dana Latham Memorial Award from Los Angeles County Bar Association Taxation Section, 1997; Jules Ritholz Memorial Merit Award from ABA Tax Section Committee on Civil and Criminal Tax Penalties, 1999; Bruce I. Hochman Award from the UCLA Tax Controversy program, 2007; and Joanne M. Garvey Award from California Bar Taxation Section, 2008; appointed by President Reagan as Judge, United States Tax Court, on September 24, 1982, for a term ending September 23, 1997; served as Chief Judge from June 1, 1996 to September 23, 1997; reappointed on November 7, 1997, for a term ending November 6, 2012, and served again as Chief Judge from November 7, 1997 to May 31, 2000.

JULIAN I. JACOBS, senior judge; born in Maryland, 1937; B.A., University of Maryland, 1958; LL.B., University of Maryland Law School, 1960; LL.M., Taxation, Georgetown Law Center, 1965; admitted to Maryland Bar, 1960; attorney, Internal Revenue Service, Washington, DC, 1961–65, and Buffalo, NY, in Regional Counsel's Office, 1965–67; entered private practice of law in Baltimore, MD, 1967; associate (1972–74) and partner (1974–84) in the Law Firm of Gordon, Feinblatt, Rothman, Hoffberger and Hollander; Chairman, study commission to improve the quality of the Maryland Tax Court, 1978; member, study groups to consider changes in the Maryland tax laws; Commissioner on a commission to reorganize and recodify article of Maryland law dealing with taxation, 1980; Lecturer, tax seminars and professional programs; Chairman, Section of Taxation, Maryland State Bar Association; adjunct professor of Law, Graduate Tax Program, University of Baltimore School of Law, 1991–93; Adjunct Professor of Law, Graduate Tax Program, University of San Diego School of Law, 2001; Adjunct Professor of Law, Graduate Tax Program, University of Denver School of Law, 2001–04; appointed by President Reagan as Judge, United States Tax Court, on March 30, 1984, for a term ending March 29, 1999; recalled on March 30, 1999, as Senior Judge to perform judicial duties from that date to the present.

JOEL GERBER, senior judge; born in Illinois, 1940; B.S., business administration, Roosevelt University, 1962; J.D., DePaul University, 1965; LL.M., Taxation, Boston University Law School, 1968; admitted to the Illinois Bar, 1965; Georgia Bar, 1974; Tennessee Bar, 1978; served with U.S. Treasury Department, Internal Revenue Service, as trial attorney, Boston, MA, 1965–72; senior trial attorney, Atlanta, GA, 1972–76; District Counsel, Nashville, TN, 1976–80; Deputy Chief Counsel, Washington, DC, 1980–84; Acting Chief Counsel, May 1983–March 1984; recipient of a Presidential Meritorious Rank Award, 1983; Secretary of the Treasury's Exceptional Service Award, 1984; Lecturer in Law, Vanderbilt University, 1976–80; appointed by President Reagan as Judge, United States Tax Court, on June 18, 1984, for a term ending June 17, 1999; served as Senior Judge on recall performing judicial duties until reappointed on December 15, 2000, for a term ending December 14, 2015; served as Chief Judge from June 1, 2004, to May 31, 2006; assumed senior status on June 1, 2006.

THOMAS B. WELLS, senior judge; born in Ohio, 1945; B.S., Miami University, Oxford, OH, 1967; J.D., Emory University Law School, Atlanta, GA, 1973; LL.M., Taxation, New York University Law School, New York, 1978; Supply Corps Officer, U.S. Naval Reserve, active duty 1967–70, Morocco and Vietnam, received Joint Service Commendation Medal; admitted to practice law in Georgia; member of law firm of Graham and Wells, P.C.; County Attorney for Toombs County, GA; City Attorney, Vidalia, GA, until 1977; law firm of Hurt, Richardson, Garner, Todd and Cadenhead, Atlanta, until 1981; law firm of Shearer and Wells, P.C. until 1986; member of American Bar Association, Section of Taxation; State Bar of Georgia, member of Board of Governors; Board of Editors, Georgia State Bar Journal; member, Atlanta Bar Association; Editor of the *Atlanta Lawyer;* active in various tax organizations, such as Atlanta Tax Forum (presently, Honorary Member); Director, Atlanta Estate Planning Council; Director, North Atlanta Tax Council; American College of Tax Counsel, Honorary Fellow; Emory Law Alumni Association's Distinguished Alumnus Award, 2001; Life Member, National Eagle Scout Association, Eagle Scout, 1960; member: Vidalia Kiwanis Club (President); recipient, Distinguished President Award; appointed by President Reagan as Judge, United States Tax Court, on October 13, 1986, for a term ending October 12, 2001; reappointed by President Bush on October 10, 2001, for a term ending October 9, 2016; served as Chief Judge from September 24, 1997 to November 6, 1997, and from June 1, 2000 to May 31, 2004. Recalled on January 1, 2011, as Senior Judge to perform judicial duties from that date to the present.

ROBERT PAUL RUWE, senior judge; born in Ohio, 1941; Roger Bacon High School, St. Bernard, OH, 1959; Xavier University, Cincinnati, OH, 1963; J.D., Salmon P. Chase College of Law (graduated first in class), 1970; admitted to Ohio Bar, 1970; Special Agent, Intelligence Division, Internal Revenue Service, 1963–70; joined Office of Chief Counsel, Internal Revenue Service in 1970, and held the following positions: Trial Attorney (Indianapolis), Director, Criminal Tax Division, Deputy Associate Chief Counsel (Litigation), and Director, Tax Litigation Division; appointed by President Reagan as Judge, United States Tax Court, on November 20, 1987, for a term ending November 19, 2002; recalled on November 20, 2002, as Senior Judge to perform judicial duties from that date to the present.

LAURENCE J. WHALEN, senior judge; born in Pennsylvania, 1944; A.B., Georgetown University, 1967; J.D., Georgetown University Law Center, 1970; LL.M., 1971; admitted to District of Columbia and Oklahoma Bars; Special Assistant to the Assistant Attorney General, Tax Division, Department of Justice, 1971–72; trial attorney, Tax Division, 1971–75; private law practice in Washington, DC, with Hamel and Park (now Hopkins, Sutter, Hamel and Park), 1977–84; also in Oklahoma City, OK, with Crowe and Dunlevy, 1984–87; member of Oklahoma Bar Association, District of Columbia Bar Association, and American Bar Association, appointed by President Reagan as Judge, United States Tax Court, on November 23, 1987, for a term ending November 22, 2002; recalled on November 23, 2002, as Senior Judge to perform judicial duties from that date to the present.

CAROLYN P. CHIECHI, senior judge; born in New Jersey, 1943; B.S. (*magna cum laude,* Class Rank: 1), Georgetown University, 1965; J.D., 1969 (Class Rank: 9); LL.M., Taxation, 1971; Doctor of Laws, Honoris Causa, 2000; practiced with law firm of Sutherland, Asbill and Brennan, Washington, DC and Atlanta, GA (partner, 1976–92; associate, 1971–76); served as attorney-adviser to Judge Leo H. Irwin, United States Tax Court, 1969–71; member, District of Columbia Bar, 1969–present (member, Taxation Section, 1973–99; member, Taxation Section Steering Committee, 1980–82, Chairperson, 1981–82; member, Tax Audits and Litigation Committee, 1986–92, Chairperson, 1987–88); member, American Bar Association, 1969–present (member, Section of Taxation, 1969–present; member, Committee on Court Procedure, 1991–present; member, Litigation Section, 1995–2000; member, Judicial Division, 1997–2000); Federal Bar Association, 1969–present (member, Section of Taxation, 1969–present; member, Judiciary Division, 1992–present); Fellow, American College of Tax Counsel; Fellow, American Bar Foundation; member, Women's Bar Association of the District of Columbia, 1992–present; Board of Governors, Georgetown University Alumni Association, 1994–97, 1997–2000; Board of Regents, Georgetown University, 1988–94, 1995–2001; National Law Alumni Board, Georgetown University, 1986–93; Board of Directors, Stuart Stiller Memorial Foundation, 1986–99; American Judicature Society, 1994–present; one of several recipients of the first Georgetown University Law Alumni Awards (1994); one of several recipients of the first Georgetown University Law Center Alumnae Achievement Awards (1998); admitted to *Who's Who in American Law, Who's Who of American Women, Who's Who in America,* and *Who's Who in the East;* appointed by President George H.W. Bush as Judge, United States Tax Court, on October 1, 1992, for a term ending September 30, 2007; serving as Senior Judge, United States Tax Court, October 1, 2007–present.

DAVID LARO, senior judge; born in Michigan, 1942; appointed by President Bush to the U.S. Tax Court in November, 1992. Formerly practiced tax law in Flint and Ann Arbor Michigan for 24 years. Graduate of New York University Law School (LL.M. in Taxation 1970), the University of Illinois Law School (J.D. 1967) and the University of Michigan (B.A. 1964). Regent of the University of Michigan, a member of the State Board of Education in Michigan, and Chairman of the State Tenure Commission in Michigan. Teaches corporate tax and business planning at Georgetown Law school, and the University of San Diego Law School. Co-Author of *Business Valuation and Taxes: Procedure, Law and Perspective* (Second edition, 2011), a 500 page text on tax valuation. At the request of the American Bar Association (CEELI), contributed written comments on the Draft Laws of Ukraine and Uzbekistan. As a consultant for Harvard University (Harvard Institute for International Development) and Georgia State University, lectured in Moscow on the subjects of tax reform and litigation. Consultant on Russian Tax Reform under a project through USAID. At the invitation of the Supreme Court of Kazakhstan in 2007, lectured to members of the Kazakhstan Judiciary, and lectured to members of the Russian Judiciary in Moscow in 2007–10. In May 2006, and June 2007, at the invitation of the State Tax Administration and other government officials, lectured in Beijing, China on economic substance. Serving as Senior Judge, U.S. Tax Court November 2007 to present.

HARRY A. HAINES, senior judge; born in Montana, 1939; B.A., St. Olaf College, 1961; J.D., University of Montana Law School, 1964; LL.M., Taxation, New York University Law School, 1966; admitted to Montana Bar and U.S. District Court, Montana, 1964; practiced law in Missoula, MT, as a partner, Law Firm of Worden, Thane and Haines, 1966–2003; adjunct professor, Law School, University of Montana, 1967–91; appointed by President George W. Bush as Judge, United States Tax Court, on April 22, 2003 for a term ending April 21, 2018. Recalled on May 30, 2009, as Senior Judge to perform judicial duties from that date to the present.

MICHAEL B. THORNTON, senior judge; born in Mississippi, 1954; B.S. in Accounting, *summa cum laude,* University of Southern Mississippi, 1976; M.S. in Accounting, 1997; M.A. in English Literature, University of Tennessee, 1979; J.D. (with distinction), Duke University School of Law, 1982; Order of the Coif, Duke Law Journal Editorial Board; admitted to District of Columbia Bar, 1982; served as Law Clerk to the Honorable Charles Clark, Chief Judge, U.S. Court of Appeals for the Fifth Circuit, 1983–84; practiced law as an Associate Attorney, Sutherland, Asbill and Brennan, Washington, DC, 1982–83 and summer 1981; Miller and Chevalier, Chartered, Washington, DC, 1985–88; served as Tax Counsel, U.S. House Committee on Ways and Means, 1988–93; Chief Minority Tax Counsel, U.S. House Committee on Ways and Means, January 1995; Attorney-Adviser, U.S. Treasury Department, February–April 1995; Deputy Tax Legislative Counsel in the Office of Tax Policy, United States Treasury Department, April 1995–February 1998; recipient of Treasury Secretary's Annual Award, U.S. Department of the Treasury, 1997; Meritorious Service Award, U.S. Department of the Treasury, 1998; appointed by President Clinton as Judge, United States Tax Court, on March 8, 1998, for a term ending March 7, 2013.

L. PAIGE MARVEL, senior judge; born in Maryland, 1949; B.A., *magna cum laude,* College of Notre Dame, 1971; J.D. with honors, University of Maryland School of Law, Baltimore, MD, 1974; Order of the Coif; member, Maryland Law Review and Moot Court Board; Garbis and Schwait, P.A., associate (1974–76) and shareholder (1976–85); shareholder, Garbis, Marvel and Junghans, P.A., 1985–86; shareholder, Melnicove, Kaufman, Weiner, Smouse and Garbis, P.A., 1986–88; partner, Venabel, Baetjer and Howard LLP, 1988–98; member, American Bar Association, Section of Taxation, Vice-Chair, Committee Operations, 1993–95; Council Director 1989–92; Chair, Court Procedure Committee, 1985–87; Maryland State Bar Association, Board of Governors, 1988–90, and 1996–98; Chair, Taxation Section 1982–83; Federal Bar Association, Section of Taxation, Section Council, 1984–90; Fellow, American Bar Foundation; Fellow, Maryland Bar Foundation; fellow and former Regent, American College of Tax Counsel, 1996–98; member, American Law Institute; advisor, ALI *Restatement of Law, Third, The Law Governing Lawyers* 1988–98; University of Maryland Law School Board of Visitors, 1995–2001; Loyola/Notre Dame Library, Inc. Board of Trustees, 1996–2003; Advisory Committee, University of Baltimore Graduate Tax Program, 1986–present; Co-editor, Procedure Department, The Journal of Taxation, 1990–98; member, Commissioner's Review Panel on IRS Integrity, 1989–91; member and Chair, Procedure Subcommittee, Commission to Revise the Annotated Code of Maryland (Tax Provisions), 1981–87; member, Advisory Commission to the Maryland State Department of Economic and Community Development, 1978–81; recipient, President's Medal, College of Notre Dame, 2006; Jules Ritholz award, ABA Tax Section's Civil and Criminal Tax Penalties Comm., 2004; First Annual Tax Excellence Award, Maryland State Bar Association Tax Section, 2002; named one of Maryland's Top 100 Women, 1998; recipient, ABA Tax Section's Distinguished Service Award, 1995; MSBA Distinguished Service Award, 1982–83; listed in Best Lawyers in America, 1991–98, *Who's Who in America, Who's Who in American Law, Who's Who in the East;* author of various articles and book chapters on tax and tax litigation topics; appointed by President Clinton as Judge, United States Tax Court, on April 6, 1998, for a term ending April 5, 2013.

SPECIAL TRIAL JUDGES OF THE COURT

Robert N. Armen, Jr.; Lewis R. Carluzzo; John F. Dean; Daniel A. Guy; Peter J. Panuthos (chief special trial judge).

COURT STAFF

Clerk.—Robert R. Di Trolio, 521–4600.
General Counsel.—Douglas Snoeyenbos, 521–3390.
Deputy General Counsel.—Fig Ruggieri, 521–3390.
Director of Human Resources.—Ellene P. Footer, 521–4700.
Reporter of Decisions.—Sheila A. Murphy, 521–4577.
Librarian.—Nancy Ciliberti, 521–4585.

UNITED STATES COURT OF APPEALS FOR THE ARMED FORCES[1]

450 E Street, NW., 20442–0001, phone 761–1448, fax 761–4672

JAMES E. BAKER, chief judge; born in New Haven, CT, March 25, 1960; education: BA., Yale University, 1982; J.D., Yale Law School, 1990; Attorney, Department of State, 1990–93; Counsel, President's Foreign Intelligence Advisory Board/Intelligence Oversight Board, 1993–94; Deputy Legal Advisor, National Security Counsel, 1994–97; Special Assistant to the President and Legal Advisor, National Security Counsel, 1997–2000; military service: U.S. Marine Corps and U.S. Marine Corp Reserve; nominated by President Clinton to serve on the U.S. Court of Appeals for the Armed Forces; began service on September 19, 2000, and became Chief Judge on October 1, 2011.

CHARLES E. ERDMANN, associate judge; born in Great Falls, MT, June 26, 1946; B.A., Montana State University, 1972; J.D., University of Montana Law School, 1975; Air Force Judge Advocate Staff Officers Course, 1981; Air Command and Staff College, 1992; Air War College, 1994; Military Service: U.S. Marine Corps, 1967–70; Air National Guard, 1981–2002 (retired as a Colonel); Assistant Montana Attorney General, 1975–76; Chief Counsel, Montana State Auditor's Office, 1976–78; Chief Staff Attorney, Montana Attorney General's Office, Antitrust Bureau; Bureau Chief, Montana Medicaid Fraud Bureau, 1980–82; General Counsel, Montana School Boards Association, 1982–86; private practice of law, 1986–95; Associate Justice, Montana Supreme Court, 1995–97; Office of High Representative of Bosnia and Herzegovina, Judicial Reform Coordinator, 1998–99; Office of High Representative of Bosnia and Herzegovina, Head of Human Rights and Rule of Law Department, 1999; Chairman and Chief Judge, Bosnian Election Court, 2000–01; Judicial Reform and International Law Consultant, 2001–2002; appointed by President George W. Bush to serve on the U.S. Court of Appeals for the Armed Forces on October 9, 2002, commenced service on October 15, 2002.

SCOTT W. STUCKY, associate judge; born in Hutchinson, KS, January 11, 1948; B.A. (*summa cum laude*), Wichita State University, 1970; J.D., Harvard Law School, 1973; M.A., Trinity University, 1980; LL.M. with highest honors, George Washington University, 1983; Federal Executive Institute, 1988; Harvard Program for Senior Officials in National Security, 1990; National War College, 1993; admitted to bar, Kansas and District of Columbia; U.S. Air Force, judge advocate, 1973–78; U.S. Air Force Reserve, 1982–2003 (retired as colonel); married to Jean Elsie Seibert of Oxon Hill, MD, August 18, 1973; children: Mary-Clare, Joseph; private law practice, Washington, DC, 1978–82; branch chief, U.S. Nuclear Regulatory Commission, 1982–83; legislative counsel and principal legislative counsel, U.S. Air Force, 1983–96; General Counsel, Committee on Armed Services, U.S. Senate, 1996–2001 and 2003–06; Minority Counsel, 2001–03; National Commander-in-Chief, Military Order of the Loyal Legion of the United States, 1993–95; Board of Directors, Adoption Service Information Agency, 1998–2002 and 2004–07; Board of Directors, Omicron Delta Kappa Society, 2006–present; member, Federal Bar Association (Pentagon Chapter), Judge Advocates Association, The District of Columbia Bar; OPM LEGIS Fellow, office of Senator John Warner (R–VA), 1986–87; member and panel chairman, Air Force Board for Correction of Military records, 1989–96; nominated by President George W. Bush to serve on the U.S. Court of Appeals for the Armed Forces on November 15, 2006; confirmed by the Senate, December 9, 2006; began service on December 20, 2006.

MARGARET A. RYAN, associate judge; born in Chicago, IL, May 23, 1964; B.A. (*cum laude*), Knox College; J.D. (*summa cum laude*), University of Notre Dame Law School; recipient of the William T. Kirby Legal Writing Award and the Colonel William J. Hoynes

[1] Prior to October 5, 1994, United States Court of Military Appeals.

Award for Outstanding Scholarship; active duty in the U.S. Marine Corps, 1986–99, serving as a communications officer, staff officer, company commander, platoon commander and operations officer in units within the II and III Marine Expeditionary Forces and as a judge advocate in Okinawa, Japan, and Quantico, VA; also served as Aide de Camp to General Charles C. Krulak, the 31st Commandant of the Marine Corps; law clerk to the Honorable J. Michael Luttig, U.S. Court of Appeals for the Fourth Circuit, and law clerk to the Honorable Clarence Thomas, Associate Justice of the Supreme Court of the United States; litigation partner at the law firm of Bartlik Beck Herman Palenchar & Scott LLP and partner in litigation and appellate practices at the law firm Wiley Rein Fielding LLP; nominated by President George W. Bush to serve on the U.S. Court of Appeals for the Armed Forces on November 15, 2006; confirmed by the Senate on December 9, 2006; began service on December 20, 2006.

SENIOR JUDGES

WILLIAM HORACE DARDEN, senior judge; born in Union Point, GA, May 16, 1923; son of William W. and Sara (Newsom) Darden; B.B.A., University of Georgia, 1946; LL.B., University of Georgia, 1948; admitted to bar of Georgia and to practice before the Georgia Supreme Court, 1948; active duty in U.S. Navy from July 1, 1943 to July 3, 1946, when released to inactive duty as lieutenant (jg.); married to Mary Parrish Viccellio of Chatham, VA, December 31, 1949; children: Sara Newsom, Martha Hardy, William H., Jr., Daniel Hobson; secretary to U.S. Senator Richard B. Russell, 1948–51; chief clerk of U.S. Senate Committee on Armed Services, 1951–53; professional staff member and later chief of staff, U.S. Senate Committee on Armed Services, February 1953 to November 1968; received recess appointment as judge of the U.S. Court of Military Appeals from President Johnson on November 5, 1968, to succeed the late Judge Paul J. Kilday; took oath of office on November 13, 1968; nominated by President Johnson for the unexpired part of the term of the late Judge Paul J. Kilday ending May 1, 1976; confirmed by Senate on January 14, 1969; designated Chief Judge by President Nixon on June 23, 1971; resigned December 29, 1973; elected to become Senior Judge on February 11, 1974.

WALTER THOMPSON COX III, senior judge; born in Anderson, SC, August 13, 1942; son of Walter T. Cox and Mary Johnson Cox; married to Vicki Grubbs of Anderson, SC, February 8, 1963; children: Lisa and Walter; B.S., Clemson University, 1964; J.D. (*cum laude*), University of South Carolina School of Law, 1967; graduated Defense Language Institute (German), 1969; graduated basic course, the Judge Advocate General's School, Charlottesville, VA, 1967; studied procurement law at that same school, 1968; active duty, U.S. Army judge advocate general's corps, 1964–72 (1964–67, excess leave to U.S.C. Law School); private law practice, 1973–78; elected resident judge, 10th Judicial Circuit, South Carolina, 1978–84; also served as acting associate justice of South Carolina supreme court, on the judicial council, on the circuit court advisory committee, and as a hearing officer of the judicial standards commission; member: bar of the Supreme Court of the United States; bar of the U.S. Court of Military Appeals; South Carolina Bar Association; Anderson County Bar Association; the American Bar Association; the South Carolina Trial Lawyers Association; the Federal Bar Association; and the Bar Association of the District of Columbia; has served as a member of the House of Delegates of the South Carolina Bar, and the Board of Commissioners on Grievances and Discipline; nominated by President Reagan, as judge of U.S. Court of Military Appeals, June 28, 1984, for a term of 15 years; confirmed by the Senate, July 26, 1984; sworn-in and officially assumed his duties on September 6, 1984; retired on September 30, 1999 and immediately assumed status of Senior Judge on October 1, 1999 and returned to full active service until September 19, 2000.

EUGENE R. SULLIVAN, senior judge; born in St. Louis, MO, August 2, 1941; son of Raymond V. and Rosemary K. Sullivan; married to Lis U. Johansen of Ribe, Denmark, June 18, 1966; children: Kim A. and Eugene R. II; B.S., U.S. Military Academy, West Point, 1964; J.D., Georgetown Law Center, Washington, DC, 1971; active duty with the U.S. Army, 1964–69; service included duty with the 3rd Armored Division in Germany, and the 4th Infantry Division in Vietnam; R&D assignments with the Army Aviation Systems Command; one year as an instructor at the Army Ranger School, Ft. Benning, GA; decorations include: Bronze Star, Air Medal, Army Commendation Medal, Ranger and Parachutist Badges, Air Force Exceptional Civilian Service Medal; following graduation from law school, clerked with U.S. Court of Appeals (8th Circuit), St. Louis, 1971–72; private law practice, Washington, DC, 1972–74; assistant special counsel, White House, 1974; trial attorney, U.S. Department of Justice, 1974–82; deputy general counsel, Department of the Air Force, 1982–84; general counsel of the Department of Air Force, 1984–86; Governor of Wake Island, 1984–86; presently serves on the Board of Governors for the West Point Society of the District of Columbia; the American Cancer Society (Montgomery County Chapter); nominated by President Reagan, as judge, U.S. Court of Military Appeals on February 25, 1986, and confirmed by the Senate on May 20, 1986, and assumed his office on May 27, 1986; President George H.W. Bush named him the chief judge of the U.S. Court of Military Appeals, effective October 1, 1990, a position he held for five years; he retired on September 30, 2001 and immediately assumed status of Senior Judge and returned to full active service until Sept. 30, 2002.

H.F. "SPARKY" GIERKE, senior judge; born in Williston, ND, March 13, 1943; son of Herman F. Gierke, Jr., and Mary Kelly Gierke; children: Todd, Scott, Craig, and Michelle; B.A., University of North Dakota, 1964; J.D., University of North Dakota, 1966; graduated basic course, the Judge Advocate General's School, Charlottesville, VA, 1967; graduated military judge course, the Judge Advocate General's School, Charlottesville, VA, 1969; active duty, U.S. Army judge advocate general's corps, 1967–71; private practice of law, 1971–83; served as a justice of the North Dakota supreme court from October 1, 1983 until appointment to U.S. Court of Military Appeals; admitted to the North Dakota Bar, 1966; admitted to practice law before all North Dakota Courts, U.S. District Court for the District of North Dakota, U.S. District Court for the Southern District of Georgia, U.S. Court of Military Appeals, and U.S. Supreme Court; served as president of the State Bar Association of North Dakota in 1982–83; served as president of the North Dakota State's Attorneys Association in 1979–80; served on the board of governors of the North Dakota Trial Lawyers Association from 1977–83; served on the board of governors of the North Dakota State Bar Association from 1977–79 and from 1981–84; served as vice chairman and later chairman of the North Dakota Judicial Conference from June 1989 until November 1991; fellow of the American Bar Foundation and the American College of Probate Counsel; member of the American Bar Association, American Judicature Society, Association of Trial Lawyers of America, Blue Key National Honor Fraternity, Kappa Sigma Social Fraternity, University of North Dakota President's Club; in 1984, received the Governor's Award from Governor Allen I. Olson for outstanding service to the State of North Dakota; in 1988 and again in 1991, awarded the North Dakota National Leadership Award of Excellence by Governor George A. Sinner; in 1989, selected as the Man of the Year by the Delta Mu Chapter of the Kappa Sigma Fraternity and as Outstanding Greek Alumnus of the University of North Dakota; also awarded the University of North Dakota Sioux Award (UND's alumni association's highest honor); in 1983–84, served as the first Vietnam era state commander of the North Dakota American Legion; in 1988–89, served as the first Vietnam era national commander of the American Legion; nominated by President George H.W. Bush, October 1, 1991; confirmed by the Senate, November 14, 1991; sworn-in and assumed office on the U.S. Court of Military Appeals, November 20, 1991; on October 1, 2004, he became the Chief Judge until his retirement on September 30, 2006, and assumed the status of Senior Judge on October 1, 2006.

SUSAN J. CRAWFORD, senior judge; born in Pittsburgh, PA, April 22, 1947; daughter of William E. and Joan B. Crawford; married to Roger W. Higgins of Geneva, NY, September 8, 1979; one child, Kelley S. Higgins; B.A., Bucknell University, Pennsylvania, 1969; J.D. (*cum laude*), Dean's Award, Arthur McClean Founder's Award, New England School of Law, Boston, MA, 1977; history teacher and coach of women's athletics, Radnor High School, Pennsylvania, 1969–74; associate, Burnett and Eiswert, Oakland, MD, 1977–79; Assistant State's Attorney, Garrett County, Maryland, 1978–80; partner, Burnett, Eiswert and Crawford, 1979–81; instructor, Garrett County Community College, 1979–81; deputy general counsel, 1981–83, and general counsel, Department of the Army, 1983–89; special counsel to Secretary of Defense, 1989; inspector general, Department of Defense, 1989–91; member: bar of the Supreme Court of the United States; bar of the U.S. Court of Military Appeals, Maryland Bar Association, District of Columbia Bar Association, American Bar Association, Federal Bar Association, and the Edward Bennett Williams American Inn of Court; member: board of trustees, 1989–present, and Corporation, 1992–present, of New England School of Law; board of trustees, 1988–present, Bucknell University; nominated by President Bush as judge, U.S. Court of Military Appeals, February 19, 1991, for a term of 15 years; confirmed by the Senate on November 14, 1991, sworn in and officially assumed her duties on November 19, 1991; on October 1, 1999, she became the Chief Judge for a term of five years; retired on September 30, 2006 and assumed the status of Senior Judge on October 1, 2006.

ANDREW S. EFFRON, senior judge; born in Stamford, CT, September 18, 1948; A.B., Harvard College, 1970; J.D., Harvard Law School, 1975; The Judge Advocate General's School, U.S. Army, 1976, 1983; legislative aide to the late Representative William A. Steiger, 1970–76 (two years full-time, the balance between school semesters); judge advocate, Office of the Staff Judge Advocate, Fort McClellan, Alabama, 1976–77; attorney-adviser, Office of the General Counsel, Department of Defense, 1977–87; Counsel, General Counsel, and Minority Counsel, Committee on Armed Services, U.S. Senate, 1987–96; nominated by President Clinton to serve on the U.S. Court of Appeals for the Armed Forces, June 21, 1996; confirmed by the Senate, July 12, 1996; took office on August 1, 1996; assumed his duties on August 1, 1996. On October 1, 2006, he became Chief Judge for a five year term, and immediately assumed status as Senior Judge on October 1, 2011.

OFFICERS OF THE U.S. COURT OF APPEALS FOR THE ARMED FORCES

Clerk of the Court.—William A. DeCicco.
Chief Deputy Clerk of the Court.—David A. Anderson.
Deputy Clerk for Opinions.—Patricia Mariani.
Court Executive.—Keith Roberts.
Librarian.—Agnes Kiang.

UNITED STATES COURT OF APPEALS
FOR VETERANS CLAIMS

625 Indiana Avenue, NW., Suite 900, 20004, phone (202) 501–5970

BRUCE E. KASOLD, chief judge; born in New York, 1951; B.S., United States Military Academy, 1973; J.D., *cum laude*, University of Florida, 1979; LL.M., Georgetown University, 1982; Honors Graduate, the Judge Advocate General's School Graduate Program, 1984; admitted to the bars of the U.S. Supreme Court, the Florida Supreme Court, the District of Columbia Court of Appeals; member: Florida Bar, District of Columbia Bar, the Federal Bar Association, Order of the Coif; retired from the U.S. Army, Lieutenant Colonel, Air Defense Artillery and Judge Advocate General's Corp, 1994; commercial litigation attorney, Holland & Knight Law Firm, 1994–95; Chief Counsel, U.S. Senate Committee on Rules and Administration, 1995–98; Chief Counsel, Secretary of the Senate and Senate Sergeant at Arms, 1998–2003; appointed by President George W. Bush to the U.S. Court of Appeals for Veterans Claims on December 13, 2003; sworn in December 31, 2003.

LAWRENCE B. HAGEL, judge; born in Washington, IN, 1947; B.S., United States Naval Academy, 1969; J.D., University of the Pacific McGeorge School of Law, 1976; LL.M. (Labor Law, with highest honors) The National Law Center, George Washington University, 1983; admitted to the bars of the U.S. Supreme Court, the United States Court of Appeals for the Fourth, Ninth, Tenth, D.C. and Federal Circuits, U.S. Court of Appeals for the Armed Forces, U.S. Court of Appeals for Veterans Claims, Supreme Court of the States of Iowa and California and the District of Columbia; commissioned in the U.S. Marine Corps, second lieutenant, infantry officer 1969–72 service in Vietnam and Puerto Rico; Marine Corps Judge Advocate 1973–90, assignments concentrated in criminal and civil litigation; Deputy General Counsel and General Counsel, Paralyzed Veterans of America, 1990–2003; appointed by President George W. Bush in December 2003, to the U.S. Court of Appeals for Veterans Claims; confirmed by the U.S. Senate to the Court of Appeals on December 9, 2003; sworn in January 2, 2004.

WILLIAM A. MOORMAN, judge; born in Chicago, IL, January 23, 1945; B.A., University of Illinois at Champaign-Urbana, 1967; J.D., University of Illinois College of Law, 1970; commissioned in the United States Air Force, second lieutenant, Reserve Officers Training Corps, 1970; entered active duty, 1971; Judge Advocate General's Corps, 1972–2002, serving as the senior attorney at every level of command, culminating his active military service with his appointment as the Judge Advocate General of the United States Air Force; military decorations include the Superior Service Medal with oak leaf cluster, the Legion of Merit with oak leaf cluster, the Joint Meritorious Service Medal, and the Meritorious Service Medal with four oak leaf clusters; retired from the Air Force in April 2002, in the grade of Major General; Counselor to the General Counsel, Department of Veterans Affairs, 2002; Assistant to the Secretary for Regulation Policy and Management, Department of Veterans Affairs, 2003; appointed by President George W. Bush as Acting Assistant Secretary of Management for the Department of Veterans Affairs, August 2004; author: ''Executive Privilege and the Freedom of Information Act: Sufficient Protection for Aircraft Mishap Reports?'', 21 *Air Force Law Review* 581 (1979); ''Cross-Examination Techniques,'' 27 *Air Force Law Review* 105 (1987); ''Fifty Years of Military Justice: Does the UCMJ Need To Be Changed?'', 48 *Air Force Law Review* 185 (2000); ''Humanitarian Intervention and International Law in the Case of Kosovo,'' 36 *New England Law Review* 775 (2002); ''Serving Our Veterans Through Clearer Rules,'' 56 *Administrative Law Review* 207 (2004); recipient: Albert M. Kuhfeld Outstanding Young Judge Advocate of the Air Force Award 1979, Stuart R. Reichart Outstanding Senior Attorney of the Air Force Award 1992, University of Illinois College of Law Distinguished Alumnus Award 2001, Department of Veterans Affairs Exceptional Service Award 2004; nominated for appointment to the U.S. Court of Appeals for Veterans Claims on September 21, 2004, by President George W. Bush; confirmed by the U.S. Senate November 20, 2004; sworn in December 16, 2004.

ALAN G. LANCE, SR., judge; born in McComb, OH, April 27, 1949; B.A. in english and history, distinguished military graduate, South Dakota State University, 1971; commissioned U.S. Army, June 1971; graduated University of Toledo School of Law and Law Review, 1973; admitted to the U.S. Supreme Court, U.S. Court of Military Appeals, State of Ohio, State of Idaho; commissioned U.S. Army, Judge Advocate Generals Corps, 1974 and served as Claims Officer, defense counsel, Chief of Defense Counsel, Legal Assistance Officer, Administrative Law Officer and in the absence of a military Judge, military Magistrate for the 172nd Infantry Brigade (Alaska) 1974–77; Army Commendation Medal 1977; served as the Command Judge Advocate, Corpus Christi Army Depot, 1977–78; engaged in private practice of law, Ada County, Idaho, 1978–94; elected to the Idaho House of Representatives, 1990, and served as Majority Caucus chairman, 1992–94; elected as Idaho Attorney General (31st) in 1994 and 1998; Distinguished Alumnus Award, University of Toledo School of Law, 2002; inducted into the Ohio Veterans Hall of Fame, November 2004; nominated as a Judge of the United States Court of Appeals for Veterans Claims by President George W. Bush; confirmed by the U.S. Senate to the Court of Appeals for Veterans Claims, November 2004 and sworn in on December 17, 2004.

ROBERT N. DAVIS, judge; born in Kewanee, IL, September 20, 1953; graduated from Davenport Central High School, Davenport, IA, 1971; B.A., University of Hartford, 1975; J.D. Georgetown University Law Center, 1978; admitted to the bars of the U.S. Supreme Court, the Ninth Circuit Court of Appeals; the State of Virginia; and the State of Iowa; career record 1978–83 appellate attorney with the Commodity Futures Trading Commission; 1983–88 attorney with the United States Department of Education, Business and Administrative Law Division of the Office of General Counsel; 1983 Governmental exchange program with the United States Attorneys office, District of Columbia; Special Assistant United States Attorney; 1988–2001 Professor of Law, University of Mississippi School of Law; 2001–05 Professor of Law, Stetson University College of Law; Published extensively in the areas of constitutional law, administrative law, national security law and sports law. Founder and Faculty Editor-in-Chief, Journal of National Security Law, arbitrator/mediator with the American Arbitration Association and the United States Postal Service. Gubernatorial appointment to the National Conference of Commissioners on Uniform State Laws 1993–2000. Joined the United States Navy Reserve Intelligence Program in 1988. Presidential recall to active duty in 1999, Bosnia and 2001 for the Global War on Terrorism. Military decorations include Joint Service Commendation Medal, Joint Service Achievement Medal, Navy Achievement Medal, NATO Medal, Armed Forces Expeditionary Medal, Armed Forces Reserve Medal with ''M'' device, Overseas Service Ribbon, National Defense Ribbon, Joint Meritorious Unit Award, and Global War on Terrorism Medal. Nominated for appointment by President George W. Bush on March 23, 2003; confirmed by the United States Senate on November 21, 2004; Commissioned on December 4, 2004 as a Judge, United States Court of Appeals for Veterans Claims.

MARY J. SCHOELEN, judge; born in Rota, Spain; B.A., political science, University of California at Irvine, 1990; J.D., George Washington University Law School, 1993; admitted to the State Bar of California; law clerk for the National Veterans Legal Services Project, 1992–93; legal intern to the U.S. Senate Committee on Veterans' Affairs, 1994; staff attorney for Vietnam Veterans of America's Veterans Benefits Program, 1994–97; Minority Counsel, U.S. Senate Committee on Veterans' Affairs, 1997–2001; Minority General Counsel, March 2001–June 2001; Deputy Staff Director, Benefits Programs/General Counsel, June 2001–03; Minority Deputy Staff Director, Benefits Programs/General Counsel, 2003–04; nominated by President George W. Bush; appointed a Judge of the United States Court of Appeals for Veterans Claims; confirmed by the U.S. Senate to the United States Court of Appeals for Veterans Claims on November 20, 2004; sworn in December 20, 2004.

CORAL WONG-PIETSCH, judge, born in Waterloo, IA, Judge Pietsch has a distinguished career in public service, both in the military and as a civilian. She was commissioned in the U.S. Army Judge Advocate General's Corps and served six years on active duty. Judge Pietsch continued her service in the U.S. Army Reserve and rose to the rank of Brigadier General. She became the first woman to be promoted to the rank of Brigadier General in the U.S. Army Judge Advocate General's Corps and the first woman of Asian ancestry to be promoted to Brigadier General in the Army. Until her appointment to the bench, Judge Pietsch held the position of Senior Attorney and Special Assistant at Headquarters, U.S. Army Pacific located in Honolulu, Hawaii. In this position, she provided and managed legal services in support of the U.S. Army Pacific's mission to train Army Forces for military operations and peacetime engagements aimed at promoting regional stability. As part of the 2007 ''surge'' in Iraq, Judge Pietsch volunteered as a Department of Defense civilian to deploy to Iraq for a year where she was seconded to the U.S. Department of State to serve as the Deputy Rule of Law Coordinator for the Baghdad Provincial Reconstruction Team. During her deployment to Iraq, Judge Pietsch assisted with numerous civil society projects involving a variety of Rule of Law partners, including the Iraqi Jurist Union, Iraqi Bar Association, law schools, and international rights, women's rights and human rights organizations. She evaluated and sought funding for numerous projects aimed at building capacity within the Iraqi legal community to include the establishment, in close collaboration with the Iraqi Bar Association, of a Legal Aid Clinic at one of Iraq's largest detention facilities. In 2006 Judge Pietsch was appointed by the Governor of Hawaii to the Hawaii Civil Rights Commission where she served for seven years. Shortly after the appointment, the Governor selected Judge Pietsch as its Chair. Earlier in her civilian legal career, Judge Pietsch had been appointed a Deputy Attorney General for the State of Hawaii advising the State Department of Health, State Department of Agriculture, and the State Criminal History Records Division. Judge Pietsch's academic degrees include a bachelor of arts, master of arts, and a juris doctor degree. She was also a Senior Executive Fellow at the Harvard University Kennedy School of Government, is a graduate of the Defense Leadership and Management Program, and a graduate of the Army War College. Her awards and decorations include the Distinguished Service Medal, Legion of Merit, Meritorious Service Medal, Joint Service Commendation Medal, Decoration for Exceptional Civilian Service, the Meritorious Civilian Service Medal, Superior Civilian Performance Medal, and the Global War on Terrorism Medal. She has been the recipient of the Organization of Chinese Americans Pioneer Award, the Hawaii Women Lawyers Attorney of the Year Award, the Honolulu YWCA Achievement in Leadership Award, the Catholic University Alumni Achievement Award, the Federal Executive Board Award for Excellence, the U.S. Army Pacific Community Service Award and recognized for lifetime accomplishments by the Women Veterans Igniting the Spirit of Entrepreneurship. Judge Pietsch is admitted to the bars of the United States Supreme Court, the Ninth Circuit Court of Appeals, U.S. District Court of the District of Hawaii, State Bar of Hawaii, State Bar of Iowa, and the United States Court of Appeals for the Armed Forces; nominated by President Barack Obama and subsequently appointed a Judge of the U.S. Court of Appeals for Veterans Claims on May 24, 2012 and sworn in June 2012.

MARGARET BARTLEY, judge; born in Pittsburgh, PA, 1959; B.S., cum laude, Pennsylvania State University, 1981; J.D., cum laude, American University Washington College of Law, 1993; admitted to the bars of the State of Maryland and the United States Court of Appeals for the Federal Circuit; law clerk to now-retired Judge Jonathan R. Steinberg of the United States Court of Appeals for Veterans Claims, 1993–94; staff attorney for National Veterans Legal Services Program, 1994–2005; senior staff attorney for National Veterans Legal Services Program, 2005–12; editor of the NVLSP veterans' law quarterly, *The Veterans Advocate,* 2004–12; Director of Outreach and Education for the Veterans Consortium Pro Bono Program, 2005–12; nominated as a Judge of the United States Court of Appeals for Veterans Claims on June 21, 2011, by President Barack Obama; confirmed by the U.S. Senate May 21, 2012 and sworn in June 28, 2012.

WILLIAM S. GREENBERG, judge, Judge Greenberg was a partner of McCarter & English, LLP. He initially joined the firm as an associate following a judicial clerkship in 1968, then returned as a partner in 1993. The majority of his career has involved litigation in Federal and state courts. Judge Greenberg had been a Certified Civil Trial Attorney by the Supreme Court of New Jersey since 1983. He served as Chairman of the Judicial and Prosecutorial Appointments Committee of the New Jersey State Bar Association, which considers all candidates to be a judge or prosecutor submitted by the Governor of New Jersey. He was President of the Association of Trial Lawyers of America, New Jersey, (The New Jersey Association for Justice) and has served as Trustee of the New Jersey State Bar Association and of the New Jersey State Bar Foundation. He also served as a member of the New Jersey Supreme Court Committee on the Admission of Foreign Attorneys. He established and chaired the New Jersey State Bar Association (public service/pro bono) program of military legal assistance for members of the Reserve Components called to active duty after September 11, 2001. He was a member of the New Jersey Supreme Court Civil Practice Committee. With the approval of the Secretary of Defense, on the recommendation of the White House, Judge Greenberg became Chairman of the Reserve Forces Policy Board in 2009, a Board established by the Secretary of Defense in 1951 and by Act of Congress in 1952. On July 26, 2011, Judge Greenberg was awarded the Secretary of Defense Medal for Outstanding Public Service, the second highest civilian award in the Defense Department, at a public ceremony in the Pentagon, and completed his term in August 2011. In 2006 his *Civil Trial Handbook,* Volume 47 of the *New Jersey Practice Series,* was published by Thomson/West. A special 20th anniversary issue was published in 2009, to commemorate the 1989 publication of its predecessor, *Trial Handbook for New Jersey Lawyers.* A retired Brigadier General, he served as a member of the New Jersey World War II Memorial Commission. In June 2009 he received the highest honor granted by the New Jersey State Bar Foundation, its medal of honor for his work in establishing the military legal assistance program, and especially in his public service representation of soldiers at Walter Reed Army

Medical Center during their Physician Disability Hearings. His article in the June 2007 issue of *New Jersey Lawyer Magazine* describes the program in detail. He has served as special litigation counsel to the Adjutants General Association of the United States and was special litigation counsel *pro bono* to the National Guard Association of the United States. Judge Greenberg was a Commissioner of the New Jersey State Commission of Investigation. He also served as Assistant Counsel to the Governor of New Jersey and as Commissioner of the New Jersey State Scholarship Commission. Professor Greenberg served as the first Adjunct Professor of Military Law at the Seton Hall University School of Law. He was chosen the New Jersey Lawyer of the Year for 2009 by the *New Jersey Law Journal.* He received the Distinguished Alumnus Award from the Johns Hopkins University in 2010, and the Rutgers Law School Public Service Award in 2010 for his work in developing and leading the efforts to represent wounded and injured soldiers at Walter Reed. Judge Greenberg is admitted in New Jersey, New York and the District of Columbia. He is a member of the bar of the Supreme Court of the United States, and of the Third, Fourth and Federal Circuits, the Southern District of New York, and the United States Court of Appeals for the Armed Forces. Judge Greenberg is a graduate of the Johns Hopkins University (AB, 1964) and Rutgers University Law School (JD, 1967). He is married to the former Betty Kaufmann Wolf of Pittsburgh. They have three children, Katherine of New York, Anthony of Baltimore, and Elizabeth of New York; nominated to the United States Court of Appeals for Veterans Claims by President Barack Obama on November 15, 2012, confirmed by the United States Senate on December 21, 2012, appointed by the President on December 27, 2012, and took the judicial oath on December 28, 2012, for a term of fifteen years.

Officers of the U.S. Court of Veterans Appeals

Clerk of the Court.—Gregory O. Block, 501–5970.
Chief Deputy Clerk Operations Manager.—Anne P. Stygles.
Counsel to the Clerk.—Cary P. Sklar.
Senior Staff Attorney (Central Legal Staff).—Cynthia Brandon-Arnold.
Deputy Executive Officer.—Robert J. Bieber.
Librarian.—Allison Fentress.

UNITED STATES JUDICIAL PANEL ON MULTIDISTRICT LITIGATION

Thurgood Marshall Federal Judiciary Building, Room G–255, North Lobby,
One Columbus Circle, NE., 20002, phone (202) 502–2800, fax 502–2888

(National jurisdiction to centralize related cases pending in multiple circuits and districts under 28 U.S.C. §§ 1407 & 2112)

Chairman.—John G. Heyburn II, U.S. District Judge, Western District of Kentucky.
Judges:
Paul J. Barbadoro, U.S. District Judge, District of New Hampshire.
Marjorie O. Rendall, U.S. Court of Appeals Judge, Third Circuit.
Charles R. Breyer, Senior U.S. District Judge, Northern District of California.
Lewis A. Kaplan, Senior U.S. District Judge, Southern District of New York.
Sarah S. Vance, Chief Judge, U.S. District Court, Eastern District of Louisiana.
Panel Executive.—Thomasenia P. Duncan.
Clerk.—Jeffery N. Lüthi.

ADMINISTRATIVE OFFICE OF THE UNITED STATES COURTS

Thurgood Marshall Federal Judiciary Building

One Columbus Circle, NE., 20544, phone (202) 502–2600

Director.—James C. Duff, 502–3000.
Deputy Director.—Jill C. Sayenga, 502–3015.
Chief, Office of:
Audit.—Rick Lewis, 502–1000.
Long-Range Planning.—Brian Lynch, 502–1300.
Management, Planning and Assessment.—Cathy A. McCarthy, 502–1300.
Associate Director and General Counsel.—William R. Burchill, Jr., 502–1100.
Deputy General Counsel.—Robert K. Loesche.
Assistant Director, Judicial Conference Executive Secretariat.—Laura C. Minor, 502–2400.
Deputy Assistant Directors: Jeffrey A. Hennemuth, Wendy Jennis.
Assistant Director, Legislative Affairs.—Cordia A. Strom, 502–1700.
Deputy Assistant Director.—Daniel A. Cunningham.
Chief, Judicial Impact Office.—Richard A. Jaffe.
Assistant Director, Public Affairs.—David A. Sellers, 502–2600.
Assistant Director, Office of Court Administration.—Noel J. Augustyn, 502–1500.
Deputy Assistant Director.—Glen K. Palman.
Chief of:
Appellate Court and Circuit Administration Division.—Gary Bowden, 502–1520.
Bankruptcy Court Administration Division.—Glen K. Palman, 502–1540.
Court Administration Policy Staff.—Abel J. Mattos, 502–1560.
District Court Administration Division.—Robert Lowney, 502–1570.
Public Access and Records Management Division.—Michel M. Ishakian, 502–1500.
Technology Division.—Gary L. Bockweg, 502–2500.
Assistant Director, Office of Defender Services.—Ted Lidz, 502–3030.
Deputy Assistant Director.—Steven G. Asin.
Chief of:
Information Technology Division.—George M. Drakulich.
Legal, Policy and Training Division.—Richard A. Wolff.
Program Budget, Operations and Assessment Division.—Steven G. Asin (acting).
Assistant Director, Office of Facilities and Security.—Ross Eisenman, 502–1200.
Deputy Assistant Director.—William J. Lehman.
Office of Court Security Office.—Edward M. Templeman, 502–1280.
Chief of:
Judiciary Emergency Preparedness Office.—William J. Lehman.
Security and Facilities Policy Staff.—Melanie F. Gilbert.
Space and Facilities Division.—John D. Casey, 502–1340.
Assistant Director, Office of Finance and Budget.—George H. Schafer, 502–2000.
Deputy Assistant Director.—Michael N. Milby.
Chief of:
Accounting and Financial Systems Division.—Charles S. Glenn, 502–2200.
Budget Division.—James R. Baugher, 502–2100.
Financial Liaison and Analysis Office.—Penny Jacobs Fleming, 502–2028.
Assistant Director, Office of Human Resources.—Patricia J. Fitzgibbons, 502–1170.
Deputy Assistant Director.—Nancy E. Ward.
Chief of:
Benefits Division.—Cynthia Roth, 502–1160.
Business Technology Optimization Division.—Christopher D. Mays, 502–3210.
Court Personnel Management Division.—Patricia E. Tuccio, 502–3100.
Fair Employment Practices Office.—Trudi M. Morrison, 502–1380.
Judges Compensation and Retirement Services Office.—Carol S. Sefren, 502–1380.

Policy and Strategic Initiatives Office.—Harvey L. Jones, 502–3185.
Assistant Director, Office of Information Technology.—Joseph R. Peters, 502–2300.
Deputy Assistant Director.—Vacant.
Chief Technology Officer.—Richard D. Fennell.
Chief of:
IT Infrastructure Management Division.—Timothy Hanlon, 502–2640.
IT Policy and Resource Management Office.—Terry A. Cain, 502–3300.
IT Technology Management Services Division.—Robert D. Morse, 502–2377.
IT Security Office.—Bethany DeLude, 502–2350.
IT Systems Deployment and Support Division.—Ronald E. Blankenship, 502–2700.
Assistant Director for Internal Services.—Doreen Bydume, 502–4200.
Chief of:
AO Administrative Services Division.—Iris Guerra, 502–1220.
AO Information and Technology Services Division.—John C. Chang, 502–2830.
AO Personnel Division.—Cheri Thompson Reid, 502–3800.
AO Procurement Management Division.—William Roeder, 502–1330.
Assistant Director for Judges Programs.—Peter G. McCabe, 502–1800.
Deputy Assistant Director.—R. Townsend Robinson, 502–1800.
Chief of:
Article III Judges Division.—Michele E. Reed (acting), 502–1860.
Bankruptcy Judges Division.—Amanda Anderson, 502–1900.
Magistrate Judges Division.—Thomas C. Hnatowski, 502–1830.
Rules Committee Support Office.—Peter G. McCabe, 502–1820.
Statistics Division.—Steven R. Schlesinger, 502–1440.
Assistant Director, Office of Probation and Pretrial Services.—John M. Hughes, 502–1600.
Deputy Assistant Director.—Matthew G. Rowland.
Chief of:
Criminal Law Policy Staff.—John Fitzgerald.
Programs Administration Division.—Nancy Beatty Gregoire.
Special Projects Office.—Nancy Lee Bradshaw.
Technology Division.—Nicholas B. DiSabatino.

FEDERAL JUDICIAL CENTER

One Columbus Circle, NE., 20002–8003, phone (202) 502–4000

Director.—Judge Jeremy D. Fogel, 502–4160, fax 502–4099.
Deputy Director.—John S. Cooke, 502–4060, fax 502–4099.
Director of:
Communications Policy and Design Office.—Sylvan A. Sobel, 502–4250, fax 502–4077.
Education Division.—Bruce M. Clarke, 502–4257, fax 502–4299.
Federal Judicial History Office.—Bruce A. Ragsdale, 502–4181, fax 502–4077.
International Judicial Relations Office.—Mira Gur-Arie, 502–4191, fax 502–4099.
Research Division.—James B. Eaglin, 502–4070, fax 502–4199.
Information Technology Office.—Esther DeVries, 502–4223, fax 502–4288.

DISTRICT OF COLUMBIA COURTS

H. Carl Moultrie I Courthouse, 500 Indiana Avenue, NW., 20001
phone (202) 879–1010

Executive Officer.—Anne B. Wicks, 879–1700.
Deputy Executive Officer.—Cheryl R. Bailey, 879–1700; fax 879–4829.
Director, Governmental and Public Relations.—Leah Gurowitz, 879–1700.

DISTRICT OF COLUMBIA COURT OF APPEALS

430 E Street, NW., 20001

phone (202) 879–1010

Chief Judge.—Eric T. Washington.

Associate Judges:

Stephen H. Glickman.
John R. Fisher.
Anna Blackburne-Rigsby.
Phyllis D. Thompson.
Kathryn A. Oberly.
Corinne Beckwith.
Catharine F. Easterly.
Roy W. McLeese.

Senior Judges:

Theodore R. Newman, Jr.
William C. Pryor.
Annice M. Wagner.
James A. Belson.
Frank Q. Nebeker.
John M. Steadman.
John A. Terry.
John M. Ferren.
Frank E. Schwelb.
Inez Smith Reid.
Warren R. King.
Michael W. Farrell.
Vanessa Ruiz.

Clerk.—Julio Castillo, 879–2725.

Chief Deputy Clerk.—Tracy Nutall, 879–2773.
Administration Director.—Reginald Turner, 879–2755.
Admissions Director.—Vacant, 879–2714.
Public Office Operations Director.—Terry Lambert, 879–2702.
Senior Staff Attorney.—Rosanna Mason, 879–2718.

SUPERIOR COURT OF THE DISTRICT OF COLUMBIA

500 Indiana Avenue, NW., 20001

phone (202) 879–1010

Chief Judge.—Lee F. Satterfield.

Associate Judges:

Jennifer M. Anderson.
Judith Bartnoff.
Ronna L. Beck.
Patricia A. Broderick.
A. Franklin Burgess, Jr.
Zoe Bush.
John M. Campbell.
Russell F. Canan.
Erik P. Christian.
Jeanette Clark.
Natalia Combs Greene.
Laura A. Cordero.
Harold Cushenberry, Jr.
Carol Dalton.
Danya A. Dayson.
Marisa Demeo.
Jennifer A. DiToro.
Herbert B. Dixon, Jr.
Todd E. Edelson.
Anthony Epstein.
Gerald I. Fisher.
Wendell P. Gardner, Jr.
Brian Holeman.
Alfred S. Irving.
Craig Iscoe.
Gregory Jackson.
William M. Jackson.
J. Ramsey Johnson.
Anita Josey-Herring.
Ann O'Regan Keary.
Kimberley S. Knowles.
Peter Krauthamer.
Neal E. Kravitz.
Milton C. Lee
Lynn Leibowitz.
José M. López.
Judith N. Macaluso.
John McCabe.
Juliet J. McKenna.
Robert E. Morin.
Thomas J. Motley.
John M. Mott.
Stuart G. Nash.
Michael R. O'Keefe.
Robert D. Okun.
Florence Y. Pan.
Heidi Pasichow.
Hiram E. Puig-Lugo.
Maribeth Raffinan.
Michael L. Rankin.
Robert I. Richter.
Robert Rigsby.
Maurice Ross.
Michael J. Ryan.

Fern Flanagan Saddler.
Judith Smith.
Frederick H. Weisberg.
Yvonne Williams.
Rhonda Reid Winston.
Melvin R. Wright.

Senior Judges:

Mary Ellen Abrecht.
Geoffrey M. Alprin.
John H. Bayly.
Leonard Braman.
Arthur L. Burnett.
Kaye R. Christian.
Linda Kay Davis.
Frederick D. Dorsey.
Stephanie Duncan-Peters.
Stephen F. Eilperin.
Henry F. Greene.
Brook Hedge.
Rufus G. King III
Richard A. Levie.
Cheryl M. Long.
Bruce S. Mencher.
Zinora Mitchell-Rankin.
Gregory E. Mize.
Truman A. Morrison III.
Judith E. Retchin.
Nan R. Shuker.
Robert S. Tignor.
Linda D. Turner.
Curtis Von Kann.
Ronald P. Wertheim.
Susan R. Winfield.
Peter H. Wolf.
Patricia A. Wynn.
Joan Zeldon.

Magistrate Judges:

Janet Albert.
Errol Arthur.
Joseph E. Beshouri.
Rainey R. Brandt.
Diane M. Brenneman.
Julie Breslow.
Diana Harris Epps.
Tara Fentress.
S. Pamela Gray.
Andrea L. Harnett.
Karen Howze.
Noel Johnson.
Michael J. McCarthy.
Aida Melendez.
Elizabeth Mullin.
Lloyd U. Nolan.
William Nooter.
Lori Parker.
Richard H. Ringell.
Gretchen Rohr.
Mary Grace Rook.
Kenia Seoane-Lopez.
Frederick J. Sullivan.
Elizabeth Wingo.

Clerk of the Court.—Duane B. Delaney, 879–1400.

GOVERNMENT OF THE DISTRICT OF COLUMBIA

John A. Wilson Building, 1350 Pennsylvania Avenue, NW., 20004
phone (202) 724–8000

[All area codes within this section are (202)]

COUNCIL OF THE DISTRICT OF COLUMBIA

Council Chairman (at Large).—Phil Mendelson, Suite 504, 724–8032.
Chairman Pro Tempore.—Kenyan McDuffie.
Council Members (at Large):
David A. Catania, Suite 404, 724–7772.
Anita Bonds, Suite 402, 724–8064.
Vincent Orange, Sr., Suite 107, 724–8174.
David Grosso, Suite 406, 724–8105.
Council Members:
Jim Graham, Ward 1, Suite 105, 724–8181.
Jack Evans, Ward 2, Suite 106, 724–8058.
Mary M. Cheh, Ward 3, Suite 108, 724–8062.
Muriel Bowser, Ward 4, Suite 110, 724–8052.
Kenyan McDuffie, Ward 5, Suite 506, 724–8028.
Thomas Wells, Ward 6, Suite 402, 724–8072.
Yvette M. Alexander, Ward 7, Suite 400, 724–8068.
Marion Barry, Ward 8, Suite 102, 724–8045.
Council Officers:
Secretary to the Council.—Nyasha Smith, Suite 5, 724–8080.
Budget Director.—Jennifer Budoff, Suite 508, 724–8139.
General Counsel.—David Zvenyach, Suite 4, 724–8026.
D.C. Auditor.—Yolanda Branche, 717 14th Street, NW., 727–3600.

EXECUTIVE OFFICE OF THE MAYOR

6th Floor, phone (202) 727–6263, fax 727–6561

Mayor of the District of Columbia.—Hon. Vincent C. Gray.
Confidential Assistant to the Mayor.—Sedrick Muhammad.
Chief of Staff.—Christopher Murphy.
Special Assistant to the Chief of Staff.—Stephanie Bland, 3rd Floor, 727–2643, fax 727–8527.
Deputy Chief of Staff.—Sheila Bunn.
Deputy Mayor for—
Education.—Abigail Smith, Suite 303, 727–3636, fax 727–8198.
Human Services.—Beatriz "BB" Otero.
Planning and Economic Development.—Victor Hoskins, Suite 317, 727–6365, fax 727–6703.
Public Safety and Justice.—Paul Quander, Jr.
Attorney General.—Irvin B. Nathan, 441 4th Street, NW., Suite 1100 South, 727–3400, fax 347–8922.
Inspector General.—Charles Willoughby, Esq., 717 14th Street, NW., 5th Floor, 727–2540, fax 727–9846.
General Counsel.—Brian K. Flowers, Suite 300, 727–7681, fax 724–7743.
Secretary of the District of Columbia.—Cynthia Brock-Smith, Suite 419, 727–6306, fax 727–3582.
Director of:
Budget and Finance.—Eric Goulet, Suite 211, 727–3380, fax 727–5931.
Communications.—Pedro Ribeiro, Suite 311, 727–5011, fax 727–8527.
Office of Community Relations and Services.—Steve Glaude, Suite 327, 442–8150, fax 727–2357.

Office of Policy and Legislative Affairs.—Janene Jackson, Suite 531, 727–6979, fax 727–3765.

OFFICE OF THE CITY ADMINISTRATOR

Suite 513, phone (202) 478–9200, fax (202) 727–9878

City Administrator.—Allen Y. Lew.
Executive Assistant to City Administrator.—J. Laverne Moss.

COMMISSIONS

Arts and Humanities, 200 I (Eye) Street SE., Suite 1400, Washington, DC 20003, 724–5613, fax 727–4135, e-mail: lionell.thomas@dc.gov, website: http://dcarts.dc.gov/DC/DCARTS.
Executive Director.—Lionel Thomas.
Chairperson.—Judith F. Terra.

Judicial Disabilities and Tenure, 515 5th Street, NW., Building A, Room 246, Washington, DC 20001, 727–1363, fax 727–9718, e-mail: cathaee.hudgins@dc.gov, website: http://cjdt.dc.gov/DC/CJDT.
Executive Director.—Cathaee Hudgins.
Chairperson.—Hon. Gladys Kessler.

Judicial Nominations, 515 5th Street, NW., Suite 235, Washington, DC 20001, 879–0478, fax 879–0755, e-mail: kim.whatley@dc.gov, website: http://jnc.dc.gov/DC/JNC.
Executive Director.—Kim M. Whatley.
Chairperson.—Hon. Emmet G. Sullivan.

Serve DC, Frank D. Reeves Municipal Center, 2000 14th Street, NW., Suite 101, Washington, DC 20009, 727–7200, fax 727–9942, e-mail: jeffrey.richardson@dc.gov, website: http://serve.dc.gov/page/about-serve-dc.
Executive Director.—Jeffrey Richardson.
Chairperson.—Peter Brusoe.

Washington Metropolitan Area Transit, 8701 Georgia Avenue, Suite 808, Silver Spring, MD 20910–3700, (301) 427–0140, fax 588–5262, e-mail: wmorrow@wmatc.gov, website: http://www.wmatc.gov.
Executive Director/General Counsel.—William S. Morrow, Jr.
Chairperson.—Lawrence Brenner.

DEPARTMENTS

Child and Family Services Agency, 400 6th Street, SW., 5th Floor, 20024, 442–6100, fax 727–6505.
Director.—Brenda Donald.

Consumer and Regulatory Affairs, 941 North Capitol Street, NE., 20002, 442–4400, fax 442–9445.
Director.—Nicholas A. Majett.

Corrections, 1923 Vermont Avenue, NW., Room 207 North, 20001, 673–7316, fax 671–2043.
Director.—Thomas Faust.

Environment, 1200 First Street, NE., 5th Floor, 20002, 535–2600, fax 673–6993.
Director.—Keith Anderson.

Employment Services, 4058 Minnesota Avenue, NE., 20019, 724–7000, fax 673–6993.
Director.—Dr. Lisa Maria Mallory.

Fire and Emergency Medical Services, 1923 Vermont Avenue, NW., Suite 201, 20001, 673–3320, fax 462–0807.
Fire Chief.—Kenneth B. Ellerbe.

Health, 899 North Capitol Street, NE., 5th Floor, 20002, 442–5955, fax 442–4795.

Director.—Dr. Joxel Garcia.

Housing and Community Development, 1800 Martin Luther King, Jr. Avenue, SE., 20020, 442–7200, fax 645–6730.
Director.—Michael Kelley.

Human Services, 64 New York Avenue, NE., 6th Floor, 20002, 671–4200, fax 671–4325.
Director.—David A. Berns.

Insurance, Securities and Banking, 810 1st Street, NE., Suite 701, 20002, 727–8000, fax 535–1196.
Commissioner.—William P. White.

Mental Health, 64 New York Avenue, NE., 4th Floor, 20002, 673–7440, fax 673–3433.
Director.—Stephen T. Baron.

Metropolitan Police, 300 Indiana Avenue, NW., 20001, phone 311 or (202) 737–4404 if calling from outside DC, fax 727–9524.
Police Chief.—Cathy L. Lanier.

Motor Vehicles, 301 C Street, NW., 20001, 727–5000, fax 727–4653.
Director.—Lucinda M. Babers.

Parks and Recreation, 3149 16th Street, NW., 20010, 673–7647, fax 673–2087.
Director.—Jesus Aguirre (until October 1).

Public Works, 2000 14th Street, NW., 6th Floor, 20009, 673–6833, fax 671–0642.
Director.—William O. Howland, Jr.

Small and Local Business Development, 441 4th Street, NW., Suite 970 North, 20001, 727–3900, fax 724–3786.
Director.—Robert Summers (acting).

Transportation, 55 M Street, SE., Suite 400, 20003, 673–6813, fax 671–0650.
Director.—Terry Bellamy.

Youth Rehabilitation Services, 450 H Street, NW., 10th Floor, 20001, 576–8175, fax 727–4434.
Director.—Neil Stanley.

OFFICES

Administrative Hearings, One Judiciary Square, 441 4th Street, NW., 20001, 442–9091, fax 442–9451.
Chief Judge.—Mary Oates Walker.

Aging, 441 4th Street, NW., Suite 900 South, 20001, 724–5622, fax 724–4979.
Director.—John M. Thompson, Ph.D.

Asian and Pacific Islander Affairs, 441 4th Street, NW., Suite 721 North, 20001, 727–3120, fax 727–9655.
Executive Director.—Soohyun "Julie" Koo.

Attorney General, 441 4th Street, NW., Suite 400 South, 20001, 727–3400, fax 347–8922.
Attorney General.—Irvin B. Nathan.

Boards and Commissions, 1350 Pennsylvania Avenue, NW., Suite 302, 20004, 727–1372, fax 727–2359.
Director.—Daryl Gorman.

Cable Television and Telecommunications, 3007 Tilden Street, NW., Pod P, 20008, 671–0066, fax 332–7020.
Director.—Eric E. Richardson (acting).

Chief Financial Officer, 1350 Pennsylvania Avenue, NW., Suite 203, 20004, 727–2476, fax 727–1643.
Chief Financial Officer.—Natwar M. Gandhi.

Chief Medical Examiner, 1910 Massachusetts Avenue, SE., Building 27, 20003, 698–9000, fax 698–9100.
Chief Medical Examiner.—Dr. Marie-Lydie Pierre-Louis.

Chief Technology Officer, 441 4th Street, NW., Suite 930 South, 20001, 727–2277, fax 727–6857.
Chief Technology Officer.—Rob Mancini.

Communications Office, 1350 Pennsylvania Avenue, NW., Suite 310, 20004, 727–5011, fax 727–8527.
Director.—Pedro Ribeiro.

Office of Community Affairs, 1350 Pennsylvania Avenue, NW., Suite 327, 20004, 442–8150, fax 727–5931.
Director.—Stephen Glaude.

Contracting and Procurement, 441 4th Street, NW., Suite 700 South, 20001, 727–0252, fax 727–0245.
Chief Procurement Officer.—James D. Staton.

Emergency Management Agency, 2720 Martin Luther King, Jr. Avenue, SE., 20032, 727–6161, fax 715–7288.
Director.—Jennifer Greene.

Employee Appeals, 1100 4th Street, SW., Suite 620 East, 20024, 727–0004, fax 727–5631.
Executive Director.—Sheila Barfield, Esq.

Finance and Resource Management, 441 4th Street, NW., Suite 890 North, 20001, 727–0333, fax 727–0659.
Director of Finance Operations.—Mohamed Mohamed.

Human Resources, 441 4th Street, NW., Suite 330 South, 20001, 442–9600, fax 727–6827.
Director.—Shawn Stokes.

Human Rights, 441 4th Street, NW., Suite 570 North, 20001, 727–4559, fax 727–9589.
Director.—Gustavo F. Velasquez.

Labor Relations and Collective Bargaining, 441 4th Street, NW., Suite 820 North, 20001, 724–4953, fax 727–6887.
Director.—Natasha Campbell.

Latino Affairs, 2000 14th Street, NW., 2nd Floor, 20009, 671–2825, fax 673–4557.
Director.—Roxana Olivas.

Lesbian, Gay, Bisexual and Transgender Affairs, 1350 Pennsylvania Avenue, NW., Suite 327, 20004, 727–9493, fax 727–5931.
Director.—Sterling Washington.

Motion Picture and Television Development, 3007 Tilden Street, NW., 4th Floor, 20008, 727–6608, fax 727–3246.
Director.—Crystal Palmer.

Office of Planning, 1100 4th Street, SW., Suite E650, 20024, 442–7600, fax 442–7638.
Director.—Harriet Tregoning.

Policy and Legislative Affairs, 1350 Pennsylvania Avenue, NW., Suite 533, 20004, 727–6979, fax 727–3765.
Director.—Janene Jackson.

Department of Real Estate Services, 2000 14th Street, NW., 8th Floor, 20009, 724–4400, fax 727–9877.
Director.—Brian J. Hanlon.

Risk Management, 441 4th Street, NW., Suite 800 South, 20001, 727–8600, fax 727–8319.
Director.—Phillip A. Lattimore.

Office of the State Superintendent of Education, 810 First Street, NE., 9th Floor, 20002, 727–6436, fax 727–2019.
Superintendent.—Interim Emily Durso.

Unified Communications, 2720 Martin Luther King Jr. Avenue, SE., 20032, 730–0524, fax 730–1425.
Interim Director.—Chris Geldart.

Veterans Affairs, 441 4th Street, NW., Suite 570 South, 20001, 724–5454, fax 727–7117.
Interim Director.—Matthew J. Cary.

Victim Services, 1350 Pennsylvania Avenue, NW., Suite 407, 20004, 727–3934, fax 727–1617.
Director.—Melissa Hook.

Zoning, 441 4th Street, NW., Suite 200 South, 20001, 727–6311, fax 727–6072.
Director.—Jamison L. Weinbaum.

INDEPENDENT AGENCIES

Advisory Neighborhood Commissions, 1350 Pennsylvania Avenue, NW., Room 8, 20004, 727–9945, fax 727–0289.
Executive Director.—Gottlieb Simon.

Alcoholic Beverage Regulation Administration, 2000 14th Street, NW., Suite 400 South, 20009, 442–4423, fax 442–9563.
Director.—Fred Moosally.

Board of Elections and Ethics, 441 4th Street, NW., Suite 250 North, 20001, 727–2525, fax 347–2648.
Chairperson of the Board.—Cliff Tatum.

Criminal Justice Coordinating Council, 441 4th Street, NW., Suite 727 North, 20001, 442–9283, fax 724–3691.
Executive Director.—Mannone Butler.

District of Columbia Court of Appeals, 430 E Street, Room 115, 20001, 879–2701, fax 626–8840.
Chief Judge.—Eric T. Washington.

District of Columbia Housing Authority, 1133 North Capitol Street, NE., 20001, 535–1500, fax 535–1740.
Executive Director.—Adrianne Todman.

District of Columbia Public Defender Service, 633 Indiana Avenue, NW., 20001, 628–1200, fax 824–2784.
Director.—Avis Buchanan.

District of Columbia Public Library, 901 G Street, NW., Suite 400, 20001, 727–1101, fax 727–1129.
Director.—Ginnie Cooper.

District of Columbia Public Schools, 825 North Capitol Street, NW., Suite 9026, 20002, 442–4226, fax 442–5026.
Chancellor.—Kaya Henderson.

District of Columbia Retirement Board, 900 7th Street, NW., 2nd Floor, 20001, 343–3200, fax 566–5000.
Executive Director.—Eric Stanchfield.

District of Columbia Sentencing and Criminal Code Revision Commission, 441 4th Street, NW., Suite 830 South, 20001, 727–8822, fax 727–7929.
Executive Director.—Barbara Tombs-Souvey.

District Lottery and Charitable Games Control Board, 2101 Martin Luther King Jr. Avenue, SE., 20020, 645–8000, fax 645–7914.
Executive Director.—Buddy Roogow.

Housing Finance Agency, 815 Florida Avenue, NW., 20001, 777–1600, fax 986–6705.
Executive Director.—Harry D. Sewell.

Metropolitan Washington Council of Governments, 777 North Capitol Street, NE., 20002, 962–3200, fax 962–3201.
Executive Director.—Dave Robertson.

People's Counsel, 1133 15th Street, NW., Suite 500, 20005, 727–3071, fax 727–1014.
People's Counsel.—Sandra Mattavous-Frye, Esq.

Police Complaints, 1400 I Street, NW., Suite 700, 20005, 727–3838, fax 727–9182.
Executive Director.—Philip K. Eure.

Public Charter School Board, 3333 14th Street, NW., Suite 210, 20010, 328–2660, fax 328–2661.
Interim Executive Director.—Jeremy Williams.

Public Employee Relations Board, 1100 4th Street, SW., Suite E630, 20024, 727–1822, fax 727–9116.
Executive Director.—Keturah Harley (acting).

Public Service Commission, 1333 H Street, NW., Suite 200 West Tower, 20005, 626–5100, fax 393–1389.
Chairperson.—Betty Ann Kane.

Superior Court of the District of Columbia, H. Carl Moultrie I Courthouse, 500 Indiana Avenue, NW., 20001, 879–1010.
Chief Judge.—Lee F. Satterfield.

Taxicab Commission, 2041 Martin Luther King Jr. Avenue, SE.. Suite 204, 20020, 645–6018, fax 889–3604.
Chairperson.—Dena C. Reed.

Washington Convention Center Authority, 801 Mount Vernon Place, NW., 20001, 249–3012, fax 249–3133.
President and CEO.—Greg O'Dell.

Destination DC, 1212 New York Avenue, NW., Suite 600, 20005, 904–0616 or 249–3012, fax 789–7037.
President and CEO.—Elliot Ferguson.

Water and Sewer Authority, 5000 Overlook Avenue, SW., 20032, 787–2000, fax 787–2210.
Chairman.—William M. Walker.
General Manager.—George S. Hawkins.

Workforce Investment Council, 4058 Minnesota Avenue, NE., 20009, 671–1900, fax 673–6993.
Chairperson.—Vacant.

OTHER

Board of Real Property Assessments and Appeals, 441 4th Street, NW., Suite 430, 20001, 727–6860, fax 727–0392.
Chairperson.—Towanda Paul–Bryant.

Contract Appeals Board, 441 4th Street, NW., Suite N350, 727–6597, fax 727–3993.
Chief Administrative Judge.—Marc D. Loud, Sr.

Justice Grants Administration, 1350 Pennsylvania Avenue, NW., Suite 327A, 20004, 727–6239, fax 727–1617.
Director.—Josh Weber.

Rehabilitation Services Administration, 1125 15th Street, NW., 20005, 730–1700, fax 730–1516.
Administrator.—Vacant.

DISTRICT OF COLUMBIA POST OFFICE LOCATIONS

900 Brentwood Road, NE., 20066–9998, General Information (202) 636–1200

Postmaster.—Gerald A. Roane.

CLASSIFIED STATIONS

Station	Phone	Location / Zip Code
Anacostia	(301) 423–9091/ 9092	3719 Branch Ave., Temple Hills, MD 20748
Ben Franklin	523–2386	1200 Pennsylvania Ave., NW., 20044
B.F. Carriers	636–2289	900 Brentwood Rd., NE., 20004
Benning	523–2391	3937–½ Minnesota Ave., NE., 20029
Bolling AFB	767–4419	Bldg. 10, Brookley Ave., 20332
Brightwood	726–8119	6323 Georgia Ave., NW., 20
Brookland	523–2126	3401 12th St., NE., 20017
Calvert	523–2908	2336 Wisconsin Ave., NW., 20007
Cleveland Park	523–2396	3430 Connecticut Ave., NW., 20008
Columbia Heights	523–2192	6510 Chillum Pl., NW., 20010
Congress Heights	523–2112	400 Southern Ave., SE., 20032
Customs House	523–2195	3178 Bladensburg Rd., NE., 20018
Dulles	(703) 471–9497	Dulles International Airport, 20041
Farragut	523–2507	1145 19th St., NW., 20033

CLASSIFIED STATIONS—CONTINUED

Station	Phone	Location / Zip Code
Fort Davis	842–4964	3843 Pennsylvania Ave., SE., 20020
Fort McNair	523–2144	300 A. St., SW., 20319
Frederick Douglass	842–4959	Alabama Ave., SE., 20020
Friendship	523–2130	4005 Wisconsin Ave., NW., 20016
Georgetown	523–2406	1215 31st St., NW., 20007
Government Mail	523–2138 / 2139	3300 V Street, NE., 20018–9998
Headsville	357–3029	Smithsonian Institute, 20560
Kalorama	523–2906	2300 18th St., NW., 20009
Lamond Riggs	523–2041	6200 North Capitol St., NW., 20011
LeDroit Park	483–0973	416 Florida Ave., NW., 20001
L'Enfant Plaza	268–4970	458 L'Enfant Plaza, SW., 20026
Main Office Window	636–2130	Curseen / Morris P&DC, 900 Brentwood Rd., NE., 20066–9998
Martin L. King, Jr	523–2001	1400 L St., NW., 20043
McPherson	842–1229	1750 Pennsylvania Ave., NW., 20038
Mid City	....	Temporarily Closed
NASA	358–0235	600 Independence Ave., SW., 20546
National Capitol	523–2368	2 Massachusetts Ave., NE., 20002
Naval Research Lab	767–3426	4565 Overlook Ave., 20390
Navy Annex	(703) 920–0815	1668 D Street, 20335
Northeast	388–5216	1563 Maryland Ave., NE., 20002
Northwest	523–2570	5632 Connecticut Ave., NW., 20015
Palisades	842–2291	5136 MacArthur Blvd., NW., 20016
Pavilion Postique	523–2571	1100 Pennsylvania Ave., NW., 20004
Pentagon	(703) 695–6835	Concourse Pentagon (Army-20301 / 20310; Air Force-20330; Navy-20350)
Petworth	523–2681	4211 9th St., NW., 20011
Postal Mus	523–2022	2 Massachusetts Ave., NW., 20002
Randle	584–6807	2341 Pennsylvania Ave., SE., 20023
River Terrace	523–2988	3621 Benning Rd., NE., 20019
Southeast	523–2174	327 7th St., SE., 20003
Southwest	523–2597	45 L St., SW., 20024
State Department	523–2574	2201 C St., NW., 20520
14th/T Street	232–6301	2000 14th St., NW., 20009
Tech World	523–2019	800 K St., NW., 20001
Temple Heights	523–2563	1921 Florida Ave., NW., 20009
Twentieth Street	523–2411	2001 M St., NW., 20036
U.S. Naval	433–2216	940 M St., SE., 20374
V Street	636–2272 / 2273	Section 2, Curseen / Morris P&DC, 900 Brentwood Rd., NE., 20002–9998
Walter Reed	....	6800 Georgia Ave., NW., 20012
Ward Place	523–2109	2121 Ward Pl., NW., 20037
Washington Square	523–3632	1050 Connecticut Ave., NW., 20035
Watergate	965–6278	2512 Virginia Ave., NW., 20037
Woodridge	523–2195	2211 Rhode Island Ave., NE., 20018

INTERNATIONAL ORGANIZATIONS

EUROPEAN SPACE AGENCY (E.S.A.)

Headquarters: 8–10 Rue Mario Nikis, 75738 Paris Cedex 15, France
phone 011–33–1–5369–7654, fax 011–33–1–5369–7560

Chairman of the Council.—Johann-Dietrich Woerner.
Director General.—Jean-Jacques Dordain.
Member Countries:

Austria	Ireland	Romania
Belgium	Italy	Spain
Denmark	Luxembourg	Sweden
Finland	Netherlands	Switzerland
France	Norway	United Kingdom
Germany	Poland	Czech Republic
Greece	Portugal	

Cooperative Agreement.—Canada.

European Space Operations Center (ESOC), Robert-Bosch-Str. 5, D–64293 Darmstadt, Germany, phone 011–49–6151–900, fax 011–49–6151–90495.

European Space Research and Technology Center (ESTEC), Keplerlaan 1, NL–2201, AZ Noordwijk, ZH, The Netherlands, phone 011–31–71–565–6565, Telex: 844–39098, fax 011–31–71–565–6040.

European Space Research Institute (ESRIN), Via Galileo Galilei, Casella Postale 64, 00044 Frascati, Italy, phone 011–39–6–94–18–01, fax 011–39–6–9418–0280.

European Space Astronomy Centre (ESAC), P.O. Box, E–28691 Villanueva de la Cañada, Madrid, Spain, phone 011–34 91 813 11 00, fax: 011–34 91 813 11 39.

European Astronaut Centre (EAC), Linder Hoehe, 51147 Cologne, Germany, phone 011–49–220360–010, fax 011–49–2203–60–1103.

European Centre for Space Applications and Telecommunications (ECSAT), Atlas Building, Harwell Science & Innovation Campus, Didcot, Oxfordshire, OX11 0QX, United Kingdom, phone 011–44 1235 567900.

Euopean Space Agency Washington Office (EWO), 955 L'Enfant Plaza, SW., Suite 7800, Washington, DC 20024.
Head of Office.—Micheline Tabache (202) 488–4158, fax 488–4930, micheline.tabache@esa.int.

INTER-AMERICAN DEFENSE BOARD

2600 16th Street, NW., 20441, phone (202) 939–6041, fax 319–2791

Chairman.—Lt. Gen. Werther Araya Menghini, Chile.
Vice Chairman.—Lt. Gen. Nicasio Rios, Paraguay.
Chairman's Executive Officer.—CDR Juan Pablo Willumsen, Chile.
Director General.—LTG Bento Costa Lima de Albuquerque Jr., Brazil.
Deputy Secretary for—
Administration.—COL Mark Jeffris, United States.
Conference.—CMG Tome Albertino de Sousa Machado, Brazil.

CHIEFS OF DELEGATION

Antigua and Barbuda.—COL Trevor Thomas.
Argentina.—Gral Brig Jorge Mario Vega.

Barbados.—LTC Ricardo da Costa Vickers.
Belize.—Kendall Belisle.
Boliva.—Vacant.
Brazil.—CA Alexandre Araujo.
Canada.—MG Nicolas Matern.
Chile.—GD Alberto Gonzalez Martin.
Colombia.—COL Alexander Godoy.
Dominican Republic.—GB Pedro Valenzuela.
Ecuador.—Vacant.
El Salvador.—COL Enrique Antonio Acosta Bonilla.
Guatemala.—COL Jorge Vernel Camey Colon.
Guyana.—COL Kemraj Persaud.
Haiti.—Minister Counselor Charles Leon.
Honduras.—Vacant.
Jamaica.—COL Anthony Anderson.
Mexico.—GB Victor Hugo Aguirre Serna.
Nicaragua.—COL Armando Alaniz.
Panama.—Commisionado Omar Ariel Pinzon Martin.
Paraguay.—COL Pedro Rolando Ortiz Cabral.
Peru.—GB Marco Jaymez Rebosio.
Suriname.—AMB Niermala Hindori-Badrising.
Trinidad and Tobago.—COL Colin Mitchell.
United States.—BG Peter E. Gersten.
Uruguay.—General Wile Ariel Purtscher.
Venezuela.—Vacant.

INTER-AMERICAN DEFENSE COLLEGE

Director.—RADM Jeffrey Allen Lemmons.
Vice Director.—CA Figueiredo Fernando.
Chief of Studies.—CA Francisco Yabar.

INTER-AMERICAN DEVELOPMENT BANK

1300 New York Avenue, NW., 20577, phone (202) 623–1000

http://www.iadb.org

OFFICERS

President.—Luis Alberto Moreno.
  Chief, Office of the President.—Luis Giorgio.
Executive Vice President.—Julie T. Katzman (United States).
Chief Advisor.—Juan Pablo Bonilla.
Director, Office of Evaluation and Oversight.—Cheryl Gray.
Manager of the Research Department and Chief Economist.—Jose Juan Ruiz Gomez.
Executive Auditor.—Jorge Da Silva.
Manager, Office of External Relations—Marcelo Cabrol.
Ombudsperson.—Doris Campos-Infantino.
Secretary.—German Quintana.
Manager, Office of Outreach and Partnerships.—Bernardo Guillamón.
Advisor, Office of Risk Management.—Gustavo De Rosa.
Manager, Office of Strategic Planning and Development Effectiveness.—Verónica Zavala.
Chief, Office of Institutional Integrity.—Maristella Aldana.
Vice-President for Countries.—Roberto Vellutini.
  Country Manager, Office of:
    Department Andean Group.—Carola Álvarez.
    Department Caribbean Group.—Gerard S. Johnson.
    Department Central America, Mexico, Panama and Dominican Republic.—Gina Montiel.
    Department Southern Cone.—José Luis Lupo.
Vice President for Sectors and Knowledge.—Santiago Levy.
  Manager of:
    Infrastructure and Environment Sector.—Alexandre Meira da Rosa.
    Institutional Capacity and Finance Sector.—Ana María Rodríguez-Ortiz.

Knowledge and Learning.—Federico Basañes.
Social Sector.—Héctor Salazar a.i.
Trade and Integration.—Antoni Estevadeorval.
Vice President for Finance and Administration.—Jaime Sujoy.
Manager of:
Budget and Administrative Services.—Yeshvanth Edwin.
Finance Department.—Edward Bartholomew.
Human Resources.—Claudia Bock-Valotta.
Information Technology.—Simon Gauthier.
Legal Department.—Jorge Alers.
Vice President for Private Sector and Non-Sovereign Guaranteed Operations.—Hans Schul.
Manager of:
Office of the Multilateral Investment Fund.—Nancy Lee.
Opportunities for the Majority Sector.—Luiz Ros.
Structured and Corporate Financing Department.—Hans Schulz.

BOARD OF EXECUTIVE DIRECTORS

Argentina and Haiti.—Gabriela V. Costa.
Alternate.—Federico Chinchilla.
Austria, Denmark, Finland, France, Norway, Spain, and Sweden.—María Pérez Ribes.
Alternate.—Per O. Bastoe.
Bahamas, Barbados, Guyana, Jamaica, Trinidad and Tobago.—Kurt M. A. Kisto.
Alternate.—Zulfikar Ally.
Belgium, Germany, Israel, Italy, The Netherlands, and Switzerland.—Leo Kreuz.
Alternate.—Ulrike Metzger.
Belize, Costa Rica, El Salvador, Guatemala, Honduras and Nicaragua.—Carla Anahí Herrera Ramos.
Alternate.—Marlon Ramsses Tabora Muñoz.
Bolivia, Paraguay and Uruguay.—Luis Hernando Larrazabal.
Alternate.—Hugo Rafael Cáceres.
Brazil and Suriname.—Ricardo Carneiro.
Alternate.—Sergio Portugal.
Canada.—James Haley.
Alternate.—Carol Nelder-Corvari.
Chile and Ecuador.—Alejandro Foxley.
Alternate.—Xavier Santillán.
Colombia and Peru.—Juan Carlos Echeverry.
Alternate.—Kurt Burneo.
Croatia, Japan, Korea, Portugal, Slovenia and United Kingdom.—Yasuhiro Atsumi.
Alternate.—Hironori Kawauchi.
Dominican Republic and Mexico.—Ángeles González.
Alternate.—Muriel A. Alfonseca.
Panama and Venezuela.—Adina Mercedes Bastidas Castillo.
Alternate.—Antonio De Roux.
United States of America.—Gustavo Arnavat.

INTER-AMERICAN TROPICAL TUNA COMMISSION

8901 La Jolla, Shores Drive, La Jolla, CA 92037–1508
phone (858) 546–7100, fax (858) 546–7133, http://www.iattc.org

Director.—Guillermo A. Compeán.

Commissioners:
Belize:
Abilio Dominguez, IMMARBE/International Merchant Marine Registry of Belize, Marina Towers, Suite 204, Newtown Barracks, Belize City, Belize, phone (501) 223–5026, fax (501) 223–5070; e-mail: abilio@immarbe.com.
James Azueta, Belize Fisheries Department, C/O Marine Towers, Suite 204, Newtown Barracks, Belize City, Belize, phone (501) 223–2187, fax (501) 223–5070; e-mail: jamesazueta_bz@yahoo.com.
Valerie Lanza, IMMARBE/International Merchant Marine Registry of Belize, Marina Towers, Suite 204, Newtown Barracks, Belize City, Belize, phone (501) 223–5026, fax (501) 223–5070; e-mail: valerie@immarbe.com, immarbe@btl.net.

Felicia Cruz, Belize Fisheries Department, C/O Marine Towers, Suite 204, Newtown Barracks, Belize City, Belize, phone (501) 224–4552 ext. 29; e-mail: feliciacruzbz@gmail.com.

Canada:

Larry Teague, British Columbia Tuna Fishermen's Association (BCTFA), Box 372, Shawnigan Lake, British Columbia V0R 2W0, Canada, phone (250) 743–5002; e-mail: bctfa@shaw.ca.

Sylvie Lapointe, Fisheries, and Oceans Canada/Peches et Océans Canada, 200 Kent Street, Station 8E240, Ottawa, ONT K1A 0E6, Canada, phone (613) 993–6853, fax (613) 993–5995; e-mail: sylvie.lapointe@dfo-mpo.gc.ca.

China:

Gang Zhao, Ministry of Agriculture, Room 1216 Jingchao Mansion, No. 5, Nongzhanguan Nanlu, Chaoyang District, Beijing 100125, People's Republic of China, phone (86–10) 6585–4085, fax (86–10) 6585–0551; e-mail: admin@tuna.org.cn.

Hai Yan Zhou, Ministry of Foreign Affairs, No. 2 Chao Yang Men Nan Da Jie, Beijing, 100701, People's Republic of China, phone (86–10) 6596–3266, fax (86–10) 6596–3276; e-mail: zhou_haiyan@mfa.gov.cn.

Xiaobing, Liu, Bureau of Fisheries of the Ministry of Agriculture, No. 11 Nong Zhan Guan Nan Li, Beijing, 100026 People's Republic of China, phone (86–10) 6419–2928, (86–10) 6419–2974, fax (86–10) 6419–2951; e-mail: inter-coop@agri.gov.cn.

Colombia:

Carlos Alberto Robles Cocuyame, Ministerio de Agricultura y Desarrollo Rural, Avenida Jiménez 7–65, Bogotá, D.C 001, Colombia, phone (57–1) 334–1199 ext. 310 (57–1) 283–3977, fax (57–1) 334–1199; e-mail: carlos.robles@minagricultura.gov.co.

Juan Carlos Cadena, Ministerio de Comercio Industria y Turismo, Calle 28 No. 13A–15 piso 6, Bogotá, Colombia, phone (57–1) 606–7530, fax (57–1) 606–7534; e-mail: jcadena@mincomercio.gov.co.

Paula Caballero Gómez, Ministerio de Relaciones Exteriores, Calle 10 No. 5–51 Palacio de San Carlos, Bogotá, DC, Colombia, phone (57–1) 381–4265, fax (57–1) 381–4747; e-mail: paula.caballero@cancilleria.gov.co.

Elizabeth Taylor Jay, Ministerio de Ambiente y Desarrollo Sostenible, Calle 35 No. 24–48, Bogota, Colombia, phone (57–1) 288–2132, (57–1) 332–3400; e-mail: etaylor@minambiente.gov.co.

Costa Rica:

Asdrúbal Vásquez, Ministerio de Agricultura y Ganadería, Oriental del TEC, 300 mts. Sur. Oeste, Cartago, 549–7050, Costa Rica, phone (506) 2234–1498, fax (506) 2253–4321; e-mail: vazqueza1@ice.co.cr, vasqueza@sardimar.com.

Lic. Bernal A. Chavarría V., Ministerio de Agricultura y Ganadería, Sabana Sur, 400 Sur, 25 Este de la Contraloría General de la República San José, San José 1000 Costa Rica, phone (506) 2290–8868 (506) 8822–4709, fax (506) 2232–4651; e-mail: bchavarria@lsg-cr.com, bchavarria@bcvabogados.com.

Lic. Luís Dobles Ramírez, INCOPESCA / Instituto Costarricense de Pesca y Acuicultura Contiguo a Consejo Nacional de Producción Yamuni Avenida 10 San José, San José 1000 Costa Rica, phone (506) 2248–1130, fax (506) 2248–1196; e-mail: ludora@ice.co.cr, rocioperezp@yahoo.es.

Xinia Chaves Quirós, Ministerio de Agricultura y Ganadería, Sabana Sur, antiguo Colegio La Salle, San José, Costa Rica, phone: (506) 2231–1023 fax: (506) 2231–0145 e-mail: viceministra-xchaves@mag.go.cr

Ecuador:

Ing. Luís Torres Navarrete, Subsecretaría de Recursos Pesqueros, Víctor Manuel Rendón 1006 y Lorenzo de Garaicoa, Guayaquil, Guayas, Ecuador, phone (593–4) 256–0993 (593–4) 256–4300 ext. 103, fax (593–4) 230–0636; e-mail: luis.torres@pesca.gov.ec, probecuador@gye.satnet.net.

Jimmy Martínez, Ministerio de Agricultura Ganadería, Acuacultura y Pesca, Av. 3 y Calle12, Manta, Manabí, Ecuador, phone (593–5) 262–7930; e-mail: jimmy.martinez@pesca.gob.ec

Guillermo Morán, Ministerio de Agricultura, Ganadería, Acuacultura y Pesca, Av. Fco. De Orellana, Ed. Ministerio del Litoral, Piso 12 Guayaquil, Ecuador, phone: (593–4) 268–1005; e-mail: viceministroap@magap.gob.ec.

Ramón Montaño Cruz, Subsecretaría de Recursos Pesqueros, Av. 3 y Calle 12 Manta Ecuador, phone (593–5) 262–7930, fax (593–5) 262–7911; e-mail: rmontano@pesca.gov.ec.

El Salvador:

Gustavo Antonio Portillo, CENDEPESCA, Final 1a. Avenida Norte y Avenida Manuel Gallardo, Santa Tecla. El Salvador, phone (503) 2534–9882, (503) 7820–4560, fax (503) 2534–9885; e-mail: gustavo.portillo@mag.gob.sv.

Hugo Alexander Flores, Ministerio De Agricultura y Ganadería Final 1a. Av. Norte y Av. Manuel Gallardo, Santa Tecla El Salvador.

Manuel Calvo García-Benavides, Calvopesca / Grupo Calvo, Plaza de Carlos Trías Bertrán, no. 7, 6a. Planta, Madrid, 28020, Spain, phone (34–91) 782–3300, fax (34–91) 561–5304; e-mail: mane.calvo@calvo.es.

Salvador Cokkom Siu Navarro DGPA (CENDEPESCA)-MAG, Final 1a. Ave. Norte y Ave. Manuel Gallardo, Santa Tecla La Libertad, El Salvador, phone (503) 2534–9880, fax (503) 2534–9885; e-mail: salvador.siu@mag.gob.sv.

European Union:

Angela Martini, European Commission, Rue Joseph II, 99, Brussels, 1049, Belgium, phone (32–2) 299–4276, fax (32–2) 299–5570; e-mail: Angela.MARTINI@ec.europa.eu.

Luis Molledo, European Commission, Rue Joseph II, 99, Brussels, 1049, Belgium, phone (32–2) 299–4276, fax (32–2) 299–5570; e-mail: luis.molledo@ec.europa.eu.

France:

Christiane Laurent-Monpetit, Ministere de l'Intérieur, de l'Outre-Mer et des Collectivites T., 27, rue Oudinot, Paris, 75358 F SPO7, France, phone (33–1) 5369–2466, fax (33–1) 5369–2065; e-mail: christiane.laurent-monpetit@outre-mer.gouv.fr.

Thomas Roche, Ministry of Ecology, Sustainable Development and Energy, Secretariat d'Etat a la Mer, 3 Place Fontenoy, Paris, 75700, France, phone (33–1) 4081–9120, fax (33–1) 4955–8200; e-mail: thomas.roche@developpement-durable.gouv.fr.

Marie-Sophie Dufau-Richet, Secretariat d'Etat a la Mer, 16 Boulevard Raspail, Paris, 75700, France, phone (33–1) 5363–4153, fax (33–1) 5363–4178; e-mail: Amarie.sophie.dufau-richet@pm.gouv.fr.

Michel Sallenave, Haut Commissariat de la République Française en Polynésie, 43 Avenue Bruat. BP 115, Papeete, 98713, French Polynesia, phone (689) 468–517, fax (689) 468–600; e-mail: michel.sallenave@polynesie-francaise.pref.gouv.fr.

Guatemala:

Jose Sebastian Marcucci, Ministerio de Agricultura, Ganadería y Alimentación, Km. 22 Carretera al Pacífico, Ed.La Ceiba, 3er. Nivel. Guatemala, Guatemala, phone (502) 6640–9320, fax (502) 2413–7035; e-mail:

William René Méndez, Ministerio de Agricultura, Ganadería y Alimentación, 3er. Nivel. Edificio la Ceiba, Carretera al Pacífico, Km. 22 B. Villanueva Guatemala, phone (502) 6640–9320 (502) 6640–9334, fax (502) 6640–9321; e-mail: wrmyjamp@hotmail.com.

Carlos F. Marín, Ministerio de Agricultura, Ganadería y Alimentación, Km. 22 Carretera al Pacífico, Edif. La Ceiba, 3er. Nivel, Villa Nueva, Guatemala, phone (502) 6640–9320, fax (502) 6640–9321; e-mail: cfmarin1058@gmail.com.

Lic. Bryslie Siomara Cifuentes Velasco, Ministerio de Agricultura, Ganadería y Alimentación, Km. 22 Carretera al Pacífico, Edificio La Ceiba, 3er. Nivel, Guatemala, Guatemala, phone (502) 6640–9320, fax (502) 6640–9321; e-mail: brysliec@hotmail.com, bcifuentes@maga.gob.gt.

Japan:

Masahiro Ishikawa, Federation of Japan Tuna Fisheries Cooperative Associations, 2–3–22 Kudankita Chiyoda-Ku, Tokyo, Japan, phone (81–3) 3264–6167 (81–3) 3264–6161, fax (81–3) 3234–7455; e-mail: section1@intldiv.japantuna.or.jp.

Kengo Tanaka, Fisheries Agency of Japan, 1–2–1 Kasumigaseki, Chiyoda-ku, Chiyoda-Ku, Tokyo, 100–8907, Japan, phone (81–3) 3502–8204, fax (81–3) 3502–0571; e-mail: kengo_tanaka@nm.maff.go.jp

Akima Umezawa, Ministry of Foreign Affairs, 2–2–1 Kasumigaseki, Tokyo, 100–8919, Japan, phone (81–3) 5501–8000, fax (81–3) 5501–8332; e-mail: akima.umezawa@mofa.go.jp.

Kiribati: (Contacts, not appointed Commissioners)

Raikaon Tumoa, Ministry of Fisheries and Marine Resources Development, P.O. Box 64 Bairiki, Tarawa, Kiribati, phone: (686) 28061. Fax: (686) 28295 e-mail: raikaont@mfmrd.gov.ki.

Elliot Ali, Ministry of Fisheries and Marine Resources Development, P.O. Box 64 Bairiki, Tarawa, Kiribati, phone: (686) 28061. Fax: (686) 28295 e-mail: elliota@mfmrd.gov.ki.

Aketa Tanga, Ministry of Fisheries and Marine Resources Development, P.O. Box 64 Bairiki, Tarawa, Kiribati, phone: (686) 28061. Fax: (686) 28295 e-mail: aketat@mfmrd.gov.ki.

Korea:

Dr. Il Jeong Jeong, Ministry of Food, Agriculture, Forestry and Fisheries, 88, Gwanmun-do, Gwacheon-si, Gyeonggi-do, 427–719, Republic of Korea, phone (82–2) 500–2422, fax (82–2) 503–9174; e-mail: ijeong@korea.kr, icdmomaf@chol.com.

Jongwha Bang, Ministry of Oceans and Fisheries, Government Complex Bldg., #2, Gwacheon, Gyeonggi-do, 427–719 Republic of Korea, phone (82–2) 500–2414, fax (82–2) 503–9174; e-mail: bjh125@Korea.kr,

Jeongseok Park, Ministry of Food, Agriculture, Forestry and Fisheries, Government Complex Gwacheon, Jungang-dong 1, Gwacheon, Gyeonggi-do, Republic of Korea, phone (82–2) 500–2426, fax (82–2) 503–9174; e-mail: jspark2@mifaff.go.kr.

México:

Mario Aguilar, CONAPESCA / Comisión Nacional de Pesca y Acuacultura Av. Camarón Sábalo S/N, 6to. Piso, Mazatlán, Sin 82100, México, phone (52–669) 915–6900, fax (52–669) 915–6904; e-mail: mario.aguilar@conapesca.gob.mx.

Carlos Gabriel Enriquez, CONAPESCA / Comisión Nacional de Acuicultura y Pesca, Av. Camarón Sábalo S/N, 6to. Piso, Mazatlán, Sin 82100, México, phone (52–669) 915–6900, fax (52–669) 915–6904; e-mail: carlos.enriquez@conapesca.gob.mx.

Michel Dreyfus, Instituto Nacional de la Pesca, Km 97.5 carretera Tijuana-Ensenada Ensenada, B.C. 22890, México, phone (52–646) 174–6085, fax (52–646) 174–6135; e-mail: dreyfus@cicese.mx.

Raúl Romo Trujillo, Instituto Nacional de la Pesca, Pitágoras #1320, Piso 8vo. Col. Sta Cruz Atoyac, México, D.F. 03310 México, phone (52–55) 3781–9501 (52–55) 3871–9502, fax (52–55) 3626–8421; e-mail: raul.romo@inapesca.sagarpa.gob.mx.

Nicaragua:

Armando Segura, Cámara de la Pesca de Nicaragua / CAPENIC, Av. 27 de Mayo, Managua, Nicaragua, phone (505) 2266–6704, fax (505) 2222–5818; e-mail: capenic@ibw.com.ni.

Danilo Rosales Pichardo, INPESCA / Instituto Nicaragüense de la Pesca y Acuicultura, Del Busto José Martí 5c al Este barrio Largaespada, Managua, Nicaragua, phone (505) 2251–0487, fax (505) 2248–7149; e-mail: drosales@inpesca.gob.ni.

Julio César Guevara Q, INATUN / Industrial Atunera de Nicaragua, Balboa Ancón, Panamá City, 0843–02264, Panamá, phone (507) 6400 3849, fax (507) 204–4651; e-mail: juliocgq@gmail.com, cpesca@g-elysium.com.

Steadman Fagoth, INPESCA / Instituto Nicaragüense de la Pesca y Acuicultura, Del Busto Jose Marti, 5 cuadras al Este, Bo. Largaespada Managua, Nicaragua, phone (505) 248–7149 (505) 248–7851 ext. 109; e-mail: cpaiz@inpesca.gob.ni, sfagoth@mific.gob.ni.

Panamá:

Giovanni Lauri, ARAP / Autoridad de los Recursos Acuáticos de Panamá, Altos de Curundu, C. Manuel Melo, Edificio 571 Panamá City 0819–05850, Panamá, phone (507) 511–6015 (507) 511–6000 ext. 304 / 303, fax (507) 511–6071; e-mail: glauri@arap.gob.pa, giovanni.lauri@gmail.com.

Raúl Delgado, ARAP / Autoridad de los Recursos Acuáticos de Panamá Edif. El Paso Elevado, frente a la intersección de Vía Transístmica, Panamá City, Panamá, phone (507) 511–6057, fax (507) 511–6013; e-mail: rdelgado@arap.gob.pa.

Perú:

Luis R. Arribasplata Campos, Ministerio de Relaciones Exteriores, Jr. Lampa 545, Cercado de Lima, Perú, phone (51–1) 204–2400; e-mail: larribasplata@rree.gob.pe.

Gladys Cárdenas, Instituto del Mar del Perú, Esquina de Gamarra y General Valle s/n Chucuito-Callao Lima, Perú, phone (51–1) 420–0144 (51–1) 4297–630, fax (51–1) 420–0144; e-mail: gcardenas@imarpe.gob.pe.

Ernesto Enrique Peña Haro Calderón, Ministerio de Producción (Pesquería), Calle 1 Oeste #60, Urb. Córpac, San Isidro, Lima 27, Perú, phone (51–1) 224–3423, fax (51–1) 224–2381; e-mail: epena@produce.gob.pe

Taipei China:

Chung-Hai Kwoh, Fisheries Agency, Council of Agriculture, No. 2 Chaochow Street, Taipei, 100, Taiwan, phone (886–2) 3343–6114, fax (886–2) 3343–6268; e-mail: chunghai@fa.gov.tw, chunghai@ms1.fa.gov.tw.

Hong-Yen Huang, Fisheries Agency, No. 1 Fishing Harbor North 1st. Rd., Kaohsiung, Taiwan, 80672, Taiwan, phone (886–7) 823–9828, fax (886–7) 815 8278; e-mail: hangyen@ms1.fa.gov.tw, chiennan@ms1.fa.gov.tw.

Ding-Rong Lin, Fisheries Agency, Department of Deep Sea Fisheries, Council of Agriculture, Executive Yuan, No. 2, Chao-Chow Street, Taipei 100, Taiwan, phone: (886–2) 3343–6126. Fax: (886–2) 3343–6128, e-mail: dingrong@ms1.fa.gov.tw.

Ted Tien-Hsiang Tsai, Fisheries Agency, International Fisheries Affairs, Deep Sea Fisheries Division, No. 2 Chao-Chow St, Taipei, Taiwan, phone: (886–2) 3343–6045, fax: (886–2) 3343–6128, e-mail: ted@ms1.fa.gov.tw.

USA:

Donald Hansen, Pacific Fishery Management Council, 79 Marbell, San Clemente, CA 92673, USA, phone (949) 240–8892; e-mail: don@danawharfsportfishing.com.

Ed Stockwell, U.S. Commissioner-IATTC, 14 Fescue Ct., Florence, KY 41042, USA, phone (859) 384–4720, fax (859) 384–7433; e-mail: ed.stockwell@insigntbb.com, kittyfescue@prodigy.net.

Rodney McInnis, NOAA/National Marine Fisheries Service, 501 West Ocean Blvd., Suite 4200, Long Beach, CA 90802–4213, USA, phone (562) 980–4005, fax (562) 980–4018; e-mail: rod.mcinnis@noaa.gov, miki.hirano@noaa.gov.

William Fox, U.S. Commissioner, P.O. Box 60633, San Diego, CA 92166, USA, phone (202) 495–4397, fax (619) 222–2489; e-mail: bill.fox@wwfus.org.

Vanuatu:

Christophe Emelee, Vanuatu Government Agent, P.O. Box 1640, Club Hippique Vanuatu, Port Vila, Sheffa 1640, Vanuatu, phone (678) 774–0219, fax (678) 29012; e-mail: tunafishing@vanuatu.com.vu.

Dimitri Malvirlani, Vanuatu IATTC Commissioner, Marine Quay, P.O. Box 320, Port-Vila, Vanuatu, phone (678) 23128, fax (678) 22949; e-mail: vma@vanuatu.com.vn.

Laurent Parente, Vanuatu IATTC Commissioner, P.O. Box 1435, Port Vila Vanuatu, phone (336) 9951–1207; e-mail: laurentparente-vanuatu-imo@hotmail.com.

Roy M. Joy, Embassy of Vanuatu, Avenue de Tervueren 380 Chemin de Ronde, Brussels 1150, Belgium, phone (32–2) 771–7494, fax (32–2) 771–7494; e-mail: rjoy@vanuatuembassy.net, joyroymickey@gmail.com.

Venezuela:

Alvin Delgado Martínez, FUNDATUN–PNOV, Av. Ppal. EL dique Edf. San Pablo, PH Cumaná, Sucre, 6101, Venezuela, phone (58–293) 433–0431, fax (58–293) 433–0431; e-mail: adelgadopnov@cantv.net, fundatunpnov@yahoo.com.

Yenry Alberto Urrea Márquez, INSOPESCA/Instituto Socialista de la Pesca y Acuacultura Av. Principal El Bosque, entre Avds. Sta. Isabel y Sta. Lucía, Torre Credicard, piso 9, Caracas, Venezuela, phone (58–212) 461–9225 (58–212) 509–0384, fax (58–212) 574 3587; e-mail: ori@insopesca.gob.ve, presidencia@inapesca.gob.ve.

Nancy Tablante, INSOPESCA/Instituto Socialista de la Pesca y Acuicultura, Av. Principal El Bosque, entre Avds. Sta. Isabel y Sta. Lucía, Torre Credicard, piso 9, Caracas, DC Venezuela, phone (58–212) 953–9972, fax (58–212) 952–0707; e-mail: ntablante@hotmail.com.

INTERNATIONAL BOUNDARY AND WATER COMMISSION, UNITED STATES AND MEXICO

UNITED STATES SECTION

The Commons, Building C, Suite 100, 4171 North Mesa, El Paso, TX 79902–1441

phone (915) 832–4100, fax 832–4190, http://www.ibwc.gov

Commissioner.—Edward Drusina, 832–4101.
Foreign Affairs Secretary.—Sally Spencer, 832–4105.
Principal Engineers: John Merino, 832–4749; Carlos Peña, 832–4160.
Human Resources Director.—Vacant, 832–4114.
General Counsel/Legal Advisor.—Luisa Alvarez, 832–4791.

MEXICAN SECTION

Avenida Universidad, No. 2180, Zona de El Chamizal, A.P. 1612–D, C.P. 32310,

Ciudad Juarez, Chihuahua, Mexico

P.O. Box 10525, El Paso, TX 79995

phone 011–52–16–13–7311 or 011–52–16–13–7363 (Mexico)

Commissioner.—Roberto F. Salmon Castello.
Foreign Affairs Secretary.—Jose de Jesus Luevano Grano.
Principal Engineers: Gilberto Elizalde Hernandez, L. Antonio Rascon Mendoza.

INTERNATIONAL BOUNDARY COMMISSION, UNITED STATES AND CANADA

UNITED STATES SECTION

2000 L Street, NW., Suite 615, 20036, phone (202) 736–9100

Commissioner.—Kyle Hipsley (acting).
Deputy Commissioner.—Kyle Hipsley.
Administrative Officer.—Tracy Morris.

CANADIAN SECTION

615 Booth Street, Room 555, Ottawa, ON, Canada K1A 0E9, phone (613) 944–4515

Commissioner.—Peter Sullivan.
Deputy Commissioner.—Daniel Fortin.

INTERNATIONAL COTTON ADVISORY COMMITTEE

Headquarters: 1629 K Street, NW., Suite 702, 20006, secretariat@icac.org
phone (202) 463–6660, fax 463–6950

(Permanent Secretariat of the Organization)

MEMBER COUNTRIES

Argentina
Australia
Belgium
Brazil
Burkina Faso
Cameroon
Chad
China (Taiwan)
Colombia
Côte d'Ivoire
Egypt
France
Germany
Greece
India
Iran
Italy
Kazakhstan
Kenya
Korea, Republic of
Mali
Mozambique
Nigeria
Pakistan
Peru
Poland
Russia
South Africa
Spain
Sudan
Switzerland
Tanzania
Togo
Turkey
Uganda
United States
Uzbekistan
Zambia
Zimbabwe

Executive Director.—Terry P. Townsend.
Statistician.—Caterina Au.
Director of Trade Analysis: Andrei Guitchounts.
Senior Economist: Alejandro Plastina.
Head of Technical Information Section.—M. Rafiq Chaudhry.

INTERNATIONAL JOINT COMMISSION, UNITED STATES AND CANADA

UNITED STATES SECTION

2000 L Street, NW., Suite 615, 20036

phone (202) 736–9000, fax 632–2006, http://www.ijc.org

Chair.—Lana B. Pollack.
Commissioners: Dereth Glance, Richard Moy.
Secretary.—Charles A. Lawson.
Legal Advisor.—Susan Daniel.
Engineering Advisor.—Mark Colosimo.
Public Information Officer.—Frank Bevacqua.
Ecologist.—Victor Serveiss.
GIS Coordinator.—Michael Laitta.
Policy Advisor.—David Dempsey.

Senior Advisor.—Joseph Babb.

CANADIAN SECTION

234 Laurier Avenue West, Ottawa, Ontario Canada K1P 6K6
phone (613) 995–2984, fax 993–5583

Chairman.—Hon. Joe Comuzzi.
Commissioners: Benoit Bouchard, Gordon Walker.
Secretary.—Camille Mageau.
Legal Advisor.—Gavin Murphy.
Public Affairs Adviser.—Bernard Beckhoff.
Engineering Advisers: Jean-Francois Cantin, David Fay.
Senior Adviser.—Nick Heisler.
Senior Science Adviser.—Ted Yuzyk.

GREAT LAKES REGIONAL OFFICE

Eighth Floor, 100 Ouellette Avenue, Windsor, Ontario Canada N9A 6T3
phone (519) 257–6700 (Canada), (313) 226–2170 (U.S.)

Director.—Stephen Locke.
Public Affairs Officer.—John Nevin.
Physical Scientists: Antonette Arvai, Raj Bejankiwar, Jennifer Boehme, Mark Burrows, Matthew Child, Lizhu Wang, John E. Wilson.

INTERNATIONAL LABOR ORGANIZATION

Headquarters: 4, route des Morillons, CH-1211, Geneva 22, Switzerland

phone 41–22–799–6111, http://www.ilo.org

Washington Office, 1808 I Street, NW., Suite 900, 20006

phone (202) 617–3952, fax 617–3960, http://www.ilo.org/washington

Liaison Office with the United Nations

One Dag Hammarskjöld Plaza, 885 Second Avenue, 30th Floor, New York, NY 10017

phone (212) 697–0150, fax 697–5218, http://www.ilo.org/newyork

International Labor Office (Permanent Secretariat of the Organization)
Headquarters Geneva:
Director-General.—Guy Ryder.
Washington:
Director.—Nancy Donaldson.
Deputy Director.—Erick Zeballos.
New York:
Director.—Telma Viale.
Deputy Director.—Vinicius Pinheiro.

INTERNATIONAL MONETARY FUND

700 19th Street, NW., 20431, phone (202) 623–7000

http://www.imf.org

MANAGEMENT AND SENIOR OFFICERS

Managing Director.—Christine Lagarde.
First Deputy Managing Director.—David Lipton.
Deputy Managing Directors: Naoyuki Shinohara, Nemat Shafik, Min Zhu.
Economic Counselor.—Olivier Blanchard.
Financial Counselor.—Jose Vinals.

Institute for Capacity Development Director.—Sharmini A. Coorey.
Legal Department General Counsel.—Sean Hagan.
Departmental Directors:
African.—Antoinette Monsio Sayeh.
Asia and Pacific.—Anoop Singh.
Budget and Planning.—Daniel Citrin.
European.—Reza Moghadam.
Communications.—Gerard T. Rice.
Finance.—Andrew Tweedie.
Fiscal Affairs.—Carlo Cottarelli.
Internal Audit and Inspection.—G. Russell Kincaid.
Middle East and Central Asia.—Masood Ahmed.
Monetary and Capital Markets.—Jose Vinals.
Strategy, Policy, and Review.—Siddharth Tiwari.
Research.—Olivier Blanchard.
Secretary.—Jianhai Lin.
Statistics.—Louis Marc Ducharme.
Technology and General Services.—Frank Harnischfeger.
Western Hemisphere.—Alejandro Werner.
Director, Regional Office for Asia and the Pacific.—Odd Per Brekk.
Director, Europe Offices.—Emmanuel van der Meensbrugghe.
Director and Special Representative to the United Nations.—Axel Albert Emil Bertuch-Samuels.
Independent Evaluations Office.—Moises J. Schwartz.

EXECUTIVE DIRECTORS AND ALTERNATES

Executive Directors:
Ahmed Abdulkarim Alkholifey, represents Saudi Arabia.
Herve M. Jodon de Villeroche, represents France.
Audun Groenn, represents Denmark, Estonia, Finland, Iceland, Latvia, Lithuania, Norway, Sweden.
Paulo Nogueira Batista Jr., represents Brazil, Cape Verde, Dominican Republic, Ecuador, Guyana, Haiti, Nicaragua, Panama, Suriname, Timor-Leste, Trinidad and Tobago.
Thomas Hockin, represents Antigua and Barbuda, the Bahamas, Barbados, Belize, Canada, Dominica, Grenada, Ireland, Jamaica, St. Kitts and Nevis, St. Lucia, St. Vincent and the Grenadines.
Moeketsi Majoro, represents Angola, Botswana, Burundi, Eritrea, Ethiopia, Gambia, Kenya, Lesotho, Malawi, Mozambique, Namibia, Nigeria, Sierra Leone, South Africa, Sudan, Swaziland, Tanzania, Uganda, Zambia, Zimbabwe.
Rakesh Mohan, represents Bangladesh, Bhutan, India, Sri Lanka.
Wimboh Santoso, represents Brunei Darussalam, Cambodia, Fiji, Indonesia, Lao People's Democratic Republic, Malaysia, Myanmar, Nepal, Singapore, Thailand, Tonga, Vietnam.
Daniel Heller, represents Azerbaijan, Kyrgyz Republic, Poland, Switzerland, Tajikistan, Turkmenistan, Uzbekistan, Serbia.
Jose Rojas, represents Colombia, Costa Rica, El Salvador, Guatemala, Honduras, Mexico, Spain, Venezuela (Republica Bolivariana de).
Johann Prader, represents Austria, Belarus, Belgium, Czech Republic, Hungary, Kazakhstan, Luxembourg, Slovak Republic, Slovenia, Turkey.
Kossi Assimaidou, represents Benin, Burkina Faso, Cameroon, Cape Verde, Central African Republic, Chad, Comoros, Congo (Democratic Republic of), Congo (Republic of), Côte d'Ivoire, Djibouti, Equatorial Guinea, Gabon, Guinea, Guinea-Bissau, Madagascar, Mali, Mauritania, Mauritius, Niger, Rwanda, São Tomé and Principe, Senegal, Togo.
Arrigo Sadun, represents Albania, Greece, Italy, Malta, Portugal, San Marino.
Meg Lundsager, represents United States.
Daikichi Momma, represents Japan.
Jafar Mojarrad, represents Afghanistan (Islamic Republic of), Algeria, Ghana, Iran (Islamic Republic of), Morocco, Pakistan, Tunisia.
Pablo Garcia-Silva, represents Argentina, Bolivia, Chile, Paraguay, Peru, Uruguay.
Hubert Temmeyer, represents Germany.
A. Shakour Shaalan, represents Bahrain, Egypt, Iraq, Jordan, Kuwait, Lebanon, Libya Arab, Jamahiriya, Maldives, Oman, Qatar, Syrian Arab Republic, United Arab Emirates, Yemen (Republic of).
Aleksei V. Mozhin, represents Russian Federation.
Jong-Won Yoon, represents Australia, Kiribati, Korea, Marshall Islands, Micronesia (Federated States of), Mongolia, New Zealand, Palau, Papua New Guinea, Philippines, Samoa, Seychelles, Solomon Islands, Vanuatu.

Menno Snel, represents Armenia, Bosnia and Herzegovina, Bulgaria, Croatia, Cyprus, Georgia, Israel, Macedonia (former Yugoslav Republic of), Moldova, Montenegro Republic, Netherlands, Romania, Ukraine.
Tao Zhang, represents China.
Steve Field, represents United Kingdom.

INTERNATIONAL ORGANIZATION FOR MIGRATION

Headquarters: 17 Route Des Morillons (P.O. Box 71), CH1211

Geneva 19, Switzerland, phone +41.22.798.61.50

Washington Mission: 1752 N Street, NW., Suite 700, 20036, phone (202) 862–1826

New York Mission: 122 East 42nd Street, 48th Floor

New York, NY 10168–1610, phone (212) 681–7000

HEADQUARTERS

Director General.—William Lacy Swing (United States).
Deputy Director General.—Laura Thompson (Costa Rica).
Washington Chief of Mission.—Luca Dalloglio (Italy).
New York Chief of Mission.—Michel Tonneau (Belgian).
Permanent Observer to the United Nations.—Michele Klein Solomon (United States).

MEMBER STATES

Afghanistan
Albania
Algeria
Angola
Antigua and Barbuda
Argentina
Armenia
Australia
Austria
Azerbaijan
Bahamas
Bangladesh
Belarus
Belgium
Belize
Benin
Bolivia (Plurinational State of)
Bosnia and Herzegovina
Botswana
Brazil
Bulgaria
Burkina Faso
Burundi
Cambodia
Cameroon
Canada
Cape Verde
Central African Republic
Chile
Colombia
Congo
Costa Rica
Côte d'Ivoire
Croatia
Cyprus
Czech Republic
Democratic Republic of the Congo
Denmark
Djibouti
Dominican Republic
Ecuador
Egypt
El Salvador
Estonia
Ethiopia
Finland
France
Gabon
Gambia
Georgia
Germany
Ghana
Greece
Guatemala
Guinea
Guinea-Bissau
Guyana
Haiti
Holy See
Honduras
Hungary
India
Iran, Islamic Republic of
Ireland
Israel
Italy
Jamaica
Japan
Jordan
Kazakhstan
Kenya
Kyrgyzstan
Latvia
Lesoto
Liberia
Libya
Lithuania
Luxembourg
Madagascar
Malawi
Maldives
Mali
Malta
Mauritania
Mauritius
Mexico
Micronesia
Mongolia
Montenegro
Morocco
Mozambique
Myanmar
Namibia
Nauru
Nepal
Netherlands
New Zealand
Nicaragua
Nigeria
Niger
Norway
Pakistan
Panama
Papua New Guinea
Paraguay
Peru
Philippines
Poland
Portugal
Republic of Korea
Republic of Moldova
Romania
Rwanda

Saint Vincent and the Grenadines
Senegal
Serbia
Seychelles
Sierra Leone
Slovakia
Slovenia
Somalia
South Africa
South Sudan
Spain
Sri Lanka
Sudan
Suriname
Swaziland
Sweden
Switzerland
Tajikistan
Thailand
Timor-Leste
Togo
Trinidad and Tobago
Tunisia
Turkey
Uganda
Ukraine
United Kingdom of Great Britain and Northern Ireland
United Republic of Tanzania
United States of America
Uruguay
Vanuatu
Venezuela, Bolivarian Republic of
Vietnam
Yemen
Zambia
Zimbabwe

STATES WITH OBSERVER STATUS

Bahrain
Bhutan
China
Cuba
Indonesia
Qatar
Russian Federation
San Marino
Sao Tomé and Principe
Saudi Arabia
The former Yugoslav Republic of Macedonia
Turkmenistan

IOM OVERSEAS LIAISON AND OPERATIONAL OFFICES

Afghanistan, Herat, Kabul
Albania, Tirana
Angola, Luanda
Argentina, Buenos Aires *
Armenia, Yerevan
Australia, Canberra *
Austria, Wien *
Azerbaijan, Baku
Bahrain, Manama
Bangladesh, Dhaka *
Belarus, Minsk
Belgium / Luxembourg, Bruxelles *
Bolivia, La Paz
Bosnia and Herzegovina, Sarajevo
Bulgaria, Sofia
Burkina Faso, Ouagadougou
Burundi, Bujumbura
Cambodia, Phnom Penh
Cameroun, Yaoundé
Canada, Ottawa, Toronto
Cape Verde, Praia
Chad, N'Djamena, Abeche
Chile, Santiago de Chile
China, Hong Kong
Colombia, Santafé de Bogotá
Congo, (Republic of the) Brazzaville
Congo, (Democratic Republic of), Kinshasa, Bukavu, Bunia, Goma, Kamako, Kananga, Kasindi, Kimpese, Kisangani, Yema
Costa Rica, San José *
Cote D'Ivoire, Abidjan
Croatia, Zagreb
Czech Republic, Praha
Dominican Republic, Santo Domingo
Denmark, Copenhagen
Djibouti, Djibouti
Ecuador, Quito
Egypt, Cairo *
El Salvador, San Salvador
Estonia, Tallinn
Ethiopia, Addis Ababa
Finland, Helsinki *
France, Paris
Gambia, Banjul
Georgia, Tbilisi
Germany, Berlin, Nuremberg
Ghana, Accra North
Greece, Athens
Guatemala, Ciudad de Guatemala
Guinea, Conakry, N'Zerekore
Guyana, Georgetown
Haiti, Port au Prince, Cap-Haitien, Gonaives, Jacmel
Honduras, Tegucigalpa
Hungary, Budapest *
India, Hyderabad
Indonesia, Jakarta, Banda Aceh, Mataram Kupang, Situbondo, Yogkakarta, Nias
Iran, Tehran
Iraq, Baghdad, Basrah, Erbil
Ireland, Dublin
Italy, Roma *
Jamaica, Kingston
Japan, Tokyo
Jordan, Amman
Kazakhstan, Almaty
Kenya, Nairobi *
Kosovo, Pristina, Gjilan, Mitrovica, Peje,
Kuwait, Kuwait City
Kyrgyzstan, Bishkek City
Laos, Vientiane
Latvia, Riga
Lebanon, Beirut
Liberia, Monrovia
Libya, Tripoli
Lithuania, Vilnius
Macedonia, Skopje
Malaysia, Kuala Lumpur
Maldives, Male
Mali, Bamako
Malta, Valletta
Marshall Islands, Majuro
Mauritania, Nouakchott
Mauritius, Port Louis
Mexico, Mexico DF
Moldova, (Republic of) Chisinau
Montenegro, Podgorica
Morocco, Rabat
Mozambique, Maputo
Myanmar, Yangon
Nauru (Republic of), Central Pacific
Nepal, Kathmandu
Netherlands, Den Haag
Nicaragua, Managua
Niger, Niamey
Nigeria, Abuja
Norway, Oslo
Pakistan, Islamabad *
Panama, Panama
Papua New Guinea, Port Moresby
Paraguay, Asuncion
Peru, Lima *
Philippines, Metro Manila *

Poland, Warszawa
Portugal, Lisboa
Romania, Bucharest
Russian Federation, Moscow
Rwanda, Kigali
Saudi Arabia, Riyadh
Senegal, Dakar *
Serbia, Belgrade
Sierra Leone, Freetown
Slovak Republic, Bratislava
Slovenia, Ljubljana
Solomon Islands, Honiara
Somalia, Somaliland
South Africa, Pretoria *
South Korea, Seoul
South Sudan, Juba, Aweil, Bentiu, Damazin,
Spain, Madrid
Sri Lanka, Colombo
Sudan, Khartoum
Switzerland, Geneva
Syria, Damascus
Tajikistan, Dushanbe
Tanzania, Dar es Salaam
Thailand, Bangkok *
Timor Leste, Dili
Togo, Lome
Trinidad and Tobago, Port of Spain
Tunisia, Tunis
Turkey, Ankara
Turkmenistan, Ashgabad
Uganda, Kampala
Ukraine, Kyiv
United Kingdom, London
United States of America, Washington *, New York *, Los Angeles, Miami,
Uruguay, Montevideo
Uzbekistan, Tashkent
Venezuela, Caracas
Vietnam, Hanoi, Ho Chi Minh City
Yemen, Yemen
Zambia, Lusaka
Zimbabwe, Harare

INTERNATIONAL PACIFIC HALIBUT COMMISSION
UNITED STATES AND CANADA

Headquarters/Mailing address: 2320 West Commodore Way, Suite 300, Seattle, WA 98199–1287

phone (206) 634–1838, fax 632–2983

American Commissioners:
Dr. Jim Balsiger, National Marine Fisheries Service, P.O. Box 21668, Juneau, AK 99802, (907) 586–7221, fax 586–7249.
Ralph G. Hoard, 1444 Madrona Drive, P.O. Box 79003, Seattle, WA 98122–3518.
Phillip Lestenkof, P.O. Box 288, St. Paul Island, AK 99660, (907) 546–2597.

Canadian Commissioners:
David Boyes, 499 Powerhouse Rd., Courtenay, BC, Canada V9N9L1 (250) 388–2188.
Michael Pearson, 200 Kent Street, Rm W088, Ottawa Ontario, Canada K1A0E6, (613) 990–9574
Paul Ryall, Suite 200, 401 Burrard St., Vancouver, BC, Canada V6C3S4 (604) 666–0115.

Director and Secretary (ex officio).—Dr. Bruce M. Leaman, 2320 West Commodore Way, Suite 300, Seattle, WA 98199–1287.

ORGANIZATION OF AMERICAN STATES

17th Street and Constitution Avenue, NW., 20006
phone (202) 458–3000, fax 458–3967

PERMANENT MISSIONS TO THE OAS

Antigua and Barbuda.—Ambassador Deborah Mae-Lovell, Permanent Representative, 3216 New Mexico Avenue, NW., 20016, phone 362–5122 / 5166 / 5211, fax 362–5225.

Argentina.—Ambassador Nilda Garre, Permanent Representative, 1816 Corcoran Street, NW., 20009, phone 387–4142 / 4146 / 4170, fax 328–1591.

The Bahamas.—Ambassador Elliston Rahming, Permanent Representative, 2220 Massachusetts Avenue, NW., 20008, phone319–2660 to 2667, fax 319–2668.

Barbados.—Ambassador John E. Beale, Permanent Representative, 2144 Wyoming Avenue, NW., 20008, phone 939–9200 / 9201 / 9202, fax 332–7467.

Belize.—Ambassador Nestor Mendez, Permanent Representative, 2535 Massachusetts Avenue, NW., 20008–3098, phone 332–9636, ext. 228, fax 332–6888.

Bolivia.—Ambassador Diego Pary, Permanent Representative, 2728 34th Street, NW., 20008, phone 785–0218 / 0219 / 0224, fax 296–0563.

Brazil.—Breno Dias Da Costa, Interim Representative, 2600 Virginia Avenue, NW., Suite 412, 20037, phone 333–4224 / 4225/4226, fax 333–6610.

Canada.—Ambassador Allan Culham, Permanent Representative, 501 Pennsylvania Avenue, NW., 20001, phone 682–1768, Ext. 7724, fax 682–7624.

---

* Mission with Regional Functions.

Chile.—Ambassador Dario Paya, Permanent Representative, 2000 L Street, NW., Suite 440, 20036, phone 887–5475 / 5476 / 5477, fax 775–0713.

Colombia.—Ambassador Andres Gonzalez Diaz, Permanent Representative, 1609 22nd Street, NW., 20008, phone 332–8003 / 8004, fax 234–9781.

Costa Rica.—Ambassador Edgar Ugalde, Permanent Representative, 2112 S Street, NW., Suite 300, 20008, phone 234–9280 / 9281, fax 986–2274.

Dominica.—Ambassador Hubert J. Charles, Permanent Representative, 3216 New Mexico Avenue, NW., 20016, phone 364–6781, fax 364–6791.

Dominican Republic.—Ambassador Pedro Verges, Permanent Representative, 1715 22nd Street, NW., 20008, phone 332–9142 / 0616 / 0772, fax 232–5038.

Ecuador.—Ambassador Fernando Suarez Moreno, Interim Representative, 2600 Virginia Ave., NW., Suite 212, 20037, phone 234–1494/1692 / 8053, fax 667–3482.

El Salvador.—Ambassador Joaquin Alexander Maza Martelli, Permanent Representative, 2308 California St., NW., 20008, phone 595–7546 / 7545, fax 232–4806.

Grenada.—Ambassador Angus Friday, Permanent Representative, 1701 New Hampshire Avenue, NW., 20009, phone 265–2561, fax 265–2468.

Guatemala.—Ambassador Jose Rodrigo Vielmann De Leon, Permanent Representative, 1507 22nd Street, NW., 20037, phone 833–4015 / 4016 / 4017, fax 833–4011.

Guyana.—Ambassador Bayney R. Karran, Permanent Representative, 2490 Tracy Place, NW., 20008, phone 265–6900 / 6901, fax 232–1297.

Haiti.—Ambassador Duly Brutus, Permanent Representative, 2311 Massachusetts Avenue, NW., 20008, phone 332–4090 / 4096, fax 518–8742.

Honduras.—Ambassador Leonidas Rosa Bautista, Permanent Representative, 3007 Tilden St., N.W., Suite 4M–400, 20008, phone 244–5430/5653 / 5260, no fax.

Jamaica.—Ambassador Stephen C. Vasciannie, Permanent Representative, 1520 New Hampshire Avenue, NW., 20036, phone 986–0121 / 0123 / 452–0660, fax 452–9395.

Mexico.—Ambassador Emilio Rabasa Gamboa, Permanent Representative, 2440 Massachusetts Avenue, NW., 20008, phone 332–3663 / 3664 / 3984, fax 234–0602.

Nicaragua.—Ambassador Denis Ronaldo Moncada Colindres, Permanent Representative, 1627 New Hampshire Avenue, NW., 20009, phone 332–1643 / 1644 / 939–6536, fax 745–0710.

Panama.—Ambassador Arturo Vallarino, Permanent Representative, 2201 Wisconsin Avenue, NW., Suite C–100, 20007, phone 965–4826 / 4819, fax 965–4836.

Paraguay.—Ambassador Elisa Ruiz Diaz Bareiro, Permanent Representative, 2022 Connecticut Avenue, NW., 20008, phone 232–8020 / 8021 / 8022, fax 244–3005.

Peru.—Ambassador Juan Federico Jimenez Mayor, Permanent Representative, 1901 Pennsylvania Avenue, NW., Suite 402, 20006, phone 232–2281/2282 / 1973, fax 466–3068.

Saint Kitts and Nevis.—Ambassador Jacinth Lorna Henry-Martin, Permanent Representative, 3216 New Mexico Avenue, NW., 20016, phone 686–2636, fax 686–5740.

Saint Lucia.—Ambassador Sonia Johnny, Permanent Representative, 3216 New Mexico Ave., NW., 20016, phone 364–6792 thru 6795, fax 364–6723.

Saint Vincent and The Grenadines.— Ambassador La Celia A. Prince, Permanent Representative, 3216 New Mexico Avenue, NW., 20016, phone 364–6730, fax 364–6736.

Suriname.—Ambassador Niermala Badrising, Permanent Representative, 3400 International Place, NW., Suite 4L, 20008, phone 629–4402/4401 / 4392, fax 629–4769.

Trinidad and Tobago.—Ambassador Neil Parsan, Permanent Representative, 1708 Massachusetts Avenue, NW., 20036–1903, phone 467–6490, fax 785–3130.

United States of America.—Ambassador Carmen Lomellin, Permanent Representative, WHA / USOAS Bureau of Western Hemisphere Affairs, Department of State, Room 5914, 20520–6258, phone 647–9376, fax 647–0911 / 6973.

Uruguay.—Ambassador Milton Romani, Permanent Representative, 1913 I (Eye) St., NW., 4th Floor, 20006, phone 223–1961, fax 223–1966.

Venezuela.—Ambassador Roy Chaderton Matos, Permanent Representative, 1099 30th Street, NW., Second Floor, 20007, phone 342–5837 / 5838 / 5839 / 5840 / 5841, fax 625–5657.

GENERAL SECRETARIAT

Secretary General.—Jose Miguel Insulza, 370–5000.

Chief of Staff to the Secretary General.—Ambassador Hugo De Zela, 370–0300.

Assistant Secretary General.—Albert R. Ramdin, 370–0261, fax 458–3011.

Chief of Staff to the Assistant Secretary General.—Carmen de la Pava, 370–0195.

Executive Secretary for—

Integral Development.—Sherry Tross, 370–9014.

Inter-American Commission on Human Rights.—Emilio Alvarez Icaza, 370–9000.

Secretary for—

Administration and Finance.—Gerald Anderson, 370–5401.

Multidimensional Security.—Adam Blackwell, 370–9959.
Political Affairs.—Kevin Casas Zamora, 370–9962.
External Relations.—Alfonso Quinonez, 370–0281.
Legal Services.—Jean Michel Arrighi, 370–0741.
Director for—
Summits Secretariat.—Alfonso Quinonez, 370–0281.
Press and Communications.—Patricia Esquenazi, 370–5437.

ORGANIZATION FOR ECONOMIC CO-OPERATION AND DEVELOPMENT

Headquarters: Paris, France, www.oecd.org

Washington Center, 2001 L Street, NW., Suite 650, 20036, phone (202) 785–6323, fax 785–0350,Washington.contact@oecd.org, www.oecd.org/washington

PARIS HEADQUARTERS

Secretary-General.—Angel Gurría.
Deputy Secretaries-General: William C. Danvers, Yves Leterme, Pier Carlo Padoan, Rintaro Tamaki.
Chief Economist.—Pier Carlo Padoan.

WASHINGTON CENTER

Head of Center.—Jill A. Schuker.
Member Countries:

Australia
Austria
Belgium
Canada
Chile
Czech Republic
Denmark
Estonia
Finland
France
Germany
Greece
Hungary
Iceland
Ireland
Israel
Italy
Japan
Korea
Luxembourg
Mexico
Netherlands
New Zealand
Norway
Poland
Portugal
Slovak Republic
Slovenia
Spain
Sweden
Switzerland
Turkey
United Kingdom
United States

OECD WASHINGTON CENTER

2001 L Street, NW., Suite 650, 20036, phone (202) 785–6323, fax 785–0350

http://www.oecd.org/washington

Head of Center.—Jill A. Schuker.

PAN AMERICAN HEALTH ORGANIZATION (PAHO)

REGIONAL OFFICE OF THE WORLD HEALTH ORGANIZATION

525 23rd Street, NW., 20037, phone (202) 974–3000

fax 974–3663

Director.—Dr. Carissa Etienne, 974–3408.
Deputy Director.—Dr. Jon Andrus, 974–3178.
Assistant Director..—Dr. Jose Romero Teruel, a.i., 974–3404.
Director of Administration.—Guillermo Birmingham, 974–3412.

PAHO / WHO FIELD OFFICES

OPS / WHO OFICINAS DE LOS REPRESENTANTES EN LOS PAISES

Barbados and Eastern Caribbean Countries (OECC serves the following countries, territories and departments: Antigua and Barbuda, Barbados, Dominica, Grenada, St. Kitts and Nevis,

Saint Lucia, St. Vincent and the Grenadines. Overseas Territories (Anguilla, British Virgin Islands, Montserrat).—Dr. Ernest Pate, a.i., Dayralls and Navy Garden Roads, Christ Church, (P.O. Box 508), Bridgetown, Barbados, phone (246) 426–3860 / 435–9263, fax 228–5402, email: ECC@ecc.paho.org, http://www.cpc.paho.org.

Caribbean Program Coordination, CPC.—Dr. Ernest Pate, Caribbean Program Coordinator, Dayralls and Navy Garden Roads, Christ Church, Bridgetown, Barbados (P.O. Box 508), (French Antilles: Guadaloupe, Martinique, St. Martin and St. Bartholomew, French Guiana), phone (246) 426–3860/3865 427–9434, fax 436–9779, email: email@cpc.paho.org, http://www.cpc.paho.org.

PAHO / WHO Representatives:

Argentina.—Dr. Pier Paolo Balladelli, Marcelo T. de Alvear 684, 4o. piso, 1058 Buenos Aires, Argentina, phone (54–11) 4319–4200, fax 4319–4201, e-mail: info@ops.org.ar, http://www.ops.org.ar.

Bahamas (Also serves Turks and Caicos).—Dr. Gerarda Eijkemans, 2nd Floor, Grosvenor Medical Centre, Grosvenor Close, Shirley Street, Nassau, Bahamas, phone (242) 326–7299 / 356–4730, fax 326–7012, e- mail: email@bah.paho.org.

Belize.—Dr. Gerardo de Cosio, 4792 Coney Drive, Coney Drive Business Plaza, 3rd Floor, P.O. Box 1834, Belize City, Belize, phone (501–2) 2448–85 / 2339–46, fax 2309–17, e-mail: admin@blz.paho.org, http://www.blz.paho.org.

Bolivia.—Dr. Michel Thieren, Calle Victor Sanjines 2678, Edificio Torre Barcelona, pisos 1, 6 y 7, Zona Sopocachi, Casillas Postales 9790 y 2504, La Paz, Bolivia, phone (591–2) 2412–465 / 313, fax 2412–598, e-mail: pwrbol@bol.ops-oms.org, http://www.ops.org.bo.

Brazil.—Dr. Joaquin Molina, Setor de Embaixadas Norte, Lote 19, 70800–400, Brasília, (Caixa Postal 08–629, 70312–970, Brasilia, D.F., Brasil), phone (55–61) 3251–9455 / 9549 /9500, fax 3223–0269, e-mail: email@bra.ops-oms.org, http://www.opas.org.br/.

Chile.—Dr. Roberto del Aguila, a.i. Av. Dag Hammarskjold 3269, Vitacura, Santiago, Chile. (Casilla No. 177, CP 7630412), phone (56–2) 437–4600 / 4605, fax 207–4717, e-mail: email@chi.ops-oms.org, http://www.chi.ops-oms.org.

Colombia.—Dr. Gina Watson, Carrera 7 No. 74–21, Piso 9, Edificio Seguros Aurora, Apartado Aéreo 253367, Santa Fe de Bogotá, D.C., Colombia, phone (57–1) 314–4141 / 254–7050, fax 254–7070, e-mail: ops-col@latino.net.co, http://www.col.ops-oms.org/.

Costa Rica.—Dr. Jorge Luis Prosperi, Calle 16, Avenida 6 y 8, Distrito Hospital, (Apartado 3745), San Jose, Costa Rica, phone (506) 2258–5810 / 2521–7045, fax 2258–5830, e-mail: email@cor.ops-oms.org, http://www.cor.ops-oms.org.

Cuba.—Dr. Jose Luis Di Fabiio, Calle 4 No. 407, entre 17 y 19 Vedado, (Casilla diplomatica 68), La Habana, Cuba C.P. 10400, phone (53–7) 831–8944 / 837–5808, fax 833–2075 /66–2075, e-mail: pwr@cub.ops-oms.org or cruzmari@cub.ops-oms.org, http://www.cub.ops-oms.org.

Dominican Republic.—Dr. Lilian Reneau-Vernon, Edificio OPS / OMS, y Defensa Civil, Calle Pepillo Salcedo - Recta Final, Plaza de la Salud, Ensanche La Fe, (Apartado Postal 1464), Santo Domingo, Republica Dominicana, phone (809) 562–1519 / 544–3241/ 542–6177, fax 544–0322, e-mail: email@dor.ops-oms.org, http://www.dor.ops-oms.org.

Ecuador.—Dr. Manuel Peña, a.i., Amazonas N. 2889 y Mariana de Jesus, Quito, Ecuador, phone (593–2) 2460–330 / 296 / 215, fax 2460–325, e-mail: email@ecu.ops-oms.org, http://www.opsecu.org.ec.

El Salvador.—Dr. José Ruales, 73 Avenida Sur No. 135, Colonia Escaló n, (Apartado Postal1072, Sucursal Centro), San Salvador, El Salvador, phone (503) 2511–9500/9504/ 9501, fax 2511–9555, e-mail: email@els.ops-oms.org, http://www.ops.org.sv/.

Guatemala.—Dr. Guadalupe Verdejo, Edificio Etisa, Plaza Españ a, 7a Avenida12–23, Zona 9, (Apartado Postal 383), Guatemala, Guatemala, phone (011–502) 2329–4200 / 2334–3803 / 2331–0583, fax 2334–3804, http://www.ops.org.gt.

Guyana.—Eng. Adrianus Vlugman, a.i., Lot 8 Brickdam Stabroek, (P.O. Box 10969), Georgetown, Guyana, phone (592) 225–3000 / 227–5159, fax 226–6654 /227–4205, e-mail: email@guy.paho.org.

Haiti.—Dr. Jean Luc Poncelet, No. 295 Avenue John Brown, (Boite Postale 1330), Port-au-Prince, Haiti, phone (509) 2814–3000/3001/3002/3005, fax 2814–3089, e-mail: email@hai.ops-oms.org.

Honduras.—Dr. Alma Morales, a.i., Edificio Imperial, 6o.y 7o.piso, Avenida Republica de Panam , Frente a la Casa de Naciones Unidas, Tegucigalpa M.D.C., Honduras, phone (504) 2221–6091 / 6098 / 6102, fax 2221–6103, e-mail: pwr@hon.ops-oms.org, http://www.paho-who.hn.

Jamaica (also serves Bermuda and Cayman).—Ms. Margareta Skold, 8 Gibraltar Way, University of the West Indies, Mona Campus, Kingston 7, Jamaica, (P.O. Box 384, Cross Roads, P.O., Kingston 5) phone (876) 927–1540, fax 927–2657, e-mail: email@jam.ops-oms.org.

México.—Dr. Maureen Birmingham, Horacio No 1855, 3er. Piso, Of. 305, Colonia Los Morales, Polanco, Del. Miguel Hidalgo, México D.F., 11510, México, phone (52–55) 5890–0880 / 5989–0870, fax 5395–5681, e-mail: e-mail@mex.ops-oms.org, http://www.mex.ops-oms.org.

Nicaragua.—Dr. Jose Gomez, a.i., Complejo Nacional de Salud, Camino a la Sabana, Apartado Postal 1309, Managua, Nicaragua, phone (505) 2289–4200 / 4800, fax 2289–4999, e-mail: email@nic.ops-oms.org, http://www.ops.org.ni.

Panamá.—Dr. Federico Hernandez Pimentel, Ministerio de Salud de Panamá, Ancon, Avenida Gorgas, Edificio 261, 2o piso, (Casilla Postal 0843–3441), Panamá, Panamá, phone (507) 262–0030 / 1996, fax 262–4052, e-mail: email@pan.ops-oms.org, http://ops-oms.org.pa.

Paraguay.—Dr. Gustavo Vargas, a.i., Edificio ''Faro del Rio'' Mcal Lopez 957 Esq. Estados Unidos, (Casilla de Correo 839), Asunció n, Paraguay, phone (595–21) 450–495 / 449–864/ fax 450–498, e-mail: email@par.ops-oms.org, http://www.par.ops-oms.org.

Perú.—Dr. Luis Fernando Leanes, Los Pinos 251, Urbanizacion Camacho, La Molina, Lima12, Perú, phone (51–1) 319–5700 / 5781, fax 437–8289, e-mail: email@per.ops-oms.org, http://www.per.ops.oms.org.

Puerto Rico.—Dr. Raú l Castellanos Bran, P.O. Box 70184, San Juan, Puerto Rico 00936, phone (787) 274–7608, fax 250–6547 / 767–8341.

Suriname.—Dr. Guillermo Troya, Burenstraat #33, (P.O. Box 1863), Paramaribo, Suriname, phone (597) 471–676 / 425–355, fax 471–568, e-mail: email@sur.paho.org.

Trinidad and Tobago.—Dr. Bernadette Theodore-Gandi, Sweet Briar Place, First Floor, 10–12 Sweet Briar Road, St. Clair, Trinidad, phone (868) 624–7524 / 4376 / 2078/625–4492, fax 624–5643, email: email@trt.paho.org.

Uruguay.—Dr. Eduardo Levcovitz, Ave. Brasil 2697, Aptos. 5, 6 y 8, Esquina Coronel Alegre, Codigo Postal 11300, (Casilla de Correo 1821), Montevideo, Uruguay, phone (598–2) 707–2589 / 3590, fax 707–3530, e-mail: pwr@uru.ops-oms.org, http://www.ops.org.uy/.

Venezuela (Also serves Netherlands Antilles).—Dra. Celia Riera, Avenida Sexta entre 5a y 6a, Transversal No. 43, Quinta OPS/OMS, Urbanizacion Altamira, Caracas 1060, Venezuela, (Apartado 6722 - Carmelitas, Caracas 1010, Venezuela) phone (58–212) 206–5022 / 5000, 265–0403 fax 261–6069, e-mail: email@ven.ops-oms.org, http://www.ops-oms.org.ve/.

CENTERS

Caribbean Epidemiology Center (CAREC).—Dr. Beryl Irons, 16–18 Jamaica Boulevard, Federation Park, (P.O. Box 164), Port-of-Spain, Trinidad, phone (1–868) 622–4262, fax 622–2792, e-mail: email@carec.ops-oms.org.

Caribbean Food and Nutrition Institute (CFNI).—Dr. Fitzroy J. Henry, University of the West Indies, (P.O. Box 140–Mona), Kingston 7, Jamaica, phone (1–876), 977–6726, fax 927–2657, e-mail: e-mail@cfni.paho.org.

Latin American and Caribbean Center on Health Sciences Information (BIREME).—Mr. Adalberto Otranto Tardelli, Rua Botucatu 862, Vila Clementino, (Caixa Postal 20381), CEP.04023–062, Sao Paulo, SP, Brasil, phone (55–11) 5576–9800 / 5572–3226, fax 575–8868 / 5549–2590, e-mail: email@bireme.ops-oms.org.

Latin American and Caribbean Center on Health Sciences Information (BIREME).—Mr. Adalberto Otranto Tardelli, Rua Botucatu 862, Vila Clementino, (Caixa Postal 20381), CEP.04023–062, Sao Paulo, SP, Brasil, phone (55–11) 5576–9800 / 5572–3226, fax 575–8868 / 5549–2590, e-mail: email@bireme.ops-oms.org.

Latin American Center for Perinatology and Human Development (CLAP).—Dr. Ricardo Fescina, Hospital de Clinicas, Piso 16, (Casilla de Correo 627, 11000 Montevideo, Uruguay), 11600 Montevideo, Uruguay, phone (598–2) 487–2929, fax 487–2593, e-mail: postmaster@clap.ops-oms.org.

Pan American Foot-and-Mouth Disease Center (PANAFTOSA).—Dr. Ottorino Cosivi, Avenida Presidente Kennedy 7778, (Antiga Estrada Rio-Petropolis), São Bento, Duque de Caxias, CEP 25040–004, (Caixa Postal 589), 20001–970 Rio de Janeiro, Brasil, phone (55–21) 3661–9000 / 9005 / 9002, fax 3661–9001, e-mail: panaftosa@panaftosa.pos-oms.org.

Pan American Health and Education Foundation (PAHEF).—Dr. Don I. Thorpe, 525 Twenty-Third St., NW., Washington, DC 20037, phone (202) 974–3416, fax 974–3636.

Regional Program on Bioethics.—Dr. Carla Saenz, Bioethics Regional Advisor, Pan American Health Organization, PAHO GDR, phone (202) 974–3263, fax: 974–3663.

PAHO HIV Caribbean Office.—112–114 Duke Street, Port-of-Spain, Trinidad W.I., phone (868) 624–0400 / 623–9417, fax 974–8001.

United States-Mexico Border.—Dr. Maria Teresa Cerqueira, 5400 Suncrest Dr., Suite C-4, El Paso, TX 79912, United States of America, phone (915) 845–5950, fax 845–4361, email: email@fep.paho.org, http://www.fep.paho.org/.

PERMANENT JOINT BOARD ON DEFENSE, CANADA–UNITED STATES

CANADIAN SECTION

National Defence Headquarters, MG George R. Pearkes Building, Ottawa, ON Canada K1A OK2, phone (613) 992–4423

Members:

Canadian Co-Chairman.—Hon. Laurie Hawn, P.C., C.D., M.P.
Military Policy.—CDR Gilles Couturier, Director, of General Plans.
Defence Policy.—Jill Sinclair, Assistant Deputy, Minister Policy.
Foreign Affairs.—Patrick Wittman, DFAIT Director General, Security and Intelligence Bureau.
Privy Council Office.—MG David Millar, Director of Operations.
Canada Joint Operations Command.—MG Mike Hood, Director of Staff CJOC.
NORAD.—LTG Alain Parent, Deputy Commander NORAD.
Public Safety.—Megan Nichols, Director General, Border Policy and International Affairs.
Military Secretary.—CDR Corey Bursey, Directorate of Western Hemisphere Policy.
Political Secretary.—Jordon Zed, DFADT Directorate of International Defence Relations, (613) 867–1234.

UNITED STATES SECTION

JCS, J–5, Western Hemisphere Directorate, Pentagon, Room 2E773, 20318

phone (703) 695–4955

Members:

US Co-Chair: Former Congressman John Spratt
Military Policy (Joint Staff).—BG Peter Gersten, room 2E773, 695–4955.
Defense Policy (OSD).—Todd Rosenblum, room 5D435, 697–5664.
State Department.—Mathew Rooney, Deputy Assistant Secretary for Western Hemisphere Affairs.
National Security Council.—Greg Schiffer (202) 456–9136.
USNORTHCOM.—MG John Newell.
NORAD.—MG John Newell.
DHS.—RDML June Ryan (202) 447–3675.
Military Secretary.—MAJ Jesse Lamarand, 695–4955.
Political Secretary.—Edith Backman, Department of State (202) 647–2475.

SECRETARIAT OF THE PACIFIC COMMUNITY

B.P. D5, 98848 Noumea Cedex, New Caledonia, phone (687) 26.20.00, fax 26.38.18

E-mail: spc@spc.int, http://www.spc.int

Director-General.—Dr. Colin Tukuitonga.
Senior Deputy Director General, Suva.—Fekitamoeloa Utoikamanu.
Deputy Director General, Noumea.—Richard Mann.
Director of Corporate Services.—Leslie Walker.
Director of Programme Support Services.—Richard Mann.
Director of Public Health Division.—William Parr.
Director of Fisheries, Aquaculture and Marine Ecosystems Division.—Michael Batty.
Director of Land Resources Division.—Inoke Ratukalou (acting).
Director of Economic Development Division.—John Hogan.
Director of the Applied Geoscience and Technology (SOPAC) Division.—Dr. Russell Howorth.
Director Education, Training and Human Development Division.—Fekitamoeloa Utoikamanu.
Head Strategic Engagement, Policy and Planning Facility.—Patricia Sachs-Cornish (acting).
Head Statistics for Development Programme.—Gerald Haberkorn.

U.S. Contact: Bureau of East Asian and Pacific Affairs, Office of Australia, New Zealand and Pacific Island Affairs, Department of State, Washington, DC 20520, phone (202) 736–4741, fax 647–0118

Member Countries and Territories of the SPC:

American Samoa
Australia
Cook Islands
Federated States of Micronesia
Fiji
France
French Polynesia
Guam
Kiribati
Marshall Islands
Nauru
New Caledonia
New Zealand
Northern Mariana Islands
Palau
Papua New Guinea
Pitcairn Islands
Samoa
Solomon Islands
Tokelau
Tonga
Tuvalu
United States
Vanuatu
Wallis and Futuna

SECRETARIAT OF THE PACIFIC REGIONAL ENVIRONMENTAL PROGRAMME

P.O. Box 240, Apia, Samoa, phone (685) 21929, fax (685) 20231

E-mail: sprep@sprep.org, http://www.sprep.org

Director.—David Sheppard.
Deputy Director.—Kosi Latu.
Director of:
Biodiversity and Ecosystem Management Programme.—Stuart Chape.
Climate Change Programme.—Netatua Pelesikoti.
Environmental Monitoring Governance.—Sefanaia Nawadra.
Waste Management and Pollution Control.—David Haynes.

U.S. Contact: Bureau of Oceans and International Environmental and Scientific Affairs, Office of Ocean and Polar Affairs, Department of State, Washington, DC 20520 phone (202) 647–3262

Member Countries and Territories of SPREP:

American Samoa
Australia
Cook Islands
Federated States of Micronesia
Fiji
France
French Polynesia
Kiribati
Marshall Islands
Nauru
New Caledonia
New Zealand
Niue
Northern Mariana Islands
Palau
Papua New Guinea
Samoa
Solomon Islands
Tokelau
Tonga
Tuvalu
United Kingdom
United States
Vanuatu
Wallis and Futuna

UNITED NATIONS

GENERAL ASSEMBLY

The General Assembly is composed of all 193 United Nations Member States.

SECURITY COUNCIL

The Security Council has 15 members. The United Nations Charter designates five States as permanent members, and the General Assembly elects ten other members for two-year terms. The term of office for each non-permanent member of the Council ends on 31 December of the year indicated in parentheses next to its name.

The five permanent members of the Security Council are China, France, Russian Federation, United Kingdom and the United States.

The ten non-permanent members of the Council in 2013 are Argentina (2014), Australia (2014), Azerbaijan (2013), Guatemala (2013), Luxembourg (2014), Morocco (2013), Pakistan (2013), Republic of Korea (2014), Rwanda (2014), and Togo (2013).

ECONOMIC AND SOCIAL COUNCIL

The Economic and Social Council has 54 members, elected for three-year terms by the General Assembly. The term of office for each member expires on 31 December of the year indicated in parentheses next to its name. Voting in the Council is by simple majority; each member has one vote. In 2011, the Council is composed of the following 54 States:

Albania (2015)
Austria (2014)
Belarus (2014)
Benin (2015)
Bolivia (Plurinational State of) (2015)
Brazil (2014)
Bulgaria (2013)
Burkina Faso (2014)
Cameroon (2013)
Canada (2015)
China (2013)
Colombia (2015)
Croatia (2015)
Cuba (2014)
Denmark (2013)
Dominican Republic (2014)
Ecuador (2013)
El Salvador (2014)
Ethiopia (2014)
France (2014)
Gabon (2013)
Haiti (2015)
India (2014)
Indonesia (2014)
Ireland (2014)
Japan (2014)
Kuwait (2015)
Kyrgyzstan (2015)
Latvia (2013)
Lesotho (2014)
Libya (2014)
Malawi (2013)
Mauritius (2015)
Mexico (2013)
Nepal (2015)
Netherlands (2015)
New Zealand (2013)
Nicaragua (2013)
Nigeria (2014)
Pakistan (2013)
Qatar (2013)
Republic of Korea (2013)
Russian Federation (2013)
San Marino (2015)
Senegal (2013)
South Africa (2015)
Spain (2014)
Sudan (2015)
Sweden (2013)
Tunisia (2015)
Turkey (2014)
Turkmenistan (2015)
United Kingdom of Great Britain and Northern Ireland (2013)
United States of America (2015)

TRUSTEESHIP COUNCIL

The Trusteeship Council has five members: China, France, Russian Federation, United Kingdom and the United States. With the independence of Palau, the last remaining United Nations trust territory, the Council formally suspended operation on 1 November 1994. By a resolution adopted on that day, the Council amended its rules of procedure to drop the obligation to meet annually and agreed to meet as occasion required—by its decision or the decision of its President, or at the request of a majority of its members or the General Assembly or the Security Council.

INTERNATIONAL COURT OF JUSTICE

The International Court of Justice has 15 members, elected by both the General Assembly and the Security Council. Judges hold nine-year terms.

The current composition of the court is as follows: President Peter Tomka (Slovakia); Vice-President Bernardo Sepulveda-Amor (Mexico). Judges: Hisashi Owada (Japan), Ronny Abraham (France), Kenneth Keith (New Zealand), Mohamed Bennouna (Morocco), Leonid Skotnikov (Russian Federation), Antonio Augusto Cancado Trindade (Brazil), Abdulqawi Ahmed Yusuf (Somalia), Christopher Greenwood (United Kingdom of Great Britain and Northern Ireland), Xue Hanqin (China), Joan E. Donoghue (United States of America), Giorgio Gaja (Italy), Julia Sebutinde (Uganda), Dalveer Bhandari (India).

The Registrar of the Court is Mr. Philippe Couvreur (Belgium).

UNITED NATIONS SECRETARIAT

One United Nations Plaza, New York, NY 10017, (212) 963–1234, http://www.un.org.

Secretary General.—Ban Ki-moon (Republic of Korea).
Deputy Secretary.— Jan Eliasson (Sweden).

EXECUTIVE OFFICE OF THE SECRETARY-GENERAL

Chief of Staff.—Susana Malcorra (Argentina).
Assistant Secretary-General for Policy Coordination and Strategic Planning.—Robert C. Orr (United States).
Spokesman.—Martin Nesirky.

OFFICE OF INTERNAL OVERSIGHT SERVICES

Under-Secretary-General.—Carman Louise Lapointe (Canada).

OFFICE OF LEGAL AFFAIRS

Under-Secretary-General and Legal Counsel.—Miguel de Serpa Soares (Portugal).
Assistant Secretary General.—Stephen Mathias.

DEPARTMENT OF POLITICAL AFFAIRS

Under-Secretary-General.—Jeffrey Feltman (United States).
Assistant Secretary-Generals: Óscar Fernandez-Taranco, Tayé-Brook Zerihoun.

DEPARTMENT FOR DISARMAMENT AFFAIRS

Under-Secretary-General.—Angela Kane (Germany).

DEPARTMENT OF PEACE-KEEPING OPERATIONS

Under-Secretary-General.—Hervé Ladsous (France).
Assistant Secretary-Generals: Edmond Mulet (Guatemala), Dimitry Titov (Russia).
Military Adviser.—Lieutenant General Maqsood Ahmed (Pakistan).

OFFICE FOR THE COORDINATION OF HUMANITARIAN AFFAIRS

Under-Secretary-General, Humanitarian Affairs and Emergency Relief Coordinator.—Valerie Amos (United Kingdom).
Assistant Secretary General/Deputy Emergency Relief Coordinator.—Kyung-wha Kang (Republic of Korea).

DEPARTMENT OF ECONOMIC AND SOCIAL AFFAIRS

Under-Secretary-General.—Wu Hongbo (China).
Assistant Secretary-Generals: Shamshad Akhtar (Pakistan), Thomas Gass (Switzerland).

DEPARTMENT OF GENERAL ASSEMBLY AND CONFERENCE MANAGEMENT

Under-Secretary-General.—Tegegnework Gettu (Ethiopia).
Assistant Secretary-General.—Franz Baumann (Germany).

DEPARTMENT OF PUBLIC INFORMATION

Under-Secretary-General.—Peter Launsky-Tieffenthal (Austria).

DEPARTMENT OF MANAGEMENT

Under-Secretary-General.—Yukio Takasu (Japan).
Assistant Secretary-General, Controller.—Maria Eugenia Cesar (Mexico).
Assistant Secretary-General, Human Resources Management.—Catherine Pollard (Guyana).
Assistant Secretary-General, Central Support Services.—Stephen Cutts (United Kingdom).
Assistant Secretary-General, Capital Master Plan.—Michael Adlerstein (United States).

OFFICE OF THE SPECIAL REPRESENTATIVE OF THE SECRETARY-GENERAL FOR CHILDREN AND ARMED CONFLICT

Under-Secretary-General.—Leila Zerrougui (Algeria).

UNITED NATIONS FUND FOR INTERNATIONAL PARTNERSHIPS

Executive Director.—Amir A. Dossal (United Kingdom).

UNITED NATIONS AT GENEVA (UNOG)

Palais des Nations, 1211 Geneva 10, Switzerland, phone (41–022) 917–1234.
Director-General of UNOG/Assistant Secretary-General.—Michael Moller (Denmark).

UNITED NATIONS AT VIENNA (UNOV)

Vienna International Centre, P.O. Box 500, 1400 Vienna, Austria, phone (43–1) 26060.
Director-General.—Yury Fedotov (Russian Federation).

UNITED NATIONS INFORMATION CENTRE

1775 K Street, NW., Suite 400, Washington, DC 20006

phone: (202) 331–8670, fax: (202) 331–9191, email: unicdc@unic.org

http://www.unicwash.org

Director.—Rodney Bent (United States).

REGIONAL ECONOMIC COMMISSIONS

Economic Commission for Africa (ECA), Menelik II Ave., P.O. Box 3001, Addis Ababa Ethiopia, phone (251–11) 551–7200, fax (251–1) 551–4416.
Executive Secretary.—Carlos Lopes (Guinea-Bissau).
Economic Commission for Europe (ECE) Palais des Nations, 1211 Geneva 10, Switzerland, phone (41–22) 917–4444.
Executive Secretary.—Sven Alkalaj (Bosnia and Herzegovina).
Economic Commission for Latin America and the Caribbean (ECLAC), Casilla 179–D, Santiago, Chile, phone (56–2) 2210–2000, fax (56–2) 208–0252.
Executive Secretary.—Alicia Bárcena Ibarra (Mexico).
Economic and Social Commission for Asia and the Pacific (ESCAP), United Nations Building, Rajadamnern Nok Avenue, Bangkok Thailand, phone (66–2) 288–1234, fax (66–2) 288–1000.
Executive Secretary.—Noeleen Heyzer (Singapore).
Economic and Social Commission for Western Asia (ESCWA), P.O. Box 11–8575, Riad El-Solh Square, Beirut, Lebanon, phone 9611–981301, fax 9611–981510.
Executive Secretary.—Rima Khalaf (Jordan).
Regional Commissions, New York Office, (ECE, ESCAP, ECLAC, ECA, ESCWA), fax 963–1500, phone 212 963–8088.
Director.—Amr Nour (Egypt).
Social Affairs Officer.—Daniela Simioni.
Programme Officer.—Andrew Allimadi.
Senior Staff Assistant and Webmaster.—Ansley Lancourt.
Staff Assistant.—Yesenia Copperman.

FUNDS, PROGRAMMES, AND BODIES OF THE UNITED NATIONS

Advisory Committee on Administrative and Budgetary Questions (ACABQ), One United Nations Plaza, New York, NY 10017, phone (212) 963–0677, (212) 963–1649.
Executive Secretary.—Shari Klugman.
Chairman.—Carlos G. Ruiz Massieu (Mexico).

Office of the High Commissioner for Human Rights, Palais des Nations, 8–14 Avenue de la Paix, 1211 Geneva 10, Switzerland, phone (41–022) 917–9220.
High Commissioner for Human Rights.—Navanethem Pillay (South Africa).

International Civil Service Commission (ICSC), Two United Nations Plaza, New York, NY 10017, phone (212) 963–5465.
Chairman.—Kingston Rhodes (Sierra Leone).

Joint Inspection Unit (JIU), Palais des Nations, 1211 Geneva 10, Switzerland, phone (41–22) 917–3044.
Chairman.—Istvan Posta (Hungary).

Panel of External Auditors of the UN, One United Nations Plaza, New York, NY 10017, phone (212) 963–5623.
Executive Secretary to the Board.—Anjana Das.
Chairman of the Board.—Jagbans Singh (India).

United Nations Human Settlements Programme (UN–HABITAT), UN Office at Nairobi, P.O. Box 30030, Nairobi, 00100, Kenya, phone (254–20) 762–1234.
Executive Director.—Joan Clos (Spain).

United Nations Children's Fund (UNICEF), UNICEF House, 3 UN Plaza, New York, NY 10017, phone (212) 326–7000.
Executive Director.—Anthony Lake (USA).

United Nations Conference on Trade and Development (UNCTAD), Palais des Nations, 8–14 Avenue de la Paix, 1211 Geneva 10, Switzerland, phone (41–22) 917–1234.
Secretary General.—Mukhisa Kituyi (Kenya).

United Nations Development Fund for Women (UNIFEM), Part of UN Women as of July 2010.
Executive Director.—Inés Alberdi.

United Nations Development Programme (UNDP), 1 United Nations Plaza, New York, NY 10017, phone (212) 906–5000.
Administrator.—Helen Clark (New Zealand).

United Nations Development Programme (UNDP), Liaison Office, 1775 K Street, NW., Suite 420, Washington, DC 20006, phone (202) 331–9130.
Director.—William K. Davis (United States).

United Nations Environment Programme (UNEP), P.O. Box 30552, Nairobi, Kenya, phone (254–20) 762–1234.
Executive Director.—Achim Steiner.

United Nations High Commissioner for Refugees (UNHCR), Case Postale 2500, CH–1211 Geneve 2 Depot, Switzerland, phone (41–22) 739–8111.
High Commissioner.—António Manuel de Oliveira Gutterres (Portugal).

United Nations High Commissioner for Refugees (UNHCR), Regional Office for the United States and the Caribbean, 1775 K Street, NW., Third Floor, Washington, DC 20006, phone (202) 296–5191.
Regional Representative.—Shelly Pitterman.

United Nations Institute for Disarmament Research (UNIDIR), Palais des Nations, 1211 Geneva 10, Switzerland, phone (41–022) 917–3186.
Director.—Theresa Hitchens (United Kingdom).

United Nations Institute for Training and Research (UNITAR), Palais des Nations, CH–1211 Geneva 10, Switzerland, phone (41–22) 917–8400.
Executive Director.—Sally Fegan-Wyles (Ireland).

United Nations International Drug Control Programme (UNODC), P.O. Box 500, A–1400 Vienna, Austria, phone (43–1) 26060.
Executive Director.—Yury Fedotov (Russian Federation).

United Nations International Research and Training Institute for the Advancement of Women (INSTRAW), Part of UN Women as July 2010.

United Nations Interregional Crime and Justice Research Institute (UNICRI), Viale Maestri del Lavoro, 10, 10127 Turin, Italy, phone (39–011) 6537–111.
Director.—Jonathan Lucas (Seychelles).

United Nations Office for Project Services (UNOPS), P.O. Box 2695, 2100 Copenhagen, Denmark, phone (45–4) 533–5000.
Executive Director.—Jan Mattsson (Sweden).

United Nations Population Fund (UNFPA), 220 East 42nd Street, New York, NY 10017, phone (212) 297–5000.
Executive Director.—Babatunde Osotimehin (Nigeria).

United Nations Relief and Works Agency for Palestine Refugees in the Near East (UNRWA), Headquarters Amman, P.O. Box 140157, Amman 11814, Jordan, phone (+ 962 6) 580–8100. Headquarters Gaza, P.O. Box 371, Gaza City, phone (+ 972 8) 288–7701.
Commissioner-General.—Pierre Krähenbühl (Switzerland).

United Nations Research Institute for Social Development (UNRISD), Palais des Nations, 1211 Geneva 10, Switzerland, phone (41–22) 917–3020.
Deputy Director (Officer in Charge).—Sarah Cook (United Kingdom).

United Nations Volunteers Programme (UNV), Postfach 260 111, D–53153 Bonn, Germany, phone (49–228) 815–2000.
Executive Coordinator.—Richard Dictus (Netherlands).

United Nations Entity for Gender Equality and the Empowerment of Women (UN Women), 220 East 42nd Street, New York, NY 10017, phone (646) 781–4400.
Director.—Phumzile Mlambo-Ngcuka (South Africa).

World Food Programme (WFP), Via C.G.Viola 68, Parco dei Medici, 00148 Rome, Italy, phone (39–6) 65131.
Executive Director.—Ertharin Cousin (United States).

United Nations University (UNU), 5–53–70 Jingumae, Shibuya-ku, Tokyo 150–8925, Japan, phone (81–3) 5467–1212.
Rector.—David Malone (Canada).

SPECIALIZED AGENCIES

Food and Agriculture Organization (FAO), Viale delle Terme di Caracalla, 00153 Rome, Italy, phone (39–6) 57051.
Director-General.—José, Graziano da Silva (Brazil).

Food and Agriculture Organization, Liaison Office for North America, Suite 800-B, 2121 K Street, NW., Washington, DC 20037, phone (1–202) 653–2400.
Director.—Nicholas Nelson (United States).

International Civil Aviation Organization (ICAO), 999 University Street, Montreal, Quebec H3C 5H7, Canada, phone (1–514) 954–8219.
Secretary-General.—Raymond Benjamin (France).

International Fund for Agricultural Development (IFAD), Via Paolo di Dono, 44, 00142 Rome, Italy, phone (39–6) 54591.
President.—Kanayo F. Nwanze (Nigeria).

External Affairs Department, IFAD North American Liaison Office, 1775 K Street, NW., Suite 410, Washington, DC 20006, phone (1–202) 331–9099.
Liaison Officer.—Thomas Pesek (United States).

International Labour Organization (ILO), 4, Routes des Morillons, CH–1211 Geneva 22, Switzerland, phone (41–22) 799–6111.
Director-General.—Guy Ryder (United Kingdom).

ILO Washington Branch Office, 1801 I Street, NW., 9th Floor, Washington, DC 20006, phone (1–202) 617–3952.
Director.—Nancy Donaldson.

International Maritime Organization (IMO), 4 Albert Embankment, London SE1 7SR, United Kingdom, phone (44–20) 7735–7611.
Secretary-General.—Koji Sekimizu (Japan).

International Monetary Fund (IMF), 700 19th Street, NW., Washington, DC 20431, phone (1–202) 623–7000.
Managing Director.—Christine Lagarde (France).

International Telecommunications Union (ITU), Palais des Nations, 1211 Geneva 20, Switzerland, phone (41–22) 730–5111.
Secretary-General.—Hamadoun Touré (Mali).

United Nations Educational, Scientific and Cultural Organization (UNESCO), 7 Place de Fontenoy, 75352 Paris 07 SP, France, phone (33–01) 4568–1000.
Director-General.—Irina Bokova (Bulgaria).

United Nations Industrial Development Organization (UNIDO), Vienna International Centre, Wagramerstr. 5, P.O. Box 300, A–1400 Vienna, Austria, phone (43–1) 26026–0.
Director-General.—Li Yong (China).

Universal Postal Union (UPU), International Bureau, Case Postale 312, 3015 Berne, Switzerland, phone (41–31) 350–3111.
Director-General.—Bishar Abdirahman Hussein (Kenya).

World Bank Group, 1818 H Street, NW., Washington, DC 20433, phone (1–202) 473–1000.
President.—Jim Yong Kim (United States).

World Health Organization (WHO), 20 Avenue Appia, 1211 Geneva 27, Switzerland, phone (41–22) 791–2111.
Director-General.—Margaret Chan (China).

Pan American Health Organization/World Health Organization Regional Office for the Americas, 525 23rd Street, NW., Washington, DC 20037, phone (1–202) 974–3000.
Director.—Carissa F. Etienne (Dominica).

World Intellectual Property Organization (WIPO), 34, chemin des Colombettes, CH–1211 Geneva 20, Switzerland, phone (41–22) 338–9111.
Director General.—Francis Gurry (Australia).

World Meteorological Organization (WMO), 7bis, avenue de la Paix, Case Postale 2300, CH–1211 Geneva 2, Switzerland, phone (41–22) 730–8111.
Secretary-General.—Michel Jarraud (France).

RELATED BODY

International Atomic Energy Agency (IAEA), P.O. Box 100, Wagramer Strasse 5, A–1400 Vienna, Austria, phone (431) 2600–0.
Director General.—Yukiya Amano (Japan).

(The IAEA is an independent intergovernmental organization under the aegis of the UN).

SPECIAL AND PERSONAL REPRESENTATIVES AND ENVOYS OF THE SECRETARY-GENERAL

AFRICA

Africa:
Special Adviser to the Secretary-General on Africa, OSAA.—Maged Abdelaziz (Egypt).
High Representative for the Least Developed Countries, Landlocked Developing Countries and Small Island Developing States, UN-OHRLLS.—Gyan Chandra Acharya (Nepal).

African Union:
Special Representative of the Secretary-General to the African Union, UNOAU.—Haile Menkerios (South Africa).

Burundi:
Special Representative of the Secretary-General for Burundi and Head of the UN Office in Burundi.—Parfait Onanga-Anyanga (Gabon).
Deputy Special Representative and UN Resident Coordinator, Resident Representative and Humanitarian Coordinator for Burundi, BNUB.—Rosine Sori-Coulibaly (Burkina Faso).

Central Africa:
Special Representative of the Secretary-General and Head of UNOCA.—Abou Moussa (Chad).

Central African Republic:
Special Representative of the Secretary-General and Head of the United Nations Integrated Peacebuilding Office in the Central African Republic.—Babacar Gaye (Senegal).
Deputy Special Representative of the Secretary-General in the Central African Republic and UN Resident Coordinator and Resident Representative, BINUCA.—Kaarina Immonen (Finland).

Cote d'Ivoire:

Special Representative of the Secretary-General for Cote d'Ivoire and Head of UNOCI.—Aïchatou Mindaoudou Souleymane (Niger).

Deputy Special Representative of the Secretary-General for Cote d'Ivoire, UNOCI.—Arnauld Antone Akodjenou (Benin).

Deputy Special Representative of the Secretary-General, UN Resident Coordinator, Humanitarian Coordinator and UNDP Resident Representative, UNOCI.—M'Baye Babacar Cisse (Senegal).

Democratic Republic of the Congo:

Special Representative of the Secretary-General for the Democratic Republic of the Congo and Head of MONUSCO.—Martin Kobler (Germany).

Deputy Special Representative of the Secretary-General for the Democratic Republic of the Congo, UN Resident Coordinator and Humanitarian Coordinator, MONUSCO.—Moustapha Soumaré (Mali).

Deputy Special Representative of the Secretary-General for the Democratic Republic of the Congo, Rule of Law, MONUSCO.—Abdallah Wafy (Niger).

Equatorial Guinea and Gabon:

Special Adviser to the Secretary-General and Mediator in the border dispute between Equatorial Guinea and Gabon.—Nicolas Michel (Switzerland).

Great Lakes Region:

Special Representative of the Secretary-General for the Great Lakes Region.—Mary Robinson (Ireland).

Special Advisor to the Special Envoy of the Secretary-General to the Great Lakes Region.—Modibo Touré (Mali).

Guinea-Bissau:

Special Representative of the Secretary-General and Head of UNOGBIS.—José Ramos-Horta (Timor-Leste).

Liberia:

Special Representative of the Secretary-General.—Karin Landgren (Sweden).

Deputy Special Representative for Recovery and Good Governance.—Aeneas Chapinga Chuma (Zimbabwe).

Deputy Special Representative for Rule of Law.—Henrietta Joy Tamrat Samuel (Ghana).

Libya:

Special Representative of the Secretary-General and Head of the United Nations Support Mission in Libya.—Tarek Mitri (Lebanon).

Deputy Special Representative of the Secretary-General, Resident Coordinator and Humanitarian Coordinator.—Georg Charpentier (Finland).

Mali:

Special Representative of the Secretary-General and Head of Mission, MINUSMA.—Albert Gerard Koenders (Netherlands).

Deputy Special Representative of the Secretary-General in MINUSMA.—Abdoulaye Bathily (Senegal).

Deputy Special Representative of the Secretary-General in MINUSMA and UN Resident Coordinator, Humanitarian Coordinator and Resident Representative of UNDP.—David Gressly (United States).

Sahel:

Special Envoy of the Secretary-General for the Sahel.—Romano Prodi (Italy).

Sierra Leone:

Executive Representative of the Secretary-General for the UN Integrated Peacebuilding Office in Sierra Leone.—Jens Anders Toyberg-Frandzen (Denmark).

Somalia:

Special Representative of the Secretary-General for Somalia and Head of Mission, UNSOM.—Nicholas Kay (United Kingdom).

Deputy Special Representative of the Secretary-General for Somalia.—Fatiha Serour (Algeria).

Sudan and South Sudan:

Special Envoy of the Secretary-General for Sudan and South Sudan.—Haile Menkerios (South Africa).

South Sudan:

Special Representative of the Secretary-General and Head of UNMISS.—Hilde Johnson (Norway)

Deputy Special Representative of the Secretary-General, UNMISS.—Raisedon Zenenga (Zimbabwe).

Deputy Special Representative of the Secretary-General, Resident Coordinator, Humanitarian Coordinator and Resident Representative, UNMISS.—Toby Lanzer (United Kingdom).

Sudan/Abyei:

Head of Mission and Force Commander, UNISFA.—Major General Yohannes Gebremeskel Tesfamariam (Ethiopia).

Sudan/Darfur:

Joint African Union-United National Special Representative for Darfur, Head of UNAMID and Joint Chief Mediator.—Mohamed Ibn Chambas (Ghana).

Deputy Joint Special Representative for Political Affairs, UNAMID.—Joseph Mutaboba (Rwanda).

Deputy Joint Special Representative for Operations and Management, UNAMID.—Mohamed Yonis (Somalia).

West Africa:

Special Representative of the Secretary-General and Head of UNOWA.—Said Djinnit (Algeria).

Western Sahara:

Special Representative of the Secretary-General for Western Sahara and Head of MINURSO.—Wolfgang Weisbrod-Weber (Germany).

Personal Envoy of the Secretary-General for Western Sahara.—Christopher Ross (United States).

THE AMERICAS

Guyana/Venezuela:

Personal Representative of the Secretary-General on the Border Controversy between Guyana and Venezuela.—Norman Girvan (Jamaica).

Haiti:

Special Representative of the Secretary-General and Head of Mission, MINUSTAH.—Sandra Honoré (Trinidad and Tobago).

Deputy Special Representative of the Secretary-General, MINUSTAH.—Carl Alexandre (United States).

Deputy Special Representative of the Secretary-General and United Nations Resident Coordinator and Humanitarian Coordinator, MINUSTAH.—Peter de Clercg (Netherlands).

Special Adviser to the Secretary-General for Community Based Medicine and Lessons from Haiti.—Paul Farmer (United States).

ASIA AND THE PACIFIC

Afghanistan:

Special Representative of the Secretary-General for Afghanistan and Head of UNAMA.—Ján Kubis (Slovakia).

Deputy Special Representative of the Secretary-General, UN Resident Coordinator and UN Humanitarian Coordinator for Afghanistan, UNAMA.—Mark Bowden (United Kingdom).

Deputy Special Representative of the Secretary-General (Political) for UNAMA.—Nicholas Haysom (South Africa).

Central Asia:

Special Representative of the Secretary-General and Head of the UN Regional Centre for Preventive Diplomacy for Central Asia.—Miroslav Jenca (Slovakia).

India-Pakistan:

Chief Military Observer and Head of Mission, UNMOGIP.—Young-Bum Choi (Republic of Korea).

Myanmar:

Special Adviser of the Secretary-General for Myanmar.—Vijay Nambiar (India).

Timor Leste:

Special Adviser of the Secretary-General for Timor-Leste.—Noeleen Heyzer (Singapore).

EUROPE

Cyprus:

Special Representative of the Secretary-General and Head of Mission, UNFICYP.—Lisa Buttenheim (United States).

Special Adviser to the Secretary-General on Cyprus.—Alexander Downer (Australia).

Former Yugoslav Republic of Macedonia-Greece:

Personal Envoy of the Secretary-General for the Greece-RYROM talks.—Matthew Nimetz (United States).

Georgia:

United Nations Representative.—Antti Turunen (Finland).

Kosovo:

Special Representative of the Secretary-General and Head of Mission, UNMIK.—Farid Zarif (Afghanistan).

MIDDLE EAST

Middle East:

Special Coordinator for the Middle East Peace Process and Personal Representative of the Secretary-General to the Palestine Liberation Organization and the Palestinian Authority.—Robert H. Serry (Netherlands).

Deputy Special Coordinator for the Middle East Peace Process/United Nations Coordinator for Humanitarian Aid and Development Activities in the Occupied Palestinian Territory.—James W. Rawley (United States).

Special Envoy for the Implementation of Security Council Resolution 1559.—Terje Roed-Larsen (Norway).

Head of Mission and Chief of Staff of UNTSO.—Major General Michael Finn (Ireland).

Iraq (UNAMI):

Special Representative of the Secretary-General for Iraq and Head of Mission, UNAMI.—Nickolay Miadenov (Bulgaria).

Deputy Special Representative of the Secretary-General for Political Affairs, UNAMI.—György Busztin (Hungary).

Deputy Special Representative of the Secretary-General (Development and Humanitarian Support) and Resident Coordinator/Humanitarian Coordinator for Iraq, UNAMI.—Jacqueline Carol Badcock (United Kingdom).

Kuwait:

Humanitarian Envoy of the Secretary-General.—Abdullah al Matouq (Kuwait).

Lebanon:

Special Coordinator of the Secretary-General for Lebanon.—Derek Plumbly (United Kingdom).

Deputy Special Coordinator of the Secretary-General for Lebanon, UN Resident Coordinator and UNDP Resident Representative.—Robert Watkins (Canada).

Head of Mission and Force Commander of UNIFIL.—Major General Paolo Serra (Italy).

Syria:

Joint Special Representative of the United Nations and the League of Arab States for Syria.—Lakhdar Brahimi (Algeria).

Deputy Joint Special Representative of the United Nations and the League of Arab States for Syria.—Nasser Al-Kidwa (Palestine).

Special Coordinator of the OPCW-UN Mission.—Sigrid Kaag (Netherlands).

Syria Golan Heights:

Head of Mission and Force Commander of the UN Disengagement Observer Force (UNDOF).—Major-General Iqbal Singh Singha (India).

Yemen:

Special Adviser to the Secretary-General on Yemen.—Jamal Benomar (Great Britain).

OTHER HIGH LEVEL APPOINTMENTS

Alliance of Civilizations:

High Representative.—Nassir Abdulaziz al-Nasser (Qatar).

Avian and Human Influenza (Bird flu):

Senior United Nations System Coordinator for Avian and Human Influenza.—David Nabarro (United Kingdom).

Children and Armed Conflict:

Special Representative.—Leila Zerrougui (Algeria).

Disaster Reduction:

Special Representative.—Margareta Wahlström (Sweden).

Financing for Development:

Special Adviser.—Phillipe Douste-Blazy (France).

Global Education:

Special Representative.—Gordon Brown (United Kingdom).

HIV / AIDS in Africa:
Special Envoy.—Speciosa Wandira-Kasibwe (Uganda).

HIV / AIDS in Asia and in the Pacific:
Special Envoy.—Prasada Rao V.R. Jonnalagadda (India).

HIV / AIDS in the Caribbean Region:
Special Envoy.—Edward Green (Gyana).

HIV / AIDS in Eastern Europe and Central Asia:
Special Envoy.—Michel Kazatchkine (France).

Inter-Regional Policy Cooperation:
Special Adviser.—Juan Somovía (Chile).

Malaria and Financing of Health-Related Millennium Development Goals:
Special Envoy.—Ray Chambers (United States).

Migration:
Special Representative.—Peter Sutherland (Ireland).

Millennium Development Goals:
Special Adviser.—Jeffrey D. Sachs (United States).

Prevention of Genocide:
Special Advisor.—Adama Dieng (Senegal).

Post-2015 Development Planning:
Special Adviser.—Amina Mohammed (Nigeria).

Sport for Development and Peace:
Special Adviser.—Wilfried Lemke (Germany).

United Nations International School (UNIS):
Special Representative.—Michael Alderstein (United States).

Violence Against Children:
Special Representative.—Marta Santos Pais (Portugal).

World Summit on Information Society:
Special Adviser.—Nitin Desai (India).

Youth:
Envoy.—Ahmad Alhendawi (Jordan).

WORLD BANK GROUP

The World Bank Group comprises five organizations: the International Bank for Reconstruction and Development (IBRD), the International Development Association (IDA), the International Finance Corporation (IFC), the Multilateral Investment Guarantee Agency (MIGA) and the International Centre for the Settlement of Investment Disputes (ICSID).

Headquarters: 1818 H Street, NW., 20433, (202) 473–1000

INTERNATIONAL BANK FOR RECONSTRUCTION AND DEVELOPMENT

President.—Jim Yong Kim.
Managing Director and Chief Operating Officer.—Sri Mulyani.
Managing Director and Chief Financial Officer.—Bertrand Badre.
Managing Director.—Caroline Anstey.
Chairperson, Inspection Panel.—Eimi Watanabe.
Senior Vice President.—Pamela Cox.
Senior Vice President and General Counsel.—Anne-Marie Leroy.
Senior Vice President, Development Economics, and Chief Economist.—Kaushik Basu.
Vice President and Head, Human Development Network.—Keith Hansen (acting).
Vice President and Chief Information Officer, WBG Information and Technology Solutions.—Stephanie von Friedeburg.
Vice President and Controller.—Charles McDonough.
Vice President, Budget, Performance Review and Strategic Planning.—Pedro Alba.
Vice President and Corporate Secretary.—Jorge F. Calderon.
Vice President and Treasurer.—Madelyn Antoncic.
Vice President of:
Africa.—Makhtar Diop.
East Asia and Pacific.—Axel vanTrotsenburg.

South Asia.—Philippe Le Houerou.

Vice President and Network Head Sustainable Development Network.—Rachel Kyte.

Vice President, World Bank Group External and Corporate Relations.—Cyril Muller.

North American Affairs (External Affairs) Special Representative.—Craig M. Albright.

Europe (External and Corporate Relations) Special Representative.—Stefan Emblad.

UN External Affairs, Special Representative.—Dominique Bichara.

Japan-External and Corporate Relations, Special Representative.—Mika Iwasaki (acting).

Human Resources.—Sean McGrath.

Latin America and the Caribbean.—Hasan A. Tuluy.

Middle East and North Africa.—Inger Andersen.

Vice President of Europe and Central Asia.—Laura Tuck (acting).

Vice President and Network Head, Operations Policy and Country Services.—Kyle Peters.

Vice President and Network Head Poverty Reduction and Economic Management Network.—Jaime Saavedra Chanduvi (acting).

Vice President and Network Head Financial and Private Sector Development (World Bank and IFC).—Janamitra Devan.

Resource Mobilization and Cofinancing.—Joachim von Amsberg.

Vice President and Bank Group Risk Officer.—Bertrand Badre (acting).

Vice President, Change, Knowledge and Learning.—Sanjay Pradhan.

Director-General, Independent Evaluation.—Caroline Heider.

Vice President, Concessional Finance and Global Partnerships.—Joachim von Amsberg.

Vice President and Auditor-General.—Clare Brady.

Vice President, Institutional Integrity.—Leonard McCarthy.

Vice President and World Bank Group Chief Ethics Officer.—Xian Zhu.

Senior Director, General Services.—Van Pulley.

OTHER WORLD BANK OFFICES

London: Millbank Tower, 12th Floor, 21–24 Millbank, London SW1P 4QP.

Geneva: 3, Chemin Louis Dunant, CP 66, CH 1211, Geneva 10, Switzerland.

Paris: 66, Avenue d'Iena, 75116 Paris, France.

Brussels: Avenue Marnix 17, 2nd floor, 1000 Brussels, Belgium.

Tokyo: Fukoku Seimei Building, 10th Floor, 2–2–2 Uchisawai-cho, Chiyoda-Ku, Tokyo 100, Japan.

Sydney: CML Building Level 19–14, Martin Place, Sydney, NSW 2000, Australia.

Berlin: Reichpietschufer 20, 10785 Berlin, Germany.

BOARD OF EXECUTIVE DIRECTORS

Bahrain, Egypt (Arab Republic of), Iraq, Jordan, Kuwait, Lebanon, Libya, Maldives, Oman, Qatar, Syrian Arab Republic, United Arab Emirates, Yemen (Republic of).

Executive Director.—Merza H. Hasan (Kuwait).

Alternate.—Karim Wissa (Arab Republic of Egypt).

Saudi Arabia.

Executive Director.—

Alternate.—Ibrahim M. I. Alturki.

Austria, Belarus, Belgium, Czech Republic, Hungary, Kazakhstan, Luxembourg, Slovak Republic, Slovenia, Turkey.

Executive Director.—Gino Alzetta (Belgium).

Alternate.—Gulsum Yazganarikan (Turkey).

Australia, Cambodia, Kiribati, Korea (Republic of), Marshall Islands, Micronesia (Federated States of), Mongolia, New Zealand, Palau, Papua New Guinea, Samoa, Solomon Islands, Vanuatu.

Executive Director.—Michael Willock (Australia).

Alternate.—Bok-Hwan Yu (Republic of Korea).

Albania, Greece, Italy, Malta, Portugal, San Marino, Timor-Leste.

Executive Director.—Piero Cipollone (Italy).

Alternate.—Nuno Mota Pinto (Portugal).

United States.

Executive Director.—Vacant.

Alternate.—Sara Margalit Aviel.

Brazil, Colombia, Dominican Republic, Ecuador, Haiti, Panama, Philippines, Suriname, Trinidad and Tobago.

Executive Director.—Roberto Tan (Philippines).

Alternate.—Rogerio Studart (Brazil).

Germany.

Executive Director.—Ingrid Hoven.

Alternate.—Wilhelm Rissmann.

Afghanistan, Algeria, Ghana, Iran (Islamic Republic of), Morocco, Pakistan, Tunisia.

Executive Director.—Omar Bougara (Algeria).

Alternate.—Muhammad Azeem-ul-Haq (Pakistan).

France.

Executive Director.—Herve de Villeroche.

Alternate.—Jean-Paul Julia.

Benin, Burkina Faso, Cameroon, Cape Verde, Central African Republic, Chad, Comoros, Congo (Democratic Republic of), Congo (Republic of), Cote d'lvoire, Djibouti, Equatorial Guinea, Gabon, Guinea, Guinea-Bissau, Madagascar, Mali, Mauritania, Mauritius, Niger, Rwanda, Sao Tome and Principe, Senegal, Togo.

Executive Director.—Agapito Mendes Dias (Sao Tome and Principe).

Alternate.—Mohamed Sikieh Kayad (Djibouti).

Fiji, Indonesia, Lao People's Democratic Republic, Malaysia, Myanmar, Nepal, Singapore, Thailand, Tonga, Vietnam.

Executive Director.—Sundaran Annamalai (Malaysia).

Alternate.—Boonchai Charassangsomboon (Thailand).

Denmark, Estonia, Finland, Iceland, Latvia, Lithuania, Norway, Sweden.

Executive Director.—Satu-Leena Santala (Finland).

Alternate.—Giedre Balcytyte (Lithuania).

Russian Federation.

Executive Director.—Vadim Nikolaevich Grishin.

Alternate.—Eugene Miagkov.

Costa Rica, El Salvador, Guatemala, Honduras, Mexico, Nicaragua, Spain, Venezuela (Republica Bolivariana de).

Executive Director.—Huan Jose Bravo (Mexico).

Antigua and Barbuda, Bahamas (The), Barbados, Belize, Canada, Dominica, Grenada, Guyana, Ireland, Jamaica, St. Kitts and Nevis, St. Lucia, St. Vincent and the Grenadines.

Executive Director.—Marie-Lucie Morin (Canada).

Alternate.—Janet Harris (St. Kitts and Nevis).

Armenia, Bosnia and Herzegovina, Bulgaria, Croatia, Cyprus, Georgia, Israel, Macedonia (former Yugoslav Republic of), Moldova, Netherlands, Romania, Ukraine.

Executive Director.—Frank Heemskerk (Netherlands).

Alternate.—Roman Zhukovskyi (Ukraine)

Japan.

Executive Director.—Hideaki Suzuki.

Alternate.—Yota Ono.

Argentina, Bolivia, Chile, Paraguay, Peru, Uruguay.

Executive Director.—Cesar Guido Forcieri (Argentina).

Alternate.—Ricardo Raineri (Chile).

United Kingdom.

Executive Director.—Gwen Hines.

Angola, Nigeria, South Africa.

Executive Director.—Mansur Muhtar (Nigeria).

Alternate.—Ana Lourenco (Angola).

Botswana, Burundi, Eritrea, Ethiopia, Gambia (The), Kenya, Lesotho, Liberia, Malawi, Mozambique, Namibia, Seychelles, Sierra Leone, Sudan, Swaziland, Tanzania, Uganda, Zambia, Zimbabwe.

Executive Director.—Denny H. Kalyalya (Zambia).

Alternate.—Louis Rene Peter Larose (Seychelles).

Bangladesh, Bhutan, India, Sri Lanka.

Executive Director.—Mukesh N. Prasad (India).

Alternate.—Mohammad Tareque (Bangladesh).

Azerbaijan, Serbia and Montenegro, Kyrgyz Republic, Poland, Switzerland, Tajikistan, Turkmenistan, Uzbekistan, Yugoslavia (Fed. Rep. of), Switzerland, Yemen, Republic of.

Executive Director.—Jorg Frieden (Switzerland).

Alternate.—Wieslaw Szczuka (Poland).

China.

Executive Director.—Shaolin Yang.

Alternate.—Bin Han.

INTERNATIONAL DEVELOPMENT ASSOCIATION

[The officers, executive directors, and alternates are the same as those of the International Bank for Reconstruction and Development.]

INTERNATIONAL FINANCE CORPORATION

President.—Jim Yong Kim.

Executive Vice President.—Jin-Yong Cai.
Vice President and Chief Operating Officer.—Rashad-Rudolf Kaldany.
Vice President and Corporate Secretary.—Jorge Familiar Calderon.
Vice President:
Human Resource.—Sean McGrath.
Financial and Private Sector Development.—Janamitra Devan.
Risk Management and Portfolio.—Saadia Khairi.
Director-General, Independent Evaluation.—Caroline Heider.
Compliance Advisor/Ombudsman (IFC/MIGA).—Meg Taylor.
Vice President and General Counsel.—Ethiopis Tafara.
Vice President, Business Advisory Services.—Snezana Stoiljkovic.
Vice President, East Asia and Pacific.—Karin Finkelston.
Vice President, Sub-Saharan Africa, Latin America and the Caribbean.—Jean Philippe Prosper.
Vice President, Eastern and Southern Europe, Central Asia, Middle East and North Africa.—Dimitris Tsitsiragos.
Vice President, Global Industries.—Rashad Kaldany.
CEO, IFC Asset Management Company.—Gavin Wilson.
Director, Corporate Relations.—Bruce Moats.
Chief Information Officer and Director, Corporate Business Technologies.—Stephanie von Friedeburg.
Director, Office of:
Accounting and Financial Operations.—Bernard Lauwers.
Partnerships and Advisory Services.—Anita Bhatia.
Portfolio and Operational Risk.—Alzbeta Klein.
Corporate Strategy.—Christian Grossman.
Investment and Credit Risk.—Vivek Pathak.
Development Impact.—Nigel Twose.
East and Southern Africa.—Cheikh O. Seydi.
Environment, Social and Governance.—William Bulmer.
Global Equity.—Edwin Frank Taverner.
Financial Markets.—James Peter Srciven.
Financial Markets Asia.—Vacant.
Human Resources.—Eva Mennel-Hartung.
Inclusive Business Models.—Toshiya Masuoka.
Indicators and Analysis.—Augusto Lopez Claros.
Infrastructure and Natural Resources.—Bernard Sheahan.
Integrated Risk Management.—Avi Hofman.
Investment Climate.—Pierre Guislain.
Manufacturing, Agribusiness and Services.—Atul Mehta.
Manufacturing, Agribusiness and Services, Asia.—Vipul Prakash.
Manufacturing, Agribusiness and Services, Middle East and North Africa.—Guy M. Ellena.
Risk Management.—Maria da Graca Domingues.
Trade and Supply Chain.—Georgina Baker.
Special Operations.—Saran G. Kebet-Koulibaly.
Treasury Client Solutions.—Monish Mahurkar.
Syndicated Loans and Management.—Stefania Berla.
West and Central Africa.—Yolande Duhem.

MULTILATERAL INVESTMENT GUARANTEE AGENCY

President.—Jim Yong Kim.
Executive Vice President.—Keiko Honda.
Vice President and General Counsel, Legal Affairs and Claims Group.—Ana-Mita Betancourt.
Compliance Advisor/Ombudsman (IFC/ICC AND MIGA).—Meg Taylor.
Vice President and Chief Operating Officer.—Michel Wormser.
Operations Group.—Edith Quintrell.
Director and Chief Economist, Economics and Policy Group.—Ravi Vish.
Director and Chief Financial Officer, Finance and Risk Management Group.—Lakshmi Shyam-Sunder.

FOREIGN DIPLOMATIC OFFICES IN THE UNITED STATES

AFGHANISTAN

Embassy of Afghanistan
2341 Wyoming Avenue, NW., Washington, DC 20008
phone (202) 483–6410, fax 483–6488
His Excellency Eklil Ahmad Hakimi
Ambassador E. and P.
Consular Offices:
California, Los Angeles
New York, New York

AFRICAN UNION

Delegation of the African Union Mission
2200 Pennsylvania Avenue, NW., Floor 4 Washington, DC 20037
Embassy of the African Union
phone (202) 293–8006, fax 429–7130
Her Excellency Amina Salum Ali
Ambassador (Head of Delegation)

ALBANIA

Embassy of the Republic of Albania
1312 18th Street, NW., Washington, DC 20036
phone (202) 223–4942, fax 628–7342
His Excellency Gilbert Galanxhi
Ambassador E. and P.
Consular Offices:
Connecticut, Greenwich
Georgia, Avondale Estates
Louisiana, New Orleans
Massachusetts, Boston
Michigan, West Bloomfield
Missouri, Blue Springs
New York, New York
North Carolina, Southern Pines
Ohio, Cleveland
Texas, Houston

ALGERIA

Embassy of the Democratic Republic of Algeria
2118 Kalorama Road, NW., Washington, DC 20008
phone (202) 265–2800, fax 667–2174
His Excellency Abdallah Baali
Ambassador E. and P.
Consular Office: New York, New York

ANDORRA

Embassy of Andorra
2 United Nations Plaza, 27th Floor, New York, NY 10017
phone (212) 750–8064, fax 750–6630
His Excellency Narcis Casal De Fonsdeviela
Ambassador E. and P.
Consular Office: California, La Jolla

ANGOLA

Embassy of the Republic of Angola
2100–2108 16th Street, NW., Washington, DC 20009
phone (202) 785–1156, fax 785–1258
His Excellency Alberto Do Carmo Bento Ribeiro
Ambassador E. and P.
Consular Offices:
New York, New York
Texas, Houston

ANTIGUA AND BARBUDA

Embassy of Antigua and Barbuda
3216 New Mexico Avenue, NW., Washington, DC 20016
phone (202) 362–5122, fax 362–5225
Her Excellency Deborah Mae Lovell
Ambassador E. and P. / Consul General
Consular Offices:
District of Columbia, Washington
Florida, Miami
New York, New York
Puerto Rico, Guaynabo

ARGENTINA

Embassy of the Argentine Republic
1600 New Hampshire Avenue, NW., Washington, DC 20009
phone (202) 238–6400, fax 332–3171
Her Excellency Maria Cecilia Nahon
Ambassador E. and P.
Consular Offices:
California, Los Angeles
Florida, Miami
Georgia, Atlanta
Illinois, Chicago
New York, New York
Texas, Houston

ARMENIA

Embassy of the Republic of Armenia
2225 R Street, NW., Washington, DC 20008
phone (202) 319–1976, fax 319–2982
His Excellency Tatoul Markarian
Ambassador E. and P.

Consular Offices:
- California, Glendale
- District of Columbia, Washington

AUSTRALIA

Embassy of Australia
1601 Massachusetts Avenue, NW., Washington, DC 20036
phone (202) 797–3000, fax 797–3331
His Excellency Kim Christian Beazley
Ambassador E. and P.
Consular Offices:
- California, San Francisco
- Colorado, Denver
- District of Columbia, Washington
- Hawaii, Honolulu
- Illinois, Chicago
- New York, New York
- Texas, Houston
- Trust Territories of the Pacific Islands:
  - Kolonia, Micronesia
  - Pago Pago

AUSTRIA

Embassy of Austria
3524 International Court, NW., Washington, DC 20008–3035
phone (202) 895–6700, fax 895–6773
His Excellency Hans Peter Manz
Ambassador E. and P.
Consular Offices:
- Alaska, Anchorage
- Arizona, Scottsdale
- California:
  - Los Angeles
  - San Francisco
- Florida:
  - Estero
  - Hollywood
  - Orlando
- Georgia, Atlanta
- Hawaii, Honolulu
- Illinois, Chicago
- Louisiana, New Orleans
- Massachusetts, Boston
- Michigan, Detroit
- Minnesota, St. Paul
- Missouri:
  - Kansas City
  - St. Louis
- New York, New York
- Ohio, Columbus
- Oregon, Portland
- Pennsylvania:
  - Philadelphia
  - Pittsburgh
- Puerto Rico, San Juan
- South Carolina, Cowpens
- Texas, Houston
- Utah, Salt Lake City
- Virgin Islands, St. Thomas
- Virginia, Richmond
- Washington, Seattle

AZERBAIJAN

Embassy of the Republic of Azerbaijan
2741 34th Street, NW., Washington, DC 20008
phone (202) 337–3500, fax 337–5911
His Excellency Elin Suleymanov
Ambassador E. and P.
Consular Offices:
- California, Los Angeles
- New Mexico, Santa Fe

BAHAMAS

Embassy of the Commonwealth of The Bahamas
2220 Massachusetts Avenue, NW., Washington, DC 20008
phone (202) 319–2660, fax 319–2668
Mr. Freddie Cleveland Tucker
Counselor (Charge D'Affaires Ad Interim)
Consular Offices:
- District of Columbia, Washington
- Florida, Miami
- Georgia, Atlanta
- New York, New York

BAHRAIN

Embassy of the Kingdom of Bahrain
3502 International Drive, NW., Washington, DC 20008
phone (202) 342–0741, fax 362–2192
Her Excellency Huda Ezra Ebrahim Nonoo
Ambassador E. and P.
Consular Offices:
- California, San Diego
- New York, New York

BANGLADESH

Embassy of the People's Republic of Bangladesh
3510 International Drive, NW., Washington, DC 20008
phone (202) 244–0183, fax 244–5366
His Excellency Akramul Qader
Ambassador E. and P.
Consular Offices:
- California, Los Angeles
- Hawaii, Honolulu
- Louisiana, New Orleans
- New York, New York

BARBADOS

Embassy of Barbados
2144 Wyoming Avenue, NW., Washington, DC 20008
phone (202) 939–9200, fax 332–7467
His Excellency John Ernest Beale

Ambassador E. and P.
Consular Offices:
California:
Los Angeles
San Francisco
Florida, Miami
Georgia, Atlanta
Illinois, Chicago
Kentucky, Louisville
Louisiana, New Orleans
Michigan, Detroit
New York, New York
Oregon, Portland
South Carolina, Charleston
Texas, Sugar Land

BELARUS

Embassy of the Republic of Belarus
1619 New Hampshire Avenue, NW., Washington, DC 20009
phone (202) 986–1604, fax 986–1805
Mrs. Marina Kravchenko
Counselor (Charge D'Affaires Ad Interim)
Consular Offices:
District of Columbia, Washington
New York, New York

BELGIUM

Embassy of Belgium
3330 Garfield Street, NW., Washington, DC 20008
phone (202) 333–6900, fax 333–3079
His Excellency Jan Jozef Matthysen
Ambassador E. and P. / Consul General
Consular Offices:
Arizona, Phoenix
California:
Los Angeles
San Diego
San Francisco
Colorado, Denver
Connecticut, Greenwich
District of Columbia, Washington
Florida, Miami
Georgia, Atlanta
Hawaii, Honolulu
Illinois:
Chicago
Moline
Kansas, Kansas City
Kentucky, Louisville
Louisiana, New Orleans
Maryland, Baltimore
Massachusetts, Boston
Michigan, Bloomfield Hills
Minnesota, St. Paul
New York, New York
Ohio, Cincinnati
Oregon, Portland
Pennsylvania:
Philadelphia
Pittsburgh
Puerto Rico, San Juan
Texas:
Fort Worth
Houston
San Antonio
Utah, Salt Lake City
Virginia, Virginia Beach
Washington, Seattle
Wisconsin, Milwaukee

BELIZE

Embassy of Belize
2535 Massachusetts Avenue, NW., Washington, DC 20008
phone (202) 332–9636, fax 332–6888
His Excellency Nestor E. Mendez
Ambassador E. and P.
Consular Offices:
California:
Los Angeles
San Francisco
District of Columbia, Washington
Florida, Coral Gables
Georgia, Atlanta
Illinois:
Belleville
Des Plaines
Louisiana, New Orleans
Michigan, Detroit
Nevada, Las Vegas
North Carolina, Wilmington
Ohio, Dayton
Puerto Rico, San Juan
Texas:
Dallas
Houston
San Antonio

BHUTAN

Consular Offices:
District of Columbia, Washington
New York, New York
Washington, Edmonds

BOLIVIA

Embassy of the Republic of Bolivia
3014 Massachusetts Avenue, NW., Washington, DC 20008
phone (202) 483–4410, fax 328–3712
Mrs. Rosayda Zubieta De Bersatti
Minister / Counselor (Charge D'Affaires, Ad Interim)
Consular Offices:
California, Los Angeles
District of Columbia, Washington

Florida, Miami
Minnesota, Maple Grove
New York, New York
Puerto Rico, San Juan

BOSNIA AND HERZEGOVINA

Embassy of Bosnia and Herzegovina
2109 E Street, NW., Washington, DC 20037
phone (202) 337–1500, fax 337–1502
Her Excellency Jadranka Negodic
Ambassador E. and P.
Consular Offices:
Illinois, Chicago
New York, New York

BOTSWANA

Embassy of the Republic of Botswana
1531–1533 New Hampshire Avenue, NW., Washington, DC 20036
phone (202) 244–4990, fax 244–4164
Her Excellency Tebelelo Seretse
Ambassador E. and P.
Consular Offices:
California:
San Francisco
Santa Monica
Michigan, Southfield

BRAZIL

Brazilian Embassy
3006 Massachusetts Avenue, NW., Washington, DC 20008
phone (202) 238–2700, fax 238–2827
His Excellency Mauro Luiz Iecker Vieira
Ambassador E. and P.
Consular Offices:
Arizona, Tempe
California:
La Jolla
Los Angeles
San Francisco
Connecticut, Hartford
District of Columbia, Washington
Florida, Miami
Georgia, Atlanta
Hawaii, Honolulu
Illinois, Chicago
Louisiana, New Orleans
Massachusetts, Boston
Nevada, Las Vegas
New York, New York
Pennsylvania, Philadelphia
Tennessee, Memphis
Texas, Houston
Trust Territories of the Pacific Islands:
Hong Kong
Utah, Salt Lake City
Virginia, Norfolk
Washington, Seattle

BRUNEI

Embassy of the State of Brunei Darussalam
3520 International Court, NW., Washington, DC 20008
phone (202) 237–1838, fax 885–0560
His Excellency Dato Yusoff Abd Hamid
Ambassador E. and P.

BULGARIA

Embassy of the Republic of Bulgaria
1621 22nd Street, NW., Washington, DC 20008
phone (202) 387–0174, fax 234–7973
Her Excellency Elena B. Poptodorova Petrova
Ambassador E. and P.
Consular Offices:
California:
Los Angeles
Palm Springs
Sacramento
District of Columbia, Washington
Florida, Boca Raton
Illinois, Chicago
Maine, Portland
Massachusetts, Newton
Nevada, Las Vegas
New York, New York
Pennsylvania:
Media
West Homestead
South Carolina, Columbia

BURKINA FASO

Embassy of Burkina Faso
2340 Massachusetts Avenue, NW., Washington, DC 20008
phone (202) 332–5577, fax 667–1882
His Excellency Seydou Bouda
Ambassador E. and P.
Consular Offices:
California, Los Angeles
Louisiana, New Orleans

BURMA

Embassy of the Union of Burma
2300 S Street, NW., Washington, DC 20008
phone (202) 332–3344, fax 332–4351
His Excellency Than Swe
Mrs. Khin Win Yee
Ambassador E. and P.
Consular Office: New York, New York

BURUNDI

Embassy of the Republic of Burundi
2233 Wisconsin Avenue, NW., Suite 212, Washington, DC 20007
phone (202) 342–2574, fax 342–2578
Her Excellency Angele Niyuhire
Ambassador E. and P.

Consular Office: California, Los Angeles

CAMBODIA

Royal Embassy of Cambodia
4530 16th Street, NW., Washington, DC 20011
phone (202) 726–7742, fax 726–8381
His Excellency Heng Hem
Ambassador E. and P.
Consular Offices:
California, Long Beach
Massachusetts, Lowell
Pennsylvania, Philadelphia
Washington, Seattle

CAMEROON

Embassy of the Republic of Cameroon
2349 Massachusetts Avenue, NW., Washington, DC 20008
phone (202) 265–8790, fax 387–3826
His Excellency Bienvenu Joseph C. Foe Atangana
Ambassador E. and P.
Consular Offices:
California, San Francisco
Texas, Houston

CANADA

Embassy of Canada
501 Pennsylvania Avenue, NW., Washington, DC 20001
phone (202) 682–1740, fax 682–7726
His Excellency Gary Albert Doer
Ambassador E. and P.
Consular Offices:
California:
Los Angeles
Palo Alto
San Diego
San Francisco
Colorado, Denver
District of Columbia, Washington
Florida, Miami
Georgia, Atlanta
Illinois, Chicago
Louisiana, New Orleans
Iowa, Des Moines
Louisiana, New Orleans
Maine, Portland
Massachusetts, Boston
Michigan, Detroit
Minnesota, Minneapolis
Missouri, St. Louis
Montana, Nashua
New Jersey, Princeton
New York, New York
North Dakota, Bismarck
Oregon, Portland
Pennsylvania, Philadelphia
Puerto Rico, San Juan
Tennessee, Memphis
Texas:
Dallas
Houston
San Antonio
Virginia, Richmond
Washington, Seattle

CAPE VERDE

Embassy of the Republic of Cape Verde
3415 Massachusetts Avenue, NW., Washington, DC 20007
phone (202) 965–6820, fax 965–1207
Her Excellency Maria De Fatima Da Veiga
Ambassador E. and P.
Consular Office: Massachusetts, Boston

CENTRAL AFRICAN REPUBLIC

Embassy of Central African Republic
1618 22nd Street, NW., Washington, DC 20008
phone (202) 483–7800, fax 332–9893
His Excellency Stanislas Moussa Kembe
Ambassador E. and P.
Consular Offices:
California, Los Angeles
New York, New York

CHAD

Embassy of the Republic of Chad
2401 Massachusetts Avenue, NW., Washington, DC 20008
phone (202) 462–4009, fax 265–1937
His Excellency Djoumbe Maitine
Ambassador E. and P.

CHILE

Embassy of the Republic of Chile
1732 Massachusetts Avenue, NW., Washington, DC 20036
phone (202) 785–1746, fax 887–5579
His Excellency Felipe Bulnes Serrano
Ambassador E. and P.
Consular Offices:
Arizona, Phoenix
California:
Los Angeles
San Diego
San Francisco
District of Columbia, Washington
Florida:
Miami
Orlando
Georgia, Atlanta
Hawaii, Honolulu
Illinois, Chicago
Louisiana, New Orleans
Massachusetts, Boston
Michigan, Grosse Pointe Park

Missouri, Kansas City
Nevada, Las Vegas
New York, New York
Pennsylvania, Philadelphia
Puerto Rico, San Juan
South Carolina, Charleston
Texas:
Dallas
Houston
Washington, Olympia

CHINA

Embassy of the People's Republic of China
3505 International Place, NW., Washington, DC 20008
phone (202) 495–2000, fax 495–2138
His Excellency Tiankaicui
Ambassador E. and P.
Consular Offices:
California:
Los Angeles
San Francisco
Illinois, Chicago
New York, New York
Texas, Houston

COLOMBIA

Embassy of Colombia
2118 Leroy Place, NW., Washington, DC 20008
phone (202) 387–8338, fax 232–8643
His Excellency Carlos Alfredo Urrutia Valenzuela
Ambassador E. and P.
Consular Offices:
California:
Beverly Hills
San Francisco
District of Columbia, Washington
Florida:
Miami
Orlando
Georgia, Atlanta
Illinois, Chicago
Massachusetts, Boston
New Jersey, Newark
New York, New York
Puerto Rico, San Juan
Texas, Houston

COMOROS

Embassy of the Union of Comoros
866 United Nations Plaza, Suite 418, New York, NY 10017
phone (212) 750–1637, fax 750–1657
His Excellency Roubanikaambi
Ambassador E. and P.
Consular Office: Illinois, Chicago

CONGO, DEMOCRATIC REPUBLIC OF

Embassy of the Democratic Republic of Congo
1726 M Street, NW., Suite 601, Washington, DC 20036
phone (202) 234–7690, fax 234–2609
Her Excellency Faida Mitifu
Ambassador E. and P.
Consular Office: New York, New York

CONGO, REPUBLIC OF THE

Embassy of the Republic of the Congo
1720 16th Street, NW., Washington, DC 20011
phone (202) 726–5500, fax 726–1860
His Excellency Serge Mombouli
Ambassador E. and P.
Consular Office: Louisiana, New Orleans

COOK ISLANDS

Consular Office: California, Los Angeles

COSTA RICA

Embassy of Costa Rica
2114 S Street, NW., Washington, DC 20008
phone (202) 234–2945, fax 265–4795
Her Excellency Meta Shanon Figueres Boggs
Ambassador E. and P.
Consular Offices:
Arizona, Tucson
California, Los Angeles
Colorado, Denver
District of Columbia, Washington
Florida, Miami
Georgia, Atlanta
Massachusetts, Boston
Minnesota, St. Paul
New York, New York
Texas:
Austin
Dallas
Houston

CÔTE D'IVOIRE

Embassy of the Republic of Côte d'Ivoire
2424 Massachusetts Avenue, NW., Washington, DC 20008
phone (202) 797–0300, fax 462–9444
His Excellency Daouda Diabate
Ambassador E. and P.
Consular Offices:
California, San Francisco
Connecticut, Stamford
Florida, Orlando
Michigan, Detroit
Texas, Houston

CROATIA

Embassy of the Republic of Croatia
2343 Massachusetts Avenue, NW., Washington, DC 20008
phone (202) 588–5899, fax 588–8936
His Excellency Josip Paro
Ambassador E. and P.
Consular Offices:
- California, Los Angeles
- District of Columbia, Washington
- Illinois, Chicago
- Kansas, Kansas City
- Louisiana, New Orleans
- New York, New York
- Pennsylvania, Pittsburgh
- Texas, Houston
- Washington, Seattle

CYPRUS

Embassy of the Republic of Cyprus
2211 R Street, NW., Washington, DC 20008
phone (202) 462–5772, fax 483–6710
Ms. Olympia Neocleous
Counselor (Charge D'Affaires Ad Interim)
Consular Offices:
- California:
  - Los Angeles
  - San Francisco
- District of Columbia, Washington
- Georgia, Chamblee
- Illinois, Chicago
- Louisiana, New Orleans
- Michigan, Dearborn
- New York, New York
- North Carolina, Jacksonville
- Oregon, Portland
- Texas, Houston
- Washington, Seattle

CZECH REPUBLIC

Embassy of the Czech Republic
3900 Spring of Freedom Street, NW., Washington, DC 20008
phone (202) 274–9100, fax 966–8540
His Excellency Petr Gandalovic
Minister/Counselor (Charge D'Affaires Ad Interim)
Consular Offices:
- Alaska, Anchorage
- California:
  - Los Angeles
  - San Francisco
- Colorado, Boulder
- Florida:
  - Ft. Lauderdale
  - Orlando
- Georgia, Atlanta
- Hawaii, Honolulu
- Illinois, Chicago
- Louisiana, New Orleans
- Massachusetts, Wellesley
- Minnesota, St. Paul
- Missouri, Kansas City
- Montana, Livingston
- New York:
  - Buffalo
  - New York
- Oregon, Portland
- Pennsylvania:
  - Philadelphia
  - Pittsburgh
- Puerto Rico, San Juan
- Texas, Houston
- Utah, Salt Lake City
- Washington, Seattle

DENMARK

Royal Danish Embassy
3200 Whitehaven Street, NW., Washington, DC 20008
phone (202) 234–4300, fax 328–1470
His Excellency Peter Taksoe Jensen
Ambassador E. and P.
Consular Offices:
- Alabama, Mobile
- Alaska, Anchorage
- Arizona, Scottsdale
- California:
  - Los Angeles
  - Sacramento
  - San Diego
- Colorado, Denver
- Florida:
  - Hollywood
  - Jacksonville
  - Tampa
- Georgia, Macon
- Hawaii, Honolulu
- Illinois, Chicago
- Indiana, Indianapolis
- Iowa, Des Moines
- Kansas, Kansas City
- Louisiana, New Orleans
- Maryland, Baltimore
- Massachusetts, Boston
- Michigan, Detroit
- Minnesota, Minneapolis
- Nebraska, Omaha
- New York, New York
- Ohio, Cleveland
- Oregon, Portland
- Pennsylvania:
  - Philadelphia
  - Pittsburgh
- Puerto Rico, San Juan
- South Carolina, Charleston
- Tennessee, Nashville

Texas:
Dallas
Houston
Utah, Salt Lake City
Virgin Islands, St. Thomas
Virginia, Virginia Beach
Washington, Seattle
Wisconsin, Milwaukee

DJIBOUTI

Embassy of the Republic of Djibouti
1156 15th Street, NW., Suite 515, Washington, DC 20005
phone (202) 331–0270, fax 331–0302
His Excellency Roble Olhaye
Ambassador E. and P.

DOMINICA

Embassy of the Commonwealth of Dominica
3216 New Mexico Avenue, NW., Washington, DC 20016
phone (202) 364–6781, fax 364–6791
His Excellency Hubert John Charles
Ambassador E. and P.
Consular Offices:
New York, New York
Puerto Rico, Guaynabo

DOMINICAN REPUBLIC

Embassy of the Dominican Republic
1715 22nd Street, NW., Washington, DC 20008
phone (202) 332–6280, fax 265–8057
His Excellency Anibal De Castro Rodriguez
Ambassador E. and P.
Consular Offices:
California, Glendale
Florida, Miami
Illinois, Chicago
Louisiana, New Orleans
Massachusetts, Boston
New York, New York
Puerto Rico:
Mayaguez
San Juan

ECUADOR

Embassy of Ecuador
1050 30th Street, NW., Washington, DC 20007
phone (202) 234–7200, fax 667–3482
Her Excellency Saskia Nathalie Cely Suarez
Minister (Charge D'Affaires A.I.)
Consular Offices:
Arizona, Phoenix
California:
Los Angeles
San Francisco
Connecticut, New Haven
District of Columbia, Washington
Florida, Miami
Georgia, Atlanta
Illinois, Chicago
Louisiana, New Orleans
Massachusetts, Boston
Minnesota, Minneapolis
Nevada, Las Vegas
New Jersey, Newark
New York:
New York
Woodside
Puerto Rico, San Juan
Texas:
Dallas
Houston

EGYPT

Embassy of the Arab Republic of Egypt
3521 International Court, NW., Washington, DC 20008
phone (202) 895–5400, fax 244–4319
His Excellency Mohamed Mostafa Mohamed Tawfik
Ambassador E. and P.
Consular Offices:
California, Los Angeles
Illinois, Chicago
New York, New York
Texas, Houston

EL SALVADOR

Embassy of El Salvador
1400 16th Street, NW., Suite 100, Washington, DC 20036
phone (202) 265–9671, fax 232–3763
His Excellency Ruben Ignacio Zamora Rivas
Ambassador E. and P.
Consular Offices:
Arizona:
Fountain Hills
Tucson
California:
Chula Vista
Costa Mesa
Los Angeles
Oakland
San Francisco
Santa Ana
District of Columbia, Washington
Florida, Coral Gables
Georgia, Woodstock
Illinois, Chicago
Indiana, Indianapolis
Louisiana, New Orleans
Nevada, Las Vegas
New Jersey, Elizabeth
New York:

Brentwood
New York
Pennsylvania, Philadelphia
Puerto Rico, Bayamon
Texas:
Dallas
Houston
Utah, Salt Lake City
Virginia, Woodbridge
Washington, Seattle

EQUATORIAL GUINEA

Embassy of the Republic of Equatorial Guinea
2020 16th Street, NW., Washington, DC 20009
phone (202) 518–5700, fax 518–5252
Mr. Roman Obama Ekua
Second Secretary (Charge D'Affaires Ad Interim)
Consular Office: Texas, Houston

ERITREA

Embassy of the State of Eritrea
1708 New Hampshire Avenue, NW., Washington, DC 20009
phone (202) 319–1991, fax 319–1304
Mr. Berhane Gebrehiwet Solomon
First Secretary (Charge D'Affaires Ad Interim)
Consular Office: District of Columbia, Washington

ESTONIA

Embassy of Estonia
2131 Massachusetts Avenue, NW., Washington, DC 20008
phone (202) 588–0101, fax 588–0108
Her Excellency Marina Kaljurand
Ambassador E. and P.
Consular Offices:
Arizona, Scottsdale
California:
Los Angeles
San Francisco
Florida:
Miami
St. Petersburg
Georgia, Atlanta
Illinois, Chicago
Nebraska, Lincoln
New Hampshire, Portsmouth
New York, New York
North Carolina, Huntersville
South Carolina, Charleston
Texas, Houston
Washington, Seattle

ETHIOPIA

Embassy of Ethiopia
3506 International Drive, NW., Washington, DC 20008
phone (202) 364–1200, fax 686–9551
His Excellency Girma Birru Geda
Ambassador E. and P.
Consular Offices:
California, Los Angeles
New York, New York
Texas, Houston
Washington, Seattle

EUROPEAN UNION

Delegation of the European Commission
2175 K Street, NW., Washington, DC 20037
phone (202) 862–9500, fax 429–1766
His Excellency Joao Vale De Almeida
Ambassador (Head of Delegation)

FIJI

Embassy of the Republic of the Fiji Islands
2000 M Street, NW., Suite 710, Washington, DC 20036
phone (202) 466–8320, fax 466–8325
His Excellency Winston Thompson
Ambassador E. and P.
Consular Offices:
California:
El Segundo
San Francisco
Oregon, Portland
Texas, Dallas

FINLAND

Embassy of Finland
3301 Massachusetts Avenue, NW., Washington, DC 20008
phone (202) 298–5800, fax 298–6030
Her Excellency Ritva Inkerikoukku Ronde
Ambassador E. and P.
Consular Offices:
Alabama, Birmingham
Alaska, Anchorage
Arizona, Phoenix
California:
Los Angeles
San Diego
San Francisco
Colorado, Highlands Ranch
Connecticut, Norwich
Florida:
Lake Worth
Miami
Georgia, Atlanta
Hawaii, Honolulu
Illinois, Chicago
Louisiana, New Orleans
Maryland, Baltimore
Massachusetts, Boston
Michigan:
Farmington
Hancock

Minnesota:
- Minneapolis
- Virginia

Missouri, Saint Louis
New Jersey, Newark
New York, New York
Pennsylvania, Philadelphia
Puerto Rico, San Juan
Texas:
- Dallas
- Houston

Utah, Salt Lake City
Virginia, Norfolk
Washington, Seattle

FRANCE

Embassy of France
4101 Reservoir Road, NW., Washington, DC 20007
phone (202) 944–6000, fax 944–6166
His Excellency Francois Marie Delattre
Ambassador E. and P.
Consular Offices:
Alabama, Auburn University
Alaska, Anchorage
Arizona, Phoenix
Arkansas, Little Rock
California:
- Los Angeles
- Los Gatos
- Sacramento
- San Diego
- San Francisco

Colorado, Denver
Connecticut, Hartford
District of Columbia, Washington
Florida:
- Clearwater
- Jacksonville
- Miami
- Orlando

Georgia:
- Atlanta
- Savannah

Guam, Tamuning
Hawaii, Honolulu
Idaho, Boise
Illinois, Chicago
Indiana, Indianapolis
Iowa, Indianola
Kentucky, Louisville
Louisiana:
- Lafayette
- New Orleans
- Shreveport

Maine, Portland
Massachusetts, Boston
Michigan, Southfield
Minnesota, Minneapolis
Mississippi, Hattiesburg
Missouri:
- Kansas City
- Saint Louis

Montana, Hamilton
Nebraska, Omaha
Nevada:
- Las Vegas
- Reno

New Hampshire, Manchester
New Jersey, Princeton
New Mexico, Albuquerque
New York:
- Buffalo
- New York

North Carolina:
- Charlotte
- Raleigh

Ohio:
- Cincinnati
- Cleveland

Oklahoma, Oklahoma City
Oregon, Portland
Pennsylvania:
- Philadelphia
- Pittsburgh

Puerto Rico, San Juan
Rhode Island, Providence
South Carolina:
- Greenville
- Mount Pleasant

Tennessee, Nashville
Texas:
- Austin
- Dallas
- Houston
- San Antonio

Utah, Salt Lake City
Vermont, Burlington
Virgin Islands, St. Thomas
Virginia, Norfolk
Washington, Seattle
Wyoming, Dubois

GABON

Embassy of the Gabonese Republic
2034 20th Street, NW., Suite 200, Washington, DC 20009
phone (202) 797–1000, fax 332–0668
His Excellency Michael Moussa Adamo
Ambassador E. and P.
Consular Office: New York, New York

GAMBIA

Embassy of The Gambia
1424 K Street, NW., Suite 600, Washington, DC 20005

phone (202) 785–1379, fax 785–1430
His Excellency Alieu Momodou Ngum
Ambassador E. and P.
Consular Office: Florida, Miami

GEORGIA

Embassy of the Republic of Georgia
2209 Massachusetts Avenue, NW., Washington, DC 20008
phone (202) 387–2390, fax 393–4537
His Excellency Archil Gegeshidze
Ambassador E. and P.
Consular Offices:
- California, Orange
- District of Columbia, Washington
- Georgia, Atlanta
- Massachusetts, Boston
- New York, New York
- South Carolina, Charleston

GERMANY, FEDERAL REPUBLIC OF

Embassy of the Federal Republic of Germany
4645 Reservoir Road, NW., Washington, DC 20007
phone (202) 298–4000, fax 298–4249
His Excellency Dr. Niels Peter Georg Ammon
Ambassador E. and P.
Consular Offices:
- Alabama, Birmingham
- Alaska, Anchorage
- Arizona, Phoenix
- California:
  - Los Angeles
  - San Diego
  - San Francisco
- Colorado, Denver
- Connecticut, Farmington
- District of Columbia, Washington
- Florida:
  - Miami
  - Naples
  - Orlando
- Georgia:
  - Atlanta
  - Savannah
- Hawaii, Honolulu
- Illinois, Chicago
- Indiana, Indianapolis
- Iowa, Indianola
- Kansas, Leawood
- Kentucky, Louisville
- Louisiana, New Orleans
- Maine, Portland
- Massachusetts, Boston
- Michigan, Auburn Hills
- Minnesota, Minneapolis
- Mississippi, Jackson
- Missouri, St. Louis
- Nevada, Las Vegas
- New Mexico, Albuquerque
- New York:
  - Buffalo
  - New York
- North Carolina, Charlotte
- Ohio:
  - Cincinnati
  - Cleveland
- Oklahoma, Oklahoma City
- Oregon, Portland
- Pennsylvania:
  - Philadelphia
  - Pittsburgh
- Puerto Rico, San Juan
- South Carolina, Greer
- Tennessee, Nashville
- Texas:
  - Dallas
  - Houston
  - San Antonio
- Trust Territories of the Pacific Islands:
  - Manila, Philippines
  - Wellington, New Zealand
- Utah, Salt Lake City
- Virginia, Virginia Beach
- Washington, Mercer Island

GHANA

Embassy of Ghana
3512 International Drive, NW., Washington, DC 20008
phone (202) 686–4520, fax 686–4527
His Excellency Daniel Ohene Agyekum
Ambassador E. and P.
Consular Offices:
- New York, New York
- Texas, Houston

GREECE

Embassy of Greece
2217 Massachusetts Avenue, NW., Washington, DC 20008
phone (202) 939–1300, fax 939–1324
His Excellency Christos Panagopoulos
Ambassador E. and P.
Consular Offices:
- California:
  - Los Angeles
  - San Francisco
- Florida, Tampa
- Georgia, Atlanta
- Illinois, Chicago
- Louisiana, New Orleans
- Massachusetts, Boston
- New York, New York

Texas, Houston

GRENADA

Embassy of Grenada
1701 New Hampshire Avenue, NW., Washington, DC 20009
phone (202) 265–2561, fax 265–2468
Her Excellency Gillian Margaret Susan Bristol
Ambassador E. and P.
Consular Offices:
Florida, Ft. Lauderdale
Illinois, Chicago
Michigan, Northville
New York, New York
Puerto Rico, Guaynabo

GUATEMALA

Embassy of Guatemala
2220 R Street, NW., Washington, DC 20008
phone (202) 745–4952, fax 745–1908
His Excellency Jose Francisco Villagran De Leon
Ambassador E. and P.
Consular Offices:
Alabama, Montgomery
Arizona, Phoenix
California:
Los Angeles
San Diego
San Francisco
Colorado, Denver
Florida:
Ft. Lauderdale
Jupiter
Miami
Georgia, Atlanta
Illinois, Chicago
Louisiana:
Lafayette
New Orleans
Maryland, Silver Spring
Massachusetts, Newton
Missouri, Kansas City
Nevada, North Las Vegas
New York, New York
North Carolina, Charlotte
Oklahoma, Oklahoma City
Oregon, Portland
Pennsylvania, Philadelphia
Puerto Rico, San Juan
South Carolina, Columbia
Tennessee, Memphis
Texas:
Houston
San Antonio
Washington, Seattle
Wisconsin, Madison

GUINEA

Embassy of the Republic of Guinea
2112 Leroy Place, NW., Washington, DC 20008
phone (202) 986–4300, fax 986–3800
His Excellency Blaise Cherif
Ambassador E. and P.
Consular Office: California, Santa Monica

GUYANA

Embassy of Guyana
2490 Tracy Place, NW., Washington, DC 20008
phone (202) 265–6900, fax 232–1297
His Excellency Bayney Ram Karran
Ambassador E. and P.
Consular Offices:
Florida, Miami
New York, New York
Texas, Houston

HAITI

Embassy of the Republic of Haiti
2311 Massachusetts Avenue, NW., Washington, DC 20008
phone (202) 332–4090, fax 745–7215
His Excellency Paul Getty Altidor
Ambassador E. and P.
Consular Offices:
California, San Francisco
Florida:
Miami
Orlando
Georgia, Atlanta
Illinois, Chicago
Louisiana, New Orleans
Massachusetts, Boston
New Jersey, Trenton
New York, New York
Pennsylvania:
Philadelphia
Pottsville
Puerto Rico, San Juan
Texas, Houston

HOLY SEE

Apostolic Nunciature
3339 Massachusetts Avenue, NW., Washington, DC 20008
phone (202) 333–7121, fax 337–4036
His Excellency Reverend Carlo Maria Vigano
Apostolic Nuncio

HONDURAS

Embassy of Honduras
3007 Tilden Street, NW., Suite 4–M, Washington, DC 20008
phone (202) 966–2604, fax 966–9751
His Excellency Jorge Ramon Hernandez Alcerro
Ambassador E. and P.

Consular Offices:
- Arizona, Phoenix
- California:
  - Los Angeles
  - San Diego
  - San Francisco
- Florida:
  - Miami
  - Tampa
- Georgia, Atlanta
- Hawaii, Honolulu
- Illinois, Chicago
- Louisiana:
  - Baton Rouge
  - New Orleans
- Maryland, Baltimore
- Massachusetts, Belmont
- Missouri, St. Louis
- Nevada, Reno
- New York, New York
- Texas, Houston

HUNGARY

Embassy of the Republic of Hungary

3910 Shoemaker Street, NW., Washington, DC 20008

phone (202) 362–6730, fax 966–8135

His Excellency Gyoergy Bela Szapary

Ambassador E. and P.

Consular Offices:
- California:
  - Los Angeles
  - Sacramento
  - San Francisco
- Colorado, Denver
- District of Columbia, Washington
- Florida:
  - Miami
  - Sarasota
- Georgia, Morrow
- Hawaii, Honolulu
- Illinois, Chicago
- Louisiana, Metairie
- Massachusetts, Boston
- Missouri, St. Louis
- New York, New York
- Ohio, Cleveland
- Puerto Rico, Mayaguez
- Texas, Houston
- Utah, Sandy
- Washington, Seattle

ICELAND

Embassy of Iceland

1156 15th Street, NW., Suite 1200, Washington, DC 20005

phone (202) 265–6653, fax 265–6656

His Excellency Gudmundur Arnistefansson

Ambassador E. and P.

Consular Offices:
- Alaska, Anchorage
- Arizona, Phoenix
- California:
  - Los Angeles
  - San Diego
  - San Francisco
- Colorado, Englewood
- Florida:
  - Orlando
  - Plantation
- Georgia, Atlanta
- Illinois, Chicago
- Kentucky, Louisville
- Louisiana, New Orleans
- Massachusetts, Boston
- Michigan, Detroit
- Minnesota, Minneapolis
- Missouri, Grandview
- New York, New York
- North Dakota, Grand Fork
- Oregon, Portland
- Pennsylvania, Harrisburg
- Puerto Rico, Guaynabo
- South Carolina, Charleston
- Texas:
  - Austin
  - Dallas
- Utah, Salt Lake City
- Virginia, Norfolk
- Washington, Seattle
- Wisconsin, Madison

INDIA

Embassy of India

2107 Massachusetts Avenue, NW., Washington, DC 20008

phone (202) 939–7000, fax 483–3972

Her Excellency Nirupama Rao

Ambassador E. and P.

Consular Offices:
- California, San Francisco
- District of Columbia, Washington
- Georgia, Atlanta
- Illinois, Chicago
- New York, New York
- Texas, Houston

INDONESIA

Embassy of the Republic of Indonesia

2020 Massachusetts Avenue, NW., Washington, DC 20036

phone (202) 775–5200, fax 775–5365

His Excellency Dino Patti Djalal

Ambassador E. and P.

Consular Offices:

California:
Los Angeles
San Francisco
Hawaii, Honolulu
Illinois, Chicago
New York, New York
Texas, Houston

IRAQ

Embassy of the Republic of Iraq
3421 Massachusetts Avenue, NW., Washington, DC 20007
phone (202) 742–1600, fax 462–5066
His Excellency Jabir Habeb Jabir Hemaidawi
Ambassador E. and P.
Consular Offices:
California, Los Angeles
Michigan, Southfield

IRELAND

Embassy of Ireland
2234 Massachusetts Avenue, NW., Washington, DC 20008
phone (202) 462–3939, fax 232–5993
His Excellency Michael Collins
Ambassador E. and P.
Consular Offices:
California:
Los Angeles
San Francisco
Colorado, Denver
Florida, Orlando
Georgia, Atlanta
Hawaii, Honolulu
Illinois, Chicago
Louisiana, New Orleans
Massachusetts, Boston
Missouri, St. Louis
Nevada, Las Vegas
New York, New York
Pennsylvania, Pittsburgh
Texas, Houston
Washington, Seattle

ISRAEL

Embassy of Israel
3514 International Drive, NW., Washington, DC 20008
phone (202) 364–5500, fax 364–5607
His Excellency Michael Scott Oren
Ambassador E. and P.
Consular Offices:
California:
Los Angeles
San Francisco
District of Columbia, Washington
Florida, Miami
Georgia, Atlanta
Illinois, Chicago
Massachusetts, Boston
New York, New York
Pennsylvania, Philadelphia
Texas, Houston

ITALY

Embassy of Italy
3000 Whitehaven Street, NW., Washington, DC 20008
phone (202) 612–4400, fax 518–2151
His Excellency Claudio Bisogniero
Ambassador E. and P.
Consular Offices:
Alaska, Anchorage
Arizona, Scottsdale
California:
Fresno
Los Angeles
Sacramento
San Diego
San Francisco
San Jose
Colorado, Denver
Connecticut, Hartford
Florida:
Miami
Orlando
Georgia:
Atlanta
Savannah
Hawaii, Honolulu
Illinois, Chicago
Indiana, Indianapolis
Kansas, Leawood
Louisiana, New Orleans
Maryland, Baltimore
Massachusetts:
Boston
Worcester
Michigan, Detroit
Mississippi, Hattiesburg
Missouri, St. Louis
Nevada, Las Vegas
New Jersey, Newark
New York:
Buffalo
Mineola
Mt. Vernon
New York
Rochester
North Carolina, Charlotte
Ohio, Cleveland
Oregon, Portland
Pennsylvania:
Philadelphia
Pittsburgh

Puerto Rico, San Juan
Rhode Island, Providence
South Carolina, Charleston
Texas, Houston
Utah, Salt Lake City
Virginia, Norfolk
Washington, Seattle

JAMAICA

Embassy of Jamaica
1520 New Hampshire Avenue, NW., Washington, DC 20036
phone (202) 452–0660, fax 452–0081
His Excellency Stephen Charles Vasciannie
Ambassador E. and P.
Consular Offices:
California:
Los Angeles
San Francisco
District of Columbia, Washington
Florida, Miami
Georgia, Atlanta
Illinois, Chicago
Massachusetts, Boston
New Hampshire, Concord
New York, New York
Pennsylvania, Philadelphia
Texas:
Dallas
Houston
Virginia, Richmond
Washington, Seattle

JAPAN

Embassy of Japan
2520 Massachusetts Avenue, NW., Washington, DC 20008
phone (202) 238–6700, fax 328–2187
His Excellency Kenichiro Sasae
Ambassador E. and P.
Consular Offices:
Alaska, Anchorage
Arizona, Tempe
California:
Los Angeles
San Diego
San Francisco
Colorado, Denver
Connecticut, Simsbury
District of Columbia, Washington
Florida:
Miami
Orlando
Georgia, Atlanta
Guam, Agana
Hawaii:
Hilo
Honolulu
Idaho, Boise
Illinois, Chicago
Indiana, Indianapolis
Kansas, Prairie Village
Kentucky, Lexington
Louisiana, New Orleans
Massachusetts, Boston
Michigan, Detroit
Minnesota, Minneapolis
Missouri, St. Louis
Nebraska, Omaha
Nevada, Las Vegas
New Mexico, Albuquerque
New York:
Buffalo
New York
North Carolina, Durham
Northern Mariana Islands, Mariana Islands
Ohio, Dublin
Oklahoma, Oklahoma City
Oregon, Portland
Pennsylvania, Philadelphia
Puerto Rico, San Juan
Tennessee, Nashville
Texas:
Dallas
Houston
Washington, Seattle

JORDAN

Embassy of the Hashemite Kingdom of Jordan
3504 International Drive, NW., Washington, DC 20008
phone (202) 966–2664, fax 966–3110
Her Excellency Dr. Alia Mohamad Ali Hatough Bouran
Ambassador E. and P.
Consular Offices:
California, San Francisco
Illinois, Chicago
Michigan, Detroit

KAZAKHSTAN

Embassy of the Republic of Kazakhstan
1401 16th Street, NW., Washington, DC 20036
phone (202) 232–5488, fax 232–5845
His Excellency Kairat Umarov
Ambassador E. and P.
Consular Offices:
California:
San Francisco
Santa Monica
District of Columbia, Washington
Louisiana, Baton Rouge
New York, New York
North Dakota, Fargo
Texas, Katy

KENYA

Embassy of the Republic of Kenya
2249 R Street, NW., Washington, DC 20008
phone (202) 387–6101, fax 462–3829
His Excellency Elkanah Odembo Absalom
Ambassador E. and P.
Consular Offices:
California, Los Angeles
New York, New York

KIRIBATI

Consular Office: Hawaii, Honolulu

KOREA

Embassy of the Republic of Korea
2450 Massachusetts Avenue, NW., Washington, DC 20008
phone (202) 939–5600, fax 387–0250
His Excellency Youngjin Choi
Ambassador E. and P.
Consular Offices:
Alaska, Anchorage
Arizona, Tucson
California:
Los Angeles
San Francisco
Colorado, Denver
Connecticut, Stamford
District of Columbia, Washington
Florida, Miami
Georgia, Atlanta
Guam, Agana
Hawaii, Honolulu
Illinois, Chicago
Louisiana, New Orleans
Massachusetts, Boston
Michigan, Southfield
Missouri, Saint Louis
Nevada, Reno
New York, New York
Oklahoma, Oklahoma City
Oregon, Portland
Pennsylvania, Philadelphia
Puerto Rico, San Juan
Texas:
Dallas
Houston
Utah, Salt Lake City
Washington, Seattle

KOSOVO REPUBLIC

Embassy of the Republic of Kosovo
900 19th Street, NW., Suite 400, Washington, DC 20006
phone (202) 380–3581, fax 380–3628
His Excellency Akan Ismaili
Ambassador E. and P.
Consular Office: New York, New York

KUWAIT

Embassy of the State of Kuwait
2940 Tilden Street, NW., Washington, DC 20008
phone (202) 966–0702, fax 966–0517
His Excellency Sheikh Salem Abdullah Al Jaber Al-Sabah
Ambassador E. and P.
Consular Office: California, Los Angeles

KYRGYZSTAN

Embassy of the Kyrgyz Republic
2360 Massachusetts Avenue, NW., Suite 600, Washington, DC 20008
phone (202) 449–9823, fax 386–7550
His Excellency Muktar Djumaliev
Ambassador E. and P.
Consular Offices:
District of Columbia, Washington
Montana, Helena
New Jersey, South Plainfield
New York, New York
Texas, Houston
Washington, Maple Valley

LATVIA

Embassy of Latvia
2306 Massachusetts Avenue, NW., Washington, DC 20008
phone (202) 328–2840, fax 328–2860
His Excellency Andris Razans
Ambassador E. and P.
Consular Offices:
Alaska, Palmer
California:
Mill Valley
Rancho Santa Margarita
Connecticut, Greenwich
Florida, Ft. Lauderdale
Illinois, Chicago
Massachusetts, Needham
Michigan, West Bloomfield
Minnesota, Minneapolis
New York:
Buffalo
New York
Ohio, Cincinnati
Oregon, Salem
Pennsylvania, Philadelphia
Rhode Island, North Kingstown
Texas, Houston
Washington, Snohomish

LEBANON

Embassy of Lebanon
2560 28th Street, NW., Washington, DC 20008
phone (202) 939–6300, fax 939–6324
His Excellency Antoine Chedid
Ambassador E. and P.

Consular Offices:
- California, Los Angeles
- Massachusetts, Boston
- Michigan, Detroit
- New York, New York
- North Carolina, Raleigh
- Texas, Houston

LESOTHO

Embassy of the Kingdom of Lesotho
2511 Massachusetts Avenue, NW., Washington, DC 20008
phone (202) 797–5533, fax 234–6815
His Excellency Eliachim Molapisebatane
Ambassador E. and P.
Consular Offices:
- Louisiana, New Orleans
- Texas, Austin

LIBERIA

Embassy of the Republic of Liberia
5201 16th Street, NW., Washington, DC 20011
phone (202) 723–0437, fax 723–0436
His Excellency Jeremiah Congbeh Sulunteh
Ambassador E. and P.
Consular Offices:
- California:
  - Los Angeles
  - San Francisco
- District of Columbia, Washington
- Florida, Tampa
- Georgia, Atlanta
- Illinois, Chicago
- Michigan, Detroit
- New York, New York
- Pennsylvania, Philadelphia

LIBYA

Embassy of the Libyan Arab Jamahiriya
2600 Virginia Avenue, NW., Suite 705, Washington, DC 20037
phone (202) 944–9601, fax 944–9606
His Excellency Ali Suleiman Aujali
Ambassador E. and P.
Consular Office: District of Columbia, Washington

LIECHTENSTEIN

Embassy of the Principality of Liechtenstein
2900 K Street, NW., Suite 602B, Washington, DC 20007
phone (202) 331–0590, fax 331–3221
Her Excellency Claudia Fritsche
Ambassador E. and P.
Consular Offices:
- California, Los Angeles
- Georgia, Macon
- Illinois, Chicago
- Oregon, Portland

LITHUANIA

Embassy of the Republic of Lithuania
2622 16th Street, NW., Washington, DC 20009
phone (202) 234–5860, fax 328–0466
His Excellency Zygimantas Pavilionis
Ambassador E. and P.
Consular Offices:
- Alaska, Anchorage
- Arizona, Phoenix
- California:
  - Lafayette
  - Santa Monica
- Colorado, Aspen
- Florida:
  - Palm Beach
  - St. Petersburg
- Georgia, Marietta
- Illinois, Chicago
- Michigan:
  - Farmington
  - Lansing
- Minnesota, Stillwater
- Nevada, Las Vegas
- New Hampshire, Manchester
- New York:
  - New York
  - Webster
- Ohio, Cleveland
- Oregon, Portland
- Pennsylvania, Philadelphia
- Texas, Houston
- Washington, Seattle

LUXEMBOURG

Embassy of Grand Duchy of Luxembourg
2200 Massachusetts Avenue, NW., Washington, DC 20008
phone (202) 265–4171, fax 328–8270
His Excellency Jean Louis Wolzfeld
Ambassador E. and P.
Consular Offices:
- Arizona, Scottsdale
- California:
  - San Francisco
  - Woodland Hills
- Colorado, Louisville
- Florida, Estero
- Georgia, Atlanta
- Hawaii, Kapolei
- Illinois, Elburn
- Indiana, Indianapolis
- Louisiana, New Orleans
- Massachusetts, Boston
- Michigan, Auburn Hills
- Minnesota, Edina
- Missouri, Kansas City
- New York, New York
- Ohio, Cleveland

Oregon, Portland
Texas, Ft. Worth
Washington, Seattle
Wisconsin, Grafton

MACEDONIA

Embassy of the Republic of Macedonia
2129 Wyoming Avenue, NW., Washington, DC 20008
phone (202) 667–0501, fax 667–2131
His Excellency Zoran Jolevski
Ambassador E. and P.
Consular Offices:
Arizona, Tucson
California:
Ontario
San Diego
Florida:
Hollywood
Naples
Illinois, Chicago
Michigan, Southfield
New Jersey, Clifton
New York, New York
Ohio, Columbus

MADAGASCAR

Embassy of the Republic of Madagascar
2374 Massachusetts Avenue, NW., Washington, DC 20008
phone (202) 265–5525, fax 265–3034
Mrs. Velotiana Rakotoanosy Raobelina
Counselor (Charge D'Affaires Ad Interim)
Consular Offices: New York, New York

MALAWI

Embassy of Malawi
2408 Massachusetts Avenue, NW., Washington, DC 20008
phone (202) 721–0270, fax 721–0288
His Excellency Stephen Dick Tennyson Matenje
Ambassador E. and P.

MALAYSIA

Embassy of Malaysia
3516 International Court, NW., Washington, DC 20008
phone (202) 572–9700, fax 572–9882
His Excellency Dato Othman Bin Hashim
Ambassador E. and P.
Consular Offices:
California, Los Angeles
Hawaii, Honolulu
New York, New York
Oregon, Portland

MALDIVES

Embassy of the Republic of Maldives
800 2nd Avenue, Suite 400E, New York, NY 10017
phone (212) 599–6195, fax 661–6405
His Excellency Ahmed Sareer
Ambassador E. and P.

MALI

Embassy of the Republic of Mali
2130 R Street, NW., Washington, DC 20008
phone (202) 332–2249, fax 332–6603
His Excellency Al-Maamoun Baba Lamine Keita
Ambassador E. and P.
Consular Offices:
California, Cupertino
Florida, Ft. Lauderdale
Georgia, Atlanta
Louisiana, New Orleans

MALTA

Embassy of Malta
2017 Connecticut Avenue, NW., Washington, DC 20008
phone (202) 462–3611, fax 387–5470
Mr. Dennis Grech
First Secretary (Charge D'Affaires Ad Interim)
Consular Offices:
Arizona, Phoenix
California:
Los Angeles
San Francisco
District of Columbia, Washington
Florida, Miami
Georgia, Atlanta
Illinois, Barrington
Louisiana, Metairie
Massachusetts, Bellmont
Michigan:
Detroit
Taylor
Minnesota, St. Paul
New York, New York
Pennsylvania, Philadelphia
Tennessee, Kingsport
Texas:
Dallas
Houston
Washington, Seattle

MARSHALL ISLANDS

Embassy of the Republic of the Marshall Islands
2433 Massachusetts Avenue, NW., 1st Floor, Washington, DC 20008
phone (202) 234–5414, fax 232–3236
His Excellency Charles Rudolph Paul
Ambassador E. and P.
Consular Offices:
Arkansas, Springdale
Guam, Agana
Hawaii, Honolulu

MAURITANIA

Embassy of the Islamic Republic of Mauritania
2129 Leroy Place, NW., Washington, DC 20008
phone (202) 232–5700, fax 319–2623
His Excellency Mohamed Lemine El Haycen
Ambassador E. and P.
Consular Office: Pennsylvania, Newtown Square

MAURITIUS

Embassy of the Republic of Mauritius
4301 Connecticut Avenue, NW., Suite 441, Washington, DC 20008
phone (202) 244–1491, fax 966–0983
His Excellency Somduth Soborun
Ambassador E. and P.
Consular Offices:
- California:
  - Los Angeles
  - San Francisco

MEXICO

Embassy of Mexico
1911 Pennsylvania Avenue, NW., Washington, DC 20006
phone (202) 728–1600, fax 728–1698
His Excellency Eduardo Tomas Medina Mora Icaza
Ambassador E. and P.
Consular Offices:
- Alaska, Anchorage
- Arizona:
  - Douglas
  - Nogales
  - Phoenix
  - Tucson
  - Yuma
- Arkansas, Little Rock
- California:
  - Calexico
  - Fresno
  - Los Angeles
  - Oxnard
  - Sacramento
  - Salinas
  - San Bernardino
  - San Diego
  - San Francisco
  - San Jose
  - Santa Ana
- Colorado, Denver
- District of Columbia, Washington
- Florida:
  - Jacksonville
  - Miami
  - Orlando
- Georgia, Atlanta
- Hawaii, Honolulu
- Idaho, Boise
- Illinois, Chicago
- Indiana, Indianapolis
- Louisiana, New Orleans
- Massachusetts, Boston
- Michigan, Detroit
- Minnesota, St. Paul
- Missouri, Kansas City
- Nebraska, Omaha
- Nevada, Las Vegas
- New Mexico, Albuquerque
- New York, New York
- North Carolina:
  - Charlotte
  - Raleigh
- Oregon, Portland
- Pennsylvania, Philadelphia
- Puerto Rico, San Juan
- Texas:
  - Austin
  - Brownsville
  - Dallas
  - Del Rio
  - Eagle Pass
  - El Paso
  - Houston
  - Laredo
  - McAllen
  - Midland
  - San Antonio
- Utah, Salt Lake City
- Virginia, Richmond
- Washington, Seattle
- Wisconsin, Madison

MICRONESIA

Embassy of the Federated States of Micronesia
1725 N Street, NW., Washington, DC 20036
phone (202) 223–4383, fax 223–4391
His Excellency Asterio R. Takesy
Ambassador E. and P.
Consular Offices:
- Guam, Tamuning
- Hawaii, Honolulu

MOLDOVA

Embassy of the Republic of Moldova
2101 S Street, NW., Washington, DC 20008
phone (202) 667–1130, fax 667–1204
His Excellency Igor Munteanu
Ambassador E. and P.
Consular Offices:
- District of Columbia, Washington
- Florida, Miami
- New York, New York
- North Carolina, Hickory

MONACO

Embassy of Monoco

3400 International Drive, NW., Suite 2K–100, Washington, DC 20008
phone (202) 234–1530, fax 244–7656
His Excellency Gilles Alexandre Noghes
Ambassador E. and P.
Consular Offices:
California:
Los Angeles
San Francisco
Florida, Miami
Georgia, Atlanta
Illinois, Chicago
Louisiana, New Orleans
Massachusetts, Boston
Nevada, Las Vegas
New York, New York
Texas, Dallas

MONGOLIA

Embassy of Mongolia
2833 M Street, NW., Washington, DC 20007
phone (202) 333–7117, fax 298–9227
His Excellency Altangerel Bulgaa
Ambassador E. and P.
Consular Offices:
California, San Francisco
Colorado, Denver
District of Columbia, Washington
Georgia, Atlanta
Illinois, Chicago
Montana, Bozeman
New York, New York
Texas, Houston
Utah, Springville

MONTENEGRO

Embassy of the Republic of Montenegro
1610 New Hampshire Avenue, NW., Washington, DC 20009
phone (202) 234–6108, fax 234–6109
His Excellency Professor Srdan Darmanovic
Ambassador E. and P.
Consular Offices:
Colorado, Denver
New York, New York

MOROCCO

Embassy of the Kingdom of Morocco
1601 21st Street, NW., Washington, DC 20009
phone (202) 462–7980, fax 265–0161
His Excellency Mohammed Rachad Bouhlal
Ambassador E. and P.
Consular Offices:
California, Los Angeles
Colorado, Denver
Hawaii, Honolulu
Illinois, Chicago
Kansas, Kansas City
Kentucky, Louisville
Massachusetts, Cambridge
New York, New York
Texas, Dallas
Utah, Bountiful

MOZAMBIQUE

Embassy of the Republic of Mozambique
1525 New Hampshire Avenue, NW., Washington, DC 20036
phone (202) 293–7146, fax 835–0245
Her Excellency Amelia Narciso Matos Sumbana
Ambassador E. and P.

NAMIBIA

Embassy of the Republic of Namibia
1605 New Hampshire Avenue, NW., Washington, DC 20009
phone (202) 986–0540, fax 986–0443
His Excellency Martin Andjaba
Ambassador E. and P.
Consular Offices:
California, San Jose
Florida, Orlando
Michigan, Detroit
Nevada, Las Vegas

NAURU

Embassy of the Republic of Nauru
800 Second Avenue, New York, NY 10017
phone (212) 937–0074, fax 937–0079
Her Excellency Marlene Inemwin Moses
Ambassador E. and P.
Consular Offices:
Guam, Agana
Hawaii, Honolulu
Trust Territories of the Pacific Islands:
Pago Pago

NEPAL

Embassy of Nepal
2131 Leroy Place, NW., Washington, DC 20008
phone (202) 667–4550, fax 667–5534
His Excellency Shankar Prasad Sharma
Ambassador E. and P.
Consular Offices:
California:
Auburn
Los Angeles
San Francisco
Vista
Colorado, Boulder
Hawaii, Naalehu
Illinois, Chicago
Maryland, Baltimore
Massachusetts, Boston
New York, New York

NETHERLANDS

Royal Netherlands Embassy
4200 Linnean Avenue, NW., Washington, DC 20008
phone (202) 244–5300, fax 362–3430
His Excellency Regina Veronica Maria Bos Jones
Ambassador E. and P.
Consular Offices:
Arizona, Phoenix
California:
Los Angeles
San Francisco
Colorado, Denver
District of Columbia, Washington
Florida:
Jacksonville
Miami
Orlando
Georgia, Atlanta
Hawaii, Honolulu
Illinois, Chicago
Louisiana, New Orleans
Massachusetts, Boston
Michigan:
Grand Rapids
New Baltimore
Minnesota, Minneapolis
Missouri, St. Louis
New York, New York
North Carolina, Raleigh
Ohio, Cleveland
Oregon, Beaverton
Puerto Rico, Guaynabo
Texas, Houston
Trust Territories of the Pacific Islands:
Manila, Phillipines
Utah, Salt Lake City
Washington, Bellevue

NEW ZEALAND

Embassy of New Zealand
37 Observatory Circle, NW., Washington, DC 20008
phone (202) 328–4800, fax 667–5227
His Excellency Michael Kenneth Moore
Ambassador E. and P.
Consular Offices:
California:
Burlingame
El Macero
San Diego
Santa Monica
District of Columbia, Washington
Georgia, Atlanta
Guam, Tamuning
Hawaii, Honolulu
Illinois, Chicago
New Hampshire, Boston
New York, New York
Oregon, Portland
Texas, Houston
Trust Territories of the Pacific Islands:
Pago Pago
Utah, Salt Lake City
Vermont, Shelburne
Washington, Seattle

NICARAGUA

Embassy of the Republic of Nicaragua
1627 New Hampshire Avenue, NW., Washington, DC 20009
phone (202) 939–6570, fax 939–6545
His Excellency Francisco Obadiah Campbell Hooker
Ambassador E. and P.
Consular Offices:
California:
Los Angeles
San Francisco
District of Columbia, Washington
Florida, Miami
Georgia, Atlanta
Louisiana, Baton Rouge
Massachusetts, Springfield
New York, New York
North Carolina, Charlotte
Texas, Houston

NIGER

Embassy of the Republic of Niger
2204 R Street, NW., Washington, DC 20008
phone (202) 483–4224, fax 483–3169
His Excellency Maman Sambo Sidikou
Ambassador E. and P.

NIGERIA

Embassy of the Federal Republic of Nigeria
3519 International Court, NW., Washington, DC 20008
phone (202) 986–8400, fax 362–6541
His Excellency Adebowale Ibidapo Adefuye
Ambassador E. and P.
Consular Offices:
Georgia, Atlanta
New York, New York

NORWAY

Royal Norwegian Embassy
2720 34th Street, NW., Washington, DC 20008
phone (202) 333–6000, fax 337–0870
His Excellency Wegger Christian Strommen
Ambassador E. and P.
Consular Offices:
Alabama, Mobile
Alaska, Anchorage
Arizona, Glendale
California:
Los Angeles

San Diego
San Francisco
Colorado, Denver
Florida:
Jacksonville
Miami
Pensacola
Tampa
Georgia, Atlanta
Hawaii, Honolulu
Illinois, Chicago
Iowa, Des Moines
Louisiana, New Orleans
Massachusetts, Boston
Michigan, Detroit
Minnesota, Minneapolis
Montana, Billings
Nebraska, Omaha
New York, New York
North Dakota, Fargo
Oklahoma, Tulsa
Oregon, Portland
Pennsylvania, Philadelphia
Puerto Rico:
Ponce
San Juan
South Carolina, Charleston
South Dakota, Sioux Falls
Texas:
Dallas
Houston
Utah, Salt Lake City
Virginia, Norfolk
Washington, Seattle
Wisconsin, Madison

OMAN

Embassy of the Sultanate of Oman
2535 Belmont Road, NW., Washington, DC 20008
phone (202) 387–1980, fax 745–4933
Her Excellency Hunaina Sultan Ahmed al-Mughairy
Ambassador E. and P.
Consular Office: Pennsylvania, Pittsburgh

PAKISTAN

Embassy of Pakistan
3517 International Court, NW., Washington, DC 20008
phone (202) 243–6500, fax 686–1544
Her Excellency Sherry Rehman
Ambassador E. and P.
Consular Office:
California, Los Angeles
Connecticut, Rocky Hill
Illinois, Chicago
Maine, Portland
Massachusetts, Boston
Missouri, St. Louis
New York, New York
Pennsylvania, Philadephia
Texas, Houston

PALAU

Embassy of the Republic of Palau
1700 Pennsylvania Avenue, NW., Suite 400, Washington, DC 20006
phone (202) 452–6814, fax 452–6281
His Excellency Hersey Kyota
Ambassador E. and P.
Consular Offices:
California:
Carlsbad
La Canada Flintridge
Guam, Tamuning
Hawaii, Honolulu
Illinois, Chicago

PANAMA

Embassy of the Republic of Panama
2862 McGill Terrace, NW., Washington, DC 20008
phone (202) 483–1407, fax 483–8416
His Excellency Mario Ernesto Jaramillo Castillo
Ambassador E. and P.
Consular Offices:
Arkansas, Fayetteville
California, Long Beach
District of Columbia, Washington
Florida:
Miami
Tampa
Louisiana, New Orleans
New York, New York
Pennsylvania, Philadelphia
Puerto Rico, San Juan
Texas:
Austin
Houston

PAPUA NEW GUINEA

Embassy of Papua New Guinea
1779 Massachusetts Avenue, NW., Suite 805, Washington, DC 20036
phone (202) 745–3680, fax 745–3679
Mr. Elias Rahuromo Wohengu
Mrs. Relvie Wohengu
Minister (Charge D'Affaires Ad Interim)
Consular Offices:
California, Los Angeles
Texas, Houston

PARAGUAY

Embassy of Paraguay
2400 Massachusetts Avenue, NW., Washington, DC 20008
phone (202) 483–6960, fax 234–4508
His Excellency Fernando Antonio Pfannl Caballero
Ambassador E. and P.

Consular Offices:
Arizona, Tucson
California, Los Angeles
Florida, Miami
New York, New York
Texas:
Bellaire
Fort Worth

PERU

Embassy of Peru
1700 Massachusetts Avenue, NW., Washington, DC 20036
phone (202) 833–9860, fax 659–8124
His Excellency Harold Winston Forsyth Mejia
Ambassador E. and P.
Consular Offices:
Arizona, Mesa
California:
Los Angeles
San Francisco
Colorado, Denver
Connecticut, Hartford
District of Columbia, Washington
Florida:
Miami
Tampa
Georgia, Atlanta
Hawaii, Honolulu
Illinois, Chicago
Massachusetts, Boston
Missouri, St. Louis
New Jersey, Paterson
New York, New York
Oklahoma, Oklahoma City
Puerto Rico, San Juan
Texas:
Dallas
Houston
Utah, Salt Lake City
Washington, Seattle

PHILIPPINES

Embassy of the Republic of the Philippines
1600 Massachusetts Avenue, NW., Washington, DC 20036
phone (202) 467–9300, fax 467–9417
His Excellency Jose Lampa Cuisia, Jr.
Ambassador E. and P.
Consular Offices:
Alaska, Juneau
California:
Los Angeles
San Francisco
District of Columbia, Washington
Florida, North Miami
Georgia, Atlanta
Guam, Tamuning
Hawaii, Honolulu
Illinois, Chicago
Michigan, Livonia
New York, New York
Northern Mariana Islands, Saipan
Oregon, Portland
Trust Territories of the Pacific Islands:
Mariana Islands
Virgin Islands, St. Thomas

POLAND

Embassy of the Republic of Poland
2640 16th Street, NW., Washington, DC 20009
phone (202) 234–3800, fax 328–6271
His Excellency Ryszard Marian Schnepf
Ambassador E. and P.
Consular Offices:
Alaska, Anchorage
Arizona, Phoenix
California:
Belmont
Los Angeles
San Francisco
Colorado, Longmont
District of Columbia, Washington
Florida, Miami
Georgia, Atlanta
Hawaii, Honolulu
Idaho, Ketchum
Illinois, Chicago
Massachusetts, Boston
Missouri, St. Louis
Nevada, Las Vegas
New York, New York
North Carolina, Raleigh
Ohio, Oxford
Pennsylvania:
Philadephia
Pittsburgh
Puerto Rico, Catano
Tennessee, Knoxville
Texas, Houston

PORTUGAL

Embassy of Portugal
2012 Massachusetts Avenue, NW., Washington, DC 20036
phone (202) 328–8610, fax 462–3726
His Excellency Nuno F. Alves Salvador E Brito
Ambassador E. and P.
Consular Offices:
California:
Los Angeles
San Francisco
Tulare
Connecticut, Waterbury

Florida:
Miami
Orlando
Hawaii, Honolulu
Illinois, Chicago
Louisiana, New Orleans
Massachusetts:
Boston
New Bedford
New Jersey, Newark
New York, New York
North Carolina, Durham
Pennsylvania, Philadephia
Puerto Rico, San Juan
Rhode Island, Providence
Texas, Houston

QATAR

Embassy of the State of Qatar
2555 M Street, NW., Suite 200, Washington, DC 20037
phone (202) 274–1600, fax 237–0061
His Excellency Mohamed Abdulla M Al Rumaihi
Ambassador E. and P.
Consular Office: Texas, Houston

ROMANIA

Embassy of Romania
1607 23rd Street, NW., Washington, DC 20008
phone (202) 332–4846, fax 232–4748
His Excellency Adrian Cosmin Vierita
Ambassador E. and P.
Consular Offices:
Arizona, Temple
California:
Los Angeles
San Francisco
District of Columbia, Washington
Florida, Hollywood
Georgia, Atlanta
Illinois, Chicago
Indiana, Indianapolis
Louisiana, New Orleans
Massachusetts, Boston
Michigan, Detroit
Minnesota, Minneapolis
Nevada, Las Vegas
New York, New York
Ohio, Cleveland
Oklahoma, Norman
Oregon, Portland
Pennsylvania, Philadelphia
Texas:
Dallas
Houston
Utah, Salt Lake City
Virginia, Norfolk

RUSSIA

Embassy of the Russian Federation
2650 Wisconsin Avenue, NW., Washington, DC 20007
phone (202) 298–5700, fax 298–5735
His Excellency Sergey Ivanovich Kislyak
Ambassador E. and P.
Consular Offices:
Alaska, Anchorage
California:
Fair Oaks
San Francisco
Colorado, Denver
District of Columbia, Washington
Florida, Pinellas Park
Minnesota, Minneapolis
New York, New York
Puerto Rico, San Juan
Texas, Houston
Utah, Salt Lake City
Washington, Seattle

RWANDA

Embassy of the Republic of Rwanda
1714 New Hampshire Avenue, NW., Washington, DC 20009
phone (202) 232–2882, fax 232–4544
His Excellency James Kimonyo
Ambassador E. and P.
Consular Offices:
Illinois, Geneva
Massachusetts, Boston
Texas, Houston

SAMOA

Embassy of the Independent State of Samoa
800 2nd Avenue, 4th Floor, New York, NY 10017
phone (212) 599–6196, fax 599–0797
His Excellency Aliioaiga Feturielisaia
Ambassador E. and P.
Consular Offices:
American Samoa, Pago Pago
California, Torrance
Florida, Melbourne

SAN MARINO

Embassy of Republic of San Marino
2650 Virginia Avenue, NW., Washington, DC 20037
phone (202) 250–1535
His Excellency Paolo Rondelli
Ambassador E. and P.
Consular Offices:
District of Columbia, Washington
Hawaii, Honolulu
Michigan, Troy
New York, New York

SAO TOME AND PRINCIPE

Embassy of Sao Tome and Principe
1211 Connecticut Avenue, NW., Suite 300, Washington, DC 20036
phone (202) 775–2075, fax 775–2077
His Excellency Ovidio Pequeno
Ambassador E. and P.
Consular Offices:
- Georgia, Atlanta
- Illinois, Chicago

SAUDI ARABIA

Royal Embassy of Saudi Arabia
601 New Hampshire Avenue, NW., Washington, DC 20037
phone (202) 342–3800, fax 944–3113
His Excellency Adel A M Al Jubeir
Ambassador E. and P.
Consular Offices:
- California, Los Angeles
- District of Columbia, Washington
- New York, New York
- Texas, Houston

SENEGAL

Embassy of the Republic of Senegal
2112 Wyoming Avenue, NW., Washington, DC 20008
phone (202) 234–0540, fax 332–6315
His Excellency Cheikh Niang
Ambassador E. and P.
Consular Offices:
- Florida, Miami
- Georgia, Atlanta
- Louisiana:
  - Baton Rouge
  - New Orleans
- Missouri, Clayton
- New York, New York
- Rhode Island, Providence

SERBIA

Embassy of the Republic of Serbia
2134 Kalorama Road, NW., Washington, DC 20008
phone (202) 332–0333, fax 332–3933
His Excellency Vladimir Petrovic
Ambassador E. and P.
Consular Offices:
- Colorado, Denver
- Illinois, Chicago
- Louisiana, Metairie
- New York, New York
- Ohio, Cleveland
- Wyoming, Cheyenne

SEYCHELLES

Embassy of the Republic of Seychelles
800 2nd Avenue, Suite 400C, New York, NY 10017
phone (212) 972–1785, fax 972–1786
Her Excellency Marie Louise Cecile Potter
Ambassador E. and P.
Consular Offices:
- Alaska, Anchorage
- Arizona, Sun City
- New York, New York
- Washington, Seattle

SIERRA LEONE

Embassy of Sierra Leone
1701 19th Street, NW., Washington, DC 20009
phone (202) 939–9261, fax 483–1793
His Excellency Bockari Kortu Stevens
Ambassador E. and P.
Consular Office:
- Florida, Miami
- Georgia, Decatur
- Illinois, Chicago
- Massachusetts, Boston
- Pennsylvania, Philadephia
- Texas, Houston

SINGAPORE

Embassy of the Republic of Singapore
3501 International Place, NW., Washington, DC 20008
phone (202) 537–3100, fax 537–0876
His Excellency Ashok Kumar
Ambassador E. and P.
Consular Offices:
- California, San Francisco
- Florida, Miami
- Illinois, Chicago
- New York, New York

SLOVAK REPUBLIC

Embassy of the Slovak Republic
3523 International Court, NW., Washington, DC 20008
phone (202) 237–1054, fax 237–6438
His Excellency Peter Kmec
Ambassador E. and P.
Consular Offices:
- California:
  - Los Angeles
  - San Francisco
- Colorado, Denver
- District of Columbia, Washington
- Florida, Miami
- Illinois, Chicago
- Indiana, Indianapolis
- Massachusetts, Weston
- Michigan, Detroit
- Minnesota, Bloomington
- Missouri, Kansas City
- New York, New York
- Pennsylvania, Pittsburgh

South Carolina, Columbia
Texas, Dallas

SLOVENIA

Embassy of the Republic of Slovenia
1525 New Hampshire Avenue, NW., Washington, DC 20036
phone (202) 332–9332, fax 667–4563
His Excellency Roman Kirn
Ambassador E. and P.
Consular Offices:
California, San Francisco
Colorado, Denver
Florida, Miami Beach
Georgia, Atlanta
Hawaii, Honolulu
Illinois, Chicago
Kansas, Mission Hills
Michigan, Dearborn
Minnesota, St. Paul
New York, New York
Ohio, Cleveland
Tennessee, Knoxville
Texas, Houston

SOLOMON ISLANDS

Embassy of the Solomon Islands
800 2nd Avenue, Suite 400L, New York, NY 10017
phone (212) 599–6192, fax 661–8925
His Excellency Collin David Beck
Ambassador E. and P.

SOUTH AFRICA

Embassy of the Republic of South Africa
3051 Massachusetts Avenue, NW., Washington, DC 20008
phone (202) 232–4400, fax 265–1607
His Excellency Ebrahim Rasool
Ambassador E. and P.
Consular Offices:
Alabama, Mobile
California, Los Angeles
Illinois, Chicago
Kansas, Kansas City
Louisiana, New Orleans
Minnesota, Minneapolis
New York, New York
Texas, Dallas
Utah, Salt Lake City
Wisconsin, Milwaukee

SOUTH SUDAN

Embassy of the Republic of South Sudan
1233 20th Street, NW., Suite 602 Washington, DC 20036
phone (202) 293–7940, fax 293–7941
His Excellency Akec Khoc Aciew Khoc
Ambassador E. and P.

SPAIN

Embassy of Spain
2375 Pennsylvania Avenue, NW., Washington, DC 20037
phone (202) 452–0100, fax 833–5670
His Excellency Ramon Gil Casares Satrustegui
Ambassador E. and P.
Consular Offices:
Alabama, Birmingham
Alaska, Anchorage
Arizona, Phoenix
California:
Los Angeles
San Diego
San Francisco
Colorado, Englewood
District of Columbia, Washington
Florida:
Miami
Orlando
Pensacola
Tampa
Georgia, Atlanta
Hawaii, Honolulu
Idaho, Boise
Illinois, Chicago
Louisiana, New Orleans
Massachusetts, Boston
Michigan, Ann Arbor
Missouri:
Kansas City
St. Louis
New Jersey, Newark
New Mexico:
Albuquerque
Santa Fe
New York, New York
Ohio:
Cincinnati
Cleveland
Oklahoma, Oklahoma City
Puerto Rico:
Hato Rey
San Juan
Texas:
Corpus Christi
Dallas
El Paso
Houston
Utah, Salt Lake City
Washington, Seattle

SRI LANKA

Embassy of the Democratic Socialist Republic of Sri Lanka
2148 Wyoming Avenue, NW., Washington, DC 20008

phone (202) 483–4025, fax 232–7181
His Excellency Jaliya Chitran Wickramasuriya
Ambassador E. and P.
Consular Offices:
- Arizona, Phoenix
- California, Los Angeles
- Georgia, Atlanta
- Hawaii, Honolulu
- Illinois, Chicago
- Massachusetts, Boston
- New Jersey, Newark
- New Mexico, Santa Fe
- New York, New York
- Texas, Houston

ST. KITTS AND NEVIS

Embassy of St. Kitts and Nevis
3216 New Mexico Avenue, NW., Washington, DC 20016
phone (202) 686–2636, fax 686–5740
Her Excellency Jacinth Lorna Henry Martin
Ambassador E. and P.
Consular Offices:
- California, Los Angeles
- District of Columbia, Washington
- Florida, Miami
- Georgia, Atlanta
- New York, New York
- Pennsylvania, Philadelphia
- Puerto Rico, Guaynabo
- Texas, Dallas
- Virgin Islands, St. Thomas

ST. LUCIA

Embassy of St. Lucia
3216 New Mexico Avenue, NW., Washington, DC 20016
phone (202) 364–6792, fax 364–6723
His Excellency Dr. Michael Louis
Ambassador E. and P.
Consular Offices:
- California, Los Angeles
- Florida, Coral Gables
- New York, New York
- Puerto Rico, Guaynabo
- Virgin Islands, St. Croix

ST. VINCENT AND THE GRENADINES

Embassy of St. Vincent and the Grenadines
3216 New Mexico Avenue, NW., Washington, DC 20016
phone (202) 364–6730, fax 364–6736
Her Excellency La Celia A. Prince
Ambassador E. and P.
Consular Offices:
- California, Los Angeles
- Florida, Groveland
- Louisiana, New Orleans
- New York, New York
- Puerto Rico, Guaynabo

SUDAN

Embassy of the Republic of the Sudan
2210 Massachusetts Avenue, NW., Washington, DC 20008
phone (202) 338–8565, fax 667–2406
Mr. Emad Mirghani Abdelhamid Altohamy
Minister (Charge D'Affaires Ad Interim)

SURINAME

Embassy of the Republic of Suriname
4301 Connecticut Avenue, NW., Suite 460, Washington, DC 20008
phone (202) 244–7488, fax 244–5878
His Excellency Subhas Chandra Mungra
Ambassador E. and P.
Consular Offices:
- Florida, Miami
- Louisiana, New Orleans

SWAZILAND

Embassy of the Kingdom of Swaziland
1712 New Hampshire Avenue, NW., Washington, DC 20009
phone (202) 234–5002, fax 234–8254
His Excellency Reverend Abednego Mandla Ntshangase
Ambassador E. and P.

SWEDEN

Embassy of Sweden
2900 K Street, NW., Washington, DC 20007
phone (202) 467–2600, fax 467–2699
His Excellency Sven Jonas Hafstroem
Ambassador E. and P.
Consular Offices:
- Alaska, Anchorage
- Arizona, Scottsdale
- California:
  - San Diego
  - San Francisco
- Colorado, Denver
- District of Columbia, Washington
- Florida:
  - Ft. Lauderdale
  - Tampa
- Georgia, Atlanta
- Hawaii, Honolulu
- Illinois, Chicago
- Kansas, Merriam
- Louisiana, New Orleans
- Massachusetts, Boston
- Michigan, Ann Arbor
- Minnesota, Minneapolis

Missouri, St. Louis
Nebraska, Omaha
Nevada, Las Vegas
New York:
Jamestown
New York
North Carolina, Raleigh
Ohio, Cleveland
Pennsylvania, Ardmore
Puerto Rico, San Juan
Texas:
Dallas
Houston
Utah, Salt Lake City
Virgin Islands, St. Thomas
Virginia, Norfolk
Washington, Seattle
Wisconsin, Milwaukee

SWITZERLAND

Embassy of Switzerland
2900 Cathedral Avenue, NW., Washington, DC 20008
phone (202) 745–7900, fax 387–2564
His Excellency Manuel Sager
Ambassador E. and P.
Consular Offices:
Arizona, Scottsdale
California:
Los Angeles
San Francisco
Colorado, Boulder
District of Columbia, Washington
Florida:
Miami
Orlando
Georgia, Atlanta
Hawaii, Honolulu
Illinois, Chicago
Indiana, Indianapolis
Louisiana, New Orleans
Massachusetts, Boston
Michigan, Dearborn
Minnesota, Minneapollis
Missouri, Kansas City
Nevada, Las Vegas
New York:
New York
Williamsville
North Carolina, Charlotte
Ohio, Cleveland
Oklahoma, Edmond
Pennsylvania:
Philadelphia
Pittsburgh
Puerto Rico, San Juan
Texas:
Dallas
Houston
Trust Territories of the Pacific Islands:
Pago Pago
Utah, Sandy
Washington, Mercer Island

SYRIA

Embassy of the Syrian Arab Republic
2215 Wyoming Avenue, NW., Washington, DC 20008
phone (202) 232–6313, fax 234–9548
Mr. Mounir Koudmani
Minister-Counselor (Charge D'Affaires Ad Interim)
Consular Offices:
District of Columbia, Washington
Michigan, Detroit
Texas, Houston

TAJIKISTAN

Embassy of the Republic of Tajikistan
1005 New Hampshire Avenue, NW., Washington, DC 20037
phone (202) 223–6090, fax 223–6091
His Excellency Nuriddin Shamsov
Ambassador E. and P.
Consular Office: District of Columbia, Washington

TANZANIA

Embassy of the United Republic of Tanzania
1232 22nd Street, NW., Washington, DC 20037
phone (202) 939–6125, fax 797–7408
Mrs. Lily Letawo Munanka
Minister-Counselor (Charge D'Affaires Ad Interim)
Consular Offices:
California, San Rafael
Georgia, Atlanta
Illinois, St. Louis
Louisiana, New Orleans
Michigan, Grosse Pointe Farms
Minnesota, Minneapolis
New Mexico, Albuquerque
Pennsylvania, Philadephia

THAILAND

Embassy of Thailand
1024 Wisconsin Avenue, NW., Washington, DC 20007
phone (202) 944–3600, fax 944–3611
His Excellency Chaiyong Satjipanon
Ambassador E. and P.
Consular Offices:
Alabama, Montgomery
California, Los Angeles
Colorado, Denver
Florida, Coral Gables
Georgia, Atlanta
Hawaii, Honolulu

Illinois, Chicago
Louisiana, New Orleans
Massachusetts, Boston
New York, New York
Oklahoma, Broken Arrow
Oregon, Portland
Puerto Rico, Hato Rey
Texas:
Dallas
Houston
Utah, Salt Lake City

TIMOR LESTE

Embassy of the Democratic Republic of Timor Leste
4201 Connecticut Avenue, NW., Suite 504, Washington, DC 20008
phone (202) 966–3202, fax 966–3205
His Excellency Constancio Da Conceicao Pinto
Ambassador E. and P.

TOGO

Embassy of the Republic of Togo
2208 Massachusetts Avenue, NW., Washington, DC 20008
phone (202) 234–4212, fax 232–3190
His Excellency Edawe Limbiye Kadangha Bariki
Ambassador E. and P.
Consular Offices:
California, Chatsworth
Florida, Miami

TONGA

Embassy of the Kingdom of Tonga
250 East 51st Street, New York, NY 10022
phone (917) 369–1025, fax 369–1024
His Excellency Sonatane Tua Taumoepeau Tupou
Ambassador E. and P.
Consular Offices:
California, San Francisco
Hawaii, Honolulu

TRINIDAD AND TOBAGO

Embassy of the Republic of Trinidad and Tobago
1708 Massachusetts Avenue, NW., Washington, DC 20036
phone (202) 467–6490, fax 785–3130
His Excellency Dr. Neil Nadesh Parsan
Ambassador E. and P.
Consular Offices:
Florida, Miami
New York, New York
Puerto Rico, San Juan
Texas, Houston

TUNISIA

Embassy of Tunisia
1515 Massachusetts Avenue, NW., Washington, DC 20005
phone (202) 862–1850, fax 862–1858
Ambassador Mokhtar Chaouachi
Mrs. Aicha Hamrit Chaouachi
Ambassador E. and P.
Consular Offices:
California, San Francisco
Florida, Miami
New York, New York
Texas, Dallas

TURKEY

Embassy of the Republic of Turkey
2525 Massachusetts Avenue, NW., Washington, DC 20008
phone (202) 612–6700, fax 612–6744
His Excellency Namik Tan
Ambassador E. and P.
Consular Offices:
California:
Fair Oaks
Los Angeles
Oakland
Georgia, Atlanta
Illinois, Chicago
Maryland, Baltimore
Massachusetts, Boston
Michigan, Farmington
Mississippi, Jackson
Missouri, Kansas City
New York, New York
Texas, Houston
Washington, Seattle

TURKMENISTAN

Embassy of Turkmenistan
2207 Massachusetts Avenue, NW., Washington, DC 20008
phone (202) 588–1500, fax 588–0697
His Excellency Meret Bairamovich Orazov
Ambassador E. and P.

TUVALU

Embassy of Tuvalu
800 Second Avenue, Suite 400D, New York, NY 10017
phone (212) 490–0534
His Excellency Afelee Falema Pita
Ambassador E. and P.

UGANDA

Embassy of the Republic of Uganda
5911 16th Street, NW., Washington, DC 20011
phone (202) 726–0416, fax 726–1727
Mr. Alfred Nnam
Minister (Charge D'Affaires Ad Interim)
Consular Offices:
California:
Los Angeles

San Diego
Colorado, Aurora
Florida, Jupiter
Georgia, Macon
Illinois, Chicago
New York, New York
Pennsylvania, Harrisburg
Texas, Dallas
Washington, Gig Harbor

UKRAINE

Embassy of Ukraine
3350 M Street, NW., Washington, DC 20007
phone (202) 349–2920, fax 333–0817
His Excellency Olexander Motsyk
Ambassador E. and P.
Consular Offices:
Alabama, Birmingham
Arizona, Tucson
California, San Francisco
District of Columbia, Washington
Georgia, Alpharetta
Illinois, Chicago
Michigan, Detroit
New York, New York
Ohio, Cleveland
Texas, Houston
Utah, Salt Lake City

UNITED ARAB EMIRATES

Embassy of the United Arab Emirates
3522 International Court, NW., Washington, DC 20008
phone (202) 243–2400, fax 243–2432
His Excellency Yousif Mana Saeed Alotaiba
Ambassador E. and P.

UNITED KINGDOM

British Embassy
3100 Massachusetts Avenue, NW., Washington, DC 20008
phone (202) 588–6500, fax 588–7870
His Excellency Sir Peter John Westmacott
Ambassador E. and P.
Consular Offices:
Alaska, Anchorage
Arizona, Phoenix
California:
Los Angeles
San Diego
San Francisco
Colorado, Denver
District of Columbia, Washington
Florida:
Miami
Orlando
Tallahassee
Georgia, Atlanta
Illinois, Chicago
Louisiana, New Orleans
Massachusetts, Boston
Michigan, Detroit
Minnesota, Minneapolis
Nevada, Las Vegas
New York, New York
North Carolina, Charlotte
Ohio, Cleveland
Oklahoma, Tulsa
Oregon, Portland
Pennsylvania:
Philadelphia
Pittsburgh
Puerto Rico, San Juan
Tennessee, Nashville
Texas:
Dallas
Houston
San Antonio
Trust Territories of the Pacific Islands:
Nuku'alofa, Tonga
Utah, Salt Lake City
Washington, Bellevue

URUGUAY

Embassy of Uruguay
1913 I Street, NW., Washington, DC 20006
phone (202) 331–1313, fax 331–8142
His Excellency Juan Carlos Pita Alvariza
Ambassador E. and P.
Consular Offices:
California:
Los Angeles
Sacramento
San Francisco
District of Columbia, Washington
Florida, Miami
Illinois, Chicago
Louisiana, Jefferson
Nevada, Reno
New York, New York
Pennsylvania, Philadephia
Puerto Rico, San Juan
Texas, Houston
Utah, Salt Lake City

UZBEKISTAN

Embassy of the Republic of Uzbekistan
1746 Massachusetts Avenue, NW., Washington, DC 20036
phone (202) 293–6803, fax 293–6804
His Excellency Ilhomjon Tuychievich Nematov
Ambassador E. and P.
Consular Offices:
District of Columbia, Washington
Georgia, Greensboro
New York, New York

Washington, Seattle

VANUATU

Consular Office: Northern Mariana Islands, Saipan

VENEZUELA

Embassy of the Bolivarian Republic of Venezuela
1099 30th Street, NW., Washington, DC 20007
phone (202) 342–2214, fax 342–6820
Mr. Angelo Agustin Rivero Santos
Minister-Counselor (Charge D'Affaires Ad Interim)
Consular Offices:
California, San Francisco
Florida, Miami
Illinois, Chicago
Louisiana, New Orleans
Massachusetts, Boston
New York, New York
Puerto Rico:
Hato Rey
San Juan
Texas, Houston

VIETNAM

Embassy of Vietnam
1233 20th Street, NW., Suite 400, Washington, DC 20036
phone (202) 861–0737, fax 861–0917
His Excellency Cuong Quoc Nguyen
Ambassador E. and P.
Consular Offices:
California, San Francisco
New York, New York
Texas, Houston

YEMEN

Embassy of the Republic of Yemen
2319 Wyoming Avenue, NW., Washington, DC 20008
phone (202) 965–4760, fax 337–2017
Mr. Adel Ali Ahmed Alsunaini
Counselor (Charge D'Affaires Ad Interim)
Consular Offices:
California, San Francisco
District of Columbia, Washington
Michigan, Dearborn

ZAMBIA

Embassy of the Republic of Zambia
2419 Massachusetts Avenue, NW., Washington, DC 20008
phone (202) 265–9717, fax 332–0826
His Excellency Palan Mulonda
Ambassador E. and P.

The following is a list of countries with which diplomatic relations have been severed:

After each country, in parenthesis, is the name of the country's protecting power in the United States.

CUBA (Switzerland)
IRAN (Pakistan)

PRESS GALLERIES*

SENATE PRESS GALLERY

The Capitol, Room S–316, phone 224–0241

www.dailypress.senate.gov

Director.—Laura Lytle

Senior Media Relations Coordinators:
Amy H. Gross
Kristyn K. Socknat
Media Coordinators:
Elizabeth B. Crowley
John E. Mulligan III
Samantha J. Yeider

HOUSE PRESS GALLERY

The Capitol, Room H–315, phone 225–3945

Superintendent.—Annie Tin
Deputy Superintendent.—Justin J. Supon
Assistant Superintendents:
Ric Anderson
Laura Reed
Drew Cannon
Molly Cain

STANDING COMMITTEE OF CORRESPONDENTS

Siobhan Hughes, Wall Street Journal, Chairwoman
Peter Urban, Stephens Media Group, Secretary
Colby Itkowitz, Washington Post
Kate Hunter, Bloomberg News
Emily Ethridge, CQ Roll Call

RULES GOVERNING PRESS GALLERIES

1. Administration of the press galleries shall be vested in a Standing Committee of Correspondents elected by accredited members of the Galleries. The Committee shall consist of five persons elected to serve for terms of two years. Provided, however, that at the election in January 1951, the three candidates receiving the highest number of votes shall serve for two years and the remaining two for one year. Thereafter, three members shall be elected in odd-numbered years and two in even-numbered years. Elections shall be held in January. The Committee shall elect its own chairman and secretary. Vacancies on the Committee shall be filled by special election to be called by the Standing Committee.

2. Persons desiring admission to the press galleries of Congress shall make application in accordance with Rule VI of the House of Representatives, subject to the direction and control of the Speaker and Rule 33 of the Senate, which rules shall be interpreted and administered by the Standing Committee of Correspondents, subject to the review and an approval by the Senate Committee on Rules and Administration.

*Information is based on data furnished and edited by each respective Gallery.

3. The Standing Committee of Correspondents shall limit membership in the press galleries to bone fide correspondents of repute in their profession, under such rules as the Standing Committee of Correspondents shall prescribe.

4. An applicant for press credentials through the Daily Press Galleries must establish to the satisfaction of the Standing Committee of Correspondents that he or she is a full-time, paid correspondent who requires on-site access to congressional members and staff. Correspondents must be employed by a news organization:

(a) with General Publication periodicals mailing privileges under U.S. Postal Service rules, and which publishes daily; or

(b) whose principal business is the daily dissemination of original news and opinion of interest to a broad segment of the public, and which has published continuously for 18 months.

The applicant must reside in the Washington, D.C. area, and must not be engaged in any lobbying or paid advocacy, advertising, publicity or promotion work for any individual, political party, corporation, organization, or agency of the U.S. Government, or in prosecuting any claim before Congress or any federal government department, and will not do so while a member of the Daily Press Galleries.

Applicants' publications must be editorially independent of any institution, foundation or interest group that lobbies the federal government, or that is not principally a general news organization.

Failure to provide information to the Standing Committee for this determination, or misrepresenting information, can result in the denial or revocation of credentials.

5. Members of the families of correspondents are not entitled to the privileges of the Galleries.

6. The Standing Committee of Correspondents shall propose no changes in these rules except upon petition in writing signed by not less than 100 accredited members of the galleries. The above rules have been approved by the Committee on Rules and Administration.

JOHN A. BOEHNER,
Speaker of the House of Representatives.

CHARLES E. SCHUMER,
Chair, Senate Committee on Rules and Administration.

MEMBERS ENTITLED TO ADMISSION

PRESS GALLERIES

Abdullah, Halimah: McClatchy Newspapers
Abel, Allen: National Post
Abrams, James: Associated Press
Abrams, Sandra: Reuters
Abruzzese, Sarah: Washington Times
Achenbach, Joel: Washington Post
Ackerman, Andrew: Bond Buyer
Adair, William: St. Petersburg Times
Adams, Christopher: McClatchy Newspapers
Adams, Rebecca: Congressional Quarterly
Adams, Richard: London Guardian
Adamy, Janet: Wall Street Journal
Adcock, Beryl: McClatchy Newspapers
Adler, Joseph: American Banker
Adofo, Adjoa: Congressional Quarterly
Aemisegger, Celine: EFE News Services
Agres, Theodore: Washington Times
Ahearn, David: Defense Daily
Ahlrich, Alan: Congressional Quarterly
Ahn, Sung Joong: Korea Times
Akers, Mary Ann: Washington Post
Akinwande, Ifedayo: Congressional Quarterly
Alamiri, Yasmeen: Saudi Press Agency
Alandete, David: El Pais
Alberta, Timothy: Wall Street Journal
Alberts, Sheldon: Canwest News Service
Alexander, Charles: Reuters
Ali, Syed: Congressional Quarterly
Allen, Amanda: Congressional Quarterly
Allen, JoAnne: Reuters
Allen, Jonathan: Congressional Quarterly
Allen, Kent: Congressional Quarterly
Allen, Ross: Argus Media
Allen, Victoria: Reuters
Allison, Wes: St. Petersburg Times
Alonso-Zaldivar, Ricardo: Associated Press
Alpert, Bruce: New Orleans Times-Picayune
Al-Sowayel, Naila: Saudi Press Agency
Alvarez, Marina: Los Angeles Times
Ammann, Beat: Neue Zuercher Zeitung
Anderson, Andre: McClatchy Newspapers
Anderson, Joanna: Congressional Quarterly
Anderson, Mark: Dow Jones Newswires
Andrews, Edmund: New York Times
Angle, Martha: Congressional Quarterly
Anstey, Christopher: Bloomberg News
Antonen, Mel: USA Today
Anyz, Daniel: Hospodarske Noving Daily
Appelbaum, Binyamin: Washington Post
Apuzzo, Matt: Associated Press
Argetsinger, Amy: Washington Post
Arimoto, Takashi: Sankei Shimbun
Arita, Tsukasa: Kyodo News
Armstrong, Andrew: Congressional Quarterly
Arnold, John Jay: Associated Press
Ashburn, Emma: Asahi Shimbun
Asher, James: McClatchy Newspapers
Asher, Julie: Catholic News Service
Ashizuka, Tomoko: Nikkei
Aslam, Abid: Inter Press Service
Asseo, Laurie: Bloomberg News
Attias, Melissa: Congressional Quarterly
Aukofer, Frank: Artists & Writers Syndicate
Aversa, Jeannine: Associated Press
Awaji, Ai: Jiji Press
Ayuso Determeyer, Sylvia: German Press Agency-DPA
Azpiazu, Maria: EFE News Services
Babaeva, Svetlana: RIA Novosti
Babcock, Charles: Bloomberg News
Babington, Charles: Associated Press
Bacon, Jr., Perry: Washington Post
Baert, Patrick: Agence France-Presse
Baker, Peter: New York Times
Baldor, Lolita: Associated Press
Baldwin, Thomas: London Times
Ball, Michael: Argus Media
Balz, Daniel: Washington Post
Banales, Jorge: EFE News Services
Banks, Adelle: Religion News Service
Baquet, Dean: New York Times
Barakat, Matthew: Associated Press
Barker, James: Congressional Quarterly
Barker, Jeffrey: Baltimore Sun
Barkley, Tom: Dow Jones Newswires
Barnes, Julian: Los Angeles Times
Barnes, Robert: Washington Post
Baron, Ana: Clarin
Barrera, Ruben: Notimex Mexican News Agency
Barrett, Barbara: McClatchy Newspapers
Barrett, Devlin: Associated Press
Barrett, Terrence: Bloomberg News
Bartash, Jeffrey: MarketWatch
Bartscht, Jill: Washington Post
Bartz, Diane: Reuters
Bashir, Mustafa: Saudi Press Agency
Bater, Jeffrey: Dow Jones Newswires
Baumann, David: Congressional Quarterly
Baygents, Ronald: Kuwait News Agency
Bayle, Juan Cañete: El Periodico
Baylis, Jamie: Congressional Quarterly

MEMBERS ENTITLED TO ADMISSION—Continued

Bazar, Emily: USA Today
Bazinet, Kenneth: New York Daily News
Beary, Brian: Europolitics
Beattie, Alan: Financial Times
Beattie, Jeff: Energy Daily
Beatty, Andrew: Agence France-Presse
Becker, Bernard: New York Times
Beckner, Steven: Market News International
Bell, Peter: Congress Daily
Bellantoni, Christina: Washington Times
Bello, Marisol: USA Today
Bendavid, Naftali: Wall Street Journal
Bender, Adam: Communications Daily
Bender, Bryan: Boston Globe
Benenson, Robert: Congressional Quarterly
Benesova, Dagmar: World Business Press
Benjamin, Matthew: Bloomberg News
Benkelman, Susan: Congressional Quarterly
Benoit, Daphne: Agence France-Presse
Benson, Clea: Congressional Quarterly
Berley, Max: Bloomberg News
Berry, Deborah: Gannett News Service
Berry, John: Bloomberg News
Bettelheim, Adriel: Congressional Quarterly
Bicknell, Arwen Adams: Congressional Quarterly
Bicknell, John: Congressional Quarterly
Biddle, Joanna: Agence France-Presse
Bilski, Christina: Nikkei
Birnbaum, Jeffrey: Washington Times
Birnbaum, Michael: Washington Post
Biskupic, Joan: USA Today
Bivins, Larry: Gannett News Service
Bjerga, Alan: Bloomberg News
Blackledge, Brett: Associated Press
Blackstone, Brian: Dow Jones Newswires
Bland, Melissa: Reuters
Blinch, Russell: Reuters
Bliss, Jeffrey: Bloomberg News
Blum, Justin: Bloomberg News
Blumenthal, Les: McClatchy Newspapers
Boadle, Anthony: Reuters
Bohan, Caren: Reuters
Bold, Michael: McClatchy Newspapers
Boles, Corey: Dow Jones Newswires
Bolstad, Erika: McClatchy Newspapers
Borak, Donna: Associated Press
Borenstein, Seth: Associated Press
Bostick, Romaine: Bloomberg News
Bourge, Christian: Washington Times
Bouza, Teresa: EFE News Services
Bowen, Joel: Congressional Quarterly
Bowman, Curtis Lee: Scripps Howard News Service
Boyd, Robert: McClatchy Newspapers
Boyer, David: Philadelphia Inquirer
Brady, Erik: USA Today
Braithwaite, Tom: Financial Times
Brandmaier, Frank: German Press Agency-DPA
Branson, Louise: USA Today
Brasher, Philip: Des Moines Register
Brauchli, Marcus: Washington Post
Braun, Stephen: Associated Press
Bravin, Jess: Wall Street Journal
Bridis, Ted: Associated Press
Brinsley, John: Bloomberg News
Broder, David: Washington Post
Broder, John: New York Times
Broder, Jonathan: Congressional Quarterly
Brodie, Michael: LRP Publications
Brodmann, Ronald: Congressional Quarterly
Brooks, David: New York Times
Brooks, David: La Jornada
Brown, David: Washington Post
Brown, DeNeen: Washington Post
Brune, Thomas: Newsday
Buddhavarapu, Bhagyashree: Singapore Straits Times
Bull, Alister: Reuters
Bumiller, Elisabeth: New York Times
Burger, Timothy: Bloomberg News
Burgess, Jeff: New York Times
Burke, Daniel: Religion News Service
Burns, Judith: Dow Jones Newswires
Burns, Robert: Associated Press
Burr, Thomas: Salt Lake Tribune
Burt, Andy: Bloomberg News
Buskirk, Howard: Communications Daily
Bussey, John: Wall Street Journal
Butler, Desmond: Associated Press
Cadei, Emily: Congressional Quarterly
Cadiz, Antonieta: La Opinion
Calmes, Jackie: New York Times
Calvo-Platero, Mario: Il Sole 24 Ore
Camia, Catalina: USA Today
Campo, Marcello: ANSA Italian News Agency
Canellos, Peter: Boston Globe
Canham, Matt: Salt Lake Tribune
Caño, Antonio: El Pais
Cantu, Leslie: Communications Daily
Capaccio, Anthony: Bloomberg News
Caplan, Abby: Argus Media
Cappiello, Dana: Associated Press
Carmichael, Lachlan: Agence France-Presse
Carney, Dan: USA Today
Carney, David: Tech Law Journal
Carney, Timothy: Washington Examiner
Carpenter, Amanda: Washington Times
Carroll, James: Congressional Quarterly
Carroll, James: Louisville Courier Journal
Carter, Sara: Washington Times
Cartwright, Linda: Congressional Quarterly
Casabona, Elizabeth: Fairchild News Service
Cass, Connie: Associated Press
Cassata, Donna: Associated Press
Casteel, Chris: Oklahoman
Cermak, Christopher: German Press Agency-DPA

MEMBERS ENTITLED TO ADMISSION—Continued

Chadbourn, Margaret: Bloomberg News
Chaddock, Gail: Christian Science Monitor
Chamberlain, Kenneth: Congress Daily
Chan, Sammie: Gannett News Service
Chandler, Michael: Washington Post
Chandra, Shobhana: Bloomberg News
Chandrasekaran, Rajiv: Washington Post
Chang, Tsung-Chih: United Daily News
Chaplain, Myriam: Agence France-Presse
Charles, Deborah: Reuters
Chebium, Raju: Gannett News Service
Chen, Edwin: Bloomberg News
Chen, Kathy: Wall Street Journal
Chen, Shawn: Associated Press
Chew, Cassie: Wall Street Journal
Chiantaretto, Mariuccia: Il Giornale
Chikazawa, Moriyasu: Kyodo News
Chinni, Dante: Christian Science Monitor
Chipman, Kimberly: Bloomberg News
Cho, David: Washington Post
Cho, Nam: Segye Times
Choate, Patricia: Scripps Howard News Service
Choi, Hyung Du: Munwha Ilbo
Chong, Christina Young: Korea Times
Christensen, Mike: Congressional Quarterly
Christian, Molly: Argus Media
Christie, Rebecca: Bloomberg News
Chu, Keith: Western Communications
Chun, Young Sik: Munwha Ilbo
Chwallek, Gabriele: German Press Agency-DPA
Cillizza, Chris: Washington Post
Cindemir, Mehmet: Hurriyet
Clampitt, Brian: Asahi Shimbun
Clark, Colin: Military.com
Clark, Lesley: Miami Herald
Clarke, David: Congressional Quarterly
Clearwater, Cindy: Reuters
Clerico, Luciano: ANSA Italian News Agency
Clymer, Adam: New York Times
Cocco, Marie: Washington Post Writer's Group
Codrea, George: Congressional Quarterly
Cohen, Sarah: Washington Post
Cohn, Peter: Congress Daily
Coile, Zachary: San Francisco Chronicle
Cole, August: Wall Street Journal
Coleman, Michael: Albuquerque Journal
Collins, Michael: Scripps Howard News Service
Collinson, Stephen: Agence France-Presse
Colvin, Ross: Reuters
Condon, Stephanie: CNET News.com
Condon, Jr., George: Congress Daily
Conery, Ben: Washington Times
Conkey, Christopher: Wall Street Journal
Conlon, Charles: Congressional Quarterly
Connealy, Erin: Asahi Shimbun
Conners, Maureen: Congressional Quarterly
Connolly, Catherine: Washington Post
Conrad, Dennis: Associated Press
Conway, Neal: Congressional Quarterly
Cook, David: Christian Science Monitor
Cooke, Anthony: Dow Jones Newswires
Coomes, Jessica: Congressional Quarterly
Cooney, Jessica Benton: Congressional Quarterly
Cooper, Helene: New York Times
Cooper, Kent: Political Money Line
Cooper, Richard: Los Angeles Times
Cooper, Sonya: Bloomberg News
Copeland, Libby: Washington Post
Copeland, Peter: Scripps Howard News Service
Corbett, Rebecca: New York Times
Corbett Dooren, Jennifer: Dow Jones Newswires
Corbin, Kenneth: Internetnews.com
Corchado, Alfredo: Dallas Morning News
Cornwell, Susan: Reuters
Cowan, Richard: Reuters
Craig, Tim: Washington Post
Cranford, John: Congressional Quarterly
Crawley, John: Reuters
Crites, Alice: Washington Post
Crittenden, Michael: Dow Jones Newswires
Crutsinger, Martin: Associated Press
Cunningham, Sarah: Reuters
Curl, Joseph: Washington Times
Curran, Timothy: Washington Post
Cushman, Jr., John: New York Times
da Costa, Mario Navarro: ABIM
Daly, Matthew: Associated Press
Daniel, Douglass: Associated Press
Daniels, Alex: Arkansas Democrat-Gazette
Dann, Carey: Congress Daily
Dao, James: New York Times
Davenport, Coral: Congressional Quarterly
Davenport, J. Christian: Washington Post
Davidson, Joe: Washington Post
Davidson, Julie: LRP Publications
Davidson, Kate: Congressional Quarterly
Davidson, Paul: USA Today
Davidz, Elizabeth: Associated Press
Davies, Anne: Sydney Morning Herald
Davies, Frank: San Jose Mercury News
Davis, Aaron: Washington Post
Davis, David: Congressional Quarterly
Davis, Julie: Associated Press
Davis, Robert: Wall Street Journal
Davis, Susan: Wall Street Journal
DeBard, Amanda: Washington Times
Debusmann, Bernd: Reuters
Decamme, Guillaume: Agence France-Presse
Dechter, Gadi: Bloomberg News
Decker, Brett: Washington Times
Decker, Susan: Bloomberg News
DeFrank, Thomas: New York Daily News
Deguchi, Tomohiro: Kyodo News
Del Giudice, Vincent: Bloomberg News

MEMBERS ENTITLED TO ADMISSION—Continued

Del Riccio, Cristiano: ANSA Italian News Agency
Delgado, Jose: El Nuevo Dia
DeLuce, Daniel: Agence France-Presse
DeMarco, Edward: Bloomberg News
Demirjian, Karoun: Congressional Quarterly
Dennis, Brady: Washington Post
Deparle, Jason: New York Times
Dermody, William: USA Today
Deshimaru, Sachiko: Nikkei
Desmond, Harold: Reuters
Dessouky, Dean: Saudi Press Agency
Diaz, Kevin: Minneapolis Star Tribune
Diaz-Briseno, Jose: Reforma Newspaper
Dick, Jason: Congress Daily
Dickerson, Christine: IFR Markets
Dickson, David: Washington Times
Dickson, Virgil: Communications Daily
Dilanian, Ken: USA Today
Dinan, Stephen: Washington Times
Dineen, John: Congressional Quarterly
Dixon, Kim: Reuters
Dlouhy, Jennifer: Hearst Newspapers
Dobbyn, Timothy: Reuters
Dodge, Catherine: Bloomberg News
Doering, Christopher: Reuters
Doggett, Tom: Reuters
Dolan, Christopher: Washington Times
Dolinger, David Allen: Wall Street Journal
Dombey, Daniel: Financial Times
Dominello, Amy: Media General News Service
Donmoyer, Ryan: Bloomberg News
Donnelly, John: Congressional Quarterly
Dorell, Oren: USA Today
Dorning, Mike: Chicago Tribune
Douglas, William: McClatchy Newspapers
Dowd, Maureen: New York Times
Downing, James: Restructuring Today
Doyle, Leonard: London Independent
Doyle, Michael: McClatchy Newspapers
Drajem, Mark: Bloomberg News
Drake, Bruce: Congressional Quarterly
Drawbaugh, Kevin: Reuters
Dreazen, Yochi: Wall Street Journal
Drinkard, Jim: Associated Press
Drobnyk, Josh: Allentown Morning Call
Drummond, Bob: Bloomberg News
Dufour, Jeff: Washington Examiner
Duggan, Loren: Congressional Quarterly
Duggan, Paul: Washington Post
Duin, Julia: Washington Times
Dumain, Emma: Congressional Quarterly
Dunham, Richard: Houston Chronicle
Dunham, Will: Reuters
Dunphy, Harry: Associated Press
Dutton, Audrey: Bond Buyer
Dvorak, Petula: Washington Post
Dwyer, Paula: New York Times
Earle, Geoff: New York Post
Eaton, Sabrina: Cleveland Plain Dealer
Eckert, Paul: Reuters
Eckert, Toby: Congressional Quarterly
Eckstrom, Kevin: Religion News Service
Edmonds, Jr., Ronald: Associated Press
Edney, Anna: Congress Daily
Eggen, Daniel: Washington Post
Eichelberger, Curtis: Bloomberg News
Eilperin, Juliet: Washington Post
Eisler, Peter: USA Today
Eisman, Dale: Virginian-Pilot
El Hamti, Maribel: EFE News Services
El Nasser, Haya: USA Today
Elboghdady, Dina: Washington Post
Elkins, Donald: Associated Press
Ellicott, Val: Gannett News Service
Elliott, Geoff: Australian
Elliott, Philip: Associated Press
Ellis, Kristi: Fairchild News Service
Elsibai, Nadine: Bloomberg News
Emerling, Gary: Washington Times
Enoch, Daniel: Bloomberg News
Epstein, Edward: Congressional Quarterly
Espo, David: Associated Press
Ethridge, Emily: Congressional Quarterly
Evans, Ben: Associated Press
Eversley, Melanie: USA Today
Faen, Wang: Xinhua News Agency
Fahrenthold, David: Washington Post
Faler, Brian: Bloomberg News
Fallis, David: Washington Post
Farah, Samer: Reuters
Farhi, Paul: Washington Post
Farnam, Timothy: Wall Street Journal
Farrell, John Aloysius: GlobalPost
Favole, Jared: Dow Jones Newswires
Fears, Darryl: Washington Post
Fein, Geoff: Defense Daily
Feld, Karen: Capital Connections
Feldman, Carole: Associated Press
Feldmann, Linda: Christian Science Monitor
Felker, Edward: Washington Times
Feller, Ben: Associated Press
Felsenthal, Mark: Reuters
Fendrich, Howard: Associated Press
Ferrari, Francisco: Agence France-Presse
Ferraro, Thomas: Reuters
Ferrechio, Susan: Washington Examiner
Ferrer, Sandra: Agence France-Presse
Fessenden, Helen: Congress Daily
Fetterman, Mindy: USA Today
Fields, Gary: Wall Street Journal
Fingerhut, Eric: Jewish Telegraphic Agency
Finn, Peter: Washington Post
Fireman, Ken: Bloomberg News
Fisher, Marc: Washington Post

MEMBERS ENTITLED TO ADMISSION—Continued

Fitzgerald, Alison: Bloomberg News
Flaherty, Anne: Associated Press
Flaherty, Mary Pat: Washington Post
Flanders, Gwen: USA Today
Flattau, Edward: Global Horizons Syndicate
Fletcher, Michael: Washington Post
Flitter, Emily: American Banker
Ford, Matt: Associated Press
Forsythe, Michael: Bloomberg News
Fournier, Ron: Associated Press
Fowler, Daniel: Congressional Quarterly
Fowler, Maria: Gannett News Service
Fox, Margaret: Reuters
Fox, Michael: Congress Daily
Fram, Alan: Associated Press
Frank, Thomas: USA Today
Fraze, Barbara: Catholic News Service
Freedman, Dan: Hearst Newspapers
Freeman, Sholnn: Washington Post
Freking, Kevin: Associated Press
Friedman, Daniel: Congress Daily
Friedman, Robert: Scripps Howard News Service
Fritze, John: USA Today
Frommer, Frederic: Associated Press
Fry, Jamey: Congressional Quarterly
Fudo, Takashi: Jiji Press
Fuhrig, Frank: German Press Agency-DPA
Fullerton, Jane: Arkansas Democrat-Gazette
Funk, Lynne: Bond Buyer
Furlow, Robert: Associated Press
Furukawa, Masakazu: Tokyo Chunichi Shimbun
Galan, Frederic: Agence France-Presse
Gallagher, Brian: USA Today
Gallu, Joshua: Bloomberg News
Gamboa, Suzanne: Associated Press
Gambrell, Kathy: Congress Daily
Gaouette, Nicole: Bloomberg News
Gardiner, Andrew: USA Today
Gardner, Amy: Washington Post
Gates-Davis, Marilyn: Congressional Quarterly
Gaul, Gilbert: Washington Post
Gaynair, Gillian: Associated Press
Gearan, Anne: Associated Press
Gehrke, Robert: Salt Lake Tribune
Gensheimer, Lydia: Congressional Quarterly
Geracimos, Ann: Washington Times
Gerhart, Ann: Washington Post
Ghosh-Siminoff, Sasha: Congressional Quarterly
Gibson, William: South Florida Sun-Sentinel
Gienger, Viola: Bloomberg News
Gilbert, Craig: Milwaukee Journal Sentinel
Gillman, Todd: Dallas Morning News
Gillum, Jack: USA Today
Giroux, Gregory: Congressional Quarterly
Glass, Pamela: Le Mauricien
Glass, Robert: Associated Press
Glod, Maria: Washington Post
Goad, Ben: Riverside Press-Enterprise
Goldbacher, Raymond: USA Today
Goldberg, Jonathan: Congressional Quarterly
Golden, Rodrek: Reuters
Goldenberg, Suzanne: London Guardian
Goldfarb, Zachary: Washington Post
Goldman, Julianna: Bloomberg News
Goldschlag, William: New York Daily News
Goldschmidt, Jim: McClatchy Newspapers
Goldsmith, Reese: Congressional Quarterly
Goldstein, Amy: Washington Post
Goldstein, Avram: Bloomberg News
Goldstein, Daniel: Platts News Service
Goldstein, David: Kansas City Star
Golle, Vince: Bloomberg News
Goller, Howard Scot: Reuters
Gomez, Alan: USA Today
Gomez, Sergio: El Tiempo
Gomez, Shawn: Associated Press
Gomlak, Norman: Congressional Quarterly
Gonzalez, Francisco: EFE News Services
Goode, Darren: Congress Daily
Goodman, Adrianne: New York Times
Goodridge, Elizabeth: New York Times
Gorcester, Andrew: Jiji Press
Gordon, Greg: McClatchy Newspapers
Gordon, Marcy: Associated Press
Gorman, Siobhan: Wall Street Journal
Goto, Shihoko: Congress Daily
Gowen, Annie: Washington Post
Graham-Silverman, Adam: Congressional Quarterly
Grancharov, Givco: Argus Media
Gray, Andrew: Reuters
Greenberg, Brigitte: Bloomberg News
Greene, Robert: Bloomberg News
Greiling Keane, Angela: Bloomberg News
Greve, Frank: McClatchy Newspapers
Grier, Peter: Christian Science Monitor
Griffith, Stephanie: Agence France-Presse
Grim, Ryan: Huffington Post
Grimaldi, James: Washington Post
Groppe, Maureen: Gannett News Service
Gruenwald, Juliana: Congress Daily
Guenther, Markus: Westdeutsche Allgemeine
Guevara, Tomas: El Diario de Hoy
Guggenheim, Ken: Associated Press
Guha, Krishna: Financial Times
Guihaire, Edouard: Agence France-Presse
Gulino, Denny: Market News International
Gutman, Roy: McClatchy Newspapers
Ha, Taewon: Korea Dong-A Ilbo
Haberkorn, Jennifer: Washington Times
Hackett, Laurel: Scripps Howard News Service
Hagenbaugh, Barbara: USA Today
Hager, George: USA Today
Hall, Kevin: McClatchy Newspapers
Hall, Mimi: USA Today

MEMBERS ENTITLED TO ADMISSION—Continued

Hallock, Kimberly: Congressional Quarterly
Hallow, Ralph: Washington Times
Hamalainen, Aloysia: St. Louis Post-Dispatch
Hamann, Carlos: Agence France-Presse
Hamburger, Thomas: Los Angeles Times
Hampton, Olivia: Agence France-Presse
Hananel, Sam: Associated Press
Hannett, Thomas: Congressional Quarterly
Hargrove, Thomas: Scripps Howard News Service
Harland, Janis: New York Times
Harper, Jennifer: Washington Times
Harris, Charles: Yomiuri Shimbun
Harris, Gardiner: New York Times
Harris, Hamil: Washington Post
Hart, Dan: Bloomberg News
Hart, Kim: Washington Post
Hartnagel, Nancy: Catholic News Service
Hartson, Merrill: Associated Press
Hatch, David: Congress Daily
Hawkings, David: Congressional Quarterly
Hayakawa, Toshiyuki: Sekai Nippo
Haygood, Wil: Washington Post
Hazar, Hasan: Turkiye Daily
Healy, James: USA Today
Healy, Robert: Congressional Quarterly
Heath, Brad: USA Today
Heavey, Susan: Reuters
Hebert, H. Josef: Associated Press
Hedgpeth, Dana: Washington Post
Hefling, Kimberly: Associated Press
Heilprin, John: Associated Press
Heller, Marc: Watertown Daily Times
Hendel, Caitlin: Congressional Quarterly
Henderson, Gregory: Associated Press
Hendrickx, Frank: Netherlands Press Association
Hendrie, Paul: Congressional Quarterly
Henriksson, Karin: Svenska Dagbladet
Henry, John: Associated Press
Hernandez, Jose: El Universal
Hernandez, Raymond: New York Times
Herrmann, Frank: Rheinische Post
Herszenhorn, David: New York Times
Hess, David: Congress Daily
Hess, Pamela: Associated Press
Hesse, Monica: Washington Post
Higgins, David: Congressional Quarterly
Higgins, Sean: Investor's Business Daily
Higuchi, Takuya: Jiji Press
Hill, Charlotte: Agence France-Presse
Hill, Patricia: Washington Times
Hillyer, Quin: Washington Times
Hilsenrath, Jon: Wall Street Journal
Hinton, Earl: Associated Press
Hitt, Greg: Wall Street Journal
Hoffecker, Leslie: Congressional Quarterly
Hoffman, Lisa: Scripps Howard News Service
Hogberg, David: Investor's Business Daily
Holland, Jesse: Associated Press
Holland, Steve: Reuters
Holly, Christopher: Energy Daily
Holzer, Jessica: Dow Jones Newswires
Holzer, Linda: USA Today
Homan, Timothy: Bloomberg News
Homma, Keiichi: Yomiuri Shimbun
Hon, Chua Chin: Singapore Straits Times
Hong, Liu: Xinhua News Agency
Honore, Hugues: Agence France-Presse
Hook, Janet: Los Angeles Times
Hopkins, Cheyenne: American Banker
Hortobagyi, Monica: USA Today
Horwich, Lee: USA Today
Hoskinson, Charles: Congressional Quarterly
Hossain, Farhana: New York Times
Hotakainen, Rob: McClatchy Newspapers
House, Billy: Congress Daily
Hoy, Anne: Congressional Quarterly
Hsu, Spencer: Washington Post
Hu, Fang: Xinhua News Agency
Hudson, Audrey: Washington Times
Hughes, Darrell: Dow Jones Newswires
Hughes, John: Bloomberg News
Hughes, Siobhan: Dow Jones Newswires
Hughey, Ann: Bloomberg News
Hui, Ju: China Youth Daily
Hull, Anne: Washington Post
Hulse, Carl: New York Times
Hultman, Tamela: AllAfrica.com
Hume, Lynn: Bond Buyer
Hunley, Jonathan: News and Messenger
Hunt, Albert: Bloomberg News
Hunt, Kasie: Congress Daily
Hunt, Terence: Associated Press
Hunter, Kathleen: Congressional Quarterly
Hurley, Lawrence: Los Angeles Daily Journal
Hurley, Liam: Saudi Press Agency
Hurst, Steven: Associated Press
Hurt, Charles: New York Post
Hussain, Abdul-Hussain: Al Rai
Hussein, Sara: Agence France-Presse
Hwang, Jae Hoon: Yonhap News Agency
Hyde, Justin: Detroit Free Press
Hyong, Hwang Doo: Yonhap News Agency
Iafolla, Robert: Los Angeles Daily Journal
Ignatiou, Michail: Ethnos Greece
Ikeda, Nestor: Associated Press
Irons, John: Congressional Quarterly
Irwin, Walton Neil: Washington Post
Issenberg, Sasha: Boston Globe
Itkowitz, Colby: Congressional Quarterly
Ito, Hiroshi: Asahi Shimbun
Ito, Kosuke: Jiji Press
Ivanovich, David: Argus Media
Ives-Halperin, Benton: Congressional Quarterly
Iwamoto, Masako: Nikkei

MEMBERS ENTITLED TO ADMISSION—Continued

Iwata, Nakahiro: Tokyo Chunichi Shimbun
Jackler, Rosalind: USA Today
Jackman, Thomas: Washington Post
Jackson, David: USA Today
Jackson, Henry: Associated Press
Jackson, Herbert: Bergen Record
Jackson-Randall, Maya: Dow Jones Newswires
Jakes, Lara: Associated Press
Jalonick, Mary Clare: Associated Press
James, Frank: Chicago Tribune
Jamrisko, Michelle: Kyodo News
Jansen, Bart: Congressional Quarterly
Jehl, Douglas: New York Times
Jelinek, Pauline: Associated Press
Jenkins, Chris: Washington Post
Jennings, Angel: Wall Street Journal
Jensen, Kristin: Bloomberg News
Jessen, Kory: Associated Press
Jha, Lalit: India Press Trust
Jha, Shweta: Congressional Quarterly
Jiang, Guopeng: Xinhua News Agency
Johnson, Annie: Congressional Quarterly
Johnson, Carrie: Washington Post
Johnson, Fawn: Dow Jones Newswires
Johnson, Kevin: USA Today
Johnson, Matthew: Congressional Quarterly
Johnston, David: New York Times
Johnston, Nicholas: Bloomberg News
Jones, David: Washington Times
Jones, Kerry: Congressional Quarterly
Jordan, Alethea: Gannett Washington Bureau
Jordan, Bryant: Military.com
Jordan, Charles: Congress Daily
Joshi, Jitendra: Agence France-Presse
Jourdier, Marc: Agence France-Presse
Joy, Patricia: Congressional Quarterly
Junius, Dennis: Associated Press
Justsen, Klaus: Jyllands-Posten
Kaiser, Emily: Reuters
Kaiser, Robert: Washington Post
Kajita, Takehito: Kyodo News
Kalish, Brian: Dow Jones Newswires
Kamalick, Joseph: ICIS News
Kamen, Al: Washington Post
Kampeas, Ron: Jewish Telegraphic Agency
Kane, Paul: Washington Post
Kang, Cecilia: Washington Post
Kaper, Stacy Lynn: American Banker
Kapochunas, Rachel: Congressional Quarterly
Karam, Joyce: Al-Hayat
Karey, Gerald: Platts News Service
Karush, Sarah: Associated Press
Kasperowicz, Pete: IFR Markets
Kastner, Kevin: Market News International
Kato, Takefumi: Jiji Press
Kato, Yoichi: Asahi Shimbun
Katsuda, Toshihiko: Asahi Shimbun
Katz, Ian: Bloomberg News
Keating, Dan: Washington Post
Keefe, Bob: Atlanta Journal Constitution
Keefe, Stephen: Nikkei
Kelley, Matthew: USA Today
Kellman Blazar, Laurie: Associated Press
Kelly, Dennis: USA Today
Kelly, Erin: Gannett News Service
Kemper, Bob: Congress Daily
Kendall, Brent: Dow Jones Newswires
Kercheval, Nancy: Bloomberg News
Kerr, Jennifer: Associated Press
Kerry, Frances: Reuters
Kertes, Noella: Congressional Quarterly
Kessler, Glenn: Washington Post
Khaledi, Kayvon: Congressional Quarterly
Kiefer, Francine: Christian Science Monitor
Kiely, Eugene: USA Today
Kiely, Kathy: USA Today
Kilian, Martin: Tages Anzeiger
Kim, Angela: Congressional Quarterly
Kim, Anne: Congressional Quarterly
Kim, Eun: Gannett News Service
Kim, Hong Yeol: Korea Economic Daily
Kim, Jae Hong: Yonhap News Agency
Kim, Jin Ho: Kyunghyang Shinmun
Kim, Jungwook: Joongang Ilbo
Kim, Kyun Mi: Seoul Shinmun
Kim, Myung Ho: Kukmin Daily
Kimura, Kazuhiro: Kyodo News
King, Ledyard: Gannett News Service
King, Llewellyn: Energy Daily
King, Peter: Congressional Quarterly
King, Jr., Neil: Wall Street Journal
Kipling, Bogdan: Kipling News Service
Kirchhoff, Suzanne: USA Today
Kirk, Jim: Bloomberg News
Kirkpatrick, David: New York Times
Kirsanov, Dmitry: Itar-Tass News Agency
Kishi, Masayuki: Hokkaido Shimbun
Kishida, Yoshiki: Jiji Press
Kittross, David: LRP Publications
Kivlan, Terence: Congress Daily
Klimek, Eric: Associated Press
Kluever, Reymer: Sueddeutsche Zeitung
Klug, Foster: Associated Press
Kniazkov, Maxim: Agence France-Presse
Knott, Alex: Congressional Quarterly
Knowlton, Brian: International Herald Tribune
Knox, Olivier: Agence France-Presse
Kobayashi, Toshiya: Akahata
Koch, Wendy: USA Today
Kodjak-Fitzgerald, Alison: Bloomberg News
Koh, Seung Il: Yonhap News Agency
Komarow, Steven: Associated Press
Komatsu, Kenichi: Mainichi Shimbun
Komori, Yoshihisa: Sankei Shimbun

MEMBERS ENTITLED TO ADMISSION—Continued

Konjevoda, Jerry: IFR Markets
Kopecki, Dawn: Bloomberg News
Korade, Matthew: Congressional Quarterly
Koring, Paul: Toronto Globe and Mail
Kornblut, Anne: Washington Post
Kotecki, Emily: Washington Post
Kramer, Reed: AllAfrica.com
Kranish, Michael: Boston Globe
Krawzak, Paul: Congressional Quarterly
Kreisher, Otto: Congress Daily
Krieger, Hilary Leila: Jerusalem Post
Kroepsch, Adrianne: Congressional Quarterly
Kuhnhenn, Jim: Associated Press
Kuk, Kiyon: Segye Times
Kumar, Arun: Indo-Asian News Service
Kumar, Dinesh: Communications Daily
Kunkle, Fredrick: Washington Post
Kuno, Shuko: Jiji Press
Kurose, Yoshinari: Yomiuri Shimbun
Kurtz, Howard: Washington Post
Kusano, Kazuhiko: Mainichi Shimbun
Kwon, Taeho: Hankyoreh Daily
La Franchi, Howard: Christian Science Monitor
Labaton, Stephen: New York Times
Labbe, Theola: Washington Post
Labriny, Azeddine: Saudi Press Agency
Lakashmanan, Indira: Bloomberg News
Lake, Eli: Washington Times
Lambert, Lisa: Reuters
Lambrecht, William: St. Louis Post-Dispatch
Lambro, Donald: Washington Times
Landay, Jonathan: McClatchy Newspapers
Landers, James: Dallas Morning News
Landers, Peter: Wall Street Journal
Landler, Mark: New York Times
Lane, Charles: Washington Post
Lane, Kamala: Associated Press
Langan, Michael: Agence France-Presse
Langley, Monica: Wall Street Journal
Lanham, Yuko: Asahi Shimbun
Lanman, Scott: Bloomberg News
Lanteaume, Sylvie: Agence France-Presse
Lardner, Richard: Associated Press
Laris, Michael: Washington Post
Larkin, Catherine: Bloomberg News
Lawder, David: Reuters
Lawrence, Jill: USA Today
Layton, Lyndsey: Washington Post
Leah, Carliner: Congressional Quarterly
Leahy, Michael: Washington Post
Leary, Alex: St. Petersburg Times
Lebling, Madonna: Washington Post
Lee, Byonghan: Korea Times
Lee, Chang-Yul: Korea Times
Lee, Do Woon: Seoul Shinmun
Lee, Ha Won: Chosun Ilbo
Lee, Jong Kook: Korea Times
Lee, Keehong: Korea Dong-A Ilbo
Lee, Matthew: Associated Press
Lee, Sang Il: Joongang Ilbo
Leeds, Charles: Los Angeles Times-Washington Post News Service
Lefkow, David Christopher: Agence France-Presse
Lehmann, Chris: Congressional Quarterly
Leibovich, Mark: New York Times
Leiby, Richard: Washington Post
Leinwand, Donna: USA Today
Leissner, Janet: Associated Press
Lengell, Sean: Washington Times
Leocha, Charles: Tripso.com
Leonatti, Andrew: Congress Daily
Leonhardt, David: New York Times
Lesnes, Corine: Le Monde
Lesparre, Michael: Votes in Congress Service
Lester, William: Associated Press
Leubsdorf, Carl: Dallas Morning News
Lever, Robert: Agence France-Presse
Levey, Noam: Los Angeles Times
Levin, Adam: Congressional Quarterly
Levin, Alan: USA Today
Levinson, Nathan: Congressional Quarterly
Lewis, Charles: Hearst Newspapers
Lewis, Finlay: Congressional Quarterly
Lewis, Neil: New York Times
Li, Jing: China News Service
Li, Zhenyu: China Press
Lichtblau, Eric: New York Times
Liebert, Larry: Bloomberg News
Lightman, David: McClatchy Newspapers
Lin, Betty: World Journal
Lindell, Cecile: Daily Deal
Lindeman, Eric: Energy Daily
Lipari, James: Associated Press
Liptak, Adam: New York Times
Lipton, Eric: New York Times
Litvan, Laura: Bloomberg News
Liu, Kuen-yuan: Central News Agency
Liu, Lina: Xinhua News Agency
Liu, Ping: China Times
Lizamá, Orlando: EFE News Services
Lloyd, Janice: USA Today
Lobe, James: Inter Press Service
Lobianco, Tom: Washington Times
Lobsenz, George: Energy Daily
Locker, Ray: USA Today
Lockhead, Carolyn: San Francisco Chronicle
Lomax, Simon: Bloomberg News
Lopez, Jose: Notimex Mexican News Agency
Lorber, Sarah Jane: New York Times
Lott, John: Washington Times
Loubette, Celine: Agence France-Presse
Loven, Jennifer: Associated Press
Lovenheim, Sarah: Washington Post
Lowe, Christian: Military.com
Lowy, Joan: Associated Press

MEMBERS ENTITLED TO ADMISSION—Continued

Lozano, Laurent: Agence France-Presse
Lubold, Gordon: Christian Science Monitor
Luce, Edward: Financial Times
Luft, Kerry: Tribune Company
Lynch, David: USA Today
Lynch, Sarah: Dow Jones Newswires
Lytle, Tamara: Freelance
Macaron, Joe: Kuwait News Agency
Macaskill, Ewen: London Guardian
MacGillis, Alec: Washington Post
Mack, Kristen: Washington Post
Magner, Mike: Congress Daily
Mahabir, Karen: Associated Press
Maher, Aya: Asahi Shimbun
Make, Jonathan: Communications Daily
Malandain, Lucile: Agence France-Presse
Malenic, Maria: Defense Daily
Maler, Sandra: Reuters
Mann, Jason: Congress Daily
Mann, William: Associated Press
Mann, Windsor: Washington Times
Manning, Stephen: Associated Press
Mannion, James: Agence France-Presse
Mansfield, Matthew: Argus Media
Mantell, Ruth: MarketWatch
Mao, Li: Science & Technology Daily
Marcus, Aliza: Bloomberg News
Marcus, Ruth: Washington Post
Marenco, Julio Ernesto: La Prensa Grafica of El Salvador
Margasak, Lawrence: Associated Press
Margetta, Robert James: Congressional Quarterly
Marimow, Anne: Washington Post
Marino, Marie: Gannett News Service
Marklein, Mary Beth: USA Today
Markon, Jerome: Washington Post
Marrero, Diana: Milwaukee Journal Sentinel
Marsh, Julia: Yomiuri Shimbun
Marshall, Stephen: USA Today
Martin, Gary: San Antonio Express-News
Marutani, Hiroshi: Nikkei
Mascaro, Lisa: Las Vegas Sun
Mason, Jeff: Reuters
Mathes, Michael: Agence France-Presse
Mathews, Mark: Orlando Sentinel
Matthews, Robert Guy: Wall Street Journal
Matthews, William: Congressional Quarterly
Mattingly, Phil: Congressional Quarterly
Maynard, Michael: MarketWatch
Mazzetti, Mark: New York Times
McAuliff, Michael: New York Daily News
McCabe, Scott: Washington Examiner
McCarthy, Meghan: Congressional Quarterly
McCarthy, Mike: German Press Agency-DPA
McCarty, Courtney: Congressional Quarterly
McCarty, Mark: Medical Device Daily
McCaslin, John: Washington Times
McConnell, William: Daily Deal
McCormick, John: Chicago Tribune
McCoy, J. J.: Restructuring Today
McCutcheon, Chuck: Congressional Quarterly
McDermott, Ryan: Communications Daily
McDonald, Greg: Congressional Quarterly
McElhatton, Jr., James: Washington Times
McFeatters, Dale: Scripps Howard News Service
McGaughy, Lauren: Asahi Shimbun
McGreal, Chris: London Guardian
McKeever, Amy: Mainichi Shimbun
McKendry, Ian: Market News International
McKinnon, John: Wall Street Journal
McLean, Demian: Bloomberg News
McManus, Doyle: Los Angeles Times
McNeil, Margaret: MarketWatch
McPike, Erin: Congress Daily
McQuillan, Mark: Bloomberg News
McQuillen, William: Bloomberg News
Meadows, Clifford: New York Times
Meckler, Laura: Wall Street Journal
Meek, James: New York Daily News
Meinert, Peer: German Press Agency-DPA
Mekay, Emad: America In Arabic News Agency
Mekay, Emad: Inter Press Service
Melvin, Jasmin: Reuters
Memmott, Mark: USA Today
Memoli, Michael: Real Clear Politics
Mercer, Marsha: Mercer Media
Merida, Kevin: Washington Post
Merle, Renae: Washington Post
Meszoly, Robin: Bloomberg News
Metzler, Natasha: Associated Press
Meyer, Joshua: Los Angeles Times
Michaels, David: Dallas Morning News
Michaels, Jim: USA Today
Michalski, Patty: USA Today
Middleton, Chris: Bloomberg News
Miga, Andrew: Associated Press
Mikes, Zoltan: World Business Press
Mikkelsen, Randall: Reuters
Milbank, Dana: Washington Post
Miller, Greg: Los Angeles Times
Miller, Kristie: La Salle News Tribune
Miller, Mark: TVNewsday.com
Miller, Reuben: Merger Market of Financial Times
Miller, Richard: Bloomberg News
Miller, Steven: Washington Times
Miller, William: Washington Post
Milligan, Susan: Boston Globe
Millikin, David: Agence France-Presse
Mills, Betty: Griffin-Larrabee News Service
Miniter, Richard: Washington Times
Miroff, Nick: Washington Post
Mitchell, Joshua: Dow Jones Newswires
Miyazaki, Takeo: Yomiuri Shimbun
Mochizuki, Hirotsugu: Asahi Shimbun
Mohammed, Arshad: Reuters

MEMBERS ENTITLED TO ADMISSION—Continued

Molotsky, Irvin: Congress Daily
Moltz, David: Inside Higher Ed
Monge, Yolanda: El Pais
Montet, Virginie: Agence France-Presse
Montgomery, David: Washington Post
Montgomery, Lori: Washington Post
Morales, Armando: La Razon
Moran, Tessa: IFR Markets
Morello, Carol: Washington Post
Morgan, David: Reuters
Morris, Damiko: Associated Press
Morris, David: Congress Daily
Morse, Dan: Washington Post
Morton, Joseph: Omaha World-Herald
Moses, Rebekah: Asahi Shimbun
Moss, Daniel: Bloomberg News
Mott, Gregory: Bloomberg News
Mozgovaya, Natasha: Haaretz Daily
Mufson, Steven: Washington Post
Mulligan, John: Providence Journal
Mullins, Brody: Wall Street Journal
Mummolo, Jonathan: Washington Post
Mundy, Alicia: Wall Street Journal
Munoz-Acebes, Cesar: EFE News Services
Murayama, Yusuke: Asahi Shimbun
Murphy, Kathleen: Congressional Quarterly
Murray, Brendan: Bloomberg News
Murray, William: Oil Daily
Murti, Bhattiprolu: Dow Jones Newswires
Muscat, Sabine: Financial Times Deutschland
Mussenden, Sean: Media General News Service
Muth, Chaz: Catholic News Service
Mutikani, Lucia: Reuters
Myers, Jim: Tulsa World
Myers, Michael: Myers News Service
Mykkanen, Pekka: Helsingin Sanomat
Nagourney, Adam: New York Times
Nahmias, Melinda: Congressional Quarterly
Nail, Dawson: Communications Daily
Najor, Pamela: Argus Media
Nakamura, David: Washington Post
Nakashima, Ellen: Washington Post
Nakaya, Yuji: Kyodo News
Nasaw, Daniel: London Guardian
Nather, David: Congressional Quarterly
Nayar, Krishnan: Calcutta Telegraph
N'Diaye, Yali: Market News International
Neergaard, Lauran: Associated Press
Neubauer, Chuck: Washington Times
Neuman, Johanna: Los Angeles Times
Newhall, Marissa: Washington Post
Newman, Christopher: Argus Media
Nicholas, Peter: Los Angeles Times
Nichols, Hans: Bloomberg News
Niedowski, Erika: Abu Dhabi National
Nielsen, David: Scripps Howard News Service
Niles, Ryan: Wall Street Journal
Nishimura, Hiroshi: Akahata
Nishina, Michi: Kyodo News
Nixon, Ron: New York Times
Njuguna, Wangui: LRP Publications
Nkansah, E. Roy: Congressional Quarterly
Noel, Essex: Reuters
Noone, Dennis: Gannett Washington Bureau
Norington, Brad: Australian
Norman, Jane: Congressional Quarterly
Northey, Hannah: Argus Media
Norton, C. JoAnne: Bloomberg News
Norton, Emily: Congressional Quarterly
Noyes, Andrew: Congress Daily
Nutting, Brian: Congressional Quarterly
Nutting, Rex: MarketWatch
Nylen, Leah: Congressional Quarterly
O'Brien, Nancy: Catholic News Service
O'Connell, James: Bloomberg News
O'Connor, Sarah: Financial Times
O'Keefe, Edward: Washington Post
O'Neil, Anne: Argus Media
O'Reilly II, Joseph: Bloomberg News
Odion-Esence, Brai: Market News International
Odle, John Robert: Kyodo News
Ogata, Toshihiko: Asahi Shimbun
Ogawa, Satoshi: Yomiuri Shimbun
Ogle, Alexander: Agence France-Presse
Ohji, Tomoko: Mainichi Shimbun
Ohlemacher, Stephen: Associated Press
Ohlsson, Erik: Dagens Nyheter
Ohsumi, Ryu: Nikkei
Oikawa, Masaya: Mainichi Shimbun
Oishi, Itaru: Nikkei
Okada, Akihiro: Yomiuri Shimbun
Okamuto, Michiro: Yomiuri Shimbun
Olchowy, Mark: Associated Press
Oliphant, James: Chicago Tribune
Olson, Elizabeth: New York Times
Orndorff, Mary: Birmingham News
Orol, Ronald: MarketWatch
Orr, J. Scott: Newark Star-Ledger
Ostermann, Dietmar: Frankfurter Rundschau
Ota, Alan: Congressional Quarterly
Ourlian, Robert: Los Angeles Times
Overberg, Paul: USA Today
Ozyurt, Ahu: Milliyet
Pace, David: Associated Press
Page, Clarence: Chicago Tribune
Page, Susan: USA Today
Pakhomov, Alexander: Itar-Tass News Agency
Palank, Jacqueline: Dow Jones Newswires
Paletta, Damian: Wall Street Journal
Paley, Amit: Washington Post
Palmer, Avery: Congressional Quarterly
Palmer, Doug: Reuters
Palomo, Elvira: EFE News Services
Papantoniou, Lambros: Eleftheros Typos

MEMBERS ENTITLED TO ADMISSION—Continued

Parisi, Christina: Congressional Quarterly
Parisse, Emmanuel: Agence France-Presse
Park, Jungbin: Yonhap News Agency
Park, Kwang Duk: Korea Times
Park, Sang Hyun: Yonhap News Agency
Parker, Ashley: New York Times
Parker, Kathleen: Washington Post Writer's Group
Parks, Daniel: Congressional Quarterly
Parsons, Christi: Chicago Tribune
Passenheim, Antje: German Press Agency-DPA
Patel, Yogettaben: Dow Jones Newswires
Patrick, Richard: USA Today
Pattison, Mark: Catholic News Service
Pear, Robert: New York Times
Pearlstein, Steven: Washington Post
Peck, Louis: Congress Daily
Pelofsky, Jeremy: Reuters
Pena, Maria: EFE News Services
Perez, Anthony J.: USA Today
Perez, Evan: Wall Street Journal
Perine, Keith: Congressional Quarterly
Perkins, Mary: Yomiuri Shimbun
Perrone, Matthew: Associated Press
Pershing, Ben: Washington Post
Peterson, Molly: Bloomberg News
Phelps, Timothy: Los Angeles Times
Phillips, Kathleen: New York Times
Phillips, Lauren: Congressional Quarterly
Phillips, Michael: Wall Street Journal
Philpott, Thomas: Military Update
Pianin, Eric: Washington Post
Picani, Silvia: La Nacion
Pickard-Cambridge, Claire: Argus Media
Picket, Kerry: Washington Times
Pickler, Nedra: Associated Press
Pincus, Walter: Washington Post
Pine, Art: Congress Daily
Pitney, Nico: Huffington Post
Piper, Greg: Communications Daily
Piven, Benjamin: Yomiuri Shimbun
Pleming, Sue: Reuters
Plocek, Joseph: Market News International
Plungis, Jeff: Bloomberg News
Poirier, John: Reuters
Ponnudurai, Parameswaran: Agence France-Presse
Pope, Charles: Oregonian
Posner, Michael: Congress Daily
Potter, Mitchell: Toronto Star
Povich, Elaine: Congress Daily
Powell, Stewart: Hearst Newspapers
Power, Stephen: Wall Street Journal
Poyraxlar, Elcin: Cumhuriyet
Preciphs, Joi: Bloomberg News
Price, Deborah: Detroit News
Priest, Dana: Washington Post
Pruitt, Claude: USA Today
Przybyla, Heidi: Bloomberg News
Puente, Maria: USA Today
Pugh, Anthony: McClatchy Newspapers
Pulizzi, Henry: Dow Jones Newswires
Purce, Melinda: Associated Press
Purger, Tibor: Magyar Szo
Putman, Eileen: Associated Press
Puzzanghera, James: Los Angeles Times
Qiang, Zou: China Legal Daily
Qianliang, Yu: Xinhua News Agency
Quaid, Libby: Associated Press
Quinn, Andrew: Reuters
Raasch, Charles: Gannett News Service
Radnofsky, Louise: Wall Street Journal
Raimon, Marcelo: ANSA Italian News Agency
Rajagopalan, Sethuraman: Pioneer - India
Rajghatta, Chidanand: Times of India
Ramadan, Wafik: L'Orient - Le Jour
Ramaswamy, Anindita: German Press Agency-DPA
Rampton, Roberta: Reuters
Rankin, Robert: McClatchy Newspapers
Rascoe, Ayesha: Reuters
Rastello, Sandrine: Bloomberg News
Ratnam, Gopal: Bloomberg News
Raum, Thomas: Associated Press
Ray, Eric: Congressional Quarterly
Ray, Rachel: London Daily Telegraph
Raymond, Anthony: Political Money Line
Raymond, Jill: Congressional Quarterly
Reber, Paticia: German Press Agency-DPA
Recio, Maria: Fort Worth Star-Telegram
Redden, Elizabeth: Inside Higher Ed
Reddy, Sudeep: Wall Street Journal
Rehmann, Marc: Congressional Quarterly
Rehrmann, Laura: Gannett News Service
Reichard, John: Congressional Quarterly
Reid, Timothy: London Times
Reilly, Sean: Mobile Register
Rein, Lisa: Washington Post
Ren, Haijun: Xinhua News Agency
Retter, Daphne: New York Post
Reynolds, David: Dow Jones Newswires
Reynolds, Maura: Los Angeles Times
Reynolds Lewis, Katherine: Freelance
Ricci, Andrea: Reuters
Rice, Charles: Merger Market of Financial Times
Richardson, Betty: Congressional Quarterly
Richert, Catharine: Congressional Quarterly
Richey, Warren: Christian Science Monitor
Richter, Paul: Los Angeles Times
Richwine, Lisa: Reuters
Rickett, Keith: Associated Press
Rickman, Jonathan: Energy Daily
Riddell, Kelly: Bloomberg News
Riechmann-Kepler, Deb: Associated Press
Riley, Kim: LRP Publications
Riley, Lauren: Saudi Press Agency
Riley, Michael: Denver Post

MEMBERS ENTITLED TO ADMISSION—Continued

Riley, Michael: Congressional Quarterly
Risen, James: New York Times
Riskind, Jonathan: Columbus Dispatch
Rizzo, Katherine: Congressional Quarterly
Robb, Gregory: MarketWatch
Robbins, James: Washington Times
Roberts, Roxanne: Washington Post
Robinson, Eugene: Washington Post
Robinson, James: Los Angeles Times
Robinson, John: Defense Daily
Rogin, Joshua: Congressional Quarterly
Rohner, Mark: Bloomberg News
Roig, Carlos: USA Today
Roig-Franzia, Manuel: Washington Post
Romano, Lois: Washington Post
Roosevelt, Ann: Defense Daily
Rose, Matthew: Wall Street Journal
Rosen, James: McClatchy Newspapers
Rosenberg, Elizabeth: Argus Media
Rosenkrantz, Holly: Bloomberg News
Ross, Sonya: Associated Press
Roth, Bennett: Congressional Quarterly
Rowland, Kara: Washington Times
Rowley, James: Bloomberg News
Ruane, Michael: Washington Post
Rubin, Richard: Congressional Quarterly
Rucker, Patrick: Reuters
Rucker, Philip: Washington Post
Ruf, Renzo: Der Bund
Rugaber, Chris: Associated Press
Rulon Herman, Malia: Gannett Washington Bureau
Runningen, Roger: Bloomberg News
Rutenberg, Jim: New York Times
Rutherford, Emelie: Defense Daily
Ryan, Kiki: Washington Examiner
Ryan, Timothy: Reuters
Ryu, Jae-Hoon: Hankyoreh Daily
Sacks, Stephen: Tokyo Chunichi Shimbun
Sadeqi, Sherouq: Kuwait News Agency
Sadowski, Dennis: Catholic News Service
Saito, Nobuhiro: Mainichi Shimbun
Salant, Jonathan: Bloomberg News
Salcedo, Michele: Associated Press
Samukawa, Akira: Kyodo News
Sanchez, Humberto: Congress Daily
Sands, David: Washington Times
Sands, Ken: Congressional Quarterly
Sanger, David: New York Times
Sanner, Ann: Associated Press
Santini, Jean-Louis: Agence France-Presse
Saslow, Eli: Washington Post
Satter, Andrew: Congressional Quarterly
Savage, Charlie: New York Times
Savage, David: Los Angeles Times
Scally, William: William Scally Reports
Scannell, Kara: Wall Street Journal
Schatz, Amy: Wall Street Journal
Schatz, Joseph: Congressional Quarterly
Scheuble, Kristy: Bloomberg News
Schlesinger, Jacob: Wall Street Journal
Schlisserman, Courtney: Bloomberg News
Schmick, William: Bloomberg News
Schmid, Randolph: Associated Press
Schmidt, Robert: Bloomberg News
Schmitt, Eric: New York Times
Schneider, Andrew: Seattle Post-Intelligencer
Scholtes, Jennifer: Congressional Quarterly
Schoof, Renee: McClatchy Newspapers
Schouten, Fredreka: USA Today
Schroeder, Peter: Bond Buyer
Schroeder, Robert: MarketWatch
Schulte, Brigid: Washington Post
Schwed, Craig: Gannett News Service
Schweid, Barry: Associated Press
Scott, Heather: Market News International
Scully, Megan: Congress Daily
Seeley, Tina: Bloomberg News
Seib, Gerald: Wall Street Journal
Seibel, Mark: McClatchy Newspapers
Seper, Jerry: Washington Times
Sevastopulo, Demetri: Financial Times
Shackelford, Lucy: Washington Post
Shalal-Esa, Andrea: Reuters
Shane, Scott: New York Times
Shanker, Thomas: New York Times
Shapira, Ian: Washington Post
Shaw, John: Market News International
Shear, Michael: Washington Post
Sheikh, Nezar: Saudi Press Agency
Shepardson, David: Detroit News
Sheridan, Kerry Colleen: Agence France-Presse
Sheridan, Mary Beth: Washington Post
Sherman, Mark: LRP Publications
Sherman, Mark: Associated Press
Sherman, Paul: CapitalBeat.com
Sherzai, Magan: Agence France-Presse
Shields, Gerard: Baton Rouge Advocate
Shields, Mark: Creators Syndicate
Shields, Todd: Bloomberg News
Shimada, Akihiro: Tokyo Chunichi Shimbun
Shuppy, Anne: Congressional Quarterly
Sia, Richard: Congress Daily
Sichelman, Lew: United Media
Siddons, Andrew: Yomiuri Shimbun
Sidorov, Dmitry: Kommersant
Sidoti, Elizabeth: Associated Press
Silva, Mark: Chicago Tribune
Silvassy, Kathleen: Congressional Quarterly
Simmons, Christine: Associated Press
Simmons, Deborah: Washington Times
Simon, Neil: Media General News Service
Simon, Richard: Los Angeles Times
Simpson, Cameron: Wall Street Journal
Sisk, Richard: New York Daily News

MEMBERS ENTITLED TO ADMISSION—Continued

Sisto, Carrie: Argus Media
Sitov, Andrei: Itar-Tass News Agency
Skarzenski, Ronald: New York Times
Skorneck, Carolyn: Associated Press
Skotzko, Stacey: Congressional Quarterly
Slater, James: Agence France-Presse
Sloan, Steven: American Banker
Smith, Donna: Reuters
Smith, Elliot Blair: Bloomberg News
Smith, Jeffrey: Washington Post
Smith, Sylvia: Fort Wayne Journal Gazette
Smith, Veronica: Agence France-Presse
Smolkin, Rachel: USA Today
Snider, Michael: USA Today
Sniffen, Michael: Associated Press
Sobczyk, Joseph: Bloomberg News
Soga, Ian: Bloomberg News
Solomon, Deborah: Wall Street Journal
Solomon, John: Washington Times
Solomon, Jonathan: Wall Street Journal
Somashekhar, Sandhya: Washington Post
Somerville, Glenn: Reuters
Southall, Ashley: New York Times
Sowdwer-Staley, Megan: Congressional Quarterly
Spang, Thomas: Berliner Zeitung
Spangler, Todd: Detroit Free Press
Sparks, Sarah: LRP Publications
Spence, Matthew: London Times
Spence, Tony: Catholic News Service
Spencer, Samuel: Restructuring Today
Spiegel, Peter: Wall Street Journal
Spieler, Matthew: Congressional Quarterly
Spillius, Alexander: London Daily Telegraph
St. George, Donna: Washington Post
Stanek, Steven: Abu Dhabi National
Starks, Tim: Congressional Quarterly
Stein, Robert: Washington Post
Stempleman, Neil: Reuters
Stephens, Joe: Washington Post
Stern, Christopher: Bloomberg News
Stern, Seth: Congressional Quarterly
Sternberg, Steve: USA Today
Sternberg, William: USA Today
Sternstein, Aliya: Congressional Quarterly
Stevenson, Richard: New York Times
Stewart, Bruce Scott: Sankei Shimbun
Stewart, Nikita: Washington Post
Stockman, Farah: Boston Globe
Stohr, Greg: Bloomberg News
Stolberg, Sheryl: New York Times
Stone, Andrea: USA Today
Storey, David: Reuters
Stoughton, Stephenie: Associated Press
Stout, David: New York Times
Straus, Miriam: Congressional Quarterly
Stripling, John: ICIS News
Strobel, Warren: McClatchy Newspapers
Strohm, Chris: Congress Daily
Strong, Thomas: Associated Press
Stuever, Hank: Washington Post
Sturgeon, William: Tokyo Chunichi Shimbun
Sugimoto, Ichiro: Kyodo News
Sugita, Hiroki: Kyodo News
Sullivan, Andy: Reuters
Sullivan, Bartholomew: Scripps Howard News Service
Sullivan, Eileen: Associated Press
Sun, Lena: Washington Post
Superville, Darlene: Associated Press
Surzhanskiy, Andrey: Itar-Tass News Agency
Susami, Fumitaka: Kyodo News
Swann, Christopher: Bloomberg News
Swarns, Rachel: New York Times
Sweeney, Jeanne: LRP Publications
Sweet, Lynn: Chicago Sun-Times
Swindell, Bill: Congress Daily
Syeed, Nafeesa: Associated Press
Symes, Frances: Congressional Quarterly
Tachino, Junji: Asahi Shimbun
Tackett, Michael: Bloomberg News
Taillefer, Pierre: Agence France-Presse
Takahashi, Hiroyuki: Jiji Press
Takei, Toru: Kyodo News
Talev, Margaret: McClatchy Newspapers
Talley, Ian: Dow Jones Newswires
Tandon, Shaun: Agence France-Presse
Tankersley, James: Chicago Tribune
Tanzi, Alex: Bloomberg News
Tate, Curtis: McClatchy Newspapers
Tavara, Santiago: Notimex Mexican News Agency
Taylor, Andrew: Associated Press
Taylor, Marisa: McClatchy Newspapers
Teitelbaum, Michael: Congressional Quarterly
Temple-West, Patrick: Bond Buyer
Tessler, Joelle: Associated Press
Tetreault, Stephan: Stephens Media Group
Theimer, Sharon: Associated Press
Theobald, William: Gannett News Service
Thibodeaux, Sarah: Congressional Quarterly
Thibodeaux, Troy: Associated Press
Thiruvengadam, Meena: Dow Jones Newswires
Thomas, Helen: Hearst Newspapers
Thomas, Ken: Associated Press
Thomas, Richard: Votes In Congress Service
Thomasson, Dan: Scripps Howard News Service
Thomma, Steven: McClatchy Newspapers
Thompson, Cheryl: Washington Post
Thompson, Krissah: Washington Post
Thompson, Marilyn: Washington Post
Thompson, Robert: Washington Post
Tilove, Jonathan: New Orleans Times-Picayune
Tobe, Hajime: Kyodo News
Tokito, Mineko: Yomiuri Shimbun
Toles, Tom: Washington Post
Toloui-Semnani, Neda: Congressional Quarterly

MEMBERS ENTITLED TO ADMISSION—Continued

Tomasky, Michael: London Guardian
Tomkin, Robert: Congressional Quarterly
Tompson, Trevor: Associated Press
Toppo, Gregory: USA Today
Torobin, Jeremy: Bloomberg News
Torres, Carlos: Bloomberg News
Torres, Craig: Bloomberg News
Torry, Jack: Columbus Dispatch
Torry, Saundra: USA Today
Tranausky, Todd: Argus Media
Trankovits, Laszlo: German Press Agency-DPA
Trejos, Nancy: Washington Post
Trescott, Jacqueline: Washington Post
Trottman, Melanie: Wall Street Journal
Trowbridge, Gordon: Detroit News
Trygstad, Kyle: Real Clear Politics
Tsao, Nadia Y.F.: Liberty Times
Tucker, Boyd Neely: Washington Post
Tumgoren, Serdar: Congressional Quarterly
Tumulty, Brian: Gannett News Service
Tunks, Larry: Congressional Quarterly
Turley, Melissa: LRP Publications
Turque, Bill: Washington Post
Tyson, Ann Scott: Washington Post
Tyson, James: Bloomberg News
Ukai, Satoshi: Asahi Shimbun
Urano, Eri: Tokyo Chunichi Shimbun
Urban, Peter: Connecticut Post
Urdaneta, Diego: Agence France-Presse
Uy, Erin: LRP Publications
Vadala, Gregory: Congressional Quarterly
Val Mitjavila, Eusebio: La Vanguardia
Valentino, Paolo: Corriere Della Sera
Valery, Chantal: Agence France-Presse
Van Nostrand, Jim: McClatchy Newspapers
Vanden Brook, Tom: USA Today
Vanderbilt, Sarah: Congressional Quarterly
Vanderhaar, William: Associated Press
Vargas, Jose Antonio: Washington Post
Vargas, Theresa: Washington Post
Varsalona, Devin: Congressional Quarterly
Vaughan, Martin: Dow Jones Newswires
Veigle, Anne: Communications Daily
Vekshin, Alison: Bloomberg News
Venkannaiah, Krishna: Hindustan Times
Vergano, Dan: USA Today
Vicini, James: Reuters
Vidal Liy, Macarena: EFE News Services
Vineys, Kevin: Associated Press
Vogel, Stephen: Washington Post
Vogt, Christophe: Agence France-Presse
Volpe, Paul: Washington Post
Von Marschall, Christoph: Der Tagesspiegel
Vorman, Julie: Reuters
Wagman, Robert: Newspaper Enterprise
Wagner, Daniel: Associated Press
Wagner, John: Washington Post
Waitz, Nancy: Reuters
Walcott, John: McClatchy Newspapers
Wald, Matthew: New York Times
Walker, Emily: Medpagetoday.com
Wallbank, Derek: Congressional Quarterly
Wallsten, Peter: Los Angeles Times
Walters, Anne: German Press Agency-DPA
Wang, Herman: Chattanooga Times Free Press
Wang, Stephanie: Asahi Shimbun
Wang, Yu-Ting: Communications Daily
Wangsness, Lisa: Boston Globe
Ward, Andrew: Financial Times
Ward, Jon: Washington Times
Warminsky, Joseph: Congressional Quarterly
Warner, Judith: New York Times
Warren, Timothy: Washington Times
Warrick, Joby: Washington Post
Watanabe, Hiroo: Sankei Shimbun
Watson, Traci: USA Today
Watters, Susan: Fairchild News Service
Wayne, Alexander: Congressional Quarterly
Wayne, Leslie: New York Times
Webber, Caitlin: Congressional Quarterly
Weekes Jr., Michael: Reuters
Wehrman, Jessica: Dayton Daily News
Wei, Jing: Xinhua News Agency
Wei, Wang: Xinhua News Agency
Weiner, Mark: Syracuse Post-Standard
Weinstein, Matthew: Congressional Quarterly
Weir, Kytja: Washington Examiner
Weisman, Jonathan: Wall Street Journal
Weiss, Eric: Washington Post
Weiss, Miles Geoffrey: Bloomberg News
Welch, James: USA Today
Wellisz, Chris: Bloomberg News
Wells, Letitia: McClatchy Newspapers
Wells, Robert: Dow Jones Newswires
Werner, Erica: Associated Press
Wessel, David: Wall Street Journal
West, Paul: Baltimore Sun
Westbrook, Jesse: Bloomberg News
Westley, Brian: Associated Press
Wetzstein, Cheryl: Washington Times
Weyl, Ben: Congressional Quarterly
White, Dina: Chicago Tribune
White, Gordon: Washington Telecommunications Services
White, Joseph: Wall Street Journal
White, Josh: Washington Post
White, Keith: Congress Daily
White, Jr., Joseph: Associated Press
Whitesides, John: Reuters
Whitmire, Guy: Congressional Quarterly
Whitten, Daniel: Bloomberg News
Whoriskey, Peter: Washington Post
Wilkison, David: Associated Press
Williams, Jr., Joseph: Boston Globe
Williamson, Elizabeth: Wall Street Journal

MEMBERS ENTITLED TO ADMISSION—Continued

Willis, Robert: Bloomberg News
Wilson, George: Congress Daily
Wilson, Patricia: Reuters
Wilson, Scott: Washington Post
Winicour, Daniel: Congressional Quarterly
Winski, Joe: Bloomberg News
Wirzbicki, Alan: Boston Globe
Witcover, Jules: Tribune Media Services
Witkowski, Nancy Benac: Associated Press
Woellert, Lorraine: Bloomberg News
Wolf, Daniel: Scripps Howard News Service
Wolf, Jim: Reuters
Wolf, Richard: USA Today
Wolfe, Frank: LRP Publications
Wolfe, Kathryn: Congressional Quarterly
Woo, Yee Ling: Congressional Quarterly
Wood, David: Baltimore Sun
Woodward, Bob: Washington Post
Woodward, Calvin: Associated Press
Wu, Qing Cai: China News Service
Wuetherich, Peter: Agence France-Presse
Wutkowski, Karey: Reuters
Wynn, Randall: Congressional Quarterly
Xian, Wen: China People's Daily
Xiangwen, Ge: Xinhua News Agency
Xiao-Jing, Du: China Press
Xiong, Min: 21st Century Business Herald
Xuejiang, Li: China People's Daily
Yada, Toshihiko: Yomiuri Shimbun
Yamada, Tetsuro: Yomiuri Shimbun
Yamamoto, Hideya: Sankei Shimbun
Yamour, Heather: Kuwait News Agency
Yan, Feng: Xinhua News Agency
Yancey, Matthew: Associated Press
Yang, Liming: China Youth Daily
Yang, Quinchuan: Xinhua News Agency
Yano, Kimiko: Kyodo News
Yasunaga, Tatsuro: Kyodo News
Yaukey, John: Gannett News Service
Yen, Hope: Associated Press
Yoder, Eric: Washington Post
Yoest, Patrick: Dow Jones Newswires
Yoneyama, Yusuke: Nikkei
Yoon, Kyongho: Maeil Business Newspaper
York, Byron: Washington Examiner
Yost, Pete: Associated Press
Young, Donna: BioWorld Today
Young, Kerry: Congressional Quarterly
Young, Mark: Media General News Service
Younglai, Rachelle: Reuters
Youssef, Nancy: McClatchy Newspapers
Yu, Donghui: China Press
Zabarenko, Deborah: Reuters
Zacharia, Janine: Bloomberg News
Zagaroli, Lisa: McClatchy Newspapers
Zajac, Andrew: Chicago Tribune
Zak, Dan: Washington Post
Zakaria, Tabassum: Reuters
Zamora Barcelo, Jordi: Agence France-Presse
Zapor, Patricia: Catholic News Service
Zeitvogel, Karin: Agence France-Presse
Zeleny, Jeff: New York Times
Zeller, Shawn: Congressional Quarterly
Zhang, Jane: Wall Street Journal
Zhao, Yi: Xinhua News Agency
Zhu, Xingfu: Shanghai Wenhui Daily
Zibel, Alan: Associated Press
Ziener, Markus: Handelsblatt
Zimmerman, Carol: Catholic News Service
Zitner, Aaron: Los Angeles Times
Zlodorev, Dmitri: Itar-Tass News Agency
Zongker, Brett: Associated Press
Zoroya, Gregg: USA Today
Zoupaniotis, Apostolos: Cyprus News Agency
Zremski, Jerry: Buffalo News
Zwelling, Michael: Restructuring Today

NEWSPAPERS REPRESENTED IN PRESS GALLERIES

House Gallery 225–3945, 225–6722 Senate Gallery 224–0241

AARGAUER ZEITUNG—(202) 403–7115; 5884 Woodfield Estates Drive, Alexandria, VA 22310: Renzo Ruf.

ABC NEWSPAPER—(202) 588–0207; 1750 P Street, NW., Apartment 306, Washington, DC 20003: Emilio Blasco.

ABIM—(703) 243–2104; 1344 Merrie Ridge Road, McLean, VA 22101: Mario Navarro da Costa.

AGENCE FRANCE-PRESSE—(202) 289–0700; 1500 K Street, NW., Suite 600, Washington, DC 20005: Marc-Antoine Baudoux, Joanna Biddle, Leon Bruneau, Jerome Cartillier, David Clark, Stephen Collinson, Ivan Couronne, Martin de Montvalon, Daniel DeLuce, Fabienne Faur, Aldo Gamboa, Stephanie Griffith, Carlos Hamann, Olivia Hampton, Paul Handley, Maxim Kniazkov, Joseph Krauss, Michelle Kwajafa, Michael Langan, Sylvie Lanteaume, David Lefkow, Robert Lever, Arthur MacMillan, Robert MacPherson, James Mannion, Michael Mathes, Becca Milfeld, David Millikin, Virginie Montet, Veronika Oleksyn, Lauren Ortiz, Raphaelle Picard, Tangi Quemener, Matthieu Rabechault, Anne Renaut, Nicolas Revise, Ramon Sahmkow, Celia Sampol, Jean-Louis Santini, Naomi Seck, Kerry Colleen Sheridan, Marisha Sherry, Magan Sherzai, James Slater, Veronica Smith, Susan Stumme, Shaun Tandon, Jeremy Tordjman, Diego Urdaneta, Chantal Valery, Gregor Waschinski, Daniel Woolls, Jordi Zamora Barcelo.

AKAHATA—(202) 393–5238; 978 National Press Building, Washington, DC 20045: Minetaka Shimada.

ALBUQUERQUE JOURNAL—(202) 329–4743; 116 6th Street, SE., Apartment 3, Washington, DC 20003: Michael Coleman.

AL-HAYAT—(202) 783–5544; 1185 National Press Building, Washington, DC 20045: Joyce Karam.

ALLAFRICA.COM—(202) 546–0777; 922 M Street, SE., Washington, DC 20003: Tamela Hultman, Reed Kramer.

ALLENTOWN MORNING CALL—(202) 824–8216; 1090 Vermont Avenue, NW., Suite 1000, Washington, DC 20005: Colby Itkowitz.

AMERICAN BANKER—(212) 803–8200; 4401 Wilson Boulevard, Suite 910, Arlington VA 22209: Joseph Adler, Donna Borak, Victoria Finkle.

ANATOLIA NEWS AGENCY—(202) 550–0904; 401 12th Street South, #1206, Arlington, VA 22202: Bariskan Toroglu, Ozkul Toroglu.

ANNIE GROER WRITER-AT-LARGE—(202) 338–8581; 2500 Q Street, Suite 640, Washington, DC 20007: Anne Groer.

ARA—(914) 954–5521; 410 Cedar Street, NW., Apartment 6, Washington, DC 20012: Joan Faus Catasus, Nuria Ferragutcasas.

ARGUS MEDIA—(202) 775–0240; 1012 14th Street, NW., Suite 1500, Washington, DC 20005: Alexander Alexandrov, Michael Ball, Abby Caplan, Molly Christian, Edward Epstein, Elizabeth Fox, David Givens, Haik Gugarats, John Heltman, David Ivanovich, Benjamin Kaldunski, Celia Lamb, Joanna Marsh, Lauren Masterson, Christopher Newman, William Peters, Claire Pickard-Cambridge, Courtney Schlisserman, Jessica Sondgeroth, Todd Tranausky, Stephanie Tsao, Matthew Volkov, Robert Willis.

ARKANSAS DEMOCRAT-GAZETTE—(202) 662–7690; 1190 National Press Building, 529 14th Street, NW., Washington, DC 20045: Alex Daniels, Sarah Wire.

ARLNOW—(703) 271–0520; 1400 Key Boulevard, Suite 100, Arlington, VA 22209: Scott Brodbeck, Aaron Kraut, Ethan Rothstein.

ARTISTS & WRITERS SYNDICATE—(703) 820–4232; 6325 Beachway Drive, Falls Church, VA 22044: Frank Aukofer.

ASAHI SHIMBUN—(202) 783–1000; 1022 National Press Building, 529 14th Street, NW., Washington, DC 20045: Conor Cislo, Jonathan Harper, Daisuke Igarashi, Tetsu Kobayashi, Jeeah Lee, Aya Maher, Jonathan Meza, Hirotsugu Mochizuki, Kent Mullen, Shiro Namekata, Atsushi Okudera, Takashi Oshima, Abraham Robinson, Jesse Walter, Ikki Yamakawa, Takeshi Yamawaki.

ASSOCIATED PRESS—(202) 641–9000; 1100 13th Street, NW., Washington, DC 20005-4076: James Abrams, Jennifer Agiesta, Luis Alonso, Ricardo Alonso-Zaldivar, Stacy Anderson, Matt Apuzzo, John Jay Arnold, Philip Avner, Charles Babington, Lolita Baldor, Matthew Barakat, Wendy Benjaminson, Josh Boak, Seth Borenstein, Stephen Braun, Ted Bridis, Sarah Brumfield, Robert Burns, Desmond Butler, Sally Buzbee, Alicia Caldwell, Dina Cappiello, Connie Cass, Donna Cassata, Lauren Cooper, Martin Crutsinger, Matthew Daly, Douglass Daniel, Alex Dominguez, Kimberly Dozier, Jim Drinkard, Harry Dunphy, Donald Elkins, Philip Elliott, David Espo, Carole Feldman, Howard Fendrich, Anne Flaherty, Alan Fram, Kevin Freking, Frederic Frommer, Adrian Fullwood, Robert Furlow, Suzanne Gamboa, Jack Gillum, Robert Glass, Adam Goldman, Shawn Gomez, Marcy Gordon, Jessica Gresko, Ken Guggenheim, Sam Hananel, Merrill Hartson, Kimberly Hefling, Earl Hinton, Jesse Holland, Terence

NEWSPAPERS REPRESENTED—Continued

Hunt, Steven Hurst, Henry Jackson, Lara Jakes, Mary Clare Jalonick, Pauline Jelinek, Kasey Jones, Dennis Junius, Amanda Kell, Laurie Kellman Blazar, Jennifer Kerr, Bradley Klapper, Eric Klimek, Jim Kuhnhenn, Richard Lardner, Josh Lederman, Matthew Lee, William Lester, James Lipari, Joan Lowy, Sunil Malhotra, Andrew Miga, Michelle Minkoff, Lauran Neergaard, Ben Nuckols, Stephen Ohlemacher, Mark Olchowy, Marjorie Olster, David Pace, Julie Pace, Matthew Pennington, Matthew Perrone, Nedra Pickler, Melinda Purce, Eileen Putman, Libby Quaid, Thomas Raum, Sonya Ross, Chris Rugaber, Michele Salcedo, Michael Sandler, Mark Sherman, Elizabeth Sidoti, Michael Sniffen, Thomas Strong, Eileen Sullivan, Darlene Superville, Andrew Taylor, Ken Thomas, Eric Tucker, Kevin Vineys, Dennis Vohar, Ryan Webb, Erica Werner, Joseph White, Jr., Trish Wilson, Paul Wiseman, Nancy Witkowski, Brian Witte, Calvin Woodward, Matthew Yancey, Hope Yen, Pete Yost, Katherine Zezima, Brett Zongker.

ATLANTA JOURNAL CONSTITUTION—(202) 777–7033; 400 North Capitol Street, NW., Suite 750, Washington, DC 20001: Daniel Malloy.

AUSTIN AMERICAN-STATESMAN—(512) 445–3672; 400 North Capitol Street, Suite 750, Washington, DC 20001: Jonathan Tilove.

AUSTRALIAN FINANCIAL REVIEW—(202) 383–3790; 1310 G Street, NW., Suite 750, Washington, DC 20005: John Kehoe, Ben Potter.

BADISCHE ZEITUNG—(202) 588–9351; 1327 Euclid Street, NW., Apartment 403, Washington, DC 20009: Jens Schmitz.

BALTIMORE SUN—(410) 979–2052; 1090 Vermont Avenue, NW., Suite 1000, Washington, DC 20005: Jeffrey Barker, Matthew Brown, John Fritze.

BATON ROUGE ADVOCATE—(225) 819–7424; 22 Finale Drive, Silver Spring, MD 20901: Jordan Blum.

BEND BULLETIN—(202) 662–7456; 1220 National Press Building, Washington, DC 20045: Andrew Clevenger.

BERLINER ZEITUNG—(301) 564–0861; 1318 Emerald Street, NE., Washington, DC 20002: Damir Fras.

BIRMINGHAM NEWS—(202) 744–5574; 1621 South Oakland Street, Arlington, VA 22204: Mary Orndorff Troyan.

BLOOMBERG NEWS—(202) 624–1820; 1399 New York Avenue, NW., 11th Floor, Washington, DC 20005: Hector Alfaro, Cesca Antonelli, Stephanie Armour, Laurie Asseo, Terry Atlas, Charles Babcock, Brad Baker, Alvin Banks, Matthew Barry, Michael Bender, Amanda Bennett, Clea Benson, Max Berley, Alan Bjerga, Justin Blum, Romaine Bostick, Kevin Brancato, Kristin Broughton, Silla Brush, Julie Bykowicz, Anthony Capaccio, Margaret Carlson, Shobhana Chandra, Kristin Cohen, Kevin Costelloe, Jamie Coughlin, Jeanne Cummings, Laura Curtis, Julie Davis, Susan Decker, Gail DeGeorge, Courtney Dimling, Catherine Dodge, Mike Dorning, Carter Dougherty, Mark Drajem, Bob Drummond, Loren Duggan, Elizabeth Dwoskin, Paula Dwyer, Anna Edney, David Ellis, Eric Engleman, Daniel Enoch, Brian Faler, Emma Fidel, Ken Fireman, Christopher Flavelle, Sara Forden, Juliann Francis, Timothy Franklin, Don Frederick, Joshua Gallu, Nicole Gaouette, Stephen Geimann, James Gibney, Gregory Giroux, Anthony Gnoffo, Susan Goldberg, Julianna Goldman, Vince Golle, Michael Gourdin, Ainhoa Goyeneche, Brendan Greeley, Joshua Green, Rick Greenwood, Angela Greiling Keane, Jesse Hamilton, Dan Hart, Kathleen Hayden, Kristen Hinman, Leslie Hoffecker, Allan Holmes, Timothy Homan, Cheyenne Hopkins, Clark Hoyt, John Hughes, Ann Hughey, Albert Hunt, Kathleen Hunter, Ronnell Ingram, Danielle Ivory, Flavia Jackson, Anastasia Jakabcin, Michelle Jamrisko, Nicholas Johnston, Daniel Joyce, Ian Katz, Jeff Kearns, Nancy Kercheval, Katarzyna Klimasinska, Steven Komarow, Weston Kosova, Alexander Kowalski, Samuel Kussin-Shoptaw, Indira Lakashmanan, Lisa Lerer, David Lerman, Cameron Leuthy, Alan Levin, Robert Levinson, Larry Liebert, Walter Little, Laura Litvan, Eduardo Londres, Jr., Meera Louis, David Lynch, William Matthews, Philip Mattingly, David McLaughlin, Mark McQuillan, Brian Meehan, Robin Meszoly, David Michaels, Chris Middleton, Kathleen Miller, Kevin Miller, Richard Miller, Kenneth Monahan, Jon Morgan, Daniel Moss, Gregory Mott, Brendan Murray, Michael Newman, Hans Nichols, Brian Nutting, Joseph O'Reilly II, Daniel Parks, Timothy Pennix, Jeff Plungis, Sonya Pollard, Joi Preciphs, Heidi Przybyla, Sandrine Rastello, Gopal Ratnam, Sanford Reback, Maura Reynolds, Michael Riley, Katherine Rizzo, Mark Rohner, Stephen Rose, Holly Rosenkrantz, Bennett Roth, James Rowley, Richard Rubin, Roger Runningen, Jonathan Salant, Marvin Salmeron, Ana Saraiva, Kristy Scheuble, Robert Schmidt, Jodi Schneider, Tom Schoenberg, William Selway, Michael Shepard, Todd Shields, Mark Silva, Jeanna Smialek, Elliot Smith, Andrea Snyder, Jim Snyder, Joseph Sobczyk, Victoria Stilwell, Greg Stohr, Stephanie Stoughton, Fred Strasser, Chris Strohm, Gregory Sullivan, Nick Taborek, Michael Tackett, Margaret Talev, Alex Tanzi, Daniel Taylor, Roxana Tiron, Carlos Torres, Craig Torres, James Tyson, John Walcott, Derek Wallbank, Stephen Walsh, Elizabeth Wasserman, Alexander Wayne, Caitlin Webber, Miles Weiss, Chris Wellisz, Chloe Whiteaker, Del Quentin Wilber, Dana Wilkie, Brian Wingfield, Lorraine Woellert, Tsaneo Yamahiro, Andrew Zajac, Joshua Zumbrun.

BOND BUYER—(571) 403–3843; 4401 Wilson Boulevard, Suite 910, Arlington, VA 22203: Jennifer DePaul, Kyle Glazier, Lynn Hume, Naomi Jogoda.

NEWSPAPERS REPRESENTED—Continued

BOSTON GLOBE—(202) 857–5050; 1130 Connecticut Avenue, NW., Suite 520, Washington, DC 20036: Bryan Bender, Noah Bierman, Tracy Jan, Michael Kranish, Lisa Grace Lednicer, Christopher Rowland, Stephanie Vallejo, Matthew Viser.

BUFFALO NEWS—(202) 234–3188; 1715 15th Street, NW., #24, Washington, DC 20009: Jerry Zremski.

BUZZFEED.COM—1130 Connecticut Avenue, NW., Washington, DC 20001: Joseph Feder, Jacob Fischler, Chris Geidner, Rosie Gray, Benny Johnson, Evan McMorris-Santoro, Kate Nocera, John Stanton.

CALCUTTA TELEGRAPH—(301) 654–6008; 5500 Friendship Boulevard, Suite 1217, Chevy Chase, MD 20815: Krishnan Nayar.

CANADIAN PRESS—(202) 641–9734; 1100 13th Street, NW., Washington, DC 20045: Alexander Panetta.

CENTER FOR PUBLIC INTEGRITY—(202) 466–1300; 910 17th Street, NW., 7th Floor, Washington, DC 20006: Paul Abowd, Michael Beckel, Douglas Birch, David Donald, Joseph Eaton, Susan Ferriss, Alison Fitzgerald, Ronnie Greene, Chris Hamby, David Heath, David Levinthal, James Morris, Reity O'Brien, Julie Patel, Fred Schulte, Jeffrey Smith, Alan Suderman, Daniel Wagner, Gordon Witkin.

CHATTANOOGA TIMES FREE PRESS—(423) 280–2025; 1190 National Press Building, Washington, DC 20045: Chris Carroll.

CHICAGO SUN-TIMES—(202) 320–6044; 3831 Windom Place, NW., Washington, DC 20016: Lynn Sweet.

CHICAGO TRIBUNE—(202) 824–8376; 1090 Vermont Avenue, NW., Suite 1000, Washington, DC 20005: Clarence Page, Christi Parsons, Katherine Skiba, Dina White.

CHINA NEWS SERVICE—(703) 527–1409; 1020 North Stafford Street, Apartment 100, Arlington, VA 22201: Qingcai Wu.

CHINA PEOPLE'S DAILY—(202) 661–8185; 529 14th Street, NW., Suite 450, Washington, DC 20045: Boya Li, Chengliang Wu, Wen Xian, Yang Zhang, Liao Zhengjun.

CHINA REVIEW NEWS AGENCY—(703) 725–0720; 2021 Brooks Square Place, Falls Church, VA 22043: Donghui Yu.

CHINA TIMES—(301) 530–8301; 9706 Holmhurst Road, Bethesda, MD 20817: Ping Liu.

CHOSUN ILBO—(703) 865–8310; 1291 National Press Building, Washington, DC 20045: Sung Kim.

CHRISTIAN SCIENCE MONITOR—(202) 481–6680; 910 16th Street, NW., Suite 200, Washington, DC 20006: Gail Chaddock, David Cook, Linda Feldmann, David Grant, Peter Grier, Francine Kiefer, Howard LaFranchi, Anna Mulrine, Kateland Oakes, Warren Richey, Mark Trumbull.

CIVIL BEAT—(808) 377–0561: Adrienne LaFrance, Kery Murakami.

CLARIN—(202) 737–4850; 988 National Press Building, Washington, DC 20045: Armando Perez, Ana Baron Supervielle.

CLEVELAND PLAIN DEALER—(202) 638–1366; 930 National Press Building, 529 14th Street, NW., Washington, DC 20006: Sabrina Eaton, Stephen Koff.

COLORADO OBSERVER—(410) 867–9239; 3600 New York Avenue, NE., Washington, DC 20002: Audrey Hudson Flanagan.

COLUMBUS DISPATCH—(202) 777–7015; 400 North Capitol Street, Suite 850, Washington, DC 20001: Jack Torry, Jessica Wehrman.

COMMUNICATIONS DAILY—(202) 872–9202; 2115 Ward Court, NW., Washington, DC 20037: Bryce Baschuk, Howard Buskirk, John Hendel, Kamala Lane, Jonathan Make, Matthew Schwartz, Katherine Tummarello.

CONNECTICUT MIRROR—(301) 613–7007; Ana Radelat.

CQ ROLL CALL—(202) 650–6500; 77 K Street, NE., Washington, DC 20002: Rebecca Adams, Ambreen Ali, Amanda Allen, Joanna Anderson, Dennis Arndt, Melissa Attias, Jasmine Baker, Susan Benkelman, Ted Benson, John Bicknell, John Boyd, Philip Brasher, Jonathan Broder, Cory Brown, Dena Bunis, Emily Cadei, George Cahlink, Lauren Camera, Scott Campbell, Charlene Carter, Sarah Chacko, Mike Christensen, George Codrea, Charles Conlon, Kristin Coyner, John Cranford, Jessica Cuellar, John Dineen, John Donnelly, Julie Ershadi, Emily Ethridge, Peter Feltman, Ellyn Ferguson, Jamisha Ford, Matthew Fuller, Karin Fuog, Lauren Gardner, Emil Georgi, Dan Germain, Steve Gettinger, Stacey Goers, Sam Goldfarb, John Gramlich, Georgina Gustin, Tamar Hallerman, Clayton Hanson, David Harrison, Robert Healy, Caitlin Hendel, Paul Hendrie, Hannah Hess, Amanda Hicks, Henry Hoffman, Emily Holden, Anne Hoy, John Hunter, Nathan Hurst, Robert Huttinger, John Irons, Benton Ives-Halperin, Paul Jenks, Patricia Joy, Noella Kertes, Elham Khatami, Angela Kim, Anne Kim, Peter King, Ashley Kongs, Matthew Korade, Geof Koss, Kaitlin Kovach, Paul Krawzak, Gil Landau, Sarah Lawrence, Randall Leonard, Adam Levin, Finlay Lewis, Alejandra Lopez, Tammy Lucas, Cristina Marcos, Robert Margetta, Cyra Master, Anna McGeehan, Catherine McGettrick, David Meyers, Tait Militana, Manuel Moya, Alex Muller, Kathleen Murphy, Gautham Nagesh, Melinda Nahmias, Eric Naing, Chris Nehls, Avigayil Niman, Jane Norman, Connor O'Brien, Katy O'Donnell, Frank Oliveri, Alexis Olson, Sandra Opanga, Alan Ota, Paul Page, Christina Parisi, Brandon Payne, Daniel Peake, Carolyn Phenicie, John Reichard, Betty Richardson, Michael Roberts, Aleksandra Robinson, Peter Rocco, Kelly Ross, Jennifer Rubio, Pam Russell, Adam Schank, Jennifer Scholtes, Megan Scully, Rebecca Shabad, Anne Shuppy, Jill Smallen, Sara Smith, Megan Sowdwer-Staley, Michael Stanaland, Tim Starks, Gail Sullivan, Michael Teitelbaum, Neda Toloui-Semnani, Robert Tomkin, Katherine Tully-McManus, Sarah Vanderbilt, Randolph Walerius, Joseph Warminsky, William Weiss, Ben Weyl, Christian

NEWSPAPERS REPRESENTED—Continued

White, Keith White, Kevin Whitelaw, Guy Whitmire, Khari Williams, Yee Woo, Christopher Wright, Randall Wynn, Tim Yoder, Kerry Young, Shawn Zeller.

CREATORS SYNDICATE—(202) 662–1255; 5777 West Century Boulevard, Suite 700, Los Angeles CA 90045: Mark Shields.

CYPRUS NEWS AGENCY—(202) 462–5772; 2211 R Street, NW., Washington, DC 20008: Apostolos Zoupaniotis.

DAILY CALLER—(202) 506–2027; 1050 17th Street, Suite 900, Washington, DC 20036: Christopher Bedford, Alexis Levinson, Giuseppe Macri, Caroline May, Neil Munro, Alex Pappas, Josh Peterson, Robert Poor, Richard Rahn, Betsy Rothstein, Jamie Weinstein.

DAILY DEAL—(202) 429–2991; 236 Massachusetts Avenue, NE., Washington, DC 20002: William McConnell.

DAILY MAIL (UK)—(646) 885–5105; David Martosko.

DALLAS MORNING NEWS—(202) 661–8410; 1252 National Press Building, 529 14th Street, NW., Washington, DC 20045: Todd Gillman, James Landers, Carl Leubsdorf, Lindenberger Michael.

DEFENSE DAILY—(703) 785–5261; 1911 Fort Meyer Drive, Suite 310, Arlington, VA 22209: Megan Eckstein, Patrick Host, Mike McCarthy, John Robinson, Ann Roosevelt, Emelie Rutherford.

DENVER POST—(202) 662–8907; 969 National Press Building, 529 14th Street, NW., Washington, DC 20045: Allison Sherry.

DER TAGESSPIEGEL—(202) 686–3947; 3200 Patterson Street, NW., Washington, DC 20015: Barbara Junge, Christoph Marshall, Christoph Von Marschall.

DETROIT FREE PRESS—(703) 854–8942; 1575 Eye Street, NW., Suite 350, Washington, DC 20005: Todd Spangler.

DETROIT NEWS—(202) 662–8736; 969 National Press Building, 529 14th Street, NW., Washington, DC 20045: Marisa Schultz, David Shepardson, Christine Tierney.

DIE TAGESZEITUNG—(202) 569–5369; 540 N Street, SW., Washington DC 20024: Dorothea Hahn.

DIGITAL FIRST MEDIA—(202) 431–2859; 2745 29th Street, NW.. Apartment 600, Washington, DC 20008: Ryan Beckwith, Amber Phillips.

DOW JONES/WALL STREET JOURNAL—(202) 862–9200; 1025 Connecticut Avenue, NW., Suite 800, Washington, DC 20036: Andrew Ackerman, Mark Anderson, Corey Boles, Rodney Christian, L. Kareema Clark, Jennifer Corbett Dooren, Michael Crittenden, David Allen Dolinger, Jared Favole, Jessica Holzer, Jonathan House, Siobhan Hughes, Brent Kendall, William Mauldin, Eric Morath, Kristina Peterson, Sarah Portlock, Jeffrey Sparshott, Ian Talley, Bill Tomson, Ryan Tracy, Tennile Tracy, Jamila Trindle, Alan Zibel.

EFE NEWS SERVICES—(202) 745–7692; 1220 National Press Building, 529 14th Street, NW., Washingon DC 20045: Jorge Banales, Teresa Bouza, Miriam Burgues, Maribel El Hamti, Alfonso Fernandez, Raquel Godos De La Puente, Lucia Leal, Jairo Mejia, Maria Pena, Jose Manuel Sanz-Mingote.

EL COMERCIO—(301) 919–8179; 8201 16th Street, Apartment 1014, Silver Spring, MD 20910: Loreto Setien.

EL DIARIO DE HOY—(703) 845–4962; 4600 South Four Mile Run Drive, Arlington, VA 22204: Tomas Guevara.

EL NUEVO DIA—(202) 662–7360; 960d National Press Building, 529 14th Street, NW., Washington, DC 20045: Jose Delgado.

EL PAIS—(202) 638–1533; 1134 National Press Building, 529 14th Street, NW., Washington, DC 20045: Antonio Caño, Christina Fernandez Pereda, Carolina Garcia, Yolanda Monge, Eva Saiz.

EL PERIODICO—(202) 679–8656; 4801 Hampden Lane, Bethesda, MD 20814: Ricardo De Francia.

EL TIEMPO—(202) 607–5929; 5597 Seminary Road, Apartment 714 South, Washington, DC 20041: Sergio Gomez.

EL UNIVERSAL—(202) 662–7190; 1193 National Press Building, 529 14th Street, NW., Washington, DC 20045: Jose Garcia.

ENERGY DAILY—(703) 236–2405; 1500 Wilson Boulevard, Suite 515, Arlington, VA 22209: Jeff Beattie, Christopher Holly, Eric Lindeman, George Lobsenz, Chad Woodworth.

ENERGY GUARDIAN—(202) 277–2487; 1934 Old Gallows Road, #350, Vienna, VA 20024: Edward Felker.

ERIE TIMES-NEWS—4712 Dorchester Drive, Erie, PA 16509: John Guerriero.

ETHNOS GREECE—(202) 361–7843; 1133 14th Street, NW., Washington, DC 20005: Michail Ignatiou.

EUROPOLITICS—(202) 758–8462; 1403 12th Street, NW., #4, Washington, DC 20005: Brian Beary.

FAIRCHILD PUBLICATIONS—(202) 955–0966; 1730 Rhode Island Avenue, Suite 603, Washington, DC 20036: Kristi Ellis, Susan Watters.

FINANCIAL TIMES—(202) 434–0972; 1023 15th Street, NW., Suite 700, Washington DC 20005: Alan Beattie, Gina Chon, Geoff Dyer, Anna Fifield, Robin Harding, Stephanie Kirchgaessner, Richard McGregor, James Politi, Aaron Stanley.

FISCAL TIMES—(202) 628–3101; 1214 National Press Building, 529 14th Street, NW., Washington DC 20045: Eric Pianin.

FRANKFURTER ALLGEMEINE ZEITUNG—(202) 986–0965; 2100 Connecticut Avenue, NW., Suite 502, Washington, DC 20016: Andreas Ross, Patrick Welter.

NEWSPAPERS REPRESENTED—Continued

FREELANCE—(202) 277-5931; 7601 Bent Oak Court, Falls Church, VA 22043: Tamara Lytle.

FREELANCE—(703) 241-2608; 2500 Q Street, Suite 640, Washington, DC 20007: Jim Myers.

GANNETT WASHINGTON BUREAU—(202) 854-8900; 1575 I Street, NW., Suite 350, Washington, DC 20005: Deborah Berry, Larry Bivins, Sammie Chan, Raju Chebium, Christopher Doering, Val Ellicott, Nicole Gaudiano Albright, Maureen Groppe, Linda Holzer, Alethea Jordan, Erin Kelly, Ledyard King, Malia Rulon Herman, Craig Schwed, Deirdre Shesgreen, William Theobald, Mary Troyan, Brian Tumulty.

GERMAN PRESS AGENCY-DPA—(202) 662-1220; 1112 National Press Building, 529 14th St NW., Washington, DC 20045: Sylvia Ayuso Determeyer, Frank Fuhrig, Margaret Johnston, Peer Meinert, Marco Mierke, Paticia Reber, Johannes Schmitt-Tegge, Anne Walters Custer.

GLOBAL HORIZONS SYNDICATE—(202) 966-8636; 1330 New Hampshire Avenue, NW., Washington, DC 20036: Edward Flattau.

GLOBE AND MAIL—(202) 662-7167; 2000 M Street, NW., Suite 330, Washington, DC 20036: Kevin Carmichael, Paul Koring.

HANDELSBLAD—(202) 957-6115; 2907 Cathedral Avenue, Washington, DC 20008: August Valk.

HANKOOK ILBO—(202) 783-2674; 986 National Press Building, Washington, DC 20045: Lee Taegyu.

HANKYOREH DAILY—(703) 989-0723; 821 National Press Building, Washington, DC 20045: Jong Park.

HEARST NEWSPAPERS—(202) 263-6400; 700 12th Street, NW., Suite 1000, Washington, DC 20005: Jennifer Dlouhy, Dan Freedman, Charles Lewis, David McCumber, Stewart Powell, Will Tucker.

HINDU, THE—(201) 701-8410; Narayan Lakshman.

HOKKAIDO SHIMBUN—(202) 783-6033; 1012 National Press Building, Washington, DC 20045: Nobutaka Sawada.

HOUSTON CHRONICLE—(202) 263-6511; 700 12th Street, NW., Suite 1000, Washington, DC 20005: Richard Dunham.

HUFFINGTON POST—(202) 567-2634; 1730 Pennsylvania Avenue, NW., #825, Washington, DC 20006: Laura Bassett, Jennifer Bendery, Mark Blumenthal, Paul Blumenthal, Zachary Carter, John Celock, Jason Cherkis, Arthur Delaney, Gabrielle Dunkley, Thomas Edsall, Ariel Edwards-Levy, Howard Fineman, Elise Foley, Christopher Gentilviso, Lucia Graves, Ryan Grim, Joshua Hersh, Dave Jamieson, Luke Johnson, Chelsea Kiene, Ethan Klapper, Paige Lavender, Michael McAuliff, Eugene Mulero, Shahien Nasiripour, Eliot Nelson, Andrew Perez, Mollie Reilly, Ryan Reilly, Michael Sacks, Brad Shannon, Sabrina Siddiqui, Sam Stein, Amanda Terkel, Jon Ward, Christina Wilkie, David Wood, William Wrigley, Jeffrey Young.

HURRIYET—(917) 340-2466; 16 Grove Ridge Court, Rockville, MD 20852: Tolga Tanis.

ICIS NEWS—(202) 836-3448; 333 North Fairfax Street, Suite 301, Alexandria, VA 22314: Joseph Kamalick.

INDIA PRESS TRUST—(301) 881-2963; 5705 Brewer House Circle, Apartment 302, Rockville, MD 20852: Lalit Jha.

INDO-ASIAN NEWS SERVICE—(703) 664-0037; 4801 Kenmore Avenue, Apartment 614, Alexandria, VA 22304: Arun Kumar.

INSIDE HIGHER ED—(202) 659-9208; 1015 18th Street, NW., Suite 1100, Washington, DC 20036: Paul Fain, Colleen Flaherty, Serena Golden, Allie Grasgreen, Douglas Lederman, Libby Nelson, Ry Riivard.

INTERNATIONAL BUSINESS TIMES—(646) 867-7100; Pema Levy.

INTERNATIONAL NEW YORK TIMES—(202) 862-0357; 1627 I Street, NW., Suite 700, Washington, DC 20006: Brian Knowlton.

IRISH TIMES—(202) 436-6223; Simon Carswell.

ITAR-TASS NEWS AGENCY—(202) 662-7080; 1004 National Press Building, 529 14th Street, NW., Washington, DC 20045: Dmitry Kirsanov, Ivan Lebedev, Andrei Sitov, Andrey Surzhanskiy, Dmitri Zlodorev.

JERUSALEM POST—(202) 758-0862; 1508 17th Street, NW., Apartment 3, Washington, DC 20036: Hilary Krieger, Michael Wilner.

JEWISH TELEGRAPHIC AGENCY—(202) 737-0935; 1025 Vermont Avenue, NW., #504, Washington, DC 20005: Ron Kampeas.

JIJI PRESS—(202) 783-4330; 550 National Press Building, NW., Washington, DC 20045: Kosuke Ito, Yoshi Kishida, Kuniaki Kitai, Satoru Kohda, Yoko Matsukawa, Kaoru Miyazawa, Tatsuya Mizumoto, Edward Pagliarulo, Nicolas Pandi, Mutsumi Tatsubo, Nishigaki Yuichiro.

JOONGANG ILBO—(202) 347-0122; 997 National Press Building, Washington, DC 20045: Jaeun Lee, Seunghee Park.

JYLLANDS-POSTEN—(202) 450-5552; 1700 Lanier Place, NW., Washington, DC 20009: Jorgen Ullerup.

KAISER HEALTH NEWS—(202) 654-1343; 1330 G Street, NW., Washington, DC 20005: Julie Appleby, Mary Agnes Carey, Carol Eisenberg, Karl Eisenhower, Marissa Evans, John Fairhall, Phil Galewitz, Jenny Gold, James Hancock, Ankita Rao, Jordan Rau, Stephanie Stapleton, Alvin Tran, Lexie Verdon, Diane Webber.

KIPLING NEWS SERVICE—(202) 686-6388; 12611 Farnell Drive, Silver Spring, MD 20906: Bogdan Kipling.

NEWSPAPERS REPRESENTED—Continued

KOREA DAILY—(703) 281–9660; 7023 Little River Turnpike, Suite 300, Annandale, VA 22003: Sungkyoon Park, Hunjeong Song, Seng Lim You.

KOREA DONG-A ILBO—(571) 623–2267; 837 National Press Building, 529 14th Street, NW., Washington, DC 20045: Suk Ho Shin.

KOREA ECONOMIC DAILY—(703) 895–0955; 821 National Press Building, 529 14th Street, NW., Washington DC 20045: Jin Jang.

KOREA TIMES—(703) 941–8002; 7601 Little River Turnpike, Annandale, VA 22203: Sung Joong Ahn, Christina Young Chong, Byonghan Lee, Chang-Yul Lee, Jong Kook Lee, Kwang Duk Park.

KUKMIN DAILY—(703) 588–2170; 909 National Press Building, 529 14th Street, NW., Washington, DC 20045: Byungwoo Bae.

KUMAMOTO NICHINICHI SHIMBUN—(301) 299–3775; 10625 Rock Run Drive, Potomac, MD 20854: Reiko Robertson.

KUWAIT NEWS AGENCY—(202) 347–5554; 906 National Press Building, Washington, DC 20045: Ronald Baygents, Sherouq Sadeqi, Heather Yamour.

KYODO NEWS—(202) 347–5767; 400 National Press Building, 529 14th Street, NW., Washington, DC 20045: Sarah Ampolsk, Takuya Arai, Tsukasa Arita, Konomi Awabayashi, Yasushi Azuma, Benjamin Dooley, Eiichiro Funahashi, Kazuhiro Haruki, Hiromasa Hayashi, Tomotaro Inoue, Jun Kaminishikawara, Dai Kaneko, Hideomi Kinoshita, Kakumi Kobayashi, Akira Samukawa, Keisuke Yoshimura, Hiroto Yoshiura.

KYUNGHYANG DAILY NEWS—(703) 624–3031: Jemin Son.

LA JORNADA—(202) 669–7760; 2708 Fourth Street, NE., Washington, DC 20002: David Brooks.

LA NACION—(202) 744–7737; 1292 National Press Building, 529 14th Street, NW., Washington, DC 20045: Silvia Pisani.

LA OPINION—(213) 369–8006; 800 4th Street, Southwest Apartment N609, Washington, DC 20024: Antonieta Cadiz, Maria Pena.

LA PRENSA GRAFICA OF EL SALVADOR—(240) 429–4296; 300 Hamilton Street, NW., Washington, DC 20011: Hector Silva Avalos.

LAS VEGAS SUN—(202) 662–7436; 1290 National Press Building, Washington, DC 20045: Karoun Demirjian.

LE MAURICIEN—(301) 728–7442; 1084 Pipestem Place, Potomac, MD 20854: Pamela Glass.

LE MONDE—(202) 248–9075; 3841 Harrison Street, NW., Washington, DC 20015: Corine Lesnes.

LE PARISIEN—(202) 269–0008; 5315 42nd Street, NW., Washington, DC 20015: Alix Bouilhaguet.

LIBERTY TIMES—(202) 879–6765; 1294 National Press Building, Washington, DC 20045: Nadia Tsao.

LONDON DAILY TELEGRAPH—(202) 393–5195; 1310 G Street, NW., Suite 750, Washington, DC 20005: Peter Foster, Raf Sanchez.

LONDON GUARDIAN—(202) 223–2560; 900 17th Street, NW., Suite 250, Washington, DC 20006: Suzanne Goldenberg, Paul Lewis, Ewen Macaskill, Daniel Roberts.

L'ORIENT - LE JOUR—(202) 342–1213; 1045 31st Street, #404, Washington, DC 20007: Wafik Ramadan.

LOS ANGELES TIMES—(202) 824–8259; 1090 Vermont Avenue, NW., Suite 1000, Washington, DC 20005: Neela Banerjee, Shashank Bengali, Brian Bennett, David Cloud, Ken Dilanian, Robert Drogin, Matea Gold, Evan Halper, Kathleen Hennessey, John Hoeffel, David Lauter, Don Lee, Noam Levey, Morgan Little, Lisa Mascaro, Melanie Mason, Michael McGough, Doyle McManus, Michael Memoli, Timothy Phelps, James Puzzanghera, Paul Richter, James Robinson, David Savage, Richard Serrano, Richard Simon, Joseph Tanfani, Paul West.

LOUISVILLE COURIER JOURNAL—(202) 906–8141; 1100 New York Avenue, NW., Washington, DC 20005: James Carroll.

LRP PUBLICATIONS—(202) 294–6357; 1901 North Moore Street, Suite 1106, Arlington, VA 22209: Emily Brown, Julie Davidson, Adam Dolge, Jean Gossman, David Kittross, Wangui Njuguna, Anjali Patel, Kim Riley, Mark Sherman, Jeanne Sweeney, Frank Wolfe.

MAEIL BUSINESS NEWSPAPER—(202) 320–0691; 909 National Press Building, 529 14th Street, NW., Washington, DC 20045: Jin Woo Lee.

MAIN JUSTICE—(202) 621–6031; 2024 P Street, NW., Washington, DC 20036: Jeffrey Benzing, Douglas Gillison (202) 621–6097, Mary Jacoby (202) 654–7049, Jennifer Koons, (202) 450–6991, David Stout, (202) 654–7000.

MAINICHI NEWSPAPERS—(202) 737–2817; Shinichiro Nishada, Marie Tanao-Archer.

MAINICHI SHIMBUN—(202) 737–2817; 340 National Press Building, 529 14th Street, NW., Washington, DC 20045: Osamu Hirachi, Masaya Oikawa, Keiichi Shirato.

MALAYA—(703) 715–8879; 10724 Midsummer Drive, Reston, VA 20191: Josefina Ilustre.

MARKET NEWS INTERNATIONAL—(202) 371–2121; 1100 National Press Building, 529 14th Street, NW., Washington, DC 20045: Steven Beckner, Denny Gulino, Kasra Kangarloo, Kevin Kastner, Ian McKendry, Karen Mracek, Yali N'Diaye, Joshua Newell, Braimoh Odion-Esene, Joseph Plocek, Heather Scott, John Shaw.

MARKETWATCH—(202) 824–0548; 1025 Connecticut Avenue, NW., Washington, DC 20036: Jeffry Bartash, Steven Goldstein, Ruth Madden, Rex Nutting, Ronald Orol, Gregory Robb, Robert Schroeder.

NEWSPAPERS REPRESENTED—Continued

MCCLATCHY NEWSPAPERS—(202) 383–6004; 700 12th Street, NW., Suite 1000, Washington, DC 20005: Christopher Adams, Beryl Adcock, Hannah Allam, James Asher, Barbara Barrett, Vera Bergengruen, Michael Bold, Erika Bolstad, Lesley Clark, Sean Cockerham, Danny Dougherty, William Douglas, Michael Doyle, Jim Goldschmidt, David Goldstein, Greg Gordon, Anders Gyllenhaal, Kevin Hall, Rob Hotakainen, Anita Kumar, Jonathan Landay, David Lightman, Julie Moos, Carol Nippert, Francisco Ordonez, Anthony Pugh, Maria Recio, James Rosen, Matthew Schofield, Renee Schoof, Mark Seibel, Curtis Tate, Marisa Taylor, Steven Thomma, Letitia Wells, Lindsay Wise.

MEDICAL DEVICE DAILY—(703) 268–5690; 4301 Connecticut Avenue, NW., Washington, DC 20008: Mark McCarty.

MEDILL NEWS SERVICE—(202) 347–8700; 1325 G Street, NW., Suite 730, Washington, DC 20005: Yichen Zhong.

MEDPAGE TODAY—(202) 230–6628; 13610 Russett Terrace, Rockville, MD 20853: Joyce Frieden, David Pittman.

MERCER MEDIA: Marsha Mercer.

MERGER MARKET OF FINANCIAL TIMES—(202) 434–1075; 1012 14th Street, NW., Suite 915, Washington, DC 20005: Raymond Barrett, David Baumann, Peter Geier, Benjamin Koconis, Cecile Lindell, Ryan Lynch, Ryan Lynch, Reuben Miller, Jennifer Smith-Parker.

MILITARY UPDATE—(703) 830–6863; P.O. Box 231111, Centreville, VA 20120: Thomas Philpott.

MILITARY.COM—(301) 908–4117; 5505 Connecticut Avenue, NW., Suite 262, Washington, DC 20015: Matthew Cox, Michael Hoffman, Bryant Jordan, Brendan McGarry, Richard Sisk.

MILLIYET—(202) 341–0494; 3700 Massachusetts Avenue, NW., Apartment 533, Washington, DC 20016: Pinar Ersoy-Bulut.

MILWAUKEE JOURNAL SENTINEL—(202) 662–2291; 940 National Press Building, 529 14th Street, NW., Washington, DC 20045: Craig Gilbert.

MINNEAPOLIS STAR TRIBUNE—(202) 408–2753; 1090 Vermont Avenue, NW., Suite 1000, Washington, DC 20005: Kevin Diaz, Corey Mitchell, Jim Spencer.

MINNPOST—(612) 455–6950; 1111 Army Navy Drive, #1230, Arlington, VA 22202: Devin Henry.

MLEX US—(202) 909–2138; 1776 Eye Street, NW., Washington, DC 20006: Jeffrey Bliss, Elizabeth Bunn, Can Celik, Flavia Fortes, Doug Halonen, Lesette Heath, Audrey Karman, Nishad Majmudar, Robert McLeod, Brittany Melling, Leah Nylen, Gabriel Pena, Neil Roland, Ira Teinowitz, Juliane von Reppert-Bismarck, Edmond Wybaillie IV, Shuting Xie.

MUNWHA ILBO—(202) 270–0148; 1149 National Press Building, Washington, DC 20045: Jea Lee.

NATIONAL JOURNAL—(202) 739–8400; 600 New Hampshire Avenue, NW., Washington, DC 20037: Timothy Alberta, George Condon, Jr., Thomas DeFrank, Chris Frates, Shane Goldmacher, Sarah Hall, Amy Harder, Billy House, Elahe Izadi, Fawn Johnson, Glen Justice, Stacy Lynn Kaper, Mike Magner, Alex Roarty, Emelie Rutherford, Margot Sanger-Katz, Sophie Yarborough.

NATIONAL JOURNAL GROUP'S GLOBAL SECURITY NEWSWIRE—(202) 266–7248; 600 New Hampshire Avenue, NW., Washington, DC 20037: Elaine Grossman, Douglas Guarino.

NEW ORLEANS TIMES-PICAYUNE—(202) 383–7861; 6303 Crathie Lane, Bethesda, MD 20816: Bruce Alpert.

NEW YORK DAILY NEWS—(202) 467–6670; 1050 Thomas Jefferson Street, Second Floor, Washington, DC 20007: Daniel Friedman, Joseph Straw, James Warren.

NEW YORK POST—(202) 393–1787; 1114 National Press Building, 529 14th Street, NW., Washington, DC 20045: Geoff Earle, Steven Miller, Gerard Shields.

NEW YORK TIMES—(202) 862–0300; 1627 I Street, NW., Suite 700, Washington, DC 20006: Jill Agostino, Leonard Apcar, Binyamin Appelbaum, Matt Bai, Peter Baker, John Broder, Elisabeth Bumiller, Jeff Burgess, Jackie Calmes, Adam Clymer, Helene Cooper, Rebecca Corbett, Maureen Dowd, Michael Gordon, Bill Hamilton, Jacob Harris, Emmarie Huetteman, Carl Hulse, David Joachim, Mark Landler, Mark Leibovich, David Leonhardt, Eric Lichtblau, Adam Liptak, Eric Lipton, Annie Lowrey, Juliet Macur, Mark Mazzetti, Clifton Meadows, Steven Myers, Ron Nixon, Ashley Parker, Alicia Parlapiano, Robert Pear, Jeremy Peters, James Risen, David Sanger, Charlie Savage, Michael Schmidt, Eric Schmitt, Scott Shane, Thomas Shanker, Michael Shear, Andrew Siddons, Ronald Skarzenski, Jada Smith, Anne Snyder, Ashley Southall, Jennifer Steinhauer, Richard Stevenson, Sheryl Stolberg, William Storey, Rachel Swarns, Sabrina Tavernise, Paul Volpe, Matthew Wald, Hannah Wallander, Jonathan Weisman, Sarah Wheaton, Derek Willis, Edward Wyatt.

NEWSDAY—(202) 408–2715; 1090 Vermont Avenue, NW., Washington, DC 20005: Thomas Brune.

NEWSPAPER ENTERPRISE—(301) 320–5559; 6008 Osceola Road, Bethesda, MD 20816: Robert Wagman.

NIKKEI—(202) 393–1388; 815 Connecticut Avenue, NW., Suite 310, Washington, DC 20006: Tomoko Ashizuka, Christina Bilski, Akio Fujii, Kazuaki Fujii, Masako Iwamoto, Stephen Keefe, Shin Nakayama, Toshiki Yazawa, Naoya Yoshino.

NISHI-NIPPON SHIMBUN—(202) 393–5120; 1012 National Press Building, 529 14th Street, NW., Washington, DC 20045: Masaharu Miyazaki, Takeshi Yamasaki.

NOTIMEX MEXICAN NEWS AGENCY—(202) 347–5227; 975 National Press Building, 529 14th Street, NW., Washington, DC 20045: Ruben Barrera, Maria Garcia, Jose Lopez Zamorano, Santiago Tavara.

NEWSPAPERS REPRESENTED—Continued

O ESTADO DE S. PAULO—(202) 248–0280; 700 13th Street, Suite 555, Washington, DC 20005: Claudia Lacerda Trevisan.

OIL DAILY—(202) 662–0723; 1411 K Street, NW., Suite 602, Washington, DC 20005: Rosa Lin, William Murray.

OKLAHOMAN—(202) 459–4921; 1015 15th Street, NW., Suite 500, Washington, DC 20005: Chris Casteel.

OMAHA WORLD-HERALD—(402) 444–1000; Omaha World-Herald Building, Omaha, NE 68102–1138: Joseph Morton.

ORANGE COUNTY REGISTER—(703) 892–0620; 1295 National Press Building, 529 14th Street, NW., Washington, DC 20045: Matthew Fleming, Elizabeth Held, David Hood, Cathy Taylor.

OREGONIAN—(202) 731–5152; 18923 Impulse Lane, Gaithersburg, MD 20879: Helen Fessenden, Charles Pope.

ORLANDO SENTINEL—(202) 824–8222; 1025 F Street, NW., Suite 700, Washington, DC 20004: Mark Matthews.

PALM BEACH POST—(202) 777–7090; 400 North Capitol Street, #750, Washington, DC 20001: Laura Green.

PHILADELPHIA INQUIRER—(215) 854–2718; 350 G Street, SW., #610, Washington, DC 20024: Thomas Fitzgerald, Jonathan Tamari.

PIONEER - INDIA—(703) 876–6149; 2731 Pleasantdale Road, #203, Vienna, VA 22180: Sethuraman Rajagopalan.

PITTSBURGH POST-GAZETTE—(703) 996–9292; 301 North Beauregard Street, Apartment 208, Alexandria, VA 22312: Tracie Mauriello.

PORTLAND PRESS HERALD—(207) 317–6256; 330 5th Street, SE., Apartment A, Washington, DC 20003: Kevin Miller.

POSTMEDIA NEWS—(301) 233–8479; 1206 National Press Building, 529 14th Street, NW., Washington, DC 20045: Allen Abel, William Marsden.

PRO PUBLICA: Sebastian Rotella.

REAL CLEAR POLITICS—(301) 412–9639; 1500 Massachusetts Avenue, NW., Washington, DC 20005: Carl Cannon, Scott Conroy, Caitlin Huey-Burns, Alexis Simendinger, Dustin Walker.

RECORD (BERGEN COUNTY, NJ)—North Jersey Media Group, 1 Garret Mountain Plaza, Woodland Park, NJ 07424: Herbert Jackson.

REFORMA NEWSPAPER—(202) 368–1523; 1009 New Hampshire Avenue, NW., Apartment 7, Washington, DC 20037: Angel Villarino-Perez.

RELIGION NEWS SERVICE—(202) 463–8777; 529 14th Street, NW., Suite 425, Washington, DC 20045: Adelle Banks, Daniel Burke, Kevin Eckstrom, Lauren Markoe.

RESTRUCTURING TODAY—(202) 384–4833; 4908 Hornbeam Drive, Rockville, MD 20853: James Downing.

RHEINISCHE POST—(202) 966–2393; 5810 Chevy Chase Parkway, NW., Washington, DC 20015: Frank Herrmann.

ROSSIIYSKAYA GAZETA—(202) 674–2842; 430 Military Road, NW., Washington, DC 20015: Igor Dunaevskiy.

RYUKYU SHIMPO—(571) 278–6828; 850 North Randolph Street, #2201, Arlington, VA 22203: Hideki Matsudo, Ryota Shimabukuro.

SALT LAKE TRIBUNE—(202) 662–8732; 969 National Press Building, 529 14th Street, NW., Washington, DC 20045: Thomas Burr, Matt Canham.

SAN ANTONIO EXPRESS-NEWS—(202) 263–6451; 700 12th Street, NW., Suite 1000, Washington, DC 20005: Gary Martin.

SAN FRANCISCO CHRONICLE—(202) 263–6573; 700 12th Street, NW., Suite 1000, Washington, DC 20005: Carolyn Lochhead.

SANKEI SHIMBUN—(202) 347–2015; 330 National Press Building, 529 14th Street, NW., Washington, DC 20045: Nobuyuki Aoki, Yosuke Inuzuka, Kosuke Kakiuchi, Norio Kokumo, Yoshihisa Komori, Rui Sasaki, Bruce Stewart.

SAUDI PRESS AGENCY—(202) 944–3890; 601 New Hampshire Avenue, NW., Washington, DC 20037: Haifa Al-Mubarak, Mustafa Bashir, Thomas Belman, Geoffrey Cunningham, Dean Dessouky, Azeddine Labriny, Lauren Riley, Nezar Sheikh.

SCIENCE & TECHNOLOGY DAILY—(703) 255–1171; Yi He, Xueke Tian.

SCOTUSBLOG: Lyle Dennison.

SCRIP—(301) 216–2433; 13109 Millhaven Place, Germantown, MD 20874: Donna Young.

SCRIPPS HOWARD NEWS SERVICE—(202) 408–1484; 1090 Vermont Avenue, Suite 1000, Washington, DC 20005: Curtis Lee Bowman, Carolyn Cerbin, Patricia Choate, Michael Collins, Carol Guensburg, Thomas Hargrove, Lisa Hoffman, Dale McFeatters, Martin Schram, Bartholomew Sullivan, Daniel Wolf.

SEATTLE TIMES—(202) 383–6108; 700 12th Street, NE., Suite 1000, Washington, DC 20005: Kyung Song.

SEGYE TIMES—(703) 207 9827; 909 National Press Building, 529 14th Street, NW., Washington, DC 20045: Hee Jun Park.

NEWSPAPERS REPRESENTED—Continued

SEKAI NIPPO—(202) 898–8292; 1133 19th Street, NW., 8th Floor, Washington, DC 20036: Toshiyuki Hayakawa.

SEOUL SHIMBUN—(202) 393–4061; 905 National Press Building, 529 14th Street, NW., Washington, DC 20045: Sang-Yeon Kim.

SMARTGRID TODAY—(888) 512 4408; 4908 Hornbeam Drive, Rockville, MD 20853: Sean Lyngaas.

SNL ENERGY—(703) 373–0657; Glen Boshant, Sean Carr, Michael Copley, Marcy Crane, Jonathan Crawford, Andrew Engblom, Darren Epps, Mark Hand, Corbin Hiar, Dan Lowrey, Michael Lustig, Bill Reilly, Bryan Schutt, Sarah Smith, Jeff Stanfield, Sean Sullivan, Esther Whieldon.

SPIEGEL ONLINE—(202) 347–5222: Sebastian Fischer.

ST. LOUIS BEACON—(301) 538–8644: Robert Koenig.

ST. LOUIS POST-DISPATCH—(202) 298–6880; 1025 Connecticut Avenue, Suite 1102, Washington, DC 20036: William Lambrecht.

STARS AND STRIPES—(202) 761–1183; 350 National Press Building, 529 14th Street, NW., Washington, DC 20045: Chris Carroll, Jennifer Hlad, Megan McCloskey.

STARS AND STRIPES—(703) 693–6957; 2500 Q Street, Suite 640, Washington, DC 20007: J.T. Rushing, Leo Shane III, (202) 761–1183.

STEPHENS MEDIA GROUP—(202) 783–1760; 666 11th Street, Suite 535, Washington, DC 20001: Stephan Tetreault, Peter Urban.

STRAITS TIMES—(202) 662–8726; 916 National Press Building, 529 14th Street, NW., Washington, DC 20045: Kean Wong.

SUEDDEUTSCHE ZEITUNG—(301) 469–0650; 8521 Meadowlark Lane, Bethesda, MD 20817: Nicolas Richter, Christian Wernicke.

SUN-SENTINEL—(202) 824–8256; 1090 Vermont Avenue, NW., Suite 1000, Washington, DC 20005: William Gibson.

SVENSKA DAGBLADET—(202) 362–8253; 3601 Connecticut Avenue, #622, Washington, DC 20008: Karin Henriksson, Gary Yerkey.

SYDNEY MORNING HERALD—(301) 272–7511; 1310 G Street, #750, Washington, DC 20005: Nicholas O'Malley.

SYRACUSE POST-STANDARD—(571) 970–3751; 3900 Fairfax Drive, Suite 1321, Arlington, VA 22203: Mark Weiner.

TAGES ANZEIGER—(202) 629–2257; 2026 16th Street, NW., #5, Washington, DC 20009: David Hesse.

TAIWAN CENTRAL NEWS AGENCY—(202) 628–2378; 1173 National Press Building, 529 14th Street, NW., Washington, DC 20045: Tony Liao Han Yuan, Shu-Yuan Lin.

TAMPA BAY TIMES—(202) 463–0575; 1100 Connecticut Avenue, Fourth Floor, Washington, DC 20036: William Adair, Rebecca Bowers, Louis Jacobson, Alex Leary.

TECH LAW JOURNAL—(202) 364–8882; 3034 Newark Street, NW., Washington, DC 20008: David Carney.

TELAM S.E.: Melisa Cabo.

THOMSON REUTERS—(202) 898–8300; 1333 H Street, Suite 500, Washington, DC 20005: Charles Abbott, Timothy Ahmann, Charles Alexander, Victoria Allen, Fred Barbash, Diane Bartz, Amanda Becker, Eric Beech, Alistair Bell, Joan Biskupic, Melissa Bland, Caren Bohan, Martin Brandt II, Alister Bull, Margaret Chadbourn, Deborah Charles, Toni Clarke, Susan Cornwell, Richard Cowan, Pedro da Costa, Stella Dawson, Alexandra de Oliveira, Gabriel Debenedetti, Kim Dixon, Timothy Dobbyn, Robert Doherty, Kevin Drawbaugh, Will Dunham, Paul Eckert, Mark Felsenthal, Thomas Ferraro, Jacqueline Frank, Tim Gardner, Rodrek Golden, Howard Scot Goller, Susan Heavey, Steve Holland, Mark Hosenball, Krista Hughes, Lawrence Hurley, Daniel Indiviglio, David Ingram, Robert Johnson, Jerry Konjevoda, Rosalind Krasny, Lisa Lambert, Jason Lange, David Lawder, Katherina Lemus, David Lindsey, Sarah Lynch, Sandra Maler, Jeff Mason, Douwe Miedema, Arshad Mohammed, David Morgan, Lucia Mutikani, Elvina Nawaguna, Essex Noel, Doug Palmer, Mitchell Rabinowitz, Roberta Rampton, Ayesha Rascoe, Andrea Ricci, Patrick Rucker, Timothy Ryan, Alina Selyukh, Jack Shafer, Andrea Shalal-Esa, John Shiffman, Eugene Shyu, Paul Simao, Ian Simpson, Matthew Spetalnick, Neil Stempleman, Emily Stephenson, Linda Stern, Phillip Stewart, David Story, Warren Strobel, Andy Sullivan, Patrick Temple-West, Marilyn Thompson, Aruna Viswanatha, Valerie Volcovici, Michael Weekes, Jr., John Whitesides, Lesley Wroughton, Karey Wutkowski, Rachelle Younglai, Sam Youngman, Anna Yukhananov, Deborah Zabarenko, Tabassum Zakaria, Patricia Zengerle.

TIMES OF INDIA—(301) 695–9348; 7505 Akfred Drive, Silver Spring, MD 20910: Chidanand Rajghatta.

TIMES OF LONDON—(202) 530–9901; 1101 17th Street, NW., Suite 601, Washington, DC 20045: Devika Bhat, Alexandra Kaye, Matthew Spence, David Taylor.

TOKYO CHUNICHI SHIMBUN—(202) 783–9479; 1012 National Press Building, NW., Washington, DC 20045: Conrad Chaffee, Chrishopher Kelly, Allison Kingery, Yasunobu Saiba, Yoichi Takeuchi, Eri Urano.

TRIBUNE MEDIA SERVICES—(202) 298–8359; 3042 Q Street, NW., Washington, DC 20007: Jules Witcover.

UNITED DAILY NEWS—(240) 428–1164; 954 National Press Building, 529 14th Street, NW., Washington, DC 20045: Chao-Ying Lai.

NEWSPAPERS REPRESENTED—Continued

UNITED MEDIA—(301) 494–0430; 3330 Blue Heron Drive, North, Chesapeake Beach, MD 20732: Lew Sichelman.

UNITED PRESS INTERNATIONAL—(202) 898–8000; 1133 19th Street, NW., Washington, DC 22030: Rafael Bernal, Gabrielle Levy, Billie Jean Shaw, Richard Tomkins.

UNIVERSAL UCLICK SYNDICATE—(703) 690–8095; 3600 New York Avenue, NE., Washington, DC 20002: Donald Lambro.

USA TODAY—(703) 854–8900; 1575 I Street, NW., Suite 350, Washington, DC 20005: William Allen, Fred Anklam, Jr., John Bacon, Jarrett Bell, Marisol Bello, Erik Brady, Catalina Camia, Paul Davidson, Susan Davis, William Dermody, Natalie DiBlasio, Linda Dono, Oren Dorell, Peter Eisler, Haya El Nasser, Gwen Flanders, Thomas Frank, Alan Gomez, George Hager, James Healy, Brad Heath, Bruce Horovitz, Meghan Hoyer, David Jackson, Bart Jansen, Kevin Johnson, Dennis Kelly, Kelly Kennedy, Gregory Korte, Jacqueline Kucinich, Donna Leger, Ray Locker, Aamer Madhani, Mary Beth Marklein, Jim Michaels, Paul Overberg, Susan Page, Claude Pruitt, Maria Puente, Cara Richardson, Christopher Schnaars, Fredreka Schouten, Paul Singer, Donovan Slack, Gregory Toppo, Geraldine Tucker, Jodi Upton, Tom Vanden Brook, Dan Vergano, James Welch, Richard Wolf, Alison Young, Gregg Zoroya.

US-REPORT (GERMANY)—(301) 299–5777; 10201 Windsor View Drive, Potomac, MD 20854: Thomas Spang.

VOTERAMA IN CONGRESS—(202) 667–9760; 1822 Corcoran Street, NW., Washington, DC 20009: Michael Lesparre, Richard Thomas.

WALL STREET JOURNAL—(202) 862–9200; 1025 Connecticut Avenue, NW., Suite 800, Washington, DC 20036: Stephanie Armour, Rebecca Ballhaus, Julian Barnes, Devlin Barrett, Susan Benkelman, Janet Booker, Jess Bravin, Thomas Burton, MaryLu Carnevale, Thomas Catan, Pedro da Costa, Gary Fields, Siobhan Gorman, James Grimaldi, Andrew Grossman, Timothy Hanrahan, Nell Henderson, Neil Hickey, Jon Hilsenrath, Janet Hook, Keith Johnson, Khalid Khattak, Neil King, Jr., Peter Landers, Carol Lee, Ben Leubsdorf, Jude Marfil, Victoria McGrane, John McKinnon, Laura Meckler, Kate Milani, Joshua Mitchell, Brody Mullins, Alicia Mundy, Sara Murray, Gautham Nagesh, Colleen Nelson, Peter Nicholas, Dion Nissenbaum, Patrick O'Connor, Robert Ourlian, Damian Paletta, Scott Patterson, Evan Perez, Michael Phillips, Louise Radnofsky, Sudeep Reddy, Matthew Rose, Amy Schatz, Gerald Seib, Melanie Trottman, David Wessel, Elizabeth Williamson, Daniel Yadron, Aaron Zitner.

WARREN COMMUNICATIONS NEWS—(202) 872–9202; 2115 Ward Court, NW., Washington, DC 20037: Jessica Arriens, Brian Feito, Erin Mershon, James Phillips, Timothy Warren.

WASHINGTON DUPONT CIRCLE NEWS—(202) 328–1121; 1735 T Street, NW., Washington, DC 20009: Irvin Molotsky.

WASHINGTON EXAMINER—(202) 903–2000; 1015 15th Street, NW., Suite 500, Washington, DC 20005: Michael Barone, Elizabeth Bedard, Paul Bedard, Rebecca Berg, Alan Blinder, Timothy Carney, Conn Carroll, Alicia Cohn, Michal Conger, Steve Contorno, Susan Crabtree, Susan Ferrechio, Mark Flatten, Joel Gehrke, Jr., Sean Higgins, Philip Klein, Joseph Lawler, Sean Lengell, Tim Mak, Jennifer Peebles, Richard Pollock, Nicole Schwab, Stephen Smith, Charles Spiering, Mark Tapscott, Byron York.

WASHINGTON POST—(202) 334–4121; 1150 15th Street, NW., Washington, DC 20071: Joel Achenbach, Nurith Aizenman, Keith Alexander, Nick Anderson, Lori Aratani, JoAnn Armao, Daniel Balz, Robert Barnes, Martin Baron, Cameron Barr, Aaron Blake, David Brown, Henri Cauvin, Chris Cillizza, Tim Craig, Timothy Curran, Joe Davidson, Aaron Davis, Marcia Davis, Mike DeBonis, Brady Dennis, Paul Duggan, Joshua duLac, Juliet Eilperin, David Fahrenthold, David Fallis, Paul Farhi, Timothy Farnam, Darryl Fears, Peter Finn, Marc Fisher, Mary Pat Flaherty, Michael Fletcher, Brian Fung, Amy Gardner, Ann Gerhart, Alma Gill, Steven Ginsberg, Zachary Goldfarb, Ashley Halsey III, Thomas Hamburger, Hamil Harris, Dana Hedgpeth, Emily Heil, Rosalind Helderman, Nia-Malika Henderson, Steve Hendrix, Melinda Henneberger, Joshua Hicks, Scott Higham, Jason Horowitz, Sari Horwitz, Spencer Hsu, Anne Hull, Jenna Johnson, Robert Kaiser, Al Kamen, Paul Kane, Dan Keating, Kimbriell Kelly, Glenn Kessler, Suzy Khimm, Ezra Klein, Sarah Kliff, Anne Kornblut, Lyndsey Layton, Carol Leonnig, Ann Marimow, Jerome Markon, Laurie McGinley, Ted Mellnik, Kevin Merida, Dana Milbank, David Montgomery, Lori Montgomery, Carol Morello, Steven Mufson, Ellen Nakashima, Robert O'Harrow, Edward O'Keefe, Lonnae O'Neal Parker, Ben Pershing, Walter Pincus, Bradford Plumer, Lisa Rein, Eli Reyes, Eugene Robinson, Manuel Roig-Franzia, Michael Ruane, Philip Rucker, Terence Samuel, Brigid Schulte, Sandhya Somashekhar, Miranda Spivack, Joe Stephens, Nikita Stewart, Stephen Stromberg, Sean Sullivan, Lena Sun, Cheryl Thompson, Krissah Thompson, Craig Timberg, Karen Tumulty, Bill Turque, Stephen Vogel, Laura Vozzella, John Wagner, Peter Wallsten, Joby Warrick, Rachel Weiner, Craig Whitlock, Peter Whoriskey, Ovetta Wiggins, Clarence Williams, Scott Wilson, Bob Woodward, Holly Yeager, Eric Yoder, Dan Zak, Matt Zapotosky.

WASHINGTON TELECOMMUNICATIONS SERVICES—(804) 695–4648; 1006 Harrison Circle, Alexandria, VA 22304: Gordon White.

WASHINGTON TIMES—(202) 636–3000; 3600 New York Avenue, NE., Washington, DC 20002: David Boyer, Tim Devaney, Richard Diamond, Stephen Dinan, Christopher Dolan, Jennifer Harper, Kellan Howell, Thomas Howell, Jr., Jacqueline Klimas, Seth McLaughlin, Emily Miller, James Morrison,

NEWSPAPERS REPRESENTED—Continued

Andrea Noble, Rowan Scarborough, Ashish Sen, David Sherfinski, Meredith Somers, Phillip Swarts, Guy Taylor, Shaun Waterman, Cheryl Wetzstein, Benjamin Wolfgang, Annie Yu.

WEN HUI DAILY—(202) 262–6781; 1600 South Eads Street, Suite 1134 North, Arlington, VA 22202: Xiaoyang Xia.

WHITE HOUSE DOSSIER—(202) 277–5416: Keith Koffler.

WILLIAM SCALLY REPORTS—(202) 362–2382; 2918 Legation Street, NW., Washington, DC 20015: William Scally.

WOLFNEWS—(202) 237–1019; 2841 Arizona Terrace, Washington, DC 20016: Mariuccia Chiantaretto.

WORLD BUSINESS PRESS—(703) 942–8318; 4706 Commons Drive, A–303, Annandale, VA 22003: Vladimir Amrich, Dagmar Benesova, Zuzana Cepla.

WORLD JOURNAL—(202) 737–6426; 954 National Press Building, 529 14th Street, NW., Washington, DC 20045: Betty Lin.

XINHUA NEWS AGENCY—(703) 647–1598; 1201 National Press Building, 529 14th Street, NW., Washington, DC 20045: Yu Fan, Pan Gao, Xiangwen Ge, Wei Ran, Hao Sun, Fengfeng Wang, Jiang Xufeng, Aijun Yi, Liu Zhanye, Linfei Zhi.

YAHOO NEWS—(202) 293–1086; 1500 K Street, NW., Suite 600, Washington, DC 20005: Phoebe Connelly, Rachel Hartman, Olivier Knox, Christopher Moody, Claude Pruitt, Walter Shapiro, Christopher Wilson.

YOMIURI SHIMBUN—(202) 783–0363; 802 National Press Building, 529 14th Street, NW., Washington, DC 20045: Janie Boschma, William DiNovi, Julian Hattem, Andrew Hill, Keiko Iizuka, Takashi Imai, Kentaro Nakajima, Tatsuo Nakajima, Akihiro Okada, Gaku Shibata, Yoshikazu Shirakawa, Ashley Sutton, Mineko Tokito, Kyoko Yamaguchi, Kunihiko Yasue.

YONHAP NEWS AGENCY—914 National Press Building, 529 14th Street, NW., Washington, DC 20045: Eui Yong Kang, Chi Lee, Seung-Gwan Lee, Woo Tak Lee, Michiko Morimoto, Hyodong Roh.

PRESS PHOTOGRAPHERS' GALLERY*

The Capitol, Room S–317, 224–6548

www.pressphotographers.senate.gov

Director.—Jeffrey S. Kent.
Deputy Director.—Mark A. Abraham.
Assistant Director.—Tricia Munro.

STANDING COMMITTEE OF PRESS PHOTOGRAPHERS

J. Scott Applewhite, *Chair,* Associated Press
Win McNamee, *Secretary-Treasurer,* Getty Images
Paul Richards, Agence France Presse
Tom Williams, CQ/Roll Call
Stephen Crowley, New York Times
Ronald Sachs, Consolidated News Pictures

RULES GOVERNING PRESS PHOTOGRAPHERS' GALLERY

1. (a) Administration of the Press Photographers' Gallery is vested in a Standing Committee of Press Photographers consisting of six persons elected by accredited members of the Gallery. The Committee shall be composed of one member each from Associated Press Photos; Reuters News Pictures or AFP Photos; magazine media; local newspapers; agency or freelance member; and one at-large member. The at-large member may be, but need not be, selected from media otherwise represented on the Committee; however no organization may have more than one representative on the Committee.

(b) Elections shall be held as early as practicable in each year, and in no case later than March 31. A vacancy in the membership of the Committee occurring prior to the expiration of a term shall be filled by a special election called for that purpose by the Committee.

(c) The Standing Committee of the Press Photographers' Gallery shall propose no change or changes in these rules except upon petition in writing signed by not less than 25 accredited members of the Gallery.

2. Persons desiring admission to the Press Photographers' Gallery of the Senate shall make application in accordance with Rule 33 of the Senate, which rule shall be interpreted and administered by the Standing Committee of Press Photographers subject to the review and approval of the Senate Committee on Rules and Administration.

3. The Standing Committee of Press photographers shall limit membership in the photographers' gallery to bona fide news photographers of repute in their profession and Heads of Photographic Bureaus under such rules as the Standing Committee of Press Photographers shall prescribe.

4. Provided, however, that the Standing Committee of Press Photographers shall admit to the Gallery no person who does not establish to the satisfaction of the Committee all of the following:

(a) That any member is not engaged in paid publicity or promotion work or in prosecuting any claim before Congress or before any department of the Government, and will not become so engaged while a member of the Gallery.

*Information is based on data furnished and edited by each respective Gallery.

(b) That he or she is not engaged in any lobbying activity and will not become so engaged while a member of the Gallery.

The above rules have been approved by the Committee on Rules and Administration.

JOHN A. BOEHNER,
Speaker, House of Representatives.

CHARLES E. SCHUMER,
Chair, Senate Committee on Rules and Administration.

MEMBERS ENTITLED FOR ADMISSION

PRESS PHOTOGRAPHERS' GALLERY

Ake, David: Associated Press Photos
Alvarez, Luis M.: Freelance
Alvarez, Miguel: Freelance
Andrews, Scott: Cannon, USA
Angerer, Drew: Freelance
Antonov, Mladen: Agence France-Presse
Applewhite, J. Scott: Associated Press Photos
Arrosi, Eddie: Freelance
Archambault, Charlie: Freelance
Ashley, Douglas G.: Suburban Communications Corp.
Augustino, Jocelyn: Freelance
Auth, Bill: Freelance
Barouh, Stan: 1105 Media
Barrett, Stephen E.: Freelance
Barrick, Matthew: Freelance
Beiser, H. Darr: USA / Today
Benic, Patrick T.: United Press International
Berglie, James: Zuma
Berg, Lisa: Freelance
Biddle, Susan: Washington Post
Binks, Porter L.: Sports Illustrated
Bivera, Johnny: Freelance
Blass, Eileen M.: USA / Today
Bleier-Schmeets, Karen: Agence France-Presse
Bloom, Richard: Freelance
Borst, Charles: Education Week
Bourg, Jim: Reuters News Pictures
Bowe, Christy: ImageCatcher News
Bowler, Dana Rene: Freelance
Brack, William D.: Black Star
Brandon, James Alex: Associated Press Photos
Brier, Joe: Freelance
Brown, Robert A.: Richmond Times Dispatch
Brown, Thomas: Gannett Government Media
Burke, Lauren: Freelance
Burnett, David: Contact Press Images
Cabrera, Mario: Vision Fotos
Calvert, Mary F.: Freelance
Cameron, Gary A.: Reuters News Pictures
Campbell, Matt: European Pressphoto Agency
Carioti, Richard A.: Washington Post
Castoro, Susan: Associated Press Photos
Cedeno, Ken: Freelance
Ceneta, Manuel B.: Associated Press Photos
Chikwendiu, Jahi: Washington Post
Chung, Andre: Freelance
Clark, Bill: Roll Call
Clement, Richard: Blooomberg Government
Cohen, Marshall H.: Bigmarsh News Photos
Connor, Kristopher Cory: Freelance
Coppage, Gary R.: Photo Press International
Crowley, Stephen: The New York Times
Curtis, Rob: Gannett Government Media
Davidson, Linda: Washington Post
De, Yongjian: China News Service
Demczuk, Gabriella: New York Times
Dharapak, Charles: Associated Press Photos
Dietsch, Kevin: United Press International
Doctorian, Sonya: Washington Post
Dougherty, Sean: USA / Today
Douliery, Olivier: Abaca
Downing, Lawrence S.: Reuters News Pictures
Du Cille, Michel: Washington Post
Duggan, James: Freelance
Eddins, Jr., Joseph M.: Washington Times
Edmonds, Ronald: Associated Press Photos
Eile, Evan: USA / Today
Elkins, Jeff: Washingtonian
Elswick, Jon: Associated Press Photos
Epstein, Linda: McCatchy Tribune
Ernst, Jonathan: Freelance
Esquivel, Robert: Herald Standard
Fabrizio, Phil: Town Courier (Gaithersburg)
Falk, Steven M.: The Philadelphia Daily News
Farrar, Anne: Washington Post
Franko, Jeff: Gannett
Frederic, Wallois: Agence France-Presse
Frey, Katherine: Washington Post
Gail, Carl Mark: Washington Post
Gainer, Denny: USA / Today
Galietta, Wendy: Washington Post
Gamarra, Ruben F.: Notimex
Gandhi, Pareshkumar A.: Rediff.com / India Abroad Pub.
Garcia, Mannie: Freelance
Geraci, Andrew: Washington Times
Gilbert, Patrice: Freelance
Glenn, Larry: Freelance
Golden, Melissa: Redux
Golon, MaryAnne: Washington Post
Graham, Douglas: Roll Call
Gripas, Yuri: Freelance
Gruber, Jack: USA / Today
Guerrucci, Aude: Polaris Images
Gunther, Brendan C.J.: European Pressphoto Agency
Hambach, Eva: Agence France-Presse
Hamburg, Harry: Freelance
Harnik, Andrew: The Washington Examiner
Harrer, Andrew: Bloomberg
Harrington, John H.: Black Star

MEMBERS ENTITLED FOR ADMISSION—Continued

Heisenfelt, Ann: Freelance
Helber, Stephen: Associated Press Photos
Henry, Dennis: European Pressphoto Agency
Hill, Robb: Freelance
Hoffman, Brendan W.: Freelance
Holt, Victor: Washington Informer
Hubbard, Garrett: USA / Today
Jennings, Graeme: Washington Examiner
Joachin, Jade-Snow: Washington Post
Jones, Leah: Freelance
Jones, Lolita: McClatchy Tribune
Jorrin, Alexander Toby: Freelance
Joseph, Marvin: Washington Post
Kahn, Greg: Freelance
Kahn, Nikki: Washington Post
Kamm, Nicholas: Agence France-Presse
Kaster, Carolyn: Associated Press Photos
Katz, Martin I.: Chesapeake News Service
Kennerly, David H.: Freelance
House, Kelci: Washingtonian
Key, Michael Patrick: Washington Blade
Kim, Hyunsoo Lee: Virginia Pilot
Kirkpatrick, T.J.: Freelance
Kittner, Sam: Freelance
Kleponis, Chris: Freelance
Kraft, Brooks: Time Magazine
Lamarque, Kevin: Reuters News Pictures
Lamkey, Jr., Rod A.: Freelance
Lane, Keith: Freelance
Lanham, Yuko: Asahi Shimbun
LaVor, Martin L.: Freelance
Lawidjaja, Rudy: Freelance
Lessig, Alan: Gannett Government Media
Levine, Lewis: Savannah Morning News
Lewis, Roy: Washington Informer
Lizik, Ron: Associated Press Photos
Loehre, Tim: USA / Today
Loeb, Saul: Agence France-Presse
LoScalzo, Jim: European Pressphoto Agency
Lynch, Liz: National Journal
Lynch, M. Patricia: Atlas Press Photo
Maddaloni, Chris: Freelance
Magana, Jose Luis: Freelance
Mahaskey, M. Scott: The Politico
Makely, John: MSNBC.com
Malet, Jeffrey: Freelance
Mallin, Jay: Freelance
Malonson, Jacqueline: Freelance
Mara, Melina: Washington Post
Markel, Brad: Capri
Marovich Jr., Pete: Freelance
Martin, Jacquelyn: Associated Press Photos
Martinez Monsivais, Pablo: Associated Press Photos
McClain, Matt: Washington Post
Mathieson, Greg E.: MAI Photo Agency
McDonnell, John: Washington Post
McNamee, Win: Getty Images
Milbrett, Jennifer: USA / Today
Miller, Robert: Washington Post
Mills, Andrew: Star-Ledger
Mills, Douglas: The New York Times
Mock-Bunning, Logan: Freelance
Morigi, Paul: Freelance
Morones, Mike: Gannett Government Media
Mount, Bonnie Jo: Washington Post
Myers, Benjamin: Freelance
Myers, Charles: McClatchy Tribune
Naji-Allah, Khalid: Freelance
Nash, Greg: The Hill
Newton, Jonathan: Washington Post
Ngan, Mandel: Agence France-Presse
Nipp, Lisa: Freelance
Nolly Araujo, Angel: Notimex
Nordby, Leslie: Freelance
O'Leary, William P: Washington Post
Owen, Clifford: Freelance
Pajic, Kamenko: NIN Magazine
Palu, Louie: Zuma Press
Panagos, Dimitrios: Greek American News Agency
Park, Maxine: USA / Today
Partlow, Wayne: Associated Press Photos
Perkins, Lucian: Washington Post
Petros, Bill: Freelance
Poleski, David: Freelance
Powers, Carol T: Freelance
Premack, Jay: Freelance
Purcell, Steven: Freelance
Radzinschi, Diego: National Law Journal
Ratliff, Walter: Associated Press Photos
Reed, Jason: Reuters News Pictures
Reed, Tom: Freelance
Reinhard, Rick: Impact Digitals
Reynolds, Michael: European Pressphoto Agency
Ricardel, Vincent: Freelance
Richards, Paul J.: Agence France-Presse
Richardson, Joey M.: McClatchy Tribune
Riley, Molly: Reuters News Pictures
Roberts, Joshua: Freelance
Robinson, Scott: Freelance
Rolfe, Judy: Freelance
Rosenbaum, Daniel: Freelance
Ryan, Patrick: Freelance
Sachs, Ronald M.: Consolidated News Pictures
Samad, Jewel: Agence France-Presse
Samperton, Kyle: Freelance
Sandys, Toni L.: Washington Post
Saunders, Ray K.: Washington Post
Savi, Ricardo: Freelance
Savoia, Stephon: Associated Press Photos
Schaeffer, Sandra L.: MAI Photo Agency
Schwartz, Michael: The Politico
Scott, Andrew: USA / Today
Semiatin, Morris: Freelance
Shelley, Allison: Freelance

MEMBERS ENTITLED FOR ADMISSION—Continued

Shinkle, John: The Politico
Simon, Martin: Corbis
Smialowski, Brendan: Freelance
Somodevilla, Kenneth: Agence France-Presse
Soares, Jared: Freelance
Soliwon, Diana: U.S. News & World Report
Squires, Derek: Tax Analysts
Swall, Lexey: Freelance
Sweets, Fredric F.: St. Louis American
Sykes, Jack W.: Professional Pilot Magazine
Szenes, Jason: Freelance
Temchine, Michael: Freelance
Theiler, Michael: Freelance
Thew, Shawn: European Pressphoto Agency
Tines, Charles: Detroit News
Trippett, Robert: Freelance
Tripplaar, Kristoffer: SIPA
Usher, Chris: Freelance
Varias, Stelios A.: Reuters News Pictures
Vick, Vanessa: Freelance
Vogel, Leigh: Freelance
Voisin, Sarah L.: Washington Post
Voss, Stephen: Freelance
Vucci, Evan: Associated Press Photos
Walker, Harry E.: McClatchy Tribune
Walsh, Susan: Associated Press Photos
Watkins, Jr., Frederick L.: Freelance
Watson, James H.: Agence France-Presse
Wells, Jonathan: Sipa Press
Williams, Tom: Roll Call
Williamson, Michael: Washington Post
Wilson, Mark L.: Getty Images
Wolf, Kevin: Freelance
Wolf, Lloyd: Freelance
Wong, Alex: Getty Images
Yim, Heesoon: Hana
Yin, Bogu: Xinhua News Agency
Zhang, Jun: Xinhua News Agency
Zhang, Weira: China News Service
Zhe, Fang: Xinhua News Agency
Ziffer, Steve: Freelance

SERVICES REPRESENTED

(Service and telephone number, office address, and name of representative)

1105 MEDIA—10 G Street, NE., Suite 500 Washington, DC 20003: Barouh, Stan.

AGENCE FRANCE PRESSE—(202) 414–0521; 1500 K Street, NW., Suite 600, Washington, DC 20005: Amalvy, Vincent; Bleier-Schmeets, Frederic Wallois; Hambach, Eva; Kamm, Nicholas; Loeb, Saul; Ngan, Mandel; Richards, Paul; Samad, Jewel; Smialowski, Brendan; Watson, James.

ASAHI SHIMBUN—(202) 783–1000; 1022 National Press Building, 529 14th Street, NW., Washington, DC 20045: Lanham, Yuko.

ASSOCIATED PRESS PHOTOS—(202) 641–9520; 1100 13th Street, NW., Suite 700, Washington, DC 20005: Ake, David; Applewhite, J. Scott; Brandon, James Alex; Castoro, Susan; Ceneta, Manuel B.; Dharapak, Charles; Elswick, Ron; Helber, Stephen; Kaster, Carolyn; Lizik, Ron; Martin, Jacquelyn; Martinez Monsivas, Pablo; Partlow, Wayne; Ratliff, Walter; Vucci, Evan; Walsh, Susan.

BIGMARSH NEWS PHOTOS—(202) 364–8332; 5131 52nd Street, NW., Washington, DC 20016: Cohen, Marshall.

BLACK STAR—(703) 547–1176; 7704 Tauxemont Road, Alexandria, VA 22308: Brack, William; Harrington, John.

BLOOMBERG—(202) 654–7300; 1399 New York Avenue, Washington, DC 20005; Harrer, Andrew.

CONSOLIDATED NEWS PICTURES—(202) 543–3203; 10305 Leslie Street, Silver Spring, MD 20902–4857: Sachs, Ronald.

CORBIS—902 Broadway, 4th Floor, New York, NY 10010: Simon, Martin.

CQ/Roll Call—(202) 650–6844; 77 K Street, NE., Washington, DC 20002: Clark, Bill; Graham, Douglas; Williams, Tom.

EFE NEWS SERVICE—7906 Georgia Avenue, Silver Spring, MD 20906: Ruben, Gamara.

EUROPEAN PRESS PHOTO—(202) 347–4694; 529 14th Street, NW., Suite 1122, Washington, DC 20045: Campbell, Matt; LoScalzo, Jim; Reynolds, Michael; Thew, Shawn.

GANNET GOVERNMENT MEDIA—(703) 750–8196; 6993 Commercial Drive, Springfield, VA 22515: Brown, Thomas; Curtis, Rob; Lessig, Alan; Morones, Mike.

GETTY IMAGES—(202) 347–2050; National Press Building, 529 14th Street, NW., Suite 1125, Washington, DC 20045: McNamee, Win; Somodevilla, Kenneth; Wilson, Mark L.; Wong, Alex.

GREEK AMERICAN NEWS AGENCY—(516) 931–2333; 37 Field Avenue, Hicksville, NY 11801: Panagos, Dimitrios.

HANA—(202) 262–4541; 11311 Park Drive, Fairfax, VA 22030: Yim, Heesoon.

HERALD STANDARD—(724) 439–7500; 8 East Church Street, Uniontown, PA 15401: Esquivel, Robert.

IMAGECATCHER NEWS—4911 Hampden Lane, Apartment #3, Bethesda, MD 20814: Bowe, Christy.

IMPACT DIGITALS—(212) 614–8406; 171 Thompson Street, #9, New York, NY 10012: Reinhard, Rick.

LA PRENSA GRAFICA OF EL SALVADOR—(503) 2241–2670; Boulevard Santa Elena, Antiguo Casadian: Alvarez, Miguel Angel.

MAI PHOTO AGENCY—(703) 968–0030; 6601 Ashmere Lane, Centreville, VA 20120: Mathieson, Greg; Schaeffer, Sandra.

MCCLATCHY TRIBUNE—(703) 383–6142; 700 12th Street, NW., Suite 1000, Washington, DC 20005: Epstein, Linda; Jones, Lolita; Myers, Charles; Richardson, Joey; Walker, Harry.

NATIONAL JOURNAL—(202) 739–8400; 600 New Hampshire Avenue, NW., Washington, DC 20037: Bloom, Richard; Carroll, Lauren.

NATIONAL LAW JOURNAL—6516 Gardenwick Road, Baltimore, MD 21209: Radzinschi, Diego.

NOTIMEX—(202) 347–5227; 529 14th Street, NW., Suite 425, Washington, DC 20045–1401: Araju, Angel Nolly.

PANOS—(617) 710–7413; Unit K, Reliance Wharf Hertford Road London, N15EW U.K.: Tatlow, Dermott.

PHOTO PRESS INTERNATIONAL—(540) 286–1045; P.O. Box 190, Goldvein, VA 22720: Coppage, Gary.

POLITICO—(703) 647–7694: Mahasky, Scott; Shinkle, John.

PRIME COLLECTIVE—(202) 285–1391; 3446 South Utah Street, Arlington, VA 22206: Hoffman, Brendan.

POLARIS IMAGES—259 West 30th Street, 13th Floor, New York, NY 10001: Guerrucci, Aude.

PROFESSIONAL PILOT MAGAZINE—3014 Colvin Street, Alexandria, VA 22314: Sykes, Jack.

REDIFF.COM/INDIA ABROAD PUB.—(646) 432–6054; 43 West 24th Street, 2nd Floor, New York, NY 10010: Gandhi, Pareshkumar.

REUTERS NEWS PICTURES—(202) 898–8333; 1333 H Street, NW., Suite 500, Washington, DC 20005: Bourg, Jim; Cameron, Gary; Downing, Lawrence; Lamarque, Kevin; Reed, Jason; Varias, Stelios.

REDUX—(212) 253–0399; 11 Hanover Square, 26th Floor, New York, NY 10005: Golden, Melissa.

SERVICES REPRESENTED—Continued

RICHMOND TIMES—(804) 649–6000; 300 East Franklin Street, Richmond, VA 23219: Brown, Robert.

SCRIPPS HOWARD NEWS SERVICE—(202) 408–2723; 1090 Vermont Avenue, NW., Washington, DC 20005: Bartz, Jason.

SAVANNAH MORNING NEWS—(912) 236–9511; 1375 Chatham Parkway, Savannah, GA 31405: Levine, Lewis.

SIPA PRESS—(212) 463–0150; 307 7th Avenue, Suite 807, New York, NY 10001: Triplar, Kristoffer.

SUBURBAN COMMUNICATIONS CORP.—(248) 568–0006; 872 Dursley Road, Bloomfield Hills, ME 48304: Ashley, Douglas.

THE DETROIT NEWS—(312) 222–2030; 615 West Lafayette Avenue, Photo Department, Detroit, MI 48226: Tines, Charles.

THE HILL—(202) 628–8525; 1625 K Street, Suite 900, Washington, DC 20006: Nash, Greg.

THE NEW YORK TIMES—(202) 862–0300; 1627 Eye Street, NW., Washington, DC 20006: Crowley, Stephen; Mills, Douglas; Damczuk, Gabriella.

THE PHILADELPHIA DAILY NEWS—(215) 854–2000; 400 North Broad Street, Philadelphia, PA 19130: Falk, Steven.

THE WASHINGTON INFORMER—(202) 561–4100; 3117 Martin L. King Avenue, SE., Washington, DC 20032: Holt, Victor.

THE WASHINGTON EXAMINER—(202) 903–2000; 1015 15th Street, NW., Suite 500, Washington, DC 20005: Jennings, Graeme.

TIME MAGAZINE—(202) 861–4062; 1130 Conneticut Avenue, Suite 900, Washington, DC 20036: Kraft, Brooks.

TOWN COURIER—(301) 330–0132; 309 Main Street, Gaithersburg, MD 20878: Fabrizio, Phil.

US NEWS AND WORLD REPORT—(202) 955–2210; 1050 Thomas Jefferson Street, NW., Washington, DC 20007: Soliwan, Diana.

THE WASHINGTON POST—(202) 334–7380; 1150 15th Street, NW., Washington, DC 20071: Biddle, Susan; Carioti, Richard; Chikwendiu, Jahi; Davidson, Linda; Doctorian, Sonya; DuCille, Michael; Farrar, Anne; Frey, Katherine; Gail, Carl; Galieta, Wendy; Golon, MaryAnne; Joachim, Jade-Snow; Joseph, Marvin; Kahn, Nikki; Mara, Melina; McClain, Matt; McDonnell, John; Miller, Mark; Miller, Robert; Mount, Bonnie; Newton, Jonathan; O'Leary, William; Perkins, Lucian; Sandys, Toni; Saunders, Ray; Voisin, Sarah; Williamson, Michael; Woodward, Tracy.

THE WASHINGTON TIMES—(202) 636–3000; 3600 New York Avenue, NE., Washington, DC 20002: Harnik, Andrew.

THE YOMIURI SHIMBUN—Room 208, National Press Building, Washington, DC 20045: Konishi, Taro.

UNITED PRESS INTERNATIONAL—(202) 898–8071; 1133 19th Street, Suite 800, Washington, DC 20036: Benic, Patrick T.; Dietsch, Kevin.

USA/TODAY—(703) 854–5216; 7950 Jones Branch Road, McLean, VA 22107: Beiser, H. Darr; Blass, Eileen; Cochran, Mick; Dougherty, Sean; Eile, Evan; Franko, Jeff; Gruber, Jack; Hubbard, Garrett; Loehrke, Tim; Milbrett, Jennifer; Park, Maxine; Scott, Andrew.

VIRINGIA PILOT—(757) 446–2000; 150 West Brambleton Avenue, Norfolk, VA 23510: Kim, Eugene; Hyunsoo Lee.

VISION PHOTOS—9708 Hale Drive, Clinton, MD 20735: Cabrera, Mario.

WASHINGTONIAN—(202) 296–3600; 1828 L Street, NW., #200, Washington, DC 20036: Propp, Andrew; Elkins, Jeff; House, Kelci.

XINHUA NEWS AGENCY—(703) 875–0082; 1740N 14th Street, Arlington, VA 22209: Zhang, Jun.

ZUMA PRESS—34189 Pacific Coast Highway, Dana Point, CA 92629: Palu, Louie.

FREELANCE

Freelance—Angerer, Drew; Charles Archambault; Eddie Arrossi; Jocelyn Augustino; Bill Auth; Stan Barouh; Stephen Barrett; Matthew Barrick; Lisa Berg; Johnny Bivera; Dana Bowler; Joe Brier; Lauren Burke; Mary Calvert; Ken Cedeno; Andre Chung; Richard Clement; Kristopher Connor; Carrie Devorah; James Duggan; Joseph Eddins, Jr.; Jonathan Ernst; Mannie Garcia; Patrice Gilbert; Larry Glenn; Yuri Gripas; Ann Heisenfelt; Robb Hill; Leah Jones; Alanander "Toby" Jorrin; Greg Kahn; David Kennerly; T.J. Kirkpatrick; Sam Kittner; Chris Kleponis; Rod Lamkey, Jr.; Keith Lane; Marty LaVor; Rudy Lawidjaja; Chris Maddaloni; Jose Luis Magana; Jeff Malet; Jay Mallin; Jacqueline Malonson; Pete Marovich; Logan Mock-Bunting; Paul Morigi; Benjamin Myers; Khalid Naji-Allah; Lisa Nipp; Leslie Nordby; Clifford Owen; Bill Petros; David Poleski; Carol Powers; Jay Premack; Steven Purcell; Tom Reed; Vincent Ricardel; Astrid Riecken; Molly Riley; Joshua Roberts; Scott Robinson; Judy Rolfe; Daniel Rosenbaum; Lance Rosenfield; Patrick Ryan; Kyle Samperton; Ricardo Savi; Morris Semiatin; Allison Shelley; Jared Soares; Lexey Swall; Jason Szenes; Michael Temchine; Michael Theiler; Robert Trippett; Chris Usher; Vanessa Vick; Leigh Vogel; Stephen Voss; Fred Watkins; Jay Westcott; Kevin Wolf; Lloyd Wolf; Steve Ziffer.

WHITE HOUSE NEWS PHOTOGRAPHERS' ASSOCIATION

P.O. Box 7119 Ben Franklin Station, Washington, DC 20044–7119

www.whnpa.org

OFFICERS

Ronald Sachs, Consolidated News, *President*
Douglas Wilkes, WTTG–TV, *Vice President*
Joshua Roberts, Freelance, *Secretary*
Jonathan Elswick, Associated Press, *Treasurer*

EXECUTIVE BOARD

Brendan Smialowski (AFP)
Charles Dharapak (Associated Press)
Andre Harnik (The Washington Times)
Rodney Batten (NBC News)
Whitney Shefte (Washington Post)
Charles MacDonald (National Geographic Channel)
Nikki Kahn, Contest Chair (Washington Post)
Pege Gilgannon, Contest Chair, Video (WJLA–TV)
Pierre Kattar, Contest Chair, Multimedia (Freelance)
Kevin Dietsch, Contest Chair, Student (UPI)
Bethany Swain, Contest Co-Chair, Student (University of Maryland)
Pablo Martinez Monsivais, Education Chair (Associated Press)

MEMBERS REPRESENTED

Abdallah, Khalil: CNN
Adlerblum, Robin: Freelance
Ake, J. David: Associated Press
Albert, Christopher: CBS News
Alberter, Jr., William: CNN
Allard, Marc: Freelance
Allen, Tom: Washington Post (Ret.)
Amarai, Kainaz: NPR
Angerer, Drew:
Applewhite, J. Scott: Associated Press
Apt Johnson, Roslyn: CBS News
Lutzky, Juana:
Ashley, Douglas: Suburban News Group & ABC TV
Assaf, Christopher: Baltimore Sun
Aubry, Tim: Reuters
Aubry, Timothy: Greenpeace Magazine
Auth, William: Freelance
Bacheler, Peter: Freelance
Bahler, Barry: Department of Homeland Security
Bahruth, William:
Baker, David: ITN
Barrick, Matthew: Caring Magazine
Batten, Rodney: NBC News
Baysden III, Earl: WTTG–TV
Beiser, H. Darr: USA Today
Benic, Patrick: UPI
Bennett, Ronald T.: Executive Branch (Ret.)
Bennett, Brian: Freelance
Berglie, James: Zuma Press
Berkman, Eliezer: Freelance
Biddle, Susan: Washington Post
Biddle, Jr., Michael: C–SPAN
Bindelglass, Perry: Freelance
Bing, Bonita: Freelance
Binks, Porter: Sports Illustrated
Bivera, Johnny: Freelance
Blaylock, Kenneth:
Bodnar, John: CNN
Boitano, Stephen: Freelance
Bourg, James: Reuters
Bowe, Christy: ImageCatcher News
Bowler, Dana Rene: Freelance
Brack, Dennis: Black Star
Brandon, Alex: Associated Press
Brantley, James: Freelance
Bridgham, Kenneth:
Brown, Randall: NBC News

MEMBERS REPRESENTED—Continued

Brown, Stephen: Freelance
Brown, Sr., Henry: ABC
Bruce, Andrea: Freelance NOOR Images
Bryan, Beverly:
Buell, Hal: AP (Ret.)
Burgess, Robert: Freelance
Burke, Jr., William C.: Page One Photography
Burnett, David: Contact Press Images
Cairns, Taylor: Student
Calvert, Mary: Washington Times
Cameron, Gary: Reuters News Pictures
Cannarozzi, Melissa: Newhouse News Service
Carioti, Ricky: Washington Post
Carlson, David: Canon
Castoro, Susan: Associated Press
Cedeno, Ken: Freelance
Ceneta, Manuel: Associated Press
Chavar, Anthony: The Washington Post
Chikwendiu, Jahi: Washington Post
Christian, George: CBS News
Chung, Andre:
Cirace, Robert: CNN (Ret.)
Cirone, Jopseph: Responsive Media
Clark, Bill: Roll Call
Clarkson, Rich: Rich Clarkson & Associates
Cohen, Marshall: Big Marsh News Photos
Cohen, Stuart: Freelance
Colburn, James: Freelance
Collins, Maxine: BBC TV
Conger, Dean:
Connor, Kristopher: Freelance
Contreras, Oliver: Washington Hispanic
Cook, Dennis: Associated Press (Ret.)
Costello II, Thomas: Asbury Park Press
Couig, Caroline: Independent Photo Editor / Web Producer
Crane, Arnold: The LaVor Group
Curran, Patrick: WTTG–TV
Curtiss, Cathaleen: AOL
D'Agostino, Matthew:
D'Angelo, Rebecca: Freelance
Daniell, Parker: Freelance
Daugherty, Bob: Associated Press (Ret.)
Davidson, Linda: Washington Post
Davis, Amy: Baltimore Sun
de la Cruz, Benedict: Washingtonpost.com
Delaney, Danita: The Washington Afro
Desfor, Max:
Devorah, Carrie: Freelance
Dharapak, Charles: Associated Press
DiBartolo, Melissa: Nikon
Dietsch, Kevin: UPI
Doane, Martin: WJLA–TV
Dorwin, Harold: Smithsonian Institution
Dougherty, Martin: CNN
Douliery, Oliver: Abaca Press
Downing, Larry: Reuters
Drapkin, Arnold: TIME Magazine
Dryden, Valerie: Freelance for Bloomberg News, NYT
duCille, Michel: Washington Post
Dukehart, Coburn: NPR Digital News
Dukehart, Jr., Thomas: WUSA–TV (Ret.)
Dunmire, John: WTTG–TV (Ret.)
Eaves, Ed: NBC News
Eddins, Joseph: Washington Times
Edmonds, Ron: Associated Press
Edrington, Michael: DMIOC
Elswick, Jonathan: Associated Press
Epstein, Linda: McClatchy Tribune
Ernst, Jonathan: Freelance
Eroglu, Levent: Australian Broadcasting Corp.
Ewing, David: Freelance / DE Media
Falk, Steven: Philadelphia Daily News
Farmer, Sharon: Freelance
Feld, Ric: Associated Press
Feldman, Randy: Viewpoint Communications, Inc.
Fielman, Sheldon: NBC News
Fine, Paul: Fine Films
Fine, Holly: Fine Films
Fitz-Patrick, Bill: Freelance
Folwell, Frank: Freelance
Fookes, Gary: Freelance (Ret.)
Ford, Nancy: IFPO / American International News
Forrest, James: WRC (Ret.)
Forte, B.J.: WTTG–TV
Foss, Philip: Speed Graphic
Foster, H. William: Freelance
Foy, Mary Lou: Washington Post (Ret.)
Frame, John: WTTG–TV
Freeman, Roland: Freelance (Ret.)
Frey, Katherine: Washington Post
Fridrich, George: Brighter Images Productions, LLC
Friedman, David: Freelance / Fox News
Fuchs, Christian: Jesuit Refugee Service / USA
Fulton, Bradley: CTV
Gaffney, Dennis: NBC News Washington
Gail, C. Mark: Washington Post
Gainer, Dennis: USA Today
Garcia, Mannie: Freelance
Garcia, Alexandra: WPNI
Geiger, Ken: National Geographic
Geissinger, Michael: Freelance
Gentilo, Richard: Associated Press
Geraci, Andrew: The Washington Times
Gilgannon, Pege: WJLA
Gilkey, David: NPR
Gmiter, Bernard: ABC News (Ret.) Freelance
Golden, Melissa: Freelance
Golon, MaryAnne: Time
Goodman, Jeffrey: NBC / Freelance
Gorman, James: Associated Press
Goulait, Bert: Freelance (Ret.)
Gould-Phillips, Carol: Current Viewpoint
Goyal, Raghubir: Asia Today & India Globe / ATN News

MEMBERS REPRESENTED—Continued

Graham, Douglas: CQ Roll Call
Demczuk, Gabriella:
Grant, Kelli: Pixways, Inc.
Greenblatt, William: UPI
Gripas, Yuri: Reuters
Gross, Jr., Eddie: CNN
Guerrucci, Aude: Ploaris
Gundy, Dorry: BBC News
Guzy, Carol: Washington Post
Hale Thomas, Susan: Freelance
Halstead, Dirck: The Digital Journalist
Hamburg, Harry: (Ret.)
Hanley, Patricia: WNET
Harmatz, Ben: Student
Harnik, Andrew: Washington Times
Harrer, Andrew: Bloomberg
Harrington, John: Freelance
Harrity, Chick: Whimsy Works
Heikes, Darryl: Freelance
Heilemann, Tami: Department of Interior
Heisenfelt, Ann: Freelance
Hill, Robert: Australian Broadcasting Corp.
Hill, Robb: Freelance
Hillian, Vanessa: Washington Post (Ret.)
Hinds, Hugh: WRC / NBC
Hoffman, Brendan: Freelance
Hoiland, Harald:
Holt, Victor: Washington Informer
Hopkins, Brian: WJLA–TV
Horan, Michael: WTTG–TV
Horn, Brad: The Washington Post
Hoyt, Michael: Catholic Standard
Hubbard, Garrett: USA Today
Huff, Daniel: Associated Press
Imai, Kesaharu: World Photo Press
Ing, Lance: WTTG–TV
Ingalls, Bill: NASA e Management
Irby, Kenneth: Poynter Institute
Isaacson-Pfueller, Jenna: Freelance
Jaeger, Kevin: WJLA–TV
Janney, Oliver: CNN America
Jenkins, David: CNN
Jennings, Graeme: Washington Examiner
Johnson, Kenneth: ABC–TV
Johnston, Frank: Washington Post
Jones, Donnamarie: DCTV
Jones, Nelson: WTTG–TV
Joseph, Marvin: Washington Post
Kahn, Nikki: Washington Post
Kang, Hyungwon: Reuters News Pictures
Kapustin, Doug: Baltimore Sun
Kaster, Carolyn: Associated Press
Kattar, Pierre:
Katz, Marty: Chesapeake News Service
Kawajiri, Chiaki: Baltimore Sun
Kelly, Colin: Army Times
Kennerly, David: Eagles Roar, Inc.
Kent, Jeffrey: Press Photographers' Gallery
Kirkpatrick, T.J.: Freelance
Kittner, Sam: Freelance
Kleber, David:
Koppelman, Mitch: Reuters Television
Kossoff-Nordby, Leslie: LK Photos
Kozak, Rick: Military Times
Kraft, Brooks: Time Magazine
Lamarque, Kevin: Reuters
Lambert, H.M.:
Lamkey, Jr., Rod:
Landy, John: BBC
Larsen, Gregory: Freelance
Lavies, Bianca: Freelance
LaVor, Marty: Freelance
Lawrence, Jeffrey:
Lee, Donald: CBS News
Levine, Lewis: Coastal News Service
Levy, Glenn Ann: Freelance
Levy, John:
Lizik, Ronald: Associated Press
Lockhart, June:
Loeb, Saul: AFP
LoScalzo, James: EPA
Love, Diane: American University in Bulgaria
Lucidon, Amanda: Independent Mulitmedia Journalist
Luna, Nathan: CTV (Canadian)
Lynaugh, Mike: Freelance
Lynch, Patricia: Retna Photo
Lynch, Elizabeth: National Journal
Lyons, Paul: NET (Ret.)
MacDonald, Charles: National Geographic Channel
MacDonald, Jim: Canadian TV Network
Maddaloni, Christopher: Roll Call
Madrid, Michael: USA Today
Magana, Jose Luis: Freelance / AP
Mager, Dickon: Sky News
Maggiolo, Vito: CNN
Makely, John: NBC News
Mallin, Jay: Freelance
Mann, Donna:
Mara, Melina: Washington Post
Marovich, Jr., Peter: Zuma Press
Martin, Gina: National Geographic
Martin, Jacquelin: AP
Martineau, Gerald: Washington Post
Martinez Monsivais, Pablo: Associated Press
Mason, Thomas: WTTG–TV
Mathieson, Greg: MAI Photo News Agency, Inc.
Mazariegos, Mark: CBS News
Maze, Stephanie: Maze Productions, Inc. / Moonstone Press, LLC
Mazer Field, Joni: Freelance
Mazzatenta, O.: Freelance
McCarthy III, Edward: Hudson Valley Black Press / Hudson Valley Press
McCarty, Dennis Page: CBS News

MEMBERS REPRESENTED—Continued

McClain, Matthew: Washington Post
McDermott, Richard: NBC Universal
McDonnell, John: Washington Post
McGinnis, Lowell: Roll Call / Contract
McGreevy, Allen: Freelance
McKenna, William: BBC World News America
McKiernan, Scott: Zuma Press
McNamee, Win: Getty Images
McNamee, Wallace: Freelance
McNay, James: Senior Editor Kobre Guide
McNeeley, Chad:
Miller, Elisa: Freelance
Mills, Doug: New York Times
Mock-Bunting, Logan: Freelance
Mole, Robert: NBC (Ret.)
Moorhead, Jeremy: CNN
Morris, Larry: Washington Post (Ret.)
Morris, Peter: CNN
Moulton, Paul: 24 years U.S. Army (Ret.), 19 TV News
Mount, Bonnie Jo: Washington Post
Mummert, John: USGA
Murphy, John: Freelance
Murtaugh, Peter: Murtaugh Productions, LLC
Natoli, Sharon: Freelance
Newton, Jonathan: Washington Post
Nguyen, Phi: U.S. House of Representatives
Nighswander, Marcia: Ohio University
Nikpour, Javad: Metropole Photo
Nishimura, Kent: Student
Nolan, David: Nolan & Company
Norling, Richard: Freelance
O'Leary, William: Washington Post
O'Neill, Claire: NPR
Ortez, George: (Ret.) Since 1980
Osterreicher, Mickey: NPPA
Palu, Louie: Zuma Press
Panzer, Chester: NBC–WRC
Parcell, James: Washington Post (Ret.)
Partlow, Wayne: Associated Press
Pekala, Bill: Nikon
Perkins, Lucian: Freelance
Petros, Bill: Freelance
Pinczuk, Samuel:
Pinczuk, Murray: Freelance
Polich, John: (Ret.)
Poole, John: NPR
Popper, Andrew:
Postovit, David: Hearst Television WNB
Potasznik, David: Point of View Production Services, Inc.
Powell, Jr., William: NBC/Retired
Powers, Carol: Freelance
Proser, Michael: ABC–News
Raker, Lester: ABC News
Reed, Jason: Reuters
Rensberger, Scott: Freelance
Reynolds, Michael: European Pressphoto Agency
Ribeiro, Luiz: The New York Post
Richards, Paul: AFP
Richardson, Charlotte: Freelance
Riecken, Astrid: Washington Times
Riley, Molly: Freelance
Roberts, Joshua: Freelance
Robinson, Sr., Clyde:
Ronay, Vivian: Freelance
Rose, Jamie: Momenta Group, LLC
Rossman, Megan: WPNI
Roth, Jr., Johnie: NBC (Ret.)
Russek II, Ronald: UPI
Sachs, Ronald: Consolidated News Photos
Salisbury, Barbara:
Samad, Jewel: AFP
Sandys, Toni: Washington Post
Sardari, Kaveh: Sardari Group, Inc.
Satter, Andrew: Roll Call
Saunders, Ray: Washington Post
Schauble, Justin: Persistent Video Productions
Schlegel, Barry: Team Video Services, Inc. / CNN
Schmick, Paul: Freelance (Ret.)
Schneider, Jack: NBC–TV
Schwartz, Herb: CBS News
Semiatin, Morris: Morris Semiatin-Photographer
Shaffir, Kimberlee: CBS News
Shannon, Dennis: CBS News
Sharrett, Luke: Photographer
Shefte, Whitney: Washingtonpost.com
Shelley, Allison: Freelance
Shepherd, Ray:
Sheppard, Kevin: Sky News
Sheras, Michael: Canon USA, Inc.
Shinkle, John: Politico
Shirmohammadi, Abbas: Panoramic Visions
Shlemon, Christopher: Independent TV News
Sierra, Joann: CNN
Sikes, Laura: Freelance
Silverberg, James: The Intellectual Property Group, PLLC
Sisco, Paul: (Ret.)
Skeans, Jr., Ronald: BBC
Smialowski, Brendan: AFP
Smith, Andrew: CCTV
Smith, Patrick: Freelance
Smith, Jason: WTTG–TV
Sommer, Emilie: Freelance
Somodevilla, Kenneth: Getty Images
Stein, Norman: TASC, Inc.
Stein III, Arthur: Freelance
Stephenson, Al: Freelance
Stoddard, Mark: Freelance
Suban, Mark: Nikon
Suddeth, Rick: Freelance
Swain, Bethany Anne:
Sweetapple, Daniel: Australian Broadcasting Corp.
Swenson, Gordon: ABC (Ret.)
Swiatkowski, Edward:

MEMBERS REPRESENTED—Continued

Sykes, Jack: Professional Pilot Magazine
Tessmer, Joseph: Freelance
Thalman, Mark: Across the Pond Productions
Thew, Shawn: European Pressphoto Agency
Thomas, Margaret:
Thomas, Ronald: Freelance Photographer / AV Specialist
Tiffen, Steve: The Tiffen Company
Tolbert IV, George Dalton: Freelance / U.S. Senate (Ret.)
Trippett, Robert: Freelance
Tripplaar, Kristoffer: Freelance
Tsuboi, Kazuo: World Photo Press
Uhl, Kim: CNN
Umrani, Anthony: CNN
Usher, Chris: Freelance
Valeri, Charlene: National Geographic
Varias, Stelios: Reuters
Vicario, Virginia: ABC News
Vineys, Kevin: Associated Press
Vogel, Leigh: Freelance
Voisin, Sarah: Washington Post
Voss, Stephen: Freelance
Vucci, Evan: Associated Press
Walker, Diana: Freelance
Wallace, Jim: Smithsonian Institution
Walsh, Susan: Associated Press
Walz, Mark: CNN
Ward, Fred: Black Star
Watkins, Frederick:
Watrud, Donald: WTTG–TV
Watson, James: AFP
Weik, David: ABC Television News (Ret.)
Wenzelberg, Charles: New York Post
Wescott, William: Politico
Wiegman, Jr., Dave: NBC (Ret.)
Wilkes, Douglas: WTTG–TV
Williams, Milton: Freelance (Ret.)
Williams, Robert: NBC News
Williams, Thomas: Roll Call Newspaper
Williamson, Michael: Washington Post
Wilson, Mark: Getty Images
Wilson, Jim: New York Times Photo
Witte, Joel: CCTV
Wolf, Kevin: Freelance
Wollenberg, Roger:
Wong, Alex: Getty Images
Woodward, Tracy:
Wu, Enoch: Freelance
Yaklyvich, Brian: CNN
Yarmuth, Floyd: CNN
Zervos, Stratis: Freelance-Zervos Video Productions, LLC

RADIO AND TELEVISION CORRESPONDENTS' GALLERIES*

SENATE RADIO AND TELEVISION GALLERY

The Capitol, Room S–325, 224–6421

Director.—Michael J. Mastrian
Deputy Director.—Ellen Eckert
Senior Media Coordinators: Michael Lawrence, Erin Yeatman
Media Coordinator.—Chris Bois

HOUSE RADIO AND TELEVISION GALLERY

The Capitol, Room H–320, 225–5214

Director.—Olga Ramirez Kornacki
Deputy Director.—Andy Elias
Senior Media Logistics Coordinator.—Kim Oates
Media Logistics Coordinators: Anthony Kellaher, Kinsey Harvey, Ryan Dahl
Media Logistics Assistant.—Leah Kaplan

EXECUTIVE COMMITTEE OF THE RADIO AND TELEVISION CORRESPONDENTS' GALLERIES

Frank Thorp, NBC, *Chair*
Fred Haberstick, C–SPAN, *Vice Chair*
Gerald Bodlander, AP Radio & TV, *Treasurer*
Alicia Budich, CBS
Lisa Desjardins, CNN
John Parkinson, ABC
Jason Scanlon, FOX

RULES GOVERNING RADIO AND TELEVISION CORRESPONDENTS' GALLERIES

1. Persons desiring admission to the Radio and Television Galleries of Congress shall make application to the Speaker, as required by Rule 34 of the House of Representatives, as amended, and to the Committee on Rules and Administration of the Senate, as required by Rule 33, as amended, for the regulation of the Senate wing of the Capitol. Applicants shall state in writing the names of all radio stations, television stations, systems, or news-gathering organizations by which they are employed and what other occupation or employment they may have, if any. Applicants shall further declare that they are not engaged in the prosecution of claims or the promotion of legislation pending before Congress, the Departments, or the independent agencies, and that they will not become so employed without resigning from the Galleries. They shall further declare that they are not employed in any legislative or executive department or independent agency of the Government, or by any foreign govern-

*Information is based on data furnished and edited by each respective Gallery.

ment or representative thereof; that they are not engaged in any lobbying activities; that they do not and will not, directly or indirectly, furnish special information to any organization, individual, or group of individuals for the influencing of prices on any commodity or stock exchange; that they will not do so during the time they retain membership in the Galleries. Holders of visitors' cards who may be allowed temporary admission to the Galleries must conform to all the restrictions of this paragraph.

2. It shall be a prerequisite to membership that the radio station, television station, system, or news-gathering agency which the applicant represents shall certify in writing to the Radio and Television Correspondents' Galleries that the applicant conforms to the foregoing regulations.

3. The applications required by the above rule shall be authenticated in a manner that shall be satisfactory to the Executive Committee of the Radio and Television Correspondents' Galleries who shall see that the occupation of the Galleries is confined to bona fide news gatherers and/or reporters of reputable standing in their business who represent radio stations, television stations, systems, or news-gathering agencies engaged primarily in serving radio stations, television stations, or systems. It shall be the duty of the Executive Committee of the Radio and Television Correspondents' Galleries to report, at its discretion, violation of the privileges of the Galleries to the Speaker or to the Senate Committee on Rules and Administration, and pending action thereon, the offending individual may be suspended.

4. Persons engaged in other occupations, whose chief attention is not given to—or more than one-half of their earned income is not derived from—the gathering or reporting of news for radio stations, television stations, systems, or news-gathering agencies primarily serving radio stations or systems, shall not be entitled to admission to the Radio and Television Galleries. The Radio and Television Correspondents' List in the Congressional Directory shall be a list only of persons whose chief attention is given to or more than one-half of their earned income is derived from the gathering and reporting of news for radio stations, television stations, and systems engaged in the daily dissemination of news, and of representatives of news-gathering agencies engaged in the daily service of news to such radio stations, television stations, or systems.

5. Members of the families of correspondents are not entitled to the privileges of the Galleries.

6. The Radio and Television Galleries shall be under the control of the Executive Committee of the Radio and Television Correspondents' Galleries, subject to the approval and supervision of the Speaker of the House of Representatives and the Senate Committee on Rules and Administration.

Approved.

JOHN A. BOEHNER,
Speaker, House of Representatives.

CHARLES E. SCHUMER,
Chair, Senate Committee on Rules and Administration.

MEMBERS ENTITLED TO ADMISSION

RADIO AND TELEVISION CORRESPONDENTS' GALLERIES

Aaron, John: WTOP Radio
Aaronson, Trevor: Aljazeera International
Abbey, Francis: ABC News
Abbott, Stacey: National Public Radio
Abdallah, Khalil: CNN
Abdalwahab, Yamen: Al Arabiya TV
Abdelouahabi, Mohamed: CNN
Abdulgawad, Atef: AP–Broadcast
Abdulkareem, Akram: American Press and TV Services (APTVS)
Abdullah, Halimah: CNN
Abdullah, Halimah: NBC News
Abe, Takaaki: Nippon TV Network
Abernethy, Bob: Religion & Ethics Newsweekly
Abeshouse, Bob: Aljazeera International
Aboud, Abdushakur: Voice of America
Abramson, Larry: National Public Radio
Abtar, Rana: Middle East Broadcasting Networks (MBN)
Abu Diab, Naser: AP–Broadcast
Abu-Hamdyia, Reema: RTTV America
Abuelhawa, Daoud: Al Arabiya TV
Aburahma, Eyad: Aljazeera Satellite Channel (Peninsula)
Acevedo, Juan: WFDC–TV Univision
Acharya, Niharika: Bloomberg Radio & TV
Ackerman, Tom: Aljazeera International
Ackland, Matthew: WTTG–Fox Television
Acle, Elizabeth: National Public Radio
Acosta, Jim: CNN
Adams, Angelyn: Al Arabiya TV
Adams, Douglas A.: NBC News
Adams, Karen: CBS News
Adams, Lauren: Lilly Broadcasting
Aden, Houssein: Voice of America
Adkinson, Janet: Rural TV News
Adkinson, Jeff: AP–Broadcast
Adlerblum, Robin: CBS News
Agnew, Jonathan: Medill News Service
Agnew, Singeli: Aljazeera International
Ahlers, Mike: CNN
Ahlquist, Greg: Fox News
Ahmadyar, Najibullah: Voice of America
Ahmed, Ali: Middle East Broadcasting Networks (MBN)
Ahmed, Ibrahim: Voice of America
Ahmed, M.: Voice of America
Ahuja Kaul, Gitika: ABC News
Aich, Atirath: China Central TV Bureau
Aidoo, Jennifer: BBC
Aiello, Jr., Augustine "Bud": National Public Radio
Aigner-Treworgy, Adam: CNN
Akey, Zachary: CBS News
Akhavi, Khodayar: Aljazeera International
Akkad, Reem: Aljazeera International
Al Allak, Firas: Sky News Arabia
Al Juboori, Haitham: Aljazeera Satellite Channel (Peninsula)
Al Khirsan, Fatima: TIMA
Al-Kwaik, Biesan: Aljazeera Satellite Channel (Peninsula)
Alami, Mohammed: Aljazeera Satellite Channel (Peninsula)
Alamiri, Yasmeen: WJLA–TV / Newschannel 8
Alan, Harvey: NBC News
Alarcon, Nefi: CNN
Alarian, Laila: Aljazeera International
Albano, Thomas: CBS News
Albert, Christopher: CBS News
Alberter, William: CNN
Alcazar, Carlos: Hispanic Communications Network
Alcazar, Obdulia: Hispanic Communications Network
Aldag, Jason: Washingtonpost.com
Alderman, Ashley: Fox News
Alderman, Debbie: EWTN
Alegret, Gustau: RAC1
Alexander, Clinton N.: CBS News
Alexander, Kenneth: C–Span
Alexander, Marc: Aljazeera International
Alexander, Peter: NBC News
Alexander, Robert: WJLA–TV / Newschannel 8
Alfa, Nadine: Reuters Radio & TV
Alfarone, Debra: WUSA–TV
Alford, Kelly: Middle East Broadcasting Networks (MBN)
Alfred, Zachary: Aljazeera International
Ali, Raad: ABS Network
Aliaga, Julio: China Central TV Bureau
Aliakbar, Nihad: AP–Broadcast
Alikozai, Hasib: Voice of America
Alinejad, Sina: BBC
Allahyari, Gholamreza: Voice of America
Allard, John: ABC News
Allbritton, Robert: WJLA–TV / Newschannel 8
Alldredge, Thomas: C–Span
Allen, Brian: Voice of America
Allen, Darrell: Voice of America
Allen, Keith: Reuters Radio & TV
Allen, Kevin: CBS News
Allison, Lynn Quarles: WETA
Allman, Bryan: WJLA–TV / Newschannel 8

MEMBERS ENTITLED TO ADMISSION—Continued

Alnwick, Melanie: WTTG–Fox Television
Alonso, Paola: WZDC–TV
Alqadiree, Faisal: ABC News
Alrawi, Khaldoun: TIMI
Altman, Joshua: The Hill
Alvey, Jay: WRC–TV / NBC–4
Amenta, Katherine: WJLA–TV / Newschannel 8
Amin, Sameen: Aljazeera International
Amirault-Michel, Theresa: C–Span
Ammerman, Stuart: CBS News
Anastasi, Patrick: CNBC
Andersen, Angela: German TV ARD
Anderson, Charles: WETA
Anderson, Patrick: Swiss Broadcasting
Anderson, Shavon: ABC News
Anderson, Wynne: NBC News
Andree, Eric: AP–Broadcast
Andrews, Wyatt: CBS News
Aneiva, Roberto: NBC News
Angelini, Mark: RTTV America
Angle, James L.: Fox News
Ankarlo, Kris: CBS News
Anthony, Tony: Morningside Partners, LLC
Anyse, Alana: CBS News
Aoyama, Kazuhiro: Nippon TV Network
Applegate, Van: WJLA–TV / Newschannel 8
Arabasadi, Arash: Voice of America
Aragon, Kathy: CNN
Archer, Nelson: CNN
Archuleta, Eddie: CBS News
Arena, Bruno: AP–Broadcast
Arenander, Inger: Swedish Broadcasting
Arenas, Andrea: Feature Story News
Arensberg, Chloe: CBS News
Arenstein, Howard: CBS News
Arero, Sora: Voice of America
Armfield, Robert: Fox News
Armstrong, Patricia: NBC News
Armstrong, Thomas: ABC News
Armwood, Adrian: CBS News
Arnesen, Ingrid: Aljazeera International
Aros, Donald: CBS News
Art, Jeremy: C–Span
Artesona, Eva: TV3–Televisio De Catalunya
Aryankalavil, Babu: Middle East Broadcasting Networks (MBN)
Asberg, Stefan: Swedish Broadcasting
Asher, Julie: TF1–French TV
Asi, Marjan: American Press and TV Services (APTVS)
Assmann, Karin: Spiegel German TV
Atif, Muhammad: Voice of America
Atkinson, Emily: CNN
Attallah, Amjad: Aljazeera International
Attkisson, Sharyl: CBS News
Atwood, Kylie: CBS News
Auerbach, Jonathan: CNN
Augenstein, Neal: WTOP Radio
Augustus, Shannon: C–Span
Auster, Bruce: National Public Radio
Austin, Gail: Hearst Television, Inc.
Austin, Jonathan: CTV Canadian TV
Austin, Kenneth: NBC News
Avila, James: ABC News
Avila, Martha: RCN–TV (Colombia)
Avrutine, Matthew: CNN
Awada, Mohamad: Sky News Arabia
Ayala, Jorge: Notimex
Azais, Jean-Pascal: Swiss Broadcasting
Azzam, Heni: Aljazeera Satellite Channel (Peninsula)
Azzizadey, Arash: Voice of America
Babb, Carla: Voice of America
Babich, Jennifer: Time Warner Cable
Bacon, Jr., Perry: NBC News
Baghi, Baubak: Aljazeera Satellite Channel (Peninsula)
Bagley, Guy: China Central TV Bureau
Bagnall, Thomas: Voice of America
Bagnato, Barry: CBS News
Bai, Fan: China Central TV Bureau
Baier, Bret: Fox News
Baik, Sungwon: Voice of America
Bailey, John: NBC News
Bailor, Michelle: C–Span
Baker, Dai: Independent Television News (ITN)
Baker, Les: Fox News
Baker, Nancy: CNN
Baker, Ray: WHUR
Baker, Sarah: CNN
Baldwin, Travis Renee: ABC News
Balinovic, Daniel: Reuters Radio & TV
Balkhy, Ibrahim: Aol Huffington Post
Ballou, Jeff: Aljazeera International
Banaszak, Brendan: National Public Radio
Banhawy, Fahd: American Press and TV Services (APTVS)
Banks, Erik: CNN
Banks, James: Eurovision Americas, Inc.
Banks, Josh: Fox News
Banks, Mark: ABC News
Banks, Morris: CBS News
Bannigan, Mike: Fox Business Network
Bannister, Craig: CNSnews.com
Baragona, Steve: Voice of America
Barajas, Joshua: The Newshour with Jim Lehrer
Barber, Paul: Agence France Presse (AFP–TV)
Barbour, Charles: Eye–To–Eye Video
Barnard, Bob: WTTG–Fox Television
Barnes, Audrey: WTTG–Fox Television
Barnes, David: CTV–Community TV of PG County
Barnes, Peter: Fox Business Network
Barnett, James: CNN
Barnhart, Marsha: Radio Free Asia
Barnwell, Taurean: NHK–Japan Broadcasting Corporation

MEMBERS ENTITLED TO ADMISSION—Continued

Barr, Bruce: CBS News
Barreda, Eric: NHK–Japan Broadcasting Corporation
Barrett, Calvin: Fox News
Barrett, Natasha: WJLA–TV / Newschannel 8
Barrett, Ted: CNN
Barringer, Reginald: CBS News
Bartee, Fatima: Aljazeera International
Barton, Tomoko: Fuji TV Japan
Basch, Michelle: WTOP Radio
Bash, Dana: CNN
Bash, David: WETA
Basinger, Stuart: Fox News
Baskerville, Kia: CBS News
Bassas, Antoni: TV3–Televisio De Catalunya
Bassiouny, Omar: WTOP Radio
Batten, Rodney: NBC News
Battistella, Marilisa: CBS News
Battle, Courtney: CNN
Baumann, Robert: Diversified Communications, Inc. (DCI)
Baumel, Susan: Voyage Productions
Bautista, Mark: CBN News
Bayrak, Emel: Turkish Radio and Television (TRT)
Bays, James: Aljazeera International
Beahn, James: WTTG–Fox Television
Beall, Gary: NBC News
Bearne, Adam: Eurovision Americas, Inc.
Beban, Paul: Aljazeera International
Becker, Bruce: Fox Business Network
Becker, Chris: Fox News
Becker, Eddie: Free Speech TV (FSTV)
Becker, Farrel: CBS News
Becker, Frank: WJLA–TV / Newschannel 8
Bediako, Regina: NHK–Japan Broadcasting Corporation
Behringer, Charles: Aljazeera Satellite Channel (Peninsula)
Bejarano, Mark: National Public Radio
Belizaire, Jacquelin: Voice of America
Bell, Brad: WJLA–TV / Newschannel 8
Bella, Timothy: Aljazeera International
Bellantoni, Christina: The Newshour with Jim Lehrer
Bellinger, Larry: NBC News
Bellis, Michael: ABC News
Bena, John: CNN
Bender, Jason: C–Span
Benetato, Michael: NBC News
Benincasa, Robert: National Public Radio
Benitez, Barbara: Aljazeera International
Benjamin, Brian: ABC News
Bennett, Geoffrey: Time Warner Cable
Bennett, Justin: NBC News
Bennett, Mark R.: CBS News
Bennewitz, Alexa: CNN
Bensen, Jackie: WRC–TV / NBC–4
Benson, Miles: Link TV
Benson, Pamela S.: CNN
Bentouila, Elkheir: Middle East Broadcasting Networks (MBN)
Bentz, Leslie: CNN
Bentz, Thomas: CNN
Berenstein, Erica: The New York Times on the Web
Berger, Judson: Fox News
Bergmann, Christina: Deutsche Welle TV
Berko, Art: Viewpoint Communications
Berman, David: CNN
Bernal, Richard: CNN
Bernardini, Laura: CNN
Bernstein, Joshua: Aljazeera International
Berry, Andrea: WRC–TV / NBC–4
Berry, Carolyn: CNN
Berryman, Jonathan: CNN
Berryman, Kimberly: CNN
Berti, Barbara: Al Jazeera America
Betsill, Brett: C–Span
Bevington, Ben: BBC
Bey, Jamila: Voice of Russia
Beyer, Kevin: Diversified Communications, Inc. (DCI)
Beyer, William: WTTG–Fox Television
Bezdrob, Shayla: Fox News
Bharania, Anoopam: Reuters Radio & TV
Bhatia, Varuna: Fox News
Biasizzo, Gabriele: Storyhouse Productions
Biat, Clemant: TF1–French TV
Biddle, Michael: C–Span
Bidwell, Wendy: Talk Radio News Service
Bilal, Sadiq: AP–Broadcast
Biliovschi Smith, Mihaela: Antena 3 TV
Bilkre, Jared: RTTV America
Billing, Christen: Radio Free Asia
Binswanger, Joshua: Morningside Partners, LLC
Bintrim, Tim: Voice of America
Bishara, Marwan: Aljazeera International
Bisson, Jean-Francois: Canadian Broadcasting Corporation (CBC)
Bivens, Laquasha: CNN
Black, Phillip M.: ABC News
Black, Sam: Aljazeera International
Blackburn, Regina: NBC News
Blackman, Jay: NBC News
Blackman, John: NBC News
Blackwill, Sarah: NBC News
Blair, Adam: Independent Television News (ITN)
Blake, Andrew: RTTV America
Blake, Paul: BBC
Blakely, Kevin: CNN
Blakley, Jonathan: National Public Radio
Blanchard, Lauren: Fox News
Blanco, Hugo: AP–Broadcast
Blanco, Iscar: Voice of America
Blitzer, Wolf: CNN
Block, Melissa: CNN

MEMBERS ENTITLED TO ADMISSION—Continued

Block, Melissa: National Public Radio
Blooston, Victoria: NBC News
Blount, Jeffrey: NBC News
Blue, James: BET Nightly News
Blyden, Rudolph: WTTG–Fox Television
Boag, Keith: Canadian Broadcasting Corporation (CBC)
Bodlander, Gerald: AP–Broadcast
Bodnar, John: CNN
Boerma, Lindsay: CBS News
Boghos, Rafi: MBC—Dubai
Bohannon, Garrett: Eurovision Americas, Inc.
Bohannon, Joseph: NBC News
Bohn, Kevin: CNN
Bois, Chris: Radio TV Gallery
Boland, Barbara: CNSnews.com
Bolden, Warren: CNN
Bolduan, Katherine: CNN
Bolter, Brian: WTTG–Fox Television
Bond, Larry: Voice of America
Bonds, Howard: Aljazeera International
Bondy, Kim: Aljazeera International
Bonewald, Jason: Fox News Radio
Bonner, Susan: Canadian Broadcasting Corporation (CBC)
Booker, Brakkton: National Public Radio
Boone, Dannie: C–Span
Bordbar, Robert: Voice of America
Borger, Gloria: CNN
Boring, Perianne: RTTV America
Borniger, Herta: German TV ARD
Boser, Kirsten: NBC News
Bosland, Katie: ABC News
Bost, Mark: WUSA–TV
Boston, Tyrone: CNN
Boswell, Craig: Fox News
Botti, David: BBC
Boughton, Bryan: Fox News
Bourar, Hicham: Middle East Broadcasting Networks (MBN)
Bowen, Timothy: WETA
Bowman, Jennifer: WJLA–TV / Newschannel 8
Bowman, Michael: Voice of America
Bowman, Tom: National Public Radio
Boyd, Wayne F.: ABC News
Brablec, Radek: National Public Radio
Braddel, Andrew: AP–Broadcast
Bradley, Emily: CBS News
Bradley, Tahman: ABC News
Bragale, Charles: WRC–TV / NBC–4
Bramson, Robert E.: ABC News
Branche, Glennwood: ABC News
Brannon, Timothy: Voice of America
Bransford, Fletcher: Fox News
Brasch, Darci: WTOP Radio
Bratton, Regina: Fox News
Braun, Joshua: CNN
Brawner, Donald: WETA
Brawner, Greta: C–Span
Bray, James: BBC
Brazhnikov, Alexey: RTTV America
Bream, Shannon: Fox News
Breese, Shiny: Radio Free Asia
Breiterman, Charles: ABC News
Breitner, Stephan: France 2 Television
Brennan, Allison: CNN
Brennan, Margaret: CBS News
Brevner, Michael: CNN
Brewster, Shaquuille: Hearst Television, Inc.
Brieger, Annette: German TV ZDF
Bright, Whitney: CBS News
Brinkerhoff, Sarah: Fox News
Britch, Ray: CNN
Britt, Lanna: Fox News
Brittain, Becky: CNN
Brockell, Gillian: Federal News Radio 1500 AM
Brockell, Gillian: Washingtonpost.com
Brody, David: CBN News
Broffman, Craig A.: CNN
Broleman, Michael: NBC Newschannel
Bronstein, Scott: CNN
Brooks, Kurt: WUSA–TV
Brooks, Sam: ABC News
Broom, William: WUSA–TV
Brower, Brooke: NBC News
Brown, April: The Newshour with Jim Lehrer
Brown, Ashley: WRC–TV / NBC–4
Brown, Beth: Hearst Television, Inc.
Brown, Donald: C–Span
Brown, Edgar: Fox News
Brown, Henry M.: ABC News
Brown, Jeffrey: The Newshour with Jim Lehrer
Brown, Jerome: Voice of America
Brown, Kimberly: Voice of Russia
Brown, Kristin: Fox News
Brown, Malcolm: Feature Story News
Brown, Megan: Fox News
Brown, Paul: C–Span
Brown, Randall: NBC News
Brown, Taylor: BBC
Brown, Tracy Ann: AP–Broadcast
Browning, Robert: C–Span
Bruce, Mary: ABC News
Brueggeman, Tia: CNN
Brumbaugh, Kathleen: AP–Broadcast
Brumfiel, Geoff: National Public Radio
Bruns, David: AP–Broadcast
Brusk, Steven: CNN
Bryant, Aubrey: WUSA–TV
Brzezinski, Mika: NBC News
Bua, Jon-Christopher: Sky News
Bubaris, Philomena: Al Jazeera America
Buck, Melanie: CNN
Buckhorn, Burke: CNN
Buckley, Daniel: WRC–TV / NBC–4

MEMBERS ENTITLED TO ADMISSION—Continued

Buckley, Julia Redpath: National Public Radio
Buddenhagen, Kristina: C–Span
Budich, Alicia: CBS News
Buehler, Paul: WTTG–Fox Television
Buel, Meredith: Voice of America
Buellmann, Rolf: German Public Radio (ARD)
Buesinger, Jennifer: CNN
Bullard Harmon, Susan: CBS News
Bullard, John: ABC News
Bullard, Larry: WRC–TV / NBC–4
Bullock, Peter: Reuters Radio & TV
Bundock, Susan J.: C–Span
Bunyan, Maureen: WJLA–TV / Newschannel 8
Burch, Jennifer: CNN
Burdick, Leslie: C–Span
Burgarella, Hunter: CNN
Burgdorf, Louis: NBC News
Burgot, Maryse: France 2 Television
Burke, James: C–Span
Burke, Michael: Voice of America
Burkhard, Betsy: Fox News
Burlij, Terence: The Newshour with Jim Lehrer
Burnett, Gordon: Radio Free Asia
Burns, Alison: Cox Broadcasting
Burton, Matthew: ABC News
Buse, Askan: German TV ZDF
Buse, Gabriele: German TV ZDF
Bustamante, Antonio: TIMI
Butcher, Robert E.: National Public Radio
Butler, Erica: NBC News
Butler, Erica: Time Warner Cable
Butler, James: Diversified Communications, Inc. (DCI)
Butler, Joan: Voice of America
Butler, Norman: NBC News
Byrne, Maria: BBC
Byrnes, Dennis: National Public Radio
Cabral, Juan: CNN
Cahill Murphy, Kathy: C–Span
Caicedo-Smit, Cristina: WZDC–TV
Caifa, Karin: CNN
Calas, Olivier: Agence France Presse (AFP–TV)
Calder, William: CBS News
Caldwell, Leigh Ann: CBS News
Caldwell, Traci: CBS News
Calfat, Marcel: Canadian Broadcasting Corporation (CBC)
Callahan, Michael: Bloomberg Radio & TV
Callebs, Sean: China Central TV Bureau
Calo-Christian, Nancy: C–Span
Calvi, Jason: EWTN
Camarda, Tim: Eye–To–Eye Video
Cameron, Carl: Fox News
Campbell, Arch: WJLA–TV / Newschannel 8
Campbell, Christopher: Aljazeera Satellite Channel (Peninsula)
Campbell, Colin: American Press and TV Services (APTVS)
Campbell, Colleen: EWTN
Campbell, Kyla: Cox Broadcasting
Candia, Kirsten: German TV ZDF
Cannon, Catherine: CBS News
Canty, James: CBS News
Cao, Yu: Xinhua
Caperton, Katherine: XM Satellite Radio
Caplan, Craig: C–Span
Capomaccio-Even, Anne-Marie: Radio France Internationale
Capra, Anthony: NBC News
Carabello Torres, Karla: RCN–TV (Colombia)
Caravello, David: CBS News
Carbonne, Frederic: Radio France Internationale
Cardoze, Jacques: France 2 Television
Carey, Julie: WRC–TV / NBC–4
Carlson, Brett: Global TV Canada
Carlson, Brett: NBC Newschannel
Carlson, Christopher: ABC News
Carlson, Frank: The Newshour with Jim Lehrer
Carlson, Steve: Fox News
Carlsson, Bjorn: Swedish Broadcasting
Carlsson, Lisa: Swedish Broadcasting
Carney, Keith: FedNet
Carpeaux, Emily: Feature Story News
Carpel, Michael: Fox News
Carr, Evan: WJLA–TV / Newschannel 8
Carr, Martin: WETA
Carrere, Hillary: Kaiser Health News
Carrick, Kenneth: C–Span
Carroll Campbell, Colleen: EWTN
Carter, Brianne: WJLA–TV / Newschannel 8
Carter, Dave: WRC–TV / NBC–4
Carter, Jr., Walter: Fox News
Cartier, Marcel: RTTV America
Casanas, Juan: Fox News
Casey, Elizabeth: Al Jazeera America
Casey, Elizabeth: C–Span
Casey, Libby: C–Span
Casey, Sean: WRC–TV / NBC–4
Cassano, Joseph: WRC–TV / NBC–4
Cassidy, David: Belo Capital Bureau
Castaneda, Diana: RCN–TV (Colombia)
Castiel, Carol: Voice of America
Castro, David: Hispanic Communications Network
Castro, Pablo: Hispanic Communications Network
Cater, Franklyn: National Public Radio
Catherine, Carl: ABC News
Catrett, David Keith: CNN
Causey, Mike: Federal News Radio 1500 AM
Cavaiola, Michael: C–Span
Centanni, Steve: Fox News
Cento, Carmen: Voice of America
Cetta, Denise: CBS News
Chaggaris, Steven: CBS News
Chakraborty, Barnini: Fox News
Chalian, David: CNN
Chalian, David: Politico.com

MEMBERS ENTITLED TO ADMISSION—Continued

Chamberlain, Richard: WJLA–TV / Newschannel 8
Chang, Ailsa: National Public Radio
Chang, Ching-Yi: Hong Kong Phoenix Satellite Television
Chang, Darzen: WETA
Chang, Min: New Tang Dynasty TV
Chang, Peggy: Voice of America
Chang, Wen-Hsiang: Ettv
Chang, Xiao: Voice of America
Changuris, Zeke: WJLA–TV / Newschannel 8
Chapman, Irwin: Bloomberg Radio & TV
Chapman, Karolina: Aljazeera International
Chapman, Michael W.: CNSnews.com
Chappell, Bill: National Public Radio
Chappell, Jill: CNN
Chaput, Isaac: National Public Radio
Charles, Dan: National Public Radio
Charles-Messance, Axel: France 2 Television
Charpa, Silvia: German Broadcasting Systems–ARD
Chase, David: Cox Broadcasting
Chattman, Tanya: C–Span
Chavar, A.J.: The New York Times on the Web
Chaytor, David: Aljazeera International
Chen, Guang: China Central TV Bureau
Chen, Joie: Aljazeera International
Chen, Yi Qiu: Hong Kong Phoenix Satellite Television
Chenevey, Steve: WJLA–TV / Newschannel 8
Cheng, He: China Central TV Bureau
Cherkaoui, Adil: Aljazeera Satellite Channel (Peninsula)
Cherkasov, Andrey: Channel One Russian TV
Cherkuru, Kavitha: Aljazeera International
Chernenkoff, Kelly: Fox News
Cherouny, Robert: Aljazeera International
Chevez, Carlos: National Public Radio
Chiba, Yuko: NHK–Japan Broadcasting Corporation
Chichakyan, Gayane: RTTV America
Chick, Jane S.: CBS News
Childs, Lete: NBC News
Ching, Nike: Voice of America
Chinn Lucie, Surae: WUSA–TV
Chmurak, Elizabeth: CNN
Cho, Eunjung: Voice of America
Cho, Hans: JTBC
Cho, Seungho: Yonhap News TV
Cho, Sungwon: Korean Broadcasting Systems
Chocarro, Silvia: Radio France Internationale
Choi, Kyoosik: Korean Broadcasting Systems
Chomiak, Catherine: NBC News
Christian, George: CBS News
Chumbley, Spencer: Aljazeera International
Chung, E-Ting: CTI–TV (Taiwan)
Chung, Hakyun: Seoul Broadcasting System (SBS)
Chung, Patrick: NBC News
Cilberti, David: Ventana Productions
Cinque, Vicente: TV Globo International
Claar, Matthew: C–Span
Clark, Grant: Aljazeera International
Clark, James: C–Span
Clark, Maggie: Stateline.org
Clark, Stephen: Fox News
Clarke, John: Reuters Radio & TV
Clary, Gregory: CNN
Claudet, Marie: Canadian Broadcasting Corporation (CBC)
Clemann, William: WUSA–TV
Clemons, Bobby: CNN
Cloherty, Jack: ABC News
Cloherty, Megan: WTOP Radio
Clugston, Gregory: SRN News (Salem)
Clune, Sarah: The Newshour with Jim Lehrer
Cockerham, Richard: Fox News
Cockey, William: RTTV America
Cocklin, Anne: ABC News
Cocklin, Stephen: ABC News
Codianni, Ashley: Now This News
Cofske, Harvey: Irish Radio & TV (RTE)
Cohan, Stacey: CNN
Cohen, Josh: C–Span
Cohen, Margot: WJLA–TV / Newschannel 8
Cohen, Thomas: CNN
Cohencious, Rebecca: Native American Television
Coil, Holly: NBC Newschannel
Cole, Bryan: Fox News
Colella, Anthony: WTTG–Fox Television
Coleman, Ashley: WJLA–TV / Newschannel 8
Coleman, Steven: AP–Broadcast
Coleman, Thomas: CBS News
Coles, David: The Newshour with Jim Lehrer
Colimore, Eric: Fox News
Coll, Dennis: National Public Radio
Collender, Howard: Mobile Video Services, LTD
Collins, Bruce D.: C–Span
Collins, Maxine: BBC
Collins, Pat: WRC–TV / NBC–4
Colombo-Abdullah, Flavia: AP–Broadcast
Colton, Michael: Canadian Broadcasting Corporation (CBC)
Comer, Donnie: CNN
Compton, Ann: ABC News
Conan, Neal: National Public Radio
Concaugh, Jr., Joseph: Diversified Communications, Inc. (DCI)
Condon, Stephanie: CBS News
Conetta, Christine: RTTV America
Coney, Carol: CBS News
Conlin, Sheila: NBC Newschannel
Conneen, Mike: WJLA–TV / Newschannel 8
Conner, Eric: Fox News
Connolly, Camille: CBS News
Connors, Ben: Washingtonpost.com
Conroy, Margaret: NBC News
Contreras, Glenda: Telemundo Network
Contreras, Jorge: Univision
Conway, Jon: RTTV America

MEMBERS ENTITLED TO ADMISSION—Continued

Cook, Gina: Fox News
Cook, James L.: C–Span
Cook, Peter: Bloomberg Radio & TV
Cooke, David M.: Diversified Communications, Inc. (DCI)
Coolidge, Richard: ABC News
Cooper, Aaron: CNN
Cooper, Caroline: Aljazeera International
Cooper, John: CBS News
Cooper, Kyle: WTOP Radio
Cooper, Rebecca J.: WJLA–TV / Newschannel 8
Cooper, Jr., Nero: NBC News
Copeland, Natasha: WRC–TV / NBC–4
Corba, Jacqueline: Politico.com
Corcoran, Patricia: WTTG–Fox Television
Cordes, Margaret: WUSA–TV
Cordes, Nancy: CBS News
Corner, Cleve: C–Span
Cornish-Emery, Audie: National Public Radio
Correa, Lina: Voice of America
Correa, Pedro: Telemundo Network
Cortes, William: Telesur
Cortez, William: Telesur
Costa, Tim: CBS News
Costantini, Bob: NBC News
Costello, Amanda: CNN
Costello, Thomas: NBC News
Costen, Chantal: BET Nightly News
Cote, Timothy: ABC News
Coudoux, Sylvain: NHK–Japan Broadcasting Corporation
Coulter, Pam: CBS News
Courson, Paul: CNN
Courtney, Eric: Diversified Communications, Inc. (DCI)
Courtney, Sarah: Fox News
Cousins, Bria: CNBC
Couvillion, Ron: ABC News
Cowan, Jane: Australian Broadcasting Corporation
Cox, Jerry: This Is America with Dennis Wholey
Cox, Oliver: NBC News
Coyte, Benjamin: CNN
Craca, Thomas: CBS News
Craig, Jill: Voice of America
Craig, John: Diversified Communications, Inc. (DCI)
Crane, Steve: Cronkite News Service
Cratty, Carol A.: CNN
Cravedi, Dennis: C–Span
Crawford, Bob: China Central TV Bureau
Crawford, James: CNN
Crawford, Jan: CBS News
Crawford, Woody: Voice of America
Crawley, John: CNN
Crawley, Plummer: CNBC
Cridland, Jeffrey: WUSA–TV
Cross, Christopher: Fox News Radio
Crosswhite-Chigbue, Karla: CNN
Crowley, Candy: CNN
Crowley, Dennis: CNSnews.com
Crowther, Philip: AP–Broadcast
Crum, John: CBS News
Crupi, Nick: Voice of America
Crutchfield, Curtis: CTV–Community TV of PG County
Cruz, Johnny: Wall Street Journal
Cucchiara, Natalie: NBC News
Cuddy, Matthew: CNBC
Cui, Lingnan: China Central TV Bureau
Culhane, Patricia: Aljazeera International
Cullen, Michael: National Public Radio
Cullum, James: Talk Radio News Service
Culver, David: WRC–TV / NBC–4
Culver, G. Doug: WJLA–TV / Newschannel 8
Cunha, John: CNN
Curran, Maurice: WTTG–Fox Television
Curran, Patrick J.: WTTG–Fox Television
Currence, Robert: Voice of America
Currier, Liam: C–Span
Curry, Daryl: WTTG–Fox Television
Curry, Thomas: NBC News
Curtis, Alexander: C–Span
Curtis, Heather: CBS News
Curtis, Jessica: Fox News Radio
Curtis, Jodie: Fox News
Czaplinski, Michael: National Public Radio
Czimmek, Stefan: Deutsche Welle TV
Czzowitz, Greg: C–Span
D'Ambrosi, Frederick: WUSA–TV
d'Annibale, Thomas J.: ABC News
Dabney, Shaneika: CNN
Daguillard, Robert: Voice of America
Dahl, Heather: Feature Story News
Dahl, Ryan: Radio TV Gallery
Dakin, Carla: CBS News
Dalal, Ali: China Central TV Bureau
Dalbah, Mohammad: Aljazeera Satellite Channel (Peninsula)
Dalmasy, Patricia: Voice of America
Dalton, Benjamin: TV Tokyo
Daly, John: CBS News
Damdul, Dorjee: Radio Free Asia
Danahar, Paul: BBC
Dang, Bing: China Central TV Bureau
Daniel, Roger: One America
Danielewicz, Joe: CBS News
Danielewicz, Joe: NBC Newschannel
Daniels, Pete: C–Span
Danilenko, Greg: CNN
Danilko, Derek: AP–Broadcast
Dann, Caroline: NBC News
Dargakis, Minas: Voice of America
Dargham, Alain: Middle East Broadcasting Networks (MBN)
Daschle, Kelly: AP–Broadcast
Date, Shirish: National Public Radio

MEMBERS ENTITLED TO ADMISSION—Continued

Dauchess, Matthew: C–Span
Daugherty, Jeffery: Voice of America
Davenport, Anne: The Newshour with Jim Lehrer
David, Ameera: RTTV America
Davidsen, Dana: CNN
Davie, Bianca: AP–Broadcast
Davieaud, Helene: TF1–French TV
Davies, Elizabeth: BBC
Davis, Clinton: WTTG–Fox Television
Davis, Derek: Aljazeera International
Davis, Jennifer: Fox News
Davis, Mitch: Fox News
Davis, Patrick A.: CNN
Davis, Tanya: C–Span
Davis, Teresa: BBC
Dawi, Akmal: Voice of America
Dawkins, Julian: The Newshour with Jim Lehrer
Dawood, Mohammed: American Press and TV Services (APTVS)
Dawson, Wendy: Fox News
Day, Kara: CNN
de Diego, Javier: CNN
de Franceschi, Jela: Voice of America
de Guise, Louis: Canadian Broadcasting Corporation (CBC)
de Jong, Wessel: Nos Dutch Public Radio & TV (VRT)
de Saint Hippolyte, Stan: AP–Broadcast
de Schaetzen, Emilie: Eurovision Americas, Inc.
Deahl, Jess: National Public Radio
Debre, Guillaume: TF1–French TV
Decker, Jonathan: XM Satellite Radio
DeFoe, Joe: WJLA–TV / Newschannel 8
DeFrank, Debra: Fox News
DeFrank, Joe: Fox News
Dehghanpour, Siamak: Voice of America
Delargy, Christine: Politico.com
DelSignore, Matthew: CBS News
Deluca, Joan: Voice of America
DeMar, Brian: National Public Radio
DeMarco, Lauren: WTTG–Fox Television
DeMark, Michael: Adventure Hill ENG
Demas, William: ABC News
DeMoss, Gary: CBS News
Deng, Agot: Talk Radio News Service
Dennert, Mary Pat: Fox News
DePuyt, Bruce: WJLA–TV / Newschannel 8
Deroche, Sylvie: Swiss Broadcasting
Derrien, Mathieu: TF1–French TV
DeRuy, Emily: Univision
deSaracho, Dinah: Televisa News Network (ECO)
Desbois, Laurent: France 2 Television
Deshishku, Stacia: CNN
Desjardins, Lisa: CNN
Desvarieux, Jessica: Real News Network
Detrow, Jon: AP–Broadcast
DeVito, Andrea: Fox News
Dhue, Stephanie: CNBC
Diakides, Anastasia: CNN
Diaz, Juan: Telemundo Network
Diaz-Briseno, Jose: MundoFox
Dibella, Rick: CNN
DiCarlo, Patricia: CNN
Dickey, Sloan: Wall Street Journal
Diggs, Bridget: C–Span
Dillard, Juanita: ABC News
DiPietro, AnnaMaria: WJLA–TV / Newschannel 8
Disselkamp, Henry: ABC News
Divaris, Oliver: German TV ZDF
Dixon, Greg: National Public Radio
Dixson, Charles H.: CBS News
Doan, Daniela: ABC News
Doane, Martin C.: WJLA–TV / Newschannel 8
Dockins, Pamela: Voice of America
Doell, Michelle: C–Span
Doherty, Brian: Fox News
Doherty, Peter M.: ABC News
Dohr-Grill, Karin: German TV ARD
Dolce, Stephen: CNN
Dolge, Michelle: CBS News
Dolma, Dawa: Radio Free Asia
Dolma, Rigdhen: Radio Free Asia
Domen, John: CBS News
Donahue, Dan: CNN
Donahue, Edward: AP–Broadcast
Donald, Bill: Eye–To–Eye Video
Donald, William: Eye–To–Eye Video
Donaldson, Mark: RCN–TV (Colombia)
Donelan, Jennifer: WJLA–TV / Newschannel 8
Donner, Jason: Fox News
Donovan, Beth: National Public Radio
Donovan, Brian: ABC News
Donovan, Christopher: NBC News
Doocy, Peter: Fox News
Dore, Margaret: CBS News
Doren, Jennifer: WJLA–TV / Newschannel 8
Dorman, Jason: C–Span
Dorn, Jason: AP–Broadcast
Dosani, Sanya: Aljazeera International
Doty, Steve: Washington Examiner
Dougherty, Jill: CNN
Dougherty, Martin: CNN
Dougherty, Paul G.: ABC News
Douglas, Denise: CTV–Community TV of PG County
Dowlatshahi, Tala: Talk Radio News Service
Downes, Richard: Irish Radio & TV (RTE)
Downey, Truval: The Newshour with Jim Lehrer
Doyle Belvedere, Jessica: WUSA–TV
Doyle, Brian: Talk Radio News Service
Doyle, Geoffrey: Fox News
Drag, Nicole: CNN
Dress, Marc: Metro Teleproductions
Drew, Emily: China Central TV Bureau
Druce, Ian: BBC
Du, Yubin: China Central TV Bureau

MEMBERS ENTITLED TO ADMISSION—Continued

Duberstein, David: CNN
Dubrovskiy, Philipp: Russian State TV and Radio (RTR)
Duckham, Justin: Talk Radio News Service
Dufresne, Louise: CBS News
Dugan, William: CTV Canadian TV
Dukakis, Alexandra: ABC News
Dukeman, Paige: Fox News
Dumont Baron, Yanik: Canadian Broadcasting Corporation (CBC)
Dunbar, Dennis: EWTN
Duncan, Victoria: NBC News
Duncombe, Lyndsay: Canadian Broadcasting Corporation (CBC)
Dunkin, John: ABC News
Dunlavey, Dennis: ABC News
Dunlavey, Thomas: CNN
Dunlop, William: Eurovision Americas, Inc.
Dunn, Lauren: WRC–TV / NBC–4
Dunnan, Victoria: CNN
Dunston, Louisa: CBS News
Dupree, Jamie: Cox Broadcasting
Duran, Humberto: RCN–TV (Colombia)
Durand, Lucho: Aljazeera International
Durham, Deborah: Univision
Durham, Timothy: Aljazeera International
Durkin, Edward: WRC–TV / NBC–4
Durnin, Gordon: Aljazeera International
Dwyer, Devin: ABC News
Dyer, Lois: CBS News
Eades, Jr., Paul: C–Span
Eaton, Hugh: National Public Radio
Echevarria, Pedro L.: C–Span
Echols, Jerry: Fox News
Eck, Christina: German Press Agency
Eckert, Barton: WTOP Radio
Eckert, Julie: Now This News
Edmondson, William: Fox News
Edoro, Jesusemen: CTV–Community TV of PG County
Edson, Rich: Fox Business Network
Edwards, Brian: CBN News
Edwards, Bruce: Canadian Broadcasting Corporation (CBC)
Edwards, John: NBC News
Edwards, William: Agence France Presse (AFP–TV)
Eidinger, Karen: WTTG–Fox Television
Eisenbarth, Ronald: C–Span
Eizeldin, Sam: American Press and TV Services (APTVS)
Ejedepang-Koge, Nkwenten: Middle East Broadcasting Networks (MBN)
El-Hamalawy, Mahmoud: Aljazeera Satellite Channel (Peninsula)
Elahmed, Mohamad: Sky News Arabia
Eldridge, James W.: Fox News
Eldridge, Michael: Federal News Service
Elfers, Steve: USA Today
Elgazar, Hosny: AP–Broadcast
Elgin, John: Middle East Broadcasting Networks (MBN)
Elhassani, Camille: Aljazeera International
Elkomy, Dalia: AP–Broadcast
Ellard, Nancy: NBC Newschannel
Ellenwood, Gary: C–Span
Elliot, Kathryn: EWTN
Elliott, Angel: BET Nightly News
Elving, Ronald: National Public Radio
Elvington, Daniel Glenn: ABC News
Emanuel, Mike: Fox News
Emberland, Annie: NBC News
Emery, Edie: CNN
Endara, Betty: Voice of America
Enders, David: Aljazeera International
Engel, Matthew: CBS News
Engel, Seth: C–Span
Ensign, Ernie: WJLA–TV / Newschannel 8
Enzmann, Jacqueline: Fuji TV Japan
Epatko, Larisa: The Newshour with Jim Lehrer
Erbe, Bonnie: To The Contrary (Persephone Productions)
Ernst, Aaron: Aljazeera International
Ernst, Charlotte: TV2–Denmark
Ernst, Manuel: German TV ARD
Esfandiari, Golnaz: Radio Free Europe
Esquivel, Patricia: C–Span
Estes, Diane: The Newshour with Jim Lehrer
Estrada, Rodolfo: AP–Broadcast
Eustis, Robert: ABC News
Evans, Laura: WTTG–Fox Television
Evans, Tyler: Fox News
Fabian, Jordan: Univision
Fabic, Greg: C–Span
Faerber, Fritz: AP–Broadcast
Fagen, Joel: Fox News
Falcone, Michael: ABC News
Falvella-Garraty, Susan: Fox Business Network
Fancher, Diane: Stateline.org
Fant, Barbara: NBC News
Fantacone, John L.: CBS News
Fantis, Manny: WUSA–TV
Farkas, Daniel: Middle East Broadcasting Networks (MBN)
Farkas, Mark: C–Span
Farley, Tim: XM Satellite Radio
Farmer, Christopher: Environment & Energy Publishing, LLC
Farnan, Shane: Talk Radio News Service
Farzam, Parichehr: Voice of America
Farzaneh, Sam: BBC
Fasching, Sophie: Austrian Radio & TV (ORF)
Fattahi, Kambiz: BBC
Fauqueux-Veit, Hannelore: Austrian Radio & TV (ORF)
Feeney, Joseph: C–Span

MEMBERS ENTITLED TO ADMISSION—Continued

Fehr, Stephen: Stateline.org
Feist, Sam: CNN
Felder, Marco: One America
Feldman, Randy: Viewpoint Communications
Fell, Jackie: Cox Broadcasting
Fendley, Gail: Religion & Ethics Newsweekly
Fendrick, Anne-Marie: NHK–Japan Broadcasting Corporation
Fente, Henok: Voice of America
Fenton, Amy: Fox News
Fenton-Smith, Richard: BBC
Ferder, Bruce: Voice of America
Ferguson, Patrick: Canadian Broadcasting Corporation (CBC)
Feria, Liza: Reuters Radio & TV
Ferrigno, Tony: WJLA–TV / Newschannel 8
Ferrise, Patrick: XM Satellite Radio
Fessler, Pam: National Public Radio
Fetzer, Robert: Diversified Communications, Inc. (DCI)
Fiegel, Eric James: CNN
Field, Andy: ABC News
Field, Joan: BBC
Field, Matthew: NHK–Japan Broadcasting Corporation
Fielman, Sheldon: NBC News
Fierro, Juan Martinez: Cope Radio (Spain)
Fifield, Paul: EWTN
Filburn, Sean: RTTV America
Finamore, Charles: ABC News
Finch, Laura: C–Span
Finch, Mark: Fox News
Fingar, Craig: CNN
Finkel, Ben: Viewpoint Communications
Finnegan, Conor: CNN
Finnerty, Robert: Fox News Radio
Finney, Richard: Radio Free Asia
Fioraliso, Ted: Lilly Broadcasting
Fischer, Elizabeth: NBC News
Fischer, Kathryn: RTTV America
Fischer, Sara: CNN
Fischer, Tanya: Eurovision Americas, Inc.
Fishel, Justin: Fox News
Fisher Forehand, Kristin: WUSA–TV
Fisher, Alan: Aljazeera International
Fisher, Siobhan: ABC News
Fitzgerald, Tom: WTTG–Fox Television
Fitzpatrick, Meagan: Canadian Broadcasting Corporation (CBC)
Flaherty, Jordan: Aljazeera International
Flaherty, Lindsay: Mobile Video Services, LTD
Flanagan, Danielle: WUSA–TV
Fleeson, Richard: C–Span
Fleischer, Victoria: The Newshour with Jim Lehrer
Fleutte, Dan: Diversified Communications, Inc. (DCI)
Flood, Randolph: Native American Television
Floquet, Michel: TF1–French TV
Flores, Cesar: BT Video Productions
Flores, Meghan: AP–Broadcast
Flori, Stefano: EWTN
Fodrea, Linda: Fox News
Foellmer, Kristin: German TV ZDF
Fogarty, Kevin: Reuters Radio & TV
Fogarty, Patrick: AP–Broadcast
Foran, Laura: Fox News
Forcier, Vincent: WETA
Ford, Christopher: CNN
Ford, Michael: Diversified Communications, Inc. (DCI)
Ford, Patrick: CNN
Ford, Sam: WJLA–TV / Newschannel 8
Forde, Kaelyn. Aljazeera International
Foreman, Thomas: CNN
Forman, David: NBC News
Forsythe, Jonathan: Washingtonpost.com
Forte, B.J.: WTTG–Fox Television
Forte, Bernard: WRC–TV / NBC–4
Forte, Victor: Diversified Communications, Inc. (DCI)
Forzato, Jamie: WTOP Radio
Foster Mathewson, Lesli: WUSA–TV
Foster, Carl: C–Span
Foster, Rebecca: Feature Story News
Foster, Scott: NBC News
Foster, Shanica: CBS News
Foster, Tom: CBS News
Foty, Thomas: CBS News
Foukara, Abderrahim: Aljazeera Satellite Channel (Peninsula)
Fouladvand, Hida: Aljazeera International
Fournelis, Yianis: WTTG–Fox Television
Fowler, Insley: CNN
Fowler, Maria: USA Today
Fowler, Richard: Talk Radio News Service
Fox, Darren: Voice of America
Fox, David: ABC News
Fox, Maggie: NBC News
Fox, Michael: Aljazeera Satellite Channel (Peninsula)
Fox, Peggy: WUSA–TV
Foxwell, Stacey: National Public Radio
Frado, John: CBS News
Fraley, Jason: WTOP Radio
Frame, John: WTTG–Fox Television
Frandino, Nathan: Voice of Russia
Frankel, Bruce: TF1–French TV
Franks, Tim: BBC
Frasier, Jordan: NBC News
Frates, Chris: CNN
Frazao, Kristin: Sinclair Broadcast Group
Frazier, Dwight: WTTG–Fox Television
Frazier, William: C–Span
Fredrickson, Drew: NBC News
Frei, Matt: Independent Television News (ITN)
French, Alva: NBC News

MEMBERS ENTITLED TO ADMISSION—Continued

French, F. Patrick: ABC News
French, Francis: ABC News
French, Mark: CBS News
Frieden, Terry: CNN
Friedman, Dave: Fox News
Friedman, Matthew: AP–Broadcast
Fritz, Mike: The Newshour with Jim Lehrer
Fritz, Sabrina: German Public Radio (ARD)
Fry, Darren: Voice of America
Fry, Jim: Voice of America
Fu, Peng: China Central TV Bureau
Fuerste, Madelin: Fox News
Fuhr, Michael: WUSA–TV
Fujioka, Chie: Nippon TV Network
Fulton, Bradley: CTV Canadian TV
Furlow, Tony: CBS News
Furman, Hal E.: CBS News
Fuseya, Hiroto: NHK–Japan Broadcasting Corporation
Fuss, Brian: CBS News
Fuss, Robert J.: CBS News
Futrowsky, David: Voice of America
Fyanes, Jo Ann Marie: ABC News
Gabriel, Oscar Wells: AP–Broadcast
Gacka, Monica: Fox News
Gaetano, Lawrence: NBC News
Gaffney, Dennis: NBC News
Gaffney, John: NBC News
Gaines, Anetra: WUSA–TV
Gaines, Mosheh: ABC News
Galdabini, Christian: Fox News
Gallacher, Andy: Aljazeera International
Gallagher, Bill: C–Span
Gallagher, John: C–Span
Gallagher, Tim: Sky News
Gallasch, Hillery: German TV ARD
Galowin, Craig: C–Span
Gama, Ismael: CNN
Gamboa, Suzanne: NBC News
Ganesan, Meena: The Newshour with Jim Lehrer
Gangel, Jamie: NBC News
Gao, Qi: China Central TV Bureau
Gao, Sheryl: China Central TV Bureau
Garay, Gavino: RTTV America
Garber, Scott: CNN
Garcia, Alexandra: Washingtonpost.com
Garcia, Gina: CBS News
Garcia, Guillermo: Reuters Radio & TV
Garcia, Jon D.: ABC News
Gardella, Richard: NBC News
Gardner, Leslie: C–Span
Gargagliano, Richard: Native American Television
Garifo, Stephen: WUSA–TV
Garlock, John: C–Span
Garner, Dave: WTOP Radio
Garner, Jean: Aljazeera International
Garner, Melodie: CNN
Garraty, Susan: CNN
Garraty, Timothy C.: CNN
Garrison, Lynsea: BBC
Garriss, Kristin: NBC News
Gary, Garney: C–Span
Gaskin, Keith: NBC News
Gasparello, Linda: White House Chronicle
Gassot, Philippe: ARTE TV
Gatewood-Gill, Danielle: WUSA–TV
Gaudino, Ralph: NBC News
Gauthier, Arthur R.: ABC News
Gavasheli, Mindia: RTTV America
Gay, Gerard: EWTN
Gebremariam, Solomon: Voice of America
Geewax, Marilyn: National Public Radio
Geffroy, Amelie: TF1–French TV
Geier, Wolfgang: Austrian Radio & TV (ORF)
Gelb, Amos: Medill News Service
Gelevska, Irina: Macedonia Radio Television (MRTV)
Gelius, Jon: Norwegian Broadcasting
Gelles, David: CNN
Gembara, Deborah: Reuters Radio & TV
Genberg, Toni: Link TV
Gentilo, Richard: AP–Broadcast
Gentry, Pamela: BET Nightly News
Gentry, Robert: TV Asahi
George, Pavithra: Reuters Radio & TV
George, Susannah: National Public Radio
Georges, Marc: BBC
Geyelin, Philip: CBS News
Ghandour, Michel: Middle East Broadcasting Networks (MBN)
Ghanem, Pierre: Al Arabiya TV
Ghattas, Kim: BBC
Giaimo, Melissa: CNN
Giammetta, Max: WTTG–Fox Television
Gibeman, Rachel: CNN
Gibson, Jake: Fox News
Gibson, Jenna: CBS News
Gibson, Kendis: WJLA–TV / Newschannel 8
Gibson, Rob: WRC–TV / NBC–4
Gibson, Sheri Lynn: NBC Newschannel
Gibson, Teneille: WRC–TV / NBC–4
Gibson-Reid, Lerita: WRC–TV / NBC–4
Gilchrist, Aaron: WRC–TV / NBC–4
Gilgannon, Pege: WJLA–TV / Newschannel 8
Gilliam, Dirk: CBS News
Gillis, Gary: Fox News
Gilman, Jeff: WTTG–Fox Television
Gimbel, Tara: ABC News
Ginebra, Nelson: NBC Newschannel
Ginsburg, Benson: CBS News
Giraldo, Edwin: Caracoal Radio
Girard, David: ABC News
Girsch, Emily: Fox News
Giusto, Thomas: ABC News
Gjelten, Tom: National Public Radio
Glass, Pat: ABC News

MEMBERS ENTITLED TO ADMISSION—Continued

Glassman, Matt: WRC–TV / NBC–4
Gleitsmann, Verena: Austrian Radio & TV (ORF)
Glennon, John: Fox News
Gliha, Lori: Aljazeera International
Globensky, Manon: Canadian Broadcasting Corporation (CBC)
Glover, Aronica: CBN News
Gobet, Pierre: Swiss Broadcasting
Goddard, Andre: CNN
Godfrey, Autria: WJLA–TV / Newschannel 8
Godinho, Joanna: China Central TV Bureau
Godsick, Andrew L.: NBC Newschannel
Goff, Angie: WRC–TV / NBC–4
Goggans, Stephanie: CNN
Gold, Avra: NBC News
Gold, Emily: NBC News
Gold, Lawrence: AP–Broadcast
Gold, Peter: Fuji TV Japan
Goldberg, Jeff: WJLA–TV / Newschannel 8
Goldman, David: CTV–Community TV of PG County
Goldman, Jeff Scott: CBS News
Goldrick, Michael: WRC–TV / NBC–4
Goler, Wendell: Fox News
Gomes, Karina: Aljazeera International
Goncalves Perry, Delia: WUSA–TV
Goncalves-de-Oliveira, Alexandra: The Hill
Gongadze, Myroslava: Voice of America
Gonsar, Dhondup: Radio Free Asia
Gonyea, Don: National Public Radio
Gonzales, Erika: WRC–TV / NBC–4
Gonzales, Mario: RCN–TV (Colombia)
Gonzalez, Antonio R.: German TV ARD
Gonzalez, John: WJLA–TV / Newschannel 8
Gooch, Diane: Talk Radio News Service
Good, Chris: ABC News
Goodall, Sam: CBS News
Goodknight, Charles A.: WRC–TV / NBC–4
Goodman, Jeffrey: NBC News
Goodrich, Megan: C–Span
Goolsby, Wyatt: EWTN
Gorap, Pema: Voice of America
Gorbutt, Richard: CNN
Gordemer, Barry: National Public Radio
Gordon, Claire: Aljazeera International
Gordon, Herbert: WRC–TV / NBC–4
Gorman, Elizabeth: Aljazeera International
Gorman, James W.: AP–Broadcast
Gould, Robert: C–Span
Gracey, Allison: CNN
Gracey, David: CNN
Gradison, Robin: ABC News
Gram, Steffen William: Danish Broadcasting Corporation
Grams, Michael: Diversified Communications, Inc. (DCI)
Granda, Marco: RCN–TV (Colombia)
Granger, Nicholle: Nippon TV Network
Grant, Megan: CNN
Grasso, Neil: CBS News
Graumann, Eva: German TV ARD
Graves, Lindsay: NBC News
Gray, Bill: C–Span
Gray, James: CNN
Gray, Justin: Cox Broadcasting
Gray, Noah: CNN
Graydon, James: CNN
Grayson, Gisele: National Public Radio
Greebaum, Adam: Voice of America
Green, Jessie J.: WTOP Radio
Green, Richard: Voice of America
Green, Shannon: USA Today
Greenbaum, Adam: Voice of America
Greenberger, Scott: Stateline.org
Greenblatt, Alan: National Public Radio
Greenblatt, Larry: Viewpoint Communications
Greenblatt, Mark: Scripps Howard
Greene, David: National Public Radio
Greene, James M.: NBC News
Gregory, David: NBC News
Greiner, Nicholas P.: ABC News
Grether, Nicole: Aljazeera International
Grether, Nicole: AP–Broadcast
Grieder, Samantha: Tokyo Broadcasting System
Griffin, Jennifer: Fox News
Griffin, Kevin: NBC News
Griffin, Regina: WUSA–TV
Griffitts, William: Mobile Video Services, LTD
Griggs, Kendall: WJLA–TV / Newschannel 8
Grigsby, Lee: Eurovision Americas, Inc.
Grobe, Stefan: Euronews
Groome, Marsha: NBC News
Gross, Andrew F.: NBC News
Gross, David: CBS News
Gross, Josh: CBS News
Gross, Jr., Eddie S.: CNN
Grow, Erica: WUSA–TV
Grzech, Cherie: Fox News
Guastadisegni, Richard: WJLA–TV / Newschannel 8
Guerouani, Fayrouz: AP–Broadcast
Guest, Frank: Federal News Service
Guevara Frey, Eric: Swiss Broadcasting
Guez, Bertrand: TF1–French TV
Guise, Gregory: WUSA–TV
Guo, Chun: China Central TV Bureau
Guo, Mantong: Xinhua
Gura, David: Marketplace Radio
Gursky, Gregg L.: Fox News
Gustafson, David: Aljazeera International
Gustafson, Heather: Fox News
Gutmann, Hanna: Washington Radio and Press Service
Gutmann, Melanie: C–Span
Gutowski, Stephen: CNSnews.com
Guzman, Armando: Azteca America
Guzman, Wilber: WZDC–TV

MEMBERS ENTITLED TO ADMISSION—Continued

Haan, Mike: Freelance
Haberstick, Fred: C–Span
Habib, Elias: Al Arabiya TV
Hackney, David: WJLA–TV / Newschannel 8
Haddad, Karim: Aljazeera International
Haddad, Margot: Canal Plus French TV
Haddad, Tammy: Feature Story News
Haefeli, Brian: ABC News
Hage, Jesse: Aljazeera International
Hager, Mary: CBS News
Hager, Nathan: CBS News
Haggerty, Patrick: This Week In Agribusiness (RFD–TV)
Hahn, Jay: Eurovision Americas, Inc.
Hahn, Stephen: ABC News
Haim, Laura: Canal Plus French TV
Halkett, Kimberly: Aljazeera International
Hall, Kata: Fox News
Hall, Richard: C–Span
Hall, Sylvia: Fox Business Network
Haller, Sylvia: NBC News
Haller, Tom: Aljazeera International
Halloran, Liz: National Public Radio
Hallstead, Daniel: ABC News
Hallstead, Daniel: NBC News
Halpern, Jared: Fox News Radio
Halpern, Lacey: Fox News
Hamberg, Steven: Viewpoint Communications
Hamby, Peter: CNN
Hamilton, Caleb: FedNet
Hamilton, Chris: Aljazeera International
Hamilton, Christopher: Middle East Broadcasting Networks (MBN)
Hamilton, James: Aljazeera International
Hampton, Adele: The Hill
Hamza, Mwamoyo: Voice of America
Hanazawa, Yuichiro: NHK–Japan Broadcasting Corporation
Handelsman, Steve: NBC Newschannel
Haning, Evan: CBS News
Hanley, Patricia: Religion & Ethics Newsweekly
Hanneman, Kirk: Federal News Service
Hanneman, Wendy: Federal News Service
Hannigan, Kevin: NBC News
Hanson, Chris: C–Span
Hanson, David: NBC News
Harder Nielsen, Charlotte: Danish Broadcasting Corporation
Harding, Alejandro: Diversified Communications, Inc. (DCI)
Harding, Alison: CNN
Harding, Bill: CBS News
Harding, Claus: Diversified Communications, Inc. (DCI)
Harkness, Stephen: C–Span
Harlan, Jeremy: CNN
Harleston, Robb: C–Span
Harper, Nick: Feature Story News
Harper, Steven: Eurovision Americas, Inc.
Harrington, Candice: NBC News
Harrington, Elizabeth: CNSnews.com
Harris, Donna: WJLA–TV / Newschannel 8
Harris, Kasey: C–Span
Harris, Leon: WJLA–TV / Newschannel 8
Harris, Richard: National Public Radio
Harris, Roy: Diversified Communications, Inc. (DCI)
Harrison, Bruce: WUSA–TV
Harrison-Atlas, Dustin: Link TV
Hartman, Brian Robert: ABC News
Harton, Marcus: Voice of America
Harvey, Alan: NBC News
Harwood, John: CNBC
Hasegawa, Kento: Nippon TV Network
Haselton, Brennan: WTOP Radio
Hash, James: WUSA–TV
Hass, Thomas: Aljazeera International
Hassan, Alegra: CBN News
Hassan, Mohamed: Voice of America
Hassel-Schumacher, Bettina: German TV ARD
Hasselmann, Silke: German Public Radio (ARD)
Hastings Wotring, Melanie: WJLA–TV / Newschannel 8
Hatfield, William: NBC News
Hawkins, Arielle: CNN
Hawkins, Nyia: AP–Broadcast
Hawkins, Shonty: WUSA–TV
Hayes, Ralikh: Real News Network
Haynes, Maurice: C–Span
Haynes, Oscar: Voice of America
Hays, Guerin: Al Jazeera America
Haywood, Barry: ABC News
He, Alan: CBS News
He, Wenjin: China Central TV Bureau
Healey, Sean: NBC News
Heath, Kendall A.: ABC News
Hecht, Barry: Diversified Communications, Inc. (DCI)
Heffley, William: C–Span
Heidarpour, Sarah: NBC News
Heina, Martin: Fox News
Heiner, Stephen: Middle East Broadcasting Networks (MBN)
Helgason, Sveinn: Icelandic National Broadcasting Service
Helgren, Jamie: CNN
Helman, Jonathan: CNN
Helton, John: CNN
Henderson, Susan: AP–Broadcast
Hendin, Robert: CBS News
Hendren, John: Aljazeera International
Henneberg, Mary Janne: Fox News
Henrehan, John: WTTG–Fox Television
Henry, Chas: CBS News
Henry, Ed: Fox News
Henry, Jonelle P.: C–Span

MEMBERS ENTITLED TO ADMISSION—Continued

Henry, Shirley: CNN
Herbas, Francis: Fox News
Herbst, Florens: German TV ARD
Herd, Phillip: BBC
Heritage, Robert: NBC News
Hermelijn, Ryan: Nos Dutch Public Radio & TV (VRT)
Hernandez-Arthur, Simon: CNN
Hernon, Louise: NBC News
Herrera, Angelica: Voice of America
Herrera, Esequiel: ABC News
Herrera, Ruben: German TV ZDF
Herridge, Catherine: Fox News
Herrod, Michael: Independent Television News (ITN)
Hesson, Ted: Univision
Hibbitts, Mi Jeong Y.: Voice of America
Hickey, Neil: Wall Street Journal
Hickman, Stacy: Fox News
Hicks, Desiree: National Public Radio
Hidaka, Masano: Diversified Communications, Inc. (DCI)
Hidaka, Yoshio: Diversified Communications, Inc. (DCI)
Higgins, Ricardo: WRC–TV / NBC–4
Hill, Dallas: C–Span
Hill, Jane: BBC
Hill, Martin: Fox News
Hill, Robert: Australian Broadcasting Corporation
Hiller, Andrew: Voice of Russia
Hindes, Walter: SRN News (Salem)
Hinds, Hugh: WRC–TV / NBC–4
Hines, Andrea: ABC News
Hinman, Katie: CNN
Hinton, Christy: C–Span
Hirouchi, Hitoshi: NHK–Japan Broadcasting Corporation
Hishchynsky, James: NBC News
Ho, King: Radio Free Asia
Hoang, Channhu: Radio Free Asia
Hochman, Jordana: National Public Radio
Hodge, Darnley: NBC Newschannel
Hoese, Christine: Mobile Video Services, LTD
Hoffman, Brian: AP–Broadcast
Hoffman, Michelle: Agence France Presse (AFP–TV)
Hoffman, Tami: Sky News
Hofmann, Maximilian: Deutsche Welle TV
Hofstedt, Loic: Agence France Presse (AFP–TV)
Holbert, William: CNN
Holden, Michael: C–Span
Holland, John: NBC News
Holland, Sarah B.: CNN
Holland, TaShick: National Public Radio
Hollenbeck, Paul: Bt Video Productions
Holm, Gro: Norwegian Broadcasting
Holman, Kwame: The Newshour with Jim Lehrer
Holmes, Horace: WJLA–TV / Newschannel 8
Holton, Jennifer: Fox News
Holtzman, Geoff: Talk Radio News Service
Honegger, Arthur: Swiss Broadcasting
Hong, Hyunjin: Korean Broadcasting Systems
Hooley, Gemma: National Public Radio
Hoover, Toni: CBS News
Hopkins, Adrienne Moira: Fox News
Hopkins, Brian: WJLA–TV / Newschannel 8
Hopper, Dave: BBC
Hopper, Michael: Aljazeera International
Horan, Michael: WTTG–Fox Television
Horchler, Andreas: German Broadcasting Systems–ARD
Horie, Tomoko: Nippon TV Network
Hormuth, Tom: WJLA–TV / Newschannel 8
Horn, Brad: Washingtonpost.com
Horn, Caroline: CBS News
Horn, Charles: Viewpoint Communications
Horne, LaTanya: WJLA–TV / Newschannel 8
Horrigan, Derek: CNN
Horsley, Scott: National Public Radio
Hosford, Matthew Alan: ABC News
Hotta, Takashi: TV Asahi
House, Amanda: One America
Houssein, Aden: Voice of America
Houston, Karen Gray: WTTG–Fox Television
Hovell, Bret: CBS News
Hovell, Dean: Voice of America
Howard, Cory R.: Fox News
Howell, George: C–Span
Howell, Margaret: RTTV America
Howell, Melissa: CBS News
Hoye, Matthew: CNN
Hoye, Sarah: Aljazeera International
Hristova, Rozalia: BBC
Hsieh, Yi-Pe: C–Span
Hssaini, Nasser: Aljazeera Satellite Channel (Peninsula)
Htike Oo, Thein: Voice of America
Hu, Elise: National Public Radio
Huang, Cindy: The Newshour with Jim Lehrer
Hubbard, Marge: CBS News
Hubert, Jason: ABC News
Hubert-Hogg, Aja: China Central TV Bureau
Huckeby, Paul: Fox News
Huether, Andy: National Public Radio
Huff, Dan: AP–Broadcast
Huff, Priscilla: Feature Story News
Hughes, Dana: ABC News
Hughes, James: NBC News
Hughes, Jillian: CBS News
Hughes, Kate: C–Span
Hughes, Katherine: C–Span
Hughes, Megan: Bloomberg Radio & TV
Hume, Brit: Fox News
Humeau, Thierry: Aljazeera International
Hunt, Kasie: NBC News
Hunter, Amy: WTOP Radio

MEMBERS ENTITLED TO ADMISSION—Continued

Hunter, Melanie: CNSnews.com
Hunter, Paul: Canadian Broadcasting Corporation (CBC)
Hunter, Tracie: C–Span
Hurley, Charles: CNN
Hurst, Whitney: Aljazeera International
Hurt, James: NBC Newschannel
Husain, Zulega: Aljazeera International
Hussain, Iftikhar: Voice of America
Hussin, Utami: Voice of America
Hutcherson, Kim: Aljazeera International
Hutcherson, Trudy: Aljazeera International
Hutchinson, Heather: WRC–TV / NBC–4
Hybels, Amy: CBS News
Hydeck, Michael: WUSA–TV
Hylton, Winston: WJLA–TV / Newschannel 8
Hyman, Mark: Sinclair Broadcast Group
Iacone, Amanda: WTOP Radio
Iadarola, Lea: CNN
Iannelli, Nick: WTOP Radio
Ibragimova, Roza: China Central TV Bureau
Ibrahim, Hend: American Press and TV Services (APTVS)
Ibrahim, Yasmeen: CNN
Ibrahim, Zena: TIMI
Ichihara, Mai: TV Asahi
Ide, Charles: WETA
Ifill, Gwen: The Newshour with Jim Lehrer
Illenseer, Erik: German TV ZDF
Im, Ko Woon: WUSA–TV
Im, Ko: CBS News
Iman, Falastine: Voice of America
Ing, Lance: WTTG–Fox Television
Ingle, Cynthia: C–Span
Ingle, Julian: Aljazeera International
Inglis, Mike: Sky News
Ingram, Julian: WJLA–TV / Newschannel 8
Inoue, Yusuke: TV Asahi
Inserra, Donna: CBS News
Inskeep, Robert: NBC News
Inskeep, Steve: National Public Radio
Irons, Mark: EWTN
Irwin, Sarah: Reuters Radio & TV
Isella, Elena: Fox News
Isham, Christopher: CBS News
Isikoff, Michael: NBC News
Italiano, Michael: AP–Broadcast
Ivey, Michael: Voice of America
Jaakson, Uelle-Mall: Austrian Radio & TV (ORF)
Jackson, George: WJLA–TV / Newschannel 8
Jackson, Hallie: Hearst Television, Inc.
Jackson, Jerry: CBS News
Jackson, Jill: CBS News
Jackson, Katharine: Reuters Radio & TV
Jackson, Robert: National Public Radio
Jackson, Roberta: C–Span
Jackson, Ryan: ABC News
Jackson, Samuel: WJLA–TV / Newschannel 8
Jacobi, Steve: CBN News
Jacobs, Adia: CNN
Jacobson, Rebecca: The Newshour with Jim Lehrer
Jaconi, Michelle: CNN
Jaeger, Kevin: WJLA–TV / Newschannel 8
Jaffe, Charly: BBC
Jaffe, Gary: Voice of America
Jaffe, Michael: WJLA–TV / Newschannel 8
James, Frank: National Public Radio
James, Karen: CNBC
James, Thomas: WUSA–TV
Jamison, Dennis: CBS News
Jamshidi, Kaveh: Voice of America
Janaka, Junko: NHK–Japan Broadcasting Corporation
Janney, Oliver: CNN
Janosky, Jesse: WJLA–TV / Newschannel 8
Jansen, Lesa: CNN
Japaridze, NuNu: CNN
Jaramillo, Laura: RCN–TV (Colombia)
Jarboe, Brian: National Public Radio
Jarrett, Rick: National Public Radio
Jarvis, Julie: NBC Newschannel
Jaskot, Sheila: CBS News
Javers, Eamon: CNBC
Javinsky, Jim: Talk Radio News Service
Jay, Courtney: CBS News
Jay, Paul: Real News Network
Jazzaa, Ziad: Al Arabiya TV
Jeannet, Francois: Swiss Broadcasting
Jeffcoat, Jan: WUSA–TV
Jefferson, Richard: CBS News
Jeffrey, Terence: CNSnews.com
Jenkins, David: CNN
Jenkins, Gene: CBN News
Jenkins, Rhonda: Fox News
Jenkins, William G.: Fox News
Jennings, Alicia: NBC News
Jennings, Jr., Edward B.: ABC News
Jensen, Heidi: ABC News
Jermin, Ede: WRC–TV / NBC–4
Jessen, Peder: Eurovision Americas, Inc.
Jessup, John: CBN News
Jevremovic, Jela: Voice of America
Jewett, Stefanie: CNN
Jewsevskyj, George: Fox News
Jia, Elizabeth: WUSA–TV
Jia, Li: China Central TV Bureau
Jiang, Xin: China Central TV Bureau
Jibai, Wafaa: BBC
Jikamshi, Kabir Isa: Deutsche Welle TV
Jimenez, Martin: Fox Business Network
Jing, Hui: New Tang Dynasty TV
Joehnk, Astrid: German Public Radio (ARD)
Johns, Joseph: CNN
Johnson, Aaron: ABC News
Johnson, Aja: CNN
Johnson, Bruce: WUSA–TV

MEMBERS ENTITLED TO ADMISSION—Continued

Johnson, Carrie: National Public Radio
Johnson, Douglas: Voice of America
Johnson, Fletcher: Aljazeera International
Johnson, Fletcher: NBC News
Johnson, Irene: WRC–TV / NBC–4
Johnson, Jennifer: NBC Newschannel
Johnson, Kevin: Cox Broadcasting
Johnson, Kia: Reuters Radio & TV
Johnson, Rich: Fox News Radio
Johnson, Rolanda: German TV ZDF
Johnson, Sandy: Stateline.org
Johnson, Shanica: CBS News
Johnson, Stephanie: WTTG–Fox Television
Johnston, Derek Leon: ABC News
Johnston, Jeffrey: CBS News
Joho, Haruka: Fuji TV Japan
Jonas, Megan: C–Span
Jones, Alvin: FedNet
Jones, Andrew: C–Span
Jones, Athena: CNN
Jones, Dawn Marie: FedNet
Jones, Gwyneth: NBC News
Jones, Jay: CNN
Jones, Joey: Sky News
Jones, Joyce: BET Nightly News
Jones, Lyrone Steven: WTTG–Fox Television
Jones, Morris: WJLA–TV / Newschannel 8
Jones, Nelson: WTTG–Fox Television
Jones, Shawn: WJLA–TV / Newschannel 8
Jones, Stephen: C–Span
Jones, Susan: CNSnews.com
Jones, Tara: BET Nightly News
Jones, Torrance: Fox News
Jones, Victoria: Talk Radio News Service
Jong, Wessel: Nos Dutch Public Radio & TV (VRT)
Joo, Mae: Fox News
Joost, Nathalie: Fox News
Jordan, Nyshicka: WJLA–TV / Newschannel 8
Jordan, Richard: WRC–TV / NBC–4
Jordan, Rosiland: Aljazeera International
Joseph, Akilah: Aljazeera International
Joseph, Daniel: CNSnews.com
Joseph, Roxanne: NBC News
Joslyn, James: WJLA–TV / Newschannel 8
Joy, Richard: Ventana Productions
Joyner, Arcelious: Middle East Broadcasting Networks (MBN)
Jubar, Muriel: Aljazeera International
Judd, Donald: CBS News
Juergens, Hans: ABC News
Juez-Moreno, Beatriz: RCN–TV (Colombia)
Juma, Mamatjan: Radio Free Asia
Just, Sara: ABC News
Kabasawa, Ichiro: NHK–Japan Broadcasting Corporation
Kabbaj, Abdelhakim: TIMI
Kabbaj, Hakim: AP–Broadcast
Kabiruddin, Sakar: Voice of America
Kades, Cathy: CBS News
Kajiwara, Takamoto: NHK–Japan Broadcasting Corporation
Kalman, Nick: Fox News
Kamat, Anjali: Aljazeera International
Kane, James: ABC News
Kane, Jason: The Newshour with Jim Lehrer
Kane, Richard: CBS News
Kang, Kang: China Central TV Bureau
Kangarlou, Tara: CNN
Kanneth, Polson: ABC News
Kaplan, Bill: Metro Teleproductions
Kaplan, Leah: Radio TV Gallery
Kapp, Bonney: CBS News
Karl, Jonathan: ABC News
Kashfi, Monna: China Central TV Bureau
Kashgary, Jilil: Radio Free Asia
Kato, Atsushi: NHK–Japan Broadcasting Corporation
Katz, Barry: C–Span
Katz, Craig: CBS News
Kauzlarich, Mark: Al Arabiya TV
Kavanaugh, John: NBC News
Kawamoto, Mitsuo: TV Tokyo
Kaye, Matthew: The Berns Bureau, Inc.
Kaye, Stephanie: C–Span
Kearns, Kara: NBC News
Keator, John C.: National Public Radio
Keedy, Matthew: CBN News
Kehoe, Steve: C–Span
Keilar, Brianna: CNN
Keith, Tamara: National Public Radio
Kelbling, Julia: Storyhouse Productions
Kelemen, Michele: National Public Radio
Keller, Kathleen: CBS News
Kellerman, Mike: Xinhua
Kelley, Alice: German TV ZDF
Kelley, Brian: Link TV
Kelley, Colleen: Fox News
Kelley, Jon: C–Span
Kelley, Pamela: CNN
Kelly, Colin: Gannett Government Media Corp.
Kelly, Terence: NBC News
Kenigsberg, Sara: Now This News
Kennedy, Robert: C–Span
Kennedy, Sean: CNN
Kennedy, Suzanne: WJLA–TV / Newschannel 8
Kenney, Colleen: WTTG–Fox Television
Kent, Peter: NBC News
Kenyon, Linda: SRN News (Salem)
Kerchner, Eric C.: ABC News
Kerley, David P.: ABC News
Kern, Barkley: C–Span
Kerr, David: EWTN
Kerr, Roxane: C–Span
Kerr, Ryan: Bloomberg Radio & TV
Kerwin, Chris: WRC–TV / NBC–4
Kessler, Jonathan L.: ABC News

MEMBERS ENTITLED TO ADMISSION—Continued

Ketcham, Lew: C–Span
Kettlewell, Christian: AP–Broadcast
Keuper, Dirk: German TV ARD
Keyes, Allison: National Public Radio
Khairy, Khaled: Middle East Broadcasting Networks (MBN)
Khalaf, Lina: Aljazeera Satellite Channel (Peninsula)
Khan, Azmat: Aljazeera International
Khan, Mariam: Lilly Broadcasting
Khananayev, Grigory: Fox News
Kharel, Nilu: Sagarmatha Television
Kharel, Ram C.: Sagarmatha Television
Khawaja, Noorulain: Aljazeera International
Khawly, Joseph: Sky News Arabia
Khedrup, Tsewang: Voice of America
Khristenko, Alexander: Russian State TV and Radio (RTR)
Kiang, Kylene: Aljazeera International
Kianpour, Suzanne: BBC
Kidd, Sally F.: Hearst Television, Inc.
Kieffer, Vivian: Radio Free Asia
Kiernan, Ryan: NBC News
Kiesch, Zachary: WRC–TV / NBC–4
Kill, Adrian: Diversified Communications, Inc. (DCI)
Killion, Nikole: Hearst Television, Inc.
Killough, Ashley: CNN
Kim, Andrew: MBC–TV Korea (Munhwa)
Kim, Chulho: Korean Broadcasting Systems
Kim, JaeEun: Korean Broadcasting Systems
Kim, Lauren: Yonhap News TV
Kim, SungJin: Korean Broadcasting Systems
Kim, William: Voice of America
Kimani, Julia: CBS News
Kinew, Wab: Aljazeera International
King Lilleston, Kristi: WTOP Radio
King, John: CNN
King, Kevin G.: WUSA–TV
King, Kevin: C–Span
King, Llewellyn: White House Chronicle
King, Nathan: China Central TV Bureau
Kinlaw, Worth: CNN
Kinney, George P.: CNN
Kinney, Jeff: CNN
Kirby, Michael: FedNet
Kirkland, Pamela: Washingtonpost.com
Kirkland, Pamela: XM Satellite Radio
Kirst, Anna: Austrian Radio & TV (ORF)
Kistner, William: Hearst Television, Inc.
Kiyasu, Adilson: CNN
Klayman, Elliot: Eye–To–Eye Video
Kleim, Peter: N–TV German News Channel
Klein, Alexander: N–TV German News Channel
Klein, Kent: Voice of America
Klein, Markus: German TV ZDF
Klein, Richard: ABC News
Klein, Rob: Metro Teleproductions
Klein, Stacey: NBC News
Klenk, Ann: NBC News
Kline, Deirdre: Middle East Broadcasting Networks (MBN)
Klinger, Carol: National Public Radio
Klopp, Felicitas: German TV ARD
Klos, Daniel: CBS News
Knantz, Alejandra: National Public Radio
Knapp, Timothy: Mobile Video Services, LTD
Knautz, Alejandra: National Public Radio
Knezek, Paul: Eurovision Americas, Inc.
Knight, Benjamin: Australian Broadcasting Corporation
Knighton, David: C–Span
Knoller, Mark: CBS News
Knott, John: ABC News
Koerber, Ashley: Fox News
Koh, Thomas: Korean Broadcasting Systems
Kokufuda, Kaoru: Tokyo Broadcasting System
Konno, Hiroaki: Nippon TV Network
Kono, Torao: NHK–Japan Broadcasting Corporation
Koolhof, Vanessa M.: WJLA–TV / Newschannel 8
Kopp, Emily: Federal News Radio 1500 AM
Koran, Laura: CNN
Korff, Jay: WJLA–TV / Newschannel 8
Kornely, Michael: Voice of America
Kos, Martin: Bt Video Productions
Kosnar, Michael: NBC News
Koster, Jesse: Voice of America
Kotke, Wolfgang: German TV ZDF
Kotuby, Stephanie: CNN
Kovach, Robert S.: CNN
Kozel, Sandy: AP–Broadcast
Krahenbül, Raquel: TV Globo International
Kramer, Kent: Radio One
Kraus, Melissa: Fox News Radio
Kreinbihl, Mary: Fox Business Network
Kreindler, Virginia: NBC Newschannel
Kretman, Les: Boston University Washinton Center
Kreuz, Greta: WJLA–TV / Newschannel 8
Krohn, Tina-Jane: Storyhouse Productions
Kroll, Donald Eugene: ABC News
Krolowitz, Benjamin: ABC News
Krupnik, Kathryn: Fox News
Ksiazek, Whitney: Fox News
Ku, Nancy: Fuji TV Japan
Kube, Courtney: NBC News
Kubo, Kensuke: Nippon TV Network
Kucinich, Jackie: Washingtonpost.com
Kulman, Betsy: Aljazeera International
Kumpf, Sarah: German Broadcasting Systems–ARD
Kupper, Carmen: German TV ZDF
Kurzius, Rachel: RTTV America
Kutler, Rebecca: CNN
Kwajafa, Michelle: Agence France Presse (AFP–TV)
Kyaw Thein, Kyaw: Voice of America
Kyaw, Ko: Radio Free Asia

MEMBERS ENTITLED TO ADMISSION—Continued

LaBella, Mike: ABC News
Labott, Elise: CNN
Laboy, Felix: C–Span
Lacey, Donna: Fox News
Lai, Daniel: Hong Kong Phoenix Satellite Television
Lamb, Brian: C–Span
Lambidakis, Stephanie: CBS News
Lamonica, Ely: Voyage Productions
LaMonica, Gabe: CNN
LaMonica, Jay: Aljazeera International
Landay, Woodrow: Australian Broadcasting Corporation
Landy, John: BBC
Lane, Christopher: WETA
Langkilde, Johannes: Danish Broadcasting Corporation
Langley, Kevin: National Public Radio
Lanier, Peter: CNN
Lannigan, Katherine: Aljazeera International
Lanningham, Kyle: Swedish Broadcasting
Lanningham, Sarah: Eurovision Americas, Inc.
Lanzendoerfer, Nancy: N24 German TV
Larade, Darren: C–Span
LaRosa, Michael: NBC News
Larotonda, Matt: ABC News
Larsen, Greg: CBS News
Larson, Lauren: Federal News Radio 1500 AM
Laslo, Matt: Laslo Congressional Bureau
Latendresse, Richard: Groupe TVa
Latremoliere, France: NBC News
Laughlin, Ara: CTV–Community TV of PG County
Laughlin, James: CBN News
Laville, Molly: C–Span
Lawn, Connie: Audio Video News
Lawrence, Chris: CNN
Lawrence, John: Ventana Productions
Lawrence, Joshalyn: Verizon
Lawrence, Michael: Radio TV Gallery
Lawton, Kim: Religion & Ethics Newsweekly
Layne, Christopher: WRC–TV / NBC–4
Lazar, Robert: C–Span
Lazarev, Anatoly: Channel One Russian TV
Lazo, Larry: CNN
Leake, Myron: ABC News
Lebedeva, Natasha: NBC News
LeCroy, Philip: Fox News
Leddon, Jerome: C–Span
Lee, Christina: Washingtonpost.com
Lee, Donald A.: CBS News
Lee, Edward: WETA
Lee, Erik: WUSA–TV
Lee, Jennifer: Hong Kong Phoenix Satellite Television
Lee, Jinsook: MBC–TV Korea (Munhwa)
Lee, JuHan: Korean Broadcasting Systems
Lee, KangDuk: Korean Broadcasting Systems
Lee, Pei-Hua: TV Asahi
Lee, Sangbok: JTBC
Leidelmeyer, Ronald: WRC–TV / NBC–4
Leidsmar, George: Telemundo Network
Leigh, Danielle: NBC Newschannel
Leiken, Katherine: German TV ZDF
Lenghi, Abdulmola: WUSA–TV
Lent, David: German TV ARD
Leong, Dexter: CBS News
Leong, Ming: WJLA–TV / Newschannel 8
Leroy, Jean-Pierre: Voice of America
Leshan, Bruce: WUSA–TV
Lesser, Howard: Washington Radio and Press Service
Lester, Paul: WUSA–TV
Levenson, Michael: Verizon
Levine, Adam: CNN
LeVine, Indira: WJLA–TV / Newschannel 8
Levine, Michael: Fox News
Levkovich, Denis: Feature Story News
Levy, Adam: CNN
Lewis, Aidan: BBC
Lewis, Dorothy: CNN
Lewis, Edward: Fox News
Lewis, Jerry S.: WETA
Lewis, John B.: WJLA–TV / Newschannel 8
Lewis, Misha: CNN
Lewis, Victoria: Washingtonpost.com
Lewkowict, David: Fox News
Lewnes, Lisa: Reuters Radio & TV
Lhundup, Tenzin: Voice of America
Li, Meng: China Central TV Bureau
Li, Wo Tak: Radio Free Asia
Li, Xiang: China Central TV Bureau
Liasson, Mara: National Public Radio
Liberto, Jennifer: CNN
Libin, Louis: Talk Radio News Service
Libretto, John: NBC News
Licht, Christopher: NBC News
Liedl, Jonathan: EWTN
Lien, Arthur: NBC News
Lien, Jonathan: CBS News
Liesegang, Albert: Diversified Communications, Inc. (DCI)
Liffiton, Bruce: CBS News
Lilling, Dave: Metro Teleproductions
Lim, Lister: Aljazeera International
Lim, Sang: MBC–TV Korea (Munhwa)
Lin, Chuan: New Tang Dynasty TV
Lin, Dongwei: China Central TV Bureau
Lin, Joy: Fox News
Lin, Yu: Xinhua
Linares, Moises: WZDC–TV
Lindblom, Mark: C–Span
Lindsay, Tahira: CTV–Community TV of PG County
Lindsey, Melvin: ABC News
Lipes, Joshua: Radio Free Asia
Liptak, Kevin: CNN
Little, Craig: WTTG–Fox Television

MEMBERS ENTITLED TO ADMISSION—Continued

Littleton, Philip: CNN
Litzinger, Sam: CBS News
Liu, Libo: Voice of America
Liu, Xiyang: China Central TV Bureau
Livelli, Kevin: CBS News
Lloyd, Brian: C–Span
Lockhart, Kathleen: NBC News
Lodoe, Kalden: Radio Free Asia
Loebach, Joseph W.: NBC News
Loeschke, Paul: C–Span
Logan, Lara: CBS News
Logan, Russell: C–Span
Logreira, Diana: Voice of America
Loker, Jessica: Fox News
Long, Culver: Reuters Radio & TV
Long, James V.: NBC News
Long, Kelle: NBC News
Lopez, Edwing: Azteca America
Lopez, Juan Carlos: CNN
Lopez, Meghan: RTTV America
Lora, Willie A.: CNN
Lord, Bill: WJLA–TV / Newschannel 8
Lorenzen, Elizabeth: Native American Television
Lothian, Daniel: CNN
Loughlin, Ryan: Aljazeera International
Lovelace, Jr., Anthony: Native American Television
Lover, Gary: C–Span
Lowman, Wayne: Fox News
Lowther, Jason: Viewpoint Communications
Lozano, Alicia: WTOP Radio
Lu, Liyuan: Voice of America
Lu, Tao: Hong Kong Phoenix Satellite Television
Lucas, Dave: WJLA–TV / Newschannel 8
Lucas, Fred: CNSnews.com
Lucas, Mary Grace: CNN
Lucchini, Maria Rosa: WFDC–TV Univision
Ludden, Jennifer: National Public Radio
Lukas, Jayne: Global TV Canada
Lumley, Tom: Aljazeera International
Luna, Nathan: Hearst Television, Inc.
Lutterbeck, Deborah: Reuters Radio & TV
Luzader, Doug: Fox News
Luzquinos, Julio: NBC News
Ly, Sherri: WTTG–Fox Television
Lyles, Robert: WJLA–TV / Newschannel 8
Lynch, Pearse: BBC
Lynds, Stacia: Fox News
Lynn, Gary: NBC News
Lyon, Michael: Fox News
Lyons, Judy: Bloomberg Radio & TV
Lyons, Nancy: CBS News
Ma, Jing: China Central TV Bureau
Mabry, Krystal: CNN
Macaluso, Michelle: Fox News
Macaya, Melissa: CNN
MacDonald, Neil: Canadian Broadcasting Corporation (CBC)
Macedo, Kate: Bloomberg Radio & TV
MacFarlane, Scott: Cox Broadcasting
Macholz, Wolfgang: German TV ZDF
Macias, Mitzi: Voice of America
MacKay, Jim: CBS News
MacNeil, Lachlan Murdoch: ABC News
MacVicar, Sheila: Aljazeera International
Maer, Peter: CBS News
Magaziner, Paris: CBS News
Mager, Dickon: Sky News
Maggiolo, Vito: CNN
Mahdi, Ali: Middle East Broadcasting Networks (MBN)
Mahdy, Emad: TIMA
Maher, Heather: Radio Free Europe
Majchrowitz, Mike: Fox News Radio
Malbon, Joy: CTV Canadian TV
Malewitz, James: Stateline.org
Malhotr, Ashish: Aljazeera International
Mallonnee, Mary Kay: WJLA–TV / Newschannel 8
Malone, Freddie: NBC News
Malone, James: Voice of America
Maltas, Michael: Fox News
Manby, Mary: NBC News
Mandelson, Adam: Eurovision Americas, Inc.
Manduley, Christina: CNN
Mann, Jon: WJLA–TV / Newschannel 8
Mannos, Sofia: Voice of Russia
Mansour, Fadi: Aljazeera Satellite Channel (Peninsula)
Maounis, Nico: AP–Broadcast
Marantz, Michael: WTTG–Fox Television
Marchione, Mark Anthony: CNN
Marchitto, Tom: National Public Radio
Marcum, James: WJLA–TV / Newschannel 8
Marcus, Gale: ABC News
Mardell, Mark: BBC
Marder, Jennifer: The Newshour with Jim Lehrer
Marenco, Julio: RCN–TV (Colombia)
Marin, Irene: RTTV America
Marion, Marvin: Voice of America
Marks, Carole: Talk Radio News Service
Marks, Simon: Feature Story News
Markwell, Lindle: BBC
Marno, Joseph: Aljazeera International
Marno, Mike: Aljazeera International
Maroney, Sean: Voice of America
Marquez, William: BBC
Marquis, Melissa: National Public Radio
Marrapodi, Eric: CNN
Marriott, Marc: NBC News
Marsh, Rene: CNN
Marshall, Brittany: NBC News
Marshall, Madeline: Politico.com
Marshall, Serena: ABC News
Marshall, Steve: CBS News
Marshall-Genzer, Nancy: Marketplace Radio
Martin Ewing, Samara: WUSA–TV
Martin, Abigail: RTTV America

MEMBERS ENTITLED TO ADMISSION—Continued

Martin, Ben: Independent Television News (ITN)
Martin, David: CBS News
Martin, Greg: NBC News
Martin, Joseph: WUSA–TV
Martin, Jr., James: ABC News
Martin, Lori: Fox News
Martin, Michel: National Public Radio
Martin, Rachel: National Public Radio
Martin, Wisdom: WTTG–Fox Television
Martinez, Carlos: WRC–TV / NBC–4
Martinez, Luis: ABC News
Martinez, Mercedes: Aljazeera International
Martino, Jeff: Canadian Broadcasting Corporation (CBC)
Mas, Lillian: WFDC–TV Univision
Mashack, Julie: Religion & Ethics Newsweekly
Mashkova, Victoria: Voice of Russia
Mason, Julie: XM Satellite Radio
Mass, Lilian: WFDC–TV Univision
Massey, Emily: CNN
Massimi, Alice: Fox News
Massini, Regis: France 2 Television
Mastrian, Michael: Radio TV Gallery
Mathias, Joseph: NBC News
Matkosky, Tim: Cox Broadcasting
Matt, Francis: FedNet
Mattera, Jason: America's Radio News Network
Matthews, Chris: NBC News
Matthews, Lisa N.: AP–Broadcast
Matthews, Molly: Fox News
Matthews, Ronald H.: CBS News
Matthews, Valerie: C–Span
Matza, Max: BBC
Matzka, Jeffrey: SRN News (Salem)
Maurer, Pola: German TV ARD
Maxwell, Brandon: CNN
May, Adam: Aljazeera International
May, Tim: Fox News
Mayer, Charles: National Public Radio
Maynard, Melissa: Stateline.org
Mazariegos, Luis: To The Contrary (Persephone Productions)
Mazariegos, Mark: CBS News
Mazrieva, Eva: Voice of America
Mazyck, Robin: CBN News
Mazza, Mathieu: German TV ARD
McAleese, Kevin: Feature Story News
McAndrew, Ken: C–Span
McArdle, John: C–Span
McCabe, Valerie: France 2 Television
McCalley, Sean: Federal News Radio 1500 AM
McCann, Michael: C–Span
McCann, Sean: C–Span
McCarren, Andrea: WUSA–TV
McCarty, D. Jay: CBS News
McCarty, D. Page: CBS News
McCarty, D.: CBS News
McCash, Douglas: German TV ZDF
McCaughan, Timothy: CNN
McClam, Kevin: Fox News
McClellan, Daniel: CBS News
McClellan, Max: CBS News
McCloskey, George: Fox News
McClure, Tipp K.: Reuters Radio & TV
McConnell, Dave: WTOP Radio
McConnell, Dugald: CNN
McDermott, Richard: Fox News
McDevitt, Lauren: Hearst Television, Inc.
McDonald, William: Talk Radio News Service
McDonough, Constance: Fox News
McDougall, Ian: Reuters Radio & TV
McEachern, Terrance: Fox News
McFarland, Patty: NBC News
McGarrity, Gerard: C–Span
McGarvy, Sean: Fox News
McGarvy, Sean: WTTG–Fox Television
McGinley, Stephen: Voice of America
McGinnis, Susan: CBS News
McGinniss, Richard: NBC News
McGinty, Derek: WUSA–TV
McGlinchy, Jim: CBS News
McGrath, Megan: WRC–TV / NBC–4
McGraw, Katherine: Fox News
McGreevy, Allen: BBC
McGuire, Gitte: Danish Broadcasting Corporation
McGuire, Michael: CBS News
McHenry, Robert: ABC News
McIntosh, Denise: CNN
McKellog, JullieAnn: Washingtonpost.com
McKelway, Doug: Fox News
McKenna, Duncan: CBS News
McKinley, Robert: CBS News
McKinney, Lee: NBC News
McKnight, William: CNN
McLellan, Jennifer: XM Satellite Radio
McLendon, Alyssa: CNN
McManamon, Erin T.: Hearst Television, Inc.
McManus, Erika: Fox News
McManus, Nicole: NBC Newschannel
McMichael IV, Samuel J.: CNN
McMinn, Nan Hee: AP–Broadcast
McMullan, Michael: CNN
McNabb, Lindsey: CNN
McNair, Erik T.: ABC News
McNary, Kirstin: Fox News Radio
McPike, Erin: CNN
McWhinney, David: Aljazeera International
Meagher, Edward: CNN
Means, Jeffrey: Voice of America
Mears, Carroll Ann: NBC News
Mears, William: CNN
Medina, Christie: CNN
Medvee, Dennis: National Public Radio
Meech, James: CNN
Mees, John: CTV Canadian TV

MEMBERS ENTITLED TO ADMISSION—Continued

Meghani, Sagar: AP–Broadcast
Mei, Yan: China Central TV Bureau
Meier, Kenneth: Verizon
Meier, Markus: Austrian Radio & TV (ORF)
Mejia, Douglas: WZDC–TV
Melendy, David R.: AP–Broadcast
Melhem, Omar: Al Arabiya TV
Melhem, Richard: Al Arabiya TV
Melick, Rob: NBC News
Melillo, Lisa: Comcast NBC
Meluza, Lourdes: Univision
Memmott, Mark: National Public Radio
Men, Kimseng: Voice of America
Mendelson, Beth: Voice of America
Mendez, Karen: WFDC–TV Univision
Mendoza, Natalia: TF1–French TV
Meng, Lingqi: China Central TV Bureau
Meraz, Gregorio: Televisa News Network (ECO)
Merena, Michael: National Public Radio
Mergener, Tara: CBS News
Merica, Daniel: CNN
Merobshoev, Seeno: C–Span
Merritt, Megan: Bloomberg Radio & TV
Merson, Austin: CNN
Messer, Christopher: Aljazeera Satellite Channel (Peninsula)
Mesthos, George: CBS News
Metcalfe, Rhoda: Canadian Broadcasting Corporation (CBC)
Metzger, Edward: BBC
Metzger, Jessica: CNN
Metzger, Justin: C–Span
Metzger, Rochelle: CTV–Community TV of PG County
Meyer, Alison: CNSnews.com
Meyer, Guillaume: Agence France Presse (AFP–TV)
Meyer, Kerry: Diversified Communications, Inc. (DCI)
Michaud, Robert: Aljazeera International
Micklos, Gregg: CBS News
Miglierina, Tomas: Swiss Broadcasting
Miklaszewski, James: NBC News
Mikols, Glenn: Eurovision Americas, Inc.
Mikutsky, David: ABC News
Mila, Lorenzo: TVE – Spanish Public Television
Milam, Greg: Sky News
Milford, Robert H.: Mobile Video Services, LTD
Millar, Christopher: NBC News
Millar, Lisa: Australian Broadcasting Corporation
Miller, Andrew Peter: C–Span
Miller, Avery: ABC News
Miller, Jake: CBS News
Miller, Jason: Federal News Radio 1500 AM
Miller, Josh: WJLA–TV / Newschannel 8
Miller, Joshua: Sinclair Broadcast Group
Miller, Lawrence: This Week In Agribusiness (RFD–TV)
Miller, Mitchell: WTOP Radio
Miller, Sunlen Mari: ABC News
Miller, Tim: Middle East Broadcasting Networks (MBN)
Mills, Chris: Fox Business Network
Mills, Joe: National Public Radio
Mills, Kate: C–Span
Millward, Craig: CNSnews.com
Milton, Pat: CBS News
Miner, Jenny: Fox News
Ming, Daniel: Aljazeera International
Minner, Richard: NBC News
Minoso, Guillermo: National Public Radio
Minott, Gloria: WPFW–FM
Miran, Alec: CNN
Mirfakhraei, Hooshmand: Voice of America
Mirsaeedi, Guita: Voice of America
Mishev, Risto: Macedonia Radio Television (MRTV)
Mitchell, Andrea: NBC News
Mitchell, Carrie: Federal News Service
Mitchell, Justin: Voice of Russia
Mitnick, Steven: NBC News
Miyake, Yuko: TV Tokyo
Mizukami, Takashi: NHK–Japan Broadcasting Corporation
Mock, Mike: Aljazeera International
Mok, Joseph: Voice of America
Molestina, Kenny: WUSA–TV
Molinares-Hess, Ione Indira: CNN
Molineaux, Diana: Radio Marti
Mollenbeck, Andrew: WTOP Radio
Moller, Jeffrey: CNN
Mollet, Melissa: WRC–TV / NBC–4
Monack, David: C–Span
Monange, Arielle: France 2 Television
Monosso, Jeff: Fox News Radio
Monroe, Bryan: CNN
Monroe, Kristian: RTTV America
Monsalve, Juliana: WZDC–TV
Montague, William: Norwegian Broadcasting
Montanaro, Domenico: NBC News
Monte, John: Viewpoint Communications
Montenegro, Lori: Telemundo Network
Montoro, Victor: C–Span
Mooar, Brian: NBC Newschannel
Moon, Ho Chul: MBC–TV Korea (Munhwa)
Mooney, Alex: CNN
Moore, Garrette: C–Span
Moore, Jack: Federal News Radio 1500 AM
Moore, Jacob: CBN News
Moore, Linwood: C–Span
Moore, Robert: Independent Television News (ITN)
Moore, Terrence: Metro Networks
Moore, W. Harrison: Middle East Broadcasting Networks (MBN)
Moorer, Willie: Voice of America
Moorhead, Jeremy: CNN

MEMBERS ENTITLED TO ADMISSION—Continued

Morada, Ray: NBC News
Morales, Isabel: CNN
Moran, Amanda: CBS News
Moreno, Julio: Radio Valera Venezuela
Morgan, Donald: CBS News
Morgan, Marcia: National Public Radio
Morgan, Nancy: WETA
Mori, Sumiko: Fuji TV Japan
Morris, Allie: The Newshour with Jim Lehrer
Morris, Amy: CBS News
Morris, Holly: WTTG–Fox Television
Morris, Peter: CNN
Morrisette, Roland: Bloomberg Radio & TV
Morrissey, John: AP–Broadcast
Morse, Richard: Fox News
Mortazavi, Negar: Voice of America
Mortman, Howard: C–Span
Morton, Dan: C–Span
Mortreux, Vincent: TF1–French TV
Moseley, Virginia: CNN
Moser, Martin: Link TV
Mosk, Matthew: ABC News
Mosley, Matthew: Fuji TV Japan
Moubray, Virginia: Middle East Broadcasting Networks (MBN)
Mounts, Ronald: WJLA–TV / Newschannel 8
Mowry, Brandon: WJLA–TV / Newschannel 8
Moynihan, Mark: The Newshour with Jim Lehrer
Mozaffari, Shaheen: NBC News
Mozgovaya, Natalia: Voice of America
Mueller, Sarah: CNN
Mueller-Thum, Sabine: German Broadcasting Systems–ARD
Muhammad, Alverda: National Scene News
Muhammad, Askia: National Scene News
Muhammad, Seleena M.: Fox News
Mui, Elaine: Voice of Russia
Muir, Robert: Reuters Radio & TV
Mullen, Christopher: WUSA–TV
Mullon, Tiffany: The Newshour with Jim Lehrer
Munford, Corey: Radio Free Asia
Munoz, Luis: Middle East Broadcasting Networks (MBN)
Muntu, Roger: Voice of America
Murai, Kiyoshi: Tokyo Broadcasting System
Muratani, Tateki: Nippon TV Network
Murphy, John: CBS News
Murphy, Lauren: Metro Networks
Murphy, Richard: WTTG–Fox Television
Murphy, Terry: C–Span
Murray, Mark: NBC News
Murray, Matthew: WRC–TV / NBC–4
Murray, Megan: Fox News
Murray, Timothy K.: Ventana Productions
Murry, Rosetta: CNN
Mursa, Alexander: RTTV America
Murtaugh, Peter: BBC
Musha, Jilili: Radio Free Asia
Muskat, Steven: NBC Newschannel
Musselwhite-Tobey, Kate: Washingtonpost.com
Myers, Bryan: Aljazeera International
Myers, Dwayne: WJLA–TV / Newschannel 8
Myers, Lisa: NBC News
Myrick, Yetta: C–Span
Nado, Jill: Fox News Radio
Naidoo, Anand: China Central TV Bureau
Naing, Thet: Voice of America
Najarian, Sarkis: Radio Free Asia
Najjar, Raqaiyah: China Central TV Bureau
Nakano, Junko: NHK–Japan Broadcasting Corporation
Nania, Rachel: WTOP Radio
Nannes, Steven: CNN
Napier, Joyce: Canadian Broadcasting Corporation (CBC)
Narahari, Priya: Eurovision Americas, Inc.
Narisi, Stephen: N24 German TV
Nash, Todd: Ventana Productions
Nason, Andrew: C–Span
Nassar, Mohamed El Hussin: Middle East Broadcasting Networks (MBN)
Nasser, Mohamed: AP–Broadcast
Nathan, Nancy: NBC News
Naylor, Brian: National Public Radio
Naylor, Robert: Voice of America
Neal, Jason: NBC News
Neal, Michelle: NBC News
Neely, Bill: Independent Television News (ITN)
Neely, Brett: Minnesota Public Radio
Negron, Mynellies: WFDC–TV Univision
Neil, Tara: BBC
Nelson, Christopher: National Public Radio
Nelson, Donna: NBC News
Nelson, Graham: Tokyo Broadcasting System
Nelson, James: Fox News
Nelson, Joseph: Washington Bureau News Service
Nelson, Marie: BET Nightly News
Nelson, Suzanne: CNN
Nettles, Meredith: ABC News
Neubauer, Kristin: Reuters Radio & TV
Neumann, Robin: German TV ARD
Nevins, Elizabeth: NBC News
Newberry, Tom: NBC Newschannel
Nguyen, Anh: Fox News
Nguyen, Thao: Voice of America
Nha, Kevin: Korean Broadcasting Systems
Ni, Chia-Hui: TVBS
Nicci, Nicholette: CNN
Nicholas, Eric: Comcast NBC
Nicholas, Eric: FedNet
Nichols, Hans: Bloomberg Radio & TV
Nicolaidis, Virginia: CNN
Niemann, Stefan: German TV ARD
Nikuradze, David: Rustavi 2 Broadcasting Company
Ninan, Reena: ABC News
Ninh, Trang (Nicole): C–Span

MEMBERS ENTITLED TO ADMISSION—Continued

Niu, Yun: China Central TV Bureau
Nixon, Adam: Middle East Broadcasting Networks (MBN)
Noble, Jeffrey: ABC News
Nocciolo, Ernest G.: CNN
Nolen, John: CBS News
Nomi, Kyle: TV Asahi
Non, Jennifer: Fox News
Noor, Areej: Aljazeera International
Noor, Matiullah Abid: Voice of America
Nordstrom, Mette: Finnish Broadcasting Company (YLE)
Norins, Jamie: Diversified Communications, Inc. (DCI)
Norling, Richard A.: ABC News
Norris, Christopher: NBC Newschannel
Norris, Donna: C–Span
Norris, James: Middle East Broadcasting Networks (MBN)
Northam, Jackie: National Public Radio
Nottingham, Danielle: CBS News
Novosel, James: NBC News
Nunez, Jorge: Ntv–Russia Broadcasting Company
Nunez, Jorge: RCN–TV (Colombia)
Nunez, Shoshannah: CBN News
Nurenberg, Gary: WUSA–TV
Nutter, Marguerite: National Public Radio
O'Berry, D. Kerry: Fox News
O'Brien, David: NBC News
O'Brien, Jane: BBC
O'Brien, Mike: NBC News
O'Brien, Soledad: Aljazeera International
O'Connell, Benjamin: C–Span
O'Connell, Mike: Federal News Radio 1500 AM
O'Connell, Mike: NBC Newschannel
O'Connell, Rosalie: Voice of America
O'Connor, Kerry: Fox News
O'Donnell, Kelly: NBC News
O'Donnell, Patrick: Eye–To–Eye Video
O'Gara, Patrick: ABC News
O'Hara, Jessica: Fox News
O'Hara, William: Diversified Communications, Inc. (DCI)
O'Malley, Ryan: Fox News
O'Neill, Emily: Independent Television News (ITN)
O'Regan, Michael: WRC–TV / NBC–4
O'Shea, Jr., Daniel J.: ABC News
O'Sullivan, Dylan: Middle East Broadcasting Networks (MBN)
Oberti, Ralf: Aljazeera International
Oblaender, Carsten: Storyhouse Productions
Och, Andy: Fox News
Odom, Quillie: Fox News
Offermann, Claudia: German TV ZDF
Oinounou, Mosheh: CBS News
Olabanji, Olajumoke: WJLA–TV / Newschannel 8
Olick, Diana: CNBC
Oliger, Brian: WTOP Radio
Ollove, Michael: Stateline.org
Ollstein, Alice: Free Speech Radio News
Olmsted, Alan: C–Span
Olson, Anna: Fox News
Omara, Kamal: AP–Broadcast
Oo, Aung: Voice of America
Oo, Thar: Voice of America
Orchard, Mark: Aljazeera International
Orellana-Canas, Ernesto: Telemundo Network
Orenstein, Jayne: Washingtonpost.com
Orgel, Paul: C–Span
Orr, Bob: CBS News
Ortiz, Fabien: France 2 Television
Ortiz, Felix: WUSA–TV
Osinski, Krystyna: TIMI
Ouafi, Mohamed: AP–Broadcast
Overby, Peter: National Public Radio
Overton, Heather: C–Span
Owen, Andrea: ABC News
Owliaei, Negin: Aljazeera International
Oyebanjo, Nike: C–Span
Ozden, Erkan: Danish Broadcasting Corporation
Ozden, Erkan: Swedish Broadcasting
Ozsancak, Hakan: China Central TV Bureau
Pacheco, Antonio: WETA
Padilla-Cirino, Mercy: Hispanic Communications Network
Pagan, Louis: AP–Broadcast
Page, David: CBN News
Page, Steven: CNN
Paggini, Thomas: Swiss Broadcasting
Paitchadze, Khatia: TV 9 (Georgia)
Palai, Andre: CBS News
Palca, Joe: National Public Radio
Palchikoff, Kim: Voice of Russia
Palmer, Hope: NBC News
Pang, Jin: New Tang Dynasty TV
Pannell, Ian: BBC
Panov, Alexander: Rtvi / Echo–TV
Panzer, Chester: WRC–TV / NBC–4
Papadeas, Tabatha: CBN News
Papinashvili, Aleksandre: Rustavi 2 Broadcasting Company
Parabaniuk, Julia: Voice of America
Park, Bunsoo: MBC–TV Korea (Munhwa)
Park, Crystal: Voice of Russia
Park, Jihee: Eurovision Americas, Inc.
Park, Jinkyung: Korean Broadcasting Systems
Park, Jung-Woo: Radio Free Asia
Park, Kathy: WJLA–TV / Newschannel 8
Parker, Andre: CNN
Parker, Beth: WTTG–Fox Television
Parker, Eric: Federal News Service
Parker, Robert Geoffrey: CNN
Parkinson, John R.: ABC News
Parks, Bob: CNSnews.com
Parks, Corwin: CNSnews.com
Parmet, Morgan: NBC News

MEMBERS ENTITLED TO ADMISSION—Continued

Parsell, Robert: Voice of America
Pathammavong, Kingsavanh: Voice of America
Patience, Keenan: Verizon
Patrick, Dan: WJLA–TV / Newschannel 8
Patruznick, Michael: C–Span
Patsalos, Connie: NBC News
Patsko, Daniel: ABC News
Patterson, Leigh: Agence France Presse (AFP–TV)
Patterson, Stephen: CNN
Paul, John: Federal News Service
Paulert, Ruediger: German TV ARD
Paxton, Bradford S.: Fox News
Paylor, Eddie: NBC News
Peaches, Sandra: CTV–Community TV of PG County
Peacock, Grant: Euronews
Peaks, Gershon: Reuters Radio & TV
Pearson, Hampton: CNBC
Pearson, Mark: WUSA–TV
Peebles, Daniel: CBS News
Pegues, Jeffrey: CBS News
Pellenberg, Wayne: WJLA–TV / Newschannel 8
Peltier, Yves: Canadian Broadcasting Corporation (CBC)
Penaloza, Marisa: National Public Radio
Pennell, Elizabeth: Morningside Partners, LLC
Peppers, Greg: AP–Broadcast
Peralta, Eyder: National Public Radio
Percha, Julie: Washingtonpost.com
Perez, Carlos: CNN
Perez, Evan: CNN
Perez, Rafael: WFDC–TV Univision
Perez, Simone: C–Span
Pergam, Andrew: Washingtonpost.com
Pergram, Chad: Fox News
Peries, Sharmini: Real News Network
Perkins, Anthony: WTTG–Fox Television
Perkins, Douglas: NBC News
Perkins, Vernon: C–Span
Perl, Drora: Galei–Tzahal (Israel Army Radio)
Perlmutter-Gumbiner, Elyse: NBC News
Perlow, Rebecca: CNN
Perna, Lindsey: CNN
Perrell, Thomas: CNN
Perry, Cal: Voice of America
Perry, Christina: C–Span
Perry, Jr., Timothy: The Newshour with Jim Lehrer
Persinko, Tim: Viewpoint Communications
Peslis, Chris: Fox News
Pessin, Don: Reuters Radio & TV
Peters, Roslyn: WJLA–TV / Newschannel 8
Peterson III, Robert: CBS News
Peterson, Gordon: WJLA–TV / Newschannel 8
Petitte, Patti: WRC–TV / NBC–4
Petraitis, Gerald: AP–Broadcast
Petroka, Katelyn: CNN
Pettit, Debra: NBC News
Peyton, Michael: CBS News
Pflugh, Chelsea: C–Span
Pham, Jacqueline: Fox News
Pham, Sherisse: CNN
Phelps, Jordyn: ABC News
Philip, Abby: ABC News
Philippe, Jean: Voice of America
Philippon, Alan: CNN
Phillips, Steven: Reuters Radio & TV
Piacente, Ellen: Morningside Partners, LLC
Pick, Lauren: Fox News
Pigott, Bernard: Fox News Radio
Pinczuk, Murray: NHK–Japan Broadcasting Corporation
Pinkerton, Elizabeth: Talk Radio News Service
Pinto, Susanna: EWTN
Pinzon, Wingel: Telemundo Network
Piper, Jeff: WRC–TV / NBC–4
Pipkin, Chase: Hearst Television, Inc.
Pitocco, Nickolas: C–Span
Pitt, Christopher: BBC
Pizarro, Fernando: Univision
Plante, William: CBS News
Plater, Christopher: WRC–TV / NBC–4
Pliszak, Richard K.: ABC News
Plotkin, Mark: WTTG–Fox Television
Poch, Reasey: Voice of America
Poduch, Shelby: NBC News
Polantz, Katelyn: The Newshour with Jim Lehrer
Poley, Michelle: CNN
Policastro, Jacqueline: Lilly Broadcasting
Polmer, Brendan: CNN
Ponnudurai, Parameswaran: Radio Free Asia
Poole, John: National Public Radio
Porsella, Claude L.: Radio France Internationale
Porter, Almon: C–Span
Porter, Christina: C–Span
Porter, Dee: Australian Broadcasting Corporation
Porter, Taylor: C–Span
Portnoy, Steven A.: ABC News
Postovit, David: Hearst Television, Inc.
Potts, Charlotte: German TV ARD
Potts, Nina-Maria: Feature Story News
Potts, Tracie: NBC Newschannel
Poulson, Theresa: Washingtonpost.com
Pound, Edward: Aljazeera International
Pourziaiee, Mehrnoosh: BBC
Povich, Elaine: Stateline.org
Powell, Brian William: Radio Free Asia
Powell, Lee: AP–Broadcast
Prah, Pamela M.: Stateline.org
Prann, Elizabeth: Fox News
Preloh, Anne: C–Span
Presto, Suzanne: Voice of America
Preston, Mark: CNN
Presutti, Carolyn: Voice of America
Price, Tolleah: CBS News
Prokupecz, Shimon: CNN
Pronko, Tony: C–Span

MEMBERS ENTITLED TO ADMISSION—Continued

Ptacek, Russell: WUSA–TV
Publicover, Robert: WTOP Radio
Pugliese, Pat: CNBC
Pulido, Hector: TVE – Spanish Public Television
Purbaugh, Michael J.: ABC News
Putzel, Christopher: Aljazeera International
Qi, Xinh: Xinhua
Quadrani, Federico: CNN
Qudah, Mohammad: ABS Network
Quinn, Diana: CBS News
Quinn, John: Voice of America
Quinn, Mary: ABC News
Quinnette, John: NBC News
Quinonez, Omar A.: Aljazeera International
Quiroz, Silvana: WFDC–TV Univision
Qureshi, Sophia: Aljazeera International
Rabin, Carrie: CBS News
Rabin, Mark: CBS News
Rachou, Carol: CNN
Rad, Ali: Fox News
Radu, Bogdan: CNN
Rady, Meaghan: NBC News
Rafferty, Andrew: NBC News
Rafferty, Meghan: CNN
Rager, Bryan: Reuters Radio & TV
Ragle, Brian: The Newshour with Jim Lehrer
Raiford, Roger: Aljazeera International
Ramadan, Wafik: AP–Broadcast
Ramchandani, Lavina: Hearst Television, Inc.
Ramos, Raul: WFDC–TV Univision
Randev, Sonia: CTV–Community TV of PG County
Randle, Debbie: BBC
Raney, Adam: Aljazeera International
Rankin, James: CNN
Rapalo, Manuel: RTTV America
Rastogi, Shruti: Sky News
Rathner, Jeffrey: WETA
Ratliff, Walter: AP–Broadcast
Ratner, Ellen: Talk Radio News Service
Ratner, Victor: ABC News
Rattansi, Shihab: Aljazeera International
Raval, Nikhil: C–Span
Raviv, Daniel: CBS News
Ray, Alonzo: NBC News
Ray, Douglas: CBS News
Raz, Guy: National Public Radio
Reap, Patrick: Bloomberg Radio & TV
Reardon, Beth: Federal News Radio 1500 AM
Reddy, Pallavi: CNN
Reed, Todd: Aljazeera International
Reeve, Richard: WJLA–TV / Newschannel 8
Reeves, Alea: Aljazeera International
Reeves, Austin: WTTG–Fox Television
Reeves, TraLanenia: Hearst Television, Inc.
Reffess, Melanie: NHK–Japan Broadcasting Corporation
Reid, Charles: CBS News
Reid, Jonathan: CBN News
Reilly, Robert: C–Span
Reinsel, Edward: Fox News
Reis, Chester: NBC News
Remillard, Michele: C–Span
Ren, Meixing: Hong Kong Phoenix Satellite Television
Renken, David: Fox News
Rensberger, Scott: TV2–Denmark
Resnick, Jon: AP–Broadcast
Reuter, Cynthia: C–Span
Reyes, Elaine: China Central TV Bureau
Reyes, Victor: Telemundo Network
Reynolds, Catherine: CBS News
Reynolds, Douglas: ABC News
Reynolds, Gioconda: Voice of America
Reynolds, Judy: Religion & Ethics Newsweekly
Reynolds, Robert: Aljazeera International
Reynolds, Talesha: NBC News
Rezaei, Kaveh: USA Today
Rhee, Alice: Washingtonpost.com
Rhee, Sung Chul: SBS
Rhodes, Elizabeth: Fox News
Ricalde, Katheryn: Fox News
Rice, Ben: WJLA–TV / Newschannel 8
Rice, Rodney: Verizon
Richard, Sylvain: Canadian Broadcasting Corporation (CBC)
Rickard, Michael: WTTG–Fox Television
Riddle, Casey: CNN
Riddlesberger, Scott: Voice of America
Ridolfi, Sarah: Fox News
Riess, Steffanie: German TV ZDF
Riggs, Giaco: NBC News
Riggs, James: NBC News
Rigney, Paul: C–Span
Riha, Anne Marie: Fox News
Riley, Justin: Voice of America
Rincon, Kevin: CBS News
Ringe, Linda: Voice of America
Rios, Delia: C–Span
Rios-Hernandez, Raul: CNN
Ritchie, Thomas: AP–Broadcast
Rivas-Vasquez, Victoria: Telemundo Network
Rizzi, Jared: XM Satellite Radio
Rizzo, Anthony: WUSA–TV
Rizzo, Jennifer: CNN
Roane Skehan, Andrea: WUSA–TV
Robbins, Christina: Fox News
Robbins, Diana: German TV ARD
Robbins, Francisco: CBS News
Robbins, Michael: Fox News
Robert, Olivier: Eye–To–Eye Video
Roberts, Bryan: WTTG–Fox Television
Roberts, Corinne: ABC News
Roberts, Eugene: ABC News
Roberts, Jean Pierre: Eurovision Americas, Inc.
Roberts, John: Fox News
Robertson, Greg: CNN

MEMBERS ENTITLED TO ADMISSION—Continued

Robertson, Tamara: Fox News
Robinson, Daniel: Voice of America
Robinson, David: CNN
Robinson, Kelvin: WRC–TV / NBC–4
Robinson, Margaret: The Newshour with Jim Lehrer
Robinson, Querry: NBC News
Robinson, Ralph: Voice of America
Robinson, Veronica: WTOP Radio
Roca, Xavier: TV3–Televisio De Catalunya
Rocha, Juan: Ventana Productions
Rocha, Samuel: Reuters Radio & TV
Rocque, Tiffany: C–Span
Rodeffer, Mark: C–Span
Rodriguez, Eduardo: AP–Broadcast
Rodriguez, Eduardo: TIMI
Rodriguez, Janet: China Central TV Bureau
Rodriguez, Martine: C–Span
Rodriguez, Susan: CNN
Rodriguez, Valdemar: RCN–TV (Colombia)
Roeckerath, Christoph: German TV ZDF
Roeller, Ulf-Jensen: German TV ZDF
Roemer, Hildrun: German TV ZDF
Rohrbeck, Douglas: Fox News
Rokus, Brian: CNN
Roland, Abu Bakr: ABC News
Roller, Richard L.: ABC News
Rollins, Bonnie: NBC Newschannel
Roof, Peter: NBC Newschannel
Root, Sean: The Hill
Root, Tom: Fox News Radio
Ropeik, Matthew: TV Tokyo
Rose, Art: WTOP Radio
Rose, Francis: Federal News Radio 1500 AM
Rose, Jeff: WJLA–TV / Newschannel 8
Roselli, H. Michael: CNN
Rosen, Ira: CBS News
Rosen, James: Fox News
Rosen, Rachel: CNN
Rosen, Shari: CNBC
Rosenberg, Gary: ABC News
Rosenberg, Howard: CBS News
Rosenfield, Jim: WRC–TV / NBC–4
Ross Taylor, Allyson: CBS News
Ross, Jane: Reuters Radio & TV
Ross, Katie: CBS News
Ross, Mary Katherine: CBS News
Rossetti-Meyer, Misa: Diversified Communications, Inc. (DCI)
Roth, Linda: CNN
Roth, Theodore: ABC News
Rovner, Julie: National Public Radio
Rowe, Hildrun: German TV ZDF
Rowe, Tom: Reuters Radio & TV
Rowland, Kara: Fox News
Rowls, Megan: WJLA–TV / Newschannel 8
Royce, Lindy: CNN
Roycraft, David: WUSA–TV
Royster, Meredith: WTTG–Fox Television
Ruby, Tracy: C–Span
Rudd, Michael: WJLA–TV / Newschannel 8
Ruderman, Jared: CBS News
Rudman, Kristin: Fox News
Rudnick, Natasha: Washingtonpost.com
Ruff, David: CNN
Ruff, Jennifer: C–Span
Ruffini, Christina: CBS News
Ruffini, Joseph: CBS News
Ruggiero, Diane: CNN
Ruhl, Lisa: Washington Examiner
Rushing, Ian: CBN News
Rushing, Joshua: Aljazeera International
Ruskin, Elizabeth: Alaska Public Radio Network
Russell, Eugene: WTTG–Fox Television
Russell, Keith: WRC–TV / NBC–4
Russell-Sluchansky, Carmen: Voice of Russia
Russert, Luke: NBC News
Rust, Emily: CNN
Ryan, Fred: WJLA–TV / Newschannel 8
Ryan, Kate: WTOP Radio
Rydell, Kate: CBS News
Ryntjes, Daniel: Feature Story News
Rysak, F. David: WTTG–Fox Television
Sababa, Ghassan: Aljazeera Satellite Channel (Peninsula)
Sabatinelli, Blake: WJLA–TV / Newschannel 8
Sachs, Rob: Voice of Russia
Sacks, Howard: NBC News
Sacks, Sam: RTTV America
Sadighi, Shahla: Voice of America
Saenz, Katherine: ABC News
Safronov, Rustem: Voice of Russia
Sagalyn, Daniel: The Newshour with Jim Lehrer
Saine-Spang, Cynthia: Voice of America
Sakar, Kabiruddin: Voice of America
Salan, Jennifer: Aljazeera International
Salas, Pedro: CNN
Salayma, Vera: Aljazeera Satellite Channel (Peninsula)
Salazar, Marcela: CNN
Salazar, Sulema: WZDC–TV
Saleeby, Rick: CNN
Sali, Sanil: Aljazeera International
Salim, Yuni: Voice of America
Saloomey, Kristen: Aljazeera International
Sammon, Bill: Fox News
Sampaio, Frederico: C–Span
Samperio, Aurora: Telesur
Sampson, Thomas: AP–Broadcast
Sampy, David: Independent Television News (ITN)
Samtani, Monika: WUSA–TV
Samuel, Stacey: CNN
Sanchez, Frances: CNN
Sanchez, George D.: ABC News
Sanchez, Jose: AP–Broadcast
Sanchez, Pablo: Univision
Sanchez, Robert: CBS News

MEMBERS ENTITLED TO ADMISSION—Continued

Sanders, Molly: C–Span
Sanders-Smith, Sherry: C–Span
Sandiford, Michelle: C–Span
Sands-Sadowitz, Geneva: The Hill
Sanfuentes, Antoine: NBC News
Sanfuentes, Jose Antoine: NBC News
Sang, Stanley: C–Span
Sanna, Nicholas: Verizon
Sansone, Joseph: CNN
Santa-Rita, Joad: Voice of America
Santayana, Michelle: CNN
Santo, Vincent: C–Span
Santos, Marcia: RTP Portuguese Public Television
Sanvido, Colleen: NBC News
Sapin, Paul: Aljazeera International
Sarfo-Kantanka, Johnson: C–Span
Sargent, Mark: WTTG–Fox Television
Sargent, Thayer: CNN
Sasaki, Tomoaki: ABC News
Sassenberg, Thomas: Storyhouse Productions
Satchell, David: WUSA–TV
Satterfield, John: WETA
Saulny, Susan: ABC News
Savage, Craig: Fox News
Savchenko, Yulia: Voice of America
Savoy, Gregory: Reuters Radio & TV
Sawera, Thomas: German TV ARD
Sayegh, Jr., Tony: Talk Radio News Service
Sbalcio, Ian: RTTV America
Scalise, Michelle: CBS News
Scanlan, William: C–Span
Scanlon, Jason: Fox News
Scarpelli, Leah: National Public Radio
Schaber, Steven: Voice of Russia
Schaefer, Robert: National Public Radio
Schantz, Douglas N.: CNN
Scharf, Jason: Eurovision Americas, Inc.
Schatz, Rebecca: China Central TV Bureau
Scheiner, Eric: CNSnews.com
Scheuer, John: C–Span
Schieffer, Bob: CBS News
Schiff, Brian: Voice of America
Schlegel, Barry C.: CNN
Schlenker, Aungthu: Radio Free Asia
Schliess, Gero: Deutsche Welle TV
Schloemer, Peter: German TV ZDF
Schmickler, Marion: German TV ARD
Schmidt, Andrea: Aljazeera International
Schneider, Corine: Aljazeera International
Schneider, Edward: Voice of America
Schneider, Fred: CBS News
Schneider, James: WETA
Schoenholtz, Howard: ABC News
Schoenmann, Donald: Eye–To–Eye Video
Schoffstall, Joe: CNSnews.com
Schonder, Gabrielle: CBS News
Schott, Sonia: Radio Valera Venezuela
Schultze, Emily: CNN
Schuster, Henry: CBS News
Schwab, Michael: Politico.com
Schwandt, Kimberly: Fox News
Schwarz, Gabriella: CNN
Schweiger, Ellen: C–Span
Schwetje, Lars: German TV ZDF
Sciacca, Jody: Fox News
Scoggins, Jennifer: CNN
Scott, Beth: NBC News
Scott, Ellen: China Central TV Bureau
Scott, Heather: CBS News
Scott, James: WJLA–TV / Newschannel 8
Scott, Linda: The Newshour with Jim Lehrer
Scott, Raquel: CNN
Scotto, Michael: Time Warner Cable
Scriabine, Raisa: Link TV
Scritchfield, Andrew: NBC News
Scruggs, Wesley: NBC News
Scuiletti, Justin: The Newshour with Jim Lehrer
Scully, Steven: C–Span
Seabrook, Andrea: Decode DC
Seabrook, Peter: Decode DC
Seabrook, Willliam: WETA
Seaby, Gregory: CNN
Sealock, Danella: WRC–TV / NBC–4
Searls, James: WJLA–TV / Newschannel 8
Searls, James: WUSA–TV
Sears, Abby: Fox News
Sears, Carl: NBC News
Sears, Taylor: Fox News
Seder, Molly: Voice of Russia
Seem, Thomas H.: CBS News
Segraves, Mark: WRC–TV / NBC–4
Seher, Jason: CNN
Seidman, Joel: NBC News
Seipel, Arnie: National Public Radio
Seium, Michael: Diversified Communications, Inc. (DCI)
Seldin, Jeff: Voice of America
Selma, Reginald G.: CNN
Semenova, Anna: Russian State TV and Radio (RTR)
Semler, Ashley: BBC
Seo, Ja Ryen: Korean Broadcasting Systems
Serbu, Jared: Federal News Radio 1500 AM
Serfaty, Sunlen: CNN
Serhan, Ali: AP–Broadcast
Serper, Noelle: Religion & Ethics Newsweekly
Serrano, Randy: WZDC–TV
Serwer, Adam: NBC News
Setsang, Pema: Voice of America
Seymour, Allison: WTTG–Fox Television
Shackelford, Rachael: CNN
Shaddick, Lorna: Feature Story News
Shaffir, Gregory: CBS News
Shakhbaz, Samir: Voice of Russia
Shakhov, Dmytro: Rtvi / Echo–TV

MEMBERS ENTITLED TO ADMISSION—Continued

Shalhoup, Joseph: NBC News
Shammo, Hakim: Voice of America
Shannon, Brad: Aol Huffington Post
Shannon, Dennis: CBS News
Shannon, Holly: WJLA–TV / Newschannel 8
Shannon, Michael: ABC News
Shapiro, Ari: National Public Radio
Shapiro, Dmitry: Voice of Russia
Shapiro, Joseph: National Public Radio
Sharma, B.K.: WJLA–TV / Newschannel 8
Sharp, Cynthia: AP–Broadcast
Shastri, Namgyal: Voice of America
Shaughnessy, Lawrence: CNN
Shaw, Cathy: National Public Radio
Shaw, Joseph: NHK–Japan Broadcasting Corporation
Shaylor, John: CNN
Sheerin, Jude: BBC
Shefte, Whitney: Washingtonpost.com
Shelton, Steve: Fox News
Shen, Chen: China Central TV Bureau
Sheng, Qing: China Central TV Bureau
Sheppard, Kevin: Sky News
Sherling, Eric: CNN
Sherman, Roger: Voice of America
Sherry, Marisha: Agence France Presse (AFP–TV)
Sherwood, Tom: WRC–TV / NBC–4
Shi, Ying: Voice of America
Shields, Daniel: Fox News Radio
Shields, Michael: Voice of America
Shikaki, Muna: Al Arabiya TV
Shim, Min: Seoul Broadcasting System (SBS)
Shimbori, Satoko: TV Asahi
Shin, Donguk: Seoul Broadcasting System (SBS)
Shipman, Claire: ABC News
Shire, Robert: German TV ARD
Shlemon, Chris: Independent Television News (ITN)
Shoffner, Harry: BBC
Shogren, Elizabeth: National Public Radio
Shoji, Shin: NHK–Japan Broadcasting Corporation
Shon, Robert: WTTG–Fox Television
Shore, Zach: WTOP Radio
Showell, Andre: BET Nightly News
Shull, Roger: Reuters Radio & TV
Siaden-Pena, Christian: RCN–TV (Colombia)
Sides, James: Metro Teleproductions
Siegel, Robert C.: National Public Radio
Siegfriedt, Anita: Fox News
Sills, Cecil John: NBC Newschannel
Silman III, Jimmie: WUSA–TV
Silva, Juan: MundoFox
Silva-Braga, Brook: Washingtonpost.com
Silva-Pinto, Lauren: Austrian Radio & TV (ORF)
Silva-Pinto, Luis Fernando: TV Globo International
Silver, David: NBC News
Silverberg, Hank: WTOP Radio
Silverleib, Alan: CNN
Silverman, Art: National Public Radio
Silverman, Gabe: Washingtonpost.com
Silverman, Rachel: Feature Story News
Silverman, Sandrine: To The Contrary (Persephone Productions)
Silverstein, Zachary: Talk Radio News Service
Simaan, Angela: Al Arabiya TV
Simeone, Ron: NBC News
Simkins, George: Voice of America
Simmons, Gregory: ABC News
Simmons, Sarah: WTTG–Fox Television
Simms, Jeffery: CNN
Simon, Jeff: Washingtonpost.com
Simon, Scott: National Public Radio
Simpson, Cynne: WJLA–TV / Newschannel 8
Simpson, Mariam: Aljazeera International
Sims, Colin: Reuters Radio & TV
Sina, Ralph: German TV ARD
Singh, Praveen: Talk Radio News Service
Sinn, Rebecca: WJLA–TV / Newschannel 8
Sipos, Joseph: Voice of America
Skeans, Ron: BBC
Skeen, Kimberly: CBS News
Skene, Mathieu: Aljazeera International
Skinski, Kathleen: CNN
Skopek, Aaron: NBC News
Slafka, Kristi: CNN
Slansky, Heike: German TV ZDF
Slattery, Julie: Bloomberg Radio & TV
Slen, Peter: C–Span
Slewka, Stephanie: German TV ZDF
Slie, Charles: NBC News
Sloan, Tyler: CNN
Sloane, Ward C.: CBS News
Slobogin, Kathy: Aljazeera International
Small, Matt: AP–Broadcast
Smith, Andrew: China Central TV Bureau
Smith, Anthony: Diversified Communications, Inc. (DCI)
Smith, Brent: CNN
Smith, Christie: NBC Newschannel
Smith, Cindy: ABC News
Smith, Cynthia: Fox News
Smith, Derrin: Antena 3 TV
Smith, Helena: National Public Radio
Smith, James E.: ABC News
Smith, Jason H.: WTTG–Fox Television
Smith, John: WRC–TV / NBC–4
Smith, Lindley: C–Span
Smith, Mark S.: AP–Broadcast
Smith, Martin: Sky News
Smith, Max: WTOP Radio
Smith, Michael: WETA
Smith, Phillip: Aljazeera International
Smith, William: Belo Capital Bureau
Smoot, Kelly: CNN
Smyth, Chris: Hearst Television, Inc.
Sneed, Kimberly: NBC News

MEMBERS ENTITLED TO ADMISSION—Continued

Snider, Katie: To The Contrary (Persephone Productions)
Soberon, Santiago: Storyhouse Productions
Sobocinski, Matt: Politico.com
Socolovsky, Jerome: Voice of America
Soe, Khin Maung: Radio Free Asia
Sok, Pov: Voice of America
Sokolova, Elena: Russian State TV and Radio (RTR)
Solash, Richard: Radio Free Europe
Soler, Esteve: TV3–Televisio De Catalunya
Soley, Joan: BBC
Solodovnikov, Mikhail: RTTV America
Solorzano, Gilbert: NBC News
Soltermann, Beat: Swiss Broadcasting
Sommers, Chloe: CNN
Sommerville, Shona: Sky News
Sonnheim, Jon: Cox Broadcasting
Sorensen, Eric D.: Global TV Canada
Sorenson, Ben: C–Span
Sorenson, Randall: Diversified Communications, Inc. (DCI)
Soric, Miodrag: Deutsche Welle TV
Soucy, Peggy: Eurovision Americas, Inc.
Sozio, George A.: ABC News
Sparrow, Thomas: BBC
Spear, Anita: WUSA–TV
Speck, Alan: C–Span
Spector, Teresa: Fox News
Speiser, Matthew: CNN
Spellman, James: China Central TV Bureau
Spencer, Darcy: WRC–TV / NBC–4
Spencer, Kim: Link TV
Sperry, Todd: CNN
Spevak, Joe: WTTG–Fox Television
Spiegler, Theodore: CBS News
Spire, Richard: CNN
Spodak, Cassandra: CNN
Spoerry, Philip Scott: CNN
Sprankle, James: Fox News
Springer, Drake: Fox News
Springer, Steven: Voice of America
Sproul, Robin: ABC News
Sreevinasan, Hari: The Newshour with Jim Lehrer
Srivastava, Amish: Voice of America
St. Jean, Johnny: C–Span
St. John, Jonathan: Fox Business Network
Stafford, Charlotte: Independent Television News (ITN)
Stakelbeck, Erick: CBN News
Stalnaker, Kurt: National Public Radio
Stamberg, Susan: National Public Radio
Stanke, Donald E.: WTTG–Fox Television
Starikoff, Gary: C–Span
Stark, Lisa: ABC News
Starling, Alison: WJLA–TV / Newschannel 8
Starr, Barbara: CNN
Starr, Penny: CNSnews.com
Staton, Thomas M.: ABC News
Staudinger, Christian: Austrian Radio & TV (ORF)
Stay, Daniel J.: Fox News
Stead, Scott: CNN
Steers, Julia: CBS News
Stefany, Steve: ABC News
Stein, Cari: To The Contrary (Persephone Productions)
Stein, Rob: National Public Radio
Steinberger, Daniel: ABC News
Steinhauser, Lesley: Irish Radio & TV (RTE)
Steinhauser, Paul: CNN
Steinman, Mindy: C–Span
Steinmetz, Jesper: TV2–Denmark
Stemple, Lexi: Fox News
Stephens, LaTonya: XM Satellite Radio
Stephens, Mark: WRC–TV / NBC–4
Sterling, Vaughn: CNN
Stevens, Seneca: Fox News
Stevenson, John: CNN
Stewart, Andrew: SRN News (Salem)
Stewart, Kathy: WTOP Radio
Stewart, Martina: CNN
Stewart, Robin: Ventana Productions
Stickley, Robin: Global TV Canada
Stirewalt, Chris: Fox News
Stix, Gabriel: CBS News
Stoddard, Mark S.: ABC News
Stoddard, Rick: C–Span
Stodter, John: Federal News Service
Stone, Evie: National Public Radio
Stone, Jessica: China Central TV Bureau
Stone, Shomari: WRC–TV / NBC–4
Storkel, Scott: Voice of America
Stout, Matthew: Fox News
Stoutzenberger, Timothy: CNN
Strand, Paul: CBN News
Straub, Terry: Diversified Communications, Inc. (DCI)
Street, Jonathan: One America
Streitfeld, Rachel: CNN
Strickland, Kenneth: NBC News
Strickler, Laura: CBS News
Stringer, Ashley: CNBC
Strothe, Stephen: N24 German TV
Stuard, Christopher: WJLA–TV / Newschannel 8
Stubbs, James: NBC News
Su, Xiaoxiao: China Central TV Bureau
Suarez, Rafael: The Newshour with Jim Lehrer
Suddeth, James: Fox News
Suddeth, Rick: Fox News
Sughroue, Jon: NBC News
Suiters, Kimberly: CBS News
Sulasma, Olli-Pekka: Finnish Broadcasting Company (YLE)
Sullivan, Laura: National Public Radio
Sullivan, Lee: CBS News
Sullivan, Robert: NBC News

MEMBERS ENTITLED TO ADMISSION—Continued

Summers, Elizabeth: The Newshour with Jim Lehrer
Summers, Patrick: Fox News
Sumrel, John: Fox News
Sun, Ping: China Central TV Bureau
Suphaphon, Songphot: Voice of America
Suto, Ena: TV Asahi
Suzara, Jennifer: Fox News
Svoboda, Sarah: BBC
Swagler, Craig: CBS News
Swain, Bethany: Mobile Video Services, LTD
Swain, Susan: C–Span
Swain, Todd: Mobile Video Services, LTD
Swanson, Carl: Voice of America
Sweeney, Robert: WRC–TV / NBC–4
Sweetapple, Dan: Australian Broadcasting Corporation
Swicord, Jeffrey: Voice of America
Sylvester, John: Fox News Radio
Sylvester, Lisa: CNN
Symanski, Mary: C–Span
Szajkowski, Vara: BBC
Szeltner, Catherine: EWTN
Szematowicz, Daniel: CNN
Szypulski, Tom: Aljazeera International
Tabet, Joseph: Middle East Broadcasting Networks (MBN)
Taguchi, Mai: Nippon TV Network
Taing, Sarada: Radio Free Asia
Taira, So: Tokyo Broadcasting System
Takagane, Yuka: NHK–Japan Broadcasting Corporation
Takashima, Miho: Tokyo Broadcasting System
Talarico, Julie: Fox News
Talley, Lauren: Religion & Ethics Newsweekly
Tamerlani, George: Reuters Radio & TV
Tanaka, Edson: RTP Portuguese Public Television
Tanaka, Masayoshi: NHK–Japan Broadcasting Corporation
Tang, Qin: China Central TV Bureau
Tanno, Kiyoshi: Nippon TV Network
Tanzeem, Ayesha: Voice of America
Tapper, Jake: CNN
Tashi, Yeshi: Radio Free Asia
Tasillo, Mary Ellen: Fox News
Tate, Simon: Aljazeera International
Tate, Tiffany: BET Nightly News
Tatton-Brown, Anna: BBC
Tavcar, Erik: Reuters Radio & TV
Taylor, Audrey: ABC News
Taylor, Christina: C–Span
Taylor, Jacqueline: Fox News
Taylor, John: WRC–TV / NBC–4
Taylor, Rolf: National Public Radio
Taylor, Russell: C–Span
Tea, Brandon: CBS News
Teboe, Mark: Aljazeera International
Teclab, Minia: Voice of America
Teeples, Joseph: C–Span
Tejerina, Pilar: Aljazeera International
Temin, Thomas: Federal News Radio 1500 AM
Terpstra, Patrick: Cox Broadcasting
Terrett, John: Al Jazeera America
Terrett, John: Aljazeera International
Terry, Janet: WUSA–TV
Test, Test: ABC News
Tevault, Neil David: National Public Radio
Tha, Kyaw: Voice of America
Thalman, Mark: Ventana Productions
Thanos, Georgeanne: ABC News
Thein, Kyaw: Voice of America
Theisen, Michael: Voice of America
Thelin, David: NBC News
Thiedman, Will: C–Span
Thoman, Eric: C–Span
Thomas, Amy: ABC News
Thomas, Charley: CBS News
Thomas, Charlie: CBS News
Thomas, Christopher: CTV–Community TV of PG County
Thomas III, James B.: CNN
Thomas, Pierre: ABC News
Thomas, Sharahn: National Public Radio
Thomas, Shari: ABC News
Thomas, Shawna: NBC News
Thomas, Will: WTTG–Fox Television
Thompson Anderson, Laetitia: WRC–TV / NBC–4
Thompson, Cameron: CBS News
Thompson, Jeremy: Sky News
Thompson, Joseph: WETA
Thompson, Ron: Radio One
Thompson, Shaleem: Reuters Radio & TV
Thompson, Tisha: WRC–TV / NBC–4
Thomson, Sylvia: Canadian Broadcasting Corporation (CBC)
Thorne, C. Patrick: Washington Bureau News Service
Thornes, Troy: CBS News
Thornton, Ronald: NBC News
Thorp, Frank: NBC News
Thuman, Scott: WJLA–TV / Newschannel 8
Tiller, Arthur: C–Span
Tillman, Thomas E.: CBS News
Tilman, Brandon: C–Span
Tin, Annie: C–Span
Titera, Lindzie: CNN
Tobia, Peter: The Newshour with Jim Lehrer
Tobianski, Sarah: C–Span
Todd, Brian: CNN
Todd, Chuck: NBC News
Tolliver, Terri: WTTG–Fox Television
Toman, George: NBC Newschannel
Tomlinson, Blair: Gannett Government Media Corp.
Tomlinson, Lucas: Fox News
Tong, Scott: Marketplace Radio
Toribio, Adoracion: TVE – Spanish Public Television

MEMBERS ENTITLED TO ADMISSION—Continued

Torlone, Lauren: C–Span
Torpey, Robert: Fox News
Toso, Nicolas: CNN
Totenberg, Nina: National Public Radio
Towers, Lucy: Independent Television News (ITN)
Trabandt, Anne: Fox News
Tracey, Bree: Fox News
Trainor, Thomas: Eurovision Americas, Inc.
Trammell, Michael: WUSA–TV
Tran, Hoa Ai: Radio Free Asia
Trauzzi, Monica: Environment & Energy Publishing, LLC
Travers, Karen Lynn: ABC News
Travis, Shannon: CNN
Traynham, Peter C.: CBS News
Traynham, Robert: Comcast NBC
Triay, Andres P.: CBS News
Trosclair, Clayton: Eurovision Americas, Inc.
Trowbridge, Alexander: Politico.com
Tschida, Stephen: WJLA–TV / Newschannel 8
Tserenbaljid, Uyanga: German TV ZDF
Tsereteli, Rusudan: TV 9 (Georgia)
Tsou, Chris: Ventana Productions
Tsugawa, Takafumi: Tokyo Broadcasting System
Tuan, Shih-Yuan: TVBS
Tucker, Elke: German TV ZDF
Tull, Anthony: WRC–TV / NBC–4
Tuman, Anna: NBC News
Tuohey, Kenneth: CNN
Turner, Carla: Canadian Broadcasting Corporation (CBC)
Turner, Catherine: Aljazeera International
Turner, Chris: CNN
Turner, Hayley: Fox News
Turner, Mikea: CTV–Community TV of PG County
Turner, Robert: Independent Television News (ITN)
Turner, Sue: Belo Capital Bureau
Turner, William: EWTN
Turnham, Stephen: Aljazeera International
Turrell, Elizabeth: WUSA–TV
Tuszynski, Tom: Al Arabiya TV
Tutman, Dan D.: CBS News
Tvegard, Anders: Norwegian Broadcasting
Tweed, Robert: CNN
Tyers, Rebecca: Independent Television News (ITN)
Tyler, Brett: CNN
Tyler, Lamonte: Fox News
Tyler, Thomas: Diversified Communications, Inc. (DCI)
Tyree, Wade: ABC News
Ubeda, Anna: TVE – Spanish Public Television
Uceda, Claudia: WFDC–TV Univision
Uchoa, Pablo: BBC
Uhl, Kim: CNN
Ulbrich-Strothe, Sabine: N24 German TV
Ulery, Brad: Reuters Radio & TV
Uliano, Dick: WTOP Radio
Ulloa, Melinda: CBS News
Ulloa, Melinda: Reuters Radio & TV
Ulloa, Victor: CBS News
Umeh, Maureen: WTTG–Fox Television
Umrani, Anthony R.: CNN
Underhill, Justine: RTTV America
Upadhyay, Brajesh: BBC
Uprety, Sharmila: Sagarmatha Television
Urban, Mark: BBC
Urbanski, Tina: NBC News
Urbina, Luis: TV Globo International
Ure, Laurie: CNN
Ureta, Juan: NBC News
Uribe, Juvenal: Morningside Partners, LLC
Urquhart, Jonathan: BBC
Usero, Adriana: RTTV America
Vaidyanathan, Rajini: BBC
Valentine, Demetress: CNN
Valentine, Natalie: Comcast NBC
Van Cleave, Kristopher: WJLA–TV / Newschannel 8
Van de Mark, Ellen: CNN
Van der Bellen, Erin: WUSA–TV
van der Veen, Jacob: TIMI
Van Susteren, Greta: Fox News
Vance, Denise: AP–Broadcast
Vandenbrink, Rachel: Radio Free Asia
VanderVeen, Jacob: Mobile Video Services, LTD
VanderVeen, Lawrence: Mobile Video Services, LTD
Vanderveen, Paul: Voice of America
VanHaren, Joel: Aljazeera International
Vargas, Luke: Talk Radio News Service
Vasel, Kathryn: Fox Business Network
Vasquez, Jennifer: BBC
Vasquez, Jennifer: NBC Newschannel
Vaughan, Scott: Reuters Radio & TV
Vaughan, Vincent: WJLA–TV / Newschannel 8
Vaughn Sandoval, Hillary: Fox News
Vaughn, Mike: WJLA–TV / Newschannel 8
Vela, Hatzel: WJLA–TV / Newschannel 8
Veldkamp, Joel: Talk Radio News Service
Vennell, Vicki A.: ABC News
Vera, Jaime: WZDC–TV
Verdugo, Adam: NBC News
Ververs, Vaughn: NBC News
Vestal, Christine: Stateline.org
Vicario, Virginia A.: ABC News
Viczian, Ilona: Aljazeera International
Viers, Dana: ABC News
Viers, Dana: CNN
Vigil, Marcos: ABC News
Vila, Xavier: Catalunya Radio
Villarreal, Alexandra: Voice of America
Villone Garcia, Patricia: CTV–Community TV of PG County
Vincent, Michael: Australian Broadcasting Corporation
Vinson, Bryce: Fox News

MEMBERS ENTITLED TO ADMISSION—Continued

Viqueira, Michael: Aljazeera International
Virji, Anar: Aljazeera International
Vishnevoy, Dmitry: Channel One Russian TV
Visioli, Todd: Fox News
Visley, Andrew G.: AP–Broadcast
Vitale, Joseph: Voice of America
Vitorovich, Susan: NBC News
Vizcarra, Mario: Univision
Vlahos, Kelley Beaucar: Fox News
Vock, Daniel: Stateline.org
Vogel, Erin: Fox News
Vogel, Phil: Fox News
Vohra, Sweta: Aljazeera International
Volkov, Dmitri: Channel One Russian TV
Volokhonovich, Vera: RTTV America
von Bonsdorff, Juri: Eurovision Americas, Inc.
Vosti, Andrea: Swiss Broadcasting
Voth, Charles: WETA
Vu, Tu H.: CNN
Vukmer, David: NBC News
Vurnis, Ambrose: WRC–TV / NBC–4
Wafa, Mohamed: Middle East Broadcasting Networks (MBN)
Waghorn, Dominic: Sky News
Waghorn, Noel: AP–Broadcast
Wagner, Paul: WTTG–Fox Television
Waheed, Amina: Aljazeera International
Wahl, Elizabeth: RTTV America
Wais, Soran: CNN
Wait, Kevin: National Public Radio
Waldman, Elliot: Tokyo Broadcasting System
Walker, Amanda: Sky News
Walker, Jackie Lyn: ABC News
Walker, James: WJLA–TV / Newschannel 8
Walker, Sebastian: Aljazeera International
Walker, William: CBS News
Wall, Katherine: NBC News
Wallace, Chris: Fox News
Wallace, Gregory: CNN
Wallace, John L.: Fox News
Wallace, Neil: Fox News
Wallick, Doug: NBC News
Walsche, Suhshannah: ABC News
Walsh, Deirdre: CNN
Walsh, Hannah: Sky News
Walsh, Mary: CBS News
Walter, Jonathan: Fox News
Walter, Mike: China Central TV Bureau
Walters, Amy: Aljazeera International
Walters, Amy: National Public Radio
Walton-James, Vickie: National Public Radio
Walz, Mark: CNN
Wang, Bingru: Hong Kong Phoenix Satellite Television
Wang, Fenghua: China Central TV Bureau
Wang, Guan: China Central TV Bureau
Wang, Hui: China Central TV Bureau
Wang, Jin: Aljazeera International
Wang, Meng: China Central TV Bureau
Wang, Taofeng: Hong Kong Phoenix Satellite Television
Wang, Yang: New Tang Dynasty TV
Waqfi, Wajd: Aljazeera Satellite Channel (Peninsula)
Ward, Derrick: WRC–TV / NBC–4
Ward, Kenric: Talk Radio News Service
Ward, Patrick: Fox News
Warfield, R.T.: China Central TV Bureau
Warner, Craig: CBS News
Warner, Tarik: WRC–TV / NBC–4
Warr, Kara: WJLA–TV / Newschannel 8
Warren, Thomas: WTOP Radio
Wasgien, Sonja: German TV ARD
Washburn, Kevin: C–Span
Washington Anderson, Robert: WJLA–TV / Newschannel 8
Washington, Erick: CBS News
Washington, Ervin: Aljazeera International
Washington, Kyeshia: CNN
Washington, Richard: WTTG–Fox Television
Washington, Travis: WJLA–TV / Newschannel 8
Watkins, Duane: China Central TV Bureau
Watkins, Duane: WTTG–Fox Television
Watrud, Don: WTTG–Fox Television
Watson, Katy: BBC
Watson, Walter: National Public Radio
Watts, Andrew: National Public Radio
Wayessa, Dhaba: Voice of America
Weakly, David: NBC News
Webb, Tracey: CNN
Webber, Joseph: Fox News
Webster, Aaron: Fox News
Webster, Richard: Talk Radio News Service
Weeks, Linton: National Public Radio
Wegmann, Christopher: Radio One
Wehinger, Amy: Fox News
Wei, Xing: China Central TV Bureau
Wei, Xuejiao: China Central TV Bureau
Weidenbosch, Glenn: China Central TV Bureau
Weinberg, Ali: ABC News
Weinbloom, Hank: Fox News Radio
Weinfeld, Michael: AP–Broadcast
Weinstein, Richard: C–Span
Weinstock, Roy: WRC–TV / NBC–4
Weisbrod, Eric: CNN
Weiss, Alexis: CNN
Weiss, Ellen: Scripps Howard
Weiss, Jessica: CNN
Welker, Kristen: NBC News
Weller, George D.: ABC News
Welna, David: National Public Radio
Welsh, Meghan: Fox News
Welter, Juergen: German TV ARD
Werner, Katarina: BBC
Wertheimer, Linda: National Public Radio
West, David: Verizon

MEMBERS ENTITLED TO ADMISSION—Continued

Westerwelle, Fabian: ABC News
Wheeler, Brian: Aljazeera International
Wheelock, Robert: Aljazeera International
White, Amanda: CNN
White, Douglas: ABC News
White, Edward: CNN
White, James: Metro Networks
White, Mark: CBS News
Whiteman, Caroline: Fox News
Whiteside, John P.: ABC News
Whitley, John H.: CBS News
Whitley, Walter: Fox News
Whitney, Michael: Washington Bureau News Service
Whitsett, Kyrie: Nippon TV Network
Whitson, Ricardo: CBS News
Whittington, Christopher: NBC News
Wholey, Dennis: This Is America with Dennis Wholey
Widmer, Chris: CBS News
Wiedenbauer, Heidi: Cox Broadcasting
Wiggins, Dion: WUSA–TV
Wiggins, Christopher: NBC Newschannel
Wik, Snorre: Aljazeera International
Wild, Whitney: WJLA–TV / Newschannel 8
Wilde, Winston: NBC News
Wilk, Wendy: Hearst Television, Inc.
Wilkes, Douglas H.: WTTG–Fox Television
Wilkins, Tracee: WRC–TV / NBC–4
Williams, Abigail: NBC News
Williams, Armstrong: Sinclair Broadcast Group
Williams, Brenna: NBC News
Williams, Colleen: Fox News
Williams, David: Fox News
Williams, James: NBC News
Williams, Jeffrey L.: Cox Broadcasting
Williams, John: Fox News
Williams, Keith: WUSA–TV
Williams, Kenneth E.: CBS News
Williams, Louis Pete: NBC News
Williams, Matt: Independent Television News (ITN)
Williams, Robert T.: NBC News
Williams, Steven: WTTG–Fox Television
Williamson, Christopher: NBC News
Willingham, Val: CNN
Willis, Anne Marie: Fox News
Willis, David: BBC
Wilson, Kristin: CNN
Wilson, Mark: CBS News
Wilson, Stephanie: WUSA–TV
Winborn, Tracy: CBN News
Windham, Ronald: WJLA–TV / Newschannel 8
Winterhalter, Ruthann: C–Span
Winters, Ronald: ABC News
Wiseman, Frederick: CNN
Wishon, Jennifer: CBN News
Witte, Joel: China Central TV Bureau
Woldearegay, Eden: Agence France Presse (AFP–TV)
Wolf, Zachary: ABC News
Wolf, Zachary: CNN
Wolfe, Lisa: Federal News Radio 1500 AM
Wood, Christopher: C–Span
Wood, Skip: WJLA–TV / Newschannel 8
Wood, Winston: Voice of America
Woodall, Crystal: CBN News
Woodruff, Judy: The Newshour with Jim Lehrer
Woodsome, Kathleen: Voice of America
Woolbright, Melinda: WRC–TV / NBC–4
Wordock, Colleen: Bloomberg Radio & TV
Workman, Paul: CTV Canadian TV
Wortman, Alexander: NHK–Japan Broadcasting Corporation
Wotshela, Gringo: BBC
Wright, Benjamin: BBC
Wright, Dale: WJLA–TV / Newschannel 8
Wright, James: Aljazeera International
Wright, Kelly: Fox News
Wright, Natalie: Independent Television News (ITN)
Wright, Tammy: Aljazeera International
Wrona, Marcin: TVN Poland
Wu, Hanying: China Central TV Bureau
Wu, Wei: New Tang Dynasty TV
Wyszogrodzki, Marcin: TVN Poland
Xavier, Wilkins: Aljazeera International
Xiang, Dong: New Tang Dynasty TV
Xiao, Hejia: China Central TV Bureau
Xie, Chenguang: China Central TV Bureau
Xue, Bin: New Tang Dynasty TV
Yack, Angie: CNN
Yaeger, Christopher: Federal News Service
Yager, Joshua: CBS News
Yaklyvich, Brian: CNN
Yam, Raymond: Voice of America
Yamaguchi, Daisuke: NHK–Japan Broadcasting Corporation
Yamaguchi, Noriyuki: Tokyo Broadcasting System
Yamasaki, Takeshi: NHK–Japan Broadcasting Corporation
Yancy, Shawn: WTTG–Fox Television
Yang, Carter: CBS News
Yang, Chunfang: New Tang Dynasty TV
Yang, Daniel: The Newshour with Jim Lehrer
Yang, Eun: WRC–TV / NBC–4
Yang, Hee: Radio Free Asia
Yang, Jian: China Central TV Bureau
Yang, Lianhua: American Chinese Television (ACT)
Yang, Sungwon: Radio Free Asia
Yang, Yang: Bloomberg Radio & TV
Yarborough, Rick: WRC–TV / NBC–4
Yarmuth, Floyd: CNN
Yates, H. William: CBS News
Yates, Mark: Australian Broadcasting Corporation
Yavas, Ahmet: TRT

MEMBERS ENTITLED TO ADMISSION—Continued

Yazaki, Anthony: NHK–Japan Broadcasting Corporation
Ybarra, Margaret: Talk Radio News Service
Ydstie, John: National Public Radio
Yellin, Jessica: CNN
Yeretzian, Leeza: Aljazeera International
Yeshi, Lobsang: Radio Free Asia
Yianopoulos, Karen: Middle East Broadcasting Networks (MBN)
Yin, Chunsheng: China Central TV Bureau
Yin, Phillip: China Central TV Bureau
Ying, Francis: Kaiser Health News
Yoon, Robert: CNN
Yoshikawa, Junichi: TV Asahi
Yoshioka, Jumpei: NHK–Japan Broadcasting Corporation
Yospyn, Joshua: WJLA–TV / Newschannel 8
Young, Jeff: Voice of America
Young, Jeremy: Aljazeera International
Young, Jr., Jerome: CBN News
Young, Melissa A.: ABC News
Young, Robert Latimer: C–Span
Young, Saundra: CNN
Young, V. Alan: NBC News
Younis, Omar: Reuters Radio & TV
Yousef, Dania: Aljazeera International
Yu, Annie: WTTG–Fox Television
Yu, James: Korean Broadcasting Systems
Yu, John: New Tang Dynasty TV
Yun, Samean: Radio Free Asia
Yun, Taeho: Korean Broadcasting Systems
Yunjin, Li: American Chinese Television (ACT)
Zaatar, Marwan: Middle East Broadcasting Networks (MBN)
Zairi, Said: ABS Network
Zajko, Robert: Diversified Communications, Inc. (DCI)
Zanatta, Dennis: TV Globo International
Zang, Guohua: CTI–TV (Taiwan)
Zann, Julie: CNN
Zariquiey, Juan Pablo: WZDC–TV
Zaru, Deena: CNN
Zayed, Nahedah: Aljazeera International
Zderic, Srdjan: Aljazeera International
Zechar, David: ABC News
Zeffler, Markus: BBC
Zeledon, Franklin: Morningside Partners, LLC
Zeleny, Jeff: ABC News
Zell, Charles: FedNet
Zervos, Stratis: ABC News
Zhang, Fangfang: Voice of America
Zhang, Shuo: China Central TV Bureau
Zhang, Xiaoyan: Voice of America
Zhao, Zhengyi: Sinovision
Zheng, Haoran: New Tang Dynasty TV
Zhodzishsky, Ilya: RTTV America
Zhu, Haiqing: China Central TV Bureau
Zhu, Xiaomeng: China Central TV Bureau
Zia, Ahmad: Voice of America
Zickel, Kathryn: Voice of Russia
Ziegenbein, Darren: WRC–TV / NBC–4
Ziegler, Julia: Federal News Radio 1500 AM
Zimerman, Ariel: RCN–TV (Colombia)
Zimmerman, Douglas: Environment & Energy Publishing, LLC
Zmidzinski, Andy: WJLA–TV / Newschannel 8
Zoldan, Ari: Talk Radio News Service
Zosso, Elizabeth: Middle East Broadcasting Networks (MBN)
Zou, Sara: C–Span
Zou, Yun: China Central TV Bureau
Zwart, Wouter: Nos Dutch Public Radio & TV (VRT)
Zwillich, Todd: WNYC

NETWORKS, STATIONS, AND SERVICES REPRESENTED

Senate Gallery 224–6421 House Gallery 225–5214

24/7 NEWS—8403 Colesville Road, #1500, Silver Spring, MD 20910: Terrence Moore, Lauren Murphy.

ABC NEWS—1717 DeSales Street, NW., Washington, DC 20036: Gitika Ahuja Kaul, John Allard, Faisal Alqadiree, James Avila, Phillip M. Black, Katie Bosland, Tahman Bradley, Robert E. Bramson, Glennwood Branche, Sam Brooks, Henry M. Brown, Mary Bruce, Christopher Carlson, Jack Cloherty, Ann Compton, Richard Coolidge, Thomas J. d'Annibale, Henry Disselkamp, Peter M. Doherty, Alexandra Dukakis, Dennis Dunlavey, Devin Dwyer, Daniel Glenn Elvington, Michael Falcone, Charles Finamore, Siobhan Fisher, Mosheh Gains, Jon D. Garcia, Arthur R. Gauthier, Tara Gimbel, Thomas Giusto, Christopher Good, Robin Gradison, Brian Robert Hartman, Kendall A. Heath, Esequiel Herrera, Matthew Alan Hosford, Dana Hughes, Heidi Jensen, Sara Just, James Kane, Polson Kanneth, Jonathan Karl, David P. Kerley, Richard Klein, John Knott, Donald Eugene Kroll, Benjamin Krolowitz, Matthew Larotonda, Lachlan Murdoch MacNeil, Gale Marcus, Serena Marshall, James Martin, Jr., Luis Martinez, Erik T. McNair, Sunlen Mari Miller, Avery Miller, Matthew Mosk, Meredith Nettles, Reena Ninan, Andrea Owen, John R. Parkinson, Jordyn Phelps, Abby Phillip, Richard K. Pliszak, Steven A. Portnoy, Mary Quinn, Victor Ratner, Corinne Roberts, Gary Rosenberg, Katherine Saenz, George D. Sanchez, Susan Saulny, Howard Schoenholtz, Claire Shipman, Gregory Simmons, James E. Smith, Cindy Smith, Robin Sproul, Lisa Stark, Steve Stefany, Daniel Steinberger, Audrey Taylor, Georgeanne Thanos, Amy Thomas, Pierre Thomas, Karen Lynn Travers, Vicki A. Vennell, Virginia A. Vicario, Shushannah Walshe, Fabian Westerwelle, Douglas White, Zachary Wolf, Melissa A. Young, Jeff Zeleny.

ABS NETWORK—50 F Street, NW., Suite 1C, Washington, DC 20001: Saad Ali.

AGENCE FRANCE PRESSE (AFP–TV)—1500 K Street, NW., Washington, DC 20005: Paul Barber, Olivier Calas, William Edwards, Michelle Hoffman, Loic Hofstedt, Michelle Kwajafa, Guillaume Meyer, Leigh Paterson, Marisha Sherry, Eden Woldearegay.

AL ARABIYA TV—National Press Building, 529 14th Street, NW., Suite 530, Washington, DC 20045: Yamen Abdalwahab, Angelyn Adams, Pierre Ghanem, Elias Habib, Ziad Jazzaa, Omar Melhem, Richard Melhem, Muna Shikaki, Angela Simaan, Tom Tuszynski.

ALASKA PUBLIC RADIO NETWORK—810 East Ninth Avenue, Anchorage, AL 99501: Peter Granitz, Elizabeth Ruskin.

ALJAZEERA INTERNATIONAL—1627 K Street, NW., Suite 4006, Washington, DC 20006: Trevor Aaronson, Bob Abeshouse, Tom Ackerman, Singeli Agnew, Khodayar Akhavi, Reem Akkad, Laila Alarian, Marc Alexander, Zachery Alfred, Sameen Amin, Ingrid Arnesen, Amjad Attallah, Jeff Ballou, Fatima Bartee, James Bays, Paul Beban, Timothy Bella, Barbara Benitez, Josh Bernstein, Barbara Berti, Marwan Bishara, Sam Black, Howard Bonds, Kim Bondy, Elizabeth Casey, Karolina Chapman, Joie Chen, Kavitha Cherkuru, Spencer Chumbley, Grant Clark, Caroline Cooper, Patricia Culhane, Derek Davis, Sanya Dosani, Lucho Durand, Timothy Durham, Gordon Durnin, Camille Elhassani, Dave Enders, Aaron Ernst, Alan Fisher, Jordan Flaherty, Hida Fouladvand, Andy Gallacher, Jean Garner, Lori Gilha, Karina Gomes, Claire Gordon, Elizabeth Gorman, Nicole Grether, David Gustafson, Karim Haddad, Jesse Hage, Kimberly Halkett, James Hamilton, Chris Hamilton, John Hendren, Michael Hopper, Sarah Hoye, Whitney Hurst, Zulega Husain, Kim Hutcherson, Julian Ingle, Fletcher Johnson, Rosiland Jordan, Akilah Joseph, Muriel Jubar, Anjali Kamat, Azmat Khan, Noorulain Khawaja, Kylene Kiang, Wab Kinew, Betsy Kulman, Jay LaMonica, Katherine Lannigan, Lister Lim, Ryan Loughlin, Tom Lumley, Sheila MacVicar, Ashish Malhotra, Joseph Marno, Mike Marno, Mercedes Martinez, Adam May, David McWhinney, Bryan Meyers, Robert Michaud, Daniel Ming, Areej Noor, Soledad O'Brien, Mark Orchard, Negin Owliaei, Ed Pound, Christof Putzel, Omar Quinonez, Sophia Qureshi, Roger Raiford, Shihab Rattansi, Todd Reed, Alea Reeves, Robert Reynolds, Joshua Rushing, Jennifer Salan, Sanil Sali, Kristen Saloomey, Paul Sapin, Andrea Schmidt, Corine Schneider, Mariam Simpson, Mathieu Skene, Kathy Slobogin, Phillip Smith, Tom Szypulski, Simon Tate, Mark Teboe, Pilar Tejerina, John Terrett, Catherine Turner, Stephen Turnham, Joel VanHaren, Ilona Viczian, Michael Viquera, Anar Virji, Sweta Vohra, Sebastian Walker, Amy Walters, Jin Wang, Ervin Washington, Brian Wheeler, Robert Wheelock, Snorre Wik, Tammy Wright, James Wright, Wilkins Xavier, Leeza Yeretzian, Jeremy Young, Dania Yousef, Nahedah Zayed, Srdjan Zderic.

ALJAZEERA SATELLITE CHANNEL (PENINSULA)—1627 K Street, NW., Suite 200, Washington, DC 20006: Biesan Abu-Kwaik, Eyad Aburahma, Haitham Al Juboori, Mohammed Alami, Heni Azzam, Baubak Baghi, Charles Behringer, Christopher Campbell, Adil Cherkaoui, Mohammad Dalbah, Mahmoud El-Hamalawy, Abderrahim Foukara, Michael Fox, Nassredine "Nasser" Hssaini, Lina Khalaf, Fadi Mansour, Christopher Messer, Ghassan Sababa, Vera Salayma, Wajd Waqfi.

NETWORKS, STATIONS, AND SERVICES REPRESENTED—Continued

AMERICAN CHINESE TELEVISION (ACT)--722 Ridgemont Avenue, Rockville, MD 20850: Yunjin Li, Lianhua Yang.

AMERICAN PRESS AND TV SERVICES (APTVS)—1919 M Street, NW., Washington, DC 20036: Akram Abdulkareem, Marjan Asi, Fahd Banhawy, Colin Campbell, Mohammed Dawood, Sam Eizeldin, Hend Ibrahim.

AMERICA'S RADIO NEWS NETWORK—2020 Pennsylvania Avenue, NW., #906, Washington, DC 20006: Jason Mattera.

ANTENA 3 TV—4901 Seminary Road, #1513, Alexandria, VA 22311: Mihaela Biliovschi Smith, Derrin Smith.

AOL HUFFINGTON POST MEDIA GROUP—1730 Pennsylvania Avenue, Washington, DC 20006: Brad Shannon.

AP–BROADCAST—1100 13th Street, NW., Suite 700, Washington, DC 20005: Jeff Adkinson, Nihad Aliakbar, Eric Andree, Hugo Blanco, Gerald Bodlander, Andrew Braddel, Tracy Ann Brown, Kathleen Brumbaugh, David Bruns, Steven Coleman, Flavia Colombo-Abdullah, Derek Danilko, Kelly Daschle, Bianca Davie, Jon Detrow, Edward Donahue, Jason Dorn, Rodolfo Estrada, Fritz Faerber, Meghan Flores, Patrick Fogarty, Matthew Friedman, Oscar Gabriel, Richard Gentilo, Lawrence Gold, James W. Gorman, Nicole Grether, Nyia Hawkins, Susan Henderson, Brian Hoffman, Dan Huff, Michael Italiano, Christian Kettlewell, Sandy Kozel, Nico Maounis, Lisa N. Matthews, Nan Hee McMinn, Sagar Meghani, David Melendy, John Morrissey, Kamal Omara, Louis Pagan, Greg Peppers, Gerald Petraitis, Lee Powell, Walter Ratliff, Jon Resnick, Thomas Ritchie, Cynthia Sharp, Matt Small, Mark S. Smith, Denise Vance, Andrew G. Visley, Noel Waghorn, Michael Weinfeld.

ARD—GERMAN BROADCASTING SYSTEMS—1200 Eton Court, NW., Suite 1000, Washington, DC 20007: Silvia Charpa, Andreas Horchler, Sarah Kumpf.

ARTE TV—2000 M Street, NW., Washington, DC 20036: Philippe Gassot.

AUDIO VIDEO NEWS—3622 Stanford Circle, Falls Church, VA 22041: Connie Lawn.

AUSTRALIAN BROADCASTING CORPORATION—2000 M Street, NW., Suite 660, Washington, DC 20036: Jane Cowan, Robert Hill, Benjamin Knight, Woodrow Landay, Lisa Millar, Dee Porter, Dan Sweetapple, Michael Vincent, Mark Yates.

AUSTRIAN RADIO & TV (ORF)—1206 Eton Court, NW., Washington, DC 20007: Sophie Fasching, Hannelore Fauqueux-Veit, Wolfgang Geier, Verena Gleitsmann, Uelle-Mall Jaakson, Anna Kirst, Markus Meier, Lauren Silva-Pinto, Christian Staudinger.

AZTECA AMERICA—400 North Capitol, NW., Suite 361, Washington, DC 20001: Armando Guzman, Edwing Lopez.

BBC—2000 M Street, NW., #800, Washington, DC 20009: Paul Adams, Lukman Ahmed, Sina Alinejad, Glenn Osten Anderson, Jonathan Beale, Ben Bevington, David Botti, James Bray, Taylor Brown, Robert Brown, Maria Byrne, Maria Byrne, Maxine Collins, Kathleen Dailey, Paul Danahar, Elizabeth Davies, Teresa Davis, Ian Druce, Jonny Dymond, Kate Farrell, Sam Farzaneh, Kambiz Fattahi, Richard Fenton-Smith, Tim Franks, Marc Georges, Kim Ghattas, Phillip Herd, Jane Hill, Rozalia Hristova, Wafaa Jibai, Majid Joneidi, Katty Kay, Suzanne Kianpour, John Landy, Gavin Lee, Aidan Lewis, Pearse Lynch, Mohammad Manzarpour, Mark Mardell, Lindle Markwell, William Marquez, Tara McKelvey, Edward Metzger, Tara Neill, Ian Pannell, Amir Payam, Christopher Pitt, Mehrnoush Pourziaiee, Debbie Randle, Ashley Semler, Jude Sheerin, Michael Shuval, Ron Skeans, Joan Soley, Thomas Sparrow, Franz Strasser, Sarah Svoboda, Vara Szajkowski, Anna Tatton-Brown, Pablo Uchoa, Brajesh Upadhyay, Mark Urban, Jonathan Urquhart, Rajini Vaidyanathan, Kathryn Watson, David Willis, Simon Wilson, Ben Wright.

BELO CAPITAL BUREAU—1325 C Street, NW., Suite 250, Washington, DC 20005: David Cassidy, William Smith, Sue Turner.

BET NIGHTLY NEWS—400 North Capitol Street, NW., Suite 361, Washington, DC 20001: Pamela Gentry, Joyce Jones, Tara Jones, Marie Nelson, Andre Showell, Tiffany Tate.

BLOOMBERG RADIO & TV—1399 New York Avenue, NW., 11th Floor, Washington, DC 20005: Niharika Acharya, Jon Bascom, Michael Callahan, Irwin Chapman, Peter Cook, Ben Geldon, Megan Hughes, Lori Jennings, Ryan Kerr, Judy Lyons, Kate Macedo, Todd Moday, Hans Nichols, Patrick Reap, Julie Slattery, Ellen Uchimiya, Colleen Wordock, Yang Yang.

BOSTON UNIVERSITY WASHINGTON CENTER—1776 Massachusetts Avenue, NW., Washington, DC 20036: Les Kretman.

BT VIDEO PRODUCTIONS—7117 Wolftree Lane, Rockville, MD 20852: Cesar Flores, Paul Hollenbeck, Martin Kos.

CANADIAN BROADCASTING CORPORATION (CBC)—National Press Building, 529 14th Street, NW., Suite 500, Washington, DC 20045: Jean-Francois Bisson, Keith Boag, Susan Bonner, Marcel Calfat, Marie Claudet, Louis de Guise, Yanik Dumont Baron, Lyndsay Duncombe, Bruce Edwards, Patrick Ferguson, Meagan Fitzpatrick, Paul Hunter, Neil MacDonald, Joyce Napier, Yves Peltier, Sylvain Richard, Sylvia Thomson.

CANAL PLUS FRENCH TV—1100 13 Street, NW., Suite 400, Washington, DC 20001: Margot Haddad, Laura Haim.

NETWORKS, STATIONS, AND SERVICES REPRESENTED—Continued

CARACOL RADIO—1320 Fairmont Street, #103, Washington, DC 20009: Edwin Giraldo.

CATALUNYA RADIO—311 Fallsworth Place, Walkersville, MD 21793: Xavier Vila.

CBN NEWS—1919 M Street, NW., Suite 100, Washington, DC 20036: Mark Bautista, David Brody, Aronica Glover, Alegra Hassan, Steve Jacobi, Gene Jenkins, John Jessup, Matthew Keedy, Robin Mazyck, Jacob Moore, Shoshannah Nunez, David Page, Tamatha Papadeas, Johnathan Reid, Ian Rushing, Erick Stakelbeck, Paul Strand, Tracy Winborn, Jennifer Wishon, Crystal Woodall, Jerome Young, Jr.

CBS NEWS—2020 M Street, NW., Washington, DC 20036: Karen Adams, Zachary Akey, Thomas Albano, Christopher Albert, Clinton N. Alexander, Kevin Allen, Stuart Ammerman, Wyatt Andrews, Kris Ankarlo, Alana Anyse, Chloe Arensberg, Howard Arenstein, Sharyl Attkisson, Kylie Atwood, Barry Bagnato, Morris Banks, Bruce Barr, Reginald Barringer, Kia Baskerville, Farrel Becker, Mark R. Bennett, Lindsay Boerma, Emily Bradley, Margaret Brennan, Whitney Bright, Alicia Budich, Susan Bullard Harmon, Leigh Ann Caldwell, Traci Caldwell, Catherine Cannon, Denise Cetta, Steve Chaggaris, Jane S. Chick, George Christian, Stephanie Condon, Carol (Pat) Coney, John Cooper, Nancy Cordes, Tim Costa, Pam Coulter, Jan Crawford, Walter Cronkite, John Crum, Heather Curtis, John Daly, Matthew DelSignore, Charles H. Dixson, Michelle Dolge, John Domen, Louise Dufresne, Louisa Dunston, Lois Dyer, John L. Fantacone, John Frado, Tony Furlow, Hal E. Furman, Brian Fuss, Robert J. Fuss, Gina Garcia, Jenna Gibson, Benson Ginsburg, Jeff Scott Goldman, Neil Grasso, David Gross, Josh Gross, Mary Hager, Nathan Hager, Evan Haning, Alan He, Robert Hendin, Chas Henry, Toni Hoover, Caroline Horn, Brett Hovell, Melissa Howell, Jillian Hughes, Amy Hybels, Christopher Isham, Jill Jackson, Dennis Jamison, Sheila Jaskot, Courtney Jay, Richard Jefferson, Shanica Johnson, Jeffrey Johnston, Donald Judd, Bonney Kapp, Craig Katz, Julia Kimani, Daniel Klos, Mark Knoller, Stephanie Lambidakis, Donald A. Lee, Jonathan Lien, Sam Litzinger, Kevin Livelli, Lara Logan, Nancy Lyons, Jim MacKay, Peter Maer, Paris Magaziner, Steve Marshall, David Martin, Mark Mazariegos, D. Page McCarty, Max McClellan, Susan McGinnis, Jim McGlinchy, Michael McGuire, Duncan McKenna, Robert McKinley, George Mesthos, Gregg Micklos, Jake Miller, Pat Milton, Donald Morgan, Amy Morris, John Nolen, Danielle Nottingham, Mosheh Oinounou, Bob Orr, Jeffrey Pegues, Michael Peyton, William Plante, Tolleah Price, Diana Quinn, Carrie Rabin, Daniel Raviv, Charles Reid, Catherine Reynolds, Kevin Rincon, Francisco Robbins, Ira Rosen, Howard Rosenberg, Katie Ross, Allyson Ross Taylor, Jared Ruderman, Christina Ruffini, Kate Rydell, Rob Sanchez, Michelle Scalise, Bob Schieffer, Fred Schneider, Gabrielle Schonder, Henry Schuster, Heather Scott, Thomas H. Seem, Gregory Shaffir, Dennis Shannon, Kimberly Skeen, Ward C. Sloane, Gabriel Stix, Laura Strickler, Kimberly Suiters, Lee Sullivan, Craig Swagler, Cameron Thompson, Thomas E. Tillman, Peter C. Traynham, Andres P. Triay, Dan D. Tutman, Victor Ulloa, William Walker, Mary Walsh, Craig Warner, Erick Washington, Mark White, John H. Whitley, Ricardo Whitson, Kenneth E. Williams, Joshua Yager, Carter Yang, H. William Yates.

CHANNEL ONE RUSSIAN TV—1100 13th Street, NW., Suite 400, Washington, DC 20005: Andrey Cherkasov, Anatoly Lazarev, Dmitry Vishnevoy.

CHINA CENTRAL TV BUREAU—1099 New York Avenue, NW., Washington, DC 20001: Atirath Aich, Dalal Ali, Julio Aliaga, Guy Bagley, Fan Bai, Sean Callebs, Guang Chen, He Cheng, Bob Crawford, Lingnan Cui, Bing Dang, Emily Drew, Yubin Du, Peng Fu, Qi Gao, Sheryl Gao, Joanna Godinho, Chun Guo, Wenjin He, Aja Hubert-Hogg, Roza Ibragimova, Li Jia, Xin Jiang, Kang Kang, Monna Kashfi, Nathan King, Wenyun Li, Meng Li, Xiang Li, Xiyang Liu, Jing Ma, Yan Mei, Lingqi Meng, Anand Naidoo, Ruqaiyah Najjar, Yun Niu, Hakan Ozsancak, Elaine Reyes, Janet Rodriguez, Rebecca Schatz, Ellen Scott, Chen Shen, Qing Sheng, Andrew Smith, James Spellman, Jessica Stone, Xiaoxiao Su, Ping Sun, Qin Tang, Mike Walter, Hui Wang, Guan Wang, Meng Wang, Fenghua Wang, RT Warfield, Duane Watkins, Xuejiao Wei, Xing Wei, Glenn Weidenbosch, Snorre Wik, Joel Witte, Hanying Wu, Hejia Xiao, Chenguang Xie, Jian Yang, Phillip Yin, Chunsheng Yin, Shuo Zhang, Peng Zhao, Haiqing Zhu, Xiaomeng Zhu, Yun Zou.

CNBC—1025 Conneticut Avenue, NW., Washington, DC 20836: Patrick Anastasi, Bria Cousins, Plummer Crawley, Matthew Cuddy, Stephanie Dhue, John Harwood, Karen James, Eamon Javers, Diana Olick, Hampton Pearson, Pat Pugliese, Shari Rosen, Ashley Stringer.

CNN—820 1st Street, NE., Washington, DC 20002: Khalil Abdallah, Mohamed Abdelouahabi, Halimah Abdullah, Jim Acosta, Mike Ahlers, Adam Aigner-Treworgy, Nefi Alarcon, William Alberter, Kathy Aragon, Nelson Archer, Emily Atkinson, Jonathan Auerbach, Matthew Avrutine, Sarah Baker, Nancy Baker, Laquasha Banks, Erik Banks, James Barnett, Ted Barrett, Dana Bash, Courtney Battle, John Bena, Alexa Bennewitz, Pamela S. Benson, Thomas Bentz, Leslie Bentz, David Berman, Richard Bernal, Laura Bernardini, Kimberly Berryman, Kevin Blakley, Wolf Blitzer, Melissa Block, John Bodnar, Kevin Bohn, Warren Bolden, Katherine Bolduan, Gloria Borger, Tyrone Boston, Joshua Braun, Allison Brennan, Michael Brevner, Ray Britch, Craig A. Broffman, Scott Bronstein, Steven Brusk, Burke Buckhorn, Jennifer Buesinger, Jennifer Burch, Hunter Burgarella, Juan Cabral, Karin Caifa, David Keith Catrett, David Chalian, Jill Chappell, Elizabeth Chmurak, Gregory Clary, Bobby Clemons, Thomas Cohen, Aaron Cooper, Christie Corologos-Medina, Paul Courson, Benjamin Coyte, Carol A. Cratty, James Crawford, John Crawley, Karla Crosswhite-Chigbue, Candy Crowley, John Cunha,

NETWORKS, STATIONS, AND SERVICES REPRESENTED—Continued

Shaneika Dabney, Greg Danilenko, Dana Davidsen, Patrick A. Davis, Kara Day, Javier de Diego, Stacia Deshishku, Lisa Desjardins, Anastasia Diakides, Rick DiBella, Patricia DiCarlo, Stephen Dolce, Daniel Donahue, Jill Dougherty, Martin Dougherty, Nicole Drag, David Duberstein, Thomas Dunlavey, Victoria Dunnan, Edie Emery, Sam Feist, Eric James Fiegel, Craig Fingar, Conor Finnegan, Sara Fischer, Patrick Ford, Christopher Ford, Thomas Foreman, Insley Fowler, Chris Frates, Terry Frieden, Scott Garber, Melodie Garner, Susan Garraty, Timothy C. Garraty, David Gelles, Melissa Giaimo, Rachel Giberman, Andre Goddard, Stephanie Goggans, Richard Gorbutt, David Gracey, Allison Gracey, Megan Grant, James Gray, James Graydon, Eddie S. Gross, Jr. Peter Hamby, Alison Harding, Jeremy Harlan, Arielle Hawkins, Jamie Helgren, Jonathan Helman, John Helton, Shirley Henry, Simon Hernandez-Arthur, Katherine Hinman, William Holbert, Sarah B. Holland, Derek Horrigan, Emily Howell, Matthew Hoye, Charles Hurley, Lea Iadarola, Yasmeen Ibrahim, Adia Jacobs, Michelle Jaconi, Oliver Janney, Lesa Jansen, NuNu Japaridze, David Jenkins, Stefanie Jewett, Joseph Johns, Athena Jones, Jay Jones, Brianna Keilar, Pamela Kelley, Sean Kennedy, Ashley Killough, John King, Worth Kinlaw, George P. Kinney, Jeff Kinney, Adilson Kiyasu, Laura Koran, Stephanie Kotuby, Robert S. Kovach, Rebecca Kutler, Elise Labott, Gabe LaMonica, Peter Lanier, Chris Lawrence, Larry Lazo, Adam Levine, Adam Levy, Dorothy Lewis, Jennifer Liberto, Kevin Liptak, Philip Littleton, Juan Carlos Lopez, Willie A. Lora, Daniel Lothian, Mary Grace Lucas, Krystal Mabry, Vito Maggiolo, Christina Manduley, Mark Anthony Marchione, Eric Marrapodi, Rene Marsh, Timothy McCaughan, Dugald McConnell, Denise McIntosh, William McKnight, Alyssa McLendon, Samuel J. McMichael IV, Michael McMullan, Erin McPike, Edward Meagher, William Mears, James Meech, Daniel Merica, Austin Merson, Jessica Metzger, Alec Miran, Ione Indira Molinares-Hess, Jeffrey Moller, Bryan Monroe, Alex Mooney, Jeremy Moorhead, Isabel Morales, Peter Morris, Virginia Moseley, Sarah Mueller, Rosetta Murry, Steven Nannes, Suzanne Nelson, Nicholette Nicci, Virginia Nicolaidis, Ernest G. Nocciolo, Steven Page, Andre Parker, Robert Geoffrey Parker, Melanie Parks, Stephen Patterson, Carlos Perez, Evan Perez, Rebecca Perlow, Lindsey Perna, Thomas Perrell, Katelyn Petroka, Sherisse Pham, Alan Philippon, Michelle Poley, Brendan Polmer, Mark Preston, Shimon Prokupecz, Federico Quadrani, Carol Rachou, Bogdan Radu, Meghan Rafferty, Pallavi Reddy, Becky Rieksks, Raul Rios-Hernandez, Jennifer Rizzo, Greg Robertson, David Robinson, Susan Rodriguez, Brian Rokus, H. Michael Roselli, Rachel Rosen, Linda Roth, Lindy Royce-Bartlett, David Ruff, Diane Ruggiero, Pedro Salas, Marcela Salazar, Rick Saleeby, Stacey Samuel, Frances Sanchez, Joseph Sansone, Amanda Sansone, Michelle Santayana, Thayer Sargent, Douglas N. Schantz, Barry C. Schlegel, Emily Schultze, Gabriella Schwarz, Jennifer Scoggins, Raquel Scott, Gregory Seaby, Jason Seher, Reginald G. Selma, Sunlen Serfaty, Rachael Shackelford, Lawrence Shaughnessy, John (Jay) Shaylor, Eric Sherling, Alan Silverleib, Jeffery Simms, Kathleen Skinski, Kristi Slafka, Tyler Sloan, Brent Smith, Kelly Smoot, Chloe Sommers, Matthew Speiser, Todd Sperry, Richard Spire, Cassandra Spodak, Philip Scott Spoerry, Barbara Starr, Scott Stead, Paul Steinhauser, Vaughn Sterling, John Stevenson, Martina Stewart, Timothy Stoutzenberger, Rachel Streitfeld, Lisa Sylvester, Daniel Szematowicz, Jake Tapper, James B. Thomas III, Lindzie Titera, Brian Todd, Nicolas Toso, Shannon Travis, Kenneth Tuohey, Chris Turner, Robert Tweed, Brett Tyler, Kim Uhl, Anthony R. Umrani, Laurie Ure, Ellen Van de Mark, Dana Viers, Tu H. Vu, Soran Wais, Gregory Wallace, Deirdre Walsh, Mark Walz, Tracey Webb, Eric Weisbrod, Jessica Weiss, Alexis Weiss, Amanda White, Edward White, Val Willingham, Frederick Wiseman, Zachary Wolf, Angie Yack, Brian Yaklyvich, Floyd Yarmuth, Jessica Yellin, Robert Yoon, Saundra Young, Julie Zann, Deena Zaru.

CNSNEWS.COM—325 South Patrick Street, Alexandria, VA 22314: Craig Bannister, Barbara Boland, Michael W. Chapman, Melanie Hunter, Terence Jeffrey, Susan Jones, Dan Joseph, Alison Meyer, Craig Millward, Corwin Parks, Bob Parks, Eric Scheiner, Penny Starr.

COMCAST NBC—101 Constitution Avenue, NW., Suite L 150, Washington, DC 20001: Lisa Melillo, Robert Traynham, Natlie Valentine.

COPE RADIO (SPAIN)—4904 Bett Road, NW., Washington, DC 20016: Juan Martinez Fierro.

COX BROADCASTING—400 North Capitol Street, NW., #750, Washington, DC 20001: Kyla Campbell, David Chase, Jamie Dupree, Jackie Fell, Justin Gray, Kevin Johnson, Jon Sonnheim, Patrick Terpstra, Heidi Wiedenbauer, Jeffrey L. Williams.

CRONKITE NEWS SERVICE—1834 Connecticut Avenue, NW., Washington, DC 20009: Stephen Crane.

C–SPAN—400 North Capitol Street, NW., #650, Washington, DC 20001: Kenneth Alexander, Thomas Alldredge, Theresa Amirault-Michel, Jeremy Art, Shannon Augustus, Michelle Bailor, Jason Bender, Brett Betsill, Michael Biddle, Dannie Boone, Greta Brawner, Paul Brown, Donald Brown, Robert Browning, Kristina Buddenhagen, Susan J. Bundock, Leslie Burdick, James Burke, Kathy Cahill Murphy, Nancy Calo-Christian, Craig Caplan, Kenneth Carrick, Elizabeth Casey, Michael Cavaiola, Tanya Chattman, Matthew Claar, James Clark, Josh Cohen, Bruce D. Collins, James L. Cook, Cleve Corner, Dennis Cravedi, Liam Currier, Alexander Curtis, Greg Czzowitz, Pete Daniels, Matthew Dauchess, Tanya Davis, Heather DeManche, Bridget Diggs, Michelle Doell, Jason Dorman, Paul Eades, Jr., Pedro L. Echevarria, Ronald Eisenbarth, Gary Ellenwood, Seth Engel, Patricia Esquivel, Greg Fabic, Mark Farkas, Joesph Feeney, Laura Finch, Richard Fleeson, Carl Foster, William Frazier, John Gallagher, Bill Gallagher, Craig Galowin, Leslie Gardner, John Garlock, Garney Gary, Robert Gould, Bill Gray,

NETWORKS, STATIONS, AND SERVICES REPRESENTED—Continued

Melanie Gutmann, Fred Haberstick, Richard Hall, Chris Hanson, Stephen Harkness, Robb Harleston, Kasey Harris, Maurice Haynes, William Heffley, Jonelle P. Henry, Dallas Hill, Christy Hinton, Michael Holden, George Howell, Yi-Pe Hsieh, Katherine Hughes, Tracy Hunter, Cynthia Ingle, Roberta Jackson, Megan Jonas, Andrew Jones, Stephen Jones, Barry Katz, Stephanie Kaye, Steve Kehoe, Jon Kelley, Robert Kennedy, Barkley Kern, Roxane Kerr, Lew Ketcham, Kevin King, David Knighton, Felix Laboy, Brian Lamb, Darren Larade, Molly Laville, Robert Lazar, Jerome Leddon, Mark Lindblom, Brian Lloyd, Paul Loeschke, Russell Logan, Gary Lover, Valerie Matthews, Ken McAndrew, John McArdle, Sean McCann, Michael McCann, Gerard McGarrity, Seeno Merobshoev, Justin Metzger, Andrew Peter Miller, Kate Mills, David Monack, Victor Montoro, Linwood Moore, Garrette Moore, Howard Mortman, Dan Morton, Terry Murphy, Yetta Myrick, Andrew Nason, Trang (Nicole) Ninh, Donna Norris, Benjamin O'Connell, Alan Olmsted, Paul Orgel, Nike Oyebanjo, Michael Patruznick, Simone Perez, Vernon Perkins, Christina Perry, Chelsea Pflugh, Nickolas Pitocco, Taylor Porter, Almon Porter, Anne Preloh, Tony Pronko, Nikhil Raval, Robert Reilly, Michelle Remillard, Cynthia Reuter, Paul Rigney, Delia Rios, Tiffany Rocque, Mark Rodeffer, Martine Rodriguez, Jennifer Ruff, Frederico Sampaio, Molly Sanders, Sherry Sanders-Smith, Michelle Sandiford, Stanley Sang, Vincent Santo, Johnson Sarfo-Kantanka, William Scanlan, John Scheuer, Ellen Schweiger, Steven Scully, Peter Slen, Lindley Smith, Ben Sorenson, Alan Speck, Johnny Street, Jean, Gary Starikoff, Mindy Steinman, Rick Stoddard, Susan Swain, Mary Symanski, Russell Taylor, Christina Taylor, Joseph Teeples, Eric Thoman, Arthur Tiller, Brandon Tilman, Annie Tin, Sarah Tobianski, Lauren Torlone, Kevin Washburn, Richard Weinstein, Ruthann Winterhalter, Christopher Wood, Robert Latimer Young, Sara Zou.

CTI–TV (TAIWAN)—7 Monona Court, Derwood, MD 20855: E-Ting Chung, Guohua Zang.

CTV CANADIAN TV—2000 M Street, NW., Suite, #330, Washington, DC 20036: Jonathan Austin, William Dugan, Bradley Fulton, Joy Malbon, John Mees, Paul Workman.

CTV–COMMUNITY TV OF PRINCE GEORGE'S COUNTY—9475 Lottsford Road, Largo, MD 20774: David Barnes, Curtis Crutchfield, Jesusemen Edoro, David Goldman, Ara Laughlin, Rochelle Metzger, Sandra Peaches, Sonia Randev, Christopher Thomas, Mikea Turner, Patricia Villone Garcia.

DANISH BROADCASTING CORPORATION—2000 M Street, NW., Suite 890, Washington, DC 20036: Steffen William Gram, Johannes Langkilde, Gitte McGuire, Charlotte Nielsen, Erkan Oezden.

DECODE DC—3112 Cheverly Avenue, Cheverly, MD 20785: Andrea Seabrook, Peter Seabrook.

DEUTSCHE WELLE TV—2000 M Street, NW., Suite 335, Washington, DC 20036: Christina Bergmann, Maximillian Hofmann, Gero Schliess, Miodrag Soric.

DIVERSIFIED COMMUNICATIONS, INC. (DCI)—2000 M Street, NW., 3rd Floor, Washington, DC 20036: James Butler, Joseph Concaugh, Jr., David M. Cooke, Robert Fetzer, Michael Grams, Yoshiki Hidaka, Masano Hidaka, Adrian Kill, Jamie Norins, Terry Straub, Robert Zajko.

ENVIRONMENT & ENERGY PUBLISHING, LLC—122 C Street, NW., Suite 722, Washington, DC 20001: Christopher Farmer, Monica Trauzzi, Douglas Zimmerman.

ETTV—1825 K Street, NW., Washington, DC 20036: Wen-Hsiang Chang.

EURONEWS—1717 DeSales Street, NW., Washington, DC 20036: Stefan Grobe.

EUROVISION AMERICAS, INC.—2000 M Street, NW., Suite 300, Washington, DC 20036: James Banks, Adam Bearne, Garrett Bohannon, Emilie de Schaetzen, William Dunlop, Tanya Fischer, Lee Grigsby, Jay Hahn, Steven Harper, Paul Knezek, Sarah Lanningham, Adam Mandelson, Glenn Mikols, Priya Narahari, Jihee Park, Jean Pierre Roberts, Jason Scharf, Peggy Soucy, Thomas Trainor, Clayton Trosclair, Juri von Bonsdorff.

EWTN Global Catholic Network—750 First Street, NE., Suite 1115, Washington, DC 20002: Debbie Alderman, Jason Calvi, Colleen Carroll Campbell, Dennis Dunbar, Kathryn Elliott, Paul Fifield, Stefano Flori, Gerry Gay, Wyatt Goolsby, Mark Irons, David Kerr, Jonathan Liedl, Susanna Pinto, Catherine Szeltner, William Turner.

EYE–TO–EYE VIDEO—4614 Chevy Chase Boulevard, Chevy Chase, MD 20815: Elliot Klayman, Patrick O'Donnell.

FEATURE STORY NEWS—1730 Rhode Island Avenue, Suite 405, Washington, DC 20036: Andrea Arenas, Malcolm Brown, Emily Carpeaux, Heather Dahl, Rebecca Foster, Tammy Haddad, Nick Harper, Priscilla Huff, Denis Levkovich, Simon Marks, Kevin McAleese, Nina Potts, Daniel Ryntjes, Lorna Shaddick, Rachel Silverman.

FEDERAL NEWS RADIO 1500 AM—3400 Idaho Avenue, NW., Washington, DC 20016: Gillian Brockell, Mike Causey, Emily Kopp, Lauren Larson, Sean McCalley, Jason Miller, Jack Moore, Mike O'Connell, Beth Reardon, Francis Rose, Jared Serbu, Thomas Temin, Lisa Wolfe, Julia Ziegler.

FEDERAL NEWS SERVICE—1000 Vermont Avenue, NW., Washington, DC 20005: Michael Eldridge, Frank Guest, Kirk Hanneman, Wendy Hanneman, Carrie Mitchell, Eric Parker, John Paul, John Stodter, Christopher Yaeger.

FEDNET—50 F Street, NW., Suite 1C, Washington, DC 20001: Keith Carney, Caleb Hamilton, Dawn Jones, Alvin Jones, Michael Kirby, Eric Nicholas, Charles Zell.

FINNISH BROADCASTING COMPANY (YLE)—2000 M Street, NW., Suite 890, Washington, DC 20036: Mette Nordstroem, Olli-Pekka Sulasma.

NETWORKS, STATIONS, AND SERVICES REPRESENTED—Continued

FOX BUSINESS NETWORK—400 North Capitol Street, NW., Washington, DC 20001: Mike Bannigan, Peter Barnes, Bruce Becker, Rich Edson, Sylvia Hall, Martin Jimenez, Mary Kreinbihl, Chris Mills, Jonathan Street.

FOX NEWS—400 North Capitol Street, NW., Washington, DC 20001: Greg Ahlquist, Ashley Alderman, James L. Angle, Trabandt Anne, Robert Armfield, Bret Baier, Les Baker, Josh Banks, Calvin Barrett, Stuart Basinger, Chris Becker, Judson Berger, Shayla Bezdrob, Varuna Bhatia, Lauren Blanchard, Craig Boswell, Bryan Boughton, Fletcher Bransford, Regina Bratton, Shannon Bream, Sarah Brinkerhoff, Lanna Britt, Edgar Brown, Megan Brown, Kristin Brown, Betsy Burkhard, Carl Cameron, Steve Carlson, Michael Carpel, Walter Carter, Jr., Juan Casanas, Steve Centanni, Barnini Chakraborty, Kelly Chernenkoff, Stephen Clark, Richard Cockerham, Bryan Cole, Eric Colimore, Eric Conner, Sarah Courtney, Jodie Curtis, Mitch Davis, Wendy Dawson, Joe DeFrank, Debra DeFrank, Michael DeMark, Mary Pat Dennert, Andrea DeVito, Brian Doherty, Jason Donner, Peter Doocy, Paige Dukeman, Jerry Echols, William Edmondson, James W. Eldridge, Mike Emanuel, Tyler Evans, Joel Fagen, Mark Finch, Justin Fishel, Linda Fodrea, Madelin Fuerste, Monica Gacka, Jake Gibson, Gary Gillis, Wendell Goler, Jennifer Griffin, Cherie Grzech, Gregg L. Gursky, Heather Gustafson, Brian Haefeli, Kata Hall, Lacey Halpern, Guerin Hays, Mary Janne Henneberg, Ed Henry, Francis Herbas, Catherine Herridge, Stacy Hickman, Martin Hill, Adrienne Moira Hopkins, Cory R. Howard, Paul Huckeby, Brit Hume, Elena Isella, Rhonda Jenkins, William G. Jenkins, George Jewsevskyj, Torrance Jones, Mae Joo, Nathalie Joost, Nick Kalman, Colleen Kelley, Grigory Khananayev, Kathryn Krupnik, Whitney Ksiazek, Donna Lacey, Philip LeCroy, Michael Levine, Edward Lewis, David Lewkowict, Joy Lin, Jessica Loker, Wayne Lowman, Doug Luzader, Stacia Lynds, Michael Lyon, Michelle Macaluso, Mike Maltas, Lori Martin, Molly Mathews, Tim May, Kevin McClam, George McCloskey, Sean McGarvy, Katherine McGraw, Doug McKelway, Richard Morse, Seleena M. Muhammad, James Nelson, Kerry O'Connor, Quillie Odom, Jessica O'Hara, Anna Olson, Ryan O'Malley, Bradford S. Paxton, Chad Pergram, Chris Peslis, Jacqueline Pham, Lauren Pick, Elizabeth Prann, David Renken, Elizabeth Rhodes, Katheryn Ricalde, Sarah Ridolfi, Anne Marie Riha, Michael Robbins, Christina Robbins, John Roberts, Tamara Robertson, Douglas Rohrbeck, James Rosen, Kara Rowland, Kristin Rudman, Bill Sammon, Craig Savage, Jason Scanlon, Kimberly Schwandt, Jody Sciacca, Abby Sears, Steve Shelton, Anita Siegfriedt, Teresa Spector, James Sprankle, Drake Springer, Daniel J. Stay, Lexi Stemple, Seneca Stevens, Chris Stirewalt, Matthew Stout, Patrick Summers, John Sumrel, Jennifer Suzara, Julie Talarico, Mary Ellen Tasillo, Lucas Tomlinson, Robert Torpey, Bree Tracey, Lamonte Tyler, Greta Van Susteren, Bryce Vinson, Todd Visioli, Erin Vogel, Phil Vogel, Chris Wallace, John L. Wallace, Neil Wallace, Jonathan Walter, Joseph Webber, Amy Wehinger, Meghan Welsh, Caroline Whiteman, Walter Whitley, Colleen Williams, John Williams, Anne Marie Willis, Kelly Wright.

FOX NEWS RADIO—5353 Cassons Neck Road, Cambridge, MD 21613: Jason Bonewald, Christopher Cross, Jessica Curtis, Mitch Davis, Robert Finnerty, Jared Halpern, Rich Johnson, Melissa Kraus, Mike Majchrowitz, Kirstin McNary, Jeff Monosso, Jill Nado, Bernard Pigott, Tom Root, Daniel Shields, John Sylvester, Hank Weinbloom.

FRANCE 2 TELEVISION—2000 M Street, NW., Suite 320, Washington, DC 20036: Maryse Burgot, Jacques Cardoze, Laurent Desbois, Regis Massini, Valerie McCabe, Arielle Monange, Fabien Ortiz.

FREE SPEECH RADIO NEWS—2390 Champlain Street, NW., Washington, DC 20009: Alice Ollstein.

FREE SPEECH TV (FSTV)—1844 Mintwood Place, NW., Washington, DC 20009: Eddie Becker.

FUJI TV JAPAN—529 14th Street, NW., Suite 330, Washington, DC 20045: Tomoko Barton, Jacqueline Enzmann, Peter Gold, Haruka Joho, Sumiko Mori, Matthew Mosley.

GALEI-TZAHAL (ISRAEL ARMY RADIO)—112 Shaw Avenue, Silver Spring, MD 20904: Drora Perl.

GANNETT GOVERNMENT MEDIA CORP—6883 Commercial Drive, Springfield, VA 22159: Colin Kelly, Blair Tomlinson.

GERMAN PRESS AGENCY—1112 National Press Building, Washington, DC 20045: Christina Eck.

GERMAN PUBLIC RADIO (ARD)—1200 Eton Court, NW., Washington, DC 20007: Rolf Buellmann, Sabrina Fritz, Silke Hasselman, Astrid Joehnk.

GERMAN TV ARD—3132 M Street, NW., Washington, DC 20007: Herta Borniger, Karin Dohr-Grill, Hillery Gallasch, Martin Ganslmeier, Antonio Gonzalez, Eva Graumann, Bettina Hassel Schumacher, Dirk Keuper, Felicitas Klopp, Pola Maurer, Robin Neumann, Stefan Niemann, Ruediger Paulert, Diana Robbins, Thomas Sawera, Marion Schmickler, Ralph Sina, Sonja Wasgien, Juergen Welter.

GLOBAL TV CANADA—400 North Capitol Street, NW., #850, Washington, DC 20001: Eric D. Sorensen, Robin Stickley.

GROUPE TVA—820 1st Street, NE., Washington, DC 20002: Richard Latendresse.

HEARST TELEVISION—1100 13th Street, NW., #425, Washington, DC 20005: Gail Austin, Shaquille Brewster, Beth Brown, Hallie Jackson, Sally F. Kidd, Nikole Killion, Nathan Luna, Lauren McDevitt, Erin T. McManamon, Chase Pipkin, David Postovit, Lavina Ramchandani, Chris Smyth, Wendy Wilk.

HISPANIC COMMUNICATIONS NETWORK—1126 16th Street, NW., 3rd Floor, Washington, DC 20036: Carlos Alcazar, Obdulia Alcazar, Pablo Castro, David Castro, Mercy Padilla-Cirino.

HONG KONG PHOENIX SATELLITE TELEVISION—101 Constitution Avenue, NW., #920 East, Washington, DC 20001: Ching-yi Chang, Yi Qiu Chen, Daniel Lai, Jennifer Lee, Tao LU, Meixing Ren, Bingru Wang, Taofeng Wang.

NETWORKS, STATIONS, AND SERVICES REPRESENTED—Continued

ICELANDIC NATIONAL BROADCASTING SERVICE—3320 Ardley Court, Falls Church, VA 22041: Sveinn Helgason.

INDEPENDENT TELEVISION NEWS (ITN)—400 North Capitol Street, NW., #899, Washington, DC 20008: Adam Blair, Matt Frei, Michael Herrod, Ben Martin, Robert Moore, William Neely, Emily O'Neill, David Sampy, Chris Shlemon, Charlotte Stafford, Lucy Towers, Robert Turner, Rebecca Tyers, Matt Williams, Natalie Wright.

IRISH RADIO & TV (RTE)—1750 16th Street, NW., #53, Washington, DC 20009: Harvey Cofske, Richard Downes, Lesley Steinhauser.

JTBC—529 14th Street, NW., Suite 997, Washington, DC 20045: Hans Cho, Sangbok Lee.

KAISER HEALTH NEWS—1330 G Street, NW., Washington, DC 20005: Hillary Carrere, Francis Ying.

KOREAN BROADCASTING SYSTEMS—529 14th Street, NW., Suite 1055, Washington, DC 20045: Sungwon Cho, Hyunjin Hong, Sungjin Kim, Thomas Koh, JuHan Lee, KangDuk Lee, Kevin Nha, Jinkyung Park, Ja Ryen Seo, James Yu.

KPCC—1750 K Street, NW., Washington, DC 20024: Kitty Felde.

LASLO CONGRESSIONAL BUREAU—1705 East West Highway, #519, Silver Spring, MD 20910: Dana Beierle, Mallory Hemerlein, Matt Laslo.

LILLY BROADCASTING—1220 Peach Street, Erie, PA 16501: Lauren Adams, Theodore Fioraliso, Mariam Khan, Jacqueline Policastro.

LINK TV—8715 Persimmon Tree Road, Potomac, MD 20814: Miles Benson, Brian Kelley, Raisa Scriabine, Kim Spencer.

MACEDONIA RADIO TELEVISION (MRTV)—1500 Massachusetts Avenue, NW., Washington, DC 20005: Irina Gelevska, Riste Mishev.

MARKETPLACE RADIO—1750 K Street, NW., Suite 300, Washington, DC 20006: David Gura, Nancy Marshall-Genzer, Scott Tong.

MBC—DUBAI—529 14th Street, NW., Suite 530, Washington, DC 20045: Nadia Bilbassy-Charters, Rafi Boghos.

MBC-TV KOREA (MUNHWA)—529 14th Street, NW., #1131, Washington, DC 20045: Andrew Kim, Jinsook Lee, Sang Ki Lim, Ho Chul Moon, Bumsoo Park.

MEDILL NEWS SERVICE—1325 G Street, NW., #730, Washington, DC 20005: Jonathan Agnew, Amos Gelb.

METRO TELEPRODUCTIONS—1400 East West Highway, Suite 628, Silver Spring, MD 20910: Dave Lilling.

MIDDLE EAST BROADCASTING NETWORK (MBN)—7600-D Boston Boulevard, Springfield, VA 22153: Rana Abtar, Ali Ahmed, Kelly Alford, Babu Aryankalavil, Elkheir Bentouila, Hisham Bourar, Alain Dargham, Nkwenten Ejedepang-Koge, John Elgin, Daniel Farkas, Michel Ghandour, Christopher Hamilton, Stephen Heiner, Arcelious Joyner, Khaled Khairy, Deirdre Kline, Ali Mahdi, Tim Miller, W. Harrison Moore, Virginia Moubray, Luis Munoz, Mohamed Nassar, Adam Nixon, James Norris, Joseph Tabet, Mohamed Wafa, Karen Yianopoulos, Marwan Zaatar, Elizabeth Zosso.

MINNESOTA PUBLIC RADIO NEWS—1750 K Street, NW., Suite 300, Washington, DC 20006: Brett Neely.

MOBILE VIDEO SERVICES, LTD.—1620 I Street, NW., #1000, Washington, DC 20006: Howard Collender, Lindsay Flaherty, William Griffitts, Christine Hoese, Timothy Knapp, Robert H. Milford, Todd Swain, Lawrence VanderVeen, Jacob VanderVeen.

MORNINGSIDE PARTNERS, LLC—4200 Forbes Road Suite 200, Lanham, MD 20706: Tony Anthony, Joshua Binswanger, Elizabeth Pennell, Ellen Piacente, Juvenal Uribe, Franklin Zeledon.

MUNDOFOX—1333 H Street, NW., Suite 8 West, Washington, DC 20005: Jose Diaz-Briseno, Juan Silva.

N24 GERMAN TV—1620 I Street, NW., Suite 1000, Washington, DC 20006: Stephen Strothe, Sabine Ulbrich-Strothe.

NATIONAL PUBLIC RADIO—635 Massachusetts Avenue, NW., Washington, DC 20001: Stacey Abbott, Larry Abramson, Elizabeth Acle, Augustine "Bud" Aiello, Jr. Bruce Auster, Brendan Banaszak, Mark Bejarano, Robert Benincasa, Jonathan Blakley, Melissa Block, Brakkton Booker, Tom Bowman, Radek Brablec, Geoff Brumfiel, Julia Redpath Buckley, Robert E Butcher, Dennis Byrnes, Franklyn Cater, Ailsa Chang, Bill Chappell, Isaac Chaput, Dan Charles, Carlos Chevez, Dennis Coll, Neal Conan, Audie Cornish-Emery, Michael Cullen, Michael Czaplinski, Shirish Date, Jess Deahl, Brian DeMar, Greg Dixon, Beth Donovan, Hugh Eaton, Ronald Elving, Pam Fessler, Stacey Foxwell, Marilyn Geewax, Susannah George, Tom Gjelten, Don Gonyea, Barry Gordemer, Gisele Grayson, David Greene, Liz Halloran, Richard Harris, Desiree Hicks, Jordana Hochman, TaShick Holland, Gemma Hooley, Scott Horsley, Elise Hu, Andy Huether, Steve Inskeep, Robert Jackson, Frank James, Brian Jarboe, Rick Jarrett, Carrie Johnson, John C. Keator, Tamara Keith, Michele Kelemen, Allison Keyes, Carol Klinger, Alejandra Knautz, Kevin Langley, Mara Liasson, Jennifer Ludden, Tom Marchitto, Melissa Marquis, Michel Martin, Rachel Martin, Dennis Medvee, Mark Memmott, Michael Merena, Joe Mills, Guillermo Minoso, Marcia Morgan, Brian Naylor, Christopher Nelson, Jackie Northam, Marguerite Nutter, Peter Overby, Joe Palca, Marisa Penaloza, Eyder Peralta, John Poole, Guy Raz, Julie Rovner, Leah Scarpelli, Robert Schaefer, Arnie Seipel, Joseph Shapiro, Ari Shapiro, Cathy Shaw, Elizabeth Shogren, Robert

NETWORKS, STATIONS, AND SERVICES REPRESENTED—Continued

C. Siegel, Art Silverman, Scott Simon, Helena Smith, Kurt Stalnaker, Susan Stamberg, Rob Stein, Evie Stone, Laura Sullivan, Rolf Taylor, Neil Tevault, Sharahn Thomas, Nina Totenberg, Kevin Wait, Amy Walters, Vickie Walton-James, Walter Watson, Andrew Watts, Linton Weeks, David Welna, Linda Wertheimer, John Ydstie.

NATIONAL SCENE NEWS—1718 M Street, NW., #333, Washington, DC 20036: Askia Muhammad, Alverda Muhammad.

NATIVE AMERICAN TELEVISION—444 N. Capitol Street, NW., Suite 524, Washington, DC 20001: Rebecca Cohencious, Robert Cohencious, Randolph Flood, Richard Gargagliano, Elizabeth Lorenzen, Anthony Lovelace, Jr.

NBC NEWS—4001 Nebraska Avenue, NW., Washington, DC 20016: Halimah Abdullah, Douglas A. Adams, Peter Alexander, Roberto Aneiva, Kenneth Austin, Perry Bacon, Jr., Rodney Batten, Gary Beall, Larry Bellinger, Michael Benetato, Justin Bennett, Regina Blackburn, John Blackman, Jay Blackman, Sarah Blackwill, Victoria Blooston, Jeffrey Blount, Joseph Bohannon, Kirsten Boser, Brooke Brower, Randall Brown, Mika Brzezinski, Louis Burgdorf, Norman Butler, Anthony Capra, Lete Childs, Catherine Chomiak, Patrick Chung, Margaret Conroy, Nero Cooper, Jr., Bob Costantini, Thomas Costello, Oliver Cox, Natalie Cucchiara, Tom Curry, Caroline Dann, Christopher Donovan, Victoria Duncan, John Edwards, Barbara Fant, Sheldon Fielman, Elizabeth Fischer, David Forman, Scott Foster, Maggie Fox, Jordan Frasier, Drew Fredrickson, Alva French, Lawrence Gaetano, Dennis Gaffney, Suzanne Gamboa, Jamie Gangel, Richard Gardella, Keith Gaskin, Ralph Gaudino, Emily Gold, Avra Gold, Jeffrey Goodman, James M. Greene, David Gregory, Marsha Groome, Andrew F. Gross, Sylvia Haller, Kevin Hannigan, David Hanson, Candice Harrington, Alan Harvey, William Hatfield, Sarah Heidarpour, Robert Heritage, John Holland, James Hughes, Kasie Hunt, Michael Isikoff, Alicia Jennings, Gwyneth Jones, Roxanne Joseph, Kara Kearns, Terence Kelly, Ryan Kiernan, Stacey Klein, Ann Klenk, Michael Kosnar, Courtney Kube, Michael LaRosa, Natasha Lebedeva, John Libretto, Christopher Licht, Arthur Lien, Kathleen Lockhart, Joseph W. Loebach, James V. Long, Gary Lynn, Freddie Malone, Mary Manby, Marc Marriott, Greg Martin, Chris Matthews, Patty McFarland, Richard McGinniss, Lee McKinney, Carroll Ann Mears, Rob Melick, James Miklaszewski, Christopher Millar, Richard Minner, Andrea Mitchell, Steven Mitnick, Domenico Montanaro, Ray Morada, Shaheen Mozaffari, Mark Murray, Lisa Myers, Nancy Nathan, Jason Neal, Michelle Neal, Donna Nelson, Elizabeth Nevins, David O'Brien, Mike O'Brien, Kelly O'Donnell, Hope Palmer, Morgan Parmet, Connie Patsalos, Eddie Paylor, Elyse Perlmutter-Gumbiner, Debra Pettit, Shelby Poduch, John Quinnette, Meaghan Rady, Andrew Rafferty, Alonzo Ray, Chester Reis, Talesha Reynolds, Giaco Riggs, Querry Robinson, Luke Russert, Howard Sacks, Colleen Sanvido, Beth Scott, Andrew Scritchfield, Wesley Scruggs, Carl Sears, Joel Seidman, Adam Serwer, Joseph Shalhoup, David Silver, Ron Simeone, Aaron Skopek, Kimberly Sneed, Gilbert Solorzano, Kenneth Strickland, Jon Sughroue, Robert Sullivan, David Thelin, Shawna Thomas, Ronald Thornton, Frank Thorp, Chuck Todd, Tina Urbanski, Adam Verdugo, Vaughn Ververs, Susan Vitorovich, David Vukmer, Katherine Wall, David Weakly, Ali Weinberg, Kristen Welker, Christopher Whittington, Winston Wilde, Robert T. Williams, Louis "Pete" Williams, Abigail Williams, Brenna Williams, Christopher Williamson, V. Alan Young, Jr.

NBC NEWSCHANNEL—400 North Capitol Street, Suite 850, Washington, DC 20001: Sheila Conlin, Nancy Ellard, Sheri Lynn Gibson, Andrew L. Godsick, Steve Handelsman, James Hurt, Julie Jarvis, Jennifer Johnson, Virginia Kreindler, Danielle Leigh, Nicole McManus, Brian Mooar, Steven Muskat, Tom Newberry, Mike O'Connell, Tracie Potts, Bonnie Rollins, Cecil John Sills, Christopher Wiggins.

NEW TANG DYNASTY TV—229 W 28th Street, Ste. 1200, New York, NY 10001: Min Chang, Hui Jing, Chuan Lin, Jin Pang, Yang Wang, Wei Wu, Dong Xiang, Bin Xue, Chunfang Yang, John Yu, Haoran Zheng.

NHK-JAPAN BROADCASTING CORPORATION—2030 M Street, NW., Suite 706, Washington, DC 20036: Taurean Barnwell, Regina Bediako, Yuko Chiba, Sylvain Coudoux, Matthew Field, Hiroto Fuseya, Yuichiro Hanazawa, Hiroshi Hirouchi, Ichiro Kabasawa, Takamoto Kajiwara, Atsushi Kato, Torao Kono, Takashi Mizukami, Joseph Shaw, Shin Shoji, Yuka Takagane, Junko Tanaka, Masayoshi Tanaka, Alexander Wortman, Daisuke Yamaguchi, Takeshi Yamasaki, Anthony Yazaki, Jumpei Yoshioka.

NIPPON TV NETWORK—529 14th Street, NW., #1036, Washington, DC 20045: Takaaki Abe, Kazuhiro Aoyama, Chie Fujioka, Kento Hasegawa, Tomoko Horie, Hiroaki Konno, Kensuke Kubo, Tateki Muratani, Kiyoshi Tanno, Kyrie Whitsett.

NORWEGIAN BROADCASTING—2000 M Street, NW., #890, Washington, DC 20036: Gro Holm, Anders Tvegard.

NOS DUTCH PUBLIC RADIO & TV (VRT)—2000 M Street, NW., #365, Washington, DC 20036: Wessel Jong, Wouter Zwart.

NOWTHIS NEWS—2000 Massachusetts Avenue, NW., Washington, DC 20036: Ashley Codianni, Julie Eckert, Sara Kenigsberg.

N-TV GERMAN NEWS CHANNEL—1100 13th Street, NW., Suite 400, Washington, DC 20005: Alexander Kleim, Peter Kleim.

ONE AMERICA—3600 New York Avenue, NE., Washington, DC 20002: Charles Herring, Amanda House.

NETWORKS, STATIONS, AND SERVICES REPRESENTED—Continued

POLITICO—101 Constitution, Washington, DC 20001: David Chalian, Jacqueline Corba, Christine Delargy, Madeline Marshall, Michael Schwab, Matt Sobocinski.

RADIO FRANCE—6404 Stratford Road, Chevy Chase, MD 20815: Frederic Carbonne.

RADIO FRANCE INTERNATIONALE—3700 Massachusetts Avenue, NW., #538, Washington, DC 20016: Anne-Marie Capomaccio, Silvia Chocarro, Claude L. Porsella.

RADIO FREE ASIA—2025 M Street, NW., Suite 300, Washington, DC 20036: Marsha Barnhart, Christen Billing, Shiny Li Breese, Gordon Burnett, Dorjee Damdul, Rigdhen Dolma, Richard Finney, Dhondup Gonsar, King Ho, Channhu Hoang, Mamatjan Juma, Jilil Kashgary, Vivian Kieffer, Ko Kyaw, Joshua Lipes, Kalden Lodoe, Corey Munford, Sarkis Najarian, Jung-Woo Park, Parameswaran Ponnudurai, Brian William Powell, Aungthu Schlenker, Khin Maung Soe, Sarada Taing, Yeshi Tashi, Hoa Ai Tran, Rachel Vandenbrink, Sungwon Yang, Hee Jung Yang, Lobsang Yeshi, Samean Yun.

RADIO FREE EUROPE—1201 Connecticut Avenue, NW., Washington, DC 20036: Golnaz Esfandiari, Heather Maher, Richard Solash.

RADIO MARTI—4201 Northwest 77th Avenue, Miami, FL 33166: Diana Molineaux.

RADIO ONE—5900 Princess Garden Pkwy 7th Floor, Lanham, MD 20706: Kent Kramer, Ron Thompson, Christopher Wegmann.

RADIO VALERA VENEZUELA—529 14th Street, NW., 8th Floor, Washington, DC 20045: Julio Moreno, Sonia Schott.

RCN–TV (COLOMBIA)—1333 H Street, NW., Washington, DC 20005: Martha Avila, Diana Castaneda, Mark Donaldson, Mario Gonzalez, Marco Granda, Laura Jaramillo, Beatriz Juez, Julio Marenco, Jorge Nuñez, Valdemar Rodriguez, Christian Siaden-Peña.

REAL NEWS NETWORK—700 12th Street, NW., Suite 1000, Washington, DC 20005: Jessica Desvarieux, Ralikh Hayes, Paul Jay, Sharmini Peries.

RELIGION & ETHICS NEWSWEEKLY—1333 H Street, NW., 6th Floor, Washington, DC 20005: Robert Abernethy, Gail Fendley, Patricia Hanley, Arnolds Labaton, Kim Lawton, Julie Mashack, Judy Reynolds, Noelle Serper, Lauren Talley.

REUTERS RADIO & TV—1333 H Street, NW., 6th Floor, Washington, DC 20005: Nadine Alfa, Keith Allen, Daniel Balinovic, Anoopam Bharania, Peter Bullock, John Clarke, Liza Feria, Kevin Fogarty, Marie Frail, Guillermo Garcia, Deborah Gembara, Pavithra George, Sarah Irwin, Katharine Jackson, Kia Johnson, Deborah Lutterbeck, Robert Muir, Kristin Neubauer, Gershon Peaks, Don Pessin, Steven Phillips, Jane Ross, Tom Rowe, Roger Shull, George Tamerlani, Scott Vaughan, Omar Younis.

RTP PORTUGUESE PUBLIC TELEVISION—2000 M Street, NW., #372, Washington, DC 20036: Marcia Santos, Edson Tanaka.

RTTV America—1325 G Street, NW., Suite 250, Washington, DC 20005: Reema Abu-Hamdyia, Mark Angelini, Jared Bilkre, Andrew Blake, Perianne Boring, Alexey Brazhnikov, Mark Bulla, Gayane Chichakyan, Christine Conetta, Jon Conway, Ameera David, Sean Filburn, Kathryn Fischer, Mindia Gavasheli, Margaret Howell, Rachel Kurzius, Meghan Lopez, Irene Marin, Abigail Martin, Kristian Monroe, Alexander Mursa, Manuel Rapalo, Samuel Sacks, Ian Sbalcio, Mikhail Solodovnikov, Justine Underhill, Vera Volokhonovich, Elizabeth Wahl, Ilya Zhodzishsky.

RTVI/ECHO–TV—1001 Pennsylvania Avenue, NW., Suite 6310, Washington, DC 20004: Alexander Panov, Dmytro Shakhov.

RUSSIAN STATE TV AND RADIO (RTR)—2000 N Street, NW., Suite 810, Washington, DC 20007: Philipp Dubrovskiy, Alexander Khristenko, Anna Semenova, Elena Sokolova.

RUSTAVI 2 BROADCASTING COMPANY—1111 Army Navy Drive, Unit 127, Arlington, VA 22202: David Nikuradze, Aleksandre Papinashvili.

SAGARMATHA TELEVISION—9655 Hawkshead Drive, Lorton, VA 22079: Nilu Kharel, Ram C. Kharel, Sharmila Uprety.

SCRIPPS HOWARD NEWS SERVICE—1090 Vermont Aveneue, NW., Washington, DC 20005: Matt Anzur, Christopher Cantergiani, Mark Greenblatt, Lawan Hamilton, Jim Osman, Ellen Weiss.

SINCLAIR BROADCAST GROUP—10706 Beaver Dam Road., Cockeysville, MD 21030: Kristin Frazao, Mark Hyman, Joshua Miller.

SIRIUS XM SATELLITE RADIO—1500 Eckington Place NE, Washington, DC 20002: Katherine Caperton, Jonathan Decker, Tim Farley, Patrick Ferrise, Pamela Kirkland, Julie Mason, Jennifer McLellan, Jared Rizzi, LaTonya Stephens.

SKY NEWS—400 North Capitol Street, NW., #550, Washington, DC 20001: Jon-Christopher Bua, Tim Gallagher, Tami Hoffman, Mike Inglis, Joey Jones, Dickon Mager, Greg Milam, Kevin Sheppard, Martin Smith, Jeremy Thompson, Dominic Waghorn, Amanda Walker, Hannah Walsh.

SKY NEWS ARABIA—400 North Capitol, Suite 770, Washington, DC 20001: Mohamad Awada, Mouhamad El Ahmed, Joseph Khawly.

SPIEGEL GERMAN TV—1202 National Press Building, Washington, DC 20045: Karin Assmann.

SRN NEWS (SALEM)—1901 North Moore Street, #201, Arlington, VA 22209: Gregory Clugston, Walter Hindes, Linda Kenyon, Jeffrey Matzka, Andrew Stewart.

STATELINE.ORG—1615 L Street, NW., Washington, DC 20016: Maggie Clark, Diane Fancher, Stephen Fehr, Scott Greenberger, Jake Grovum, Sandy Johnson, James Malewitz, Melissa Maynard, Michael Ollove, Elaine Povich, Pamela M. Prah, Christine Vestal, Daniel Vock.

NETWORKS, STATIONS, AND SERVICES REPRESENTED—Continued

STORY HOUSE PRODUCTIONS—2233 Wisconsin Avenue, NW., #420, Washington, DC 20007: Gabriele Biasizzo, Santiago Chillari Soberon, Julia Kelbling, Tina-Jane Krohn, Carsten Oblaender, Thomas Sassenberg.

SWEDISH BROADCASTING—2000 M Street, NW., Suite 890, Washington, DC 20036: Inger Arenander, Stefan Asberg, Lisa Carlsson, Leif Carlsson, Kyle Lanningham.

SWISS BROADCASTING—2000 M Street, NW., Suite 370, Washington, DC 20036: Sylvie Deroche, Pierre Gobet, Eric Guevara Frey, Arthur Honegger, Thomas Paggini, Beat Soltermann, Andrea Vosti.

TALK RADIO NEWS SERVICE—236 Massachusetts Avenue, NE., Suite 306, Washington, DC 20002: Zack Baddorf, Wendy Bidwell, James Cullum, Agot Deng, Tala Dowlatshahi, Brian Doyle, Justin Duckham, Shane Farnan, Diane Gooch, Geoff Holtzman, James Javinsky, Victoria Jones, Carole Marks, William McDonald, Elizabeth Pinkerton, Ellen Ratner, Tony Elias Sayegh, Zachary Silverstein, Luke Vargas, Joel Veldkamp, Kenric Ward, Ari Zoldan.

TELEMUNDO NETWORK—400 North Capitol Street, NW., Suite 850, Washington, DC 20001: Glenda Contreras, Lori Montenegro, Victor Reyes.

TELESUR—1825 K Street, NW., Suite 710, Washington, DC 20006: Aurora Samperio.

TELEVISA NEWS NETWORK (ECO)—1825 K Street, NW., Suite 710–G, Washington, DC 20006: Gregorio Meraz.

TF1-FRENCH TV—2000 M Street, NW., Suite 870, Washington, DC 20036: Julie Asher, Clement Biat, Helene Davieaud, Guillaume Debre, Mathieu Derrien, Michel Floquet, Bruce Frankel, Amelie Geffroy, Bertrand Guez, Vincent Mortreux.

THE BERNS BUREAU, INC.—SDG 40, Washington, DC 20510: Matthew Kaye.

THE HILL—1625 K Street, NE., Suite 900, Washington, DC 20006: Joshua Altman, Adele Hampton, Sean Root.

THE NEWSHOUR WITH JIM LEHRER—3620 South 27th Street, Arlington, VA 22206: Joshua Barajas, Christina Bellantoni, April Brown, Terence Burlij, Frank Carlson, Sarah Clune, David Coles, Anne Davenport, Truval Downey, Larisa Epatko, Victoria Fleischer, Mike Fritz, Meena Ganesan, Kwame Holman, Cindy Huang, Gwen Ifill, Rebecca Jacobson, Jason Kane, Diane Lincoln Estes, Jennifer Marder, Allie Morris, Mark Moynihan, Tiffany Mullon, Timothy Perry, Jr., Katelyn Polantz, Brian Ragle, Margaret Robinson, Daniel Sagalyn, Justin Scuiletti, Hari Sreenivasan, Rafael Suarez, Elizabeth Summers, Peter Tobia, Judy Woodruff, Daniel Yang.

THIS IS AMERICA WITH DENNIS WHOLEY—1333 H Street, NW., Washington, DC 20005: Jerry Cox, Dennis Wholey.

THIS WEEK IN AGRIBUSINESS (RFD–TV)—9915 Hillridge Drive, Kensington, MD 20895: Patrick Haggerty, Lawrence Miller.

TIMA—1620 I Street, NW., Suite 1000, Washington, DC 20006: Fatima Alkhirsan, Khaldoun Alrawi, Antonio Bustamante, Zena Ibrahim, Abdelhakim Kabbaj, Emad Mahdy, Krystyna Osinski, Eduardo Rodriguez, Jacob van der Veen.

TIME WARNER CABLE, Washington Bureau—400 North Capitol, NW., Suite G–95, Washington, DC 20001: Jennifer Babich, Geoffrey Bennett, Erica Butler, Michael Scotto.

TO THE CONTRARY (PERSEPHONE PRODUCTIONS)—1819 L Street, NW., 7th Floor, Washington, DC 20036: Bonnie Erbe, Luis Mazariegos, Sandrine Silverman, Cari Stein.

TOKYO BROADCASTING SYSTEM—1088 National Press Building, Washington, DC 20045: Samantha Grieder, Kiyoshi Murai, So Taira, Miho Takashima, Elliot Waldman, Noriyuki Yamaguchi.

TURKISH RADIO TELEVISION (TRT)—529 14th Street, NW., #1273, Washington, DC 20045: Emel Bayrak, Ahmet Yavas.

TV 9 (GEORGIA)—5800 Quantrell Avenue, Apartment 922, Alexandria, VA 22312: Khatia Paitchadze, Rusudan Tsereteli.

TV ASAHI—529 14th Street, NW # 1280, Washington, DC 20045: Robert Gentry, Takashi Hotta, Mai Ichihara, Yusuke Inoue, Satoko Shimana Shimbori, Ena Suto, Junichi Yoshikawa.

TV GLOBO INTERNATIONAL—2141 Wisconsin Avenue, NW., Suite L, Washington, DC 20007: Vicente Cinque, Raquel Krahenbuhl, Luis Fernando Silva-Pinto, Luis Urbina, Dennis Zanatta.

TV TOKYO—1333 H Street, NW 5th Floor, Washington, DC 20005: Benjamin Dalton, Mitsuo Kawamoto, Yuko Miyake, Matt Ropeik.

TV2–DENMARK—2000 M Street, NW., Suite 375, Washington, DC 20036: Charlotte Ernst, Scott Rensberger, Jesper Steinmetz.

TV3–TELEVISIO DE CATALUNYA—2000 M Street, NW., Suite 830, Washington, DC 20036: Eva Artesona, Antoni Bassas, Xavier Roca, Esteve Soler.

TVBS—2500 Wisconsin Avenue, Washington, DC 20007: Chia-Hui Ni, Shih-Yuan Tuan.

TVE–SPANISH PUBLIC TELEVISION—2000 M Street, NW., #325, Washington, DC 20036: Lorenzo Mila, Hector Pulido, Adoracion Toribio, Anna Ubeda.

TVN POLAND—7429 Chummley Court, Falls Church, VA 22043: Marcin Wrona, Marcin Wyszogrodzki.

UNIVISION—101 Constitution Avenue, NW., Suite 810E, Washington, DC 20001: Jorge Contreras, Emily Deruy, Deborah Durham, Jordan Fabian, Ted Hesson, Lourdes Meluza, Fernando Pizarro, Pablo Sanchez, Mario Vizcarra.

NETWORKS, STATIONS, AND SERVICES REPRESENTED—Continued

USA TODAY—7950 Jones Branch Drive, McLean, VA 22107: Steve Elfers, Maria Fowler, Shannon Green, Kaveh Rezaei.

VENTANA PRODUCTIONS—1819 L Street, NW., Washington, DC 20036: Richard Joy, John Lawrence, Timothy K. Murray, Juan Rocha, Robin Stewart, Mark Thalman, Christopher Tsou.

VIEWPOINT COMMUNICATIONS—8607 2nd Avenue, Suite 400, Silver Spring, MD 20910: Art Berko, Randy Feldman, Ben Finkel, Larry Greenblatt, Steven Hamberg, Charles Horn.

VOICE OF AMERICA—330 Independence Avenue, SW., Washington, DC 20237: Abdushakur Aboud, Houssein Aden, Najibullah Ahmadyar, Ibrahim Ahmed, M. Ahmed, Hasib Alikozai, Gholamreza Allahyari, Brian Allen, Darrell Allen, Muhammad Atif, Arash Azzizadeh, Carla Babb, Thomas Bagnall, Sungwon Baik, Steve Baragona, Jacqueline Belizaire, Iscar Blanco, Larry Bond, Robert Bordbar, Michael Bowman, Timothy Brannon, Jerome Brown, Meredith Buel, Michael Burke, Joan Butler, Carol Castiel, Carmen Cento, Peggy Chang, Nike Ching, Eunjung Cho, Lina Correa, Woody Crawford, Nick Crupi, Robert Currence, Robert Daguillard, Patricia Dalmasy, Minas Dargakis, Jeffery Daugherty, Akmal Dawi, Jela de Franceschi, Siamak Dehghanpour, Joan Deluca, Pamela Dockins, Betty Endara, Parichehr Farzam, Henok Fente, Bruce Ferder, Darren Fox, James Fry, David Futrowsky, Solomon Gebremariam, Myroslava Gongadze, Pema Gorap, Richard Green, Adam Greenbaum, Mwamoyo Hamza, Marcus Harton, Mohamed Hassan, Mi Jeong Y. Hibbitts, Thein Htike Oo, Iftikhar Hussain, Utami Hussin, Falastine Iman, Michael Ivey, Gary Jaffe, Kaveh Jamshidi, Douglas Johnson, Tsewang Khedrup, William Kim, Kent klein, Michael Kornely, Jesse Koster, Jean-Pierre Leroy, Tenzin Lhundup, Libo Liu, Diana Logriera, Liyuan Lu, James Malone, Marvin Marion, Sean Maroney, Eva Mazrieva, Stephen McGinley, Jeffrey Means, Kimseng Men, Beth Mendelson, Hooshmand Mirfakhraei, Guita Mirsaeedi, Joseph Mok, Negar Mortazavi, Roger Muntu, Thet Su Naing, Robert Naylor, Thao Nguyen, Matiullah Abid Noor, Thar Nyunt Oo, Rosalie O'Connell, Aung Lwin Oo, Julia Parabaniuk, Robert Parsell, Cal Perry, Jean Philippe, Reasey Poch, Suzanne Presto, Carolyn Presutti, John Quinn, Gioconda Reynolds, Scot Riddlesberger, Justin Riley, Linda Ringe, Daniel Robinson, Ralph Robinson, Shahla Sadighi, Cynthia Saine-Spang, Kabiruddin Sakar, Yuni Salim, Joad Santa-Rita, Yulia Savchenko, Brian Schiff, Edward Schneider, Jeff Seldin, Pema Setsang, Namgyal Shastri, Roger Sherman, Michael Shields, George Simkins, Joseph Sipos, Jerome Socolovsky, Pov Sok, Steven Springer, Amish Srivastava, Scott Storkel, Songphot Suphaphon, Carl Swanson, Jeffrey Swicord, Ayesha Tanzeem, Minia Teclab, Kyaw Zan Tha, Kyaw Thein, Michael Theisen, Alexandra Villarreal, Joseph Vitale, Winston Wood, Kathleen Woodsome, Raymond Yam, Jeff Young, Xiaoyan Zhang, Ahmad Zia.

VOICE OF RUSSIA—1325 G Street, NW., Suite 750, Washington, DC 20005: Andrew Hiller, Victoria Mashkova, Crystal Park, Rob Sachs, Rustem Safronov, Molly Seder, Samir Shakhbaz, Kate Zickel.

VOYAGE PRODUCTIONS—565 Pennsylvania Avenue, NW., #302, Washington, DC 20001: Susan Baumel, Ely Lamonica.

WASHINGTON BUREAU NEWS SERVICE—7425 Savan Point Way, Columbia, MD 21045: Joseph Nelson, C. Patrick Thorne, Michael Whitney.

WASHINGTON POST—1150 15th Street, NW., Washington, DC 20071: Jason Aldag, Gillian Brockell, A.J. Chavar, Ben Connors, Jonathan Forsythe, Alexandra Garcia, Brad Horn, Pamela Kirkland, Jackie Kucinich, Christina Lee, Victoria Lewis, Julie Ann McKellogg, Kate Musselwhite-Tobey, Jayne Orenstein, Julie Percha, Andrew Pergam, Theresa Poulson, Alice Rhee, Natasha Rudnick, Whitney Shefte, Brook Silva-Braga, Jeffrey Simon.

WASHINGTON RADIO AND PRESS SERVICE—6702 Pawtucket Road, Bethesda, MD 20817: Hanna Gutmann, Howard Lesser.

WETA—2775 South Quincy Street, Arlington, VA 22206: Lynn Allison, Charles Anderson, David Bash, Timothy Bowen, Donald Brawner, Martin Carr, Darzen Chang, Vincent Forcier, Charles Ide, Christopher Lane, Edward Lee, Jerry S. Lewis, Nancy Gerstman Morgan, Antonio Pacheco, Jeffrey Rathner, John Satterfield, James Schneider, Willliam Seabrook, Charles Voth.

WFDC–TV UNIVISION—101 Constitution Avenue, NW., Suite L–100, Washington, DC 20001: Juan Acevedo, Maria Rosa Lucchini, Lilian Mass, Karen Menedez, Mynellies Negron, Rafael Perez, Silvana Quiroz, Raul Ramos, Claudia Uceda.

WHITE HOUSE CHRONICLE—1042 Wisconsin Avenue, NW., Washington, DC 20007: Linda Gasparello, Llewellyn King.

WHUR—529 Bryant Street, NW., Washington, DC 20059: Ray Baker.

WJLA–TV / NEWSCHANNEL 8—1100 Wilson Boulevard, Arlington, VA 22209: Yasmeen Alamiri, Robert Alexander, Robert Allbritton, Bryan Allman, Katherine Amenta, Van Applegate, Natasha Barrett, Frank Becker, Brad Bell, Jennifer Bowman, Maureen Bunyan, Arch Campbell, Evan Carr, Brianne Carter, Richard Chamberlain, Zeke Changuris, Steve Chenevey, Margot Cohen, Ashley Coleman, Mike Conneen, Rebecca J. Cooper, G. Doug Culver, Joe DeFeo, Bruce DePuyt, AnnaMaria DiPietro, Martin C. Doane, Jennifer Donelan, Jennifer Doren, Ernie Ensign, Tony Ferrigno, Sam Ford, Kendis Gibson, Pege Gilgannon, Autria Godfrey, Jeff Goldberg, John Gonzalez, Kendall Griggs, Richard Guastadisegni, David Hackney, Mark Hanner, Leon Harris, Donna Harris, Melanie Hastings Wotring, Horace Holmes, Brian Hopkins, Tom Hormuth, LaTanya Horne, George Jackson, Samuel Jackson, Kevin Jaeger, Michael Jaffe, Jesse Janosky, Morris Jones, Nyshicka Jordan, James Joslyn, Suzanne Kennedy, Vanessa M.

NETWORKS, STATIONS, AND SERVICES REPRESENTED—Continued

Koolhof, Jay Korff, Greta Kreuz, Ming Leong, Indira LeVine, John B. Lewis, Bill Lord, Dave Lucas, Mary Kay Mallonee, Jon Mann, James Marcum, Brandon Mowry, Dwayne Myers, Jummy Olabanji, Kathy Park, Dan Patrick, Wayne Pellenberg, Gordon Peterson, Ben Rice, Jeff Rose, Thomas Roussey, Megan Rowls, Michael Rudd, Fred Ryan, Blake Sabatinelli, James Scott, James Searls, Holly Shannon, B.K. Sharma, Cynne Simpson, Rebecca Sinn, Alison Starling, Christopher Stuard, Scott Thuman, Stephen Tschida, Kristopher Van Cleave, Mike Vaughn, Hatzel Vela, James Walker, Kara Warr, Travis Washington, Robert Washington Anderson, Whitney Wild, Ron Windham, Skip Wood, Dale Wright, Andy Zmidzinski.

WNYC—1642 C Beekman Place, Washington, DC 20009: Todd Zwillich.

WPFW–FM—2390 Champlain Street, NW., Washington, DC 20009: Gloria Minott.

WRC–TV / NBC–4—4001 Nebraska Avenue, NW., #6, Washington, DC 20016: Jay Alvey, Jackie Bensen, Andrea Berry, Charles Bragale, Ashley Brown, Daniel Buckley, Larry Bullard, Julie Carey, Sean Casey, Joseph Cassano, Pat Collins, Natasha Copeland, David Culver, Lauren Dunn, Edward Durkin, Bernard Forte, Rob Gibson, Teneille Gibson, Aaron Gilchrist, Matt Glassman, Angie Goff, Michael Goldrick, Erika Gonzalez, Charles A. Goodknight, Herbert Gordon, Ede Jermin, Irene Johnson, Richard Jordan, Chris Kerwin, Zachary Kiesch, B. Layne, Ronald Leidelmeyer, Carlos Martinez, Megan McGrath, Michael O'Regan, Chester Panzer, Patti Petitte, Jeff Piper, Kelvin Robinson, Jim Rosenfield, Keith Russell, Danella Sealock, Mark Segraves, Tom Sherwood, Darcy Spencer, Mark Stephens, Shomari Stone, Robert Sweeney, John Taylor, Tisha Thompson, Anthony Tull, Adam Tuss, Roy Weinstock, Melinda Woolbright, Eun Yang, Rick Yarborough, Darren Ziegebein.

WTOP RADIO—3400 Idaho Avenue, NW., Washington, DC 20016: John Aaron, Neal Augenstein, Michelle Basch, Omar Bassiouny, Darci Brasch, Megan Cloherty, Jamie Forzato, Jason Fraley, Dave Garner, Jessie J. Green, Brennan Haselton, Amy Hunter, Amanda Iacone, Nick Iannelli, Kristi King Lilleston, Dave McConnell, Mitchell Miller, Andrew Mollenbeck, Rachel Nania, Brian Oliger, Robert Publicover, Veronica Robinson, Art Rose, Kate Ryan, Zach Shore, Hank Silverberg, Max Smith, Dick Uliano, Thomas Warren.

WTTG–FOX TELEVISION—5151 Wisconsin Avenue, NW., Washington, DC 20016: Matthew Ackland, Melanie Alnwick, Bob Barnard, Audrey Barnes, James Beahn, William Beyer, Rudolph Blyden, Paul Buehler, Anthony Colella, Patricia Corcoran, Daryl Curry, Lauren DeMarco, Karen Eidinger, Laura Evans, Tom Fitzgerald, Yianis Fournelis, John Frame, Dwight Frazier, Max Giammetta, Jeff Gilman, John Henrehan, Michael Horan, Karen Gray Houston, Lance Ing, Nelson Jones, Colleen Kenney, Craig Little, Sherri Ly, Michael Marantz, Wisdom Martin, Holly Morris, Richard Murphy, Beth Parker, Anthony Perkins, Michael Rickard, Bryan Roberts, Meredith Royster, Eugene Russell, F. David Rysak, Mark Sargent, Allison Seymour, Robert Shon, Sarah Simmons, Jason H. Smith, Joe Spevak, Donald E. Stanke, Will Thomas, Terri Tolliver, Maureen Umeh, Paul Wagner, Duane Watkins, Don Watrud, Douglas H. Wilkes, Steven Williams, Shawn Yancy, Annie Yu.

WUSA–TV—4100 Wisconsin Avenue, NW., Washington, DC 20016: Debra Alfarone, Mark Bost, Kurt Brooks, William Broom, Aubrey Bryant, Surae Chinn Lucie, William Clemann, Margaret Cordes, Jeffrey Cridland, Frederick D'Ambrosi, Jessica Doyle Belvedere, Manny Fantis, Kristin Fisher Forehand, Danielle Flanagan, Lesli Foster Mathewson, Peggy Fox, Michael Fuhr, Anetra Gaines, Stephen Garifo, Danielle Gatewood-Gill, Delia Goncalves Perry, Regina Griffin, Erica Grow, Gregory Guise, Bruce Harrison, James Hash, Shonty Hawkins, Michael Hydeck, Ko Im, Thomas James, Jan Jeffcoat, Elizabeth Jia, Bruce Johnson, Kevin G. King, Erik Lee, Abdulmola Lenghi, Bruce Leshan, Paul Lester, Joseph Martin, Samara Martin Ewing, Andrea McCarren, Derek McGinty, Kenny Molestina, Christopher Mullen, Gary Nurenberg, Felix Ortiz, Mark Pearson, Russell Ptacek, Anthony Rizzo, Andrea Roane Skehan, David Roycraft, Monika Samtani, David Satchell, James Searls, Jimmie Silman III, Anita Spear, Janet Terry, Michael Trammell, Elizabeth Turrell, Erin Van der Bellen, Dion Wiggins, Keith Williams, Stephanie Wilson.

WZDC–TV—2775 Quincy Street, Arlington, VA 22206: Paola Alonzo, Cristina Caicedo, Wilber Guzman, Moises Linares, Douglas Mejia, Lizeth Monsalve, Sulema Salazar, Randy Serrano, Jaime Vera, Juan Pablo Zariquiey.

XINHAU—1740 North 14th Street, Arlington, VA 22209: Yu Cao, Mantong Guo, Mike Kellerman, Yu Lin, Xing Qi.

YONHAP NEWS TV—529 14th Street, NW., Washington, DC 20045: Seungho Cho, Lauren Kim.

ZDF GERMAN TV—1077 31st Street, NW., Washington, DC 20007: Annette Brieger, Gabriele Buse, Askan Buse, Kirsten Candia, Oliver Divaris, Ruben Herrera, Erik Illenseer, Wolfgang Macholz, Claudia Offermann, Steffanie Riess, Christoph Roeckerath, Ulf-Jensen Roeller, Hildrun Roemer, Peter Schloemer, Heike Slansky, Uyanga Tserenbaljid, Elke Tucker.

FREELANCE

Freelancers: Francis Abbey, Rund Abdelfatah, Atef Abdulgawad, Naser Abu Diab, Robin Adlerblum, Jennifer Aidoo, Firas Alallak, Raad Ali, Angela Andersen, Patrick Anderson, Arash Arabasadi, Edward Archuletta, Bruno Arena, Sora Arero, Thomas Armstrong, Patricia Armstrong, Adrian Armwood, Donald Aros,

NETWORKS, STATIONS, AND SERVICES REPRESENTED—Continued

Jean-Pascal Azais, Travis Renee Baldwin, Mark Banks, Marilisa Battistella, Robert Baumann, Michael Bellis, Eric Bender, Brian Benjamin, Carolyn Berry, Jonathan Berryman, Kevin Beyer, Sadiq Bilal, Tim Bintrim, Paul Blake, James Blue, Warren Bolden, Bruce Bookhultz, Wayne F. Boyd, Paul Brandus, Charles Breiterman, Michael Broleman, Adam Brookes, Alison Burns, Matthew Burton, William Calder, James Canty, David Caravello, Brett Carlson, Brett Carlson, Dave Carter, Carl Catherine, Xiao Chang, Axel Charles-Messance, David Chaytor, Robert Cherouny, Stephen Cocklin, Anne Cocklin, Stacey Cohan, Holley Coil, Thomas Coleman, Donnie Comer, Camille Connolly, Gina Cook, Kyle Cooper, Pedro Correa, William Cortes, Chantal Costen, Timothy Cote, Eric Courtney, Ron Couvillion, Thomas Craca, Jill Craig, Philip Crowther, Maurice Curran, Patrick Curran, Stefan Czimmek, Carla Dakin, Joe Danielewicz, Joseph Danielewicz, Clinton Davis, Jennifer Davis, Stan de Saint Hippolyte, Michael DeMark, William Demas, Gary DeMoss, Juan Carlos Diaz, Juanita Dillard, Daniela Doan, Brian Donovan, Margaret Dore, Paul G. Dougherty, Denise Douglas, Geoffrey Doyle, Marc Dress, Barton Eckert, Brian Edwards, Arlene Eiras, Hosny Elgazar, Dalia Elkomy, Angel Elliott, Matthew Engel, Manuel Ernst, Robert Eustis, Anne-Marie Fendrick, Amy Fenton, Andy Field, Dan Fleutte, Kristin Foellmer, Laura Foran, Michael Ford, Kaelyn Forde, Victor Forte, Jr., Tom Foster, Thomas Foty, David Fox, Francis Patrick French, Mark French, Dave Friedman, Jo Ann Marie Fyanes, Christian Galdabini, Ismael Gama, Lynsea Garrison, Toni Genberg, Phil Geyelin, LeRita Gibson Reid, Dirk Gilliam, Nelson Ginebra, David Girard, Emily Girsch, Pat Glass, John Glennon, Sam Goodall, Lindsay Graves, Noah Gray, Nicholas P. Greiner, Kevin Griffin, David Grip, Fayrouz Guerouani, Mike Haan, Brian HaeFeli, Stephen Hahn, Tom Haller, Daniel Hallstead, Bill Harding, Claus Harding, Alejandro Harding, Roy Harris, Dustin Harrison-Atlas, ''Lara'' Jacqueline Hartzenbusch, Thomas Hass, Oscar Haynes, Barry Haywood, Sean Healey, Barry Hecht, Martin Heina, Karen Hendren, Florens Herbst, Ryan Hermelijn, Louise Hernon, Ricardo Higgins, Hugh Hinds, Andrea Hines, Darnley Hodge, David Hopper, Dean Hovell, Marge Hubbard, Jason Hubert, Thierry Humeau, Trudy Hutcherson, Heather Hutchinson, Winston Hylton, Ko Im, Julian Ingram, Donna Inserra, Jerry Jackson, Ryan Jackson, Charly Jaffe, Edward B. Jennings, Jr., Peder Jessen, Kabir Jikamshi, Aja Johnson, Fletcher Johnson, Rolanda Johnson, Stephanie Johnson, Aaron Johnson, Derek Leon Johnston, Shawn Jones, Hans Juergens, Cathy Kades, Richard Kane, Tara Kangarlou, Bill Kaplan, Mark Kauzlarich, John Kavanaugh, Kathleen Keller, Alice Kelley, Peter Kent, Eric Kerchner, Jonathan L. Kessler, Rob Klein, Ashley Koerber, Kaoru Kokufuda, Wolfgang Kotke, Carmen Kupper, Michael LaBella, Nancy Lanzendoerfer, Greg Larsen, France Latremoliere, James Laughlin, Myron Leake, George Leidsmar, Katherine Leiken, David Lent, Dexter Leong, Misha Lewis, Lisa Lewnes, Albert Liesegang, Bruce Liffiton, Tahira Lindsay, Melvin Lindsey, Jane Little, Culver Long, Jason Lowther, Jayne Lukas, Julio Luzqunios, Robert Lyles, Melissa Macaya, Mitzi Macias, Lindsey MacNabb, Jeff Martino, Emily Massey, Alice Massimi, Ronald H. Matthews, Max Matza, Brandon Maxwell, Joan Mazer Field, Mathieu Mazza, Donald McCarty, Douglas McCash, Daniel McClellan, Tipp K. McClure, Rich McDermott, Constance McDonough, Ian McDougall, Terrance McEachern, Allen McGreevy, Robert McHenry, Erika McManus, Tara Mergener, Megan Merritt, Rhoda Metcalfe, Kerry Meyer, David Mikutsky, Jenny Miner, Justin Mitchell, Mike Mock, Melissa Mollet, William Montague, John Monte, Willie Moorer, Amanda Moran, Martin Moser, Ronald Mounts, Natalia Mozgovaya, John Murphy, Megan Murray, Matthew Murray, Peter Murtaugh, Stephen Narisi, Todd Nash, Mohamed Nasser, Graham Nelson, Anh Nguyen, Jeffrey Noble, Richard A. Norling, Christopher Norris, James Novosel, Patrick O'Gara, D. O'Berry, Ralf Oberti, Jane O'Brien, Andy Och, William O'Hara, Daniel J. O'Shea, Jr., Mohamed Ouafi, Andre Palai, Kingsavanh Pathammavong, Daniel Patsko, Grant Peacock, Daniel Peebles, Douglas Perkins, Tim Persinko, Robert Peterson, Murray Pinczuk, Wingel Pinzon, Roslyn Plater, Christopher Plater, Mark Plotkin, Charlotte Potts, Michael J. Purbaugh, Omar A. Quinonez, Mark Rabin, Ali Rad, Bryan Rager, Wafik Ramadan, James Rankin, Shruti Rastogi, Doug Ray, Richard Reeve, Austin Reeves, Melanie Reffess, Ed Reinsel, Douglas Reynolds, Casey Riddle, Olivier Robert, Eugene Roberts, Sam Rocha, Eduardo Rodriguez, Abu Bakr Roland, Richard L. Roller, Peter Roof, Misa Rossetti-Meyer, Theodore Roth, Joseph Ruffini, Thomas Sampson, Jose Sanchez, Dinah Saracho, Tomoaki Sasaki, Gregory Savoy, Donald Schoenmann, Lars Schwetje, Taylor Sears, Michael Seium, Ali Serhan, Hakim Shammo, Michael Shannon, Ying Shi, Robert Shire, Harry Shoffner, James Sides, Colin Sims, Stephanie Slewka, Charles Slie, Anthony Smith, Christie Smith, John Smith, Cynthia Smith, Shona Somerville, Randall Sorenson, George A. Sozio, Theodore Spiegler, Thomas M. Staton, Kathy Stewart, Mark S. Stoddard, James Stubbs, James Suddeth, Rick Suddeth, Bethany Swain, Erik Tavcar, Jacqueline Taylor, Brandon Tea, Charlie Thomas, Shari Thomas, Shaleem Thompson, Joseph Thompson, Troy Thornes, George Toman, Hayley Turner, Brad Ulery, Melinda Ulloa, Melinda Ulloa, Luis Urbina, Juan Ureta, Demetress Valentine, Paul Vanderveen, Jennifer Vasquez, Jennifer Vasquez, Hillary Vaughn Sandoval, Marcos Vigil, Kelley Vlahos, Ambrose Vurnis, Jackie Lyn Walker, Douglas Wallick, Patrick Ward, Derrick Ward, Tarik Warner, Kyeshia Washington, Aaron Webster, George D. Weller, Katarina Werner, John P. Whiteside, Chris Widmer, Tracee Wilkins, Armstrong Williams, David Williams, James Williams, Chris Williamson, Kristin Wilson, Mark Wilson, Ronald Winters, Gringo Wotshela, Joshua Yospyn, David Zechar, Markus Zeffler, Stratis Zervos, Fangfang Zhang, Ariel Zimerman.

PERIODICAL PRESS GALLERIES*

HOUSE PERIODICAL PRESS GALLERY

The Capitol, H–304, 225–2941

Director.—Robert M. Zatkowski
Deputy Director.—Gerald Rupert, Jr.
Assistant Directors: Jenn Walters, Ryan Hamel

SENATE PERIODICAL PRESS GALLERY

The Capitol, S–320, 224–0265

Director.—Edward V. Pesce
Deputy Director.—Justin Wilson
Assistant Director.—Shawna Blair

EXECUTIVE COMMITTEE OF CORRESPONDENTS

Heather Rothman, BNA News, *Chairman*
Jay Newton-Small, Time Magazine, *Secretary*
Meg Shreve, Tax Notes, *Treasurer*
Manu Raju, Politico
Rebekah Metzler, U.S. News & World Report
Jason Dick, Roll Call
Alexander Bolton, The Hill

RULES GOVERNING PERIODICAL PRESS GALLERIES

1. Persons eligible for admission to the Periodical Press Galleries must be bona fide resident correspondents of reputable standing, giving their chief attention to the gathering and reporting of news. They shall state in writing the names of their employers and their additional sources of earned income; and they shall declare that, while a member of the Galleries, they will not act as an agent in the prosecution of claims, and will not become engaged or assist, directly or indirectly, in any lobbying, promotion, advertising, or publicity activity intended to influence legislation or any other action of the Congress, nor any matter before any independent agency, or any department or other instrumentality of the Executive Branch; and that they will not act as an agent for, or be employed by the Federal, or any State, local or foreign government or representatives thereof; and that they will not, directly or indirectly, furnish special or "insider" information intended to influence prices or for the purpose of trading on any commodity or stock exchange; and that they will not become employed, directly or indirectly, by any stock exchange, board of trade or other organization or member thereof, or brokerage house or broker engaged in the buying and selling of any security or commodity. Applications shall be submitted to the Executive Committee of the Periodical Correspondents' Association and shall be authenticated in a manner satisfactory to the Executive Committee.

2. Applicants must be employed by periodicals that regularly publish a substantial volume of news material of either general, economic, industrial, technical, cultural, or trade character. The periodical must require such Washington coverage on a continuing basis and must be owned and operated independently of any government, industry, institution, association, or lobbying organization. Applicants must also be employed by a periodical that is published for profit and is supported chiefly by advertising or by subscription, or by a periodical meeting the conditions in this paragraph but published by a nonprofit organization that, first, operates independently of any government, industry, or institution and, second, does

*Information is based on data furnished and edited by each respective Gallery.

not engage, directly or indirectly, in any lobbying or other activity intended to influence any matter before Congress or before any independent agency or any department or other instrumentality of the Executive Branch. House organs are not eligible.

3. Members of the families of correspondents are not entitled to the privileges of the Galleries.

4. The Executive Committee may issue temporary credentials permitting the privileges of the Galleries to individuals who meet the rules of eligibility but who may be on short-term assignment or temporarily residing in Washington.

5. Under the authority of Rule 6 of the House of Representatives and of Rule 33 of the Senate, the Periodical Galleries shall be under the control of the Executive Committee, subject to the approval and supervision of the Speaker of the House of Representatives and the Senate Committee on Rules and Administration. It shall be the duty of the Executive Committee, at its discretion, to report violations of the privileges of the Galleries to the Speaker or the Senate Committee on Rules and Administration, and pending action thereon, the offending correspondent may be suspended. The committee shall be elected at the start of each Congress by members of the Periodical Correspondents' Association and shall consist of seven members with no more than one member from any one publishing organization. The committee shall elect its own officers and a majority of the committee may fill vacancies on the committee. The list in the Congressional Directory shall be a list only of members of the Periodical Correspondents' Association.

JOHN A. BOEHNER,
Speaker, House of Representatives.

CHARLES E. SCHUMER,
Chair, Senate Committee on Rules and Administration.

MEMBERS ENTITLED TO ADMISSION

PERIODICAL PRESS GALLERIES

Abbott, Ryan M.: Courthouse News Service
Abdul-Alim, Jamaal: Diverse: Issues In Higher Education
Abramson, Julie L.: National Journal
Ackerman, Spencer J.: Wired.com
Ackley, Kate: Roll Call
Acree, Stephanie M.: BNA News
Adams, Caralee J.: Education Week
Adams, Shar: Epoch Times
Adragna, Anthony: BNA News
Aftab, Mirza Z.: BNA News
Albergo, Paul F.: BNA News
Alberts, Sheldon D.: The Hill
Albon, Courtney: Inside Washington Publishers
Alexis, Alexei: BNA News
Al-Faruque, Ferdous: Washington Business Information
Allen, Jonathan J.: Politico
Allen, Michael P.: Politico
Altman, Alex: Time Magazine
Altman, George: Gannett Government Media Corp.
Altscher, Judy K.: The Hill
Amber, Michelle L.: BNA News
Ambrosio, Patrick: BNA News
Amolsch, Christopher: FTC: Watch
Anderson, Heather M.: Credit Union Times
Anselmo, Joseph C.: Aviation Week
Antoine, LaTrina: BNA News
Antonides, David Scott: Tax Notes
Aplin, Donald G.: BNA News
Aquino, John T.: BNA News
Arnett, Autumn: Diverse: Issues In Higher Education
Arora, Jaime K.: Tax Notes
Ashton, Jerome C.: BNA News
Ashworth, Jerry: Thompson Information Services
Asker, James R.: Aviation Week
Assam, Cecelia M.: BNA News
Atkins, Pamela S.: BNA News
Atwood, John Filar: CCH Inc.
August, Melissa A.: Time Magazine
Aulino, Margaret: BNA News
Ault, Alicia: IMNG Medical Media
Ayers, Cameron S.: Thompson Information Services
Ayers, Carl A.: UCG
Bachman, Kathryn M.: Adweek
Bade, Rachael: Politico
Baker, Samuel: The Hill
Ball, Molly: Atlantic Monthly
Ballasy, Nicholas A.: Credit Union Times
Baltic, Sarah E.: McGraw-Hill Co.
Bancroft, John R.: Inside Mortgage Finance
Barash, Martina S.: BNA News
Barbagallo, Paul: BNA News
Barclay, Douglas: Broadband Census
Bardwell, Brian D.: Tax Notes
Barkoukis, Leah E.: Townhall Magazine
Barnes, Fred W.: Weekly Standard
Barnes, James A.: National Journal
Baron, Kevin: Foreign Policy Magazine
Barron-Lopez, Laura: The Hill
Barry, Sean A.: BNA News
Barry, Theresa A.: BNA News
Baschuk, Bryce: BNA News
Basken, Paul A.: Chronicle of Higher Education
Bason, Tamlin H.: BNA News
Basu, Sandra L.: U.S. Medicine
Bater, Jeffrey P.: BNA News
Baumann, Jeannie: BNA News
Bazinet, Kenneth: Kiplinger Washington Editors
Beasley, Stephanie M.: Inside Washington Publishers
Beaven, Lara W.: Inside Washington Publishers
Becker, Bernard A.: The Hill
Behr, Peter B.: Environment & Energy Publishing
Behsudi, Adam: Inside Washington Publishers
Belogolova, Olga: Inside Washington Publishers
Belz, Emily C.: World Magazine
Bender, Melanie: Washingtonian
Bennett, Alison E.: BNA News
Bennett, Cory: National Journal
Bennett, John T.: Gannett Government Media Corp.
Bennett, Kate: Washingtonian
Benson, Guy P.: Townhall Magazine
Benton, Nicholas F.: Falls Church News Press
Ben-Yosef, Andrea L.: BNA News
Berger, James R.: Washington Trade Daily
Berger, Mary L.: Washington Trade Daily
Bergin, Ulrike M.: Tax Notes
Berke, Kenneth H.: Government Contractor
Berman, Dan: Politico
Berman, Matt: National Journal
Berman, Russell L.: The Hill
Bertuca, Anthony F.: Inside Washington Publishers
Bettelheim, Adriel: Roll Call
Beutler, Brian A.: Talking Points Memo
Beyoud, Lydia: BNA News
Biggs, Alicia E.: BNA News
Billings, Deborah D.: BNA News
Bivins, Amy E.: BNA News
Bland, Scott: Hotline
Blank, Peter L.: Kiplinger Washington Editors

MEMBERS ENTITLED TO ADMISSION, PERIODICAL PRESS GALLERIES—Continued

Block, Jonathan M.: Crain Communications
Blotner, David: Capitol Forum
Blumenstyk, Goldie: Chronicle of Higher Education
Bobic, Igor: Talking Points Memo
Boehm, Rachel: BNA News
Bogardus, Kevin J.: The Hill
Boliek, Brooks: Politico
Bolton, Alexander: The Hill
Bomster, Mark W.: Education Week
Bonaquist, Maria: Tax Notes
Bondioli, Sara E.: Roll Call
Borchersen-Keto, Sarah A.: CCH Inc.
Bottemiller Evich, Helena: Politico
Boudreau, Catherine: BNA News
Bouve, Andrew: Slate
Boyles, Virginia: Health Market Survey
Boyles, William R.: Health Market Survey
Bracken, Leonard A.: BNA News
Bradford, Hazel M.: Crain Communications
Bradner, Eric: Politico
Brandolph, David B.: BNA News
Brannen, Kate: Politico
Braun, Kevin D.: Environment & Energy Publishing
Bravender, Robin: Environment & Energy Publishing
Brennan, Kevin: Hotline
Brenneman, Ross E.: Education Week
Bresnahan, John: Politico
Brevetti, Rossella E.: BNA News
Bridgeford, Lydell C.: BNA News
Brint, Juliana R.: McGraw-Hill Co.
Broderick, Brian J.: BNA News
Brooks, George A.: Inside Mortgage Finance
Brostoff, Tera E.: BNA News
Brown, Alex D.: Hotline
Brown, Carrie Budoff: Politico
Brown, Janet M.: Press Associates
Brown, Jill: Atlantic Information Services
Brownstein, Andrew D.: Thompson Information Services
Brownstein, Ronald J.: National Journal
Bruce, Robert: BNA News
Bruninga, Susan E.: BNA News
Bruno, Michael: Aviation Week
Bryant, Meg: Washington Business Information
Buford, Talia N.: Politico
Bullock, Lorinda M.: IMNG Medical Media
Burns, Alexander I.: Politico
Busch, Alaina V.: Inside Washington Publishers
Bushweller, Kevin C.: Education Week
Butler, Amy: Aviation Week
Byers, Alex: Politico
Byers, Dylan: Politico
Cahn, Emily: Roll Call
Cain, Derrick: Agri-Pulse
Calabresi, Massimo T.: Time Magazine
Caldwell, Christopher S.: Weekly Standard
Callahan, Madelyn R.: BNA News
Campbell, Christopher: Washingtonian
Caplan-Bricker, Nora: New Republic
Carey, William J.: Aviation International News
Carlile, Amy V.: Environment & Energy Publishing
Carlson, Jeffrey E.: CCH Inc.
Carney, Eliza Newlin: Roll Call
Carney, Jordain: Hotline
Carpenter, John: CCH Inc.
Carpenter, Zoe: Nation
Carr, Jennifer: Tax Notes
Casabona, Elizabeth M.: Thompson Information Services
Cash, Catherine: McGraw-Hill Co.
Cassidy, William B.: Journal of Commerce
Castelli, Christopher: Inside Washington Publishers
Casuga, Jay-Anne B.: BNA News
Catalini, Michael: National Journal
Cavanagh, Sean M.: Education Week
Cavas, Christopher P.: Gannett Government Media Corp.
Caygle, Heather N.: BNA News
Cecala, Guy David D.: Inside Mortgage Finance
Cervantes, Bobby: Politico
Chambers, Francesca A.: Red Alert Politics
Chan, Megan: Politico
Chemnick, Jean M.: Environment & Energy Publishing
Chen, Yang: Epoch Times
Cheney, Kyle: Politico
Chi, Tina M.: BNA News
Chibbaro, Jr., Louis M.: Washington Blade
Childers, Andrew J.: BNA News
Chokshi, Niraj: National Journal
Chronister, Gregory: Education Week
Cinquegrani, Gayle C.: BNA News
Cirilli, Kevin: Politico
Clapp, Stephen C.: Food Chemical News
Clark, Charles S.: Government Executive
Clark, Drew: Broadband Census
Clarke, Dave: Politico
Clemmitt, Marcia A.: CQ Researcher
Clemons, Steven: Atlantic Monthly
Clift, Eleanor: Newsweek
Coffin, James B.: Public Lands News
Cogan, Marin: New Republic
Cohen, Janey: BNA News
Cohen, Richard: FCW
Cole, Christopher M.: Inside Washington Publishers
Collins, Brian: National Mortgage News
Colman, Zachary A.: The Hill
Compart, Andrew: McGraw-Hill Co.
Compton, Kimberly Claire: BNA News
Connole, Patrick J.: Atlantic Information Services
Conroy, Declan A.: Food Protection Report
Cook, Jr., Charles E.: Cook Political Report
Cook, Nancy: National Journal
Cook, Robert C.: BNA News
Cook, Steven: BNA News

MEMBERS ENTITLED TO ADMISSION, PERIODICAL PRESS GALLERIES—Continued

Coomes, Jessica M.: BNA News
Cooper, Matthew: National Journal
Cooper, Perry E.: BNA News
Cooper, Stephen K.: CCH Inc.
Correa, Frances: IMNG Medical Media
Corrin, Amber: FCW
Cottle, M. Michelle: Newsweek
Cowden, Richard H.: BNA News
Cox, Ramsey C.: The Hill
Coyle, Marcia: National Law Journal
Craig, Geoffrey W.: McGraw-Hill Co.
Craver, Martha L.: Kiplinger Washington Editors
Crawford, Elizabeth R.: Elsevier Business Intelligence
Croft, John W.: Aviation Week
Cronin, Anne T.: Politico
Crowley, Michael: Time Magazine
Cunningham, Paige: Politico
Curran, John P.: Telecommunications Reports
Cusack, Robert: The Hill
Daigle, Rachael K.: BNA News
Dalphonse, Sherri: Washingtonian
Dalton, Matthew: Tax Notes
Daly, Richard F.: Crain Communications
Darcey, Susan W.: Elsevier Business Intelligence
Davenport, Coral: National Journal
Davidson-Choma, Katherine: Politico
Davies, Stephen A.: Endangered Species and Wetlands Report
Davis, Jeffrey J.: Transportation Weekly
Davis, Kristin G.: Gannett Government Media Corp.
Davis, Michelle: Education Week
Davis, S. Diane: BNA News
Davis, Steve W.: Atlantic Information Services
Davis, William R.: Tax Notes
Day, Jeff: BNA News
de la Isla, Jose: Hispanic Link News Service
Deigh, Gloria: BNA News
Dela Rosa, Darrell D.: CQ Researcher
Delargy, Christine: Politico
DeLeon, Carrie R.: Telecommunications Reports
Dellerson, Danielle R.: BNA News
Demko, Paul J.: Crain Communications
Dennis, Steven T.: Roll Call
DePaul, Jennifer: Tax Notes
Derrick, Joshua C.: World Magazine
Devaney, Tim: The Hill
Diamond, Phyllis: BNA News
Dias, Elizabeth: Time Magazine
Dick, Jason J.: Roll Call
Dickerson, John F.: Slate
Dickinson, Lauren: National Journal
DiCosmo, Bridget: Inside Washington Publishers
Diegmueller, Karen: Education Week
Dillon, Jeremy L.: Exchange Monitor Publications
DiMascio, Jennifer: Aviation Week
DiSciullo, Joseph: Tax Notes
Divis, Dee A.: Inside GNSS
Dixit, Rachana: Inside Washington Publishers
Dixon, Darius A.: Politico
Dixon, Kim: Politico
Dobson, William J.: Slate
Doherty, Daniel P.: Townhall Magazine
Dolley, Steven D.: McGraw-Hill Co.
Dombrowski, Cathy H.: Elsevier Business Intelligence
Domone, Dana J.: BNA News
Donlan, Thomas G.: Barron's
Donovan, Douglas: Chronicle of Higher Education
Dorrian, Patrick F.: BNA News
Douglas, Genevieve: BNA News
Dovere, Edward-Isaac: Politico
Downey, Kirstin E.: FTC: Watch
Downey, Theodore: Capitol Forum
Doyle, Kenneth P.: BNA News
Doyle, Susan: BNA News
Draper, Robert L.: GQ Magazine
Drew, Russell: Inside Washington Publishers
Dube, Elliott: BNA News
Dube, Jr., Lawrence E.: BNA News
Dudley, Julianne E.: Weekly Standard
Duffy, Jennifer E.: Cook Political Report
Duffy, Michael W.: Time Magazine
Dumain, Emma N.: Roll Call
Durkin, Erin: Inside Washington Publishers
Dutra, Antonio: BNA News
Dwyer, Diana: New Republic
Easley, Jonathan: The Hill
Eastland, Terry: Weekly Standard
Easton, Nina J.: Fortune Magazine
Eckstein, Megan A.: Inside Washington Publishers
Edney, Hazel Trice T.: Trice Edney Newswire
Edwards, Charles J.: Thompson Information Services
Edwards, Jewel W.: BNA News
Edwards, Thomas J.: CD Publications
Ege, Konrad: Freitag
Eggerton, John S.: Broadcasting & Cable
Ehart, William: CEO Update
Eisele, Albert: The Hill
Eisenstein, Michael: BNA News
Elbasha, Diana: Washingtonian
Elfin, Dana: BNA News
Elgatian, Tawny A.: BNA News
Elliott, Amy S.: Tax Notes
Ellis, Isobel: National Journal
Emma, Caitlin Z.: Politico
Epstein, Ethan R.: Weekly Standard
Epstein, Jennifer: Politico
Epstein, Reid: Politico
Ertel, Karen L.: BNA News
Esquivel, J. Jesus: Proceso
Estepa, Jessica M.: Environment & Energy Publishing
Evans, Josh: Broadband Census
Everett, John B.: Politico

MEMBERS ENTITLED TO ADMISSION, PERIODICAL PRESS GALLERIES—Continued

Everstine, Brian: Gannett Government Media Corp.
Ewing, Philip: Politico
Fabey, Michael J.: Aviation Week
Faler, Brian: Politico
Farmer, Liz: Governing
Fath, Meredith: Tax Notes
Feeney, William: National Journal
Fellman, Samuel: Gannett Government Media Corp.
Fellow, Avery: BNA News
Fellows, Jody C.: Falls Church News Press
Ferguson, Andrew: Weekly Standard
Ferguson, Brett A.: BNA News
Ferullo, Michael A.: BNA News
Festa, Elizabeth D.: National Underwriter
Fialka, John J.: Environment & Energy Publishing
Field, Kelly E.: Chronicle of Higher Education
Fischer, Jonathan L.: Washington City Paper
Fischer, Karin E.: Chronicle of Higher Education
Fisher, Julia: New Republic
Fitton, Jacqueline: Elsevier Business Intelligence
Fleming, Nora: Education Week
Fletcher, Kenneth R.: Exchange Monitor Publications
Flood, Brian: BNA News
Foran, Clare: National Journal
Forbes, Sean I.: BNA News
Fournier, Ronald: National Journal
Fox, Lauren: U.S. News & World Report
Francis, Laura: BNA News
Franke-Ruta, Garance: Atlantic Monthly
Franklin, Mary Beth: Crain Communications
Frantz, Karen D.: Exchange Monitor Publications
Freda, Diane: BNA News
Freebairn, William A.: McGraw-Hill Co.
French, Lauren: Politico
Fried, Lissa: Tax Notes
Friedman, Linda: Tax Notes
Friedman, Lisa F.: Environment & Energy Publishing
Fryer-Biggs, Zachary: Gannett Government Media Corp.
Fung, Brian: National Journal
Galentine, Elizabeth R.: Employee Benefit Adviser
Gannon, John: BNA News
Gantz, Rachel: UCG
Gardner, Donald L.: Chronicle of Higher Education
Garland, Susan B.: Kiplinger Washington Editors
Garner, Wilson Lynn: BNA News
Garofalo, Patrick: U.S. News & World Report
Gates-Davis, Marilyn: Roll Call
Gattoni-Celli, Luca: Tax Notes
Gatz, Nicholas T.: Falls Church News Press
Gavin, Patrick: Politico
Gaynor, Michael: Washingtonian
Geisel, Jerome M.: Crain Communications
Geman, Ben: The Hill
Gentile, Gary: McGraw-Hill Co.
Gerecht, Michael S.: CD Publications
Gerstein, Joshua A.: Politico
Gewertz, Catherine: Education Week
Gibson, Ginger S.: Politico
Gilbert, Natasha: Nature
Gilbert, Sophie: Washingtonian
Gilcrest, Laura H.: McGraw-Hill Co.
Gillespie, Lisa: Inside Washington Publishers
Gilmer, Ellen M.: Environment & Energy Publishing
Gilston, Meredith L.: Gilston-Kalin Communications
Gilston, Samuel M.: Gilston-Kalin Communications
Gingery, Derrick J.: Elsevier Business Intelligence
Ginsberg, Heather: Townhall Magazine
Gizzi, John: Newsmax
Glass, Andrew J.: Politico
Glass, Kevin W.: Townhall Magazine
Gleeson, Michael: Tax Notes
Gloger, Katja: Stern
Glover, Mary: Washingtonian
Glueck, Katie: Politico
Gnezditskaia, Anastasia: McGraw-Hill Co.
Goad, Benjamin: The Hill
Goindi, Geeta: Express India
Gold, Hadas: Politico
Goldwyn, Brant: CCH Inc.
Gonzales, Nathan: Rothenberg Political Report
Gonzalez, Sarah: Agri-Pulse
Goode, Darren T.: Politico
Goodin, Emily L.: The Hill
Goodwine, Velma: Research Institute of America Group
Gould, Joseph M.: Gannett Government Media Corp.
Goyal, Raghubir: Asia Today
Graff, Garrett: Washingtonian
Graham, David A.: Atlantic Monthly
Gray, Steven U.: Ebony
Gray, William T.: Synopsis
Green, Charles A.: National Journal
Green, Miranda C.: Inside Washington Publishers
Greenblum, Ariel: Tax Notes
Greene, Virginia W.: National Law Journal
Greenhalgh, Keiron: McGraw-Hill Co.
Gregg, Diana I.: BNA News
Gregory, Patrick: BNA News
Griffith, Cara L.: Tax Notes
Gross, Grant J.: IDG News Service
Gruber, Amelia M.: Government Executive
Gruenberg, Mark J.: Press Associates
Gruss, Michael: Space News
Guida, Victoria: Inside Washington Publishers
Guillen, Alexander C.: Politico
Guniganti, Pallavi: Global Competition Review
Gurdon, Hugo: The Hill
Gutman, James H.: Atlantic Information Services
Haas, Joseph A.: Elsevier Business Intelligence
Haberkorn, Jennifer A.: Politico
Hagstrom, Jerry: National Journal
Hallerman, Tamar: Exchange Monitor Publications

MEMBERS ENTITLED TO ADMISSION, PERIODICAL PRESS GALLERIES—Continued

Halper, Daniel M.: Weekly Standard
Hamilton, Amy L.: Tax Notes
Hamrick, Mark: Bankrate.com
Hancock, Benjamin: Inside Washington Publishers
Handley, Megan M.: U.S. News & World Report
Haniffa, Aziz A.: India Abroad
Hansard, Sara E.: BNA News
Hansen, Brian: McGraw-Hill Co.
Hansen, David: BNA News
Harball, Elizabeth: Environment & Energy Publishing
Harbrecht, Douglas A.: Kiplinger Washington Editors
Hardy, Michael: FCW
Harkins, Gina A.: Gannett Government Media Corp.
Harris, John F.: Politico
Harris, Shane: Washingtonian
Haseley, Donna L.: Inside Washington Publishers
Havard, Katherine: Weekly Standard
Hawkings, Jr., David: Roll Call
Hayes, Peter S.: BNA News
Healy, Amber M.: Food Chemical News
Hedberg, Lars-Eric: BNA News
Hegstad, Maria A.: Inside Washington Publishers
Heitin, Liana: Education Week
Helbling, Laura: Elsevier Business Intelligence
Heller, Marc R.: BNA News
Helminski, Edward L.: Exchange Monitor Publications
Hemingway, Mark W.: Weekly Standard
Hennig, Jutta: Inside Washington Publishers
Herb, Jeremy: The Hill
Herness, Sarah E.: Exchange Monitor Publications
Hess, Ryan E.: MII Publications
Hicks, Kathleen B.: Townhall Magazine
Hill, Keith M.: BNA News
Hill, Richard: BNA News
Hillman, G. Robert: Politico
Hiruo, Elaine: McGraw-Hill Co.
Ho, Soyoung: Research Institute of America Group
Hobbs, M. Nielsen: Elsevier Business Intelligence
Hobbs, Susan R.: BNA News
Hobson, Margaret Kriz: Environment & Energy Publishing
Hodge, Hope: Gannett Government Media Corp.
Hoffman, Rebecca E.: BNA News
Hoffman, William: Tax Notes
Hofmann, Mark A.: Crain Communications
Hohmann, James P.: Politico
Holeywell, Ryan M.: Governing
Holland, William: McGraw-Hill Co.
Hollander, Catherine: National Journal
Hollis, April: Washington Business Information
Holmes, Gwendolyn C.: BNA News
Hooper, Molly K.: The Hill
Hoover, Kent D.: Washington Business Journal
Hopkins, Chris: National Journal
Hopkinson, Jenny: Politico
Horowitz, Jay: BNA News
Horwood, Rachel J.: Economist
Howell, Katie J.: Environment & Energy Publishing
Hudson, Elizabeth L.: Inside Washington Publishers
Hudson, Jasmin M.: McGraw-Hill Co.
Hudson, John: Foreign Policy Magazine
Huffman, Jason: Politico
Huisman, Matthew L.: National Law Journal
Hujer, Marc A.: Der Spiegel
Humphrey, Shonda: Tax Notes
Hyland, Kristyn J.: BNA News
Iafolla, Robert: BNA News
Ichniowski, Thomas F.: McGraw-Hill Co.
Iekel, John F.: Thompson Information Services
Ioffe, Julia: New Republic
Ip, Gregory W.: Economist
Irfan, Umair: Environment & Energy Publishing
Irgang, Anke B.: UCG
Isenstadt, Alex: Politico
Jackson, Jr., David Randall: Tax Notes
Jackson, Valarie N.: McGraw-Hill Co.
Jacobs, Benjamin: Newsweek
Jacobs, Jeremy P.: Environment & Energy Publishing
Jacobson, Todd K.: Exchange Monitor Publications
Jaffe, Alexandra: The Hill
Jaffe, Harry: Washingtonian
James, Betty W.: Government Contractor
Jaworski, Thomas: Tax Notes
Jenning, Linda Kramer: Glamour Magazine
Jin, Yan: Caijing Magazine
Johnsen, Erika L.: Townhall Magazine
Johnson, Alisa A.: BNA News
Johnson, Christopher: Washington Blade
Johnson, Katie: BNA News
Johnson, Nicole: Gannett Government Media Corp.
Johnson, Regina: McGraw-Hill Co.
Johnston, Stephanie S.: Tax Notes
Jones, Caroline E.: Washington City Paper
Jones, George G.: CCH Inc.
Jonson, Nick G.: McGraw-Hill Co.
Joseph, Cameron E.: The Hill
Jost, Kenneth W.: CQ Researcher
Jowers, Karen G.: Gannett Government Media Corp.
Joynt, Carol R.: Washingtonian
Judis, John: New Republic
Judson, Jennifer A.: Inside Washington Publishers
Juliano, Nick: Environment & Energy Publishing
Kady, Martin J. II: Politico
Kalish, Brian M.: Employee Benefit Adviser
Kamens, Jessie K.: BNA News
Kaplan, Hugh B.: BNA News
Kaplan, Karen H.: Nature
Kaplan, Rebecca: National Journal
Kapur, Sahil: Talking Points Memo
Kashino, Marisa M.: Washingtonian
Kasperowicz, Peter I.: The Hill
Kaufman, Bruce S.: BNA News

MEMBERS ENTITLED TO ADMISSION, PERIODICAL PRESS GALLERIES—Continued

Kaufmann, Gregory R.: Nation
Kavruck, Deborah A.: Washington Counseletter
Kelly, Catherine A.: Elsevier Business Intelligence
Kelly, Lauren: Atlantic Information Services
Kenen, Joanne L.: Politico
Kern, Rebecca M.: Elsevier Business Intelligence
Khan, Naureen: National Journal
Kim, Seung Min: Politico
Kime, Patricia N.: Gannett Government Media Corp.
King, Pamela L.: Environment & Energy Publishing
King, Robert C.: Washington Business Information
King, Robert P.: Politico
Kingsley, Kim: Politico
Kinstler, Linda: New Republic
Kirby, Paul S.: Telecommunications Reports
Kirkland, Joel G.: Environment & Energy Publishing
Kirkland, John R.: BNA News
Kitchens, Alison: Washingtonian
Kitfield, James: National Journal
Klein, Alyson: Education Week
Klimas, Jacqueline: Gannett Government Media Corp.
Klimko, Frank J.: CD Publications
Klingst, Martin E.: Die Zeit
Kneller, Susan R.: BNA News
Knight, Christopher: Inside Washington Publishers
Knobbe, Martin: Stern
Koebler, Jason T.: U.S. News & World Report
Koelemay, Jeffrey: BNA News
Kondracke, Morton M.: Roll Call
Konkel, Frank R.: FCW
Koo, Jimmy H.: BNA News
Kopan, Tal: Politico
Koszczuk, Jaculine M.: National Journal
Kovski, Alan D.: BNA News
Kraushaar, Josh: National Journal
Kubetin, Sally: IMNG Medical Media
Kubetin, William Randy: BNA News
Kukuk, Brad A.: Mine Safety and Health News
Kummer, Luke J.: Washington Diplomat
Kunkelman, Sarah: BNA News
Kurtz, David M.: Talking Points Memo
Kurtz, Josh: Environment & Energy Publishing
Kurtzleben, Danielle: U.S. News & World Report
Kushin, Philip H.: BNA News
Kushner, Adam: National Journal
Kwidzinski, Anna: BNA News
LaBrecque, Louis C.: BNA News
Lacey, Anthony: Inside Washington Publishers
Laffler, Mary Jo: Elsevier Business Intelligence
Laing, Keith A.: The Hill
Laise, Eleanor: Kiplinger Washington Editors
Lake, Eli J.: Newsweek
Lambert, Kevin C.: BNA News
Lamothe, Daniel G.: Gannett Government Media Corp.
Laping, Karen McBeth: McGraw-Hill Co.
LaRoss, David R.: Inside Washington Publishers
Larson, Cathleen R.: BNA News
Larson, Samantha: GQ Magazine
Last, Jonathan V.: Weekly Standard
Lavers, Michael: Washington Blade
Lawrence, Jill: National Journal
Lawson, Alex R.: Inside Washington Publishers
Learner, Neal: Atlantic Information Services
Leatherman, Jacquelyn D.: CCH Inc.
Lee, Min Jung: Politico
Lee, Steve K.: BNA News
Leeuwenburgh, Todd H.: Thompson Information Services
Lehmann, Evan W.: Environment & Energy Publishing
Lejeune, Tristan: Employee Benefit News
Leone, Daniel: Space News
Leopold, George H.: EE Times
Lesesne, William F.: Research Institute of America Group
Lesniewski, Niels P.: Roll Call
Leven, Rachel P.: BNA News
Levin, Joshua: Slate
Levine, Susan: Politico
Levy, Pema: Talking Points Memo
Liang, John: Inside Washington Publishers
Lillis, Michael P.: The Hill
Lindeman, Ralph: BNA News
Ling, Katherine: Environment & Energy Publishing
Littleton, Julia A.: Environment & Energy Publishing
Livingston, Rebecca A.: Roll Call
Lizza, Ryan: New Yorker
Loatman, Michael O.: BNA News
Logan, Lee: Inside Washington Publishers
Lokshin, Maria L.: BNA News
Long Rayburn, Karen S.: UCG
Lopez, Kathryn J.: National Review
Lorenzo, Aaron E.: BNA News
Losey, Stephen: Gannett Government Media Corp.
Loveless, William E.: McGraw-Hill Co.
Lowe, Christian A.: U.S. News & World Report
Lowe, Paul D.: Aviation International News
Lowther, William A.: Mail on Sunday
Lubold, Gordon: Foreign Policy Magazine
Lunney, Kellie: Government Executive
Lustig, Joe: BNA News
Maas, Angela K.: Atlantic Information Services
MacDonald, Neil A.: Technology Commercialization
MacGillis, Alec: New Republic
Macy, Daniel J.: Thompson Information Services
Madara, Matthew: Tax Notes
Madden, Mike: Washington City Paper
Mahoney, Brian: Law360
Maine, Amanda: CCH Inc.
Maixner, Edward: Kiplinger Washington Editors
Mak, Tim K.: Politico

MEMBERS ENTITLED TO ADMISSION, PERIODICAL PRESS GALLERIES—Continued

Mandel, Jennifer A.: Environment & Energy Publishing
Manley, Mary Ann G.: BNA News
Mann, Jason: National Journal
Manzo, Kathleen: Education Week
Marchessault, Anna: BNA News
Marks, Joseph H.: Government Executive
Maron, Dina: Scientific American
Marron, Jessica: McGraw-Hill Co.
Marshall, Aarian M.: Agri-Pulse
Marshall, Christa: Environment & Energy Publishing
Marshall, Madeline: Politico
Martin, Juliann: Tax Notes
Martinez, Jennifer M.: The Hill
Martinson, Erica L.: Politico
Marx, Claude: FTC: Watch
Massey, Nathanael: Environment & Energy Publishing
Matus, Victorino L.: Weekly Standard
Mauro, Anthony E.: National Law Journal
Maze, Richard: Gannett Government Media Corp.
Mazmanian, Adam: FCW
Mazumdar, Anandashankar: BNA News
McAllister, William H.: Linn's Stamp News & Coin World
McArdle, John E.: Environment & Energy Publishing
McAuley, David: BNA News
McBride, Courtney: Hotline
McBride, Edward P.: Economist
McCabe, Neil: Human Events
McCalmont, Lucy: Politico
McCarter, Mickey: HS Today
McCleskey, Ellen E.: BNA News
McCord, Quinn T.: Hotline
McCormack, John M.: Weekly Standard
McCormack, Richard A.: Manufacturing & Technology News
McCormally, Kevin: Kiplinger Washington Editors
McCracken, Rebecca P.: BNA News
McCutcheon, Chuck A.: National Journal
McDevitt, Caitlin A.: Politico
McElwaine, Sandra: Newsweek
McElwee, Joshua J.: National Catholic Reporter
McEvoy, Margaret: BNA News
McFarland, Pamela E.: McGraw-Hill Co.
McGann, Laura K.: Politico
McGill, Brian: National Journal
McGolrick, Susan J.: BNA News
McGowan, Kevin P.: BNA News
McInerney, Susan M.: BNA News
McIntosh, Toby: BNA News
McKewen, Darren: BNA News
McKinney, Amber: BNA News
McLeary, Paul J.: Gannett Government Media Corp.
McMahon, Francine M.: The Hill
McMahon, Robert: McGraw-Hill Co.
McManus, Erin: BNA News
McNeil, Michele: Education Week
McPherson, Lindsey: Tax Notes
McTague, James A.: Barron's
Meacham, Jane: Thompson Information Services
Mechcatie, Elizabeth: IMNG Medical Media
Medici, Andrew S.: Gannett Government Media Corp.
Mehta, Aaron N.: Gannett Government Media Corp.
Meinecke, Elisabeth C.: Townhall Magazine
Merrion, Paul Robert: Crain Communications
Mershon, Erin: Politico
Metzler, Rebekah W.: U.S. News & World Report
Meyers, Jessica: Politico
Miley, John T.: Kiplinger Washington Editors
Milhiser, Ellen B.: Synopsis
Milk, Leslie: Washingtonian
Miller, Zeke: Time Magazine
Millman, Jason: Politico
Milone, Tiffany F.: BNA News
Mimms, Sarah: Hotline
Mishory, Jordana L.: Inside Washington Publishers
Mitchell, Charles F.: Inside Washington Publishers
Mitchell, Ellen: Inside Washington Publishers
Mixter, Bronwyn: BNA News
Moeller, Philip: U.S. News & World Report
Mokhiber, Russell J.: Corporate Crime Reporter
Mola, Roger A.: Aviation International News
Molnar, Michele: Education Week
Monastersky, Richard A.: Nature
Moore, Andrew: McGraw-Hill Co.
Moore, Michael D.: BNA News
Moore, Miles David: Crain Communications
Morales, Cecilio: MII Publications
Morella, Michael: U.S. News & World Report
Morello, Lauren: Nature
Morring, Jr., Frank: Aviation Week
Morris, David: Kiplinger Washington Editors
Morris, Jefferson F.: Aviation Week
Moss, Teresa: Tax Notes
Mracek, Karen L.: Kiplinger Washington Editors
Mulero, Eugene: Environment & Energy Publishing
Mullen, Laura: Capitol File
Mullins, Luke: Washingtonian
Mullins, Richard A.: Aviation Week
Munoz, Amanda: Townhall Magazine
Munoz, Carlo: The Hill
Munsil, Leigh: Politico
Muolo, Paul: Inside Mortgage Finance
Muradian, Vardges: Gannett Government Media Corp.
Murphy, Joan F.: Food Chemical News
Mutcherson-Ridley, Joyce: CCH Inc.
Narayanan, Nayantara: Environment & Energy Publishing
Nardella, Lauren: Elsevier Business Intelligence
Nartker, Michael: Exchange Monitor Publications
Nather, David R.: Politico

MEMBERS ENTITLED TO ADMISSION, PERIODICAL PRESS GALLERIES—Continued

Natter, Ari J.: BNA News
Naylor, Sean D.: Gannett Government Media Corp.
Needham, Vicki: The Hill
Nelson, Eric: Politico
Nelson, Gabe: Crain Communications
Nelson, Libby A.: Politico
Nelson, Steven E.: U.S. News & World Report
Neuhauser, Alan: U.S. News & World Report
Neumeyer, Benjamin: Capitol Forum
Newell, Ashley C.: Tax Notes
Newhauser, Daniel J.: Roll Call
Newkumet, Christopher J.: McGraw-Hill Co.
Newmyer, Tory G.: Fortune Magazine
Newton-Small, Jay: Time Magazine
Nichols, William D.: Politico
Nicholson, Jonathan: BNA News
Nicks, Denver: Time Magazine
Noh, Chang: McGraw-Hill Co.
Norman, Brett: Politico
Norris, Karen: Thompson Information Services
Northey, Hannah M.: Environment & Energy Publishing
Novack, Sophie: National Journal
Obey, Douglas: Inside Washington Publishers
O'Brien, Cortney: Townhall Magazine
Odom, Che L.: BNA News
Ogburn, Stephanie: Environment & Energy Publishing
Ognanovich, Nancy: BNA News
Oliphant, James: National Journal
Olsen, Florence E.: BNA News
Opfer, Christopher R.: BNA News
Orchowski, Margaret: Hispanic Outlook in Higher Education
Orr, Elizabeth: Washington Business Information
Orth, Maureen: Vanity Fair
Ortman, Emily M.: Roll Call
Osnos, Evan: New Yorker
Osterman, Kelsey N.: Red Alert Politics
Ostroff, James J.: McGraw-Hill Co.
O'Sullivan, William: Washingtonian
O'Toole, Charles C.: Tax Notes
O'Toole, Thomas: BNA News
Otto, Nick: Washington Business Information
Pai, Tanya: Washingtonian
Pak, Janne Kum Cha: USA Journal
Palleschi, Amanda: Inside Washington Publishers
Palmer, Anna A.: Politico
Palmer, Doug: Politico
Parillo, Kristen A.: Tax Notes
Parker, Laura: Vanity Fair
Parker, Stuart H.: Inside Washington Publishers
Parti, Tarini: Politico
Paschal, Mack Arthur: BNA News
Patterson, James B.: Kiplinger Washington Editors
Patton, Oliver B.: Heavy Duty Trucking
Pavlich, Catherine M.: Townhall Magazine
Pazanowski, Bernard J.: BNA News
Pazanowski, Mary Anne: BNA News
Pecquet, Julian J.: The Hill
Pekow, Charles W.: Community College Week
Peleo-Lazar, Chris: Hotline
Penn, Benjamin: BNA News
Perelman, Isabella: BNA News
Perine, Keith B.: BNA News
Perlman, Howard: BNA News
Perry, Suzanne: Chronicle of Higher Education
Peterka, Amanda E.: Environment & Energy Publishing
Peters, Katherine M.: Government Executive
Petersen, Laura A.: Environment & Energy Publishing
Peterson, Denise: Elsevier Business Intelligence
Peterson, Kyle O.: American Spectator
Pettingell, Dolia E.: Poder
Phillips, Bergrek: Tax Notes
Piegari, Nick: IMNG Medical Media
Piemonte, Philip M.: Federal Employees News Digest
Pierce, Emily K.: Roll Call
Pinneau, Trina L.: Tax Notes
Pitts, Edward Lee: World Magazine
Plank, Kendra Casey: BNA News
Plautz, Jason: Environment & Energy Publishing
Plotz, David: Slate
Plunkett, A.J.: UCG
Pluviose, David: Diverse: Issues In Higher Education
Pollak, Suzanne: Washington Jewish Week
Ponnuru, Ramesh: National Review
Postal, Arthur D.: National Underwriter
Powers, Martha C.: Mid-Atlantic Research
Preston, Caroline S.: Chronicle of Higher Education
Prideaux, John: Economist
Prior, Jon: Politico
Prochnau, William W.: Vanity Fair
Purdum, Todd S.: Vanity Fair
Purple, Matthew: American Spectator
Pyper, Julia M.: Environment & Energy Publishing
Quinn, Melissa A.: Red Alert Politics
Quinn, Peter C.: BNA News
Quinones, Manuel G.: Environment & Energy Publishing
Quinton, Sophie A.: National Journal
Radford, Bruce W.: Public Utilities Fortnightly
Radick, Lea: Elsevier Business Intelligence
Rainey, Ryan: Inside Washington Publishers
Rajala, Liisa N.: Kiplinger Washington Editors
Raju, Manu K.: Politico
Ramonas, Andrew D.: National Law Journal
Rapp, David: Roll Call
Reardon, Sara: Nature
Reed, John: Foreign Policy Magazine
Reeves, Dawn L.: Inside Washington Publishers
Reilly, Sean C.: Gannett Government Media Corp.
Reinhard, Beth: National Journal

MEMBERS ENTITLED TO ADMISSION, PERIODICAL PRESS GALLERIES—Continued

Reis, Patrick C.: Politico
Reishus, Mark: Thompson Information Services
Rennie, David: Economist
Reske, Henry: Tax Notes
Resnick, Brian: National Journal
Ressler, Thomas S.: Inside Mortgage Finance
Restuccia, Andrew: Politico
Reynolds, David: Inside Washington Publishers
Rhodan, Maya: Time Magazine
Ricaurte Knebel, Kristen C.: BNA News
Richardson, Nathaline: BNA News
Richman, Sheldon B.: BNA News
Rickman, Johnathan A.: Washington Business Information
Ricks, Markeshia: Gannett Government Media Corp.
Rieger, John M.: Roll Call
Ripps, Alexander: BNA News
Risen, Thomas: U.S. News & World Report
Ritger, Clara: National Law Journal
Rizzuto, Pat: BNA News
Robelen, Erik: Education Week
Roberts, Edward S.: Credit Union Journal
Roberts, Gillian: Employee Benefit Adviser
Robertson, Matthew: Epoch Times
Robillard, Kevin P.: Politico
Robinson, Kimberly S.: BNA News
Rodibaugh, Jennifer: CCH Inc.
Roem, Dan: Hotline
Rogers, Alex: Time Magazine
Rogers, David E.: Politico
Rogers, Jennifer: Washington City Paper
Rogers, Lance: BNA News
Rohrer, S. Scott: National Journal
Rojas, Warren A.: Roll Call
Rolfsen, Bruce R.: BNA News
Roller, Emma: Slate
Romano, Lois: Politico
Romero, Melissa: Washingtonian
Romm, Tony: Politico
Rosche, Jedd M.: Politico
Rose, Michael F.: BNA News
Rose, Phil: Professional Pilot Magazine
Roston, Aram: Gannett Government Media Corp.
Rothenberg, Stuart: Rothenberg Political Report
Rothman, Heather M.: BNA News
Rousselle, Christine: Townhall Magazine
Rudd, Jr., Terrence: IMNG Medical Media
Ruger, Todd M.: National Law Journal
Ruoff, Alex: BNA News
Russo, Eugene I.: Nature
Ryan, Denise: BNA News
Ryan, Jr., Frederick J.: Politico
Ryan, Laura: National Journal
Saenz, Cheryl L.: BNA News
Saiyid, Amena H.: BNA News
Saletan, William B.: Slate
Salzano, Carlo J.: Waterways Journal
Sama, Anita: CEO Update
Sami, Tamra S.: Elsevier Business Intelligence
Sammon, Richard T.: Kiplinger Washington Editors
Samuels, Christina: Education Week
Samuelsohn, Darren S.: Politico
Sanborn, James K.: Gannett Government Media Corp.
Sanchez, Humberto: Roll Call
Sander, Libby C.: Chronicle of Higher Education
Sands, Derek O.: McGraw-Hill Co.
Sandza, Richard W.: Gannett Government Media Corp.
Sangillo, Gregg Thomas: National Journal
Santos, Maria T.: Weekly Standard
Sarlin, Benjamin V.: Talking Points Memo
Sasso, Brendan S.: The Hill
Saunders, Karen J.: BNA News
Savage, Luiza C.: Maclean's
Savoie, Andy: McGraw-Hill Co.
Sawchuk, Stephen A.: Education Week
Sawyer, David: Tax Notes
Saxena, Varum: Elsevier Business Intelligence
Scarcella, Michael A.: National Law Journal
Scheid, Brian J.: McGraw-Hill Co.
Scherer, Michael B.: Time Magazine
Scherman, Bob: Satellite Business News
Schewel, Matthew A.: Inside Washington Publishers
Schieken, William: Government Contractor
Schiff, Daniel A.: Elsevier Business Intelligence
Schlesinger, Robert: U.S. News & World Report
Schneider, Martin A.: Exchange Monitor Publications
Schneider, Troy K.: FCW
Schoeff, Jr., Mark: Crain Communications
Schogol, Jeffrey Duff: Gannett Government Media Corp.
Scholtz, Maria K.: Thompson Information Services
Schomisch, Jeffrey W.: Thompson Information Services
Schor, Elana A.: Environment & Energy Publishing
Schreckinger, Benjamin: National Journal
Schroeder, Peter C.: The Hill
Schultheis, Emily: Politico
Schwab, Nicole: U.S. News & World Report
Schwartz, David H.: BNA News
Schweitzer, Allison: Washington City Paper
Scott, Dean T.: BNA News
Scott, Dylan L.: Governing
Seitz-Wald, Alexander L.: Salon.com
Seligman, Lara: Inside Washington Publishers
Selingo, Jeffrey: Chronicle of Higher Education
Seman, Sarah: Townhall Magazine
Semnani, Neda T.: Roll Call
Severns, Maggie: Politico
Sfiligoj, Mark L.: Kiplinger Washington Editors
Shabad, Rebecca D.: The Hill
Shah, Nirvi H.: Politico
Sharn, Lori: CEO Update
Sharpe, Stephanie: McGraw-Hill Co.

MEMBERS ENTITLED TO ADMISSION, PERIODICAL PRESS GALLERIES—Continued

Sheets, Scott Andrew: Tax Notes
Shen, Helen H.: Nature
Shepard, Steven G.: Hotline
Sheppard, Douglas: Tax Notes
Sherman, Jake S.: Politico
Shiner, Meredith H.: Roll Call
Shinkman, Paul: U.S. News & World Report
Shreve, Meg: Tax Notes
Siciliano, John: Inside Washington Publishers
Sidman, Jessica: Washington City Paper
Simmons, Quintin: Tax Notes
Simon, Elizabeth V.: BNA News
Simon, Roger M.: Politico
Sinderbrand, Rebecca: Politico
Sink, Justin T.: The Hill
Skinner, Liz: Crain Communications
Slaughter, David A.: Thompson Information Services
Sloan, Steven P.: Politico
Small, John R.: BNA News
Smelson, Cheryl: BNA News
Smith, Joseph J.: NewBay Media
Smith, Katie: Roll Call
Smith, Lee H.: Weekly Standard
Smolkin, Rachel: Politico
Sneed, Tierney M.: U.S. News & World Report
Snell, Kelsey: Politico
Snider, Adam K.: Politico
Snider, Ann E.: Environment & Energy Publishing
Snow, Justin: Metro Weekly
Snow, Nicholas J.: Oil & Gas Journal
Snyder, Katharine: Mine Safety and Health News
Sobczak, Blake: Environment & Energy Publishing
Sobel, Julie: Hotline
Sobieraj Westfall, Sandra J.: People Magazine
Sobocinski, Matthew: Politico
Sodergreen, John: Scudder Publishing Group
Soderstrom, Nathan: Capitol Forum
Solomon, Burt: National Journal
Somerville, Glenn F.: Kiplinger Washington Editors
Sommer, William: Washington City Paper
Soraghan, Michael: Environment & Energy Publishing
Sorcher, Sara: National Journal
Southern, E. Richard: Government Contractor
Sparks, Sarah D.: Education Week
Spence, Charles F.: General Aviation News
Spicer, Malcolm E.: Elsevier Business Intelligence
Spiegel, Anna: Washingtonian
Splete, Heidi: IMNG Medical Media
Spotswood, Stephen: U.S. Medicine
Sprague, John: Budget & Program
Sprenger, Sebastian: Inside Washington Publishers
Sritharan, Naresh: BNA News
Stahl, Jeremy: Slate
Stam, John H.: BNA News
Stanage, Niall G.: The Hill
Stangler, Cole H.: In These Times
Stanton, Lynn E.: Telecommunications Reports
Stark, Holger: Der Spiegel
Starosta, Gabriel: Inside Washington Publishers
Stecker, Tiffany A.: Environment & Energy Publishing
Stein, Jeffrey: Newsweek
Stein, Michelle: Inside Washington Publishers
Steinberg, Julie A.: BNA News
Steinke, Scott A.: Elsevier Business Intelligence
Steinmetz, Katherine: Time Magazine
Stephani, Justin: Employee Benefit News
Sternberg, Steve: U.S. News & World Report
Sternstein, Aliya E.: Government Executive
Stewart, David D.: Tax Notes
Stewart, Joshua P.: Gannett Government Media Corp.
Stiles, Andrew J.: National Review
Stimson, James A.: BNA News
Stimson, Leslie P.: NewBay Media
Stoddard, Alexandra B.: The Hill
Stokeld, Frederick W.: Tax Notes
Straub, Noelle C.: Environment & Energy Publishing
Strauss, Daniel L.: The Hill
Strawbridge, James: Inside Washington Publishers
Strong, Jonathan: National Review
Sturges, Peyton M.: BNA News
Suderman, Alan H.: Washington City Paper
Sullivan, Monica C.: National Journal
Sullivan, Peter: The Hill
Summers, Juana: Politico
Sun, Zhongyan: Epoch Times
Supiano, Beckie M.: Chronicle of Higher Education
Sutter, Susan M.: Elsevier Business Intelligence
Sutton, Eileen: BNA News
Swann, James L.: BNA News
Sweeney, Ray F.: CD Publications
Sweetman, Bill A.: Aviation Week
Swift, James A.: Weekly Standard
Swisher, Larry: BNA News
Szakonyi, Mark D.: Journal of Commerce
Tahir, Darius A.: Elsevier Business Intelligence
Tan, Angelica: Kiplinger Washington Editors
Tang, Chia-Chieh: Caixin Media
Tarallo, Mark: CEO Update
Tau, Byron C.: Politico
Tavangar, Sayeh: McGraw-Hill Co.
Taylor II, B.J.: Atlantic Information Services
Taylor, Jessica L.: Rothenberg Political Report
Taylor, Joy M.: Kiplinger Washington Editors
Taylor, Philip A.: Environment & Energy Publishing
Taylor, Jr., Stuart: National Journal
Taylor, Thomas P.: BNA News
Taylor, Vincent E.: UCG
Teichert, Erica: Law360
Terris, Ben: National Journal
Terzian, Philip: Weekly Standard
Teske, Steve J.: BNA News

MEMBERS ENTITLED TO ADMISSION, PERIODICAL PRESS GALLERIES—Continued

Thibodeau, Patrick: IDG Communications
Thomas, David: Inside Washington Publishers
Thomas, Kevin: CCH Inc.
Thomas, Michelle E.: Washingtonian
Thompson, Mark J.: Time Magazine
Thompson, Wendy S.: DC Spotlight Newspaper
Thrush, Glenn H.: Politico
Tice, James S.: Gannett Government Media Corp.
Tiernan, Tom: McGraw-Hill Co.
Tilghman, Andrew S.: Gannett Government Media Corp.
Tillman, Zoe M.: National Law Journal
Tinkelman, Joe A.: BNA News
Tipograph, Joseph: Capitol Forum
Titus, Elizabeth: Politico
Toeplitz, Shira: Roll Call
Tomasky, Michael J.: Newsweek
Tomson, Bill: Politico
Topor, Eric D.: BNA News
Toporek, Bryan: Education Week
Torrance, Kelly J.: Weekly Standard
Tosh, Dennis A.: Thompson Information Services
Touhey, Noel Emmanuel: The Hill
Travis, Jesse T.: BNA News
Tremulis, Christopher: McGraw-Hill Co.
Tricchinelli, Robert: BNA News
Trilling, Stefanie S.: BNA News
Trindle, Jamila: Foreign Policy Magazine
Trinko, Katrina M.: National Review
Troop, Donald: Chronicle of Higher Education
Trowbridge, Alexander: Politico
Trujillo, Frank: The Hill
Trygstad, Kyle K.: Roll Call
Twachtman, Gregory: Elsevier Business Intelligence
Tyler, Eleanor: BNA News
Ujifusa, Andrew: Education Week
Vaidyanathan, Gayathri: Environment & Energy Publishing
van den Berg, David T.: Tax Notes
Van Dongen, Rachel: Politico
Vandehei, James: Politico
Vasilogambros, Matt: National Journal
Velarde, Andrew: Tax Notes
Viadero, Debra: Education Week
Victor, Kirk: National Journal
Viebeck, Elise J.: The Hill
Villacorta, Natalie: Politico
Vissiere, Helene A.: Le Point
Vittorio, Andrea: BNA News
Voelker, Jessica: Washingtonian
Vogel, Kenneth P.: Politico
Volz, Dustin: National Journal
Waddell, Melanie L.: Investment Advisor Magazine
Wadman, Meredith K.: Nature
Waldman, Katy: Slate
Walsh, Kenneth T.: U.S. News & World Report
Walsh, Mark F.: Education Week
Wang, Herman D.: McGraw-Hill Co.
Ward, Mary E.: McGraw-Hill Co.
Ware, Patricia A.: BNA News
Warmbrodt, Zachary: Politico
Warren, Michael R.: Weekly Standard
Wasserman, David N.: Cook Political Report
Wasson, Erik L.: The Hill
Weaver, Dustin A.: The Hill
Weber, Rick: Inside Washington Publishers
Webster, Henry C.: McGraw-Hill Co.
Webster, James C.: Webster Communications
Wechsler, Jill: Pharmaceutical Executive
Weible, Jack: BNA News
Weigel, David A.: Slate
Weinger, Mackenzie K.: Politico
Weisgerber, Marcus A.: Gannett Government Media Corp.
Weixel, Nathaniel L.: BNA News
Welsh, Teresa M.: U.S. News & World Report
Wheeler, Blair L.: Gannett Government Media Corp.
Whieldon, Esther: McGraw-Hill Co.
Whitaker, Joel: Whitaker Newsletters
White III, Frank: BNA News
White, Gillian B.: Kiplinger Washington Editors
White, Rodney A.: McGraw-Hill Co.
Whittington, Lauren: Roll Call
Wiener, Aaron M.: Washington City Paper
Wieser, Eric M.: McGraw-Hill Co.
Wilczek, Yin: BNA News
Wilding, Alexandra M.: CD Publications
Wilhelm, Ian L.: Chronicle of Higher Education
Wilkerson, John S.: Inside Washington Publishers
Wille, Jacklyn N.: BNA News
Williams, Jake: Capitol Forum
Williams, Jeffrey: Satellite Business News
Williams, Lauren C.: UCG
Williams, Mark A.: BNA News
Williams, Walter: CEO Update
Wills, Denise M.: Washingtonian
Wilson, Daniel: Law360
Wilson, Megan: The Hill
Wilson, Stanley E.: Institutional Investor
Windsor, Joseph K.: Government Contractor
Winn, Melissa: Washington Business Information
Winston, Kate: McGraw-Hill Co.
Winter, Allison A.: Environment & Energy Publishing
Wisniowski, Charles M.: Inside Mortgage Finance
Wolfe, Kathryn A.: Politico
Wong, Kristina: The Hill
Wong, Scott B.: Politico
Wood, Graeme: Atlantic Monthly
Woodruff, Betsy A.: National Review
Wooldridge, Leslie: Capitol File
Wooten, Casey: BNA News
Wortherly, Kenya: BNA News
Wright, Austin: Politico
Wu, Xiuli: Epoch Times

MEMBERS ENTITLED TO ADMISSION, PERIODICAL PRESS GALLERIES—Continued

Wyckoff, Whitney: Environment & Energy Publishing
Yachnin, Jennifer: Environment & Energy Publishing
Yager, Christopher J.: The Hill
Yaksick, Jr., George L.: CCH Inc.
Yamazaki, Kazutami: Washington Watch
Yang, Bettina: Duowei Times
Yarrison, Mary: Washingtonian
Yehle, Emily: Environment & Energy Publishing
Yglesias, Matthew: Slate
Yingling, Jennifer S.: The Hill
Yochelson, Mindy: BNA News
Yohannan, Suzanne M.: Inside Washington Publishers
Yonkman, David L.: Newsmax
Young, Sam: Tax Notes
Yuill, Barbara: BNA News
Zalan, Kira: U.S. News & World Report
Zaman, Gulnar: Tax Notes
Zaneski, Cyril T.: Environment & Energy Publishing
Zapler, Mike: Politico
Zhang, Tao: Caixin Media
Zigmond, Jessica A.: Crain Communications
Zornick, George L.: Nation
Zubrzycki, Jaclyn A.: Education Week
Zurcher, Anthony W.: Congressional Digest

PERIODICALS REPRESENTED IN PRESS GALLERIES

House Gallery 225–2941, Senate Gallery 224–0265

ADWEEK—(703) 212–0540; 31 Arell Court, Alexandria, VA 22304: Kathryn M. Bachman.

AGRI-PULSE—(202) 547–5588; 1400 Independence Avenue, SW., 1639 South Building, Washington, DC 20250: Derrick Cain, Sarah Gonzalez, Aarian M. Marshall.

AMERICAN SPECTATOR—(703) 807–2011; 1611 North Kent Street, Suite 901, Arlington, VA 22209: Kyle O. Peterson, Matthew Purple.

ASIA TODAY—(202) 271–1100; 27025 McPherson Square Street, Washington, DC 20038: Raghubir Goyal.

ATLANTIC INFORMATION SERVICES—(202) 775–9008; 1100 17th Street, NW., Suite 300, Washington, DC 20036: Jill Brown, Patrick J. Connole, Steve W. Davis, James H. Gutman, Lauren Kelly, Neal Learner, Angela K. Maas, B.J. Taylor II.

ATLANTIC MONTHLY—(202) 266–7000; 600 New Hampshire Avenue, NW., Washington, DC 20037: Molly Ball, Steven Clemons, Garance Franke-Ruta, David A. Graham, Graeme Wood.

AVIATION INTERNATIONAL NEWS—(301) 230–4520; 5605 Alderbrook Court, #T6, Rockville, MD 20851: William J. Carey, Paul D. Lowe, Roger A. Mola.

AVIATION WEEK—(202) 383–2300; 1200 G Street, NW., Washington, DC 20005: Joseph C. Anselmo, James R. Asker, Michael Bruno, Amy Butler, John W. Croft, Jennifer DiMascio, Michael J. Fabey, Frank Morring, Jr., Jefferson F. Morris, Richard A. Mullins, Bill A. Sweetman.

BANKRATE.COM—(202) 450–4465; National Press Building, Suite 841, Washington, DC 20045: Mark Hamrick.

BARRON'S—(202) 862–6606; 1025 Connecticut Avenue, NW., Suite 800, Washington, DC 20036: Thomas G. Donlan, James A. McTague.

BNA NEWS—(703) 341–3000; 1801 South Bell Street, Arlington, VA 22202: Stephanie M. Acree, Anthony Adragna, Mirza Z. Aftab, Paul F. Albergo, Alexei Alexis, Michelle L. Amber, Patrick Ambrosio, LaTrina Antoine, Donald G. Aplin, John T. Aquino, Jerome C. Ashton, Cecelia M. Assam, Pamela S. Atkins, Margaret Aulino, Martina S. Barash, Paul Barbagallo, Sean A. Barry, Theresa A. Barry, Bryce Baschuk, Tamlin H. Bason, Jeffrey P. Bater, Jeannie Baumann, Alison E. Bennett, Andrea L. Ben-Yosef, Lydia Beyoud, Alicia E. Biggs, Deborah D. Billings, Amy E. Bivins, Rachel Boehm, Catherine Boudreau, Leonard A. Bracken, David B. Brandolph, Rossella E. Brevetti, Lydell C. Bridgeford, Brian J. Broderick, Tera E. Brostoff, Robert Bruce, Susan E. Bruninga, Madelyn R. Callahan, Jay-Anne B. Casuga, Heather N. Caygle, Tina M. Chi, Andrew J. Childers, Gayle C. Cinquegrani, Janey Cohen, Kimberly Claire Compton, Robert C. Cook, Steven Cook, Jessica M. Coomes, Perry E. Cooper, Richard H. Cowden, Rachael K. Daigle, S. Diane Davis, Jeff Day, Gloria Deigh, Danielle R. Dellerson, Phyllis Diamond, Dana J. Domone, Patrick F. Dorrian, Genevieve Douglas, Kenneth P. Doyle, Susan Doyle, Elliott Dube, Lawrence E. Dube, Jr., Antonio Dutra, Jewel W. Edwards, Michael Eisenstein, Dana Elfin, Tawny A. Elgatian, Karen L. Ertel, Avery Fellow, Brett A. Ferguson, Michael A. Ferullo, Brian Flood, Sean I. Forbes, Laura Francis, Diane Freda, John Gannon, Wilson Lynn Garner, Diana I. Gregg, Patrick Gregory, Sara E. Hansard, David Hansen, Peter S. Hayes, Lars-Eric Hedberg, Marc R. Heller, Keith M. Hill, Richard Hill, Susan R. Hobbs, Rebecca E. Hoffman, Gwendolyn C. Holmes, Jay Horowitz, Kristyn J. Hyland, Robert Iafolla, Alisa A. Johnson, Katie Johnson, Jessie K. Kamens, Hugh B. Kaplan, Bruce S. Kaufman, John R. Kirkland, Susan R. Kneller, Jeffrey Koelemay, Jimmy H. Koo, Alan D. Kovski, William Randy Kubetin, Sarah Kunkelman, Philip H. Kushin, Anna Kwidzinski, Louis C. LaBrecque, Kevin C. Lambert, Cathleen R. Larson, Steve K. Lee, Rachel P. Leven, Ralph Lindeman, Michael O. Loatman, Maria L. Lokshin, Aaron E. Lorenzo, Joe Lustig, Mary Ann G. Manley, Anna Marchessault, Anandashankar Mazumdar, David McAuley, Ellen E. McCleskey, Rebecca P. McCracken, Margaret McEvoy, Susan J. McGolrick, Kevin P. McGowan, Susan M. McInerney, Toby McIntosh, Darren McKewen, Amber McKinney, Erin McManus, Tiffany F. Milone, Bronwyn Mixter, Michael D. Moore, Ari J. Natter, Jonathan Nicholson, Che L. Odom, Nancy Ognanovich, Florence E. Olsen, Christopher R. Opfer, Thomas O'Toole, Mack Arthur Paschal, Bernard J. Pazanowski, Mary Anne Pazanowski, Benjamin Penn, Isabella Perelman, Keith B. Perine, Howard Perlman, Kendra Casey Plank, Peter C. Quinn, Kristen C. Ricaurte Knebel, Nathaline Richardson, Sheldon B. Richman, Alexander Ripps, Pat Rizzuto, Kimberly S. Robinson, Lance Rogers, Bruce R. Rolfsen, Michael F. Rose, Heather M. Rothman, Alex Ruoff, Denise Ryan, Cheryl L. Saenz, Amena H. Saiyid, Karen J. Saunders, David H. Schwartz, Dean T. Scott, Elizabeth V. Simon, John R. Small, Cheryl Smelson, Naresh Sritharan, John H. Stam, Julie A. Steinberg, James A. Stimson, Peyton M. Sturges, Eileen Sutton, James L. Swann, Larry Swisher, Thomas P. Taylor, Steve J. Teske, Joe A. Tinkelman, Eric D. Topor, Jesse T. Travis, Robert Tricchinelli, Stefanie S. Trilling, Eleanor Tyler, Andrea Vittorio, Patricia A. Ware, Jack Weible, Nathaniel L. Weixel, Frank White III, Yin Wilczek, Jacklyn N. Wille, Mark A. Williams, Casey Wooten, Kenya Wortherly, Mindy Yochelson, Barbara Yuill.

BROADBAND CENSUS—(202) 580–8196; 1100 Connecticut Avenue, NW., Suite 725, Washington, DC 20036: Douglas Barclay, Drew Clark, Josh Evans.

BROADCASTING & CABLE—(571) 830–6440; 8015 Hatteras Lane, Springfield, VA 22151: John S. Eggerton.

BUDGET & PROGRAM—(202) 328–3860; 1408 Teal Court, Frederick, MD 21703: John Sprague.

PERIODICALS REPRESENTED IN PRESS GALLERIES—Continued

CAIJING MAGAZINE—(202) 525–2117; 3133 Connecticut Avenue, NW., 110A, Washington, DC 20008: Yan Jin.

CAIXIN MEDIA—(202) 375–9744; 708 15th Street, South #5, Arlington, VA 22202: Chia-Chieh Tang, Tao Zhang.

CAPITOL FILE—(202) 293–8025; 1301 Pennsylvania Avenue, NW., Suite 925, Washington, DC 20004: Laura Mullen, Leslie Wooldridge.

CAPITOL FORUM—(202) 601–2300; 1829 M Street, NW., Washington, DC 20036: David Blotner, Theodore Downey, Benjamin Neumeyer, Nathan Soderstrom, Joseph Tipograph, Jake Williams.

CCH INC.—(202) 842–7355; 1015 15th Street, NW., 10th Floor, Washington, DC 20005: John Filar Atwood, Sarah A. Borchersen-Keto, Jeffrey E. Carlson, John Carpenter, Stephen K. Cooper, Brant Goldwyn, George G. Jones, Jacquelyn D. Leatherman, Amanda Maine, Joyce Mutcherson-Ridley, Jennifer Rodibaugh, Kevin Thomas, George L. Yaksick, Jr.

CD PUBLICATIONS—(301) 588–6380; 8204 Fenton Street, Silver Spring, MD 20910: Thomas J. Edwards, Michael S. Gerecht, Frank J. Klimko, Ray F. Sweeney, Alexandra M. Wilding.

CEO UPDATE—(202) 721–7656; 1990 M Street, NW., 8th Floor, Washington, DC 20036: William Ehart, Anita Sama, Lori Sharn, Mark Tarallo, Walter Williams.

CHRONICLE OF HIGHER EDUCATION—(202) 466–1000; 1255 23rd Street, NW., Suite 700, Washington, DC 20037: Paul A. Basken, Goldie Blumenstyk, Douglas Donovan, Kelly E. Field, Karin E. Fischer, Donald L. Gardner, Suzanne Perry, Caroline S. Preston, Libby C. Sander, Jeffrey Selingo, Beckie M. Supiano, Donald Troop, Ian L. Wilhelm.

COMMUNITY COLLEGE WEEK—(301) 493–6926; 5225 Pooks Hill Road, #1118 N, Bethesda, MD 20814: Charles W. Pekow.

CONGRESSIONAL DIGEST—(202) 258–2122; 3307 M Street, NW., Suite 301, Washington, DC 20007: Anthony W. Zurcher.

COOK POLITICAL REPORT—(202) 739–8525; 600 New Hampshire Avenue, NW., Suite 400, Washington, DC 20037: Charles E. Cook, Jr., Jennifer E. Duffy, David N. Wasserman.

CORPORATE CRIME REPORTER—(202) 737–1680; 1209 National Press Building, Washington, DC 20045: Russell J. Mokhiber.

COURTHOUSE NEWS SERVICE—(443) 783–1463; 125 Chester Avenue, Annapolis, MD 21403: Ryan M. Abbott.

CQ RESEARCHER—(202) 729–1800; 2300 N Street, NW., Suite 800, Washington, DC 20037: Marcia A. Clemmitt, Darrell D. Dela Rosa, Kenneth W. Jost.

CRAIN COMMUNICATIONS—(202) 662–7200; 814 National Press Building, Washington, DC 20045: Jonathan M. Block, Hazel M. Bradford, Richard F. Daly, Paul J. Demko, Mary Beth Franklin, Jerome M. Geisel, Mark A. Hofmann, Paul Robert Merrion, Miles David Moore, Gabe Nelson, Mark Schoeff, Jr., Liz Skinner, Jessica A. Zigmond.

CREDIT UNION JOURNAL—(202) 243–8714; 4401 Wilson Boulevard, Arlington, VA 22203: Edward S. Roberts.

CREDIT UNION TIMES—(202) 370–4822; 1301 Connecticut Avenue, NW., #300, Washington, DC 20036: Heather M. Anderson, Nicholas A. Ballasy.

DC SPOTLIGHT NEWSPAPER—(301) 288–7997; P.O. Box 3121, Gaithersburg, MD 20885: Wendy S. Thompson.

DER SPIEGEL—(202) 347–5222; 1202 National Press Building, Washington, DC 20045: Marc A. Hujer, Holger Stark.

DIE ZEIT—(301) 312–8453; 4701 Willard Avenue, #1214, Chevy Chase, MD 20815: Martin E. Klingst.

DIVERSE: ISSUES IN HIGHER EDUCATION—(703) 385–2981; 10520 Warwick Avenue, Suite B–8, Fairfax, VA 22030: Jamaal Abdul-Alim, Autumn Arnett, David Pluviose.

DUOWEI TIMES—(301) 658–6808; P.O. Box 3353, Gaithersburg, MD 20885: Bettina Yang.

EBONY—(312) 371–2814; P.O. Box 21262, Washington, DC 20009: Steven U. Gray.

ECONOMIST—(202) 429–0890; 1730 Rhode Island Avenue, NW., Suite 1210, Washington, DC 20036: Rachel J. Horwood, Gregory W. Ip, Edward P. McBride, John Prideaux, David Rennie.

EDUCATION WEEK—(301) 280–3100; 6935 Arlington Road, Suite 100, Bethesda, MD 20814: Caralee J. Adams, Mark W. Bomster, Ross E. Brenneman, Kevin C. Bushweller, Sean M. Cavanagh, Gregory Chronister, Michelle Davis, Karen Diegmueller, Nora Fleming, Catherine Gewertz, Liana Heitin, Alyson Klein, Kathleen Manzo, Michele McNeil, Michele Molnar, Erik Robelen, Christina Samuels, Stephen A. Sawchuk, Sarah D. Sparks, Bryan Toporek, Andrew Ujifusa, Debra Viadero, Mark F. Walsh, Jaclyn A. Zubrzycki.

EE TIMES—(703) 772–7440; 1639 York Mills Lane, Reston, VA 20194: George H. Leopold.

ELSEVIER BUSINESS INTELLIGENCE—(240) 221–4500; 5635 Fishers Lane, Suite 6000, Rockville, MD 20852: Elizabeth R. Crawford, Susan W. Darcey, Cathy H. Dombrowski, Jacqueline Fitton, Derrick J. Gingery, Joseph A. Haas, Laura Helbling, M. Nielsen Hobbs, Catherine A. Kelly, Rebecca M. Kern, Mary Jo Laffler, Lauren Nardella, Denise Peterson, Lea Radick, Tamra S. Sami, Varum Saxena, Daniel A. Schiff, Malcolm E. Spicer, Scott A. Steinke, Susan M. Sutter, Darius A. Tahir, Gregory Twachtman.

PERIODICALS REPRESENTED IN PRESS GALLERIES—Continued

EMPLOYEE BENEFIT ADVISER—(571) 403–3840; 4401 Wilson Boulevard, Suite 910, Arlington, VA 22203: Elizabeth R. Galentine, Brian M. Kalish, Gillian Roberts.

EMPLOYEE BENEFIT NEWS—(571) 403–3871, 4401 Wilson Boulevard, Suite 910, Arlington, VA 22203: Tristan Lejeune, Justin Stephani.

ENDANGERED SPECIES AND WETLANDS REPORT—(202) 744–1535; 6609 Westmoreland Avenue, Takoma Park, MD 20912: Stephen A. Davies.

ENVIRONMENT & ENERGY PUBLISHING—(202) 628–6500; 122 C Street, NW., Suite 722, Washington, DC 20001: Peter B. Behr, Kevin D. Braun, Robin Bravender, Amy V. Carlile, Jean M. Chemnick, Jessica M. Estepa, John J. Fialka, Lisa F. Friedman, Ellen M. Gilmer, Elizabeth Harball, Margaret Kriz Hobson, Katie J. Howell, Umair Irfan, Jeremy P. Jacobs, Nick Juliano, Pamela L. King, Joel G. Kirkland, Josh Kurtz, Evan W. Lehmann, Katherine Ling, Julia A. Littleton, Jennifer A. Mandel, Christa Marshall, Nathanael Massey, John E. McArdle, Eugene Mulero, Nayantara Narayanan, Hannah M. Northey, Stephanie Ogburn, Amanda E. Peterka, Laura A. Petersen, Jason Plautz, Julia M. Pyper, Manuel G. Quinones, Elana A. Schor, Ann E. Snider, Blake Sobczak, Michael Soraghan, Tiffany A. Stecker, Noelle C. Straub, Philip A. Taylor, Gayathri Vaidyanathan, Allison A. Winter, Whitney Wyckoff, Jennifer Yachnin, Emily Yehle, Cyril T. Zaneski.

EPOCH TIMES—(301) 515–5422; 7529 Standish Place, Suite 260, Rockville, MD 20855: Shar Adams, Yang Chen, Matthew Robertson, Zhongyan Sun, Xiuli Wu.

EXCHANGE MONITOR PUBLICATIONS—(202) 296–2814; 4301 Connecticut Avenue, NW., Suite 132, Washington, DC 20008: Jeremy L. Dillon, Kenneth R. Fletcher, Karen D. Frantz, Tamar Hallerman, Edward L. Helminski, Sarah E. Herness, Todd K. Jacobson, Michael Nartker, Martin A. Schneider.

EXPRESS INDIA—(703) 599–6623; 1541 Wellingham Court, Vienna, VA 22182: Geeta Goindi.

FALLS CHURCH NEWS PRESS—(703) 532–3267; 200 Little Falls Street, Suite 508, Falls Church, VA 22046: Nicholas F. Benton, Jody C. Fellows, Nicholas T. Gatz.

FCW—(703) 876–5100; 8609 Westwood Center Drive, Suite 500, Vienna, VA 22182: Richard Cohen, Amber Corrin, Michael Hardy, Frank R. Konkel, Adam Mazmanian, Troy K. Schneider.

FEDERAL EMPLOYEES NEWS DIGEST—(703) 891–8554; 8609 Westwood Center Drive, Suite 500, Vienna, VA 22182: Philip M. Piemonte.

FOOD CHEMICAL NEWS—(703) 595–2255; 3 East Cliff Street, Alexandria, VA 22301: Stephen C. Clapp, Amber M. Healy, Joan F. Murphy.

FOOD PROTECTION REPORT—(703) 548–3146; P.O. Box 25277, Alexandria, VA 22313: Declan A. Conroy.

FOREIGN POLICY MAGAZINE—(202) 728–7300; 11 Dupont Circle, NW., Suite 600, Washington, DC 20036: Kevin Baron, John Hudson, Gordon Lubold, John Reed, Jamila Trindle.

FORTUNE MAGAZINE—(202) 861–4000; 1130 Connecticut Avenue, NW., Suite 900, Washington, DC 20036: Nina J. Easton, Tory G. Newmyer.

FREITAG—(301) 699–3908; 4506 32nd Street, Mt. Rainier, MD 20712: Konrad Ege.

FTC: WATCH—(703) 684–7171; 604 Cameron Street, Alexandria, VA 22314: Christopher Amolsch, Kirstin E. Downey, Claude Marx.

GANNETT GOVERNMENT MEDIA CORP.—(703) 750–7400; 6883 Commercial Drive, Springfield, VA 22159: George Altman, John T. Bennett, Christopher P. Cavas, Kristin G. Davis, Brian Everstine, Samuel Fellman, Zachary Fryer-Biggs, Joseph M. Gould, Gina A. Harkins, Hope Hodge, Nicole Johnson, Karen G. Jowers, Patricia N. Kime, Jacqueline Klimas, Daniel G. Lamothe, Stephen Losey, Richard Maze, Paul J. McLeary, Andrew S. Medici, Aaron N. Mehta, Vardges Muradian, Sean D. Naylor, Sean C. Reilly, Markeshia Ricks, Aram Roston, James K. Sanborn, Richard W. Sandza, Jeffrey Duff Schogol, Joshua P. Stewart, James S. Tice, Andrew S. Tilghman, Marcus A. Weisgerber, Blair L. Wheeler.

GENERAL AVIATION NEWS—(301) 698–6186; 6351 Spring Ridge Parkway, #322, Frederick, MD 21701: Charles F. Spence.

GILSTON-KALIN COMMUNICATIONS—(301) 570–4544; 4816 Sweetbirch Drive, Rockville, MD 20853: Meredith L. Gilston, Samuel M. Gilston.

GLAMOUR MAGAZINE—(703) 317–4949; 6100 Edgewood Terrace Alexandria, VA 22307: Linda Kramer Jenning.

GLOBAL COMPETITION REVIEW—(202) 706–7031; 2401 Pennsylvania Avenue, NW., Suite 300, Washington, DC 20037: Pallavi Guniganti.

GOVERNING—(202) 862–8802; 1100 Connecticut Avenue, NW., #1300, Washington, DC 20036: Liz Farmer, Ryan M. Holeywell, Dylan L. Scott.

GOVERNMENT CONTRACTOR—(202) 772–8295; 1100 13th Street, NW., Suite 200, Washington, DC 20005: Kenneth H. Berke, Betty W. James, William Schieken, E. Richard Southern, Joseph K. Windsor.

GOVERNMENT EXECUTIVE—(202) 739–8501; 600 New Hampshire Avenue, NW., Washington, DC 20037: Charles S. Clark, Amelia M. Gruber, Kellie Lunney, Joseph H. Marks, Katherine M. Peters, Aliya E. Sternstein.

GQ MAGAZINE—(202) 615–5003; 1420 K Street, SE.,Washington, DC 20003: Robert L. Draper, Samantha Larson.

PERIODICALS REPRESENTED IN PRESS GALLERIES—Continued

HEALTH MARKET SURVEY—(202) 277–1994; 3767 Oliver Street, NW., Washington, DC 20015: Virginia Boyles, William R. Boyles.

HEAVY DUTY TRUCKING—(703) 683–9935; 320 Mansion Drive, Alexandria, VA 22302: Oliver B. Patton.

THE HILL—(202) 628–8500; 1625 K Street, NW., Suite 900, Washington, DC 20006: Sheldon D. Alberts, Judy K. Altscher, Samuel Baker, Laura Barron-Lopez, Bernard A. Becker, Russell L. Berman, Kevin J. Bogardus, Alexander Bolton, Zachary A. Colman, Ramsey C. Cox, Robert Cusack, Tim Devaney, Jonathan Easley, Albert Eisele, Ben Geman, Benjamin Goad, Emily L. Goodin, Hugo Gurdon, Jeremy Herb, Molly K. Hooper, Alexandra Jaffe, Cameron E. Joseph, Peter I. Kasperowicz, Keith A. Laing, Michael P. Lillis, Jennifer M. Martinez, Francine M. McMahon, Carlo Munoz, Vicki Needham, Julian J. Pecquet, Brendan S. Sasso, Peter C. Schroeder, Rebecca D. Shabad, Justin T. Sink, Niall G. Stanage, Alexandra B. Stoddard, Daniel L. Strauss, Peter Sullivan, Noel Emmanuel Touhey, Frank Trujillo, Elise J. Viebeck, Erik L. Wasson, Dustin A. Weaver, Megan Wilson, Kristina Wong, Christopher J. Yager, Jennifer S. Yingling.

HISPANIC LINK NEWS SERVICE—(202) 234–0280; 1420 N Street, NW., Washington, DC 20005: Jose de la Isla.

HISPANIC OUTLOOK IN HIGHER EDUCATION—(202) 236–5595; 2627 O Street, NW., Washington, DC 20007: Margaret Orchowski.

HOTLINE—(202) 739–8400; 600 New Hampshire Avenue, NW., Washington, DC 20037: Scott Bland, Kevin Brennan, Alex D. Brown, Jordain Carney, Courtney McBride, Quinn T. McCord, Sarah Mimms, Chris Peleo-Lazar, Dan Roem, Steven G. Shepard, Julie Sobel.

HS TODAY—(202) 427–8780; P.O. Box 5843, Washington, DC 20016: Mickey McCarter.

HUMAN EVENTS—(202) 216–0600; One Massachusetts Avenue, NW., Suite 600, Washington, DC 20001: Neil McCabe.

IDG COMMUNICATIONS—(202) 361–2011; 2630 Adams Mill Road, NW., #304, Washington, DC 20009: Patrick Thibodeau, Grant J. Gross.

IMNG MEDICAL MEDIA—(240) 221–4500; 5635 Fishers Lane, Suite 6000, Rockville, MD 20852: Alicia Ault, Lorinda M. Bullock, Frances Correa, Sally Kubetin, Elizabeth Mechcatie, Nick Piegari, Terrence Rudd, Jr., Heidi Splete.

IN THESE TIMES—(203) 940–3329; 1208 Holbrook Street, NE., #2, Washington, DC 20002: Cole H. Stangler.

INDIA ABROAD—(703) 899–1419; 2747 Centreville Road, Herndon, VA 20171: Aziz A. Haniffa.

INSIDE GNSS—(703) 920–9041; 1014 17th Street, South Arlington, VA 22202: Dee A. Divis.

INSIDE MORTGAGE FINANCE—(301) 951–1240; 7910 Woodmont Avenue, Suite 1000, Bethesda, MD 20814: John R. Bancroft, George A. Brooks, Guy David D. Cecala, Paul Muolo, Thomas S. Ressler, Charles M. Wisniowski.

INSIDE WASHINGTON PUBLISHERS—(703) 416–8500; 1919 South Eads Street, #201, Arlington, VA 22202: Courtney Albon, Stephanie M. Beasley, Lara W. Beaven, Adam Behsudi, Olga Belogolova, Anthony F. Bertuca, Alaina V. Busch, Christopher Castelli, Christopher M. Cole, Bridget DiCosmo, Rachana Dixit, Russell Drew, Erin Durkin, Megan A. Eckstein, Lisa Gillespie, Miranda C. Green, Victoria Guida, Benjamin Hancock, Donna L. Haseley, Maria A. Hegstad, Jutta Hennig, Elizabeth L. Hudson, Jennifer A. Judson, Christopher Knight, Anthony Lacey, David R. LaRoss, Alex R. Lawson, John Liang, Lee Logan, Jordana L. Mishory, Charles F. Mitchell, Ellen Mitchell, Douglas Obey, Amanda Palleschi, Stuart H. Parker, Ryan Rainey, Dawn L. Reeves, David Reynolds, Matthew A. Schewel, Lara Seligman, John Siciliano, Sebastian Sprenger, Gabriel Starosta, Michelle Stein, James Strawbridge, David Thomas, Rick Weber, John S. Wilkerson, Suzanne M. Yohannan.

INSTITUTIONAL INVESTOR—(202) 393–0728; 1319 F Street, NW., Suite 805, Washington, DC 20004: Stanley E. Wilson.

INVESTMENT ADVISOR MAGAZINE—(202) 370–4810; 1301 Connecticut Avenue, NW., Suite 300, Washington, DC 20036: Melanie L. Waddell.

JOURNAL OF COMMERCE—(202) 499–2285; 700 12th Street, NW., Suite 700, Washington, DC 20005: William B. Cassidy, Mark D. Szakonyi.

KIPLINGER WASHINGTON EDITORS—(202) 887–6400; 1100 13th Street, NW., Suite 750, Washington, DC 20005: Kenneth Bazinet, Peter L. Blank, Martha L. Craver, Susan B. Garland, Douglas A. Harbrecht, Eleanor Laise, Edward Maixner, Kevin McCormally, John T. Miley, David Morris, Karen L. Mracek, James B. Patterson, Liisa N. Rajala, Richard T. Sammon, Mark L. Sfiligoj, Glenn F. Somerville, Angelica Tan, Joy M. Taylor, Gillian B. White.

LAW360—(571) 305–2529; 617 21st Street, South, Arlington, VA 22202: Brian Mahoney, Erica Teichert, Daniel Wilson.

LE POINT—(202) 244–6656; 3234 McKinley Street, NW., Washington, DC 20015: Helene A. Vissiere.

LINN'S STAMP NEWS & COIN WORLD—(703) 385–6996; 10121 Ratcliffe Manor Drive, Fairfax, VA 22030: William H. McAllister.

MACLEAN'S—(703) 534–1283; 6316 24th Street, North Arlington, VA 22207: Luiza C. Savage.

MAIL ON SUNDAY—(202) 549–9032; 510 Constitution Avenue, NE., Washington, DC 20002: William A. Lowther.

PERIODICALS REPRESENTED IN PRESS GALLERIES—Continued

MANUFACTURING & TECHNOLOGY NEWS—(703) 750–2664; P.O. Box 36, Annandale, VA 22003: Richard A. McCormack.

MCGRAW-HILL CO.—(202) 383–2000; 1200 G Street, NW., Suite 1000, Washington, DC 20005: Sarah E. Baltic, Juliana R. Brint, Catherine Cash, Andrew Compart, Geoffrey W. Craig, Steven D. Dolley, William A. Freebairn, Gary Gentile, Laura H. Gilcrest, Anastasia Gnezditskaia, Keiron Greenhalgh, Brian Hansen, Elaine Hiruo, William Holland, Jasmin M. Hudson, Thomas F. Ichniowski, Valarie N. Jackson, Regina Johnson, Nick G. Jonson, Karen McBeth Laping, William E. Loveless, Jessica Marron, Pamela E. McFarland, Robert McMahon, Andrew Moore, Christopher J. Newkumet, Chang Noh, James J. Ostroff, Derek O. Sands, Andy Savoie, Brian J. Scheid, Stephanie Sharpe, Sayeh Tavangar, Tom Tiernan, Christopher Tremulis, Herman D. Wang, Mary E. Ward, Henry C. Webster, Esther Whieldon, Rodney A. White, Eric M. Wieser, Kate Winston.

METRO WEEKLY—(202) 638–6830; 1425 K Street, NW., Suite 350, Washington, DC 20005: Justin Snow.

MID-ATLANTIC RESEARCH—(410) 366–2531; 2805 St. Paul Street, Baltimore, MD 21218: Martha C. Powers.

MII PUBLICATIONS—(202) 495–1879; 1800 I Street, NW., Suite 301, Washington, DC 20006: Ryan E. Hess, Cecilio Morales.

MINE., SAFETY AND HEALTH NEWS—(703) 217–8270; 5935 4th Street, North Arlington, VA 22203: Brad A. Kukuk, Katharine Snyder.

NATION—(202) 546–2239; 110 Maryland Avenue, NE., Suite 308, Washington, DC 20002: Zoe Carpenter, Gregory R. Kaufmann, George L. Zornick.

NATIONAL CATHOLIC REPORTER—(408) 406–5609; 400 North Capitol Street, NW., Suite G–80, Washington, DC 20001: Joshua J. McElwee.

NATIONAL JOURNAL—(202) 739–8400; 600 New Hampshire Avenue, NW., Washington, DC 20037: Julie L. Abramson, James A. Barnes, Cory Bennett, Matt Berman, Ronald J. Brownstein, Michael Catalini, Niraj Chokshi, Nancy Cook, Matthew Cooper, Coral Davenport, Lauren Dickinson, Isobel Ellis, William Feeney, Clare Foran, Ronald Fournier, Brian Fung, Charles A. Green, Jerry Hagstrom, Catherine Hollander, Chris Hopkins, Rebecca Kaplan, Naureen Khan, James Kitfield, Jaculine M. Koszczuk, Josh Kraushaar, Adam Kushner, Jill Lawrence, Jason Mann, Chuck A. McCutcheon, Brian McGill, Sophie Novack, James Oliphant, Sophie A. Quinton, Beth Reinhard, Brian Resnick, S. Scott Rohrer, Laura Ryan, Gregg Thomas Sangillo, Benjamin Schreckinger, Burt Solomon, Sara Sorcher, Monica C. Sullivan, Stuart Taylor, Jr., Ben Terris, Matt Vasilogambros, Kirk Victor, Dustin Volz.

NATIONAL LAW JOURNAL—(202) 457–0686; 1100 G Street, NW., Suite 900, Washington, DC 20005: Marcia Coyle, Virginia W. Greene, Matthew L. Huisman, Anthony E. Mauro, Andrew D. Ramonas, Clara Ritger, Todd M. Ruger, Michael A. Scarcella, Zoe M. Tillman.

NATIONAL MORTGAGE NEWS—(571) 403–3837; 4401 Wilson Boulevard, Suite 910, Arlington, VA 22203: Brian Collins.

NATIONAL REVIEW—(202) 543–9226; 233 Pennsylvania Avenue, SE, 3rd Floor, Washington, DC 20003: Kathryn J. Lopez, Ramesh Ponnuru, Andrew J. Stiles, Jonathan Strong, Katrina M. Trinko, Betsy A. Woodruff.

NATIONAL UNDERWRITER—(202) 370–4819; 1301 Connecticut Avenue, NW., Suite 300, Washington, DC 20036: Elizabeth D. Festa, Arthur D. Postal.

NATURE—(202) 737–2355; 968 National Press Building, Washington, DC 20045: Natasha Gilbert, Karen H. Kaplan, Richard A. Monastersky, Lauren Morello, Sara Reardon, Eugene I. Russo, Helen H. Shen, Meredith K. Wadman.

NEW REPUBLIC—(202) 508–4482; 525 9th Street, NW., Suite 600, Washington, DC 20004: Nora Caplan-Bricker, Marin Cogan, Diana Dwyer, Julia Fisher, Julia Ioffe, John Judis, Linda Kinstler, Alec MacGillis.

NEW YORKER—(202) 955–0960; 1730 Rhode Island Avenue, NW., Suite 603, Washington, DC 20036: Ryan Lizza, Evan Osnos.

NEWBAY MEDIA—(703) 852–4600; 5285 Shawnee Road, Suite 100, Alexandria, VA 22312: Joseph J. Smith, Leslie P. Stimson.

NEWSMAX—(202) 465–8730; 1900 K Street, NW., Suite 1120, Washington, DC 20006: John Gizzi, David L. Yonkman.

NEWSWEEK—(202) 626–2000; 1750 Pennsylvania Avenue, NW., Suite 1220, Washington, DC 20006: Eleanor Clift, M. Michelle Cottle, Benjamin Jacobs, Eli J. Lake, Sandra McElwaine, Jeffrey Stein, Michael J. Tomasky.

OIL & GAS JOURNAL—(703) 533–1552; 7013 Jefferson Avenue, Falls Church, VA 22042: Nicholas J. Snow.

PEOPLE MAGAZINE—(202) 861–4000; 1130 Connecticut Avenue, NW., Suite 900, Washington, DC 20036: Sandra J. Sobieraj Westfall.

PHARMACEUTICAL EXECUTIVE—(301) 656–4634; 7715 Rocton Avenue, Chevy Chase, MD 20815: Jill Wechsler.

PODER—(703) 707–0236; 2300 Darius Lane, Reston, VA 20191: Dolia E. Pettingell.

POLITICO—(703) 647–7999; 1100 Wilson Boulevard, 6th Floor, Arlington, VA 22209: Jonathan J. Allen, Michael P. Allen, Rachael Bade, Dan Berman, Brooks Boliek, Helena Bottemiller Evich, Eric Bradner,

PERIODICALS REPRESENTED IN PRESS GALLERIES—Continued

Kate Brannen, John Bresnahan, Carrie Budoff Brown, Talia N. Buford, Alexander I. Burns, Alex Byers, Dylan Byers, Bobby Cervantes, Megan Chan, Kyle Cheney, Kevin Cirilli, Dave Clarke, Anne T. Cronin, Paige Cunningham, Katherine Davidson-Choma, Christine Delargy, Darius A. Dixon, Kim Dixon, Edward-Isaac Dovere, Caitlin Z. Emma, Jennifer Epstein, Reid Epstein, John B. Everett, Philip Ewing, Brian Faler, Lauren French, Patrick Gavin, Joshua A. Gerstein, Ginger S. Gibson, Andrew J. Glass, Katie Glueck, Hadas Gold, Darren T. Goode, Alexander C. Guillen, Jennifer A. Haberkorn, John F. Harris, G. Robert Hillman, James P. Hohmann, Jenny Hopkinson, Jason Huffman, Alex Isenstadt, Martin J. Kady II, Joanne L. Kenen, Seung Min Kim, Robert P. King, Kim Kingsley, Tal Kopan, Min Jung Lee, Susan Levine, Tim K. Mak, Madeline Marshall, Erica L. Martinson, Lucy McCalmont, Caitlin A. McDevitt, Laura K. McGann, Erin Mershon, Jessica Meyers, Jason Millman, Leigh Munsil, David R. Nather, Eric Nelson, Libby A. Nelson, William D. Nichols, Brett Norman, Anna A. Palmer, Doug Palmer, Tarini Parti, Jon Prior, Manu K. Raju, Patrick C. Reis, Andrew Restuccia, Kevin P. Robillard, David E. Rogers, Lois Romano, Tony Romm, Jedd M. Rosche, Frederick J. Ryan, Jr., Darren S. Samuelsohn, Emily Schultheis, Maggie Severns, Nirvi H. Shah, Jake S. Sherman, Roger M. Simon, Rebecca Sinderbrand, Steven P. Sloan, Rachel Smolkin, Kelsey Snell, Adam K. Snider, Matthew Sobocinski, Juana Summers, Byron C. Tau, Glenn H. Thrush, Elizabeth Titus, Bill Tomson, Alexander Trowbridge, Rachel Van Dongen, James Vandehei, Natalie Villacorta, Kenneth P. Vogel, Zachary Warmbrodt, Mackenzie K. Weinger, Kathryn A. Wolfe, Scott B. Wong, Austin Wright, Mike Zapler.

PRESS ASSOCIATES—(202) 898–4825; 2605 P Street, NW., Suite A, Washington, DC 20007: Janet M. Brown, Mark J. Gruenberg.

PROCESO—(202) 737–1538; 529 14th Street, NW., Suite 1117, Washington, DC 20045: J. Jesus Esquivel.

PROFESSIONAL PILOT MAGAZINE—(703) 370–0606; 30 South Quaker Lane, Suite 300, Alexandria, VA 22314: Phil Rose.

PUBLIC LANDS NEWS—(703) 553–0552; 133 South Buchanan Street, Arlington, VA 22204: James B. Coffin.

PUBLIC UTILITIES FORTNIGHTLY—(703) 847–7733; 11410 Isaac Newton Square, Suite 220, Reston, VA 20190: Bruce W. Radford.

RED ALERT POLITICS—(202) 903–2000; 1150 17th Street, NW., Suite 504, Washington, DC 20036: Francesca A. Chambers, Kelsey N. Osterman, Melissa A. Quinn.

RESEARCH INSTITUTE OF AMERICA GROUP—(202) 842–1240; 1275 K Street, NW., Suite 875, Washington, DC 20005: Velma Goodwine, Soyoung Ho, William F. Lesesne.

ROLL CALL—(202) 650–6000; 77 K Street, NE., 8th Floor, Washington, DC 20002: Kate Ackley, Adriel Bettelheim, Sara E. Bondioli, Emily Cahn, Eliza Newlin Carney, Steven T. Dennis, Jason J. Dick, Emma N. Dumain, Marilyn Gates-Davis, David Hawkings, Jr., Morton M. Kondracke, Niels P. Lesniewski, Rebecca A. Livingston, Daniel J. Newhauser, Emily M. Ortman, Emily K. Pierce, David Rapp, John M. Rieger, Warren A. Rojas, Humberto Sanchez, Neda T. Semnani, Meredith H. Shiner, Katie Smith, Shira Toeplitz, Kyle K. Trygstad, Lauren Whittington.

ROTHENBERG POLITICAL REPORT—(202) 546–2822; 13305 Morning Field Way Potomac, MD 20854: Nathan Gonzales, Stuart Rothenberg, Jessica L. Taylor.

SALON.COM—(202) 630–2227; 2206 1st Street, NW., Washington, DC 20001: Alexander L. Seitz-Wald.

SATELLITE BUSINESS NEWS—(202) 785–0505; 5614 Connecticut Avenue, NW., #300, Washington, DC 20015: Bob Scherman, Jeffrey Williams.

SCIENTIFIC AMERICAN—(202) 626–2532; 968 National Press Building, Washington, DC 20045: Dina Maron.

SCUDDER PUBLISHING GROUP—(410) 923–0688; 1145 Generals Highway, Crownsville, MD 21032: John Sodergreen.

SLATE—(202) 261–2066; 1350 Connecticut Avenue, Suite 400, Washington, DC 20036: Andrew Bouve, John F. Dickerson, William J. Dobson, Joshua Levin, David Plotz, Emma Roller, William B. Saletan, Jeremy Stahl, Katy Waldman, David A. Weigel, Matthew Yglesias.

SPACE NEWS—(571) 356–9532; 1414 Prince Street, Suite 300, Alexandria, VA 22314: Michael Gruss, Daniel Leone.

STERN—(646) 546–8458; 2480 16th Street, NW., #719, Washington, DC 20009: Katja Gloger, Martin Knobbe.

SYNOPSIS—(301) 728–4988; 20312 Aspenwood Lane, Montgomery Village, MD 20886: William T. Gray, Ellen B. Milhiser.

TALKING POINTS MEMO—(202) 758–3048; 1615 L Street, NW., Suite 310, Washington, DC 20036: Brian A. Beutler, Igor Bobic, Sahil Kapur, David M. Kurtz, Pema Levy, Benjamin V. Sarlin.

TAX NOTES—(703) 533–4400; 400 South Maple Avenue, Suite 400, Falls Church, VA 22046: David Scott Antonides, Jaime K. Arora, Brian D. Bardwell, Ulrike M. Bergin, Maria Bonaquist, Jennifer Carr, Matthew Dalton, William R. Davis, Jennifer DePaul, Joseph DiSciullo, Amy S. Elliott, Meredith Fath, Lissa Fried, Linda Friedman, Luca Gattoni-Celli, Michael Gleeson, Ariel Greenblum, Cara L. Griffith, Amy L. Hamilton, William Hoffman, Shonda Humphrey, David Randall Jackson, Jr., Thomas Jaworski, Stephanie S. Johnston, Matthew Madara, Juliann Martin, Lindsey McPherson, Teresa Moss,

PERIODICALS REPRESENTED IN PRESS GALLERIES—Continued

Ashley C. Newell, Charles C. O'Toole, Kristen A. Parillo, Bergrek Phillips, Trina L. Pinneau, Henry Reske, David Sawyer, Scott Andrew Sheets, Douglas Sheppard, Meg Shreve, Quintin Simmons, David D. Stewart, Frederick W. Stokeld, David T. van den Berg, Andrew Velarde, Sam Young, Gulnar Zaman.

TECHNOLOGY COMMERCIALIZATION—(703) 522–6648; P.O. Box 100595, Arlington, VA 22210: Neil A. MacDonald.

TELECOMMUNICATIONS REPORTS—(202) 842–8923; 1015 15th Street, NW., 10th Floor, Washington, DC 20005: John P. Curran, Carrie R. DeLeon, Paul S. Kirby, Lynn E. Stanton.

THOMPSON INFORMATION SERVICES—(202) 872–4000; 4340 East-West Highway, Suite 300, Bethesda, MD 20814: Jerry Ashworth, Cameron S. Ayers, Andrew D. Brownstein, Elizabeth M. Casabona, Charles J. Edwards, John F. Iekel, Todd H. Leeuwenburgh, Daniel J. Macy, Jane Meacham, Karen Norris, Mark Reishus, Maria K. Scholtz, Jeffrey W. Schomisch, David A. Slaughter, Dennis A. Tosh.

TIME MAGAZINE—(202) 861–4000; 1130 Connecticut Avenue, NW., Suite 900, Washington, DC 20036: Alex Altman, Melissa A. August, Massimo T. Calabresi, Michael Crowley, Elizabeth Dias, Michael W. Duffy, Zeke Miller, Jay Newton-Small, Denver Nicks, Maya Rhodan, Alex Rogers, Michael B. Scherer, Katherine Steinmetz, Mark J. Thompson.

TOWNHALL MAGAZINE—(703) 247–1251; 1901 North Moore Street, Suite 701, Arlington, VA 22209: Leah E. Barkoukis, Guy P. Benson, Daniel P. Doherty, Heather Ginsberg, Kevin W. Glass, Kathleen B. Hicks, Erika L. Johnsen, Elisabeth C. Meinecke, Amanda Munoz, Cortney O'Brien, Catherine M. Pavlich, Christine Rousselle, Sarah Seman.

TRANSPORTATION WEEKLY—(703) 371–1226; 2301 North Stafford Street, Arlington, VA 22207: Jeffrey J. Davis.

TRICE EDNEY NEWSWIRE—(202) 291–9310; 6817 Georgia Avenue, NW., Suite 218, Washington, DC 20012: Hazel Trice T. Edney.

U.S. MEDICINE—(202) 488–0611: Sandra L. Basu, Stephen Spotswood.

U.S. NEWS & WORLD REPORT—(202) 955–2000; 1050 Thomas Jefferson Street, NW., Washington, DC 20007: Lauren Fox, Patrick Garofalo, Megan M. Handley, Jason T. Koebler, Danielle Kurtzleben, Christian A. Lowe, Rebekah W. Metzler, Philip Moeller, Michael Morella, Steven E. Nelson, Alan Neuhauser, Thomas Risen, Robert Schlesinger, Nicole Schwab, Paul Shinkman, Tierney M. Sneed, Steve Sternberg, Kenneth T. Walsh, Teresa M. Welsh, Kira Zalan.

UCG—(301) 287–2700; 9737 Washingtonian Boulevard, Suite 200, Gaithersburg, MD 20878: Carl A. Ayers, Rachel Gantz, Anke B. Irgang, Karen S. Long Rayburn, A.J. Plunkett, Vincent E. Taylor, Lauren C. Williams.

USA JOURNAL—(202) 714–7330; P.O. Box 714, Washington, DC 20044: Janne Kum Cha Pak.

VANITY FAIR—(202) 244–3424; 5146 Klingle Street, NW., Washington, DC 20016: Maureen Orth, Laura Parker, William W. Prochnau, Todd S. Purdum.

WASHINGTON BLADE—(202) 747–2077; 1712 14th Street, NW., Washington, DC 20009: Louis M. Chibbaro, Jr., Christopher Johnson, Michael Lavers.

WASHINGTON BUSINESS INFORMATION—(703) 538–7600; 300 North Washington Street, Suite 200, Falls Church, VA 22046: Ferdous Al-Faruque, Meg Bryant, April Hollis, Robert C. King, Elizabeth Orr, Nick Otto, Johnathan A. Rickman, Melissa Winn.

WASHINGTON BUSINESS JOURNAL—(703) 258–0845; 1555 Wilson Boulevard, Suite 400, Arlington, VA 22204: Kent D. Hoover.

WASHINGTON CITY PAPER—(202) 332–2100; 1400 I Street, NW., #900, Washington, DC 20005: Jonathan L. Fischer, Caroline E. Jones, Mike Madden, Jennifer Rogers, Allison Schweitzer, Jessica Sidman, William Sommer, Alan H. Suderman, Aaron M. Wiener.

WASHINGTON COUNSELETTER—(202) 244–6709; 5712 26th Street, NW., Washington, DC 20015: Deborah A. Kavruck.

WASHINGTON DIPLOMAT—(301) 933–3552; P.O. Box 1345, Silver Spring, MD 20915: Luke J. Kummer.

WASHINGTON JEWISH WEEK—(301) 230–2222; 11900 Parklawn Drive, Suite 300, Rockville, MD 20852: Suzanne Pollak.

WASHINGTON TRADE DAILY—(301) 946–0817; P.O. Box 1802, Wheaton, MD 20915: James R. Berger, Mary L. Berger.

WASHINGTON WATCH—(301) 263–9023; 5923 Onondaga Road, Bethesda, MD 20816: Kazutami Yamazaki.

WASHINGTONIAN—(202) 296–3600; 1828 L Street, NW., Suite 200, Washington, DC 20036: Melanie Bender, Kate Bennett, Christopher Campbell, Sherri Dalphonse, Diana Elbasha, Michael Gaynor, Sophie Gilbert, Mary Glover, Garrett Graff, Shane Harris, Harry Jaffe, Carol R. Joynt, Marisa M. Kashino, Alison Kitchens, Leslie Milk, Luke Mullins, William O'Sullivan, Tanya Pai, Melissa Romero, Anna Spiegel, Michelle E. Thomas, Jessica Voelker, Denise M. Wills, Mary Yarrison.

WATERWAYS JOURNAL—(703) 524–2490; 5220 North Carlin Springs Road, Arlington, VA 22203: Carlo J. Salzano.

WEBSTER COMMUNICATIONS—(703) 525–4013; 3835 9th Street North, #401W, Arlington, VA 22203: James C. Webster.

PERIODICALS REPRESENTED IN PRESS GALLERIES—Continued

WEEKLY STANDARD—(202) 293–4900; 1150 17th Street, NW., Suite 505, Washington, DC 20036: Fred W. Barnes, Christopher S. Caldwell, Julianne E. Dudley, Terry Eastland, Ethan R. Epstein, Andrew Ferguson, Daniel M. Halper, Katherine Havard, Mark W. Hemingway, Jonathan V. Last, Victorino L. Matus, John M. McCormack, Maria T. Santos, Lee H. Smith, James A. Swift, Philip Terzian, Kelly J. Torrance, Michael R. Warren.

WHITAKER NEWSLETTERS—(240) 583–0280; P.O. Box 224, Spencerville, MD 20868: Joel Whitaker.

WIRED.COM—(202) 294–9523; 1816 New Hampshire Avenue, #908, Washington, DC 20009: Spencer J. Ackerman.

WORLD MAGAZINE—(202) 445–0454; 310 Laverne Avenue, Alexandria, VA 22305: Emily C. Belz, Joshua C. Derrick, Edward Lee Pitts.

CONGRESSIONAL DISTRICT MAPS

ALABAMA—Congressional Districts—(7 Districts)

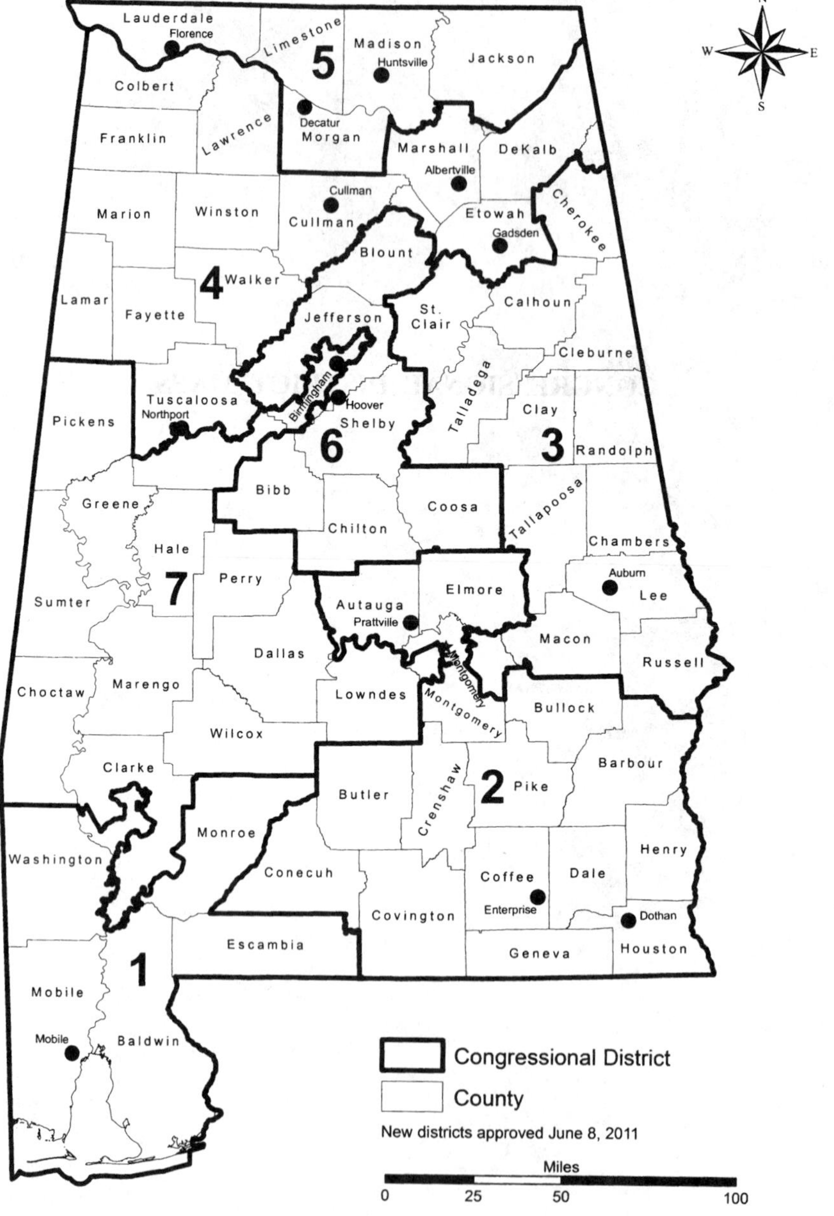

ALASKA—Congressional District—(1 District At Large)

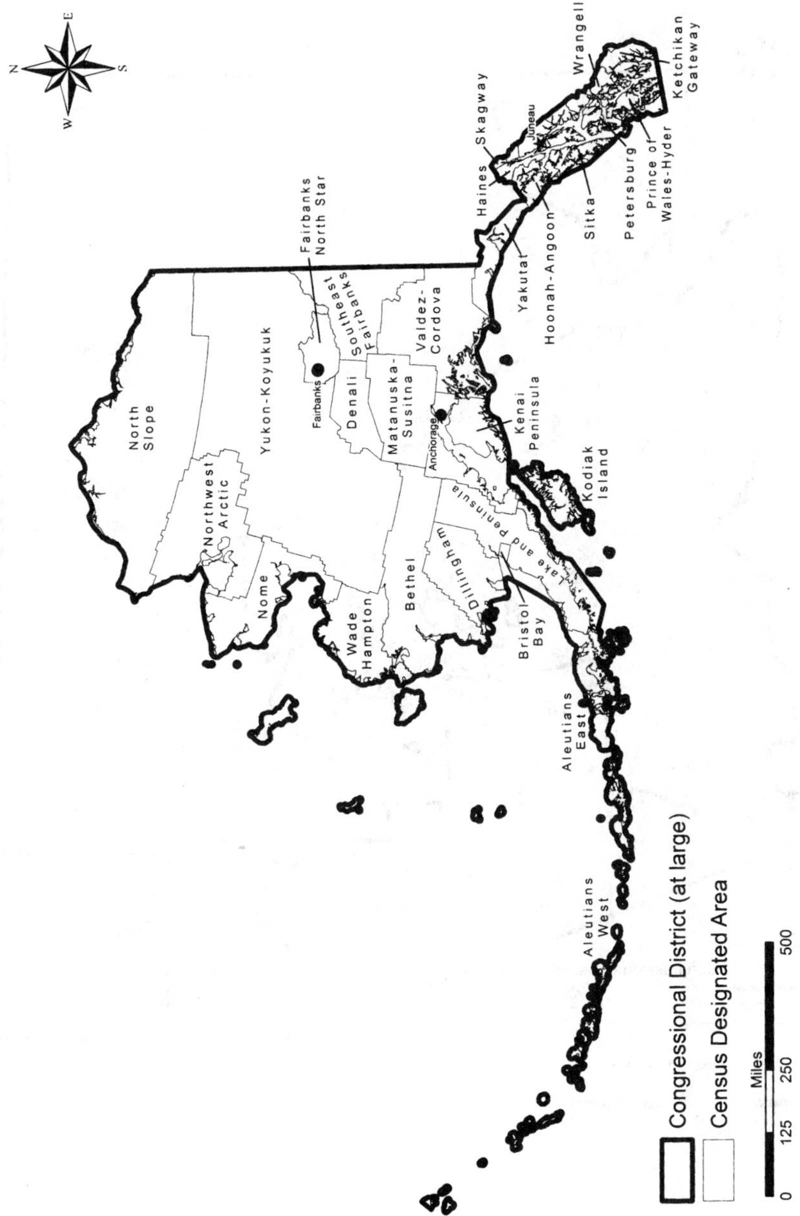

ARIZONA—Congressional Districts—(9 Districts)

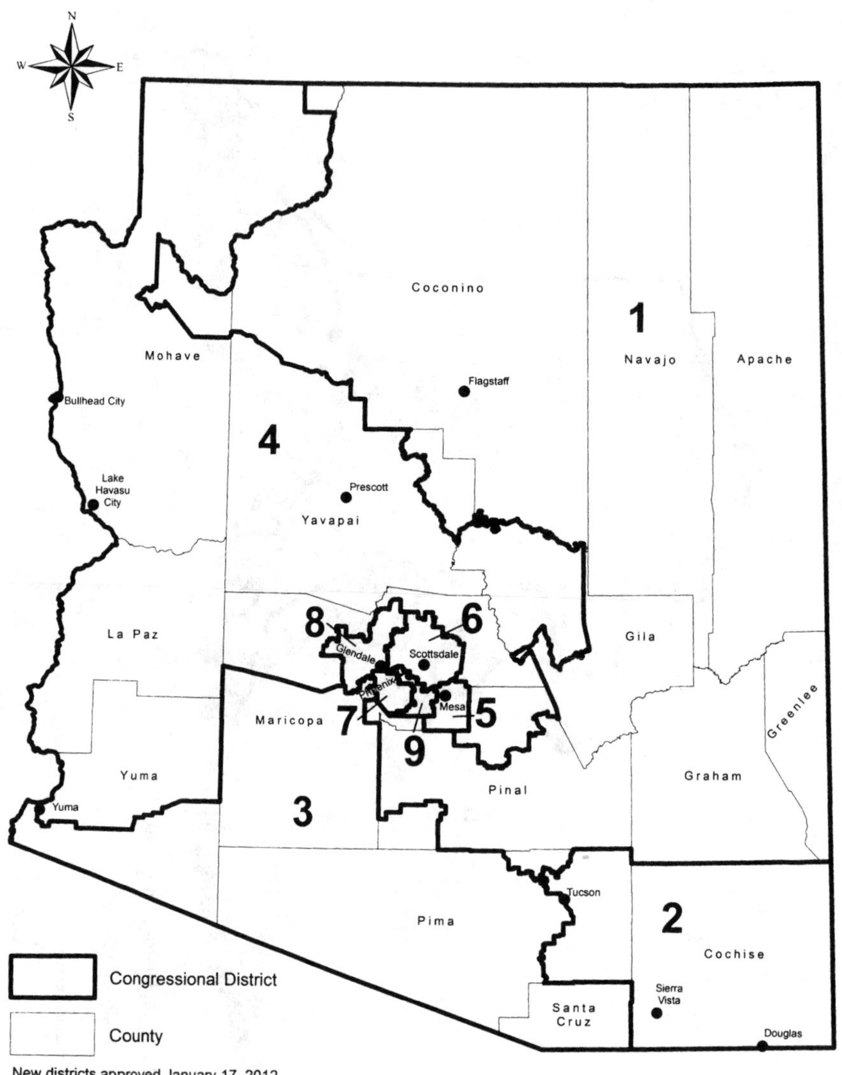

ARKANSAS—Congressional Districts—(4 Districts)

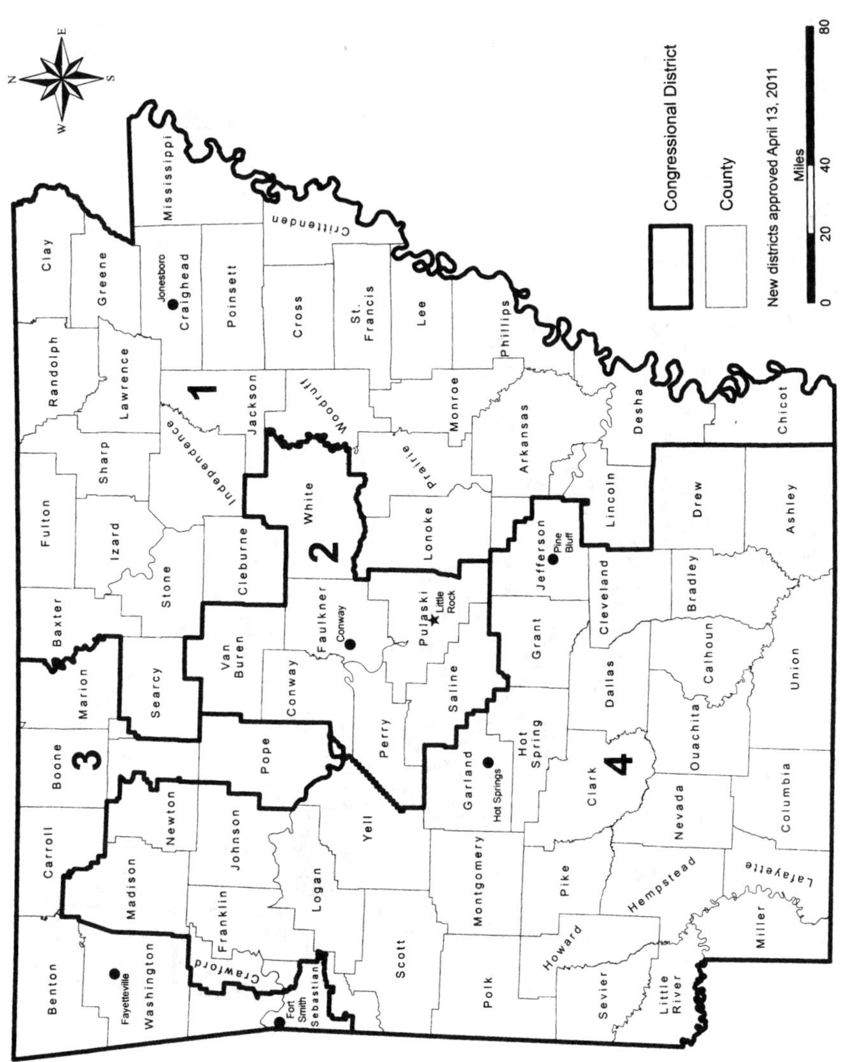

CALIFORNIA—Congressional Districts—(53 Districts)

Congressional District

County

New districts approved August 15, 2011

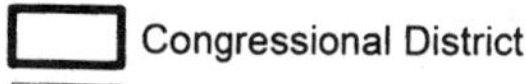

COLORADO—Congressional Districts—(7 Districts)

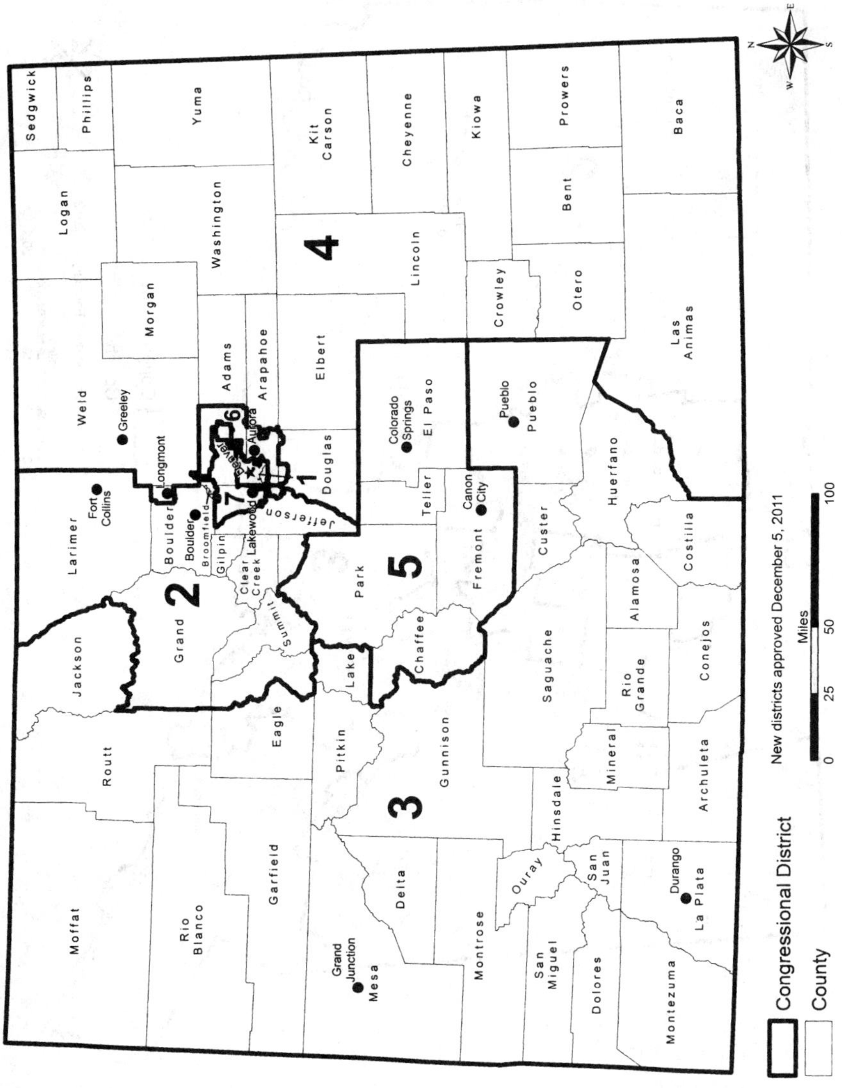

CONNECTICUT—Congressional Districts—(5 Districts)

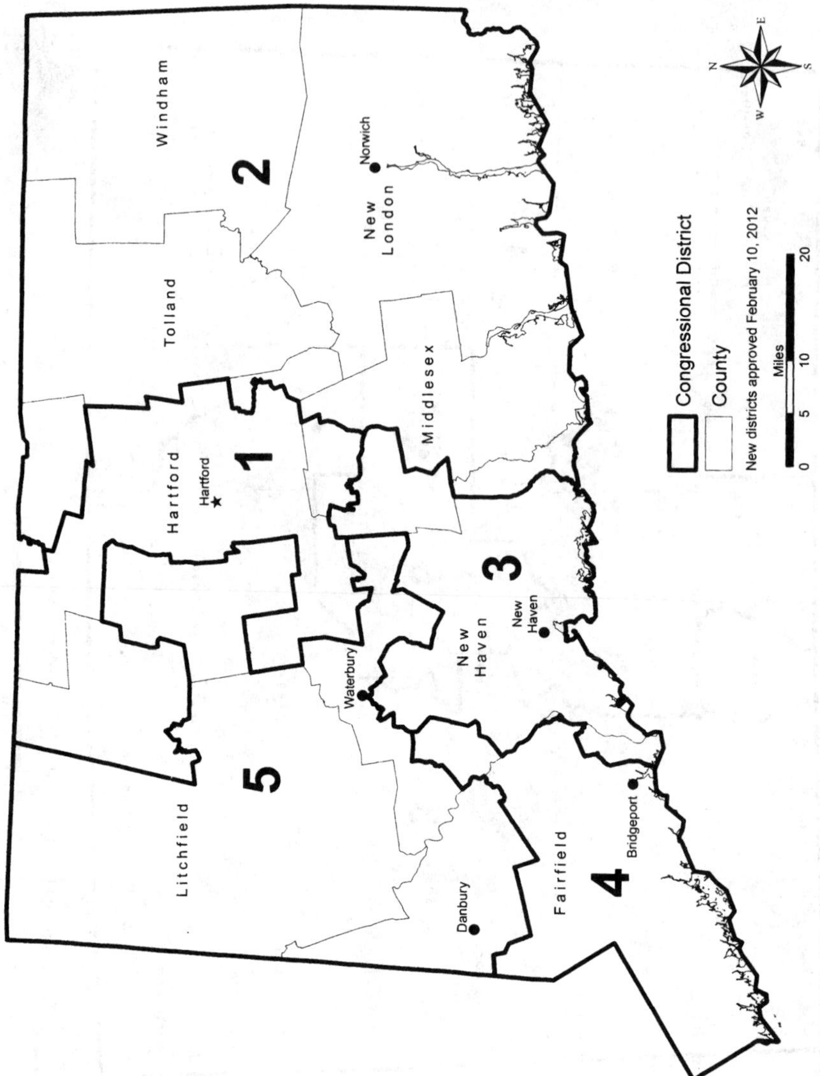

DELAWARE—Congressional District—(1 District At Large)

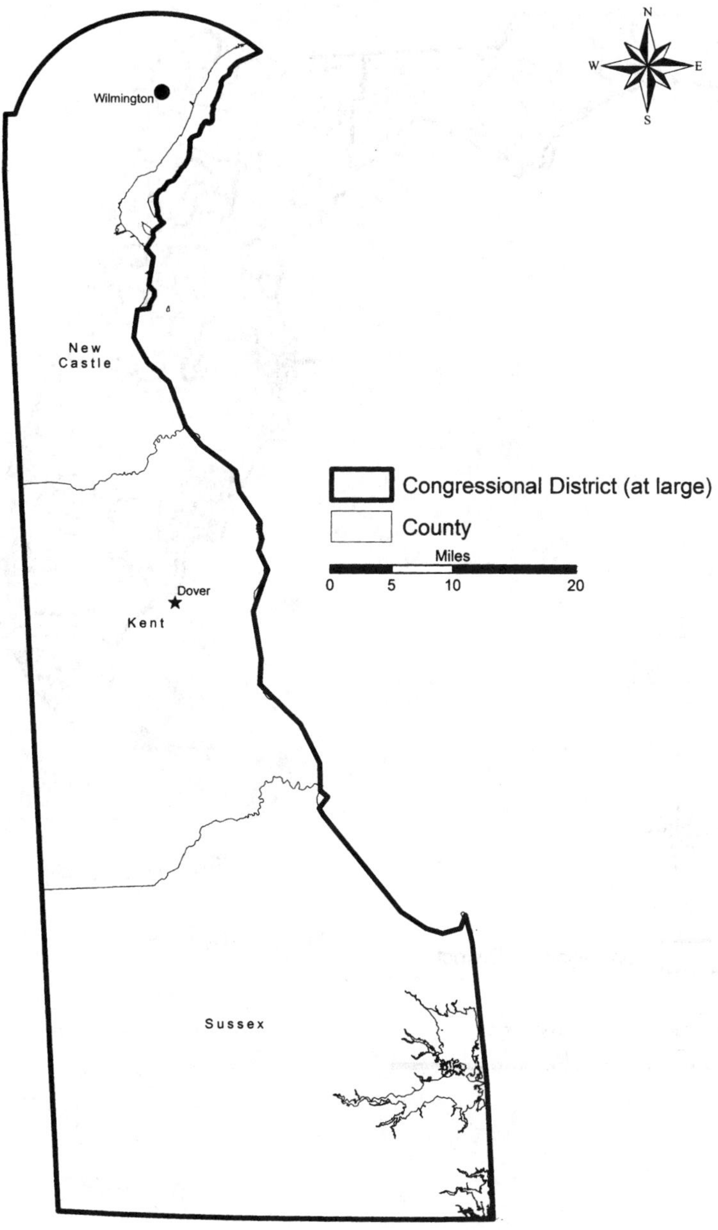

FLORIDA—Congressional Districts—(27 Districts)

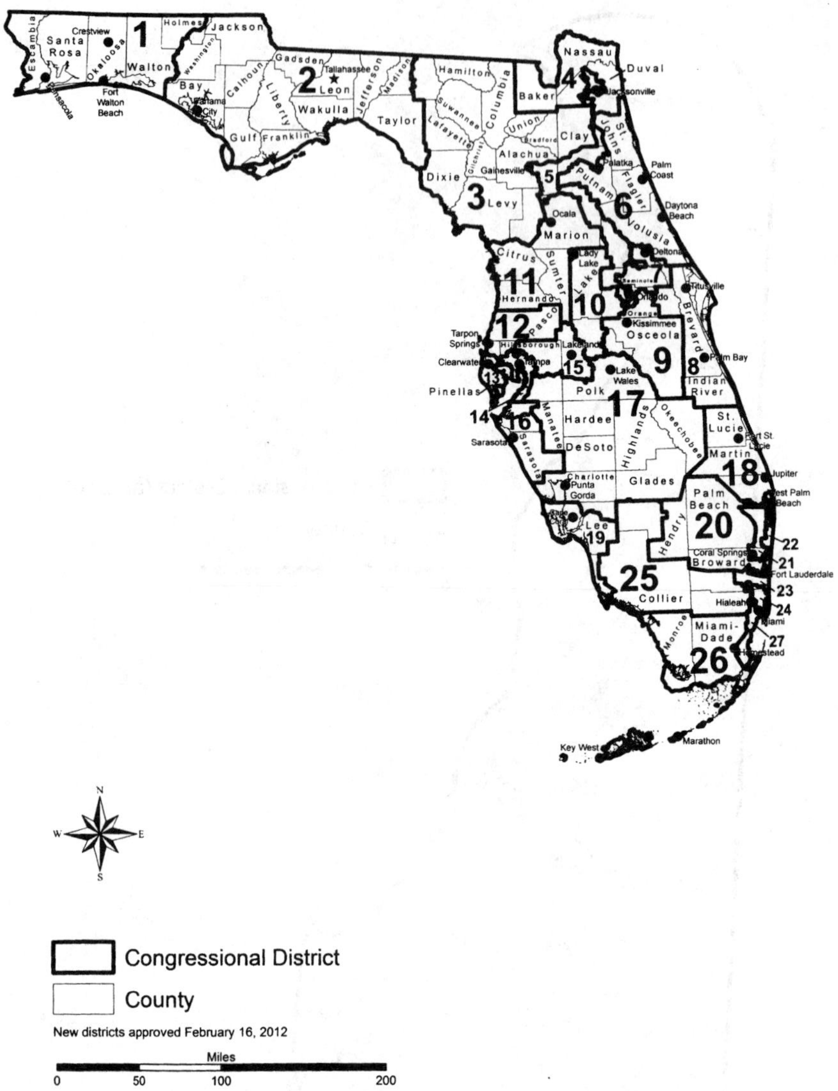

Congressional District

County

New districts approved February 16, 2012

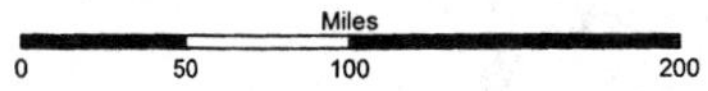

GEORGIA—Congressional Districts—(14 Districts)

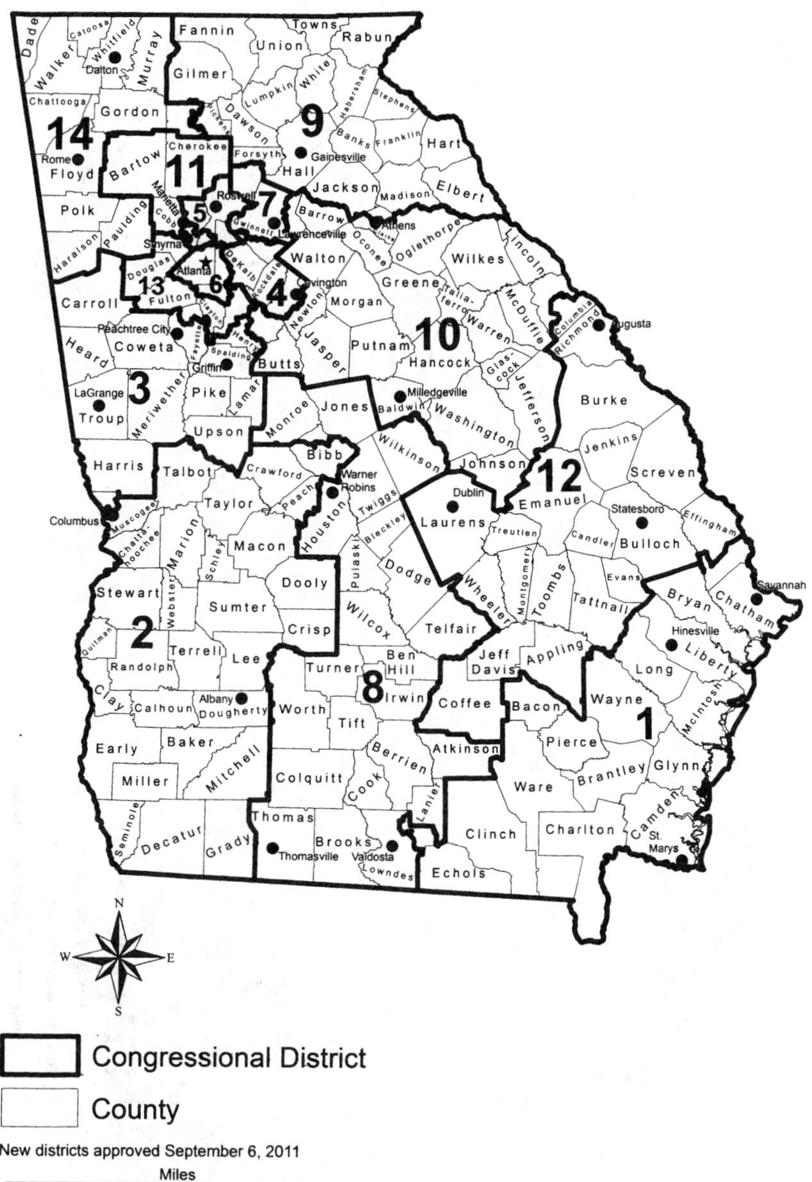

HAWAII—Congressional Districts—(2 Districts)

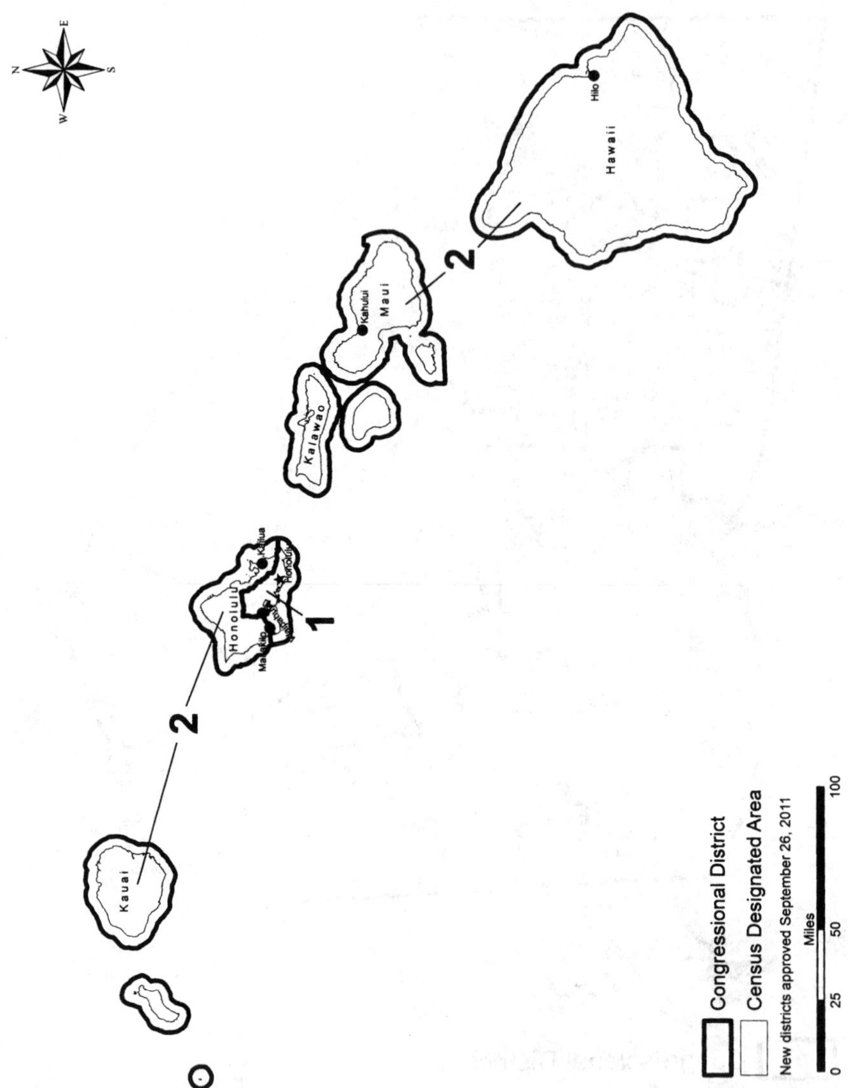

IDAHO—Congressional Districts—(2 Districts)

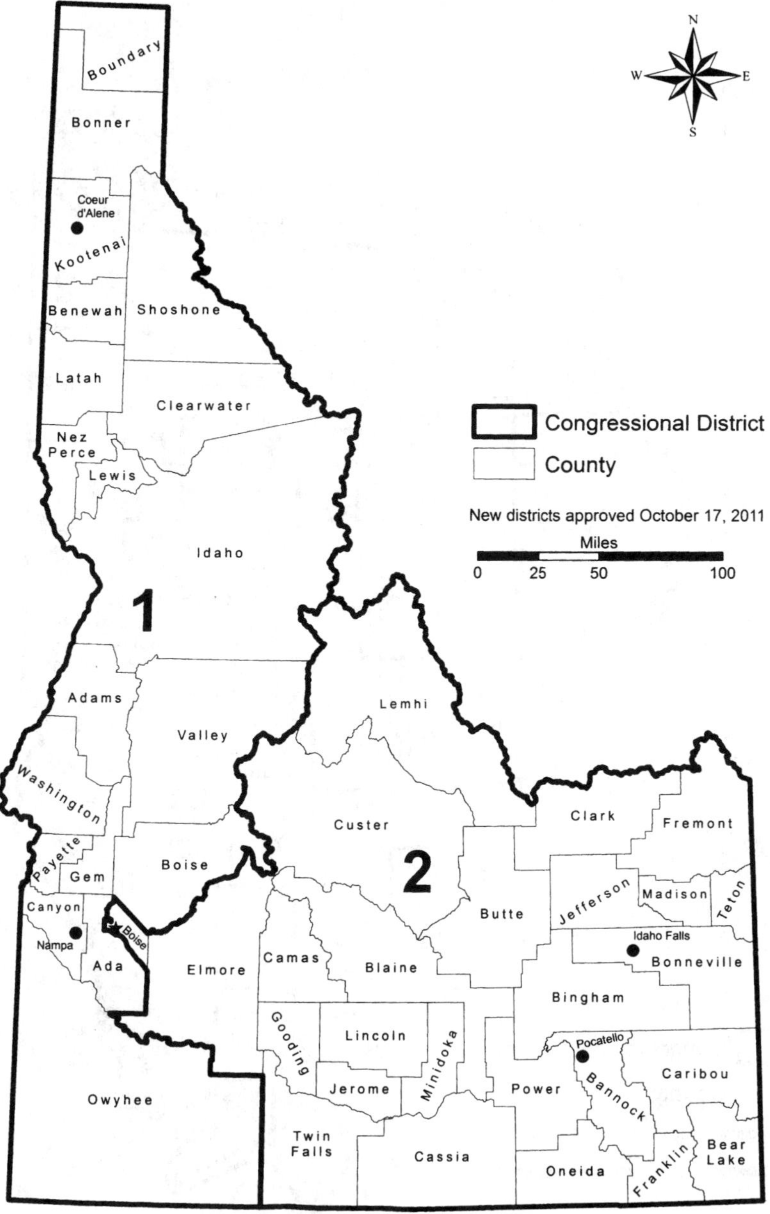

ILLINOIS—Congressional Districts—(18 Districts)

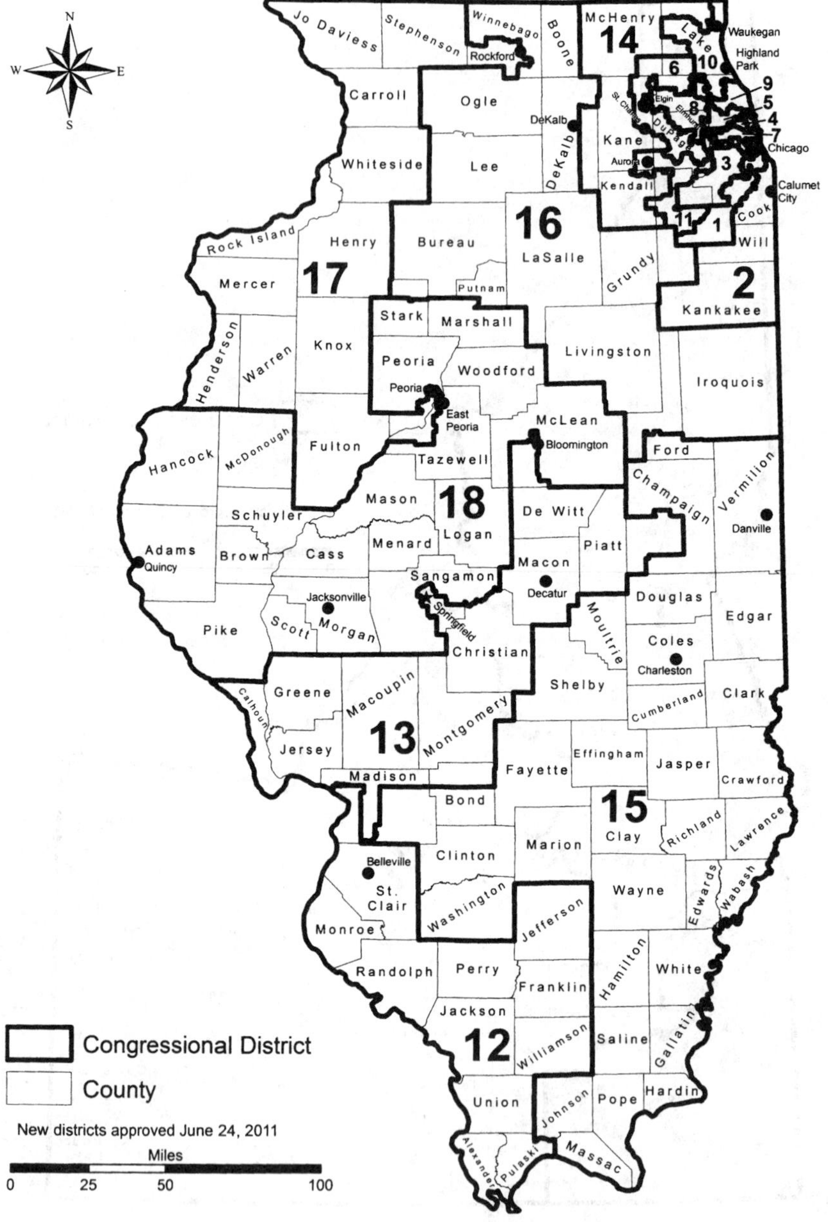

INDIANA—Congressional Districts—(9 Districts)

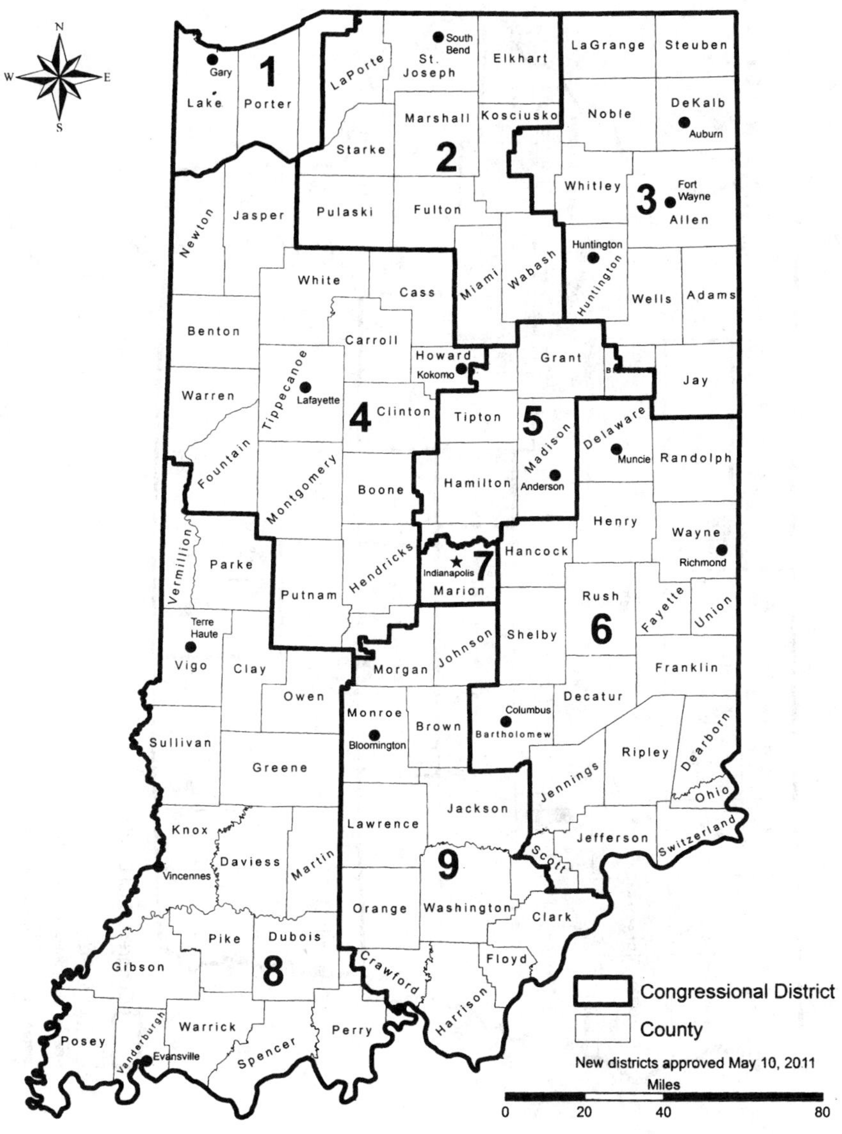

IOWA—Congressional Districts—(4 Districts)

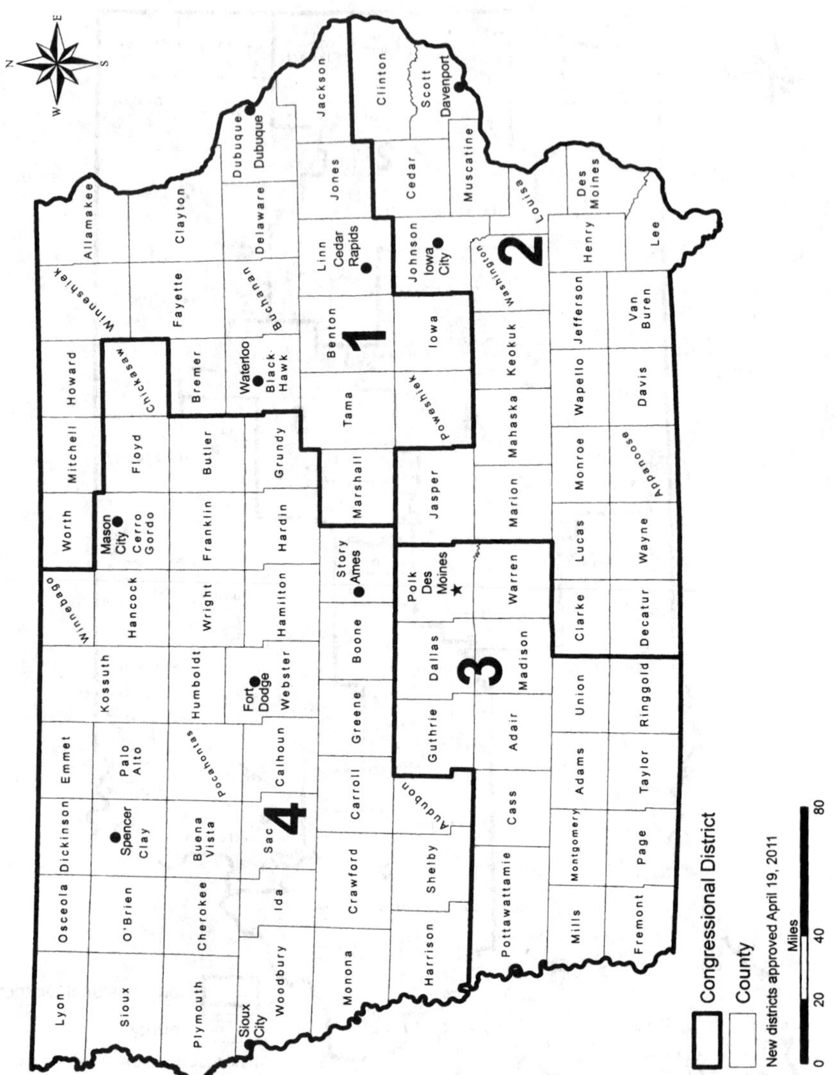

KANSAS—Congressional Districts—(4 Districts)

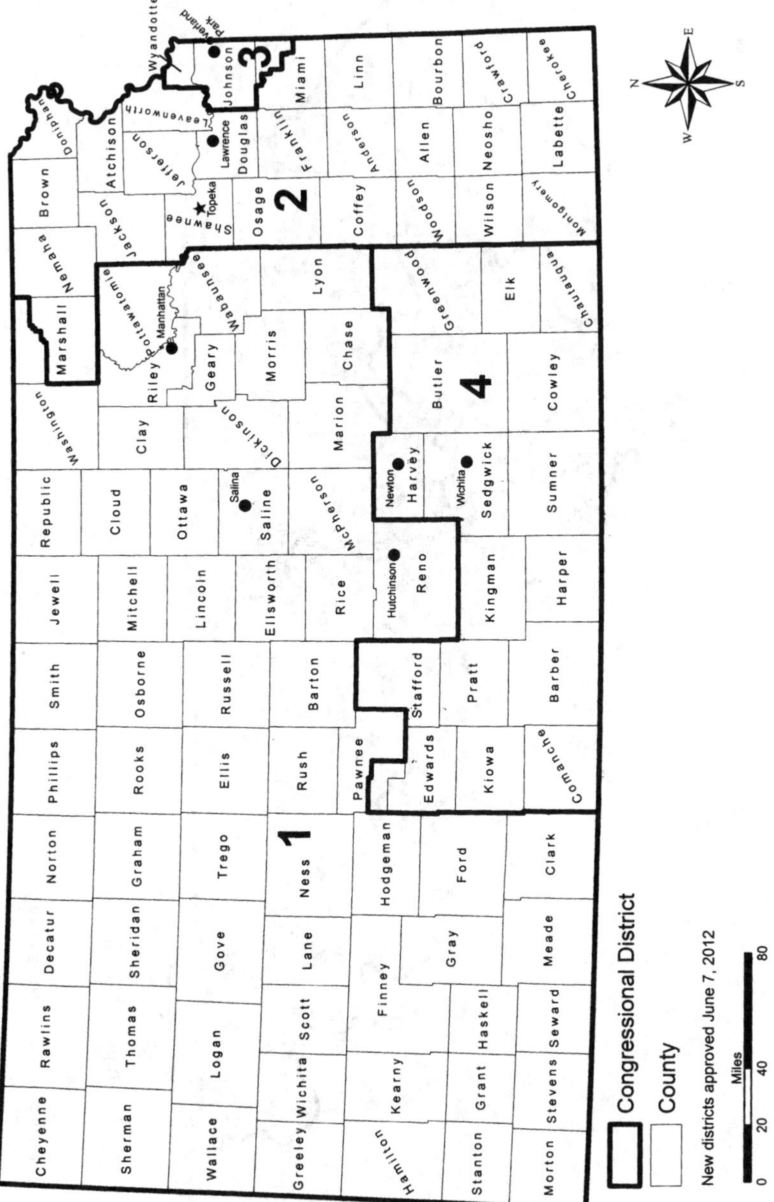

KENTUCKY—Congressional Districts—(6 Districts)

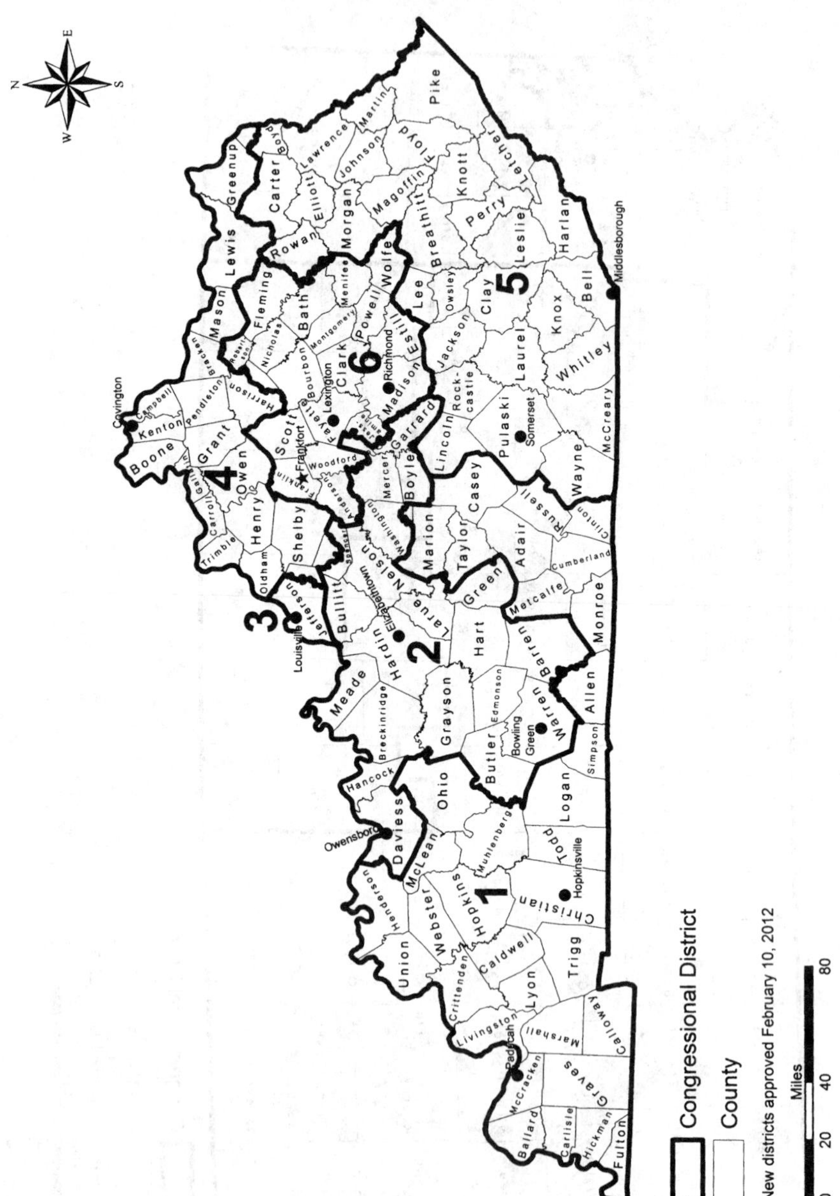

LOUISIANA—Congressional Districts—(6 Districts)

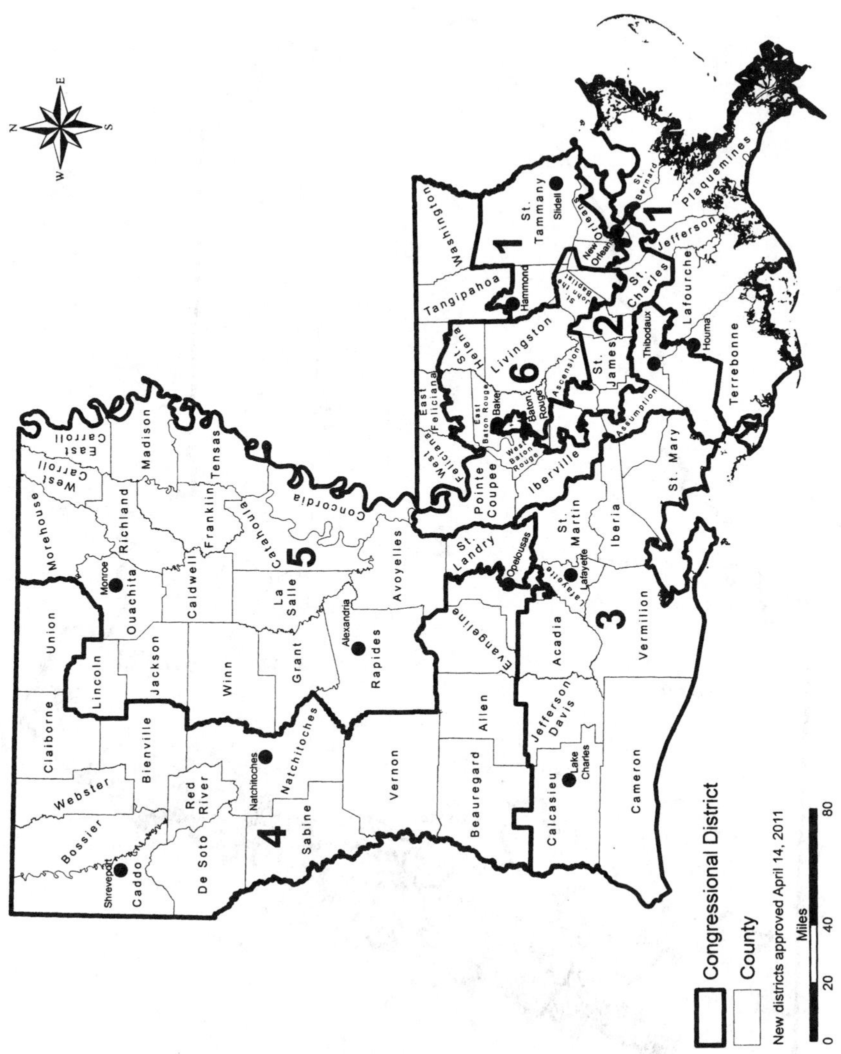

MAINE—Congressional Districts—(2 Districts)

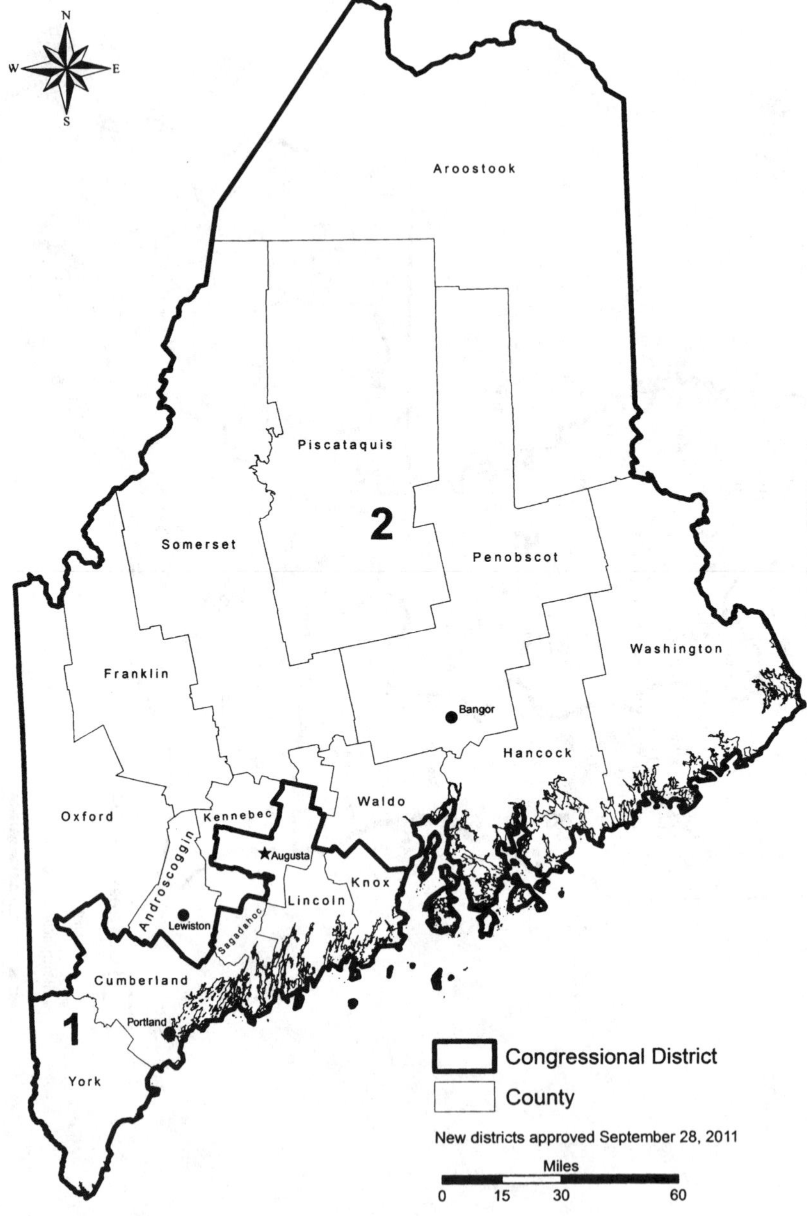

MARYLAND—Congressional Districts—(8 Districts)

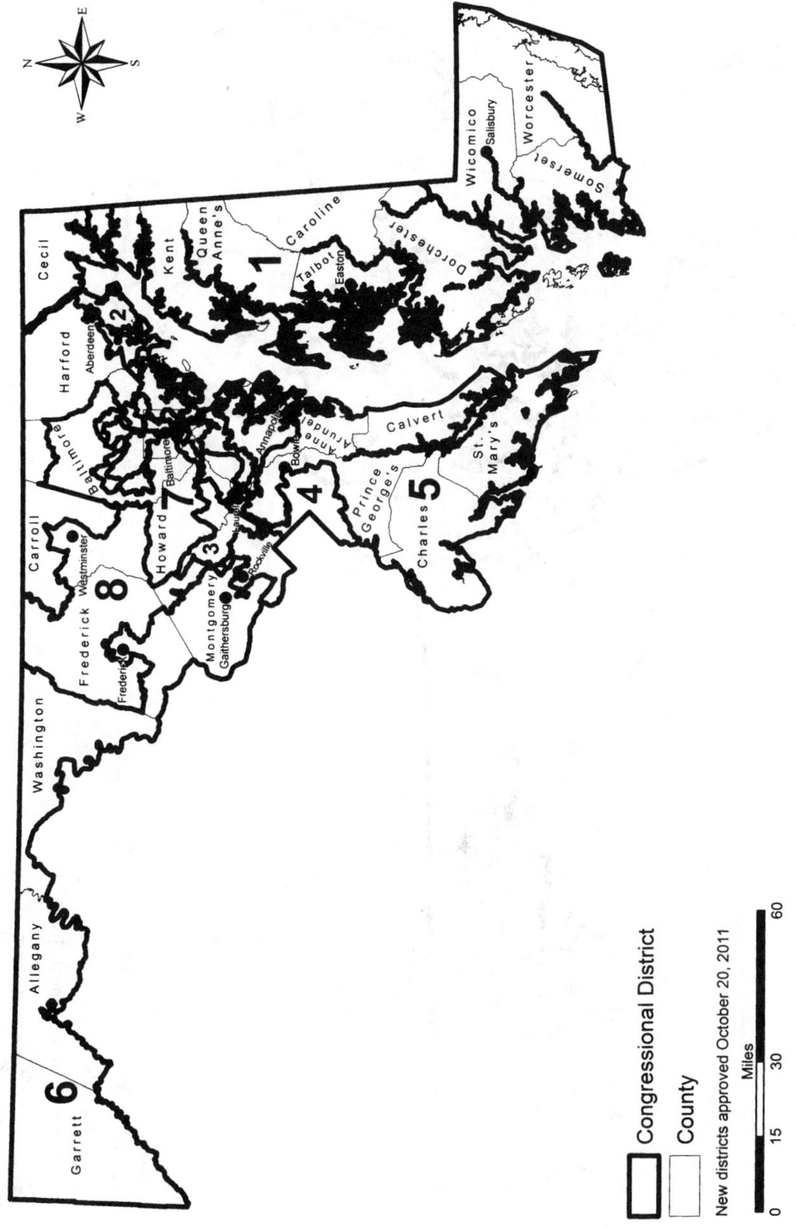

MASSACHUSETTS—Congressional Districts—(9 Districts)

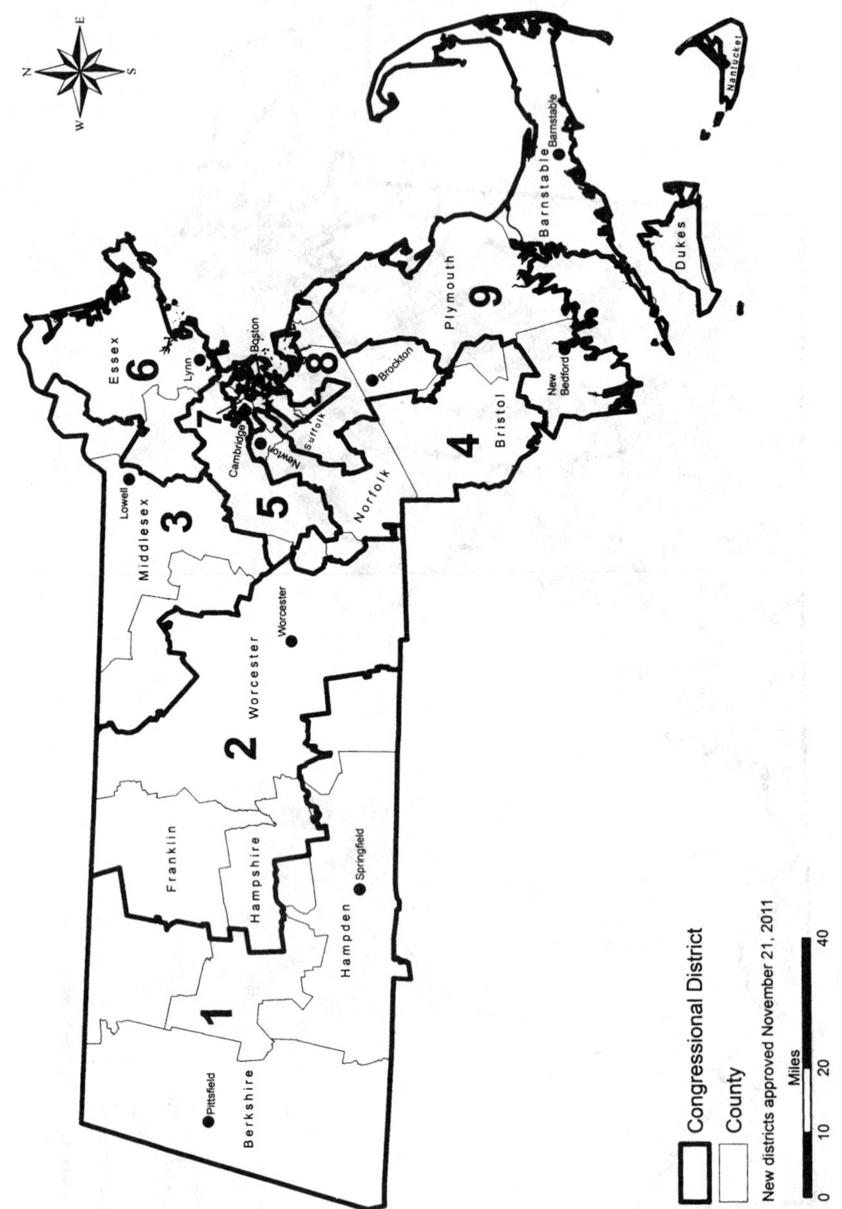

MICHIGAN—Congressional Districts—(14 Districts)

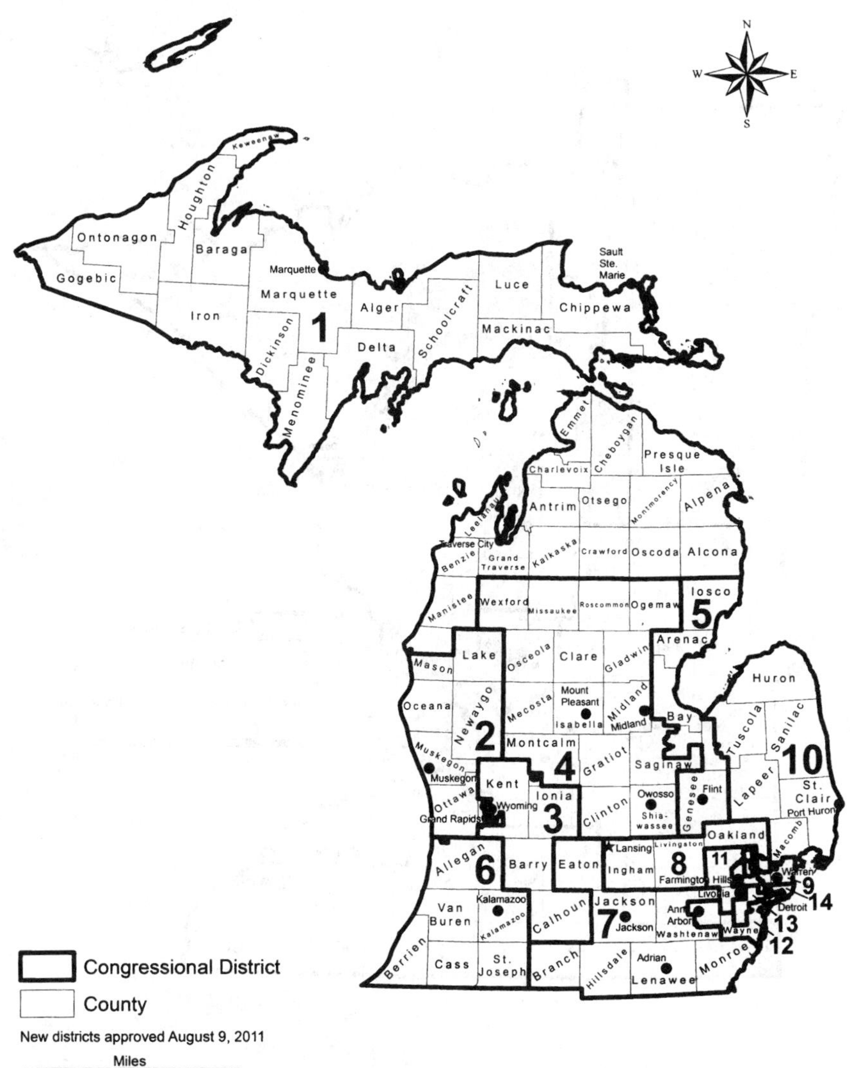

MINNESOTA—Congressional Districts—(8 Districts)

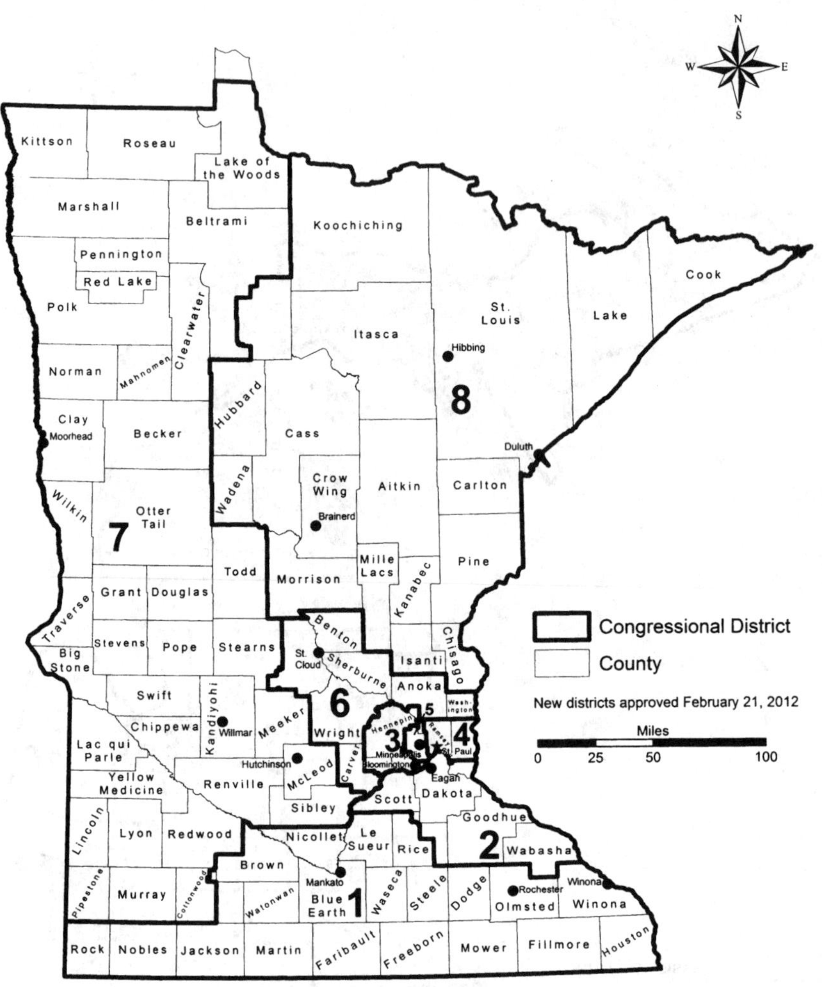

MISSISSIPPI—Congressional Districts—(4 Districts)

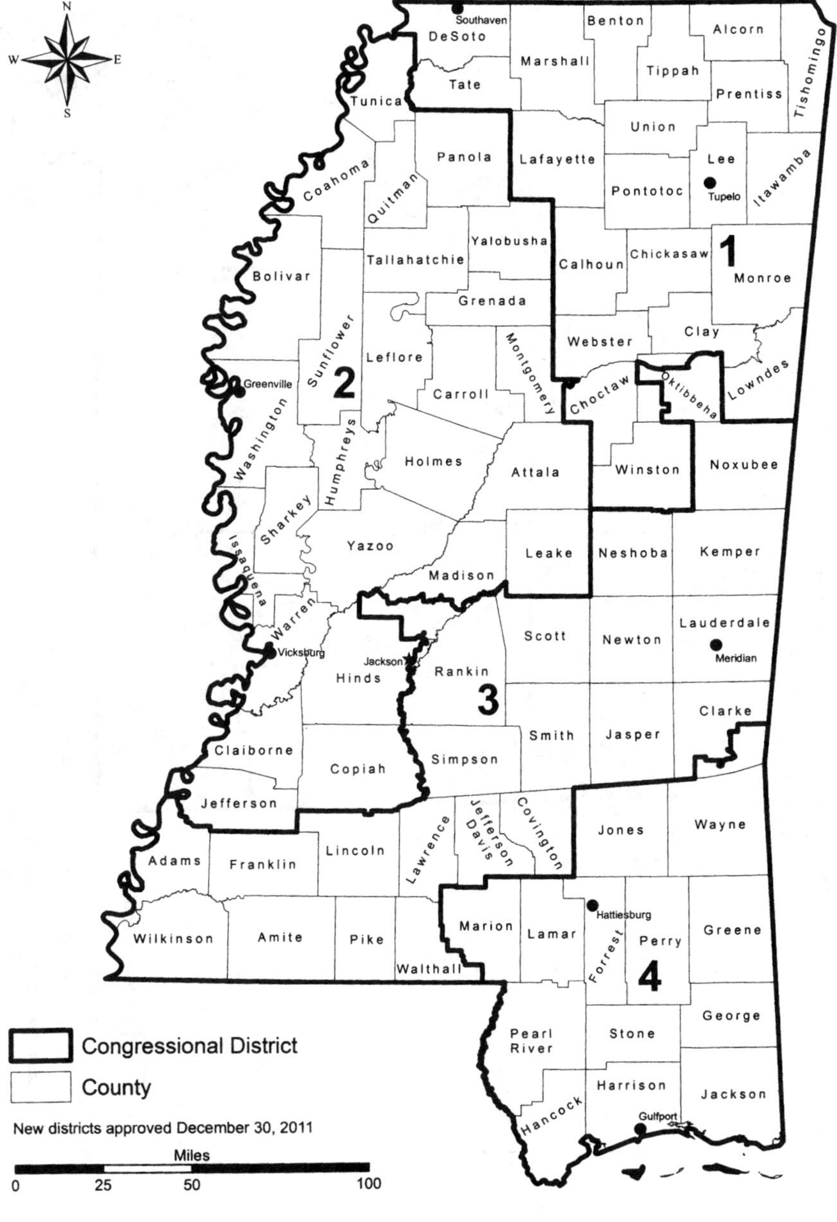

MISSOURI—Congressional Districts—(8 Districts)

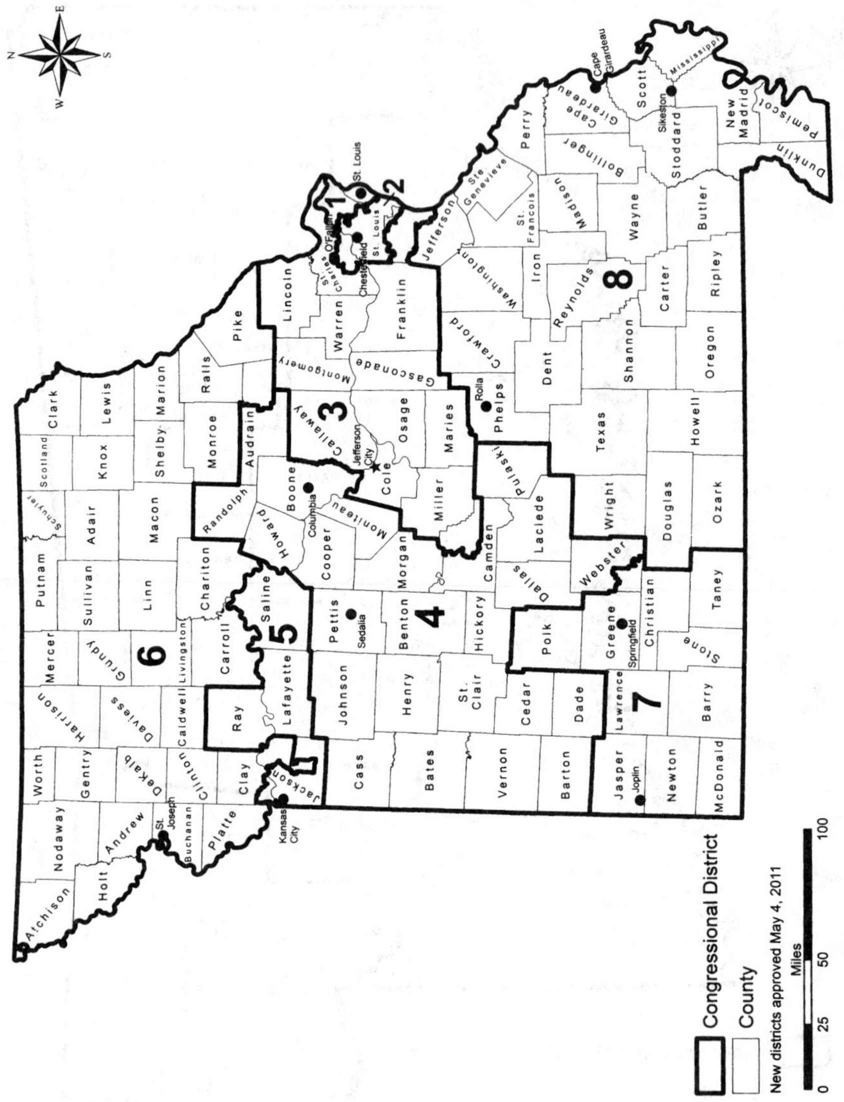

MONTANA—Congressional District—(1 District At Large)

NEBRASKA—Congressional Districts—(3 Districts)

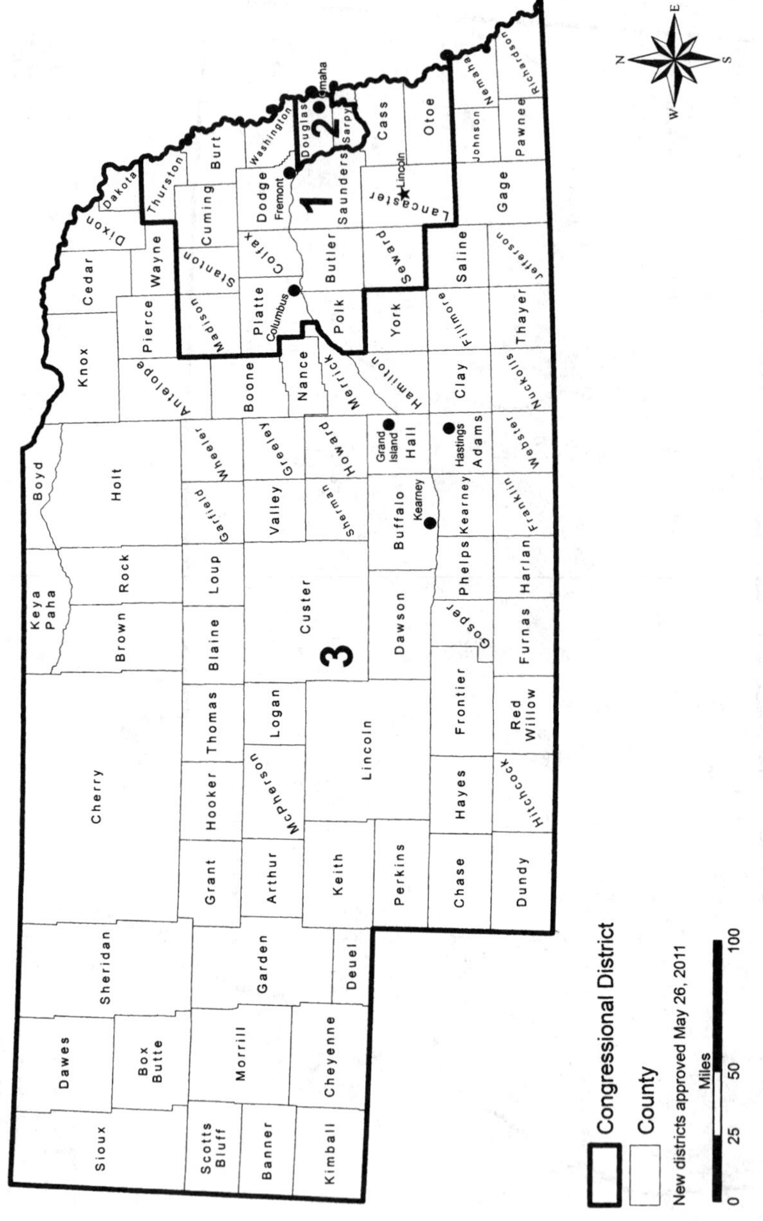

NEVADA—Congressional Districts—(4 Districts)

NEW HAMPSHIRE—Congressional Districts—(2 Districts)

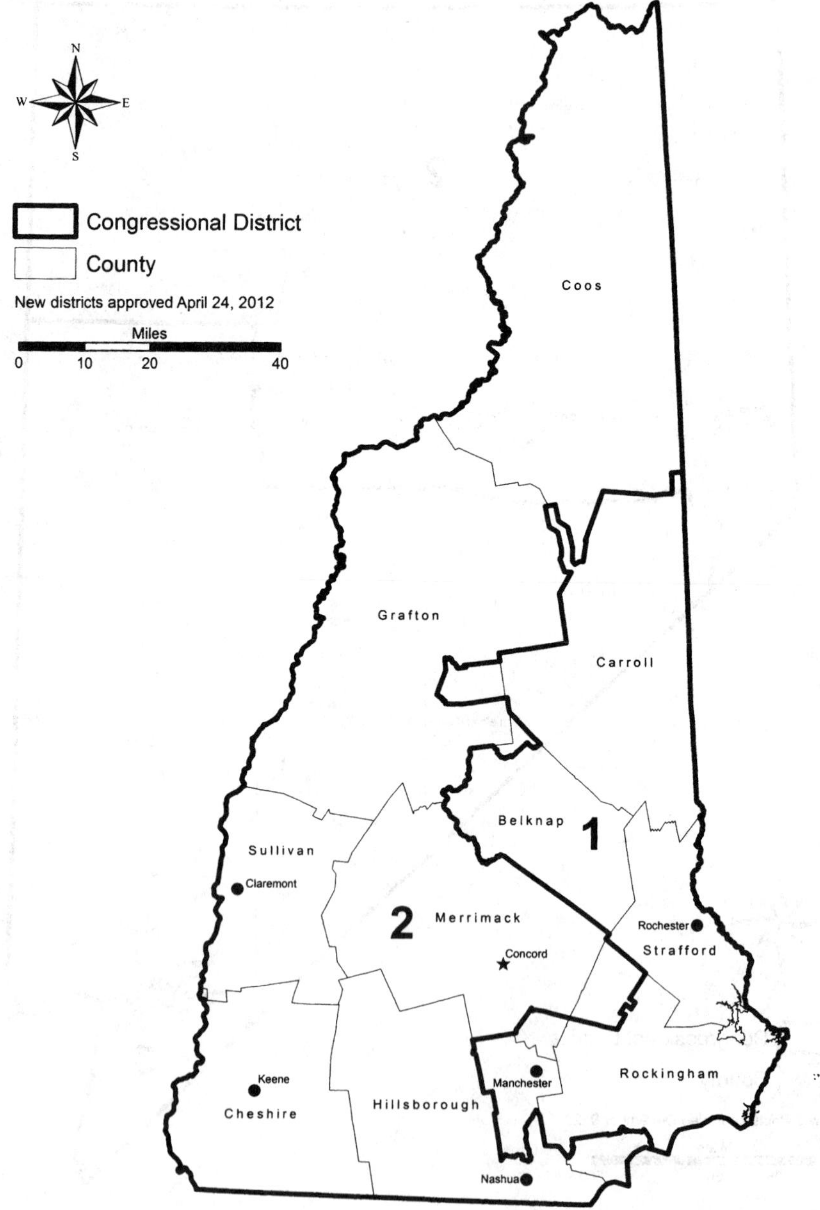

NEW JERSEY—Congressional Districts—(12 Districts)

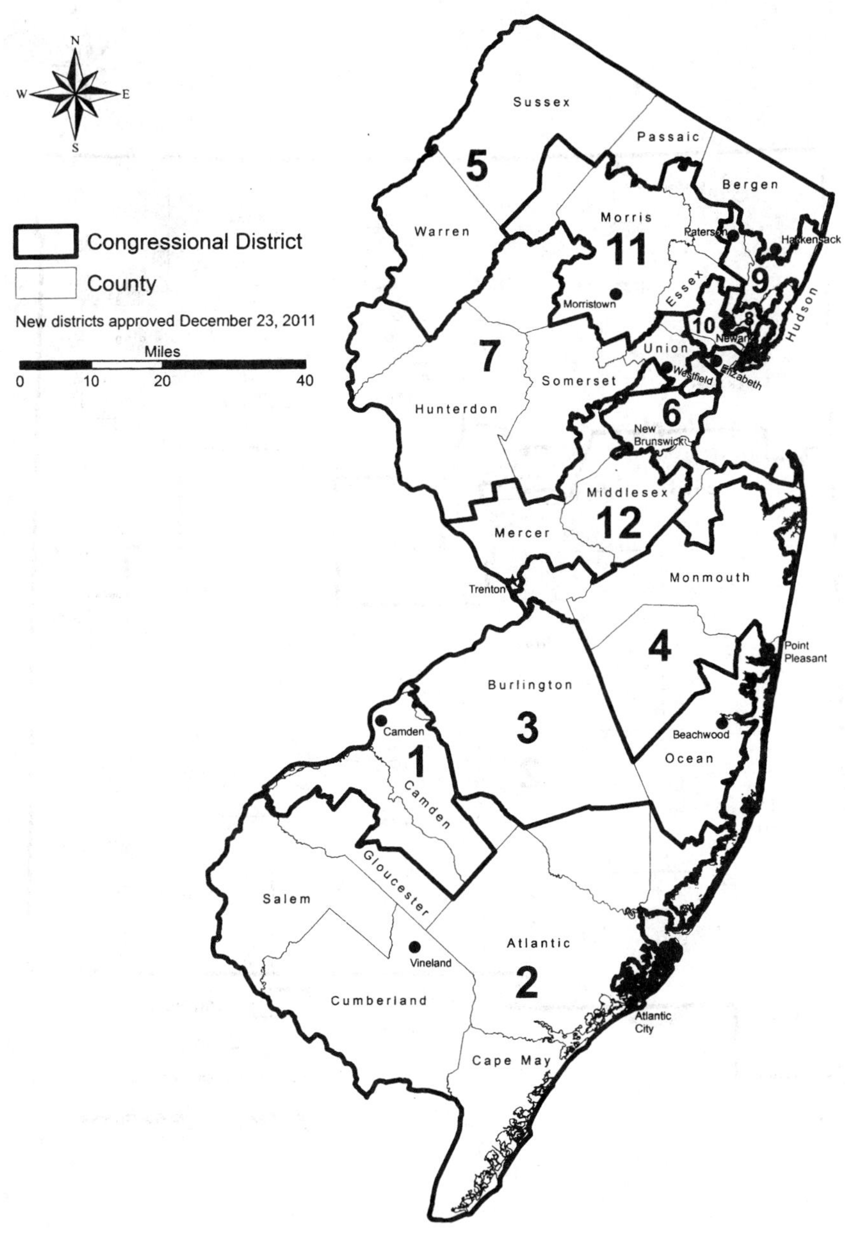

NEW MEXICO—Congressional Districts—(3 Districts)

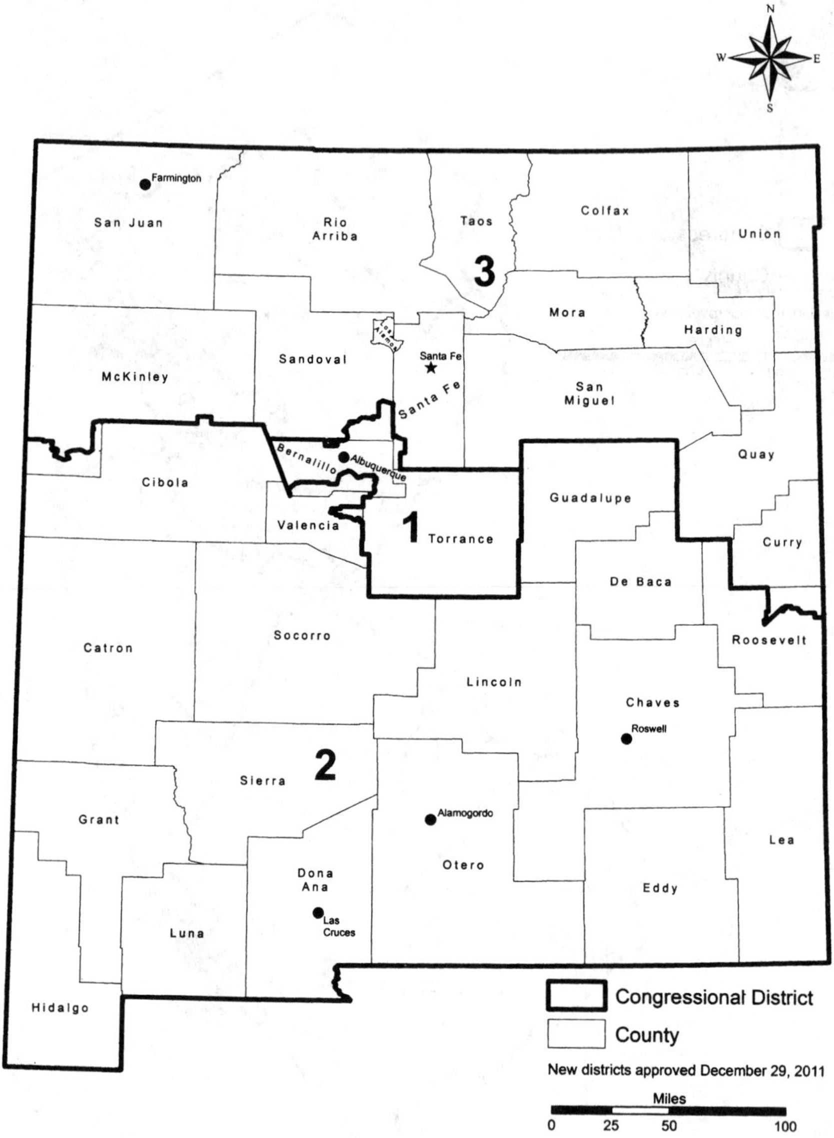

NEW YORK—Congressional Districts—(27 Districts)

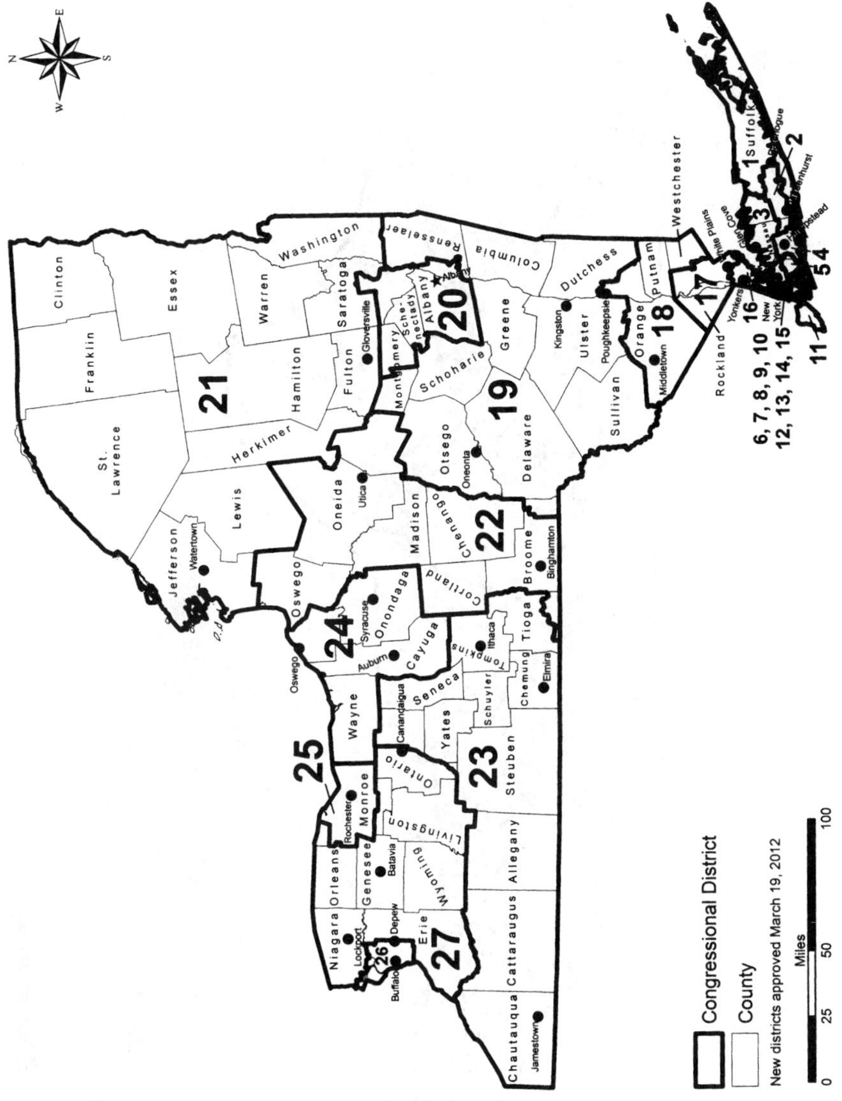

NORTH CAROLINA—Congressional Districts—(13 Districts)

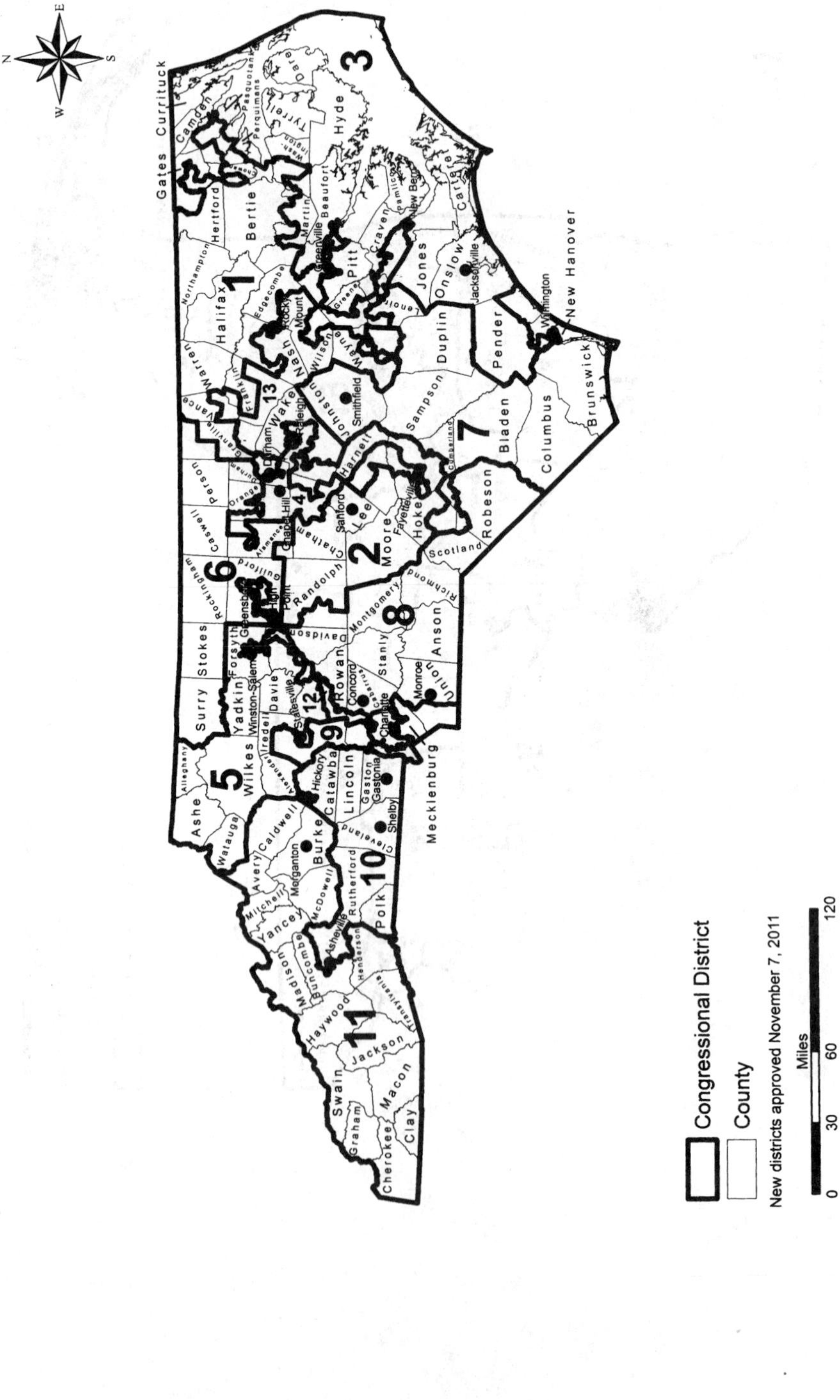

Congressional District

County

New districts approved November 7, 2011

Miles

0 30 60 120

NORTH DAKOTA—Congressional District—(1 District At Large)

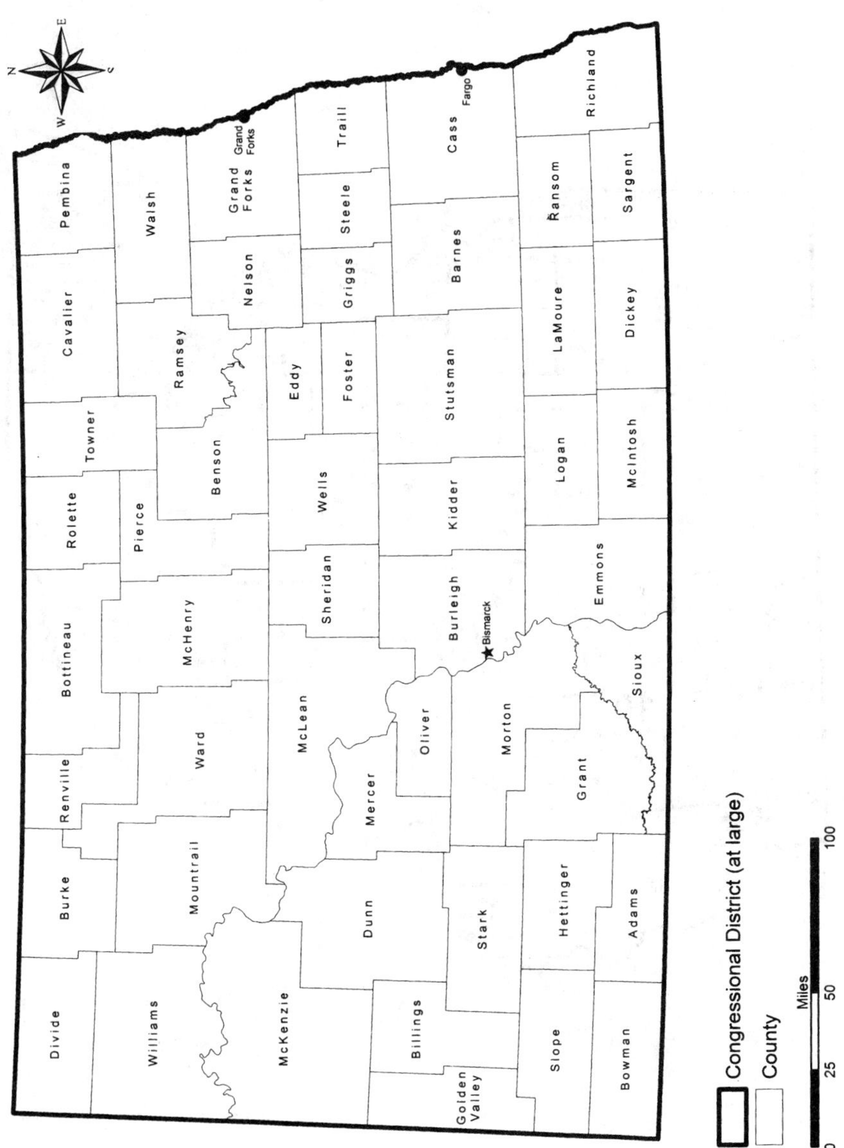

OHIO—Congressional Districts—(16 Districts)

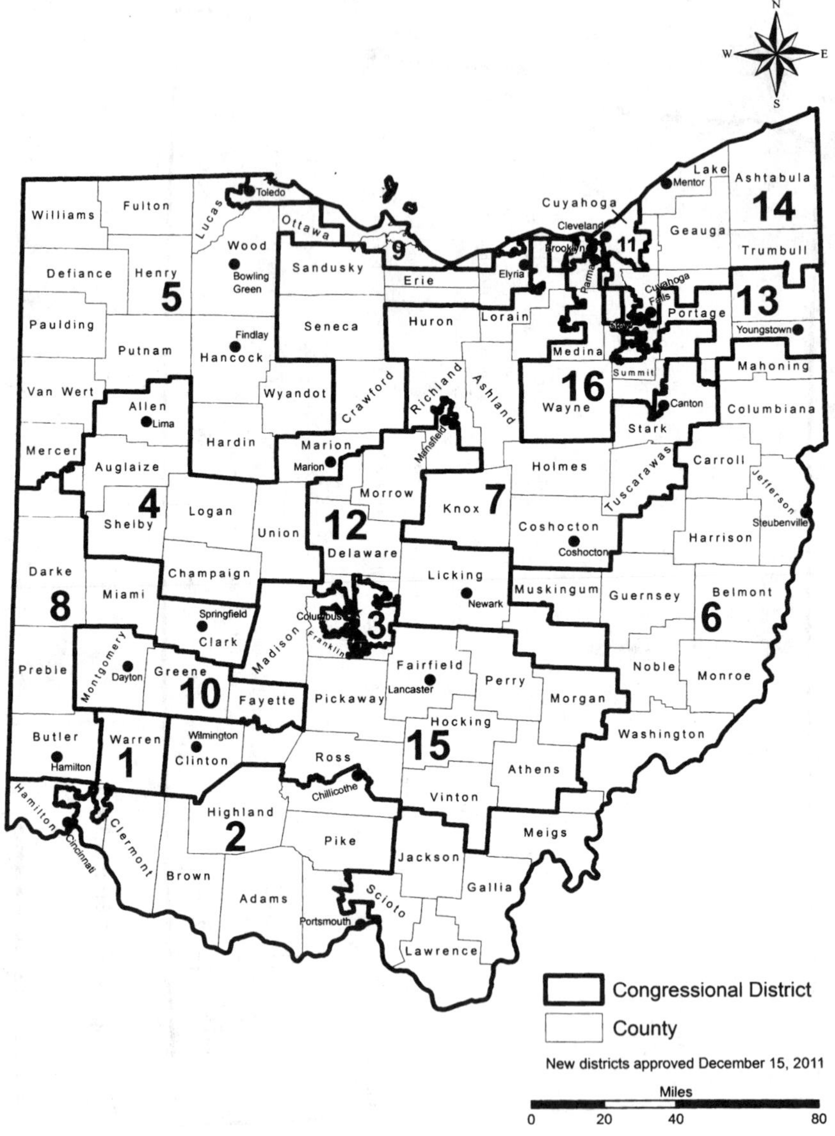

OKLAHOMA—Congressional Districts—(5 Districts)

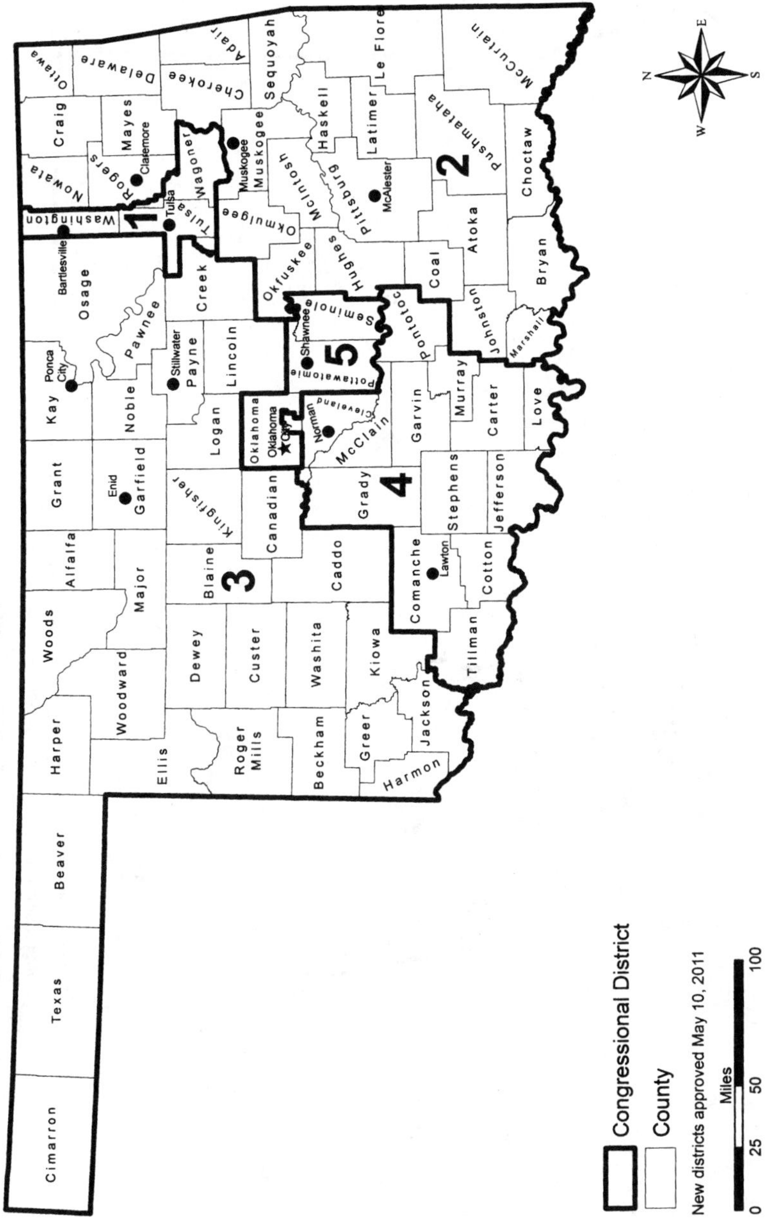

OREGON—Congressional Districts—(5 Districts)

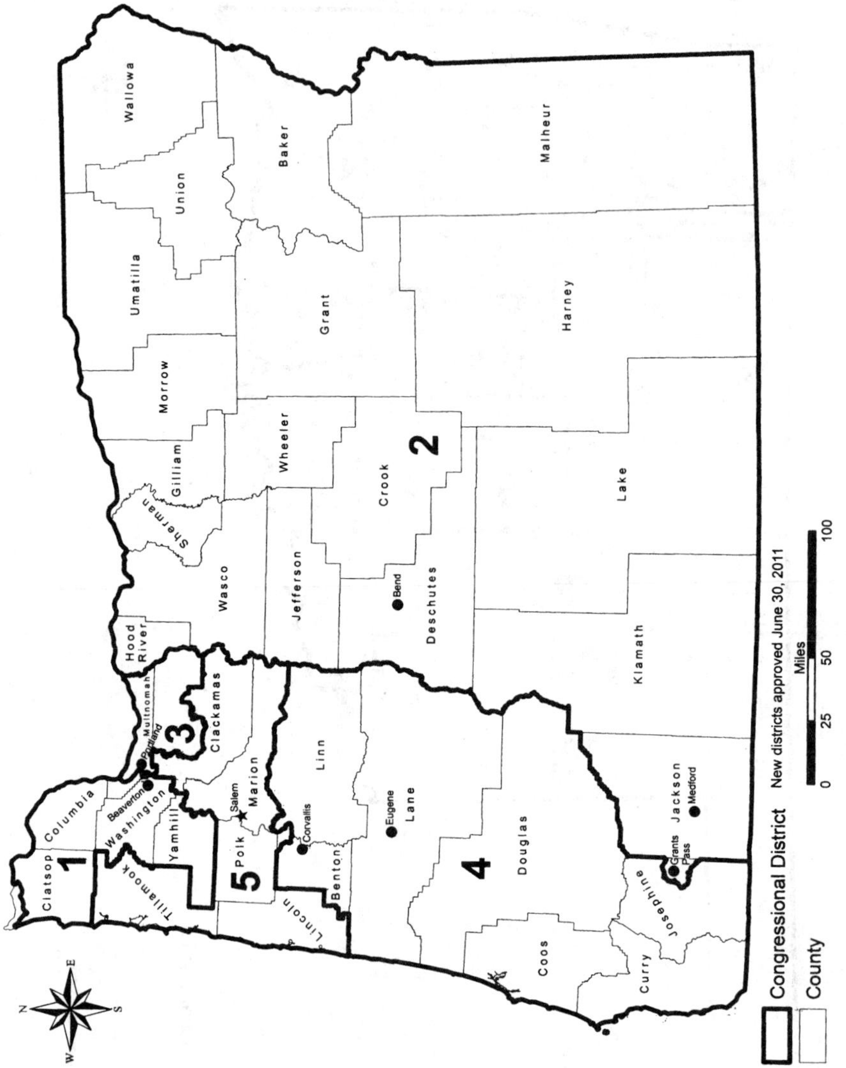

PENNSYLVANIA—Congressional Districts—(18 Districts)

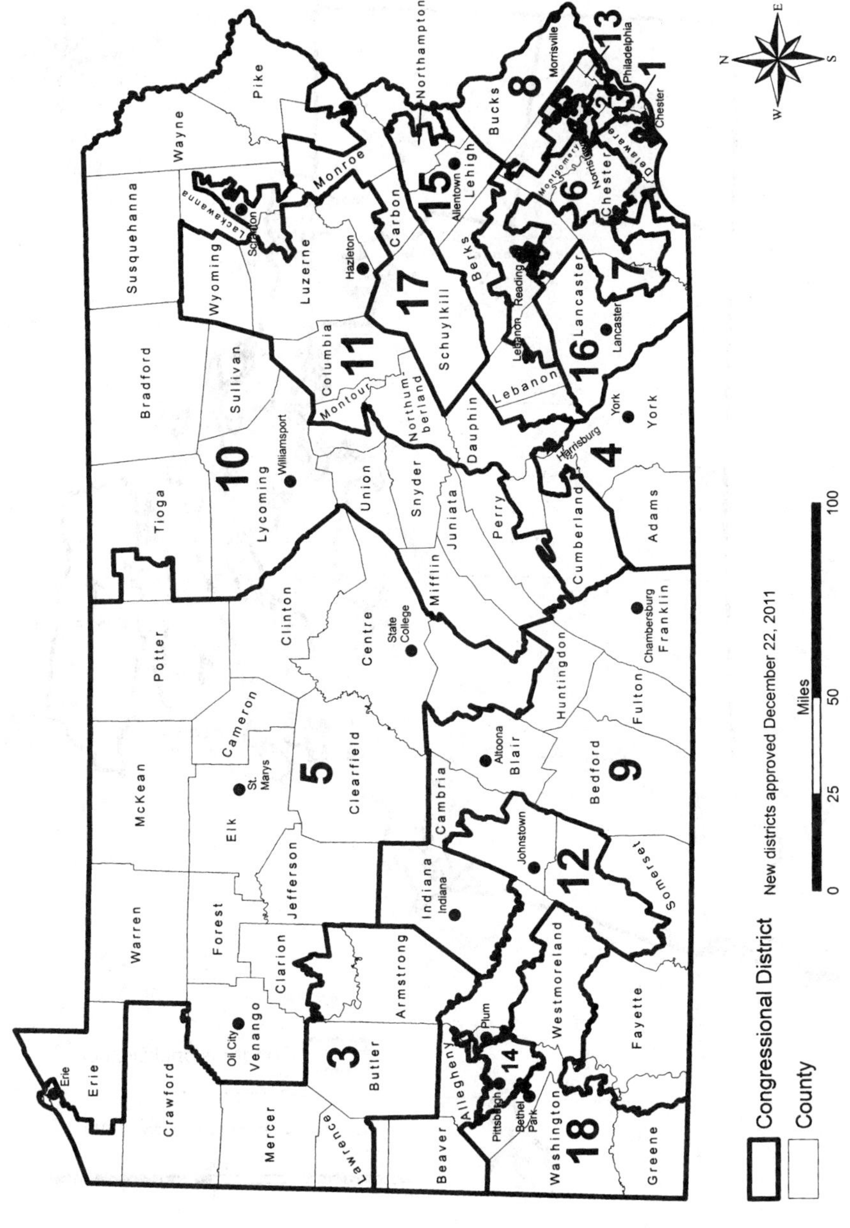

RHODE ISLAND—Congressional Districts—(2 Districts)

SOUTH CAROLINA—Congressional Districts—(7 Districts)

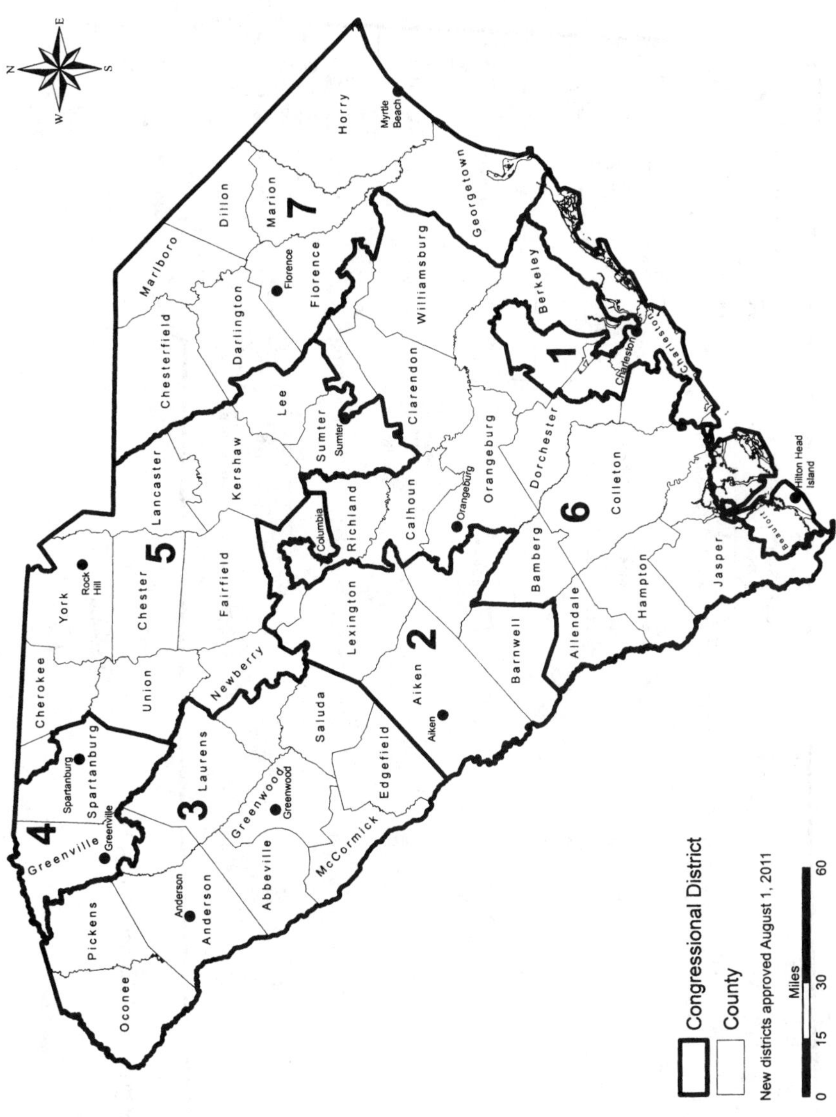

SOUTH DAKOTA—Congressional District—(1 District At Large)

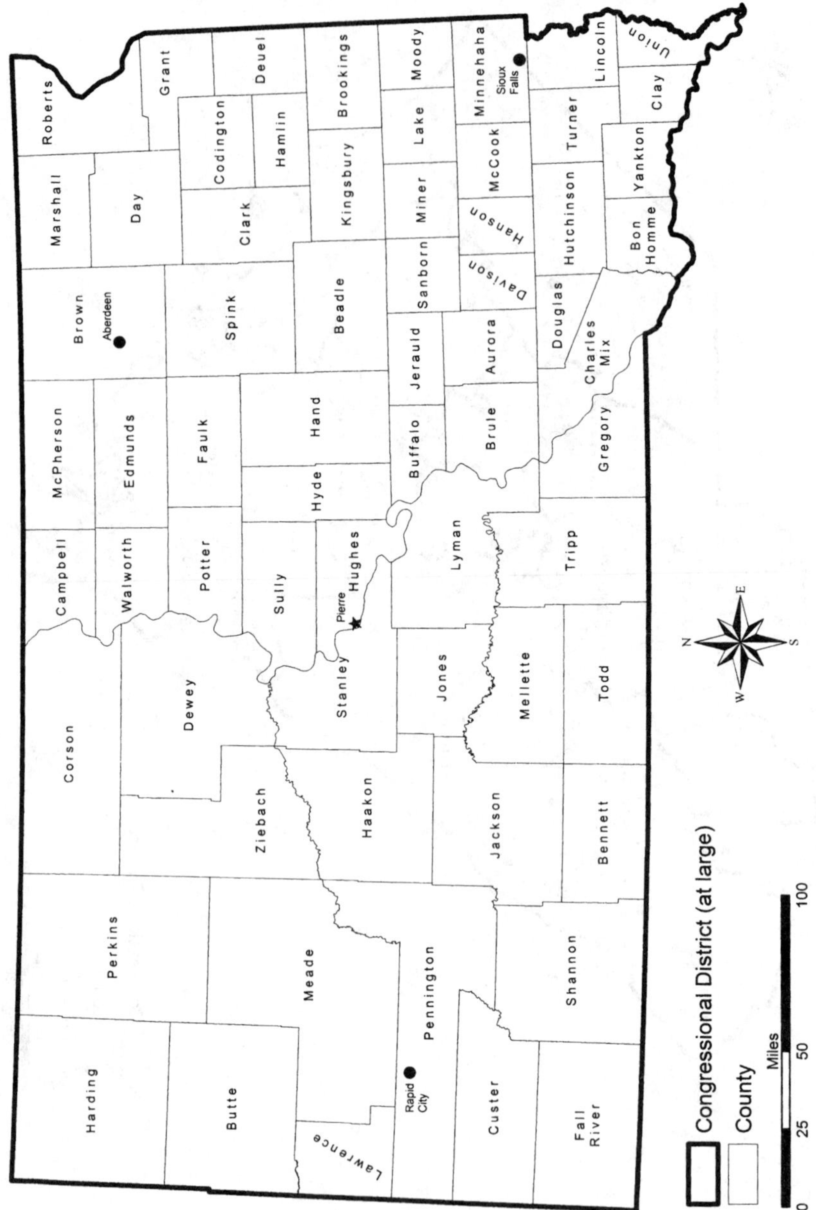

TENNESSEE—Congressional Districts—(9 Districts)

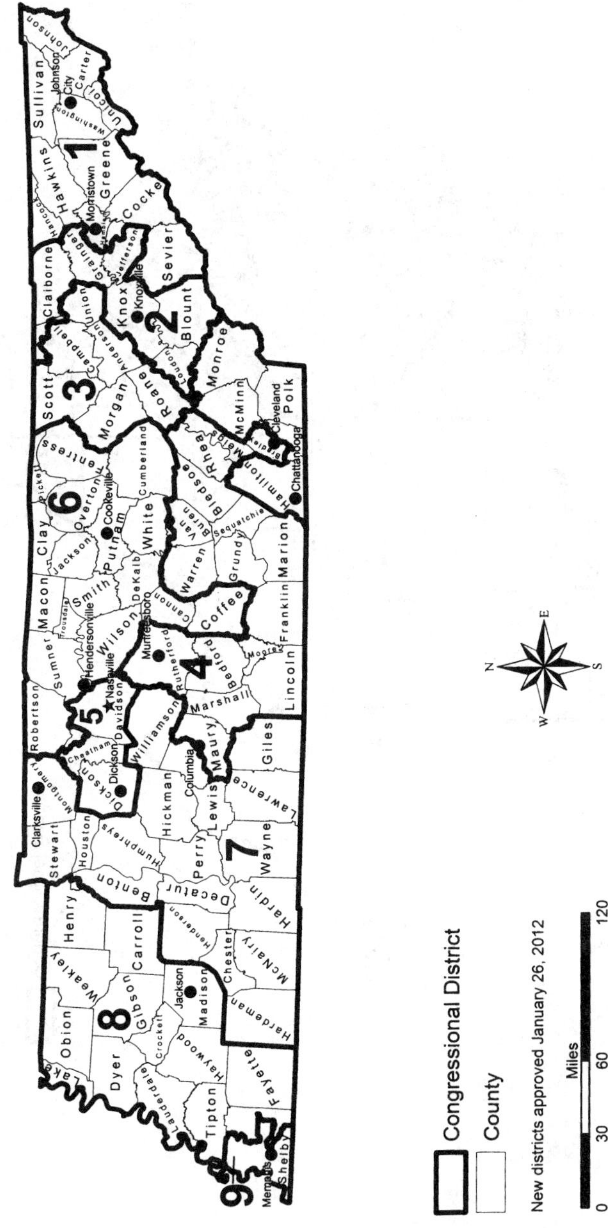

TEXAS—Congressional Districts—(36 Districts)

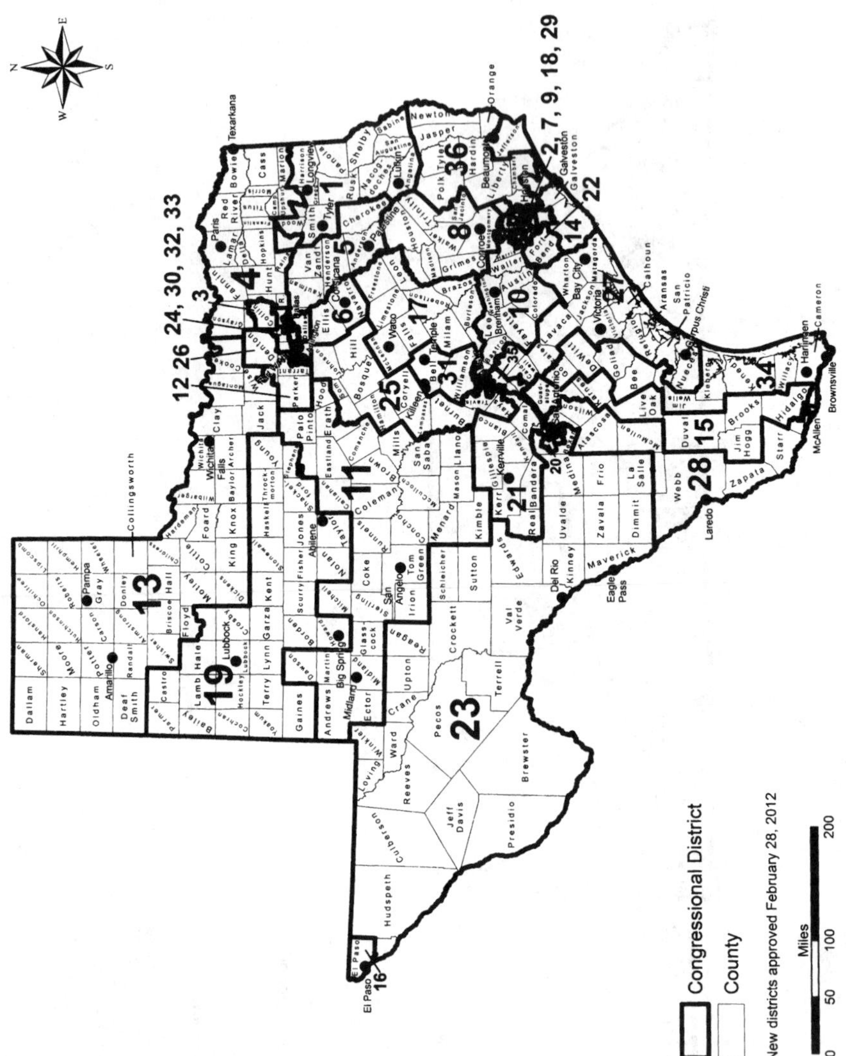

UTAH—Congressional Districts—(4 Districts)

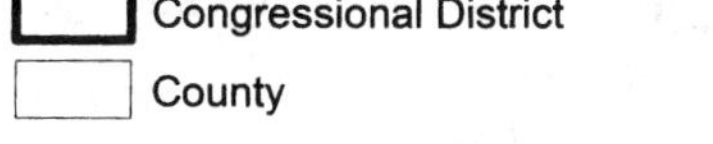

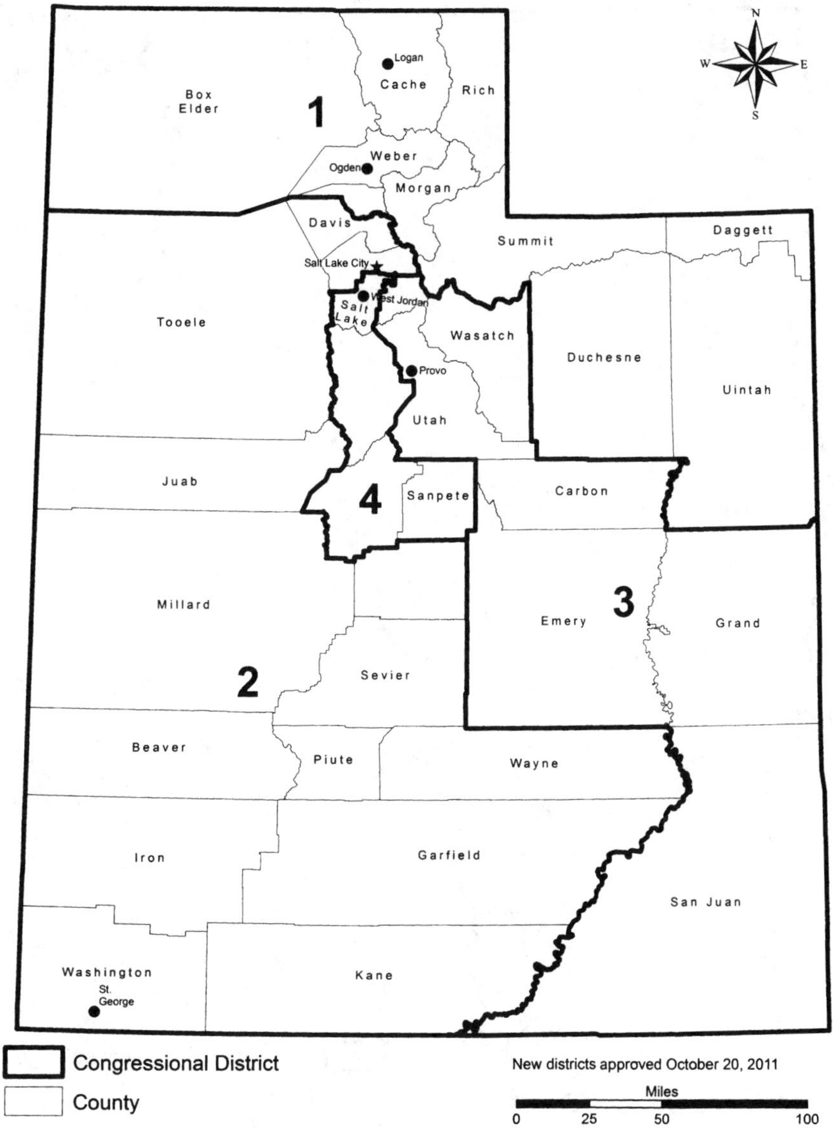

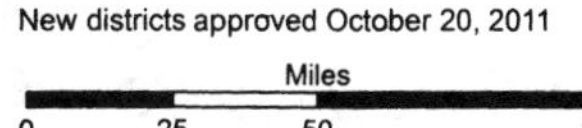

VERMONT—Congressional District—(1 District At Large)

VIRGINIA—Congressional Districts—(11 Districts)

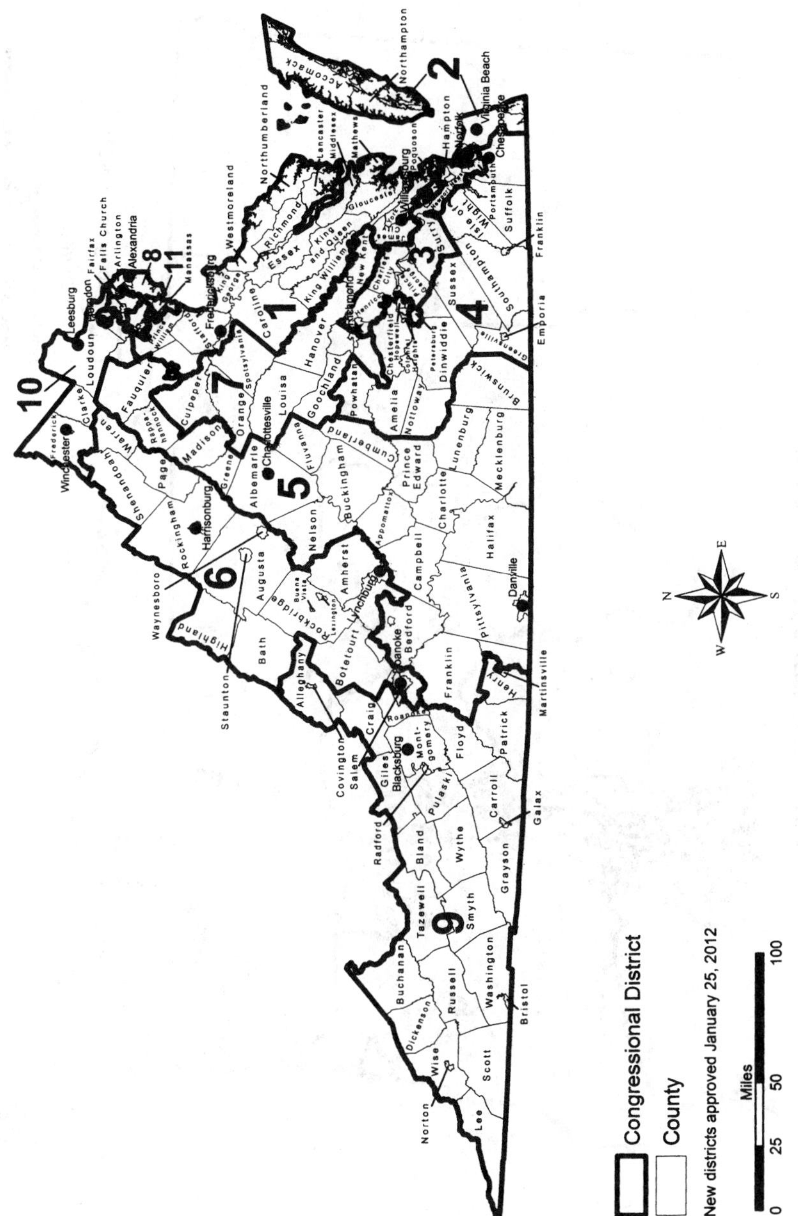

WASHINGTON—Congressional Districts—(10 Districts)

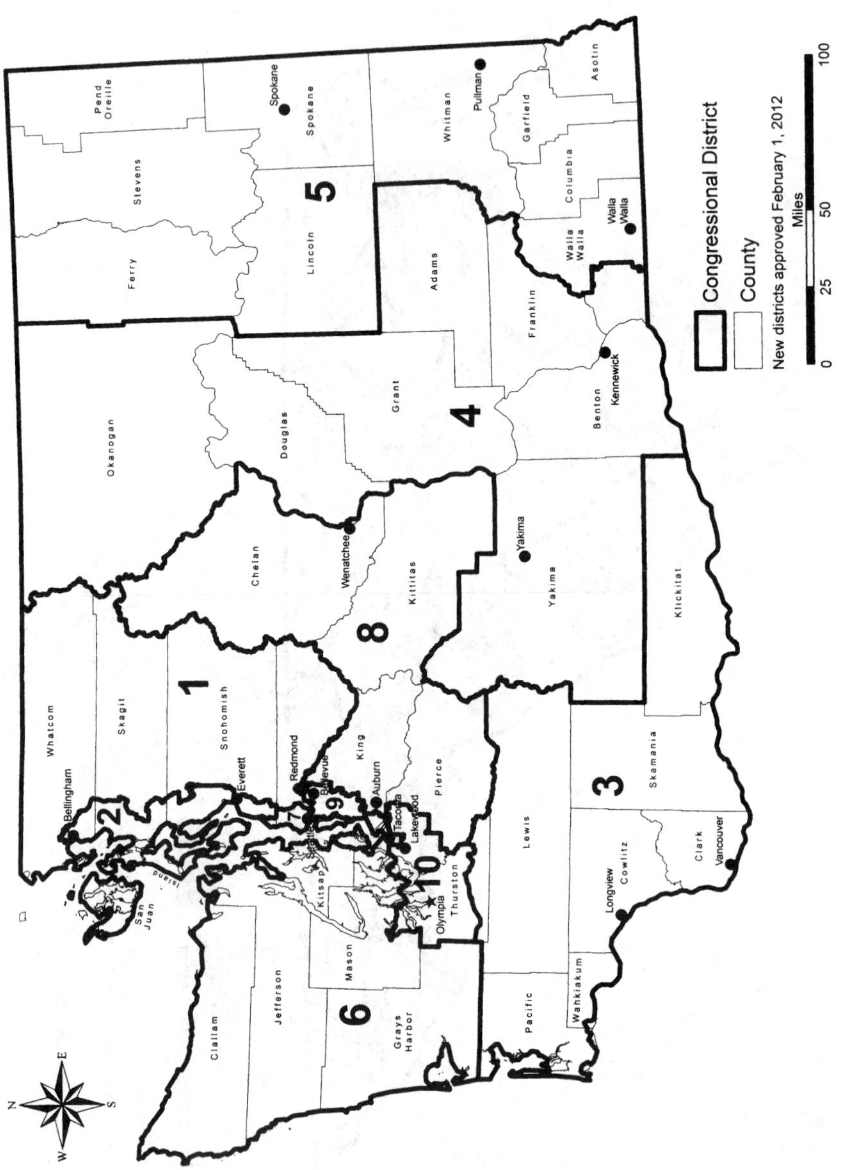

WEST VIRGINIA—Congressional Districts—(3 Districts)

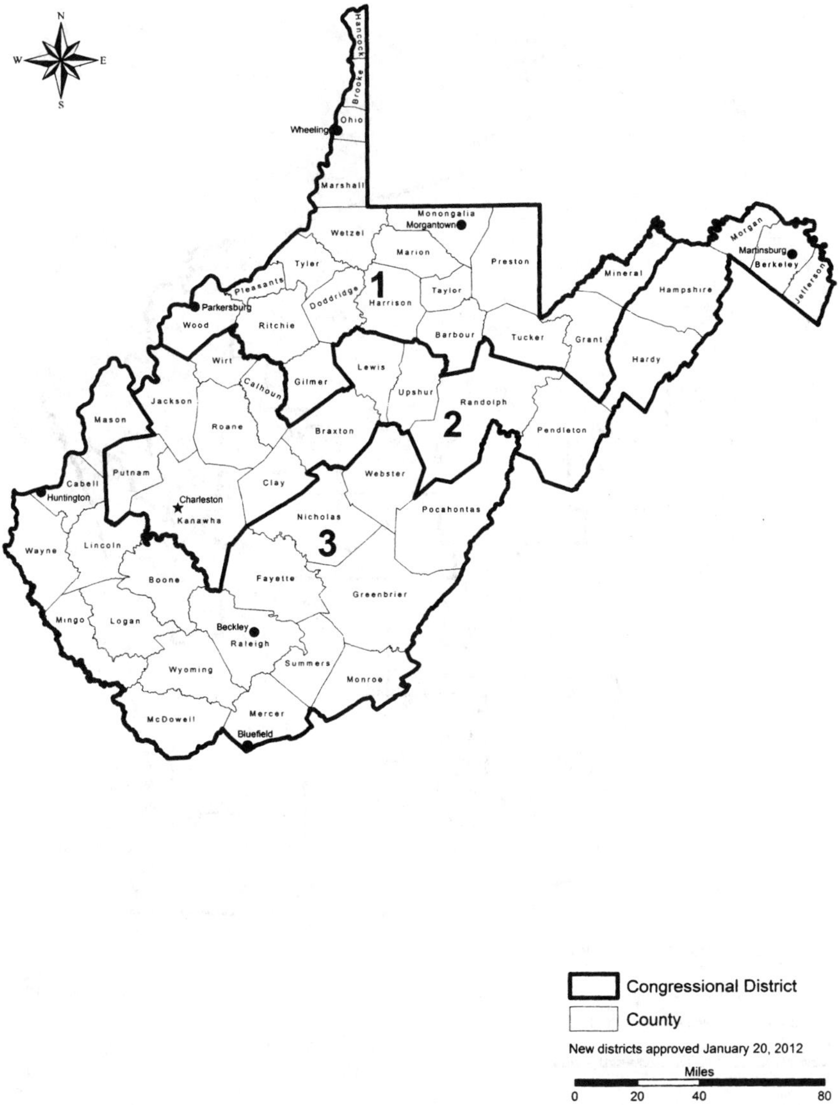

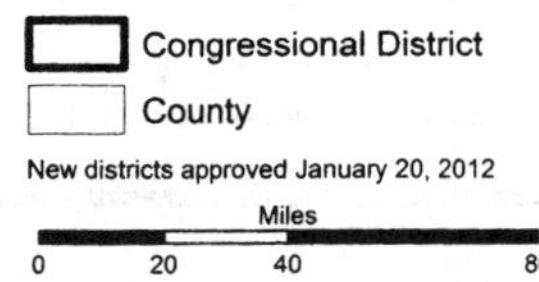

WISCONSIN—Congressional Districts—(8 Districts)

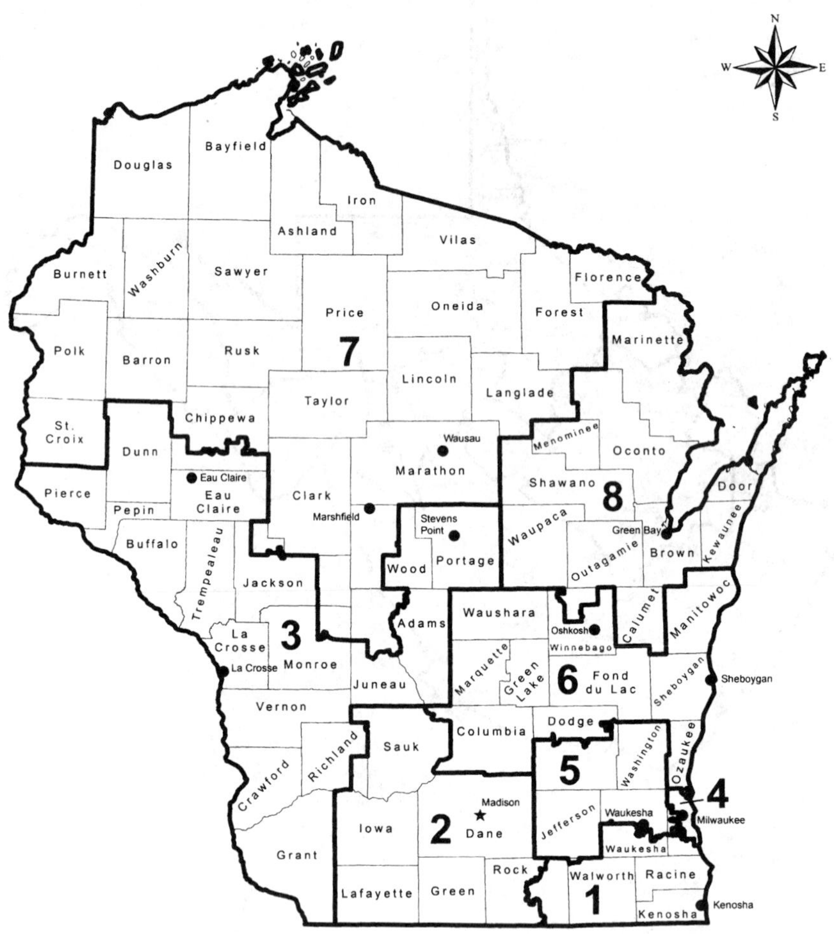

Congressional District

County

New districts approved August 9, 2011

Miles

0 25 50 100

WYOMING—Congressional District—(1 District At Large)

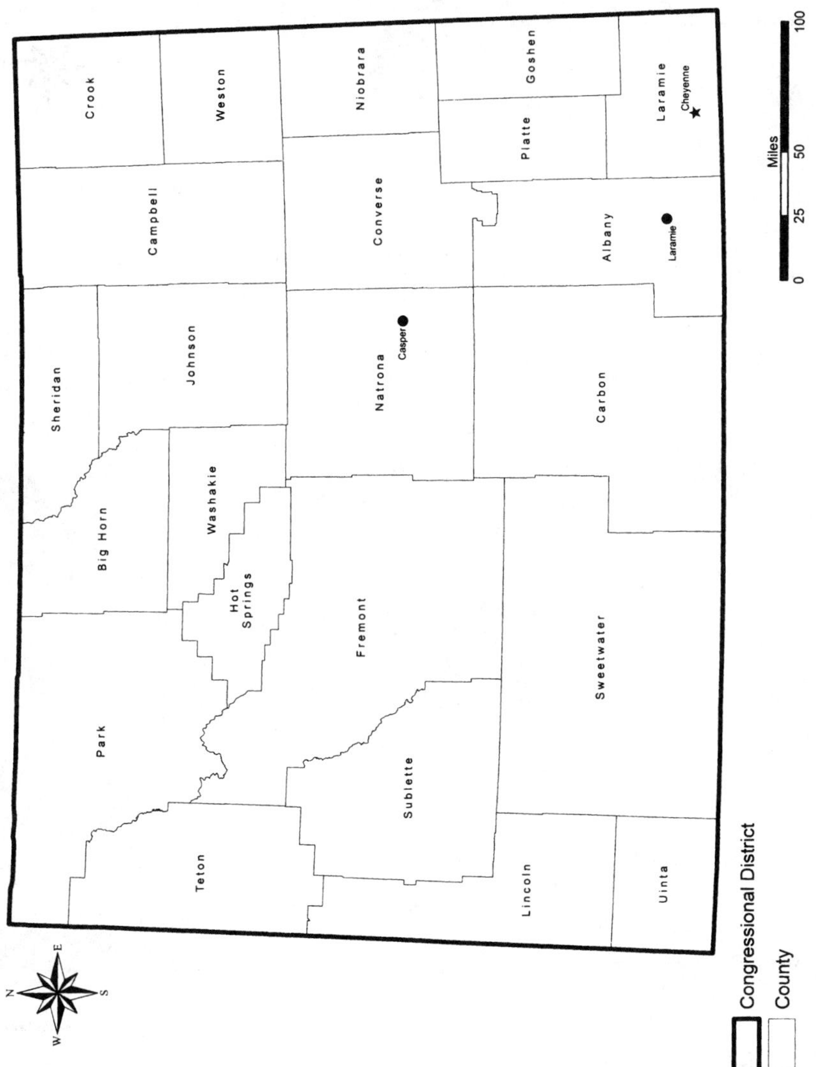

AMERICAN SAMOA—(1 Delegate At Large)

Swains Island

Eastern

Manu'a

Western

Rose Island

Islands

Miles

0 20 40 80

DISTRICT OF COLUMBIA—(1 Delegate At Large)

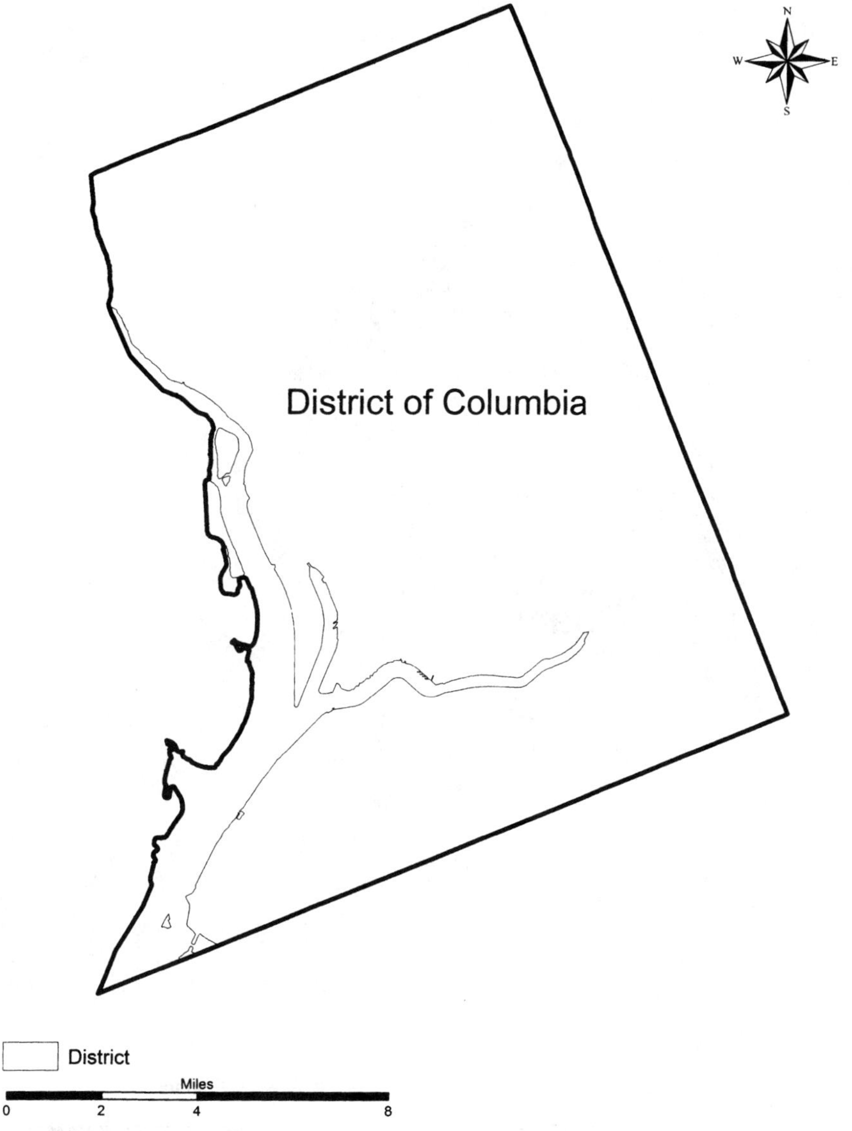

N
W E
S

District of Columbia

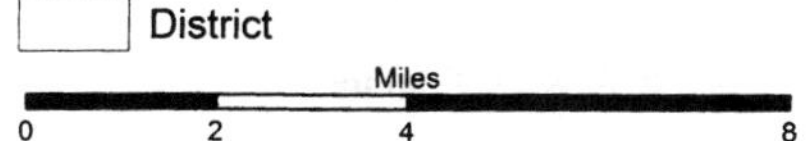

GUAM—(1 Delegate At Large)

NORTHERN MARIANA ISLANDS—(1 Delegate At Large)

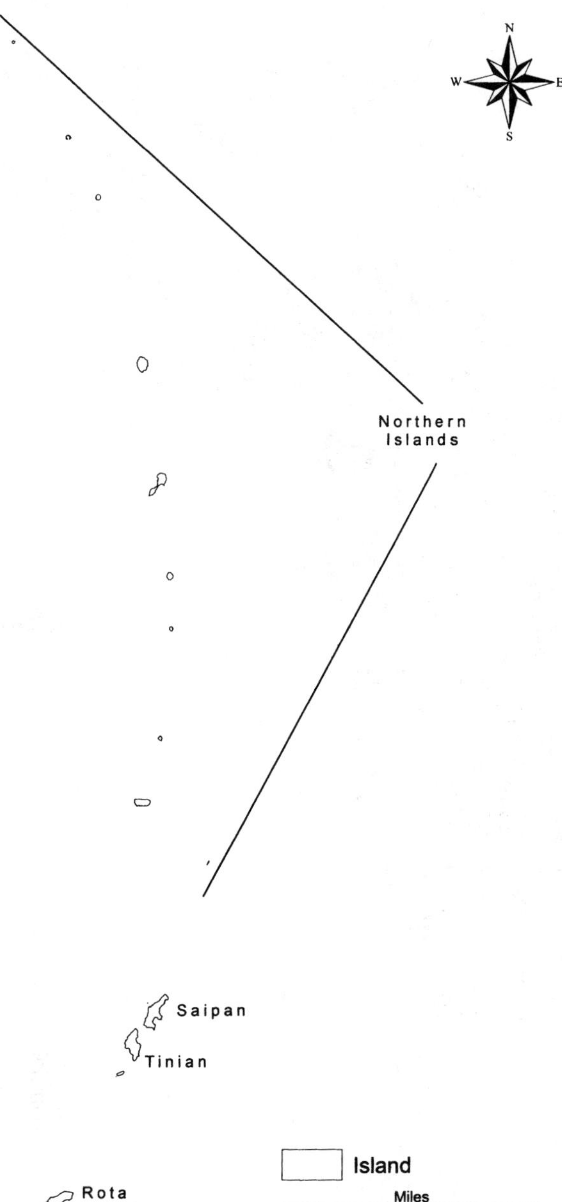

PUERTO RICO—(1 Resident Commissioner At Large)

THE VIRGIN ISLANDS OF THE UNITED STATES—(1 Delegate At Large)

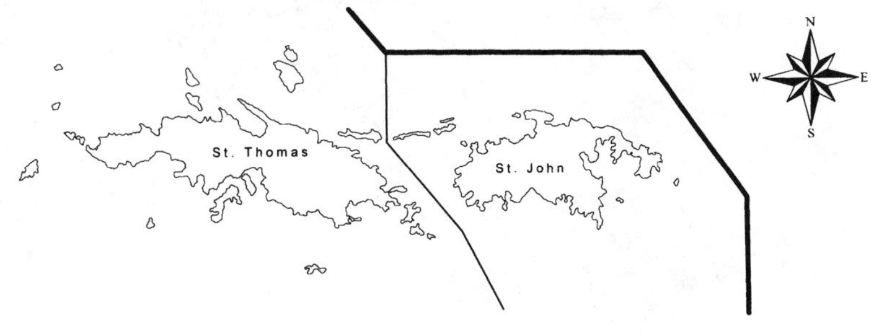

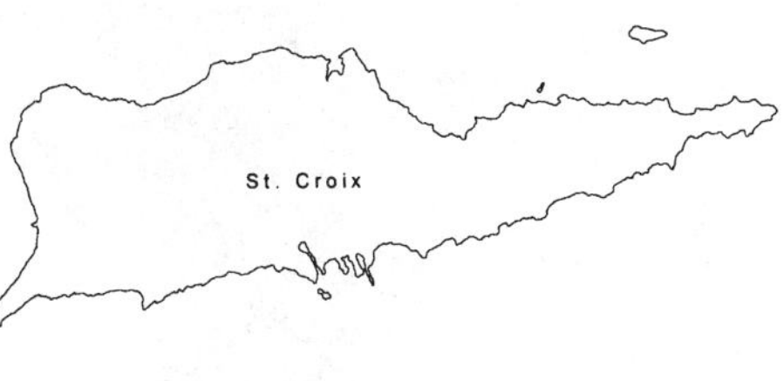

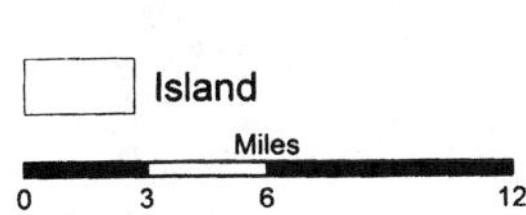

NAME INDEX

D

E

G

K

O

Margin Index:
To use, bend book and align index marker with black-edged page mark in text.